Small Business Sourcebook

ISSN 0883-3397

Small Business Sourcebook

The Entrepreneur's Resource

FORTY-SECOND EDITION

Volume 1

Specific Small Business Profiles

(Entries 1-8085)

Holly M. Selden
Project Editor

Small Business Sourcebook, 42nd edition

Project Editor: Holly M. Selden

Editorial Support Services: Pranav Kokate

Composition and Electronic Prepress: Carolyn Roney

Manufacturing: Rita Wimberley

© 2025 Gale, a Cengage Company

ALL RIGHTS RESERVED. No part of this work covered by the copyright herein may be reproduced, transmitted, stored, or used in any form or by any means graphic, electronic, or mechanical, including but not limited to photocopying, recording, scanning, digitizing, taping, Web distribution, information networks, or information storage and retrieval systems, except as permitted under Section 107 or 108 of the 1976 United States Copyright Act, without the prior written permission of the publisher.

This publication is a creative work fully protected by all applicable copyright laws, as well as by misappropriation, trade secret, unfair competition, and other applicable laws. The authors and editors of this work have added value to the underlying factual material herein through one or more of the following: unique and original selection, coordination, expression, arrangement, and classification of the information.

For product information and technology assistance, contact us at
Gale Customer Support, 1-800-877-4253.
For permission to use material from this text or product,
submit all requests online at www.cengage.com/permissions.
Further permissions questions can be emailed to
permissionrequest@cengage.com.

While every effort has been made to ensure the reliability of the information presented in this publication, Gale, part of Cengage Group, does not guarantee the accuracy of the data contained herein. Gale accepts no payment for listing and inclusion in the publication of any organization, agency, institution, publication, service, or individual does not imply endorsement of the editors or publisher. Errors brought to the attention of the publisher and verified to the satisfaction of the publisher will be corrected in future editions.

Gale, part of Cengage Group
5191 Natorp Blvd.
Mason, OH 45040

978-1-5358-7663-6 (set)
978-1-5358-7664-3 (vol. 1)
978-1-5358-7665-0 (vol. 2)
978-1-5358-7666-7 (vol. 3)
978-1-5358-7667-4 (vol. 4)
978-1-5358-7668-1 (vol. 5)
978-1-5358-7669-8 (vol. 6)

ISSN 0883-3397

This title is also available as an e-book.
978-1-5358-7670-4
Contact your Gale sales representative for ordering information.

Contents

Volume 1
Introduction vii
User's Guide ix
List of Small Business Profiles xv
Standard Industrial Classification (SIC) Codes for
 Profiled Small Businesses xix
Licensing Assistance Programs xxxiii
Guide to Publishers xxxvii
Glossary lxxxix

Small Business Profiles 1

    Provides start-up information, associations and other organizations, educational programs, directories of educational programs, reference works, sources of supply, statistical sources, trade periodicals, video/audio media, trade shows and conventions, consultants, franchises and business opportunities, computerized databases, computer systems/software, libraries, and research centers.

Volume 2
Introduction vii
User's Guide ix
List of Small Business Profiles xv
Standard Industrial Classification (SIC) Codes for
 Profiled Small Businesses xix

Small Business Profiles 623

Volume 3
Introduction vii
User's Guide ix
List of General Small Business Topics xv

General Small Business Topics 1253

    Includes associations and other organizations, educational programs, directories of educational programs, reference works, sources of supply, statistical sources, trade periodicals, video/audio media, trade shows and conventions, consultants, computerized databases, computer systems/software, libraries, and research centers.

Volume 4
Introduction vii
User's Guide ix
List of General Small Business Topics xv

General Small Business Topics 1827

Volume 5
Introduction vii
User's Guide ix

State Listings 2393

    Offers sources of small business assistance by state, territory, and Canadian province, including small business development centers, small business assistance programs, SCORE offices, better business bureaus, chambers of commerce, minority business assistance programs, financing and loan programs, procurement assistance programs, incubators/research and technology parks, educational programs, legislative assistance, small business development consultants, and publications.

Volume 6
Introduction vii
User's Guide ix

State Listings 2951

Federal Government Assistance 3111

    Lists U.S. federal government agencies and offices, including regional, branch, and district offices, which focus on small business issues, programs, assistance, and policy.

Master Index 3167

Introduction

The appeal of small business ownership remains perpetually entrenched in American culture as one of the most viable avenues for achieving the American Dream. To many entrepreneurs, going into business for themselves represents financial independence, an increased sense of identity and self-worth, and the fulfillment of personal goals. Small business owners strive to make their mark in today's competitive marketplace by establishing healthy businesses that can, over time, become legacies handed down from one generation to the next. Entrepreneurs from each generation tackle the obstacles and adversities of the current business and economic climate to test their business savvy and generate opportunities. Today's entrepreneurs face many of the problems of their predecessors, as well as some distinctly new challenges.

With the rightsizing, downsizing, and reorganization of corporate America, many individuals have decided to confront the risks of developing and operating their own businesses. Small business ownership is rapidly becoming a viable alternative to what is perceived as an equally unstable corporate environment. These entrepreneurs, many of whom have firsthand experience with the problems and inefficiencies inherent in today's large corporations, seek to improve upon an archaic business model and to capitalize on their own ingenuity and strengths. Led by their zeal, many would-be entrepreneurs let their desire, drive, and determination overshadow the need for business knowledge and skill. Ironically, aids in obtaining these components of entrepreneurial success are widely available, easily accessible, and often free of charge.

Small Business Sourcebook (*SBS*) is a six-volume annotated guide to nearly 17,000 listings of live and print sources of information designed to facilitate the start-up, development, and growth of specific small businesses, as well as more than 19,500 similar listings on general small business topics. An additional 12,500 state-specific listings and nearly 1,100 U.S. federal government agencies and offices specializing in small business issues, programs, and assistance are also included. *SBS* covers more than 300 specific small business profiles more than 100 general small business topics.

Features of This Edition

This edition of *Small Business Sourcebook* has been revised and updated, incorporating thousands of changes to names, addresses, contacts, and descriptions of listings from the previous edition. We have also added several hundred podcasts that will help users better understand topics on entrepreneurship and small business ownership.

Contents and Arrangement

The geographical scope of *SBS* encompasses the United States and Canada, with expanded coverage for resources pertaining to international trade and for resources that have a U.S. or Canadian distributor or contact. Internet sites that are maintained outside of the U.S. and Canada are also included if they contain relevant information for North American small businesses. Resources that do not relate specifically to small businesses are generally not included.

The information presented in *SBS* is grouped within four sections: Specific Small Business Profiles, General Small Business Topics, State Listings, and Federal Government Assistance. Detailed outlines of these sections may be found in the Users' Guide following this Introduction. Also included is a Master Index to Volumes 1 through 6.

Specific Small Business Profiles This section includes the following types of resources: start-up information, associations and other organizations, educational programs, directories of educational programs, reference works, sources of supply, statistical sources, trade periodicals, videos and podcasts, trade shows and conventions, consultants, franchises, and business opportunities, computerized databases, computer systems/software, Internet databases, libraries, and research centers. All resources are arranged by business type. Entries range from Accounting Service to Word Processing Service, and include such businesses as Cannabis Dispensaries, Computer Consulting, Food Trucks, and Web Site Design.

General Small Business Topics This section offers such resources as associations, books, periodicals, articles, pamphlets, educational programs, directories of educational

INTRODUCTION

programs, trade shows and conventions, consultants, computerized databases, Internet databases, software, libraries, and research centers. All resources in this section are arranged alphabetically by business topic.

State Listings Entries include government, academic, and commercial agencies and organizations, as well as select coverage of relevant state-specific publications. Listings are arranged alphabetically by state, territory, and Canadian province. Some examples include small business development consultants, SCORE offices, financing and loan programs, better business bureaus, and chambers of commerce.

Federal Government Assistance Listings Entries include federal organizations and agencies specializing in small business issues, programs, assistance, and policy. Listings are arranged alphabetically by U.S. government agency or office; regional or branch offices are listed alphabetically by state.

Master Index All entries in Volumes 1 through 6 are arranged in one alphabetic index for convenience.

Entries in *SBS* include (as appropriate and available):

- Organization, institution, or product name
- Contact information, including contact name, address and phone, toll-free, and fax numbers
- Author/editor, date(s), and frequency
- Availability, including price
- Brief description of purpose, services, or content
- Company and/or personal E-mail addresses
- Web site addresses

SBS also features the following:

Guide to Publishers—An alphabetic listing of nearly 1,000 companies, associations, institutions, and individuals that publish the periodicals, directories, guidebooks, and other publications noted in the Small Business Profiles and General Topics sections. Users are provided with full contact information, including address, phone, fax, and e-mail and URL when available. The Guide to Publishers facilitates contact with publishers and provides a one-stop resource for valuable information.

Method of Compilation

SBS was compiled by consulting small business experts and entrepreneurs, as well as a variety of resources, including direct contact with the associations, organizations, and agencies through Internet research or materials provided by those listees; government resources; and data obtained from other relevant Gale directories. *SBS* was reviewed by a team of small business advisors, all of whom have numerous years of expertise in small business counseling and identification of small business information resources. The last and perhaps most important resource we utilize is direct contact with our readers, who provide valuable comments and suggestions to improve our publication. *SBS* relies on these comprehensive market contacts to provide today's entrepreneurs with relevant, current, and accurate information on all aspects of small business.

Available in Electronic Formats

Licensing. Small Business Sourcebook is available for licensing. The complete database is provided in a fielded format and is deliverable on various forms of media. For more information, contact Gale's Business Development Group at 1-800-877-GALE, or visit our website at www.gale.com.

Comments and Suggestions Welcome

Associations, agencies, business firms, publishers, and other organizations that provide assistance and information to the small business community are encouraged to submit material about their programs, activities, services, or products. Comments and suggestions from users of this directory are also welcomed and appreciated. Please contact:

Project Editor
Small Business Sourcebook
27555 Executive Dr., Ste. 270
Farmington Hills, MI 48331
Gale, part of Cengage Group
URL: www.gale.com

User's Guide

Small Business Sourcebook (*SBS*) provides information in a variety of forms and presentations for comprehensive coverage and ease of use. The directory contains four parts within six volumes:

- Specific Small Business Profiles
- General Small Business Topics
- State Listings
- Federal Government Assistance

Information on specific businesses is arranged by type of business; the many general topics that are of interest to the owners, operators, or managers of all small businesses are grouped in a separate section for added convenience. Users should consult the various sections to benefit fully from the information *SBS* offers. For example, an entrepreneur with a talent or interest in the culinary arts could peruse a number of specific small business profiles, such as Restaurant, Catering Service, Cooking School, Specialty/Gourmet Food/Wine Shop, Food Truck, Healthy Restaurant, or Candy/Chocolate Shop. Secondly, the General Small Business Topics section could be consulted for any applicable subjects, such as Service Industry, Retailing, Franchising, and other relevant topics. Then, the appropriate state within the State Listings section would offer area programs and offices providing information and support to small businesses, including venture capital firms and small business development consultants. Finally, the Federal Government Assistance section could supply relevant government offices, such as procurement contacts.

Features Included in Volumes 1 and 2

List of Small Business Profiles. This list provides an alphabetic outline of the small businesses profiled. The page number for the beginning of each profile is indicated.

Standard Industrial Classification (SIC) Codes for Profiled Small Businesses. This section lists four-digit SIC codes and corresponding classification descriptions for the small businesses profiled in this edition. The SIC system, which organizes businesses by type, is a product of the Statistical Policy Division of the U.S. Office of Management and Budget. Statistical data produced by government, public, and private organizations is usually categorized according to SIC codes, thereby facilitating the collection, comparison, and analysis of data as well as providing a uniform method for presenting statistical information. Hence, knowing the SIC code for a particular small business increases access and the use of a variety of statistical data from many sources.

Guide to Publishers. This resource lists alphabetically the companies, associations, institutions, and individuals that publish the periodicals, directories, guidebooks, and other publications noted in the "Small Business Profiles" and "General Topics" sections. Users are provided with full contact information, including address, phone, fax, and e-mail and URL when available. The "Guide" facilitates contact with publishers and provides a one-stop resource for valuable information.

Glossary of Small Business Terms. This glossary defines nearly 400 small business terms, including financial, governmental, insurance, procurement, technical, and general business definitions. Cross-references and acronyms are also provided.

Small Business Profiles A-Z. More than 300 small business profiles are represented in volumes 1 and 2. Profiles are listed alphabetically by business type. Each profile may contain up to sixteen subheadings that correlate to a resource type; entries within are listed alphabetically. These resource types are detailed below:

- ***Start-up Information***—Includes periodical articles, books, manuals, book excerpts, kits, and other sources of information. Entries offer title; publisher; address; phone, fax, toll-free numbers; company e-mail and URL addresses; and a description. Bibliographic data is provided for cited periodical articles whenever possible.

- ***Associations and Other Organizations***—Includes trade and professional associations whose members gather and disseminate information of interest to small business owners. Entries offer the association's

Small Business Sourcebook • 42nd Edition

USER'S GUIDE

name; address; phone, toll-free and fax numbers; company e-mail address; contact name; purpose and objective; a description of membership; telecommunication services; and a listing of its publications, including publishing frequency.

- **Educational Programs**—Includes university and college programs, schools, training opportunities, association seminars, correspondence courses, and other educational programs. Entries offer name of program or institution, sponsor name, address, phone, toll-free and fax numbers, e-mail and URL addresses; and description of program.

- **Directories of Educational Programs**—Includes directories and other publications that list educational programs. Entries offer name of publication; publisher name, address, and phone, toll-free and fax numbers; editor; frequency or date of publication; price; and description of contents, including directory arrangement and indexes.

- **Reference Works**—Includes handbooks, manuals, textbooks, guides, directories, dictionaries, encyclopedias, and other published reference materials. Entries offer name of publication; publisher name, address, and phone, toll-free and fax numbers; e-mail and URL addresses; and, when available, name of author or editor, publication year or frequency, and price. A brief description is often featured.

- **Sources of Supply**—Includes buyer's guides, directories, special issues of periodicals, and other publications that list sources of equipment, supplies, and services related to the operation of the profiled small business. Entries offer publication name; publisher name, address, and phone, toll-free and fax numbers; e-mail and URL addresses; and, when available, editor's name, frequency or publication year, and price. A brief description of the publication, including directory arrangement and indexes, is often provided.

- **Statistical Sources**—Includes books, reports, pamphlets, and other sources of statistical data of interest to an owner, operator or manager of the profiled small business, such as wage, salary, and compensation data; financial and operating ratios; prices and costs; demographics; and other statistical information. Entries offer publication/data source name; publisher (if applicable); address; phone, toll-free and fax numbers of data source; publication date or frequency; and price. A brief description of the publication/data source is often provided.

- **Trade Periodicals**—Includes trade journals, newsletters, magazines, and other serials that offer information about the management and operation of the profiled small business. Such periodicals often contain industry news; trends and developments; reviews; articles about new equipment and supplies; and other information related to business operations. Entries offer publication name; publisher name, address, phone, toll-free and fax numbers, and e-mail and URL addresses; editor name; publication frequency; and price. A brief description of the publication's content is also included, when known.

- **Video/Audio Media**—Includes videos, podcasts, and other audiovisual media offering information on the profiled small business. Entries offer program title; creator or distributor name, address, phone, toll-free and fax numbers, and e-mail and URL addresses; description of program; price; and format(s).

- **Trade Shows and Conventions**—Includes tradeshows, exhibitions, expositions, conventions, and other industry meetings that provide prospective and existing business owners with the opportunity to meet and exchange information with their peers, review commercial exhibits, establish business or sales contacts, and attend educational programs. Entries offer event name; sponsor or management company name, address, phone, toll-free and fax numbers, and e-mail and URL addresses; a description of the event, including audience, frequency, principal exhibits, and dates and locations of event for as many years ahead as provided by the event's sponsor.

- **Consultants**—Includes consultants and consulting organizations that provide services specifically related to the profiled small business. Entries offer individual consultant or consulting organization name, address, and phone, toll-free and fax numbers; company and individual e-mail addresses; and a brief description of consulting services. (For e-mail and URL addresses, see the Small Business Development Consultants subheadings in the State Listings section in Volume 2.)

- **Franchises and Business Opportunities**—Includes companies granting franchise licenses for enterprises falling within the scope of the profiled small business, as well as other non-franchised business opportunities that operate within a given network or system. Entries offer franchise name, address, phone, toll-free and fax numbers, and e-mail and URL addresses, as well as a description of the franchise or business opportunity, which has been expanded whenever possible to include the number of existing franchises, the founding date of the franchise, franchise fees, equity capital requirements, royalty fees, any managerial assistance offered, and available training.

- **Computerized Databases**—Includes diskettes, magnetic tapes, CD-ROMs, online systems, and other computer-readable databases. Entries offer database name; producer name, address, phone, toll-free and fax numbers, e-mail and URL addresses; description; and available format(s), including vendor name.

(Many university and public libraries offer online information retrieval services that provide searches of databases, including those listed in this category.)

- *Computer Systems/Software*—Includes software and computerized business systems designed to assist in the operation of the profiled small business. Entries offer name of the software or system; publisher name, address, phone, toll-free and fax numbers; price; and description.

- *Libraries*—Includes libraries and special collections that contain material especially applicable to the profiled small business. Entries offer library or collection name; parent organization (where applicable); address; phone, toll-free and fax numbers; e-mail and URL addresses; contact name and title; scope of collection; and description of holdings, subscriptions, and services.

- *Research Centers*—Includes university-related and independently operated research institutes and information centers that generate, through their research programs, data related to the operation of the profiled small business. Also listed are associations and other business-related organizations that conduct research programs. Entries offer name of organization; address; phone, toll-free and fax numbers; company web site address; contact name and personal e-mail; a description of principal fields of research or services; publications, including title and frequency; and related conferences.

Features Included in Volumes 3 and 4

General Small Business Topics. This section offers chapters on different topics in the operation of any small business, for example, venture capital and other funding, or compensation. Chapters are listed alphabetically by small business topic; entries within each chapter are arranged alphabetically, within up to 14 subheadings, by resource type:

- *Associations and Other Organizations*—Includes trade and professional associations that gather and disseminate information of interest to small business owners. Entries offer the association's name; address; phone, toll-free and fax numbers; organization e-mail and URL addresses; contact name; purpose and objectives; a description of membership; telecommunication services; and a listing of its publications, including publishing frequency.

- *Educational Programs*—Includes university and college programs, schools, training opportunities, association seminars, correspondence courses, and other educational programs. Entries offer name of program or institution, sponsor name, address, phone, toll-free and fax numbers, e-mail and URL addresses, and description of program.

- *Directories of Educational Programs*—Includes directories and other publications that list educational programs. Entries offer name of publication; publisher name, address, phone, toll-free and fax numbers, and e-mail and URL addresses; editor; frequency or date of publication; price; and description of contents, including arrangement and indexes.

- *Reference Works*—Includes articles, handbooks, manuals, textbooks, guides, directories, dictionaries, encyclopedias, and other published reference materials. Entries offer title of article, including bibliographic information; name of publication; publisher name, address, phone, toll-free and fax numbers, and e-mail and URL addresses; and, when available, name of author or editor, publication year or frequency, and price. A brief description is often featured.

- *Sources of Supply*—Includes buyer's guides, directories, special issues of periodicals, and other publications that list sources of equipment, supplies, and services. Entries offer publication name; publisher name, address, phone, toll-free and fax numbers, and e-mail and URL addresses; editor's name, frequency or publication year, price, and a brief description of the publication, when available.

- *Statistical Sources*—Includes books, reports, pamphlets, and other sources of statistical data of interest to an owner, operator, or manager of a small business, such as wage, salary, and compensation data; financial and operating ratios; prices and costs; demographics; and other statistical information. Entries offer publication/data source name; publisher (if applicable); address; phone, toll-free and fax numbers of data source; publication date or frequency; and price. A brief description is often provided.

- *Trade Periodicals*—Includes journals, newsletters, magazines, and other serials. Entries offer name of publication; publisher name, address, phone, toll-free and fax numbers, and e-mail and URL addresses; and name of editor, frequency, and price. A brief description of the periodical's content is included when known.

- *Video/Audio Media*—Includes videos, podcasts, and other audiovisual media. Entries offer program title; distributor name, address, phone, toll-free and fax numbers, and e-mail and URL addresses; price; description of program; and format(s).

- *Trade Shows and Conventions*—Includes tradeshows, exhibitions, expositions, seminars, and conventions. Entries offer event name; sponsor or management company name, address, phone, toll-free and fax numbers, and e-mail and URL addresses; frequency of event; and dates and locations of the event for as many years ahead as known.

USER'S GUIDE

- *Consultants*—Includes consultants and consulting organizations. Entries offer individual consultant or consulting organization name, address, and phone, toll-free and fax numbers; company and individual e-mail addresses; and a brief description of consulting services. (See also Consultants in the State Listings section.)

- *Computerized Databases*—Includes diskettes, CD-ROMs, magnetic tape, online systems and other computer-readable databases. Entries offer database name; producer, address, phone, toll-free and fax numbers, and e-mail and URL addresses; description; and available format(s), including vendor name. (Many university and public libraries offer online information retrieval services that provide searches of databases, including those listed in this category.)

- *Computer Systems/Software*—Includes software and computerized business systems. Entries offer name of the software or system; publisher name, address, phone, toll-free and fax numbers, and e-mail and URL addresses; price; and description.

- *Libraries*—Includes libraries and special collections that contain material applicable to the small business topic. Entries offer library or collection name, parent organization (where applicable), address, phone and fax numbers, e-mail and URL addresses, scope of collection, and description of holdings and services.

- *Research Centers*— Includes university-related and independently operated research institutes and information centers that generate, through their research programs, data related to specific small business topics. Entries offer name of organization, address, phone, toll-free and fax numbers, e-mail and URL addresses, a description of principal fields of research or services, and related conferences.

Features Included in Volumes 5 and 6

State Listings. This section lists various sources of information and assistance available within given states, territories, and Canadian provinces; entries include governmental, academic, and commercial agencies, and are arranged alphabetically within up to 15 subheadings by resource type:

- *Small Business Development Center Lead Office*— Includes the lead small business development center (SBDC) for each state.

- *Small Business Development Centers*—Includes any additional small business development centers (SBDC) in the state, territory, or province. SBDCs provide support services to small businesses, including individual counseling, seminars, conferences, and learning center activities.

- *Small Business Assistance Programs*—Includes state small business development offices and other programs offering assistance to small businesses.

- *SCORE Offices*—Includes SCORE office(s) for each state. The Service Corps of Retired Executives Association (SCORE), a volunteer program sponsored by the Small Business Administration, offers counseling, workshops, and seminars across the U.S. for small business entrepreneurs.

- *Better Business Bureaus*—Includes various better business bureaus within each state. By becoming a member of the local Better Business Bureau, a small business owner can increase the prestige and credibility of his or her business within the community, as well as make valuable business contacts.

- *Chambers of Commerce*—Includes various chambers of commerce within each state. Chambers of Commerce are valuable sources of small business advice and information; often, local chambers sponsor SCORE counseling several times per month for a small fee, seminars, conferences, and other workshops to its members. Also, by becoming a member of the local Chamber of Commerce, a small business owner can increase the prestige and credibility of his or her business within the community, as well as make valuable business contacts.

- *Minority Business Assistance Programs*—Includes minority business development centers and other sources of assistance for minority-owned business.

- *Financing and Loan Programs*—Includes venture capital firms, small business investment companies (SBIC), minority enterprise small business investment companies (MESBIC), and other programs that provide funding to qualified small businesses.

- *Procurement Assistance Programs*—Includes state services such as counseling, set-asides, and sheltered-market bidding, which are designed to aid small businesses in bidding on government contracts.

- *Incubators/Research and Technology Parks*— Includes small business incubators, which provide newly established small business owners with work sites, business services, training, and consultation; also includes research and technology parks, which sponsor research and facilitate commercialization of new technologies.

- *Educational Programs*—Includes university and college programs, as well as those sponsored by other organizations that offer degree, nondegree, certificate, and correspondence programs in entrepreneurship and in small business development.

- *Legislative Assistance*—Includes committees, subcommittees, and joint committees of each state's senate and house of representatives that are concerned with small business issues and regulations.

- **Consultants**—Includes consultants and consulting firms offering expertise in small business development.
- **Publications**—Includes publications related to small business operations within the profiled state.
- **Publishers**—Includes publishers operating in or for the small business arena within the profiled state.
- **Early Stage Financing**—Includes organizations offering early-stage capital needed to launch and grow new businesses.
- **Venture Capital Firm**—Includes organizations offering financial support to small, early-stage and emerging firms.

Federal Government Assistance. This section lists federal government agencies and offices, many with additional listings for specific offices, as well as regional or district branches. Main agencies or offices are listed alphabetically; regional, branch, or district offices are listed after each main office or agency.

Master Index. This index provides an alphabetic listing of all entries contained in Volumes 1 through 6. Citations are referenced by their entry numbers. Publication titles are rendered in italics.

List of Small Business Profiles

This list is an outline of the small businesses profiled in this edition of Small Business Sourcebook. The beginning page number of each profile is provided.

Abstracting and Indexing Service 1	Blind Cleaning/Installation 133	Commercial/Graphic Art Business 275
Accounting Service 2	Body Care Shop 134	Commercial Mail Receiving Agency ...282
Adult Day Care Center 14	Book Publishing 136	Compact Disc/Record Store 284
Advertising Service 17	Bookbinder 147	Computer Consulting 285
Airbag Replacement/Service Centers ...29	Bookkeeping 149	Computer Data Storage Company 290
Air Charter Service 30	Bookstore 154	Computer Learning/Training Center ...295
Air-Conditioning/Heating and Cooling Contractor 34	Bottled Water Service 158	Computer Maintenance and Repair Service 298
Air Purification/Cleaning Service 41	Bowling Alley 160	Computer Programming and Data Processing Service 300
Ambulance Service 43	Brewpub and Microbrewery 162	Computer Store 306
Amusement Arcade 44	Bridal Shop/Bridal Consultant 167	Computer System Integrators 310
Amusement/Water Park 46	Building/Home Inspection Service 170	Computerized Billing Service 314
Animal Breeder 49	Building Maintenance/ Custodial Service 173	Computerized Matching Service 315
Animal Clinic 53	Bulletin Board Service 179	Concession Stand Business 316
Antique Shop 58	Business Broker Service 180	Concierge/Virtual Assistant Service 320
Apartment Locating Service 61	Business Consulting Service 183	Consignment Shop 321
Appliance Store 63	Business Services Operation 199	Construction Company 324
Appraisal Service 65	Butcher Shop 203	Consumer Electronics Store 354
Aquarium Maintenance/ Leasing Service 68	Cable Network 205	Convenience Store 357
Archery/Target/Shooting Range 70	Calligraphy Service 208	Cooking School 360
Architectural Restoration/ Conservation 72	Camera Shop 210	Copy Shop 363
Art Gallery 79	Campground Management 211	Cosmetics Business 365
Art Supplies Store 83	Candy/Chocolate Shop 214	Costume Shop 369
Assisted Living Facilities 84	Car Alarm and Stereo Store 217	Craft Artisan 371
Association Management Service 87	Car Inspection Service 218	Craft/Hobby Business 376
Auctioneer/Broker 89	Car Towing Service 219	Create-Your-Own... Store 380
Auto Supply Store 91	Car Wash 220	Credit Card Issuing Service 381
Automobile Detailing/ Painting Service 95	Career Counseling 221	Credit Repair Service 383
Automobile/Truck Leasing Service 97	Carpentry Service 225	Credit Reporting and Collection Service 385
Automotive Repair Shop 100	Catering Service 228	Damage Restoration Service 389
Baby Store 101	Cellular Phone/ Telephone Business 231	Dance School 391
Bagel Shop 103	Charter Boat Service 238	Delicatessen/Sandwich Shop 395
Bait and Tackle Shop 105	Check Cashing Service 239	Desktop Publishing Company 399
Bakery/Doughnut Shop 107	Children's Apparel Shop 240	Dial-It Services 402
Bar/Nightclub 112	Children's Day Care Center 242	Disc Jockey Service 403
Beauty Salon/Day Spa 116	Chimney Sweeping Business 247	Dispensary (Cannabis) 404
Beauty Supply Center 117	Christmas Decoration Store 248	Domestic Help/Maid Service 410
Bed and Breakfast Operation 119	Christmas Tree Farm 249	Driving School 413
Beekeeping 121	Cleaning Service 252	Drug Store/Pharmacy 416
Beeper/Paging Service 126	Clipping Service 254	Dry Cleaning Service/Coin-Operated Laundry 424
Bicycle Shop 127	Clothing Designer 255	Editorial/Freelance Writing Business ..427
Billiards Hall 129	Clothing Store 260	Electrical Contractor 434
Blacktop Surfacing Business 130	Coffee Service 265	Electrical Lighting Supply Store 438
	Coin/Stamp Dealer 268	
	Comic Book/Collectibles Store 273	

LIST OF SMALL BUSINESS PROFILES

Electronic/Online Publishing 440
Employee Leasing Service 441
Employment Agency 442
Engraving/Monogramming Service 446
Environmental Consultant 447
Environmental Store 465
Estate Planning 477
Estate Sales Business 480
Event/Wedding Planning 481
Executive Recruiting Agency 483
Fashion Accessories/
   Design Business 485
Film and Video
   Production Operation 487
Financial Planning Service 492
Fish and Seafood Store 518
Fish Farm 520
Fitness Service/Health Club/Personal
   Trainer 525
Floor Covering/
   Restoration Business 526
Florist 528
Food Delivery Service 531
Food Truck 535
Freight Forwarding Service 539
Fund-Raising Consultant 542
Funeral Service 551
Fur Farm 554
Fur Store 555
Furniture Restoration Service 556
Gambling Organization/Service 558
Genealogy Service 564
Gift Basket Service 572
Gift/Card Shop 573
Glass Repair and
   Replacement Service 575
Golf Shop 577
Gourmet Coffee/Tea House 580
Graphic Design 584
Greenhouse/Garden Center/
   Nursery Business 585
Greeting Card Publishing 592
Grocery Store 594
Gunsmith/Gun Shop 602
Hair Replacement/
   Electrolysis Clinic 604
Hair Salon/Barber Shop 605
Handwriting Analysis Consultant 609
Hardware Store 610
Hat Store 612
Hazardous Waste Disposal Business . 613
Health Food Store 617
Healthy Restaurant 623
Hearing Aid Testing and
   Fitting Service 626
Herb Farm 628
Home Accessory Store 631
Home Furnishings Store 633
Home Improvement/Construction/
   Repair 636
Home Health Care Service 637
Horse Riding Academy 642

Hotel/Motel/Resort/
   Accommodation Operator 646
Ice Cream/Frozen Yogurt Shop 658
Image Consultant 664
Import/Export Service 667
Incubator 674
Information Broker 677
Insulation Contractor 679
Insurance Agency 680
Interior Design Service 691
Internet/Online Service Provider 696
Investment/Securities Broker 707
Jewelry Store 740
Job Training/Retraining 743
Kiosk/Pushcart/Vendor Business 745
Landscape Equipment and Supplies .. 748
Landscaping Service 750
Laundromat 757
Law Firm 760
Lawn Maintenance Service 761
Limousine Service 765
Lingerie Shop 767
Liquor Store 768
Literary Agency 771
Locksmith 772
Luggage and Leather
   Goods Business 774
Lumberyard 775
Machine Shop/Metalworking Shop 779
Mail Order Business 783
Management Consulting Service 785
Manufacturer's Representative 794
Marine Shop 796
Market Research and Analysis 800
Martial Arts Studio 806
Masonry, Stonework, and Plastering
   Contractors 807
Massage Therapist 811
Mediation Service 813
Medical and Dental Instrument
   Manufacturing 816
Medical Claims Service 821
Medical Laboratory Service 823
Medical Supplies Store 827
Medical Transcription Service 829
Messenger/Delivery/
   Subpoena Service 830
Miniature Golf Course Operation 831
Modeling School/Agency 832
Mortgage Broker 833
Motorcycle/Moped Store 840
Movie Theatre Operation 841
Moving/Storage Service 843
Music School 845
Music Shop 852
Musical Instrument Repair/Piano
   Tuning Service 856
Nail Salon 858
Nanny Service 859
New Age Services and Supplies 860
New and Used Car Dealer 862
Newsletter Publishing 870
Novelty Items Business 871

Nursing Home/Long-Term
   Care Center 872
Nutritional Consultant/Diet Planner 878
Office Design Service 884
Office Supply/Equipment Store 887
Online/Retail/E-Commerce 889
Paint/Wall Covering Center 898
Painting Contractor 900
Party Entertainment Service 903
Party/Reunion Planning Service 904
Pawnbroker 905
Payroll Preparation Service 906
Periodical/Newspaper Publishing 908
Personal Shopping Service 913
Pest Control Service 915
Pet Boarding/Grooming Service 918
Pet Cemetery 922
Pet Obedience School 923
Pet Shop 925
Pet Sitting Service 930
Photo Finishing Center 933
Photographer, Commercial 934
Photographic Studio 937
Physical Fitness Center 939
Physical Therapy Clinic/Practice 947
Pizzeria 951
Plant Leasing Service 956
Plumbing Service 957
Porcelain Refinishing Service 962
Power Washing Service 963
Prepaid Phone Card Business 964
Print/Frame Shop 965
Printing Business 967
Private Investigation/Personal
   Security Service 972
Private Label Product
   Manufacturer/Retailer 974
Professional Organizer 975
Property Management 978
Public Relations Consultant 982
Public Warehousing/
   Ministorage Operation 986
Quick Oil Change Service 989
Radio Station 991
Radon Testing Service 996
Real Estate Agency 997
Real Estate Investment Service 1015
Recording Studio 1032
Recreational Vehicle Dealer 1035
Recycling Business 1037
Rental Service 1042
Restaurant 1048
Resume Service 1074
Roofing Contractor 1075
Satellite Dish Service 1077
Screen Printing Business 1078
Security Systems Service 1079
Seminar Planner/Lecturer 1087
Service Station/Auto Repair
   and Service Shop 1089
Sewer and Drain
   Cleaning Business 1095
Sewing Center 1098

LIST OF SMALL BUSINESS PROFILES

Shoe Repair Shop 1100	Tattoo Parlor 1151	Translating/Interpreting Service 1204
Shoe Store 1101	Tax Preparation Business 1155	Travel Agency 1207
Sign Shop 1104	Taxicab/Van Shuttle Service 1166	Trucking Business 1213
Silk Plant Shop 1106	Taxidermy Service 1169	Tutoring Service 1218
Skating Rink Operation 1107	Teacher Supply Store 1170	Typesetting Business 1222
Ski Shop 1109	Telemarketing Service 1171	Typing/Stenographic Service 1225
Software Publishing 1111	Telephone Answering Service 1172	Upholstery/Carpet Services 1226
Solar Energy Design/	Television/Radio Repair Service 1173	Vending Machine Merchandising
Contracting Business 1121	Television Station 1174	and Service Business 1228
Specialized Staffing 1127	Temporary Employment Agency 1180	Video Production 1230
Specialty/Gourmet Foods/	Tennis Court/Racquet	Vision Center 1231
Wine Shop 1129	Club Operation 1183	Voice Mail Service 1236
Sporting Goods Store 1134	Tire Dealer 1185	Water Conditioning Service 1237
Sports Promotional Service 1138	Tobacco Shop 1187	Web Site Design 1240
Surveying Service 1144	Tour Guide Operation/	Weight Reduction/Control Center 1247
Swimming Pool/Hot Tub Business 1146	Adventure Service 1190	Welcome Service 1249
Tailor Shop 1148	Toy Business 1195	Window Dressing Business 1250
Talent Agency 1149	Trade Show/Conference	Word Processing Service 1251
Tanning Parlor/Sauna 1150	Management Service 1198	

Standard Industrial Classification (SIC) Codes for Profiled Small Businesses

Included here are the four-digit SIC codes and corresponding classification descriptions for the businesses profiled in this edition. The SIC system, which organizes businesses by type, is a product of the Statistical Policy Division of the U.S. Office of Management and Budget. Statistical data produced by government, public, and private organizations usually are categorized according to SIC codes, thereby facilitating the collection, comparison, and analysis of data as well as providing a uniform method for presenting statistical information. Hence, knowing the SIC code for a particular small business increases the access to, and the use of, a variety of statistical data from many sources. The following SIC codes were obtained from the 1987 edition of the Standard Industrial Classification Manual, the most recent version available. (The term "nec" stands for "not elsewhere classified.")

Accounting Service
- 7291 — Tax return preparation services
- 8721 — Accounting, auditing, and bookkeeping services

Adult Day Care Center
- 8322 — Individual and family social services (includes adult day care centers)

Advertising Service
- 7311 — Advertising agencies (includes advertising consultants)
- 7312 — Outdoor advertising agencies
- 7313 — Radio, television, and publishers' advertising representatives
- 7319 — Advertising, nec
- 7331 — Direct mail advertising services
- 8999 — Services, nec (includes advertising copywriters)

Airbag Replacement Service Centers
- 7538 — General automotive repair shops
- 7539 — Automotive repair shops, nec

Air Charter Service
- 4512 — Air transportation, scheduled (includes air cargo and passenger carriers)
- 4513 — Air courier services
- 4522 — Air transportation, nonscheduled (includes charter service)

Air-conditioning/Heating and Cooling Contractor
- 1711 — Plumbing, heating, and air-conditioning contractors

Air Purification/Cleaning Service
- 7699 — Repair shops and related services, nec (includes furnace cleaning service)

Ambulance Service
- 4119 — Local passenger transportation, nec (includes ambulance service, road)
- 4522 — Air transportation, nonscheduled (includes ambulance service, air)

Amusement Arcade
- 7993 — Coin-operated amusement devices

Amusement/Water Park
- 7996 — Amusement parks
- 7999 — Amusement and recreation services, nec (includes waterslides and wave pools)

Animal Breeder
- 0279 — Animal specialties, nec (includes kennels, breeding and raising own stock)
- 0752 — Animal specialty services, except veterinary (includes breeding of animals other than farm animals)

Animal Clinic
- 0742 — Veterinary service for animal specialties (includes animal hospitals for pets and other animals)

Antique Shop
- 5932 — Used merchandise stores (includes retail antique stores)

- 7641 — Reupholstery and furniture repair (includes antique furniture repair and restoration)
- 7699 — Repair shops and related services, nec (includes antique repair and restoration, except furniture)

Apartment Locating Service
- 6531 — Real Estate Agents and Managers

Appliance Store
- 5722 — Household appliance stores

Appraisal Service
- 7389 — Business services, nec (includes appraisers, except real estate)
- 6531 — Real estate agents and managers (includes appraisers, real estate)

Aquarium Maintenance/Leasing Service
- 7359 — Equipment rental and leasing, nec
- 8999 — Services, nec

Archery/Target/Shooting Range
- 7999 — Amusement and recreation services, nec (includes archery ranges, shooting galleries, shooting ranges, and trap-shooting facilities, except membership)

Architectural Restoration/Conservation
- 8712 — Architectural Services

Art Gallery
- 5932 — Used merchandise stores (includes retailers of art objects)

SIC CODES FOR PROFILED SMALL BUSINESSES

5999	Miscellaneous retail stores, nec (includes art dealers)
8412	Museums and art galleries (includes noncommercial art galleries)

Art Supplies Store

5999	Miscellaneous retail stores, nec (includes retail artists' supplies and materials stores)

Assisted Living Facilities

8051	Skilled nursing care facilities (includes extended care facilities and skilled nursing homes)
8052	Intermediate care facilities (includes intermediate care nursing homes)
8059	Nursing and personal care facilities, nec (includes rest homes with health care)

Association Management Service

8611	Business associations
8621	Professional membership organizations
8631	Labor unions and similar labor organizations
8641	Civic, social, and fraternal associations
8699	Membership organizations, nec
8741	Management services (does not include operating staff)

Auctioneer/Broker

5154	Livestock (includes wholesale livestock auctioning)
5999	Miscellaneous retail stores, nec (includes retail general merchandise auction rooms)
7389	Business services, nec (includes auctioneering services)

Auto Supply Store

5531	Auto and home supply stores

Automobile Detailing/Painting Service

7532	Automotive paint shops
7542	Carwashes (includes detailing, cleaning and polishing, new autos on a contract or fee basis; washing and polishing, automotive; waxing and polishing, automotive)

Automobile/Truck Leasing Service

7513	Truck rental and leasing, without drivers
7514	Passenger car rental, without drivers
7515	Passenger car leasing, without drivers

Baby Store

5999	Miscellaneous retail stores, nec (includes retail baby)

Bagel Shop

2051	Bread and other bakery products, except cookies and crackers (includes bagels)
5461	Retail bakeries (includes retail bagel stores)

Bait and Tackle Shop

5941	Sporting goods stores and bicycle shops (includes bait and tackle shops and fishing equipment, retail)

Bakery/Doughnut Shop

5461	Retail bakeries

Bar/Nightclub

5813	Drinking places alcoholic beverages (includes bars, cocktail lounges, saloons, tap rooms, taverns, and like establishments)

Beauty Supply Center

5087	Service establishment equipment and supplies (includes wholesale barber shop and beauty parlor equipment and supplies)

Bed and Breakfast Operation

7011	Hotels and motels (includes bed and breakfast inns)

Beekeeping

0279	Animal specialties, nec (includes apiaries and bee farms)

Beeper/Paging Service

4812	Radiotelephone communications (includes beeper and paging services)

Bicycle Shop

5941	Sporting goods stores and bicycle shops
7699	Repair shops and related services, nec (includes bicycle repair shops)

Billiards Hall

7999	Amusement and recreation services, nec (includes billiard parlors)

Blacktop Surfacing Business

1771	Concrete work (includes blacktop work: private driveways and private parking areas contractors)

Blind Cleaning/Installation

2431	Millwork (includes wood blinds and shutters)
2591	Drapery hardware and window blinds and shades

Body Care Shop

5999	Miscellaneous retail stores, nec (includes cosmetics stores)

Book Publishing

2731	Books; publishing or publishing and printing

Bookbinder

2789	Bookbinding and related work

Bookkeeping

8721	Accounting, auditing, and bookkeeping services

Bookstore

5932	Used merchandise stores (includes used book retailers)
5942	Bookstores

Bottled Water Service

5149	Groceries and related products, nec (includes natural spring and mineral water bottling and distribution services)

SIC CODES FOR PROFILED SMALL BUSINESSES

| 5499 | Miscellaneous food stores (includes mineral water, retail) |

Bowling Alley

| 7933 | Bowling centers |

Brewpub and Microbrewery

| 2082 | Malt beverages |

Bridal Shop/Bridal Consultant

| 5621 | Women's clothing stores (includes retail bridal shops, except custom designers) |

Building/Home Inspection Service

| 7389 | Business services, nec (includes safety inspection, except automotive) |

Building Maintenance/Custodial Service

| 7349 | Building cleaning and maintenance services, nec (includes interior building cleaning services, contract janitorial services, and like enterprises) |

Bulletin Board Service

| 4822 | Telegraph and other message communications (includes electronic mail services) |
| 7379 | Computer related services, nec |

Business Broker Service

| 7389 | Business services, nec (includes business brokers buying and selling business enterprises) |

Business Consulting Service

| 8748 | Business consulting services, nec |

Business Services Operation

| 8744 | Facilities support management services (includes base maintenance, providing personnel on continuing basis) |

Butcher Shop

| 5423 | Meat and fish (seafood) markets, including freezer provisioners |

| 5499 | Miscellaneous food stores (includes retail poultry dealers) |

Cable Network

1623	Water, Sewer, Pipeline, and Communications and Power Line Construction (includes cable television line construction-contractors)
1731	Electrical Work (includes cable television hookup-contractors)
4841	Cable and Other Pay Television Services

Calligraphy Service

| 7389 | Business services, nec (includes lettering services) |

Camera Shop

| 5946 | Camera and photographic supply stores |
| 7699 | Repair shops and related services, nec (includes camera repair shops) |

Campground Management

| 7033 | Recreational vehicle parks and campsites |

Candy/Chocolate Shop

| 5441 | Candy, nut, and confectionery stores |

Car Alarm and Stereo Store

| 5531 | Auto and home supply stores (includes automobile accessory dealers, retail) |
| 5731 | Radio, television, and consumer electronics stores (includes automotive stereo equipment, retail) |

Car Inspection Service

| 7549 | Automotive services, except repair services and car washes(includes inspection service, automotive) |

Car Towing Service

| 7549 | Automotive services, except repair services and car washes (includes automotive towing and wrecker services) |

Car Wash

| 7542 | Car washes |

Career Counseling

| 7389 | Business services, nec (includes career counseling service) |

Carpentry Service

| 1751 | Carpentry work |

Catering Service

| 5812 | Eating places (includes caterers) |

Cellular Phone/Telephone Business

| 4812 | Radiotelephone communications |
| 5999 | Miscellaneous retail stores, nec (includes telephone stores, retail) |

Charter Boat Service

| 4499 | Water transportation service, nec (includes boat rental, commercial) |

Check Cashing Service

| 6099 | Functions related to depository banking, nec (includes check cashing agencies) |

Children's Apparel Shop

5611	Men's and boys' clothing stores
5641	Children's and infants' wear stores
5651	Family clothing stores
5699	Miscellaneous apparel and accessory stores (includes children's wear)
5932	Used merchandise stores (includes retail second hand clothing stores)

Children's Day Care Center

| 8351 | Child day care services |

Chimney Sweeping Business

| 7349 | Building cleaning and maintenance services, nec (includes chimney cleaning service) |

Christmas Decoration Store

| 5999 | Miscellaneous retail stores, nec |

Christmas Tree Farm

| 0811 | Timber tracts (includes Christmas tree growing) |

Clipping Service

| 7389 | Business services, nec (includes press clipping service) |

Clothing Designer

2311	Men's and boys' suits, coats, and overcoats
2325	Men's and boys' separate trousers and slacks
2329	Men's and boys' clothing, nec
2331	Women's, misses', and juniors' blouses and shirts
2335	Women's, misses', and juniors' dresses
2337	Women's, misses', and juniors' suits, skirts, and coats
2361	Girls', children's, and infants' dresses, blouses, and shirts

Clothing Store

5611	Men's and boys' clothing and accessory stores
5621	Women's clothing stores
5632	Women's accessory and specialty stores
5641	Children's and infants' wear stores
5651	Family clothing stores
5699	Miscellaneous apparel and accessory stores
5932	Used merchandise stores (includes retail secondhand clothing stores)

Coffee Service

| 5149 | Groceries and related products, nec (includes coffee, wholesale) |

Coin/Stamp Dealer

| 5961 | Catalog and mail order houses (includes retail mail order coin and stamp businesses) |
| 5999 | Miscellaneous retail stores, nec |

Comic Book/Collectibles Store

| 5999 | Miscellaneous retail stores, nec |

Commercial/Graphic Art Business

| 7336 | Commercial art and graphic design |

Commercial Mail Receiving Agency

| 7389 | Business services, nec (includes post office contract stations) |

Compact Disc/Record Store

| 5735 | Recorded and prerecorded tape stores |

Computer Consulting

| 7379 | Computer related services, nec (includes computer consultants) |

Computer Data Storage Company

| 3572 | Computer storage devices |

Computer Learning/Training Center

| 8243 | Data processing schools |

Computer Maintenance and Repair Service

| 7378 | Computer maintenance and repair |

Computer Programming and Data Processing Service

| 7374 | Computer processing and data preparation services |

Computer Store

| 5734 | Computer and computer software stores |

Computer System Integrators

7371	Computer programming services
7373	Computer integrated systems design
7379	Computer related services, nec (includes computer consultants and database developers)

Computerized Billing Service

| 7374 | Computer processing and data preparation and processing services |

Computerized Matching Service

| 7299 | Miscellaneous personal services, nec (includes dating services) |
| 7375 | Information retrieval services |

Concession Stand Business

| 5812 | Eating places (includes concession stands in airports and sports arenas, and refreshment stands) |
| 7999 | Amusement and recreation services, nec (concession operators and amusement concessions) |

Consignment Shop

| 5932 | Used merchandise stores (includes clothing stores, secondhand retail; furniture stores, secondhand retail; home furnishing stores, secondhand retail) |

Construction Company

| 1521 | General contractors—single family houses |
| 1522 | General contractors—residential buildings other than single-family |

Consumer Electronics Store

| 5731 | Radio, television, and consumer electronics stores |

Convenience Store

| 5411 | Grocery stores (includes retail convenience food stores) |

Cooking School

| 8299 | Schools and educational services, nec (includes cooking schools) |

Copy Shop

| 7334 | Photocopying and duplicating services |

Cosmetics Business

| 2844 | Perfumes, cosmetics, and other toilet preparations |
| 5122 | Drugs, drug proprietaries, and druggists' sundries (includes cosmetics—wholesale) |

SIC CODES FOR PROFILED SMALL BUSINESSES

5963	Direct selling establishments (includes canvassers, headquarters for retail sale of merchandise, and direct selling organizations—retail)
5999	Miscellaneous retail stores, nec (includes cosmetics-stores—retail)

Costume Shop

7299	Miscellaneous personal services, nec (includes costume rental)
7922	Theatrical producers and miscellaneous theatrical services(includes theatrical costume design)

Craft Artisan

3269	Pottery products, nec (includes art and ornamental ware; pottery; ceramic articles for craft shops; cookware; crockery; china, earthenware and stoneware figures; kitchen articles; coarse earthenware; lamp bases; and vases)

Craft/Hobby Shop

5945	Hobby, toy, and game shops (includes retail hobby stores and craft kit and supply retailers)
5947	Gift, novelty, and souvenir shops pottery; ceramic articles for craft shops; cookware; crockery; china, earthenware and stoneware figures; kitchen articles; coarse earthenware; lamp bases; and vases)

Create Your Own...Store

3269	Pottery Products, nec
5947	Gift, Novelty, and Souvenir Shops
5999	Miscellaneous retail stores, nec

Credit Card Issuing Service

6153	Short-Term Business Credit Institutions, Except Agricultural (includes credit card service, collection by central agency)

7389	Business Services, nec (includes credit card service collection by individual firms)

Credit Repair Service

7299	Miscellaneous personal services, nec (includes debt counseling and adjustment services)

Credit Reporting and Collection Service

7322	Adjustment and collection services
7323	Credit reporting services

Damage Restoration Service

1790	Special trade contractors, nec (includes cleaning building exteriors, damp-proofing buildings, dewatering, fireproofing buildings, steam cleaning of building exteriors, and waterproofing)

Dance School

7911	Dance studios, schools, and halls

Delicatessen/Sandwich Shop

5812	Eating places (includes sandwich bars or shops and submarine sandwich shops)

Desktop Publishing Company

2711	Publishing, or publishing and printing newspapers
2721	Publishing, or publishing and printing periodicals
2731	Publishing, or publishing and printing books
2741	Miscellaneous publishing

Dial-it Services

4813	Telephone communications, except radiotelephone

Disc Jockey Service

8999	Services, nec

Domestic Help/Maid Service

7349	Building cleaning and maintenance services, nec (includes housekeeping and office cleaning services)

8811	Private households (includes private households employing cooks, maids, and other domestic help)

Driving School

8249	Vocational schools, nec (includes truck driving schools)
8299	Schools and educational services, nec (includes automobile driving instruction)

Drug Store/Pharmacy

5912	Drug stores and proprietary stores

Dry Cleaning Service/Coin-Operated Laundry

7215	Coin-operated laundries and dry cleaning services
7216	Dry cleaning plants, except rug cleaning

Editorial/Freelance Writing Business

8999	Services, nec (includes writing and ghostwriting services)

Electrical Contractor

1731	Electrical work (includes trade contractors engaged in on-site electrical work)

Electrical Lighting Supply Store

5719	Miscellaneous home furnishings stores (includes retail lamp and shade shops)

Employee Leasing Service

7363	Help supply services

Employment Agency

361	Employment agencies

Engraving/Monogramming Service

3479	Coating, engraving, and allied services, nec (includes jewelry and silverware engraving)
7389	Business services, nec (includes advertising embroidery services, embossing services, and identification engraving services)

SIC CODES FOR PROFILED SMALL BUSINESSES

Environmental Consultant
8748   Business consulting services, nec

Environmental Store
5999   Miscellaneous retail stores, nec

Estate Planning
8811   Private Households

Estate Sales Business
6530   Real estate agents and managers

Executive Recruiting Agency
7361   Employment agencies (includes executive placement)

Fashion Accessories/Design Business
3961   Costume jewelry and costume novelties, except precious metal
5137   Women's, children's, and infants' clothing and accessories
5632   Women's accessory and specialty stores

Film and Video Production Operation
7812   Motion picture and videotape production services

Financial Planning Service
282   Investment Advice

Fish and Seafood Store
5421   Meat and fish (seafood) markets, including freezer provisioners

Fish Farm
0273   Animal aquaculture (includes fish farms except hatcheries)

Floor Covering/Restoration Business
5713   Floor covering stores—retail

Florist
5992   Florists

Food Delivery Service
5812   Eating places

5963   Direct selling establishments (includes door-to-door selling organizations and mobile lunch wagons)
5999   Miscellaneous retail stores, nec

Freight Forwarding Service
4731   Arrangement of transportation of freight and cargo (includes freight forwarding services)

Fund-Raising Consultant
7389   Business services, nec (includes fund raising on a contract or fee basis)

Funeral Service
7261   Funeral services and crematories

Fur Farm
0271   Fur-bearing animals and rabbits

Fur Store
5632   Women's accessory and specialty stores (includes fur shops and furriers)

Furniture Restoration Service
7641   Reupholstery and furniture repair

Gambling Organizations/Service
7011   Hotels and Motels (includes casino hotels)
7993   Coin-Operated Amusement Devices
7999   Amusement and Recreation Services, nec (includes gambling establishments not primarily operating coin-operated machines and lotteries, operation of)
9311   Public Finance Taxation, and Monetary Policy (includes gambling control boards-government and lottery control boards-government)

Genealogy Service
7299   Miscellaneous personal services, nec (includes genealogical investigation service)

Gift Basket Service
5961   Catalog and mail-order houses

Gift/Card Shop
5943   Stationery stores
5947   Gift, novelty, and souvenir shops (includes card shops)

Glass Repair and Replacement Service
1751   Carpentry work (includes prefabricated window and door installation)
7536   Automotive glass replacement shops

Golf Shop
5941   Sporting goods stores and bicycle shops (includes retail golf goods and equipment stores)

Gourmet Coffee/Tea House
5499   Miscellaneous food stores (includes coffee stores, retail)
5812   Eating places (includes coffee shops)

Greenhouse/Garden Center/Nursery Business
0181   Ornamental floricultural and nursery products (includes greenhouses for floral products, growing of nursery stock, growing of potted plants)
5261   Retail nurseries, lawn and garden supply stores (includes nursery stock, seeds, and bulbs, retail)

Greeting Card Publishing
2771   Greeting card publishing and printing
8999   Services, nec (includes hand painting of greeting cards)

Grocery Store
5411   Grocery stores

Gunsmith/Gun Shop
5941   Sporting goods stores and bicycle shops (includes firearms, retail)

| 7699 | Repair shops and related services, nec (includes gunsmith shops) |

Hair Replacement/Electrolysis Clinic

| 7299 | Miscellaneous personal services, nec (includes depilatory salons, electrolysis, and hair weaving or replacement services) |

Hair Salon/Barber Shop

| 7231 | Beauty shops (includes beauty and barber shops combined) |
| 7241 | Barber shops |

Handwriting Analysis Consultant

| 7389 | Business services, nec (includes handwriting analysis) |

Hardware Store

| 5251 | Hardware stores |

Hat Store

| 5611 | Men's and boys' clothing and accessory stores (includes retail hat stores) |
| 5621 | Women's accessory and specialty stores (includes retail millinery stores) |

Hazardous Waste Disposal Business

| 4953 | Refuse systems (includes hazardous waste material disposal sites) |

Health Food Store

| 5499 | Miscellaneous food stores (includes health food stores) |

Healthy Restaurants

| 5812 | Eating Places |

Hearing Aid Testing and Fitting Service

| 5999 | Miscellaneous retail stores, nec (includes hearing aids, retail) |
| 8099 | Health and allied services, nec (includes hearing testing service) |

Herb Farm

0191	General farms, primarily crop
2833	Medical chemicals and botanical products (includes herb grinding, grading, and milling)
5499	Miscellaneous food stores (includes spice and herb stores)

Home Accessory Store

| 5714 | Drapery, curtain, and upholstery stores |
| 5719 | Miscellaneous home furnishings stores |

Home Furnishings Store

5712	Furniture stores
5719	Miscellaneous home furnishings stores
5932	Used merchandise stores (including antique and secondhand retail furniture stores)

Home Health Care Service

| 8082 | Home health care services |

Horse Riding Academy

| 752 | Animal specialty services, except veterinary (includes boarding and training horses) |

Hotel/Motel/Resort Operation

| 7011 | Hotels and motels (includes resort hotels) |

Ice Cream/Frozen Yogurt Shop

5451	Dairy products stores (includes retail packaged ice cream stores)
5812	Eating places (includes retail dairy bars)
563	Direct selling establishments (includes ice cream wagons)

Image Consultant

| 8299 | Schools and educational services, nec (includes personal development schools) |
| 8743 | Public relations services |

Import/Export Service

| 4731 | Arrangement of the transportation of freight and cargo |

Incubator

| 7389 | Business services, nec |
| 8748 | Business consulting services, nec |

Information Broker

| 7375 | Information retrieval services |

Insulation Contractor

| 1742 | Plastering, dry wall, acoustical, and insulation work (includes insulation installation contractors) |

Insurance Agency

| 6411 | Insurance agents, brokers, and services |

Interior Design Service

| 7389 | Business services, nec (includes interior decoration consulting services and interior design services) |

Internet/Online Service Provider

| 4822 | Telegraph and other message communications (includes electronic mail services) |
| 7379 | Computer related services, nec |

Investment/Securities Broker

| 6211 | Security brokers, dealers, and flotation companies |

Jewelry Store

5632	Women's accessory and specialty stores (includes costume jewelry stores)
5944	Jewelry stores
7631	Watch, clock, and jewelry repair

Job Training/Retraining

| 8331 | Job training and vocational rehabilitation services (includes job training) |

Kiosk/Pushcart/Vendor Business

| 5812 | Eating places (includes box lunch stands, concession stands, food bars, hamburger and hot dog stands, ice cream stands, refreshment stands, and soft drink stands) |

SIC CODES FOR PROFILED SMALL BUSINESSES

Landscaping Service
0781   Landscape counseling and planning services
0782   Lawn and garden services
0783   Ornamental shrub and tree services

Lawn Maintenance Service
0782   Lawn and garden services
0783   Ornamental shrub and tree services

Limousine Service
4119   Local passenger transportation, nec (includes hearse and limousine rental, with drivers)
7514   Passenger car rental (includes limo rental, w/o drivers)

Lingerie Shop
5632   Lingerie stores, retail

Liquor Store
5921   Liquor stores

Literary Agency
7389   Business services, nec (includes agents and brokers for authors and non-performing artists)

Locksmith
7699   Repair shops and related services, nec (includes locksmith shops and made-to order lock parts)

Luggage and Leather Goods Business
5948   Luggage and leather goods stores

Lumberyard
5211   Lumber and other building materials dealers

Machine Shop/Metalworking Shop
3541   Machine tools, metal cutting types
3542   Machine tools, metal forming types
3544   Special dies and tools, die sets, jigs and fixtures, and industrial molds
3545   Cutting tools, machine tool accessories, and machinists' precision measuring devices
3549   Metalworking machinery, nec

Mail Order Business
5961   Catalog and mail order houses

Management Consulting Service
8742   Management consulting services

Manufacturer's Representative
7389   Business services, nec

Marine Shop
5551   Boat dealers (includes retail marine supply dealers)

Market Research and Analysis
8732   Commercial, economic, sociological, and educational research
8742   Management consulting services

Martial Arts Studio
7999   Amusement and recreation services, nec (includes Judo and Karate instruction)

Masonry, Stonework, and Plastering Contractors
1741   Masonry, stone setting, and other stonework
1742   Plastering, dry wall, acoustical, and insulation work

Massage Therapist
7299   Massage parlor
8049   Offices and clinics of health practitioners, nec

Mediation Service
7389   Business services, nec (includes arbitration and conciliation services)

Medical and Dental Instrument Manufacturing
3841   Surgical and medical instruments and apparatus
3843   Dental equipment and supplies

Medical Claims Service
6411   Insurance agents, brokers, and service (includes processing of medical claims on a contract or fee basis)

Medical Laboratory Service
8071   Medical laboratories

Medical Supplies Store
5047   Medical, dental, and hospital equipment and supplies

Medical Transcription Service
7374   Computer processing and data preparation and processing services

Messenger/Delivery/Subpoena Service
4215   Courier services, except by air (includes letter, mail, package, and parcel delivery services)
4822   Telegraph and other message communication (includes cablegrams, mailgrams, electronic mail, and other message services)
7389   Business services, nec (includes process serving services)

Miniature Golf Course Operation
7999   Amusement and recreation services, nec (includes miniature golf course operations)

Modeling School/Agency
7363   Help supply services (includes modeling services)
8299   Schools and educational services, nec (includes modeling schools)

Mortgage Broker
6162   Mortgage bankers and loan correspondents (includes mortgage brokers using own money)
6163   Loan brokers (includes mortgage brokers arranging for loans but using money of others)
6211   Security brokers, dealers, and flotation companies (includes buying and selling mortgages)

SIC CODES FOR PROFILED SMALL BUSINESSES

Motorcycle/Moped Store
5571	Motorcycle dealers

Movie Theatre Operation
7832	Motion picture theatres, except drive-ins
7833	Drive-in motion picture theatres

Moving Service
4212	Local trucking, without storage (includes furniture and other moving services)
4214	Local trucking, with storage (includes furniture and household goods moving services)

Music School
8299	Schools and educational services, nec (includes music schools)

Music Shop
5736	Musical instrument stores
5932	Used merchandise stores (includes retailers of secondhand musical instruments)
7699	Repair shops and related services, nec (includes musical instrument repair shops)

Musical Instrument Repair/Piano Tuning Service
7699	Repair shops and related services, nec (includes musical instrument repair shops and piano tuning and repair)

Nail Salon
7231	Beauty shops (includes manicure and pedicure salons)

Nanny Service
7299	Miscellaneous personal services, nec (includes babysitting bureaus)

New Age Services and Supplies
5999	Miscellaneous retail stores, nec
8999	Services, nec

New and Used Car Dealer
5511	Motor vehicle dealers (new and used)
5521	Motor vehicle dealers (used only)

Newsletter Publishing
2721	Periodicals; publishing or publishing and printing
2741	Miscellaneous publishing (includes business service newsletters publishing and/or printing)

Novelty Items Business
2499	Wood products, nec (includes wood and wood fiber novelties)
2514	Metal household furniture (includes metal novelty furniture)
2679	Converted paper and paperboard products, nec (includes paper novelties)
3199	Leather goods, nec (includes leather novelties)
3229	Pressed and blown glass and glassware, nec (includes novelty glassware made in glassmaking plants)
3231	Glass products, made of purchased glass (includes glass novelties)
3499	Fabricated metal products, nec (includes metal novelties and specialties, except advertising novelties)
3961	Costume jewelry and costume novelties, except precious metal and gems
3999	Manufacturing industries, nec (includes bone, beaded and shell novelties)

Nursing Home/Long-Term Care Center
8051	Skilled nursing care facilities
8052	Intermediate care facilities (includes intermediate care nursing homes)
8059	Nursing and personal care facilities, nec (includes convalescent homes, rest homes, and like facilities)

Nutritional Consultant/Diet Planner
7299	Miscellaneous personal services, nec (includes diet workshops)

8049	Offices and clinics of health practitioners, nec (includes offices of nutritionists and offices of dietitians)

Office Design Service
7389	Business services, nec (includes interior decorating and design services)

Office Supply/Equipment Store
5943	Stationery stores (includes retail office forms and supplies stores)

Online/Retail/E-Commerce
5734	Computer and computer software stores
7375	Information retrieval services

Paint/Wall Covering Center
5231	Paint, glass, and wallpaper stores

Painting Contractors
1721	Painting and paperhanging contractors

Party Entertainment Services
7929	Bands, orchestras, actors, and other entertainers and entertainment groups

Party/Reunion Planning Service
7359	Equipment rental and leasing, nec (includes party supplies rental and leasing)
8999	Services, nec

Pawnbroker
5932	Used merchandise stores (includes pawnshops)

Payroll Preparation Service
8721	Accounting, auditing, and bookkeeping services (includes payroll accounting service)

Periodical/Newspaper Publishing
2721	Periodicals; publishing or publishing and printing

Personal Shopping Service
7299	Miscellaneous personal services, nec (includes shopping services for individuals)

SIC CODES FOR PROFILED SMALL BUSINESSES

Pest Control Service

0851   Forestry services (includes forest pest control)

7342   Disinfecting and pest control services

Pet Boarding/Grooming Service

0279   Animal specialties, nec (includes breeding kennels)

0752   Animal specialty services (includes boarding kennels, dog grooming services, and related services)

Pet Cemetery

0782   Lawn and garden services (includes independent cemetery upkeep services)

6531   Real estate agents and managers (includes cemetery management services)

6553   Cemetery subdividers and developers (includes animal cemetery operations)

Pet Obedience School

0752   Animal specialty services, except veterinary (includes training of pets and other animal specialties)

Pet Shop

5999   Miscellaneous retail stores, nec (includes pet shops)

Pet Sitting Service

0752   Animal specialty services, except veterinary

Photo Finishing Center

7384   Photo finishing laboratories

7819   Services allied to motion picture production (includes motion picture film processing)

Photographer, Commercial

7335   Commercial photography

Photographic Studio

7221   Photographic studios, portrait

Physical Fitness Center

7991   Physical fitness facilities

Physical Therapy Clinic/Practice

8049   Offices and clinics of health practitioners, nec (includes offices of physical therapists)

Pizzeria

5812   Eating places (includes pizza parlors and pizzerias)

Plant Leasing Service

7359   Equipment rental and leasing, nec (includes plants)

Plumbing Service

1711   Plumbing, heating, and air-conditioning contractors

Porcelain Refinishing Service

1799   Special trade contractors, nec

Power Washing Service

1799   Special trade contractors, nec (includes cleaning of building exteriors)

7349   Building cleaning and maintenance services, nec (includes cleaning of building interiors)

7542   Car washes (includes automotive washing and polishing)

Prepaid Phone Card Business

4812   Radiotelephone communications

4813   Telephone communications, except radiotelephone

Print/Frame Shop

7699   Repair shops and related services, nec (includes custom picture framing services)

Printing Business

2752   Commercial printing, lithographic

2754   Commercial printing, gravure

2759   Commercial printing, nec

2761   Manifold business form printers

Private Investigation/Personal Security Service

7381   Detective, guard, and armored car services

Private Label Product Manufacturer/Retailer

3999   Manufacturing industries, nec

5399   Miscellaneous general merchandise stores

5499   Miscellaneous food stores 5699 Miscellaneous apparel and accessory stores

5999   Miscellaneous retail stores, nec

Professional Organizer

7299   Miscellaneous personal services, nec

7389   Business services, nec

Property Management

6531   Real estate agents and managers

Public Relations Consultant

8743   Public relations services

Public Warehousing/Ministorage Operation

4221   Farm product warehousing and storage

4222   Refrigerated warehousing and storage

4225   General warehousing and storage

4226   Special warehousing and storage, nec (includes fur storage, household goods warehousing and storage, whiskey warehousing, and like enterprises)

Quick Oil Change Service

5541   Gasoline service stations (includes automobile service stations—retail)

7538   General automotive repair shops

Radio Station

4832   Radio broadcasting stations

Radon Testing Service

1799   Special trade contractors, nec

8734   Testing laboratories

Real Estate Agency

6531   Real estate agents and managers

SIC CODES FOR PROFILED SMALL BUSINESSES

Real Estate Investment Service

6798   Real estate investment trusts

Recording Studio

7399   Business services, nec (includes recording studios operating on a contract or fee basis)

Recreational Vehicle Dealer

5561   Recreational vehicle dealers

Recycling Business

5093   Scrap and waste materials

Rental Service

7299   Miscellaneous personal services, nec (includes clothing rental)

7352   Medical equipment rental and leasing

7353   Heavy construction equipment and leasing

7359   Equipment rental and leasing, nec

7377   Computer rental and leasing

7999   Amusement and recreation services, nec (includes pleasure boat rental, canoe and rowboat rental, bicycle, motorcycle and moped rental, and sporting goods rental)

Restaurant

5812   Eating places (includes sit-down, carry-out, and fast food)

Resume Service

7338   Secretarial and court reporting services (includes resume writing services)

Roofing Contractor

1761   Roofing, siding, and sheet metal work

Satellite Dish Service

4841   Cable and other pay television services (includes direct broadcast satellite services and satellite master antenna systems services)

Screen Printing Business

2261   Finishers of broadwoven fabrics of cotton (includes printing and finishing of cotton broadwoven fabrics)

2262   Finishers of broadwoven fabrics of manmade fiber and silk (includes printing manmade fiber and silk broadwoven fabrics)

2759   Commercial printing, nec (includes screen printing on glass, plastics, paper, and metal, including highway signs)

Security Systems Service

7382   Security systems services

Seminar Planner/Lecturer

8999   Services, nec (including lecturers)

Service Station/Auto Repair and Service Shop

5541   Gasoline service stations

7532   Top, body, and upholstery repair shops and paint shops

7533   Automotive exhaust system repair shops

7534   Tire retreading and repair shops

7536   Automotive glass replacement shops

7537   Automotive transmission repair shops

7538   General automotive repair shops

7539   Automotive repair shops, nec

Sewer and Drain Cleaning Business

7699   Repair shops and related services, nec (includes sewer cleaning and rodding and septic tank cleaning)

Sewing Center

5722   Household appliance stores (includes retail sewing machine stores)

5949   Sewing, needlework, and piece goods stores

7699   Repair shops and related services, nec (includes sewing machine repair shops)

Shoe Repair Shop

7251   Shoe repair shops and shoeshine parlors

Shoe Store

5661   Shoe stores

Sign Shop

3993   Signs and advertising specialties

7389   Business services, nec (includes sign painting shops)

Silk Plant Shop

5999   Miscellaneous retail stores, nec (includes artificial flowers—retail)

Skating Rink Operation

7999   Amusement and recreation services, nec (includes ice and roller skating rink operations)

Ski Shop

5941   Sporting goods stores and bicycle shops

Software Publishing

7372   Packaged software

Solar Energy Design/Contracting Business

1711   Plumbing, heating, and air-conditioning contractors (includes solar heating apparatus contractors)

1742   Plastering, dry wall, acoustical, and insulation work (includes solar reflecting insulation film contractors)

Specialized Staffing

7361   Employment Agencies

7363   Help Supply Services

Specialty/Gourmet Foods/Wine Shop

5499   Miscellaneous food stores

5921   Liquor stores (includes packaged wine—retail)

Sporting Goods Store

5941   Sporting goods stores and bicycle shops

Sports Promotional Services

7941   Professional Sports Clubs and Promoters

SIC CODES FOR PROFILED SMALL BUSINESSES

Surveying Service

8713   Surveying services (includes surveying: land, water, and aerial)

Swimming Pool/Hot Tub Business

1799   Special trade contractors, nec (includes swimming pool construction contractors)

5999   Miscellaneous retail stores, nec (includes hot tubs, retail)

7389   Business services, nec (includes swimming pool cleaning and maintenance services)

7999   Amusement and recreation services, nec (includes swimming pool operations)

Tailor Shop

5699   Miscellaneous apparel and accessory stores (includes custom tailor shops) 7219 Laundry and garment services, nec (includes tailor shops, except custom or merchant tailors)

Talent Agency

7922   Theatrical producers and miscellaneous theatrical services (includes agents)

Tanning Parlor/Sauna

7299   Miscellaneous personal services (includes steam baths and tanning salons)

Tattoo Parlor

7299   Miscellaneous personal services, nec (includes tattoo parlors)

Tax Preparation Business

7291   Tax return preparation services

8721   Accounting, auditing, and bookkeeping services

Taxicab/Van Shuttle Service

4121   Taxicabs

Taxidermy Service

7699   Repair shops and related services, nec (includes taxidermy)

Teacher Supply Store

5999   Miscellaneous retail stores, nec

Telemarketing Service

7389   Business services, nec (includes telemarketing services operating on a contract or fee basis)

Telephone Answering Service

7389   Business services, nec (includes answering services)

Television/Radio Repair Service

7622   Radio and television repair shops

Television Station

4833   Television broadcasting stations

Temporary Employment Agency

7363   Help supply services (includes temporary help services

Tennis Court/Racquet Club Operation

7997   Membership sports and recreation clubs (includes racquetball and tennis clubs)

7999   Amusement and recreation services, nec (includes nonmembership racquetball and tennis court operations)

Tire Dealer

5531   Auto and home supply stores (includes retail tire dealers) 7534 Tire retreading and repair shops

Tobacco Shop

5993   Tobacco stores and stands

Tour Guide Operation/Adventure Service

4725   Tour operations

7999   Amusement and recreation services, nec (includes tour guides)

Toy Business

5945   Hobby, toy, and game shops

Trade Show/Conference Management Service

7389   Business services, nec (includes trade show arrangement)

Translating/Interpreting Service

7389   Business services, nec (includes translation service)

Travel Agency

4724   Travel agencies

Trucking Business

4212   Local trucking, without storage services

4213   Trucking, except local

4214   Local trucking, with storage services

Tutoring Service

8299   Schools and educational services, nec (includes tutoring services)

Typesetting Business

2791   Typesetting

Typing/Stenographic Service

7338   Secretarial and court reporting services (includes stenographic and typing services)

Upholstery/Carpet Services

1752   Floor laying and other floor work, nec (includes carpet laying and removing services)

5714   Drapery, curtain, and upholstery stores (includes upholstery materials stores)

7217   Carpet and upholstery cleaning

Vending Machine Merchandising and Service Business

5962   Automatic merchandising machine operators (includes retail sale of products through vending machines)

7359   Equipment rental and leasing services, nec (includes vending machine rental businesses)

SIC CODES FOR PROFILED SMALL BUSINESSES

Vision Center

5995　　Optical goods stores

Voice Mail Service

4813　　Telephone communications, except radiotelephone (includes voice telephone communications)

Water Conditioning Service

7389　　Business services, nec (includes water softener services)

Web Site Design

7371　　Computer programming services (includes custom computer programs or systems software development and computer software systems analysis and design)

Weight Reduction/Control Center

7991　　Physical fitness facilities (includes reducing facilities and slenderizing salons)

Welcome Service

7389　　Business service, nec (includes welcoming service)

Window Dressing Business

3993　　Signs and advertising specialties (includes advertising displays, except printed, and window and lobby cutouts and displays)

7319　　Advertising, nec (includes display advertising services, except outdoor)

Word Processing Service

7338　　Secretarial and court reporting services (includes word processing services)

Licensing Assistance Programs

Included here are state offices that provide information and assistance to small business owners and entrepreneurs concerning business licensing requirements and regulations.

ALABAMA

Dept. of Revenue—Business Licensing
50 N. Ripley
Montgomery, AL 36130
334-242-1170
URL: http://www.revenue.alabama.gov/business-license

ALASKA

Division of Corporations, Business and Professional Licensing
PO Box 110806
Juneau, AK 99811-0806
907-465-2550
Fax: 907-465-2974
Email: businesslicense@alaska.gov
URL: www.commerce.alaska.gov/web/cbpl/BusinessLicensing.aspx

ARIZONA

Arizona Commerce Authority
100 N. 7th Ave., Ste. 400
Phoenix, AZ 85007
602-845-1200
URL: https://www.azcommerce.com/small-business/quick-links/business-licensing

ARKANSAS

Arkansas Dept. of Labor and Licensing
900 W Capitol Ave, Ste 400
Little Rock, AR 72201
501-682-4500
Fax: 501-682-4535
Email: asklabor@arkansas.gov
URL: https://labor.arkansas.gov/licensing

CALIFORNIA

Department of Consumer Affairs
1625 N. Market Blvd.
Sacramento, CA 95834
Email: DCA@dca.ca.gov
Toll-Free: 800-952-5210
URL: http://www.dca.ca.gov

COLORADO

Dept. of Regulatory Agencies
1560 Broadway, Ste. 110
Denver, CO 80202
303-894-7855
Toll-Free: 800-886-7675
URL: https://dora.colorado.gov/

CONNECTICUT

Dept. of Consumer Protection—DCP License Services Division
450 Columbus Blvd., Ste. 901
Hartford, CT 06103
860-713-6100
URL: https://portal.ct.gov/dcp

DELAWARE

Dept. of State — Professional Regulation Division
Cannon Bldg., Ste. 203
861 Silver Lake Blvd., Ste. 203
Dover, DE 19904
302-744-4500
Fax: 302-739-2711
URL: http://dpr.delaware.gov

DISTRICT OF COLUMBIA

Dept. of Licensing and Consumer Protection
1100 4th St., SW
Washington, DC 20024
202-671-4500
Email: dlcp@dc.gov
URL: http://dlcp.dc.gov

FLORIDA

Department of Business & Professional Regulation
2601 Blair Stone Rd.
Tallahassee, FL 32399-1027
850-487-1395
URL: https://www2.myfloridalicense.com/

GEORGIA

Georgia Secretary of State—Professional Licensing Boards Division
237 Coliseum Dr.
Macon, GA 31217-3858
404-424-9966
URL: https://www.sos.ga.gov/licensing-division-georgia-secretary-states-office

HAWAII

Department of Business, Economic Development & Tourism
No. 1 Capital District Bldg.
250 S Hotel St.
Honolulu, HI 96813
808-586-2355
URL: https://dbedt.hawaii.gov/

IDAHO

Division of Occupational and Professional Licenses
Street Address:
11341 W. Chinden Blvd.
Boise, ID 83714
Mailing Address:
PO Box 83720
Boise, ID 83720-0063
208-334-3233
Email: dopl@dopl.idaho.gov
URL: https://dopl.idaho.gov

ILLINOIS

Illinois Department of Financial & Professional Regulation
320 W. Washington St., 3rd Fl.
Springfield, IL 62786
888-473-4858
URL: https://idfpr.illinois.gov

INDIANA

Professional Licensing Agency
Indiana Government Center South,
Room W072

LICENSING ASSISTANCE PROGRAMS

402 West Washington St.
Indianapolis, IN 46204
317-232-2960
URL: https://www.in.gov/pla/

IOWA

Professional Licensing Division
8120 Jennings Dr.
Cedar Falls, IA 50614
319-273-5444
Email: info@iasourcelink.com
URL: https://license.iasourcelink.com/

KANSAS

Secretary of State - Business Services Div.
Memorial Hall, 1st Fl.
120 SW 10th Ave.
Topeka, KS 66612-1594
785-296-4564
Email: kssos@ks.gov
URL: https://sos.ks.gov/businesses/businesses.html

KENTUCKY

Business One Stop
500 Metro St.
Frankfort, KY 40601
800-626-2250
URL: https://onestop.ky.gov/resources/Pages/feedback.aspx

LOUISIANA

Secretary of State—Commercial Div.
URL: https://www.sos.la.gov/BusinessServices/Pages/default.aspx

MAINE

URL: http://www.maine.gov/portal/business/licensing.html

MARYLAND

Department of Labor — Division of Occupational and Professional Licensing
PO Box 29622
Baltimore, MD 21201
410-230-6231
Email: dlopl-labor@maryland.gov
URL: http://www.dllr.state.md.us/license/

MASSACHUSETTS

Division of Occupational Licensure
1 Federal St.
Boston, MA 02110
617-701-8600
URL: https://www.mass.gov/orgs/division-of-occupational-licensure

MICHIGAN

Dept. of Licensing and Regulatory Affairs
Street address:
611 W Ottawa St.
Lansing, MI 48933-1070
Mailing address:
PO Box 30004
Lansing, MI 48909-7504
517-241-0199
Fax: 517-241-9416
Email: BPLHelp@Michigan.gov
URL: http://www.michigan.gov/lara

MINNESOTA

Commerce Dept.
85 7th Place East, Ste. 280
St. Paul, MN 55101
651-539-1500
URL: https://mn.gov/commerce/

MISSISSIPPI

Mississippi Secretary of State—Business Services & Regulation
Street address:
125 S Congress St.
Jackson, MS 39201
Mailing address:
PO Box 136
Jackson, MS 39205-0136
601-359-1633
Toll-Free: 800-256-3494
Fax: 601-576-2546
URL: www.sos.ms.gov/business-services-regulation

MISSOURI

Missouri Division of Professional Registration
Street address:
3605 Missouri Blvd.
Jefferson City, MO 65102
Mailing address:
PO Box 1335
Jefferson City, MO 65102-1335
573-751-0293
Email: profreg@pr.mo.gov
URL: https://www.pr.mo.gov/

MONTANA

Department of Labor and Industry
PO Box 1728
Helena, MT 59624
406-444-2840
URL: https://dli.mt.gov/

NEBRASKA

Secretary of State Business Services
1201 N Street, Suite 120
Lincoln, NE 68508
402-471-2554
Fax: 402-471-3237
URL: https://sos.nebraska.gov/business-services/new-business-information

NEVADA

Nevada Secretary of State
101 N Carson St., Ste. 3
Carson City, NV 89701
775-684-5708
URL: https://www.nvsos.gov/sos

NEW HAMPSHIRE

Department of Business and Economic Affairs
1 Eagle Square, Ste. 100
Concord, NH 03301
603-271-2591
URL: https://www.nheconomy.com/

NEW JERSEY

New Jersey Division of Consumer Affairs
124 Halsey St.
Newark, NJ 07102
973-504-6200
Email: AskConsumerAffairs@dca.lps.state.nj.us
URL: www.njconsumeraffairs.gov

NEW MEXICO

Regulation & Licensing Department
2550 Cerrillos Rd
Santa Fe, NM 87505
505-476-4500
URL: https://www.rld.nm.gov/

NEW YORK

New York State Dept. of State, Division of Licensing Services
Street address:
1 Commerce Plz.
99 Washington Ave., 6th Fl.
Albany, NY 12231
518-474-4429
Fax: 518-473-6648
Email: licensing@dos.ny.gov
URL: https://dos.ny.gov/licensing-services

NORTH CAROLINA

Dept. of the Secretary of State Business Registration
PO Box 29622
Raleigh, NC 27626-0622
919-814-5400
URL: https://www.sosncgov/divisions/business_registration

NORTH DAKOTA

Secretary of State—Business Information and Registration
600 E. Boulevard Ave., Dept. 108
Bismarck, ND 58505-0500
701-328-2900
800-352-0867
URL: https://sos.nd.gov/business/business-services

OHIO

Department of Commerce
77 S. High St., 20th Fl.
Columbus, OH 43215
614-466-4100
URL: http://www.com.ohio.gov/

OKLAHOMA

Dept. of Commerce
900 N Stiles Ave.
Oklahoma City, OK 73104
405-815-8552
Toll-Free: 800-879-6552
https://www.okcommerce.gov/

OREGON

Secretary of State—Corporate Division
255 Capitol St. NE, Ste. 151
Salem, OR 97310-1327
503-986-2200
URL: https://sos.oregon.gov/business/Pages/default.aspx

PENNSYLVANIA

Bureau of Professional & Occupational Affairs
Secretary of Commonwealth (State Dept.)
Street address:
2525 N 7th Street
Harrisburg, PA 17110
Mailing address:
PO Box 2649
Harrisburg, PA 17105
833-367-2762
URL: https://www.pa.gov/agencies/dos/department-and-offices/bpoa.html

RHODE ISLAND

Department of State - Business Services Division
148 W River St.
Providence, RI 02904
401-222-3040
Email: corporations@sos.ri.gov
URL: https://www.sos.ri.gov/divisions/business-services

SOUTH CAROLINA

Department of Labor, Licensing and Regulation
Synergy Business Park, Kingstree Bldg.
110 Centerview Dr.
Columbia, SC 29210
803-896-4300
URL: https://llr.sc.gov

SOUTH DAKOTA

Dept. of Labor & Regulation: Boards, Commissions & Councils
123 W. Missouri Ave.
Pierre, SD 57501
605-773-3101
Fax: 605-773-6184
URL: https://dlr.sd.gov/boards_commissions_councils.aspx

TENNESSEE

Dept. of Commerce & Insurance Licensing & Regulations
500 James Robertson Pkwy.
Nashville, TN 37243-0565
615-741-2241
URL: https://www.tn.gov/commerce/licensing-regulations.html

TEXAS

Department of Licensing & Regulation
Street address:
920 Colorado
Austin, TX 78701
Mailing address:
PO Box 12157
Austin, TX 78711
512-463-6599
Toll-Free: 800-803-9202
URL: https://www.tdlr.texas.gov

UTAH

Dept. of Commerce—Div. of Professional Licensing
Street address:
Heber M. Wells Building, 4th Fl.
160 East 300 South
Salt Lake City, Utah 84111
Mailing address:
PO Box 146741
Salt Lake City, UT 84114-6741
801-530-6628
Email: dopl@utah.gov
URL: https://dopl.utah.gov

VERMONT

Office of Professional Regulation
89 Main St.
Montpelier, VT 05602
802-828-1505
URL: https://sos.vermont.gov/opr/

VIRGIN ISLANDS

Government of the U.S. Virgin Islands— Department of Licensing and Consumer Affairs
Golden Rock Shopping Center
3000 Estate Golden Rock, Ste. 9
St. Croix, VI 00820
340-713-3522
Fax: 340-718-6982
URL: http://dlca.vi.gov

VIRGINIA

Department of Professional and Occupational Regulations
9960 Maryland Dr., Ste. 400
Richmond, VA 23233-1485
804-367-8500
URL: www.dpor.virginia.gov

WASHINGTON

Department of Licensing
PO Box 9030
Olympia, WA 98507-9030
360-902-3900
URL: http://www.dol.wa.gov/business

WEST VIRGINIA

Division of Labor - Licensing
State Capitol Complex - Bldg. 3, Rm. 200
1900 Kanawha Blvd. E
Charleston, WV 25305
304-558-7890
URL: https://labor.wv.gov/licensing

WISCONSIN

Department of Safety and Professional Services
4822 Madison Yards Way
Madison, WI 53705
608-266-2112
Toll-Free: 877-617-1565
URL: https://dsps.wi.gov

WYOMING

Secretary of State - Business Div.
Herschler Building East
122 W 25th St., Ste. 101
Cheyenne, WY 82002-0020
307-777-7311
Email: Business@wyo.gov
URL: https://sos.wyo.gov/Business/Default.aspx

Guide to Publishers

This Guide lists alphabetically by name the companies, associations, institutions, and individuals who publish the periodicals (magazines, journals, etc.), directories, guide books, and other publications noted in the "Small Business Profiles" and "General Topics" sections. In these two sections, you will see "Pub:" (publisher) noted following publication names. This note provides the name of the entity that publishes the work.

If you should need to directly contact the publisher, you can locate the contact information in this Guide. Note that some publications listed provide the specific name and e-mail address of an individual to be contacted regarding the publication; this information can be found in the text of the entry. Please use that contact information when available. Listings in this *Guide* provide full publisher name, address, phone and fax numbers, and e-mail and URL when available.

NUMERICS

1105 Media Inc.
9201 Oakdale Ave., Ste. 101
Chatsworth, CA 91311
Free: 866-410-1321
URL: http://1105media.com/home.aspx

A

A. and C. Black
50 Bedford Sq.
London WC1B 3DP, United Kingdom

A/N Group Inc.
29 Stiles Dr.
Melville, NY 11747-1013

Abbeyfield Houses Society of Canada
38 Lakeside Ave.
Toronto, ON, Canada M1N 3C1
Ph: (416)699-4599
Co. E-mail: info@abbeyfield.ca
URL: http://abbeyfield.ca
Facebook: www.facebook.com/
 AbbeyfieldBluff

ABC Book Publishing
20609 NE Lakeside Dr.
Fairview, OR 97024
Ph: (503)780-7322

ACA International (ACA)
3200 Courthouse Ln.
Eagan, MN 55121-1585
Ph: (952)926-6547
Free: 800-269-1607
Co. E-mail: comm@acainternational.org
URL: http://www.acainternational.org
Facebook: www.facebook.com/acaintl
Linkedin: www.linkedin.com/company/aca
 -international

Academy of Management (AOM)
100 Summit Lake Dr., Ste. 110
Valhalla, NY 10595
Ph: (914)326-1800
Fax: (914)326-1900
Co. E-mail: membership@aom.org
URL: http://aom.org
Facebook: www.facebook.com/
 aomconnect
Linkedin: www.linkedin.com/company/
 aomconnect
YouTube: www.youtube.com/user/
 AcademyOfManagement

Acoustic Guitar
101 Desosticr He.
San Anselmo, CA 94979
URL: http://acousticguitar.com
Facebook: www.facebook.com/
 AcousticGuitarMagazine

Action Communication Inc.
ON, Canada
Ph: (520)792-0326
Free: 800-214-6011
Fax: (520)792-2709
URL: http://www.actioncommunications
 .com

Active Interest Media (PMY)
2143 Grand Ave.
Des Moines, IA 50312
URL: http://www.aimmedia.com
Linkedin: www.linkedin.com/company/
 active-interest-media

Advanced Research Media, Inc.
21 Bennetts Rd., Ste. 101
East Setauket, NY 11733

Adventure Cycling Association
150 E Pine St.
Missoula, MT 59807
Ph: (406)721-1776
Free: 800-755-2453
Fax: (406)721-8754
Co. E-mail: info@adventurecycling.org
URL: http://www.adventurecycling.org
Facebook: www.facebook.com/
 adventurecycling
YouTube: www.youtube.com/user/
 AdvCyclingAssoc

Adventure Publishing Group Inc.
307 7th Ave., Ste. 1601
New York, NY 10001
Ph: (212)575-4510
Fax: (212)575-4521
URL: http://www.adventurepublishinggroup
 .com

Advertising Age
685 3rd Ave.
New York, NY 10017
Ph: (212)210-0100
Free: 877-320-1721
Co. E-mail: customerservice@adage.com
URL: http://adage.com
Facebook: www.facebook.com/AdAge
Linkedin: www.linkedin.com/company/ad
 -age
Instagram: www.instagram.com/adage

The Advertising Research Foundation (ARF)
432 Park Ave. S 4th Fl.
New York, NY 10016
Ph: (212)751-5656
Fax: (212)689-1859
Co. E-mail: membership@thearf.org
URL: http://thearf.org
Facebook: www.facebook.com/ARF
Linkedin: www.linkedin.com/company/
 advertising-research-foundation
YouTube: www.youtube.com/user/
 TheARFvideos

Adweek L.P.
261 Madison Ave., 8th Fl.
New York, NY 10016
Ph: (212)493-4262
Co. E-mail: info@adweek.com
URL: http://www.adweek.com
Facebook: www.facebook.com/adweek
Linkedin: www.linkedin.com/company/
 adweek
Instagram: www.instagram.com/adweek
YouTube: www.youtube.com/channel/
 UCKhCJRTHHLuW2iW7XQtcfyQ

AIP Publishing LLC
1305 Walt Whitman Rd., Ste. 110
Melville, NY 11747
Ph: (516)576-2200

Co. E-mail: help@aip.org
URL: http://publishing.aip.org
Facebook: www.facebook.com/
 AIPPublishing
Linkedin: www.linkedin.com/company/aip
 -publishing

Air Age Publishing Inc.
88 Danbury Rd.
Wilton, CT 06897
Ph: (203)431-9000
Co. E-mail: production@airage.com
URL: http://www.airage.com

Air Conditioning Contractors of America Association (ACCA)
1520 Belle View Blvd. No 5220
Alexandria, VA 22307
Ph: (703)575-4477
Co. E-mail: membership@acca.org
URL: http://www.acca.org/home
Facebook: www.facebook.com/
 accontractors
Linkedin: www.linkedin.com/company/
 accausa
YouTube: www.youtube.com/c/accamerica

Alaska Business Publishing Company Inc.
501 W N Lights Blvd., Ste. 100
Anchorage, AK 99503
Ph: (907)276-4373
Fax: (907)279-2900
URL: http://www.akbizmag.com
Facebook: www.facebook.com/
 AKBusinessMonth
Linkedin: www.linkedin.com/company/
 alaska-business-monthly
Instagram: www.instagram.com/akbizmag

Alexander Communications Group Inc.
36 Midvale Rd., Ste. 2E
Mountain Lakes, NJ 07046
Ph: (973)265-2300
Co. E-mail: info@alexcommgrp.com
URL: http://www.alexcommgrp.com

Alexander Graham Bell Association for the Deaf & Hard of Hearing (AG Bell)
3417 Volta Pl. NW
Washington, DC 20007
Ph: (202)337-5220
Co. E-mail: info@agbell.org
URL: http://agbell.org
Facebook: www.facebook.com/
 AGBellAssociation
Linkedin: www.linkedin.com/company/ag
 -bell-association-for-the-deaf-and-hard-of
 -hearing
Instagram: www.instagram.com/
 agbellassociation

Alexander Research & Communications Inc.
36 Midvale Rd., Ste. 2E
Mountain Lakes, NJ 07046
Ph: (973)265-2300

Fax: (973)402-6056
Co. E-mail: info@alexcommgrp.com
URL: http://www.alexcommgrp.com

Alive Publishing Group Inc. (APG)
100-12751 Vulcan Way
Richmond, BC, Canada V6V 3C8
Free: 800-663-6580
Co. E-mail: editorial@alive.com
URL: http://www.alive.com
Facebook: www.facebook.com/alive.health
 .wellness
Instagram: www.instagram.com/alivehealth
YouTube: www.youtube.com/user/
 aliveMagazineOnline
Pinterest: www.pinterest.com/alivemag

Allen and Unwin Proprietary Ltd.
83 Alexander St.
Crows Nest, NSW 2065, Australia
Ph: 61 2 8425 0100
URL: http://www.allenandunwin.com
Facebook: www.facebook.com/
 AllenandUnwinBooks
Instagram: www.instagram.com/
 allenandunwin
YouTube: www.youtube.com/user/
 Allenandunwin
Pinterest: www.pinterest.com/
 allenandunwin

Alliance of Area Business Publishers (AABP)
287 Richards Ave.
Norwalk, CT 06850
Ph: (203)515-9294
Co. E-mail: sandersonmgt@gmail.com
URL: http://www.bizpubs.org

Allured Business Media
336 Gundersen Dr., Ste. D
Carol Stream, IL 60188-2403
Ph: (630)653-2155
Fax: (630)653-2192
Co. E-mail: customerservice@allured.com
URL: http://www.allured.com

Allworth Press
307 W 36th St., 11th Fl.
New York, NY 10018
Ph: (212)643-6816
Free: 800-733-3000
Fax: (212)643-6819
URL: http://www.skyhorsepublishing.com/
 allworth-press
Facebook: www.facebook.com/
 allworthpressbooks

ALM Media Properties LLC.
150 E 42nd St.
New York, NY 10017
Ph: (212)457-9400
Free: 877-256-2472

Co. E-mail: customercare@alm.com
URL: http://www.alm.com
Facebook: www.facebook.com/
 ALMMediaLLC
Linkedin: www.linkedin.com/company/alm
YouTube: www.youtube.com/channel/
 UCQYPgRdn5I6ZUgwXVp9ekLw

ALOA Security Professionals Association, Inc. (ALOA)
1408 N Riverfront Blvd., Ste. 303
Dallas, TX 75207
Ph: (214)819-9733
Free: 800-532-2562
Fax: (214)819-9736
Co. E-mail: education@aloa.org
URL: http://www.aloa.org
Facebook: www.facebook.com/ALOA.org

A.M. Best Company Inc.
1 Ambest Rd.
Oldwick, NJ 08858-0700
Ph: (908)438-2200
Free: 800-424-2378
Co. E-mail: customer_support@ambest
 .com
URL: http://web.ambest.com
Linkedin: www.linkedin.com/company/
 ambestcompany
YouTube: www.youtube.com/channel/
 UCYZCqtqc7_OlinFo9L_PgIw

American Accounting Association (AAA)
9009 Town Ctr., Pkwy.
Lakewood Ranch, FL 34202
Ph: (941)921-7747
Fax: (941)923-4093
Co. E-mail: info@aaahq.org
URL: http://aaahq.org

American Advertising Federation (AAF)
1101 K St. NW, Ste. 420
Washington, DC 20005
Ph: (202)898-0089
URL: http://www.aaf.org
Facebook: www.facebook.com/aafnational
Linkedin: www.linkedin.com/company/
 aafnational
Instagram: www.instagram.com/
 aafnational

American Animal Hospital Association (AAHA)
14142 Denver W Pkwy., Ste. 245
Lakewood, CO 80401
Free: 800-252-2242
Co. E-mail: dpo@aaha.org
URL: http://www.aaha.org
Linkedin: www.linkedin.com/company/
 aahaofficia
YouTube: www.youtube.com/aahavets

American Association of Bioanalysts (AAB)
906 Olive St., Ste. 1200
Saint Louis, MO 63101-1448

GUIDE TO PUBLISHERS

Ph: (314)241-1445
Fax: (314)241-1449
Co. E-mail: aab@aab.org
URL: http://www.aab.org/aab/default.asp
Facebook: www.facebook.com/AAB.MT
Linkedin: www.linkedin.com/company/
　american-assoication-of-bioanalysts

American Association of Individual Investors (AAII)
625 N Michigan Ave.
Chicago, IL 60611
Ph: (312)280-0170
Free: 800-428-2244
Fax: (312)280-9883
URL: http://www.aaii.com

American Association for Physician Leadership (AAPL)
PO Box 96503
Washington, DC 20090
Free: 800-562-8088
Fax: (813)287-8993
Co. E-mail: info@physicianleaders.org
URL: http://www.physicianleaders.org
Facebook: www.facebook.com/
　physicianslead
Linkedin: www.linkedin.com/company/
　physicianslead
YouTube: www.youtube.com/user/
　physicianleaders

American Bar Association (ABA)
321 N Clark St.
Chicago, IL 60654
Ph: (312)988-5000
Free: 800-285-2221
Co. E-mail: service@americanbar.org
URL: http://www.americanbar.org
Facebook: www.facebook.com/
　AmericanBarAssociation
Linkedin: www.linkedin.com/company/
　american-bar-association
Instagram: www.instagram.com/
　americanbarassociation

American Beekeeping Federation (ABF)
136 Everett Rd.
Albany, NY 12205
Ph: (518)694-9793
Co. E-mail: info@abfnet.org
URL: http://www.abfnet.org
Facebook: www.facebook.com/
　AmericanBeekeepingFederation
Instagram: www.instagram.com/
　americanbeekeepingfederation
YouTube: www.youtube.com/channel/
　UCpf26uL2FYrjnbnxUYTY_dA

American Board of Family Medicine (ABFM)
1648 McGrathiana Pky., Ste. 550
Lexington, KY 40511-1247
Free: 877-223-7437
Fax: (859)335-7516

Co. E-mail: help@theabfm.org
URL: http://www.theabfm.org
YouTube: www.youtube.com/channel/
　UCZGo4ySK579YwKWcf-v2UdQ

American Boat & Yacht Council (ABYC)
613 Third St., Ste. 10
Annapolis, MD 21403
Ph: (410)990-4460
Fax: (410)990-4466
Co. E-mail: info@abycinc.org
URL: http://abycinc.org
Facebook: www.facebook.com/abycinc
Linkedin: www.linkedin.com/company/abyc
Instagram: www.instagram.com/
　ABYC_BoatSafety
YouTube: www.youtube.com/user/
　ABYCAnnapolis

American Business Women's Association (ABWA)
PO Box 4757
Overland Park, KS 66204-0757
Free: 800-228-0007
Co. E-mail: webmail@abwa.org
URL: http://www.abwa.org
Facebook: www.facebook.com/ABWA.NationalOrganization
Linkedin: www.linkedin.com/company/
　american-business-women-s-association
　-national
Instagram: www.instagram.com/
　americanbusinesswomensassn

American Camp Association (ACA)
5000 State Rd. 67 N
Martinsville, IN 46151-7902
Ph: (765)342-8456
Free: 800-428-2267
Fax: (765)342-2065
URL: http://www.acacamps.org
Facebook: www.facebook.com/ACACamps
Linkedin: www.linkedin.com/company/
　american-camp-association
YouTube: www.youtube.com/user/
　AmericanCampAssoc

American Cat Fanciers Association (ACFA)
PO Box 1949
Nixa, MO 65714-1949
Ph: (417)725-1530
Fax: (417)725-1533
Co. E-mail: acfa@aol.com
URL: http://www.acfacat.com
Facebook: www.facebook.com/acfacat
YouTube: www.youtube.com/channel/
　UCdsli659X0yrXVwnLnRAa8Q
Pinterest: www.pinterest.com/acfacat

American Ceramic Society (ACERS)
550 Polaris Pky., Ste. 510
Westerville, OH 43082
Ph: (614)890-4700
Free: 866-721-3522
Fax: (614)899-6109

Co. E-mail: customerservice@ceramics
　.org
URL: http://ceramics.org
Facebook: www.facebook.com/acersnews
Linkedin: www.linkedin.com/company/the
　-american-ceramic-society
YouTube: www.youtube.com/user/
　ceramicsociety

American Chemical Society Philadelphia Section
Dept. of Chemistry
University of Pennsylvania
231 S 34th St.
Philadelphia, PA 19104-6323
Ph: (215)898-6042
Co. E-mail: philaacs@gmail.com
URL: http://phillyacs.org
Facebook: www.facebook.com/
　PhilaSectionACS

American Chemical Society (ACS)
1155 16th St. NW
Washington, DC 20036
Ph: (202)872-4600
Free: 800-333-9511
Co. E-mail: service@acs.org
URL: http://www.acs.org
Facebook: www.facebook.com/
　AmericanChemicalSociety
Linkedin: www.linkedin.com/company/
　american-chemical-society

American City Business Journals, Inc. (ACBJ)
120 W Morehead St.
Charlotte, NC 28202
Co. E-mail: circhelp@bizjournals.com
URL: http://www.acbj.com

American College of Healthcare Executives (ACHE)
300 S Riverside Pl., Ste. 1900
Chicago, IL 60606-6698
Ph: (312)424-2800
Fax: (312)424-0023
Co. E-mail: contact@ache.org
URL: http://www.ache.org
Facebook: www.facebook.com/
　ACHEConnect
Linkedin: www.linkedin.com/company/
　american-college-of-healthcare
　-executives
Instagram: www.instagram.com/
　acheconnect
YouTube: www.youtube.com/user/
　ACHEhealthexecs

American Counseling Association (ACA)
PO Box 31110
Alexandria, VA 22310-9998
Ph: (703)823-9800
Free: 800-347-6647
Fax: (800)473-2329

Co. E-mail: acamemberservices@counseling.org
URL: http://www.counseling.org/#
Facebook: www.facebook.com/American.Counseling.Association
Linkedin: www.linkedin.com/company/american-counseling-association
Instagram: www.instagram.com/americancounselingassociation

American Craft Council (ACC)
1224 Marshall St. NE, Ste. 200
Minneapolis, MN 55413
Ph: (612)206-3100
Fax: (612)355-2330
Co. E-mail: council@craftcouncil.org
URL: http://craftcouncil.org
Facebook: www.facebook.com/CraftCouncil
Instagram: www.instagram.com/craftcouncil
YouTube: www.youtube.com/user/AmericanCraftCouncil
Pinterest: www.pinterest.com/craftcouncil

American Culinary Federation (ACF)
6816 Southpoint Pky., Ste. 400
Jacksonville, FL 32216
Ph: (904)824-4468
Fax: (904)940-0741
Co. E-mail: helpdesk@acfchefs.org
URL: http://www.acfchefs.org
Facebook: www.facebook.com/ACFChefs
Linkedin: www.linkedin.com/company/american-culinary-federation
Instagram: www.instagram.com/ACF_CHEFS

American Farm Bureau Federation (AFBF)
600 Maryland Ave. SW, Ste. 1000W
Washington, DC 20024
Ph: (202)406-3600
Co. E-mail: info@fb.org
URL: http://www.fb.org
Facebook: www.facebook.com/AmericanFarmBureau
Linkedin: www.linkedin.com/company/american-farm-bureau-federation
Instagram: www.instagram.com/americanfarmbureau
YouTube: www.youtube.com/user/farmbureautv

American Foundry Society (AFS)
1695 North Penny Ln.
Schaumburg, IL 60173
Ph: (847)824-0181
Free: 800-537-4237
Fax: (847)824-7848
Co. E-mail: afs@afsinc.net
URL: http://www.afsinc.org
Facebook: www.facebook.com/americanfoundrysociety
Linkedin: www.linkedin.com/company/american-foundry-society

American Future Systems Inc.
370 Technology Dr.
Malvern, PA 19355
Ph: (610)695-8600
Free: 800-220-5000
Fax: (610)647-8089
Co. E-mail: customer_service@pbp.com
URL: http://www.pbp.com

American Health Care Association (AHCA)
1201 L St. NW
Washington, DC 20005
Ph: (202)842-4444
Fax: (202)842-3860
Co. E-mail: help@ltctrendtracker.com
URL: http://www.ahcancal.org/Pages/default.aspx
Facebook: www.facebook.com/ahcancal
YouTube: www.youtube.com/user/ahcancalstream

American Home Furnishings Alliance (AHFA)
1912 Eastchester Dr., Ste. 100
High Point, NC 27265
Ph: (336)884-5000
Co. E-mail: info@ahfa.us
URL: http://www.ahfa.us
Facebook: www.facebook.com/AHFAToday

American Horse Council (AHC)
1616 H St. NW, 7th Fl.
Washington, DC 20006
Ph: (202)296-4031
Co. E-mail: jbroadway@horsecouncil.org
URL: http://www.horsecouncil.org
Facebook: www.facebook.com/AmericanHorseCouncil
Instagram: www.instagram.com/americanhorsecouncil
YouTube: www.youtube.com/channel/UCdBtNkiAZffIDV7Nx92swzg

American Institute of Certified Public Accountants (AICPA)
220 Leigh Farm Rd.
Durham, NC 27707-8110
Ph: (919)402-4500
Free: 888-777-7077
Fax: (919)402-4505
Co. E-mail: aicpaspamreporting@gmail.com
URL: http://www.aicpa.org/home

American International Automobile Dealers Association (AIADA)
500 Montgomery St., Ste. 800
Alexandria, VA 22314
Ph: (703)519-7810
Free: 800-462-4232
Co. E-mail: goaiada@aiada.org
URL: http://www.aiada.org
Facebook: www.facebook.com/AIADA.News
Linkedin: www.linkedin.com/company/aiada
YouTube: www.youtube.com/user/aiadaorg2011

American-International Charolais Association (AICA)
11700 NW Plz. Cir.
Kansas City, MO 64153
Ph: (816)464-5977
Fax: (816)464-5759
Co. E-mail: info@charolaisusa.com
URL: http://www.charolaisusa.com
Facebook: www.facebook.com/CharolaisUSA

American Law Institute Continuing Legal Education (ALICLE)
4025 Chestnut St.
Philadelphia, PA 19104-3099
Ph: (215)243-1600
Free: 800-253-6397
Fax: (215)243-1664
Co. E-mail: custserv@ali-cle.org
URL: http://www.ali-cle.org
Linkedin: www.linkedin.com/company/american-law-institute-continuing-legal-education-ali-cle-
YouTube: www.youtube.com/channel/UCPTs9jgMa3LoFr6rlme0sHw

American Lock Collectors Association (ALCA)
c/o David Rankl
13151 Millersburg Rd. SW
Massillon, OH 44647
Ph: (330)833-1438
Co. E-mail: dlr41@aol.com
URL: http://alca.name/menu.htm

American Management Association (AMA)
1601 Broadway
New York, NY 10019
Ph: (212)586-8100
Free: 800-262-9699
Fax: (212)903-8168
Co. E-mail: customerservice@amanet.org
URL: http://www.amanet.org
Facebook: www.facebook.com/AmericanManagementAssn
Linkedin: www.linkedin.com/company/american-management-association
Instagram: www.instagram.com/americanmanagementassociation
YouTube: www.youtube.com/user/AmericanManagement

American Marketing Association (AMA)
130 E Randolph St., 22nd Fl.
Chicago, IL 60601
Ph: (312)542-9000

Free: 800-262-1150
Co. E-mail: customersupport@ama.org
URL: http://www.ama.org
Facebook: www.facebook.com/
  AmericanMarketing
Linkedin: www.linkedin.com/company/
  american-marketing-association

American Massage Therapy Association (AMTA)
500 Davis St., Ste. 900
Evanston, IL 60201
Free: 877-905-2700
Co. E-mail: info@amtamassage.org
URL: http://www.amtamassage.org
Facebook: www.facebook.com/
  AMTAmassage
Linkedin: www.linkedin.com/company/
  american-massage-therapy-association
Instagram: www.instagram.com/
  amtamassage
YouTube: www.youtube.com/
  amtamassage

American Numismatic Association (ANA)
818 N Cascade Ave.
Colorado Springs, CO 80903
Ph: (719)632-2646
Free: 800-367-9723
Fax: (719)634-4085
Co. E-mail: ana@money.org
URL: http://www.money.org
Facebook: www.facebook.com/
  numismatics
Instagram: www.instagram.com/
  AmericanNumismatic
YouTube: www.youtube.com/user/
  AmericanNumismatic

American Philatelic Society (APS)
100 Match Factory Pl.
Bellefonte, PA 16823
Ph: (814)933-3803
Fax: (814)933-6128
Co. E-mail: info@stamps.org
URL: http://stamps.org
Facebook: www.facebook.com/american
  .philatelic.society

American Physical Therapy Association (APTA)
3030 Potomac Ave., Ste. 100
Alexandria, VA 22305-3085
Ph: (703)684-2782
Free: 800-999-2782
Fax: (703)684-7343
Co. E-mail: memberservices@apta.org
URL: http://www.apta.org
Facebook: www.facebook.com/
  AmericanPhysicalTherapyAssociation
Linkedin: www.linkedin.com/company/
  american-physical-therapy-association
Instagram: www.instagram.com/aptapics
YouTube: www.youtube.com/user/
  APTAvideo

American Polygraph Association (APA)
118 Lee Pky. Dr., Ste. 205
Chattanooga, TN 37414-0037
Ph: (423)892-3992
Free: 800-272-8037
Fax: (423)894-5435
URL: http://www.polygraph.org
Facebook: www.facebook.com/
  AmericanPolygraphAssociation

American Public Health Association (APHA)
800 I St. NW
Washington, DC 20001
Ph: (202)777-2742
Fax: (202)777-2534
Co. E-mail: membership.mail@apha.org
URL: http://www.apha.org
Facebook: www.facebook.com/
  AmericanPublicHealthAssociation
Linkedin: www.linkedin.com/company/
  american-public-health-association
Instagram: www.instagram.com/
  AmericanPublicHealth
YouTube: www.youtube.com/user/aphadc

American Purchasing Society (APS)
8 E Galena Blvd., Ste. 406
Aurora, IL 60506
Ph: (630)859-0250
Fax: (630)859-0270
Co. E-mail: propurch@propurch.com
URL: http://www.american-purchasing.com

American Quarter Horse Association (AQHA)
1600 Quarter Horse Dr.
Amarillo, TX 79104
Ph: (806)376-4811
Fax: (806)349-6411
Co. E-mail: hlane@aqha.org
URL: http://www.aqha.com
Facebook: www.facebook.com/aqha1
Instagram: www.instagram.com/
  officialaqha
YouTube: www.youtube.com/user/
  aqhavideo
Pinterest: www.pinterest.com/aqha1

American Quilt Study Group (AQSG)
1610 L St.
Lincoln, NE 68508-2509
Ph: (402)477-1181
Fax: (402)477-1181
Co. E-mail: aqsg2@americanquiltstudy-
  group.org
URL: http://www.americanquiltstudygroup
  .org
Facebook: www.facebook.com/
  americanquiltstudygroup
Instagram: www.instagram.com/
  americanquiltstudygroup
YouTube: www.youtube.com/channel/
  UCnSdyh7Ji7GLiumC9-c9Xkg

American Rental Association (ARA)
1900 19th St.
Moline, IL 61265
Free: 800-334-2177
Fax: (309)764-1533
Co. E-mail: marketing@ararental.org
URL: http://www.ararental.org
Facebook: www.facebook.com/
  ARAHeadquarters
Linkedin: www.linkedin.com/company/
  american-rental-association

American Salers Association (ASA)
PO Box 850
Big Horn, WY 82833
Ph: (303)770-9292
Fax: (303)770-9302
Co. E-mail: communications@salersusa
  .org
URL: http://www.salersusa.org
Facebook: www.facebook.com/
  SalersBreed
YouTube: www.youtube.com/channel/
  UC9doSo2ye6i8yupCGKyKnjw

American Society of Agricultural and Biological Engineers (ASABE)
2950 Niles Rd.
Saint Joseph, MI 49085
Ph: (269)429-0300
Fax: (269)429-3852
Co. E-mail: hq@asabe.org
URL: http://www.asabe.org
Facebook: www.facebook.com/ASABEorg
Linkedin: www.linkedin.com/company/
  asabeorg
Instagram: www.instagram.com/asabeorg
YouTube: www.youtube.com/user/
  AgBioEngineering

American Society of Andrology (ASA)
1061 E Main St., Ste. 300
East Dundee, IL 60118
Ph: (847)752-5355
Co. E-mail: info@andrologysociety.org
URL: http://andrologysociety.org
Facebook: www.facebook.com/
  AndrologyASA
Linkedin: www.linkedin.com/company/
  american-society-of-andrology

American Society of Civil Engineers (ASCE)
1801 Alexander Bell Dr.
Reston, VA 20191
Ph: (703)295-6300
Free: 800-548-2723
Co. E-mail: customercare@asce.org
URL: http://www.asce.org
Facebook: www.facebook.com/ASCE.org
Linkedin: www.linkedin.com/company/
  american-society-of-civil-engineers/
Instagram: instagram.com/asce_hq
YouTube: www.youtube.com/user/
  AmerSocCivilEng

GUIDE TO PUBLISHERS

American Society for Clinical Pathology (ASCP)
33 West Monroe St., Ste. 1600
Chicago, IL 60603
Ph: (312)541-4999
Fax: (312)541-4998
Co. E-mail: pdinfo@ascp.org
URL: http://www.ascp.org/content#
Facebook: www.facebook.com/ASCP.Chicago

American Society of Journalists and Authors (ASJA)
355 Lexington Ave. 15th Fl.
New York, NY 10017-6603
Ph: (212)997-0947
Co. E-mail: asjaoffice@asja.org
URL: http://asja.org
Facebook: www.facebook.com/ASJAinc

American Society of Landscape Architects (ASLA)
636 Eye St. NW
Washington, DC 20001-3736
Ph: (202)898-2444
Free: 888-999-2752
Fax: (202)898-1185
Co. E-mail: info@asla.org
URL: http://www.asla.org
Facebook: www.facebook.com/NationalASLA
Instagram: www.instagram.com/nationalasla
Pinterest: www.pinterest.com/NationalASLA

American Society for Microbiology (ASM)
1752 N St. NW
Washington, DC 20036
Ph: (202)737-3600
Co. E-mail: service@asmusa.org
URL: http://www.asm.org
Facebook: www.facebook.com/asmfan
Linkedin: www.linkedin.com/company/american-society-for-microbiology
YouTube: www.youtube.com/channel/UCBxWzf49gVHz0Ksgw_N8brw

American Society for Nutrition (ASN)
9211 Corporate Blvd., Ste. 300
Rockville, MD 20850
Ph: (240)428-3650
Fax: (240)404-6797
Co. E-mail: info@nutrition.org
URL: http://www.nutrition.org
Facebook: www.facebook.com/AmerSocNutr
Linkedin: www.linkedin.com/company/american-society-for-nutrition

American Society of Plant Biologists (ASPB)
15501 Monona Dr.
Rockville, MD 20855-2768
Co. E-mail: info@aspb.org
URL: http://my.aspb.org
Facebook: www.facebook.com/myASPB
Linkedin: www.linkedin.com/company/american-society-of-plant-biologists

American Society for Public Administration (ASPA)
1730 Rhode Island Ave. NW, Ste. 500
Washington, DC 20036
Ph: (202)393-7878
Fax: (202)638-4952
Co. E-mail: info@aspanet.org
URL: http://www.aspanet.org
Facebook: www.facebook.com/ASPANational

American Solar Energy Society (ASES)
2525 Arapahoe Ave. Ste. E4 253
Boulder, CO 80302
Ph: (303)443-3130
Co. E-mail: info@ases.org
URL: http://www.ases.org
Facebook: www.facebook.com/americansolarenergysociety
Linkedin: www.linkedin.com/company/ases-solar
Instagram: www.instagram.com/ases_solar
YouTube: www.youtube.com/channel/UCF9nNtHuTDY4NrA4ObpxVkA

American Supply Association (ASA)
1200 N Arlington Heights Rd., Ste. 150
Itasca, IL 60143
Ph: (630)467-0000
Fax: (630)467-0001
Co. E-mail: info@asa.net
URL: http://www.asa.net
Facebook: www.facebook.com/americansupplyassociation
Linkedin: www.linkedin.com/company/american-supply-association-asa

American Translators Association (ATA)
225 Reinekers Ln., Ste. 590
Alexandria, VA 22314
Ph: (703)683-6100
Fax: (703)683-6122
Co. E-mail: ata@atanet.org
URL: http://www.atanet.org
Facebook: www.facebook.com/AmericanTranslatorsAssociation
Linkedin: www.linkedin.com/company/american-translators-association
Instagram: www.instagram.com/americantranslatorsassn
YouTube: www.youtube.com/c/AmericanTranslatorsAssociationATA

American Veterinary Medical Association (AVMA)
1931 N Meacham Rd., Ste. 100
Schaumburg, IL 60173-4360
Free: 800-248-2862
Fax: (847)925-1329
URL: http://www.avma.org
Facebook: www.facebook.com/avmavets
Linkedin: www.linkedin.com/company/avma
Instagram: www.instagram.com/avmavets
YouTube: www.youtube.com/user/AmerVetMedAssn

American Window Cleaner Magazine (AWCMAG)
750-B NW Broad St.
Southern Pines, NC 28387
URL: http://www.awcmag.com
Facebook: www.facebook.com/AWCmag
Instagram: www.instagram.com/awcmag

Amos Media Co.
1660 Campbell Rd., Ste. A
Sidney, OH 45365
Ph: (937)498-2111
Free: 800-253-4555
Co. E-mail: cuserv@amosmedia.com
URL: http://www.amosmedia.com
Facebook: www.facebook.com/AmosMediaInc

Annex Buisness Media
105 Donly Drive St. S
Simcoe, ON, Canada N3Y 4N5
Ph: (519)429-3966
Free: 800-265-2827
Fax: (519)428-3327
URL: http://www.annexbusinessmedia.com
Linkedin: www.linkedin.com/company/annex-publishing-&-printing-inc
YouTube: www.youtube.com/channel/UCzZ752yOqSdu5Wmr-QEdCnA

Antique Bottle and Glass Collector
102 Jefferson St.
East Greenville, PA 18041
URL: http://www.glassworksauctions.com

Apartment News Publications Inc.
15502 Graham St.
Huntington Beach, CA 92649
Ph: (714)893-3971
Free: 800-931-6666
Fax: (714)893-6484
URL: http://www.aptmags.com
Facebook: www.facebook.com/apartmentnewspublications
YouTube: www.youtube.com/user/ApartmentNews

APhA Academy of Pharmacy Practice and Management (APhA-APPM)
2215 Constitution Ave., NW
Washington, DC 20037
Ph: (202)628-4410
Free: 800-237-2742
Fax: (844)390-3782

Co. E-mail: infocenter@aphanet.org
URL: http://www.pharmacist.com/apha-appm
Facebook: www.facebook.com/APhAPharmacists
Linkedin: www.linkedin.com/company/american-pharmacists-association
YouTube: www.youtube.com/channel/UCKAj5RelarIgcZyA8kbiBQA

Apparel News Group
127 E 9th St., Ste. 806
Los Angeles, CA 90015
Ph: (213)627-3737
Fax: (213)623-5707
Co. E-mail: info@apparelnews.net
URL: http://www.apparelnews.net
Facebook: www.facebook.com/ApparelNews
Linkedin: www.linkedin.com/company/california-apparel-news
Instagram: www.instagram.com/apparelnews
Pinterest: www.pinterest.com/apparelnews

Applied Arts Inc.
PO Box 1233
Toronto, ON, Canada M4P 3E4
Ph: (416)510-0909
Fax: (416)510-0913
Co. E-mail: customerservice@appliedarts-mag.com
URL: http://www.appliedartsmag.com
Facebook: www.facebook.com/AppliedArtsMag
Linkedin: www.linkedin.com/company/applied-arts-magazine
Instagram: www.instagram.com/appliedartsmag
Pinterest: www.pinterest.ca/awards0196

Appraisal Institute of Canada (AIC)
403-200 Catherine St.
Ottawa, ON, Canada K2P 2K9
Ph: (613)234-6533
Fax: (613)234-7197
Co. E-mail: info@aicanada.ca
URL: http://www.aicanada.ca
Linkedin: www.linkedin.com/company/appraisal-institute-of-canada

Appraisers Association of America (AAA)
212 W 35th St., 11th Fl. S
New York, NY 10001
Ph: (212)889-5404
Fax: (212)889-5503
Co. E-mail: referrals@appraisersassociation.org
URL: http://www.appraisersassociation.org
Facebook: www.facebook.com/appraisersassociation

Arbor Day Foundation (ADF)
211 N 12th St.
Lincoln, NE 68508
Ph: (402)474-5655
Free: 888-448-7337
Co. E-mail: info@arborday.org
URL: http://www.arborday.org
Facebook: www.facebook.com/arborday
Linkedin: www.linkedin.com/company/arbor-day-foundation
Instagram: www.instagram.com/arbordayfoundation
YouTube: www.youtube.com/channel/UCaUfpc8WmwJWQqzRupURzRw
Pinterest: www.pinterest.com/arborday

The Arc Carroll County
180 Kriders Church Rd.
Westminster, MD 21158
Ph: (410)848-4124
Fax: (410)876-5317
URL: http://arccarroll.org
Facebook: www.facebook.com/thearccarrollcounty
Instagram: www.instagram.com/thearccarroll
YouTube: www.youtube.com/channel/UCZJHn76dRpB8fsDlRHuWHeQ

Architectural Engineering Institute of ASCE (AEI)
c/o American Society of Civil Engineers
1801 Alexander Bell Dr.
Reston, VA 20191
Co. E-mail: aei@asce.org
URL: http://www.asce.org/communities/institutes-and-technical-groups/architectural-engineering-institute

Archway Publishing
1663 Liberty Dr.
Bloomington, IN 47403
Free: 844-669-3957
Co. E-mail: customersupport@archway-publishing.com
URL: http://www.archwaypublishing.com/en
Facebook: www.facebook.com/ArchwayPublishing

Arizona Daily Star
PO Box 26887
Tucson, AZ 85726-6887
Free: 800-695-4492
Co. E-mail: circulation@tucson.com
URL: http://tucson.com
Facebook: www.facebook.com/ArizonaDailyStar
Linkedin: www.linkedin.com/company/arizona-daily-star
Instagram: www.instagram.com/arizonadailystar
YouTube: www.youtube.com/channel/UCeYHpGha-z3ahTum2tpvf-g
Pinterest: www.pinterest.com/tucsonstar

Arkansas Business Publishing Group
114 Scott St.
Little Rock, AR 72201
Ph: (501)372-1443
Free: 888-322-6397
URL: http://www.arkansasbusiness.com
Facebook: www.facebook.com/ArkansasBusiness
Linkedin: www.linkedin.com/company/arkansas-business-publishing-group
YouTube: www.youtube.com/user/ArkansasBusiness

The Art of Eating LLC.
PO Box 333
Saint Johnsbury, VT 05819
Co. E-mail: mail@artofeating.com
URL: http://www.artofeating.com
Instagram: www.instagram.com/artofeating

Artech House Inc.
685 Canton St.
Norwood, MA 02062
Ph: (781)769-9750
Free: 800-225-9977
Fax: (781)769-6334
Co. E-mail: artech@artechhouse.com
URL: http://us.artechhouse.com
Facebook: www.facebook.com/pages/Artech-House-Publishers/144926394008
Linkedin: www.linkedin.com/company/artech-house

ARTnews L.L.C.
475 Fifth Ave., 16th Fl.
New York, NY 10017
Ph: (212)398-1690
Free: 800-284-4625
Co. E-mail: arncustserv@cdsfulfillment.com
URL: http://www.artnews.com
Facebook: www.facebook.com/artnewsmag
Instagram: www.instagram.com/artnews
YouTube: www.youtube.com/channel/UC08Z3HFs8ds6YtClAvbtVeQ
Pinterest: www.pinterest.com/artnewsmag

ASET - The Neurodiagnostic Society
312 SW Greenwich Dr., Ste. 669
Lees Summit, MO 64082
Ph: (816)931-1120
Co. E-mail: info@aset.org
URL: http://www.aset.org
Facebook: www.facebook.com/ASETsociety
Linkedin: www.linkedin.com/company/aset-society
YouTube: www.youtube.com/c/ASETTheNeurodiagnosticSociety

ASIS International (ASIS)
1625 Prince St.
Alexandria, VA 22314-2882
Ph: (703)519-6200
Fax: (703)519-6299

Co. E-mail: asis@asisonline.org
URL: http://www.asisonline.org
Facebook: www.facebook.com/
 ASISInternational
YouTube: www.youtube.com/user/
 ASISInternational

ASM International
9639 Kinsman Rd.
Novelty, OH 44073
Ph: (440)338-5151
Co. E-mail: memberservicecenter@asminternational.org
URL: http://www.asminternational.org
Facebook: www.facebook.com/
 asminternational
Linkedin: www.linkedin.com/company/asm
 -international/
Instagram: www.instagram.com/
 asminternational/
YouTube: www.youtube.com/channel/
 UCTxjfUb2cfxvZQQtBiyMCag

ASME International (ASME)
Two Park Ave.
New York, NY 10016-5990
Free: 800-843-2763
Co. E-mail: customercare@asme.org
URL: http://www.asme.org
Facebook: www.facebook.com/ASME.org
Linkedin: www.linkedin.com/company/
 asme
Instagram: www.instagram.com/
 asmedotorg

The Asphalt Contractor
201 N Main St.
Fort Atkinson, WI 53538
Co. E-mail: support@forconstructionpros
 .com
URL: http://www.forconstructionpros.com

Asphalt Emulsion Manufacturers Association (AEMA)
800 Roosevelt Rd., Bldg. C-312
Glen Ellyn, IL 60137
Ph: (630)942-6579
Co. E-mail: alim@cmservices.com
URL: http://www.aema.org
Facebook: www.facebook.com/aema.social
Linkedin: www.linkedin.com/company/
 asphalt-emulsion-manufacturers
 -association

Asphalt Recycling and Reclaiming Association (ARRA)
800 Roosevelt Rd., Bldg. C-312
Glen Ellyn, IL 60137
Ph: (630)942-6578
URL: http://www.arra.org
Facebook: www.facebook.com/arra.social
Linkedin: www.linkedin.com/company/
 asphalt-recycling-&-reclaiming
 -association

Associated Builders and Contractors, Inc. (ABC)
440 1st St. NW, Ste. 200
Washington, DC 20001
Ph: (202)595-1505
Co. E-mail: gotquestions@abc.org
URL: http://www.abc.org
Facebook: www.facebook.com/
 ABCNational
Linkedin: www.linkedin.com/company/
 associated-builders-and-contractors
Instagram: www.instagram.com/
 abc_national
YouTube: www.youtube.com/user/
 theabcnational

Associated Construction Publications
1030 E Washington St., Ste. 201
Indianapolis, IN 46202
Ph: (317)423-2325
Co. E-mail: info@acppubs.com
URL: http://www.acppubs.com
Facebook: www.facebook.com/pages/
 Associated-Construction-Publications/
 272109932894183
Linkedin: www.linkedin.com/company/
 associated-construction-publications
 -acp-

Associated Equipment Distributors (AED)
650 E Algonquin Rd., Ste. 305
Schaumburg, IL 60173
Ph: (630)574-0650
Co. E-mail: help@aednet.org
URL: http://aednet.org
Linkedin: www.linkedin.com/company/
 associated-equipment-distributors
YouTube: www.youtube.com/channel/
 UCqMEitw-IIsr0wONSAaeHXA

Associated General Contractors of America (AGC)
2300 Wilson Blvd., Ste. 300
Arlington, VA 22201
Ph: (703)548-3118
Free: 800-242-1767
Fax: (703)548-3119
Co. E-mail: info@agc.org
URL: http://www.agc.org
Facebook: www.facebook.com/AGCofA
Linkedin: www.linkedin.com/company/
 agcofa
YouTube: www.youtube.com/user/
 agcofamerica

Associated Humane Societies (AHS)
124 Evergreen Ave.
Newark, NJ 07114-2133
Ph: (973)824-7080
Fax: (973)824-2720
Co. E-mail: info@ahscares.org
URL: http://ahscares.org

Associated Press (AP)
200 Liberty St.
New York, NY 10281
Co. E-mail: info@ap.org
URL: http://www.ap.org/en
Facebook: www.facebook.com/APNews
Linkedin: www.linkedin.com/company/
 associated-press
YouTube: www.youtube.com/ap

Association for the Advancement of Medical Instrumentation (AAMI)
901 N Glebe Rd., Ste. 300
Arlington, VA 22203
Ph: (703)525-4890
Fax: (703)276-0793
Co. E-mail: customerservice@aami.org
URL: http://www.aami.org
Facebook: www.facebook.com/
 aamiconnect
Instagram: www.instagram.com/
 aamiconnect
YouTube: www.youtube.com/user/
 aamiconnect

Association of American University Presses (AAUP)
1412 Bwdy., ste. 2135
New York, NY 10018
Ph: (212)989-1010
Fax: (212)989-0275
Co. E-mail: info@aaupnet.org
URL: http://aupresses.org
Facebook: www.facebook.com/
 universitypresses

Association of Asphalt Paving Technologists (AAPT)
6776 Lake Dr., Ste. 215
Lino Lakes, MN 55014
Ph: (651)293-9188
Fax: (651)293-9193
Co. E-mail: aapt@asphalttechnology.org
URL: http://www.asphalttechnology.org
Facebook: www.facebook.com/asphalttech

Association of Bridal Consultants (ABC)
632 Federal Rd., Ste. 2
Brookfield, CT 06804
Ph: (860)355-7000
Fax: (203)775-0037
Co. E-mail: info@bridalassn.com
URL: http://bridalassn.com
Facebook: www.facebook.com/
 AssocBridalConsultants
YouTube: www.youtube.com/channel/
 UC77N7hfAwxl4k6sAiD72O6Q

Association of Clinicians for the Underserved (ACU)
1575 I St. NW, Ste. 300
Washington, DC 20005
Free: 844-422-8247
Fax: (703)562-8801
Co. E-mail: acu@clinicians.org
URL: http://clinicians.org
Facebook: www.facebook.com/

CliniciansfortheUnderserved
Linkedin: www.linkedin.com/company/
association-of-clinicians-for-the
-underserved
YouTube: www.youtube.com/channel/
UCZg-CFN7Wuev5qNUWt69u0w

Association for Computing Machinery - Manor College Student Chapter
700 Fox Chase Rd.
Jenkintown, PA 19046
Ph: (215)885-2360
Fax: (215)576-6564
Co. E-mail: enroll@manor.edu
URL: http://www.manor.edu
Facebook: www.facebook.com/
ManorCollegePA

Association for Computing Machinery (ACM)
1601 Broadway
10th Fl.
New York, NY 10019-7434
Ph: (212)869-7440
Free: 800-342-6626
Fax: (212)944-1318
Co. E-mail: acmhelp@acm.org
URL: http://www.acm.org
Facebook: www.facebook.com/
AssociationForComputingMachinery
Linkedin: www.linkedin.com/company/
association-for-computing-machinery
Instagram: www.instagram.com/
theofficialacm
YouTube: www.youtube.com/user/
TheOfficialACM

Association for Computing Machinery - Special Interest Group on Array Programming Languages
Department of Computer Science
151 Engineer's Way
Charlottesville, VA 22904
Ph: (212)869-7440
Free: 800-342-6626
Fax: (212)944-1318
Co. E-mail: acmhelp@acm.org
URL: http://www.sigir.org/index.html

Association for Computing Machinery - University of Wyoming (ACM)
PO Box 3315
Laramie, WY 82071-3315
Co. E-mail: acm@cs.uwyo.edu
URL: http://www.uwyo.edu/cosc/current-
_students/resources.html

Association for Diagnostics & Laboratory Medicine (ADLM)
900 7th St. NW Ste. 400
Washington, DC 20001
Ph: (202)857-0717
Free: 800-892-1400
Fax: (202)887-5093
Co. E-mail: custserv@aacc.org
URL: http://www.aacc.org
Facebook: www.facebook.com/myADLM
Linkedin: www.linkedin.com/company/
myadlm
Instagram: www.instagram.com/myadlm
YouTube: www.youtube.com/@myadlm

Association for Manufacturing Technology (AMT)
7901 Jones Branch Dr., Ste. 900
McLean, VA 22102-4206
Ph: (703)893-2900
Free: 800-524-0475
Fax: (703)893-1151
Co. E-mail: amt@amtonline.org
URL: http://www.amtonline.org/home
Facebook: www.facebook.com/amtnews
Linkedin: www.linkedin.com/company/
amtonline
YouTube: www.youtube.com/user/
amtinsight

Association of Nutrition and Foodservice Professionals (ANFP)
406 Surrey Woods Dr.
Saint Charles, IL 60174
Ph: (630)587-6336
Free: 800-323-1908
Fax: (630)587-6308
Co. E-mail: info@anfponline.org
URL: http://www.anfponline.org
Facebook: www.facebook.com/
ANFPonline
Linkedin: www.linkedin.com/company/
association-of-nutrition-&-foodservice
-professionals
Instagram: www.instagram.com/anfponline
Pinterest: www.pinterest.com/anfp3581

Association of Ontario Land Surveyors (AOLS)
1043 McNicoll Ave.
Toronto, ON, Canada M1W 3W6
Ph: (416)491-9020
Free: 800-268-0718
Fax: (416)491-2576
Co. E-mail: info@aols.org
URL: http://www.aols.org
Facebook: www.facebook.com/
AssociationOfOntarioLandSurveyors
Linkedin: www.linkedin.com/groups/
4083207
YouTube: www.youtube.com/channel/
UCGAWsVKuElp1QfBDz743Ovw

Association of Professional Chaplains (APC)
2800 W Higgins Rd., Ste. 295
Hoffman Estates, IL 60169
Ph: (847)240-1014
Fax: (847)240-1015
Co. E-mail: info@professionalchaplains
.org
URL: http://www.professionalchaplains.org
Facebook: www.facebook.com/groups/
ProfChap
Linkedin: www.linkedin.com/company/
association-of-professional-chaplains

Association of Professional Genealogists (APG)
PO Box 2369
Poulsbo, WA 98370
Ph: (303)465-6980
Co. E-mail: admin@apgen.org
URL: http://www.apgen.org
Facebook: www.facebook.com/
AssociationofProfessionalGenealogists
Linkedin: www.linkedin.com/company/
association-of-professional-genealogists
-apg
Instagram: www.instagram.com/
APgenealogists

Association de la construction du Quebec (ACQ)
9200 boul. Metropolitain E
Montreal, QC, Canada H1K 4L2
Ph: (514)354-0609
Free: 888-868-3424
Fax: (514)354-8292
Co. E-mail: info@acq.org
URL: http://www.acq.org
Facebook: www.facebook.com/
ACQprovinciale
Linkedin: www.linkedin.com/company/
association-de-la-construction-du-qu-bec
YouTube: www.youtube.com/user/
ACQprovinciale

Association of Schools and Colleges of Optometry (ASCO)
6110 Executive Blvd.
Rockville, MD 20847
Ph: (301)231-5944
Fax: (301)770-1828
URL: http://www.optometriceducation.org
Facebook: www.facebook.com/
OptometricEducation
Linkedin: www.linkedin.com/company/
association-of-schools-and-colleges-of
-optometry
Instagram: www.instagram.com/
optometriced
YouTube: www.youtube.com/channel/
UCmws13yqQhOpSlR2qKjxizQ

Association for Talent Development (ATD)
1640 King St.
Alexandria, VA 22313-1443
Ph: (703)683-8100
Free: 800-628-2783
Fax: (703)683-1523

Co. E-mail: customercare@td.org
URL: http://www.td.org
Facebook: www.facebook.com/ATD
Linkedin: www.linkedin.com/company/15989
Instagram: www.instagram.com/atdnational
Pinterest: www.pinterest.com/ATDofficial

Association of Writers & Writing Programs (AWP)
5700 Rivertech Ct., Ste. 225
Riverdale Park, MD 20737-1250
Ph: (696)696-7700
Co. E-mail: awp@awpwriter.org
URL: http://www.awpwriter.org
Facebook: www.facebook.com/AWPWriter
Linkedin: www.linkedin.com/company/awp-writer
Pinterest: www.pinterest.com/awpwriter

Athletic Business Publications Inc. (AB)
22 E Mifflin St., Ste. 910
Madison, WI 53703
Ph: (608)249-0186
URL: http://www.athleticbusiness.com
Facebook: www.facebook.com/athleticbusiness
Linkedin: www.linkedin.com/company/athletic-business
Instagram: www.instagram.com/athleticbiz
YouTube: www.youtube.com/user/AthleticBusinessMag

The Atlanta Journal-Constitution (AJC)
223 Perimeter Ctr. Pky.
Atlanta, GA 30346
Free: 800-933-9771
Co. E-mail: customercare@ajc.com
URL: http://www.ajc.com
Facebook: www.facebook.com/ajc

Atlantic Boating Almanac
3 Church Cir., Ste. 109
Annapolis, MD 21401
Free: 800-481-6277
Fax: (800)487-6277
Co. E-mail: editor@prostarpublications.com
URL: http://www.prostarpublications.com

Atlantic Publishing Co. (APG)
1405 SW 6th Ave.
Ocala, FL 34471
Ph: (352)622-1825
Co. E-mail: sales@atlantic-pub.com
URL: http://www.atlantic-pub.com
Facebook: www.facebook.com/AtlanticPublishing
Instagram: www.instagram.com/atlanticpublishinggroup

Atlantic Spinners and Handweavers (ASH)
c/o Scott Manor House, 15 Fort Sackville Rd.
Bedford, NS, Canada B4A 2G6
Co. E-mail: info@ashguild.ca
URL: http://ashguild.ca
Facebook: www.facebook.com/people/Atlantic-Spinners-and-Handweavers-ASH/100064574386936

Audio Engineering Society UK (AES)
London, United Kingdom
Co. E-mail: info@aes-uk.org
URL: http://www.aes-uk.org
Facebook: www.facebook.com/aesuk
YouTube: www.youtube.com/aesuksection

Austin Business Journal (ABJ)
515 Congress Ave., Ste. 1100
Austin, TX 78701
Ph: (512)494-2500
Fax: (512)494-2525
Co. E-mail: austin@bizjournals.com
URL: http://www.bizjournals.com/austin
Facebook: www.facebook.com/ATXBizJournal
Linkedin: www.linkedin.com/company/austin-business-journal
Instagram: www.instagram.com/austin_business_journal

AuthorHouse Inc.
1663 Liberty Dr.
Bloomington, IN 47403
Free: 833-262-8899
Co. E-mail: customersupport@authorhouse.com
URL: http://www.authorhouse.com/en
Facebook: www.facebook.com/AuthorHouse
Linkedin: www.linkedin.com/company/authorhouse
Pinterest: www.pinterest.com/authorhouse

Automotive Body Parts Association (ABPA)
400 Putnam Pke., Ste. J, No. 503
Smithfield, RI 02917-2442
Ph: (401)949-0912
Free: 800-323-5832
Fax: (401)262-0193
Co. E-mail: info@autobpa.com
URL: http://www.autobpa.com
Facebook: www.facebook.com/autobpa

Automotive Engine Rebuilders Association (AERA)
875 Feinberg Ct., Ste. 106
Cary, IL 60013
Ph: (815)526-7600
Free: 888-326-2372
Fax: (815)526-7601
Co. E-mail: info@aera.org
URL: http://www.aera.org
Instagram: www.instagram.com/engineprofessionalmag
YouTube: www.youtube.com/c/AERAEngineBuildersAssociation/videos

Automotive Service Association (ASA)
8209 Mid Cities Blvd., Ste. 100
North Richland Hills, TX 76182-4712
Ph: (817)514-2900
Co. E-mail: info@asashop.org
URL: http://www.asashop.org
Facebook: www.facebook.com/ASAshop
Linkedin: www.linkedin.com/company/automotive-service-association
Instagram: www.instagram.com/asa_national
YouTube: www.youtube.com/user/asawebops

Awards and Personalization Association
8735 W Higgins Rd., Ste. 300
Chicago, IL 60631
Ph: (847)375-4800
Fax: (847)375-6480
Co. E-mail: info@awardspersonalization.org
URL: http://awardspersonalization.org
Instagram: www.instagram.com/apa_hq

AWC Business Solutions
PO Box 282
Kensington Park, SA 5068, Australia
Ph: 61 08 8331 3231
Fax: 61 08 8331 3234
Co. E-mail: andrew.cole@awcsolutions.com.au
URL: http://www.awcsolutions.com.au

Azure Publishing Inc.
213 Sterling Rd., Ste. 206
Toronto, ON, Canada M6R 2B2
Ph: (416)203-9674
Fax: (416)203-9842
Co. E-mail: azure@azureonline.com
URL: http://www.azuremagazine.com
Facebook: www.facebook.com/AzureMagazine
Linkedin: www.linkedin.com/company/azure-magazine
Instagram: www.instagram.com/azuremagazine
YouTube: www.youtube.com/channel/UCvrVZE9TPyBGrqlB49F6JyQ
Pinterest: www.pinterest.ca/azuremagazine

B

Babcox Media Inc.
3550 Embassy Pky.
Akron, OH 44333-8318
Ph: (330)670-1234
Fax: (330)670-0874
URL: http://babcox.com
Facebook: www.facebook.com/BabcoxMedia
Linkedin: www.linkedin.com/company/babcox-media
Instagram: www.instagram.com/babcoxmedia
YouTube: www.youtube.com/channel/UCdFtzC7zhlqQrx0JpH2DzeA

Baker & Taylor, Inc.
2810 Coliseum Ctr. Dr., Ste. 300
Charlotte, NC 28217
Ph: (704)998-3100
Free: 800-775-1800
Co. E-mail: btinfo@baker-taylor.com
URL: http://www.baker-taylor.com
Facebook: www.facebook.com/
 BakerandTaylor
Linkedin: www.linkedin.com/company/
 baker-&-taylor
Instagram: www.instagram.com/
 baker_and_taylor
YouTube: www.youtube.com/user/
 BakerandTaylorTV

Ball Publishing
622 Town Rd.
West Chicago, IL 60186
Ph: (630)231-3675
Free: 888-888-0013
Fax: (630)231-5254
Co. E-mail: info@ballpublishing.com
URL: http://www.ballpublishing.com

Ballantine/ Del Rey/Fawcett/Ivy Books
1745 Broadway, 3rd Fl.
New York, NY 10019
URL: http://www.penguinrandomhouse.biz/
 media/logos

Baltimore Business Journal
36 S Charles St., Ste. 2500
Baltimore, MD 21201
Ph: (410)576-1161
Fax: (410)752-3112
Co. E-mail: baltimore@bizjournals.com
URL: http://www.bizjournals.com/baltimore
Facebook: www.facebook.com/
 baltimorebizjournal

The B&B and Country Inn Marketplace
926 Lenoir Rhyne Blvd. SE
Hickory, NC 28602
Ph: (828)781-2659
Co. E-mail: mariettehnc@gmail.com
URL: http://mariettesells.com
Facebook: www.facebook.com/pages/The
 -BB-and-Country-Inn-MarketPlace/
 185762208155714

Bangor Daily News (BDN)
1 Merchants Pl.
Bangor, ME 04402
Ph: (207)990-8000
Free: 800-432-7964
Co. E-mail: customerservice@bangordaily-
 news.com
URL: http://www.bangordailynews.com
Facebook: www.facebook.com/
 bangordailynews
Instagram: www.instagram.com/
 bangordailynews

Bard Press (BP)
5275 Mccormick Mountain D
Austin, TX 78734
Ph: (503)616-3092
Co. E-mail: info@bardpress.com
URL: http://bardpress.com
Linkedin: www.linkedin.com/company/bard
 -press

Barron's Editorial & Corporate Headquarters
1211 Avenue of the Americas
New York, NY 10036
URL: http://www.barrons.com

Barron's Educational Series Inc.
250 Wireless Blvd.
Hauppauge, NY 11788
Free: 866-506-1949
Co. E-mail: support@barronseduc.com
URL: http://www.barronseduc.com
Facebook: www.facebook.com/
 barronspublishing

Baum Publications Ltd.
124-2323 Boundary Rd.
Vancouver, BC, Canada V5M 4V8
Ph: (604)291-9900
Free: 888-286-3630
Fax: (604)291-1906
Co. E-mail: info@baumpub.com
URL: http://baumpub.com

Bay Area Poets Coalition Inc. (BAPC)
1791 Solano Ave., No. A11
Berkeley, CA 94707-2209
Ph: (510)859-7734
Co. E-mail: bapc.poetalk@gmail.com
URL: http://sites.google.com/site/
 bayareapoetscoalition
Facebook: www.facebook.com/Bay-Area
 -Poets-Coalition-231192550254579

The Beauty Industry Report (BIR)
15500 Pearl Rd., Ste. 360949
Cleveland, OH 44136-9998
Ph: (440)846-6022
Fax: (440)846-6024
URL: http://www.bironline.com

Bee Publishing Company Inc.
5 Church Hill Rd.
Newtown, CT 06470
Ph: (203)426-3141
Fax: (203)426-5169
Co. E-mail: editor@thebee.com
URL: http://www.newtownbee.com
Facebook: www.facebook.com/
 TheNewtownBee

Before and After
PO Box 7616
Citrus Heights, CA 95621-7616
Ph: (916)784-3880
URL: http://www.bamagazine.com
Facebook: www.facebook.com/pages/
 Before-After-magazine/83669057302

BenBella Books Inc.
10440 N Central Expy., Ste. 800
Dallas, TX 75231-2264
Co. E-mail: feedback@benbellabooks.com
URL: http://benbellabooks.com
Facebook: www.facebook.com/
 benbellabooks
Instagram: www.instagram.com/
 benbellabooks
YouTube: www.youtube.com/channel/
 UCkSpoNqFKMgoheQjnk9DRew

Bennett, Coleman & Company Ltd. (BCCL)
Times of India Office, 3rd Fl., Dr. D.N. Rd,
 Fort
Mumbai 400002, India
URL: http://bccl.in

Bennett Communications Inc.
424 W 800 N, Ste. 201
Orem, UT 84057
Ph: (801)802-0200
URL: http://bennettcommunications.com

Benzinga.com
1 Campus Martius Ste. 200
Detroit, MI 48226
Free: 877-440-9464
Co. E-mail: info@benzinga.com
URL: http://www.benzinga.com
Facebook: www.facebook.com/Benzinga
Linkedin: www.linkedin.com/company/
 benzinga
Instagram: www.instagram.com/benzinga
YouTube: www.youtube.com/benzinga

Berkley Books
375 Hudson St.
New York, NY 10014
URL: http://www.penguin.com/berkley
 -overview

Berkley Trade/Penguin Group USA Inc.
375 Hudson St.
New York, NY 10014
Facebook: www.facebook.com/
 PenguinGroupUSA

Best-Met Publishing Company Inc.
5537 Twin Knolls Rd., Ste. 438
Columbia, MD 21045
Ph: (410)730-5013
Co. E-mail: office@foodtradenews.com
URL: http://www.foodtradenews.com

BIA/Kelsey
14901 Bogle Dr., Ste. 101
Chantilly, VA 20151
Ph: (703)818-2425
Co. E-mail: info@bia.com
URL: http://www.bia.com
Facebook: www.facebook.com/biakelsey
Linkedin: www.linkedin.com/company/
 biaadvisorysrvs
YouTube: www.youtube.com/user/
 BIAmediacenter

The Billings Gazette
401 N Broadway
Billings, MT 59101
Ph: (406)657-1200
Free: 800-762-6397
Fax: (406)657-1208
URL: http://billingsgazette.com
Facebook: www.facebook.com/
  billingsgazette
Instagram: www.instagram.com/
  billingsgazette
YouTube: www.youtube.com/user/
  BillingsGazette

Bio-Integral Resource Center (BIRC)
PO Box 7414
Berkeley, CA 94707
Ph: (510)524-2567
Fax: (510)524-1758
Co. E-mail: birc@igc.org
URL: http://www.birc.org
Facebook: www.facebook.com/Bio-Integral
  -Resource-Center-434226623308463

BK Royston Publishing
PO Box 4321
Jeffersonville, IN 47131
Ph: (502)802-5385
Co. E-mail: bkroystonpublishing@gmail
  .com
URL: http://bkroystonpublishing.com
Facebook: www.facebook.com/
  BkRoystonPublishing
Instagram: www.instagram.com/
  bkroystonpublishing
YouTube: www.youtube.com/channel/
  UCxZ6hPU4Ut4OwyObBuSDOMA

Black Enterprise
500 7th Ave., 12th Fl.
New York, NY 10018
Ph: (212)242-8000
Fax: (212)886-9618
Co. E-mail: benyc_ads@blackenterprise
  .com
URL: http://www.blackenterprise.com
Facebook: www.facebook.com/
  BLACKENTERPRISE
Linkedin: www.linkedin.com/company/
  black-enterprise
Instagram: www.instagram.com/
  blackenterprise
YouTube: www.youtube.com/user/
  BEMultiMedia

Black Tennis Magazine Inc.
3548 Rio Grande Cir.
Dallas, TX 75233

Block Communications Inc. (BCI)
405 Madison Ave., Ste. 2100
Toledo, OH 43604
Ph: (419)724-6212
URL: http://www.blockcommunications
  .com

Bloomberg Businessweek
731 Lexington Ave.
New York, NY 10022
Free: 800-635-1200
Fax: (212)617-9065
URL: http://www.businessweek.com

Bloomberg L.P.
731 Lexington Ave.
New York, NY 10022
Ph: (212)318-2000
Co. E-mail: inquiry1@bloomberg.net
URL: http://www.bloomberg.com
Facebook: www.facebook.com/
  bloombergbusiness
Linkedin: www.linkedin.com/company/
  bloomberg
Instagram: www.instagram.com/
  bloombergbusiness
YouTube: www.youtube.com/channel/
  UCIALMKvObZNtJ6AmdCLP7Lg

Bluestocking Press
PO Box 1134
Eagle, ID 83616-1134
Free: 800-959-8586
Fax: (800)959-8586
Co. E-mail: customerservice@bluestock-
  ingpress.com
URL: http://www.bluestockingpress.com

BNP Media
2401 W Big Beaver Rd., Ste. 700
Troy, MI 48084
Ph: (248)362-3700
URL: http://www.bnpmedia.com
Facebook: www.facebook.com/BnpMedia
Linkedin: www.linkedin.com/company/bnp
  -media
Instagram: www.instagram.com/
  bnp_media

Boat Owners Association of the United States
5323 Port Royal Rd.
Springfield, VA 22151
Free: 800-937-3300
URL: http://www.boatus.com
Facebook: www.facebook.com/BoatUS
Linkedin: www.linkedin.com/company/
  boatus
Instagram: www.instagram.com/boatus
YouTube: www.youtube.com/boatus

Bobit Business Media (BBM)
3520 Challenger St.
Torrance, CA 90503
Ph: (310)533-2400
URL: http://www.bobitbusinessmedia.com
Facebook: www.facebook.com/
  bobitbusinessmedia

Bollinger Capital Management Inc. (BCM)
1200 Aviation Blvd.,Ste. 201
Redondo Beach, CA 90278
Ph: (310)798-8855

Co. E-mail: info@bollingercapital.com
URL: http://www.bollingercapital.com
Linkedin: www.linkedin.com/company/
  bollinger-capital-management

Bonnier LLC
517 N Virginia Ave.
Winter Park, FL 32790
Ph: (407)628-4802
URL: http://www.bonniercorp.com

Booklocker.com Inc.
11550 S Main St., Ste. 150
Trenton, GA 30752
Fax: (305)768-0261
URL: http://booklocker.com

Boston Business Journal
70 Franklin St. 8th Fl.
Boston, MA 02110
Ph: (617)330-1000
Fax: (617)330-1015
Co. E-mail: boston@bizjournals.com
URL: http://www.bizjournals.com/boston
Facebook: www.facebook.com/
  BostonBusinessJournal

The Bowser Report
PO Box 5156
Williamsburg, VA 23188
Ph: (757)877-5979
Co. E-mail: customerservice@thebowser-
  report.com
URL: http://www.thebowserreport.com
Facebook: www.facebook.com/
  thebowserreport
YouTube: www.youtube.com/channel/
  UCa7eSUnaMZGYrYXnBavywFg

BPS Communications
1001 Easton Rd.
Willow Grove, PA 19090
Ph: (215)830-8467
Co. E-mail: info@bpscommunications.com
URL: http://www.bpscommunications.com

Brewery Collectibles Club of America (BCCA)
747 Merus Ct.
Fenton, MO 63026-2092
URL: http://www.bcca.com
Instagram: www.instagram.com/
  brewerycollectibles
YouTube: www.youtube.com/channel/
  UCk3zx_LEg2BuBuy6lpxo-2A

Brick Industry Association (BIA)
12007 Sunrise Valley Dr., Ste. 430
Reston, VA 20191
Ph: (703)620-0010
Fax: (703)620-3928

Co. E-mail: socialmedia@bia.org
URL: http://www.gobrick.com
Facebook: www.facebook.com/
brickindustry
Linkedin: www.linkedin.com/groups/
1931504/profile
Instagram: www.instagram.com/
brickindustry
YouTube: www.youtube.com/user/
BrickIndustry
Pinterest: www.pinterest.com/brickindustry

BridgeTower Media (BTM)
7025 Albert Pick Rd.
Greensboro, NC 27409
Ph: (612)317-9420
Free: 877-615-9536
Co. E-mail: customerservice@bridgetowermedia.com
URL: http://www.bridgetowermedia.com
Facebook: www.facebook.com/
bridgetowermedia
Linkedin: www.linkedin.com/company/
bridgetower-media

BrightFocus Foundation
22512 Gateway Center Dr.
Clarksburg, MD 20871
Free: 800-437-2423
Fax: (301)258-9454
Co. E-mail: info@brightfocus.org
URL: http://www.brightfocus.org
Facebook: www.facebook.com/
BrightFocusFoundation
Linkedin: www.linkedin.com/company/
brightfocus-foundation
Instagram: www.instagram.com/
brightfocus
YouTube: www.youtube.com/c/
BrightfocusOrg
Pinterest: www.pinterest.com/
BrightFocusFdn

Broadway Books (BB)
1714 NE Broadway
Portland, OR 97232
Ph: (503)284-1726
Co. E-mail: bookbroads@broadwaybooks.net
URL: http://www.broadwaybooks.net
Facebook: www.facebook.com/Broadway-Books-41493694630
Instagram: www.instagram.com/
broadwaybooks
YouTube: www.youtube.com/bookbroads

Broadway Business
1745 Broadway
New York, NY 10019
URL: http://www.randomhouse.com/crown/
broadway-business-books

BUC International Corp.
1314 NE 17th Ct.
Fort Lauderdale, FL 33305
Ph: (954)565-6715
Free: 800-327-6929
Fax: (954)561-3095
Co. E-mail: orders@buc.com
URL: http://www.buc.com

The Buffalo News, Inc. (BNI)
1 News Plz.
Buffalo, NY 14240
Ph: (716)842-1111
Free: 800-777-8640
Co. E-mail: subscriberservices@buffnews.com
URL: http://buffalonews.com
Facebook: www.facebook.com/
TheBuffaloNews
YouTube: www.youtube.com/user/
BuffaloNewsVideo

Building Green Inc. (BG)
122 Birge St., Ste. 30
Brattleboro, VT 05301
Ph: (802)257-7300
Free: 800-861-0954
Co. E-mail: support@buildinggreen.com
URL: http://www.buildinggreen.com
Facebook: www.facebook.com/bgsocial
Linkedin: www.linkedin.com/company/
buildinggreen-inc

Business Courier
101 W 7th St.
Cincinnati, OH 45202
Ph: (513)621-6665
Fax: (513)621-2462

Business Ethics
Ansonia St.
New York, NY 10023
Ph: (646)688-3620
Fax: (212)202-3561
Co. E-mail: editorial@business-ethics.com
URL: http://business-ethics.com

Business Ethics Quarterly
PO Box 7147
Charlottesville, VA 22906
Free: 800-444-2419
Fax: (434)220-3301
URL: http://sbeonline.org/?page_id=633

Business First
465 Main St.
Buffalo, NY 14203-1793
Ph: (716)541-1600
Fax: (716)854-3394
Co. E-mail: buffalo@bizjournals.com
URL: http://www.bizjournals.com/buffalo
Facebook: www.facebook.com/
BfloBusinessFirst
Linkedin: www.linkedin.com/company/
buffalo-business-first
Instagram: www.instagram.com/bflobizfirst

Business First
300 Marconi Blvd., Ste. 105
Columbus, OH 43215
Ph: (614)461-4040
Fax: (614)365-2980
Co. E-mail: columbus@bizjournals.com
URL: http://www.bizjournals.com/columbus
Facebook: www.facebook.com/
ColumbusBusinessFirst
Linkedin: www.linkedin.com/company/
american-city-business-journals
Instagram: www.instagram.com/
columbusbiz1st

Business Intelligence Program
333 Ravenswood Ave.
Menlo Park, CA 94025
Ph: (650)859-4600
Fax: (650)859-4544
Co. E-mail: info@sric-bi.com

The Business Journal
825 N Jefferson St., Ste. 200
Milwaukee, WI 53202
Ph: (414)278-7788
Fax: (414)278-7028
Co. E-mail: milwaukee@bizjournals.com
URL: http://www.bizjournals.com/
milwaukee

Business North Carolina (BNC)
1230 W Morehead St., Ste. 308
Charlotte, NC 28208
Ph: (704)523-6987
Fax: (704)523-4211
Co. E-mail: circulation@businessnc.com
URL: http://www.businessnc.com
Facebook: www.facebook.com/
BusinessNC
Linkedin: www.linkedin.com/company/
business-north-carolina
Instagram: www.instagram.com/
businessnorthcarolina
YouTube: www.youtube.com/channel/
UCZj5pjytIsyXj-JLHOu4baQ

Business Research Services, Inc. (BRS)
7720 Wisconsin Ave., Ste. 213
Bethesda, MD 20814
Ph: (301)229-5561
Free: 800-845-8420
Fax: (301)229-6133
Co. E-mail: brspubs@sba8a.com
URL: http://www.sba8a.com

C

California Trucking Association (CTA)
4148 E Commerce Way
Sacramento, CA 95834
Ph: (916)373-3500
Co. E-mail: membership@caltrux.org
URL: http://www.caltrux.org
Facebook: www.facebook.com/caltrux

Cambridge University Press
1 Liberty Plz., Fl. 20
New York, NY 10013-2473
Ph: (212)337-5000

GUIDE TO PUBLISHERS

Co. E-mail: subscriptions_newyork@cambridge.org
URL: http://www.cambridge.org
Facebook: www.facebook.com/CambridgeUniversityPress

Canada Wide Media Ltd. (CW)
130 - 4321 Still Creek Rd.
Burnaby, BC, Canada V5C 6S7
Ph: (604)299-7311
Co. E-mail: sales@canadawide.com
URL: http://canadawide.com
Linkedin: www.linkedin.com/company/canada-wide-media

Canadian Apparel Federation (CAF)
116 Albert St., Ste. 404
Ottawa, ON, Canada K1P 5G3
Ph: (613)231-3220
URL: http://www.apparel.ca

Canadian Association of Token Collectors (CATC)
c/o Ian Spears, Secretary-Treasurer
3280 Bloor St., W Ste. 1140
Toronto, ON, Canada M8X 2X3
Co. E-mail: ian.speers@utoronto.ca
URL: http://www.nunetcan.net/catc.htm

Canadian Co-Operative Wool Growers Ltd. (CCWG)
c/o Ontario Stockyards Inc. 3807 Hwy. No.89
Cookstown, ON, Canada L0L 1L0
Ph: (705)458-4800
Free: 866-458-4800
Fax: (705)458-0186
Co. E-mail: cookstown@ccwg.ca
URL: http://wool.ca

Canadian Council for Small Business and Entrepreneurship (CCSBE)
6382 Young St.
Halifax, NS, Canada B3L 2A1
URL: http://ccsbe.org

Canadian Honey Council (CHC)
51519, No. 218, R.R., Ste. 220
Sherwood Park, AB, Canada T8E 1H1
Free: 877-356-8935
Co. E-mail: chc-ccm@honeycouncil.ca
URL: http://honeycouncil.ca

Canadian Institute of Geomatics (CIG)
100 E 900 Dynes Rd.
Ottawa, ON, Canada K2C 3L6
Co. E-mail: admin@cig-acsg.ca
URL: http://www.cig-acsg.ca
Facebook: www.facebook.com/TheCanadianInstituteOfGeomatics

Canadian Money Saver Inc.
470 Weber St. N, Ste. 104
Waterloo, ON, Canada N2L 6J2
Ph: (519)772-7632

Co. E-mail: moneyinfo@canadianmoneysaver.ca
URL: http://www.canadianmoneysaver.ca
Facebook: www.facebook.com/CanadianMoneySaver
Linkedin: www.linkedin.com/company/canadian-moneysaver-inc
Instagram: www.instagram.com/canadian_money_saver
YouTube: www.youtube.com/user/canadianmoneysaver

Canadian Science Publishing (CSP)
1840 Woodward Dr., Ste. 1
Ottawa, ON, Canada K2C 0P7
Ph: (613)656-9846
Free: 844-223-8144
Fax: (613)656-9838
Co. E-mail: cjp@cdnsciencepub.com
URL: http://www.cdnsciencepub.com
Facebook: www.facebook.com/cdnsciencepub
Linkedin: www.linkedin.com/company/canadian-science-publishing
YouTube: www.youtube.com/user/cdnsciencepub

Canadian Society of Cinematographers (CSC)
3085 Kingston Rd., Ste. 131
Toronto, ON, Canada M1M 1P1
Ph: (416)266-0591
Co. E-mail: info@csc.ca
URL: http://csc.ca
Instagram: www.instagram.com/canadiancinematographer
YouTube: www.youtube.com/channel/UCPNOY3YiUTCjmp-mTa9MMDg

Canadian Veterinary Medical Association (CVMA)
339 Booth St.
Ottawa, ON, Canada K1R 7K1
Ph: (613)236-1162
Free: 800-567-2862
Fax: (613)236-9681
Co. E-mail: admin@cvma-acmv.org
URL: http://www.canadianveterinarians.net
Facebook: www.facebook.com/CanadianVeterinaryMedicalAssociation
YouTube: www.youtube.com/user/CVMAACMV

Cannabis Culture
307 W Hastings St.
Vancouver, BC, Canada V6B 1H6
Ph: (604)682-1172
Co. E-mail: shipping@cannabisculture.com
URL: http://cannabisculturehq.com
Facebook: www.facebook.com/CCMagazineOnline
Instagram: www.instagram.com/cannabiscultureofficial
YouTube: www.youtube.com/user/PotTVNetwork

The Cannabis Marketing Lab
PO Box 2711
Pismo Beach, CA 93448
Linkedin: www.linkedin.com/company/mj-marketing-labs

Cannabis Now
8495 W 3rd St., Ste. D-105
Los Angeles, CA 90048
Ph: (323)452-9200
Co. E-mail: retail@cannabisnow.com
URL: http://cannabisnow.com
Facebook: www.facebook.com/cnmagazine
Instagram: www.instagram.com/cannabisnow

Canola Council of Canada (CCC)
400-167 Lombard Ave.
Winnipeg, MB, Canada R3B 0T6
Ph: (204)982-2100
Free: 866-834-4378
Co. E-mail: admin@canolacouncil.org
URL: http://www.canolacouncil.org
Facebook: www.facebook.com/CanolaWatchCCC
YouTube: www.youtube.com/channel/UCpROV-G7e-MnkPQHLcjcTBA

Cape Cod Media Group
319 Main St.
Hyannis, MA 02601
Ph: (508)775-1200
Free: 800-286-2233
Co. E-mail: news@capecodonline.com
URL: http://www.capecodtimes.com
Facebook: www.facebook.com/capecodtimes
Instagram: www.instagram.com/capecodtimes

Cape Cod Times
319 Main St.
Hyannis, MA 02601
Ph: (508)775-1200
Free: 800-286-2233
Co. E-mail: news@capecodonline.com
URL: http://www.capecodtimes.com
Facebook: www.facebook.com/capecodtimes
Instagram: www.instagram.com/capecodtimes

Capitol Information Group Inc.
20 Pidgeon Hill Dr., Ste. 202
Sterling, VA 20165
Ph: (703)905-8000
Free: 800-832-2330
Co. E-mail: customerservice@investingdaily.com
URL: http://capinfogroup.com

Career Press Inc.
12 Parish Dr.
Wayne, NJ 07470
URL: http://redwheelweiser.com/imprints/career-press

GUIDE TO PUBLISHERS

Casket and Funeral Supply Association of America (CFSA)
3502 Woodview Trace, Ste. 300
Indianapolis, IN 46268
Ph: (847)295-6630
Fax: (847)295-6647
Co. E-mail: info@cfsaa.org
URL: http://www.cfsaa.org
Facebook: www.facebook.com/funeralsuppliers

Cat Fanciers' Association (CFA)
260 E Main St.
Alliance, OH 44601
Ph: (330)680-4070
Fax: (330)680-4633
Co. E-mail: marketing@cfa.org
URL: http://cfa.org
Facebook: www.facebook.com/CFAcats
Instagram: www.instagram.com/cfa.cats
YouTube: www.youtube.com/channel/UCU2UK7DB_1nshLXgtlj7yDQ
Pinterest: www.pinterest.com/CFAcats

Catholic Health Association of the United States (CHA)
4455 Woodson Rd.
Saint Louis, MO 63134
Ph: (314)427-2500
Free: 800-230-7823
Fax: (314)427-0029
Co. E-mail: servicecenter@chausa.org
URL: http://www.chausa.org
Facebook: www.facebook.com/catholichealthassociation
Instagram: www.instagram.com/thechausa
YouTube: www.youtube.com/user/catholichealthassoc
Pinterest: www.pinterest.com/thechausa

CBJ L.P.
18500 Von Karman Ave., Ste. 150
Irvine, CA 92612
Ph: (949)833-8373
Fax: (949)833-8751
URL: http://www.ocbj.com
Facebook: www.facebook.com/OrangeCountyBusinessJournal
Linkedin: www.linkedin.com/company/ocbj
Instagram: www.instagram.com/ocbizjournal
YouTube: www.youtube.com/channel/UCw4oUCN7DGEdfEKeFo1ocGA

CBJ L.P.
4445 Eastgate Mall, Ste. 200
San Diego, CA 92121

CCIM Institute
430 N Michigan Ave., Ste. 700
Chicago, IL 60611
Ph: (312)321-4460
URL: http://www.ccim.com
Facebook: www.facebook.com/cciminstitute
Linkedin: www.linkedin.com/company/ccim-institute
YouTube: www.youtube.com/user/CCIMInstitute

C.E. Publications Inc.
11711 N Creek Pkwy S, Ste. 112
Bothell, WA 98011
Ph: (425)806-5200
Fax: (425)806-5585
Co. E-mail: staff@cjhunter.com
URL: http://www.cjhunter.com/cepublications/index.html

Ceilings and Interior Systems Construction Association (CISCA)
1010 Jorie Blvd., Ste. 30
Oak Brook, IL 60523
Ph: (630)584-1919
Fax: (866)560-8537
Co. E-mail: cisca@cisca.org
URL: http://www.cisca.org/i4a/pages/index.cfm
Facebook: www.facebook.com/ciscaassociation

Cengage Learning, Inc.
5191 Natorp Blvd.
Mason, OH 45040
Ph: (513)229-1000
URL: http://www.cengagegroup.com

Center for Science in the Public Interest (CSPI)
1250 I St. NW Ste. 500
Washington, DC 20005
Ph: (202)332-9110
Fax: (202)265-4954
Co. E-mail: cspi@cspinet.org
URL: http://www.cspinet.org
Facebook: www.facebook.com/cspinet
Instagram: www.instagram.com/cspi_nutritionaction
YouTube: www.youtube.com/user/cspitv
Pinterest: www.pinterest.com/cspinutrition

Cereals & Grains Association (CGA)
3285 Northwood Cir., Ste. 100
Saint Paul, MN 55121
Ph: (651)454-7250
Fax: (651)454-0766
Co. E-mail: info@cerealsgrains.org
URL: http://www.cerealsgrains.org/Pages/default.aspx
Facebook: www.facebook.com/cerealsgrains
Linkedin: www.linkedin.com/company/cerealsgrains

CFA Institute
915 E High St.
Charlottesville, VA 22902
Ph: (434)951-5499
Co. E-mail: info@cfainstitute.org
URL: http://www.cfainstitute.org
Facebook: www.facebook.com/CFAInstitute
Linkedin: www.linkedin.com/company/cfainstitute

Chain Store Guide (CSG)
3710 Corporex Pk. Dr., Ste. 310
Tampa, FL 33619
Free: 800-927-9292
Fax: (813)627-6888
Co. E-mail: info@csgis.com
URL: http://www.chainstoreguide.com
Facebook: www.facebook.com/ChainStoreGuide
Linkedin: www.linkedin.com/company/chain-store-guide

Charlotte Business Journal (CBJ)
550 S Caldwell St., Ste. 910
Charlotte, NC 28202
Ph: (704)973-1100
Fax: (704)973-1102
Co. E-mail: charlotte@bizjournals.com
URL: http://www.bizjournals.com/charlotte
Facebook: www.facebook.com/charlottebizjournal
Instagram: www.instagram.com/cbjnewsroom

Chattanooga Publishing Company Inc.
400 E 11th St.
Chattanooga, TN 37403-4203
Co. E-mail: circulationcs@timesfreepress.com

Cheese Reporter Publishing Co.
2810 Crossroads Dr., Ste. 3000
Madison, WI 53718
Ph: (608)246-8430
Fax: (608)246-8431
Co. E-mail: marketing@cheesereporter.com
URL: http://www.cheesereporter.com

The Chemical Educator
2640 S Bear Claw Way
Meridian, ID 83642
Ph: (208)440-1866
Co. E-mail: chemeducator@gmail.org
URL: http://www.chemeducator.org

Chemical Institute of Canada (CIC)
90-2420 Bank St.
Ottawa, ON, Canada K1V 8S1
Ph: (613)232-6252
Fax: (613)232-5862
Co. E-mail: info@cheminst.ca
URL: http://www.cheminst.ca
Linkedin: www.linkedin.com/company/chemical-institute-of-canada

Chicago Home & Garden
208 So Lasalle St., Ste. 814
Chicago, IL 60604-1101

GUIDE TO PUBLISHERS

Chicago Review Press Inc. (CRP)
814 N Franklin St.
Chicago, IL 60610
Ph: (312)337-0747
Free: 800-888-4741
Fax: (312)337-5110
Co. E-mail: frontdesk@chicagoreview-press.com
URL: http://www.chicagoreviewpress.com
Facebook: www.facebook.com/chireviewpress
Instagram: www.instagram.com/chireviewpress

Child Welfare League of America (CWLA)
727 15th St. NW Ste. 1200
Washington, DC 20005
Ph: (202)688-4200
Co. E-mail: cwla@cwla.org
URL: http://www.cwla.org
Facebook: www.facebook.com/CWLAUpdates

Children's Book Insider L.L.C. (CBI)
901 Columbia Rd.
Fort Collins, CO 80525
Ph: (970)495-0056
Co. E-mail: mail@cbiclubhouse.com
URL: http://writeforkids.org
Facebook: www.facebook.com/WriteKidsBooks
YouTube: www.youtube.com/user/cbiclubhouse

Christian Camp and Conference Association (CCCA)
PO Box 62189
Colorado Springs, CO 80962-2189
Ph: (719)260-9400
Free: 888-922-2287
Fax: (719)260-6398
Co. E-mail: support@ccca.org
URL: http://www.ccca.org/ccca/default.asp
Facebook: www.facebook.com/cccaorgconnect
Pinterest: www.pinterest.com/christiancamp

The Chronicle of Philanthropy
1255 Twenty-third St. N, 7th Fl.
Washington, DC 20037
Ph: (202)466-1200
Fax: (202)466-2078
Co. E-mail: editor@philanthropy.com
URL: http://www.philanthropy.com
Facebook: www.facebook.com/ChronicleOfPhilanthropy
Linkedin: www.linkedin.com/company/the-chronicle-of-philanthropy
YouTube: www.youtube.com/channel/UCk0hYi2US2LASzODBika_6w
Pinterest: www.pinterest.com/cophilanthropy

CIO
PO Box 9208
Framingham, MA 01701
Ph: (508)872-0080

Clarkson Potter
222 Rosewood Dr.
Danvers, MA 01923
URL: http://crownpublishing.com

Close-Up Media Inc.
13400 Sutton Pk. Dr. S, Ste. 1504
Jacksonville, FL 32224
Ph: (904)463-8580
Fax: (904)992-3945
Co. E-mail: info@closeupmedia.com
URL: http://closeupmedia.com

Closing the Gap Inc. (CTG)
PO Box 68
Henderson, MN 56044
Ph: (507)248-3294
Fax: (507)248-3810
Co. E-mail: info@closingthegap.com
URL: http://www.closingthegap.com
Facebook: www.facebook.com/ATClosingTheGap
Instagram: www.instagram.com/atclosingthegap

The Clute Institute for Academic Research
8119 Shaffer Pky. A10
Littleton, CO 80127
Ph: (303)904-4750
URL: http://www.cluteinstitute.com
Facebook: www.facebook.com/cluteinstitute
Linkedin: www.linkedin.com/company/the-clute-institute
YouTube: www.youtube.com/c/cluteinstitute

CNW Group Ltd.
88 Queens Quay W, Ste. 3000
Toronto, ON, Canada M5J 0B8
Ph: (416)863-5639
Free: 877-269-7890
URL: http://www.newswire.ca
Facebook: www.facebook.com/CisionCA
Linkedin: www.linkedin.com/company/cnw-group

CNW Publishing, Editing and Promotion Inc.
45 Main St.
North Stratford, NH 03590
Ph: (603)922-8338
Fax: (603)922-8339
Co. E-mail: info@writers-editors.com
URL: http://www.writers-editors.com
Facebook: www.facebook.com/WritersEditorsNetwork

Coastal Communications Corp.
2700 N Military Trl., Ste. 120
Boca Raton, FL 33431-6394
Ph: (561)989-0600
Fax: (561)989-9509
URL: http://www.themeetingmagazines.com

The Collectors Club (CC)
22 E 35th St.
New York, NY 10016-3806
Ph: (212)683-0559
Co. E-mail: info@collectorsclub.org
URL: http://www.collectorsclub.org

College Art Association (CAA)
50 Broadway, 21st Fl.
New York, NY 10004
Ph: (212)691-1051
Fax: (212)627-2381
Co. E-mail: nyoffice@collegeart.org
URL: http://www.collegeart.org
Facebook: www.facebook.com/caavisual
YouTube: www.youtube.com/c/CAAvisual

Colorado Calligraphers' Guild
PO Box 102672
Denver, CO 80250-2672
Co. E-mail: info@coloradocalligraphers.com
URL: http://www.coloradocalligraphers.com
Facebook: www.facebook.com/coloradocalligraphers
Instagram: www.instagram.com/coloradocalligraphers

Colorado Society of Certified Public Accountants (COCPA)
7887 E Belleview Ave., Ste. 200
Englewood, CO 80111-6076
Ph: (303)773-2877
Free: 800-523-9082
Co. E-mail: info@cocpa.org
URL: http://www.cocpa.org
Facebook: www.facebook.com/cocpa
Instagram: www.instagram.com/co_cpas
YouTube: www.youtube.com/user/CSCPA

Columbus Times
2230 Buena Vista Rd.
Columbus, GA 31906
Ph: (706)405-6518
Co. E-mail: columbustimes706@gmail.com
URL: http://www.columbustimes.com

Communication Publications & Resources
2807 N Parham Rd., Ste. 200
Richmond, VA 23294
Free: 800-780-4066
URL: http://www.briefingsmediagroup.com

Communications Concepts Inc.
6604 Richmond Rd., Ste. 19
Williamsburg, VA 23188-7233
Ph: (703)643-2200

Co. E-mail: info@apexawards.com
URL: http://www.apexawards.com
Facebook: www.facebook.com/
 ApexAwardsForPublicationExcellence
Linkedin: www.linkedin.com/in/apexawards

CompTIA
3500 Lacey Rd., Ste. 100
Downers Grove, IL 60515
Ph: (630)678-8300
Free: 866-835-8020
Fax: (630)678-8384
Co. E-mail: membership@comptia.org
URL: http://www.comptia.org
Facebook: www.facebook.com/CompTIA
Linkedin: www.linkedin.com/company/
 comptia
Instagram: www.instagram.com/
 comptiaphotos
YouTube: www.youtube.com/comptiatv

ComputerTalk Associates Inc.
492 Norristown Rd., Ste. 2501
Blue Bell, PA 19422
Co. E-mail: info@computertalk.com
URL: http://computertalk.com

Comtex News Network Inc.
295 Madison Ave., 12th Fl.
New York, NY 10017
Ph: (212)688-6240
Fax: (212)688-6241
Co. E-mail: cs@comtex.com
URL: http://www.comtex.com

Concepts Travel Media Ltd.
130 Queens Quay W, Ste. 512
Toronto, ON, Canada M5A 0P6
Ph: (416)365-1500
Fax: (416)365-1504
Co. E-mail: travelweek@travelweek.ca
URL: http://www.travelweek.ca
Linkedin: www.linkedin.com/company/
 travelweek
YouTube: www.youtube.com/user/
 travelweek

Conde Nast Publications
1 World Trade Ctr.
New York, NY 10007
Ph: (515)243-3273
Free: 800-405-8085
Co. E-mail: communications@condenast
 .com
URL: http://www.condenast.com
Linkedin: www.linkedin.com/company/
 conde-nast
Instagram: www.instagram.com/condenast

Conseil Canadien du Bois (CCB)
99 Bank St., Ste. 400
Ottawa, ON, Canada K1P 6B9
Ph: (613)747-5544
Fax: (613)747-6264
URL: http://cwc.ca/en/home
Linkedin: www.linkedin.com/company/
 canadian-wood-council
YouTube: www.youtube.com/c/
 CanadianWoodCouncil

Construction Financial Management Association (CFMA)
100 Village Blvd., Ste. 200
Princeton, NJ 08540
Ph: (609)452-8000
Free: 888-421-9996
Fax: (609)452-0474
Co. E-mail: info@cfma.org
URL: http://cfma.org
Facebook: www.facebook.com/
 ConstructionFinancialManagementAsso-
 ciation
Linkedin: www.linkedin.com/company/cfma
YouTube: www.youtube.com/user/
 CFMAPrinceton

Construction Specifications Institute (CSI)
123 N Pitt St., Ste. 450
Alexandria, VA 22314
Free: 800-689-2900
Co. E-mail: csi@csinet.org
URL: http://www.csiresources.org/home
Facebook: www.facebook.com/
 CSIConstruction
YouTube: www.youtube.com/user/
 CSIConstruction

Consumer Reports Books (CR)
101 Truman Ave.
Yonkers, NY 10703
URL: http://www.consumerreports.org/cr
 -store

Consumer Technology Association (CTA)
1919 S Eads St.
Arlington, VA 22202
Ph: (703)907-7600
Co. E-mail: copyright@cta.tech
URL: http://www.cta.tech
Facebook: www.facebook.com/
 ConsumerTechnologyAssociation
Linkedin: www.linkedin.com/company/
 consumer-technology-association
Instagram: www.instagram.com/cta

Contact Lens Manufacturers Association (CLMA)
PO Box 29398
Lincoln, NE 68529
Ph: (402)465-4122
Free: 800-344-9060
Fax: (402)465-4187
URL: http://www.clma.net

Contact Lens Society of America (CLSA)
PO Box 253
Highland Lakes, NJ 07422
Free: 800-296-9776
Fax: (888)275-9098
Co. E-mail: clsa@clsa.info
URL: http://www.clsa.info
Facebook: www.facebook.com/
 ContactLensSociety

Convenience Distribution Association (CDA)
11250 Roger Bacon Dr. 8
Reston, VA 20190
Ph: (703)208-3358
Free: 800-482-2962
Fax: (703)573-5738
Co. E-mail: info@cdaweb.net
URL: http://www.cdaweb.net
Facebook: www.facebook.com/
 conveniencedistribution

Conway Inc.
6625 The Corners Pky., Ste. 200
Peachtree Corners, GA 30092
Ph: (770)446-6996
Co. E-mail: info@conway.com
URL: http://conway.com
Linkedin: www.linkedin.com/company/
 conway-data-inc-

COR Healthcare Resources
PO Box 50507
Santa Barbara, CA 93150
Ph: (805)564-2177
Fax: (805)564-2146
Co. E-mail: info@corhealth.com

Corbin Manufacturing & Supply Inc.
600 Industrial Cir.
White City, OR 97503
Ph: (541)826-5211
Fax: (541)826-8669
Co. E-mail: sales@corbins.com
URL: http://www.corbins.com

Cosmic Awareness Communications (CAC)
PO Box 115
Olympia, WA 98507
Fax: (360)352-6294
Co. E-mail: info@cosmicawareness.org
URL: http://cosmicawareness.org
Facebook: www.facebook.com/cacdotorg

Council of Educators in Landscape Architecture (CELA)
110 Horizon Dr., Ste. 210
Raleigh, NC 27615
Ph: (919)674-4185
Fax: (919)459-2075
Co. E-mail: thecela.org@gmail.com
URL: http://thecela.org
Facebook: www.facebook.com/thecela
Linkedin: www.linkedin.com/company/
 council-of-educators-in-landscape
 -architecture
Instagram: www.instagram.com/
 thecelaofficial

GUIDE TO PUBLISHERS

Country Dance and Song Society (CDSS)
116 Pleasant St., Ste. 345
Easthampton, MA 01027-2759
Ph: (413)203-5467
Fax: (413)203-5471
Co. E-mail: address@cdss.org
URL: http://www.cdss.org
Facebook: www.facebook.com/cdss.org
Instagram: www.instagram.com/CDSSorg
YouTube: www.youtube.com/user/CDSSorg

Country Sampler Group
306 E Parr Rd.
Berne, IN 46711
Free: 800-829-0425
Co. E-mail: customer_service@countrysampler.us
URL: http://www.countrysampler.com
Facebook: www.facebook.com/CountrySamplerMagazine
Instagram: www.instagram.com/countrysamplermagazine
YouTube: www.youtube.com/user/CountrySamplerMag

Crain Associated Enterprises Inc. - American Trade Magazines
150 N Michigan Ave.
Chicago, IL 60601
Ph: (312)649-5200
Co. E-mail: customer-service@crain.com
URL: http://www.crain.com/index.html
Facebook: www.facebook.com/craincommunicationsinc
Linkedin: www.linkedin.com/company/crain-communications

Crain Communications Inc.
700 W St. Clair Ave., Ste. 310
Cleveland, OH 44113-1256
Ph: (216)522-1383
Co. E-mail: info@crain.com
URL: http://www.crain.com
Facebook: www.facebook.com/CrainCommunicationsInc
Linkedin: www.linkedin.com/company/crain
Instagram: www.instagram.com/craincommunications

Crain Communications Inc.
1155 Gratiot Ave.
Detroit, MI 48207-2732
Ph: (313)446-6000
Co. E-mail: info@crain.com
URL: http://www.crain.com
Facebook: www.facebook.com/CrainCommunicationsInc
Linkedin: www.linkedin.com/company/crain-communications
Instagram: www.instagram.com/craincommunications

Crain Communications, Inc.
685 3rd Ave.
New York, NY 10017
Ph: (212)210-0100
Free: 877-824-9379
Co. E-mail: customerservice@crainsnewyork.com
URL: http://crainsnewyork.com

CreateSpace
PO Box 81226
Seattle, WA 98108
Fax: (206)266-7010
Co. E-mail: copyright@createspace.com
URL: http://www.createspace.com
Facebook: www.facebook.com/CreateSpace

Creative Magazine Inc.
31 Merrick Ave., Ste. 60
Merrick, NY 11566
Ph: (516)378-0800
Fax: (516)378-0884
Co. E-mail: info@creativemag.com
URL: http://www.creativemag.com

Crittenden Research Inc.
3544 E 17th, Ste. 201
Ammon, ID 83406
Free: 800-857-1916
Co. E-mail: membership@crittendenresearch.com
URL: http://crittendenreport.com
Linkedin: www.linkedin.com/company/crittenden-real-estate-finance

Cross Country Skier L.L.C.
PO Box 550
Cable, WI 54821
Ph: (715)798-5500
Free: 800-827-0607
URL: http://www.crosscountryskier.com
Facebook: www.facebook.com/xcskiermag
Instagram: www.instagram.com/xcskiermag

Cruz Bay Publishing Inc.
Ph: (303)253-6412
Co. E-mail: clmcustserv@cdsfulfillment.com
URL: http://www.aimmedia.com

CSIRO Publishing
Unipark Bldg., 1 Level 1, 195 Wellington Rd.
Clayton, VIC 3168, Australia
Ph: 61 3 9545 8400
Co. E-mail: info@eurospan.co.uk
URL: http://www.publish.csiro.au
Facebook: www.facebook.com/pages/CSIRO-PUBLISHING/70534682887
Linkedin: www.linkedin.com/company/csiro-publishing
Instagram: www.instagram.com/csiropublishing

Currency
1745 Broadway
New York, NY 10019
Free: 800-726-0600
URL: http://crownpublishing.com

Cutter Information Corp.
37 Broadway, Ste. 1
Arlington, MA 02474
Ph: (781)648-8700
Co. E-mail: service@cutter.com
URL: http://www.cutter.com

Cycle News
26341 Jefferson Ave., Ste. G
Murrieta, CA 92562
Ph: (949)863-7082
Co. E-mail: editor@cyclenews.com
URL: http://www.cyclenews.com
Facebook: www.facebook.com/CycleNews
Instagram: www.instagram.com/cyclenews
YouTube: www.youtube.com/user/CycleNews

D

Dadant and Sons Inc.
51 S 2nd St.
Hamilton, IL 62341
Ph: (217)847-3324
Free: 888-922-1293
Fax: (217)847-3660
Co. E-mail: dadant@dadant.com
URL: http://www.dadant.com
Facebook: www.facebook.com/DadantAndSons
Instagram: www.instagram.com/dadantbeekeeping
YouTube: www.youtube.com/user/DadantBeekeeping

Dance Magazine Inc. (DM)
535 Fifth Ave. 4th Fl.
New York, NY 10017
Free: 800-331-1750
Co. E-mail: dancemagazine@sfsdayton.com
URL: http://www.dancemagazine.com/#gsc.tab=0
Facebook: www.facebook.com/DanceMagazine
Linkedin: www.linkedin.com/showcase/dance-magazine
Instagram: www.instagram.com/dancemagazine
YouTube: www.youtube.com/c/dancemagazine
Pinterest: www.pinterest.com/dancemagazine

Dartnell Corporation
2222 Sedwick Dr.
Durham, NC 27713
Free: 800-223-8720
Fax: (919)287-2643
Co. E-mail: customerservice@dartnellcorp.com
URL: http://www.dartnellcorp.com

GUIDE TO PUBLISHERS

Data Conversion Laboratory (DCL)
61-18 190th St., Ste. 205
Fresh Meadows, NY 11365
Ph: (718)357-8700
URL: http://www.dataconversionlaboratory.com
Linkedin: www.linkedin.com/company/dclab
YouTube: www.youtube.com/channel/UCrs_D323yvVDBGV8FbdWmMw

David Hall Rare Coins (DHRC)
PO Box 27190
Santa Ana, CA 92799
Ph: (949)567-1325
Free: 800-759-7575
Fax: (949)231-1293
Co. E-mail: info@davidhall.com
URL: http://davidhall.com
Facebook: www.facebook.com/DavidHallRareCoins
YouTube: www.youtube.com/channel/UCtgKFZCe-3OLK6gV0CL9p0A

Destiny Productions for Print, Radio and Cable Promotions
3395 S Jones Blvd., No. 217
Las Vegas, NV 89146-6729

Detroit Free Press Inc.
160 W Fort St.
Detroit, MI 48226
Free: 800-395-3300
Co. E-mail: custserv@michigan.com
URL: http://freep.com
Facebook: www.facebook.com/detroitfreepress

Development Concepts Inc.
7820 Sudley Rd., Ste. 100
Manassas, VA 20109
Ph: (703)361-7300
Free: 800-361-1055
Fax: (703)335-9486
Co. E-mail: query2@impactpublications.com
URL: http://www.impactpublications.com
Facebook: www.facebook.com/ImpactPublications

The Dickinson Press
1815 First St. W
Dickinson, ND 58602
Ph: (701)225-8111
Co. E-mail: pcotton@thedickinsonpress.com
URL: http://www.thedickinsonpress.com
Facebook: www.facebook.com/thedickinsonpress

Dietitians of Canada
99 Yorkville Ave., 2nd Fl.
Toronto, ON, Canada M5R 1C1
Ph: (416)596-0857
Fax: (416)596-0603

Co. E-mail: contactus@dietitians.ca
URL: http://www.dietitians.ca
Facebook: www.facebook.com/DietitiansCAN
YouTube: www.youtube.com/user/DietitiansCAN

Directors Guild of America Inc. (DGA)
7920 Sunset Blvd.
Los Angeles, CA 90046
Ph: (310)289-2000
Free: 800-421-4173
Co. E-mail: dgawebsupport@dga.org
URL: http://www.dga.org

Diversity Information Resources, Inc. (DIR)
2300 Kennedy St. NE, Ste. 230
Minneapolis, MN 55413
Ph: (612)781-6819
Co. E-mail: info@diversityinforesources.com
URL: http://www.diversityinforesources.com
Facebook: www.facebook.com/DiversityInformationResources
YouTube: www.youtube.com/channel/UCFikCMXHK2fca1zBDygfyOw
Pinterest: www.pinterest.com/dirmarketing

DL Perkins L.L.C.
1364 E 43rd Ct.
Tulsa, OK 74105
Ph: (918)748-7995
URL: http://www.acquisitionadvisors.com
Linkedin: www.linkedin.com/company/acquisition-advisors

DNA Press
Pottstown, PA
Free: 800-888-4741
Fax: (312)337-5985
URL: http://www.dnapress.com

Dogwise Publishing
403 S Mission St.
Wenatchee, WA 98801
Free: 800-776-2665
Co. E-mail: mail@dogwise.com
URL: http://www.dogwise.com
Facebook: www.facebook.com/dogwise
Instagram: www.instagram.com/dogwise.books

Dolan Media Newswires
31 E Platte Ave., Ste. 300
Colorado Springs, CO 80903
Ph: (719)634-5905

Dolan Media Newswires
401 S Boston Ave., Ste. 105
Tulsa, OK 74103
Ph: (918)295-0098

Dotdash Meredith
28 Liberty St., 7th Fl
New York, NY 10005

Ph: (212)204-4000
Co. E-mail: security@dotdash.com
URL: http://www.about.com

Doubleday
1745 Broadway
New York, NY 10019
URL: http://knopfdoubleday.com
Facebook: www.facebook.com/DoubledayBooks
Instagram: www.instagram.com/doubledaybooks
YouTube: www.youtube.com/user/knopfdoubleday

Dow Jones And Co.
890 Ridge Rd.
Princeton, NJ 08540
URL: http://www.dowjones.com

Dow Jones & Company Inc.
1211 Avenue of the Americas
New York, NY 10036
Free: 800-568-7625
Co. E-mail: support@dowjones.com
URL: http://dowjones.com
Facebook: www.facebook.com/dowjones

Driving School Association of the Americas (DSAA)
Communications Office
634E. Main St.
Lansdale, PA 19446
Free: 800-270-3722
Fax: (215)699-3015
Co. E-mail: info@dsaa.org
URL: http://dsaa.org
Facebook: www.facebook.com/thedsaa
YouTube: www.youtube.com/channel/UC0J1XzGtg8DzrYwRW3NB1pg

Drycleaning and Laundry Institute International (DLI)
14700 Sweitzer Ln.
Laurel, MD 20707
Free: 800-638-2627
Co. E-mail: techline@dlionline.org
URL: http://www.dlionline.org
Linkedin: www.linkedin.com/company/drylauninst
Instagram: www.instagram.com/drylauninst

DTI
2700 Lake Cook Rd.
Riverwoods, IL 60015
URL: http://www.wolterskluwer.com/en/solutions/tax-accounting-us

Dun & Bradstreet Holdings, Inc. (D&B)
5335 Gate Pkwy.
Jacksonville, FL 32256
Ph: (904)648-6350

Co. E-mail: info@dnb.com
URL: http://www.dnb.com
Facebook: www.facebook.com/
 DunBradstreet
Linkedin: www.linkedin.com/company/dun
 -&-bradstreet

duPont Publishing Inc.
4600 140th Ave. N, Ste. 210
Clearwater, FL 33762
Ph: (727)573-9339
Free: 800-233-1731
URL: http://www.dupontregistry.com
Facebook: www.facebook.com/
 dupontregistry
Linkedin: www.linkedin.com/company/
 dupontregistry
Pinterest: www.pinterest.com/
 dupontregistry

Dustbooks (DB)
PO Box 100
Paradise, CA 95967
Ph: (530)877-6110
Fax: (530)877-0222
URL: http://www.dustbooks.com

E

Earl G. Graves Ltd.
500 7th Ave., 12th Fl.
New York, NY 10018
Ph: (212)242-8000
Fax: (212)886-9618
URL: http://www.blackenterprise.com
Facebook: www.facebook.com/
 blackenterprise
Linkedin: www.linkedin.com/company/
 black-enterprise
Instagram: www.instagram.com/
 blackenterprise
YouTube: www.youtube.com/user/
 BEMultiMedia

Earth Action Network
1536 Crest Dr.
Los Angeles, CA 90035
URL: http://www.discoverthenetworks.org/
 organizations/earth-action-network-ean

Earth Island Institute (EII)
2150 Allston Way, Ste. 460
Berkeley, CA 94704
Ph: (510)859-9100
Co. E-mail: carrie@earthisland.org
URL: http://www.earthisland.org
Facebook: www.facebook.com/
 EarthIslandInstitute
Linkedin: www.linkedin.com/company/
 earth-island-institute
Instagram: www.instagram.com/
 earth_island_institute
YouTube: www.youtube.com/user/
 EarthIslandJournal

Eaton-Moghannam Publishing
696 San Ramon Valley Blvd., Ste. 214
Danville, CA 94526
Ph: (925)743-1083

EB Golf Media, LLC
6 E 43rd St., 12th Fl.
New York, NY 10017
Free: 800-876-7726
Co. E-mail: dpo@golf.com
URL: http://www.golf.com
Facebook: www.facebook.com/golf
Instagram: www.instagram.com/golf_com
YouTube: www.youtube.com/channel/
 UCzdMqRWzdF0JUJRIVa-dgDw

EBSCO Information Services
10 Estes St.
Ipswich, MA 01938
Ph: (978)356-6500
Free: 800-653-2726
Co. E-mail: information@ebsco.com
URL: http://www.ebsco.com
Facebook: www.facebook.com/
 EBSCOInfoServices
Linkedin: www.linkedin.com/company/
 ebsco-information-services
Instagram: www.instagram.com/
 ebscoinformationservices
YouTube: www.youtube.com/user/
 ebscopublishing

Ecco Books
195 Broadway
New York, NY 10007
URL: http://eccobooks.tumblr.com
Facebook: www.facebook.com/eccobooks
Instagram: www.instagram.com/eccobooks
YouTube: www.youtube.com/user/
 EccoBooks

Economist Newspaper Ltd.
90 New Montgomery St., Ste. 418
San Francisco, CA 94105
Co. E-mail: impactinfo@economist.com
URL: http://impact.economist.com/?re-
 gionId=6

Editage
214 Carnegie Center, Ste. 102
Princeton, NJ 08540
Ph: (267)332-0051
Free: 833-979-0061
Fax: (267)332-0052
Co. E-mail: request@editage.com
URL: http://www.editage.com
Facebook: www.facebook.com/Editage
Linkedin: www.linkedin.com/showcase/
 editage
Instagram: www.instagram.com/
 editage_official
YouTube: www.youtube.com/user/editage

Editorial Freelancers Association (EFA)
266 W 37th St., 20th Fl.
New York, NY 10018
Ph: (212)920-4816
Free: 866-929-5425
Co. E-mail: office@the-efa.org
URL: http://www.the-efa.org
Facebook: www.facebook.com/
 editorialfreelancersassociation
Linkedin: www.linkedin.com/company/
 editorial-freelancers

Edward Elgar Publishing Inc. (EE)
The William Pratt House, 9 Dewey Ct.
Northampton, MA 01060-3815
Ph: (413)584-5551
Fax: (413)584-9933
Co. E-mail: elgarsales@e-elgar.com
URL: http://www.e-elgar.com

Electronic Security Association (ESA)
2222 S Service Rd., Ste. 230
Dallas, TX 75261
Ph: (972)807-6800
Co. E-mail: membership@esaweb.org
URL: http://esaweb.org
Facebook: www.facebook.com/ESAonline
Linkedin: www.linkedin.com/company/
 electronic-security-association-esa
YouTube: www.youtube.com/channel/
 UCkDpqx-b1-f-DQ_THIVmcZA

Electronics Technicians Association International (ETA)
5 Depot St.
Greencastle, IN 46135
Ph: (765)653-8262
Free: 800-288-3824
Fax: (765)653-4287
Co. E-mail: eta@etai.org
URL: http://www.etai.org
Facebook: www.facebook.com/
 ETAInternational
YouTube: www.youtube.com/user/
 ETAINTL

Elsevier Advanced Technology Publications
Kelly School of Business
Indiana University
1309 E 10th St.
Bloomington, IN 47405
Ph: (812)855-6342
Fax: (812)856-4971

Elsevier B.V.
Radarweg 29
1043 NX Amsterdam, Netherlands
Ph: 31 20 485-3911
URL: http://www.elsevier.com

Elsevier Inc.
Ste. 800, 230 Pk. Ave.
New York, NY 10169
Ph: (212)309-8100
URL: http://www.elsevier.com

Elsevier Inc.
50 High St., Ste. 21
North Andover, MA 01845
Free: 866-344-2088

Co. E-mail: customercare@elsevier.com
URL: http://www.elsevier.com
Facebook: www.facebook.com/
 ElsevierConnect
Linkedin: www.linkedin.com/company/
 elsevier/about
YouTube: www.youtube.com/c/elsevier

Elsevier Ltd.
The Blvd., Langford Ln., Kidlington
Oxford OX5 1GB, United Kingdom
Ph: 44 1865 843-000
Fax: 44 1865 843-010
URL: http://www.elsevier.com/en-in

Elsevier Technology Publications
230 Pk. Ave., Ste. 800
New York, NY 10169
Ph: (212)309-8100
Co. E-mail: permissionshelpdesk@elsevier
 .com
URL: http://www.elsevier.com
Facebook: www.facebook.com/
 ElsevierConnect
Linkedin: www.linkedin.com/company/
 elsevier
YouTube: www.youtube.com/c/elsevier

Emerald Group Publishing Limited
120 Beacon St., Ste. 202
Somerville, MA 02143

Emerald Inc.
Harvard Square
1 Mifflin Place, Ste. 400
Cambridge, MA 02138
Ph: (617)576-5782

Employee Relocation Council (ERC)
4401 Wilson Blvd., Ste. 510
Arlington, VA 22203
Ph: (703)842-3400
Fax: (703)527-1552
Co. E-mail: CustomerCare@World-
 wideERC.org
URL: http://www.worldwideerc.org/Pages/
 index.aspx

Endeavor Business Media, LLC
331 54th Ave. N
Nashville, TN 37209
Free: 800-547-7377
URL: http://www.endeavorbusinessmedia
 .com

EnsembleIQ
8550 W. Bryn Mawr Ave. Ste. 200
Chicago, IL 60631
Free: 877-687-7321
URL: http://www.progressivegrocer.com

Entree Travel
695 Olive Rd.
Santa Barbara, CA 93108
Ph: (805)969-5848
URL: http://www.entreenews.com

Entrepreneur Media Inc.
18061 Fitch
Irvine, CA 92614
Ph: (212)221-9595
Co. E-mail: events@entrepreneur.com
URL: http://www.entrepreneur.com

Environmental News Network (ENN)
URL: http://www.enn.com
Facebook: www.facebook.com/environ-
 mental.news.network
Linkedin: www.linkedin.com/company/enn

EPM Communications Inc.
19 W 21st St., Ste. 303
New York, NY 10010

Equipment Marketing and Distribution Association (EMDA)
PO Box 1208
Statham, GA 30666
Ph: (319)354-5156
Co. E-mail: celeste@emda.net
URL: http://www.emda.net
Facebook: www.facebook.com/EMDAnews
Linkedin: www.linkedin.com/company/
 emda-equipment-marketing-&
 -distribution-association
Instagram: www.instagram.com/
 emda_news

Erie Times News
205 W 12th St.
Erie, PA 16534
Free: 800-352-0043
URL: http://www.goerie.com
Facebook: www.facebook.com/GoErie

Escapees, Inc.
100 Rainbow Dr.
Livingston, TX 77351
Ph: (936)327-8873
Free: 888-757-2582
Fax: (936)327-4388
Co. E-mail: clubbusiness@escapees.com
URL: http://www.escapees.com

Executive Business Media Inc.
825 Old Country Rd.
Westbury, NY 11590
Ph: (516)334-3030
Fax: (516)334-3059
Co. E-mail: ebm-mail@ebmpubs.com
URL: http://www.ebmpubs.com

Exhibit Builder Magazine
123 St. W
Seattle, WA 98125
Co. E-mail: info@exhibitbuilder.net
URL: http://exhibitbuilder.net

F

Fabricare Canada
100 Lakeshore Rd. E
Oakville, ON, Canada L6J 6M9

Co. E-mail: canadianfabricare@fabricare
 .org
URL: http://www.fabricarecanada.com

Fabricators and Manufacturers Association, International (FMA)
2135 Point Blvd.
Elgin, IL 60123
Ph: (815)399-8700
Free: 888-394-4362
Co. E-mail: info@fmanet.org
URL: http://www.fmanet.org
Facebook: www.facebook.com/
 FabricatorsAndManufacturers
Linkedin: www.linkedin.com/company/
 fabricators-&-manufacturers-association
 -int'l-fma-
YouTube: www.youtube.com/FMAnetorg

Fahy-Williams Publishing Inc. (FWPI)
171 Reed St.
Geneva, NY 14456
Ph: (315)789-0458
URL: http://www.fwpi.com

Fandata Publications
Fredericksburg, VA
Ph: (703)913-5575
Co. E-mail: email@fandata.com
URL: http://www.fandata.com

Farm Journal Media Inc.
1550 NW Hwy., Ste. 403
Park Ridge, IL 60068
Ph: (847)653-8904
Fax: (847)298-7169
Co. E-mail: customerservice@farmjournal
 .com
URL: http://www.farmjournalmedia.com/
 office-locations
Facebook: www.facebook.com/
 FarmJournal

Fastline
4900 Fox Run Rd.
Buckner, KY 40010
Free: 800-626-6409
Fax: (502)222-0615
Co. E-mail: helpdesk@fastline.com
URL: http://www.fastline.com
Facebook: www.facebook.com/
 FastlineFarm
YouTube: www.youtube.com/user/
 FastlineVideos

FCW
50 Charles Lindbergh Blvd., Ste. 100
Uniondale, NY 11553
Fax: (516)227-1342
URL: http://www.floorcoveringweekly.com
Facebook: www.facebook.com/
 floorcoveringweekly

Federick News-Post
351 Ballenger Center Dr.
Frederick, MD 21703
Ph: (301)662-1177

Co. E-mail: citydesk@newspost.com
URL: http://www.fredericknewspost.com
Facebook: www.facebook.com/
fredericknewspost

Feed-Lot Magazine
336 S Ln.
Dighton, KS 67839
Ph: (620)397-2838
Free: 800-798-9515
Co. E-mail: feedlot@st-tel.net
URL: http://www.feedlotmagazine.com
Facebook: www.facebook.com/
FeedlotMagazine

Ferdic Inc.
PO Box 28
Camp Hill, PA 17001
Ph: (717)731-1426
Co. E-mail: info@fdaweb.com
URL: http://www.fdaweb.com/default.php

Fifth Estate (FE)
PO Box 201016
Ferndale, MI 48220
Co. E-mail: fe@fifthestate.org
URL: http://www.fifthestate.org
Facebook: www.facebook.com/
FifthEstateMag

Film Society of Lincoln Center
70 Lincoln Ctr. Plz.
New York, NY 10023-6595
Ph: (212)875-5610
Free: 888-313-6085
Co. E-mail: members@filmlinc.org
URL: http://www.filmlinc.org
Facebook: www.facebook.com/filmlinc
YouTube: www.youtube.com/user/
filmlincdotcom

Financial Planning Association (FPA)
1290 Broadway, Ste. 1625
Denver, CO 80203
Ph: (303)759-4900
Free: 800-322-4237
Co. E-mail: info@onefpa.org
URL: http://www.financialplanningassocia-
tion.org
Facebook: www.facebook.com/
FinancialPlanningAssociation
Linkedin: www.linkedin.com/company/
financial-planning-association
YouTube: www.youtube.com/fpatelevision

The Financial Times Ltd.
No. 1, Southwark Bridge
London SE1 9HL, United Kingdom
URL: http://www.ft.com

Find/SVP
17 Oxford St.
Rochester, NY 14607
Ph: (212)645-4500
Free: 800-346-3787
Fax: (212)645-7681
Co. E-mail: infoadvisor@findsvp.com

Florida Department of Agriculture and Consumer Services (FDACS-DPI) Division of Plant Industry
1911 SW 34th St.
Gainesville, FL 32608-7100
Ph: (352)395-4600
Free: 888-397-1517
Co. E-mail: plantindustry@fdacs.gov
URL: http://www.fdacs.gov/Divisions
-Offices/Plant-Industry
Facebook: www.facebook.com/FDACSDPI
YouTube: www.youtube.com/user/fdacsdpi
Pinterest: www.pinterest.com/FDACSDPI

Florida International University Chaplin School of Hospitality & Tourism Management
3000 NE 151st St.
North Miami, FL 33181
Ph: (305)919-4500
Co. E-mail: hospitality@fiu.edu
URL: http://hospitality.fiu.edu
Facebook: www.facebook.com/
FIUHospitality
Instagram: www.instagram.com/
fiuhospitality
YouTube: www.youtube.com/user/
FIUHospitality

Florida Times-Union
1 Independent Dr., Ste. 200
Jacksonville, FL 32202
Ph: (904)359-4255
Co. E-mail: circserv@jacksonville.com
URL: http://www.jacksonville.com

Food Institute (FI)
330 Changebridge Rd., Ste. 101
Pine Brook, NJ 07058
Ph: (201)791-5570
Free: 855-791-5570
Co. E-mail: questions@foodinstitute.com
URL: http://www.foodinstitute.com
Facebook: www.facebook.com/
foodinstitutenj
Linkedin: www.linkedin.com/company/the
-food-institute
Instagram: www.instagram.com/
foodinstitute
YouTube: www.youtube.com/channel/
UCYAPI0TXNtJa04aQre4h4pA

Foodservice Consultants Society International (FCSI)
PO Box 4961
Louisville, KY 40204
Ph: (502)379-4122
Co. E-mail: info@fcsi.org
URL: http://www.fcsi.org

For Dummies
111 River St.
Hoboken, NJ 07030
URL: http://www.dummies.com
Facebook: www.facebook.com/
ForDummies
Instagram: www.instagram.com/
fordummies
YouTube: www.youtube.com/user/
fordummies

Forbes Media LLC
499 Washington Blvd.
Jersey City, NJ 07310
Ph: (212)620-1887
Free: 800-295-0893
URL: http://www.forbes.com
Linkedin: www.linkedin.com/company/
forbes-magazine

Fortune Media IP Limited
40 Fulton St.
New York, NY 10038
URL: http://fortune.com

Forum Publishing Co.
383 E Main St.
Centerport, NY 11721
Free: 800-635-7654
Co. E-mail: forumpublishing@aol.com
URL: http://www.forum123.com

Foundation of the Flexographic Technical Association (1974)
3920 Veterans Memorial Hwy., Ste. 9
Bohemia, NY 11716-1074
URL: http://www.flexography.org

Frances Lincoln Ltd.
The Old Brewery, 6 Blundell St.
London N7 9BH, United Kingdom
Ph: 44 20 7700 6700
Fax: 44 20 7700 8066
Co. E-mail: marketinguk@quarto.com
URL: http://www.quartoknows.com

Free Press Inc. (FP)
PO Box 60238
Florence, MA 01062
Ph: (202)265-1490
Co. E-mail: info@freepress.net
URL: http://www.freepress.net
Facebook: www.facebook.com/freepress
Instagram: www.instagram.com/
freepressaction

Free Press/Simon and Schuster Inc.
1230 Ave. of the Americas
New York, NY 10020
URL: http://www.simonandschuster.com

French-Canadian Genealogical Society of Connecticut (FCGSC)
53 Tolland Green
Tolland, CT 06084
Ph: (860)872-2597
Co. E-mail: info@fcgsc.org
URL: http://www.fcgsc.org

GUIDE TO PUBLISHERS

FT Press
Upper Saddle River, NJ
URL: http://www.informit.com/promotions/
　pearson-ft-press-141135
Linkedin: www.linkedin.com/company/ft
　-press

Funeral Consumers Alliance (FCA)
33 Patchen Rd.
South Burlington, VT 05403
Ph: (802)865-8300
Co. E-mail: fca@funerals.org
URL: http://www.funerals.org

Future P.L.C.
Quay House, The Ambury
Bath BA1 1UA, United Kingdom
Ph: 44 1225 442-244
Co. E-mail: support@futurenet.com
URL: http://www.futureplc.com
Linkedin: www.linkedin.com/company/
　future-publishing

G

Gale, part of Cengage Group
27555 Executive Dr., Ste. 270
Farmington Hills, MI 48331
Free: 800-877-4253
Co. E-mail: gale.customerservice@cengage.com
URL: http://www.gale.com
Facebook: www.facebook.com/
　GaleCengage
Linkedin: www.linkedin.com/showcase/
　gale
YouTube: www.youtube.com/user/
　GaleCengage

Gallup, Inc.
The Gallup Bldg.
901 F St. NW
Washington, DC 20004
Ph: (202)715-3030
Free: 888-486-9104
Fax: (202)715-3045
Co. E-mail: galluphelp@gallup.com
URL: http://gallup.com
Facebook: www.facebook.com/gallup
Linkedin: www.linkedin.com/company/
　gallup
Instagram: www.instagram.com/gallup
YouTube: www.youtube.com/channel/
　UC2dTfkMAnl7_kco6QK7sQuA

Gardner Business Media Inc. (GBMI)
6915 Valley Ave.
Cincinnati, OH 45244-3029
Ph: (513)527-8800
Fax: (513)527-8801
URL: http://www.gardnerweb.com
Facebook: www.facebook.com/
　GardnerBusinessMedia
Linkedin: www.linkedin.com/company/
　gardner-business-media-inc-

Gasoline and Automotive Service Dealers Association, Ltd. (GASDA)
6 Walker Way
Albany, NY 12205
Ph: (516)371-6201
URL: http://rsgda.com

The Gazette
30 E Pikes Peak Ave., Ste. 100
Colorado Springs, CO 80903
Ph: (719)632-5511
Free: 866-632-NEWS
Co. E-mail: customercare@gazette.com
URL: http://gazette.com
Facebook: www.facebook.com/
　springsgazette
YouTube: www.youtube.com/user/
　springsgazette

Gearhead Communications L.L.C.
3 Research Ctr.
Marion, IA 52302
Ph: (319)447-5550
Free: 877-704-4327
Fax: (319)447-5599
URL: http://www.premierguitar.com
Facebook: www.facebook.com/
　premierguitar
YouTube: www.youtube.com/premierguitar

Genealogical Institute Inc.
56 W Main St.
Tremonton, UT 84337
Ph: (435)257-6649
Fax: (435)257-4685
Co. E-mail: arlene@arleneeakle.com
URL: http://arleneeakle.com

Genealogical Publishing Company Inc. (GPC)
3600 Clipper Mill Rd., Ste. 229
Baltimore, MD 21211

George Washington University Institute for European, Russian and Eurasian Studies (IERES)
1957 E St. NW
Washington, DC 20052
Ph: (202)994-6340
Co. E-mail: ieresgwu@gwu.edu
URL: http://ieres.elliott.gwu.edu
Facebook: www.facebook.com/ieresgwu
Instagram: www.instagram.com/ieresgwu
YouTube: www.youtube.com/channel/
　UC2XOXU6qVVoSOB-LKtK3I7Q

GIE Media Inc.
5811 Canal Rd.
Valley View, OH 44125
Ph: (216)393-0300
Free: 800-456-0707
Co. E-mail: info@giemedia.com
URL: http://www.giemedia.com
Facebook: www.facebook.com/
　giemediainc

Gift and Decorative Accessories Center Association
1350 Broadway, 17th Fl., Ste. 1715
New York, NY 10018
Ph: (917)934-2830

The Giving Institute (GI)
1660 International Dr., Ste. 600
McLean, VA 22102
Ph: (312)981-6794
Co. E-mail: info@givinginstitute.org
URL: http://www.givinginstitute.org
Linkedin: www.linkedin.com/company/
　giving-institute

GL Brands, Inc.
3939 Belt Line Rd., Ste. 350
Addison, TX 75001
Ph: (720)717-3646
Free: 888-811-4367
Co. E-mail: info@glbrands.com
URL: http://glbrands.com
Linkedin: www.linkedin.com/company/
　glbrandsinc

Glass Patterns Quarterly Inc. (GPQ)
8300 Hidden Valley Rd.
Westport, KY 40077
Ph: (502)222-5631
Fax: (502)222-4527
Co. E-mail: info@theflowmagazine.com
URL: http://www.glasspatterns.com

Glaucoma Research Foundation (GRF)
251 Post St., Ste. 600
San Francisco, CA 94108
Ph: (415)986-3162
Co. E-mail: question@glaucoma.org
URL: http://glaucoma.org
Facebook: www.facebook.com/glaucoma
　.org
Linkedin: www.linkedin.com/company/
　glaucoma-research-foundation
Instagram: www.instagram.com/
　glaucomaresearch
YouTube: www.youtube.com/GRFvideos
Pinterest: www.pinterest.com/
　glaucomaresearch

Global Investment Technology
909 3rd Ave., 27th Fl.
New York, NY 10022
Ph: (212)370-3700
Fax: (212)370-4606
Co. E-mail: info@globalinv.com
URL: http://www.globalinv.com

The Globe & Mail Inc.
351 King St. E, Ste. 1600
Toronto, ON, Canada M5A 0N1

Ph: (416)585-5172
URL: http://www.globeandmailcentre.com
Facebook: www.facebook.com/
 globeandmailcentre
Instagram: www.instagram.com/
 globeandmailcentre
Pinterest: www.pinterest.com/
 globeandmailcentre

Government Publishing Office (GPO)
732 N Capitol St. NW
Washington, DC 20401
Ph: (202)512-1800
Free: 866-512-1800
Fax: (202)512-1293
Co. E-mail: contactcenter@gpo.gov
URL: http://www.gpo.gov
Facebook: www.facebook.com/USGPO
Linkedin: www.linkedin.com/company/u.s
 .-government-printing-office
Instagram: www.instagram.com/usgpo
YouTube: www.youtube.com/user/
 gpoprinter
Pinterest: www.pinterest.com/usgpo

G.R. Leonard and Co.
181 N Vermont Ave.
Glendora, CA 91741
Ph: (626)914-3200
Free: 800-574-5250
Co. E-mail: info@leonardsguide.com
URL: http://www.leonardsguide.com

Grand Central Publishing (GCP)
1290 Ave., of the Americas
New York, NY 10104
Free: 800-890-0625
URL: http://www.hachettebookgroup.com
Facebook: www.facebook.com/
 GrandCentralPub
Instagram: www.instagram.com/
 grandcentralpub
YouTube: www.youtube.com/channel/
 UCvUxnjFAd57CcM25e95K6Qg
Pinterest: www.pinterest.com/
 grandcentralpub

Grand Circle Corp. (GCC)
347 Congress St.
Boston, MA 02210
URL: http://www.gct.com/?icid=global:logo

Greater Phoenix Chamber of Commerce
2575 E Camelback Rd., Ste. 410
Phoenix, AZ 85016
Ph: (602)495-2195
Fax: (602)495-8913
Co. E-mail: info@phoenixchamber.com
URL: http://phoenixchamber.com
Facebook: www.facebook.com/
 phxchamber
Linkedin: www.linkedin.com/company/
 42478
Instagram: www.instagram.com/
 phxchamber
YouTube: www.youtube.com/user/
 PhoenixChamber

Greenleaf Book Group Press
PO Box 91869
Austin, TX 78709
Ph: (512)891-6100
Fax: (512)891-6150
Co. E-mail: orders@greenleafbookgroup
 .com
URL: http://www.greenleafbookgroup.com
Facebook: www.facebook.com/GBGAustin
Instagram: www.instagram.com/
 GreenleafBookGr
YouTube: www.youtube.com/channel/
 UC13WupgwAWIE1TqpW0XqsQg
Pinterest: www.pinterest.com/
 greenleafbookgroup

Greenwood Electronic Media (GEM)
130 Cremona Dr., Ste. C
Santa Barbara, CA 93117
URL: http://publisher.abc-clio.com

Grey House Publishing
4919 Rte. 22
Amenia, NY 12501-0056
Ph: (518)789-8700
Free: 800-562-2139
Fax: (518)789-0556
URL: http://www.greyhouse.com
Facebook: www.facebook.com/
 greyhousepub

Grey House Publishing Canada Inc. (GHP)
3 - 1500 Upper Middle Rd.
Oakville, ON, Canada L6M 3H5
Ph: (416)644-6479
Free: 866-433-4739
Fax: (416)644-1904
Co. E-mail: info@greyhouse.ca
URL: http://greyhouse.ca
Facebook: www.facebook.com/
 GreyHouseCanada
Linkedin: www.linkedin.com/company/grey
 -house-publishing-canada
YouTube: www.youtube.com/user/
 greyhousecanada
Pinterest: www.pinterest.com/
 greyhousecanada

Grimes and Associates Inc.
24 Daisy St.
Ladera Ranch, CA 92694
Ph: (949)388-4848
Co. E-mail: info@vowsmagazine.com
URL: http://www.vowsmagazine.com
Facebook: www.facebook.com/
 VOWSMAGAZINE
Instagram: www.instagram.com/
 vowsmagazine

Group C Media Inc.
The Galleria
2 Bridge Ave., Ste. 231
Red Bank, NJ 07701
Ph: (732)842-7433
Free: 800-524-0337
Fax: (732)758-6634
URL: http://groupcmedia.com
Pinterest: www.pinterest.com/groupcmedia

Guild of Book Workers (GBW)
521 5th Ave.
New York, NY 10175
Co. E-mail: communications@guildofbook-
 workers.org
URL: http://guildofbookworkers.org

H

Handmade Business
N7528 Aanstad Rd.
Iola, WI 54945
Ph: (715)445-5000
Free: 800-331-0038
Fax: (715)445-4053
Co. E-mail: customercare@jonespublish-
 ing.us
URL: http://handmade-business.com
Facebook: www.facebook.com/
 handmadebusinessmag
Instagram: www.instagram.com/explore/
 tags/handmadebusinessmagazine

Happy About
20660 Stevens Creek Blvd., Ste. 210
Cupertino, CA 95014
Ph: (408)257-3000
Co. E-mail: info@happyabout.com
URL: http://www.happyabout.com
Facebook: www.facebook.com/happyabout

Harper Business
195 Broadway
New York, NY 10007
Co. E-mail: harper.business@harpercollins
 .com
URL: http://www.harpercollins.com/pages/
 harperbusiness
Facebook: www.facebook.com/
 harperbusiness
Linkedin: www.linkedin.com/showcase/
 harper-business

HarperCollins Leadership
195 Broadway
New York, NY 10007
Co. E-mail: hcleadership@harpercollins
 .com
URL: http://www.harpercollinsleadership
 .com
Facebook: www.facebook.com/
 harpercollinsleadership
Instagram: www.instagram.com/
 hcleadership

HarperCollins Publishers L.L.C. (HCP)
195 Broadway
New York, NY 10007
Ph: (212)207-7000
Free: 800-242-7737

Co. E-mail: hello@harpercollins.com
URL: http://www.harpercollins.com
Facebook: www.facebook.com/
  HarperCollins
Instagram: www.instagram.com/
  harpercollins

Harris Publishing, Inc.
520 Pk. Ave.
Idaho Falls, ID 83402
Ph: (208)524-7000
Free: 800-638-0135
Fax: (208)522-5241
Co. E-mail: customerservice@harrispub-
  lishing.com
URL: http://www.harrispublishing.com

Harvard Business Press
300 N Beacon St.
Watertown, MA 02472
Ph: (617)783-7600
Free: 800-545-7685
Fax: (617)783-7666
Co. E-mail: custserv@hbsp.harvard.edu
URL: http://cb.hbsp.harvard.edu/cbmp/
  pages/content/contact

Harvard Business Publishing (HBP)
20 Guest St., Ste. 700
Brighton, MA 02135
Free: 800-795-5200
Co. E-mail: corporate@harvardbusiness
  .org
URL: http://www.harvardbusiness.org
Facebook: www.facebook.com/
  HBPCorpLearning
Linkedin: www.linkedin.com/company/
  harvard-business-publishing-corporate
  -learning
YouTube: www.youtube.com/channel/
  UCTStHSp2-io68j_3jjvQmgA

Harvard Business Review Press (HBR)
20 Guest St., Ste. 700
Brighton, MA 02135
Ph: (617)783-7400
Fax: (617)783-7664
URL: http://hbr.org
Facebook: www.facebook.com/HBR
Linkedin: www.linkedin.com/company/
  harvard-business-review

Harvey W. Watt and Company Inc. (HW)
PO Box 20787
Atlanta, GA 30320
Ph: (404)767-7501
Free: 800-241-6103
Fax: (404)761-8276
Co. E-mail: pilot@harveywatt.com
URL: http://www.harveywatt.com

Hatton-Brown Publishers Inc.
225 Hanrick St.
Montgomery, AL 36104
Ph: (332)834-1170
Free: 800-669-5613

Co. E-mail: hbmail@hattonbrown.com
URL: http://www.hattonbrown.net
Facebook: www.facebook.com/
  Hbpublishers
Linkedin: www.linkedin.com/company/
  hatton-brown-publishers-inc-
Instagram: www.instagram.com/
  hattonbrown

Haymarket Media Inc.
461 From Rd., Ste. 198
Paramus, NJ 07652
Ph: (201)799-4800
URL: http://www.haymarket.com
Linkedin: www.linkedin.com/company/
  haymarket-media-group
Instagram: www.instagram.com/haymarket
  .media

HCM Publishing
c/o Mapletree Publishing
6233 Howard Ln.
Highlands Ranch, CO 80126
Ph: (303)791-9024
Free: 800-537-0414
Fax: (303)791-9028

Hearst Magazines Inc.
300 W 57th St.
New York, NY 10019
Ph: (212)649-2000
Co. E-mail: feedback@hearst.com
URL: http://www.hearst.com/magazines
Facebook: www.facebook.com/HearstCorp
Linkedin: www.linkedin.com/company/
  hearst
Instagram: www.instagram.com/hearst

Herb Society of America (HSA)
9019 Kirtland Chardon Rd.
Kirtland, OH 44094
Ph: (440)256-0514
Co. E-mail: herbs@herbsociety.org
URL: http://www.herbsociety.org
Facebook: www.facebook.com/
  herbsocietyofamerica
Instagram: www.instagram.com/
  herbsocietyofamerica
Pinterest: www.pinterest.com/
  HerbSocietyAmer

Heritage Books Inc.
5810 Ruatan St.
Berwyn Heights, MD 20740
Free: 800-876-6103
Fax: (800)297-9954
Co. E-mail: info@heritagebooks.com
URL: http://heritagebooks.com
Facebook: www.facebook.com/
  HeritageBooksNow
Pinterest: www.pinterest.com/
  heritagebooksinc

Hightimes Holding Corp.
2110 Narcissus Ct.
Venice, CA 90291
Ph: (323)609-7631

Free: 844-933-3287
URL: http://hightimes.com

Hobby Merchandiser (HM)
58 Gables Way
Jackson, NJ 08527
Ph: (732)262-2268
URL: http://www.hobbymerchandiser.com

Hobby Publications Inc.
83 South St., Ste. 307
Freehold, NJ 07728
Ph: (732)536-5160
Fax: (732)536-5761
URL: http://www.hobbypub.com

Home Builders Association of Southeastern Michigan (HBA)
30400 Telegraph RD.
Bingham Farms, MI 48025
Ph: (248)737-4477
Co. E-mail: builders@builders.org
URL: http://www.builders.org
Facebook: www.facebook.com/
  HBAofSoutheasternMichigan

The Home Shop Machinist
PO Box 629
Traverse City, MI 49685
Ph: (231)946-3712
Free: 800-447-7367
Fax: (231)946-6180
Co. E-mail: info@schsm.org
URL: http://homeshopmachinist.net

Horizon Publishing Company LLC. (HPC)
7412 Calumet Ave.
Hammond, IN 46324-2622

The Horn Book Inc.
300 The Fenway Main College Building,
  Ste. C316
Boston, MA 02129
Free: 800-325-1170
Co. E-mail: info@hbook.com
URL: http://www.hbook.com
Facebook: www.facebook.com/
  TheHornBook
Instagram: www.instagram.com/
  thehornbook
Pinterest: www.pinterest.com/thehornbook

Houston Business Journal (HBJ)
5444 Westheimer, Ste. 1560
Houston, TX 77056
Ph: (713)688-8811
Fax: (713)963-0482
Co. E-mail: houston@bizjournals.com
URL: http://www.bizjournals.com/houston
Facebook: www.facebook.com/
  houstonbusinessjournals
Linkedin: www.linkedin.com/company/
  houston-business-journal
Instagram: www.instagram.com/
  houbizjournal

GUIDE TO PUBLISHERS

Houston Chronicle
PO Box 4260
Houston, TX 77210
Ph: (713)362-7171
Co. E-mail: help@houstonchronicle.com
URL: http://www.houstonchronicle.com
Facebook: www.facebook.com/chroncom
Instagram: www.instagram.com/
  houstonchron
Pinterest: www.pinterest.com/
  houstonchron

Hudson River Sloop Clearwater (HRSC)
724 Wolcott Ave.
Beacon, NY 12508
Ph: (845)265-8080
Co. E-mail: office@clearwater.org
URL: http://www.clearwater.org
Facebook: www.facebook.com/
  sloopclearwater
Instagram: www.instagram.com/
  sloopclearwater
YouTube: www.youtube.com/user/
  HRSloopClearwater

Human Factors and Ergonomics Society (HFES)
2001 K St., NW Third Fl. N
Washington, DC 20006
Ph: (202)367-1114
Fax: (202)367-2114
Co. E-mail: info@hfes.org
URL: http://www.hfes.org
Facebook: www.facebook.com/
  HFESociety
YouTube: www.youtube.com/channel/
  UCQpwTrRsKhcQFxVjOuzOrSg

Hunterdon County Historical Society (HCHS)
114 Main St.
Flemington, NJ 08822
Ph: (908)782-1091
URL: http://hunterdonhistory.org
Facebook: www.facebook.com/
  hunterdonhistory
Instagram: www.instagram.com/
  hunterdonhistory
YouTube: www.youtube.com/channel/
  UCX9cK_e2bXmC-iGr-l9fRdg

Huntington Press (HP)
3665 Procyon St.
Las Vegas, NV 89103
Ph: (702)252-0655
Free: 800-244-2224
Fax: (702)252-0675
Co. E-mail: orders@huntingtonpress.com
URL: http://www.huntingtonpress.com

I

ICD Publications
28 Liberty St.
New York, NY 10005

Ice Sports Industry (ISI)
539 W. Commerce St., No. 7250
Dallas, TX 75208
Ph: (972)735-8800
Fax: (972)735-8815
Co. E-mail: info@skateisi.org
URL: http://www.skateisi.org
Facebook: www.facebook.com/skateisi
Instagram: www.instagram.com/skateisi

Idaho Business Review (IBR)
4696 W Overland Rd., Ste. 180
Boise, ID 83705
Ph: (208)336-3768
Free: 877-615-9536
Fax: (208)336-5534
URL: http://idahobusinessreview.com
Facebook: www.facebook.com/
  IdahoBusinessReview
Linkedin: www.linkedin.com/company/
  idaho-business-review
Instagram: www.instagram.com/ibrnews
YouTube: www.youtube.com/channel/
  UC59PCuG4AfDCN_TkgX26x2A

IEEE-USA
2001 L St. NW, Ste. 700
Washington, DC 20036-4910
Ph: (202)785-0017
Fax: (202)785-0835
Co. E-mail: ieeeusa@ieee.org
URL: http://ieeeusa.org/default.asp

IGI Global
701 E Chocolate Ave.
Hershey, PA 17033
Ph: (717)533-8845
Free: 866-342-6657
Fax: (717)533-8661
Co. E-mail: cust@igi-global.com
URL: http://www.igi-global.com
Facebook: www.facebook.com/IGIglobal
Linkedin: www.linkedin.com/company/
  igiglobal

Illinois State Genealogical Society (ISGS)
PO Box 10195
Springfield, IL 62791-0195
Ph: (217)789-1968
Co. E-mail: isgsoffice@ilgensoc.org
URL: http://www.ilgensoc.org
Facebook: www.facebook.com/ILGenSoc

Illuminating Engineering Society of North America
120 Wall St., 17th Fl.
New York, NY 10005-4026
Ph: (212)248-5000
Fax: (212)248-5018
URL: http://www.ies.org
Facebook: www.facebook.com/TheIES
Linkedin: www.linkedin.com/company/
  illuminating-engineering-society
Instagram: www.instagram.com/the_iesorg

Incisive Media Inc.
22nd Fl.
New York, NY 10004
URL: http://www.incisivemedia.com
Linkedin: www.linkedin.com/company/
  incisive-media
Instagram: www.instagram.com/
  incisivemedia

Inc. Magazine
Seven World Trade Ctr.
New York, NY 10007-2195
Ph: (217)389-5377
Free: 800-234-0999
Co. E-mail: mail@inc.com
URL: http://www.inc.com
Facebook: www.facebook.com/Inc
Instagram: www.instagram.com/
  incmagazine

Independent Book Publishers Association (IBPA)
1020 Manhattan Beach Blvd., Ste. 204
Manhattan Beach, CA 90266
Ph: (310)546-1818
Co. E-mail: info@ibpa-online.org
URL: http://www.ibpa-online.org
Facebook: www.facebook.com/IBPAonline
Instagram: www.instagram.com/
  ibpalovesindies
YouTube: www.youtube.com/user/
  ibpavideo

Independent Lubricant Manufacturers Association (ILMA)
675 N Washington St., Ste. 275
Alexandria, VA 22314
Ph: (703)684-5574
Fax: (703)350-4919
Co. E-mail: ilma@ilma.org
URL: http://www.ilma.org
Linkedin: www.linkedin.com/company/
  independent-lubricant-manufacturers
  -association-ilma-
YouTube: www.youtube.com/channel/
  UCOqmIJwTCY-h7qgNXK01hSQ

Inderscience Publishers
United Kingdom
Co. E-mail: info@inderscience.com
URL: http://www.inderscience.com

Indiana Association of Plumbing Heating Cooling Contractors (IAPHCC)
9595 Whitley Dr., Ste. 208
Indianapolis, IN 46240
Ph: (317)575-9292
Fax: (317)575-9378
URL: http://www.iaphcc.com
Facebook: www.facebook.com/Indiana
  -PHCC-137787886322669

Indiana Historical Society Press
450 W Ohio St.
Indianapolis, IN 46202
Ph: (317)232-1882

GUIDE TO PUBLISHERS

Co. E-mail: membership@indianahistory.org
URL: http://indianahistory.org
Linkedin: www.linkedin.com/company/indianahistory
Instagram: www.instagram.com/indianahistory
YouTube: www.youtube.com/user/indianahistoricalsoc
Pinterest: www.pinterest.com/indianahistory

Informa Business Media, Inc.
7900 International Dr., Ste. 650
Bloomington, MN 55425
Co. E-mail: info@informa.com
URL: http://www.informa.com
Facebook: www.facebook.com/InformaPLC
Linkedin: www.linkedin.com/company/informa

Informa USA, Inc.
605 Third Ave., Fl. 20-22
New York, NY 10158
URL: http://www.informa.com
Linkedin: www.linkedin.com/company/informa

Informa USA Inc.
1990 Main St., Regus - Sarasota Courthouse, Offices 733 & 769, Ste. 750
Sarasota, FL 34236
URL: http://www.informa.com
Facebook: www.facebook.com/InformaPLC
Linkedin: www.linkedin.com/company/informa

Information Gatekeepers Inc. (IGI)
PO Box 606
Winchester, MA 01890
Ph: (617)782-5033
Fax: (617)507-8338
Co. E-mail: info@igigroup.com
URL: http://www.igigroup.com

Information Today Inc. (ITI)
143 Old Marlton Pke.
Medford, NJ 08055-8750
Ph: (609)654-6266
Free: 800-300-9868
Fax: (609)654-4309
Co. E-mail: custserv@infotoday.com
URL: http://www.infotoday.com

Innovative Properties Worldwide, Inc.
1750 Wewatta St., Ste. 1821
Denver, CO 80202
Ph: (720)476-4920
URL: http://goipw.com
Linkedin: www.linkedin.com/company/innovative-properties-worldwide-inc

Innovative Publishing Company LLC
PO Box 908
Edgartown, MA 02539
URL: http://innovativepublishing.net

Inside Mortgage Finance Publications Inc.
7910 Woodmont Ave., Ste. 1000
Bethesda, MD 20814-7019
Ph: (301)951-1240
Free: 800-570-5744
Fax: (301)656-1709
URL: http://www.insidemortgagefinance.com
Linkedin: www.linkedin.com/company/inside-mortgage-finance-publications

Inside Washington Publishers (IWP)
1919 S Eads St., Ste. 100
Arlington, VA 22202
Ph: (703)416-8500
Free: 800-424-9068
Co. E-mail: custsvc@iwpnews.com
URL: http://iwpnews.com/index.html

INSIGHT Into Diversity (IID)
50 Crestwood Executive Ctr., Ste. 526
Saint Louis, MO 63126
Ph: (314)200-9955
Co. E-mail: info@insightintodiversity.com
URL: http://www.insightintodiversity.com
Facebook: www.facebook.com/insightintodiversity
Linkedin: www.linkedin.com/company/insight-into-diversity

L'Institut d'Administration Publique du Canada (IAPC)
1075 Bay St., Ste. 401
Toronto, ON, Canada M5S 2B1
Ph: (416)924-8787
Fax: (416)924-4992
Co. E-mail: ipac@ipac.ca
URL: http://www.ipac.ca/?
Facebook: www.facebook.com/IPACIAPC
Linkedin: www.linkedin.com/company/institute-of-public-administration-of-canada

Institute of Museum & Library Services (IMLS)
955 L'Enfant Plz. N SW, Ste. 4000
Washington, DC 20024-2135
Ph: (202)653-4657
Co. E-mail: imlsinfo@imls.gov
URL: http://www.imls.gov
Facebook: www.facebook.com/USIMLS
YouTube: www.youtube.com/channel/UC_3YQWDq3Rqvo1y2L9cxKEw

Institute of Real Estate Management (IREM)
430 N Michigan Ave., Ste. 500
Chicago, IL 60611
Ph: (312)329-6000
Free: 800-837-0706
Fax: (800)338-4736
Co. E-mail: getinfo@irem.org
URL: http://www.irem.org
Facebook: www.facebook.com/InstituteofRealEstateManagement
Linkedin: www.linkedin.com/company/institute-of-real-estate-management
YouTube: www.youtube.com/user/IREMinfo

Institute of Scrap Recycling Industries (ISRI)
1250 H St. NW, Ste. 400
Washington, DC 20005
Ph: (202)662-8500
Fax: (202)624-9256
Co. E-mail: info@isri.org
URL: http://www.isri.org
Facebook: www.facebook.com/isri1987
Instagram: www.instagram.com/isrinews
YouTube: www.youtube.com/user/ISRI1987

Institute for Supply Management (ISM)
309 W Elliot Rd., Ste. 113
Tempe, AZ 85284-1556
Ph: (480)752-6276
Fax: (480)752-7890
Co. E-mail: membersvcs@ismworld.org
URL: http://www.ismworld.org
Facebook: www.facebook.com/InstituteForSupplyManagement
Linkedin: www.linkedin.com/company/institute-for-supply-management
Instagram: www.instagram.com/supplymanagement
YouTube: www.youtube.com/ismorg

Institutional Investor L.L.C.
225 Park Ave. S
New York, NY 10003
Ph: (212)224-3300
Co. E-mail: ukizy@institutionalinvestor.com
URL: http://www.institutionalinvestor.com
Facebook: www.facebook.com/iimag
Linkedin: www.linkedin.com/company/institutional-investor

Institutional Real Estate Inc. (IREI)
2010 Crow Canyon Pl., Ste. 455
San Ramon, CA 94583
Ph: (925)244-0500
Fax: (925)244-0520
Co. E-mail: circulation@irei.com
URL: http://irei.com
Facebook: www.facebook.com/pages/InstitutionalRealEstateInc/182772375186991
Linkedin: www.linkedin.com/company/institutional-real-estate-inc.
Instagram: www.instagram.com/institutionalrealestateinc
YouTube: www.youtube.com/channel/UCiOsFmt13whvvgXFv7OmmyQ

International Association of Horticultural Producers (AIPH)
Horticulture House, Manor Ct., Oxfordshire
Chilton OX11 0RN, United Kingdom
Ph: 44 1235 776230
Co. E-mail: info@aiph.org
URL: http://www.aiph.org
Facebook: www.facebook.com/TheAIPH
Linkedin: www.linkedin.com/company/aiph
Instagram: www.instagram.com/aiphglobal
YouTube: www.youtube.com/channel/UCDIz-pEBx4q0HEf5TWMGX4A

International Association of Insurance Professionals (IAIP)
One Glenlake Pkwy., Ste. 1200
Atlanta, GA 30328
Ph: (404)789-3153
Free: 800-766-6249
Fax: (404)240-0998
Co. E-mail: membership@iaip-ins.org
URL: http://www.internationalinsuranceprofessionals.org/default.aspx
Facebook: www.facebook.com/theinsuranceprofessionals
Linkedin: www.linkedin.com/groups/International-Association-Insurance-Professionals-IAIP-4067452

International Association of Plumbing and Mechanical Officials (IAPMO)
4755 E Philadelphia St.
Ontario, CA 91761
Ph: (909)472-4100
Fax: (909)472-4150
Co. E-mail: iapmo@iapmo.org
URL: http://www.iapmo.org
Facebook: www.facebook.com/IAPMO
Instagram: www.instagram.com/iapmo
YouTube: www.youtube.com/user/IAPMOGroup

International Bottled Water Association (IBWA)
1700 Diagonal Rd., Ste. 650
Alexandria, VA 22314
Ph: (703)683-5213
Free: 800-WAT-ER11
Co. E-mail: ibwainfo@bottledwater.org
URL: http://www.bottledwater.org
Facebook: www.facebook.com/bottledwatermatters
Instagram: www.instagram.com/bottledwatermatters
YouTube: www.youtube.com/user/BottledWaterMatters
Pinterest: www.pinterest.com/luvbottledwater

International Brotherhood of Teamsters - Graphic Communications Conference
25 Louisiana Ave. NW
Washington, DC 20001
URL: http://teamster.org/divisions/graphic-communications-conference

International Business Times (IBT)
33 Whitehall St., 7th Fl.
New York, NY 10004
Ph: (646)781-7381
Co. E-mail: info@ibtimes.co.uk
URL: http://www.ibtimes.com
Facebook: www.facebook.com/IBTimes
Linkedin: www.linkedin.com/company/international-business-times

International Cinematographers Guild (ICG)
7755 Sunset Blvd.
Los Angeles, CA 90046-3911
Ph: (323)876-0160
Free: 877-424-4685
Fax: (323)876-6383
URL: http://www.icg600.com
Facebook: www.facebook.com/ICGLocal600
Instagram: www.instagram.com/icglocal600
YouTube: www.youtube.com/channel/UCnAUjDliPHYuy9Bv1z4PStQ

International City/County Management Association (ICMA)
777 N Capitol St. NE Ste. 500
Washington, DC 20002-4201
Ph: (202)962-3680
Free: 800-745-8780
Fax: (202)962-3500
Co. E-mail: customerservices@icma.org
URL: http://icma.org
Facebook: www.facebook.com/ICMAORG
Linkedin: www.linkedin.com/company/icma
YouTube: www.youtube.com/user/ICMAvideos

International Council on Hotel, Restaurant, and Institutional Education (ICHRIE)
3900 Westerre Pky, Ste. 300
Richmond, VA 23233
Ph: (804)346-4800
Fax: (804)346-5009
Co. E-mail: membership@chrie.org
URL: http://www.chrie.org
Facebook: www.facebook.com/ichrie
Linkedin: www.linkedin.com/company/internationalchrie

International Economic Development Council (IEDC)
1275 K St., Ste. 300
Washington, DC 20005-4083
Ph: (202)223-7800
Fax: (202)223-4745
Co. E-mail: marketing@iedconline.org
URL: http://www.iedconline.org
Facebook: www.facebook.com/iedcONLINE
Linkedin: www.linkedin.com/company/international-economic-development-council

International Franchise Association (IFA)
1900 K St., NW, Ste. 700
Washington, DC 20006
Ph: (202)628-8000
Co. E-mail: info@franchise.org
URL: http://www.franchise.org
Facebook: www.facebook.com/IFA.DC
Linkedin: www.linkedin.com/company/international-franchise-association
Instagram: www.instagram.com/franchising411
YouTube: www.youtube.com/user/ifadc

International Home Furnishings Center (IHFC)
209 S Main St.
High Point, NC 27260
Ph: (336)888-3700
URL: http://www.andmorehighpointmarket.com/ihfc

International Risk Management Institute, Inc. (IRMI)
12222 Merit Dr., Ste. 1600
Dallas, TX 75251-2266
Ph: (972)960-7693
Free: 800-827-4242
Fax: (972)371-5120
URL: http://www.irmi.com
Facebook: www.facebook.com/IRMIowl
Linkedin: www.linkedin.com/company/irmiowl/about
YouTube: www.youtube.com/user/IRMIdotcom

International Society of Certified Employee Benefit Specialists (ISCEBS)
18700 W Bluemound Rd.
Brookfield, WI 53045-2936
Ph: (262)786-8771
Fax: (262)786-8670
Co. E-mail: iscebs@iscebs.org
URL: http://www.iscebs.org/home

International Textile and Apparel Association (ITAA)
2221 Gates Dr.
Tallahassee, FL 32312
Ph: (850)408-5145
Co. E-mail: executive_director@online.org
URL: http://itaaonline.org
Linkedin: www.linkedin.com/company/international-textile-and-apparel-association

International Trumpet Guild (ITG)
PO Box 2688
Davenport, IA 52809-2688
Ph: (563)676-2435
Co. E-mail: membership@trumpetguild.org
URL: http://www.trumpetguild.org
Facebook: www.facebook.com/InternationalTrumpetGuild

International Wealth Success Inc. (IWS)
PO Box 186

Merrick, NY 11566-0186
Ph: (516)766-5850
Free: 800-323-0548
Fax: (516)766-5919
URL: http://www.iwsmoney.com
Facebook: www.facebook.com/
  InternationalWealthSuccessInc

International Wood Products Association (IWPA)
4214 King St.
Alexandria, VA 22302
Ph: (703)820-6696
Fax: (703)820-8550
Co. E-mail: info@iwpawood.org
URL: http://www.iwpawood.org
Facebook: www.facebook.com/
  International-Wood-Products-Association-98537846310
Linkedin: www.linkedin.com/company/
  international-wood-products-association

Investment Adviser Association (IAA)
818 Connecticut Ave. NW, Ste. 600
Washington, DC 20006
Ph: (202)293-4222
Co. E-mail: iaaservices@investmentadviser.org
URL: http://investmentadviser.org
YouTube: www.youtube.com/channel/
  UCSiGYqDq5SkIDOUbwE-Nsjw

Investment Weekly News
100 City View, Ste. 125
3330 Cumberland Blvd.
Atlanta, GA 30339
Ph: (770)507-7777

Iowa Grocery Industry Association (IGIA)
2540 106th St., Ste. 102
Urbandale, IA 50322
Ph: (515)270-2628
Co. E-mail: info@iowagrocers.com
URL: http://www.iowagrocers.com
Facebook: www.facebook.com/
  IowaGrocers

Island Press Center For Resource Economics
2000 M St. NW, Ste. 480-B
Washington, DC 20036-3307
Ph: (202)232-7933
Fax: (202)234-1328
URL: http://islandpress.org

I.T. Financial Management Association (ITFMA)
PO Box 30188
Santa Barbara, CA 93130
Ph: (805)687-7390
URL: http://www.itfma.com

Ivan Levison and Associates
14 Los Cerros Dr.
Greenbrae, CA 94904
Ph: (415)461-0672
Co. E-mail: ivan@levison.com
URL: http://www.levison.com

J

J. Ross Publishing Inc. (JRP)
151 N Nob Hill Rd., No. 476
Plantation, FL 33324
Ph: (954)727-9333
Fax: (561)892-0700
Co. E-mail: customerservice@jrosspub.com
URL: http://jrosspub.com

JL Com Publishing Company L.L.C.
26 Hawthorn Dr.
Succasunna, NJ 07876-2112
Free: 888-235-2997
Fax: (973)252-7552
URL: http://www.lawpublish.com

John Wiley & Sons, Inc.
111 River St.
Hoboken, NJ 07030-5774
Ph: (201)748-6000
Fax: (410)955-0298
Co. E-mail: cs-journals@wiley.com
URL: http://www.wiley.com/en-us

John Wiley & Sons Ltd.
9600 Garsington Rd.
Oxford OX4 2DQ, United Kingdom
Ph: 44 1865 776868
Fax: 44 1865 714591
Co. E-mail: customer@wiley.com
URL: http://www.wiley.com
Facebook: www.facebook.com/
  JohnWileySons
Linkedin: www.linkedin.com/company/john-wiley-and-sons

John Wiley & Sons, Ltd.
The Atrium, Southern Gate, Chichester
West Sussex PO19 8SQ, United Kingdom

Joint Commission Resources (JCR)
1515 W 22nd St., Ste. 1300W
Oak Brook, IL 60523
Ph: (630)268-7400
Free: 877-223-6866
Co. E-mail: support@jcrinc.com
URL: http://www.jcrinc.com
Facebook: www.facebook.com/
  jointcommissionresources
Linkedin: www.linkedin.com/company/joint-commission-resources
YouTube: www.youtube.com/user/
  JointCommResources

Jola Publications
4601 Washburn Av. S.
Minneapolis, MN 55410
Ph: (612)529-5001
Free: 866-206-4495
Fax: (612)605-4645
Co. E-mail: medical@jolapub.com
URL: http://www.jolapub.com

Jossey-Bass
111 River St.
Hoboken, NJ 07030
Free: 855-827-4630
Co. E-mail: josseybasseducation@wiley.com
URL: http://www.wiley.com/learn/jossey-bass

Journal of the Canadian Economics Association
CP 35006
1221 Fleury E
Montreal, QC, Canada H2C 3K4
Ph: (646)257-5906

Journal Star
1 News Plaza
Peoria, IL 61643
Ph: (309)686-3000

J.R. O'Dwyer Company Inc.
271 Madison Ave., Ste. 1500
New York, NY 10016
Ph: (212)679-2471
URL: http://www.odwyerpr.com

K

KAL Publications Inc.
559 S Harbor Blvd., Ste. A
Anaheim, CA 92805-4547
Ph: (714)563-9300
Fax: (714)563-9310
URL: http://www.kalpub.com

Kalmbach Media
21027 Crossroads Cir.
Waukesha, WI 53187-1612
Ph: (414)796-8776
Free: 800-533-6644
Co. E-mail: customerservice@kalmbach.com
URL: http://www.kalmbach.com

Kane Communications Inc.
1062 Lancaster Ave., Ste. 15-F
Bryn Mawr, PA 19010
Ph: (610)645-6940
Fax: (610)645-6943
URL: http://www.kanec.com

Katydid Press
4736 Meadowview Blvd.
Sarasota, FL 34233
Ph: (941)924-4142
Fax: (941)922-5902

Keith Key
2451 Cumberland Pkwy., Ste. 3374
Atlanta, GA 30339
Ph: (404)419-6701
Free: 800-633-4931
Fax: (404)419-6702
Co. E-mail: info@fertiltyweekly.com

Kenilworth Media Inc.
15 Wertheim Ct., Ste. 710
Richmond Hill, ON, Canada L4B 3H7
Ph: (905)771-7333
Free: 800-409-8688
Fax: (905)771-7336
Co. E-mail: sales@kenilworth.com
URL: http://www.kenilworth.com
Linkedin: www.linkedin.com/company/
 kenilworth-media-inc

Knopf Doubleday Publishing Group
1745 Broadway
New York, NY 10019
URL: http://knopfdoubleday.com

Kodály Society of Canada (KSC)
Victoria, BC, Canada
Co. E-mail: kodalybc@gmail.com
URL: http://www.kodalysocietyofcanada.ca
Facebook: www.facebook.com/groups/
 kodalysocietyofcanada

Kogan Page Ltd.
45 Gee St., 2nd Fl.
London EC1V 3RS, United Kingdom
Ph: 44 20 7278-0433
Co. E-mail: kpinfo@koganpage.com
URL: http://www.koganpage.com
Facebook: www.facebook.com/KoganPage
Linkedin: www.linkedin.com/company/
 kogan-page_2
Instagram: www.instagram.com/
 koganpage
YouTube: www.youtube.com/user/
 KoganPageBooks

Kogan Page (KP)
8 W 38th St., Ste. 902
New York, NY 10018
Ph: (212)812-4414
Co. E-mail: info@koganpage.com
URL: http://www.koganpage.com
Linkedin: www.linkedin.com/company/
 kogan-page_2
Instagram: www.instagram.com/
 koganpage
Pinterest: www.pinterest.com/
 koganpagebooks

Kon-Lin Research & Analysis Corp.
5 Water Rd.
Rocky Point, NY 11778
Ph: (631)744-8536
Fax: (631)744-3096
URL: http://www.konlin.com

Kostuch Publications Ltd.
14-3650 Langstaff Rd., Ste. 33
Woodbridge, ON, Canada L4L 9A8
URL: http://www.kostuchmedia.com

KSE Outdoor Sportsman Group LLC.
624 S Denver Ave. Ste. 300
Tulsa, OK 74119

L

L/L Research
PO Box 5195
Louisville, KY 40255-0195
URL: http://www.llresearch.org
Facebook: www.facebook.com/llresearch
Instagram: www.instagram.com/
 ll_research
YouTube: www.youtube.com/c/LLResearch

La Crosse Tribune
1407 St. Andrew St., Ste. A100
La Crosse, WI 54603
Ph: (608)782-9710
Free: 800-262-0420
Fax: (608)782-5870
URL: http://www.lacrossetribune.com
Linkedin: www.linkedin.com/company/la
 -crosse-tribune
YouTube: www.youtube.com/
 lacrossetribune

Landscape Communications Inc.
14771 Plz. Dr., Ste. A
Tustin, CA 92780
Ph: (714)979-5276
URL: http://www.landscapeonline.com

Landscape Ontario Horticultural Trades Association (LOHTA)
7856 5th Line S, RR4
Milton, ON, Canada L9T 2X8
Ph: (905)875-1805
Free: 800-265-5656
Fax: (905)875-3942
Co. E-mail: info@landscapeontario.com
URL: http://horttrades.com
Facebook: www.facebook.com/
 landscapeontario
Linkedin: www.linkedin.com/company/
 landscape-ontario
Instagram: www.instagram.com/
 landscapeontario
YouTube: www.youtube.com/
 landscapeontario

LexisNexis
3733 Park E Dr., Ste. 260
Beachwood, OH 44122
URL: http://risk.lexisnexis.com

Linn's Stamp News
Amos Media Co.
1660 Campbell Rd., Ste. A
Sidney, OH 45365
Free: 800-253-4555
Co. E-mail: edirectory@amosmedia.com
URL: http://www.linns.com

Lippincott Williams & Wilkins (LWW)
Two Commerce Sq.
2001 Market St.
Philadelphia, PA 19103
Free: 800-638-3030
Co. E-mail: customerservice@lww.com
URL: http://shop.lww.com
Facebook: www.facebook.com/
 LippincottWoltersKluwer
YouTube: www.youtube.com/user/
 LippincottPublishing

Little, Brown and Company (LB)
1290 Ave. of the Americas
New York, NY 10104
URL: http://www.hachettebookgroup.com/
 imprint/little-brown-and-company
Facebook: www.facebook.com/
 littlebrownandcompany
Instagram: www.instagram.com/littlebrown

LNRS Data Services Limited (RBI)
Quadrant House
The Quadrant, Surrey
Sutton SM2 5AS, United Kingdom

Long Island Business News (LIBN)
2150 Smithtown Ave., Ste. 7
Ronkonkoma, NY 11779
Ph: (631)737-1700
Free: 877-615-9536
Co. E-mail: service@bridgetowerm.com
URL: http://libn.com
Facebook: www.facebook.com/
 LongIslandBusinessNews
Instagram: www.instagram.com/
 libusinessnews

Luby Publishing Inc. (LPI)
47 W Polk St., Ste. 319
Chicago, IL 60605
Ph: (312)341-1110
Fax: (312)341-1469
URL: http://www.lubypublishing.com

Lucis Trust (LT)
866 United Nations Plz., Ste. 482
New York, NY 10017
Ph: (212)292-0707
Fax: (212)292-0808
Co. E-mail: newyork@lucistrust.org
URL: http://www.lucistrust.org
Facebook: www.facebook.com/
 lucistrustorg
YouTube: www.youtube.com/user/lucistrust

Lulu Press Inc.
627 Davis Dr., Ste. 300
Morrisville, NC 27560
Free: 844-212-0689
Facebook: www.facebook.com/
 LuludotcomUK

M

M. Shanken Communications Inc.
825 8th Ave., 33rd Fl.
New York, NY 10019-7475
Co. E-mail: ssenatore@mshanken.com
URL: http://www.mshanken.com

GUIDE TO PUBLISHERS

Machinery Dealers National Association (MDNA)
5568 General Washington Dr., Ste. A213D
Alexandria, VA 22312
Ph: (703)836-9300
Co. E-mail: office@mdna.org
URL: http://www.mdna.org
Facebook: www.facebook.com/ MDNAMACHINERY

Madavor Media LLC. (MM)
35 Braintree Hill Office Pk., Ste. 101
Braintree, MA 02184
Ph: (617)706-9110
Fax: (617)536-0102
Co. E-mail: info@madavor.com
URL: http://www.madavor.com
Facebook: www.facebook.com/ MadavorMedia
Linkedin: www.linkedin.com/company/ madavor-media

Magill's Choice
2 University Plz., Ste. 310
Hackensack, NJ 07601
URL: http://www.salempress.com

Maher Publications
102 N Haven Rd.
Elmhurst, IL 60126
Ph: (630)941-2030
Co. E-mail: editor@downbeat.com
URL: http://www.downbeat.com
Facebook: www.facebook.com/ downbeatmagazine

Management Accounting Quarterly (MAQ)
10 Paragon Dr., Ste. 1
Montvale, NJ 07645-1760
URL: http://in.imanet.org

Manitoba Child Care Association (MCCA)
2350 McPhillips St., 2nd Fl.
Winnipeg, MB, Canada R2V 4J6
Ph: (204)586-8587
Free: 888-323-4676
Fax: (204)589-5613
Co. E-mail: info@mccahouse.org
URL: http://mccahouse.org
Facebook: www.facebook.com/ manitobachildcare
Instagram: www.instagram.com/ manitobachildcare
YouTube: www.youtube.com/channel/ UCwVVhisEuRqnPSV-EZT4m2w

Mansueto Ventures L.L.C. (MV)
7 World Trade Ctr.,29th Fl.
New York, NY 10007-2195
Ph: (212)389-5300
Fax: (212)389-5245
Co. E-mail: mvlicensing@inc.com
URL: http://www.mansueto.com

Manufacturers' Agents N.A. (MANA)
6321 W Dempster St., Ste. 110
Morton Grove, IL 60053
Ph: (949)859-4040
Free: 877-626-2776
Fax: (949)855-2973
Co. E-mail: mana@manaonline.org
URL: http://www.manaonline.org
Facebook: www.facebook.com/MANAonline.org
YouTube: www.youtube.com/user/ MANAspeaks

Manufacturers' Mart Publications
PO Box 310
Georgetown, MA 01833
Ph: (978)352-3320
Fax: (978)352-4829
Co. E-mail: sales@airmax.net
URL: http://www.manufacturersmart.com
Facebook: www.facebook.com/people/ Manufacturers-Mart/100064876320448

Manufacturing Confectioner Publishing Corp.
711 W Water St.
Princeton, WI 54968
Ph: (920)295-6969
URL: http://gomc.com

Maria C. Smith
PO Box 75064
Houston, TX 77234
Ph: (281)857-6571
Fax: (301)261-5010
Co. E-mail: tp@globalwaterintel.com

Marijuana Business Daily
3900 S Wadsworth Blvd., Ste. 100
Lakewood, CO 80235
Ph: (720)213-5992
Co. E-mail: customerservice@mjbiz.com
URL: http://mjbiz.com
Facebook: www.facebook.com/MJBizDaily
YouTube: www.youtube.com/channel/ UC63o9UVMm_v6MI05RgKunIQ

Mariner Books
125 High St.
Boston, MA 02110
URL: http://www.harpercollins.com/pages/ marinerbooks
Facebook: www.facebook.com/ MarinerBooks

Marketing & Technology Group Inc. (MTG)
1415 N Dayton St.
Huntley, IL 60142-2643
Ph: (312)266-1716
Fax: (312)266-3385

MarketResearch.com
6116 Executive Blvd., Ste. 550
Rockville, MD 20852
Ph: (240)747-3093
Free: 800-298-5699

Fax: (240)747-3004
Co. E-mail: customerservice@marketresearch.com
URL: http://www.marketresearch.com
Facebook: www.facebook.com/ MarketResearchDotCom

Mary Ann Liebert Inc. Publishers
140 Huguenot St., 3rd Fl.
New Rochelle, NY 10801-5215
Ph: (914)740-2100
Free: 800-MLI-EBERT
Fax: (914)740-2101
Co. E-mail: info@liebertpub.com
URL: http://www.liebertpub.com

The Masonry Society (TMS)
105 S Sunset St., Ste. Q
Longmont, CO 80501-6172
Ph: (303)939-9700
Fax: (303)541-9215
Co. E-mail: info@masonrysociety.org
URL: http://masonrysociety.org

Masthead Publishing Ltd.
Unit 8-1606 Sedlescomb Dr.
Mississauga, ON, Canada L4X 1M6
Ph: (905)625-7070
URL: http://www.mastheadonline.com

Maximum Press
605 Silverthorn Rd.
Gulf Breeze, FL 32561
URL: http://www.maxpress.com

The McClatchy Company
1601 Alhambra Blvd., Ste. 100
Sacramento, CA 95816
Ph: (916)321-1855
Free: 844-445-5715
Co. E-mail: customerservice@mcclatchy.com
URL: http://www.mcclatchy.com
Facebook: www.facebook.com/ McClatchyCo
Linkedin: www.linkedin.com/company/the -mcclatchy-company

McClatchy Tribune Information Services
120 S Lawler
Mitchell, SD 57301
URL: http://www.mcclatchy.com

McClatchy-Tribune Regional News
1320 SW Broadway
Portland, OR 97201
Ph: (503)648-1131

McClatchy-Tribune Regional News
345 Cedar St.
Saint Paul, MN 55101
Ph: (651)222-1111
Free: 800-950-9080

McEntee Media Corp.
9815 Hazelwood Ave.

Strongsville, OH 44149
Ph: (440)238-6603
Fax: (440)238-6712
URL: http://www.recycle.cc

McFarland & CPI, Publishers
960 NC Hwy. 88 W
Jefferson, NC 28640
Ph: (336)246-4460
Free: 800-253-2187
Fax: (336)246-5018
Co. E-mail: info@mcfarlandpub.com
URL: http://mcfarlandbooks.com
Facebook: www.facebook.com/
 mcfarlandcopub
Linkedin: www.linkedin.com/company/
 mcfarland-and-company-inc.-publishers
Instagram: www.instagram.com/mcfpub
Pinterest: www.pinterest.com/
 mcfarlandpub

McGraw-Hill Higher Education (MHHE)
8787 Orion Pl.
Columbus, OH 43240
URL: http://www.mheducation.com/
 highered
Facebook: www.facebook.com/
 McGrawHillEducation
Linkedin: www.linkedin.com/company/
 mcgraw-hill-education

McGraw-Hill Professional
860 Taylor Station Rd.
Blacklick, OH 43004
Free: 800-338-3987
Co. E-mail: pbg_ecommerce_custserv
 @mheducation.com
URL: http://www.mhprofessional.com
Facebook: www.facebook.com/
 McGrawHillEducation
YouTube: www.youtube.com/user/
 McGrawHIllPro

McMillan Analysis Corporation (MAC)
PO Box 1323
Morristown, NJ 07962-1323
Free: 800-724-1817
Fax: (973)328-1303
URL: http://www.optionstrategist.com

Mealey's Legal News & Litigation Reports
230 Park Ave., Ste. 7
New York, NY 10169
Ph: (212)309-8100
Free: 800-543-6862
Co. E-mail: mealeyinfo@lexisnexis.com
URL: http://www.lexisnexis.com/en-us/
 products/mealeys.page

Merrell Publishers
70 Cowcross St.
London EC1M 6EJ, United Kingdom
Ph: 44 20 7928 8880
URL: http://www.merrellpublishers.com
Facebook: www.facebook.com/people/
 Merrell-Publishers/100067645952391
Instagram: www.instagram.com/
 merrellpublishers

Merriman Market Analyst (MMA)
PO Box 14934
Scottsdale, AZ 85267
Ph: (248)626-3034
Free: 800-662-3349
Fax: (248)538-5296
Co. E-mail: customerservice@mmacycles
 .com
URL: http://www.mmacycles.com
Facebook: www.facebook.com/
 merrimanmarketanalyst
Instagram: www.instagram.com/
 mma_cycles
YouTube: www.youtube.com/c/
 MerrimanMarketAnalyst

MicroDesign Resources
298 S Sunnyvale Ave. Ste. 101
Sunnyvale, CA 94086-6245
Ph: (408)328-3900
Free: 800-527-0288
Fax: (408)737-2242
Co. E-mail: cs@mdr.cahners.com

Mid-West Truckers Association Inc. (MTA)
2727 N Dirksen Pky.
Springfield, IL 62702
Ph: (217)525-0310
Co. E-mail: info@mid-westtruckers.com
URL: http://www.mid-westtruckers.com

Miller Publishing Company
12400 Whitewater Dr., Ste. 160
Minnetonka, MN 55343
Ph: (952)930-4343
Fax: (952)938-1832

Mini-Storage Messenger
10851 N Black Canyon Fwy.
Phoenix, AZ 85029
Free: 800-352-4636
Co. E-mail: msm@modernstoragemedia
 .com
URL: http://www.modernstoragemedia.com
Facebook: www.facebook.com/MiniCo
Linkedin: www.linkedin.com/company/
 modern-storage-media

Minnesota Center for Book Arts (MCBA)
1011 Washington Ave. S, No. 100
Minneapolis, MN 55415
Ph: (612)215-2520
Fax: (612)215-2545
Co. E-mail: mcba@mnbookarts.org
URL: http://www.mnbookarts.org
Facebook: www.facebook.com/mnbookarts
Instagram: www.instagram.com/
 mnbookarts
YouTube: www.youtube.com/mnbookarts

Minnesota Department of Transportation, Office of Aeronautics
395 John Ireland Blvd.
Saint Paul, MN 55155-1800
Ph: (651)296-8202
URL: http://www.dot.state.mn.us
Facebook: www.facebook.com/
 MnDOTAeronautics

Minnesota State Bar Association (MSBA)
600 Nicollet Mall, Ste. 380
Minneapolis, MN 55402
Ph: (612)333-1183
Free: 800-882-6722
Co. E-mail: info@mnbars.org
URL: http://www.mnbar.org
Linkedin: www.linkedin.com/company/
 minnesota-state-bar-association
YouTube: www.youtube.com/channel/
 UCRZBF1BvksWAi26QQalsIjQ

Missouri Botanical Garden Press (MBG Press)
4344 Shaw Blvd.
Saint Louis, MO 63110
Ph: (314)577-9547
Co. E-mail: orders@mbgpress.org
URL: http://www.mbgpress.org

Missouri Municipal League (MML)
1727 Southridge Dr.
Jefferson City, MO 65109
Ph: (573)635-9134
Fax: (573)635-9009
Co. E-mail: info@mocities.com
URL: http://www.mocities.com
Facebook: www.facebook.com/MoCities
Linkedin: www.linkedin.com/company/
 mocities

Missouri State Genealogical Association (MOSGA)
PO Box 833
Columbia, MO 65205-0833
URL: http://mosga.org
Facebook: www.facebook.com/pages/Mo
 -State-Genealogical-Assoc/
 106281609542158

The MIT Press
1 Rogers St.
Cambridge, MA 02142-1209
Ph: (617)253-5646
URL: http://mitpress.mit.edu
Linkedin: www.linkedin.com/company/the
 -mit-press
YouTube: www.youtube.com/c/
 TheMITPress
Pinterest: www.pinterest.com/mitpress

MJH Life Sciences
2 Clarke Dr., Ste. 100
Cranbury, NJ 08512

Ph: (609)716-7777
URL: http://www.mjhlifesciences.com
Linkedin: www.linkedin.com/company/mjh
-life-sciences

Mobile Air Climate Systems Association (MACS)
PO Box 88
Lansdale, PA 19446
Ph: (215)631-7020
Fax: (215)631-7017
Co. E-mail: info@macsmobileairclimate
.org
URL: http://macsmobileairclimate.org
Facebook: www.facebook.com/
MACSMobileAir
Linkedin: www.linkedin.com/company/
mobile-air-conditioning-society-macs
-worldwide
Instagram: www.instagram.com/
macs_mobile_air
YouTube: www.youtube.com/channel/UC
-aQjZ-uXWjxlaszlQkRr0g

Mondaq Ltd.
The Old Church, Quicks Road Wimbledon
London SW19 1EX, United Kingdom
Ph: 44 20 8544 8300
Co. E-mail: enquiries@mondaq.com
URL: http://www.mondaq.com
Facebook: www.facebook.com/pages/
Mondaq/191015204600071
Linkedin: www.linkedin.com/company/
mondaq-ltd

The Moneychanger
PO Box 178
Westpoint, TN 38486
Free: 888-661-4093
URL: http://the-moneychanger.com

Montana Standard
25 W Granite St.
Butte, MT 59701
Ph: (406)496-5500
Free: 800-877-1074
URL: http://mtstandard.com
Facebook: www.facebook.com/
MontanaStandard

Morgan James Publishing L.L.C.
Five Penn Plz., 23rd Fl.
New York, NY 10001
Ph: (212)655-5470
Fax: (516)908-4496
Co. E-mail: support@morganjamespub-
lishing.com
URL: http://www.morgan-james-publishing
.com
Facebook: www.facebook.com/
morganjames
Instagram: www.instagram.com/
morganjamespub
Pinterest: www.pinterest.com/
morganjamespub/morgan-james-covers

Mortgage Bankers Association (MBA)
1919 M St. NW, 5th Fl.
Washington, DC 20036
Ph: (202)557-2700
Free: 800-793-6222
Co. E-mail: education@mba.org
URL: http://www.mba.org
Facebook: www.facebook.com/
mbamortgage
Linkedin: www.linkedin.com/company/
mortgage-bankers-association
Instagram: www.instagram.com/
mortgage_bankers_association

Motion Picture Enterprises Publications Inc. (MPE)
PO Box 276
Tarrytown, NY 10591-0276
Ph: (212)245-0969
Co. E-mail: info@mpe.net
URL: http://www.mpe.net

Motivate Publishing
34th Flr., Media One Twr., Dubai Media City
Dubai, United Arab Emirates
Ph: 971 4 427-3000
Co. E-mail: motivate@motivate.ae
URL: http://motivatemedia.com

Motor Information Systems
1301 W Long Lake Rd., Ste. 300
Troy, MI 48098
Free: 800-426-6867
Co. E-mail: contact@motor.com
URL: http://www.motor.com
Facebook: www.facebook.com/
MOTORInfoSys
Linkedin: www.linkedin.com/company/
motor-information-systems
YouTube: www.youtube.com/user/
motorinfosys

MPL Communications Inc.
133 Richmond St. W, Ste. 402
Toronto, ON, Canada M5H 3M8
Ph: (416)869-1177
Free: 800-804-8846
Co. E-mail: customers@mplcomm.com
URL: http://www.adviceforinvestors.com

Multicultural Marketing Resources Inc. (MMR)
101 Fifth Ave., Ste. 10B
New York, NY 10003
Ph: (212)242-3351
URL: http://multicultural.com
Facebook: www.facebook.com/
multiculturalmarketingresources

MunaLuchi
74 High St., 2nd Fl.
Mount Holly, NJ 08060
Free: 888-501-1272

Co. E-mail: info@munaluchibridal.com
URL: http://www.munaluchibridal.com
Facebook: www.facebook.com/
munaluchibridal
Linkedin: www.linkedin.com/company/
munaluchi
YouTube: www.youtube.com/channel/
UCT08xk5dHp6iVXTvSM25zqA
Pinterest: www.pinterest.com/
munaluchibride/_created

Municipal Art Society of New York (MASNYC)
488 Madison Ave., Ste. 1900
New York, NY 10022
Ph: (212)935-3960
Fax: (212)753-1816
Co. E-mail: info@mas.org
URL: http://www.mas.org
Facebook: www.facebook.com/masnyc
Linkedin: www.linkedin.com/company/the
-municipal-art-society-of-new-yorkwww
.linkedin.com/company/the-municipal-art
-society-of-new-york
Instagram: www.instagram.com/mas_nyc
YouTube: www.youtube.com/user/
MunicipalArt

Municipal World Inc.
42860 Sparta Line
Union, ON, Canada N0L 2L0
Free: 888-368-6125
URL: http://www.municipalworld.com
Facebook: www.facebook.com/
MunicipalWorld
Linkedin: www.linkedin.com/company/
municipalworld
Instagram: www.instagram.com/
municipalworld
YouTube: www.youtube.com/user/
MunicipalWorld

Music Teachers National Association (MTNA)
600 Vine St., Ste. 1710
Cincinnati, OH 45202
Ph: (513)421-1420
Free: 888-512-5278
Co. E-mail: mtnanet@mtna.org
URL: http://www.mtna.org/MTNA/Home/
MTNA/Default.aspx?hkey=91963004
-fbe4-4711-a192-b6293aedc31c
Facebook: www.facebook.com/mtnapage
Linkedin: www.linkedin.com/company/
music-teachers-national-association
Instagram: www.instagram.com/mtnaorg
YouTube: www.youtube.com/channel/
UCdzWx_UxrOZz9HoeXsZxWig
Pinterest: www.pinterest.com/
musicteache0952

Music Trades Corp.
15 Duck Pond Rd.
Demarest, NJ 07627
Ph: (201)871-1965
URL: http://www.musictrades.com

N

NAPCO Media
1500 Spring Garden St., Ste. 1200
Philadelphia, PA 19130
Ph: (215)238-5300
Free: 800-627-2689
Co. E-mail: customerservice@napco.com
URL: http://www.napco.com

National Accrediting Agency for Clinical Laboratory Sciences (NAACLS)
5600 N River Rd., Ste. 720
Rosemont, IL 60018-5119
Ph: (773)714-8880
Fax: (773)714-8886
Co. E-mail: info@naacls.org
URL: http://www.naacls.org

National Agri-Marketing Association (NAMA)
8700 State Line Rd., Ste. 105
Leawood, KS 66206
Ph: (913)491-6500
Fax: (913)491-6502
Co. E-mail: info@nama.org
URL: http://www.nama.org
Facebook: www.facebook.com/NationalNAMA
Linkedin: www.linkedin.com/company/national-agri-marketing-association
Instagram: www.instagram.com/officialnama
YouTube: www.youtube.com/ExploreNAMA

National Agricultural Aviation Association (NAAA)
1440 Duke St.
Alexandria, VA 22314
Ph: (202)546-5722
Fax: (202)546-5726
Co. E-mail: information@agaviation.org
URL: http://www.agaviation.org
Facebook: www.facebook.com/NationalAgriculturalAviationAssociation
Instagram: www.instagram.com/agaviationnaaa

National Air Transportation Association (NATA)
818 Connecticut Ave. NW, Ste. 900
Washington, DC 20006
Ph: (202)774-1535
Free: 800-808-6282
Fax: (202)452-0837
Co. E-mail: info@nata.aero
URL: http://www.nata.aero
Facebook: www.facebook.com/nataaero
Linkedin: www.linkedin.com/company/nataaero

National Antique & Art Dealers Association of America (NAADAA)
220 E 57th St.
New York, NY 10022
Co. E-mail: naadaa.antiques@gmail.com
URL: http://naadaa.org

National Association of Concessionaires (NAC)
180 N Michigan Ave., Ste. 2215
Chicago, IL 60601
Ph: (312)236-3858
Fax: (312)236-7809
Co. E-mail: info@naconline.org
URL: http://www.naconline.org

National Association for the Education of Young Children (NAEYC)
1401 H St. NW Ste. 600
Washington, DC 20005
Ph: (202)232-8777
Free: 800-424-2460
Fax: (202)328-1846
Co. E-mail: help@naeyc.org
URL: http://www.naeyc.org
Facebook: www.facebook.com/NAEYC
Linkedin: www.linkedin.com/company/naeyc
YouTube: www.youtube.com/channel/UCoqygeWY9lnViJE5bGSE_eg

National Association of Electrical Distributors (NAED)
1181 Corporate Lk. Dr.
Saint Louis, MO 63132
Ph: (314)991-9000
Free: 888-791-2512
Co. E-mail: naedcommunications@naed.org
URL: http://www.naed.org
Facebook: www.facebook.com/NAEDorg
Linkedin: www.linkedin.com/company/national-association-of-electrical-distributors-naed-
Instagram: www.instagram.com/naed_org
YouTube: www.youtube.com/channel/UCHJLWzwi6_hy8pO_zn8ujEA

National Association of EMS Educators (NAEMSE)
250 Mt. Lebanon Blvd., Ste. 209
Pittsburgh, PA 15234
Ph: (412)343-4775
Fax: (412)343-4770
Co. E-mail: naemse@naemse.org
URL: http://naemse.org
Facebook: www.facebook.com/NAEMSE
Instagram: www.instagram.com/naemsepgh

National Association for Healthcare Quality (NAHQ)
8600 W Bryn Mawr Ave., Ste. 710 N
Chicago, IL 60631
Ph: (847)375-4720
Free: 800-966-9392
Fax: (847)375-6320
Co. E-mail: info@nahq.org
URL: http://nahq.org
Facebook: www.facebook.com/mynahq
Instagram: www.instagram.com/mynahq

National Association of Insurance Commissioners (NAIC)
1100 Walnut St., Ste. 1500
Kansas City, MO 64106-2197
Ph: (816)842-3600
Fax: (816)842-3600
Co. E-mail: help@naic.org
URL: http://content.naic.org
Facebook: www.facebook.com/NAIC.News

National Association of Investors Corp. (NAIC)
570 Kirts Blvd., Ste. 237
Troy, MI 48084
Ph: (248)583-6242
Free: 877-275-6242
Fax: (248)583-4880
Co. E-mail: service@betterinvesting.org
URL: http://www.betterinvesting.org
Facebook: www.facebook.com/betterinvesting
Linkedin: www.linkedin.com/company/betterinvesting
Instagram: www.instagram.com/betterinvesting
YouTube: www.youtube.com/betterinvesting

National Association of Realtors (NAR)
430 N Michigan Ave.
Chicago, IL 60611-4087
Free: 800-874-6500
Co. E-mail: infocentral@realtors.org
URL: http://www.nar.realtor
Facebook: www.facebook.com/NARdotRealtor
Linkedin: www.linkedin.com/company/national-association-of-realtors
Instagram: www.instagram.com/NARdotRealtor
YouTube: www.youtube.com/user/NAREALTORS

National Association of Schools of Music (NASM)
11250 Roger Bacon Dr., Ste. 21
Reston, VA 20190-5248
Ph: (703)437-0700
Fax: (703)437-6312
Co. E-mail: info@arts-accredit.org
URL: http://nasm.arts-accredit.org

National Association of State Boards of Accountancy (NASBA)
150 4th Ave. N, Ste. 700
Nashville, TN 37219-2417
Ph: (615)880-4200
Fax: (615)880-4290
Co. E-mail: cbtcpa@nasba.org
URL: http://nasba.org
Facebook: www.facebook.com/National

-Association-of-State-Boards-of
-Accountancy-NASBA-57029612379
Linkedin: www.linkedin.com/company/
nasba
Instagram: www.instagram.com/
nasbagram
YouTube: www.youtube.com/user/
NASBAorg

National Association of Tax Professionals (NATP)
3517 N McCarthy Rd.
Appleton, WI 54913
Free: 800-558-3402
Fax: (800)747-0001
Co. E-mail: natp@natptax.com
URL: http://www.natptax.com/Pages/default.aspx
Facebook: www.facebook.com/natptax
Instagram: www.instagram.com/natptax

National Association of Women Artists (NAWA)
15 Gramercy Pk. S, Ste. 301
New York, NY 10003
Ph: (646)461-0068
Co. E-mail: office@thenawa.org
URL: http://thenawa.org
Facebook: www.facebook.com/TheNAWA
Instagram: www.instagram.com/nawa_usa
YouTube: www.youtube.com/channel/
UCxlnrjtDRUaUtRB5T8sg5sg
Pinterest: www.pinterest.com/theNAWA

National Auctioneers Association (NAA)
8880 Ballentine St.
Overland Park, KS 66214
Ph: (913)541-8084
Fax: (913)894-5281
Co. E-mail: support@auctioneers.org
URL: http://www.auctioneers.org
Facebook: www.facebook.com/
naaauctioneers
YouTube: www.youtube.com/user/
NAAAuctioneers

National Auto Auction Association (NAAA)
5320 Spectrum Dr., Ste. D
Frederick, MD 21703
Ph: (301)696-0400
Fax: (301)631-1359
Co. E-mail: naaa@naaa.com
URL: http://www.naaa.com
Facebook: www.facebook.com/National
-Auto-Auction-Association-35704747404

National Bus Trader Inc.
9698 W Judson Rd.
Polo, IL 61064
Ph: (815)946-2341
Fax: (815)946-2347
Co. E-mail: reception@busmag.com
URL: http://www.busmag.com
Facebook: www.facebook.com/National
-Bus-Trader-102997628573168

National Christmas Tree Association (NCTA)
PO Box 3609
Littleton, CO 80161
Free: 800-975-5920
Fax: (303)374-6594
Co. E-mail: info@realchristmastrees.org
URL: http://realchristmastrees.org
Facebook: www.facebook.com/
ChristmasTreesandWreaths

National Community Pharmacists Association (NCPA)
100 Daingerfield Rd.
Alexandria, VA 22314
Ph: (703)683-8200
Free: 800-544-7447
Fax: (703)683-3619
Co. E-mail: kathy.doucette@ncpa.org
URL: http://ncpa.org
Facebook: www.facebook.com/
commpharmacy
Linkedin: www.linkedin.com/company/ncpa
Instagram: www.instagram.com/
commpharmacy
YouTube: www.youtube.com/user/
NCPAvids

National Conference of State Liquor Administrators (NCSLA)
6183 Beau Douglas Ave.
Gonzales, LA 70737
Ph: (225)473-7209
Fax: (225)257-4498
Co. E-mail: pamsalario@cox.net
URL: http://www.ncsla.org

National Council of Acoustical Consultants (NCAC)
3502 Woodview Trace, Ste. 300
Indianapolis, IN 46268
Ph: (317)328-0642
Fax: (317)328-4629
Co. E-mail: info@ncac.com
URL: http://ncac.com
Facebook: www.facebook.com/ncac
.acoustics
Linkedin: www.linkedin.com/company/
national-council-of-acoustical-consultants

National Council for GeoCosmic Research (NCGR)
c/o Pam Wenzel, Treasurer
5329 E C Ave.
Richland, MI 49083
Ph: (212)838-6247
Co. E-mail: treasurer@geocosmic.org
URL: http://geocosmic.org
Facebook: www.facebook.com/geocosmic

National Cutting Horse Association (NCHA)
260 Bailey Ave.
Fort Worth, TX 76107
Ph: (817)244-6188
Fax: (817)244-2015
Co. E-mail: stallion.foal@nchacutting.com
URL: http://www.nchacutting.com
Facebook: www.facebook.com/
nationalcuttinghorse
Instagram: www.instagram.com/explore/
tags/ncha
YouTube: www.youtube.com/user/
NCHAcutting

National Electrical Contractors Association (NECA)
1201 Pennsylvania Ave. NW Ste. 1200
Washington, DC 20004
Ph: (202)991-6300
Fax: (202)217-4171
Co. E-mail: education@necanet.org
URL: http://www.necanet.org
Facebook: www.facebook.com/NECANET
Linkedin: www.linkedin.com/company/
necanet
YouTube: www.youtube.com/user/
NECAadmin

National EMS Pilots Association (NEMSPA)
131 S Ctr. St.
Collierville, TN 38027
Fax: (760)563-6772
Co. E-mail: info@nemspa.org
URL: http://www.nemspa.org
Facebook: www.facebook.com/NEMSPA
Linkedin: www.linkedin.com/company/
nemspa
Instagram: www.instagram.com/
nemspa_org

National Federation of Community Broadcasters (NFCB)
PO Box 806
Paonia, CO 81428
Ph: (970)279-3411
URL: http://nfcb.org
Facebook: www.facebook.com/
CommunityRadio
Linkedin: www.linkedin.com/company/nfcb
Instagram: www.instagram.com/nfcborg

National Federation of Independent Business (NFIB)
53 Century Blvd., Ste. 250
Nashville, TN 37214
Ph: (615)874-5288
Free: 800-634-2669
URL: http://www.nfib.com
Linkedin: www.linkedin.com/company/nfib

National Fisherman (NF)
PO Box 7438
Portland, ME 04112-7437
Ph: (207)842-5608
Free: 800-959-5073
Fax: (207)842-5609

Co. E-mail: info@nationalfisherman.com
URL: http://www.nationalfisherman.com
Facebook: www.facebook.com/
nationalfisherman

National Frozen and Refrigerated Foods Association (NFRA)
4755 Linglestown Rd., Ste. 300
Harrisburg, PA 17112
Ph: (717)657-8601
Fax: (717)657-9862
Co. E-mail: nfra@nfraweb.org
URL: http://nfraweb.org

National Funeral Directors Association (NFDA)
13625 Bishop's Dr.
Brookfield, WI 53005
Ph: (262)789-1880
Free: 800-228-6332
Fax: (262)789-6977
Co. E-mail: nfda@nfda.org
URL: http://www.nfda.org
Facebook: www.facebook.com/
NationalFuneralDirectorsAssociation
Linkedin: www.linkedin.com/company/
national-funeral-directors-association
Instagram: www.instagram.com/nfda_usa
YouTube: www.youtube.com/user/nfdaweb

National Glass Association (NGA)
1945 Old Gallows Rd., Ste. 750
Vienna, VA 22182
Ph: (703)442-4890
Free: 866-342-5642
URL: http://www.glass.org
Linkedin: www.linkedin.com/company/
national-glass-association

National Guild for Community Arts Education (NGCAE)
520 8th Ave., Ste. 302
New York, NY 10018
Ph: (212)268-3337
Co. E-mail: guildinfo@nationalguild.org
URL: http://www.nationalguild.org
Facebook: www.facebook.com/
NationalGuild
Instagram: www.instagram.com/
communityartsed
YouTube: www.youtube.com/user/
communityartsed

National Health Association (NHA)
PO Box 477
Youngstown, OH 44501-0477
Ph: (330)953-1002
Fax: (330)953-1030
Co. E-mail: info@healthscience.org
URL: http://www.healthscience.org
Facebook: www.facebook.com/
NationalHealthAssociation

National Independent Automobile Dealers Association (NIADA)
4621 S Cooper St., Ste. 131-524
Arlington, TX 76017
Ph: (817)640-3838
Co. E-mail: cpo@niada.com
URL: http://niada.com
Facebook: www.facebook.com/
NationalIndependentAutomobileDealersAssociation
Linkedin: www.linkedin.com/company/
national-independent-automobile-dealers-association
Instagram: www.instagram.com/_niada
YouTube: www.youtube.com/channel/
UCwhk-6tS5PDMOpGDkxGMd_g

National Information Standards Organization (NISO)
3600 Clipper Mill Rd., Ste. 302
Baltimore, MD 21211-1948
Ph: (301)654-2512
Fax: (410)685-5278
Co. E-mail: nisohq@niso.org
URL: http://www.niso.org

National Insulation Association (NIA)
516 Herndon Pky., Ste. D
Herndon, VA 20190
Ph: (703)464-6422
Fax: (703)464-5896
URL: http://www.insulation.org
Facebook: www.facebook.com/NIAinfo
Linkedin: www.linkedin.com/company/
niainfo
YouTube: www.youtube.com/niainfo

National League for Nursing (NLN)
2600 Virginia Ave. NW, 8th Fl.
Washington, DC 20037
Ph: (202)909-2500
Free: 800-669-1656
Co. E-mail: accounting@nln.org
URL: http://www.nln.org
Facebook: www.facebook.com/
NationalLeagueforNursing
Instagram: www.instagram.com/nlnursing
YouTube: www.youtube.com/channel/
UCs69j-7ABCzIBfaM79KAa6A

National Marine Fisheries Service - Fisheries Statistics & Economics Division, F/ST1
1315 East-West Highway - Rm. 12441
Silver Spring, MD 20910-3282
Ph: (301)713-2328
Fax: (301)713-4137
URL: http://www.st.nmfs.noaa.gov/st1/fus/fus09/index.html

National Marine Representatives Association (NMRA)
238 N Sioux Rd.
Kilmarnock, VA 22482
Co. E-mail: info@nmraonline.org
URL: http://nmraonline.org
Linkedin: www.linkedin.com/company/
national-marine-representatives-association

National Opera Association (NOA)
1100 Baits Dr.
Ann Arbor, MI 48109-2085
Ph: (734)615-3784
Co. E-mail: president@noa.org
URL: http://www.noa.org
Facebook: www.facebook.com/
NATIONALOPERAASSOCIATION
Instagram: www.instagram.com/
nationaloperaassociation

National Rifle Association of America (NRA)
11250 Waples Mill Rd.
Fairfax, VA 22030
Ph: (800)672-3888
Free: 877-672-2000
URL: http://explore.nra.org
Facebook: www.facebook.com/NRA

National Roofing Contractors Association (NRCA)
10255 W Higgins Rd., Ste. 600
Rosemont, IL 60018-5607
Ph: (847)299-9070
Free: 866-275-6722
Fax: (847)299-1183
Co. E-mail: info@nrca.net
URL: http://www.nrca.net
Facebook: www.facebook.com/nrcainfo
Linkedin: www.linkedin.com/company/
national-roofing-contractors-association
Instagram: www.instagram.com/
NRCAnews
YouTube: www.youtube.com/user/
nrcanews

National Shoe Retailers Association (NSRA)
7386 N La Cholla Blvd.
Tucson, AZ 85741
Ph: (520)209-1710
Co. E-mail: memberservices@nsra.org
URL: http://www.nsra.org
Facebook: www.facebook.com/
NationalShoeRetailersAssociation
Linkedin: www.linkedin.com/company/
national-shoe-retailers-association
Instagram: www.instagram.com/
nationalshoeretailersassoc

National Skeet Shooting Association (NSSA)
5931 Roft Rd.
San Antonio, TX 78253
Ph: (210)688-3371
Free: 800-877-5338
Fax: (210)688-3014
Co. E-mail: nsca@nssa-nsca.com
URL: http://www.nssa-nsca.org
Facebook: www.facebook.com/MyNSSA
YouTube: www.youtube.com/channel/
UChzKSrY8prE-u4yZQ2J-TyA

National Ski and Snowboard Retailers Association (NSSRA)
3041 Woodcreek Dr., Ste. 210
Downers Grove, IL 60515
Ph: (224)220-1522
Fax: (847)391-9827
Co. E-mail: info@nssra.com
URL: http://www.nssra.com
Linkedin: www.linkedin.com/company/national-ski-snowboard-retailers-association-nssra

National Tank Truck Carriers (NTTC)
950 N Glebe Rd., Ste. 520
Arlington, VA 22203-4183
Ph: (703)838-1960
Co. E-mail: nttcstaff@tanktruck.org
URL: http://www.tanktruck.org
Facebook: www.facebook.com/NationalTankTruck
Linkedin: www.linkedin.com/company/national-tank-truck-carriers

National Tour Association (NTA)
101 Prosperous Pl., Ste. 350
Lexington, KY 40591
Ph: (859)264-6540
Free: 800-682-8886
Fax: (859)264-6570
Co. E-mail: headquarters@ntastaff.com
URL: http://www.ntaonline.com
Facebook: www.facebook.com/NTAnow
YouTube: www.youtube.com/user/ntaonline

National Wellness Institute (NWI)
1300 College Ct.
Stevens Point, WI 54481
Ph: (715)342-2969
Co. E-mail: nwi@nationalwellness.org
URL: http://www.nationalwellness.org
Facebook: www.facebook.com/NationalWellnessInstituteFans
Linkedin: www.linkedin.com/company/national-wellness-institute
Instagram: www.instagram.com/nationalwellnessinstitute
YouTube: www.youtube.com/channel/UCx7gMTow6vUSUVXZLYt4TiA

National Wood Carvers Association (NWCA)
PO Box 43218
Cincinnati, OH 45243
Ph: (513)561-7045
Co. E-mail: nwca@chipchats.org
URL: http://chipchats.org

National Writers Association (NWA)
10940 S Parker Rd., No. 508
Parker, CO 80134
Co. E-mail: natlwritersassn@hotmail.com
URL: http://www.nationalwriters.com/page/page/1963103.htm

Nelson Education Ltd.
1120 Birchmount Rd.
Toronto, ON, Canada M1K 5G4
Ph: (416)752-9448
Free: 800-268-2222
Co. E-mail: inquire@nelson.com
URL: http://www.nelson.com
Facebook: www.facebook.com/NelsonClassroom
Instagram: www.instagram.com/NelsonClassroom

Nelson Publishing Inc.
2504 Tamiami Trl. N
Nokomis, FL 34275

Networld Media Group (NMG)
13100 Eastpoint Park Blvd.
Louisville, KY 40223
Free: 877-441-7545
Fax: (502)241-1385
URL: http://networldmediagroup.com
Facebook: www.facebook.com/NetWorldMediaGroup
Linkedin: www.linkedin.com/company/network-media-group

New England Appraisers Association (NEAA)
6973 Crestridge Rd.
Memphis, TN 38119
Ph: (901)758-2659
Co. E-mail: etuten551@aol.com
URL: http://www.newenglandappraisers.org
Facebook: www.facebook.com/NewEnglandAppraisersAssociation

New England Historic Genealogical Society (NEHGS)
99-101 Newbury St.
Boston, MA 02116-3007
Ph: (617)536-5740
Free: 888-296-3447
Fax: (617)536-7307
URL: http://www.americanancestors.org
Facebook: www.facebook.com/nehgs
Instagram: www.instagram.com/american_ancestors
YouTube: www.youtube.com/user/AmericanAncestors

New Jersey Law Journal
NJ
URL: http://www.law.com/njlawjournal/?slreturn=20240612232908

New York State Society of Certified Public Accountants (NYSSCPA)
200 Madison Ave., 11th Fl.
New York, NY 10016
Ph: (212)719-8383
Free: 800-633-6320
Fax: (212)719-3364
Co. E-mail: membership@nysscpa.org
URL: http://www.nysscpa.org
Facebook: www.facebook.com/NYSSCPA
Instagram: www.instagram.com/nysscpa

New York University Press (NYUP)
411 Lafayette St., 6th Fl.
New York, NY 10003
Co. E-mail: nyupressinfo@nyu.edu
URL: http://nyupress.org
Facebook: www.facebook.com/nyupress
Instagram: www.instagram.com/nyupress
YouTube: www.youtube.com/nyupressonline

The News Herald (NH)
7085 Mentor Ave.
Willoughby, OH 44094
Ph: (440)951-0000
Free: 800-947-2737
Fax: (440)975-2293
Co. E-mail: comment@news-herald.com
URL: http://www.news-herald.com
Facebook: www.facebook.com/newsheraldinoh

News and Observer
160 Mine Lake Ct., Ste. 200
Raleigh, NC 27615
URL: http://www.newsobserver.com

NewsRX LLC.
PO Box 724823
Atlanta, GA 31139
Ph: (770)507-7777
Co. E-mail: info@newsrx.com
URL: http://www.newsrx.com/NewsRxWebsite
Facebook: www.facebook.com/NewsRxButter
Linkedin: www.linkedin.com/company/newsrx-llc
Instagram: www.instagram.com/newsrxbutter

NewYorkAncestry.com
1300 West Traverse Parkway
Lehi, UT 84043
Ph: (208)469-0673
Facebook: www.facebook.com/AncestryUS
Instagram: www.instagram.com/ancestry
YouTube: www.youtube.com/user/AncestryCom
Pinterest: in.pinterest.com/ancestrycom

Nightingale-Conant Corp. (NC)
1400 S Wolf Rd., Bldg. 300, Ste. 103
Wheeling, IL 60090
Free: 800-557-1660
URL: http://www.nightingale.com
Facebook: www.facebook.com/NightingaleConantCorp
YouTube: www.youtube.com/NightingaleConantCorp

Nolo
950 Parker St.
Berkeley, CA 94710
Free: 800-728-3555
Co. E-mail: customersupport@nolo.com
URL: http://www.nolo.com

Nomis Publications Inc.
8570 Foxwood Ct.
Youngstown, OH 44514
Ph: (330)965-2380
Free: 800-321-7479
Fax: (330)965-2381
Co. E-mail: info@nomispublications.com
URL: http://www.nomispublications.com
Facebook: www.facebook.com/Nomis.Publications

NorlightsPress.com
762 State Rd. 458
Bedford, IN 47421
Ph: (812)675-8054
URL: http://norlightspress.com
Facebook: www.facebook.com/northlightpress

North American Association of Floor Covering Distributors (NAFCD)
330 N Wabash Ave., Ste. 2000
Chicago, IL 60611-7621
Ph: (312)321-6836
Free: 800-383-3091
Fax: (312)673-6962
Co. E-mail: info@nafcd.org
URL: http://www.nafcd.org
Facebook: www.facebook.com/NAFCD
YouTube: www.youtube.com/user/nafcdfloorcovering

North American Building Material Distribution Association (NBMDA)
330 N Wabash Ave., Ste. 2000
Chicago, IL 60611
Ph: (312)321-6845
Free: 888-747-7862
Fax: (312)644-0310
Co. E-mail: info@nbmda.org
URL: http://www.nbmda.org
Facebook: www.facebook.com/NBMDA
Linkedin: www.linkedin.com/company/north-american-building-material-distribution-association-nbmda-
YouTube: www.youtube.com/user/NBMDAheadquarters

North American Die Casting Association (NADCA)
3250 N Arlington Heights Rd., Ste. 101
Arlington Heights, IL 60004
Ph: (847)279-0001
Fax: (847)279-0002
Co. E-mail: nadca@diecasting.org
URL: http://www.diecasting.org
Linkedin: www.linkedin.com/company/north-american-die-casting-association

North American Drama Therapy Association (NADTA)
230 Washington Ave. Ext., Ste. 101
Albany, NY 12203-3539
Ph: (518)463-8656
Free: 888-416-7167
Co. E-mail: office@nadta.org
URL: http://www.nadta.org
Facebook: www.facebook.com/NADTA.Dramatherapy
Instagram: www.instagram.com/nadta.dramatherapy
YouTube: www.youtube.com/user/DramaTherapyChannel

North Coast Media (NCM)
360 E 9th St., Ste. 1070
Skokie, IL 60076-7990
Ph: (847)763-9030
Fax: (847)763-9694
Co. E-mail: northcoastmedia@northcoastmedia.net
URL: http://www.northcoastmedia.net

North Island Publishing
8-1606 Sedlescomb Dr.
Mississauga, ON, Canada L4X 1M6
Ph: (905)625-7070
Free: 800-331-7408
Fax: (905)625-4856
Co. E-mail: circulation@northisland.ca
URL: http://www.northisland.ca

North Jersey Media Group
One Garret Mountain Plz.
Woodland Park, NJ 07424
Ph: (973)569-7100
Free: 888-282-3422
URL: http://www.northjersey.com
Facebook: www.facebook.com/northjerseycom

Northeastern Lumber Manufacturers Association (NELMA)
272 Tuttle Rd.
Cumberland Center, ME 04021
Ph: (207)829-6901
Fax: (207)829-4293
Co. E-mail: info@nelma.org
URL: http://www.nelma.org
Facebook: www.facebook.com/NortheasternLumberMfg
YouTube: www.youtube.com/user/NelmaTV

Northern Arizona Genealogical Society (NAGS)
PO Box 695
Prescott, AZ 86302
Ph: (928)778-2311
Co. E-mail: asknagsprescottaz@gmail.com
URL: http://www.nagsprescott.org

NorthStar Travel Media
116 W 32nd St., 14th Fl.
New York, NY 10001
Ph: (646)380-6240
URL: http://www.northstartravelgroup.com

Northstar Travel Media (NTM)
100 Lighting Way, 2nd Fl.
Secaucus, NJ 07094
Ph: (201)902-2000
URL: http://www.northstartravelgroup.com
Linkedin: www.linkedin.com/company/northstar-travel-media

Northwest Fuchsia Society (NWFS)
12735- 1st Ave., NW
Seattle, WA 98177-4221
URL: http://www.nwfuchsiasociety.com

Nouveau Connoisseurs Corporation
9225 SW 169th Ave.
Beaverton, OR 97007
Ph: (503)590-4329
URL: http://moniquehayward.com

NPT Publishing Group Inc.
201 Littleton Rd., 2nd Fl.
Morris Plains, NJ 07950
Ph: (973)401-0202
Fax: (973)401-0404
Co. E-mail: marketing@nptimes.com
URL: http://www.thenonprofittimes.com
Facebook: www.facebook.com/thenonprofittimes
YouTube: www.youtube.com/user/TheNonProfitTimes

NueMedia L.L.C.
36 Canyon Ln.
McFarland, WI 53558
URL: http://www.nuemediallc.net

O

Lawrence Oakly
5 Savage Ct.
Bluffton, SC 29910-4430
Ph: (843)705-5591
Fax: (843)705-5592
Co. E-mail: up415@aol.com

Obsidian Launch L.L.C.
612 Main St., Ste.1
Boonton, NJ 07005
Free: 888-244-2843
URL: http://mikemichalowicz.com

Ocala Star-Banner
2121 SW 19th Ave. Rd.
Ocala, FL 34471
Free: 800-541-2171
URL: http://www.ocala.com
Facebook: www.facebook.com/ocala.starbanner
Instagram: www.instagram.com/ocalastarbanner

Ohio State University Michael E. Moritz College of Law
55 W 12th Ave., Drinko Hall
Columbus, OH 43210-1391
Ph: (614)292-2631

Co. E-mail: lawadmit@osu.edu
URL: http://moritzlaw.osu.edu
Facebook: www.facebook.com/
osumoritzlaw
Linkedin: www.linkedin.com/school/the
-ohio-state-university-moritz-college-of
-law
Instagram: www.instagram.com/
ohio_state_law
YouTube: www.youtube.com/user/
OhioStateLaw

Oklahoma Genealogical Society (OGS)
1125 NW 50th St.
Oklahoma City, OK 73118
Ph: (405)637-1907
Co. E-mail: info@okgensoc.org
URL: http://www.okgensoc.org
Facebook: www.facebook.com/
OklahomaGenealogicalSociety

Omnigraphics Inc.
615 Griswold, Ste. 520
Detroit, MI 48226
Free: 800-234-1340
Co. E-mail: customerservice@omnigraph-
ics.com
Facebook: www.facebook.com/
omnigraphicspublishing

Oregon National Organization for the Reform of Marijuana Laws
Portland, OR
Co. E-mail: oregonnorml@gmail.com
URL: http://ornorml.org
Facebook: www.facebook.com/oregon
.norml
Instagram: www.instagram.com/
oregonnorml

Oregon Newspaper Publishers Association (ONPA)
400 2nd St., Ste. 100
Lake Oswego, OR 97034
Ph: (503)624-6397
Co. E-mail: onpa@orenews.com
URL: http://www.orenews.com

The Oregonian
1500 SW First Ave.
Portland, OR 97201
Free: 800-452-1420
URL: http://www.oregonlive.com
Facebook: www.facebook.com/
OregonianMedia
Instagram: www.instagram.com/
theoregonian
YouTube: www.youtube.com/user/
oregoniannews/videos

O'Reilly Media Inc.
1005 Gravenstein Hwy. N
Sebastopol, CA 95472
Ph: (707)827-7000
Fax: (707)829-0104
Co. E-mail: orders@oreilly.com
URL: http://www.oreilly.com
YouTube: www.youtube.com/user/
OreillyMedia

Organization of American Kodaly Educators (OAKE)
650 NE Holladay St., Ste. 1600
Portland, OR 97232
Ph: (310)441-3555
Fax: (310)441-3577
Co. E-mail: info@oake.org
URL: http://www.oake.org
Facebook: www.facebook.com/oakeorg
Instagram: www.instagram.com/
oakenational

Orlando Business Journal (OBJ)
255 S Orange Ave., Ste. 650
Orlando, FL 32801
Ph: (407)649-8470
Fax: (407)420-1625
Co. E-mail: orlando@bizjournals.com
URL: http://www.bizjournals.com/orlando
Facebook: www.facebook.com/objupdate
Linkedin: www.linkedin.com/company/
orlando-business-journal
Instagram: www.instagram.com/
orlandobizjrnl

Ormazabal Y Cia S.L.U

Oser Communications Group Inc.
1877 N Kolb
Tucson, AZ 85715
Ph: (520)721-1300
Fax: (520)721-6300
Co. E-mail: info@oser.com
URL: http://www.osercomm.com

Out Your Backdoor
OYB, 2231 Woodleaf Ct.
Okemos, MI 48864
Ph: (517)992-1010
URL: http://www.outyourbackdoor.com
Facebook: www.facebook.com/
outyourbackdoor
Instagram: www.instagram.com/
outyourbackdoor
YouTube: www.youtube.com/channel/
UCTCegrAm3X-THTkSNEJ0k0A

Owner-Operator Independent Drivers Association (OOIDA)
1 NW OOIDA Dr.
Grain Valley, MO 64029
Ph: (816)229-5791
Free: 800-444-5791
Fax: (816)427-4467
URL: http://www.ooida.com
Facebook: www.facebook.com/OOIDA
Instagram: www.instagram.com/
ooida_truckers
YouTube: www.youtube.com/user/
TruckersOOIDA

Oxford University Press Oxford Journals
Great Clarendon St.
Oxford OX2 6DP, United Kingdom
Ph: 44 1865 353907
Fax: 44 1865 353485
URL: http://academic.oup.com/journals
Facebook: www.facebook.com/
OUPAcademic
Linkedin: www.linkedin.com/showcase/oup
-academic
YouTube: www.youtube.com/c/
OUPAcademic

P

Pacific Northwest Christmas Tree Association (PNWCTA)
PO Box 660
Molalla, OR 97038
Ph: (503)364-2942
Fax: (971)314-4703
Co. E-mail: pnwchristmastrees@gmail
.com
URL: http://www.nwchristmastrees.org

PacificBasin Communications
1088 Bishop St., Ste. LL2
Honolulu, HI 96813
Ph: (808)537-9500
Fax: (808)537-6455
Co. E-mail: letters@honolulumagazine
.com
URL: http://www.honolulumagazine.com
Facebook: www.facebook.com/
honolulumag
Instagram: www.instagram.com/
honolulumag
YouTube: www.youtube.com/
honolulumagazine
Pinterest: www.pinterest.com/honolulumag

Paint and Decorating Retailers Association (PDRA)
1401 Triad Ctr. Dr.
Saint Peters, MO 63376
Free: 800-737-0107
Co. E-mail: info@pdra.org
URL: http://www.pdra.org
Pinterest: www.pinterest.com/pdra0036

Palgrave Macmillan
4 Crinan St.
London N1 9XW, United Kingdom
Ph: 44 20 78334000
Co. E-mail: palgrave@macmillan.com.au
URL: http://www.palgrave.com

Palgrave Macmillan
One New York Plz., Ste. 4500
New York, NY 10004-1562
Free: 800-777-4643
URL: http://www.palgrave.com

Panoma Press
Ivy House, Beccles Rd., Fritton

GUIDE TO PUBLISHERS

Great Yarmouth NR31 9HB, United Kingdom
Ph: 44 1582 540-506
Co. E-mail: publishing@panomapress.com
URL: http://www.panomapress.com
Facebook: www.facebook.com/
PanomaPress
Linkedin: www.linkedin.com/company/
panoma-press
Instagram: www.instagram.com/
panomapress

Panoptic Enterprises
6055 Ridge Ford Dr.
Burke, VA 22015
Ph: (703)451-5953
URL: http://www.fedgovcontracts.com

The Pantagraph
205 N Main St.
Bloomington, IL 61701
Ph: (309)829-9000
Free: 855-264-2511
Co. E-mail: custservice@pantagraph.com
URL: http://pantagraph.com
Facebook: www.facebook.com/pantagraph
Linkedin: www.linkedin.com/company/the
-pantagraph
Instagram: www.instagram.com/
thepantagraph

PC Magazine
114 Fifth Ave., 15th Fl.
New York, NY 10011
Free: 800-289-0429
Co. E-mail: pcmagdigital@emailcustomer-
service.com
URL: http://www.pcmag.com
Facebook: www.facebook.com/PCMag
Instagram: www.instagram.com/pcmag
YouTube: www.youtube.com/channel/
UCRhADYLTpsb0JA-uaLWovGw
Pinterest: www.pinterest.com/pcmag

Pearson Education Inc.
330 Hudson St.
New York, NY 10013
URL: http://www.pearson.com
Facebook: www.facebook.com/
PearsonNorthAmerica
Linkedin: www.linkedin.com/company/2137
Instagram: www.instagram.com/
pearsonofficial
YouTube: www.youtube.com/c/
PearsonNorthAmerica

Penguin Publishing Group
375 Hudson St.
New York, NY 10014
Free: 800-793-2665
Co. E-mail: consumerservices@penguin-
randomhouse.com
URL: http://www.penguin.com
Facebook: www.facebook.com/
PenguinGroupUSA
Linkedin: www.linkedin.com/company/
penguin-group-usa

Penguin Random House
1745 Broadway
New York, NY 10019
Ph: (212)782-8812
Free: 800-793-2665
Co. E-mail: customerservice@penguinran-
domhouse.com
URL: http://www.penguinrandomhouse
.com
Facebook: www.facebook.com/
PenguinRandomHouse
Linkedin: www.linkedin.com/company/
penguin-random-house-publishing
Instagram: www.instagram.com/
penguinrandomhouse
YouTube: www.youtube.com/channel/
UC4OnzY1OgwUE0XPAHpqlcvQ
Pinterest: www.pinterest.com/
penguinrandom

Personal Care Product Council
1620 L St. NW, Ste. 1200
Washington, DC 20036
Ph: (202)331-1770
Fax: (202)331-1969
Co. E-mail: membership@personalcar-
ecouncil.org
URL: http://www.personalcarecouncil.org
Facebook: www.facebook.com/Personal
-Care-Products-Council
-1443878795835012
Linkedin: www.linkedin.com/company/
464630
YouTube: www.youtube.com/user/
PersonalCareCouncil

Personal Selling Power Inc.
150 Riverside Pky., Ste. 201
Fredericksburg, VA 22406
Ph: (540)752-7000
Free: 800-752-7355
Fax: (540)752-7001
Co. E-mail: customerservice@sell-
ingpower.com
URL: http://sellingpower.com
Facebook: www.facebook.com/
SellingPowerMagazine
Linkedin: www.linkedin.com/company/
selling-power
YouTube: www.youtube.com/user/
sellingpower

PHCPPros
6201 W Howard St., Ste. 206
Niles, IL 60714
Ph: (847)564-1127
Fax: (847)564-1264
URL: http://www.phcppros.com
Facebook: www.facebook.com/PHCPPros
Linkedin: www.linkedin.com/company/
phcppros
Instagram: www.instagram.com/phcppros
YouTube: www.youtube.com/phcppros

Philadelphia Business Journal
400 Market St., Ste. 1200
Philadelphia, PA 19106
Ph: (215)238-1450
Fax: (215)238-9489
Co. E-mail: philadelphia@bizjournals.com
URL: http://www.bizjournals.com/
philadelphia
Facebook: www.facebook.com/
PhilaBusinessJournal
Linkedin: www.linkedin.com/company/
philadelphia-business-journal

The Philadelphia Inquirer
801 Market St., Ste. 300
Philadelphia, PA 19107
Ph: (215)854-2000
Free: 800-222-2765
Co. E-mail: philly_sales@philly.com
URL: http://www.inquirer.com
Facebook: www.facebook.com/
philadelphiainquirer
Instagram: www.instagram.com/
phillyinquirer

Phoenix Business Journal
101 N First Ave., Ste. 2300
Phoenix, AZ 85003
Ph: (602)230-8400
Fax: (602)230-0955
Co. E-mail: phoenix@bizjournals.com
URL: http://www.bizjournals.com/phoenix
Facebook: www.facebook.com/
phxbizjournal
Linkedin: www.linkedin.com/company/
phoenix-business-journal

Phoenix Media Corp.
100 Cummings Ctr., Ste. 211-C
Beverly, MA 01915

The Photo Review (TPR)
340 E Maple Ave., Ste. 200
Langhorne, PA 19047
URL: http://www.photoreview.org

The Photograph Collector
140 E Richardson Ave.
Langhorne, PA 19047

Photographic Society of America (PSA)
8241 S Walker Ave., Ste. 104
Oklahoma City, OK 73139
Ph: (405)843-1437
Free: 855-772-4636
URL: http://psa-photo.org
Instagram: www.instagram.com/
photographicsocietyofamerica

Pi Yee Press
4855 W Nevso Dr.
Las Vegas, NV 89103-3787
Co. E-mail: orders@bj21.com
URL: http://bj21.com

Pioneer Associates Inc.
2125 Center Ave., Ste. 305
Fort Lee, NJ 07024-5898
Ph: (201)592-7007

Fax: (201)592-7171
URL: http://www.williamspublications.com

Playtonic Communications
3409 Yonge St.
Toronto, ON, Canada M4N 3R1
URL: http://www.toysandgamesmagazine.ca

Polar Bear Alumni Association (PBAA)
718 Fairlawn Dr.
Columbus, OH 43214
Ph: (614)263-3471
URL: http://northhighpolarbears.org

Portfolio Hardcover
375 Hudson St.
New York, NY 10014
URL: http://www.penguin.com

Portfolio
1745 Broadway
New York, NY 10019
Free: 800-793-2665
Co. E-mail: portfoliopublicity@penguinrandomhouse.com
URL: http://www.penguin.com
Facebook: www.facebook.com/
  PortfolioBooks
Linkedin: www.linkedin.com/showcase/
  portfolio-penguin-random-house
Instagram: www.instagram.com/
  portfolio_books
Pinterest: www.pinterest.com/
  PortfolioBooksPRH

Portland Business Journal (PBJ)
851 SW 6th Ave., Ste. 500
Portland, OR 97204
Ph: (503)274-8733
Fax: (503)219-3450
Co. E-mail: portland@bizjournals.com
URL: http://www.bizjournals.com/portland
Facebook: www.facebook.com/
  PortlandBizJournal

Portland Press Herald
PO Box 1460
Portland, ME 04101
Ph: (207)791-6000
Co. E-mail: circulation@pressherald.com
URL: http://pressherald.com
Facebook: www.facebook.com/pressherald
Linkedin: www.linkedin.com/company/
  pressherald
Instagram: www.instagram.com/
  portlandpressherald
YouTube: www.youtube.com/channel/
  UC0sPBv78fAj46b_AaU159qQ
Pinterest: www.pinterest.com/pressherald

Potomac Books Inc.
1225 L St., Ste. 200
Lincoln, NE 68588-0630
URL: http://www.nebraskapress.unl.edu/
  potomac
Facebook: www.facebook.com/
  PotomacBooks

PR Newswire Association LLC.
200 Vesey St., 19th Fl.
New York, NY 10281
Free: 800-776-8090
Fax: (800)793-9313
Co. E-mail: info@prnasia.com
URL: http://www.prnewswire.com

Precision Metalforming Association (PMA)
6363 Oak Tree Blvd.
Independence, OH 44131
Ph: (216)901-8800
URL: http://www.pma.org/home
Facebook: www.facebook.com/
  PrecisionMetalformingAssociation
Linkedin: www.linkedin.com/company/
  precision-metalforming-association
Instagram: www.instagram.com/
  metalformingmatters
YouTube: www.youtube.com/user/
  PrecisionMetalform

Premium Source, Inc.
7101 La Vista Pl.
Longmont, CO 80503
Ph: (720)583-6693
Co. E-mail: contact@therooster.com
URL: http://therooster.com

Printworld International Inc.
PO Box 1957
West Chester, PA 19380

Productive Publications
380 Brooke Ave.
North York, ON, Canada M5M 2L6
Ph: (416)483-0634
Free: 877-879-2669
Fax: (416)322-7434
Co. E-mail: productivepublications@gmail
  .com
URL: http://www.productivepublications.ca

Professional and Technical Consultants Association (PATCA)
PO Box 2261
Santa Clara, CA 95055
Free: 800-747-2822
Fax: (866)746-1053
Co. E-mail: admin@patca.org
URL: http://patca.org
Facebook: www.facebook.com/pages/
  PATCA/48258307732
YouTube: www.youtube.com/channel/
  UCL6gesDzEPk3NPdi1g8qFJA

Profile Books Limited
29 Cloth Fair
London EC1A 7JQ, United Kingdom
Ph: 44 20 784-163-00
Co. E-mail: info@profilebooks.com
URL: http://profilebooks.com
Facebook: www.facebook.com/
  profilebooks
Instagram: www.instagram.com/profile
  .books

Project HOPE
1220 19th St. NW
Washington, DC 20036
Free: 844-349-0188
Co. E-mail: hope@projecthope.org
URL: http://www.projecthope.org
Facebook: www.facebook.com/
  ProjectHOPEorg
Linkedin: www.linkedin.com/company/
  project-hope
Instagram: www.instagram.com/
  projecthopeorg

Project Management Institute (PMI)
14 Campus Blvd.
Newtown Square, PA 19073-3299
Ph: (610)356-4600
Fax: (610)356-4647
Co. E-mail: customercare@pmi.org
URL: http://www.pmi.org
Facebook: www.facebook.com/PMInstitute
Linkedin: www.linkedin.com/company/
  pminstitute
Instagram: www.instagram.com/pmi_org
YouTube: www.youtube.com/c/pmi

Property Management Association (PMA)
7508 Wisconsin Ave., 4th Fl.
Bethesda, MD 20814
Ph: (301)657-9200
Fax: (301)907-9326
Co. E-mail: info@pma-dc.org
URL: http://www.pma-dc.org
Facebook: www.facebook.com/
  PropertyManagementAssociation
Linkedin: www.linkedin.com/company/
  property-management-association-inc
Instagram: www.instagram.com/
  propertymanagementassociation

ProStar Publications Inc.
8643 Hayden Pl.
Culver City, CA 90232-2901
Ph: (310)280-1010
Free: 800-481-6277
Fax: (310)280-1025
Co. E-mail: editor@prostarpublications
  .com
URL: http://www.prostarpublications.com

The PRS Group Inc.
290 Elwood Davis Rd., Ste. 290, Unit 3
Liverpool, NY 13088-2133
Ph: (315)431-0511
Fax: (315)431-0200

Co. E-mail: custserv@prsgroup.com
URL: http://www.prsgroup.com
Instagram: www.instagram.com/
theprsgroup

PublicAffairs
1290 Avenue of the Americas 5th Fl.
New York, NY 10104
Ph: (212)364-1100
Co. E-mail: pemail@hbgusa.com
URL: http://www.hachettebookgroup.com/
imprint/perseus/publicaffairs
Facebook: www.facebook.com/
PublicAffairs/about
Instagram: www.instagram.com/
publicaffairsbooks
YouTube: www.youtube.com/channel/
UCFvJCa-DZ7ym62-KkgeJUAA

Publicom Inc.
7522 N La Cholla Blvd.
Tucson, AZ 85741
Ph: (520)323-6144
Fax: (520)323-7412
Co. E-mail: info@wcponline.com
URL: http://www.wcponline.com

Publishers & Producers
PO Box 36
Annandale, VA 22003
Ph: (703)750-2664

Publishers Weekly (PW)
71 W 23rd St., Ste.1608
New York, NY 10010
Ph: (818)487-2069
Fax: (818)487-4550
Co. E-mail: service@publishersweekly
.com
URL: http://www.publishersweekly.com
Facebook: www.facebook.com/pubweekly
Linkedin: www.linkedin.com/company/
publishers-weekly
Instagram: www.instagram.com/pwpics

Purdue University Press (PUP)
Stewart Ctr. 190, 504 W State St.
West Lafayette, IN 47907-2058
Ph: (765)494-2038
Co. E-mail: pupress@purdue.edu
URL: http://www.thepress.purdue.edu
Facebook: www.facebook.com/
purduepress

Q

Que Publishing
Indianapolis, IN
URL: http://www.quepublishing.com

Questex L.L.C.
275 Grove St., Ste. 2-130
Newton, MA 02466
Co. E-mail: info@questex.com
URL: http://www.questex.com

R

R I D Publications
333 Commerce St.
Alexandria, VA 22314
Ph: (571)257-3957
Co. E-mail: ridinfo@rid.org
URL: http://www.rid.org
Facebook: www.facebook.com/RIDInc

R. S. Means Company Inc.
30 Patewood Dr.Bldg 2, Ste. 350
Greenville, SC 29615
Free: 888-875-7338
Fax: (864)233-9100
URL: http://www.rsmeans.com

Ramsey Press
46 Industrial Ave.
Mahwah, NJ 07430
URL: http://www.ramseysolutions.com

Randall-Reilly
3200 Rice Mine Rd. NE
Tuscaloosa, AL 35406
Free: 855-288-3783
Co. E-mail: marketing@randallreilly.com
URL: http://www.randallreilly.com
Facebook: www.facebook.com/randallreilly
Linkedin: www.linkedin.com/company/
randallreilly

Random Lengths Publications Inc.
450 Country Club Rd., Ste. 315
Eugene, OR 97401
Ph: (650)264-4099
Free: 866-271-8525
URL: http://www.rlmyprint.com/Default
.aspx

RB Publishing Co.
URL: http://www.rbpub.com
Linkedin: in.linkedin.com/company/rb
-publishing

Realtor Magazine (RM)
430 N Michigan Ave.
Chicago, IL 60611-4087
Ph: (312)329-8458
Free: 800-874-6500
URL: http://www.nar.realtor/magazine
Facebook: www.facebook.com/realtormag
Instagram: www.instagram.com/realtormag

Realtors Land Institute (RLI)
430 N Michigan Ave., Ste. 600
Chicago, IL 60611
Free: 800-441-5263
Fax: (312)329-8633
Co. E-mail: rli@realtors.org
URL: http://www.rliland.com
Facebook: www.facebook.com/RLILand
Instagram: www.instagram.com/
realtors_land_institute

Recycling Today Media Group (RTMG)
5811 Canal Rd.
Valley View, OH 44125
Ph: (216)393-0300
Free: 800-456-0707
Fax: (216)525-0515
URL: http://www.recyclingtoday.com/page/
rtmediagroup

Redleaf Press
10 Yorkton Ct.
Saint Paul, MN 55117-1065
Ph: (651)641-0508
Free: 800-423-8309
Fax: (651)641-0115
Co. E-mail: customerservice@redleafpress
.org
URL: http://www.redleafpress.org
Facebook: www.facebook.com/
RedleafPress
Pinterest: www.pinterest.com/redleafpress

RePlay Magazine
18757 Burbank Blvd., Ste. 105
Tarzana, CA 91357
Ph: (818)776-2880
Fax: (818)776-2888
Co. E-mail: editor@replaymag.com
URL: http://www.replaymag.com
Facebook: www.facebook.com/
replaymagazine

Residential Real Estate Council (RRC)
430 N Michigan Ave., Ste. 300
Chicago, IL 60611
Free: 800-462-8841
Co. E-mail: social@crs.com
URL: http://www.crs.com
Facebook: www.facebook.com/ThisIsRRC
YouTube: www.youtube.com/channel/UCH
-IXMoFJ8CrC38zCKzHdfQ

Resource Recycling Inc.
2440 NE Mlk Jr. Blvd., Ste. 202
Portland, OR 97212
Ph: (503)233-1305
Fax: (503)233-1356
Co. E-mail: info@resource-recycling.com
URL: http://resource-recycling.com
Facebook: www.facebook.com/
ResourceRecycling
Linkedin: www.linkedin.com/company/
resource-recycling-inc-

Restoration Industry Association (RIA)
1120 Rte. 73, Ste. 200
Mount Laurel, NJ 08054
Ph: (856)439-9222
Co. E-mail: info@restorationindustry.org
URL: http://www.restorationindustry.org
Facebook: www.facebook.com/
restorationindustry
YouTube: www.youtube.com/channel/
UCXUElHrn4wjzwFUv03eMTFg

RFP Corp.
1333A N Ave., Ste. 706
New Rochelle, NY 10804
Ph: (212)838-7733

GUIDE TO PUBLISHERS

Free: 800-472-7744
Fax: (212)308-7165
URL: http://www.bridalguide.com

Risk Management Association (RMA)
1801 Market St., Ste. 300
Philadelphia, PA 19103-1613
Free: 800-677-7621
Fax: (215)446-4100
Co. E-mail: rmaar@rmahq.org
URL: http://www.rmahq.org/Default.aspx
Linkedin: www.linkedin.com/company/the-risk-management-association

Riverhead Books
375 Hudson St.
New York, NY 10014
URL: http://www.penguin.com/riverhead-overview
Facebook: www.facebook.com/RiverheadBooks
Instagram: www.instagram.com/riverheadbooks

Rogers Media Inc.
One Mount Pleasant Rd., 8th Fl.
Toronto, ON, Canada M4Y 2Y5
URL: http://www.rogerssportsandmedia.com

The Rough Notes Company Inc. (RNC)
11690 Technology Dr.
Carmel, IN 46032
Ph: (317)582-1600
Free: 800-428-4384
Fax: (800)321-1909
Co. E-mail: rnc@roughnotes.com
URL: http://www.roughnotes.com
Facebook: www.facebook.com/theroughnotescompany

Routledge, Taylor & Francis Group
2-4 Park Sq., Oxfordshire
Abingdon OX14 4RN, United Kingdom
URL: http://www.routledge.com
Facebook: www.facebook.com/routledgebooks
YouTube: www.youtube.com/user/RoutledgeBooks

R.R. Bowker L.L.C.
630 Central Ave.
New Providence, NJ 07974
Free: 888-269-5372
URL: http://www.bowker.com

Rug News Magazine
5 Hanover Sq., 21st Fl.
New York, NY 10004
Ph: (212)269-2016
URL: http://Rugnewsdesign.Com

RVDA, The National RV Dealers Association (RVDA)
3930 University Dr.
Fairfax, VA 22030
Ph: (703)591-7130

Co. E-mail: info@rvda.org
URL: http://www.rvda.org
Facebook: www.facebook.com/rvlearningcenter
YouTube: www.youtube.com/user/rvlearningcenter

S

Sacramento Business Journal (SBJ)
555 Capitol Mall, Ste. 200
Sacramento, CA 95814
Ph: (916)447-7661
Fax: (916)558-7898
Co. E-mail: sacramento@bizjournals.com
URL: http://www.bizjournals.com/sacramento
Facebook: www.facebook.com/SacBiz
Instagram: www.instagram.com/sacbiz

Saddle & Bridle Inc.
375 Jackson Ave.
Saint Louis, MO 63130
Ph: (314)725-9115
Co. E-mail: submissions@saddleandbridle.com
URL: http://www.saddleandbridle.com
Facebook: www.facebook.com/saddleandbridle
Instagram: www.instagram.com/saddleandbridlemag

Sagamore Publishing L.L.C.
3611 N Staley Rd., Ste. B
Champaign, IL 61822

SAGE Publications
2455 Teller Rd.
Thousand Oaks, CA 91320
Facebook: www.facebook.com/SagePublications
Linkedin: www.linkedin.com/company/sagepublishing
Instagram: www.instagram.com/sage_publishing

Saint Louis Business Journal
Old Post Office
815 Olive St., Ste. 100
Saint Louis, MO 63101
Ph: (314)421-6200
Fax: (314)621-5031
Co. E-mail: stlouis@bizjournals.com
URL: http://www.bizjournals.com/stlouis
Facebook: www.facebook.com/stlbj
Linkedin: www.linkedin.com/company/st-louis-business-journal
Instagram: www.instagram.com/stlouisbiz

St. Louis Post-Dispatch LLC.
901 N 10th St.
Saint Louis, MO 63101
Ph: (314)340-8000
Free: 800-365-0820

Co. E-mail: service@stltoday.com
URL: http://www.stltoday.com
Facebook: www.facebook.com/STLPD
Linkedin: www.linkedin.com/company/st.-louis-post-dispatch
Instagram: www.instagram.com/stltoday
YouTube: www.youtube.com/user/STLPostDispatch
Pinterest: www.pinterest.com/stltoday

St. Martins Press/Macmillan (SMP)
120 Broadway
New York, NY 10271
Co. E-mail: trademarketing@stmartins.com
URL: http://us.macmillan.com/stmartinspress
Facebook: www.facebook.com/stmartinspress
Instagram: www.instagram.com/stmartinspress

San Diego Community Newspaper Group
1621 Grand Ave., Ste. C, 2nd Fl.
San Diego, CA 92109
Ph: (858)270-3103
URL: http://sdnews.com
Facebook: www.facebook.com/sdcng
Instagram: www.instagram.com/sdnewsgroup

The San Diego Union-Tribune
600 B St., Ste. 1201
San Diego, CA 92101
Ph: (619)293-1211
Co. E-mail: customer.service@sduniontribune.com
URL: http://www.signonsandiego.com
Facebook: www.facebook.com/SanDiegoUnionTribune
Linkedin: www.linkedin.com/company/the-san-diego-union-tribune
Instagram: www.instagram.com/sandiegouniontribune
YouTube: www.youtube.com/channel/UCKCbC7uTe7dRtKPou10JKtQ

Sandow
3651 NW 8th Ave.
Boca Raton, FL 33431
Ph: (561)961-7600
Co. E-mail: hello@sandow.com
URL: http://www.sandow.com

Santa Clara University Markkula Center for Applied Ethics
Vari Hall, Santa Clara University
500 El Camino Real
Santa Clara, CA 95053-0633
Ph: (408)554-5319
Fax: (408)554-2373
Co. E-mail: ethics@scu.edu
URL: http://www.scu.edu/ethics
Facebook: www.facebook.com/

MarkkulaCenterForAppliedEthics
Linkedin: www.linkedin.com/company/
markkula
YouTube: www.youtube.com/user/
appliedethicscenter

Scandinavian Collectors Club (SCC)
PO Box 16213
Saint Paul, MN 55116
Co. E-mail: sccpay@gmail.com
URL: http://www.scc-online.org

The Scarecrow Press Inc.
4501 Forbes Blvd., Ste. 200
Lanham, MD 20706
URL: http://NA

Schaeffer's Investment Research Inc. (SIR)
5151 Pfeiffer Rd., Ste. 450
Cincinnati, OH 45242
Ph: (513)589-3800
Free: 800-448-2080
Co. E-mail: service@sir-inc.com
URL: http://www.schaeffersresearch.com
Facebook: www.facebook.com/
schaeffersinvestmentresearch
Linkedin: www.linkedin.com/company/
schaeffer's-investment-research
Instagram: www.instagram.com/
schaeffers_research
YouTube: www.youtube.com/user/
Schaeffers

Schonfeld and Associates Inc. (SAI)
1932 Terramar Ln.
Virginia Beach, VA 23456
Free: 800-205-0030
Co. E-mail: saiinfo@saibooks.com
URL: http://saibooks.com

Schoolhouse Press
6899 Cary Bluff
Pittsville, WI 54466
Ph: (715)884-2799
Free: 800-968-5648
Co. E-mail: info@schoolhousepress.com
URL: http://www.schoolhousepress.com
Facebook: www.facebook.com/
SchoolhousePress

Scott's Directories
80 Valleybrook Dr.
Toronto, ON, Canada M3B 2S9
Ph: (416)442-2122
Free: 844-462-2076
Co. E-mail: customerservice@scottsdirectories.com
URL: http://scottsdirectories.com
Facebook: www.facebook.com/pages/
ScottsDirectories/204833802886321
Linkedin: www.linkedin.com/company/scott
-s-directories

Scranton Gillette Communications Inc.
220 N Smith St., Ste. 440
Palatine, IL 60067
Ph: (847)391-1000
URL: http://scrantongillette.com

Secured Finance Network (SFNet)
370 7th Ave., Ste. 1801
New York, NY 10001
Ph: (212)792-9390
Fax: (212)564-6053
URL: http://community.cfa.com/home
Linkedin: www.linkedin.com/company/
secured-finance-network
Instagram: www.instagram.com/
secured_finance_network

Self-Counsel Press Inc.
4152 Meridian St., Ste. 105-471
Bellingham, WA 98226
Free: 800-663-3007
Co. E-mail: orders@self-counsel.com
URL: http://www.self-counsel.com
Facebook: www.facebook.com/
selfcounselpress
Linkedin: www.linkedin.com/company/self
-counsel-press
Pinterest: www.pinterest.com/SCPBooks

Self-Help Publishers
80 Wheeler Dr.
Cambridge, ON, Canada N1P 1G3
URL: http://www.selfhelppublishers.com

SHARE
165 West 46th St., Ste. 712
New York, NY 10036
Ph: (212)719-0364
Co. E-mail: info@sharecancersupport.org

Shelby Publishing Company Inc.
517 Green St. NW
Gainesville, GA 30501
Ph: (770)534-8380
Free: 888-498-0771
Co. E-mail: circulation@shelbypublishing.com
URL: http://www.theshelbyreport.com
Facebook: www.facebook.com/
theshelbyreport
Linkedin: www.linkedin.com/company/
shelby-publishing
Instagram: www.instagram.com/
theshelbyreport
YouTube: www.youtube.com/channel/
UCflOfdAjfQvnfl30YhujSfg

Sheltie Pacesetter
Fort Wayne, IN 46804
Ph: (260)434-1566
Fax: (260)434-1566
Co. E-mail: s.pacesetter@sheltie.com
URL: http://www.sheltie.com/Sheltie_Pacesetter/Home.html

Shutterbug Productions
11 Rotherfield Ave.
Bexhill TN40 1SY, United Kingdom

SignCraft Publishing Co. Inc.
3960 Ellis Rd.
Fort Myers, FL 33905
Ph: (239)939-4644
Free: 800-204-0204
Fax: (239)939-0607
Co. E-mail: signcraft@signcraft.com
URL: http://www.signcraft.com
Facebook: www.facebook.com/
signcraftmag
Pinterest: www.pinterest.com/signcraftmag

Simon & Schuster Adult Publishing Group
1230 Avenue of the Americas
New York, NY 10020
Ph: (212)698-7000
URL: http://about.simonandschuster.biz

Simon & Schuster, Inc.
1230 Avenue of the Americas
New York, NY 10020
Ph: (212)698-7000
Free: 866-506-1949
URL: http://www.simonandschuster.com
Facebook: www.facebook.com/
Simonandschuster
Instagram: www.instagram.com/
simonandschuster
YouTube: www.youtube.com/user/
SimonSchusterVideos

Sleep Research Society (SRS)
2510 North Frontage Rd.
Darien, IL 60561
Ph: (630)737-9702
Fax: (630)737-9790
Co. E-mail: membership@srsnet.org
URL: http://sleepresearchsociety.org
Facebook: www.facebook.com/
sleepresearchsociety
Linkedin: www.linkedin.com/company/
sleep-research-society
Instagram: www.instagram.com/
researchsleep
YouTube: www.youtube.com/channel/
UCB2iKfrM7aGKzOKoTP7TA2A

Small Business Trends, LLC
15275 Collier Blvd., No., 201-367
Naples, FL 34119
Free: 888-842-1186
Co. E-mail: sbtips@gmail.com
URL: http://smallbiztrends.com
Facebook: www.facebook.com/
smallbusinesstrends
Linkedin: www.linkedin.com/company/
small-business-trends
YouTube: www.youtube.com/c/
SmallBusinessTrends
Pinterest: www.pinterest.com/
smallbiztrends

Society of Actuaries (SOA)
475 N Martingale Rd., Ste. 600
Schaumburg, IL 60173

Ph: (847)706-3500
Free: 888-697-3900
Fax: (847)706-3599
Co. E-mail: customerservice@soa.org
URL: http://www.soa.org
Facebook: www.facebook.com/
SocietyofActuaries
Linkedin: www.linkedin.com/company/
society-of-actuaries
YouTube: www.youtube.com/user/
SocietyofActuaries

Society of Architectural Historians (JSAH)
1365 N Astor St.
Chicago, IL 60610
Ph: (312)573-1365
Co. E-mail: info@sah.org
URL: http://www.sah.org
Facebook: www.facebook.com/SAH1365
Linkedin: www.linkedin.com/company/
society-of-architectural-historians
Instagram: www.instagram.com/sah1365
YouTube: www.youtube.com/user/
sahvideo1365

Society for Calligraphy (SfC)
PO Box 64174
Los Angeles, CA 90064-0174
URL: http://www.societyforcalligraphy.org
Facebook: www.facebook.com/
societyforcalligraphy
Instagram: www.instagram.com/
societyforcalligraphy

Society of Chemical Industry (SCI)
14/15 Belgrave Sq.
London SW1X 8PS, United Kingdom
Ph: 44 207 598-1500
Co. E-mail: secretariat@soci.org
URL: http://www.soci.org
Facebook: www.facebook.com/
SocietyChemicalIndustry
Linkedin: www.linkedin.com/company/
society-of-chemical-industry
YouTube: www.youtube.com/channel/
UCFx7oVS9TcDst22iMwtsBhg

Society for Human Resource Management (SHRM)
1800 Duke St.
Alexandria, VA 22314
Ph: (703)548-3440
Free: 800-283-7476
Co. E-mail: shrm@shrm.org
URL: http://www.shrm.org
Facebook: www.facebook.com/
societyforhumanresourcemanagement
Linkedin: www.linkedin.com/company/shrm
Instagram: www.instagram.com/
shrmofficial
YouTube: www.youtube.com/shrmofficial

Society of Industrial and Office Realtors (SIOR)
1201 New York Ave. NW, Ste. 350
Washington, DC 20005-6126
Ph: (202)449-8200
URL: http://www.sior.com
Facebook: www.facebook.com/SIORglobal
Linkedin: www.linkedin.com/company/sior
YouTube: www.youtube.com/siormedia

Society for the Preservation and Advancement of the Harmonica (SPAH)
PO Box 551381
Dallas, TX 75355
Co. E-mail: info@spah.org
URL: http://www.spah.org
Facebook: www.facebook.com/SPAH63
Instagram: www.instagram.com/
official_spah63
YouTube: www.youtube.com/channel/
UCbJlie6bVGh8JhVCO-XLtsg

Society of Satellite Professionals International (SSPI)
The New York Information Technology Ctr.
250 Pk. Ave., 7th Fl.
New York, NY 10177
Ph: (212)809-5199
Fax: (212)825-0075
URL: http://www.sspi.org/cpages/home
Facebook: www.facebook.com/SSPIglobal
YouTube: www.youtube.com/user/
SSPIVideo

Society for the Study of Myth and Tradition (SSMT)
Parabola
20 W 20th St., 2nd Fl.
New York, NY 10011
Free: 877-593-2521
URL: http://parabola.org

Society for Thermal Medicine (STM)
810 E 10th St.
Lawrence, KS 66044
Ph: (785)289-2056
Co. E-mail: stm@allenpress.com
URL: http://www.thermaltherapy.org/
ebusSFTM
Facebook: www.facebook.com/
SocietyforThermalMedicine
Linkedin: www.linkedin.com/company/
society-for-thermal-medicine

Solutions Business Publishing
35 Wates Way
Mitcham CR4 4HR, United Kingdom
Ph: 44 1959567806
Fax: 44 1959567809

Sosland Publishing Co.
4801 Main St., Ste. 650
Kansas City, MO 64112-2513
Ph: (816)756-1000
Free: 800-338-6201
URL: http://www.sosland.com

Sound Publishing Inc.
11323 Commando Rd. W, Unit Main
Everett, WA 98204-3532
Ph: (360)394-5800
Fax: (360)394-5829
Co. E-mail: contact@soundpublishing.com
URL: http://www.soundpublishing.com

Soundings Publications L.L.C.
10 Bokum Rd.
Essex, CT 06426
Ph: (386)246-0423
Free: 800-444-7686
Fax: (860)767-0642
Co. E-mail: sndcustserv@cdsfulfillment
.com
URL: http://www.soundingsonline.com
Facebook: www.facebook.com/
SoundingsOnline
Linkedin: www.linkedin.com/company/
soundings-online
Instagram: www.instagram.com/
soundings_online
YouTube: www.youtube.com/user/
SOUNDINGSmagazine

SourceMedia LLC
1 State St., Plz.
New York, NY 10004
Ph: (212)803-8200
Co. E-mail: help@arizent.com
URL: http://www.arizent.com
Facebook: www.facebook.com/Arizentco
Linkedin: www.linkedin.com/company/
sourcemedia

South Carolina Department of Natural Resources (SCDNR)
Rembert C. Dennis Bldg., 1000 Assembly St.
Columbia, SC 29201
Ph: (803)734-3833
Co. E-mail: licensing@dnr.sc.gov
URL: http://www.dnr.sc.gov
Facebook: www.facebook.com/SCDNR
YouTube: www.youtube.com/user/
SCNaturalResources

Southern California News Group
21860 Burbank Blvd., Ste. 200
Woodland Hills, CA 91367
URL: http://www.socalnewsgroup.com
Facebook: www.facebook.com/
socalnewsgroup
Linkedin: www.linkedin.com/company/
southern-california-news-group

Southwest Farm Press - Agribusiness Div.
6191 N State Hwy. 161, Ste. 500
Irving, TX 75038
Ph: (662)624-8503
URL: http://www.farmprogress.com/
southwest-farm-press
Facebook: www.facebook.com/
FarmPress4

Specialized Carriers and Rigging Association (SC&RA)
5870 Trinity Pky., Ste. 200

Centreville, VA 20120
Ph: (703)698-0291
Co. E-mail: info@scranet.org
URL: http://www.scranet.org
Facebook: www.facebook.com/scranet
YouTube: www.youtube.com/user/
 scranetorg

Specialty Equipment Market Association (SEMA)
1575 S Valley Vista Dr.
Diamond Bar, CA 91765
Ph: (909)610-2030
Co. E-mail: research@sema.org
URL: http://www.sema.org
Facebook: www.facebook.com/SEMA.org
Linkedin: www.linkedin.com/company/
 specialty-equipment-market-association
 -sema
YouTube: www.youtube.com/channel/
 UCfhmBjjzf8auV6zvt5mhGiA

Spiritual Counterfeits Project (SCP)
PO Box 40015
Pasadena, CA 91114-7015
Ph: (510)540-0300
Fax: (510)540-1107
Co. E-mail: access@scp-inc.org
URL: http://www.scp-inc.org

Splash Magazines
1526 Monroe St.
Shelton, WA 98584
Ph: (323)362-6282
Co. E-mail: contact@lasplash.com
URL: http://losangeles.splashmags.com
Linkedin: www.linkedin.com/in/splashmags
Instagram: www.instagram.com/
 splashmags

Spokesman Review
999 W Riverside Ave.
Spokane, WA 99201
Ph: (509)747-4422
URL: http://www.spokesman.com
Facebook: www.facebook.com/
 spokesmanreview

Spray Technology & Marketing
140 Littleton Rd., Ste. 320
Parsippany, NJ 07054
Ph: (973)331-9545
Fax: (973)331-9547
URL: http://www.spraytm.com
Facebook: www.facebook.com/
 SprayTechnologyMag

Springer London
The Campus, 4 Crinan St.
London N1 9XW, United Kingdom
Ph: 44 207 3192 2009
URL: http://www.springer.com/gb

Springer Nature Limited
Tiergartenstr. 17
69121 Heidelberg, Germany
Ph: 49 622 1487-0

Co. E-mail: corporate-communications
 @springer.com
URL: http://www.springernature.com
Linkedin: www.linkedin.com/company/
 springer-nature

Springer Publishing Co. (SPC)
902 Carnegie Ctr. Dr.
Princeton, NJ 08540
Ph: (212)431-4370
Co. E-mail: cs@springerpub.com
URL: http://www.springerpub.com
Facebook: www.facebook.com/
 springerpub
Linkedin: www.linkedin.com/company/
 springer-publishing-company
Instagram: www.instagram.com/
 springerpub
YouTube: www.youtube.com/user/
 SpringerPubCo

Springer Science + Business Media LLC.
233 Spring St.
New York, NY 10013-1578

Springer US
233 Spring St.
New York, NY 10013
Free: 866-839-0194
Fax: (212)460-1700
Co. E-mail: customerservice@springerna-
 ture.com
URL: http://www.springer.com

SRDS
5600 N. River Road, Suite 900
Rosemont, IL 60018
Free: 800-851-7737
URL: http://www.srds.com

Standard And Poor's Financial Services LLC. (S&P)
55 Water St.
New York, NY 10041
Free: 877-772-5436
URL: http://www.spglobal.com/ratings/en
YouTube: www.youtube.com/user/
 SPTVbroadcast

Standard Publishing Corp. (SP)
10 High St., Ste. 1107
Boston, MA 02110
Ph: (617)457-0600
Free: 800-682-5759
Fax: (617)457-0608
Co. E-mail: customerservice@spcpub.com
URL: http://www.spcpub.com
Linkedin: www.linkedin.com/company/
 standard-publishing-corporation

Stoddart Publishing Company, Ltd.
895 Don Mills Rd.
Toronto, ON, Canada M3C 1W3
Ph: (416)445-3333
Fax: (416)445-5967

Storey Publishing L.L.C.
210 Mass Moca Way
North Adams, MA 01247
Ph: (413)346-2100
Free: 800-441-5700
Fax: (800)865-3429
Co. E-mail: storey_feedback@hbgusa.com
URL: http://www.hachettebookgroup.com
Facebook: www.facebook.com/
 storeypublishing
Instagram: www.instagram.com/storeypub
YouTube: www.youtube.com/user/
 StoreyPublishing
Pinterest: www.pinterest.com/storeypub

Suzuki Association of the Americas (SAA)
PO Box 17310
Boulder, CO 80308
Ph: (303)444-0948
Free: 888-378-9854
Fax: (303)444-0984
Co. E-mail: info@suzukiassociation.org
URL: http://www.suzukiassociation.org

Swedish-American Chamber of Commerce Inc. (SACC)
900 3rd Ave., 29th Fl.
New York, NY 10022
Ph: (212)838-5530
URL: http://www.saccny.org
Facebook: www.facebook.com/
 saccnewyork
Linkedin: www.linkedin.com/in/swedish
 -american-chamber-of-commerce-new
 -york-69692467
Instagram: www.instagram.com/
 saccnewyork

T

Tampa Bay Business Journal (TBBJ)
4890 W Kennedy Blvd., Ste. 850
Tampa, FL 33609
Ph: (813)873-8225
Fax: (813)876-1827
Co. E-mail: tampabay@bizjournals.com
URL: http://www.bizjournals.com/tampabay
Facebook: www.facebook.com/
 TampaBusinessJournal

Tax Analysts
400 S Maple Ave., Ste. 400
Falls Church, VA 22046
Free: 800-955-2444
Co. E-mail: communications@taxanalysts
 .org
URL: http://www.taxnotes.com
YouTube: www.youtube.com/channel/
 UCXyMBsMNwoi8oolSyA7HWwg

Taylor And Francis Group
711 3rd Ave.
New York, NY 10017
URL: http://www.taylorandfrancis.com

GUIDE TO PUBLISHERS

Taylor & Francis Group (Journals)
530 Walnut St., Ste. 850
Philadelphia, PA 19106
Ph: (215)625-8900
Fax: (215)207-0050
URL: http://taylorandfrancis.com/journals

Taylor & Francis Group Limited
4 Park Sq.
Milton Pk.
Abingdon OX14 4RN, United Kingdom
Ph: 44 20 7017 6000
Co. E-mail: enquiries@taylorandfrancis
  .com
URL: http://taylorandfrancis.com
Facebook: www.facebook.com/
  TaylorandFrancisGroup
Linkedin: www.linkedin.com/company/
  taylor-&-francis-group
YouTube: www.youtube.com/user/
  TaylorandFrancis

TEACH Magazine
1655 Dupont St., Ste. 321
Toronto, ON, Canada M6P 3T1
Ph: (416)537-2103
Co. E-mail: info@teachmag.com
URL: http://teachmag.com
Facebook: www.facebook.com/teachmag
YouTube: www.youtube.com/user/
  teachmag

The Telegraph
111 E Broadway
Alton, IL 62002
Ph: (618)463-2500
URL: http://www.thetelegraph.com
Facebook: www.facebook.com/
  telegraphnews

Telegraph Media Group Limited (TMG)
111 Buckingham Palace Rd.
London SW1W 0DT, United Kingdom
Ph: 44 20 7931 2000
Co. E-mail: customerservice@telegraph
  .co.uk
URL: http://telegraphmediagroup.com
Facebook: www.facebook.com/TELE-
  GRAPH.CO.UK
Linkedin: www.linkedin.com/company/
  telegraph-media-group
Instagram: www.instagram.com/Telegraph

Territorial Newspapers
3280 E Hemisphere Loop, Ste. 180
Tucson, AZ 85706
Ph: (520)294-1200
Fax: (520)294-4040
URL: http://www.insidetucsonbusiness
  .com

Testa Communications
25 Willowdale Ave.
Port Washington, NY 11050
Ph: (516)767-2500
Fax: (516)767-9335
Co. E-mail: info@testa.com
URL: http://www.testa.com
Facebook: www.facebook.com/testacomm
Linkedin: www.linkedin.com/company/testa
  -communications

T.F.H. Publications Inc.
PO Box 427
Neptune, NJ 07754
Fax: (732)776-8763
Co. E-mail: info@tfh.com
URL: http://www.tfh.com

Thin Book Publishing Co. (TB)
70 SW Century Dr., Ste. 100-446
Bend, OR 97702
Ph: (541)382-7579
Co. E-mail: info@thinbook.com
URL: http://www.thinbook.com

Think Services
24 Willie Mays Plz.
San Francisco, CA 94107
Co. E-mail: help@10times.com
URL: http://10times.com/organizers/think
  -services
Facebook: www.facebook.com/
  10timesonline
Linkedin: www.linkedin.com/company/
  10times-events

Thomas Nelson, Inc.
PO Box 141000
Nashville, TN 37214
URL: http://www.thomasnelson.com

Thomas Publishing Company
5 Penn Plz., 17th Fl.
New York, NY 10001
Free: 800-879-6757
URL: http://www.thomasnet.com
Facebook: www.facebook.com/
  ThomasForIndustry
Linkedin: www.linkedin.com/company/
  thomasforindustry

Thompson Information Services
4340 EW Hwy.
1725 K St. NW, Ste. 700
Bethesda, MD 20814
Free: 800-677-3789
Fax: (800)999-5661
Co. E-mail: service@thompson.com
URL: http://thompson.com

Thomson Reuters Corporation
333 Bay St.
Toronto, ON, Canada M5H 2R2
Ph: (416)687-7500
URL: http://www.thomsonreuters.com
Facebook: www.facebook.com/
  thomsonreuters
Linkedin: www.linkedin.com/company/
  thomson-reuters
Instagram: www.instagram.com/
  thomsonreuters/
YouTube: www.youtube.com/
  thomsonreuters

Thomson West
610 Opperman Dr.
Eagan, MN 55123
URL: http://store.legal.thomsonreuters
  .com/law-products/Brands/Thomson
  -West/c/20287

Timber Framers Guild (TFG)
299 Pratt Rd.
Alstead, NH 03602
Free: 833-862-7376
Co. E-mail: info@tfguild.org
URL: http://www.tfguild.org
Facebook: www.facebook.com/timber
  .framers.guild

The Times
3410 Delta Dr.
Portage, IN 46368
Co. E-mail: news@portagetimes.com
URL: http://portagetimes.com
Facebook: www.facebook.com/Portage
  -Times-114569120303055

Toastmasters International (TI)
9127 S Jamaica St., Ste. 400
Englewood, CO 80112
Ph: (720)439-5050
Fax: (303)799-7753
URL: http://www.toastmasters.org
Facebook: www.facebook.com/
  ToastmastersInternationalOfficialFan-
  Page
Linkedin: www.linkedin.com/company/
  toastmasters-international
Instagram: www.instagram.com/
  toastmastersinternational
YouTube: www.youtube.com/toastmasters

Tobacco Merchants Association (TMA)
1121 Situs Ct., Ste. 370
Raleigh, NC 27606
Ph: (609)275-4900
Co. E-mail: tma@tma.org
URL: http://www.tma.org

Toolkit Media Group
2700 Lake Cook Rd.
Riverwoods, IL 60015
Ph: (847)267-7000
Free: 800-248-3248
URL: http://www.ipgbook.com/toolkit-media
  -group-publisher-CCH.php

Touchpoint Media, Inc.
10 W End, 1601 Utica Ave., S, Ste. 110
Minneapolis, MN 55416
Free: 800-597-5656
Co. E-mail: info@touchpointmedia.com
URL: http://www.touchpointmedia.com
Facebook: www.facebook.com/
  touchpointmedia
Instagram: www.instagram.com/
  touchpointmedia

GUIDE TO PUBLISHERS

Towing and Recovery Association of America, Inc. (TRAA)
700 12th St. NW, Ste. 700
Washington, DC 20005
Free: 888-392-9300
Fax: (888)392-9300
Co. E-mail: contact@traaonline.com
URL: http://traaonline.com
Facebook: www.facebook.com/
TRAAOnline

Trade Press Media Group Inc.
2100 W Florist Ave.
Milwaukee, WI 53209
Ph: (414)228-7701
Free: 800-727-7995
Fax: (414)228-1134
Co. E-mail: info@tradepress.com
URL: http://www.tradepress.com
Facebook: www.facebook.com/
TradePressMediaGroup
Linkedin: www.linkedin.com/company/
trade-press-media-group

Training Education Management (TEM)
4216 Pacific Coast Hwy., Ste. 1442
Torrance, CA 90505
Ph: (310)316-2240
Co. E-mail: info@trainingeducationmanagement.com
URL: http://trainingeducationmanagement.com
Facebook: www.facebook.com/
TrainingEduMgmt

Trajan Publishing Corp.
129 Hagar St., Unit 23
Welland, ON, Canada L3B 5V9
Ph: (905)646-7744
Free: 800-265-0720
Co. E-mail: office@trajan.ca
URL: http://www.trajan.com
Instagram: www.instagram.com/trajan_csn

Transportation and Logistics Council, Inc. (TLC)
120 Main St.
Huntington, NY 11743
Ph: (631)549-8988
Fax: (631)549-8962
URL: http://www.tlcouncil.org
Facebook: www.facebook.com/
transportationandlogisticscouncil

Travel Goods Association (TGA)
259 Nassau St., Ste.119
Princeton, NJ 08542
Free: 877-842-1938
Fax: (877)842-1938
Co. E-mail: hello@travel-goods.org
URL: http://travel-goods.org
Pinterest: www.pinterest.com/pin-builde

Travel Weekly
301 Rte. 17 N, Ste. 1150
Rutherford, NJ 07070
Ph: (201)902-2000
URL: http://www.travelweekly.com
Facebook: www.facebook.com/
travelweeklyus
Linkedin: www.linkedin.com/company/
travel-weekly
Instagram: www.instagram.com/
travelweeklyus
Pinterest: www.pinterest.com/travelweekly

Tribune News Service
560 W Grand Ave.
Chicago, IL 60654
Ph: (312)222-4131
Free: 800-346-8798
Co. E-mail: smartcontent@tribpub.com
URL: http://delivery.tribunecontentagency.com

Trusted Media Brands Inc. (TMB)
485 Lexington Ave.
New York, NY 10017
Free: 877-732-4438
URL: http://www.trustedmediabrands.com
Linkedin: www.linkedin.com/company/
trusted-media-brands-inc-

Tulsa World
PO Box 1770
Tulsa, OK 74102
Ph: (918)581-8400
Free: 800-444-6552
Fax: (918)581-8353
Co. E-mail: letters@tulsaworld.com
URL: http://www.tulsaworld.com
Facebook: www.facebook.com/tulsaworld
Instagram: www.instagram.com/tulsaworld

U

UCG Holdings L.P.
11300 Rockville Pk., Ste. 1100
Rockville, MD 20852-3030
URL: http://www.ucg.com

United Association Manufacturers' Representatives (UAMR)
PO Box 4216
Dana Point, CA 92629
Ph: (949)481-5214
Fax: (417)779-1576
Co. E-mail: info@uamr.com
URL: http://www.uamr.com

United Empire Loyalists' Association of Canada (UELAC)
50 Baldwin St., Ste. 202
Toronto, ON, Canada M5T 1L4
Ph: (416)591-1783
Co. E-mail: uelac@uelac.org
URL: http://www.uelac.org
Facebook: www.facebook.com/UELAC

United Press International Inc. (UPI)
1133 19th St. NW, Ste. 800
Washington, DC 20036
Ph: (202)898-8000
Co. E-mail: copyright@upi.com
URL: http://www.upi.com
Facebook: www.facebook.com/UPI
Linkedin: www.linkedin.com/company/
united-press-international
Pinterest: www.pinterest.com/UPI

United States Department of Agriculture (USDA)
1400 Independence Ave. SW
Washington, DC 20250
Ph: (202)720-7117
Co. E-mail: sm.sb.asksb@usda.gov
URL: http://www.usda.gov
Facebook: www.facebook.com/USDA
Linkedin: www.linkedin.com/company/usda
Instagram: www.instagram.com/usdagov
YouTube: www.youtube.com/c/UsdaGov

U.S. Department of Commerce
1401 Constitution Ave. NW
Washington, DC 20230
Ph: (202)482-2825
URL: http://www.commerce.gov
Facebook: www.facebook.com/
Commercegov
Linkedin: www.linkedin.com/company/u-s
-department-of-commerce
YouTube: www.youtube.com/channel/
UCDk7XARReoJChTwu1WojgRQ

U.S. Department of Health & Human Service Centers for Medicare & Medicaid Services (CMS)
7500 Security Blvd.
Baltimore, MD 21244
URL: http://www.cms.gov

U.S. Department of Health and Human Services Centers for Disease Control and Prevention (CDC)
1600 Clifton Rd.
Atlanta, GA 30329
Free: 800-232-4636
URL: http://www.cdc.gov
Facebook: www.facebook.com/cdc
Linkedin: www.linkedin.com/company/
centers-for-disease-control-and
-prevention
Instagram: www.instagram.com/CDCgov
YouTube: www.youtube.com/cdc
Pinterest: www.pinterest.com/cdcgov

U.S. Department of Labor Bureau of Labor Statistics (BLS)
2 Massachusetts Ave. NE
Washington, DC 20212-0001
Ph: (202)691-5200
Co. E-mail: blsdata_staff@bls.gov
URL: http://www.bls.gov
YouTube: www.youtube.com/channel/
UCijn3WBpHtx4AvSya7NER9Q

U.S. Economic Development Administration (EDA)
1401 Constitution Ave. NW, Ste. 71014
Washington, DC 20230

Ph: (202)482-2000
URL: http://www.eda.gov

U.S. Food & Drug Administration (US FDA)
10903 New Hampshire Ave. (HFI-50)
Silver Spring, MD 20993-0002
Ph: (301)796-8240
Free: 888-463-6332
URL: http://www.fda.gov
Facebook: www.facebook.com/FDA
Linkedin: www.linkedin.com/company/fda
Instagram: www.instagram.com/FDA
YouTube: www.youtube.com/user/
    USFoodandDrugAdmin
Pinterest: www.pinterest.com/usfda

U.S. Government Publishing Office (GPO)
732 N Capitol St. NW
Washington, DC 20401
Free: 866-512-1800
URL: http://www.gpo.gov
Facebook: www.facebook.com/USGPO
Linkedin: www.linkedin.com/company/u.s
    .-government-printing-office
Instagram: www.instagram.com/usgpo
YouTube: www.youtube.com/user/
    gpoprinter
Pinterest: www.pinterest.com/usgpo

United States Postal Service (USPS)
475 L'Enfant Plz. SW, Rm. 2100
Washington, DC 20260-0004
YouTube: www.youtube.com/user/uspstv/
    custom
Pinterest: www.pinterest.com/uspsstamps

The University of Chicago Press, Journals Div.
1427 E 60th St.
Chicago, IL 60637
Ph: (773)702-7700
Free: 800-621-2736
Co. E-mail: subscriptions@press.uchicago
    .edu
URL: http://www.journals.uchicago.edu
Facebook: www.facebook.com/
    UChicagoJournals

University Film and Video Association (UFVA)
Co. E-mail: home@ufva.org
URL: http://ufva.org
Facebook: www.facebook.com/
    ufvaconnection

University of Illinois Press (UIP)
1325 S Oak St., MC-566
Champaign, IL 61820-6903
Ph: (217)333-0950
Fax: (217)244-8082
Co. E-mail: uipress@uillinois.edu
URL: http://www.press.uillinois.edu
Facebook: www.facebook.com/
    UniversityofIllinoisPress
YouTube: www.youtube.com/user/
    univofillinoispress

University of Illinois (UIS)
1 University Plz.
Springfield, IL 62703-5407
Ph: (217)206-6600
Co. E-mail: admissions@uis.edu
URL: http://www.uis.edu
Linkedin: www.linkedin.com/school/
    university-of-illinois-at-springfield
Instagram: www.instagram.com/
    uisedualumni
YouTube: www.youtube.com/user/uistube

University of Minnesota Carlson School of Management Management Information Systems Research Center (MISRC)
321 Nineteenth Ave. S
Minneapolis, MN 55455-0438
URL: http://carlsonschool.umn.edu/faculty
    -research/mis-research-center

University of Montana Bureau of Business and Economic Research (UM BBER)
Gallagher Business Bldg.
32 Campus Dr., No. 6840
Missoula, MT 59812-6840
Ph: (406)243-5113
Co. E-mail: bbermail@business.umt.edu
URL: http://www.bber.umt.edu
Facebook: www.facebook.com/bbermt

University of North Carolina at Chapel Hill Highway Safety Research Center (HSRC)
130 Mason Farm Rd CB No. 3430
Chapel Hill, NC 27514
Ph: (919)962-2202
Fax: (919)962-8710
Co. E-mail: info@hsrc.unc.edu
URL: http://www.hsrc.unc.edu
Facebook: www.facebook.com/hsrcinfo

University Press of America Inc.
4501 Forbes Blvd., Ste. 200
Lanham, MD 20706
URL: http://rowman.com/Imprint/UPA

University of Toronto Press Journals Division
5201 Dufferin St.
Toronto, ON, Canada M3H 5T8
Ph: (416)667-7929
Fax: (416)667-7832
Co. E-mail: journals@utpress.utoronto.ca
URL: http://utpjournals.press
Facebook: www.facebook.com/utpjournals
Instagram: www.instagram.com/
    utpjournals

UpCity, Inc.
180 N LaSalle St., Ste. 2100
Chicago, IL 60601
Ph: (312)445-9615
Co. E-mail: info@upcity.com
URL: http://upcity.com
Facebook: www.facebook.com/upcityinc
Linkedin: www.linkedin.com/company/
    upcity

Urban Land Institute (ULI)
2001 L St., NW Ste. 200
Washington, DC 20036
Ph: (202)624-7000
Free: 800-321-5011
Fax: (202)403-3849
Co. E-mail: customerservice@uli.org
URL: http://uli.org
Facebook: www.facebook.com/ULIGlobal
Linkedin: www.linkedin.com/company/
    uliglobal
Instagram: www.instagram.com/
    urbanlandinstitute
YouTube: www.youtube.com/user/ULITV

USA Today Network
7950 Jones Branch Dr.
McLean, VA 22107-0150
URL: http://www.gannett.com/brands
Facebook: www.facebook.com/usatoday
Linkedin: www.linkedin.com/company/usa
    -today
Instagram: www.instagram.com/usatoday
YouTube: www.youtube.com/USATODAY
Pinterest: www.pinterest.com/usatoday

V

Valley Calligraphy Guild (VCG)
638 Sunnyside Dr.
Eugene, OR 97404
URL: http://valleycalligraphyguild.com

Vancouver Ballet Society (VBS)
Scotiabank Dance Ctr.
677 Davie St., Level 6
Vancouver, BC, Canada V6B 2G6
Ph: (604)681-1525
Co. E-mail: vbs@telus.net
URL: http://www.vancouverballetsociety
    .com
Facebook: www.facebook.com/
    VancouverBalletSocietyvbs
Instagram: www.instagram.com/
    vancouverballetsociety

Vegetarian Resource Group (VRG)
PO Box 1463
Baltimore, MD 21203
Ph: (410)366-8343
Co. E-mail: vrg@vrg.org
URL: http://www.vrg.org
Facebook: www.facebook.com/
    thevegetarianresourcegroup
Instagram: www.instagram.com/
    vegetarianresourcegroup

GUIDE TO PUBLISHERS

VerticalNews
2727 Paces Ferry Rd. SE, Ste. 2-440
Atlanta, GA 30339

Vickers Stock Research Corp.
61 Broadway
New York, NY 10006
Co. E-mail: clientservices@vickers-stock.com
URL: http://www.vickers-stock.com

The Virginian-Pilot
150 W Brambleton Ave.
Norfolk, VA 23510
Ph: (757)446-9000
Co. E-mail: customerservice@pilotonline.com
URL: http://www.pilotonline.com
Facebook: www.facebook.com/virginianpilot
YouTube: www.youtube.com/user/VirginianPilot

Visionaire Publishing L.L.C.
263 E 7th St., No 1
New York, NY 10009
Co. E-mail: info@visionaireworld.com
URL: http://visionaireworld.com
Instagram: www.instagram.com/visionaireworld

Voyageur Magazine
PO Box 1411
Green Bay, WI 54305
Ph: (920)437-1840
Co. E-mail: chris@browncohistoricalsoc.org
URL: http://voyageurmagazine.org
Facebook: www.facebook.com/Voyageur-Northeast-Wisconsins-Historical-Review-180983315318552
Instagram: www.instagram.com/readvoyageurmagazine

VP Demand Creation Services
2779 Aero Pk. Dr.
Traverse City, MI 49685
Ph: (231)946-3712
Free: 800-773-7798
Fax: (231)946-3289
URL: http://www.vpdemandcreation.com
Facebook: www.facebook.com/vpdemandcreationservices
Instagram: www.instagram.com/vpdemandcreationservices
YouTube: www.youtube.com/user/VillagePressInc/featured

W

Waco Tribune-Herald (WT)
215 S Second St., Ste. 301
Waco, TX 76701
Ph: (254)757-5757
Free: 800-678-8742
Co. E-mail: custservice@wacotrib.com
URL: http://wacotrib.com
Facebook: www.facebook.com/wacotrib
Linkedin: www.linkedin.com/company/waco-tribune-herald
Instagram: www.instagram.com/wacotrib

Waterfront Digital Press
2055 Oxford Ave.
Cardiff, CA 92007
Co. E-mail: marketing@waterfrontdigital-press.com
URL: http://www.waterfrontdigitalpress.com

Wayfarer Publications
2601 Silver Ridge Ave.
Los Angeles, CA 90039
Free: 800-888-9119
URL: http://www.tai-chi.com
Facebook: www.facebook.com/BluehostIndia

Wells Media Group Inc.
3570 Camino del Rio N, Ste. 100
San Diego, CA 92108
Ph: (619)584-1100
Free: 800-897-9965
Fax: (619)584-1200
URL: http://www.wellsmedia.com
Facebook: www.facebook.com/wellsmedia
Linkedin: www.linkedin.com/company/wells-media

WFC Inc.
51 Cragwood Rd., Ste. 104
South Plainfield, NJ 07080
Ph: (908)769-1160
Fax: (908)769-1171
URL: http://wholefoodsmagazine.com

Wharton School Publishing
1 Lake St.
Upper Saddle River, NJ 07458
Ph: (201)236-7113

White River Productions (WRP)
PO Box 48
Bucklin, MO 64631
Ph: (660)695-4433
Free: 877-787-2467
Co. E-mail: info@whiteriverproductions.com
URL: http://www.whiteriverproductions.com
Facebook: www.facebook.com/WhiteRiverProductions

Wholesale Florist and Florist Supplier Association (WF&FSA)
529 14th St., NW, Ste. 1280
Washington, DC 20045
Ph: (410)940-6580
Free: 888-289-3372
Co. E-mail: info@wffsa.org
URL: http://www.wffsa.org/aws/WFFSA/pt/sp/home_page
Facebook: www.facebook.com/WFFSAHQ
Linkedin: www.linkedin.com/company/wffsa
Instagram: www.instagram.com/wffsa
YouTube: www.youtube.com/channel/UCT9Tnw_jkgWDqwTvhZRzT7g

Wiley-Blackwell

Wiley-Blackwell
111 River St.
Hoboken, NJ 07030-5774
URL: http://www.wiley.com//WileyCDA/Brand/id-35.html
Linkedin: www.linkedin.com/company/wiley-blackwell

Wiley Periodicals Inc.
111 River St.
Hoboken, NJ 07030-5774
Ph: (201)748-6000
Fax: (201)748-6088
Co. E-mail: creditriskdept@wiley.com
URL: http://www.wiley.com/en-in

William Morrow (WM)
195 Broadway
New York, NY 10007
URL: http://www.harpercollins.com/pages/williammorrow
Instagram: www.instagram.com/WILLIAMMORROWBOOKS

Wine & Spirits Magazine Inc. (W&S)
2 W 32nd St., Ste. 601
New York, NY 10001
Ph: (212)695-4660
Free: 888-695-4660
Fax: (212)695-2920
Co. E-mail: info@wineandspiritsmagazine.com
URL: http://www.wineandspiritsmagazine.com
Facebook: www.facebook.com/WineSpiritsMag
Instagram: www.instagram.com/wineandspirits

Wines and Vines
65 Mitchell Blvd., Ste.A
San Rafael, CA 94903
URL: http://www.winesvines.org
Facebook: www.facebook.com/people/Wines-Vines/100035392436400
Instagram: www.instagram.com/wines_and_vines

Wizards Of The Coast LLC
1600 Lind Ave. SW, Ste. 400
Renton, WA 98057
Ph: (425)226-6500

GUIDE TO PUBLISHERS

Free: 800-342-6496
URL: http://company.wizards.com/en
Facebook: www.facebook.com/people/
 Wizards-of-the-Coast/100069224032191

Wolfe Publishing Company
2180 Gulfstream, Ste. A
Prescott, AZ 86301
Ph: (928)445-7810
Free: 800-899-7810
Fax: (928)778-5124
Co. E-mail: contact@loaddata.com
URL: http://www.wolfeoutdoorsports.com

Wolters Kluwer Health Inc.
Zuidpoolsingel 2
2400 BA Alphen aan den Rijn, Netherlands
Ph: 31 172 641-400
Co. E-mail: info@wolterskluwer.com
URL: http://www.wolterskluwer.com/en
Facebook: www.facebook.com/
 wolterskluwer
Linkedin: www.linkedin.com/company/
 wolters-kluwer
YouTube: www.youtube.com/user/
 WoltersKluwerComms

Wolters Kluwer Law and Business
28 Liberty St.
New York, NY 10005
Free: 800-638-8437
Co. E-mail: customer.service@wolterskluwer.com
URL: http://www.wolterskluwer.com
Facebook: www.facebook.com/
 WoltersKluwerLR

World Health Organization (WHO)
20, Ave. Appia
1211 Geneva, Switzerland
Ph: 41 22 7912111
Fax: 41 22 7913111
URL: http://www.who.int/en
Facebook: www.facebook.com/WHO
Linkedin: www.linkedin.com/company/
 world-health-organization
YouTube: www.youtube.com/user/who
Pinterest: www.pinterest.com/
 worldhealthorganization

World Organization of China Painters (WOCP)
2700 N Portland
Oklahoma City, OK 73107-5400
Ph: (405)521-1234
Fax: (405)521-1265
Co. E-mail: wocporg@sbcglobal.net
URL: http://www.wocporg.com
Facebook: www.facebook.com/
 WOCPMUSEUM

World Scientific Publishing Co., Inc. (WSPC)
27 Warren St., Ste. 401-402
Hackensack, NJ 07601
Ph: (201)487-9655
Free: 800-227-7562
Fax: (201)487-9656
Co. E-mail: wspc_us@wspc.com
URL: http://worldscientific.com
Facebook: www.facebook.com/
 worldscientific
Linkedin: www.linkedin.com/company/
 world-scientific-publishing
YouTube: www.youtube.com/channel/
 UCDw6b_X0ccpwcc78iMjsl_Q

Worldwide Videotex
PO Box 3273
Boynton Beach, FL 33424-3273

W.W. Norton & Company Ltd.
500 Fifth Ave.
New York, NY 10110
Ph: (212)354-5500
Free: 800-233-4830
Fax: (212)869-0856
Co. E-mail: publicity@wwnorton.com
URL: http://wwnorton.com
Facebook: www.facebook.com/wwnorton
Instagram: www.instagram.com/w.w.norton

Y

Yarn Tree Design Inc.
117 Alexander Ave.
Ames, IA 50010
Ph: (515)232-3121
Free: 800-247-3952
Fax: (515)232-0789
Co. E-mail: info@yarntree.com
URL: http://www.yarntree.com

Ye Olde Genealogie Shoppe
9605 Vandergriff Rd.
Indianapolis, IN 46239-9591
Ph: (317)862-3330
Free: 800-419-0200
Co. E-mail: orders@yogs.com
URL: http://www.yogs.com

Yuill & Associates
Ottawa, ON, Canada K2B 8C8
Co. E-mail: info@yuill-associates.com
URL: http://www.yuill-associates.com
Linkedin: www.linkedin.com/company/yuill
 -&-associates/?originalSubdomain=ca

Z

Zonda Home
4000 MacArthur, Ste. 400
Newport Beach, CA 92660
Free: 866-846-0282
Co. E-mail: supportrequest@zondahome
 .com
URL: http://zondahome.com
Facebook: www.facebook.com/
 ZondaHome
Linkedin: www.linkedin.com/company/
 zondahome
Instagram: www.instagram.com/
 zondahome

GLOSSARY

Absolute liability ❙ Liability that is incurred due to product defects or negligent actions. Manufacturers or retail establishments are held responsible, even though the defect or action may not have been intentional or negligent.

ACE ❙ See Active Corps of Executives.

Accident and health benefits ❙ Benefits offered to employees and their families in order to offset the costs associated with accidental death, accidental injury, or sickness.

Account statement ❙ A record of transactions, including payments, new debt, and deposits, incurred during a defined period of time.

Accounting system ❙ System capturing the costs of all employees and/or machinery included in business expenses.

Accounts payable ❙ See Trade credit.

Accounts receivable ❙ Unpaid accounts which arise from unsettled claims and transactions from the sale of a company's products or services to its customers.

Active Corps of Executives (ACE) ❙ (See also Service Corps of Retired Executives) A group of volunteers for a management assistance program of the U.S. Small Business Administration; volunteers provide one-on-one counseling and teach workshops and seminars for small firms.

ADA ❙ See Americans with Disabilities Act.

Adaptation ❙ The process whereby an invention is modified to meet the needs of users.

Adaptive engineering ❙ The process whereby an invention is modified to meet the manufacturing and commercial requirements of a targeted market.

Adverse selection ❙ The tendency for higher-risk individuals to purchase health care and more comprehensive plans, resulting in increased costs.

Advertising ❙ A marketing tool used to capture public attention and influence purchasing decisions for a product or service. Utilizes various forms of media to generate consumer response, such as flyers, magazines, newspapers, radio, and television.

Age discrimination ❙ The denial of the rights and privileges of employment based solely on the age of an individual.

Agency costs ❙ Costs incurred to insure that the lender or investor maintains control over assets while allowing the borrower or entrepreneur to use them. Monitoring and information costs are the two major types of agency costs.

Agribusiness ❙ The production and sale of commodities and products from the commercial farming industry.

America Online ❙ (See also Prodigy) An online service which is accessible by computer modem. The service features Internet access, bulletin boards, online periodicals, electronic mail, and other services for subscribers.

Americans with Disabilities Act (ADA) ❙ Law designed to ensure equal access and opportunity to handicapped persons.

Annual report ❙ (See also Securities and Exchange Commission) Yearly financial report prepared by a business that adheres to the requirements set forth by the Securities and Exchange Commission (SEC).

Antitrust immunity ❙ (See also Collective ratemaking) Exemption from prosecution under antitrust laws. In the transportation industry, firms with antitrust immunity are permitted—under certain conditions—to set schedules and sometimes prices for the public benefit.

Applied research ❙ Scientific study targeted for use in a product or process.

Asians ❙ A minority category used by the U.S. Bureau of the Census to represent a diverse group that includes Aleuts, Eskimos, American Indians, Asian Indians, Chinese, Japanese, Koreans, Vietnamese, Filipinos, Hawaiians, and other Pacific Islanders.

Assets ❙ Anything of value owned by a company.

Audit ❙ The verification of accounting records and business procedures conducted by an outside accounting service.

Average cost ❙ Total production costs divided by the quantity produced.

Balance Sheet ❙ A financial statement listing the total assets and liabilities of a company at a given time.

Bankruptcy ❙ (See also Chapter 7 of the 1978 Bankruptcy Act; Chapter 11 of the 1978 Bankruptcy Act) The condition in which a business cannot meet its debt obligations and petitions a federal district court either for reorganization of its debts (Chapter 11) or for liquidation of its assets (Chapter 7).

Basic research ❙ Theoretical scientific exploration not targeted to application.

Basket clause ❙ A provision specifying the amount of public pension funds that may be placed in investments not included on a state's legal list (see separate citation).

GLOSSARY

BBS ∎ *See* Bulletin Board Service.

BDC ∎ *See* Business development corporation.

Benefit ∎ Various services, such health care, flextime, day care, insurance, and vacation, offered to employees as part of a hiring package. Typically subsidized in whole or in part by the business.

BIDCO ∎ *See* Business and industrial development company

Billing cycle ∎ A system designed to evenly distribute customer billing throughout the month, preventing clerical backlogs.

Birth ∎ *See* Business birth.

Blue chip security ∎ A low-risk, low-yield security representing an interest in a very stable company.

Blue sky laws ∎ A general term that denotes various states' laws regulating securities.

Bond ∎ (*See also* General obligation bond; Taxable bonds; Treasury bonds) A written instrument executed by a bidder or contractor (the principal) and a second party (the surety or sureties) to assure fulfillment of the principal's obligations to a third party (the obligee or government) identified in the bond. If the principal's obligations are not met, the bond assures payment to the extent stipulated of any loss sustained by the obligee.

Bonding requirements ∎ Terms contained in a bond (*see* separate citation).

Bonus ∎ An amount of money paid to an employee as a reward for achieving certain business goals or objectives.

Brainstorming ∎ A group session where employees contribute their ideas for solving a problem or meeting a company objective without fear of retribution or ridicule.

Brand name ∎ The part of a brand, trademark, or service mark that can be spoken. It can be a word, letter, or group of words or letters.

Bridge financing ∎ A short-term loan made in expectation of intermediate-term or long-term financing. Can be used when a company plans to go public in the near future.

Broker ∎ One who matches resources available for innovation with those who need them.

Budget ∎ An estimate of the spending necessary to complete a project or offer a service in comparison to cash-on-hand and expected earnings for the coming year, with an emphasis on cost control.

Bulletin Board Service (BBS) ∎ An online service enabling users to communicate with each other about specific topics.

Business birth ∎ The formation of a new establishment or enterprise. The appearance of a new establishment or enterprise in the Small Business Data Base (*see* separate citation).

Business conditions ∎ Outside factors that can affect the financial performance of a business.

Business contractions ∎ The number of establishments that have decreased in employment during a specified time.

Business cycle ∎ A period of economic recession and recovery. These cycles vary in duration.

Business death ∎ The voluntary or involuntary closure of a firm or establishment. The disappearance of an establishment or enterprise from the Small Business Data Base (*see* separate citation).

Business development corporation (BDC) ∎ A business financing agency, usually composed of the financial institutions in an area or state, organized to assist in financing businesses unable to obtain assistance through normal channels; the risk is spread among various members of the business development corporation, and interest rates may vary somewhat from those charged by member institutions. A venture capital firm in which shares of ownership are publicly held and to which the Investment Act of 1940 applies.

Business dissolution ∎ For enumeration purposes, the absence of a business that was present in the prior time period from any current record.

Business entry ∎ *See* Business birth.

Business ethics ∎ Moral values and principles espoused by members of the business community as a guide to fair and honest business practices.

Business exit ∎ *See* Business death.

Business expansions ∎ The number of establishments that added employees during a specified time.

Business failure ∎ Closure of a business causing a loss to at least one creditor.

Business format franchising ∎ (*See also* Franchising) The purchase of the name, trademark, and an ongoing business plan of the parent corporation or franchisor by the franchisee.

Business and industrial development company (BIDCO) ∎ A private, for-profit financing corporation chartered by the state to provide both equity and long-term debt capital to small business owners (*see* separate citations for equity and debt capital).

Business license ∎ A legal authorization issued by municipal and state governments and required for business operations.

Business name ∎ (*See also* Business license; Trademark) Enterprises must register their business names with local governments usually on a "doing business as" (DBA) form. (This name is sometimes referred to as a "fictional name.") The procedure is part of the business licensing process and prevents any other business from using that same name for a similar business in the same locality.

Business norms ∎ *See* Financial ratios.

Business permit ∎ *See* Business license.

Business plan ∎ A document that spells out a company's expected course of action for a specified period, usually including a detailed listing and analysis of risks and uncertainties. For the small busi-ness, it should examine the proposed products, the market, the industry, the management policies, the marketing policies, produc-tion needs, and financial needs. Frequently, it is used as a pros-pectus for potential investors and lenders.

Business proposal ∎ *See* Business plan.

Business service firm ∎ A business primarily engaged in rendering services to other businesses on a fee or contract basis.

Business start ∎ For enumeration purposes, a business with a name or similar designation that did not exist in a prior time period.

Cafeteria plan ∎ *See* Flexible benefit plan.

Capacity ∎ Level of a firm's, industry's, or nation's output corresponding to full practical utilization of available resources.

Capital ∎ Assets less liabilities, representing the ownership interest in a business. A stock of accumulated goods, especially at a specified time and in contrast to income received during a specified time period. Accumulated goods devoted to production. Accumulated possessions calculated to bring income.

Capital expenditure ∎ Expenses incurred by a business for improvements that will depreciate over time.

Capital gain ∎ The monetary difference between the purchase price and the selling price of capital. Capital gains are taxed at a rate of 28% by the federal government.

Capital intensity ∎ (*See also* Debt capital; Equity midrisk venture capital; Informal capital; Internal capital; Owner's capital; Secondhand capital; Seed capital; Venture capital) The relative importance of capital in the production process, usually expressed as the ratio of capital to labor but also sometimes as the ratio of capital to output.

Capital resource ∎ The equipment, facilities and labor used to create products and services.

Caribbean Basin Initiative ∎ An interdisciplinary program to support commerce among the businesses in the nations of the Caribbean Basin and the United States. Agencies involved include: the Agency for International Development, the U.S. Small Business Administration, the International Trade Administration of the U.S. Department of Commerce, and various private sector groups.

Catastrophic care ∎ Medical and other services for acute and long-term illnesses that cost more than insurance coverage limits or that cost the amount most families may be expected to pay with their own resources.

CDC ∎ *See* Certified development corporation.

CD-ROM ∎ Compact disc with read-only memory used to store large amounts of digitized data.

Certified development corporation (CDC) ∎ A local area or statewide corporation or authority (for profit or nonprofit) that packages U.S. Small Business Administration (SBA), bank, state, and/or private money into financial assistance for existing business capital improvements. The SBA holds the second lien on its maximum share of 40 percent involvement. Each state has at least one certified development corporation. This program is called the SBA 504 Program.

Certified lenders ∎ Banks that participate in the SBA guaranteed loan program (*see* separate citation). Such banks must have a good track record with the U.S. Small Business Administration (SBA) and must agree to certain conditions set forth by the agency. In return, the SBA agrees to process any guaranteed loan application within three business days.

Champion ∎ An advocate for the development of an innovation.

Channel of distribution ∎ The means used to transport merchandise from the manufacturer to the consumer.

Chapter 7 of the 1978 Bankruptcy Act ∎ Provides for a court-appointed trustee who is responsible for liquidating a company's assets in order to settle outstanding debts.

Chapter 11 of the 1978 Bankruptcy Act ∎ Allows the business owners to retain control of the company while working with their creditors to reorganize their finances and establish better business practices to prevent liquidation of assets.

Closely held corporation ∎ A corporation in which the shares are held by a few persons, usually officers, employees, or others close to the management; these shares are rarely offered to the public.

Code of Federal Regulations ∎ Codification of general and permanent rules of the federal government published in the Federal Register.

Code sharing ∎ *See* Computer code sharing.

Coinsurance ∎ (*See also* Cost sharing) Upon meeting the deductible payment, health insurance participants may be required to make additional health care cost-sharing payments. Coinsurance is a payment of a fixed percentage of the cost of each service; copayment is usually a fixed amount to be paid with each service.

Collateral ∎ Securities, evidence of deposit, or other property pledged by a borrower to secure repayment of a loan.

Collective ratemaking ∎ (*See also* Antitrust immunity) The establishment of uniform charges for services by a group of businesses in the same industry.

Commercial insurance plan ∎ *See* Underwriting.

Commercial loans ∎ Short-term renewable loans used to finance specific capital needs of a business.

Commercialization ∎ The final stage of the innovation process, including production and distribution.

Common stock ∎ The most frequently used instrument for purchasing ownership in private or public companies. Common stock generally carries the right to vote on certain corporate actions and may pay dividends, although it rarely does in venture investments. In liquidation, common stockholders are the last to share in the proceeds from the sale of a corporation's assets; bondholders and preferred shareholders have priority. Common stock is often used in first-round start-up financing.

Community development corporation ∎ A corporation established to develop economic programs for a community and, in most cases, to provide financial support for such development.

Competitor ∎ A business whose product or service is marketed for the same purpose/use and to the same consumer group as the product or service of another.

Computer code sharing ∎ An arrangement whereby flights of a regional airline are identified by the two-letter code of a major carrier in the computer reservation system to help direct passengers to new regional carriers.

Consignment ∎ A merchandising agreement, usually referring to secondhand shops, where the dealer pays the owner of an item a percentage of the profit when the item is sold.

Consortium ∎ A coalition of organizations such as banks and corporations for ventures requiring large capital resources.

Consultant ∎ An individual that is paid by a business to provide advice and expertise in a particular area.

GLOSSARY

Consumer price index ▮ A measure of the fluctuation in prices between two points in time.

Consumer research ▮ Research conducted by a business to obtain information about existing or potential consumer markets.

Continuation coverage ▮ Health coverage offered for a specified period of time to employees who leave their jobs and to their widows, divorced spouses, or dependents.

Contractions ▮ *See* Business contractions.

Convertible preferred stock ▮ A class of stock that pays a reasonable dividend and is convertible into common stock (*See* separate citation). Generally the convertible feature may only be exercised after being held for a stated period of time. This arrangement is usually considered second-round financing when a company needs equity to maintain its cash flow.

Convertible securities ▮ A feature of certain bonds, debentures, or preferred stocks that allows them to be exchanged by the owner for another class of securities at a future date and in accordance with any other terms of the issue.

Copayment ▮ *See* Coinsurance.

Copyright ▮ A legal form of protection available to creators and authors to safeguard their works from unlawful use or claim of ownership by others. Copyrights may be acquired for works of art, sculpture, music, and published or unpublished manuscripts. All copyrights should be registered at the Copyright Office of the Library of Congress.

Corporate financial ratios ▮ (*See also* Industry financial ratios) The relationship between key figures found in a company's financial statement expressed as a numeric value. Used to evalu-ate risk and company performance. Also known as Financial averages, Operating ratios, and Business ratios.

Corporation ▮ A legal entity, chartered by a state or the federal government, recognized as a separate entity having its own rights, privileges, and liabilities distinct from those of its members.

Cost containment ▮ Actions taken by employers and insurers to curtail rising health care costs; for example, increasing employee cost sharing (*see* separate citation), requiring second opinions, or preadmission screening.

Cost sharing ▮ The requirement that health care consumers contribute to their own medical care costs through deductibles and coinsurance (*see* separate citations). Cost sharing does not include the amounts paid in premiums. It is used to control utilization of services; for example, requiring a fixed amount to be paid with each health care service.

Cottage industry ▮ (*See also* Home-based business) Businesses based in the home in which the family members are the labor force and family-owned equipment is used to process the goods.

Credit Rating ▮ A letter or number calculated by an organization (such as Dun & Bradstreet) to represent the ability and disposition of a business to meet its financial obligations.

Customer service ▮ Various techniques used to ensure the satisfaction of a customer.

Cyclical peak ▮ The upper turning point in a business cycle.

Cyclical trough ▮ The lower turning point in a business cycle.

DBA ▮ *See* Business name.

Death ▮ *See* Business death.

Debenture ▮ A certificate given as acknowledgment of a debt (*see* separate citation) secured by the general credit of the issuing corporation. A bond, usually without security, issued by a corporation and sometimes convertible to common stock.

Debt ▮ (*See also* Long-term debt; Mid-term debt; Securitized debt; Short-term debt) Something owed by one person to another. Financing in which a company receives capital that must be repaid; no ownership is transferred.

Debt capital ▮ Business financing that normally requires periodic interest payments and repayment of the principal within a specified time.

Debt financing ▮ *See* Debt capital.

Debt securities ▮ Loans such as bonds and notes that provide a specified rate of return for a specified period of time.

Deductible ▮ A set amount that an individual must pay before any benefits are received.

Demand shock absorbers ▮ A term used to describe the role that some small firms play by expanding their output levels to accommodate a transient surge in demand.

Demographics ▮ Statistics on various markets, including age, income, and education, used to target specific products or services to appropriate consumer groups.

Demonstration ▮ Showing that a product or process has been modified sufficiently to meet the needs of users.

Deregulation ▮ The lifting of government restrictions; for example, the lifting of government restrictions on the entry of new businesses, the expansion of services, and the setting of prices in particular industries.

Desktop Publishing ▮ Using personal computers and specialized software to produce camera-ready copy for publications.

Digital cash ▮ A system that allows a person to make financial transactions over the Internet. This system allows a person to purchase goods or services by transmitting a number from one computer to another.

Disaster loans ▮ Various types of physical and economic assistance available to individuals and businesses through the U.S. Small Business Administration (SBA). This is the only SBA loan program available for residential purposes.

Discrimination ▮ The denial of the rights and privileges of employment based on factors such as age, race, religion, or gender.

Diseconomies of scale ▮ The condition in which the costs of production increase faster than the volume of production.

Dissolution ▮ *See* Business dissolution.

Distribution ▮ Delivering a product or process to the user.

Distributor ▮ One who delivers merchandise to the user.

Diversified company ▮ A company whose products and services are used by several different markets.

Doing business as (DBA) ▮ *See* Business name.

Dow Jones ∎ An information services company that publishes the Wall Street Journal and other sources of financial information.

Dow Jones Industrial Average ∎ An indicator of stock market performance.

Earned income ∎ A tax term that refers to wages and salaries earned by the recipient, as opposed to monies earned through interest and dividends.

E-commerce ∎ *See* Electronic commerce.

Economic efficiency ∎ The use of productive resources to the fullest practical extent in the provision of the set of goods and services that is most preferred by purchasers in the economy.

Economic indicators ∎ Statistics used to express the state of the economy. These include the length of the average work week, the rate of unemployment, and stock prices.

Economically disadvantaged ∎ *See* Socially and economically disadvantaged.

Economies of scale ∎ *See* Scale economies.

EEOC ∎ *See* Equal Employment Opportunity Commission.

8(a) Program ∎ A program authorized by the Small Business Act that directs federal contracts to small businesses owned and operated by socially and economically disadvantaged individuals.

Electronic mail (e-mail) ∎ The electronic transmission of mail via phone lines.

Electonic commerce (e-commerce) ∎ Buying and selling goods and services through the Internet.

E-mail ∎ *See* Electronic mail.

Employee leasing ∎ A contract by which employers arrange to have their workers hired by a leasing company and then leased back to them for a management fee. The leasing company typically assumes the administrative burden of payroll and provides a benefit package to the workers.

Employee tenure ∎ The length of time an employee works for a particular employer.

Employer identification number ∎ The business equivalent of a social security number. Assigned by the U.S. Internal Revenue Service.

Enterprise ∎ An aggregation of all establishments owned by a parent company. An enterprise may consist of a single, independent establishment or include subsidiaries and other branches under the same ownership and control.

Enterprise zone ∎ A designated area, usually found in inner cities and other areas with significant unemployment, where businesses receive tax credits and other incentives to entice them to establish operations there.

Entrepreneur ∎ A person who takes the risk of organizing and operating a new business venture.

Entry ∎ *See* Business entry

Equal Employment Opportunity Commission (EEOC) ∎ A federal agency that ensures nondiscrimination in the hiring and firing practices of a business.

Equal opportunity employer ∎ An employer who adheres to the standards set by the Equal Employment Opportunity Commission (*see* separate citation).

Equity ∎ (*See also* Common Stock; Equity midrisk venture capital) The ownership interest. Financing in which partial or total ownership of a company is surrendered in exchange for capital. An investor's financial return comes from dividend payments and from growth in the net worth of the business.

Equity capital ∎ *See* Equity; Equity midrisk venture capital.

Equity financing ∎ *See* Equity; Equity midrisk venture capital.

Equity midrisk venture capital ∎ An unsecured investment in a company. Usually a purchase of ownership interest in a company that occurs in the later stages of a company's development.

Equity partnership ∎ A limited partnership arrangement for providing start-up and Seed capital to businesses.

Equity securities ∎ *See* Equity.

Equity-type ∎ Debt financing subordinated to conventional debt.

Establishment ∎ A single-location business unit that may be independent (a single-establishment enterprise) or owned by a parent enterprise.

Establishment and Enterprise Microdata File ∎ *See* U.S. Establishment and Enterprise Microdata File.

Establishment birth ∎ *See* Business birth.

Establishment Longitudinal Microdata File ∎ *See* U.S. Establishment Longitudinal Microdata File.

Ethics ∎ *See* Business ethics.

Evaluation ∎ Determining the potential success of translating an invention into a product or process.

Experience rating ∎ *See* Underwriting.

Exit ∎ *See* Business exit.

Export ∎ A product sold outside of the country.

Export license ∎ A general or specific license granted by the U.S. Department of Commerce required of anyone wishing to export goods. Some restricted articles need approval from the U.S. Departments of State, Defense, or Energy.

Extranet ∎ (*See also* Intranet) An intranet that provides various levels of accessibility to outsiders. Access to an extranet can only be obtained if you have a valid username and password.

Failure ∎ *See* Business failure.

Fair share agreement ∎ (*See also* Franchising) An agreement reached between a franchisor and a minority business organization to extend business ownership to minorities by either reducing the amount of capital required or by setting aside certain marketing areas for minority business owners.

Feasibility study ∎ A study to determine the likelihood that a proposed product or development will fulfill the objectives of a particular investor.

Federal Trade Commission (FTC) ∎ Federal agency that promotes free enterprise and competition within the U.S.

Federal Trade Mark Act of 1946 ■ *See* Lanham Act.

Fictional name ■ *See* Business name.

Fiduciary ■ An individual or group that hold assets in trust for a beneficiary.

Financial analysis ■ The techniques used to determine money needs in a business. Techniques include ratio analysis, calculation of return on investment, guides for measuring profitability, and break-even analysis to determine ultimate success.

Financial intermediary ■ A financial institution that acts as the intermediary between borrowers and lenders. Banks, savings and loan associations, finance companies, and venture capital companies are major financial intermediaries in the United States.

Financial ratios ■ *See* Corporate financial ratios; Industry financial ratios.

Financial statement ■ A written record of business finances, including balance sheets and profit and loss statements.

Financing ■ *See* First-stage financing; Second-stage financing; Third-stage financing.

First-stage financing ■ (*See also* Second-stage financing; Third-stage financing) Financing provided to companies that have expended their initial capital, and require funds to start full-scale manufacturing and sales. Also known as First-round financing.

Fiscal year ■ Any twelve-month period used by businesses for accounting purposes.

504 Program ■ *See* Certified development corporation.

Flexible benefit plan ■ A plan that offers a choice among cash and/or qualified benefits such as group term life insurance, accident and health insurance, group legal services, dependent care assistance, and vacations.

FOB ■ *See* Free on board

Format franchising ■ *See* Business format franchising; Franchising.

401(k) plan ■ A financial plan where employees contribute a percentage of their earnings to a fund that is invested in stocks, bonds, or money markets for the purpose of saving money for retirement.

Four Ps ■ Marketing terms: Product, Price, Place, and Promotion.

Franchising ■ A form of licensing by which the owner—the franchisor—distributes or markets a product, method, or service through affiliated dealers called franchisees. The product, method, or service being marketed is identified by a brand name, and the franchisor maintains control over the marketing methods employed. The franchisee is often given exclusive access to a defined geographic area.

Free on board (FOB) ■ A pricing term indicating that the quoted price includes the cost of loading goods into transport vessels at a specified place.

Frictional unemployment ■ *See* Un-employment.

FTC ■ *See* Federal Trade Commission.

Fulfillment ■ The systems necessary for accurate delivery of an ordered item, including subscriptions and direct marketing.

Full-time workers ■ Generally, those who work a regular schedule of more than 35 hours per week.

Garment registration number ■ A number that must appear on every garment sold in the U.S. to indicate the manufacturer of the garment, which may or may not be the same as the label under which the garment is sold. The U.S. Federal Trade Commission assigns and regulates garment registration numbers.

Gatekeeper ■ A key contact point for entry into a network.

GDP ■ *See* Gross domestic product.

General obligation bond ■ A municipal bond secured by the taxing power of the municipality. The Tax Reform Act of 1986 limits the purposes for which such bonds may be issued and establishes volume limits on the extent of their issuance.

GNP ■ *See* Gross national product.

Good Housekeeping Seal ■ Seal appearing on products that signifies the fulfillment of the standards set by the Good Housekeeping Institute to protect consumer interests.

Goods sector ■ All businesses producing tangible goods, including agriculture, mining, construction, and manufacturing businesses.

GPO ■ *See* Gross product originating.

Gross domestic product (GDP) ■ The part of the nation's gross national product (*see* separate citation) generated by private business using resources from within the country.

Gross national product (GNP) ■ The most comprehensive single measure of aggregate economic output. Represents the market value of the total output of goods and services produced by a nation's economy.

Gross product originating (GPO) ■ A measure of business output estimated from the income or production side using employee compensation, profit income, net interest, capital consumption, and indirect business taxes.

HAL ■ *See* Handicapped assistance loan program.

Handicapped assistance loan program (HAL) ■ Low-interest direct loan program through the U.S. Small Business Administration (SBA) for handicapped persons. The SBA requires that these persons demonstrate that their disability is such that it is impossible for them to secure employment, thus making it necessary to go into their own business to make a living.

Health maintenance organization (HMO) ■ Organization of physi-cians and other health care professionals that provides health services to subscribers and their dependents on a prepaid basis.

Health provider ■ An individual or institution that gives medical care. Under Medicare, an institutional provider is a hospital, skilled nursing facility, home health agency, or provider of certain physical therapy services.

Hispanic ■ A person of Cuban, Mexican, Puerto Rican, Latin American (Central or South American), European Spanish, or other Spanish-speaking origin or ancestry.

HMO ■ *See* Health maintenance organization.

Home-based business ■ (*See also* Cottage industry) A business with an operating address that is also a residential address (usually the residential address of the proprietor).

GLOSSARY

Hub-and-spoke system ∎ A system in which flights of an airline from many different cities (the spokes) converge at a single airport (the hub). After allowing passengers sufficient time to make connections, planes then depart for different cities.

Human Resources Management ∎ A business program designed to oversee recruiting, pay, benefits, and other issues related to the company's work force, including planning to determine the optimal use of labor to increase production, thereby increasing profit.

Idea ∎ An original concept for a new product or process.

Import ∎ Products produced outside the country in which they are consumed.

Income ∎ Money or its equivalent, earned or accrued, resulting from the sale of goods and services.

Income statement ∎ A financial statement that lists the profits and losses of a company at a given time.

Incorporation ∎ The filing of a certificate of incorporation with the secretary of state, thereby limiting the business owner's liability.

Incubator ∎ A facility designed to encourage entrepreneurship and minimize obstacles to new business formation and growth, particularly for high-technology firms, by housing a number of fledgling enterprises that share an array of services, such as meeting areas, secretarial services, accounting, research library, on-site financial and management counseling, and word processing facilities.

Independent contractor ∎ An individual considered self-employed (*see* separate citation) and responsible for paying Social Security taxes and income taxes on earnings.

Indirect health coverage ∎ Health insurance obtained through another individual's health care plan; for example, a spouse's employer-sponsored plan.

Industrial development authority ∎ The financial arm of a state or other political subdivision established for the purpose of financing economic development in an area, usually through loans to nonprofit organizations, which in turn provide facilities for manufacturing and other industrial operations.

Industry financial ratios ∎ (*See also* Corporate financial ratios) Corporate financial ratios averaged for a specified industry. These are used for comparison purposes and reveal industry trends and identify differences between the performance of a specific company and the performance of its industry. Also known as Industrial averages, Industry ratios, Financial averages, and Business or Industrial norms.

Inflation ∎ Increases in volume of currency and credit, generally resulting in a sharp and continuing rise in price levels.

Informal capital ∎ Financing from informal, unorganized sources; includes informal debt capital such as trade credit or loans from friends and relatives and equity capital from informal investors.

Initial public offering (IPO) ∎ A corporation's first offering of stock to the public.

Innovation ∎ The introduction of a new idea into the marketplace in the form of a new product or service or an improvement in organization or process.

Intellectual property ∎ Any idea/work that can be considered proprietary in nature and thus protected from infringement by others.

Internal capital ∎ Debt or equity financing obtained from the owner or through retained business earnings.

Internet ∎ A government-designed computer network that contains large amounts of information and is accessible through various vendors for a fee.

Intranet ∎ (*See also* Extranet) A web site belonging to an organization or a corporation, that is accessible only to employees, members, or others that have authorization.

Intrapreneurship ∎ The state of employing entrepreneurial principles to nonentrepreneurial situations.

Invention ∎ The tangible form of a technological idea, which could include a laboratory prototype, drawings, formulas, etc.

IPO ∎ *See* Initial public offering.

Job description ∎ The duties and responsibilities required in a particular position.

Job tenure ∎ A period of time during which an individual is continuously employed in the same job.

Joint marketing agreements ∎ Agree-ments between regional and major airlines, often involving the coordination of flight schedules, fares, and baggage transfer. These agreements help regional carriers operate at lower cost.

Joint venture ∎ Venture in which two or more people combine efforts in a particular business enterprise, usually a single transaction or a limited activity, and agree to share the profits and losses jointly or in proportion to their contributions.

Keogh plan ∎ Designed for self-employed persons and unincorporated businesses as a tax-deferred pension account.

Labor force ∎ Civilians considered eligible for employment who are also willing and able to work.

Labor force participation rate ∎ The civilian labor force as a percentage of the civilian population.

Labor intensity ∎ (*See also* Capital intensity) The relative importance of labor in the production process, usually measured as the capital-labor ratio; i.e., the ratio of units of capital (typically, dollars of tangible assets) to the number of employees. The higher the capital-labor ratio exhibited by a firm or industry, the lower the capital intensity of that firm or industry is said to be.

Labor surplus area ∎ An area in which there exists a high unemployment rate. In procurement (*see* separate citation), extra points are given to firms in counties that are designated a labor surplus area; this information is requested on procurement bid sheets.

Labor union ∎ An organization of similarly-skilled workers who collectively bargain with management over the conditions of employment.

Laboratory prototype ∎ *See* Prototype.

LAN ∎ *See* Local Area Network.

Lanham Act ∎ Refers to the Federal Trade Mark Act of 1946. Protects registered trademarks, trade names, and other service marks used in commerce.

Large business-dominated industry ∎ Industry in which a minimum of 60 percent of employment or sales is in firms with more than 500 workers.

GLOSSARY

LBO ▪ *See* Leveraged buy-out.

Leader pricing ▪ A reduction in the price of a good or service in order to generate more sales of that good or service.

Legal list ▪ A list of securities selected by a state in which certain institutions and fiduciaries (such as pension funds, insurance companies, and banks) may invest. Securities not on the list are not eligible for investment. Legal lists typically restrict investments to high quality securities meeting certain specifications. Generally, investment is limited to U.S. securities and investment-grade blue chip securities (*see* separate citation).

Leveraged buy-out (LBO) ▪ The purchase of a business or a division of a corporation through a highly leveraged financing package.

Liability ▪ An obligation or duty to perform a service or an act. Also defined as money owed.

License ▪ (*See also* Business license) A legal agreement granting to another the right to use a technological innovation.

Limited partnerships ▪ *See* Venture capital limited partnerships

Liquidity ▪ The ability to convert a security into cash promptly.

Loans ▪ *See* Commercial loans; Disaster loans; SBA direct loans; SBA guaranteed loans; SBA special lending institution categories.

Local Area Network (LAN) ▪ Computer networks contained within a single building or small area; used to facilitate the sharing of information.

Local development corporation ▪ An organization, usually made up of local citizens of a community, designed to improve the economy of the area by inducing business and industry to locate and expand there. A local development corporation establishes a capability to finance local growth.

Long-haul rates ▪ Rates charged by a transporter in which the distance traveled is more than 800 miles.

Long-term debt ▪ An obligation that matures in a period that exceeds five years.

Low-grade bond ▪ A corporate bond that is rated below investment grade by the major rating agencies (Standard and Poor's, Moody's).

Macro-efficiency ▪ (*See also* Economic efficiency) Efficiency as it pertains to the operation of markets and market systems.

Managed care ▪ A cost-effective health care program initiated by employers whereby low-cost health care is made available to the employees in return for exclusive patronage to program doctors.

Management and technical assistance ▪ A term used by many programs to mean business (as opposed to technological) assistance.

Management Assistance Programs ▪ *See* SBA Management Assistance Programs

Mandated benefits ▪ Specific treatments, providers, or individuals required by law to be included in commercial health plans.

Market evaluation ▪ The use of market information to determine the sales potential of a specific product or process.

Market failure ▪ The situation in which the workings of a competitive market do not produce the best results from the point of view of the entire society.

Market information ▪ Data of any type that can be used for market evaluation, which could include demographic data, technology forecasting, regulatory changes, etc.

Market research ▪ A systematic collection, analysis, and reporting of data about the market and its preferences, opinions, trends, and plans; used for corporate decision-making.

Market share ▪ In a particular market, the percentage of sales of a specific product.

Marketing ▪ Promotion of goods or services through various media.

Master Establishment List (MEL) ▪ A list of firms in the United States developed by the U.S. Small Business Administration; firms can be selected by industry, region, state, standard metropolitan statistical area (*see* separate citation), county, and zip code.

Maturity ▪ (*See also* Term) The date upon which the principal or stated value of a bond or other indebtedness becomes due and payable.

Medicaid (Title XIX) ▪ A federally aided, state-operated and administered program that provides medical benefits for certain low-income persons in need of health and medical care who are eligible for one of the government's welfare cash payment programs, including the aged, the blind, the disabled, and members of families with dependent children where one parent is absent, incapacitated, or unemployed.

Medicare (Title XVIII) ▪ A nationwide health insurance program for disabled and aged persons. Health insurance is available to insured persons without regard to income. Monies from payroll taxes cover hospital insurance and monies from general revenues and beneficiary premiums pay for supplementary medical insurance.

MEL ▪ *See* Master Establishment List.

Metropolitan statistical area (MSA) ▪ A means used by the government to define large population centers that may transverse different governmental jurisdictions. For example, the Washington, D.C., MSA includes the District of Columbia and contiguous parts of Maryland and Virginia because all of these geopolitical areas comprise one population and economic operating unit.

Mezzanine financing ▪ *See* Third-stage financing.

MESBIC ▪ *See* Minority enterprise small business investment corporation.

MET ▪ *See* Multiple employer trust.

Micro-efficiency ▪ (*See also* Economic efficiency) Efficiency as it pertains to the operation of individual firms.

Microdata ▪ Information on the characteristics of an individual business firm.

Mid-term debt ▪ An obligation that matures within one to five years.

Midrisk venture capital ▪ *See* Equity midrisk venture capital.

Minimum premium plan ∎ A combination approach to funding an insurance plan aimed primarily at premium tax savings. The employer self-funds a fixed percentage of estimated monthly claims and the insurance company insures the excess.

Minimum wage ∎ The lowest hourly wage allowed by the federal government.

Minority Business Development Agency ∎ Contracts with private firms throughout the nation to sponsor Minority Business Development Centers which provide minority firms with advice and technical assistance on a fee basis.

Minority Enterprise Small Business Investment Corporation (MESBIC) ∎ A federally funded private venture capital firm licensed by the U.S. Small Business Administration to provide capital to minority-owned businesses (*see* separate citation).

Minority-owned business ∎ Businesses owned by those who are socially or economically disadvantaged (*see* separate citation).

Mom and Pop business ∎ A small store or enterprise having limited capital, principally employing family members.

Moonlighter ∎ A wage-and-salary worker with a side business.

MSA ∎ *See* Metropolitan statistical area.

Multi-employer plan ∎ A health plan to which more than one employer is required to contribute and that may be maintained through a collective bargaining agreement and required to meet standards prescribed by the U.S. Department of Labor.

Multi-level marketing ∎ A system of selling in which you sign up other people to assist you, and they, in turn, recruit others to help them. Some entrepreneurs have built successful companies on this concept because the main focus of their activities is their product and product sales.

Multimedia ∎ The use of several types of media to promote a product or service. Also refers to the use of several different types of media (sight, sound, pictures, text) in a CD-ROM (*see* separate citation) product.

Multiple employer trust (MET) ∎ A self-funded benefit plan generally geared toward small employers sharing a common interest.

NAFTA ∎ *See* North American Free Trade Agreement.

NASDAQ ∎ *See* National Association of Securities Dealers Automated Quotations.

National Association of Securities Dealers Automated Quotations ∎ Provides price quotes on over-the-counter securities as well as securities listed on the New York Stock Exchange.

National income ∎ Aggregate earnings of labor and property arising from the production of goods and services in a nation's economy.

Net assets ∎ *See* Net worth.

Net income ∎ The amount remaining from earnings and profits after all expenses and costs have been met or deducted. Also known as Net earnings.

Net profit ∎ Money earned after production and overhead expenses (*see* separate citations) have been deducted.

Net worth ∎ (*See also* Capital) The difference between a company's total assets and its total liabilities.

Network ∎ A chain of interconnected individuals or organizations sharing information and/or services.

New York Stock Exchange (NYSE) ∎ The oldest stock exchange in the U.S. Allows for trading in stocks, bonds, warrants, options, and rights that meet listing requirements.

Niche ∎ A career or business for which a person is well-suited. Also, a product which fulfills one need of a particular market segment, often with little or no competition.

Nodes ∎ One workstation in a network, either local area or wide area (*see* separate citations).

Nonbank bank ∎ A bank that either accepts deposits or makes loans, but not both. Used to create many new branch banks.

Noncompetitive awards ∎ A method of contracting whereby the federal government negotiates with only one contractor to supply a product or service.

Nonmember bank ∎ A state-regulated bank that does not belong to the federal bank system.

Nonprofit ∎ An organization that has no shareholders, does not distribute profits, and is without federal and state tax liabilities.

Norms ∎ *See* Financial ratios.

North American Free Trade Agreement (NAFTA) ∎ Passed in 1993, NAFTA eliminates trade barriers among businesses in the U.S., Canada, and Mexico.

NYSE ∎ *See* New York Stock Exchange

Occupational Safety & Health Administration (OSHA) ∎ Federal agency that regulates health and safety standards within the workplace.

Optimal firm size ∎ The business size at which the production cost per unit of output (average cost) is, in the long run, at its minimum.

Organizational chart ∎ A hierarchical chart tracking the chain of command within an organization.

OSHA ∎ *See* Occupational Safety & Health Administration.

Overhead ∎ Expenses, such as employee benefits and building utilities, incurred by a business that are unrelated to the actual product or service sold.

Owner's capital ∎ Debt or equity funds provided by the owner(s) of a business; sources of owner's capital are personal savings, sales of assets, or loans from financial institutions.

P & L ∎ *See* Profit and loss statement.

Part-time workers ∎ Normally, those who work less than 35 hours per week. The Tax Reform Act indicated that part-time workers who work less than 17.5 hours per week may be excluded from health plans for purposes of complying with federal nondiscrimination rules.

Part-year workers ∎ Those who work less than 50 weeks per year.

Partnership ∎ Two or more parties who enter into a legal relationship to conduct business for profit. Defined by the U.S. Internal Revenue Code as joint ventures, syndicates, groups, pools, and other associations of two or more persons organized for profit that are not specifically classified in the IRS code as corporations or proprietorships.

GLOSSARY

Patent | A grant by the government assuring an inventor the sole right to make, use, and sell an invention for a period of 17 years.

PC | See Professional corporation.

Peak | See Cyclical peak.

Pension | A series of payments made monthly, semiannually, annually, or at other specified intervals during the lifetime of the pensioner for distribution upon retirement. The term is sometimes used to denote the portion of the retirement allowance financed by the employer's contributions.

Pension fund | A fund established to provide for the payment of pension benefits; the collective contributions made by all of the parties to the pension plan.

Performance appraisal | An established set of objective criteria, based on job description and requirements, that is used to evaluate the performance of an employee in a specific job.

Permit | See Business license.

Plan | See Business plan.

Pooling | An arrangement for employers to achieve efficiencies and lower health costs by joining together to purchase group health insurance or self-insurance.

PPO | See Preferred provider organization

Preferred lenders program | See SBA special lending institution categories

Preferred provider organization (PPO) | A contractual arrangement with a health care services organization that agrees to discount its health care rates in return for faster payment and/or a patient base.

Premiums | The amount of money paid to an insurer for health insurance under a policy. The premium is generally paid periodically (e.g., monthly), and often is split between the employer and the employee. Unlike deductibles and coinsurance or co-payments, premiums are paid for coverage whether or not benefits are actually used.

Prime-age workers | Employees 25 to 54 years of age.

Prime contract | A contract awarded directly by the U.S. Federal Government.

Private company | See Closely held corporation. Private placement A method of raising capital by offering for sale an investment or business to a small group of investors (generally avoiding registration with the Securities and Exchange Commis-sion or state securities registration agencies). Also known as Private financing or Private offering.

Pro forma | The use of hypothetical figures in financial statements to represent future expenditures, debts, and other potential financial expenses.

Proactive | Taking the initiative to solve problems and anticipate future events before they happen, instead of reacting to an already existing problem or waiting for a difficult situation to occur.

Procurement | (See also 8(a) Program; Small business set asides) A contract from an agency of the federal government for goods or services from a small business.

Prodigy | (See also America Online) An online service which is accessible by computer modem. The service features Internet access, bulletin boards, online periodicals, electronic mail, and other services for subscribers.

Product development | The stage of the innovation process where research is translated into a product or process through evaluation, adaptation, and demonstration.

Product franchising | An arrangement for a franchisee to use the name and to produce the product line of the franchisor or parent corporation.

Production | The manufacture of a product.

Production prototype | See Prototype.

Productivity | A measurement of the number of goods produced during a specific amount of time.

Professional corporation (PC) | Organized by members of a pro-fession such as medicine, dentistry, or law for the purpose of con-ducting their professional activities as a corporation. Liability of a member or shareholder is limited in the same manner as in a business corporation.

Profit and loss statement (P & L) | The summary of the incomes and costs of a company's operation during a specific period of time. Also known as Income and expense statement.

Proposal | See Business plan.

Proprietorship | The most common legal form of business ownership; about 85 percent of all small businesses are proprietorships. The liability of the owner is unlimited in this form of ownership.

Prospective payment system | A cost-containment measure included in the Social Security Amendments of 1983 whereby Medicare payments to hospitals are based on established prices, rather than on cost reimbursement.

Prototype | A model that demonstrates the validity of the concept of an invention (laboratory prototype); a model that meets the needs of the manufacturing process and the user (production prototype).

Prudent investor rule or standard | A legal doctrine that requires fiduciaries to make investments using the prudence, diligence, and intelligence that would be used by a prudent person in making similar investments. Because fiduciaries make invest-ments on behalf of third-party beneficiaries, the standard results in very conservative investments. Until recently, most state regulations required the fiduciary to apply this standard to each investment. Newer, more progressive regulations permit fiduciaries to apply this standard to the portfolio taken as a whole, thereby allowing a fiduciary to balance a portfolio with higher-yield, higher-risk invest-ments. In states with more progressive regulations, practically every type of security is eligible for inclusion in the portfolio of investments made by a fiduciary, provided that the portfolio investments, in their totality, are those of a prudent person.

Public equity markets | Organized markets for trading in equity shares such as common stocks, preferred stocks, and warrants. Includes markets for both regularly traded and nonregularly traded securities.

Public offering | General solicitation for participation in an investment opportunity. Interstate public offerings are supervised by the U.S. Securities and Exchange Commission (see separate citation).

Quality control ∎ The process by which a product is checked and tested to ensure consistent standards of high quality.

Rate of return z ∎ (*See also* Yield) The yield obtained on a security or other investment based on its purchase price or its current market price. The total rate of return is current income plus or minus capital appreciation or depreciation.

Real property ∎ Includes the land and all that is contained on it.

Realignment ∎ *See* Resource realignment.

Recession ∎ Contraction of economic activity occurring between the peak and trough (*see* separate citations) of a business cycle.

Regulated market ∎ A market in which the government controls the forces of supply and demand, such as who may enter and what price may be charged.

Regulation D ∎ A vehicle by which small businesses make small offerings and private placements of securities with limited disclosure requirements. It was designed to ease the burdens imposed on small businesses utilizing this method of capital formation.

Regulatory Flexibility Act ∎ An act requiring federal agencies to evaluate the impact of their regulations on small businesses before the regulations are issued and to consider less burdensome alternatives.

Research ∎ The initial stage of the innovation process, which includes idea generation and invention.

Research and development financing ∎ A tax-advantaged partnership set up to finance product development for start-ups as well as more mature companies.

Resource mobility ∎ The ease with which labor and capital move from firm to firm or from industry to industry.

Resource realignment ∎ The adjustment of productive resources to interindustry changes in demand.

Resources ∎ The sources of support or help in the innovation process, including sources of financing, technical evaluation, market evaluation, management and business assistance, etc.

Retained business earnings ∎ Business profits that are retained by the business rather than being distributed to the shareholders as dividends.

Revolving credit ∎ An agreement with a lending institution for an amount of money, which cannot exceed a set maximum, over a specified period of time. Each time the borrower repays a portion of the loan, the amount of the repayment may be borrowed yet again.

Risk capital ∎ *See* Venture capital.

Risk management ∎ The act of identifying potential sources of financial loss and taking action to minimize their negative impact.

Routing ∎ The sequence of steps necessary to complete a product during production.

S corporations ∎ *See* Sub chapter S corporations.

SBA ∎ *See* Small Business Administration.

SBA direct loans ∎ Loans made directly by the U.S. Small Business Administration (SBA); monies come from funds appropriated specifically for this purpose. In general, SBA direct loans carry interest rates slightly lower than those in the private financial markets and are available only to applicants unable to secure private financing or an SBA guaranteed loan.

SBA 504 Program ∎ *See* Certified development corporation.

SBA guaranteed loans ∎ Loans made by lending institutions in which the U.S. Small Business Administration (SBA) will pay a prior agreed-upon percentage of the outstanding principal in the event the borrower of the loan defaults. The terms of the loan and the interest rate are negotiated between the borrower and the lending institution, within set parameters.

SBA loans ∎ *See* Disaster loans; SBA direct loans; SBA guaranteed loans; SBA special lending institution categories.

SBA Management Assistance Programs ∎ (*See also* Active Corps of Executives; Service Corps of Retired Executives; Small business institutes program) Classes, workshops, counseling, and publications offered by the U.S. Small Business Administration.

SBA special lending institution categories ∎ U.S. Small Business Administration (SBA) loan program in which the SBA promises certified banks a 72-hour turnaround period in giving its approval for a loan, and in which preferred lenders in a pilot program are allowed to write SBA loans without seeking prior SBA approval.

SBDB ∎ *See* Small Business Data Base.

SBDC ∎ *See* Small business development centers.

SBI ∎ *See* Small business institutes program.

SBIC ∎ *See* Small business investment corporation.

SBIR Program ∎ *See* Small Business Innovation Development Act of 1982.

Scale economies ∎ The decline of the production cost per unit of output (average cost) as the volume of output increases.

Scale efficiency ∎ The reduction in unit cost available to a firm when producing at a higher output volume.

SCORE ∎ *See* Service Corps of Retired Executives.

SEC ∎ *See* Securities and Exchange Commission.

SECA ∎ *See* Self-Employment Contribu-tions Act.

Second-stage financing ∎ (*See also* First-stage financing; Third-stage financing) Working capital for the initial expansion of a com-pany that is producing, shipping, and has growing accounts receiv-able and inventories. Also known as Second- round financing.

Secondary market ∎ A market established for the purchase and sale of outstanding securities following their initial distribution.

Secondary worker ∎ Any worker in a family other than the person who is the primary source of income for the family.

Secondhand capital ∎ Previously used and subsequently resold capital equipment (e.g., buildings and machinery).

Securities and Exchange Commission (SEC) ∎ Federal agency charged with regulating the trade of securities to prevent unethical practices in the investor market.

GLOSSARY

Securitized debt ∎ A marketing technique that converts long-term loans to marketable securities.

Seed capital ∎ Venture financing provided in the early stages of the innovation process, usually during product development.

Self-employed person ∎ One who works for a profit or fees in his or her own business, profession, or trade, or who operates a farm.

Self-Employment Contributions Act (SECA) ∎ Federal law that governs the self-employment tax (*see* separate citation).

Self-employment income ∎ Income covered by Social Security if a business earns a net income of at least $400.00 during the year. Taxes are paid on earnings that exceed $400.00.

Self-employment retirement plan ∎ *See* Keogh plan.

Self-employment tax ∎ Required tax imposed on self-employed individuals for the provision of Social Security and Medicare. The tax must be paid quarterly with estimated income tax statements.

Self-funding ∎ A health benefit plan in which a firm uses its own funds to pay claims, rather than transferring the financial risks of paying claims to an outside insurer in exchange for premium payments.

Service Corps of Retired Executives (SCORE) ∎ (*See also* Active Corps of Executives) Volunteers for the SBA Management Assistance Program who provide one-on-one counseling and teach workshops and seminars for small firms.

Service firm ∎ *See* Business service firm.

Service sector ∎ Broadly defined, all U.S. industries that produce intangibles, including the five major industry divisions of transportation, communications, and utilities; wholesale trade; retail trade; finance, insurance, and real estate; and services.

Set asides ∎ *See* Small business set asides.

Short-haul service ∎ A type of transportation service in which the transporter supplies service between cities where the maximum distance is no more than 200 miles.

Short-term debt ∎ An obligation that matures in one year.

SIC codes ∎ *See* Standard Industrial Classification codes.

Single-establishment enterprise ∎ *See* Establishment.

Small business ∎ An enterprise that is independently owned and operated, is not dominant in its field, and employs fewer than 500 people. For SBA purposes, the U.S. Small Business Administration (SBA) considers various other factors (such as gross annual sales) in determining size of a business.

Small Business Administration (SBA) ∎ An independent federal agency that provides assistance with loans, management, and advocating interests before other federal agencies.

Small Business Data Base ∎ (*See also* U.S. Establishment and Enterprise Microdata File; U.S. Establishment Longitudinal Microdata File) A collection of microdata (*see* separate citation) files on individual firms developed and maintained by the U.S. Small Business Administration.

Small business development centers (SBDC) ∎ Centers that provide support services to small businesses, such as individual counseling, SBA advice, seminars and conferences, and other learning center activities. Most services are free of charge, or available at minimal cost.

Small business development corporation ∎ *See* Certified development corporation.

Small business-dominated industry ∎ Industry in which a minimum of 60 percent of employment or sales is in firms with fewer than 500 employees.

Small Business Innovation Development Act of 1982 ∎ Federal statute requiring federal agencies with large extramural research and development budgets to allocate a certain percentage of these funds to small research and development firms. The program, called the Small Business Innovation Research (SBIR) Program, is designed to stimulate technological innovation and make greater use of small businesses in meeting national innovation needs.

Small business institutes (SBI) program ∎ Cooperative arrangements made by U.S. Small Business Administration district offices and local colleges and universities to provide small business firms with graduate students to counsel them without charge.

Small business investment corporation (SBIC) ∎ A privately owned company licensed and funded through the U.S. Small Business Administration and private sector sources to provide equity or debt capital to small businesses.

Small business set asides ∎ Procurement (*see* separate citation) opportunities required by law to be on all contracts under $10,000 or a certain percentage of an agency's total procurement expenditure.

Smaller firms ∎ For U.S. Department of Commerce purposes, those firms not included in the Fortune 1000.

SMSA ∎ *See* Metropolitan statistical area.

Socially and economically disadvantaged ∎ Individuals who have been subjected to racial or ethnic prejudice or cultural bias without regard to their qualities as individuals, and whose abilities to compete are impaired because of diminished opportunities to obtain capital and credit.

Sole proprietorship ∎ An unincorporated, one-owner business, farm, or professional practice.

Special lending institution categories ∎ *See* SBA special lending institution categories.

Standard Industrial Classification (SIC) codes ∎ Four-digit codes established by the U.S. Federal Government to categorize businesses by type of economic activity; the first two digits correspond to major groups such as construction and manufacturing, while the last two digits correspond to subgroups such as home construction or highway construction.

Standard metropolitan statistical area (SMSA) ∎ *See* Metropolitan statistical area.

Start-up ∎ A new business, at the earliest stages of development and financing.

Start-up costs ∎ Costs incurred before a business can commence operations.

Start-up financing ∎ Financing provided to companies that have either completed product development and initial marketing or have been in business for less than one year but have not yet sold their product commercially.

Stock ∎ (*See also* Common stock; Convertible preferred stock) A certificate of equity ownership in a business.

Stop-loss coverage ∎ Insurance for a self-insured plan that reimburses the company for any losses it might incur in its health claims beyond a specified amount.

Strategic planning ∎ Projected growth and development of a business to establish a guiding direction for the future. Also used to determine which market segments to explore for optimal sales of products or services.

Structural unemployment ∎ *See* Un-employment.

Sub chapter S corporations ∎ Corpora-tions that are considered noncorporate for tax purposes but legally remain corporations.

Subcontract ∎ A contract between a prime contractor and a subcontractor, or between subcontractors, to furnish supplies or services for performance of a prime contract (*see* separate citation) or a subcontract.

Surety bonds ∎ Bonds providing reimbursement to an individual, company, or the government if a firm fails to complete a contract. The U.S. Small Business Administration guarantees surety bonds in a program much like the SBA guaranteed loan program (*see* separate citation).

Swing loan ∎ *See* Bridge financing.

Target market ∎ The clients or customers sought for a business' product or service.

Targeted Jobs Tax Credit ∎ Federal legislation enacted in 1978 that provides a tax credit to an employer who hires structurally unemployed individuals.

Tax number ∎ (*See also* Employer identification number) A number assigned to a business by a state revenue department that enables the business to buy goods without paying sales tax.

Taxable bonds ∎ An interest-bearing certificate of public or private indebtedness. Bonds are issued by public agencies to finance economic development.

Technical assistance ∎ *See* Management and technical assistance

Technical evaluation ∎ Assessment of technological feasibility.

Technology ∎ The method in which a firm combines and utilizes labor and capital resources to produce goods or services; the application of science for commercial or industrial purposes.

Technology transfer ∎ The movement of information about a tech-nology or intellectual property from one party to another for use.

Tenure ∎ *See* Employee tenure.

Term ∎ (*See also* Maturity) The length of time for which a loan is made.

Terms of a note ∎ The conditions or limits of a note; includes the interest rate per annum, the due date, and transferability and convertibility features, if any.

Third-party administrator ∎ An outside company responsible for handling claims and performing administrative tasks associated with health insurance plan maintenance.

Third-stage financing ∎ (*See also* First-stage financing; Second-stage financing) Financing provided for the major expansion of a company whose sales volume is increasing and that is break-ing even or profitable. These funds are used for further plant expansion, marketing, working capital, or development of an improved product. Also known as Third-round or Mezzanine financing.

Time deposit ∎ A bank deposit that cannot be withdrawn before a specified future time.

Time management ∎ Skills and scheduling techniques used to maximize productivity.

Trade credit ∎ Credit extended by suppliers of raw materials or finished products. In an accounting statement, trade credit is referred to as "accounts payable."

Trade name ∎ The name under which a company conducts business, or by which its business, goods, or services are identified. It may or may not be registered as a trademark.

Trade periodical ∎ A publication with a specific focus on one or more aspects of business and industry.

Trade secret ∎ Competitive advantage gained by a business through the use of a unique manufacturing process or formula.

Trade show ∎ An exhibition of goods or services used in a particular industry. Typically held in exhibition centers where exhibitors rent space to display their merchandise.

Trademark ∎ A graphic symbol, device, or slogan that identifies a business. A business has property rights to its trademark from the inception of its use, but it is still prudent to register all trade marks with the Trademark Office of the U.S. Department of Commerce.

Translation ∎ *See* Product development.

Treasury bills ∎ Investment tender issued by the Federal Reserve Bank in amounts of $10,000 that mature in 91 to 182 days.

Treasury bonds ∎ Long-term notes with maturity dates of not less than seven and not more than twenty-five years.

Treasury notes ∎ Short-term notes maturing in less than seven years.

Trend ∎ A statistical measurement used to track changes that oc-cur over time.

Trough ∎ *See* Cyclical trough.

UCC ∎ *See* Uniform Commercial Code. **UL** *See* Underwriters Laboratories.

Underwriters Laboratories (UL) ∎ One of several private firms that tests products and processes to determine their safety. Although various firms can provide this kind of testing service, many local and insurance codes specify UL certification.

Underwriting ∎ A process by which an insurer determines whether or not and on what basis it will accept an application for insurance. In an experience-rated plan, premiums are based on a firm's or group's past claims; factors other than prior claims are used for community-rated or manually rated plans.

Unfair competition ∎ Refers to business practices, usually unethical, such as using unlicensed products, pirating merch-andise, or misleading the public through false advertising, which give the offending business an unequitable advantage over others.

Unfunded accrued liability ∎ The excess of total liabilities, both present and prospective, over present and prospective assets.

GLOSSARY

Unemployment ∎ The joblessness of individuals who are willing to work, who are legally and physically able to work, and who are seeking work. Unemploy-ment may represent the temporary joblessness of a worker between jobs (frictional unemployment) or the joblessness of a worker whose skills are not suitable for jobs available in the labor market (structural unemployment).

Uniform Commercial Code (UCC) ∎ A code of laws governing commercial transactions across the U.S., except Louisiana. Their purpose is to bring uniformity to financial transactions.

Uniform product code (UPC symbol) ∎ A computer-readable label comprised of ten digits and stripes that encodes what a product is and how much it costs. The first five digits are assigned by the Uniform Produce Code Council, and the last five digits by the individual manufacturer.

Unit cost ∎ *See* Average cost.

UPC symbol ∎ *See* Uniform product code.

US Establishment and Enterprise Microdata (USEEM) File ∎ A cross-sectional database containing information on employment, sales, and location for individual enterprises and establishments with employees that have a Dun & Bradstreet credit rating.

US Establishment Longitudinal Microdata (USELM) File ∎ A database containing longitudinally linked sample microdata on establishments drawn from the U.S. Establishment and Enterprise Microdata file (*see* separate citation).

US Small Business Administration 504 Program ∎ *See* Certified development corporation.

USEEM ∎ *See* U.S. Establishment and Enterprise Microdata File.

USELM ∎ *See* U.S. Establishment Longitudinal Microdata File.

VCN ∎ *See* Venture capital network.

Venture capital ∎ (*See also* Equity; Equity midrisk venture capital) Money used to support new or unusual business ventures that exhibit above-average growth rates, significant potential for market expansion, and are in need of additional financing to sustain growth or further research and development; equity or equity- type financing traditionally provided at the commercialization stage, increasingly available prior to commercialization.

Venture capital company ∎ A company organized to provide seed capital to a business in its formation stage, or in its first or second stage of expansion. Funding is obtained through public or private pension funds, commercial banks and bank holding companies, small business investment corporations licensed by the U.S. Small Business Administration, private venture capital firms, insurance companies, investment management companies, bank trust departments, industrial companies seeking to diversify their investment, and investment bankers acting as intermediaries for other investors or directly investing on their own behalf.

Venture capital limited partnerships ∎ Designed for business development, these partnerships are an institutional mechanism for providing capital for young, technology-oriented businesses. The investors' money is pooled and invested in money market assets until venture investments have been selected. The general partners are experienced investment managers who select and invest the equity and debt securities of firms with high growth potential and the ability to go public in the near future.

Venture capital network (VCN) ∎ A computer database that matches investors with entrepreneurs.

WAN ∎ *See* Wide Area Network.

Wide Area Network (WAN) ∎ Computer networks linking systems throughout a state or around the world in order to facilitate the sharing of information.

Withholding ∎ Federal, state, social security, and unemployment taxes withheld by the employer from employees' wages; employers are liable for these taxes and the corporate umbrella and bankruptcy will not exonerate an employer from paying back payroll withholding. Employers should escrow these funds in a separate account and disperse them quarterly to withholding authorities.

Workers' compensation ∎ A state-mandated form of insurance covering workers injured in job-related accidents. In some states, the state is the insurer; in other states, insurance must be acquired from commercial insurance firms. Insurance rates are based on a number of factors, including salaries, firm history, and risk of occupation.

Working capital ∎ Refers to a firm's short-term investment of current assets, including cash, short-term securities, accounts receivable, and inventories.

Yield ∎ (*See also* Rate of return) The rate of income returned on an investment, expressed as a percentage. Income yield is obtained by dividing the current dollar income by the current market price of the security. Net yield or yield to maturity is the current income yield minus any premium above par or plus any discount from par in purchase price, with the adjustment spread over the period from the date of purchase to the date of maturity.

Abstracting and Indexing Service

ASSOCIATIONS AND OTHER ORGANIZATIONS

1 ■ American Society for Indexing (ASI)
1628 E Southern Ave., No. 9-223
 Tempe, AZ 85282
Ph: (480)245-6750
Co. E-mail: info@asindexing.org
URL: http://www.asindexing.org
Contact: Michele Combs, President
E-mail: president@asindexing.org
Facebook: www.facebook.com/asindexing

Description: Professional indexers, librarians, editors, publishers, and organizations employing indexers. Works to improve the quality of indexing and adherence to indexing standards; to encourage members to increase their professional indexing capabilities and performance; to advise authors, editors, and publishers on the qualifications and remuneration of indexers. **Founded:** 1968. **Publications:** *Indexer Locator*; *Education and Training in Indexing and Abstracting: A Directory*; *Directory of Indexing and Abstracting Courses and Seminars*; *The Indexer: The International Journal of Indexing* (Quarterly); *A Guide to Indexing Software*; *Generic Markup of Electronic Index Manuscripts*; *The Indexer* (Quarterly); *Indexing from A to Z*; *Key Words: American Society of Indexers* (Quarterly). **Educational Activities:** ASI Annual Conference (Annual). **Awards:** Hines Award (Irregular); ASI Excellence in Indexing Award (Annual). **Geographic Preference:** National.

2 ■ Indexing Society of Canada (ISC) [Societe Canadienne D'indexation; Societe canadienne pour l'analyse de documents (SCAD)]
100 Chapel St.
 Kitchener, ON, Canada N2H 2T5
Co. E-mail: info@indexers.ca
URL: http://indexers.ca
Contact: Jolanta Komornicka, President
Facebook: www.facebook.com/indexingsocie
 tyofcanada
Linkedin: www.linkedin.com/company/indexing-socie
 ty-of-canada-isc-sci
X (Twitter): x.com/indexerscanada

Description: Indexing and abstracting services; corporations; institutions; interested individuals. Works to: promote production and use of indexes and abstracts; further the recognition of indexers and abstracters; develop improvements in indexing and abstracting techniques; facilitate communication among members. **Founded:** 1977. **Publications:** *ISC/SCI Bulletin* (3/year); *Register of Indexers* (Annual). **Educational Activities:** Indexing Society of Canada Annual Conference (Annual). **Geographic Preference:** National.

3 ■ *ISC/SCI Bulletin*
100 Chapel St.
 Kitchener, ON, Canada N2H 2T5
Co. E-mail: info@indexers.ca
URL: http://indexers.ca
Contact: Jolanta Komornicka, President
URL(s): indexers.ca/resources/bulletin

Released: 3/year; Spring, Fall, Winter. **Price:** Free for members. **Availability:** Print; Download; Online; PDF.

REFERENCE WORKS

4 ■ "Abstracting and Indexing Still Relevant in the Digital Age" in GreenPoint Content + Publishing (August, 2015)
URL(s): www.greenpointpublishing.com/insight_html/
 abstracting-indexing.html

Released: August 2015. **Description:** Discusses how online content still benefits from clear and concise abstracts. Indexing also give users the ability to locate important information quickly, especially since the amount of digital and online content is so massive. **Availability:** Online.

5 ■ "Journal Indexing 101: Understanding the Basics" in Editage Insights (May 20, 2015)
Pub: Editage
Contact: Elvira d'Souza, President
URL(s): editage.com/insights/journal-indexing-101-un
 derstanding-the-basics

Ed: Jayashree Rajagopalan. **Description:** Provides an overview of journal indexing, including a list of databases that index published research. **Availability:** Online.

TRADE SHOWS AND CONVENTIONS

6 ■ ASI Annual Conference
American Society for Indexing (ASI)
1628 E Southern Ave., No. 9-223
 Tempe, AZ 85282
Ph: (480)245-6750
Co. E-mail: info@asindexing.org
URL: http://www.asindexing.org
Contact: Michele Combs, President
E-mail: president@asindexing.org
URL(s): www.asindexing.org/conference-2024

Frequency: Annual. **Audience:** Industry professionals. **Telecommunication Services:** info@asindexing.org.

7 ■ Indexing Society of Canada Annual Conference
Indexing Society of Canada (ISC)
100 Chapel St.
 Kitchener, ON, Canada N2H 2T5
Co. E-mail: info@indexers.ca
URL: http://indexers.ca
Contact: Jolanta Komornicka, President
URL(s): conference.indexers.ca

Frequency: Annual. **Description:** Annual national conference covering various topics of interest to indexers. **Audience:** The Society holds its conference and annual general meeting. **Principal Exhibits:** Annual national conference covering various topics of interest to indexers. **Telecommunication Services:** conference@indexers.ca.

Accounting Service

ASSOCIATIONS AND OTHER ORGANIZATIONS

8 ■ Accounting and Finance Benchmarking Consortium (AFBC)
4606 FM 1960 Rd. W, Ste. 250
Houston, TX 77069-9949
Ph: (281)440-5044
URL: http://www.afbc.org
Description: Promotes the use of benchmarking, wherein businesses compare their processes with those of their competitors, as a means of improving corporate efficiency and profitability among accounting and finance managers; facilitates exchange of information among members; conducts target operations, procurement, development, and maintenance studies; and identifies model business practices. **Founded:** 1998. **Geographic Preference:** National.

9 ■ Accounting and Financial Women's Alliance (AFWA)
2365 Harrodsburg Rd., Ste. A325
Lexington, KY 40504
Ph: (859)219-3532
Co. E-mail: afwa@afwa.org
URL: http://www.afwa.org
Contact: Stephanie Searcy, President
Facebook: www.facebook.com/AFWANational
X (Twitter): x.com/afwanational
Instagram: www.instagram.com/afwanational
Pinterest: www.pinterest.com/AFWAHQ
Description: Women accountants, educators and others in accounting dedicated to the achievement of personal, professional and economic potential. Assists women accountants in their careers and promotes development in the profession. Conducts educational and research programs. **Founded:** 1938. **Publications:** *The Edge* (Monthly); *Accounting and Financial Women's Alliance*. **Educational Activities:** Women Who Count National Conference (Annual). **Awards:** AFWA Masters Scholarships (Annual); AFWA Undergraduate Scholarships (Annual). **Geographic Preference:** National.

10 ■ AGN North America (AGN-NA)
13918 E Mississippi Ave., No. 63308
Aurora, CO 80012
Co. E-mail: info@agn.org
URL: http://agn.org/location/north-america
Contact: Heidi LaMarca, Chairman
E-mail: hlamarca@windhambrannon.com
Description: Certified public accounting firms. Provides networking resources, technical and marketing assistance, and staff training programs to members. Compiles statistics. **Founded:** 1978. **Publications:** *Client Newsletter* (Quarterly); *Tax Brochures* (Annual). **Geographic Preference:** National.

11 ■ American Academy of Attorney-CPAs (AAA-CPA)
2800 Eisenhower Ave., Ste. 210
Alexandria, VA 22314
Ph: (703)352-8064
Free: 800-ATT-YCPA
Fax: (703)683-5480
Co. E-mail: info@attorney-cpa.com
URL: http://www.attorney-cpa.com
Contact: Michele B. Friend, President
E-mail: mfriend@clarktrev.com
Facebook: www.facebook.com/americanacademyofattorneycpas
X (Twitter): x.com/attorneycpas
Description: Represents persons who are licensed both as attorneys and as certified public accountants (CPAs). Promotes high professional and ethical standards; seeks to safeguard and defend the professional and legal rights of attorney-CPAs. Conducts research on dual licensing and dual practice; maintains speakers' bureau, placement service. Compiled a list of attorney-CPAs in the United States; conducts biennial economic and practice survey. Maintains liaison with bar associations and accounting groups and offers referral service of potential clients. State groups conduct extensive self-education programs. **Founded:** 1964. **Publications:** *Membership Directory--American Association of Attorney-Certified Public Accountants Inc.*; *The Attorney-CPA* (Quarterly); *Attorney-CPA Directory*. **Educational Activities:** American Association of Attorney-Certified Public Accountants Annual Meeting and Educational Conference (Annual). **Geographic Preference:** National.

12 ■ American Accounting Association (AAA)
9009 Town Ctr., Pkwy.
Lakewood Ranch, FL 34202
Ph: (941)921-7747
Fax: (941)923-4093
Co. E-mail: info@aaahq.org
URL: http://aaahq.org
Contact: Terry J. Shevlin, Vice President
E-mail: tshevlin@uci.edu
Description: Represents professors, practitioners of accounting and other persons interested in accounting education and research. Promotes worldwide excellence in accounting education, research and practice. **Founded:** 1916. **Publications:** *Accounting Horizons* (Quarterly); *ATA Journal of Legal Tax Research* (Annual); *The Hasselback Directory*; *The Accounting Review* (6/year); *Journal of Information Systems* (3/year); *Issues in Accounting Education* (Quarterly); *Behavioral Research in Accounting* (Semiannual); *Journal of the American Taxation Association (JATA)* (Semiannual); *Auditing: A Journal of Practice & Theory* (Quarterly); *Journal of Management Accounting Research (JMAR)* (3/year). **Educational Activities:** ATA Midyear Meeting (Annual); American Accounting Association Annual Meeting (Annual). **Geographic Preference:** National.

13 ■ American Institute of Certified Public Accountants (AICPA)
220 Leigh Farm Rd.
Durham, NC 27707-8110
Ph: (919)402-4500
Free: 888-777-7077
Fax: (919)402-4505
Co. E-mail: aicpaspamreporting@gmail.com
URL: http://www.aicpa.org/home
Contact: Barry C. Melancon, President
Description: The national professional organization of Certified Public Accountants (CPAs). It sets ethical standards for the profession and U.S. auditing standards for audits of private companies, non-profit organizations, federal, state and local governments. It also develops and grades the Uniform CPA Examination. **Founded:** 1887. **Publications:** *CPA Client Bulletin* (Monthly); *AICPA Online*; *Accounting Research Studies*; *Auditing Research Monographs*; *Journal of Accountancy* (Monthly); *Not-for-Profit Entities - Best Practices in Presentation and Disclosure*; *The Practicing CPA*; *CPA Client Tax Letter* (Quarterly); *The Tax Adviser* (Monthly). **Educational Activities:** AICPA Advanced Personal Financial Planning (PFP) Conference (Annual). **Awards:** AICPA Two-Year Transfer Scholarship (Annual); AICPA Accountemps Student Scholarship Award; AICPA John L. Carey Scholarship Awards (Annual); AICPA Public Service Award for Firms; AICPA Outstanding CPA in Government Impact Award (Annual); AICPA Scholarship Award for Minority Accounting Students (Annual); AICPA/AAA Notable Contributions to Accounting Literature Award (Annual); AICPA Distinguished Achievement in Accounting Education Award (Annual); Outstanding CPA in Government Career Contribution Award (Annual); AICPA Public Service Award for Individuals (Annual); AICPA Special Recognition Award (Annual); AICPA Business Valuation Hall of Fame Award. **Geographic Preference:** National.

14 ■ American Taxation Association (ATA)
c/o LeAnn Luna, Representative
University of Tennessee-Knoxville
711 Stokely Management Ctr.
Knoxville, TN 37996
URL: http://aaahq.org/ATA
Contact: Jenny Brown, President
Facebook: www.facebook.com/aaahqata
Description: Membership comprises primarily university professors teaching federal income tax, federal estate, and/or gift tax courses; other members are practitioners, including certified public accountants. Seeks to further taxation education. Researches the impact of the tax process, particularly tax code sections, on the social and economic structure of the US. Maintains speakers' bureau. **Founded:** 1974. **Awards:** Ray M. Sommerfeld Outstanding Tax Educator Award (Annual); ATA Tax Manuscript Award (Annual); ATA Deloitte Teaching Innovation Award (Annual). **Geographic Preference:** National.

15 ■ American Woman's Society of Certified Public Accountants (AWSCPA)
1605 Wethersfield Rd.
Austin, TX 78703-3326
Contact: Margaret A. Ertewine, Officer
Description: Citizens who hold Certified Public Accountant certificates as well as those who have passed the CPA examination but do not have certificates. Works to improve the status of professional

women and to make the business community aware of the professional capabilities of the woman CPA. Conducts semi annual statistical survey of members; offers specialized education and research programs. **Founded:** 1933. **Publications:** *Membership Roster*; *AWSCPA Newsletter*; *American Woman's Society of Certified Public Accountants--Roster* (Annual). **Awards:** AWSCPA Woman of Courage Award (Annual); AWSCPA Educator of the Year Award (Annual); National Scholarships (Annual); AWSCPA Public Service Award (Annual); AWSCPA Woman CPA of the Year Award (Annual); AWSCPA National Scholarships. **Geographic Preference:** National.

16 ■ Auto Dealers CPAs
818 18th Ave. 10th Fl.
Nashville, TN 37203
Ph: (615)373-9880
Co. E-mail: info@autodealercpas.com
URL: http://autodealercpas.com
Contact: Angie Grissom, Owner
Facebook: www.facebook.com/Rainmakercompanies
X (Twitter): twitter.com/RainmakerCPAs

Description: Certified Public Accounting (CPA) firms providing financial and consulting services to automobile dealers. Seeks to advance CPA services to automobile dealers. Sponsors continuing education and training courses; conducts industry and member surveys; facilitates formation of joint ventures; makes available marketing assistance; facilitates resource sharing among members. **Founded:** 1996. **Publications:** *Auto Focus* (Quarterly). **Geographic Preference:** National.

17 ■ BKR International (BKR)
40 Wall St., Ste. 2837
New York, NY 10005
Ph: (212)964-2115
Co. E-mail: bkr@bkr.com
URL: http://bkr.com
Contact: Micheal Burch, Chief Executive Officer
E-mail: micheal.burch@bkr.com
Facebook: www.facebook.com/bkrinternational
Linkedin: www.linkedin.com/company/bkr-international
X (Twitter): x.com/bkrintl
YouTube: www.youtube.com/channel/UCHHd3Grwhp2uUG2WeOg1WWw

Description: Accounting firms in the U.S. and abroad. Seeks to create an international group of competent professional firms, which will provide services in major markets of the world and enable member firms to send/receive referrals. Helps reduce operating costs of member firms by: developing consolidated purchasing arrangements for services and supplies at the lowest possible cost; developing recruiting programs, marketing materials, and advertising to reduce the collective recruiting effort of group members; expanding the group to reduce the burden on individual member firms and increase their potential scope of services. Compiles statistics to provide member firms with data helpful to sound management decisions. Organizes clinical and administrative peer reviews to insure quality and provide management with professional counsel. Develops forms, procedures, and manuals to provide guidance and accommodate the needs of partners. **Founded:** 1989. **Publications:** *Worldwide Bulletin*. **Geographic Preference:** Multinational.

18 ■ Canadian Academic Accounting Association (CAAA) [Association Canadienne des Professeurs de Comptabilite]
439 University Ave., 5th Fl.
Toronto, ON, Canada M5G 1Y8
Ph: (416)486-5361
Fax: (416)486-6158
URL: http://www.caaa.ca
Contact: Hanen Khemakhem, President
X (Twitter): twitter.com/caaa_acpc

Description: Seeks to advance the study, teaching, and practice of accounting, broadly defined to include many related areas and disciplines of study. **Founded:** 1976. **Publications:** *Contemporary Accounting Research: Recherche Comptable Contemporaine (CAR)* (Quarterly); *Accounting Perspectives* (Quarterly); *Canadian Accounting Education and Research News* (3/year); *Contemporary Accounting Research* (Quarterly). **Geographic Preference:** National.

19 ■ Canadian Institute of Quantity Surveyors (CIQS) [Institut Canadien des Economistes en Construction]
90 Nolan Ct., Unit 19
Markham, ON, Canada L3R 4L9
Ph: (905)477-0008
Free: 866-345-1168
Fax: (905)477-6774
Co. E-mail: info@ciqs.org
URL: http://ciqs.org
Contact: Sheila Lennon, Chief Executive Officer
E-mail: ceo@ciqs.org
Facebook: www.facebook.com/canadianinstituteofquantitysurveyors
Linkedin: www.linkedin.com/company/ciqs
X (Twitter): x.com/ciqs_official
YouTube: www.youtube.com/channel/UC5l59C8R7cQN0Ngq-FvjS7g

Description: Establishes and maintains standards for certification and provides through advice to members relating to construction costs, management and administration of construction projects. **Founded:** 1959. **Publications:** *The Construction Economist* (Quarterly). **Awards:** Buster Vermeulen Memorial Award (Annual); Frank Helyar Memorial Award (Annual). **Geographic Preference:** National.

20 ■ Canadian Insurance Accountants Association (CIAA) [Association Canadienne du Comptables d'Assurance]
705-1 Eglinton Ave. E
Toronto, ON, Canada M4P 3A1
Ph: (416)840-5662
Co. E-mail: info@ciaa.org
URL: http://ciaa.org
Contact: Patrick Espeut, President
E-mail: patrick.espeut@allianz-assistance.ca
Linkedin: www.linkedin.com/company/canadian-insurance-accountants-association
X (Twitter): x.com/CIAA_Official

Description: Accountants employed in the insurance industry. Promotes excellence in the practice of insurance accounting; seeks to insure continuing professional development among members. Serves as a forum for the exchange of information among members; sponsors educational programs. **Geographic Preference:** National.

21 ■ Canadian Tax Foundation (CTF) - Douglas J. Sherbaniuk Research Centre [L'Association Canadienne d'Études Fiscales (ACEF)]
145 Wellington St. W Ste. 1400
Toronto, ON, Canada M5J 1H8
Ph: (416)599-0283
Free: 877-733-0283
Fax: (416)599-9283
Co. E-mail: ctfmembership@ctf.ca
URL: http://www.ctf.ca
Contact: Heather L. Evans, Chief Executive Officer
E-mail: hevans@ctf.ca
X (Twitter): x.com/cdntaxfdn

Description: Promotes increased awareness of the Canadian Tax Code and the social ramifications of taxation. Serves as a clearinghouse on taxation; sponsors research and educational programs. **Scope:** sponsors or directly carries out expert research in the fields of taxation and public finance, publishes the results of that research. **Services:** Interlibrary loan; copying; open to the public. **Founded:** 1945. **Holdings:** Periodicals; documents; books. **Publications:** *Annual Conference Report* (Annual); *CTF Annual Report* (Monthly); *Canadian Tax Highlights* (Monthly); *Canadian Tax Journal* (Quarterly); *Canadian Tax Papers Series*; *Finances of the Nation* (Annual); *Tax Memos*; *Tax for the Owner Manager* (Quarterly); *Taxation of Private Corporations and Their Shareholders* (Occasionally). **Geographic Preference:** National.

22 ■ *Canadian Tax Journal*
145 Wellington St. W Ste. 1400
Toronto, ON, Canada M5J 1H8
Ph: (416)599-0283
Free: 877-733-0283
Fax: (416)599-9283
Co. E-mail: ctfmembership@ctf.ca
URL: http://www.ctf.ca
Contact: Heather L. Evans, Chief Executive Officer
E-mail: hevans@ctf.ca
URL(s): www.ctf.ca/EN/EN/Publications/CTJ.aspx
Ed: Brian Carr, Kevin Milligan, Alan MacNaughton, Alan Macnaughton. **Released:** Quarterly **Price:** C$360, Nonmembers for CTJ-four hardcopy issues per year; C$460, Nonmembers for CTJ Plus-four hardcopy issues per year plus electronic access; $75, for per copy; $75, Members; C$100, for outside Canada. **Description:** Journal for professional tax practitioners, government officials, and public finance economists and university students. **Availability:** Print; PDF; Online.

23 ■ Chartered Accountants Worldwide Network USA (ACAUS)
New York, NY
Ph: (781)428-4544
URL: http://cawnetworkusa.com
Contact: Chris Easton, Co-President

Description: Chartered accountants from England, Wales, Scotland, Ireland, Canada, Australia, New Zealand and South Africa in commerce and public practice. Represents the interests of chartered accountants; promotes career development and international mobility of professionals. **Founded:** 1980. **Publications:** *Member's Directory and Handbook* (Annual). **Geographic Preference:** National.

24 ■ Chartered Professional Accountants of Canada (CPA CANADA) - Library
277 Wellington St., W
Toronto, ON, Canada M5V 3H2
Ph: (416)977-3222
Free: 800-268-3793
Fax: (416)977-8585
Co. E-mail: member.services@cpacanada.ca
URL: http://www.cpacanada.ca
Contact: Pamela Steer, President
Facebook: www.facebook.com/CPACanada
Linkedin: www.linkedin.com/company/cpa-canada
X (Twitter): x.com/CPAcanada
Instagram: www.instagram.com/cpa.canada
YouTube: www.youtube.com/cpacanada

Description: Aims to represent professional accountants in Canada by providing the highest standards of accounting, ethics, and best business practices. **Scope:** Accounting. **Founded:** 2013. **Holdings:** Figures not available. **Publications:** *CA Magazine: For Canada's Chartered Accountants*; *Directory of Canadian Chartered Accountants* (Periodic; Biennial); *CMA Magazine* (6/year). **Geographic Preference:** National.

25 ■ *The Construction Economist*
90 Nolan Ct., Unit 19
Markham, ON, Canada L3R 4L9
Ph: (905)477-0008
Free: 866-345-1168
Fax: (905)477-6774
Co. E-mail: info@ciqs.org
URL: http://ciqs.org
Contact: Sheila Lennon, Chief Executive Officer
E-mail: ceo@ciqs.org
URL(s): ciqs.org/web/08-News-Announcements-Pages/Construction-Economist-Journal.aspx
Released: Quarterly; Spring, Summer, Fall, Winter. **Description:** Provides up-to-date information on the Institute, technical articles and information on past and upcoming events. **Availability:** Print; PDF; Online.

26 ■ Construction Industry CPAs/Consultants Association (CICPAC)
4531 Bohemia Dr.
Pensacola, FL 32504
Ph: (850)723-0372
Co. E-mail: info@cicpac.com
URL: http://cicpac.com

27 ■ Accounting Service   **Small Business Profiles**

Contact: Christina Chifici, President
E-mail: cchifici@laporte.com
Facebook: www.facebook.com/CICPAC
Linkedin: www.linkedin.com/company/cicpac
Description: Certified Public Accounting (CPA) firms providing financial and consulting services to construction companies. Seeks to advance CPA services to the construction industries. Sponsors continuing education and training courses; conducts industry and member surveys; facilitates formation of joint ventures; makes available marketing assistance; facilitates resource sharing among members. **Founded:** 1989. **Educational Activities:** CICPAC Annual Conference (Annual); American Association of Attorney-Certified Public Accountants Annual Meeting and Educational Conference (Annual). **Geographic Preference:** National.

27 ■ *Contemporary Accounting Research*
439 University Ave., 5th Fl.
  Toronto, ON, Canada M5G 1Y8
Ph: (416)486-5361
Fax: (416)486-6158
URL: http://www.caaa.ca
Contact: Hanen Khemakhem, President
URL(s): www.caaa.ca/journals-and-research/con
temporary-accounting-research-caronlinelibrary
.wiley.com/journal/19113846
Ed: Hai Lu, Sarah McVay, Miguel Minutti-Meza, Partha Mohanram, Thomas Omer, Marlene Plumlee, Kristina Rennekamp, Jeffrey Hales, J.Douglas Hanna, Ole Kristian Hope, Paul Hribar, Khim Kelly, Clive Lennox, Thomas Ahrens, Peter Clarkson, Jeffrey Cohen, Kenneth Klassen, Linda Myers, Margaret Abernethy, Edward Riedl, Florin Sabac, Joseph Carcello, Fabrizio Ferri, Yves Gendron. **Released:** Quarterly **Price:** $1,105, Institutions for online only US, Canada. **Availability:** Print; Download; PDF; Online.

28 ■ CPA Firm Management Association (CAFMA) - Lending Library
7946 Clyo Rd., Ste. A
  Centerville, OH 45459
Ph: (937)222-0030
Co. E-mail: info@cpafma.org
URL: http://cpafma.org
Contact: Kim Fantaci, President
Facebook: www.facebook.com/CPAFMA
Linkedin: www.linkedin.com/company/cpafma
X (Twitter): x.com/cpafma
Description: Promotes accounting administration and office management in accounting firms and corporate accounting departments. Sponsors activities, including consulting and placement services, seminars, salary and trends surveys, and speaker's bureau. Provides a forum for representation and exchange. **Scope:** Audio collection; video programs collection; printed material collection. **Services:** Open to members; copying. **Founded:** 1984. **Holdings:** Audio and video programs; books; manuals; survey results.; Audio and video programs; books; manuals; survey results. **Publications:** *AAA Report* (Bimonthly). **Educational Activities:** CPA Firm Management Association's National Practice Management Conference (Annual). **Awards:** CPAFMA ACE Award. **Geographic Preference:** National.

29 ■ The Educational Foundation for Women in Accounting (EFWA)
151 W 4th St., Ste. 222
  Cincinnati, OH 45202
Ph: (937)424-3391
Co. E-mail: info@efwa.org
URL: http://www.efwa.org
Contact: Alexandra Miller, President
E-mail: alex@alexmiller-cpa.com
Description: Supports the advancement of women in the accounting profession through funding of education, research, career literature, publications, and other projects. **Founded:** 1966. **Publications:** *The Educator* (Semiannual). **Awards:** Women In Transition Scholarship (Annual); Women In Need Scholarships (Annual); Moss Adams Foundation Scholarship (Annual); Michele L. McDonald Memorial Scholarship (Annual); Rhonda J.B. O'Leary Memorial Scholarship (Annual); EFWA Postgraduate Scholarships (Annual). **Geographic Preference:** National.

30 ■ Healthcare Financial Management Association (HFMA)
4 Broad Plain
  Bristol BS2 0JP, United Kingdom
Ph: 44 117 929-478-9
Co. E-mail: info@hfma.org.uk
URL: http://www.hfma.org.uk
Contact: Owen Harkin, President
Facebook: www.facebook.com/HFMAUK
X (Twitter): x.com/HFMA_UK
Instagram: www.instagram.com/hfma_uk
Description: Any qualified accountant and/or financial employee working in the NHS. Promotes professional standards of financial practice in the management and audit of the NHS. **Publications:** *NHS Health Authorities*; *NHS Trust*. **Geographic Preference:** National.

31 ■ Institute of Management Accountants (IMA) - Library
10 Paragon Dr., Ste. 1
  Montvale, NJ 07645-1760
Ph: (201)573-9000
Free: 800-638-4427
Fax: (201)474-1600
URL: http://in.imanet.org
Contact: Mike DePrisco, President
Facebook: www.facebook.com/IMAnetORG
Linkedin: www.linkedin.com/company/ima-institute-of
-management-accountants
Description: Management accountants in industry, public accounting, government, and academia; other persons interested in internal and management uses of accounting. Conducts research on accounting methods and procedures and the management purposes served. Established Institute of Certified Management Accountants to implement and administer examinations for the Certified Management Accountant (CMA) program and the Certified in Financial Management (CFM) program. **Scope:** Accounting. **Founded:** 1919. **Holdings:** Figures not available. **Publications:** *Strategic Finance* (Monthly); *SF TechNotes* (Bimonthly); *Strategic Finance: Leadership Strategies in Accounting, Finance, and Information Management* (Monthly); *National Association of Accountants--Chapter Directory*; *Listing of Who's Who among Controllers Today*; *Management Accounting Quarterly* (Quarterly). **Educational Activities:** IME Annual Conference & Expo (Annual). **Awards:** Stuart Cameron & Margaret McLeod Memorial Scholarship (SCMS) (Annual); IMA Memorial Education Fund Scholarships (MEF) (Annual); Institute of Management Accountants FAR Doctoral Student Grants Program (Annual); IMA Student Case Competition (Biennial); IMA Stevenson Trophy (Annual); IMA Clark Johnson Achievement Award (Annual). **Geographic Preference:** National; Multinational.

32 ■ Interamerican Accounting Association (AIC) - Library [Asociación Interamericana de Contabilidad]
San Juan, PR
URL: http://contadores-aic.org
Contact: Aixa Gonzalez Reyes, President
E-mail: pedro.gonzález.cerrud@gmail.com
URL(s): www.ifac.org/who-we-are/membership
Facebook: www.facebook.com/aic.contabilidad
Instagram: www.instagram.com/aic.contabilidad
YouTube: www.youtube.com/c/AICdigital
Description: Objectives are to maintain high technical and ethical standards for the accounting profession; further accounting as a scientific discipline by fostering contacts between members and institutions of higher learning; provide members with information on current accounting practices and concepts. **Scope:** Accounting. **Holdings:** Figures not available. **Publications:** *Interamerican Accounting Association--Directory* (Irregular); *Interamerican Bulletin* (Monthly); *IAA Directory* (Biennial); *Interamerican Accounting Magazine* (Quarterly). **Awards:** IAA Meritorious Accountant of the Americas. **Geographic Preference:** Multinational.

33 ■ International Budget Partnership (IBP)
750 First St. NE, Ste. 700
  Washington, DC 20002
Ph: (202)792-6833
Fax: (202)792-6833
Co. E-mail: info@internationalbudget.org
URL: http://internationalbudget.org
Contact: Warren Krafchik, Executive Director
E-mail: wkrafchik@international.com
Facebook: www.facebook.com/InternationalBudge
tPartnership
Linkedin: www.linkedin.com/company/international-bu
dget-partnership
YouTube: www.youtube.com/user/IntBudgetPar
tnership/playlists
Description: Works to assist civil society organizations globally to improve budget policies and decision-making processes and reduce poverty. **Publications:** *A Guide to Budget Work for NGOs*; *IBP Newsletter* (Monthly). **Educational Activities:** IBP Conferences. **Geographic Preference:** Multinational.

34 ■ Manufacturing CPAs
188 Front St., Ste. 116-90
  Franklin, TN 37064
Ph: (615)373-9880
Co. E-mail: info@manufacturingcpas.com
URL: http://manufacturingcpas.com
Description: Provides accountants in the manufacturing industry a forum for information exchange, technical expertise, and resources. Sponsors continuing education and training courses; conducts industry and member surveys; facilitates formation of joint ventures; makes available marketing assistance; facilitates resource sharing among members. **Publications:** *Client* (Periodic). **Geographic Preference:** National.

35 ■ Moore North America
Moore Global Network Limited (MGNL)
  10400 Viking Dr., Ste. 510
  Eden Prairie, MN 55344
URL: http://www.moore-global.com
Contact: Ellen O'Sullivan, Executive Director
E-mail: eosullivan@moore-na.com
Facebook: www.facebook.com/MooreNorthAmerica
X (Twitter): x.com/MooreNAmerica
Instagram: www.instagram.com/moorenorthamerica
Description: North American public accounting and consulting firms. Aids certified public accounting firms in increasing, expanding, and diversifying their practices. Capitalizes on diversity of resources resident throughout the network to build a stronger revenue base for all members. Sponsors training programs in areas such as industry niche development, service niche development tax, staff, and computer auditing; conducts tax and management seminars. Compiles statistics. Offers networking forums, marketing assistance, and technology consulting to member firms. **Founded:** 1966. **Publications:** *MSNA Membership Directory* (Annual); *MSNA Networker* (Quarterly). **Geographic Preference:** Multinational.

36 ■ National Association of Black Accountants, Inc. (NABA)
7474 Greenway Center Dr., Ste. 1120
  Greenbelt, MD 20770
Ph: (301)474-6222
Co. E-mail: customerservice@nabainc.org
URL: http://nabainc.org
Contact: Guylaine Saint Juste, President
Facebook: www.facebook.com/NABAInc
Linkedin: www.linkedin.com/company/nabainc
X (Twitter): x.com/nabainc
YouTube: www.youtube.com/user/NABAInc
Description: Represents minority students and professionals currently working, or interested in the fields of accounting, finance, technology, consulting or general business. Seeks, promotes, develops, and represents the interests of current and future minority business professionals. **Founded:** 1969. **Publications:** *Achieve* (Semiannual); *Spectrum* (Semian-

nual); *Spectrum* (Semiannual); *National Association of Black Accountants--News Plus* (Quarterly). **Educational Activities:** NABA National Convention & Expo (Annual). **Awards:** NABA National Scholarship Program (Annual). **Geographic Preference:** National; Local.

37 ■ National Association of State Boards of Accountancy (NASBA)
150 4th Ave. N, Ste. 700
Nashville, TN 37219-2417
Ph: (615)880-4200
Fax: (615)880-4290
Co. E-mail: cbtcpa@nasba.org
URL: http://nasba.org
Contact: Ken L. Bishop, President
Facebook: www.facebook.com/National-Association-of-State-Boards-of-Accountancy-NASBA-57029612379
Linkedin: www.linkedin.com/company/nasba
X (Twitter): x.com/nasba
Instagram: www.instagram.com/nasbagram
YouTube: www.youtube.com/user/NASBAorg
Description: Comprises 54 state boards of accountancy. Serves as a forum for the boards, which administer the Uniform CPA Examination, license certified public accountants, and regulate the practice of public accountancy in the United States. Sponsors committee meetings, conferences, programs and services designed to enhance the effectiveness of its member boards. **Founded:** 1908. **Publications:** *State Board Report*; *Boards of Accountancy*. **Educational Activities:** NASBA National CPE Expo. **Awards:** William H. Van Rensselaer Public Service Award (Annual). **Geographic Preference:** National.

38 ■ National Association of Tax Professionals (NATP)
3517 N McCarthy Rd.
Appleton, WI 54913
Free: 800-558-3402
Fax: (800)747-0001
Co. E-mail: natp@natptax.com
URL: http://www.natptax.com/Pages/default.aspx
Contact: Gerard Cannito, President
Facebook: www.facebook.com/natptax
X (Twitter): x.com/NATPTAX
Instagram: www.instagram.com/natptax
Description: Serves professionals who work in all areas of tax practice, including individual practitioners, enrolled agents, certified public accountants, accountants, attorneys and certified financial planners. **Founded:** 1979. **Publications:** *TAXPRO Journal* (Quarterly); *TAXPRO Weekly* (Weekly); *TAXPRO Monthly* (Monthly). **Educational Activities:** NATP National Conference & Expo. **Awards:** NATP Tax Professional of the Year (Annual). **Geographic Preference:** National.

39 ■ National Conference of CPA Practitioners (NCCPAP)
185 Froehlich Farm Blvd.
Woodbury, NY 11797
Ph: (516)333-8282
Fax: (516)333-4099
URL: http://go.nccpap.org/home
Contact: Mark A. Stewart, Jr., President
Facebook: www.facebook.com/NCCPAP
X (Twitter): x.com/nccpap
Description: Represents the interests of CPA regional and local accounting firms. Works to enhance the professionalism of local firms. Works with the IRS and local and national government. **Founded:** 1979. **Geographic Preference:** National.

40 ■ National Society of Accountants (NSA)
1330 Braddock Pl., Ste. 540
Alexandria, VA 22314
Free: 800-966-6679
Fax: (703)549-2984
URL: http://www.nsacct.org/nsamain/nsa-homepage
Contact: Marchelle Foshee, President
E-mail: marchelle.foshee@gmail.com
Facebook: www.facebook.com/nsacct
Linkedin: www.linkedin.com/company/national-society-of-accountants
X (Twitter): x.com/NSAtax
Description: Professional organization and its affiliates represent 30,000 members who provide auditing, accounting, tax preparation, financial and estate planning, and management services to approximately 19 million individuals and business clients. Most members are sole practitioners or partners in small to mid-size accounting firms. **Founded:** 1969. **Publications:** *NSAlert* (Biweekly); *NSA Practice Advisor* (8/year); *NSPA Washington Reporter*; *National Society of Public Accountants--Yearbook*; *National Society of Public Accountants - Yearbook*; *Main Street Practitioner*; *Income and Fees of Accountants in Public Practice*. **Educational Activities:** NSA Annual Convention (Annual). **Awards:** NSA Scholarship Foundation (Annual); The Stanley H. Stearman Awards (Annual); NSA Accountant of the Year (Annual); NSA ASO of the Year (Annual). **Geographic Preference:** National.

41 ■ National Society of Accountants for Cooperatives (NSAC)
7946 Clyo Rd., Ste. A
Centerville, OH 45459
Ph: (937)222-6707
Co. E-mail: info@nsacoop.org
URL: http://nsacoop.org
Contact: Eric Krienert, President
E-mail: eric.krienert@mossadams.com
Facebook: www.facebook.com/NSACoop
Linkedin: www.linkedin.com/company/nsacoop
X (Twitter): x.com/nsacoop
Description: Employees of cooperatives, certified public accountants, auditors, chief financial officers, attorneys and bankers. Unites persons performing accounting, auditing, financial and legal services for cooperative and non-profit associations. Holds technical sessions annually. Compiles statistics. **Founded:** 1936. **Publications:** *The Cooperative Accountant* (Quarterly); *National Society of Accountants for Cooperatives--Membership Directory & Resource Guide*. **Educational Activities:** Tax, Finance & Accounting Conference for Cooperatives (Annual). **Awards:** NSAC Silver Bowl Award (Annual). **Geographic Preference:** National.

42 ■ National Tax Association (NTA)
1100 Vermont Ave. NW Ste. 650
Washington, DC 20005
Ph: (202)737-3325
Co. E-mail: nta@ntanet.org
URL: http://ntanet.org
Contact: Jennifer Blouin, President
X (Twitter): x.com/NatlTax
Description: Government and corporate tax officials, accountants, consultants, economists, attorneys, and others interested in the field of taxation. Promotes nonpartisan academics, study of taxation; encourages better understanding of the common interests of national, state, and local governments in matters of taxation and public finance; and disseminates higher quality research through publications and conferences. **Founded:** 1907. **Publications:** *National Tax Association Conference Proceedings* (Annual); *National Tax Journal (NTJ)* (Quarterly). **Awards:** Daniel M. Holland Medal (Annual); NTA Outstanding Doctoral Dissertation in Government Finance and Taxation (Annual); Steven D. Gold Award (Annual). **Geographic Preference:** National.

43 ■ PrimeGlobal
PrimeGlobal
3235 Satellite Blvd., Bldg. 400, Ste. 300
Duluth, GA 30096
Ph: (678)417-7730
Fax: (678)999-3959
Co. E-mail: communications@primeglobal.net
URL: http://www.primeglobal.net
Contact: Katie O'Bryan, Executive Director
E-mail: kobryan@primeglobal.net
Facebook: www.facebook.com/PrimeGlobalAccts
Linkedin: www.linkedin.com/company/primeglobalacct
X (Twitter): x.com/PrimeGlobalAcct
YouTube: www.youtube.com/channel/UCRVCVsNrjHhlQe5IBJ89m9Q
Description: Ensures that accounting, auditing, and management services standards are maintained. **Founded:** 1977. **Publications:** *Polaris International*. **Geographic Preference:** Multinational.

44 ■ Society of Depreciation Professionals (SDP)
12110 N Pecos St., Ste. 220
Westminster, CO 80234
Ph: (303)254-6496
Co. E-mail: admin@depr.org
URL: http://www.depr.org
Contact: Rebecca Richards, President
Linkedin: www.linkedin.com/company/depr
Description: Accountants and other individuals with an interest in the depreciation of assets. Promotes "professionalism and ethics within the art of depreciation." Serves as a forum for the discussion of issues affecting depreciation; sponsors continuing professional development courses for members. **Founded:** 1987. **Publications:** *The Journal of the Society of Depreciation Professionals* (Annual). **Geographic Preference:** National.

45 ■ Society of Professional Accountants of Canada (SPAC) [La societe des comptables professionnels du Canada; RPA Canada]
48 Village Ctr. Pl., Ste., 100
Mississauga, ON, Canada L4Z 1V9
Ph: (416)350-8145
Free: 877-515-4447
Co. E-mail: info@rpacanada.org
URL: http://rpacanada.org
Contact: Zubair Choudhry, President
Facebook: www.facebook.com/RegisteredProfessionalAccountants
Linkedin: www.linkedin.com/in/registered-professional-accountant-555378190
X (Twitter): x.com/rpacanada
YouTube: www.youtube.com/channel/UCqo7eFpci_fktegT5vwjB8A
Description: Professional accountants and individuals working to pass qualifying accountancy examinations. Promotes ongoing professional education among accountants; encourages students to enter the accounting field; works to advance the profession of accounting. Gathers and disseminates information on accounting; sponsors educational programs; conducts professional accountancy qualifying examinations. **Founded:** 1978. **Publications:** *Professional Accountant* (Quarterly). **Geographic Preference:** National.

REFERENCE WORKS

46 ■ "2011 Tax Information of Interest" in Business Owner (Vol. 35, November-December 2011, No. 6, pp. 10)
Description: Compilation of 2011 tax information to help small business take advantage of all tax incentives. **Availability:** Print; Online.

47 ■ "Accountants Get the Hook" in Canadian Business (Vol. 80, October 22, 2007, No. 21, pp. 19)
Description: Chartered Accountants of Ontario handed down the decision on Douglas Barrington, Anthony Power and Claudio Russo's professional misconduct case. The three accountants of Deloitte & Touche LLP must pay C$100,000 in fines and C$417,000 in costs. Details of the disciplinary case are presented. **Availability:** Print; Online.

48 ■ "Accounting Firm ATKG Adding Assurance Services Division" in San Antonio Business Journal (Vol. 28, July 11, 2014, No. 22, pp. 10)
Pub: American City Business Journals, Inc.
Contact: Mike Olivieri, Executive Vice President
Released: Weekly. **Price:** $4, introductory 4-week offer(Digital only). **Description:** A financial assurance services division will be added to the suite of client services offered by San Antonio, Texas-based accounting firm, ATKG. The new division will be headed by Kevin Barber. **Availability:** Print; Online.

49 ■ "Accounting Firm Weaver is Still Pursuing Growth Via Mergers" in San Antonio Business Journal (Vol. 25, January 6, 2012, No. 50, pp. 1)
Pub: Baltimore Business Journal
Contact: Rhonda Pringle, President
E-mail: rpringle@bizjournals.com
Description: Fort Worth, Texas-based Weaver LLP has worked out a merger to absorb the San Antonio-based John R. Hannah & Company LLP. The merger deal is Weaver's third in San Antonio area after it absorbed Polansky McNutt Perry & Company in 2008 and Edelman Arnold in 2009. Insights into the accounting firm's plan for Hannah are also provided. Availability: Print; Online.

50 ■ "Accounting Lags Behind: Profession Trails Others in Recruiting and Retaining Minorities" in Philadelphia Business Journal (Vol. 28, June 29, 2012, No. 20, pp. 1)
Pub: Baltimore Business Journal
Contact: Rhonda Pringle, President
E-mail: rpringle@bizjournals.com
Description: Accounting firms in the US had a low number of ethnic minorities in their talent pool, particularly African Americans and Hispanic accountants. A survey by the Pennsylvania Institute of CPAs found that 71 percent of their members do not believe their organization has a diversity recruitment and retention strategy in place. Availability: Print; Online.

51 ■ Accounting Perspectives
Pub: Wiley-Blackwell
URL(s): onlinelibrary.wiley.com/journal/19113838
Linkedin: www.linkedin.com/showcase/ap-pc
X (Twitter): x.com/AP_PC_Journal
Ed: Leslie Berger. Released: Quarterly Price: $1,105, Institutions for Online Only US, Canada, India. Description: Peer-reviewed journal covering new insights in Canadian accounting research, policy, and education. Published by Wiley on behalf of the Canadian Academic Accounting Association (CAAA). Availability: Print; PDF; Online; Download.

52 ■ "Accrual vs. Cash Accounting, Explained" in Business Owner (Vol. 35, July-August 2011, No. 4, pp. 13)
Description: Cash method versus accrual accounting methods are examined, using hypothetical situations.

53 ■ "Auditing the Auditors" in Barron's (Vol. 92, September 17, 2012, No. 38, pp. 16)
Description: The Public Company Accounting Oversight Board banned Michael T. Studer, president of the accounting firm Studer Group, because he failed to comply with auditing standards in his audits involving hinese reverse mergers. Availability: Online.

54 ■ "Cautions on Loans with Your Business" in Business Owner (Vol. 35, July-August 2011, No. 4, pp. 5)
Description: Caution must be used when borrowing from or lending to any small business. Tax guidelines for the borrowing and lending practice are also included. Availability: Print; Online.

55 ■ "Changing the Rules of the Accounting Game" in Canadian Business (Vol. 81, December 8, 2008, No. 21, pp. 19)
Description: Interference from world politicians in developing accounting standards is believed to have resulted in untested rules that are inferior to current standards. European lawmakers have recently asked to change International Financial Reporting Standards. Availability: Online.

56 ■ "Convergence Collaboration: Revising Revenue Recognition" in Management Accounting Quarterly (Vol. 12, Spring 2011, No. 3, pp. 18)
Pub: Management Accounting Quarterly
Contact: Mike DePrisco, President
Ed: Jack T. Ciesielski, Thomas R. Weirich. Description: While revenue recognition is critical, regulations have been developed on an ad hoc basis until now. The joint FASB/IASB proposed accounting standard on revenue recognition is a meaningful convergence of standards that will require a major adjustment for financial statement preparers. The proposal is a radical departure from the way revenue has been recognized by the U.S. GAAP. For industries such as consulting, engineering, construction, and technology, it could dramatically change revenue recognition, impacting the top line. The new proposed standard, its potential impact, and the critical role that contracts play is examined thoroughly. Availability: PDF; Online.

57 ■ "Crucible: Battling Back from Betrayal" in Harvard Business Review (Vol. 88, December 2010, No. 12, pp. 130)
Pub: Harvard Business Publishing
Contact: Diane Belcher, Managing Director
Ed: Daniel McGinn. Price: $8.95, PDF. Description: Stephen Greer's scrap metal firm, Hartwell Pacific, lost several million dollars due to a lack of efficient and appropriate inventory audits, accounting procedures, and new-hire reference checks for his foreign operations. Greer believes that balancing growth with control is a key component of success. Availability: Print; PDF.

58 ■ Deduct It! Lower Your Small Business Taxes
Pub: Nolo
Contact: Chris Braun, President
Ed: Stephen Fishman. Released: 19th edition. Price: $17.99, e-book; $19.99, book and e-book; $17.99, E-Book; $19.99, book and e-book; $17.99, e-book. Description: Information is provided to help small companies maximize taxable deductions. Availability: Handheld; E-book; Print; Electronic publishing; PDF.

59 ■ "The Difference Between Management and Project Management" in Contractor (Vol. 57, February 2010, No. 2, pp. 30)
Ed: H. Kent Craig. Description: There are differences when managing a two-man crew as a foreman and a 2,000 employee company as a corporate president. A project manager should have good skills in human psychology, accounting, and the knowledge of a mechanical engineer, architect, civil engineer, and also the meditative skills of a Zen master. Availability: Print; Online.

60 ■ "Do Fair Value Adjustments Influence Dividend Policy?" in Accounting and Business Research (Vol. 41, Spring 2011, No. 2, pp. 51)
Ed: Igor Goncharov, Sander van Triest. Description: The impact of positive fair value adjustments on corporate distributions is examined using a Russian setting that requires disclosure of unrealized fair value adjustments in income. It was found that there is no rise in dividends due to positive fair value adjustments and that on the contrary, a negative relationship exists between adjustments and dividend changes.

61 ■ "Economic Crisis and Accounting Evolution" in Accounting and Business Research (Vol. 41, Summer 2011, No. 3, pp. 2159)
Pub: Routledge, Taylor & Francis Group
Ed: Gregory Waymire, Sudipta Basu. Description: Financial reporting changes at the face of economic crises are studied using a punctuated equilibrium evolution. Findings show that financial reporting has a minor impact but may amplify economic crises. Attempts to enhance accounting and economic crises may not be as beneficial as planned. Availability: PDF; Online; Download.

62 ■ Employer Legal Forms Simplified
Released: First edition. Description: Business reference containing the following forms needed to handle employees in any small business environment: application, notice, confidentiality, absence, federal employer forms and notices, and many payroll forms. All forms are included on a CD that comes in both PDF and text formats. Adobe Acrobat Reader software is also included on the CD. The forms are valid in all fifty states and Washington, DC. Availability: Print.

63 ■ "Feds Finalize I-9 Form Rules Allowing Electronic Storage" in HR Specialist (Vol. 8, September 2010, No. 9, pp. 5)
Pub: Capitol Information Group Inc.
Contact: Allie Ash, Chief Executive Officer
Description: U.S. Department of Homeland Security issued regulations that give employers more flexibility to electronically sing and store I-9 employee verification forms. Availability: Print; PDF; Online.

64 ■ Finance & Accounting: How to Keep Your Books and Manage Your Finances with an MBA, a CPA, or a Ph.D

65 ■ "Finding the Right Accountant for Your Small Business" Business News Daily (February 21, 2023)
URL(s): www.businessnewsdaily.com/8039-find-small-business-accountant.html
Ed: Simone Johnson. Released: February 21, 2023. Description: Filing your small business taxes can be daunting, especially if you don't have a background in accounting. This article explains what to look for when choosing an accountant. Availability: Online.

66 ■ The Flaw of Averages: Why We Underestimate Risk in the Face of Uncertainty
Pub: John Wiley & Sons, Inc.
Contact: Christina Van Tassell, Executive Vice President Chief Financial Officer
Ed: Sam L. Savage. Released: March 26, 2012. Price: $19.95, paperback; $27.95, hardcover; $12.99, E-Book. Description: Personal and business plans are based on uncertainties on a daily basis. The common avoidable mistake individuals make in assessing risk in the face of uncertainty is defined. The explains why plans based on average assumptions are wrong, on average, in areas as diverse as finance, healthcare, accounting, the war on terror, and climate change. Availability: E-book; Print.

67 ■ "Getting More Out of Retirement" in Agency Sales Magazine (Vol. 39, November 2009, No. 10, pp. 48)
Description: Overview of the Tax Increase Prevention and Reconciliation Act, which lets employees convert to a Roth IRA in 2010. The benefits of conversion depend on age and wealth and it is best to consult a tax advisor to determine the best strategy for retirement planners. Availability: Print; Online.

68 ■ How to Start an Internet Sales Business Without Making the Government Mad
Pub: Lulu Press Inc.
Ed: Dan Davis. Released: October 01, 2011. Price: $19.95, paperback; $14.38, PDF; $14.38, e-book. Description: Small business guide for launching an Internet sales company. Topics include business structure, licenses, and taxes. Availability: E-book; Print; PDF.

69 ■ "How To: Manage Your Cash Better" in Inc. (Volume 32, December 2010, No. 10, pp. 69)
Pub: Mansueto Ventures L.L.C.
Contact: Stephanie Mehta, Chief Executive Officer
Released: December 01, 2010. Description: A monthly guide to policies, procedures and practices for managing cash for a small business. Availability: Online.

70 ■ "Inesoft Cash Organizer Desktop: A New Approach to Personal Accounts Bookkeeping" in America's Intelligence Wire (August 7, 2012)
Description: Inesoft Cash Organizer Desktop application is offering a new product for financial management on a home PC and mobile devices. The program supports the classification of money transac-

tions by category, sub-category, project, sub-project, budget planning, and world currencies (including current exchange rates), credit calculators, special reports, and more. Multiple users in the family can use the appllication. Details of the program are outlined. **Availability:** Online.

71 ■ *"Internal Auditor Wants Ethics Review of City's Billy Casper Golf Contract" in Business Courier (Vol. 27, September 10, 2010, No. 19, pp. 1)*
Pub: Business Courier

Ed: Dan Monk. **Description:** Mark Ashworth, an internal auditor for Cincinnati, Ohio is pushing for an ethics review of management contract for seven city-owned golf courses. Ashworth wants the Ohio Ethics Commission to investigate family ties between a superintendent for the Cincinnati Recreation Commission and Billy Casper Golf. **Availability:** Print; Online.

72 ■ *"Kaboom!" in Canadian Business (Vol. 81, November 10, 2008, No. 19, pp. 18)*
Description: International Financial Reporting Standards (IFRS) is a good idea in theory but was implemented in a hurry and had poor quality standards from the beginning. **Availability:** Print; Online.

73 ■ *"Lifesavers" in Black Enterprise (Vol. 41, December 2010, No. 5, pp. 38)*
Pub: Earl G. Graves Ltd.
Contact: Earl Graves, Jr., President

Ed: Tamara E. Holmes. **Description:** Profile of Interventional Nephrology Specialists Access Center and founders Dr. Omar Davis and Dr. Natarsha Grant; the center generated $5.5 million in revenue for 2009. Details on how they run their successful center are included. **Availability:** Online.

74 ■ *"Living in a 'Goldfish Bowl'" in WorkingUSA (Vol. 11, June 2008, No. 2, pp. 277)*
Description: Recent changes in laws, regulations and even the reporting format of labor organization annual financial reports in both the U.S. and Australia have received surprisingly little attention, yet they have significantly increased the amount of information available both to union members and the public in general, as reports in both countries are available via government Websites. While such financial reporting laws are extremely rare in European countries, with the exception of the UK and Ireland, the U.S. and Australian reporting systems have become among the most detailed in the world. After reviewing these changes in financial reporting and the availability of these reports, as well as comparing and contrasting the specific reporting requirements of each country, this paper then examines the cost-benefit impact of more detailed financial reporting. **Availability:** Print; Online.

75 ■ *Mergers and Acquisitions from A to Z*
Pub: HarperCollins Leadership
Contact: Donald Miller, Chief Executive Officer

Released: 2nd edition. **Price:** $19.99, Paperback. **Description:** Guide for the entire process of mergers and acquisitions, including taxes, accounting, laws, and projected financial gain. **Availability:** E-book; Print.

76 ■ *"Michael Daszkal On Going Beyond the Role of CPA" in South Florida Business Journal (Vol. 34, April 25, 2014, No. 40)*
Pub: American City Business Journals, Inc.
Contact: Mike Olivieri, Executive Vice President

Released: Weekly. **Price:** $8, Introductory 4-week offer(Digital & Print). **Description:** Michael Daszkal launched his CPA firm, Daszkal Bolton CPAs in 1994. It has grown from two people to a staff of 115, with 2013 net revenue pegged at $16 million. **Availability:** Print; Online.

77 ■ *Minding Her Own Business, 4th Ed.*
Released: 4th edition. **Description:** A guide to taxes and financial records for women entrepreneurs is presented. **Availability:** E-book; Print.

78 ■ *"My Favorite Tool for Managing Expenses" in Inc. (Volume 32, December 2010, No. 10, pp. 60)*
Pub: Inc. Magazine

Ed: J.J. McCorvey. **Description:** Web-based service called Expensify is outlined. The service allows companies to log expenses while away from the office using the service's iPhone application. **Availability:** Online.

79 ■ *"A Necessary Balancing Act: Bookkeeping" in Contractor (Vol. 56, November 2009, No. 11, pp. 22)*
Ed: Al Schwartz. **Description:** Pros and cons of getting a bookkeeper or a certified public accountant for the subcontractor are discussed. A bookkeeper can help a subcontractor get new accounting software up and running while an accountant will more than likely keep after the books at regular intervals throughout the year. **Availability:** Print; Online.

80 ■ *"New Institutional Accounting and IFRS" in Accounting and Business Research (Vol. 41, Summer 2011, No. 3, pp. 309)*
Pub: Routledge, Taylor & Francis Group

Ed: Peter Wysocki. **Description:** A new framework for institutional accounting research is presented. It has five fundamental components: efficient versus inefficient results, interdependencies, causation, level of analysis, and institutional structure. The use of the framework for evaluation accounting institutions such as the international financial reports standards (IFRS) is discussed. **Availability:** PDF; Online; Download.

81 ■ *"Olympus is Urged to Revise Board" in Wall Street Journal Eastern Edition (November 28, 2011, pp. B3)*
Pub: Dow Jones & Company Inc.
Contact: Almar Latour, Chief Executive Officer

Ed: Phred Dvorak. **Description:** Koji Miyata, once a director on the board of Japanese photographic equipment company, is urging the company to reorganize its board, saying the present group should resign their board seats but keep their management positions. The company has come under scrutiny for its accounting practices and costly acquisitions. **Availability:** Online.

82 ■ *"Place Restrictions on Your Stock Shares" in Business Owner (Vol. 35, July-August 2011, No. 4, pp. 14)*
Description: It is critical for any small business owner to be certain that the buyer or recipient of any part of the company represents that the stock is being acquired or given for investment purposes only. **Availability:** Online.

83 ■ *"Privacy Concern: Are 'Group' Time Sheets Legal?" in HR Specialist (Vol. 8, September 2010, No. 9, pp. 4)*
Pub: Capitol Information Group Inc.
Contact: Allie Ash, Chief Executive Officer

Description: Under the Fair Labor Standards Act (FLSA) employers are required to maintain and preserve payroll or other records, including the number of hours worked, but it does not prescribe a particular order or form in which these records must be kept. **Availability:** PDF; Online.

84 ■ *"Proposed Accounting Changes Could Complicate Tenants' Leases" in Baltimore Business Journal (Vol. 28, July 2, 2010, No. 8, pp. 1)*
Pub: Baltimore Business Journal
Contact: Rhonda Pringle, President
E-mail: rpringle@bizjournals.com

Ed: Daniel J. Sernovitz. **Description:** The Financial Accounting Standards Board has proposed that companies must indicate the value of real estate leases as assets and liabilities on balance sheets instead of expenses. The proposals could cause some companies to document millions of dollars in charges on their books or find difficulty in getting loans. **Availability:** Print.

85 ■ *"PwC to Add 400 Workers in North Texas" in Dallas Business Journal (Vol. 35, April 6, 2012, No. 30, pp. 1)*
Pub: Baltimore Business Journal
Contact: Rhonda Pringle, President
E-mail: rpringle@bizjournals.com

Description: London, England-headquartered PwC, formerly known as PricewaterhouseCoopers LLP, announced plans to hire 400 employees for its North Texas operations during the next 12 months. The firm provides auditing, consulting, and tax services to public, private and government clients. **Availability:** Print; Online.

86 ■ *QuickBooks 2014 on Demand*
Pub: Que Publishing

Ed: Gail Perry. **Released:** 1st edition. **Price:** $22.39, Members, e-book. **Description:** Step-by-step training for using various small business financial software programs; includes illustrated, full color explanations. **Availability:** watermarked; E-book; Print; Electronic publishing; PDF.

87 ■ *QuickBooks for the New Bean Counter: Business Owner's Guide 2006*
Description: Profile of QuickBooks software, offering insight into using the software's accounting and bookkeeping functions.

88 ■ *"Quicken Starter Edition 2008" in Black Enterprise (Vol. 38, March 1, 2008, No. 8, pp. 54)*
Pub: Earl G. Graves Ltd.
Contact: Earl Graves, Jr., President

Ed: Dale Coachman. **Description:** Profile of Quicken Starter Edition 2008 offering programs that track spending; it will also categorize tax deductible expenses. **Availability:** Online.

89 ■ *Reading Financial Reports for Dummies*
Pub: John Wiley & Sons, Inc.
Contact: Christina Van Tassell, Executive Vice President Chief Financial Officer
URL(s): www.amazon.com/gp/product/1119871360/ref=as_li_tl?ie=UTF8&tag=wiley01-20

Ed: Lita Epstein. **Released:** 4th Edition. **Price:** $27.18, paperback; $18, e-book. **Description:** The fourth edition contains more new and updated information. This book is meant as a guide to help the reader interpret and understand financial reports, annual reports, balance sheets, income statements, statements of cash flow and consolidated statements. Real-world examples are given. . **Availability:** E-book; Print.

90 ■ *Schaum's Outline of Financial Management*
Pub: McGraw-Hill Professional

Ed: Jae K. Shim, Joel G. Siegel. **Released:** Third edition. **Description:** Rules and regulations governing corporate finance, including the Sarbanes-Oxley Act are discussed. **Availability:** E-book; Print; Download.

91 ■ *Self-Employed Tax Solutions: Quick, Simple, Money-Saving, Audit-Proof Tax and Recordkeeping Basics*
Released: Second edition. **Description:** A simple system for maintaining tax records and filing tax forms for any small business is explored.

92 ■ *The Small Business Bible: Everything You Need to Know to Succeed in Your Small Business*
Pub: John Wiley & Sons, Inc.
Contact: Christina Van Tassell, Executive Vice President Chief Financial Officer

Ed: Steven D. Strauss. **Released:** Third edition. **Price:** $22.95, paperback; $14.99, E-book. **Description:** Comprehensive guide to starting and running a successful small business. Topics include bookkeeping and financial management, marketing, publicity, and advertising. **Availability:** E-book; Print.

93 ■ *Small Business for Dummies*
Pub: John Wiley & Sons, Inc.

Contact: Christina Van Tassell, Executive Vice President Chief Financial Officer
Ed: Eric Tyson, Jim Schell. **Released:** 5th Edition. **Price:** $24.99, paperback; $16.99, E-book. **Description:** Guidebook for anyone wanting to start or grow a small business; topics include information financing, budgeting, marketing, management and more. **Availability:** E-book; Print.

94 ■ *Small Business Survival Guide*
Released: First edition. **Description:** Small business expert provides strategies to start a company and survive in the 21st Century. He shows small business owners how to succeed despite challenges that can defeat any firm. His advice covers suppliers; customers and contractors; competitors and creditors; spouses, family and friends; as well as the ways lawyers, accountants and other can steal an entrepreneur's success. Ennico also describes how startups can comply with local regulations. **Availability:** E-book; Print.

95 ■ *"Small Is Bountiful for Intuit" in Barron's (Vol. 90, September 13, 2010, No. 37, pp. 22)*
Pub: Barron's Editorial & Corporate Headquarters
Ed: Mark Veverka. **Description:** Finance software maker Intuit wants to tap the underserved small business market. One analyst sees Intuit's shares rising 25 percent to 55 percent in the next 12 months from September 2010. **Availability:** Online.

96 ■ *"Smart Year-End Tax Moves" in Business Owner (Vol. 35, November-December 2011, No. 6, pp. 8)*
Description: Managing small business and individual taxes is more important in a bad economy. It is imperative to seek all tax incentives that apply to your business.

97 ■ *"Spotlight on Pensions" in Business Horizons (Vol. 51, March-April 2008, No. 2, pp. 105)*
Pub: Elsevier Advanced Technology Publications
Ed: Laureen A. Maines. **Description:** Perceptions of pension burden and risk among financial statement users is likely to increase with changes in pension accounting. These perceptions might affect decisions on pension commitments and investments. **Availability:** Online.

98 ■ *Streetwise Finance and Accounting for Entrepreneurs: Set Budgets, Manage Costs, Keep Your Business Profitable*
Description: Book offers a basic understanding of accounting and finance for small businesses, including financial statements, credits and debits, as well as establishing a budget. Strategies for small companies in financial distress are included.

99 ■ *Streetwise Small Business Book of Lists: Hundreds of Lists to Help You Reduce Costs, Increase Revenues, and Boost Your Profits!*
Price: Paperback. **Description:** Strategies to help small business owners locate services, increase sales, and lower expenses. **Availability:** Print.

100 ■ *"Surviving an IRS Audit: Tips for Small Businesses" in Agency Sales Magazine (Vol. 39, July 2009, No. 7, pp. 52)*
Description: It is a good idea to enlist the services of a tax professional even if an audit is expected to go smoothly since the IRS is likely to scrutinize the unreported income and personal as well as business expenses of a small business during an audit. **Availability:** Online.

101 ■ *"Throughput Metrics Meet Six Sigma" in Management Accounting Quarterly (Vol. 12, Spring 2011, No. 3, pp. 12)*
Pub: Management Accounting Quarterly
Contact: Mike DePrisco, President
Ed: Shaun Aghili. **Description:** Throughput accounting (TA) metrics can be combined with six sigma's DMAIC methodology and various time-tested analysis and measurement tools for added effectiveness in resolving resource constraint issues. The goal is to optimize not only the output of a specific department but that of the entire system, by implementing a cost accounting system that is conducive to system optimization while increasing product quality, process integrity, or ideally, both. **Availability:** Print; PDF; Online.

102 ■ *"UPMC Develops Own Billing Solutions" in Pittsburgh Business Times (Vol. 33, January 17, 2014, No. 27, pp. 6)*
Pub: American City Business Journals, Inc.
Contact: Mike Olivieri, Executive Vice President
Description: How University of Pittsburgh Medical Center (UPMC) Health System transformed its accounts payable department by passing its process to a subsidiary, Prodigo Solutions, is discussed. UPMC moved suppliers and purchasers to a shared electronic platform and created a digital marketplace. The system's no purchase order, no pay policy has reduced the number of rogue purchases. **Availability:** Online.

103 ■ *"Voices Boomer's Blueprint: How CPAs and Auditors Will Remain Relevant" in AccountingToday (October 2, 2019)*
URL(s): www.accountingtoday.com/opinion/boomers-blueprint-how-cpas-and-auditors-will-remain-relevant
Ed: L. Gary Boomer. **Released:** October 02, 2019. **Description:** Even with the advancement of AI, robotics, and machine learning, CPAs and auditors will remain relevant. Computers are missing the human touch. CPAs and auditors also utilize technology, which makes it beneficial to their customers because they are then getting the best of both worlds. **Availability:** Online.

STATISTICAL SOURCES

104 ■ *RMA Annual Statement Studies*
Pub: Risk Management Association
Contact: Nancy Foster, President
Released: Annual. **Description:** Contains composite balance sheets and income statements for more than 360 industries, including the accounting, auditing, and bookkeeping industries. Also contains five years of comparative historical data for discerning trends. Includes 16 commonly used ratios, computed for most of the size groupings for nearly every industry.

TRADE PERIODICALS

105 ■ *The Accounting Review*
Pub: American Accounting Association
Contact: Terry J. Shevlin, Vice President
E-mail: tshevlin@uci.edu
URL(s): aaahq.org/Research/Journals/The-Accounting-Review
Ed: Michael L. Ettredge, Prof. Stephen Zeff. **Released:** 6/year; January, March, May, July, September, and November. **Price:** $1,390, for print package of three association-wide journals; $785, for print only. **Description:** Accounting education, research, financial reporting, and book reviews. Includes job postings of organizations seeking to hire accounting professionals. **Availability:** Print; PDF; Online.

106 ■ *Auditing: A Journal of Practice & Theory*
Pub: American Accounting Association
Contact: Terry J. Shevlin, Vice President
E-mail: tshevlin@uci.edu
URL(s): aaahq.org/Research/Journals/Auditing-a-Journal-of-Practice-and-Theory
Ed: Christopher Agoglia. **Released:** Quarterly; February, May, August and November. **Price:** $176, for print only. **Description:** Trade journal covering the practice and theory of auditing for accounting professionals. **Availability:** Print; Download; PDF; Online.

107 ■ *Behavioral Research in Accounting*
Pub: American Accounting Association
Contact: Terry J. Shevlin, Vice President
E-mail: tshevlin@uci.edu
URL(s): aaahq.org/Research/Journals/Behavioral-Research-in-Accounting
Ed: Prof. Richard C. Hatfield. **Released:** Semiannual **Price:** $208, for print only. **Description:** Academic journal covering research in accounting. **Availability:** Print; PDF; Online.

108 ■ *The CPA Journal (Certified Public Accoutants)*
Pub: New York State Society of Certified Public Accountants
Contact: Liren Wei, President
URL(s): www.cpajournal.com
Facebook: www.facebook.com/TheCPAJournal
X (Twitter): x.com/thecpajournal
Released: Bimonthly **Description:** Provides analysis, perspective, and debate on the issues affecting the financial world. Includes classifieds organized by positions available or situations wanted. **Availability:** Print; Online.

109 ■ *Journal of Accountancy*
Pub: American Institute of Certified Public Accountants
Contact: Barry C. Melancon, President
URL(s): www.journalofaccountancy.com
Facebook: www.facebook.com/JournalofAccountancy
X (Twitter): x.com/AICPA_JofA
Released: Monthly **Description:** Accounting journal. **Availability:** Print; Online.

110 ■ *Journal of Accounting Research (JAR)*
Pub: John Wiley & Sons, Inc.
Contact: Christina Van Tassell, Executive Vice President Chief Financial Officer
URL(s): onlinelibrary.wiley.com/journal/1475679x
Released: 5/year **Price:** $2,000, Institutions for print and online US, Canada; $1,781, Institutions for online only US, Canada; $1,858, Institutions for print US, Canada; $218, Individuals for print and online US, Canada and India; $81, Students for print and online US and Canada, India; $2,410, Institutions for print and online India; $2,706, Institutions for print and online India; $2,514, Institutions for print India. **Description:** General interest account journal covering research in all areas of accounting and related fields. Published by Wiley in association with the Accounting Research Center (ARC) at the Chicago Booth School of Business. **Availability:** Print; PDF; Download; Online.

111 ■ *Journal of the American Taxation Association (JATA)*
Pub: American Accounting Association
Contact: Terry J. Shevlin, Vice President
E-mail: tshevlin@uci.edu
URL(s): aaahq.org/Research/Journals/The-Journal-of-the-American-Taxation-Association
Ed: Connie D. Weaver. **Released:** Semiannual; Spring and Fall. **Price:** $168, for print only; $25, Members for hard copy. **Description:** Academic journal covering accounting and taxation. **Availability:** Print; PDF; Online.

112 ■ *Journal of Management Accounting Research (JMAR)*
Pub: American Accounting Association
Contact: Terry J. Shevlin, Vice President
E-mail: tshevlin@uci.edu
URL(s): publications.aaahq.org/jmar
Ed: Karen L. Sedatole. **Released:** 3/year; Spring, Summer, Fall. **Price:** $158, for print annual. **Description:** Academic journal covering the theory and practice of management accounting by promoting applied and theoretical research. **Availability:** Print; PDF; Online.

113 ■ *NewsAccount*
Pub: Colorado Society of Certified Public Accountants
Contact: Alicia Gelinas, Co-President Co-Chief Executive Officer
E-mail: alicia@cocpa.org
URL(s): cocpa.org/membership-plans
Ed: Krista Flynt. **Released:** Bimonthly **Description:** Relays information on issues and trends affecting the Society, its members, and the accounting profession. Recurring features include letters to the editor, job

listings, a calendar of events and columns titled Committees in Action, Student Corner, SEC Corner, and Technical Update. **Availability:** Print; Online.

114 ■ *The Practicing CPA*
Pub: American Institute of Certified Public Accountants
Contact: Barry C. Melancon, President
URL(s): us.aicpa.org/publications/newsletters/thepracticingcpa
Description: Focuses on accounting practice management and the practical application of professional standards. Recurring features include letters to the editor, announcements of seminars and conferences, and bizsites. **Availability:** Print.

115 ■ *Single Audit Information Service*
Pub: Thompson Information Services
URL(s): www.thompsongrants.com/product/Single-Audit-Information-Service
Released: Monthly **Price:** $696, for print and online; $2,100, for annual; $528, for online. **Description:** Covers single audit developments. **Availability:** Online.

116 ■ *State Board Report*
Pub: National Association of State Boards of Accountancy
Contact: Ken L. Bishop, President
URL(s): nasba.org/media-resources/publications
Ed: Ken L. Bishop. **Description:** Describes the activities and concerns of the National Association of State Boards of Accountancy. Recurring features include reports of meetings. **Availability:** PDF.

TRADE SHOWS AND CONVENTIONS

117 ■ American Accounting Association Annual Meeting
American Accounting Association (AAA)
9009 Town Ctr., Pkwy.
Lakewood Ranch, FL 34202
Ph: (941)921-7747
Fax: (941)923-4093
Co. E-mail: info@aaahq.org
URL: http://aaahq.org
Contact: Terry J. Shevlin, Vice President
E-mail: tshevlin@uci.edu
URL(s): aaahq.org/Meetings/2024/Annual-Meeting
Frequency: Annual. **Audience:** Industry professionals. Dates and Locations: 2025 Aug 04-06 Hyatt Regency Chicago, Chicago, IL; 2026 Aug 03-05 Caesars Palace, Las Vegas, NV; 2027 Aug 02-04 Gaylord Palms Resort & Convention Center, Orlando, FL; 2028 Aug 07-09 Hilton Anaheim, Anaheim, CA. **Telecommunication Services:** info@aaahq.org.

118 ■ American Association of Attorney-Certified Public Accountants Annual Meeting and Educational Conference
American Academy of Attorney-CPAs (AAA-CPA)
2800 Eisenhower Ave., Ste. 210
Alexandria, VA 22314
Ph: (703)352-8064
Free: 800-ATT-YCPA
Fax: (703)683-5480
Co. E-mail: info@attorney-cpa.com
URL: http://www.attorney-cpa.com
Contact: Michele B. Friend, President
E-mail: mfriend@clarktrev.com
URL(s): www.attorney-cpa.com/2024-annual-meeting-education-conference
Frequency: Annual. **Audience:** Accountants and lawyers.

119 ■ Institute of Internal Auditors - International Conference
KPMG LLP
345 Pk. Ave.
New York, NY 10154
Ph: (212)758-9700
Fax: (212)758-9819
Co. E-mail: us-optout@kpmg.com
URL: http://kpmg.com/us/en.html
Contact: Erik Lange, Leader Partner
URL(s): iiaic.org
Facebook: www.facebook.com/iiaintlconf
X (Twitter): twitter.com/iiaic
Frequency: Annual. **Description:** Internal auditing equipment, supplies, and services, software, and computer related equipment. Hybrid event experiences. **Audience:** All levels of internal auditors from every industry. **Principal Exhibits:** Internal auditing equipment, supplies, and services, software, and computer related equipment. Hybrid event experiences. **Telecommunication Services:** sponsorships@theiia.org.

120 ■ New Jersey Accounting, Business & Technology Show & Conference
New Jersey Society of Certified Public Accountants (NJCPA)
105 Eisenhower Pky., Ste. 300
Roseland, NJ 07068
Ph: (973)226-4494
Co. E-mail: njcpa@njcpa.org
URL: http://njcpa.org
Contact: Kathleen F. Powers, President
URL(s): www.flaggmgmt.com/nj
Description: Information and technology, financial and business services, computer accounting systems, software, tax preparation, accounting, audit, practice management software - windows, and computer and business systems. Banking, insurance, financial and business software. Internet, online systems and middle market software and investment services. **Audience:** CPAs, accounting professionals, business and financial executives of New Jersey, Fortune 1000 corporations, business owners and managers, and IT managers. **Principal Exhibits:** Information and technology, financial and business services, computer accounting systems, software, tax preparation, accounting, audit, practice management software - windows, and computer and business systems. Banking, insurance, financial and business software. Internet, online systems and middle market software and investment services.

CONSULTANTS

121 ■ Accounting Aid Society (AAS)
3031 W Grand Blvd., Ste. 470
Detroit, MI 48202
Ph: (313)556-1920
Fax: (313)556-1941
Co. E-mail: info@accountingaidsociety.org
URL: http://accountingaidsociety.org
Contact: Priscilla Perkins, President
Facebook: www.facebook.com/accountingaidsociety
Linkedin: www.linkedin.com/company/533610
Instagram: www.instagram.com/accountingaidacademy
Description: Expands the financial potential of underserved community members and small businesses in Detroit and Southeast Michigan area. **Scope:** Provider of free income tax assistance programs for low and moderate income families, seniors and others in need. Assists people with local, state and federal tax filings, as well as Property Tax Refunds, Earned Income Credits, Home Heating Credits and Child Credits. Also provides information on tax rights and responsibilities, including help for those who speak English as a second language and offer aid in resolving tax disputes with the IRS. Area served: Michigan. **Founded:** 1972.

122 ■ Accounting Evolutions, Inc.
Los Angeles, CA 90064
URL: http://www.accountingevolutions.com
Contact: Debbie Koltun, Contact
E-mail: debbie@accountingevolutions.com
Description: Consultants specialize in providing onsite accounting training services. **Scope:** Consultants specialize in providing on-site accounting training services.

123 ■ Accounting Group International
10830 N Central Expy., Ste. 300
Dallas, TX 75231-2139
Contact: Richard Stein, Contact
Description: Experienced international professional business advisors in the field of taxation, audit and accounting. Provides business advice to small and medium-sized domestic, international companies and private individuals. **Geographic Preference:** Multinational.

124 ■ Accounting On Computers Inc. (AONC)
PO Box 5272
Santa Rosa, CA 95402-5272
Ph: (707)837-8634
Co. E-mail: support@aonc.com
URL: http://aonc.com
Description: Assists in adapting a new or current accounting system into one that provides the information require to manage a business. **Scope:** Assists in adapting a new or current accounting system into one that provides the information require to manage a business. **Founded:** 1994.

125 ■ Accounting Software Tutor Inc.
509 Tunney Pl.
Santa Rosa, CA 95403
Contact: Pamela Benz, Contact
Description: Firm provides accounting software solutions for small to medium-sized businesses and mission is to provide the fit accounting software solution to meet the end users needs and provides consultation, installation, training, support services, procedures and bookkeeping on MYOB accounting software. **Scope:** Firm provides accounting software solutions for small to medium-sized businesses and mission is to provide the fit accounting software solution to meet the end users needs and provides consultation, installation, training, support services, procedures and bookkeeping on MYOB accounting software.

126 ■ Accounting Solutions Unlimited L.L.C.
429 Middletown Ave.
New Haven, CT 06513
Contact: Anthony F. Beatman, Member
Description: Provider of accounting software consulting and tax preparation services. **Scope:** Provider of accounting software consulting and tax preparation services.

127 ■ Accounting Transition Advisors L.L.C.
2 Galleine Dr.
Commack, NY 11725
Free: 866-279-8550
URL: http://www.transitionadvisors.com
Contact: Joel L. Sinkin, President
E-mail: jsinkin@transitionadvisors.com
Description: Firm provides consulting for the accounting profession and offers merger and transition consulting services for public accounting firms. **Scope:** Firm provides consulting for the accounting profession and offers merger and transition consulting services for public accounting firms. **Publications:** "Six Steps to Selling Your Practice," 2002; "Planning and Paying for Partner Retirements" **Training:** Tax Season Marketing: Strategies for Client Acquisition, Retention and Year Round Fee Generation, Jan, 2012.

128 ■ Arnold S. Goldin & Associates Inc.
PO Box 276158
Boca Raton, FL 33427
Ph: (561)994-5810
Fax: (561)431-3102
URL: http://www.arnoldgoldin.com
Description: An accounting and management consulting firm. Serves clients worldwide. Provides management services. Handles monthly write-ups and tax returns. **Scope:** An accounting and management consulting firm. Serves clients worldwide. Provides management services. Handles monthly write-ups and tax returns.

129 ■ Avery, Cooper & Co.
4918-50th St.
Yellowknife, NT, Canada X1A 2P2
Ph: (867)873-3441
Free: 800-661-0787
Fax: (867)873-2353
URL: http://averycooper.com

130 ■ Accounting Service

Contact: William Senfuma, Manager
E-mail: william.senfuma@averycooper.com
Facebook: www.facebook.com/averycooperandco
Description: Provider of public accounting and auditing services. **Scope:** Provider of public accounting and auditing services. **Founded:** 1969. **Training:** Sage Software Training. **Special Services:** ACCPAC Plus; Sage Accpac ERP.

130 ■ BAPTurnkey
12 Greenway Plz., Ste. 1100, No. 103
Houston, TX 77046
Ph: (281)705-0427
Co. E-mail: customercare@bapturnkey.com
URL: http://www.bapturnkey.com
Contact: Greg Businelle, Contact
Description: A "turnkey" hardware, internet and software best practices company. Provides partners and direct hire candidates. Specializes in several industries: industrial, information technology, engineering, finance and accounting. Turnkey hardware solutions include maintenance and evaluation and support of hardware/network infrastructure. Suggest solutions to supplement current set-up. Turnkey internet solutions incorporate solid design principles. Turnkey software solutions include updating and patching software. **Scope:** A "turnkey" hardware, internet and software best practices company. Provides partners and direct hire candidates. Specializes in several industries: industrial, information technology, engineering, finance and accounting. Turnkey hardware solutions include maintenance and evaluation and support of hardware/network infrastructure. Suggest solutions to supplement current set-up. Turnkey internet solutions incorporate solid design principles. Turnkey software solutions include updating and patching software. **Founded:** 2001.

131 ■ BDO FMA LLC
600 3rd Ave., 3rd Fl.
New York, NY 10016
Ph: (212)931-9112
URL: http://www.bdofma.com
Contact: Alex Gonzalez, Director
E-mail: agonzalez@bdo.com
Description: Firm provides public and private foundations and not-for-profit organizations capacity building services such as consultation and advisory, outsourced financial and operational management, certified and customized accounting training services. **Founded:** 2021. **Publications:** "The Evolution of Human Resources Directors' Responsibilities," The CPA Journal, Jul, 2009; "The Yin and the Yang of Strong Fiscal Infrastructures and Sound Programs," Apr, 2009; "A Countywide Non-profit Call to Action," The Register Star, Feb, 2009; "Fiscal Management: How Do Nonprofits Do It," New York Nonprofit Press, Sep, 2008; "What is the proper role of a nonprofit Chief Financial Officer," CPA Journal, Feb, 2008. **Training:** Building on Quality, Strengthening Financial Management Initiative Launch, Jul, 2009; Hands- 0n Tools for Managing through Tough Times, New York, May, 2009; Creating Investment Policies For Your Nonprofit, May, 2009; Seminars In Nonprofit Excellence, Apr, 2009; The Wallace Foundation Bidders Conference, Chicago, IL, Jan, 2009; The 2009 Nonprofit Economic Climate, Jan, 2009; Nonprofit Financial Management; Certified Nonprofit Accounting Professional (CNAP) Program; FUND E-Z Software; CPAmerica Technical.

132 ■ Capital Balance L.L.C.
1105 Berea Dr.
Boulder, CO 80305
Contact: Toni L. Frank, Contact
Description: A small business accountancy engaged in offering outsourced tax preparation services, tax planning, bookkeeping, and estate and trust tax consultation services.

133 ■ CBIZ, Inc.
CBIZ, Inc.
5959 Rockside Woods Blvd. N, Ste. 600
Independence, OH 44131
Ph: (216)447-9000
Fax: (216)447-9007
Co. E-mail: cbizwomensadvantage@cbiz.com
URL: http://www.cbiz.com
Contact: Jerome P. Grisko, Jr., President
Facebook: facebook.com/cbizmhmcareers
Linkedin: www.linkedin.com/company/cbiz
X (Twitter): twitter.com/cbz
YouTube: www.youtube.com/user/CBIZSolutions
Description: Diversified services company is engaged in providing an array of professional business services which include accounting and tax, healthcare and health benefits consulting, financial advisory, valuation, risk and advisory services, payroll, property and casualty insurance, retirement planning, managed networking and hardware services primarily to small and medium-sized businesses, as well as individuals, government agencies, and not-for-profit enterprises. **Founded:** 1996. **Training:** Health Care - What The Future Holds; Consumer Driven Health Plans; Executive Plans; Health Savings Accounts; Healthy Wealthy and Wise; Legislative Update; Medicare Part D; Retirement Plans.

134 ■ CheckMark Software Inc.
323 W Drake Rd., Ste. 100
Fort Collins, CO 80526
Free: 800-444-9922
Fax: (970)225-0611
Co. E-mail: sales@checkmark.com
URL: http://www.checkmark.com
Contact: Mohammed A. Ghani, Contact
X (Twitter): x.com/CheckMark_Inc
YouTube: www.youtube.com/channel/UCpJam_8CH-fjiC4eUG--wSA
Description: Developer of accounting and payroll software. **Scope:** Developer of accounting software tools for small businesses and provides fast, easy to use, affordable accounting and payroll solutions to small and medium sized businesses. Provides payroll software and multiledger integrated accounting software. **Founded:** 1984. **Special Services:** MultiLedger; Payroll.

135 ■ Edge Marketing
Minneapolis, MN
X (Twitter): x.com/EdgeMktgInc
Description: A full service agency in the accounting and financial marketplace to help businesses market and sell their products and services to accountants and financial professionals. Also assists companies in marketing and promoting accounting and finance related products and services to many other industries. Offers effective strategic planning, creating and executing effective marketing tactics and generating publicity that builds awareness of the client's products and services and enhances the company's image. **Scope:** A full service agency in the accounting and financial marketplace to help businesses market and sell their products and services to accountants and financial professionals. Also assists companies in marketing and promoting accounting and finance related products and services to many other industries. Offers effective strategic planning, creating and executing effective marketing tactics and generating publicity that builds awareness of the client's products and services and enhances the company's image. **Founded:** 1997. **Publications:** "Marketing and PR Social Networking Best Practices".

136 ■ Goldstein And Associates
10940 Wilshire Blvd., Ste. 600
Los Angeles, CA 90024
Ph: (310)443-4109
Fax: (310)443-4110
URL: http://nicmag.ca
Contact: Steve Goldstein, Chief Executive Officer
E-mail: s.gold4@verizon.net
Description: Firm provides temporary and permanent employment placement services offer career guidance and resume writing for job applicants and also provides computer consulting to clients in the area of database applications, installation, training, and support for small and medium business accounting systems. **Publications:** Neonatal Intensive Care: The Journal of Perinatalogy/Neonatology (Bimonthly); TradeShow & Exhibit Manager (Bimonthly); TradeShow & Exhibit Manager Buyer's Guide (Annual); Tradeshow and Exhibit Manager, Medical Sonography.

137 ■ Job Finders Employment Service (JF)
1729 W Broadway, Ste. 4
Columbia, MO 65203
Ph: (573)446-4250
Free: 844-228-JOBS
Fax: (573)446-4257
Co. E-mail: info@jobfindersusa.com
URL: http://www.jobfindersusa.com
Contact: Anne Williams, Owner
E-mail: annew@jobfindersusa.com
Facebook: www.facebook.com/JobFindersEmployment
Linkedin: www.linkedin.com/company/jobfindersusa
Description: Provider of staffing and recruitment services. **Scope:** Provider of staffing and recruitment services. **Founded:** 1986.

138 ■ John N. Zaremba
1314 N State St.
Bellingham, WA 98225
Ph: (360)671-1023
Fax: (360)671-3458
URL: http://www.zarembacpa.com
Contact: Brian Paxton, Contact
E-mail: brian@zarembacpa.com
Description: Firm provides tax preparation services for individuals and businesses, financial statement preparation, consultation regarding retirement planning, and much more. **Scope:** Firm provides tax preparation services for individuals and businesses, financial statement preparation, consultation regarding retirement planning, and much more.

139 ■ McCallum & Kudravetz P.C.
250 E High St.
Charlottesville, VA 22902
Ph: (434)293-8191
Fax: (434)296-9641
URL: http://www.mkpc.com
Contact: Deborah A. Hall, Director
E-mail: dhall@mkpc.com
Description: Law firm provides real estate acquisition, conservation easements, estate planning, elder law services and much more. **Founded:** 1982.

140 ■ Midwest Computer Group L.L.C. (MCG)
6060 Franks Rd.
House Springs, MO 63051
Contact: Leon Sanford, Jr., Contact
Description: Specializes in helping businesses create accounting, marketing and business information systems, software development and database design and management. **Scope:** Specializes in helping businesses create accounting, marketing and business information systems, software development and database design and management.

141 ■ Nelson & Pickens
15280 Addison Rd., Ste. 230
Addison, TX 75001-4550
Ph: (972)380-4096
Fax: (972)380-4096
URL: http://sites.google.com/a/nelsonandpickens.com/www
Description: Full-service certified public accounting firm focused on selling, training, and supporting accounting software. **Scope:** Full-service certified public accounting firm focused on selling, training, and supporting accounting software. **Founded:** 1989.

142 ■ On-Q Software Inc.
13764 SW 11 St.
Miami, FL 33184
URL: http://www.on-qsoftware.com
Contact: Teresita Cajigas, President
Description: Developer of computer software solutions. **Scope:** Developer of computer software solutions. **Founded:** 1987.

143 ■ Penny & Associates Inc. (PA)
2748 Bur Oak Ave., Ste. 2
Markham, ON, Canada L6B 1K4

Ph: (416)907-7158
Free: 866-370-0703
Co. E-mail: info@pennyinc.com
URL: http://www.pennyinc.com
Contact: Betty Penny, Contact

Description: Firm is an accounting and management firm that offers accounting and business solutions. **Scope:** Firm is an accounting and management firm that offers accounting and business solutions. **Founded:** 1994. **Training:** Quick Books, Aug, 2001; How to Stand Up to People Without Being a Jerk; How to Build Influence and Rapport With Almost Anyone; Dealing With Dissatisfied, Different and Difficult People; Effective Public Speaking; How to Incorporate Yourself; Company Perks: Attracting & Retaining Good People; FIRST AID. **Special Services:** Quickbooks®.

144 ■ PNP Staffing Group
515 Madison Ave., Ste. 1100
 New York, NY 10022
Ph: (212)546-9091
Co. E-mail: info@pnpstaffinggroup.com
URL: http://pnpstaffinggroup.com
Facebook: www.facebook.com/PNPStaffing
X (Twitter): x.com/PNPStaffing

Description: Full service staffing agency engaged in recruiting and staffing services. The company's suite of services includes temporary, temporary-to-hire, and contract staffing, interim professional services, executive search, direct hire and consulting services. It provides comprehensive solutions in fiscal management, business models, mission and vision, public policy and reputation management. It exclusively serves not-for-profit organizations and associations across a number of market sectors. **Founded:** 1996.

145 ■ PYA GatesMoore
Resurgens Plz., Ste. 2100, 945 E Paces Ferry Rd. NE
 Atlanta, GA 30326
Ph: (404)266-9876
Free: 800-270-9629
Co. E-mail: info@pyapc.com
URL: http://www.pyapc.com
Contact: Marty Brown, President
E-mail: mbrown@pyapc.com
Facebook: www.facebook.com/pyapc
Linkedin: www.linkedin.com/company/pyapc

Description: Firm provides healthcare consulting, audit and accounting and valuation services. **Scope:** Firm provides healthcare consulting, audit and accounting and valuation services. **Founded:** 1982. **Publications:** "Practicing Medicine in the 21st Century"; "Physicians, Dentists and Veterinarians"; "Insurance Portability and Accountability Act Privacy Manual"; "How To Guide for your Medical Practice and Health Insurance Portability and Accountability Act Security Manual"; "A How To Guide for your Medical Practice"; "Cost Analysis Made Simple: A Step by Step Guide to Using Cost Accounting to Ensure Practice Profitability"; "Cost Cutting Strategies for Medical Practices"; "Cost Cutting Strategies for Medical Practices"; "Getting the Jump on Year-End Tax Planning"; "New 401(k) Safe Harbor Option: Increased Opportunities for the Physician and Practice"; "Not All Tax News is Bad News"; "Shareholder Agreements: Identifying and Addressing Five Risk Areas"; "Surprise - Your Practice has a Deferred Income Tax Liability". **Training:** Documenting and Billing High Risk Codes, 2010; Current Challenges in Ob/Gyn Recruiting, 2010; Planning for Physician Wind-down & Retirement, 2010; HITECH "How To" - Opportunities & Risks, 2010; Pediatric Coding and Audits; Recruiting and Retaining Physicians; How to Prepare for the Recovery Audit Contractors - RAC, 2010; Meaningful Use Rule, 2010; The Revenue Stream in Practice, Apr, 2008; Improving Efficiencies in a Small Family Medicine Practice, Oct, 2007; Using Compensation Models to Improve Performance, Sep, 2007; The Financial Side of Personnel Management, Sep, 2007; Pay for Performance-Is it Really Contracting for Quality?, New York State Ophthalmological Society, Sep, 2007; Beyond the Class Action Settlement Payments-Looking Prospectively at Managed Care Companies Behavior, New York State Ophthalmological Society, Sep, 2007; Protecting your clients from Embezzlement, Jun, 2007; What P4P Means to Your Medical Practice, May, 2007; Finance for the Practicing Physician, May, 2007; Trashing, Dipping and Ghosts in Medical Practices: Protecting your clients from Embezzlement, Apr, 2006.

146 ■ R. Shane Chance CPA P.C.
1000 W Aztec Blvd.
 Aztec, NM 87410
Ph: (505)334-4375
Co. E-mail: office@chancecpa.com
URL: http://www.chancecpa.com
Contact: Shane R. Chance, Contact

Description: Provider of professional tax and accounting services. **Scope:** Provider of professional tax and accounting services.

147 ■ Sphere Consulting Group LLC
811 Oak St.
 Scott, LA 70583
Contact: Dennis J. Savoie, Manager

Description: Professional services firm is focused on in-building and metro-scale radio frequency engineering design, system verification, and system validation for fiber optics, small cell, distributed antenna systems and carrier-grade wireless connection implementation networks, the companies business targets enterprise, government, wireless service providers, and system integrators. **Founded:** 2005. **Training:** Total Statewide Interoperable Communication Methodology and Approach to a Solution, 2007; Sales Process The Key to Sales Productivity, 2006; Business Retention and Expansion, Business Attraction and Recruitment, and Entrepreneurship Economic Development Strategy Approach.

148 ■ Sterling
350 W Arden Ave.
 Glendale, CA 91203
Ph: (818)241-1144
URL: http://sterling.us
Contact: Kevin Wilson, Chief Executive Officer
Linkedin: www.linkedin.com/company/sterlingpracticemanagement
X (Twitter): x.com/sterlingmanage1

Description: Offers business consulting and management training for accountants and healthcare professionals. Offers on-site training and consulting. Designs an individualized program for clients to help them achieve their goals for their practice and to improve quality of life through precise application of Hubbard technology. Creates an organization and an environment that promotes, supports and rewards people for their contribution and productivity. **Scope:** Offers business consulting and management training for accountants and healthcare professionals. Offers on-site training and consulting. Designs an individualized program for clients to help them achieve their goals for their practice and to improve quality of life through precise application of Hubbard technology. Creates an organization and an environment that promotes, supports and rewards people for their contribution and productivity. **Founded:** 1983. **Training:** How to Achieve Your Goals; How Staff Can Increase Sales in the Workplace; Handling Emotions in the Workplace; Successful Team Building; How to Be Happy, Winning and Successful as an Executive; The Secrets to Getting Great Products; Honesty and Integrity in the Workplace; How to Sell More Using the Tone Scale; Improving Business Through Communication; Successful Time Management; How to Be Happy, Winning and Successful; Increasing Productivity and Job Satisfaction.

149 ■ Steve Burns Inc.
586 Leon Ave., Ste. 104
 Kelowna, BC, Canada V1Y 6J6
Ph: (250)863-9522
URL: http://steveburns.ca
Contact: Steve Burns, Officer

Description: Firm engages in financing, accounting and taxation issues advising activities. **Scope:** Firm engages in financing, accounting and taxation issues advising activities. **Publications:** "Entrepreneurialism Okanagan Style," 2005; "Burns Business Builder Beyond the Box," 2005; "Overhauling Your Sales Effort," 2005; "The Inside/Outside Marketing Measurement System," 2005; "Overhauling Your Marketing Efforts," 2005. **Training:** Performance Management; Marketing Intelligence Part 1; Human Resource Planning/Policies; Four Ways To Grow Your Business; How To Effectively Recruit High Technology Personnel; How To Interview, Select And Hire High Technology Personnel; Making Your Business Really Fly.

150 ■ Steven E. Kramer CpA
8282 University Ave.
 La Mesa, CA 91941
Ph: (619)464-8183
URL: http://us-accountant.com/company-steven-e-kramer-in-la-mesa-ca-30036
Contact: Steven E. Kramer, Contact

Description: Provider of accounting and management services in the following areas: Estate and tax planning, income tax preparation, expert witness services, small business development, professional liability insurance and professional practice management. **Scope:** Provider of accounting and management services in the following areas: Estate and tax planning, income tax preparation, expert witness services, small business development, professional liability insurance and professional practice management. **Founded:** 1975. **Training:** Starting Your Own CPA Firm; Protecting the Small CPA Firm Against Malpractice; Sole Practitioner's Conference; Loss Prevention Conference.

151 ■ Stillwater Insurance Group
6800 S point Pkwy, Ste. 700
 Jacksonville, FL 32216
Free: 800-220-1351
Fax: (800)491-7683
Co. E-mail: ins@stillwater.com
URL: http://stillwaterinsurance.com
Contact: Mark Davey, President
Facebook: www.facebook.com/Stillwater.Insurance.Company
Linkedin: www.linkedin.com/company/stillwater-insurance-group

Description: Provides strategic planning, budget and financial management, process improvement, organizational design and assessment and college student services operations. **Scope:** Provides strategic planning, budget and financial management, process improvement, organizational design and assessment and college student services operations. **Founded:** 2000. **Publications:** "Integrated Resource Planning (Irp)," Business Officer Magazine, 2005; "The Economic Risk Conundrum," University Business Magazine; "Revenue Analysis and Tuition Strategy"; "Managing Advancement Services: Processes and Paper".

152 ■ TL Cramer Associates LLC
561 Hollywood Ave.
 Grosse Pointe Woods, MI 48236
Contact: Terry Cramer, Contact

Description: Provides management advisory services to small and mid-sized businesses. The company's consultation capabilities include corporate structure; strategic and operational focus; financial management, including accounting and cash flow; marketing and business development; business planning and implementation; human resources and administrative issues; key management; information technology; and growth and profitability advisory. **Publications:** "Biz Journals"; "Business Week for Small Business"; "Trade Pub".

FRANCHISES AND BUSINESS OPPORTUNITIES

153 ■ LedgerPlus
4643 Clyde Morris Blvd., Ste. 308
 Port Orange, FL 32129
Ph: (386)767-3006
Fax: (386)767-7005
Co. E-mail: office@ledgerplusaccountants.com
URL: http://www.ledgerplusaccountants.com
Contact: Melvin Zerrusen, Owner
E-mail: mel@ledgerplusaccountants.com

154 ■ Accounting Service　　　**Small Business Profiles**

Description: Firm provides tax management, assurance, advisory services, accounting, audit and payroll services. **Financial Assistance:** Yes **Training:** Yes.

154 ■ Liquid Capital Canada Corp.
5075 Yonge St., Ste. 700
Toronto, ON, Canada M2N 6C6
Free: 877-228-0800
URL: http://liquidcapitalcorp.com
Contact: Robert Thompson-So, President
Facebook: www.facebook.com/liquid.capital
X (Twitter): x.com/Liquid_Capital
YouTube: www.youtube.com/channel/UCgFXxyEM4Lk1FjBms-H8Rng
Description: Provider of short term financing services including factoring, financing receivables, purchase financing and much more. **Founded:** 1999. **Training:** Yes.

155 ■ Padgett Business Services (PBS)
555 High St., Ste. 102
Westwood, MA 02090
Ph: (781)219-0395
URL: http://www.padgettadvisors.com
Contact: John Barucci, Contact
Facebook: www.facebook.com/PadgettBusiness
X (Twitter): x.com/PadgettBusSvcs
Description: Padgett provides an array of services to small businesses, such as consulting, financial reporting, government compliance, payroll and tax preparation services. Padgett also offers credit card processing, pension and 125 plan administration, equipment financing and workers' compensation payment service. **Founded:** 1993. **Training:** Initial training 12 days field visits, covering marketing, operations, and software. Ongoing training and support is provided through regular seminars in marketing, operations, tax, etc. Support is delivered through toll-free telephone and a wide range of information and material is provided via the company's web site.

156 ■ Sareen & Associates
10702 Vandor Ln.
Manassas, VA 20109
Ph: (703)366-3444
Co. E-mail: info@sareentax.com
URL: http://www.sareentax.com
Contact: Arun K. Sareen, President
Facebook: www.facebook.com/SareenandAssociates
Linkedin: www.linkedin.com/company/sareen-and-associates
X (Twitter): x.com/SareenTax
YouTube: www.youtube.com/channel/UCgWdJi928UANmcyJK2kBDbg
Description: Provider of accounting, bookkeeping, taxes and payroll services. **Founded:** 1993. **Financial Assistance:** Yes

COMPUTERIZED DATABASES

157 ■ ProQuest Accounting, Tax and Banking Collection™
ProQuest LLC
789 E Eisenhower Pky.
Ann Arbor, MI 48108
Ph: (734)761-4700
Free: 800-521-0600
URL: http://www.proquest.com
Contact: Matti Shem Tov, Chief Executive Officer
URL(s): about.proquest.com/en/products-services/pq_accounting
Availability: Online. **Type:** Bibliographic.

158 ■ Tax Notes® Today
Tax Analysts
400 S Maple Ave., Ste. 400
Falls Church, VA 22046
Free: 800-955-2444
Co. E-mail: communications@taxanalysts.org
URL: http://www.taxnotes.com
Contact: Thomas L. Evans, Chairman
URL(s): www.taxnotes.com/tax-notes-today-federal
Availability: Print. **Type:** Full-text.

COMPUTER SYSTEMS/ SOFTWARE

159 ■ *BNA Income Tax Planner*
BNA Software
1801 S Bell St.
Arlington, VA 22202
Free: 800-424-2938
Fax: (800)253-0322
Co. E-mail: help@bloombergtax.com
URL: http://pro.bloombergtax.com
Contact: Lisa Fitzpatrick, President
URL(s): pro.bloombergtax.com/income-tax-planner
Description: Available for IBM computers and compatibles. Calculates federal and state individual income taxes. **Availability:** Online.

160 ■ *Website Relief*
AccountantsWorld L.L.C.
1412 Broadway, Ste.1200
New York, NY 10018
Ph: (631)232-1040
Free: 888-999-1366
Fax: (631)232-3160
Co. E-mail: marketing@accountantsworld.com
URL: http://www.accountantsworld.com
Contact: Chandra Bhansali, Chief Executive Officer
E-mail: cbhansali@accountantsworld.com
URL(s): www.accountantsworld.com/website-relief
Description: Available for IBM computers and compatibles. System prepares 53 tax forms and schedules and calculates various personal and business taxes. **Availability:** Online.

LIBRARIES

161 ■ Brooklyn Public Library Business & Career Center
10 Grand Army Plz.
Brooklyn, NY 11201
Ph: (718)230-2100
URL: http://www.bklynlibrary.org/business
Contact: Linda E. Johnson, President
Description: Offers library services for business and career. **Scope:** Business & career services. **Founded:** 1943. **Holdings:** Figures not available.

162 ■ Canada Office of the Auditor General Knowledge Centre Library
240 Sparks St.
Ottawa, ON, Canada K1A 0G6
Ph: (613)952-0213
Free: 888-761-5953
Fax: (613)957-0474
Co. E-mail: infomedia@oag-bvg.gc.ca
URL: http://www.oag-bvg.gc.ca/internet/English/admin_e_41.html
Contact: Chantal Richard, General Counsel
Facebook: www.facebook.com/OAGCanada
Linkedin: www.linkedin.com/company/office-of-the-auditor-general-of-canada
X (Twitter): x.com/OAG_BVG
Instagram: www.instagram.com/oag_bvg
YouTube: www.youtube.com/channel/UC7UiIATFGs8x6cvNJilRHVw
Scope: Accounting; auditing; public administration; finance; management. **Services:** Library open to the public by appointment. **Founded:** 1977. **Holdings:** Books. **Subscriptions:** journals and other serials.

163 ■ Deloitte & Touche - Library
555 W 5th St., Ste. 2700
Los Angeles, CA 90013-1010
URL: http://www.deloitte.com/global/en/services/tax/collections/tax-library---deloitte.html
Scope: Auditing, taxation, management consultation, actuarial services, employee benefits, valuation consultation. **Services:** Library not open to the public. **Founded:** 1845. **Holdings:** Figures not available.

164 ■ Ernst & Young Center for Business Knowledge
155 N Wacker Dr.
Chicago, IL 60606
Ph: (312)879-2000
Fax: (312)879-4000
URL: http://www.ey.com
Contact: Joon Ko, Vice President
Scope: Accounting; taxation; consulting; healthcare. **Services:** Interlibrary loan; library not open to the public. **Holdings:** 3,000 books.

165 ■ Ernst & Young Library
833 E Michigan St.
Milwaukee, WI 53202
Ph: (414)273-5900
Fax: (414)223-7200
URL: http://www.ey.com
Contact: Carmine di Sibio, Chief Executive Officer
Facebook: www.facebook.com/EY
Linkedin: www.linkedin.com/company/ernstandyoung
X (Twitter): x.com/EYnews
YouTube: www.youtube.com/ernstandyoungglobal
Scope: Taxation; tax law; accounting; auditing. **Services:** Performs searches on fee basis for clients only. **Holdings:** 1,200 books.

166 ■ Ernst & Young L.L.P., Center for Business Knowledge
One Manhattan W 401 9th Ave.
New York, NY 10001
Co. E-mail: general@gu.ey.com
URL: http://www.ey.com
Facebook: www.facebook.com/EY
Linkedin: www.linkedin.com/company/ernstandyoung
X (Twitter): x.com/EYnews
YouTube: www.youtube.com/c/ernstyoung
Description: Helps build trust and confidence in the capital markets and in economies the world over. **Scope:** Accounting and auditing; taxation; finance. **Services:** Interlibrary loan; copying; library open to clients and SLA members. **Founded:** 1953. **Holdings:** 3,500 books.

167 ■ Institute of Management Accountants (IMA) - Library
10 Paragon Dr., Ste. 1
Montvale, NJ 07645-1760
Ph: (201)573-9000
Free: 800-638-4427
Fax: (201)474-1600
URL: http://in.imanet.org
Contact: Mike DePrisco, President
Facebook: www.facebook.com/IMAnetORG
Linkedin: www.linkedin.com/company/ima-institute-of-management-accountants
Description: Management accountants in industry, public accounting, government, and academia; other persons interested in internal and management uses of accounting. Conducts research on accounting methods and procedures and the management purposes served. Established Institute of Certified Management Accountants to implement and administer examinations for the Certified Management Accountant (CMA) program and the Certified in Financial Management (CFM) program. **Scope:** Accounting. **Founded:** 1919. **Holdings:** Figures not available. **Publications:** *Strategic Finance* (Monthly); *SF TechNotes* (Bimonthly); *Strategic Finance: Leadership Strategies in Accounting, Finance, and Information Management* (Monthly); *National Association of Accountants--Chapter Directory*; *Listing of Who's Who among Controllers Today*; *Management Accounting Quarterly* (Quarterly). **Educational Activities:** IME Annual Conference & Expo (Annual). **Awards:** Stuart Cameron & Margaret McLeod Memorial Scholarship (SCMS) (Annual); IMA Memorial Education Fund Scholarships (MEF) (Annual); Institute of Management Accountants FAR Doctoral Student Grants Program (Annual); IMA Student Case Competition (Biennial); IMA Stevenson Trophy (Annual); IMA Clark Johnson Achievement Award (Annual). **Geographic Preference:** National; Multinational.

168 ■ KPMG - Research Centre
777 Dunsmuir St., 11 Fl.
Vancouver, BC, Canada V7Y 1K3
Ph: (604)691-3000
Fax: (604)691-3031
URL: http://home.kpmg/ca/en/home.html

Scope: Tax; general business; stocks. **Founded:** 1982. **Subscriptions:** journals Figures not available.

169 ■ PwC Research Centre
1250 Rene Levesque Blvd. Ouest Bureau 2500
  Montreal, QC, Canada H3B 4Y1
Ph: (514)205-5000
URL: http://www.pwc.com/gx/en/industries/
  government-public-services/public-sector-research
  -centre.html
Contact: Nicolas Marcoux, Contact
Linkedin: www.linkedin.com/company/pwc
X (Twitter): x.com/pwc
YouTube: www.youtube.com/user/PwC

Description: Public sector research center. **Scope:** Accounting, tax, management, business, finance. **Founded:** 1993. **Holdings:** Figures not available.

170 ■ U.S. Department of the Treasury - Library
Freedman's Bank Bldg., Rm. 1020, 720 Madison Pl.
  Washington, DC 20220
Ph: (202)622-2000
URL: http://home.treasury.gov/services/tours-and-li
  brary/library

Scope: Local history. **Services:** Library open to the public by appointment. **Founded:** 1789. **Holdings:** Figures not available. **Publications:** *Department of the Treasury, Departmental Offices Telephone Directory* (Annual); *Roster of Minority Financial Institutions.*

171 ■ United States Tax Court
400 2nd St. NW
  Washington, DC 20217
Ph: (202)521-0700
URL: http://www.ustaxcourt.gov
Contact: Maurice B. Foley, Chief Judge

Scope: Federal tax law - income, estate, and gift. **Services:** Interlibrary loan; library not open to the public. **Founded:** 1924. **Holdings:** 60,000 books; 9,000 bound periodical volumes; Congressional Record, Federal Register, and federal tax legislation.

172 ■ University of Kentucky - Business & Economics Information Center
105 Main Bldg.
  Lexington, KY 40506-0132
URL: http://gatton.uky.edu

Description: Center that provides various programs involving business strategies and ideas about the economy. **Scope:** Business, economics, business management, marketing, finance, accounting. **Services:** Library open to the public for reference use only. **Founded:** 1993.

Adult Day Care Center

START-UP INFORMATION

173 ■ *"Caring Concern" in Small Business Opportunities (September 2010)*
Pub: Harris Publishing, Inc.
Contact: Janet Chase, Contact
Description: Profile of Joshua Hoffman, founder and CEO of HomeWell Senior Care, Inc., provider of non-medical live-in and hourly personal care, companionship and homemaker services for seniors so they can remain in their own homes. **Availability:** Online.

174 ■ *There's Someplace Like Home: Developing an Adult Day Care Center in Your Church*
Released: 1999. **Price:** $4.50.

ASSOCIATIONS AND OTHER ORGANIZATIONS

175 ■ **Argentum**
1650 King St.
  Alexandria, VA 22314
Ph: (703)894-1805
Co. E-mail: info@argentum.org
URL: http://www.argentum.org
Contact: James Balda, President
E-mail: jbalda@argentum.org
Facebook: www.facebook.com/ArgentumSeniorLiving
Linkedin: www.linkedin.com/company/argentum1
X (Twitter): x.com/argentum
Instagram: www.instagram.com/argentumadvocates
YouTube: www.youtube.com/user/assistedlivingfed
Description: Promotes the interests of the assisted living industry and works to enhance the quality of life for the population it serves. **Founded:** 1990. **Publications:** *ALFA Alert* (Periodic); *Senior Housing Directory*; *Guide to Choosing an Assisted Living Residence*; *Senior Living Executive* (Bimonthly); *ALFA Public Policy Bulletins* (Monthly). **Awards:** Argentum Hero Awards (Annual). **Geographic Preference:** National.

176 ■ **Little Brothers Friends of the Elderly Chicago Chapter (LBFE) [Little Brothers of the Poor]**
355 N Ashland Ave.
  Chicago, IL 60607-1016
Ph: (312)455-1000
Fax: (312)455-9674
Co. E-mail: general@littlebrotherschicago.org
URL: http://lbfechicago.org
Contact: Simone Mitchell-Peterson, Chief Executive Officer
Facebook: www.facebook.com/LBFEChicago
Linkedin: www.linkedin.com/company/little-brothers---friends-of-the-elderly-chicago-chapter
X (Twitter): x.com/LBFEChicago
Instagram: www.instagram.com/lbfechicago
YouTube: www.youtube.com/channel/UCFl5WfLN6qYQqO4Ps8XOOFg

Description: Seeks to combat the isolation and loneliness often experienced by elderly people by providing friendship and special assistance. Sponsors visitation programs, holiday and birthday parties, and summer vacations. Provides transportation for shopping and doctor's visits, food packages, and other services. Offers information, referrals and contacts with other public or private agencies. **Founded:** 1959. **Publications:** *Little Brothers Bulletin* (3/year). **Geographic Preference:** Local; National.

177 ■ **National Adult Day Services Association (NADSA)**
11350 Random Hills Rd., Ste. 800
  Fairfax, VA 22030
Free: 877-745-1440
Co. E-mail: info@nadsa.org
URL: http://www.nadsa.org
Contact: Donna Hale, Executive Director
E-mail: director@nadsa.org
Facebook: www.facebook.com/NADSA2
X (Twitter): x.com/NADSA2
Description: Adult daycare practitioners; health and social service planners; individuals involved in planning and providing services for older persons. (Daycare centers offer services in a group setting ranging from active rehabilitation to social and health care.) Promotes and enhances adult daycare programs; provides services and activities for disabled older persons on a long-term basis; provides training and technical assistance and consultation services for daycare personnel; organizes funding; develops standards and guidelines for adult daycare programs; encourages adult daycare centers to participate in local area health planning activities to heighten the effectiveness of adult daycare. **Founded:** 1979. **Educational Activities:** National Adult Day Services Conference (Annual). **Awards:** Ruth Von Behren Award (Annual). **Geographic Preference:** National.

178 ■ **National Council on Aging (NCOA) - Library**
251 18th St. S Ste. 500
  Arlington, VA 22202
Ph: (571)527-3900
Co. E-mail: newsletters@ncoa.org
URL: http://www.ncoa.org
Contact: Ramsey Alwin, President
Facebook: www.facebook.com/NCOAging
Linkedin: www.linkedin.com/company/national-council-on-aging
X (Twitter): x.com/NCOAging
Instagram: www.instagram.com/ncoaging
YouTube: www.youtube.com/user/ncoaging
Description: Serves as a national voice and powerful advocate on behalf of older Americans. **Scope:** Aging. **Founded:** 1950. **Holdings:** Figures not available. **Publications:** *Abstracts in Social Gerontology* (Quarterly); *NCOA Networks* (Bimonthly); *Innovations: The Journal of the National Council on the Aging* (Quarterly). **Educational Activities:** National Council on the Aging (Annual). **Awards:** Geneva Mathiasen Award (Annual); Arthur Flemming Award (Annual); Jack Ossofsky Award (Annual); Ollie A. Randall Award (Annual); Molly Mettler Award for Leadership in Health Promotion (Annual); Claude Pepper Award for Excellence in Community-Based Long-Term Care (Annual); NISC Founders Award (Annual); NISC Research Award. **Geographic Preference:** National.

REFERENCE WORKS

179 ■ *"Advancing the Ball" in Inside Healthcare (Vol. 6, December 2010, No. 7, pp. 31)*
Description: Profile of Medicalodges an elder-care specialty company that provides both patient care and technology development. President and CEO of the firm believes that hiring good employees is key to growth for any small business. **Availability:** Online.

180 ■ *"Elder Care Costs Surge" in National Underwriter Life & Health (Vol. 114, November 8, 2020, No. 21, pp. 25)*
Ed: Trevor Thomas. **Description:** Nursing home and assisted living rates rose from 2009 to 2010, according to MetLife Mature Market Institute. Statistical data included. **Availability:** Online.

181 ■ *"Elder Care, Rx Drug Reforms Top Zoeller's Agenda" in Times (December 21, 2010)*
Pub: The Times
Ed: Sarah Tompkins. **Description:** Indiana Attorney General Greg Zoeller is hoping to develop a program in the state that will help regulate care for the elderly; freeze medical licenses for doctors involved in criminal investigations; address illegal drug use; and to establish a program to help individuals dispose of old prescription medications easily at pharmacies. **Availability:** Online.

182 ■ *"Elder-Care Seminar to Teach Ways to Avoid Falls" in Virginian-Pilot (November 25, 2010)*
Pub: The Virginian-Pilot
Contact: Kevin Goyette, Director
E-mail: kgoyette@dailypress.com
Ed: Amy Jeter. **Description:** ResCare HomeCare, a home health services firm, offers free seminars on helping to make residences safer for seniors prone to falling. **Availability:** Print; Online.

183 ■ *"EVMS Gets Grant to Train Providers for Elder Care" in Virginian-Pilot (October 29, 2010)*
Pub: The Virginian-Pilot
Contact: Kevin Goyette, Director
E-mail: kgoyette@dailypress.com
Ed: Elizabeth Simpson. **Description:** Eastern Virginia Medical School received a federal grant to train health providers in elder care. Details of the program are provided. **Availability:** Online.

184 ■ *How to Start a Home-Based Senior Care Business*
Ed: James L. Ferry. **Released:** 2nd edition. **Price:** Paperback,softback; Electronic Book. **Description:** Information is provided to start a home-based senior care business. **Availability:** E-book; Print.

185 ■ *"Silver Dollars" in Small Business Opportunities (September 2008)*
Description: Profile of Always Best Care Senior Services, a franchise created by Michael Newman, which offers non-medical In-Home Care, Personal Emergency Response Systems, and Assisted Living Placement Services to seniors; the company offers franchisees the opportunity to fill what is oftentimes a void for the seniors and their families in the community. **Availability:** Online.

186 ■ *"Starting an Adult Day Care Center: What You Need to Know for Success" in Verywell (July 30, 2019)*
URL(s): www.verywellhealth.com/starting-an-adult-day-care-center-197946
Ed: Anthony Cirillo. **Released:** July 30, 2019. **Description:** A comprehensive article discussing multiple facets for the adult day care industry. Statistics, state rules, regulations, certification, record keeping, service requirements, design environment, safety, and staffing are examined. **Availability:** Online.

TRADE PERIODICALS

187 ■ *Clinical Gerontologist: The Journal of Aging and Mental Health*
Pub: Taylor And Francis Group
Contact: Annie Callanan, Chief Executive Officer
URL(s): www.tandfonline.com/journals/wcli20
X (Twitter): x.com/clinical_gero
Ed: Dolores Gallagher-Thompson, PhD. **Released:** 5/year **Price:** $2,284, Institutions for online only; $340, Individuals for online only. **Description:** Contains practical information and research on assessment and intervention of mental health needs of aged patients. **Availability:** Print; Download; PDF; Online.

FRANCHISES AND BUSINESS OPPORTUNITIES

188 ■ **Aging Excellence**
12 Shuman Ave., Ste. 3
Augusta, ME 04330
Ph: (207)512-8894
Free: 866-988-0991
Co. E-mail: info@seniorsonthego.com
URL: http://www.seniorsonthego.com
Contact: Bethany Lawrence, President
Description: Firm provides home care and non-medical senior care services. **Founded:** 1999. **Financial Assistance:** Yes **Training:** Provides 1 week at headquarters, 2 days onsite with ongoing support.

189 ■ **CareMinders Home Care Inc.**
2475 Northwinds Pky., Ste. 200
Alpharetta, GA 30009
Contact: Brian Leonard Schleicher, Chief Executive Officer
Description: Franchiser in the home care industry. **Founded:** 2004. **Royalty Fee:** 3.75-5%. **Training:** 1 week training provided at headquarters, 2 days onsite and ongoing support.

190 ■ **Caring Senior Service**
201 E Pk. Ave., Ste. 200
San Antonio, TX 78212
Ph: (210)227-9494
Co. E-mail: cssmarketing@caringinc.com
URL: http://www.caringseniorservice.com
Contact: Jeff Salter, President
E-mail: jeff@caringinc.com
Facebook: www.facebook.com/CaringSeniorService
Linkedin: www.linkedin.com/company/73321
X (Twitter): x.com/CaringSrService
YouTube: www.youtube.com/user/caringsrservice
Pinterest: www.pinterest.com/caringsrservice
Description: Provider of home senior care services for elderly. **Founded:** 1991. **Financial Assistance:** Yes **Training:** Yes.

191 ■ **Homewatch CareGivers (HWCG)**
6251 Greenwood Plz. Blvd., Ste. 250
Greenwood Village, CO 80111
URL: http://www.homewatchcaregivers.com
Contact: Todd Houghton, President
Facebook: www.facebook.com/HomewatchCareGivers
Linkedin: www.linkedin.com/company/homewatch-caregivers
X (Twitter): x.com/hwcaregivers
Instagram: www.instagram.com/hwcaregivers
YouTube: www.youtube.com/user/hwcg500
Description: Offers services to elderly people who want to stay at home. **Founded:** 1980. **Training:** Offers pre-training, initial training, and post training program.

192 ■ **Passport Health Inc. (PH)**
1702 Whetstone Way
Baltimore, MD 21230
Ph: (410)727-0556
Co. E-mail: info@passporthealthglobal.com
URL: http://www.passporthealthusa.com
Contact: Fran Lessans, Chief Executive Officer
Facebook: www.facebook.com/PassportHealthINC
Linkedin: www.linkedin.com/company/passport-health
X (Twitter): x.com/passport_health
Instagram: www.instagram.com/passporthealth
YouTube: www.youtube.com/user/passporthealth
Description: Provider of travel medicine and immunization services in North America. **Founded:** 1994. **Training:** Provider of preventive healthcare services.

COMPUTERIZED DATABASES

193 ■ *AgeLine®*
EBSCO Information Services
10 Estes St.
Ipswich, MA 01938
Ph: (978)356-6500
Free: 800-653-2726
Co. E-mail: information@ebsco.com
URL: http://www.ebsco.com
Contact: Tim Collins, Chief Executive Officer
URL(s): www.ebsco.com/products/research-databases/ageline
Released: Weekly **Availability:** Online. **Type:** Bibliographic.

194 ■ *Consumer InSite*
Type: Full-text.

195 ■ *Health & Wellness InSite*
Type: Full-text.

LIBRARIES

196 ■ **American College of Health Care Administrators (ACHCA)**
1101 Connecticut Ave. NW, Ste. 450
Washington, DC 20036
Free: 800-561-3148
Co. E-mail: info@achca.org
URL: http://www.achca.org
Contact: Amanda Charles, Business Manager
E-mail: acharles@achca.org
Facebook: www.facebook.com/pages/The-American-College-of-Health-Care-Administrators/326597784597
X (Twitter): x.com/ACHCA
Description: Persons actively engaged in the administration of long-term care facilities, such as nursing homes, retirement communities, assisted living facilities, and sub-acute care programs. Administers professional certification programs for assisted living, sub-acute and nursing home administrators. Works to elevate the standards in the field and to develop and promote a code of ethics and standards of education and training. Seeks to inform allied professions and the public that good administration of long-term care facilities calls for special formal academic training and experience. Encourages research in all aspects of geriatrics, the chronically ill, and administration. Maintains placement service. Holds special education programs; facilitates networking among administrators. **Founded:** 1962. **Publications:** *Continuum* (Quarterly); *Balance: The Source for Administrators in Long-Term Health Care* (8/year); *ACHCA E-News* (Bimonthly). **Educational Activities:** ACHCA Annual Winter Marketplace (Annual). **Awards:** New Administrator Award (Annual); ACHCA Education Award (Annual); ACHCA Journalism Award (Annual); W.Phillip McConnell Student Scholarship Fund (Irregular); Richard L. Thorpe Fellowship (Annual); ACHCA Distinguished Assisted Living Administrator Award (Annual); ACHCA Distinguished Nursing Home Administrator Award (Annual); ACHCA New Nursing Home Administrator Award (Annual). **Geographic Preference:** National.

197 ■ **Benjamin Rose Library**
11890 Fairhill Rd.
Cleveland, OH 44120
Ph: (216)791-8000
Fax: (216)373-1813
Co. E-mail: info@benrose.org
URL: http://www.benrose.org
Description: Canisius is named for St. Peter Canisius, a renowned Dutch educator and one of the original members of the Society of Jesus. **Scope:** Research; consumer-responsive services and client advocacy. **Founded:** 1908. **Holdings:** Figures not available.

198 ■ **Philadelphia Corporation for Aging Library (PCA)**
Wallace Bldg.
642 N Broad St.
Philadelphia, PA 19130-3049
Ph: (215)765-9000
Fax: (215)765-9066
Co. E-mail: info@pcacares.org
URL: http://www.pcacares.org
Contact: Najja R. Orr, President
Facebook: www.facebook.com/PCACares.org
Linkedin: www.linkedin.com/company/philadelphia-corporation-for-aging
X (Twitter): x.com/pcacares_org
YouTube: www.youtube.com/channel/UCqY3FpDiC2Y5a1nq_1GEVZg
Scope: Local history. **Founded:** 1978.

199 ■ **Pima Council on Aging (PCOA) - Library**
8467 E Broadway Blvd.
Tucson, AZ 85710
Ph: (520)790-7262
Fax: (520)790-7577
Co. E-mail: help@pcoa.org
URL: http://pcoa.org
Contact: W. Mark Clark, President
E-mail: mclark@pcoa.org
X (Twitter): x.com/pcoaging
Description: Aims to promote dignity and respect for the aging population and to advocate for independence in the lives of Pima County's adults and their families. Advocates, plans, coordinates, develops, and delivers home-and-community-based aging services for older adults and provides supportive assistance, accurate information, and local resource connections for family caregivers. **Scope:** Aging. **Founded:** 1967. **Holdings:** Figures not available. **Geographic Preference:** Local.

200 ■ **United Way of Dane County - Imagination Library**
2059 Atwood Ave.
Madison, WI 53704
Ph: (608)246-4350
Fax: (608)246-4349
Co. E-mail: writeus@uwdc.org
URL: http://www.unitedwaydanecounty.org
Contact: Renee Moe, President
E-mail: renee.moe@uwdc.org

Facebook: www.facebook.com/unitedwaydaneco
X (Twitter): x.com/unitedwaydaneco
Instagram: www.instagram.com/unitedwaydaneco
YouTube: www.youtube.com/channel/
UCmBN7K8KWKsci6yaVqU-wmg
Description: Unite the community to achieve measurable results and change lives. **Scope:** School. **Founded:** 1971. **Holdings:** Books. **Geographic Preference:** Local.

201 ■ Virginia Commonwealth University School of Allied Health Professions - Virginia Center on Aging - Information Resources Center
900 E Leigh St., Ste. 7020
Richmond, VA 23219
Ph: (804)828-1525
Co. E-mail: vcoa@vcu.edu
URL: http://www.sahp.vcu.edu/vcoa/video-library/index.html
Contact: Dr. Edward F. Ansello, Director
E-mail: eansello@vcu.edu
Facebook: www.facebook.com/vcuvcoa
YouTube: www.youtube.com/user/alliedhelp/videos
Scope: Gerontology; mental health; sociology and the politics of aging; geriatrics; family relationships; long-term care; lifelong learning. **Services:** Library open to the public with restrictions (audio/visual materials available to Virginia residents only). **Founded:** 1978. **Holdings:** 1,500 books; 4 archives; 150 videos and DVDs.

202 ■ Western Illinois Area Agency on Aging (WIAAA) - Greta J. Brook Elderly Living and Learning Facility [Elderly Living and Learning Facility (ELLF)]
729 34th Ave.
Rock Island, IL 61201
Ph: (309)793-6800
Free: 800-322-1051
Co. E-mail: information@wiaaa.org
URL: http://www.wiaaa.org
Contact: Barbara Eskildsen, Executive Director
E-mail: beskildsen@wiaaa.org
Facebook: www.facebook.com/Western-Illinois-Area-Agency-on-Aging-502130799853006
Scope: Gerontology; senior housing; family caregiving; Medicare; Medicaid; social security; retirement planning; intergenerational programs; program development. **Services:** Interlibrary loan; senior computer center open to those fifty years of age or older; facility open to the public. **Founded:** 1973. **Holdings:** 1,108 books; 260 videotapes; 130 audio/visual materials; 35 DVDs and CDs. **Subscriptions:** 2 journals and other serials; 12 periodicals (includes journals).

RESEARCH CENTERS

203 ■ Brown University - Center for Gerontology and Health Care Research (CGHR)
121 South Main St.
Providence, RI 02903
Ph: (401)863-3604
Co. E-mail: public_health@brown.edu
URL: http://www.brown.edu/academics/public-health/cghr/home
Contact: Joan Brazier, Director
E-mail: joan_brazier@brown.edu
X (Twitter): x.com/BrownGero
Description: Integral unit of Brown University. Offers data collection, database development and training. **Scope:** Aging, chronic disease, and long-term care with particular emphasis on the assessment of function and health status and its application to diagnosis, prognosis and monitoring of long-term care. **Founded:** 1986. **Publications:** *Monograph Series*.

204 ■ Case Western Reserve University - Elderly Care Research Center (ECRC)
10900 Euclid Ave.
Cleveland, OH 44106
URL: http://caslabs.case.edu/ecrc
Contact: Dr. Eva Kahana, Director
E-mail: exk@case.edu
Description: Integral unit of Department of Sociology, Case Western Reserve University. **Scope:** Aging, health, and mental health, including public policy issues, predictors of wellness and vulnerability, environmental and social influences on well-being of the elderly, cross-national and cross-cultural comparisons, and health and mental health outcomes of stress, coping, and adaptation. **Founded:** 1967. **Publications:** *ECRC Brochure*.

Advertising Service

START-UP INFORMATION

205 ▪ *"Starting Up All Over Again: Alex Bogusky Backs Bootcamp for Advertising Startup"* in *Denver Business Journal* (Vol. 65, February 7, 2014, No. 39, pp. 8)
Pub: American City Business Journals, Inc.
Contact: Mike Olivieri, Executive Vice President
Released: February 7, 2014. **Description:** Once called the Elvis of advertising, Alex Bogusky is now launching a new startup named 'Boomtown' with an aim to cultivate a new generation of advertising, marketing, design, and media related tech companies. The end goal of boomtown will be to figure out the trend in which media as well as the relationship between brands and people is going.

ASSOCIATIONS AND OTHER ORGANIZATIONS

206 ▪ **Ad Complaints Reports**
33 Bloor St. E, Ste. 303
  Toronto, ON, Canada M4W 3H1
Ph: (416)961-6311
Co. E-mail: info@adstandards.com
URL: http://adstandards.ca
Contact: Jani Yates, Chief Executive Officer
E-mail: jani.yates@adstandards.ca
URL(s): adstandards.ca/complaints/complaints-reporting/annual-ad-complaints-report
Released: Annual **Availability:** PDF.

207 ▪ **Ad Council**
815 Second Ave., 9th Fl.
  New York, NY 10017
Co. E-mail: privacy@adcouncil.org
URL: http://www.adcouncil.org
Contact: Lisa Sherman, President
Facebook: www.facebook.com/adcouncil
Linkedin: www.linkedin.com/company/the-advertising-council
X (Twitter): x.com/adcouncil
Instagram: www.instagram.com/adcouncil
YouTube: www.youtube.com/adcouncil
Description: Produces and promotes public service campaigns on behalf of non-profit organizations and government agencies in issue areas such as improving the quality of life for children, preventative health, education, community well being, environmental preservation and strengthening of families. **Founded:** 1942. **Publications:** *PSA Bulletin* (Bimonthly); *Public Service Advertising Bulletin* (Bimonthly). **Awards:** Ad Council Silver Bell Award (Annual); Advertising Council Public Service Award (Annual). **Geographic Preference:** National.

208 ▪ **Advertising Club of New York (ACNY)**
989 Avenue of the Americas, 7th Fl.
  New York, NY 10018
Ph: (212)533-8080
Co. E-mail: info@theadvertisingclub.org
URL: http://www.theadvertisingclub.org
Contact: Mari Kim Novak, Chairman
Facebook: www.facebook.com/adclubny
X (Twitter): x.com/adclubny
Instagram: www.instagram.com/adclubny
Description: Sponsors educational and public service activities, promotional and public relations projects and talks by celebrities and advertising persons. Conducts annual advertising and marketing course, which offers classes in copywriting, special graphics, verbal communication, advertising production, sale promotion, marketing and management. Sponsors competitions and charitable programs. **Founded:** 1896. **Publications:** *ACNY Membership Roster* (Annual); *Auction Catalogue and Program* (Annual); *ANDY Souvenir Journal* (Annual). **Awards:** ANDY Awards (Annual); AC Silver Medal Award (Annual). **Geographic Preference:** National.

209 ▪ **Advertising Standards Canada (ASC) [Normes Canadiennes de la Publicité (NCP)]**
33 Bloor St. E, Ste. 303
  Toronto, ON, Canada M4W 3H1
Ph: (416)961-6311
Co. E-mail: info@adstandards.com
URL: http://adstandards.ca
Contact: Jani Yates, Chief Executive Officer
E-mail: jani.yates@adstandards.ca
Linkedin: www.linkedin.com/company/ad-standards
X (Twitter): x.com/AdStandardsCan
Description: Committed to ensuring the integrity and viability of advertising through industry self-regulation. Administers the Canada Code of Advertising Standards, accepts and reviews complaints about advertising, and provides advertising pre-clearance services. **Founded:** 1957. **Publications:** *Ad Complaints Reports* (Annual). **Geographic Preference:** National.

210 ▪ **American Academy of Advertising (AAA)**
8585 SW 12TH Ln.
  Gainesville, FL 32607
Contact: Debbie Treise, Executive Director
E-mail: dtreise@ufl.edu
Facebook: www.facebook.com/AmericanAcademyOfAdvertising
X (Twitter): x.com/adscholar
Description: Professional organization for college and university teachers of advertising and for industry professionals who wish to contribute to the development of advertising education. **Founded:** 1958. **Publications:** *Journal of Current Issues & Research in Advertising* (3/year); *American Academy of Advertising--Directory of Members* (Annual); *Journal of Advertising* (5/year); *Journal of Interactive Advertising (JIAD)* (Quarterly; Quarterly); *Proceedings of the Conference of the American Academy of Advertising*; *Membership Roster* (Annual). **Awards:** AAA Distinguished Service Award (Annual); AAA Doctoral Dissertation Grant Competition (Annual); AAA Fellow Award (Annual); AAA Journal of Advertising Best Article Award (Annual); Ivan L. Preston Outstanding Contribution to Research Award (Irregular). **Geographic Preference:** National.

211 ▪ **American Advertising Federation (AAF)**
1101 K St. NW, Ste. 420
  Washington, DC 20005
Ph: (202)898-0089
URL: http://www.aaf.org
Contact: Steve Pacheco, President
Facebook: www.facebook.com/aafnational
Linkedin: www.linkedin.com/company/aafnational
X (Twitter): x.com/AAFNational
Instagram: www.instagram.com/aafnational
Description: Works to advance the business of advertising as a vital and essential part of the American economy and culture through government and public relations; professional development and recognition; community service, social responsibility and high standards; and benefits and services to members. Operates Advertising Hall of Fame, Hall of Achievement, and National Student Advertising Competition. Maintains speaker's bureau. **Founded:** 1905. **Publications:** *Communicator* (Bimonthly); *Newsline* (Monthly); *American Advertising: The American Advertising Federation Magazine* (Quarterly); *AAF Member Newsletter*; *AAF Government Reports*; *American Advertising Federation--Speakers Directory*. **Educational Activities:** American Advertising Federation Annual Conference (Annual); ADMERICA National Conference (Annual). **Awards:** American Advertising Awards (Annual); AAF Advertising Hall of Fame (Annual); AAF Ovation Awards (Annual); National Student Advertising Competition (Annual); AAF Advertising Hall of Achievement (Annual). **Geographic Preference:** National.

212 ▪ **American Association of Advertising Agencies (AAAA)**
25 W 45th St., 16th Fl.
  New York, NY 10036
Ph: (212)682-2500
Co. E-mail: research@4as.org
URL: http://www.aaaa.org
Contact: Marla Kaplowitz, President
Facebook: www.facebook.com/aaaaorg
Linkedin: www.linkedin.com/company/4as
Instagram: www.instagram.com/4as_presents
Description: Fosters development of the advertising industry; assists member agencies to operate more efficiently and profitably. Sponsors member information and international services. Maintains multiple councils, committees, and forums. Conducts government relations. **Founded:** 1917. **Holdings:** 2,000 books; 300 VF drawers of clippings, reports, and pamphlets. **Publications:** *AAAA Publications Catalog* (Periodic); *The Reporter* (Bimonthly); *Advertising Agency Accounting/Finance/Collaboration Software Directory*; *Cable Broadcast Traffic Guide*; *American Association of Advertising Agencies--Roster and Organization* (Annual). **Awards:** O'Toole Agency Awards (Annual); O'Toole Public Service Award; O'Toole Awards for Creative and Media Excellence; ANA Multicultural Excellence Scholarship Fund (MAIP) (Annual). **Geographic Preference:** National.

213 ▪ **American Photographic Artists (APA)**
9190 W Olympic Blvd. No.212
  Beverly Hills, CA 90212-3540

Ph: (323)933-1631
Co. E-mail: membershiprep@apanational.org
URL: http://la.apanational.org
Contact: Patti Silverstein, Director
E-mail: director@apa-la.com
Facebook: www.facebook.com/APALosAngeles
X (Twitter): x.com/apanational
Instagram: www.instagram.com/apa_la

Description: Enhances dialogue among professional photographers and their clients. Suggests standards and business practices to improve the quality of professional photography; and acts as a forum for discussion of problems and solutions. Conducts discussion groups. **Founded:** 1981. **Publications:** *1999 APA National Photographer's Survey Report.* **Geographic Preference:** National.

214 ■ **AMIN Worldwide [The Advertising and Marketing Independent Network (AMIN)]**
3587 Northshore Dr.
 Wayzata, MN 55391
Ph: (613)473-4124
Co. E-mail: contact@aminworldwide.com
URL: http://www.aminworldwide.com
Contact: Ali Sizemore Mahaffy, President
Facebook: www.facebook.com/AMINWorldwide
Linkedin: www.linkedin.com/company/aminworldwide
YouTube: www.youtube.com/channel/UC7S7jayioY9J6HBEfrlIdjA

Description: Represents independent marketing agencies. **Founded:** 1932. **Geographic Preference:** Multinational.

215 ■ **Association of National Advertisers (ANA)**
Association of National Advertisers (ANA)
 155 E 44th St.
 New York, NY 10017
Ph: (212)697-5950
Fax: (212)687-7310
Co. E-mail: info@ana.net
URL: http://www.ana.net
Contact: Christine Manna, President
E-mail: cmanna@ana.net
Facebook: www.facebook.com/ANAmarketers
Linkedin: www.linkedin.com/company/association-of-national-advertisers
X (Twitter): x.com/anamarketers
Instagram: www.instagram.com/anamarketers

Description: Serves the needs of members by providing marketing and advertising industry leadership in traditional and e-marketing, legislative leadership, information resources, professional development and industry-wide networking. Maintains offices in New York City and Washington, DC. **Founded:** 1910. **Publications:** *The Advertiser* (Bimonthly); *Tie-In Promotion Service* (Annual). **Awards:** ANA Multicultural Excellence Awards (Annual). **Geographic Preference:** National.

216 ■ **Canadian Marketing Association (CMA)**
55 University Ave., Ste. 603
 Toronto, ON, Canada M5J 2H7
Ph: (416)391-2362
Free: 800-267-8805
Fax: (416)441-4062
Co. E-mail: helpdesk@thecma.ca
URL: http://thecma.ca
Contact: Alison Simpson, President
Facebook: www.facebook.com/cdnmarketing
Linkedin: www.linkedin.com/company/canadian-marketing-association
X (Twitter): x.com/Cdnmarketing
Instagram: www.instagram.com/cdnmarketing
YouTube: www.youtube.com/user/canadianmarketing

Description: Promotes growth and development in the information-based marketing industry. Facilitates communication and cooperation among members; serves as a clearinghouse on information-based marketing. **Founded:** 1967. **Publications:** *CMA Member Directory*; *Marketing Facts* (Annual); *E-Communicator* (10/year). **Educational Activities:** Canadian Marketing Association National Convention. **Geographic Preference:** National.

217 ■ *CARF Newsletter*
160 Bloor St. E, Ste. 1005
 Toronto, ON, Canada M4W 1B9
Ph: (416)413-3864
Fax: (416)413-3879

Released: Bimonthly **Price:** Included in membership. **Description:** Contains information of the latest developments in advertising research in Canada and internationally. **Availability:** Print; Online.

218 ■ *CARF Update*
160 Bloor St. E, Ste. 1005
 Toronto, ON, Canada M4W 1B9
Ph: (416)413-3864
Fax: (416)413-3879
URL(s): www.carf.ca/research/index.shtml

Released: Periodic **Description:** Includes informative papers on topics of interest to marketers, researchers and advertisers. **Availability:** Print; Online.

219 ■ **Geopath**
561 7th Ave., 12th Fl.
 New York, NY 10018
Ph: (212)972-8075
Co. E-mail: geekout@geopath.org
URL: http://geopath.org
Contact: Kevin Gleason, President
Facebook: www.facebook.com/geopathooh
Linkedin: www.linkedin.com/company/geopath
X (Twitter): x.com/geopathooh
Instagram: www.instagram.com/geopathooh
YouTube: www.youtube.com/channel/UCbxnJ2FK3IXEUbA8gPdIv2A

Description: Advertisers, advertising agencies, operators of outdoor advertising plants, bus shelter advertising companies, and backlighted display and painted bulletin companies. **Founded:** 1933. **Publications:** *Building Accountability for Out of Home Media*; *TAB Eyes On Out of Home*; *TABBriefs*; *What You Should Know About the New TAB Audit*. **Educational Activities:** Traffic Audit Bureau for Media Measurement Out of Home Media Conference & Marketing Expo (Annual). **Geographic Preference:** National.

220 ■ **Intermarket Agency Network (IAN)**
401 Mendocino Ave.
 Santa Rosa, CA 95401
Co. E-mail: info@theengineisred.com
URL: http://www.intermarketnetwork.com
Contact: Alicia Wadas, President

Description: An active network of high-powered marketing/communications agencies in the United States, Canada, Central and South America, and Europe. **Geographic Preference:** National.

221 ■ **International Advertising Association (IAA) - Library**
511 Ave. of Americas No. 4017
 New York, NY 10011
Ph: (646)849-9908
Co. E-mail: iaa@iaaglobal.org
URL: http://www.iaaglobal.org
Contact: Joel Nettey, President
Facebook: www.facebook.com/InternationalAdvertisingAssociation
Linkedin: www.linkedin.com/company/international-advertising-association
X (Twitter): x.com/iaa_global
Instagram: www.instagram.com/iaaglobal
YouTube: www.youtube.com/channel/UCULDmcOgvEd_SyFF0LS_-BQ

Description: Demonstrates to governments and consumers the benefits of advertising as the foundation of diverse, independent media. **Scope:** Advertising. **Founded:** 1938. **Holdings:** Figures not available. **Publications:** *IAA National & World News* (Quarterly); *The Case for Advertising Self-Regulation*; *IAA Annual Report* (Annual); *IAA Membership Directory*; *International Advertising Association-- Membership Directory* (Continuous). **Awards:** InterAd Student Competition (Annual); Samir Fares Award. **Geographic Preference:** National.

222 ■ **International Communications Agency Network (ICOM)**
74 Hwy. 72
 Nederland, CO 80466
URL: http://icomagencies.com
Contact: Emma Keenan, Executive Director
Linkedin: www.linkedin.com/company/icomagencies
X (Twitter): x.com/icomagencies

Description: Provides an interchange of management information, international facilities, and branch office service for partner agencies. Provides discounts on syndicated services and access to 1,000 computer databases. **Founded:** 1950. **Publications:** *Agency Client Lists* (Monthly); *The Globe* (Monthly); *Membership Directory* (Annual). **Educational Activities:** International Management Conference. **Geographic Preference:** Multinational.

223 ■ **Marketing and Advertising Global Network (MAGNET)**
Pittsburgh, PA 15202
URL: http://magnetglobal.org
Contact: Melissa Lentz, Chief Executive Officer
E-mail: melissai@magnetglobal.org
Facebook: www.facebook.com/Magnet-Global-Network-86729467810
Linkedin: www.linkedin.com/company/magnet-global-network
X (Twitter): x.com/MAGNETGLOBALNET

Description: Aims to bring about, through mutual cooperation, greater accomplishment and efficiency in the management of member advertising agencies. Other goals are: to raise standards of the advertising agency business through the exchange of information relative to agency management and all phases of advertising; to exchange information on all common problems, such as management, sales development, market studies, agency functions, and operations. **Founded:** 1946. **Publications:** *MAGNET Matters* (3/year); *This Week at MAGNET* (Weekly). **Geographic Preference:** Multinational.

224 ■ **National Advertising Review Board (NARB)**
7 Times Sq., Fl., 17, Ste. 1705
 New York, NY 10036
URL: http://bbbprograms.org/programs/all-programs

Description: Individuals from industry and the public. Sponsored by the National Advertising Review Council for the purpose of sustaining high standards of truth and accuracy in national advertising. Aims to maintain a self-regulatory mechanism that responds constructively to public complaints about national advertising and which significantly improves advertising performance and credibility. **Founded:** 1971. **Publications:** *NARB Panel Reports*. **Geographic Preference:** National.

225 ■ **She Runs It**
89-12 70th Ave.
 Forest Hills, NY 11375-6614
Ph: (212)221-7969
Fax: (212)221-8296
Co. E-mail: info@sherunsit.org
URL: http://sherunsit.org
Contact: Lynn Branigan, President
Facebook: www.facebook.com/sherunsit
X (Twitter): x.com/sherunsitorg
Instagram: www.instagram.com/sherunsitorg

Description: Women in advertising and related industries that provides a forum for professional growth, serves as catalyst for enhancement and advancement of women; promotes philanthropic endeavors. Conducts events of interest and benefit to members and non-members involved in the industry. Membership concentrated in the metropolitan New York area. **Founded:** 1912. **Awards:** Woman of the Year (Annual); AWNY President's Award (Annual); Crystal Prism Award (Annual). **Geographic Preference:** National.

226 ■ **Sign Association of Canada (SAC) [Association Canadienne de l'enseigne (ACE)]**
18 King St. E, ste.1400
 Toronto, ON, Canada M5C 1C4

Ph: (905)856-0000
Free: 877-470-9787
Fax: (905)856-0064
Co. E-mail: sacinfo@signs.org
URL: http://sac-ace.ca
Contact: Tanya Mailhot, President
Facebook: www.facebook.com/sacace
Linkedin: www.linkedin.com/company/sign-association-of-canada
X (Twitter): x.com/sacace

Description: Manufacturers of advertising signs; suppliers of sign components and services. Promotes increased use of signs in advertising. Represents members' interests. **Scope:** Conducts research and studies on advertising, sign technologies, and human resources. **Founded:** 1955. **Publications:** Signs Canada (Bimonthly). **Educational Activities:** SAC Conference (Annual). **Geographic Preference:** National.

REFERENCE WORKS

227 ■ "Abacast, Citadel Strike Radio Ad Deal" in Business Journal Portland (Vol. 27, December 31, 2010, No. 44, pp. 3)
Pub: Portland Business Journal
Contact: Andy Giegerich, Managing Editor
E-mail: agiegerich@bizjournals.com

Ed: Erik Siemers. **Description:** Software firm Abacast Inc. has partnered with Citadel Media to aid the latter's advertising sales. Citadel provides radio networks and syndicated programs to 4,200 affiliate stations. **Availability:** Print; Online.

228 ■ "Advertising Agencies" in Black Enterprise (Vol. 44, June 2014, No. 10, pp. 81)
Pub: Earl G. Graves Ltd.
Contact: Earl Graves, Jr., President

Description: A listing of the top 100 advertising agencies is presented.

229 ■ "Advertising May Take a Big Hit in Southwest/AirTran Merger" in Baltimore Business Journal (Vol. 28, October 1, 2010, No. 21, pp. 1)
Pub: Baltimore Business Journal
Contact: Rhonda Pringle, President
E-mail: rpringle@bizjournals.com

Ed: Gary Haber. **Description:** Advertising on television stations and the publishing industry in Baltimore could drop as a result of the merger between rival discount airlines Southwest Airlines and AirTran Airways. Southwest is among the top advertisers in the U.S., spending $126 million in 2009. No local jobs are expected to be affected because neither airline uses a local advertising firm. **Availability:** Print.

230 ■ "Africa Rising" in Harvard Business Review (Vol. 86, September 2008, No. 9, pp. 36)
Pub: Harvard Business Review Press
Contact: Moderna V. Pfizer, Contact

Ed: Vijay Mahajan. **Description:** Review of the book entitled, "Africa Rising: How 900 Million African Consumers Offer More Than You Think" provides advice for marketing to those on the African continent. **Availability:** Print; Online.

231 ■ "The Agency Model Is Bent But Not Broken" in Advertising Age (Vol. 79, July 7, 2008, No. 26, pp. 17)
Pub: Crain Communications, Inc.
Contact: Jessica Botos, Manager, Marketing
E-mail: jessica.botos@crainsnewyork.com

Ed: Stephen Fajen. **Description:** In the new-media environment, advertising agencies must change the way in which they do business and receive payment. **Availability:** Online.

232 ■ "The Agency-Selection Process Needs Fixing Now" in Advertising Age (Vol. 79, July 7, 2008, No. 26, pp. 18)
Pub: Crain Communications, Inc.
Contact: Jessica Botos, Manager, Marketing
E-mail: jessica.botos@crainsnewyork.com

Ed: Avi Dan. **Description:** Marketers are facing increased challenges in this sagging economic climate and must realize the importance of choosing the correct advertising agency for their company in order to benefit from a more-stable relationship that yields better business results. Advice for marketers regarding the best way to choose an agency is included. **Availability:** Online.

233 ■ "The AHA Moment" in Hispanic Business (December 2010)

Description: An interview with Gisela Girard on how competitive market conditions push buttons. Girard stepped down from her 18-month position as chairwoman the Association of Hispanic Advertising Agencies. She has more than 20 years of experience in advertising and research marketing. **Availability:** Print; Online.

234 ■ "Ampm Focus Has BP Working Overtime" in Crain's Chicago Business (April 28, 2008)
Pub: Crain Communications Inc.
Contact: Barry Asin, President

Ed: John T. Slania. **Description:** Britian's oil giant BP PLC is opening its ampm convenience stores in the Chicago market and has already begun converting most of its 78 Chicago-area gas stations to ampms. The company has also started to franchise the stores to independent operators. BP is promoting the brand with both traditional and unconventional marketing techniques such s real or simulated 3D snacks embedded in bus shelter ads and an in-store Guitar Hero contest featuring finalists from a recent contest at the House of Blues. **Availability:** Online.

235 ■ "Are Nutrient-Content Claims Always Effective? Match-Up Effects Between Product Type and Claim Type in Food Advertising" in International Journal of Advertising (Vol. 31, May 2012, No. 2, pp. 421)

Ed: Hojoon Choi, Hye-Jin Paek, Karen Whitehill King. **Released:** 2012. **Description:** Research examines the extent to which recently prevalent nutrient-content claims in food advertising are effective and how the level of effectiveness might differ between food products perceived as healthy and unhealthy. **Availability:** Online.

236 ■ "Are Offline Pushes Important to E-Commerce?" in DM News (Vol. 31, September 14, 2009, No. 23, pp. 10)
Pub: Haymarket Media Inc.
Contact: Kevin Costello, Chief Executive Officer

Description: With the importance of Internet marketing and the popularity of ecommerce increasing experts debate the relevance of more traditional channels of advertising. **Availability:** Online.

237 ■ "As Traditional Web Site Adoption Slows, Facebook and Other Social Networks Become Key Platforms for Home-Based Business Promotional and Commercial Activity Online" in Marketing Weekly News (June 16, 2012)

Description: Websites have provided an inexpensive means for businesses to market their products and services. However, home-based businesses are using social networking, email marketing, search engine optimization, search engine marketing, Website optimization for mobile devices, banner advertisements, and the use of ecommerce platforms such as eBay, Craigs list, and Amazon. **Availability:** Print; Online.

238 ■ "avVaa World Health Care Products Rolls Out Internet Marketing Program" in Health and Beauty Close-Up (September 18, 2009)

Description: avVaa World Health Care Products, Inc., a biotechnology company, manufacturer and distributor of nationally branded therapeutic, natural health care and skin products, has signed an agreement with Online Performance Marketing to launch of an Internet marketing campaign in order to broaden its presence online. The impact of advertising on the Internet to generate an increase in sales is explored. **Availability:** Online.

239 ■ "Baltimore Ravens Back to Business as NFL Lockout Ends" in Baltimore Business Journal (Vol. 29, July 29, 2011, No. 12, pp. 1)
Pub: Boston Business Journal
Contact: Carolyn M. Jones, President
E-mail: cmjones@bizjournals.com

Ed: Scott Dance. **Description:** The Baltimore Ravens football team has been marketing open sponsorship packages following the end of the National Football League lockout. Team officials are working to get corporate logos and slogans on radio and television commercials and online advertisements. **Availability:** Print; Online.

240 ■ "Being All a-Twitter" in Canadian Business (Vol. 81, December 8, 2008, No. 21, pp. 22)

Description: Marketing experts suggest that advertising strategies have to change along with new online social media. Companies are advised to find ways to incorporate social software because workers and customers are expected to continue its use. **Availability:** Print; Online.

241 ■ "Better ROI Or Your Money Back, Says Buzz Agency" in Advertising Age (Vol. 79, July 14, 2008, No. 7, pp. 1)
Pub: Crain Communications, Inc.
Contact: Jessica Botos, Manager, Marketing
E-mail: jessica.botos@crainsnewyork.com

Ed: Michael Bush. **Description:** Word-of-mouth marketing is discussed as well as the impact on the advertising industry. Although many firms specializing in this form of marketing have opened over the past few years, many marketers are reluctant to try this route. **Availability:** Online.

242 ■ "Better Than New Runs on Tried-and-True Model" in Bellingham Business Journal (Vol. February 2010, pp. 16)
Pub: Sound Publishing Inc.
Contact: Josh O'Connor, President

Ed: Ashley Mitchell. **Description:** Profile of family owned Better Than New clothing store that sells overstock items from department stores and clothing manufacturers. The stores location makes it easy to miss and its only advertising is a large sign posted outside. This is the sixth store owned by the couple, Keijeo and Sirba Halmekanqas.

243 ■ "Blue Bell Touts Non-Shrinkage" in Ice Cream Reporter (Vol. 21, July 20, 2008, No. 8, pp. 1)

Description: Blue Bell Ice Cream is promoting its decision to keep their ice cream products in a full half-gallon container rather than downsizing the package. Thirty-second television ads contrast the move by other ice cream makers to offer less for the same money. **Availability:** Online.

244 ■ "Branded Entertainment: Dealmaking Strategies & Techniques for Industry Professionals"
Pub: J. Ross Publishing Inc.
Contact: Stephen Buda, President

Released: October 01, 2014. **Price:** $39.95, hardcover, plus shipping charge extra. FL sale tax $3.36. **Description:** Branded entertainment, also known as branded content or advertainment, is an entertainment-based method that is funded by and complementary to a brand's marketing strategy. These projects are usually a partnership between brands, television or radio producers, and broadcasters. **Availability:** E-book; Print; Download.

245 ■ "Branding Your Way" in Canadian Business (Vol. 80, February 12, 2007, No. 4, pp. 31)

Description: The trend in involving consumers in brand marketing by seeking their views through contests or inviting them to produce and submit commercials through Internet is discussed. **Availability:** Online.

246 ■ "Brands' Mass Appeal" in ADWEEK (Vol. 51, June 14, 2010, No. 24)
Ed: Brian Morrissey. Description: Engineering/science crowdsourced projects tend to result from posting and/or publishing interim results as well as from other talents building upon those results to produce even better results. However, the author does not see the same results in the creative world. Availability: Online.

247 ■ "Brewing Up a Brand" in Canadian Business (Vol. 80, February 26, 2007, No. 5, pp. 68)
Description: The marketing strategies adopted by Molson Coors Brewing Company, to improve customer loyalty to the Coors Light brand, are presented. Availability: Online.

248 ■ "Campaign Ads Lucrative for Denver's TV Stations" in Denver Business Journal (Vol. 64, September 7, 2012, No. 16, pp. 1)
Pub: Baltimore Business Journal
Contact: Rhonda Pringle, President
E-mail: rpringle@bizjournals.com

Description: US presidential election campaign advertising is seen to boost the earnings of Denver, Colorado's television broadcasting sector. Presidential candidate Mitt Romney and US president Barrack Obama have spent $2.6 million on advertising in Denver.

249 ■ "Charlotte Pipe Launches Satirical Campaign" in Contractor (Vol. 57, January 2010, No. 1, pp. 6)
Description: Charlotte Pipe and Foundry Co. launched an advertising campaign that uses social media and humor to make a point about how it can be nearly impossible to determine if imported cast iron pipes and fittings meet the same quality standards as what is made in the U.S. The campaign features 'pipe whisperers' and also spoofs pipe sniffing dogs. Availability: Print; Online.

250 ■ "Citadel EFT (CDFT) Contracts With New Search Engine Optimization (SEO) and Banner Ad Web Marketing Companies" in Internet Wire (August 8, 2012)
Pub: Comtex News Network Inc.
Contact: Kan Devnani, President

Description: Citafel EFT Inc. provides credit card terminals, online, mail order and retail credit card processing services. The firm has contracted with two Web marketing companies to increase its awareness on the Internet. Availability: Print; Online.

251 ■ "CMO Nicholson Exits Pepsi as Share Declines" in Advertising Age (Vol. 79, July 7, 2008, No. 26, pp. 4)
Pub: Crain Communications, Inc.
Contact: Jessica Botos, Manager, Marketing
E-mail: jessica.botos@crainsnewyork.com

Ed: Natalie Zmuda. Description: Cie Nicholson, the chief marketing officer at Pepsi-Cola UK, is leaving the company at a time when its market share is down; the brand, which was known for its dynamic marketing, has diverted much of its attention from its core brands and shifted attention to the ailing Gatorade brand as well as Sobe Life Water and Amp. Availability: Online.

252 ■ The Complete Guide to Google Adwords: Secrets, Techniques, and Strategies You Can Learn to Make Millions
Pub: Atlantic Publishing Co.
Contact: Dr. Heather L. Johnson, Contact

Released: 2012. Description: Google AdWords, when it launched in 2002 signaled a fundamental shift in what the Internet was for so many individuals and companies. Learning and understanding how Google AdWords operates and how it can be optimized for maximum exposure, boosting click through rates, conversions, placement, and selection of the right keywords, can be the key to a successful online business. Availability: Print; Online.

253 ■ "Congress Targets Online Ad Tracking" in Inc. (Vol. 33, November 2011, No. 9, pp. 30)
Pub: Inc. Magazine

Ed: Issie Lapowsky. Description: Congressional bills dealing with behavioral tracking whereby advertising networks monitor people's online behavior and use the date to tailor ads to people's interest propose Do Not Track measures which would allow consumers to turn off online behavior tracking by clicking a button. Availability: Online.

254 ■ "Contagious: Why Things Catch On"
Pub: Simon & Schuster, Inc.
Contact: Jonathan Karp, President

Released: March 2013. Price: $26, after_pricing-text. Description: Wharton marketing professor, Jonah Berger, reveals the science of successful word-of-mouth and social media marketing that provides greater results than traditional advertising. Availability: Print.

255 ■ "Conversations Need to Yield Actions Measured in Dollars" in Advertising Age (Vol. 79, July 7, 2008, No. 26, pp. 18)
Pub: Crain Communications, Inc.
Contact: Jessica Botos, Manager, Marketing
E-mail: jessica.botos@crainsnewyork.com

Ed: Jonathan Salem Baskin. Description: New ways in which to market to consumers are discussed. Availability: Online.

256 ■ "Covario Recognized for Second Year in a Row as OMMA Award Finalist for Online Advertising Creativity in Both SEO and SEM" in Internet Wire (August 29, 2012)
Pub: Comtex News Network Inc.
Contact: Kan Devnani, President

Description: Leading independent search marketing agency, Covario, providing search engine optimization (SEO) and search engine marketing (SEM) for companies was chosen as a finalist for the Media-Post Onlien Media, Marketing and Advertising award. This is Covario's second year to be recognized for this award. Availability: Print; Online.

257 ■ "Crain's Makes Ad Sales, Custom Marketing Appointments" in Crain's Chicago Business (Vol. 34, October 24, 2011, No. 42, pp. 13)
Pub: Crain Communications Inc.
Contact: Barry Asin, President

Description: Crain's Chicago Business announced key appointments in its sales department: David Denor has been named first director of custom marketing services and Kate Van Etten will succeed Denor as advertising director. Availability: Online.

258 ■ "Culturally Incongruent Messages In International Advertising" in International Journal of Advertising (Vol. 31, May 2012, No. 2, pp. 355)
Description: Research into the effect of culturally incongruent messages in international advertising on consumer responses is presented. The results of an experiment suggest that the type of cultural values (terminal vs instrumental)and ethnic background of models (foreign vs local) significantly moderate the effectof message congruency on attitude towards the advertisement, and such effect is mediated by the number of counter-arguments. Availability: Print; Online.

259 ■ "Defend Your Research: Commercials Make Us Like TV More" in Harvard Business Review (Vol. 88, October 2010, No. 10, pp. 36)
Pub: Harvard Business Publishing
Contact: Diane Belcher, Managing Director

Ed: Leif Nelson. Price: $6, PDF. Description: Research indicates that people prefer commercial interruption over uninterrupted shows due to the break creating a reactivation of the initial pleasure when beginning a desirable activity. Availability: Online; PDF.

260 ■ "Designing Women? Apparel Apparatchic at Kmart" in Barron's (Vol. 88, March 17, 2008, No. 11, pp. 16)
Pub: Dow Jones & Company Inc.
Contact: Almar Latour, Chief Executive Officer

Ed: Robin Goldwyn Blumenthal. Description: Kmart began a nationwide search for women to represent the company in a national advertising campaign. Contestants need to upload their photos to Kmart's website and winners will be chosen by a panel of celebrity judges. The contest aims to reverse preconceived negative notions about the store's quality and service. Availability: Online.

261 ■ "Digital Publishers Team Up to Compete for More Video Ad Dollars" in The Wall Street Journal (September 23, 2019)
URL(s): www.wsj.com/articles/digital-publishers-team-up-to-compete-for-more-video-ad-dollars-11569263015

Released: September 23, 2019. Description: Three major digital publishers, BuzzFeed Inc., Group Nine Media Inc, and Insider Inc., are forming an ad sales alliance in order to sell ads as an independent body. This is an effort to compete against YouTube. Availability: Print; Online.

262 ■ "Discovery Networks" in Brandweek (Vol. 49, April 21, 2008, No. 16, pp. SR9)
Description: Provides contact information for sales and marketing personnel for the Discovery networks as well as a listing of the station's top programming and an analysis of the current season and the target audience for those programs running in the current season. The networks flagship station returned to the top 10 in 2007, averaging 1.28 million viewers.

263 ■ "Disruptive Innovators: Commonground is Transforming the Advertising Landscape by Living at the Intersection of Culture, Creativity, Content, and Technology" in Black Enterprise (Vol. 44, June 2014, No. 10, pp. 82)
Pub: Earl G. Graves Ltd.
Contact: Earl Graves, Jr., President

Description: Profile of partners, Sherman Wright and Ahmad Islam, who started the Chicago-based Commonground Marketing. The firm is an integrated, multicultural and general market advertising company. The partners met while on vacation in Cancun, Mexico.

264 ■ "Doyle: Domino's New Pizza Seasoned with Straight Talk" in Crain's Detroit Business (Vol. 26, January 11, 2010, No. 2, pp. 8)
Pub: Crain Communications Inc.
Contact: Barry Asin, President

Ed: Nathan Skid. Description: Interview with J. Patrick Doyle, the CEO of Domino's Pizza, Inc.; the company has launched a new marketing campaign that focuses on its bold new vision. Availability: Online.

265 ■ Duct Tape Marketing: The World's Most Practical Small Business Marketing Guide
Pub: Thomas Nelson, Inc.
Contact: Thomas Nelson, Publisher

Ed: John Jantsch. Released: 2007. Description: Small business owners are provided the tools and tactics necessary to market and grow a business.

266 ■ EBay Income: How ANYONE of Any Age, Location, and/or Background Can Build a Highly Profitable Online Business with eBay
Pub: Atlantic Publishing Co.
Contact: Dr. Heather L. Johnson, Contact

Description: A complete overview of eBay is given and guides any small company through the entire process of creating the auction and auction strategies, photography, writing copy, text and formatting, multiple sales, programming tricks, PayPal, accounting, creating marketing, merchandising, managing email lists, advertising plans, taxes and sales tax, best time to list items and for how long, sniping programs, international customers, opening a storefront, electronic commerce, buy-it now pricing, keywords, Google marketing and eBay secrets.

267 ■ *"The Effect of 3-D Product Visualization on the Strength of Brand Attitude"* **in International Journal of Advertising (Vol. 31, May 2012, No. 2, pp. 377)**
Description: Research investigates the effect of 3-D product visualization on attitude accessibility and attitude confidence in advertising, two non-evaluative dimensions of attitudes that have not been studied in previous research. The experiment analyzed two versions of a Website (3-D vs 2-D), in which the capacity to interact with the product has been manipulated. **Availability:** PDF; Online.

268 ■ *"The Effectiveness of Advertising That Leverages Sponsorship and Cause-Related Marketing: A Contingency Model"* **in International Journal of Advertising (Vol. 31, May 2012, No. 2, pp. 317)**
Description: Consumers are more likely to have ambivalent attitudes towards cause-related marketing (CRM) than sponsorship. Wherease consumers share similar positive perceptions of CRM and sponsorship, and attribute the motives behind them to altruism, their negative perceptions and attributions of CRM are more accessible than those of sponsorship. **Availability:** Print; Online.

269 ■ *"The Effectiveness of Regulatory (In)Congruent Ads: The Moderating Role of an Ad's Rational Versus Emotional Tone"* **in International Journal of Advertising (Vol. 31, May 2012, No. 2, pp. 397)**
Ed: Erlinde Cornelis, Leen Adams, Veroline Cauberghe. **Released:** 2012. **Price:** $42.50. **Description:** In a 2 (ad tone: emotional versus rational) x 2 (ad's regulatory focus: prevention vs promotion) x 2 (viewer's self-regulatory focus: prevention vs promotion) between-subjects experimental design, the effectiveness of fair trade campaigns is tested. The results show that, in the case of a rational ad, regulatory congruence (vs incongruence) effects were found (though only for prevention focused people), whereas in the case of an emotional ad, regulatory incongruence (vs congruence) effects were found (though only for promotion focused people). **Availability:** Print; Online.

270 ■ *"Elanco Challenges Bayer's Advantage, K9 Advantix Ad Claims"* **in Pet Product News (Vol. 64, November 2010, No. 11, pp. 11)**
Description: Elanco Animal Health has disputed Bayer Animal Health's print and Web advertising claims involving its flea, tick, and mosquito control products Advantage and K9 Advantix. The National Advertising Division of the Council of Better Business Bureaus recommended the discontinuation of ads, while Bayer Animal Health reiterated its commitment to self-regulation. **Availability:** Online.

271 ■ *"Event-Related Advertising and the Special Case of Sponsorship-Linked Advertising"* **in International Journal of Advertising (Vol. 31, February 2012, No. 1, pp. 15)**
Ed: Sarah J. Kelly, T. Bettina Cornwell, Leonard V. Coote, Anna R. McAlister. **Released:** 2012. **Description:** Corporate sponsorship is a valuable brand-building platform, typically leveraged by advertising and promotion. While advertising often 'uses news' to connect to meaningful events, sponsorship contracts create a special category of advertisers that have official rights to event affiliation. **Availability:** Print; Download; Mailing list; Online.

272 ■ *"Everyone Has a Story Inspired by Chevrolet"* **in Automotive News (Vol. 86, October 31, 2011, No. 6488, pp. S003)**
Pub: Crain Communications Inc.
Contact: Barry Asin, President
Description: Besides being a great ad slogan, 'Baseball, Hot Dogs, Apple Pie and Chevrolet', the brand conjures up memories for most everyone in our society. Louis Chevrolet had a reputation as a race car driver and lent his name to the car that has endured for 100 years. **Availability:** Online.

273 ■ *"The Evolution of Self-Regulation in Food Advertising: an Analysis of CARU Cases from 2000-2012"* **in International Journal of Advertising (Vol. 31, May 2012, No. 2, pp. 257)**
Price: $42.50. **Description:** The FTC envisions the Children's Advertising Review Unit (CARU) and the Children's Food and Beverage Advertising Initiative playing lead roles in self-regulatory efforts to address advertising's contribution to childhood obesity. Peeler (2009) notes that CARU's decisions provide comprehensive guidance to advertisers. Limited research has investigated those decisions. This study examines CARU case reports from 2000 to 2010 involving food marketers from a longitudinal perspective. **Availability:** Print; Online.

274 ■ *"Evolutionary Psychology in the Business Sciences"*
Pub: Springer Publishing Co.
Contact: Bernhard Springer, Founder
Released: First edition. **Description:** All individuals operating in the business sphere share a common biological heritage, including consumers, employers, employees, entrepreneurs, or financial traders, to name a few. The evolutionary behavioral sciences and specific business contexts including marketing, consumer behavior, advertising, innovation and creativity and invention, intertemporal choice, negotiations, competition and cooperation in organizational settings, sex differences in workplace patterns, executive leadership, business ethics, store and office design, behavioral decision making, and electronic communications and commerce are all addressed. **Availability:** E-book; Print.

275 ■ *"Fair and Lovely: Building an Integrated Model to Examine How Peer Influence Mediates the Effects of Skin-Lightening Advertisements On College Women In Singapore"* **in International Journal of Advertising (Vol. 31, February 2012, No. 1, pp. 189)**
Ed: Stella C. Chia, Yuen Ting Chay, Poh Kwan Cheong. **Released:** January 02, 2012. **Description:** Research uses an integrated model with which suggested that perceptions of peers and interpersonal communication with peers each mediate the influence of skin-lightening advertisements on college women in the South Asian country, Singapore. The model is build based on the influence-of-presumed-influence model. The study found that college women in Singapore tended to infer their peers' advertising exposure and the corresponding advertising influence on peers based on the own advertising exposure. Their exposure to the skin-lightening advertisements also induced their discussions about fair-skinned appearance with peers, resulting in favorable attitudes towards fair-skinned appearance. **Availability:** Online.

276 ■ *"Far Out: Satellite Radio Finds New Way to Tally Listeners"* **in Globe & Mail (March 14, 2007, pp. B14)**
Description: The marketing strategy adopted by satellite radio broadcasting firm XM Satellite Radio Inc. in Canada for increasing its subscriber based is discussed. **Availability:** Online.

277 ■ *"First Mariner Bank's New Ads No Passing Fancy"* **in Baltimore Business Journal (Vol. 29, September 16, 2011, No. 19, pp. 1)**
Pub: Boston Business Journal
Contact: Carolyn M. Jones, President
E-mail: cmjones@bizjournals.com
Ed: Gary Haber. **Description:** Baltimore, Maryland-based First Mariner Bank replaced Ed Hale, the bank's CEO and founder, as the pitchman for its television ads with Ravens quarterback Joe Flacco. Hales' exit from the advertisements is the result of First Mariner's struggle to raise money for recapitalization. **Availability:** Online.

278 ■ *"First, the Merger: Then, The Culture Clash. How To Fix the Little Things That Can Tear a Company Apart"* **in Inc. (January 2008)**
Ed: Elaine Appleton Grant. **Description:** Ways three CEOs handled the culture classes that followed after company mergers; companies profiled include Fuel Outdoor, an outdoor advertising company; Nelson, an interior design and architecture firm; and Beber Silverstein, an ad agency. **Availability:** Online.

279 ■ *"For Tax Preparation Agencies, Inbound Consumer Calls Trend Higher in January than April"* **in Marketing Weekly News (May 5, 2012)**
Pub: NewsRX LLC.
Contact: Kalani Rosell, Contact
Description: According to Marchex Institute, caller activity is highest in January, no April when tax deadlines loom. Online advertising campaigns for tax preparers should be optimized at the beginning of the year when peak calls occurred during the week of January 9, 2012. **Availability:** Online.

280 ■ *"A Framework for Conceptual Contributions in Marketing"* **in Journal of Marketing (Vol. 75, July 2011, No. 4, pp. 136)**
Pub: American Marketing Association
Contact: Bennie F. Johnson, Chief Executive Officer
Ed: Deborah J. MacInnis. **Description:** A look at a new framework for thinking about conceptualization in marketing is presented. Conceptual advances are essential to the vitality of the marketing discipline but recent writings indicate that advancement is slowing. The types of conceptual contributions are described, including their similarities and difference, and their importance to the field of marketing. **Availability:** PDF.

281 ■ *"Funeral Directors Get Creative As Boomers Near Great Beyond"* **in Advertising Age (Vol. 79, October 13, 2008, No. 38, pp. 30)**
Pub: Crain Communications, Inc.
Contact: Jessica Botos, Manager, Marketing
E-mail: jessica.botos@crainsnewyork.com
Ed: Lenore Skenazy. **Description:** Despite the downturn in the economy, the funeral business is thriving due to the number of baby boomers who realize the importance of making preparations for their death. Marketers are getting creative in their approach and many companies have taken into consideration the need for a more environmental friendly way to dispose of bodies and thus have created innovative businesses that reflect this need. **Availability:** Online.

282 ■ *"Google Gets Creepy"* **in Canadian Business (Vol. 85, September 17, 2012, No. 14, pp. 28)**
Ed: Jeff Beer. **Description:** Google's move to integrate its more than 70 different privacy agreements into just one has simplified the privacy deal the search engine company made with its users and improved its ability to obtain information for advertising. Google is addressing concerns about online privacy and allegations of anticompetitive practices in the U.S. and Europe. **Availability:** Online.

283 ■ *"Half of Canadian Firms to Boost Marketing Budgets"* **in Globe & Mail (January 22, 2007, pp. B1)**
Ed: Keith McArthur. **Description:** The advertising and marketing spending plans of different companies are presented. **Availability:** Online.

284 ■ *"Headwinds From the New Sod Slow Aer Lingus"* **in Barron's (Vol. 88, March 10, 2008, No. 10, pp. M6)**
Pub: Dow Jones & Company Inc.
Contact: Almar Latour, Chief Executive Officer
Ed: Sean Walters, Arindam Nag. **Description:** Aer Lingus faces a drop in its share prices with a falling US market, higher jet fuel prices, and lower long-haul passenger load factors. British media companies

Johnston Press and Yell Group are suffering from weaker ad revenue and heavier debt payments due to the credit crunch. **Availability:** Online.

285 ■ *"How to Brand-Crash the Olympics" in Canadian Business (Vol. 85, August 13, 2012, No. 13, pp. 18)*

Ed: Jeff Beer. **Description:** Several ways of taking advantage of the marketing opportunities in the 2012 London Olympics without having to spend millions in sponsorship fees are recommended. A few suggestions include securing advertising placements just outside of the brand exclusion zones, establishing presence on the Web and sponsoring an individual athlete.

286 ■ *"How to Improve Your Mobile Marketing" in Contractor (Vol. 56, October 2009, No. 10, pp. 54)*

Ed: Matt Michel. **Description:** Plumbers can improve their mobile advertising by making their logos as large as possible and positioning their logo on top of the truck so people can see it over traffic. They should also make the phone numbers small because people only take note of these when the truck is parked. **Availability:** Online.

287 ■ *How to Start a Faux Painting or Mural Business*
Pub: Allworth Press
Contact: Tad Crawford, Founder

Ed: Rebecca Pittman. **Released:** Second edition. **Price:** $24.95, paperback. **Description:** Updated and expanded to cover better ways to advertise, innovative supplies (such as Venetian plasters and stained cements), unique bidding and studio setups required for new plasters and varnishes. **Availability:** E-book; Print.

288 ■ *How to Use the Internet to Advertise, Promote, and Market Your Business or Web Site: With Little or No Money*
Pub: Atlantic Publishing Co.
Contact: Dr. Heather L. Johnson, Contact

Ed: Bruce C. Brown. **Released:** Revised third edition. **Description:** Information is given to help build, promote, and make money from your Website or brick and mortar store using the Internet, with minimal costs.

289 ■ *"An Ice Boost in Revenue; Wings Score With Expanded Corporate Sales" in Crain's Detroit Business (Vol. 25, June 1, 2009, No. 22)*
Pub: Crain Communications Inc.
Contact: Barry Asin, President

Ed: Bill Shea. **Description:** Stanley Cup finals always boost business for the Detroit area, even during a recession. The Red Wings corporate office reported corporate sponsorship revenue luxury suite rentals, Legends Club seats and advertising were up 40 percent this year over 2008. **Availability:** Print; Online.

290 ■ *"In-House Agencies Grew During COVID-19" in AdAge (November 23, 2021)*

Ed: Keira Wingate. **Released:** November 23, 2021. **Description:** Discusses the growth of in-house advertising opportunities while businesses were on lockdown due to the COVID-19 pandemic. **Availability:** Online.

291 ■ *"Infomercial King on TeleBrands, Going Broke, Making Millions" in Philadelphia Business Journal (Vol. 33, July 11, 2014, No. 22, pp. 3)*
Pub: American City Business Journals, Inc.
Contact: Mike Olivieri, Executive Vice President

Released: Weekly. **Price:** $4, Introductory 4-week offer(Digital only). **Description:** Ajit "A.J." Khubani is CEO of TeleBrands, the Fairfield, New Jersey company that brings to the American mainstream market novelty products by using infomercials, including AmberVision sunglasses and PedEgg. Though the marketing/advertising firm is worth $1 billion, Khubani's entrepreneurship career has gone through ups and downs and he has been close to bankruptcy three times. **Availability:** Print; Online.

292 ■ *Instant Income: Strategies That Bring in the Cash*
Pub: McGraw-Hill Professional

Ed: Janet Switzer. **Released:** First Edition. **Price:** $24. **Description:** Book covers small business advertising techniques, marketing, joint ventures, and sales. **Availability:** Print.

293 ■ *"Insurers No Longer Paying Premium for Advertising" in Brandweek (Vol. 49, April 21, 2008, No. 16, pp. SR3)*

Description: Insurance companies are cutting their advertising budgets after years of accelerated double-digit growth in spending due to the economic downturn, five years of record-breaking ad spend and a need to cut expenditures as claims costs rise and a competitive market keeps premiums in place. Statistical data included. **Availability:** Print; Online.

294 ■ *"Israeli Spam Law May Have Global Impact" in Information Today (Vol. 26, February 2009, No. 2, pp. 28)*
Pub: Information Today Inc.
Contact: Thomas H. Hogan, President

Ed: David Mirchin. **Description:** Israels new law, called Amendment 40 of the Communications Law, will regulate commercial solicitations including those sent without permission via email, fax, automatic phone dialing systems, or short messaging technologies. **Availability:** PDF; Online.

295 ■ *It's Not Who You Know - It's Who Knows You!: The Small Business Guide to Raising Your Profits by Raising Your Profile*
Pub: John Wiley & Sons, Inc.
Contact: Christina Van Tassell, Executive Vice President Chief Financial Officer

Ed: David Arvin. **Released:** 2nd edition. **Price:** $8.69, hardcover. **Description:** When it comes to promoting a small business or a brand, it is essential to know how valuable high-profile attention can be. But for most small companies, the cost of hiring an outside firm to increase attention can be too expensive. **Availability:** Print; Online.

296 ■ *"Joanna Crangle Named MBJ Publisher" in Sacramento Business Journal (Vol. 31, March 28, 2014, No. 5)*
Pub: American City Business Journals, Inc.
Contact: Mike Olivieri, Executive Vice President

Released: Weekly. **Description:** Joanna Crangle has been appointed the new publisher of the 'Memphis Business Journal'. She will succeed Stuart Chamblin, who is retiring as of March 31, 2014. Crangle has previously served as the newspaper's circulation director and advertising director. **Availability:** Print; Online.

297 ■ *The King of Madison Avenue: David Ogilvy and the Making of Modern Advertising*
Pub: Palgrave Macmillan

Ed: Kenneth Roman. **Released:** 2010. **Price:** $18, Paperback; $9.99, e-book. **Description:** The rise and fall of David Ogilvy, once the leader on Madison Avenue, is discussed. **Availability:** E-book; Print.

298 ■ *"Kokanee Films World's Longest Beer Commercial: Ready for a 90-Minute Feature Starring the Cast of Kokanee?' in Canadian Business (Vol. 85, July 16, 2012, No. 11-12, pp. 11)*

Ed: Jeff Beer. **Description:** Labatt Brewing Company and advertising agency Grip Ltd. produced a feature-length commercial for the Kokanee beer entitled, "The Movie Out Here", which centers on the reunion of friends in a ski town. As part of the marketing campaign, consumers can submit suggestions for props and set locations, audition for parts and vote online for the soundtrack. **Availability:** Online.

299 ■ *"Kroger Recasts Its Brand' in Supermarket News (November 6, 2019)*
URL(s): www.supermarketnews.com/retail-financial/kroger-recasts-its-brand

Ed: Russell Redman. **Released:** November 06, 2019. **Description:** The Kroger Co. has unveiled a new logo and a new brand identity that emphasizes "food first." Their new slogan is "Fresh for Everyone" while still maintaining an updated version of its classic Kroger logo. **Availability:** Online.

300 ■ *"LatinWorks Cozies Up to Chevy in Detroit' in Austin Business Journal (Vol. 31, August 12, 2011, No. 23, pp. A1)*
Pub: Austin Business Journal
Contact: Rachel McGrath, Director
E-mail: rmcgrath@bizjournals.com

Ed: Sandra Zaragoza. **Description:** Hispanic marketing agency LatinWorks opened an office in Detroit to better serve its client Chevrolet and to potentially secure more contracts from its parent company General Motors, whose offices are located nearby. **Availability:** Print; Online.

301 ■ *"Lawsuits Claim Coke Sent Illegal Ad Texts" in Atlanta Business Chronicle (June 13, 2014, 4A)*
Pub: American City Business Journals, Inc.
Contact: Mike Olivieri, Executive Vice President

Description: Coca-Cola Company is facing lawsuits in San Diego and California from consumers who claim to have received unsolicited ads to their wireless phones, thus putting Coke in violation of the Federal law, called the Telephone Consumer Protection Act. The plaintiff of the California lawsuit is seeking damages amounting to $1,500 for each text message sent. **Availability:** Print; Online.

302 ■ *"Leading Ohio Internet Marketing Firm Announces Growth in September" in Marketing Weekly News (September 26, 2009, pp. 24)*
Pub: Investment Weekly News

Description: Despite a poor economy, Webbed Marketing, a leading social media marketing and search engine optimization firm in the Midwest, has added five additional professionals to its fast-growing team. The company continues to win new business, provide more services and hire talented employees. **Availability:** Online.

303 ■ *"Local Firm Snaps up 91 Area Pizza Huts" in Orlando Business Journal (Vol. 26, January 8, 2010, No. 32, pp. 1)*
Pub: Orlando Business Journal
Contact: Julie Swyers, Director
E-mail: jswyers@bizjournals.com

Ed: Alexis Muellner, Anjali Fluker. **Description:** Orlando, Florida-based CFL Pizza LLC bought the 91 Orlando-area Pizza Hut restaurants for $35 million from parent company Yum! Brands Inc. CFL Pizza plans to distribute parts of the business to Central Florida vendors and the first business up for grabs is the advertising budget. **Availability:** Print; Online.

304 ■ *"Location-Based Advertising: Convenience and Personalization vs. Data Privacy" in Business News Daily (March 20, 2023)*
URL(s): www.businessnewsdaily.com/15049-survey-location-based-advertising.html

Ed: Andrew Martins. **Released:** March 20, 2023. **Description:** Location-based advertising can be a very useful tool for small businesses, but many consumers are against it for data privacy reasons. This article explores this concept in depth. **Availability:** Online.

305 ■ *"Lotteries Scratch Their Way to Billions" in Saint Louis Business Journal (Vol. 31, August 19, 2011, No. 52, pp. 1)*
Pub: Saint Louis Business Journal
Contact: Robert Bobroff, President
E-mail: rbobroff@bizjournals.com

Ed: Kelsey Volkmann. **Description:** Missouri Lottery reported $1 billion in sales in 2011. A six-fold increase in the lottery's advertising budget is seen to drive the revenue increase; a 4.5 percent rise in its scratch-off tickets and new sponsorships has also contributed to the development. **Availability:** Print; Online.

306 ■ *"Macy's Seeks Balance in All Things Ad-Related" in Crain's Chicago Business (Vol. 31, March 31, 2008, No. 13, pp. 19)*
Pub: Crain Communications Inc.
Contact: Barry Asin, President

Ed: Natalie Zmuda. **Description:** Macy's Inc. is seeking to balance its national television campaign with locally tailored promotions and products. **Availability:** Online.

307 ■ *"Marketers Push for Mobile Tuesday as the New Black Friday" in Advertising Age (Vol. 79, December 1, 2008, No. 44, pp. 21)*
Pub: Crain Communications, Inc.
Contact: Jessica Botos, Manager, Marketing
E-mail: jessica.botos@crainsnewyork.com

Ed: Natalie Zmuda. **Description:** Marketers are using an innovative approach in an attempt to stimulate business on the Tuesday following Thanksgiving by utilizing consumer's cell phones to alert them of sales or present them with coupons for this typically slow retail business day; with this campaign both advertisers and retailers are hoping to start Mobile Tuesday, another profitable shopping day in line with Black Friday and Cyber Monday. **Availability:** Online.

308 ■ *"Marketing in the Digital World: Here's How to Craft a Smart Online Strategy" in Black Enterprise (Vol. 40, July 2010, No. 12, pp. 47)*
Pub: Earl G. Graves Ltd.
Contact: Earl Graves, Jr., President

Ed: Sonya A. Donaldson. **Description:** Social media is an integral part of any small business plan in addressing marketing, sales, and branding strategies.

309 ■ *"Marketing at the Olympics is No Longer Worth It: An Exercise in Olympic Vanity" in Canadian Business (Vol. 85, August 13, 2012, No. 13, pp. 15)*

Ed: Bruce Philp. **Description:** The cost and return on investment of sponsoring the 2012 London Olympics is examined. Given the high price of official sponsorship in the Olympics, marketers should realize the value of the television advertising audience. **Availability:** Online.

310 ■ *Marketing Outrageously Redux: How to Increase Your Revenue by Staggering Amounts*
Pub: Bard Press
Contact: Ray Bard, Founder

Ed: Jon Spoelstra, Mark Cuban. **Released:** February 16, 2011. **Description:** Creative marketing strategies are defined. The book shows how considering marketing problems as outrageously but consistently can benefit any small business. The author talks about his own experience when there were not adequate funds for marketing and advertising and the outrageous approach he created to promote sports teams. **Availability:** Print; Electronic publishing.

311 ■ *Marketing Without Money for Small and Midsize Businesses: 300 FREE and Cheap Ways to Increase Your Sales*

Price: $11.25. **Description:** Three hundred practical low-cost or no-cost strategies to increase sales, focusing on free advertising, free marketing assistance, and free referrals to the Internet. **Availability:** Print; Online.

312 ■ *Marketing Works: Unlock Big Company Strategies for Small Business*
Description: Marketing strategies for any small business are outlined. **Availability:** Print.

313 ■ *"Mars Advertising's Orbit Grows as Other Ad Segments Fall" in Crain's Detroit Business (Vol. 25, June 1, 2009, No. 22, pp. 10)*
Pub: Crain Communications Inc.
Contact: Barry Asin, President

Ed: Bill Shea. **Description:** An electrical fire burned at Mars Advertising's headquarters in Southfield, Michigan. The company talks about its plans for regrouping and rebuilding. The family firm specializes in in-store marketing that targets consumers already in the buying mode. **Availability:** Print; Online.

314 ■ *"Medicine Men" in Canadian Business (Vol. 80, February 12, 2007, No. 4, pp. 19)*
Description: The effort of HPI Health Products' owners Dong Pedersen and Kent Pedersen to popularize their pain reliever product 'Lakota' is discussed. **Availability:** Online.

315 ■ *"Missing Ingredients In Cause-Related Advertising: The Right Formula of Execution Style and Cause Framing" in International Journal of Advertising (Vol. 31, May 2012, No. 2, pp. 231)*

Description: In traditional cause-related marketing (CRM) campaigns, marketers focus on a promoted product and ads containing CRM messesage only in small print at the bottom. Some recent marketers have choses to highlight the cause, with the product taking a lesser role in the advertising copy. The purpose of this research is to compare these two execution styles. **Availability:** Download; PDF; Online.

316 ■ *"Mobile Marketing Grows With Size of Cell Phone Screens" in Crain's Detroit Business (Vol. 24, January 14, 2008, No. 2, pp. 13)*
Pub: Crain Communications Inc.
Contact: Barry Asin, President

Ed: Bill Shea. **Description:** Experts are predicting increased marketing for cell phones with the inception of larger screens and improved technology.

317 ■ *"More Leading Retailers Using Omniture Conversion Solutions to Boost Sales and Ecommerce Performance" in Marketwired (September 22, 2009)*
Pub: Comtex News Network Inc.
Contact: Kan Devnani, President

Description: Many retailers are utilizing Omniture conversion solutions to improve the performance of their ecommerce businesses; recent enhancements to Omniture Merchandising and Omniture Recommendations help clients drive increased conversion to their Internet ventures.

318 ■ *"New Giants CEO Goes to Bat for Sponsorships" in Silicon Valley/San Jose Business Journal (Vol. 29, February 3, 2012, No. 45, pp. 1)*
Pub: Baltimore Business Journal
Contact: Rhonda Pringle, President
E-mail: rpringle@bizjournals.com

Description: New San Jose Giants baseball team, chief executive Dan Orum, is planning to increase the team's sponsorship, advertising, and ticket revenue. Orum will target technology companies and other firms as prospective sponsors. Orum's career background and achievements are also outlined. **Availability:** Print; Online.

319 ■ *"The New Science of Viral Ads: Five Techniques Can Help Companies Make Commercials That People Will Watch and Share" in Harvard Business Review (Vol. 90, April 2012, No. 4, pp. 25)*
Pub: Harvard Business Review Press
Contact: Moderna V. Pfizer, Contact

Ed: Thales Teixeira. **Price:** $6. **Description:** Guidelines include avoiding prominent brand placement, engage viewers immediately through joy and amusement use surprise but avoid shocking viewers, and target viewers who are inclined to share the ad. **Availability:** Online; PDF.

320 ■ *"New Sony HD Ads Tout Digital" in Brandweek (Vol. 49, April 21, 2008, No. 16, pp. 5)*
Description: Looking to promote Sony Electronics' digital imaging products, the company has launched another campaign effort known as HDNA, a play on the words high-definition and DNA; originally Sony focused the HDNA campaign on their televisions, the new ads will include still and video cameras as well and marketing efforts will consist of advertising in print, Online, television spots and publicity at various venues across the country. **Availability:** Online.

321 ■ *"No, Those Casino Rama Ads Aren't Running in NYC" in Globe & Mail (March 15, 2006, pp. B1)*
Ed: Keith McArthur. **Description:** The reason Casino Rama did not advertise on New York Cabs is discussed. **Availability:** Online.

322 ■ *"Nortel Makes Customers Stars in New Campaign" in Brandweek (Vol. 49, April 21, 2008, No. 16, pp. 8)*
Description: Nortel has launched a new television advertising campaign in which the business-to-business communications technology provider cast senior executives in 30-second TV case studies that show how Nortel's technology helped their businesses innovate. **Availability:** Online.

323 ■ *"Nowspeed and OneSource to Conduct Webinar: How to Develop Social Media Content That Gets Results" in Marketwired (December 14, 2009)*
Pub: Comtex News Network Inc.
Contact: Kan Devnani, President

Description: OneSource, a leading provider of global business information, and Nowspeed, an Internet marketing agency, will conduct a webinar titled "How to Develop Social Media Content That Gets Results" in order to provide marketers insight into how to develop and optimize effective social media content to get consumer results that translate into purchases and lead generation. **Availability:** Print; Mailing list; Online.

324 ■ *Obsessive Branding Disorder: The Illusion of Business and the Business of Illusion*
Pub: PublicAffairs
Contact: Jaime Leifer, Director

Ed: Lucas Conley. **Released:** 2008. **Description:** The implications of brand-centric marketing shows how defenseless consumers are against advertising because they are assaulted with 3,000 to 5,000 ads and branding stratagems that subtly dictate all aspects of their lives. **Availability:** Print; Online.

325 ■ *"Offer Your Own Authentic Truth" in South Florida Business Journal (Vol. 34, July 25, 2014, No. 53, pp. 13)*
Pub: American City Business Journals, Inc.
Contact: Mike Olivieri, Executive Vice President

Released: Weekly. **Price:** $8, introductory 4-week offer(Digital only). **Description:** Turkel Brands CEO, Bruce Turkel, was born in Miami Beach, Florida and has a bachelor's degree in design at the University of Florida. Turkel was a respected advertising agency owner and executive creative director before he began blogging on marketing and branding. He shares three tips for building a brand and creating a positive public image. **Availability:** Print; Online.

326 ■ *"Old Spice Guy (Feb.-July 2010)" in Canadian Business (Vol. 83, August 17, 2010, No. 13-14, pp. 23)*
Pub: Rogers Media Inc.
Contact: Neil Spivak, Chief Executive Officer

Ed: Andrew Potter. **Description:** Old Spice Guy was played by ex-football player and actor Isaiah Mustafa who made the debut in the ad for Old Spice Red Zone body wash that was broadcast during Super Bowl XLIV in February 2010. Old Spice Guy has become one of social marketing success but was cancelled in July when online viewership started to wane. **Availability:** Print; Online.

327 ■ *"Oliver Russell Acquiring Social Good Network"* in *Idaho Business Review* (August 29, 2014)
Pub: BridgeTower Media
Contact: Adam Reinebach, President
Description: Oliver Russell, owner of a Boise advertising firm, is acquiring the assets of startup Social Good Network, an online fundraising firm that was turned down for additional funding beyond its seed funding. Details of the deal and future plans are discussed.

328 ■ *"Olympic Challenge: The Skinny on Sponsors"* in *Barron's* (Vol. 92, July 23, 2012, No. 30, pp. 13)
Pub: Dow Jones & Company Inc.
Contact: Almar Latour, Chief Executive Officer
Ed: Jacqueline Doherty. **Description:** Sponsorship of the Olympics by Coca-Cola and McDonald's has been criticized due to the nature of their products. Representatives of the two companies, however, claim that their products are also enjoyed by athletes and can still remain part of a healthy lifestyle. **Availability:** Online.

329 ■ *"The One Thing You Must Get Right When Building a Brand"* in *Harvard Business Review* (Vol. 88, December 2010, No. 12, pp. 80)
Pub: Harvard Business Publishing
Contact: Diane Belcher, Managing Director
Ed: Patrick Barwise, Sean Meehan. **Price:** $8.95, PDF. **Description:** Four uses for new media include: communicating a clearly defined customer promise, creating trust via delivering on the promise, regularly improving on the promise, and innovating past what is familiar. **Availability:** Online; PDF.

330 ■ *"Oreos, Mercedes Join Super Bowl Ad Lineup; 90 Percent of Inventory Sold"* in *Advertising Age* (Vol. 83, October 8, 2012, No. 36, pp. 3)
Description: Mercedes-Benz and Oreo cookes, along with Coca-Cola and Best Buy, announced marketing plans to advertise during Super Bowl XLVII. **Availability:** Print; Online.

331 ■ *"Paper Tigers"* in *Conde Nast Portfolio* (Vol. 2, June 2008, No. 6, pp. 84)
Ed: Roger Lowenstein. **Description:** Newspapers are losing their advertisers and readers and circulation today is equal to that of 1950, a time when the U.S. population was half its present size. **Availability:** Print; Online.

332 ■ *"Play By Play: These Video Products Can Add New Life to a Stagnant Website"* in *Black Enterprise* (Vol. 41, December 2010, No. 5)
Pub: Earl G. Graves Ltd.
Contact: Earl Graves, Jr., President
Ed: Marcia Wade Talbert. **Description:** Web Visible, provider of online marketing products and services, cites video capability as the fastest-growing Website feature for small business advertisers. Profiles of various devices for adding video to a Website are included. **Availability:** Online.

333 ■ *"Promotional Marketing: How to Create, Implement & Integrate Campaigns That Really Work"*
Pub: Kogan Page
Released: Sixth edition. **Description:** Promotional marketing helps companies stay ahead of competition to gain new customers and keep existing ones. The guide includes new developments in the field of marketing, examining the use of digital media such as mobile devices and phones, interactive television, and Web-based advertising, as well as ways to research and evaluate promotional marketing campaigns. **Availability:** Online; PDF.

334 ■ *"Promotions Create a Path to Better Profit"* in *Pet Product News* (Vol. 64, December 2010, No. 12, pp. 1)
Ed: Joan Hustace Walker. **Description:** Pet store retailers can boost small mammal sales by launching creative marketing and promotions such as social networking and adoption days.

335 ■ *"The Proven 3 Step Formula For Growing Retail Profits: Without Having to Resort to Coupons or Discount Sales"*
Pub: CreateSpace
Released: September 24, 2014. **Price:** $4.89, paperback. **Description:** Previously published under the name, "How Some Retailers Make More Money Than Others". Retailers, whether a franchise or independent brand face challenges for increasing sales. An explanation for growing customer base without mass advertising, how to increase each customers spending, and improve gross margins are reported. A proven three-step process for increasing retail profits without the use of coupons or discounts is provided. **Availability:** Print.

336 ■ *"Psychological Ownership: A Social Marketing Advertising Message Appeal? Not for Women"* in *International Journal of Advertising* (Vol. 31, May 2012, No. 2, pp. 291)
Description: An assessment of psychological ownership as a potential persuasive advertising message appeal in the social marketing effort is examined. Psychological ownership is a feeling of possession; it occurs when individuals feel that something is their even though they cannot hold legal tide to it. **Availability:** PDF; Online.

337 ■ *"Put Power in Your Direct Mail Campaigns"* in *Contractor* (Vol. 56, September 2009, No. 9, pp. 64)
Ed: Matt Michel. **Description:** Advice on how members of the United States plumbing industry should manage direct mail marketing campaigns is offered. Determining the purpose of a campaign is recommended. Focusing on a single message, product or service is also encouraged. **Availability:** Print; Online.

338 ■ *"Quantivo Empowers Online Media Companies to Immediately Expand Audiences and Grow Online Profits"* in *Marketwired* (November 18, 2009)
Pub: Comtex News Network Inc.
Contact: Kan Devnani, President
Description: Quantivo, the leader in on-demand Behavioral Analytics, has launched a new solution that includes 22 of the most critical Internet audience behavior insights as out-of-the-box reports; Internet marketers need to understand their audience, what they want and how often to offer it to them in order to gain successful branding and campaigns online. **Availability:** Online.

339 ■ *"Reagan HQ In Limbo"* in *Austin Business Journal* (Vol. 32, April 6, 2012, No. 5, pp. A1)
Pub: American City Business Journals, Inc.
Contact: Mike Olivieri, Executive Vice President
Ed: Vicky Garza. **Description:** Reagan National Advertising has been awaiting the Austin City Council decision on whether it would be allowed to build a new headquarters that was on the drawing board for more than five years. However, approval of Reagan's plan would cut down several trees and that would violate the Heritage tree ordinance. **Availability:** Online.

340 ■ *"Regulatory Focus and Attribute Framing: Evidence of Compatibility Effects In Advertising"* in *International Journal of Advertising* (Vol. 31, February 2012, No. 1, pp. 169)
Ed: Hui-Fei Lin, Fuyuan Shen. **Released:** 2012. **Description:** Examination of the effects of regulatory focus on the framing of product attributes in advertisements is given. An experiment with a 2x2x2 between-subjects design was conducted to see if the compatibility among regulatory focus, frames and product attributes could affect advertising and brand attitudes, and purchase intention. **Availability:** Print; Online.

341 ■ *"Remember Those Great Volkswagen Ads?"*
Pub: Merrell Publishers
Contact: Hugh Merrell, Publisher

E-mail: hugh.merrell@merrellpublishers.com
Price: $65; C$72. **Description:** The Volkswagen advertising campaign of the 1960s and 1970s is rated the best and most influential of the century. Also included is a section on billboards signs used to advertise. **Availability:** Print.

342 ■ *"Research and Markets Adds Report: The U.S. Mobile Web Market"* in *Entertainment Close-Up* (December 10, 2009)
Description: Highlights of the new Research and Markets report "The U.S. Mobile Web Market: Taking Advantage of the iPhone Phenomenon" include: mobile Internet marketing strategies; the growth of mobile web usage; the growth of revenue in the mobile web market; and a look at Internet business communications, social media and networking. **Availability:** Print; Online.

343 ■ *"The Return of the Infomercial"* in *Canadian Business* (Vol. 83, September 14, 2010, No. 15, pp. 19)
Pub: Rogers Media Inc.
Contact: Neil Spivak, Chief Executive Officer
Ed: James Cowan. **Description:** Infomercials or direct response ads have helped some products succeed in the marketplace. The success of infomercials is due to the cheap advertising rates, expansion into retail stores and the products' oddball appeal. Insights into the popularity of infomercial products on the Internet and on television are given. **Availability:** Online.

344 ■ *"ROIonline Announces Streaming Video Products"* in *Marketing Weekly News* (December 5, 2009, pp. 155)
Pub: Investment Weekly News
Description: ROIonline LLC, an Internet marketing firm serving business-to-business and the industrial marketplace, has added streaming video options to the Internet solutions it offers its clients; due to the huge increase of broadband connections, videos are now commonplace on the Internet and can often convey a company's message in a must more efficient, concise and effective way that will engage a website's visitor thus delivering a high return on a company's investment. **Availability:** Print; Mailing list; Online.

345 ■ *"The Role of Advertising in Consumer Emotion Management"* in *International Journal of Advertising* (Vol. 31, May 2012, No. 2, pp. 339)
Description: Consumer research has demonstrated that emotions play an important role in the decision-making process. Individuals may use consumption or purchasing as a way to manage their emotions. This research develops a model to help explain the process by which individuals engage in consumption to manage their emotions, and examines the efficacy of an advertisement for a hedonic product that uses affect-laden language in marketing to stimulate such a process. **Availability:** Print; Online; Download.

346 ■ *"San Francisco Ad Agency Picks Boston For Its East Coast Beachhead"* in *Boston Business Journal* (Vol. 34, March 21, 2014, No. 7, pp. 4)
Pub: American City Business Journals, Inc.
Contact: Mike Olivieri, Executive Vice President
Description: H and L Partners is planning to open an office in Boston, Massachusetts. The move occurred following the company's takeover of the New England McDonald's account. The company has since recruited talent from large Boston agencies. **Availability:** Print; Online.

347 ■ *"Scepticism Towards DTC Advertising: A Comparative Study of Korean and Caucasian Americans"* in *International Journal of Advertising* (Vol. 31, February 2012, No. 1, pp. 147)
Ed: Jisu Huh, Denise E. DeLorme, Leonard N. Reid. **Description:** Studies of cultural and subcultural differences among consumers are important for advancing knowledge on direct-to-consumer prescription

Small Business Profiles

Advertising Service ■ 367

drug advertising (DTCA). This study investigates and compares scepticism towards DTCA between Korean and Caucasian Americans and the relationship of cultural values (collectivism vs individualism) and acculturation to DTCA secpticism. The results of the research is provided.

348 ■ *"Search and Discover New Opportunities"* in DM News (Vol. 31, December 14, 2009, No. 29, pp. 13)
Pub: Haymarket Media Inc.
Contact: Kevin Costello, Chief Executive Officer
Ed: Chantal Tode. **Description:** Although other digital strategies are gaining traction in Internet marketing, search marketing continues to dominate this advertising forum. Companies like American Greetings, which markets e-card brands online, are utilizing social networking sites and affiliates to generate a higher demand for their products. **Availability:** Print; Online.

349 ■ *"Seed Funding: Monsanto Plants Millions in Image Advertising"* in Saint Louis Business Journal (Vol. 31, July 29, 2011, No. 49, pp. 1)
Pub: Saint Louis Business Journal
Contact: Robert Bobroff, President
E-mail: rbobroff@bizjournals.com
Ed: Kelsey Volkman. **Description:** Monsanto kicked off a new campaign, 'St. Louis Grown' to show its commitment to the St. Louis, Missouri region after spending millions of dollars in recent years on national advertising campaigns. Monsanto had a marketing budget totaling $839 million in 2010 for both brand and corporate marketing. **Availability:** Print; Online.

350 ■ *The Seven Principles of WOM and Buzz Marketing: Crossing the Tipping Point*
Pub: Springer Science + Business Media LLC.
Ed: Panos Mourdoukoulas, George J. Siomkos. **Released:** First edition. **Description:** An examination into the reasons for some word-of-mouth marketing campaigns being effective while other fail, with a discussion about which group of consumers should be targeted, and how to turn a word-of-mouth campaign into buzz.

351 ■ *The Small Business Bible: Everything You Need to Know to Succeed in Your Small Business*
Pub: John Wiley & Sons, Inc.
Contact: Christina Van Tassell, Executive Vice President Chief Financial Officer
Ed: Steven D. Strauss. **Released:** Third edition. **Price:** $22.95, paperback; $14.99, E-book. **Description:** Comprehensive guide to starting and running a successful small business. Topics include bookkeeping and financial management, marketing, publicity, and advertising. **Availability:** E-book; Print.

352 ■ *The Social Media Bible: Tactics, Tools, and Strategies for Business Success*
Pub: John Wiley & Sons, Inc.
Contact: Christina Van Tassell, Executive Vice President Chief Financial Officer
Ed: Lon Safko. **Released:** Third edition. **Price:** $29.95, paperback; $19.99, E-Book. **Description:** Information is given to build or transform a business into social media, where customers, employees, and prospects connect, collaborate, and champion products and services in order to increase sales and to beat the competition. **Availability:** E-book; Print.

353 ■ *"Sorrell Digs Deep to Snag TNS"* in Advertising Age (Vol. 79, July 14, 2008, No. 7, pp. 1)
Pub: Crain Communications, Inc.
Contact: Jessica Botos, Manager, Marketing
E-mail: jessica.botos@crainsnewyork.com
Ed: Michael Bush. **Description:** Martin Sorrell's strategic vision for expansion in order to become the largest ad-agency holding company in the world is discussed. **Availability:** Online.

354 ■ *"Spanish Company to Offer Free Wi-Fi In Miami-Dade County"* in South Florida Business Journal (Vol. 34, April 25, 2014, No. 40)
Pub: American City Business Journals, Inc.
Contact: Mike Olivieri, Executive Vice President
Released: Weekly. **Description:** GOWEX a Madrid-based company, is offering free Wi-Fi access at 400 public spots in Miami, Florida. The firm will sell advertising over the Wi-Fi network. It has offered similar free access to users in New York, NY and in San Francisco, CA. **Availability:** Print; Online.

355 ■ *Start Your Own Fashion Accessories Business*
Pub: Entrepreneur Media Inc.
Contact: Dan Bova, Director
E-mail: dbova@entrepreneur.com
Ed: Eileen Figure Sandlin. **Released:** Second edition. **Description:** Entrepreneurs wishing to start a fashion accessories business will find important information for setting up a home workshop and office, exploring the market, managing finances, publicizing and advertising the business and more.

356 ■ *"Such Crust: Domino's Disses Pizza Hut Dough in Latest Spots"* in Advertising Age (Vol. 83, October 1, 2012, No. 35, pp. 3)
Pub: Crain Communications, Inc.
Contact: Barry Asin, President
Ed: Maureen Morrison. **Description:** Domino's Pizza reports Pizza Hut using frozen crusts in its latest advertising campaign, whereas Domino's always uses fresh dough for all of its pizzas. **Availability:** Print; Online.

357 ■ *"Suits Keep Flying in Wireless Service Marketing Wars"* in Globe & Mail (March 22, 2007, pp. B3)
Ed: Catherine McLean. **Description:** The suit filed by Telus Corp. against BCE Mobile Communications Inc. over the latter's alleged misleading advertisement in the press is discussed. **Availability:** Print; Online.

358 ■ *"Technology Companies are Increasing Their Hiring"* in Philadelphia Business Journal (Vol. 31, March 16, 2012, No. 5, pp. 1)
Pub: Baltimore Business Journal
Contact: Rhonda Pringle, President
E-mail: rpringle@bizjournals.com
Description: Technology firms in Pennsylvania have been expanding their work force. Online advertisements for computer and math science hiring have increased. **Availability:** Print; Online.

359 ■ *"This Week: McD's Eyes Ad Plan, Shifts Breakfast Biz"* in Crain's Chicago Business (Vol. 30, February 2007, No. 6, pp. 1)
Description: McDonald's is moving its national breakfast ad account from DDB Chicago to Arnold Worldwide of Boston and Moroch of Dallas in an attempt to change its marketing strategy. It is also doing a study to keep abreast of consumer trends. **Availability:** Print; Online.

360 ■ *"Titan to Become New York's Largest Provider of Phone Kiosk Advertising"* in Marketing Weekly News (September 11, 2010, pp. 150)
Pub: VerticalNews
Description: Titan will acquire from Verizon 1,900 payphones at 1,300 phone kiosk locations in New York City, New York. This transaction will triple the firm's inventory of New York Phone Kiosk media to over 5,000 advertising faces. Details are included. **Availability:** Print; Online.

361 ■ *"To Catch Up, Colgate May Ratchet Up Its Ad Spending"* in Advertising Age (Vol. 81, December 6, 2010, No. 43, pp. 1)
Pub: Crain Communications, Inc.
Contact: Jessica Botos, Manager, Marketing
E-mail: jessica.botos@crainsnewyork.com
Ed: Jack Neff. **Description:** Colgate-Palmolive Company has been losing market share in the categories of toothpaste, deodorant, body wash, dish soap and pet food. **Availability:** Online.

362 ■ *"The Top Mistakes of Social Media Marketing"* in Agency Sales Magazine (Vol. 39, November 2009, No. 9, pp. 42)
Description: One common mistake in social media marketing is having more than one image on the Internet because this ruins a business' credibility. Marketers need to put out messages that are useful to their readers and to keep messages consistent. **Availability:** Online.

363 ■ *"UEDs Would Light Up Street with News, Ads"* in Philadelphia Business Journal (Vol. 33, April 11, 2014, No. 9, pp. 8)
Pub: American City Business Journals, Inc.
Contact: Mike Olivieri, Executive Vice President
Description: Catalyst Outdoor head, Thaddeus Bartkowski, has been working on legislation to create a digital district that would permit urban experiential displays (UEDs) in a well-defined area in Center City. UEDs, which would communicate advertising and news, are being considered as a potential revenue stream for the city. The challenges in the installation of UEDs are also presented. **Availability:** Online.

364 ■ *"Ultimate Guide to Google AdWords: How to Access 100 Million People in 10 Minutes"*
Pub: Entrepreneur Media Inc.
Contact: Dan Bova, Director
E-mail: dbova@entrepreneur.com
Released: 5th edition. **Price:** $24.95, paperback. **Description:** The Google AdWords experts and analytics specialist present the techniques, tools, and tricks for using Google AdWords. The experts help small businesses to write advertising and Web site copy design, work in difficult markets, advertise, increase search engine presence, bid strategies for online auctions, financial budgeting and more. **Availability:** Print.

365 ■ *"Under Armour's Founder On Learning to Leverage Celebrity Endorsements"* in Harvard Business Review (Vol. 90, May 2012, No. 5, pp. 45)
Pub: Harvard Business Review Press
Contact: Moderna V. Pfizer, Contact
Ed: Kevin Plank. **Description:** Using his athletic apparel company Under Armour as an illustration, the author identifies two key points in effective utilization of endorsement advertising: balancing freebies with fair-price contracts, and offering stock opportunities so that celebrities can be personally engaged with growth.

366 ■ *"Unleashing the Power of Marketing"* in Harvard Business Review (Vol. 88, October 2010, No. 10, pp. 90)
Pub: Harvard Business Publishing
Contact: Diane Belcher, Managing Director
Ed: Beth Comstock, Ranjay Gulati, Stephen Liguori. **Price:** $8.95, PDF. **Description:** Chronicle of the development of General Electric's marketing framework that focused on three key factors: Principles, people and process. GE determined that successful marketing fulfills four functions: instigating, innovating, implementing, and integrating. **Availability:** Online; PDF.

367 ■ *"Unused Coupons Still Pay Off"* in Harvard Business Review (Vol. 90, May 2012, No. 5, pp. 32)
Pub: Harvard Business Review Press
Contact: Moderna V. Pfizer, Contact
Ed: Rajkumar Venkatesan, Paul Farris. **Price:** $6, hardcopy and PDF. **Description:** Unredeemed coupons have been found to create a sales lift for retailers as they increase awareness of a retailer or a brand even when consumers do not use them. Redemption rates should still be monitored however to assess campaign effectiveness. **Availability:** Print; Online.

368 ■ *"Use Social Media to Enhance Brand, Business"* in *Contractor (Vol. 56, December 2009, No. 12, pp. 14)*

Ed: Elton Rivas. **Description:** Advice on how plumbing contractors should use online social networks to increase sales is presented including such issues as clearly defining goals and target audience. An additional advantage to this medium is that advertisements can easily be shared with other users.

369 ■ *"The View From the Front Row"* in *Philadelphia Business Journal (Vol. 32, January 31, 2014, No. 51, pp. 6)*

Pub: American City Business Journals, Inc.
Contact: Mike Olivieri, Executive Vice President

Released: Weekly. **Price:** $4, introductory 4-week offer(Digital & Print). **Description:** Eric Smallwood, senior vice president of Front Row Analytics, reveals that the company conducts full-season sponsorship marketing analysis for the Seattle Seahawks. He mentions that a 30-second Super Bowl commercial could cost $4 million. Information about his favorite Super Bowl commercials is revealed. **Availability:** Print; Online.

370 ■ *"Vote Count Chocula in 2014"* in *Canadian Business (Vol. 87, July 2014, No. 7, pp. 28)*

Released: July 2014. **Description:** The current state of political marketing is criticized for exploiting the weaknesses of both the press and the electorate and is compared to brand marketing. The soul of brand marketing is perpetual accountability and marketers are expected to make sure that consumers are not disappointed.

371 ■ *"Web-Based Marketing Excites, Challenges Small Business Use"* in *Colorado Springs Business Journal (January 20, 2010)*

Pub: BridgeTower Media
Contact: Adam Reinebach, President

Ed: Becky Hurley. **Description:** Business-to-business and consumer-direct firms alike are using the fast-changing Web technologies to increase sales, leads and track consumer behavior but once a company commits to an Online marketing plan, experts believe, they must be prepared to consistently tweak and overhaul content and distribution vehicles in order to keep up. **Availability:** Online.

372 ■ *"What Is the Best Way to Promote My New Company?"* in *Legal Zoom (March 9, 2023)*

URL(s): www.legalzoom.com/articles/what-is-the-best-way-to-promote-my-new-company

Ed: Kylie Ora Lobell. **Released:** March 09, 2023. **Description:** There are several really good options for getting the word out about your new business including hiring an advertising company to handle the details or by using social media and other online options yourself. **Availability:** Online.

373 ■ *"Why Some Get Shafted By Google Pricing"* in *Advertising Age (Vol. 79, July 14, 2008, No. 7, pp. 3)*

Pub: Crain Communications, Inc.
Contact: Jessica Botos, Manager, Marketing
E-mail: jessica.botos@crainsnewyork.com

Ed: Abbey Klaassen. **Description:** Google's search advertising is discussed as well as the company's pricing structure for these ads. **Availability:** Online.

374 ■ *"Why You Need a New-Media 'Ringmaster"* in *Harvard Business Review (Vol. 88, December 2010, No. 12, pp. 78)*

Pub: Harvard Business Publishing
Contact: Diane Belcher, Managing Director

Ed: Patrick Spenner. **Price:** $8.95, PDF. **Description:** The concept of ringmaster is applied to brand marketing. This concept includes integrative thinking, lean collaboration skills, and high-speed decision cycles. **Availability:** Online; PDF.

375 ■ *"Will Mobile's Massive Growth Ever Equal Real Revenue?"* in *Advertising Age (Vol. 83, October 1, 2012, No. 35, pp. 18)*

Pub: Crain Communications Inc.
Contact: Barry Asin, President

Ed: Jason Del Rey. **Description:** Media companies are concerned over the return on investment when advertising on mobile applications. Firms lament that these ads are worth less to a small business than offline marketing programs. **Availability:** Online.

376 ■ *"With Traffic Jam in Super Bowl, Can Any Auto Brand Really Win?"* in *Advertising Age (Vol. 81, December 6, 2010, No. 43, pp. 1)*

Pub: Crain Communications, Inc.
Contact: Jessica Botos, Manager, Marketing
E-mail: jessica.botos@crainsnewyork.com

Ed: Rupal Parekh. **Description:** Car marketers are doubling down for Super Bowl XLV in Arlington, Texas and asking their ad agencies to craft commercials unique enough to break through the clutter and to capture viewers' attention. **Availability:** Online.

STATISTICAL SOURCES

377 ■ *Advertising Agencies Industry in the US - Market Research report*

URL(s): www.ibisworld.com/united-states/market-research-reports/advertising-agencies-industry/

Price: $925. **Description:** Downloadable report analyzing the current and future trends in the advertising agency industry. **Availability:** Download.

378 ■ *Advertising in Gaming - US - 2021*

URL(s): store.mintel.com/report/advertising-in-gaming-us-2021

Price: $4,366.35. **Description:** Downloadable report examining digital advertising in the video game industry. Discusses strategies along with player reactions and preferences. Report includes an executive summary, interactive databook, PowerPoint presentation, infographic overview, report PDF, and previous years data. **Availability:** PDF.

379 ■ *RMA Annual Statement Studies*

Pub: Risk Management Association
Contact: Nancy Foster, President

Released: Annual. **Description:** Contains composite balance sheets and income statements for more than 360 industries, including the accounting, auditing, and bookkeeping industries. Also contains five years of comparative historical data for discerning trends. Includes 16 commonly used ratios, computed for most of the size groupings for nearly every industry.

380 ■ *Standard & Poor's Industry Surveys*

Pub: Standard And Poor's Financial Services LLC.
Contact: Douglas L. Peterson, President

Description: Two-volume book that examines the prospects for specific industries, including trucking. Also provides analyses of trends and problems, statistical tables and charts, and comparative company analyses.

381 ■ *US Digital Advertising Market Report 2021*

URL(s): store.mintel.com/report/us-digital-advertising-market-report

Price: $4,366.35. **Description:** Downloadable report examining recent trends in digital advertising, especially with the impact the Covid-19 pandemic has had on the way people consume advertising. Includes an executive summary, interactive databook, PowerPoint Presentation, Infographic Overview, report PDF, and previous years data. **Availability:** PDF.

TRADE PERIODICALS

382 ■ *AAF Government Reports*

Pub: American Advertising Federation
Contact: Steve Pacheco, President
URL(s): www.aaf.org/Public/Public/Education-and-Resources/Newsletters/Government_Newsletter/GR-Reports-Hub.aspx?hkey=154b4f54-5025-498b-83fd-a65db6d39169

Released: Latest edition April 2024. **Description:** Supplies information on federal and state legislative and regulatory issues that affect the advertising industry. Remarks: Available online only. **Availability:** Online.

383 ■ *Advertising Compliance Service*

Pub: JL Com Publishing Company L.L.C.

Description: Functions as the only comprehensive reference source for information regarding advertising compliance requirements and issues. Subscription includes: 24 issues annually, 6 special reports, and a three-volume based volume (1,500 plus pages) for initial subscribers only. **Availability:** Online.

384 ■ *Adweek*

Pub: Adweek L.P.
Contact: Stuart Feil, Director, Publications
E-mail: stuart.feil@adweek.com
URL(s): www.adweek.com/aboutshop.adweek.com
YouTube: www.youtube.com/channel/UCKhCJRTHHLuW2iW7XQtcfyQ

Ed: Tim Nudd, Chris Ariens, Christopher Heine. **Released:** Weekly **Price:** $20, for monthly digital; $17, for digital annual; $1,200, for back issue; $199, for annual only. **Description:** Advertising news magazine. **Availability:** Print; Online.

385 ■ *Journal of Advertising Research (JAR)*

Pub: The Advertising Research Foundation
Contact: Scott McDonald, Executive
URL(s): www.journalofadvertisingresearch.com
Facebook: www.facebook.com/journalofadvertisingresearch

Ed: nanette burns. **Released:** Quarterly **Description:** Journal of advertising, marketing, and media research. **Availability:** Print; Download; PDF; Online.

CONSULTANTS

386 ■ Bob Bly
31 Cheyenne
Montville, NJ 07045
Ph: (973)263-0562
Co. E-mail: rwbly@bly.com
URL: http://www.bly.com
Contact: Bob Bly, Consultant
Facebook: www.facebook.com/BobBlyCopywriter
Linkedin: www.linkedin.com/in/bobbly
X (Twitter): x.com/Robertbly
Pinterest: www.pinterest.ph/blycopywriter

Description: An independent consultant and copywriter specializing in business-to-business, industrial, hi-tech and direct response advertising, marketing, publicity and promotion. **Scope:** An independent consultant and copywriter specializing in business-to-business, industrial, hi-tech and direct response advertising, marketing, publicity and promotion. **Founded:** 1982. **Publications:** "The Bulletproof Book Proposal "; "Finding A Good Idea For Your Book"; "A Fine Position to Be In"; "What to Do When Your Book Goes Out of Print"; "How To Write a Good Advertisement"; "31-derfully Simple Ways To Make Your Ads Generate More Inquiries.". **Training:** Active Listening; Become an Instant Guru; Get More Done In Less Time: How To Double Your Personal Productivity; How To Write A Nonfiction Book And Get It Published.

387 ■ Ideas To Go Inc. (ITG)
1730 New Brighton Blvd., Ste. 104-238
Minneapolis, MN 55413
Ph: (612)331-1570
Co. E-mail: info@ideastogo.com
URL: http://www.ideastogo.com
Contact: Beth Storz, President
Facebook: www.facebook.com/Ideastogoinc
Linkedin: www.linkedin.com/company/ideas-to-go-inc-
X (Twitter): x.com/ideastogo
Instagram: www.instagram.com/ideastogoinc
YouTube: www.youtube.com/channel/UCeUA74dfBPwjjdvZsKRKNsg

Description: A firm offering innovation services by engaging customers in idea generation sessions that includes assumption busting, insight mining, ethnography and team building. **Founded:** 1980. **Training:** Pennsylvania Manufacturing Confectioners' Association, Feb, 2010; Custom-designed creativity training; Creative Problem Solving Institute facilitator training; Received focus group moderator training, RIVA Institute. **Special Services:** Forness®, e-deation®, concentrated concept development, claimstorming, creative ethnography.

388 ■ ReCourses Inc.
4851 Vincion Rd.
  Murfreesboro, TN 37130-7909
Ph: (615)831-2277
Fax: (615)831-2277
URL: http://www.davidcbaker.com
Contact: Bob Lalasz, Chief Executive Officer
X (Twitter): x.com/ReCourses

Description: A privately held advisory firm providing business management advice to entrepreneurial experts worldwide. It is committed to a research-based, educational contribution to principals of expert firms through free position papers, webinars, a podcast, books (print, ebook, audible), and speaking engagements, as well as affordable seminars and advisory services. **Scope:** A privately held advisory firm providing business management advice to entrepreneurial experts worldwide. It is committed to a research-based, educational contribution to principals of expert firms through free position papers, webinars, a podcast, books (print, ebook, audible), and speaking engagements, as well as affordable seminars and advisory services. **Founded:** 1996. **Publications:** -"Managing (Right) for the First Time"; "Financial Management of a Marketing Firm". - "Financial Management of a Marketing Firm"; "Guidebook used worldwide for independent agencies". - "The Business of Expertise"; "How Entrepreneurial Experts Convert Insight to Impact and Wealth". **Training:** 10th Annual New Business Summit, Jan, 2013; Event - TEDx Nashville: Success from the Inside Out--Alignment & Engagement, Apr, 20163; Event - AIGA Brand Academy (Emory Executive Education @ Goizueta Business School), Apr, 2013; Measuring Economic Performance: Measuring and Enhancing Performance in a Marketing Firm, Dec, 2012; Managing Client Relationships: Being Indispensable, Growing the Account, Making Money, Nov, 2012; The Business of Design Oct, 2012; Getting a Good Start in Your Creative Career, Nov, 2011; Research and Insights, Nov, 2011; Managing Client Relationships; Research and Strategy; Financial Management: Measuring and Enhancing Performance in a Marketing Firm, Sep, 2009; Building and Leading a Staff: The When, How, and What of Growth and Culture, Sep, 2009; Doing Effective Work: Adding Significance to the Strategic Portion of Your Work for Clients, Sep, 2009; Resourcing the Creative Process: Managing Pricing, Deadlines, Budgets, Quality, and Capacity, Apr, 2009.

FRANCHISES AND BUSINESS OPPORTUNITIES

389 ■ AllOver Media Inc. (AOM)
16355 36th Ave., Ste. 700
  Minneapolis, MN 55446
Ph: (763)762-2000
Free: 800-525-8762
Co. E-mail: info@allovermedia.com
URL: http://allovermedia.com
Contact: Jeff Griffing, Chief Executive Officer
Facebook: www.facebook.com/AllOverMediaCorp
Linkedin: www.linkedin.com/company/allover-media
X (Twitter): x.com/allovermedia
Instagram: www.instagram.com/allover_media
YouTube: www.youtube.com/channel/UCTgq0ZsiK1bDl36Xk32WqJw

Description: Services: nontraditional advertising solutions. **Founded:** 2002.

390 ■ Billboard Connection (BC)
2121 Vista Pky.
  West Palm Beach, FL 33411
Free: 866-257-6025
Co. E-mail: info@billboardconnection.com
URL: http://billboardconnection.com
Contact: Donald L. Varner, President
Facebook: www.facebook.com/billboardconnection.corporate
X (Twitter): x.com/bbconnection

Description: Advertising agency specializing in out-of-home media consult with clients and place their ads on billboards, buses, taxis, airport dioramas, mall kiosks, movie theaters and more. **Founded:** 1997. **Financial Assistance:** Yes **Training:** Offers two-week training program and ongoing support.

391 ■ City Publications
1300 Parkwood Cir. SE, Ste. 100
  Atlanta, GA 30339
Ph: (770)951-0048
Co. E-mail: citypublications@outlook.com
URL: http://www.citypublication.com
Contact: Richard Houden, Chief Executive Officer

Description: Provider of direct mail advertising services. **Founded:** 2002. **Financial Assistance:** Yes **Training:** Engaged in publishing.

392 ■ Kwik Kopy Business Centers, Inc.
12715 Telge Rd.
  Cypress, TX 77429
Contact: Jay Groot, President

Description: Provider of printing and copying services. **Founded:** 2001. **Financial Assistance:** Yes **Managerial Assistance:** Provide business support, advertising, and marketing materials. **Training:** Owners attend classroom and field training, as well as ongoing training through workshops and conferences.

393 ■ Our Town America, A Franchising Corp.
13900 US Hwy. 19 N
  Clearwater, FL 33764
Free: 800-497-8360
Co. E-mail: customerservice@ourtownamerica.com
URL: http://www.ourtownamerica.com
Contact: Michael Plummer, Jr., President
Linkedin: www.linkedin.com/company/ourtown-america-inc-
X (Twitter): x.com/ourtownamerica
Instagram: www.instagram.com/ourtownamerica
YouTube: www.youtube.com/user/OurTownAmerica

Description: Firm provides direct mail advertising, community welcoming programs, mover marketing and direct mail programs. **Founded:** 1972. **Franchised:** 2005. **Equity Capital Needed:** $47,500. **Training:** Offers classroom training at headquarters followed with up to 2 weeks field training with a Franchise Training Manager who will be your ongoing sales support.

394 ■ RSVP Publications, Inc. (RSVP)
47585 Galleon Dr.
  Plymouth, MI 48170
Free: 800-360-7787
Fax: (800)726-9050
URL: http://www.rsvpadvertising.com
Contact: Kevin Cushing, President
Facebook: www.facebook.com/RsvpCorp
Linkedin: www.linkedin.com/company/rsvp-publications

Description: A direct mail advertising company. **Founded:** 1985. **Financial Assistance:** Yes **Training:** Offers 7 days training and ongoing support.

395 ■ Sign Biz Inc. (SB)
24681 La Plz., Ste. 270
  Dana Point, CA 92629
Free: 800-633-5580
Fax: (949)234-0426
Co. E-mail: sosa@signbiz.com
URL: http://www.signbiz.com
Contact: Teresa M. Young, President
Facebook: www.facebook.com/SIGNBIZ
X (Twitter): x.com/SIGNBIZ
Instagram: www.instagram.com/signbiznetwork
YouTube: www.youtube.com/signbiznetwork

Description: Visual communication stores developing digital sign making. **Founded:** 1989. **Training:** 2 weeks initial training at corporate office and 1-2 week home study program.

COMPUTERIZED DATABASES

396 ■ Ad Age
Contact: Josh Golden, Publisher
URL(s): adage.com www.crainsnewyork.com
Facebook: www.facebook.com/AdAge
X (Twitter): twitter.com/adage
Instagram: www.instagram.com/adage

Released: Weekly **Price:** Included in membership. **Description:** Magazine of marketing, media and advertising. **Availability:** Print; Online. **Type:** Full-text.

LIBRARIES

397 ■ The Advertising Research Foundation (ARF) - Library
432 Park Ave. S 4th Fl.
  New York, NY 10016
Ph: (212)751-5656
Fax: (212)689-1859
Co. E-mail: membership@thearf.org
URL: http://thearf.org
Contact: Scott McDonald, Executive
Facebook: www.facebook.com/ARF
Linkedin: www.linkedin.com/company/advertising-research-foundation
X (Twitter): x.com/The_ARF
YouTube: www.youtube.com/user/TheARFvideos

Description: Advertisers, advertising agencies, research organizations, associations, and the media are regular members of the foundation; colleges and universities are associate members. Objectives are to: further scientific practices and promote greater effectiveness of advertising and marketing by means of objective and impartial research. **Scope:** Advertising. **Founded:** 1936. **Holdings:** Figures not available. **Publications:** Journal of Advertising Research (JAR) (Quarterly). **Awards:** David Ogilvy Awards (Annual); ARF Rising Star Award (Annual); ARF Innovation Award (Annual); ARF Member Recognition Award (Annual). **Geographic Preference:** National.

398 ■ DDB Worldwide Communications Group LLC - Library [Doyle Dane Bernbach]
DDB Worldwide Communications Group LLC
  195 Broadway, 7th Fl.
  New York, NY 10007
Ph: (212)415-2000
Co. E-mail: info@ddb.com
URL: http://www.ddb.com
Contact: Alex Lubar, President
Linkedin: www.linkedin.com/company/ddb
X (Twitter): x.com/DDB_Worldwide
Instagram: www.instagram.com/ddbworldwide

Description: Provides advertising and marketing services such as direct mail, events, promotions, catalogs, and strategic services. **Services:** Interlibrary loan; SDI; full reference service; Center not open to the public except for prearranged student group tours. **Founded:** 1949. **Holdings:** 5,000 books; 200 VF drawers of pictures and print advertisements; 300 VF drawers of subject clippings; 150 VF drawers of corporation files and Annual reports; 100 pamphlet boxes of consumer analysis material; Computerized Research Library (internal database); Internet.

399 ■ International Advertising Association (IAA) - Library
511 Ave. of Americas No. 4017
  New York, NY 10011
Ph: (646)849-9908
Co. E-mail: iaa@iaaglobal.org
URL: http://www.iaaglobal.org
Contact: Joel Nettey, President
Facebook: www.facebook.com/InternationalAdvertisingAssociation
Linkedin: www.linkedin.com/company/international-advertising-association
X (Twitter): x.com/iaa_global
Instagram: www.instagram.com/iaaglobal

YouTube: www.youtube.com/channel/ UCULDmcOgvEd_SyFF0LS_-BQ

Description: Demonstrates to governments and consumers the benefits of advertising as the foundation of diverse, independent media. **Scope:** Advertising. **Founded:** 1938. **Holdings:** Figures not available. **Publications:** *IAA National & World News* (Quarterly); *The Case for Advertising Self-Regulation*; *IAA Annual Report* (Annual); *IAA Membership Directory*; *International Advertising Association-- Membership Directory* (Continuous). **Awards:** InterAd Student Competition (Annual); Samir Fares Award. **Geographic Preference:** National.

400 ■ Leo Burnett Detroit - Information Resource Center
3310 W Big Beaver Rd., Ste. 107
  Troy, MI 48084
Ph: (248)458-8300
Co. E-mail: monica.lambert@leoburnett.com
URL: http://www.leoburnett.com
Facebook: www.facebook.com/LeoBurnettDetroit
Scope: Marketing; advertising. **Services:** Copying (limited). **Founded:** 1952. **Holdings:** 3,000 books; 200,000 pictures.

401 ■ thinkTV - Library
160 Bloor St. E, Ste. 1005
  Toronto, ON, Canada M4W 1B9
Ph: (416)923-8813
Co. E-mail: info@thinktv.ca
URL: http://thinktv.ca
Contact: Catherine MacLeod, President
E-mail: catherine.macleod@thinktv.ca
Linkedin: www.linkedin.com/company/10345659
X (Twitter): x.com/thinktvca
Scope: Television; advertising. **Services:** Copying; library open to members of the advertising industry. **Founded:** 1962. **Holdings:** Figures not available.

Airbag Replacement/Service Centers

ASSOCIATIONS AND OTHER ORGANIZATIONS

402 ■ Automotive Service Association (ASA) - Library
8209 Mid Cities Blvd., Ste. 100
North Richland Hills, TX 76182-4712
Ph: (817)514-2900
Co. E-mail: info@asashop.org
URL: http://www.asashop.org
Contact: Ray Fisher, Executive Director
E-mail: rayf@asashop.org
Facebook: www.facebook.com/ASAshop
Linkedin: www.linkedin.com/company/automotive-service-association
X (Twitter): x.com/asashop
Instagram: www.instagram.com/asa_national
YouTube: www.youtube.com/user/asawebops
Description: Serves the needs of mechanical, transmission, and collision shop owners through education and representation on legislation affecting the automotive service industry. **Scope:** Automobiles; repair. **Founded:** 1951. **Holdings:** Figures not available. **Publications:** *AutoInc.* (Bimonthly). **Educational Activities:** Congress of Automotive Repair and Service (CARS) (Annual); International Autobody Congress and Exposition - NACE (Annual). **Geographic Preference:** National.

REFERENCE WORKS

403 ■ "With 54 Million to Go, This Airbag Recall is Never Going to End" in The Wall Street Journal (June 26, 2017)
URL(s): www.wsj.com/articles/bankrupt-air-bag-maker-takata-means-to-keep-limping-along-1498477869
Ed: Sean McLain, Mike Spector. **Released:** May 26, 2017. **Description:** Bankrupt Takata is still supplying parts for the nearly 54 million defective air bags just in the U.S in 2017 and it is expected to grow to over 70 million air bags by the end of 2019. Most car manufacturers are dealing with the air bag replacements and they are also receiving supplies from Autoliv Inc. **Availability:** Print; Online.

404 ■ "Your Car Repair Handbook" in Consumer Reports (September 9, 2021)
URL(s): www.consumerreports.org/car-repair/your-car-repair-handbook
Ed: Benjamin Preston. **Released:** September 21, 2021. **Description:** Owning a vehicle can get expensive, especially if repairs are needed. Even regular maintenance can add up. A breakdown of what costs to expect when doing it yourself or taking it in to the shop is given. Repairs that should be handled at a dealership, such as airbag safety, is also discussed. **Availability:** Print; Online.

TRADE PERIODICALS

405 ■ *AutoInc.*
Pub: Automotive Service Association
Contact: Ray Fisher, Executive Director
E-mail: rayf@asashop.org
URL(s): www.autoinc.org
Ed: John Clark. **Released:** Bimonthly **Price:** $35, for per year US; $40, for Canada / Mexico; $95, for international; $5, Single issue. **Description:** Covers technical and management information of interest to members; contains shop profiles, legislative news, and industry events. **Availability:** Print; PDF.

TRADE SHOWS AND CONVENTIONS

406 ■ Dayton Auto Show
Dayton Area Auto Dealers Association (DAADA)
6515 Longshore loop, Ste. 320
Dublin, OH 43017
Contact: Sara Bruce, Contact
URL(s): daytonautoshow.com/aws/OADA/pt/sp/DAS_home_page
Facebook: www.facebook.com/DaytonAutoShow
X (Twitter): twitter.com/DaytonAutoShow
Frequency: Annual. **Description:** Automobiles and automotive equipment, supplies, and services. **Audience:** General public. **Principal Exhibits:** Automobiles and automotive equipment, supplies, and services. **Telecommunication Services:** mfast@oada.com.

LIBRARIES

407 ■ U.S. National Highway Traffic Safety Administration - Technical Information Services (TIS)
1201 New Jersey Ave. SE, E12-100
Washington, DC 20590
URL: http://www.nhtsa.gov/es/about-nhtsa/electronic-reading-room
Scope: Vehicle and traffic safety information. **Services:** Copying; TIS open to the public.

RESEARCH CENTERS

408 ■ Center for Auto Safety (CAS)
4400 Jenifer St., NW Ste. 331
Washington, DC 20015-2113
Ph: (202)328-7700
Co. E-mail: contact@autosafety.org
URL: http://www.autosafety.org
Contact: Jack Gillis, President
E-mail: jack@consumerfed.org
X (Twitter): x.com/Ctr4AutoSafety
Description: Seeks to "reduce the human and economic losses wrought by the automobile and the auto industry.". **Scope:** Dedicated to advocating for auto safety, quality, and fuel economy on behalf of our members and all drivers, passengers, and pedestrians. **Founded:** 1970. **Publications:** *Lemon Times* (Quarterly); *Center for Auto Safety--Impact: A Journal of Safety News* (Bimonthly); *The Lemon Book*. **Geographic Preference:** National.

409 ■ Insurance Institute for Highway Safety (IIHS) - Library
4121 Wilson Blvd., 6th Fl.
Arlington, VA 22203
Ph: (703)247-1500
Co. E-mail: legal@iihs.org
URL: http://www.iihs.org
Contact: David Harkey, President
Facebook: www.facebook.com/iihs.org
Linkedin: www.linkedin.com/company/iihs-hldi
X (Twitter): x.com/IIHS_autosafety
Instagram: www.instagram.com/iihs_autosafety
Description: Supported by casualty insurance companies and trade associations such as American Insurers Highway Safety Alliance, American Insurance Highway Safety Association, and National Association of Independent Insurers Safety Association. **Scope:** Seeks to reduce deaths, injuries, and property damage resulting from crashes on the nation's highways. **Founded:** 1959. **Holdings:** Figures not available. **Publications:** *IIHS Annual Report* (Annual); *Shopping For a Safer Car* (Annual); *IIHS Status Report*. **Geographic Preference:** National.

Air Charter Service

ASSOCIATIONS AND OTHER ORGANIZATIONS

410 ■ Air Line Pilots Association International - Canada (ALPA) [Association Canadienne des Pilotes de Ligne Internationale]
360 Albert St., Ste. 1210
Ottawa, ON, Canada K1R 7X7
Ph: (613)569-5668
URL: http://www.alpa.org
Contact: Joe DePete, President
Description: Promotes safety and efficiency in air transportation. Collects and distributes information on professional problems and concerns. Negotiates collective employment agreements with airlines. **Founded:** 1931. **Geographic Preference:** National.

411 ■ Air Transport Association of Canada (ATAC) [Association du transport aérien du Canada]
222 Queen St., Ste. 1110
Ottawa, ON, Canada K1P 5V9
Ph: (613)233-7727
Co. E-mail: info@atac.ca
URL: http://www.atac.ca
Contact: John McKenna, President
Linkedin: www.linkedin.com/company/atac1934
X (Twitter): x.com/atac_canada
Description: Promotes a business climate beneficial to members. Represents member interests before government agencies. **Scope:** Aims to support our members in their commitment to a safe, world-leading and sustainable Canadian air transport industry. **Founded:** 1934. **Publications:** *Flightplan* (Semiannual). **Educational Activities:** ATAC Industry Symposium and Spring Reception. **Awards:** ATAC Lifetime Honoree Award (Annual); Paul Mulrooney Memorial Award of Excellence (Biennial). **Geographic Preference:** National.

412 ■ Aircraft Owners and Pilots Association (AOPA)
421 Aviation Way
Frederick, MD 21701
Ph: (301)695-2000
Free: 800-872-2672
Fax: (301)695-2375
Co. E-mail: memberservices@aopa.org
URL: http://www.aopa.org
Contact: Mark R. Baker, President
E-mail: mark@aopa.org
Facebook: www.facebook.com/AOPApilots
Linkedin: www.linkedin.com/company/aopa
X (Twitter): x.com/AOPA
YouTube: www.youtube.com/AOPALive
Description: Represents general aviation pilots and owners, 60 percent of US. are members, as are three-quarters of the nation's general aviation aircraft owners. Works to make flying safer, less expensive, and more fun. **Founded:** 1939. **Publications:** *AOPA Pilot* (Monthly); *AOPA Flight Training* (8/year); *AOPA's Airport Directory: The Pilot and FBO Flight Planning Guide*; *AOPA Pilot--General Aviation Aircraft Directory Issue*; *AOPA's Aviation U.S.A.* (Semiannual); *AOPA Airports Directory*. **Awards:** Aircraft Owners and Pilots Association Scholarships; Joseph B. Hartranft Award (Annual); Laurence P. Sharples Perpetual Award (Annual). **Geographic Preference:** National.

413 ■ Airlines for America (A4A) - Library
1275 Pennsylvania Ave. NW, Ste. 1300
Washington, DC 20004
Ph: (202)626-4000
Co. E-mail: mediarelations@airlines.org
URL: http://www.airlines.org
Contact: Nicholas E. Calio, President
Facebook: www.facebook.com/AirlinesForAmerica
Linkedin: www.linkedin.com/company/airlines-for-america
X (Twitter): x.com/airlinesdotorg
Instagram: www.instagram.com/airlinesforamerica
YouTube: www.youtube.com/user/AirlinesforAmerica
Description: Airlines engaged in transporting persons, goods and mail by aircraft between fixed terminals on regular schedules. **Scope:** Airlines. **Founded:** 1936. **Holdings:** Figures not available. **Publications:** *Air Transport* (Annual); *Economic* (Annual). **Geographic Preference:** National.

414 ■ Airport Minority Advisory Council (AMAC)
45 L St. SW
Washington, DC 20024
Ph: (703)414-2622
Co. E-mail: info@amac-org.com
URL: http://www.amac-org.com
Contact: Simeon Terry, Vice Chairman of the Board
Facebook: www.facebook.com/AirportMinorityAdvisoryCouncil
Linkedin: www.linkedin.com/company/airport-minority-advisory-council
X (Twitter): x.com/AMAC_ORG
Instagram: www.instagram.com/amac_org
YouTube: www.youtube.com/channel/UCKDJh--0mbVOvNltAz9vSiQ
Description: Advocates for equal opportunity for minorities and women in airport contracting and employment. **Founded:** 1984. **Publications:** *AMAC-ESP Informational Brochure*. **Educational Activities:** Annual Airport Business Diversity Conference (Annual). **Awards:** Airport AEC Award (Annual); Airport Concessions Innovation and Inclusion Award (Annual); AMAC Award of the Organization (Annual); AMAC Hall of Fame Award (Annual). **Geographic Preference:** National.

415 ■ Canadian Business Aviation Association (CBAA)
1 Rideau St., Ste. 700
Ottawa, ON, Canada K1N 8S7
Ph: (613)236-5611
Co. E-mail: membersupport@cbaa.ca
URL: http://www.cbaa-acaa.ca
Contact: Anthony Norejko, President
E-mail: anorejko@cbaa.ca
Linkedin: www.linkedin.com/company/canadian-business-aviation-association-cbaa-
X (Twitter): x.com/cbaacanada
Instagram: www.instagram.com/cbaacanada
YouTube: www.youtube.com/channel/UCl19bwex6vlNC5pZ3DqGO0w
Description: Companies operating or supporting business aviation, promotes business aviation; encourages safety and efficiency; makes recommendations to regulatory agencies. **Founded:** 1961. **Educational Activities:** Canadian Business Aviation Association Convention and Exhibition (Annual). **Awards:** CBAA Company Safety Award (Annual); CBAA Company Maintenance Department Safety Award (Annual); Award of Merit (Annual); CBAA Pilot Safety Award (Annual); CBAA Honorary Lifetime Membership Award (Annual); CBAA Award of Merit (Annual). **Geographic Preference:** Multinational.

416 ■ Flight Safety Foundation (FSF) - Library
c/o Dr. Hassan Shahidi, President
Chief Executive Officer
1920 Ballenger Ave., 4th Fl.
Alexandria, VA 22314
Ph: (703)739-6700
Fax: (703)739-6708
Co. E-mail: technical@flightsafety.org
URL: http://flightsafety.org
Contact: Dr. Hassan Shahidi, President
Facebook: www.facebook.com/FlightSafetyFoundation
X (Twitter): x.com/flightsafety
YouTube: www.youtube.com/channel/UCYS5ObEBNuW9s3j7SMzxvLQ
Description: Aerospace manufacturers, domestic and foreign airlines, insurance companies, fuel and oil companies, schools and miscellaneous organizations having an interest in the promotion of safety in flight. Sponsors safety audits. Compiles statistics. **Scope:** Aviation safety, including pilot decision making, human factors, aircraft passenger safety, air traffic control, maintenance, aging aircraft safety, environmental safety hazards, confidential audits of airlines and corporate fleets, and safety and security factors at airports. **Founded:** 1947. **Holdings:** Figures not available. **Publications:** *Pilots Safety Exchange*; *Flight Safety Foundation--Membership Directory*; *Accident Prevention* (Monthly); *Human Factors and Aviation Medicine* (Bimonthly). **Educational Activities:** International Air Safety Summit (IASS) (Annual); Business Aviation Safety Summit (BASS) (Annual). **Awards:** Business Aviation Meritorious Service Award (Annual); Joe Chase Award (Annual); Laura Taber Barbour Air Safety Award (Annual); Cecil A. Brownlow Publication Award (Annual); Richard Teller Crane Founder's Award (Annual). **Geographic Preference:** National.

417 ■ Helicopter Association International (HAI) [HAI Foundation]
1920 Ballenger Ave., 4th Fl.
Alexandria, VA 22314-2898
Ph: (703)683-4646

Fax: (703)683-4745
Co. E-mail: rotor@rotor.org
URL: http://rotor.org
Contact: James A. Viola, President
Facebook: www.facebook.com/HelicopterAssoc
Linkedin: www.linkedin.com/company/helicopter
 -association-international
X (Twitter): x.com/HeliAssoc
Instagram: www.instagram.com/helicopterassoc
YouTube: www.youtube.com/user/HelicopterAssoc
Description: Disseminates information concerning the use, operation, hiring, contracting, and leasing of helicopters. Maintains a collection of current helicopter service bulletins and technical data; organizes safety seminars, continuing education courses, and helicopter operator management courses. **Founded:** 1983. **Publications:** *Helicopter Association International--The Helicopter Annual* (Annual); *Heliport/Vertiport Development Guide*; *Operations Update* (Monthly); *Rotorgram* (Quarterly); *ROTOR* (Quarterly); *Heliport Directory*; *Operations and Management, Guide/Safety Manual*; *The Helicopter Annual* (Annual). **Educational Activities:** HAI HELI-EXPO (Annual). **Awards:** Commercial Helicopter Pilot Rating Scholarships (Annual); Helicopter Foundation International Maintenance Technician Certificate Scholarships (Annual); Michelle North Scholarships for Safety (Annual); Bill Sanderson Aviation Maintenance Technician Scholarships (Annual); HAI Aviation Maintenance Technician Safety Award (AMT) (Annual); HAI Operator Safety Award (Annual); HAI Salute to Excellence (Annual); The Bell Helicopter Lifetime Achievement Award (Annual); The AgustaWestland Safety Award (Annual); Sikorsky Humanitarian Service Award; HAI Excellence in Communications Award (Irregular); Maintenance Award (Irregular); Eurocopter Golden Hour Award (Annual); W. A. (Dub) Blessing Certified Flight Instructor of the Year (Annual); HAI Pilot of the Year Award (Annual); HAI Pilot Safety Award (Annual). **Geographic Preference:** Multinational; National.

418 ■ IBAC Update
999 Robert-Bourrassa Blvd., Ste. 16-33
 Montreal, QC, Canada H3C 5J9
Ph: (514)954-8054
Co. E-mail: info@ibac.org
URL: http://ibac.org
Contact: Kurt Edwards, Member
URL(s): ibac.org/news/newsletters
Released: Irregular **Description:** Contains information on the activities of the aviation community and member organizations. **Availability:** Print.

419 ■ The ICAO Journal
999 Robert-Bourassa Blvd.
 Montreal, QC, Canada H3C 5H7
Ph: (514)954-8219
Fax: (514)954-6077
Co. E-mail: icaohq@icao.int
URL: http://www.icao.int
Contact: Dr. Fang Liu, Secretary General
URL(s): www.icao.int/publications/Pages/ICAO-Journal.aspx?year=2024&lang=en
Released: Latest Edition 2024. **Description:** Contains concise account of the activities of the International Civil Aviation Organization and features additional information of interest to Contracting States and the international aeronautical world. **Availability:** Print; Online.

420 ■ International Business Aviation Council (IBAC)
999 Robert-Bourrassa Blvd., Ste. 16-33
 Montreal, QC, Canada H3C 5J9
Ph: (514)954-8054
Co. E-mail: info@ibac.org
URL: http://ibac.org
Contact: Kurt Edwards, Member
Facebook: www.facebook.com/IBACBizAv1
Linkedin: www.linkedin.com/company/18677197
X (Twitter): x.com/IBACBizAv1
Description: Aims to provide information on all aspects of international business aircraft operations; ensure that the interests of international business aviation are brought to the attention of and understood by authorities; and improve the safety, efficiency, and economic use of business aircraft operating internationally. Stresses the importance of business aviation to the economy and to the well-being of all nations and maintains liaison with international aviation organizations to ensure growth of the field throughout the world. **Founded:** 1981. **Publications:** *IBAC Update* (Irregular). **Geographic Preference:** Multinational.

421 ■ International Civil Aviation Organization (ICAO) - Library
999 Robert-Bourassa Blvd.
 Montreal, QC, Canada H3C 5H7
Ph: (514)954-8219
Fax: (514)954-6077
Co. E-mail: icaohq@icao.int
URL: http://www.icao.int
Contact: Dr. Fang Liu, Secretary General
Facebook: www.facebook.com/InternationalCivilAviationOrganization
Linkedin: www.linkedin.com/company/icao
X (Twitter): x.com/icao
YouTube: www.youtube.com/user/ICAOvideo
Description: Seeks to develop the standards and procedures in international air navigation and to foster the planning and development of international air transport so as to insure safe and orderly growth of international civil aviation. Carries out activities in air navigation, air transport, and legal matters. **Scope:** Aviation. **Founded:** 1944. **Holdings:** Figures not available. **Publications:** *ICAO Location Indicators: Doc 7910/114* (Quarterly); *ICAO Aeronautical Chart Catalogue*; *Aeronautical Information Services Provided by States: Doc 7383* (Annual); *Airport Characteristics Data Bank (ACDB)*; *ICAO Bird Strike Information System (IBIS)*; *Aeronautical Chart Manual: Doc 8697*; *ICAO Journal* (Quarterly); *The ICAO Journal*; *ICAO Designators for Aircraft Operating Agencies, Aeronautical Authorities and Services* (Quarterly). **Awards:** Edward Warner Award (Irregular). **Geographic Preference:** Multinational.

422 ■ National Air Carrier Association (NACA)
1735 N Lynn St., Ste. 105
 Arlington, VA 22209-3928
Ph: (703)358-8060
Co. E-mail: admin@naca.aero
URL: http://naca.aero
Contact: George Novak, President
Facebook: www.facebook.com/National-Air-Carrier
 -Association-191452260962499
Linkedin: www.linkedin.com/company/national-air
 -carrier-association-dc
Description: Represents U.S. certificated airlines specializing in low-cost scheduled and air charter operations. Assists members in the promotion of air transportation and serves as a liaison between members and U.S. government bodies that regulate air transportation. **Founded:** 1962. **Geographic Preference:** National.

423 ■ National Air Transportation Association (NATA)
818 Connecticut Ave. NW, Ste. 900
 Washington, DC 20006
Ph: (202)774-1535
Free: 800-808-6282
Fax: (202)452-0837
Co. E-mail: info@nata.aero
URL: http://www.nata.aero
Contact: Curt Castagna, President
Facebook: www.facebook.com/nataaero
Linkedin: www.linkedin.com/company/nataaero
X (Twitter): x.com/nataaero
Description: Represents the interests of aviation businesses nationwide. Provides vital aviation services to the airlines, the military, and business/corporate/individual aircraft owners and operators; services includes fueling, maintenance, and flight instruction. **Founded:** 1940. **Publications:** *NATAnews* (Weekly); *National Air Transportation Association Official Membership Directory*; *Wage and Salary Handbook* (Annual); *National Air Transportation Association - Aviation Resource and Membership Directory* (Annual). **Awards:** William A. "Bill" Ong Memorial Award (Annual); NATA Distinguished Service Award (Annual); NATA Aviation Journalism Award (Annual); ATP/NATA General Aviation Service Technician Award (Annual); NATA Excellence in Pilot Training Award (Annual); NATA Airport Executive Partnership Award (Annual); FAA Customer Service Excellence Award (Annual); NATA Aviation Maintenance Technician Employer Recognition Award (Annual). **Geographic Preference:** National.

424 ■ National Business Aviation Association (NBAA)
1200 G St. NW, Ste. 1100
 Washington, DC 20005
Ph: (202)783-9000
Free: 800-394-6222
Fax: (202)331-8364
Co. E-mail: info@nbaa.org
URL: http://nbaa.org
Contact: Edward M. Bolen, President
Facebook: www.facebook.com/NBAAfans
Linkedin: www.linkedin.com/company/national-business-aviation-association
X (Twitter): x.com/nbaa
Instagram: www.instagram.com/nbaaphotos
YouTube: www.youtube.com/user/NBAAvideo
Description: Companies owning and operating aircraft for business use, suppliers, and maintenance and air fleet service companies. Compiles statistics; provides literature for researchers and students. **Founded:** 1947. **Publications:** *Maintenance and Operations Bulletin* (Semiannual); *Management Guide*; *National Business Aircraft Association--Membership Directory*; *NBAA Update*; *NBAA Directory of Member Companies and Aircraft*. **Educational Activities:** European Business Aviation Convention and Exhibition (EBACE) (Annual); National Business Aviation Association Annual Meeting And Convention (Annual). **Awards:** Donald A. Baldwin Sr. Business Aviation Management Scholarship (Annual); UAA Janice K. Barden Aviation Scholarship (Annual); Al Conklin and Bill de Decker Business Aviation Management Scholarship (Annual); Leadership Conference Scholarship (Annual); International Operators Scholarship (Annual); William M. Fanning Maintenance Scholarship (Annual); Flight Attendants/Flight Technician Scholarship (Annual); Lawrence Ginocchio Aviation Scholarships (Annual); NORDAM Dee Howard/Etienne Fage Scholarships (Annual); Maintenance Technical Reward and Career Scholarship (Annual); Schedulers and Dispatchers Monetary Scholarship (Annual); U.S. Aircraft Insurance Group Professional Development Program (USAIG PDP) Scholarships; Gold Wing Award for Journalism Excellence (Annual); NBAA American Spirit Award (Irregular); John P. "Jack" Doswell Award (Annual); NBAA Flying Safety Award (Annual); Meritorious Service To Aviation Award (Annual); David W. Ewald Platinum Wing Award (Annual); Schedulers and Dispatchers Outstanding Achievement and Leadership Award (Annual); Silk Scarf Award (Annual). **Geographic Preference:** National.

425 ■ World Airlines Clubs Association (WACA)
c/o International Air Transport Association
 800 Pl. Victoria
 Montreal, QC, Canada H4Z 1M1
Ph: (438)258-3243
Fax: (514)874-9200
Co. E-mail: info@waca.org
URL: http://www.waca.org
Contact: Maga Ramasamy, President
Description: Works to provide better service to the traveling public. Seeks to increase public awareness of the contribution of the airlines to world of the contribution of the airlines to world understanding and to extend, promote, and publicize the airline/interline clubs movement. **Founded:** 1966. **Publications:** *World Airlines Clubs Association--WACA Contact* (Irregular); *Airline/Interline Club Newsletter*. **Educational Activities:** WACA Annual General Assembly (WACA AGA) (Annual). **Geographic Preference:** Multinational.

PROCUREMENT ASSISTANCE PROGRAMS

426 ■ Women in Aviation Conference
URL(s): www.wai.org/conference

Frequency: Annual. **Description:** Provides mentoring and networking for women in the aviation industry. Also hosts an exhibit hall and scholarships. **Principal Exhibits:** Provides mentoring and networking for women in the aviation industry. Also hosts an exhibit hall and scholarships.

REFERENCE WORKS

427 ■ "Black-Owned Company Signed $334 Million Deal with Houston's William P. Hobby Airport" in Black Enterprise(February 10, 2023)

Ed: Darryl Robertson. **Released:** February 10, 2023. **Description:** Black-owned Latrelle's Management signed a deal to operate over 17,000 square feet of the Hobby Airport's dining areas. **Availability:** Online.

428 ■ "Delta Rebrands Its Business Travel Tools Package" in Small Business Trends (September 5, 2022)
URL(s): smallbiztrends.com/2022/09/delta-air-lines-has-consolidated-its-set-of-business-travel-tools.html

Ed: Gabrielle Pickard-Whitehead. **Released:** September 05, 2022. **Description:** Airline carrier Delta has consolidated all of its business travel components into one program called Delta Business. **Availability:** Online.

429 ■ Minnesota Airport Directory & Travel Guide
Pub: Minnesota Department of Transportation, Office of Aeronautics
Contact: Josh Knatterud-Hubinger, Chief Financial Officer
E-mail: josh.knatterud-hubinger@state.mn.us
URL(s): www.dot.state.mn.us/aero/airportdirectory

Released: Annual; last Issue, 2023. **Description:** Covers airports and public seaplane bases in Minnesota. Includes information on approaches, ditches, lights, nearby rivers, elevation, latitude and longitude, storage facilities and repair potential. **Entries include:** Address and telephone number. **Availability:** Print; Online; Download; PDF.

430 ■ National Air Transportation Association - Aviation Resource and Membership Directory
Pub: National Air Transportation Association
Contact: Curt Castagna, President
URL(s): www.nata.aero/membership/benefitswww.nata.aero/enewsletters.aspx?newsid=826

Released: Annual **Description:** Covers more than 1,000 regular, associate, and affiliate members; regular members include airport service organizations, air taxi operators, and commuter airlines. **Entries include:** Company name, address, phone, fax number, name and title of contact. **Arrangement:** Regular members are classified by service; associate and affiliate members are alphabetical in separate sections. **Indexes:** Geographical. **Availability:** Print.

431 ■ "Uber Make JFK Airport Helocopter Taxis Available to All Users" in KFGO (October 3, 2019)
URL(s): kfgo.com/news/articles/2019/oct/03/uber-makes-jfk-airport-helicopter-taxis-available-to-all-users/943561/?refer-section=technology

Ed: Tina Bellon. **Released:** October 03, 2019. **Description:** Uber is branching out in New York City with Uber Copter. Users will now be able to book helicopter flights to JFK International airport just by using their app on their phones. This project may pave the way for Uber Air, a taxi service of electric aircraft that could help relieve road congestion. **Availability:** Online.

432 ■ "When One Business Model Isn't Enough: LAN Airlines Flourishes By Running Three Distinctly Different Operations at the Same Time" in Harvard Business Review (Vol. 90, January-February 2012, No.1-2, pp. 132)
Pub: Harvard Business Review Press
Contact: Moderna V. Pfizer, Contact

Ed: Ramon Casadesus-Masanell, Jorge Tarzijan. **Description:** Chilean carrier LAN Airlines successfully blends three distinct business models: a full-service international passenger airline, a no-frills domestic airline, and an air-cargo line. The cargo revenues complement the passenger business to ensure more fully loaded flights.

STATISTICAL SOURCES

433 ■ RMA Annual Statement Studies
Pub: Risk Management Association
Contact: Nancy Foster, President

Released: Annual. **Description:** Contains composite balance sheets and income statements for more than 360 industries, including the accounting, auditing, and bookkeeping industries. Also contains five years of comparative historical data for discerning trends. Includes 16 commonly used ratios, computed for most of the size groupings for nearly every industry.

434 ■ Standard & Poor's Industry Surveys
Pub: Standard And Poor's Financial Services LLC.
Contact: Douglas L. Peterson, President

Description: Two-volume book that examines the prospects for specific industries, including trucking. Also provides analyses of trends and problems, statistical tables and charts, and comparative company analyses.

TRADE PERIODICALS

435 ■ Air Medical Journal (AMJ)
Pub: National EMS Pilots Association
Contact: Miles Dunagan, President
E-mail: miles.dunagan@nemspa.org
URL(s): www.airmedicaljournal.com

Ed: Jacqueline C. Stocking, PhD, Eric R. Swanson, MD. **Released:** 6/year **Price:** $292, Individuals for print + online 1 year international; $241, Individuals for print and online 1 year US; $205, Individuals for online only Us , Canada; $217, Individuals for online international; $310, Individuals for print and online US. **Description:** Journal for air medical transport professionals. Official Journal of the Air & Surface Transport Nurses Association, Air Medical Physician Association, Association of Air Medical Services, International Association of Flight and Critical Care Paramedics, and National EMS Pilots Association. **Availability:** Print; Download; PDF; Online.

436 ■ Aviation Medical Bulletin
Pub: Harvey W. Watt and Company Inc.
Contact: Helen Alston, Chief Executive Officer
URL(s): www.harveywatt.com/medical-bulletin

Released: Monthly **Price:** $19.95, for one year 12 issue; $50, for 36 issue 3 year. **Description:** Provides the latest medical information for those working in the aviation field. Recurring features include news of research. **Availability:** Download; PDF.

TRADE SHOWS AND CONVENTIONS

437 ■ AOPA Aviation Summit - Aircraft Owners and Pilots Association
URL(s): www.aopa.org

Frequency: Annual. **Description:** Opportunity to interact with members face to face. **Audience:** Aviation pilots and aircraft owners. **Principal Exhibits:** Opportunity to interact with members face to face. **Telecommunication Services:** aopahq@aopa.org.

438 ■ Canadian Business Aviation Association Convention and Exhibition
Honeywell International Inc.
11 W Spring St.
Freeport, IL 61032
Free: 877-841-2840
Co. E-mail: info.sc@honeywell.com
URL: http://www.honeywell.com
Contact: Vimal Kapur, Chief Executive Officer
URL(s): www.cbaa-acaa.ca/cbaa_2024_convention.php

Frequency: Annual. **Description:** Business aircraft products and services, including avionics, paint, parts, and supplies, and federal government agencies; includes static display of business aircraft. **Audience:** Industry Professionals. **Principal Exhibits:** Business aircraft products and services, including avionics, paint, parts, and supplies, and federal government agencies; includes static display of business aircraft. Dates and Locations: 2025 Jun 10-12 Richmond, BC. **Telecommunication Services:** membersupport@cbaa.ca.

439 ■ HAI HELI-EXPO
Dodge City Community College (DC3)
2501 N 14th Ave.
Dodge City, KS 67801
Ph: (620)225-1321
Free: 800-367-3222
Fax: (620)227-9350
Co. E-mail: admit@dc3.edu
URL: http://www.dc3.edu
Contact: Dr. Harold Nolte, President
URL(s): verticon.org
X (Twitter): twitter.com/HELIEXPO

Frequency: Annual. **Description:** World's largest event devoted exclusively to the civil helicopter industry. **Audience:** Helicopter professionals. **Principal Exhibits:** World's largest event devoted exclusively to the civil helicopter industry. Dates and Locations: 2025 Mar 10-13 Kay Bailey Hutchison Convention Center, Dallas, TX. **Telecommunication Services:** verticon@verticalavi.org.

440 ■ PBExpo Aviation Technology Innovation
URL(s): pbexpo.org

Frequency: Annual. **Description:** Conference focusing on the innovations developed at PartsBase for the aviation industry. **Principal Exhibits:** Conference focusing on the innovations developed at PartsBase for the aviation industry.

CONSULTANTS

441 ■ AVITAS Inc.
14520 Avion Pky., Ste. 300
Chantilly, VA 20151
Ph: (703)476-2300
Fax: (703)860-5855
Co. E-mail: info@avitas.com
URL: http://www.avitas.com
Contact: John Vitale, President
Facebook: www.facebook.com/AVITASInc
Linkedin: www.linkedin.com/company/avitas
X (Twitter): x.com/AVITASInc

Description: Firm provides advisory and technical services for airlines, aircraft manufacturers, industry suppliers, maintenance providers, aircraft lessons and financiers, legal counsel, and government entities. **Scope:** Firm provides advisory and technical services for airlines, aircraft manufacturers, industry suppliers, maintenance providers, aircraft lessons and financiers, legal counsel, and government entities. **Founded:** 1985. **Publications:** "Bluebook of Jet Aircraft Values"; "Bluebook of Commercial Turboprop Aircraft Values"; "Bluebook of Jet Engine Values"; "BlueBook of Flight Simulator Values"; "Aircraft Block Hour Operating Costs and Operations Guide"; "SAVI - Scenario Analysis & Value Index". **Special Services:** AVITAS Analyst; Online Aircraft Appraisal Service; Online Portfolio Monitoring Service; Online Engine Appraisal Service; Online Flight Distance Calculator.

COMPUTERIZED DATABASES

442 ■ Jane's Aero Engines
URL(s): ihsmarkit.com/products/janes-aero-engines.html
Price: $1,685, Individuals for US. **Availability:** Print; Online. **Type:** Properties; Image.

443 ■ Jane's All the World's Aircraft: In Service
URL(s): ihsmarkit.com/products/janes-all-the-worlds-aircraft-in-service.html
Released: Quarterly **Availability:** Print; Download; Online. **Type:** Properties; Directory; Image.

444 ■ Jane's All the World's Aircraft: Unmanned
URL(s): ihsmarkit.com/products/janes-all-the-worlds-unmanned-aircraft.html
Released: Annual; Latest 18/19. **Price:** $1,430, Individuals for US. **Availability:** Print; Online. **Type:** Properties; Directory; Image.

LIBRARIES

445 ■ Boeing Company - Integrated Defense Systems - Business Information Center
Seal Beach, CA
URL: http://www.boeing.com/defense
Scope: Books, reports, periodicals, journals, newspapers, videos, and industry and military specifications. **Services:** Library not open to the public. **Holdings:** Figures not available.

446 ■ British Columbia Institute of Technology (BCIT) - Aerospace and Technology Campus Library
3800 Cessna Dr.
Richmond, BC, Canada V7B 0A1
Ph: (604)419-3708
Fax: (604)207-8437
URL: http://www.bcit.ca/about/visit/campuses-directions/aerospace
Contact: Kathy Kinloch, President
Facebook: www.facebook.com/bcit.ca
Linkedin: www.linkedin.com/school/bcit
X (Twitter): x.com/bcit
Instagram: www.instagram.com/lifeatbcit
Description: Aerospace research and central library. **Scope:** Aeronautics; technology. **Services:** Interlibrary loan; library open to the public with restrictions (upon purchase of a membership card). **Subscriptions:** journals Books; e-Books; DVDs and streamed video; CIT calendars; yearbooks; facts and figures; historical photographs.

447 ■ Flight Safety Foundation (FSF) - Library
c/o Dr. Hassan Shahidi, President
Chief Executive Officer
1920 Ballenger Ave., 4th Fl.
Alexandria, VA 22314
Ph: (703)739-6700
Fax: (703)739-6708
Co. E-mail: technical@flightsafety.org
URL: http://flightsafety.org
Contact: Dr. Hassan Shahidi, President
Facebook: www.facebook.com/FlightSafetyFoundation
X (Twitter): x.com/flightsafety
YouTube: www.youtube.com/channel/UCYS5ObEBNuW9s3j7SMzxvLQ
Description: Aerospace manufacturers, domestic and foreign airlines, insurance companies, fuel and oil companies, schools and miscellaneous organizations having an interest in the promotion of safety in flight. Sponsors safety audits. Compiles statistics. **Scope:** Aviation safety, including pilot decision making, human factors, aircraft passenger safety, air traffic control, maintenance, aging aircraft safety, environmental safety hazards, confidential audits of airlines and corporate fleets, and safety and security factors at airports. **Founded:** 1947. **Holdings:** Figures not available. **Publications:** *Pilots Safety Exchange*; *Flight Safety Foundation--Membership Directory*; *Accident Prevention* (Monthly); *Human Factors and Aviation Medicine* (Bimonthly). **Educational Activities:** International Air Safety Summit (IASS) (Annual); Business Aviation Safety Summit (BASS) (Annual). **Awards:** Business Aviation Meritorious Service Award (Annual); Joe Chase Award (Annual); Laura Taber Barbour Air Safety Award (Annual); Cecil A. Brownlow Publication Award (Annual); Richard Teller Crane Founder's Award (Annual). **Geographic Preference:** National.

448 ■ U.S. Federal Aviation Administration - Mike Monroney Aeronautical Center Library (MMAC)
Aerospace Medical Certification Division, AAM-300
CAMI, Bldg. 13
Oklahoma City, OK 73125
URL: http://www.faa.gov/training_testing/faa_academy
Scope: Aeronautics; airplanes; mathematics; avionics; electronics; management. **Services:** Interlibrary loan; library open to the public with restrictions. **Founded:** 1962. **Holdings:** 12,000 volumes; books; periodicals; 15,000 technical reports.

449 ■ Veryon - Library
548 Market St., Ste. 42403
San Francisco, CA 94104
Ph: (415)330-9500
Free: 800-227-4610
Co. E-mail: marketing@veryon.com
URL: http://veryon.com
Contact: Norman Happ, Chief Executive Officer
Facebook: www.facebook.com/veryonplatform
Linkedin: www.linkedin.com/company/veryonplatform
X (Twitter): x.com/veryonplatform
Instagram: www.instagram.com/veryonplatform
Description: Publisher of books related to aircraft maintenance. **Scope:** Aircraft maintenance. **Founded:** 1973. **Holdings:** Figures not available. **Publications:** *U.S. Aviation Regulatory Library*.

Air-Conditioning/Heating and Cooling Contractor

ASSOCIATIONS AND OTHER ORGANIZATIONS

450 ■ Air Conditioning Contractors of America Association (ACCA)
1520 Belle View Blvd. No 5220
Alexandria, VA 22307
Ph: (703)575-4477
Co. E-mail: membership@acca.org
URL: http://www.acca.org/home
Contact: Martin Hoover, Chairman
Facebook: www.facebook.com/accontractors
Linkedin: www.linkedin.com/company/accausa
X (Twitter): x.com/accausa
YouTube: www.youtube.com/c/accamerica
Description: Contractors involved in installation and service of heating, air conditioning, and refrigeration systems. Associate members are utilities, manufacturers, wholesalers, and other market-oriented businesses. Monitors utility competition and operating practices of HVAC manufacturers and wholesalers. Provides consulting services, technical training, and instructor certification program; offers management seminars. **Founded:** 1968. **Publications:** *ACCA Technical Bulletin*; *Air Conditioning Contractors of America Quality Contractor's Catalog of Products and Services* (Annual); *Air Conditioning Contractors of America--Membership Directory*. **Educational Activities:** ACCA Annual Conference and IE3 Expo (Annual); ACCA Conference (Annual). **Awards:** ACCA Spirit of Independence Award (Occasionally); ACCA Distinguished Service Award (Occasionally); ACCA Spirit of Federation Award (Annual). **Geographic Preference:** National.

451 ■ Air-Conditioning, Heating, and Refrigeration Institute (AHRI)
2311 Wilson Blvd., Ste. 400
Arlington, VA 22201
Ph: (703)524-8800
Co. E-mail: ahricommunications@ahrinet.org
URL: http://www.ahrinet.org
Contact: Stephen Yurek, President
Facebook: www.facebook.com/AHRIconnect
Linkedin: www.linkedin.com/company/the-air-conditioning-heating-and-refrigeration-institute
X (Twitter): x.com/AHRIConnect
YouTube: www.youtube.com/user/AHRIcommunications
Description: Represents companies that manufacture air conditioning, heating, water heating, and commercial refrigeration units. Maintains a continuing presence within Congress and government agencies to monitor and respond to policies and regulations affecting the industry and represent the collective interests of members. **Founded:** 1959. **Publications:** *CRMA Newsbreak* (Periodic); *Recommended Guidelines for Retail Food Store Design*; *Recommended Guidelines for Retail Food Store Energy Conservation*; *Voluntary Minimum Standard for Retail Food Store Refrigerators-Health and Sanitation*; *Directory of Certified Unitary Air-Conditioners, Unitary Air-Source Heat Pumps and Sound-Rated Outdoor Unitary Equipment* (Semiannual); *Directory of Certified Air-to-Air Energy Recovery Ventilation Equipment* (Periodic); *Directory of Certified Automatic Commercial Ice-Cube Machines and Ice Storage Bins*; *Directory of Certified Direct Geoexchange Heat Pumps*; *Directory of Certified Drinking Water Coolers* (Annual); *Directory of Certified Refrigerant Recovery/Recycling Equipment and Reclaimed Refrigerants, and Refrigerant Testing Laboratories* (Semiannual); *Directory of Certified Transport Refrigeration Units* (Annual); *AHRI Curriculum Guide*; *Minuteman* (Monthly); *Educational Institutions Offering Courses in Air-Conditioning and Refrigeration* (Annual); *Directory of Certified Applied Air-Conditioning Products* (Semiannual). **Educational Activities:** AHR Expo Mexico (Annual). **Geographic Preference:** National.

452 ■ American Society of Heating, Refrigerating and Air-Conditioning Engineers (ASHRAE)
180 Technology Parkway NW
Peachtree Corners, GA 30092
Ph: (404)636-8400
Free: 800-527-4723
Fax: (404)539-2129
Co. E-mail: orders@ashrae.org
URL: http://www.ashrae.org
Contact: Farooq Mehboob, President
Facebook: www.facebook.com/ASHRAEupdates
Linkedin: www.linkedin.com/company/ashrae
X (Twitter): x.com/ashraenews
Instagram: www.instagram.com/ashrae_society
YouTube: www.youtube.com/user/ASHRAEvideo
Description: Technical society of heating, ventilating, refrigeration, and air-conditioning engineers. Sponsors numerous research programs in cooperation with universities, research laboratories, and government agencies on subjects such as human and animal environmental studies, effects of air-conditioning, quality of inside air, heat transfer, flow, and cooling processes. Conducts professional development seminars. Writes method of test standards and other standards addressing energy conservation in buildings, indoor air quality, and refrigerants. Publishes extensive literature and electronic products. **Founded:** 1894. **Publications:** *American Society of Heating, Refrigerating, and Air-Conditioning Engineers-Membership Roster* (Annual); *ASHRAE Journal* (Monthly); *HVAC&R Research*; *ASHRAE Insights* (Monthly); *IAQ Applications*; *Science and Technology for the Built Environment* (Semiannual); *Duct Fitting Database* (Annual). **Educational Activities:** AHR Expo: International Air-Conditioning, Heating, Refrigerating Exposition (Annual); AHR Expo Mexico (Annual). **Awards:** Henry Adams Scholarship (Annual); American Society of Heating, Refrigerating, and Air-Conditioning Memorial Scholarships (Annual); ASHARE Undergraduate Engineering Scholarships (Annual); Willis H. Carrier Scholarships (Annual); Frank M. Coda Scholarships (Annual); Duane Hanson Scholarship (Annual); Alwin B. Newton Scholarship (Annual); Donald E. Nichols Scholarships (Annual); Reuben Trane Scholarships (Biennial); F. Paul Anderson Award (Annual); ASHRAE Award for Distinguished Public Service (Annual); Homer Addams Award (Annual); Technology Award/Award of Engineering Excellence (Annual); ASHRAE Fellows (Annual); ASHRAE Journal Paper Award (Annual); ASHRAE Technical Paper Award (Annual); Andrew T. Boggs Service Award (Annual); Lincoln Bouillon Award (Annual); E.K. Campbell Award of Merit (Annual); William J. Collins Jr. Research Promotion Award (Annual); ASHRAE Distinguished Fifty-Year Member Award (Annual); ASHRAE Distinguished Service Award (DSA) (Annual); Crosby Field Award (Annual); Louise and Bill Holladay Distinguished Fellow Award (Annual); ASHRAE Honorary Member (Annual); John F. James International Award (Annual); Ralph G. Nevins Physiology and Human Environment Award (Annual); Milton W. Garland Commemorative Refrigeration Award for Project Excellence (Annual); ASHRAE Student Design Project Competition (Annual); ASHRAE Hall of Fame (Annual); ASHRAE Standards Achievement Award (Annual). **Geographic Preference:** Multinational.

453 ■ Heating, Refrigeration and Air Conditioning Institute of Canada (HRAI) - Library
2350 Matheson Blvd. E, Ste. 101
Mississauga, ON, Canada L4W 0A5
Ph: (905)602-4700
Free: 800-267-2231
Fax: (905)602-1197
Co. E-mail: hraimail@hrai.ca
URL: http://www.hrai.ca
Contact: Sandy MacLeod, President
Facebook: www.facebook.com/HRAI.ca
X (Twitter): x.com/HRAI_Canada
YouTube: www.youtube.com/user/hraichannel
Description: Corporations engaged in the heating, refrigeration, air-conditioning, ventilation, and related industries. Seeks to advance the techniques and technologies available to members, and the heating and cooling industries as a whole. Conducts educational programs; compiles statistics. **Scope:** A nonprofit trade association of manufacturers, whole sellers and contractors in the Canadian heating, ventilation, air conditioning and refrigeration (HVACR) industry. **Founded:** 1968. **Holdings:** Figures not available. **Training:** SkillTech Academy Training and Education; Refrigeration Controls Training; Building Automation Systems; Pneumatic Controls System. **Educational Activities:** University of Innovative Distribution (Annual).

454 ■ Home Ventilating Institute (HVI)
1740 Dell Range Blvd., Ste. H
Cheyenne, WY 82009
Free: 855-484-8368
Fax: (480)559-9722
Co. E-mail: hvi@hvi.org
URL: http://www.hvi.org
Contact: Patrick Nielsen, Chairman
Facebook: www.facebook.com/homeventilating
X (Twitter): x.com/HVI_HQ
Instagram: www.instagram.com/homeventilatinginstitute

Description: Aims to serve consumers and members by advancing residential ventilation. Provides a forum for industry to meet and discuss common issues. **Founded:** 1955. **Publications:** *Home Ventilating Guide* (Periodic). **Geographic Preference:** National.

455 ■ International Association of Plumbing and Mechanical Officials (IAPMO) [IAPMO Research and Testing Inc.]
4755 E Philadelphia St.
 Ontario, CA 91761
Ph: (909)472-4100
Fax: (909)472-4150
Co. E-mail: iapmo@iapmo.org
URL: http://www.iapmo.org
Contact: D. J. Nunez, President
Facebook: www.facebook.com/IAPMO
X (Twitter): x.com/IAPMO
Instagram: www.instagram.com/iapmo
YouTube: www.youtube.com/user/IAPMOGroup

Description: Government agencies, administrative officials, sales representatives, manufacturers, associations, and members of associations related to the plumbing field. Sponsors and writes Uniform Plumbing Codes; also sponsors Uniform Mechanical Code. **Publications:** *Directory of Listed Plumbing Products for Mobile Homes and Recreational Vehicles* (Bimonthly); *Official Magazine* (Quarterly); *Backflow Prevention Journal* (Bimonthly); *2009 Idaho State Plumbing Code CD-ROM*; *Directory of Listed Plumbing Products*; *Directory of Manufactured Housing/RV Research Recommendations* (Bimonthly); *Uniform Mechanical Code Illustrated Training Manual*; *Uniform Plumbing Code Illustrated Training Manual*; *2010 Green Plumbing & Mechanical Code Supplement CD-ROM*; *2012 Uniform Plumbing Code CD-ROM*; *2012 Uniform Mechanical Code CD-ROM*; *2013 California Plumbing Code CD-ROM*; *2013 California Mechanical Code on CD-ROM*; *2011 Oregon Plumbing Specialty Code on CD-ROM*. **Educational Activities:** Annual Education and Business Conference (Annual). **Awards:** IAPMO Government Person of the Year (Annual); IAPMO Industry Person of the Year (Annual); Joseph Kneidinger Green Professional of the Year Award (Annual); IAPMO American Flag Award (Annual); George Kauffman Lifetime Achievement Award (Annual). **Geographic Preference:** National; Multinational.

456 ■ International District Energy Association (IDEA)
1800 W Pk. Dr., Ste. 350
 Westborough, MA 01581
Ph: (508)366-9339
Fax: (508)366-0019
Co. E-mail: idea@districtenergy.org
URL: http://www.districtenergy.org
Contact: Robert P. Thornton, President
E-mail: rob.idea@districtenergy.org
Facebook: www.facebook.com/InternationalDistric
 tEnergyAssociation
X (Twitter): x.com/districtenergy

Description: Foster the success of the members as leaders in providing reliable, economical, efficient, and environmentally sound district heating, district cooling, and combined heat and power. **Founded:** 1909. **Publications:** *District Heating Association--Annual Handbook* (Annual); *International District Energy Association--Membership Directory*; *District Energy* (Quarterly); *District Energy Now* (Quarterly); *Manual of District Heating*. **Educational Activities:** International District Energy Association Annual Conference and Trade Show (Annual). **Awards:** IDEA Unsung Hero Award (Occasionally); IDEA Public Sector Leadership Award (Annual); IDEA International District Energy Climate Award (Biennial); Unsung Hero Award (Occasionally); Norman R. Taylor Award (Annual); IDEA System of the Year Award (SOYA) (Annual).

457 ■ International Ground Source Heat Pump Association (IGSHPA)
312 S 4th St., Ste. 100
 Springfield, IL 62701
Free: 800-626-4747
Co. E-mail: igshpa@okstate.edu
URL: http://igshpa.org
Contact: Jeff Hammond, Executive Director
Facebook: www.facebook.com/igshpa
X (Twitter): x.com/igshpa
YouTube: www.youtube.com/c/igshpaOrg

Description: Seeks to educate the public about ground source heat pump systems and promote their use as economical energy saving systems. **Founded:** 1987. **Publications:** *Closed-Loop Ground-Source Heat Pump Systems Installation Guide*; *Grouting Procedures for Ground Source Heat Pump Systems*; *Installation Guide*; *The Source* (Bimonthly). **Educational Activities:** IGSHPA Conference and Expo (Annual); May Tech. **Geographic Preference:** Multinational.

458 ■ Masonry Heater Association of North America (MHA) - Library
2820 S Alma School Rd., Ste. 18
 Chandler, AZ 85286
Ph: (520)883-0191
Fax: (480)371-1139
Co. E-mail: execdir@mha-net.org
URL: http://www.mha-net.org
Contact: Scott Soldat-Valenzuela, Executive Director

Description: Represents builders, manufacturers and retailers of masonry heaters. Seeks to promote the industry, sponsor research and development, shape regulations, standards and codes, inform and educate the public and further the expertise and professionalism of its membership. **Scope:** Masonry; construction. **Services:** Library open to the public. **Founded:** 1981. **Holdings:** Technical papers; abstracts; preprints and datasets. **Publications:** *Masonry Heaters - The Intelligent Choice*. **Geographic Preference:** National.

459 ■ Mechanical Contractors Association of America (MCAA)
1385 Piccard Dr.
 Rockville, MD 20850
Ph: (301)869-5800
Free: 800-556-3653
Co. E-mail: help@mcaa.org
URL: http://www.mcaa.org
Facebook: www.facebook.com/mcaaeducation
Linkedin: www.linkedin.com/company/mechanical
 -contractors-association-of-america-mcaa-
X (Twitter): x.com/mcaanews

Description: Represents firms involved in heating, air conditioning, refrigeration, plumbing, piping, and mechanical service. Provides educational materials and programs to help members attain the highest level of managerial and technical expertise. **Founded:** 1889. **Publications:** *MCAA Membership Directory & Buyer's Guide*; *MCAA Membership Directory & Buyer's Guide*; *MCAA National Update* (Weekly (Mon.)); *MCAA Reporter*. **Educational Activities:** MCAA Annual Convention. **Awards:** Foster McCarl, Jr. Memorial Scholarship (Annual); MCAA Distinguished Service Award (Annual); MCAA Educator of the Year (Annual); MCAA/CNA Safety Excellence Awards (Annual). **Geographic Preference:** National.

460 ■ Mobile Air Climate Systems Association (MACS) - Library
PO Box 88
 Lansdale, PA 19446
Ph: (215)631-7020
Fax: (215)631-7017
Co. E-mail: info@macsmobileairclimate.org
URL: http://macsmobileairclimate.org
Contact: Peter J. Coll, President
E-mail: pcoll@macsmobileairclimate.org
Facebook: www.facebook.com/MACSMobileAir
Linkedin: www.linkedin.com/company/mobile-air-con
 ditioning-society-macs-worldwide
X (Twitter): x.com/MACSMobileAir
Instagram: www.instagram.com/macs_mobile_air
YouTube: www.youtube.com/channel/UC-aQjZ
 -uXWjxlaszlQkRr0g

Description: Distributors, service specialists, installers, manufacturers, and suppliers of automotive and truck air conditioners and parts. Works to disseminate information and develop specialized education. **Scope:** Automotive service technicians. **Founded:** 1981. **Holdings:** Figures not available. **Publications:** *Action* (6/year); *Shop Talk* (Monthly); *MACS Service Reports* (Monthly); *International Mobile Air Conditioning Association--Membership/Industry Contact Directory*. **Educational Activities:** MACS Annual Training Event & Trade Show (Annual). **Geographic Preference:** Multinational.

461 ■ National Environmental Balancing Bureau (NEBB)
8575 Grovemont Cir.
 Gaithersburg, MD 20877
Ph: (301)977-3698
Free: 877-800-5147
Fax: (301)977-9589
Co. E-mail: support@nebb.org
URL: http://nebb.org
Contact: Tiffany J. Meyers, Executive Vice President
E-mail: tiffany@nebb.org
Facebook: www.facebook.com/NEBBCertified
Linkedin: www.linkedin.com/company/nebb
X (Twitter): x.com/NEBB_Bldg

Description: Qualified heating, ventilation, and air-conditioning contractors specializing in the fields of air and hydronic systems balancing, sound vibration measuring, testing of heating and cooling systems, building systems commissioning, and testing of clean rooms. **Founded:** 1971. **Publications:** *Procedural Standards for TAB Environmental Systems*; *Procedural Standards for the Measurement of Sound and Vibration*. **Educational Activities:** National Environmental Balancing Bureau Annual Conference (Annual). **Geographic Preference:** National.

462 ■ Refrigerating Engineers and Technicians Association (RETA)
1725 Ferry St. SW
 Albany, OR 97322
Ph: (541)497-2955
Free: 844-801-3711
Fax: (541)497-2966
Co. E-mail: info@reta.com
URL: http://reta.com
Contact: Bengie Branham, President
E-mail: bbranham@scsengineers.com
Facebook: www.facebook.com/RETAHQ
Linkedin: www.linkedin.com/company/refrigerating
 -engineers-&-technicians-association-reta---official
 -page
X (Twitter): x.com/reta_hq

Description: Focuses on the professional development of industrial refrigeration operators and technicians. Offers self-study and on-line training courses on industrial refrigeration. Offers a nationally-recognized certification program for operators and technicians on two levels of understanding and knowledge. **Founded:** 1909. **Publications:** *RETA Breeze* (6/year). **Educational Activities:** Refrigerating Engineers and Technicians Association Convention. **Geographic Preference:** National.

463 ■ Refrigeration Service Engineers Society (RSES) - Library
PO Box 248
 Arlington Heights, IL 60006-0248
Ph: (847)297-6464
Free: 800-297-5660
Fax: (547)297-5038
Co. E-mail: general@rses.org
URL: http://rses.org
Contact: Art T. Miller, President
E-mail: hvacr@artcms.net
Facebook: www.facebook.com/rseshq

Description: Persons engaged in refrigeration, air-conditioning and heating installation, service, sales and maintenance. Conducts training courses and certification testing. Maintains a hall of fame and a speaker's bureau. **Scope:** Refrigeration, air conditioning, heating. **Founded:** 1933. **Holdings:** Figures not available. **Publications:** *Service Application Manuals (SAM)*. **Educational Activities:** Refrigeration Service Engineers Society Educational Conference (Annual). **Awards:** RSES Distinguished Service Member of the Year Award (Annual); V.V. Solomon Educator/Teacher of the Year Award (Annual); RSES Rising Star Award (Annual); RSES Speaker of the Year (Annual). **Geographic Preference:** Multinational.

464 ■ Sheet Metal and Air Conditioning Contractors' National Association (SMACNA)
4201 Lafayette Center Dr.
 Chantilly, VA 20151-1219
Ph: (703)803-2980
Fax: (703)803-3732
Co. E-mail: order@smacna.org
URL: http://www.smacna.org
Contact: Stanley E. Kolbe, Jr., Executive Director
Facebook: www.facebook.com/SMACNA
Linkedin: www.linkedin.com/company/122248
X (Twitter): x.com/smacna
Instagram: www.instagram.com/smacna
YouTube: www.youtube.com/user/SMACNAnational/feed
Description: Ventilation, air handling, warm air heating, architectural and industrial sheet metal, kitchen equipment, testing and balancing, siding, and decking and specialty fabrication contractors. Prepares standards and codes; sponsors research and educational programs on sheet metal duct construction and fire damper (single and multi-blade) construction. Engages in legislative and labor activities. **Founded:** 1943. **Publications:** SMACNA Technical Manual Collection; Architectural Sheet Metal CADD Drawings. **Educational Activities:** SMACNA's Annual Convention (Annual). **Awards:** SMACNA & College of Fellows Scholarship (Annual). **Geographic Preference:** Multinational.

REFERENCE WORKS

465 ■ "A2L Servicing Best Practices" in AC & Heating Connect (October 22, 2021)
Ed: Brad Hess. **Released:** October 22, 2021. **Description:** Discusses using A2L refrigerants in places of HFC, since HFC is being phased away due to its consideration as a high-global warming potential chemical. **Availability:** Online.

466 ■ "Adventures at Hydronicahh" in Contractor (Vol. 56, September 2009, No. 9, pp. 52)
Ed: Mark Eatherton. **Released:** Part 6. **Description:** Installations of the heating system of a lakeview room are described. The room's radiant windows are powered by electricity from a solar PV array and a propane-powered hydrogen fuel cell. The system will be programmed to use the most energy available. **Availability:** Print; Online.

467 ■ Air Conditioning Contractors of America--Membership Directory
Pub: Air Conditioning Contractors of America Association
Contact: Martin Hoover, Chairman
URL(s): www.acca.org/directories
Description: Covers member air conditioning and heating contractors, manufacturers, vocational technical schools. **Entries include:** Company name, address, phone, fax, names and titles of key personnel, description of fields, and types of work performed. **Arrangement:** Geographical. **Indexes:** Alphabetical. **Availability:** Online.

468 ■ "Alternative Energy Calls for Alternative Marketing" in Indoor Comfort Marketing (Vol. 70, June 2011, No. 6, pp. 8)
Pub: Spray Technology & Marketing
Contact: Ava Caridad, Director, Editorial
E-mail: acaridad@spraytm.com
Ed: Richard Rutigliano. **Released:** June 01, 2011. **Description:** Advice for marketing solar energy products and services is given. **Availability:** Print; Online.

469 ■ American Supply Association--Member Directory
Pub: American Supply Association
Contact: Bill Condron, President
URL(s): www.asa.net/Join-ASA/Member-Directory -PUBLIC

Released: Annual **Description:** Covers 4,000 member wholesalers handling plumbing, heating, and cooling materials and supplies. **Entries include:** Company name, address, phone, names of executives, list of products or services, fax numbers, email and website. **Arrangement:** Geographical and alphabetical. **Indexes:** Special interest divisions. **Availability:** Print.

470 ■ "Art Institute of Chicago Goes Green" in Contractor (Vol. 56, July 2009, No. 7, pp. 1)
Ed: Candace Roulo. **Description:** Art Institute of Chicago's Modern Wing museum addition will receive a certification that makes them one of the most environmentally sound museum expansions in the U.S. A modified variable-air-volume system is being used to meet temperature and humidity requirements in the building and it also has a double curtain wall to capture summer heat. **Availability:** Print; Online.

471 ■ "Be Wary of Dual-Flush Conversion Kits" in Contractor (Vol. 56, September 2009, No. 9, pp. 66)
Ed: John Koeller, Bill Gauley. **Description:** Recommendation of untested dual-flush conversion devices for tank-type toilets in the United States has been questioned. The products are being advertised as having the ability to convert single-flush to a dual-flush toilet. No evidence of water conservation from using such devices has been recorded. **Availability:** Print; Online.

472 ■ "Bioheat - Alternative for Fueling Equipment" in Indoor Comfort Marketing (Vol. 70, May 2011, No. 5, pp. 14)
Description: Profile of Worley and Obetz, supplier of biofuels used as an alternative for fueling industry equipment. **Availability:** Print; Online.

473 ■ "Canadian Hydronics Businesses Promote 'Beautiful Heat" in Indoor Comfort Marketing (Vol. 70, September 2011, No. 9, pp. 20)
Pub: Spray Technology & Marketing
Contact: Ava Caridad, Director, Editorial
E-mail: acaridad@spraytm.com
Released: September 01, 2011. **Description:** Canadian hydronics companies are promoting their systems as beautiful heat. Hydronics is the use of water as the heat-transfer medium in heating and cooling system. **Availability:** Print; Online.

474 ■ "Cash for Appliances Targets HVAC Products, Water Heaters" in Contractor (Vol. 56, October 2009, No. 10, pp. 1)
Ed: Candace Roulo. **Description:** States and territories would need to submit a full application that specifies their implementation plans if they are interested in joining the Cash for Appliances program funded by the American Recovery and Reinvestment Act. The Department of Energy urges states to focus on heating and cooling equipment, appliances and water heaters since these offer the greatest energy savings potential. **Availability:** Print; Online.

475 ■ "Certified Technicians can Increase Bottom Line" in Contractor (Vol. 56, September 2009, No. 9, pp. 37)
Ed: Ray Isaac. **Description:** Certified technicians increase the value of HVAC firms, a survey by Service Round Table has reported. The increased value has been attributed to fewer callbacks, less warranty work and greater ability to educate consumers. Meanwhile, consumers are willing to pay more for the services of certified technicians. **Availability:** Print; Online.

476 ■ "Chicago Public Schools District Builds Green" in Contractor (Vol. 56, October 2009, No. 10, pp. 5)
Ed: Candace Roulo. **Description:** Chicago Public Schools district has already built six U.S. Green Building Council LEED certified schools and one addition in five years and will continue to build new green buildings. The district has an Environmental Action Plan that strives to reduce energy usage, improve indoor air quality, and reduce contribution to climate change. **Availability:** Print; Online.

477 ■ "Combo Dorm-Field House Built to Attain LEED Gold" in Contractor (Vol. 56, September 2009, No. 9, pp. 1)
Ed: Candace Roulo, Robert P. Mader. **Description:** North Central College in Illinois has built a new dormitory that is expected to attain Leadership in Energy and Environmental Design Gold certification from the United States Green Building Council. The structure features a geo-exchange heat pump system and radiant floor heat. A description of the facility is also provided. **Availability:** Print; Online.

478 ■ "Contractors Can't Do It Alone, PHCC's Pfeffer Says" in Contractor (Vol. 56, October 2009, No. 10, pp. 3)
Ed: Robert P. Mader. **Description:** President Herbert "Skip" Pfeffer of the Plumbing-Heating-Cooling Contractors National Association says lobbying and education are the services that the association offers that a contractor cannot do individually. Pfeffer says the dues for the association are set up in a manner that allows members to pay monthly. **Availability:** Print; Online.

479 ■ "A Day Late and a Dollar Short" in Indoor Comfort Marketing (Vol. 70, March 2011, No. 3, pp. 30)
Description: A discussion involving futures options and fuel oil prices is presented. **Availability:** Online.

480 ■ "Do the Right Thing" in Contractor (Vol. 56, December 2009, No. 12, pp. 16)
Ed: Robert P. Mader. **Description:** Applewood Plumbing, Heating and Electric has won Contractor magazine's 2009 Contractor of the Year Award. The company has ranked eighth among more than 300 service companies in the United States. A brief history of the company is also provided. **Availability:** Print; Online.

481 ■ "Eco Smart Home Will Showcase Green Technology" in Contractor (Vol. 56, September 2009, No. 9, pp. 3)
Ed: Steve Spaulding. **Description:** Eco Smart World Wide is building the Eco Smart Demonstration House to promote the latest in sustainable, renewable and high-efficiency practices and products. The company will use insulated concrete forms in the construction of the building. Features and dimensions of the structure are also presented. **Availability:** Print; Online.

482 ■ "EPA to Tighten Energy Star Standards for 2011" in Contractor (Vol. 56, September 2009, No. 9, pp. 6)
Description: United States Environmental Protection Agency will tighten standards for its Energy Star for Homes program in 2011. The green trend in the construction industry has been cited as reason for the plan. The agency is adding requirements for energy-efficient equipment and building techniques. **Availability:** Print; Online.

483 ■ "Expect Action on Health Care and the Economy" in Contractor (Vol. 57, January 2010, No. 1, pp. 30)
Ed: Kevin Schwalb. **Description:** The Plumbing-Heating-Cooling Contractors National Association is working to solidify its standing in the public policy arena as the legislative agenda will focus on health care reform, estate tax and immigration reform, all of which will impact the industries. **Availability:** Print; Online.

484 ■ "Fix-It Careers: Jobs in Repair" in Occupational Outlook Quarterly (Vol. 54, Fall 2010, No. 3, pp. 26)
Pub: U.S. Department of Labor Bureau of Labor Statistics
Contact: Amrit Kohli, Director
E-mail: kohli.amrit@bls.gov

Ed: Elka Maria Torpey. **Description:** Auto mechanics and HVAC technician occupations require repair skills. Advantages for individuals with proper skills are outlined. **Availability:** Online; PDF.

485 ■ *"'Frozen' Assets: Refrigeration Goes High Tech as Hussmann Invests $7 Million in Global Hub"* in *St. Louis Business Journal (Vol. 33, September 21, 2012, No. 4, pp. 1)*
Pub: Baltimore Business Journal
Contact: Rhonda Pringle, President
E-mail: rpringle@bizjournals.com
Description: Hussmann Corporation is spending $7 million to create a high-tech innovation and clients collaboration center that will be called Global Hub, a venue for grocery food retailers, industry trend setters and through leaders. The company is also focusing on tapping the potential of convenience marts and dollar-store retailers. **Availability:** Print.

486 ■ *"Get Online Quick in the Office Or in the Field"* in *Contractor (Vol. 56, October 2009, No. 10, pp. 47)*
Ed: William Feldman, Patti Feldman. **Description:** Contractors can set up a web site in minutes using the www.1and1.com website. Verizon's Novatel MIFI 2372 HSPA personal hotspot device lets contractors go online in the field. The StarTech scalable business management system helps contractors manage daily operations. **Availability:** Print; Online.

487 ■ *"Getting the Bioheat Word Out"* in *Indoor Comfort Marketing (Vol. 70, September 2011, No. 9, pp. 32)*
Description: Ways to market advanced liquid fuels to the public are outlined. **Availability:** Print; Online.

488 ■ *"Harness the Internet to Boost Equipment Sales"* in *Indoor Comfort Marketing (Vol. 70, July 2011, No. 7, pp. 24)*
Description: Advice is given to increase HVAC/R equipment sales using the Internet. **Availability:** Online.

489 ■ *"Housing Slide Picks Up Speed"* in *Crain's Chicago Business (Vol. 31, April 19, 2008, No. 16, pp. 2)*
Pub: Crain Communications Inc.
Contact: Barry Asin, President
Ed: Eddie Baeb. **Description:** According to Tracy Cross & Associates Inc., a real estate consultancy, sales of new homes in the Chicago area dropped 61 percent from the year-earlier period which is more bad news for homebuilders, contractors and real estate agents who are eager for an indication that market conditions are improving. **Availability:** Online.

490 ■ *"How Good Advice 'Online' Can Attract Customers"* in *Indoor Comfort Marketing (Vol. 70, August 2011, No. 8, pp. 20)*
Pub: Spray Technology & Marketing
Contact: Ava Caridad, Director, Editorial
E-mail: acaridad@spraytm.com
Ed: Richard Rutigilano. **Description:** Online marketing tips for heating and cooling small businesses are explained.

491 ■ *"HVAC/R Evolution"* in *Indoor Comfort Marketing (Vol. 70, March 2011, No. 3, pp. 14)*
Description: Tools and techniques for heating, ventilation, air conditioning and refrigeration are examined.

492 ■ *"IAPMO Seeks Group Participants"* in *Contractor (Vol. 56, September 2009, No. 9, pp. 37)*
Description: International Association of Plumbing and Mechanical Officials is accepting applications for task groups that will develop its Uniform Plumbing Code and Uniform Mechanical Code. The codes are developed using American National Standards Institute accredited consensus process. Task groups are assigned to address a specific topic or problem. **Availability:** Print; Online.

493 ■ *"If the Opportunity is There, Move Boldly"* in *Indoor Comfort Marketing (Vol. 70, March 2011, No. 3)*
Pub: Spray Technology & Marketing
Contact: Ava Caridad, Director, Editorial
E-mail: acaridad@spraytm.com
Ed: Richard Rutigliano. **Released:** March 01, 2011. **Description:** Suggestions are offered to help improve air conditioning sales. **Availability:** Print; Online.

494 ■ *"Independence Station Utilizes Sustainable Technologies"* in *Contractor (Vol. 56, September 2009, No. 9, pp. 3)*
Ed: Candace Roulo. **Description:** Independence Station building in Oregon is seen to receive the most LEED points ever awarded by the United States Green Building Council. The building will use an ice-based cooling storage system, biofuel cogeneration system and phovoltaic system. Other building features and dimensions are also supplied. **Availability:** Print; Online.

495 ■ *"The Ins and Outs of Wi-Fi-Enabled Air Conditioning"* in *AC Heating and Air Conditioning Services (August 28, 2018)*
URL(s): http://www.achvac.com/article/the-ins-and-outs-of-wi-fi-enabled-air-conditioning
Released: August 28, 2018. **Description:** A variety of air conditioning systems are examined with an emphasis on smartphone and app-enabled technology to control the indoor environment. These recent advancements provide a variety of benefits to homeowners. **Availability:** Online.

496 ■ *"It's New or Improved, But Does It Work?"* in *Contractor (Vol. 57, January 2010, No. 1, pp. 22)*
Ed: Al Schwartz. **Description:** There is a place for skepticism in the HVAC and plumbing industry as not all new products that are specified may not always perform. The tradesman has the responsibility of integrating new technology into the field. **Availability:** Print; Online.

497 ■ *"Large Homes can be Energy Efficient Too"* in *Contractor (Vol. 56, October 2009, No. 10, pp. 5)*
Ed: Candace Roulo. **Description:** Eco Estate at Briggs Chaney subdivision in Silver Spring, Maryland has model houses that use sustainable technologies and products and the homes that will be built on the subdivision will feature some of the technologies featured on the model home. The energy efficient HVAC system of the model homes are discussed. **Availability:** Print; Online.

498 ■ *"The Latest on E-Verify"* in *Contractor (Vol. 56, September 2009, No. 9, pp. 58)*
Ed: Susan McGreevy. **Description:** United States government has required federal contractors to use its E-Verify program to verify the eligibility of incoming and existent employees. The use of the program is seen to eliminate Social Security mismatches. **Availability:** Print; Online.

499 ■ *"Manufacturers Become Part of Coalition"* in *Contractor (Vol. 56, July 2009, No. 7, pp. 40)*
Description: Bradford White Water Heaters, Rheem Water Heating, Rinnai America Corp., and A.O. Smith Water Heaters have joined the Consortium for Energy Efficiency in the Coalition for Energy Star Water Heaters. The coalition seeks to increase the awareness of Energy Star water heaters. **Availability:** Print; Online.

500 ■ *"A Necessary Balancing Act: Bookkeeping"* in *Contractor (Vol. 56, November 2009, No. 11, pp. 22)*
Ed: Al Schwartz. **Description:** Pros and cons of getting a bookkeeper or a certified public accountant for the subcontractor are discussed. A bookkeeper can help a subcontractor get new accounting software up and running while an accountant will more than likely keep after the books at regular intervals throughout the year. **Availability:** Print; Online.

501 ■ *"A New Day is Dawning"* in *Indoor Comfort Marketing (Vol. 70, August 2011, No. 8, pp. 18)*
Description: New trends in the HVAC/R industry regarding biofuels and bioheat are explored. **Availability:** Online.

502 ■ *"New Hydronic Heating Technologies Work"* in *Contractor (Vol. 57, January 2010, No. 1, pp. 58)*
Ed: Carol Fey. **Released:** January 01, 2010. **Description:** Technology behind hydronic heating systems is reviewed. These technologies include radiant and geothermal hydronic heating. System requirements for installing these greener forms of heating are discussed.

503 ■ *"Nexstar Super Meeting Breaks Business Barriers"* in *Contractor (Vol. 56, November 2009, No. 11, pp. 3)*
Ed: Candace Roulo. **Description:** Around 400 Nexstar members met to discuss the trends in the HVAC industry and the economic outlook for 2010. Former lead solo pilot John Foley for the Blue Angels made a presentation on how a business can increase overall productivity based on the culture of the Blue Angels. Some breakout sessions tackled how to optimize workflow and marketing. **Availability:** Print; Online.

504 ■ *"Overheating Taking Place? Pay Attention to Details.."* in *Indoor Comfort Marketing (Vol. 70, March 2011, No. 3)*
Description: Boiler facts are outlined to help the small HVAC company when servicing customers. **Availability:** PDF; Online.

505 ■ *"PHCC Convention, Show Get High Marks"* in *Contractor (Vol. 56, December 2009, No. 12, pp. 1)*
Ed: Robert P. Mader. **Description:** Plumbing-Heating-Cooling Contractors National Association has held its first convention and trade show in New Orleans, Louisiana. Attendees were treated to a variety of seminars and exhibitors during the event. Comments from event organizers are also given. **Availability:** Print; Online.

506 ■ *"Plumbing, Heating Products Shine at Greenbuild Expo"* in *Contractor (Vol. 56, December 2009, No. 12, pp. 1)*
Ed: Robert P. Mader. **Description:** Greenbuild Show held in Phoenix, Arizona has showcased the latest in plumbing and heating products. Zurn displayed its EcoVantage line of fixtures and valves during the event. Meanwhile, Sloan Valve offered its washdown 1-pint/flush Alphine urinal. **Availability:** Online.

507 ■ *"Portland Home Is First in U.S. to Use Variable Speed Inverter Technology"* in *Contractor (Vol. 56, December 2009, No. 12, pp. 5)*
Description: Daikin Altherma heat pump with inverter drive has been installed in a Portland, Oregon home. The heat pump provides a high coefficient of performance while delivering hydronic and domestic hot water functionality. Other product features and dimensions are also supplied. **Availability:** Print; Online.

508 ■ *"Programs Provide Education and Training"* in *Contractor (Vol. 56, September 2009, No. 9, pp. 56)*
Ed: William Feldman, Patti Feldman. **Description:** Opportunity Interactive's Showroom v2 software provides uses computer graphics to provide education and training on HVAC equipment and systems. It can draw heat pump balance points for a specific home. Meanwhile, Simutech's HVAC Training Simulators provide trainees with 'hands-on' HVACR training. **Availability:** Print; Online.

509 ■ *"Put Your Heating Cap On"* in *Indoor Comfort Marketing (Vol. 70, September 2011, No. 9, pp. 26)*
Description: Tools and techniques for HVAC/R technicians servicing boilers are outlined. **Availability:** PDF; Online.

510 ■ *"Rehab Center Slashes Energy Bills By Going Tankless"* in *Contractor* (Vol. 56, December 2009, No. 12, pp. 3)
Description: Melburne Health and Rehabilitation Center in Florida has reduced its energy bills by installing a tankless hot water system. Sun Plumbing was selected to install the system. The system was installed on a mechanical room that housed the old tank-type heaters. **Availability:** Print; Online.

511 ■ *"Route Optimization Impacts the Bottom Line"* in *Contractor* (Vol. 56, November 2009, No. 11, pp. 48)
Ed: Dave Beaudry. **Description:** Plumbing and HVAC businesses can save a significant amount of money from route optimization. The process begins with gathering information on a fleet and a routing software tool can determine the effectiveness of current route configurations and identify preferable route plans. **Availability:** Print; Online.

512 ■ *"RPA Preps for Building Radiant Conference, Show"* in *Contractor* (Vol. 57, January 2010, No. 1, pp. 5)
Description: Radiant Panel Association is accepting registrations for its Building Radiant 2010 Conference and Trade Show. The conference will discuss radiant heating as well as insurance and other legal matters for mechanical contractors. **Availability:** Print; Online.

513 ■ *"Selling a Job When There's Buyer's Remorse"* in *Contractor* (Vol. 56, December 2009, No. 12, pp. 37)
Ed: H. Kent Craig. **Description:** Advice on how contractors should manage low-profit jobs in the United States is presented. Efforts should be made to try and find at least one quality field foreman or superintendent. Contractors should also try to respectfully renegotiate the terms of the job. **Availability:** Online.

514 ■ *"Snappy Moves Headquarters to Marietta"* in *Atlanta Business Chronicle* (June 27, 2014, pp. 13A)
Pub: American City Business Journals, Inc.
Contact: Mike Olivieri, Executive Vice President
Description: Snappy, the leading supplier of metal pipes for the residential HVAC market is shifting its headquarters from Philadelphia to Marietta, Georgia. The company will move its employees to an existing building on Johnson Ferry Road in Marietta. Snappy will close its Philadelphia plant and will increase its manufacturing operations at other plants in Powder Springs, Georgia and Medina, New York. **Availability:** Print; Online.

515 ■ *"Solar Choices"* in *Contractor* (Vol. 56, October 2009, No. 10, pp. 32)
Ed: Tom Scheel. **Description:** Price, performance, and ease of installation of a flat plate versus an evacuated tube collector for a plumbing and heating job are compared. The better choice with regards to weight, aesthetics, efficiency in warm or cool climates, year round load, and space heating is discussed. **Availability:** Print; Online.

516 ■ *"Store Front: Invest in Energy-Efficient Equipment for Your Pet Store"* in *Pet Product News* (Vol. 66, September 2012, No. 9, pp. 43)
Ed: Leila Meyer. **Description:** Developments in energy-efficient lighting, heating, and air conditioning have allowed pet supplies stores to conduct upgrades that result in savings. Pet supplies stores have also been impressing customers by obtaining Energy Start or LEED certification. **Availability:** Print; Online.

517 ■ *"There's Always Something Unexpected"* in *South Florida Business Journal* (Vol. 34, June 6, 2014, No. 46, pp. 13)
Pub: American City Business Journals, Inc.
Contact: Mike Olivieri, Executive Vice President
Released: Weekly. **Price:** $8, introductory 4-week offer(Digital only). **Description:** Hannah Granade, CEO of Advantix Systems, likes how her job allows her to build the business and bring people together. The company, that provides cooling and dehumidification systems for industrial and commercial applications, encourages creative thinking by building an open culture. **Availability:** Print; Online.

518 ■ *"Tracking Your Fleet Can Increase Bottom Line"* in *Contractor* (Vol. 56, November 2009, No. 11, pp. 26)
Ed: Candace Roulo. **Description:** GPS fleet management system can help boost a contractor's profits, employee productivity, and efficiency. These are available as a handheld device or a cell phone that employees carry around or as a piece of hardware installed in a vehicle. These lets managers track assets and communicate with employees about jobs. **Availability:** Online.

519 ■ *"Trade Craft: Take Pride in Your Trade, Demand Excellence"* in *Contractor* (Vol. 56, October 2009, No. 10, pp. 24)
Ed: Al Schwartz. **Description:** There is a need for teaching, developing, and encouraging trade craft. An apprentice plumber is not only versed in the mechanical aspects of the trade but he also has a working knowledge of algebra, trigonometry, chemistry, and thermal dynamics. Contractors should be demanding on their personnel regarding their trade craft and should only keep and train the very best people they can hire. **Availability:** Print; Online.

520 ■ *"Two Field Service Management Solutions"* in *Contractor* (Vol. 56, November 2009, No. 11, pp. 37)
Ed: William Feldman, Patti Feldman. **Description:** Bella Solutions Field Service Software v. 4.2 is a web based solution for HVAC service contractors that enables scheduling of emergency, one-time, multi-visit or periodically recurring jobs with drag and drop appointments. VaZing is another web based solution that costs $99 per month for contractors. It can handle line-item discounting and invoices aside from scheduling. **Availability:** Print; Online.

521 ■ *"Ultra Low Sulfur Diesel: The Promise and the Reality"* in *Indoor Comfort Marketing* (Vol. 70, July 2011, No. 7, pp. 22)
Description: Impacts of ultra low sulfur diesel are examined.

522 ■ *"Water Efficiency Bills Move Through Congress"* in *Contractor* (Vol. 56, July 2009, No. 7, pp. 20)
Ed: Kevin Schwalb. **Description:** National Association, a plumbing-heating-cooling contractor, was instrumental in drafting the Water Advanced Technologies for Efficient Resource Use Act of 2009 and they are also backing the Water Accountability Tax Efficiency Reinvestment Act. The first bill promotes WaterSense-labeled products while the other promotes water conservation through tax credits. **Availability:** Print; Online.

523 ■ *"Web-Based Solutions Streamline Operations"* in *Contractor* (Vol. 56, December 2009, No. 12, pp. 28)
Ed: William Feldman, Patti Feldman. **Description:** Sage Project Lifecycle Management is a Web-based service platform for plumbing and HVAC contractors. It enables effective workflow and document management. Projectmates, on the other hand, is a Web-based enterprise-wide solution for managing both commercial plumbing and HVAC projects. **Availability:** Print; Online.

524 ■ *"What Is a Geothermal Heat Pump"* in *Indoor Comfort Marketing* (Vol. 70, August 2011, No. 8, pp. 14)
Description: Examination of geothermal heat pumps is provided, citing new trends in the industry. **Availability:** Print; Online.

525 ■ *"Yates Helps Turn Log Home Green"* in *Contractor* (Vol. 56, November 2009, No. 11, pp. 1)
Description: Dave Yates of F.W. Behler Inc. helped homeowners from James Creek, Pennsylvania achieve energy efficiency on the heating system of their log cabin. The mechanical system installed on the cabin had high-temp "THW" water-to-water geothermal system by ClimateMaster, two twin-coil indirect water heaters, and several pre-assembled, pre-engineered Hydronex panels by Watts Radiant. **Availability:** Print; Online.

526 ■ *"Yates Turns Log Home Green - Part Three"* in *Contractor* (Vol. 57, January 2010, No. 1, pp. 5)
Released: January 12, 2010. **Description:** Dave Yates of F.W. Behler Inc. discusses remodeling a log home's HVAC system with geo-to-radiant heat and thermal-solar systems. The solar heater's installation is discussed.

STATISTICAL SOURCES

527 ■ *Heating & Air-Conditioning Contractors Industry in the US - Market Research Report*
URL(s): www.ibisworld.com/united-states/market-research-reports/heating-air-conditioning-contractors-industry/
Price: $925. **Description:** Downloadable report analyzing current and future trends in the heating and air-conditioning contractors industry. **Availability:** Download.

528 ■ *RMA Annual Statement Studies*
Pub: Risk Management Association
Contact: Nancy Foster, President
Released: Annual. **Description:** Contains composite balance sheets and income statements for more than 360 industries, including the accounting, auditing, and bookkeeping industries. Also contains five years of comparative historical data for discerning trends. Includes 16 commonly used ratios, computed for most of the size groupings for nearly every industry.

TRADE PERIODICALS

529 ■ *Contractor Connection*
Pub: Indiana Association of Plumbing Heating Cooling Contractors
Contact: Tyler Frame, President
URL(s): www.iaphcc.com/contractor-connection
Released: Quarterly; Jan/Feb/Mar; Apr/May/June; July/Aug/Sept; and Oct/Nov/Dec. **Description:** Official publication of the Indiana Association of Plumbing, Heating, Cooling Contractors, Inc. **Availability:** Print; PDF.

530 ■ *Heating/Piping/Air Conditioning Engineering: The Magazine of Mechanical Systems Engineering (HPAC) (HPAC)*
Pub: Informa USA Inc.
Contact: Gareth Wright, Director
URL(s): www.hpac.com
Facebook: www.facebook.com/hpacengineering
Linkedin: www.linkedin.com/company/hpac-engineering
X (Twitter): x.com/HPACEng
Released: 6/year **Description:** Business magazine serving the growing mechanical engineered systems market in the areas of building construction, renovation, and retrofit. **Availability:** Print; Online.

531 ■ *MACS Service Reports*
Pub: Mobile Air Climate Systems Association
Contact: Peter J. Coll, President
E-mail: pcoll@macsmobileairclimate.org
URL(s): macsmobileairclimate.org/publications
Released: Monthly **Description:** Serves as the technical information publication of the Mobile Air Conditioning Society Worldwide. Recurring features include news of research, news of educational opportunities, and How to and technical articles. **Availability:** Print.

VIDEO/AUDIO MEDIA

532 ■ *The How of Business: Patrick Lange - Buying an HVAC Business*
URL(s): www.thehowofbusiness.com/518-buying-hvac-business

Ed: Henry Lopez. **Released:** April 29, 2024. **Description:** Podcast discusses considerations when buying an HVAC business.

TRADE SHOWS AND CONVENTIONS

533 ■ ACCA Annual Conference and IE3 Expo
Air Conditioning Contractors of America Association (ACCA)
1520 Belle View Blvd. No 5220
Alexandria, VA 22307
Ph: (703)575-4477
Co. E-mail: membership@acca.org
URL: http://www.acca.org/home
Contact: Martin Hoover, Chairman
URL(s): www.accaconference.com
Frequency: Annual. **Description:** Indoor environmental and energy services, supplies, and equipment. **Audience:** Industry professionals. **Principal Exhibits:** Indoor environmental and energy services, supplies, and equipment. Dates and Locations: 2025 Mar 24-27 Kalahari Resort, Austin, TX. **Telecommunication Services:** events@acca.org.

534 ■ AHR Expo: International Air-Conditioning, Heating, Refrigerating Exposition
American Society of Heating, Refrigerating and Air-Conditioning Engineers (ASHRAE)
180 Technology Parkway NW
Peachtree Corners, GA 30092
Ph: (404)636-8400
Free: 800-527-4723
Fax: (404)539-2129
Co. E-mail: orders@ashrae.org
URL: http://www.ashrae.org
Contact: Farooq Mehboob, President
URL(s): www.ahrexpo.com/about
Facebook: www.facebook.com/ahrexpo/timeline
X (Twitter): twitter.com/ahrexpo
Frequency: Annual. **Description:** Seminars, and workshops addressing HVAC&R equipment and services. **Audience:** Industry professionals. **Principal Exhibits:** Seminars, and workshops addressing HVAC&R equipment and services. Dates and Locations: 2025 Feb 10-12 Orlando, FL; 2026 Feb 02-04 Las Vegas, NV; 2027 Jan 25-27 Chicago, IL. **Telecommunication Services:** info@ahrexpo.com.

535 ■ ASHRAE Winter Conference
URL(s): www.ashrae.org/conferences/2022-winter-conference-las-vegas
Description: Provides talks, technical tours, and certification programs for those in the heating, refrigerating, and air conditioning industry. **Principal Exhibits:** Provides talks, technical tours, and certification programs for those in the heating, refrigerating, and air conditioning industry.

536 ■ HARDI Annual Conference
Mars
Usman Abad Karachi, Garden West Karachi
Karachi, Sindh 00876, Pakistan
Ph: 92 021 7644263
Fax: 92 021 2237799
Co. E-mail: hanif_mars@hotmail.com
Contact: Hanif Abdullah, Managing Director
URL(s): www.hardiconference.com
Facebook: www.facebook.com/hardihvacr
Linkedin: www.linkedin.com/company/heating-air-conditioning-&-refrigeration-distributors-international
X (Twitter): twitter.com/HARDInews
Frequency: Annual; held every December. **Description:** Event for HARDI members brings together distributors, manufacturers and other vendors ready to drive their businesses forward. **Audience:** Distributors, manufacturers and other vendors. **Principal Exhibits:** Event for HARDI members brings together distributors, manufacturers and other vendors ready to drive their businesses forward. **Telecommunication Services:** hardimail@hardinet.org.

537 ■ Process Heating and Cooling Show
URL(s): www.process-heating.com/heat-cool-show
Price: $50, Onsite; $100, Onsite Supplier or vendor.; $25, Onsite Exhibitors and sponsors. **Frequency:** Annual. **Description:** Networking and exhibit hall for manufacturing suppliers, buyers and users of process heating and cooling equipment. **Principal Exhibits:** Networking and exhibit hall for manufacturing suppliers, buyers and users of process heating and cooling equipment.

538 ■ SMACNA's Annual Convention
Sheet Metal and Air Conditioning Contractors' National Association (SMACNA)
4201 Lafayette Center Dr.
Chantilly, VA 20151-1219
Ph: (703)803-2980
Fax: (703)803-3732
Co. E-mail: order@smacna.org
URL: http://www.smacna.org
Contact: Stanley E. Kolbe, Jr., Executive Director
URL(s): www.smacna.org/learn/events/calendar/2024-smacna-annual-convention
Frequency: Annual. **Description:** Product show for manufacturers and contractors of industrial, commercial, institutional, and residential equipment. **Audience:** Contractors, industry professionals. **Principal Exhibits:** Product show for manufacturers and contractors of industrial, commercial, institutional, and residential equipment. Dates and Locations: 2025 Oct 26-29 Grand Wailea, A Waldorf Astoria Resort/Wailea Beach Resort, Wailea, HI; 2026 Oct 25-28 Signia by Hilton Bonnet Creek/Waldorf Astoria, Orlando, FL; 2027 Oct 24-27 Gaylord Pacific Resort & Convention Center, Chula Vista, CA. **Telecommunication Services:** jfranco@smacna.org.

539 ■ Thermal Management Systems Symposium (TMSS)
Thermoanalytics Inc.
23440 Airpark Blvd.
Calumet, MI 49913
Ph: (906)482-9560
Fax: (906)482-9755
Co. E-mail: sales@thermoanalytics.com
URL: http://www.thermoanalytics.com
Contact: Al Curran, Co-Founder
URL(s): www.sae.org/attend/thermal
Frequency: Annual. **Audience:** Thermal-management engineers, powertrain engineers, environmental engineers, R&D engineers, product development professionals, HVAC system engineers, executives/management and college students. Dates and Locations: 2025 Oct 14-16 Ypsilanti, MI. **Telecommunication Services:** melissa.jena@sae.org.

CONSULTANTS

540 ■ Calmac Manufacturing Corp.
3-00 Banta Pl.
Fair Lawn, NJ 07410
Ph: (201)797-1511
URL: http://www.calmac.com
Contact: Mark M. MacCracken, President
Facebook: www.facebook.com/CalmacEnergyStorage
X (Twitter): x.com/EnergyStorage
YouTube: www.youtube.com/user/CALMACEnergyStorage
Pinterest: www.pinterest.com/thermalstorage
Description: Manufacturer of thermal energy storage. **Scope:** Manufacturer of thermal energy storage. **Founded:** 1947. **Publications:** "Intelligent Building Series, Volume 1: Large Commercial Buildings," EPRI; "Energy Storage is the Answer to Looming Power Shortages, Frost and Sullivan"; "Thermal Energy Storage- Btu's in the Land of the kWh's," IEEE; "Market Evaluation for Energy Storage in the United States," KEMA; "The Future of the Electric Grid," MIT; "2020 Strategic Analysis of Energy Storage in California"; "Energy Storage Providing for a Low Carbon Future," ASHRAE Journal.

541 ■ Environmental & Engineering Services Inc. (EESI)
428 NW 5th St.
Corvallis, OR 97330
Ph: (541)754-1062
Co. E-mail: esinet5@peak.org
URL: http://www.eesinet.com
Contact: Peter Sanford, Manager
Linkedin: www.linkedin.com/company/environmental-and-engineering-services-inc-
Description: Firm provides design consulting services focused in the mechanical, plumbing and electrical disciplines and offers a wide range of HVAC, electrical and controls engineering services including feasibility assessments, master planning, budgeting, cost analysis, design, computer-aided drafting, and much more. **Founded:** 1979.

542 ■ Fanning, Fanning & Associates Inc.
2555 74th St.
Lubbock, TX 79423
Ph: (806)745-2533
Fax: (806)745-3596
Co. E-mail: nfanning@fanningfanning.com
URL: http://www.fanningfanning.com
Contact: Scott Fanning, President
Facebook: www.facebook.com/FFAconsultingengineers
Description: Specializes in engineering services including mechanical, electrical, plumbing design and plant layout, HVAC, energy conservation and management, utilities, fire protection and alarms, central heating and cooling plants and communications for institutional, commercial and industrial buildings. Offers design services for drawings, specifications and bid documents, master planning, engineering reports, estimates, analysis, feasibility studies and construction phase services. **Scope:** Specializes in engineering services including mechanical, electrical, plumbing design and plant layout, HVAC, energy conservation and management, utilities, fire protection and alarms, central heating and cooling plants and communications for institutional, commercial and industrial buildings. Offers design services for drawings, specifications and bid documents, master planning, engineering reports, estimates, analysis, feasibility studies and construction phase services.

543 ■ GHT Ltd.
1110 N Glebe Rd., Ste. 300
Arlington, VA 22201
Ph: (703)243-1200
Fax: (703)276-1376
Co. E-mail: info@ghtltd.com
URL: http://www.ghtltd.com
Contact: Patrick Kunze, President
Facebook: www.facebook.com/GHTLimited
Linkedin: www.linkedin.com/company/ght-limited
Description: Firm provides consulting on engineering design services such as telecommunications and security engineering service, life safety engineering service, utilities planning service and much more. **Scope:** Firm provides consulting on engineering design services such as telecommunications and security engineering service, life safety engineering service, utilities planning service and much more. **Founded:** 1965. **Publications:** "Critical spaces keep the pace of business humming," May, 2004; "To avoid staticlater, hire right telecom consultant," Oct, 2007. **Special Services:** LEED®.

544 ■ GPD P.C.
524 First Ave. S
Great Falls, MT 59401
Ph: (406)452-9558
URL: http://www.gpdpc.com
Contact: James Wyatt, Project Manager
Description: Firm provides professional design, mechanical and electrical engineering, refrigeration design and construction administration services. **Scope:** Firm provides professional design, mechanical and electrical engineering, refrigeration design and construction administration services.

545 ■ Lawrence G. Spielvogel Inc.
190 Presidential Blvd., No. 310
Bala Cynwyd, PA 19004
Contact: Lawrence G. Spielvogel, President
Description: Firm provides technical consulting services in energy management and mechanical and electrical engineering for buildings. Areas of activities include energy procurement, heating, ventilating and

air conditioning and plumbing, system design and much more. Serves consulting engineers, contractors, government agencies, architects and owners. **Scope:** Firm provides technical consulting services in energy management and mechanical and electrical engineering for buildings. Areas of activities include energy procurement, heating, ventilating and air conditioning and plumbing, system design and much more. Serves consulting engineers, contractors, government agencies, architects and owners.

FRANCHISES AND BUSINESS OPPORTUNITIES

546 ■ Aire Serv Heating & Air Conditioning Inc.
Neighborly
1020 N University Parks Dr.
Waco, TX 76707
Free: 800-490-7501
Fax: (877)496-2356
URL: http://www.neighborlybrands.com
Facebook: www.facebook.com/AireServLLC
Linkedin: www.linkedin.com/company/aire-serv
X (Twitter): twitter.com/AireServ
Instagram: www.instagram.com/aireservftw
YouTube: www.youtube.com/user/AireServDotCom
Pinterest: www.pinterest.com/aireservcorp

Description: Operates a franchise system offering installation, maintenance, and repair of heating, ventilation, air conditioning, and indoor air quality systems. **Founded:** 1992.

547 ■ One Hour Heating and Air Conditioning
Largo, FL
Ph: (727)245-0378
URL: http://www.onehourheatandair.com
Facebook: www.facebook.com/onehourheatandair
X (Twitter): x.com/OneHourHeatAir
Instagram: www.instagram.com/onehourheatair
YouTube: www.youtube.com/c/OneHourHea
 tingAirConditioning/featured
Pinterest: www.pinterest.com/OneHourHeatAir

Description: Provider of plumbing, home improvements, water heater and electrical appliance installation and repair services. **Founded:** 1999. **Franchised:** 2003. **Financial Assistance:** Yes **Training:** Provides 3 days training at headquarters, at model centers and training school, Internet training, onsite with ongoing support.

LIBRARIES

548 ■ Refrigeration Service Engineers Society (RSES) - Library
PO Box 248
 Arlington Heights, IL 60006-0248
Ph: (847)297-6464
Free: 800-297-5660
Fax: (547)297-5038
Co. E-mail: general@rses.org
URL: http://rses.org
Contact: Art T. Miller, President
E-mail: hvacr@artcms.net
Facebook: www.facebook.com/rseshq

Description: Persons engaged in refrigeration, air-conditioning and heating installation, service, sales and maintenance. Conducts training courses and certification testing. Maintains a hall of fame and a speaker's bureau. **Scope:** Refrigeration, air conditioning, heating. **Founded:** 1933. **Holdings:** Figures not available. **Publications:** *Service Application Manuals (SAM)*. **Educational Activities:** Refrigeration Service Engineers Society Educational Conference (Annual). **Awards:** RSES Distinguished Service Member of the Year Award (Annual); V.V. Solomon Educator/Teacher of the Year Award (Annual); RSES Rising Star Award (Annual); RSES Speaker of the Year (Annual). **Geographic Preference:** Multinational.

RESEARCH CENTERS

549 ■ American Society of Heating, Refrigerating and Air-Conditioning Engineers Research Program (ASHRAE)
180 Technology Pky. NW
 Peachtree Corners, GA 30092
URL: http://www.ashrae.org

Description: Research arm of an independent, nonprofit, international trade and professional association numbering 50,000 members and 152 local chapters. **Scope:** Sponsors research projects at colleges, universities, and private research firms on technical subjects dealing with heating, refrigeration, air conditioning, and ventilation and their effects on humans and the environment. Projects include air pollution sources in HVAC systems, evaluation of service hot water system distribution losses in residential and commercial installations, investigation and identification of indoor allergens and biological toxins that can be moved by filtration, computer algorithms for moisture loss and latent heat loads in bulk storage of fruits and vegetables, and modeling of reflected solar heat gain from neighboring structures in building energy simulation programs. **Founded:** 1960. **Publications:** *ASHRAE Handbook* (Annual); *ASHRAE Transactions* (Semiannual); *Science Tecnology for the Built Environment* (10/year). **Awards:** ASHRAE Graduate Student Grants-in-aid (Annual).

550 ■ University of California, Berkeley - California Institute for Energy and Environment (CIEE)
2150 Allston Way Ste. 280
 Berkeley, CA 94704
Ph: (510)664-7462
Co. E-mail: info@uc-ciee.org
URL: http://uc-ciee.org
Contact: Dr. Carl Blumstein, Director
E-mail: blumstei@berkeley.edu
Facebook: www.facebook.com/CIEEuc
Linkedin: www.linkedin.com/company/california-insti
 tute-for-energy-and-environment
X (Twitter): x.com/UC_CIEE
Instagram: www.instagram.com/uc_ciee

Description: Integral unit of the University of California. **Scope:** Building energy efficiency, including integrated lighting systems, commercial cooling systems, HVAC distribution systems, residential cooling systems, improved building HVAC controls; building commissioning, operations, and maintenance; air quality effects of energy efficiency, including emission reduction strategies, gas combustion systems, and alternative transportation systems. Institute seeks to secure sustainable, affordable energy for California while improving the state's economy and resources and remaining sensitive to climate change issues. **Services:** Library open to the public. **Founded:** 1989. **Holdings:** Articles; reports. **Publications:** *CIEE Technical reports*. **Educational Activities:** CIEE Project workshops, On global climate change, demand response, and transmission research.

Air Purification/Cleaning Service

ASSOCIATIONS AND OTHER ORGANIZATIONS

551 ■ Allergy/Asthma Information Association (AAIA) [Association d'information sur l'allergie et l'asthme]
200 - 5409 Eglinton Ave. W
Toronto, ON, Canada M9C 5K6
URL: http://www.aaia.ca
Facebook: www.facebook.com/AllergyAsthmaInformationAssociation
Description: Seeks to develop societal awareness of the seriousness of allergic disease, including asthma, and to enable allergic individuals, their families, and caregivers to increase control over allergy symptoms. Provides leadership in information, education, and advocacy through partnership with healthcare professionals, businesses, industry, and government. Maintains speakers' bureau. **Founded:** 1964. **Publications:** *Awareness and Info Allergie Newsletter* (Quarterly); *Awareness and Info Allergie* (Quarterly); *Allergy/Asthma Quarterly* (Quarterly). **Geographic Preference:** National.

552 ■ Indoor Air Quality Association (IAQA)
1120 Rt. 73, Ste. 200
Mount Laurel, NJ 08054
Free: 844-802-4103
Co. E-mail: info@iaqa.org
URL: http://iaqa.org
Contact: Lisa Rogers, President
E-mail: lrogers@mycometer.com
Facebook: www.facebook.com/IAQAupdates
X (Twitter): x.com/IAQAssociation
YouTube: www.youtube.com/user/IAQAvideos
Description: Promotes the exchange of indoor environmental information. Provides education and research for the safety and well-being of the general public. Advances standards, procedures and protocols in the Indoor Air Quality industry. **Founded:** 1995. **Publications:** *In the Air* (Quarterly). **Geographic Preference:** National.

553 ■ National Air Filtration Association (NAFA)
1818 Parmenter St., Ste. 300
Middleton, WI 53562
Ph: (608)310-7542
Fax: (608)492-0523
Co. E-mail: nafa@nafahq.org
URL: http://www.nafahq.org
Contact: Emily Bardach, Executive Director
E-mail: ebardach@nafahq.org
Facebook: www.facebook.com/NAFAHQ
Linkedin: www.linkedin.com/company/national-air-filtration-association
X (Twitter): x.com/nafahq
YouTube: www.youtube.com/channel/UCtcMU_PP5wM1hsHRSM57kRw
Description: Promotes the sale and use of air filtration media. Makes available technical education to members; conducts regional workshops. Offers certification for air filter sales/distributors and service technicians. Consists of companies that sell or service air filtration media to commercial and industrial users; manufacturers of air filtration media. **Founded:** 1980. **Publications:** *Air Media* (3/year). **Educational Activities:** National Air Filtration Association National Convention (Annual). **Awards:** NAFA Clean Air Award Program (Annual); NAFA Scholarship Program (Annual). **Geographic Preference:** National.

REFERENCE WORKS

554 ■ "Amazon's Top Doctor on Why Air Quality Is the Biggest Workplace Health Challenge of This Century" in CNBC (October 22, 2021)
Ed: Eric Rosenbaum. **Released:** October 22, 2021. **Description:** The Covid pandemic has many businesses looking for ways to keep their employees healthy. One of the best ways to do so is to keep the air clean within buildings by filtering out viruses and other contaminants.

555 ■ "Amistee Air Duct Acquires Ducts R Us, Looks at 2nd Competitor" in Crain's Detroit Business (Vol. 35, September 1, 2014, No. 35, pp. 5)
Pub: Crain Communications Inc.
Contact: Barry Asin, President
Description: Details of the Novi-based Amistee Air Duct Cleaning & Insulation firm's acquisition of their competitor Ducts R Us Air Duct Cleaning of Clinton Township, Michigan. Co-owners of Amistee revealed the plan to acquire another competitor in Southeast Michigan. Details of the deal are included. **Availability:** Online.

556 ■ "Chicago Public Schools District Builds Green" in Contractor (Vol. 56, October 2009, No. 10, pp. 5)
Ed: Candace Roulo. **Description:** Chicago Public Schools district has already built six U.S. Green Building Council LEED certified schools and one addition in five years and will continue to build new green buildings. The district has an Environmental Action Plan that strives to reduce energy usage, improve indoor air quality, and reduce contribution to climate change. **Availability:** Print; Online.

TRADE SHOWS AND CONVENTIONS

557 ■ National Air Filtration Association National Convention
National Air Filtration Association (NAFA)
1818 Parmenter St., Ste. 300
Middleton, WI 53562
Ph: (608)310-7542
Fax: (608)492-0523
Co. E-mail: nafa@nafahq.org
URL: http://www.nafahq.org
Contact: Emily Bardach, Executive Director
E-mail: ebardach@nafahq.org
URL(s): www.nafahq.org/annual_convention
Frequency: Annual. **Description:** Provides forums, education and certification programs for members to exchange information about technical standards, government regulations, and product information. **Audience:** Air filter and component manufacturers, sales, and service companies, and HVAC and indoor quality professionals. **Principal Exhibits:** Provides forums, education and certification programs for members to exchange information about technical standards, government regulations, and product information. **Telecommunication Services:** nafa@nafahq.org.

CONSULTANTS

558 ■ Pathogen Control Associates Inc.
270 Scientific Dr., Ste. 3
Norcross, GA 30092
Ph: (770)446-0540
Fax: (770)446-0610
Co. E-mail: info_na@pathcon.com
URL: http://www.pathcon.com
Contact: George Gorman, Co-Founder
Description: Firm provides consulting services in analysis, prevention, and eradication for a range of industries such as hospitality, banking, insurance, government, healthcare, and much more. **Scope:** Firm provides consulting services in analysis, prevention, and eradication for a range of industries such as hospitality, banking, insurance, government, healthcare, and much more. **Founded:** 1986. **Publications:** "Microbes in the Indoor Environment"; "Legionellosis: Is there a National Preventing Strategy". **Training:** Micro Organisms in Indoor Air: Health Complaints Associated With Environmental and Occupational Settings; Environmental Hazards in HealthCare Settings; Moisture and Engineering Design; Mold Remediation; Sampling Strategy; Airborne Bacteria; Legionella.

FRANCHISES AND BUSINESS OPPORTUNITIES

559 ■ Coit Services Inc. [Coit Cleaning and Restoration]
897 Hinckley Rd.
Burlingame, CA 94010
Free: 800-367-2648
Co. E-mail: info@coit.com
URL: http://www.coit.com
Facebook: www.facebook.com/COITClean
Linkedin: www.linkedin.com/company/coit-services
X (Twitter): x.com/coitclean
Instagram: www.instagram.com/coitclean
Description: Provides cleaning services in upholstery, draperies, carpeting and other flooring surfaces. **No. of Franchise Units:** 42. **No. of Company-Owned Units:** 8. **Founded:** 1950. **Franchised:**

1962. **Equity Capital Needed:** $50,000-$145,000. **Franchise Fee:** $24,000-$40,000. **Financial Assistance:** Yes **Training:** Includes 10 days in corporate office.

560 ■ Ductmedic
5200 N 57th St., Ste. 2
 Lincoln, NE 68507
Ph: (402)435-3828
Co. E-mail: info@ductmedic.com
URL: http://ductmedic.com
Contact: Bill Hippen, President
Facebook: www.facebook.com/DuctMedic
Description: Firm provides air duct cleaning and indoor air quality services. **Founded:** 1994. **Financial Assistance:** Yes **Training:** Yes.

LIBRARIES

561 ■ AECOM - Library
AECOM
 13355 Noel Rd., Ste. 400
 Dallas, TX 75240
Ph: (972)788-1000
Co. E-mail: info@aecom.com
URL: http://www.aecom.com
Contact: Lara Poloni, President
Facebook: www.facebook.com/
 AecomTechnologyCorporation
Linkedin: www.linkedin.com/company/aecom
X (Twitter): twitter.com/AECOM
Instagram: www.instagram.com/aecom
YouTube: www.youtube.com/user/
 AECOMTechnologyCorp
Description: Fully integrated provider of planning, consultation, architectural, and engineering design and construction services. **Scope:** Environment; air quality; hazardous waste. **Services:** Interlibrary loan; library not open to the public. **Founded:** 1990. **Holdings:** 5,000 books; technical and government reports; government agency rules and regulations. **Publications:** "Global Perspectives"; "Asia Beyond Growth"; "Climate Design"; "Water Reuse: Issues, Technologies, Applications"; "Wastewater Engineering: Treatment and Reuse"; "The Bigger Picture". **Educational Activities:** Air & Waste Management Association Annual Conference & Exhibition (ACE) (Annual); Core-Net Global Symposium (Irregular); American Planning Association Conference (APA) (Annual); IFMA's World Workplace Conference & Expo (Annual); ACENZ Annual Conference (Annual); ASFPM Annual National Conference (Annual); Airports Council International - Asia-Pacific Regional Assembly, Conference & Exhibition (Annual).

562 ■ Cadwalader, Wickersham & Taft Library
700 6th St., NW
 Washington, DC 20001
Ph: (202)862-2200
Co. E-mail: cwtinfo@cwt.com
URL: http://www.cadwalader.com
Scope: Law - antitrust, corporate, securities, taxation, business fraud. **Services:** Interlibrary loan; library open to the public by appointment (with restrictions). **Founded:** 1792. **Holdings:** 15,000 volumes; microforms; CD-ROM.

563 ■ California Environmental Protection Agency (CalEPA) - Library
1001 I St.
 Sacramento, CA 95814
Ph: (916)323-2514
Co. E-mail: cepacomm@calepa.ca.gov
URL: http://calepa.ca.gov
Contact: Jared Blumenfeld, Secretary
Facebook: www.facebook.com/CaliforniaEPA
Linkedin: www.linkedin.com/company/california
 -environmental-protection-agency
X (Twitter): twitter.com/CaliforniaEPA
Instagram: www.instagram.com/californiaepa
Description: Integral unit of California state government. **Scope:** Environmental protection and public health. **Services:** Open to the public for reference use only. **Founded:** 1991. **Holdings:** Books; journals; periodicals; research reports; technical reports; reference materials and DVD's. **Publications:** *Annual Governor's Report on the Environment*. **Educational Activities:** Cal/EPA Emerging Issues Conference.

RESEARCH CENTERS

564 ■ Northeastern University - Center for Nano and Microcontamination Control (CMC)
360 Huntington Ave.
 Boston, MA 02115
Ph: (617)373-6012
Fax: (617)373-3266
URL: http://cmc.sites.northeastern.edu
Contact: Ahmed Busnaina, Professor
Description: Integral unit of Northeastern University. Offers consulting services. **Scope:** Microcontamination and particulate control applied to process equipment and manufacturing. Specific areas of research include nanoparticle transport, deposition, adhesion, and removal from silicon and other substrates; modeling of particle and mass transport in semiconductor processing; particle deposition and generation in semiconductor manufacturing processes, micro and nanofabrication of interconnects and the development of Cu physically enhanced electroplating. **Publications:** *CMC Newsletter* (Daily); *Research conference report* (Biennial). **Educational Activities:** CMC Short courses; CMC Technical conference; CMC Industrial Advisory Board Meeting.

565 ■ University of California, Davis - Air Quality Group
1560 Drew Ave.
 Davis, CA 95618
URL: http://aqrc.ucdavis.edu
Facebook: www.facebook.com/UCDavisAQRC
Linkedin: www.linkedin.com/company/uc-davis-air
 -quality-research-center
X (Twitter): twitter.com/UCDavisAQRC
Description: Integral unit of Crocker Nuclear Laboratory, University of California, Davis. **Scope:** Air quality, including chemical size-analysis and source identification of air pollutants, particulate monitoring, and development of sampling equipment.

Ambulance Service

ASSOCIATIONS AND OTHER ORGANIZATIONS

566 ■ Ambulance Association of Pennsylvania (AAP)
PO Box 60183
Harrisburg, PA 17106-0183
Ph: (717)512-5609
URL: http://www.aa-pa.org
Contact: Dean Bollendorf, President
Facebook: www.facebook.com/Ambulance-Associa tion-of-Pennsylvania-116633218350101
X (Twitter): x.com/heathersharar
Description: Furthers medical transportation industry in Pennsylvania. Aims to provide the best possible patient care and service through education, communication, and support. **Geographic Preference:** State.

567 ■ American Ambulance Association (AAA)
PO Box 96503, No. 72319
Washington, DC 20090-6503
Ph: (202)802-9020
Co. E-mail: info@ambulance.org
URL: http://ambulance.org
Contact: Aarron Reinert, President
E-mail: aarronr@lrems.com
Facebook: www.facebook.com/americanambulanceassoc
Linkedin: www.linkedin.com/company/american-ambulance-association
X (Twitter): x.com/amerambassoc
Description: Represents private suppliers of ambulance service. Aims to: aid in developing private enterprise pre-hospital emergency medical treatment and medical transportation services as a viable cost-effective alternative to publicly-operated services; promote improved patient care; develop efficient medical transportation at a reasonable cost; improve personnel and equipment standards; work with organizations offering medical transportation; encourage high standards of ethics and conduct. **Founded:** 1979. **Publications:** *Medicare Reference* (Annual); *Ambulance Industry Journal* (Quarterly). **Educational Activities:** American Ambulance Association Annual Conference and Trade Show (Annual). **Geographic Preference:** National.

568 ■ Florida Ambulance Association (FAA)
c/o American Ambulance Association No 72319
Washington, DC 20090-6503
Ph: (202)802-9020
Co. E-mail: faa@ambulance.org
URL: http://www.the-faa.org
Contact: Alissa Garcia, President
E-mail: alissa@nationalhealthtransport.com
Facebook: www.facebook.com/flori daambulanceassoc
Description: Collaborates with Florida emergency services to support patient care and reimbursement. **Founded:** 1967.

569 ■ South Dakota Ambulance Association (SDAA)
PO Box 543
Spearfish, SD 57783
Ph: (605)642-8810
Fax: (605)717-0193
URL: http://sdaa.wildapricot.org
Contact: Brian Hambeck, President
E-mail: seas@rushmore.com
Facebook: www.facebook.com/people/SD-Ambu lance-Assn-SDAA/100057418392891
Description: Provides support and a code of ethics for ambulance services in South Dakota.

REFERENCE WORKS

570 ■ *Ambulance Services: Leadership and Management Perspectives*
Released: 2015. **Description:** With cuts in healthcare budgets, ambulance services are adjusting and adapting. Critical insights into the ambulance industry are examined and how these services are now operating to serve communities. **Availability:** Print.

571 ■ *"Feds Battling to Put the Brakes on Ambulance Billing Fraud" in Philadelphia Business Journal (Vol. 33, April 25, 2014, No. 11, pp. 4)*
Pub: American City Business Journals, Inc.
Contact: Mike Olivieri, Executive Vice President
Released: Weekly. **Price:** $4, introductory 4-week offer(Digital & Print). **Description:** The Department of Health and Human Services, Office of Inspector General, Federal Bureau of Investigation and the U.S. Attorney's Office are working together to crack down on ambulance companies involved in fraudulent Medicare claims. A ban on new ground ambulance companies in southeastern Philadelphia was issued due to ambulance fraud in the Philadelphia region. **Availability:** Print; Online.

572 ■ *"The Problem of Private Ambulances Services" in Current Affairs (August 30, 2018)*
URL(s): www.currentaffairs.org/2018/08/the-problem -of-private-ambulance-services
Ed: David Anderson. **Released:** August 30, 2018. **Description:** Burnout, fatigue, poor health, and low pay are rampant in the private EMS industry, which is discussed in detail along with the monopoly that American Medical Response holds in the US. The high-cost to keep the private ambulance system going is compared to what it would cost to have it fully funded through public taxes. **Availability:** Print; Online.

TRADE SHOWS AND CONVENTIONS

573 ■ American Ambulance Association Annual Conference and Trade Show
Zoll Medical Corp.
269 Mill Rd.
Chelmsford, MA 01824-4105
Ph: (978)421-9655
Free: 800-348-9011
Fax: (978)421-0025
Co. E-mail: info@zoll.com
URL: http://www.zoll.com
Contact: Jonathan A. Rennert, Chief Executive Officer
URL(s): annual.ambulance.org
Frequency: Annual. **Description:** Exhibits related to ambulance equipment, supplies, and services. **Audience:** Medical transportation professionals and trade professionals. **Principal Exhibits:** Exhibits related to ambulance equipment, supplies, and services. Dates and Locations: 2025 Jun 23-25 Central Bank Center, Lexington, KY. **Telecommunication Services:** hello@ambulance.org.

RESEARCH CENTERS

574 ■ University of California, San Francisco - San Francisco Injury Center (SFIC)
San Francisco General Hospital, Department of Surgery, Ward 3A, 1001 Potrero Ave.
San Francisco, CA 94110
Ph: (415)206-4623
Fax: (415)206-5484
Co. E-mail: du-leesa.morris@ucsf.edu
URL: http://sfic.ucsf.edu
Contact: Dr. M. Margaret Knudson, Director
E-mail: peggy.knudson@ucsf.edu
Description: Research activity of the University of California, San Francisco, at San Francisco General Hospital, one of eleven Injury Control Research Centers in the U.S. **Scope:** Acute trauma care, injury prevention and surveillance. **Founded:** 1989.

Amusement Arcade

ASSOCIATIONS AND OTHER ORGANIZATIONS

575 ■ **American Amusement Machine Association (AAMA)**
450 E Higgins Rd., Ste. 201
Elk Grove Village, IL 60007
Ph: (847)290-9088
Fax: (847)290-9121
Co. E-mail: info@coin-op.org
URL: http://coin-op.org
Contact: Joe Camarota, President
Facebook: www.facebook.com/LikeAAMA
Linkedin: www.linkedin.com/company/american
 -amusement-machine-association
X (Twitter): x.com/aama__
Description: Manufacturers and distributors of coin machines; parts suppliers and others interested in promoting and protecting the amusement machine industry. Seeks solutions to the problem of copyright infringement by foreign manufacturers, and legislative and regulatory problems facing the industry and manufacturers. Works to improve the image of the coin-operated amusement industry. Presents views to governmental decision-makers. Operates American Amusement Machine Charitable Foundation. **Founded:** 1981. **Publications:** *AAMA Membership Directory* (Annual). **Geographic Preference:** Multinational.

576 ■ **Amusement & Music Operators Association (AMOA)**
380 Terra Cotta Rd., Ste. F
Crystal Lake, IL 60012
Ph: (815)893-6010
Free: 800-937-2662
Fax: (815)893-6248
Co. E-mail: info@amoa.com
URL: http://amoa.memberclicks.net
Contact: Tim Zahn, President
URL(s): www.amoa.com
Facebook: www.facebook.com/AMOAassociation
Linkedin: www.linkedin.com/company/amoaassocia
 tion
X (Twitter): x.com/coinop
Instagram: www.instagram.com/amoa_association
Description: Firms engaged in the coin-operated music, vending and amusement business. Sponsors juke box and amusement game award programs; compiles industry statistics. Conducts research; offers specialized education programs. **Founded:** 1948. **Publications:** *Amusement and Music Operators Association--Member Directory*; *Who's Who in Amusement and Music Operators Association* (Annual). **Educational Activities:** Amusement Expo International (AEI) (Annual). **Awards:** Wayne E. Hesch Memorial Scholarship (Annual). **Geographic Preference:** National.

REFERENCE WORKS

577 ■ *"3 Questions with Andrew Tosh, CEO of GameSim Inc. - and Brother to a Star"* in *Orlando Business Journal* (Vol. 30, April 18, 2014, No. 43, pp. 8)
Pub: American City Business Journals, Inc.
Contact: Mike Olivieri, Executive Vice President
Released: Weekly. **Price:** $8, introductory 4-week offer(Digital & Print). **Description:** GameSim Inc. CEO, Andrew Tosh, says Orlando, Florida's talent pool is the reason for the company's expansion into the city. He also said that the city government's incentive programs also influenced the video game producer's choice of this location. Tosh added that the firm is set to open satellite office in other states. **Availability:** Print; Online.

578 ■ *"Ditch the Pet Store! MindJolt SGN and The Humane Society of the United States Unleash Fluff Friends Rescue"* in *Benzinga.com* (January 4, 2012)
Pub: Benzinga.com
Contact: Jason Raznick, Founder
Ed: Aaron Wise. **Description:** The Humane Society of the United States has partnered with MindJolt SGN, a multiplatform game developer and distributor, to release a mobile game called Fluff Friends Rescue. The game introduces players to the real-world challenges of rescuing pets by nursing animals back to health while running their own animal shelter.

579 ■ *"Getting Emotional Over Microsoft's Minecraft"* in *Puget Sound Business Journal* (Vol. 35, September 19, 2014, No. 22, pp. 7)
Pub: American City Business Journals, Inc.
Contact: Mike Olivieri, Executive Vice President
Description: Microsoft's acquisition of Minecraft maker Mojan AB is helps to promote STEM education. Microsoft will purchase the company for $2.5 billion. Minecraft game creator, Markus Persson, will not be joining the new Microsoft team. **Availability:** Online.

580 ■ *"Great Canadian's President Folds His Cards"* in *Globe & Mail* (February 21, 2006, pp. B4)
Ed: Peter Kennedy. **Description:** The reasons behind the resignation of Anthony Martin as president of Great Canadian Gaming Corp. are presented. **Availability:** Print; Online.

581 ■ *"Here's How an Old School Arcade Survives in the 21st Century"* in *Vice* (September 9, 2016)
URL(s): www.vice.com/en_us/article/xyg47n/video
 -game-arcades-in-2016
Ed: Kevin Wong. **Released:** September 09, 2016. **Description:** Profile of Richie Knucklez who runs a video arcade in New Jersey. His business strategy is discussed, which includes providing high-quality machines and having a family-like atmosphere. **Availability:** Online.

582 ■ *How to Get Rich*
Ed: Felix Dennis. **Released:** 2013. **Price:** $8.16, paperback. **Description:** The author, publisher of Maxim, The Week, and Stuff magazines, discusses the mistakes he made running his companies. He didn't understand that people who buy computer gaming magazines wanted a free game with each copy, as one of his rivals was offering. And he laments not diversifying into television and exploiting the Internet. **Availability:** E-book; Print.

583 ■ *Internet Pinball Database*
URL(s): www.ipdb.org/search.pl
Description: A searchable database of every pinball machine commercially made. Incluse 69,726 images, 6214 games, 4,845 other game files, and link to pinball sites. **Availability:** Online.

584 ■ *"Kiosk Outfit ecoATM Now Recycling Video Games"* in *San Diego Union-Tribune* (October 7, 2010)
Pub: The San Diego Union-Tribune
Contact: Phyllis Pfeiffer, President
E-mail: ppfeiffer@lajollalight.com
URL(s): www.sandiegouniontribune.com/sdut-kiosk
 -outfit-ecoatm-now-recycling-video-games-2010oc
 t07-story.html
Ed: Mike Freeman. **Description:** ecoATM makes automated kiosks to buy back cell phones,it will now include video games as part of their recycling center for consumer electronics. **Availability:** Print; Online.

585 ■ *"Lighter Than Air"* in *Game Developer* (Vol. 18, November 1, 2011, No. 10, pp. 38)
Pub: Think Services
Description: Floating point performance tips and tricks are outlined. Floating point allows freedom of representation when implementing algorithms and is both intuitive to set up and simple to work with; hardware is also improved so that it is faster to use floating point math as opposed to integer in many environments. **Availability:** Print; Online.

586 ■ *"Work for Play: Careers in Video Game Development"* in *Occupational Outlook Quarterly* (Vol. 55, Fall 2011, No. 3, pp. 2)
Pub: U.S. Department of Labor Bureau of Labor
 Statistics
Contact: Amrit Kohli, Director
E-mail: kohli.amrit@bls.gov
Ed: Drew Liming, Dennis Vilorio. **Description:** Game developers make a living creating the games the public enjoys playing. The video gaming industry reported sales over $10 billion in 2009 and employed 32,000 people in 34 states. Career options in video game development are featured. **Availability:** PDF; Online.

587 ■ *World Pinball Directory*
URL(s): www.daveland.com/pinball/index2.html
Description: Online database of places to play pinball in the United States, around the world, and it has links to the latest releases and upcoming tournaments and shows. **Availability:** Online.

588 ■ *"Zoo Entertainment Inc. Aims for the Sky"* in *Business Courier* (Vol. 27, September 24, 2010, No. 21, pp. 1)
Pub: Business Courier

Ed: Dan Monk. **Description:** Video game company Zoo Entertainment Inc., which is based in Norwood near Cincinnati, Ohio aims to build a strong company and to position itself for future growth. The company reported $27.6 million in revenue for the first half of 2010 and analysts project $100 million in sales for 2011. **Availability:** Print; Online.

TRADE PERIODICALS

589 ■ *RePlay Magazine*
Pub: RePlay Magazine
Contact: Key Snodgress, Director, Editorial
Facebook: www.facebook.com/replaymagazine
X (Twitter): x.com/replaymag

Ed: Steve White. **Released:** Monthly **Price:** $6, for sample copies or back issues (those dated 2011 to the present with the exception of the current year's Annual Directory; $10, Canada and Mexico for sample copies; $20, for back issues 2010 and earlier; $20, for last 12 months; $25, U.S. for directory issue international; $25, for directory issue current us& its territory; $40, for sample copies international; $40, for 1 year old; $45, Members for AMOA; $65, U.S. for 1 year; $90, Canada and Mexico for 1 year; $120, U.S. for 2 year; $160, U.S. for 3 year; $230, for 1 year international subscription. **Description:** Trade magazine covering the coin-operated amusement game industry. **Availability:** Print; Online.

TRADE SHOWS AND CONVENTIONS

590 ■ Amusement Expo International (AEI)
SmithBucklin Corp. (SB)
330 N Wabash Ave., Ste. 2000
Chicago, IL 60611
Free: 800-539-9740
Co. E-mail: info@smithbucklin.com
URL: http://smithbucklin.com
Contact: Matt Sanderson, President
E-mail: msanderson@smithbucklin.com
URL(s): www.amusementexpo.org/2025/Public/Enter.aspx

Frequency: Annual. **Description:** Informative sessions, various exhibits, relating to the Amusement Entertainment Industry. **Audience:** Industry professionals. **Principal Exhibits:** Informative sessions, various exhibits, relating to the Amusement Entertainment Industry. Dates and Locations: 2025 Mar 17-20, Las Vegas Convention Center, Las Vegas, NV. **Telecommunication Services:** brian@wtglasgow.com.

CONSULTANTS

591 ■ Amusement Consultants Ltd.
56 Harrison St.
New Rochelle, NY 10801
Ph: (914)576-7800
Fax: (914)576-3620
Co. E-mail: info@amusementconsultants.com
URL: http://www.amusementconsultants.com
Contact: Melvin Getlan, President

Description: Owns and operates amusement centers, and provides a variety of business development and management services to other independent operators. **Scope:** Owns and operates amusement centers, and provides a variety of business development and management services to other independent operators. **Founded:** 1952.

FRANCHISES AND BUSINESS OPPORTUNITIES

592 ■ Monkey Joe's Party And Play
6090 Roswell Rd.
Atlanta, GA 30328
Ph: (470)277-5721
Co. E-mail: monkjoes@gmail.com
URL: http://www.monkeyjoes.com
Contact: Daryl Dollinger, Contact
Facebook: www.facebook.com/monkeyjoes
X (Twitter): x.com/monkeyjoesparty

Description: Provider of jumps, slides, thrilling obstacle courses, development games and fun party rooms. **Founded:** 2004. **Financial Assistance:** Yes **Training:** Raving Brands University classroom and onsite training provided. From register operation to food preparation, from hiring staff to accounting procedures, you'll improve your management skills, setup back office and develop a sales and marketing plan.

Amusement/Water Park

ASSOCIATIONS AND OTHER ORGANIZATIONS

593 ■ Amusement Industry Manufacturers and Suppliers International (AIMS) [AIMS International]
PO Box 5178
 Jacksonville, FL 32247
Ph: (714)425-5747
Co. E-mail: info@aimsintl.org
URL: http://aimsintl.org
Contact: David Bromilow, President
Facebook: www.facebook.com/aimsintl
Linkedin: www.linkedin.com/company/aims-international
X (Twitter): x.com/aims_int
Instagram: www.instagram.com/aimsintl
Description: Represents manufacturers and suppliers of amusement riding devices and equipment used by amusement parks, carnivals, and traveling amusement companies. Exchanges information on safety, maintenance, state laws, transportation, and credit. Works to develop safety programs and codes at the federal and state levels; carries out public relations activities; and cooperates with the ASTM to develop voluntary standards for amusement rides and devices. **Founded:** 1994. **Publications:** Full List of AIMS Members. **Educational Activities:** AIMS Safety Seminar (Annual). **Geographic Preference:** National.

594 ■ Association Canadienne des Foires et Expositions (ACFE) [Canadian Association of Fairs and Exhibitions (CAFE)]
PO Box 21053
 Brandon, MB, Canada R7B 3W8
Co. E-mail: info@canadian-fairs.ca
URL: http://www.canadian-fairs.ca
Contact: Phil Shuchat, Vice President
E-mail: phil@superdogs.com
X (Twitter): x.com/CdnAssocofFairs
Description: Exhibition and fair operators. Seeks to advance the exhibition industry. Represents members' interests before trade organizations, government agencies, and the public. **Founded:** 1924. **Geographic Preference:** National.

595 ■ International Association of Amusement Parks and Attractions (IAAPA)
4155 West Taft Vineland Rd.
 Orlando, FL 32837
Ph: (321)319-7600
Fax: (321)319-7690
Co. E-mail: iaapa@iaapa.org
URL: http://www.iaapa.org
Contact: David Mandt, Executive Director
Facebook: www.facebook.com/IAAPAHQ
Linkedin: www.linkedin.com/company/iaapa
X (Twitter): x.com/IAAPAHQ
YouTube: www.youtube.com/user/IAAPACentral
Description: Operators of amusement parks, theme parks, tourist attractions, water parks, zoos, aquariums, museums, miniature golf courses and family entertainment centers; manufacturers and suppliers of amusement equipment and services. Conducts research programs; compiles statistics; hosts annual convention and trade show; publishes periodicals. **Founded:** 1918. **Publications:** International Directory and Buyer's Guide (Annual); Funworld (Bimonthly); Year in Review (Annual); International Association of Amusement Parks and Attractions--International Directory and Buyer's Guide: D & G (Annual); Find an Amusement Park or Attraction; International Association of Amusement Parks and Attractions International Directory and Buyers' Guide (Annual). **Educational Activities:** IAAPA Expo Europe (EAS) (Annual); IAAPA Expo Asia (Annual); Association of Amusement Parks Convention and Trade Show (Annual); IAAPA Expo (Annual). **Awards:** IAAPA Best Outdoor Advertisement Award (Annual); IAAPA Hall of Fame Awards (Annual); IAAPA Lifetime Service Award (Annual). **Geographic Preference:** Multinational.

596 ■ National Amusement Park Historical Association (NAPHA)
PO Box 871
 Lombard, IL 60148-0871
Co. E-mail: info@napha.org
URL: http://www.napha.org
Contact: Brenton Asti, Treasurer
Facebook: www.facebook.com/NationalAmusementParkHistoricalAssociation
X (Twitter): x.com/NAPHA_on_Parks
Instagram: www.instagram.com/napha_on_parks
YouTube: www.youtube.com/channel/UCdbdP2iR3G5zP0z329q7luA
Description: Persons interested in the preservation and history of past and present amusement parks. Promotes the enjoyment of amusement parks; acquires and documents information concerning amusement parks; preserves and displays memorabilia from amusement parks. Presents audiovisual shows to the public, civic groups, and libraries. **Founded:** 1978. **Publications:** NAPHA Newsflash (Monthly). **Geographic Preference:** National.

597 ■ New England Association of Amusement Parks and Attractions (NEAAPA)
PO Box 85
 Saco, ME 04072
Free: 877-999-8740
Fax: (207)283-4716
Co. E-mail: secretary@neaapa.com
URL: http://neaapa.com
Contact: Dave Oberlander, President
Facebook: www.facebook.com/NEAAPA
Linkedin: www.linkedin.com/company/neaapa
X (Twitter): x.com/neaapa1
Instagram: www.instagram.com/neaapa
YouTube: www.youtube.com/user/NEAAPA
Description: Promotes development, growth, safe operations, and success of the amusement industry in the New England region. **Founded:** 1913.

598 ■ Outdoor Amusement Business Association (OABA)
1305 Memorial Ave.
 West Springfield, MA 01089-3578
Ph: (407)848-4958
Co. E-mail: oaba@oaba.org
URL: http://oaba.org
Contact: Greg Chiecko, President
E-mail: gregc@oaba.org
Facebook: www.facebook.com/OutdoorAmusementBusinessAssn
X (Twitter): x.com/oabainfo
Instagram: www.instagram.com/outdooramusementbusinessassn
YouTube: www.youtube.com/user/OABAinfo
Description: Represents executives and employees of carnivals and fairs; ride owners; independent food and games concessionaires; manufacturers and suppliers of equipment. Promotes and lobbies on behalf of the interests of the outdoor amusement industry; provides a center for dissemination of information. **Founded:** 1965. **Publications:** Midway Marquee (Annual). **Geographic Preference:** National.

599 ■ World Waterpark Association (WWA)
8826 Santa Fe Dr., Ste. 310
 Overland Park, KS 66212
Ph: (913)599-0300
Fax: (913)599-0520
Co. E-mail: wwamemberinfo@waterparks.org
URL: http://www.waterparks.org
Contact: Damien Latham, Chairman
Facebook: www.facebook.com/WorldWaterparkAssociation
Linkedin: www.linkedin.com/company/world-waterpark-association
X (Twitter): x.com/WWA
YouTube: www.youtube.com/user/WorldWaterparkAssn
Description: Provides a forum for the discussion of information related to the water amusement park industry. **Founded:** 1981. **Publications:** World Waterpark Association--Buyers Guide (Annual); Considerations for Operating Safety; Splash & Spray (9/year); World Waterpark Magazine (WWM) (10/year). **Educational Activities:** World Waterpark Association Symposium and Tradeshow (Annual). **Geographic Preference:** National.

REFERENCE WORKS

600 ■ "5 Things You Need to Know About Water Parks, But Probably Don't" in healthychildren.org (June 6, 2019)
URL(s): www.healthychildren.org/English/safety-prevention/at-play/Pages/Water-Park-Safety.aspx
Released: June 04, 2019. **Description:** Over 85 million people visit the 1,300 water parks in the US each year. Before spending the day in the water park, five important factors are discussed which should help keep you and family safe and allow you to have an enjoyable experience. **Availability:** Online.

601 ■ The Amusement Park: 900 Years of Thrills and Spills, and the Dreamers and Schemers Who Built Them
Ed: Stephen M. Silverman. Released: 2019. Description: The story of amusement parks from the middle ages to the modern day is presented, along with the people who made these places possible to exist. Availability: Print.

602 ■ "Cedar Fair to Solicit Bids for Geauga Lake" in Crain's Cleveland Business (Vol. 28, October 8, 2007, No. 40, pp. 1)
Pub: Crain Communications Inc.
Contact: K. C. Crain, President
Ed: Stan Bullard. Description: Cedar Fair Entertainment Co. plans to seek sealed bids for the redevelopment of nearly 540 acres of their amusement park site in southwest Geauga County and northwest Portage County. Availability: Online.

603 ■ "Do Social Deal Sites Really Work? A Theme Park Chain Considers Whether the Boost In Ticket Sales Is Worth the Trouble" in Harvard Business Review (Vol. 90, May 2012, No. 5, pp. 139)
Pub: Harvard Business Review Press
Contact: Moderna V. Pfizer, Contact
Ed: Marco Bertini, Luc Wathieu, Betsy Page Sigman, Michael I. Norton. Price: $8.95. Description: A fictitious group-purchasing promotion scenario is presented, with contributors providing advice. At issue is whether deal-type promotions compromise the customer experience to the point where it offsets any marketing benefit from the deal. While one approach is to more effectively manage the traffic generated from deals, the other is to more closely target promotions to optimize outcomes. Availability: Online; PDF.

604 ■ "Experts: Orlando Great Fit for Cars Land" in Orlando Business Journal (Vol. 29, September 7, 2012, No. 12, pp. 1)
Pub: Baltimore Business Journal
Contact: Rhonda Pringle, President
E-mail: rpringle@bizjournals.com
Description: Amusement park industry experts have been talking about the potential Cars Land expansion in Walt Disney World in Orlando, Florida soon after the launch of $200 million-plus Cars attraction at Disney California Adventure Park. They believed the idea would be ingenious for the giant theme park. Insights on Walt Disney World's other popular attractions are also given. Availability: Print; Online.

605 ■ "Koneco Building Services Inc. to Add Theme Park Division" in Orlando Business Journal (Vol. 30, April 25, 2014, No. 44, pp. 3)
Pub: American City Business Journals, Inc.
Contact: Mike Olivieri, Executive Vice President
Released: Weekly. Price: $8, introductory 4-week offer(Digital & Print). Description: Koneco Building Services Inc. operations director, Ernie Falco and sales director Wolf Adler, discuss plans to add a theme park division to the Florida-based facility maintenance firm. They offer advice to other entrepreneurs and share the sacrifices they made as their business was growing. Availability: Print; Online.

606 ■ "Legoland Florida Plans $3M-$6M Expansion" in Orlando Business Journal (Vol. 29, August 24, 2012, No. 10, pp. 1)
Pub: Baltimore Business Journal
Contact: Rhonda Pringle, President
E-mail: rpringle@bizjournals.com
Description: Legoland Florida is planning to add three new pirate attractions at the amusement park in 2013. The planned attractions will be named Pirate Shores. Availability: Print; Online.

607 ■ "Legoland Florida Theme Park Construction to Start in May" in Orlando Business Journal (Vol. 26, January 29, 2010, No. 35, pp. 1)
Pub: Orlando Business Journal
Contact: Julie Swyers, Director
E-mail: jswyers@bizjournals.com
Ed: Richard Bilbao. Description: Merlin Entertainments Group purchased the closed Cypress Garden theme park in Winter Haven, Florida for $22.3 million and plans to spend a reported $100 million or more to begin transforming it into the world's largest Legoland. Winter Haven businesses are expecting a windfall from the theme park's constructions workers. Availability: Print; Online.

608 ■ "Lessons from SeaWorld's 'Blackfish' Nightmare" in Orlando Business Journal (Vol. 30, January 3, 2014, No. 28, pp. 7)
Pub: American City Business Journals, Inc.
Contact: Mike Olivieri, Executive Vice President
Released: January 03, 2014. Price: $8, introductory 4-week offer(Digital only). Description: University of Florida's crisis communications specialist and public relations (PR) professor, W. Timothy Coombs, shares his views about the PR backlash from SeaWorld's refusal to participate in the filming of the documentary 'Blackfish'. Coombs believes SeaWorld must create a public statement that defends its character and actions. Availability: Print; Online.

609 ■ "A Level of Excitement That is Second to None" in South Florida Business Journal (Vol. 35, August 8, 2014, No. 2, pp. 9)
Pub: American City Business Journals, Inc.
Contact: Mike Olivieri, Executive Vice President
Released: Weekly. Price: $8, introductory 4-week offer(Digital only). Description: Iconic Attractions Group president and CEO, John Dunlap, was born in Annapolis, Maryland and made his reputation in hospitality management by successfully running world famous zoos. Currently, Dunlap is running the Jungle Island at Miami, Florida's Watson Island. Dunlap shares his views about his business and working with animals. Availability: Print; Online.

610 ■ "Office Space" in Business Strategy Review (Vol. 25, Summer 2014, No. 2, pp. 18)
Description: Author talks about his working environment at Wild Wadi Waterpark where screams from excited customers are all part of the daily backdrop. Availability: Print; Online.

611 ■ "Six Flags Fiesta Texas Could See More Reinvestment" in San Antonio Business Journal (Vol. 28, April 25, 2014, No. 11, pp. 6)
Pub: American City Business Journals, Inc.
Contact: Mike Olivieri, Executive Vice President
Released: Weekly. Price: $4, Introductory 4-week offer(Digital & Print). Description: Six Flags Fiesta Texas benefited from Six Flags Entertainment's decision to invest $102 million in new capital expenditures. The theme park is expected to undergo more improvements as parent company focuses on international marketing opportunities. Six Flags Fiesta Texas president, Martin Bozer, shares that the amusement theme park continues to look for more way to improve its services. Availability: Print; Online.

612 ■ "Up In the Air" in The Business Journal-Serving Greater Tampa Bay (Vol. 28, July 18, 2008, No. 30, pp. 1)
Description: Views and information on Busch Gardens and on its future, are presented. The park's 3,769 employees worry for their future, after tourism industry experts have expressed concerns on possible tax cuts and other cost reductions. The future of the park, which ranks number 19 as the most visited park in the world, is expected to have a major impact on the tourism industry. Availability: Online.

STATISTICAL SOURCES

613 ■ RMA Annual Statement Studies
Pub: Risk Management Association
Contact: Nancy Foster, President
Released: Annual. Description: Contains composite balance sheets and income statements for more than 360 industries, including the accounting, auditing, and bookkeeping industries. Also contains five years of comparative historical data for discerning trends. Includes 16 commonly used ratios, computed for most of the size groupings for nearly every industry.

TRADE PERIODICALS

614 ■ Splash Magazine
Pub: Splash Magazines
Facebook: www.facebook.com/SplashMags
Linkedin: www.linkedin.com/in/splashmags
X (Twitter): x.com/SplashMagWW
Instagram: www.instagram.com/splashmags
YouTube: www.youtube.com/channel/UCVohp7KDSWvcqxgE42AF4rA
Pinterest: www.pinterest.com/splashmags
Ed: Randy Falsetta. Description: Online trade magazine covering the water leisure industry. Targets owners, managers, suppliers, and developers of private and community owned water leisure facilities, in addition to hotels and resorts with these facilities. Availability: Online.

TRADE SHOWS AND CONVENTIONS

615 ■ IAAPA Expo
International Association of Amusement Parks and Attractions (IAAPA)
4155 West Taft Vineland Rd.
Orlando, FL 32837
Ph: (321)319-7600
Fax: (321)319-7690
Co. E-mail: iaapa@iaapa.org
URL: http://www.iaapa.org
Contact: David Mandt, Executive Director
URL(s): https://www.iaapa.org/expos/iaapa-expo
Frequency: Annual. Description: Amusement, leisure, recreation, and family entertainment-related products and services. Audience: Trade industry professionals. Principal Exhibits: Amusement, leisure, recreation, and family entertainment-related products and services. Telecommunication Services: exhibitsales@iaapa.org.

616 ■ IAFE Trade Show
International Association of Fairs and Expositions (IAFE)
3043 E Cairo St.
Springfield, MO 65802
Ph: (417)862-5771
Free: 800-516-0313
Co. E-mail: iafe@fairsandexpos.com
URL: http://www.fairsandexpos.com
Contact: Marla Calico, President
URL(s): www.iafeconvention.com
Frequency: Annual. Description: Talent agencies, concessionaires, novelties, amusement devices, insurance, ribbons, plaques, attractions, and equipment. Products and services for the fair industry. Audience: IAFE members, special event producers, entertainment buyers, carnival executives, concessionaires, facility managers, Fair industry professionals. Principal Exhibits: Talent agencies, concessionaires, novelties, amusement devices, insurance, ribbons, plaques, attractions, and equipment. Products and services for the fair industry. Telecommunication Services: registration@fairsandexpos.com.

CONSULTANTS

617 ■ Amusement Consultants Ltd.
56 Harrison St.
New Rochelle, NY 10801
Ph: (914)576-7800
Fax: (914)576-3620
Co. E-mail: info@amusementconsultants.com
URL: http://www.amusementconsultants.com
Contact: Melvin Getlan, President
Description: Owns and operates amusement centers, and provides a variety of business development and management services to other independent operators. Scope: Owns and operates amusement centers, and provides a variety of business development and management services to other independent operators. Founded: 1952.

Amusement/Water Park

618 ■ Dennis G. Glore Inc. (DGG)
120 S Virginia Ave.
Eureka, MO 63025
Ph: (636)938-7887
URL: http://www.dgg-inc.com
Contact: Michael D. Glore, President
E-mail: mike.glore@dgg-inc.com
Facebook: www.facebook.com/DennisGGloreInc
Description: Firm provides consulting services in planning and design of food service facilities. **Founded:** 1971.

619 ■ KZF Design Inc. - Library
700 Broadway St.
Cincinnati, OH 45202
Ph: (513)621-6211
Co. E-mail: info@kzf.com
URL: http://kzf.com
Contact: Doug Marsh, President
E-mail: doug.marsh@kzf.com
Facebook: www.facebook.com/kzfdesign
Linkedin: www.linkedin.com/company/kzf-design
X (Twitter): x.com/KZFDesign
Instagram: www.instagram.com/kzfdesign
Description: Interdisciplinary design firm whose services include architecture, engineering, interior design, and urban planning serves both private and public sectors, including education, transportation and municipal, commercial and industrial, government, and workplace design markets. **Scope:** Engineering; architecture; interior design. **Founded:** 1956. **Holdings:** Figures not available. **Publications:** "The art of grieving," Oct, 2008; "Cincinnati Enquirer," 2008; "KZF Design moving Downtown," Feb, 2008; "Cincinnati Business Courier," Feb, 2008; "Tampa Bay Business Journal," Feb, 2008; "Work life strategy". **Special Services:** LEED®.

620 ■ Lougheed Resource Group Inc. (LRG)
17608 Deer Isle Cir.
Winter Garden, FL 34787
Ph: (407)654-1212
Co. E-mail: info@lrgconstruction.com
URL: http://lrgconstruction.com
Contact: Karen Lougheed, Owner
E-mail: karen@lrgconstruction.com
Description: Provider of building diagnostics, forensic and construction document analysis, litigation support, customized on-site risk reduction workshops, and much more for construction fields and trades related to commercial, residential, institutional, industrial, and recreational projects. **Scope:** Provider of building diagnostics, forensic and construction document analysis, litigation support, customized on-site risk reduction workshops, and much more for construction fields and trades related to commercial, residential, institutional, industrial, and recreational projects. **Founded:** 1987.

621 ■ Nyikos-Garcia Foodservice Design, Inc.
7146 Starmount Way
New Market, MD 21774
Ph: (240)683-9530
URL: http://nyikosgarcia.com
Contact: Patty Nyikos, Chief Executive Officer
E-mail: pnyikos@nyikosgarcia.com
Description: Independent professional design/consulting organization specializing in commercial foodservice and laundry facilities for hospitals, hotels, restaurants, schools, universities, employee cafeterias, correctional facilities, convention centers, nursing homes, ski resorts, amusement parks and sports stadiums. Firm also offers management consulting for marketing and feasibility purposes. **Scope:** Independent professional design/consulting organization specializing in commercial foodservice and laundry facilities for hospitals, hotels, restaurants, schools, universities, employee cafeterias, correctional facilities, convention centers, nursing homes, ski resorts, amusement parks and sports stadiums. Firm also offers management consulting for marketing and feasibility purposes. **Founded:** 1988. **Publications:** "Maryland State Department of Education School Food and Nutrition Design Manual," Jan, 1995.

622 ■ Turner Consulting Group Inc. (TCG)
7348 Georgia Ave. NW
Washington, DC 20012
Ph: (202)986-5533
Co. E-mail: talktous@tcg.com
URL: http://www.tcg.com
Contact: Daniel A. Turner, President
Facebook: www.facebook.com/TCGPositivelyDistinct
Linkedin: www.linkedin.com/company/tcginc
X (Twitter): x.com/TCGnews
Description: Provider of online information management systems, specializes in data-driven web sites and customized software solutions. **Scope:** Provider of IT and management consulting services. **Founded:** 1994.

Animal Breeder

ASSOCIATIONS AND OTHER ORGANIZATIONS

623 ■ Alpaca Breeders of the Rockies (ABR)
PO Box 1965
  Estes Park, CO 80517
Ph: (970)586-5589
Fax: (970)591-0007
Co. E-mail: abr@alpacabreeders.org
URL: http://www.alpacabreeders.org
Contact: Hillary Devin, President
E-mail: president@alpacabreeders.org
Description: Breeders of Alpacas (an Alpaca is a close relative of the Llama); processors and distributors of Alpaca products. Promotes public awareness of Alpacas; seeks to advance the Alpaca industries. Facilitates communication and cooperation among members; conducts marketing campaigns. Participates in agricultural fairs. **Founded:** 1994. **Geographic Preference:** National.

624 ■ American Border Leicester Association (ABLA)
c/o Jessica Feindt, Vice President, 8388 Green Rd.
  Fenton, MI 48430
Co. E-mail: americanborderleicesterassn@gmail.com
URL: http://borderleicesters.org
Contact: Jennifer Baird, President
E-mail: tjbaird814@earthlink.net
Facebook: www.facebook.com/ABLAsheep
Description: Owners and admirers of Border Leicester sheep. Promotes Border Leicesters as a source of wool and meat. Sets breed standards and confers certification; maintains breed registry. Sponsors competitions; conducts educational programs. **Founded:** 1973. **Publications:** *ABLA newsletter* (Quarterly). **Educational Activities:** Maryland Sheep & Wool Festival (Annual). **Geographic Preference:** National.

625 ■ American Brahmousin Council (ABC)
PO Box 88
  Whitesboro, TX 76273
Ph: (903)815-0321
Co. E-mail: rsopbc@gmail.com
URL: http://www.americanbrahmousincouncil.org
Contact: Dewon Rankin, President
Description: Breeders of Brahmousin cattle. **Geographic Preference:** National.

626 ■ American Cat Fanciers Association (ACFA)
PO Box 1949
  Nixa, MO 65714-1949
Ph: (417)725-1530
Fax: (417)725-1533
Co. E-mail: acfa@aol.com
URL: http://www.acfacat.com
Contact: Murlene Priest, President
E-mail: mpriest.acfa@gmail.com
Facebook: www.facebook.com/acfacat
YouTube: www.youtube.com/channel/UCdsli659X0yrXVwnLnRAa8Q
Pinterest: www.pinterest.com/acfacat
Description: Breeders and exhibitors of purebred cats; individuals interested in educating the public regarding the health and welfare of domesticated cats. Maintains studbook registry and licenses cat shows and cat judges. Registers pedigreed cats. **Founded:** 1955. **Publications:** *ACFA Bulletin* (7/year); *AFCA Parade of Royalty* (Annual); *Clerking Manual*; *Breeder's Directory* (Annual). **Awards:** ACFA Inter-American Award (Annual); ACFA Legacy of Achievement (Annual); ACFA Legacy of Excellence (Annual); ACFA Regional Inter-American Award (Annual). **Geographic Preference:** Multinational.

627 ■ American Dog Breeders Association (ADBA)
PO Box 1771
  Salt Lake City, UT 84110
Ph: (801)936-7513
Co. E-mail: customerservice@adba.cc
URL: http://adbadog.com
Contact: Hank Greenwood, President
Facebook: www.facebook.com/AmericanDogBreeders
X (Twitter): x.com/adba1909
Instagram: www.instagram.com/american_dog_breeders
Description: Processes genealogy information on the American Pit Bull Terrier. **Founded:** 1909. **Publications:** *American Pit Bull Terrier Gazette* (Quarterly). **Awards:** ADBA Leaders of the Future Scholarship (Annual). **Geographic Preference:** National.

628 ■ American Kennel Club (AKC)
101 Pk. Ave.
  New York, NY 10178
Ph: (212)696-8200
Co. E-mail: info@akc.org
URL: http://www.akc.org
Contact: Dennis B. Sprung, President
E-mail: dennis.sprung@akc.org
Facebook: www.facebook.com/AmericanKennelClub
X (Twitter): x.com/akcdoglovers
YouTube: www.youtube.com/user/AmericanKennelClub
Pinterest: www.pinterest.com/americankennelclub
Description: All-breed, specialty breed, obedience, and field trial dog clubs. Maintains stud book registry and pedigree records; approves standards for judging breeds eligible for registration; adopts and enforces rules governing shows, obedience trials, hunting tests, and field trials. **Scope:** Dog. **Services:** Open to the public; interlibrary loan. **Founded:** 1884. **Holdings:** Book; periodical collection; brochures; pamphlets; premium lists; show catalogs; club publications; photographs; audio-visual material. **Publications:** *Puppies*; *American Kennel Club Gazette: The Official Journal for the Sport of Purebred Dogs* (Monthly); *AKC Family Dog* (Bimonthly); *AKC Gazette--List of Clubs Issue* (Annual); *American Kennel Club Awards* (Monthly); *AKC Afield* (Monthly); *Pure-Bred Dogs - American Kennel Gazette* (Monthly). **Awards:** Awards for Canine Excellence (ACE) (Annual); AKC Breeder of the Year Award (Annual); AKC Lifetime Achievement Awards (Annual). **Geographic Preference:** National.

629 ■ Association des eleveurs Ayrshire du Canada [Ayrshire Breeders' Association of Canada (ABAC)]
4855, boul. Laurier O
  Saint-Hyacinthe, QC, Canada J2S 3V4
Ph: (450)778-3535
Fax: (450)778-3531
Co. E-mail: info@ayrshire-canada.com
URL: http://ayrshire-canada.com/en
Contact: Francois Beaudry, President
E-mail: fermefrancoisbeaudry@gmail.com
Facebook: www.facebook.com/ayrshire.canada
Instagram: www.instagram.com/ayrshirecanadaofficial
YouTube: www.youtube.com/user/Ayrshirecan
Description: Promotes improvement of the Ayrshire breed; seeks to advance the dairy industry. **Founded:** 1901. **Publications:** *Canadian Ayrshire Review* (Bimonthly). **Awards:** Ayrshire Canada's Award of Meri t (Annual); Ayrshire Master Breeder (Annual). **Geographic Preference:** National.

630 ■ Association Féline Canadienne (AFC) [Canadian Cat Association (CCA)]
Unit 118, 1 Centre St.
  Toronto, ON, Canada M1J 3B4
Ph: (905)232-3481
Co. E-mail: office@cca-afc.com
URL: http://www.cca-afc.com
Contact: Shirley Mccollow, President
Facebook: www.facebook.com/ccaafc.ca
X (Twitter): x.com/ccawebsite
Instagram: www.instagram.com/ccasocialmedia
Description: Cat breeders and fanciers. Promotes responsible pet care; seeks to improve the bloodlines of purebred cats. Serves as a clearinghouse on purebred cats; maintains breed registries; sponsors competitions. **Founded:** 1960. **Geographic Preference:** National.

631 ■ Canadian Kennel Club (CKC) [Club Canin Canadien]
5397 Eglinton Ave., W. Ste. 101
  Etobicoke, ON, Canada M9C 5K6
Ph: (416)675-5511
Free: 855-364-7252
Co. E-mail: information@ckc.ca
URL: http://www.ckc.ca
Contact: Ramune Kazlauskaite, President
Facebook: www.facebook.com/CKC4thedogs
X (Twitter): x.com/CKC4thedogs
Instagram: www.instagram.com/ckc4thedogs
YouTube: www.youtube.com/channel/UCsd-E04doM6JL1y1aNwQgKA
Description: Dog owners, breeders, and enthusiasts. Promotes responsible pet ownership; seeks to improve the bloodlines of pedigreed dogs. Sponsors educational programs for dogs and dog owners;

maintains breed registries; sets breed standards; holds competitions. **Founded:** 1888. **Publications:** *Dogs in Canada* (Monthly). **Geographic Preference:** National.

632 ■ Canadian Thoroughbred Horse Society (CTHS) - Library
PO Box 172
Rexdale, ON, Canada M9W 5L1
Ph: (416)675-3602
Fax: (416)675-9405
Co. E-mail: cthsont@idirect.com
URL: http://cthsont.com
Contact: Peter Berringer, President
Facebook: www.facebook.com/CTHSOntarioDivision
X (Twitter): x.com/CTHSOntario
Instagram: www.instagram.com/cthsontario
Description: Providers of services to horse racing and the thoroughbred horse industry. Promotes a viable future for the thoroughbred industry in Canada. **Scope:** Horses. **Founded:** 1906. **Holdings:** Figures not available. **Publications:** *Breeders' News* (Quarterly). **Awards:** CTHS Breeders' Awards (Annual). **Geographic Preference:** National.

633 ■ Cat Fanciers' Association (CFA) - Library
260 E Main St.
Alliance, OH 44601
Ph: (330)680-4070
Fax: (330)680-4633
Co. E-mail: marketing@cfa.org
URL: http://cfa.org
Contact: Mark Hannon, President
Facebook: www.facebook.com/CFAcats
X (Twitter): x.com/cfaorg
Instagram: www.instagram.com/cfa.cats
YouTube: www.youtube.com/channel/UCU2UK7DB_1nshLXgtlj7yDQ
Pinterest: www.pinterest.com/CFAcats
Description: Federation of all-breed and specialty cat clubs. Promotes the welfare of cats, register pedigrees, and license shows held under association rules. **Scope:** Cat books; stud books; past issues of the cfa yearbook; the cat fanciers' almanac. **Founded:** 1906. **Subscriptions:** 100 periodicals (includes journals) magazines 700 books.; 100 magazines Books; artwork. **Publications:** *Show Rules* (Annual); *Cat Fanciers' Association--Yearbook* (Annual); *Show Standards Booklet*; *Cat Fanciers' Almanac* (Bimonthly). **Educational Activities:** CFA Annual Meeting (Annual). **Awards:** CFA National Awards (Annual). **Geographic Preference:** National.

634 ■ Cat Fanciers' Federation (CFF)
18 Kimball Rd.
Woburn, MA 01801
Ph: (937)787-9009
Co. E-mail: cffinc@live.com
URL: http://www.cffinc.org
Contact: Ken Staples, President
E-mail: kennystaples1255@gmail.com
Description: Federation of local clubs of persons who own, breed, and exhibit cats and who are interested in the general welfare of cats. **Founded:** 1919. **Publications:** *CFF Newsletter*. **Awards:** Cat Fanciers' Federation Parade of Perfection Awards (Annual). **Geographic Preference:** National.

635 ■ Field Spaniel Society of America (FSSA)
Coleman, TX 76834
URL: http://www.fieldspanielsocietyofamerica.org
Description: Promotes responsible breeding and pet ownership; seeks to increase public awareness and appreciation of field spaniels. Maintains breed registry; conducts educational and public relations activities. **Founded:** 1978. **Publications:** *Field Spaniel Fancier* (Quarterly). **Geographic Preference:** National.

636 ■ International Sporthorse Registry, Inc. (ISR)
PO Box 504
Sycamore, IL 60178
Ph: (815)899-7803
Co. E-mail: office@isroldenburg.org
URL: http://www.isroldenburg.org
Description: Owners and breeders of sport horses. Seeks to improve sport horse bloodlines. Formulates and enforces standards of breed conformance; maintains breed registry. **Founded:** 1983. **Awards:** ISR Champion Foal Award (Annual); ISR Premium Awards for Mares; USDF All Breed Award (Annual). **Geographic Preference:** National.

637 ■ International Spotted Horse Registry Association (ISHR)
2120 Scotch Hollow Rd.
Noel, MO 64854
Ph: (417)475-6273
Free: 866-201-3098
Co. E-mail: ishrppa@aol.com
URL: http://internationalspottedhorseregistryassociation.yolasite.com
Contact: Rebecca Rogers, President
E-mail: ishrppa@aol.com
Description: International Spotted Horse Registry Association. **Founded:** 1990. **Publications:** *Rainbow Connection*. **Educational Activities:** Annual Open Online Horse Show (Annual). **Awards:** ROM Year End High Point Trophies (Annual); ISHR Year End Awards (Annual). **Geographic Preference:** Multinational.

638 ■ Michigan Emu Growers Association (MEGA)
c/o Dennis E Homant, President
2147 Thorntree Ln.
Ortonville, MI 48462
Ph: (248)324-2687
Co. E-mail: dhomant@mi.rr.com
URL: http://michemu.tripod.com
Contact: Dennis E. Homant, President
E-mail: dhomant@mi.rr.com
Description: Association of emu growers in Michigan. **Geographic Preference:** State.

639 ■ National Chincoteague Pony Association (NCPA)
2595 Jensen Rd.
Bellingham, WA 98226
Ph: (360)671-8338
Co. E-mail: gfreder426@aol.com
URL: http://www.pony-chincoteague.com
Contact: Gale Park Frederick, Director
Description: Admirers of Chincoteague ponies, a rare breed of horse which developed on Chincoteague Island off the coast of Virginia. Promotes responsible horse ownership; seeks to improve the Chincoteague pony. Facilitates communication and cooperation among members; maintains breed registry; establishes standards required for breed conformation; arranges Chincoteague pony sales. **Founded:** 1980. **Geographic Preference:** National.

640 ■ Navajo-Churro Sheep Association (NCSA)
PO Box 190840
Boise, ID 83719-0840
Co. E-mail: spindanceacres@gmail.com
URL: http://www.navajo-churrosheep.com
Contact: Kim Kerley, Contact
E-mail: kim.kerley@earthlink.net
Facebook: www.facebook.com/churrosheep
Description: Owners and breeders of Navajo-Churro sheep; fiber artists and collectors of textiles. Promotes preservation the Navajo-Churro breed of sheep. Facilitates breeding of Navajo-Churro sheep and maintains breed registry. **Founded:** 1986. **Publications:** *Catch Pen* (Quarterly). **Geographic Preference:** National.

641 ■ Oldenburg Registry North America (OLD NA)
PO Box 504
Sycamore, IL 60178
Ph: (815)899-7803
Co. E-mail: office@isroldenburg.org
URL: http://www.isroldenburg.org
Facebook: www.facebook.com/Friends-of-ISROldenburg-NA-168725279852466
Description: Owners and breeders of modern sport horses used as dressage, hunter/jumpers, and performance horses. Seeks to improve sport horse bloodlines. Maintains breed registry; formulates and enforces standards of breed conformance. **Founded:** 1983. **Awards:** Oldenburg High Score Foals Awards; Oldenburg High Score Mares Awards; USDF All Breed Award (Annual). **Geographic Preference:** National.

642 ■ Professional Handlers' Association (PHA)
17017 Norbrook Dr.
Olney, MD 20832
Ph: (301)774-2400
URL: http://www.phadoghandlers.com
Contact: Dinah Baggenstos, President
Description: Seeks to promote the interests of individuals who show purebred dogs at dog shows as a profession. Enhances the stature of professional dog handling. Provides information on purebred dogs to interested persons. Sponsors seminars and lectures. **Founded:** 1926. **Geographic Preference:** National.

643 ■ The Traditional Cat Association, Inc. (TCA)
PO Box 178
Heisson, WA 98622
URL: http://tcainc.org
Contact: Diana Fineran, Contact
E-mail: diana@traditionalcats.com
Description: Breeders and fanciers of traditional cats. Promotes, preserves, protects, and perpetuates the traditional cat. Operates kitten referral services. Conducts educational, charitable, and research programs. Sponsors competitions and shows; compiles statistics. Maintains registry, placement services, hall of fame, and museum. **Founded:** 1987. **Geographic Preference:** National.

644 ■ United Kennel Club (UKC)
100 E Kilgore Rd.
Portage, MI 49002-5584
Ph: (269)343-9020
Fax: (269)343-7037
URL: http://www.ukcdogs.com
Contact: Taylor Armstrong, Manager, Customer Service
E-mail: tarmstrong@ukcdogs.com
Facebook: www.facebook.com/ukcdogs
Linkedin: www.linkedin.com/company/united-kennel-club
X (Twitter): x.com/UKC1898
Instagram: www.instagram.com/ukcdogs
YouTube: www.youtube.com/channel/UCe1e5RcgabaqPyNPTY9Mjsw
Description: Registry for purebred dogs. Maintains records and pedigrees and establishes rules for events. **Founded:** 1898. **Publications:** *Hunting Retriever* (Bimonthly); *Bloodlines: An International Journal Devoted to Pure Bred Dogs* (Monthly); *Coonhound Bloodlines* (Monthly). **Awards:** UKC Hunting Retriever Champion (Semiannual). **Geographic Preference:** National.

REFERENCE WORKS

645 ■ *Cat Fanciers' Association--Yearbook*
Pub: Cat Fanciers' Association
Contact: Mark Hannon, President
URL(s): catalog.cfa.org/yearbook.shtml
Released: Annual; Latest edition 2019. **Price:** $45, U.S.; $45, Canada and Mexico; $45, Individuals; $45, for other locations; $15, for online; $55, for online. **Description:** Publication includes list of cat clubs, cat breeders. **Entries include:** Name, address. **Availability:** Print; Online.

646 ■ *"Dog Behaviors Like Aggression and Fearfulness are Linked to Breed Genetics" in Science News (October 1, 2019)*
URL(s): www.sciencenews.org/article/dog-breed-behavior-genetics

Ed: Jonathan Lambert. **Released:** October 01, 2019. **Description:** Scientists have discovered that many dog breeds share certain behavioral traits that are shared by genetically similar breeds. A discussion of the study is presented, which goes into some detail on which traits the geneticists focused on, and how the study was conducted with the 101 different dog breeds. **Availability:** Online.

647 ■ *Genetic Data Analysis for Plant and Animal Breeding*
Ed: Fikret Isik, James Holland, Christian Maltecca. **Released:** 2017. **Description:** Covers classic phenotypic data analysis for breeding along with discussing the tools available for analyzing DNA. **Availability:** E-book.

648 ■ *"How to Become a Licensed Dog Breeder?" in BreedingBusiness.com (October 23, 2018)*
Released: October 23, 2018. **Description:** Discusses the ins and outs of dog breeding licenses including who issues dog breeding licenses, who needs a license, information on the licensing process for commercial dog breeding, preparing for licensing inspection and how to renew licenses. **Availability:** Online.

649 ■ *"How Much Does It Cost to Be a Dog Breeder" in BreedingBusiness.com (October 7, 2017)*
Released: October 07, 2017. **Description:** Breeding dogs can be a profitable enterprise. The expenses of whelping a litter of puppies for sale can be substantial, though. This article summarizes expenses involved in dog breeding and discusses annual expenses not related to breeding, breeding-related expenses, and litter-related expenses. **Availability:** Online.

650 ■ *How Much Money Do Dog Breeders Make Monthly/Yearly*
Description: Discusses estimated startup costs associated with a dog breeding business as well as estimated profit potential and different types of dogs to breed. **Availability:** Online.

651 ■ *"How to Start a Business Breeding Dogs" in Chron (July 19, 2017)*
Ed: Jordan Meyers. **Released:** July 19, 2017. **Description:** Discusses the ins and outs of starting a dog breeding business, including start up costs, licensing, and veterinary care. **Availability:** Online.

652 ■ *How to Start a Dog Breeding Business at Home in 23 Steps*
Description: A detailed guide to starting a profitable dog breeding business with no money or experience. **Availability:** Online.

653 ■ *How to Start a Dog Breeding Business: The Complete Guide*
Ed: Allna Ral. **Released:** September 30, 2020. **Description:** Provides steps new breeders must take to start your own dog breeding business. **Availability:** Online.

654 ■ *"Is Dog Breeding Profitable?" in BreedingBusiness.com (October 21, 2016)*
Released: October 21, 2016. **Description:** Discusses factors involved in the profitability of the dog breeding business. **Availability:** Online.

655 ■ *Pros and Cons of Dog Breeding Business: Guide for Beginners*
Description: Running a successful dog breeding business requires professionalism, responsibility and commitment. This article details the pros and cons to be aware of before starting your own dog breeding business. **Availability:** Online.

656 ■ *QuickBooks for the New Bean Counter: Business Owner's Guide 2006*
Description: Profile of QuickBooks software, offering insight into using the software's accounting and bookkeeping functions.

657 ■ *"Shear Profit" in Crain's Cleveland Business (Vol. 28, October 29, 2007, No. 43, pp. 3)*
Pub: Crain Communications Inc.
Contact: K. C. Crain, President
Ed: David Bennett. **Description:** Alpaca farms are becoming a very profitable business for a number of Northeast Ohio entrepreneurs due to the high return on initial investments, tax incentives and the rise in demand for the animals. Ohio leads the country in the number of alpaca farms with roughly one-third located in Northeast Ohio. **Availability:** Online.

658 ■ *"Tax Tips for Dog Breeders" in AmericanKennelClub.com (March 21, 2016)*
Ed: Glenye Cain Oakford. **Released:** May 21, 2016. **Description:** Discusses all things related to taxes for your dog breeding business. **Availability:** Online.

659 ■ *Why You Should Start a Dog Breeding Business*
Released: September 17, 2019. **Description:** Discusses the dog breeding business industry, how to start your own breeding business, marketing, writing a business plan, startup costs, permits, pricing, and creating an online presence. **Availability:** Online.

660 ■ *Workforce Needs in Veterinary Medicine*
Released: 2013. **Description:** Examines the changing societal needs and how it relates to the U.S. veterinary medical profession. **Availability:** Print.

TRADE PERIODICALS

661 ■ *ACFA Bulletin*
Pub: American Cat Fanciers Association
Contact: Murlene Priest, President
E-mail: mpriest.acfa@gmail.com
URL(s): acfacat.com/about.htm
Released: 7/year; bi-monthly plus the October Election Issue containing the candidates, issues and ballot for voting. **Description:** Contains Association news, show schedules, news about the officers and judges, and articles of interest to cat fanciers. **Availability:** Print.

662 ■ *American Salers*
Pub: American Salers Association
Contact: Gregg Jasperson, President
URL(s): www.salersusa.org/marketing/magazine
Released: 3/year; Winter, Spring, Fall. **Description:** Trade magazine for the livestock industry. Represents Salers cattle breed. Official publication of the American Salers Association. **Availability:** Print; Online.

663 ■ *Charolais Journal*
Pub: American-International Charolais Association
URL(s): charolaisusa.com/publications.php
Ed: Molly Schoen. **Released:** Monthly; except June and July which are combined issues. **Price:** $75, U.S. for 1 year; $20, Members; $7, for Single Copies; $100, U.S. for first class; $125, for foreign; $125, Canada. **Description:** International magazine on Charolais cattle, including special interest articles, show/sale reports, and association news. **Availability:** Print; PDF.

664 ■ *Feed-Lot*
Pub: Feed-Lot Magazine
Contact: Annita Lorimor, President
E-mail: annita@feedlotmagazine.com
Facebook: www.facebook.com/FeedlotMagazine
X (Twitter): x.com/feedlotmagazine
Instagram: www.instagram.com/feedlot_magazine
Ed: Jill Dunkel. **Released:** 8/year **Description:** Trade magazine covering feedlot and cattle feeder information. **Availability:** Print; Download; Online.

665 ■ *Sheltie Pacesetter*
Pub: Sheltie Pacesetter
Contact: Nancy Lee Cathcart, Contact
Ed: Nancy Lee Cathcart. **Released:** Quarterly **Price:** $17, for 5 magazines. http://www.sheltie.com/Sheltie_Pacesetter/p%26h_rates.html. **Description:** Trade magazine covering Shetland Sheepdogs (Shelties). **Availability:** Print.

LIBRARIES

666 ■ **American Kennel Club Library (AKC Library)**
101 Pk. Ave.
New York, NY 10178
Ph: (919)233-9767
Co. E-mail: info@akc.org
URL: http://www.akc.org/about/archive
Instagram: www.instagram.com/akclibrary
Description: Contains a repository of unique data devoted to dogs that consists of approximately 15,000 volumes on purebred dog. **Scope:** Dogs - breeds, training, health, literature, art. **Services:** Copying; library open to the public by appointment. **Founded:** 1934. **Holdings:** 18,000 volumes; VF drawers of clippings, videocassettes, fine art collection; 5 dissertations. **Subscriptions:** 300 journals and other serials.

667 ■ **Cleveland Public Library - Science and Technology Department**
Louis Stokes Wing, 3rd Fl.
325 Superior Ave.
Cleveland, OH 44114
Ph: (216)623-2932
Co. E-mail: scitech@cpl.org
URL: http://cpl.org/aboutthelibrary/subjectscollections/science-and-technology
Contact: Sarah Dobransky, Manager
Scope: Physical and life sciences to applied technology; needlecraft; handicrafts; cooking; engineering; car and truck repair; chemistry; gardening; geology; health; medicine; schematics. **Services:** Interlibrary loan; copying; department open to the public. **Founded:** 1869. **Holdings:** 3,000 volumes; books; map; Photograph.

668 ■ **Glendale Public Library - Special Collections Room**
613 E Broadway
Glendale, CA 91206
URL: http://www.glendaleca.gov/our-city/visitors/historic-glendale/nell-shipman-doctor-house/doctors-office/under-the-crescent
Description: Contains reference materials, journals, books, online materials, and video and audio materials. **Scope:** Glendale and area history; California history; cats and cat genealogy. **Services:** Copying; room open to the public for reference use only (call for open hours or appointments). **Founded:** 1906. **Holdings:** 400 bound periodical volumes; city departmental reports; archives; microfilm, clippings file. **Subscriptions:** 11 journals and other serials.

669 ■ **Oregon Thoroughbred Owners & Breeders Association (OTOBA)**
1001 N Schmeer Rd.
Portland, OR 97217
Ph: (503)285-0658
Co. E-mail: office@oregontoba.com
URL: http://www.oregontoba.com
Contact: Sharon Balcom, President
Description: Serves the needs of thoroughbred breeders in Oregon. Administers the Oregon Stakes Series and owner/breeder incentive programs, and mixed thoroughbred sales. **Scope:** Thoroughbreds - life, breeding, racing. **Services:** Copying; library open to the public. **Founded:** 1944. **Holdings:** 200 books; 3 bound periodical volumes; 50 reports; microfiche; CD-ROMs. **Publications:** *Oregon Horse Magazine* (Semiannual). **Educational Activities:** Oregon Thoroughbred Owners and Breeders Association Banquet (Annual). **Awards:** OTOBA Breeder Awards. **Geographic Preference:** State.

670 ■ **Voice for Animals, Inc. (VOICE) - Library**
PO Box 120095
San Antonio, TX 78212

Ph: (210)737-3138
Co. E-mail: voice@voiceforanimals.org
URL: http://www.voiceforanimals.org
Contact: Rachel Z. Wolf, Contact

Description: Individuals with an interest in animal rights. Seeks to raise public awareness of animal rights issues. Works to abolish "the systematic abuse of nonhuman animals." Conducts educational programs. **Scope:** Animal rights. **Founded:** 1987. **Holdings:** Figures not available. **Geographic Preference:** National.

RESEARCH CENTERS

671 ■ University of California, Davis - School of Veterinary Medicine - Veterinary Genetics Laboratory (VGL)
Old Davis Rd.
  Davis, CA 95616
Ph: (530)752-2211
Fax: (530)752-3556
Co. E-mail: vglcustserv@ucdavis.edu
URL: http://vgl.ucdavis.edu
Contact: Dr. Rebecca Bellone, Director

Facebook: www.facebook.com/ucdavis.vgl
Instagram: www.instagram.com/ucdavis_vgl

Description: Integral unit of University of California, Davis. **Scope:** Genetics, genomic and forensic research of domestic and wildlife animal species, including horses, cattle, sheep, goats, camelids, dogs, cats, wild felids and canids, bears, birds and primates. Activities include DNA genotyping and mitochondria sequencing for applications in animal identification, parentage verification, forensic analyses, population structure and genetic diversity. **Founded:** 1950.

Animal Clinic

START-UP INFORMATION

672 ■ *"Elanco Challenges Bayer's Advantage, K9 Advantix Ad Claims"* in *Pet Product News* (Vol. 64, November 2010, No. 11, pp. 11)
Description: Elanco Animal Health has disputed Bayer Animal Health's print and Web advertising claims involving its flea, tick, and mosquito control products Advantage and K9 Advantix. The National Advertising Division of the Council of Better Business Bureaus recommended the discontinuation of ads, while Bayer Animal Health reiterated its commitment to self-regulation. **Availability:** Online.

ASSOCIATIONS AND OTHER ORGANIZATIONS

673 ■ **American Animal Hospital Association (AAHA)**
14142 Denver W Pkwy., Ste. 245
Lakewood, CO 80401
Free: 800-252-2242
Co. E-mail: dpo@aaha.org
URL: http://www.aaha.org
Contact: Mark Thompson, President
Linkedin: www.linkedin.com/company/aahaofficia
YouTube: www.youtube.com/aahavets
Description: Represents veterinary care providers who treat companion animals. Accredits veterinary hospitals throughout the U.S. and Canada. Conducts stringent accreditation process that covers patient care, client service and medical protocols. **Founded:** 1933. **Publications:** *NEWStat* (Weekly); *Trends® Magazine* (Monthly); *Journal of the American Animal Hospital Association (JAAHA)* (Bimonthly). **Geographic Preference:** National.

674 ■ **American Association of Feline Practitioners (AAFP)**
750 Rte. 202, Ste. 200
Bridgewater, NJ 08807
Free: 800-874-0498
Fax: (908)292-1188
Co. E-mail: info@catvets.com
URL: http://www.catvets.com
Contact: Heather O'Steen, Chief Executive Officer
Facebook: www.facebook.com/CatVets
X (Twitter): x.com/catvets
YouTube: www.youtube.com/channel/UCyiphdrt9Eal7NCR9k3ub_g
Description: Works to promote the interests and improve the public stature of feline practice and to increase the knowledge of veterinarians in the field. Cooperates with other veterinary and cat fancier organizations. **Founded:** 1971. **Publications:** *Journal of Feline Medicine and Surgery (JFMS)* (Monthly). **Educational Activities:** AAFP Conference (Annual). **Geographic Preference:** National.

675 ■ **American Association of Swine Veterinarians (AASV) - Swine Information Library**
830 26th St.
Perry, IA 50220
Ph: (515)465-5255
Fax: (515)465-3832
Co. E-mail: aasv@aasv.org
URL: http://www.aasv.org
Contact: Mary Battrell, President
Description: Represents veterinarians concerned with swine health and nutrition. Improves public stature and increases the knowledge of veterinarians in the field of swine practice. **Scope:** Swine veterinary. **Founded:** 1969. **Holdings:** 17439 papers; 821 articles; journal. **Publications:** *Journal of Swine Health & Production* (6/year); *American Association of Swine Veterinarians--Membership Directory*; *Proceedings of the AASV Annual Meeting* (Annual); *Swine Disease Manual*. **Educational Activities:** AASV Annual Meeting (Annual). **Awards:** Howard Dunne Memorial Award (Annual); AASV Meritorious Service Award (Annual); Swine Practitioner of the Year (Annual). **Geographic Preference:** Multinational.

676 ■ **American Association of Wildlife Veterinarians (AAWV)**
URL: http://www.aawv.net
Contact: John Bryan, II, President
E-mail: president@aawv.net
Description: Veterinarians in state and federal wildlife resource agencies, universities, private practice, public health service agencies, agricultural agencies, and diagnostic laboratories; veterinary students; and interested individuals. Deals with problems confronting veterinarians who work with free-ranging wildlife. Encourages colleges of veterinary medicine to increase emphasis on management of and preventive medicine for free-ranging species; educates governmental agencies and wildlife resource interest groups; promotes utilization of veterinarians in the field of wildlife resource management and research; encourages cooperation among resource management professionals and wildlife veterinarians; promotes continuing education programs for wildlife veterinarians; emphasizes interrelationships of man, domestic animals, and wildlife with disease; encourages recognition of disease syndromes as potentially influenced by habitat succession, alteration, and pollution. **Founded:** 1979. **Geographic Preference:** National.

677 ■ **American Association of Zoo Veterinarians (AAZV)**
370 Zoo Pky.
Jacksonville, FL 32218
Ph: (904)225-3275
Fax: (904)719-8741
Co. E-mail: admin@aazv.org
URL: http://www.aazv.org/default.aspx
Contact: Dr. Robert Hilsenroth, Executive Director
E-mail: rhilsenrothaazv@aol.com
Facebook: www.facebook.com/ZooVets
X (Twitter): x.com/AazvZoovets
Description: Veterinarians actively engaged in the practice of zoo and wildlife medicine for at least four years; veterinarians who do not qualify for active membership; persons interested in diseases of wildlife; students of veterinary medicine in any accredited veterinary school. **Founded:** 1946. **Publications:** *Journal of Zoo and Wildlife Medicine* (Quarterly). **Awards:** Emil Dolensek Award (Annual); Duane Ullrey Award (Annual). **Geographic Preference:** Multinational.

678 ■ **American Veterinary Medical Association (AVMA) - Library**
1931 N Meacham Rd., Ste. 100
Schaumburg, IL 60173-4360
Free: 800-248-2862
Fax: (847)925-1329
URL: http://www.avma.org
Contact: Dr. Rena Carlson, President
Facebook: www.facebook.com/avmavets
Linkedin: www.linkedin.com/company/avma
X (Twitter): x.com/AVMAvets
Instagram: www.instagram.com/avmavets
YouTube: www.youtube.com/user/AmerVetMedAssn
Description: Professional society of veterinarians. Conducts educational and research programs. Sponsors American Veterinary Medical Association Foundation and Educational Commission for Foreign Veterinary Graduates. Compiles statistics. Accredits veterinary medical education programs and veterinary technician education programs. **Scope:** Veterinary medicine. **Founded:** 1863. **Holdings:** Figures not available. **Publications:** *Veterinarians*; *AVMA Membership Directory and Resource Manual*; *AVMA Placement Service Bulletin*; *Canine Parvoviris Pamphlet*; *What You Should Know About Buying a Horse Pamphlet*; *Pet Euthanasia*; *External Parasites*; *Internal Parasites in Horses*; *When Your Animal Dies*; *Selecting an Amphibian*; *Selecting a Pet Ferret*; *Selecting a Pet Rabbit*; *Selecting a Reptile*; *Selecting a Pet Rodent*; *Toxoplasmosis*; *Veterinarians*; *What You Should Know About Canine Parvovirus Pamphlet*; *Selecting a Bird*; *Traveling with Your Pet*; *Treating Pain in Your Dog*; *Colleges of Veterinary Medicine Accredited by American Veterinary Medical Association*; *Bovine Spongiform Encephalopathy (BSE)*; *Cancer in Pets*; *Canine Distemper*; *Choosing a Veterinarian*; *Facts About CWD: Chronic Wasting Disease*; *Dog Bite Prevention*; *Equine Euthanasia*; *External Parasites*; *Feline Lower Urinary Tract Disease*; *Feline Panleukopenia*; *Heartworm Disease*; *Household Hazards*; *Internal Parasites In Cats and Dogs*; *Pet Euthanasia*; *Rabies Pamphlet*; *Selecting a Cat*; *Selecting a Dog*; *Spaying and Neutering*; *What You Should Know About Toxoplasmosis Pamphlet*; *Vaccinating Your Pet*; *The Veterinary Health Care Team*; *Veterinary Technicians*; *What You Should Know About West Nile Virus Pamphlet*; *Pet Loss & Grief*; *Anthrax*, *VMA Fact Sheet*; *Avian Influenza*; *Brucellosis Fact Sheet*; *Canine Influenza Fact Sheet*; *Chronic Wasting Disease Fact Sheet*; *Classical Swine Fever Fact Sheet*; *Equine Influenza Fact Sheet*; *Exotic Newcastle Disease Fact Sheet*; *Foot and Mouth Disease Fact Sheet*; *Glanders and Melioidosis Fact Sheet*; *Monkeypox Fact Sheet*; *Plague Fact Sheet*; *Q Fever Fact Sheet*; *Swine Influenza Fact Sheet*; *Tularemia Fact Sheet*; *Vesicular Stomatitis Fact Sheet*; *Viral Encephalitis Fact Sheet*; *Welfare*

Implications of Castration of Cattle Fact Sheet; *Welfare Implications of Dehorning and Disbudding of Cattle Fact Sheet*; *Welfare Implications of Tail Docking of Dairy Cattle Fact Sheet*; *Cancer in Animals Pamphlet*; *Canine Distemper Pamphlet*; *AVMA Directory*; *American Journal of Veterinary Research (AJVR)* (Monthly); *Vaccines and Sarcomas Pamphlet*; *Welfare Implications of Deer Velvet Fact Sheet*; *AVMA Disaster Preparedness and Response Guide*; *AVMA Membership Directory and Resource Manual*; *Economic Report on Veterinarians and Veterinary Practices*; *Journal of the American Veterinary Medical Association (JAVMA)* (Semimonthly). **Awards:** AVMA Fellowship Program (Annual); AVMA Award (Annual); Bustad Companion Animal Veterinarian of the Year Award (Annual); AVMA Royal Canin Award (Annual); AVMA Clinical Research Award (Annual); AVMA Public Service Award (Annual); AVMA Global Veterinary Service Award (Annual); AVMA Animal Welfare Award (Annual); AVMA Career Achievement in Canine Research Award (Annual); AVMA Lifetime Excellence in Research Award (Annual); AVMA Advocacy Award (Annual); AVMA Meritorious Service Award (Annual). **Geographic Preference:** National.

679 ■ Animal Health Institute (AHI)
1325 G St. NW, Ste. 700
 Washington, DC 20005-3104
Ph: (202)637-2440
Fax: (202)393-1667
URL: http://ahi.org
Contact: Alexander S. Mathews, President
E-mail: amathews@ahi.org
Facebook: www.facebook.com/AnimalsHealthy
X (Twitter): x.com/animalshealthy
Instagram: www.instagram.com/healthyanimals.heal
 thypeople
YouTube: www.youtube.com/channel/UCDWdQqZp
 2uem_tj1yyvWV2g

Description: Represents manufacturers of animal health products (vaccines, pharmaceuticals, and feed additives used in modern food production; and medicines for household pets). Works with government agencies and legislators; prepares position papers; and compiles and disseminates information. Sponsors AHI Foundation. **Founded:** 1941. **Publications:** *AHI Newsletter*. **Geographic Preference:** National.

680 ■ Association of Reptilian and Amphibian Veterinarians (ARAV)
PO Box 1868
 Mount Juliet, TN 37121
Co. E-mail: info@arav.org
URL: http://arav.org
Contact: James E. Bogan, Jr., President
Facebook: www.facebook.com/ARAVvets
X (Twitter): x.com/aravets

Description: Seeks to advance the study and practice of reptilian and amphibian veterinary medicine. Promotes the ongoing professional development of members. **Founded:** 1990. **Publications:** *Journal of Herpetological Medicine and Surgery* (Quarterly). **Awards:** ARAV Lifetime Achievement Award (Irregular). **Geographic Preference:** Multinational.

681 ■ *Canadian Journal of Veterinary Research (CJVR)*
339 Booth St.
 Ottawa, ON, Canada K1R 7K1
Ph: (613)236-1162
Free: 800-567-2862
Fax: (613)236-9681
Co. E-mail: admin@cvma-acmv.org
URL: http://www.canadianveterinarians.net
Contact: Dr. Trevor Lawson, President
URL(s): www.canadianveterinarians.net/journals-an
 d-classified-ads/canadian-journal-of-veterinary
 -research

Ed: Eva Nagy. **Released:** Quarterly **Price:** $260, Individuals for foreign; $240, Individuals for Canada; $315, Institutions. **Description:** Peer-reviewed, online only veterinary research journal, covering original research in veterinary and comparative medicine. **Availability:** PDF; Online.

682 ■ *Canadian Veterinary Journal (CVJ)*
339 Booth St.
 Ottawa, ON, Canada K1R 7K1
Ph: (613)236-1162
Free: 800-567-2862
Fax: (613)236-9681
Co. E-mail: admin@cvma-acmv.org
URL: http://www.canadianveterinarians.net
Contact: Dr. Trevor Lawson, President
URL(s): www.canadianveterinarians.net/journals-an
 d-classified-ads/the-canadian-veterinary-journal

Released: Monthly **Price:** $290, Individuals for print, foreign; $275, Individuals for print, Canada; $350, Institutions for print, Canada. **Description:** Peer-reviewed, scientific veterinary medicine journal serving the Canadian veterinary community. Publishes research articles, regular columns, news items, and business information. **Availability:** Print; PDF; Online.

683 ■ Canadian Veterinary Medical Association (CVMA) - Library [Association Canadienne des Medecins Veterinaires (ACMV)]
339 Booth St.
 Ottawa, ON, Canada K1R 7K1
Ph: (613)236-1162
Free: 800-567-2862
Fax: (613)236-9681
Co. E-mail: admin@cvma-acmv.org
URL: http://www.canadianveterinarians.net
Contact: Dr. Trevor Lawson, President
Facebook: www.facebook.com/CanadianVe
 terinaryMedicalAssociation
X (Twitter): x.com/CanVetMedAssoc
YouTube: www.youtube.com/user/CVMAACMV

Description: Veterinarians in Canada. Encourages excellence in the field of veterinary medicine; seeks to increase awareness of the importance of animals; represents the interests of members. **Scope:** Veterinary; animals. **Founded:** 1948. **Holdings:** Figures not available. **Publications:** *Canadian Veterinary Journal (CVJ)* (Monthly); *CVMA Source Guide and Directory*; *Canadian Journal of Veterinary Research (CJVR)* (Quarterly). **Educational Activities:** CVMA Convention (Annual); Canadian Veterinary Medical Association Convention (Annual). **Awards:** CVMA Industry Award (Annual); Merck Veterinary Award (Annual); CVMA Small Animal Practitioner Award (Annual); CVMA President's Award (Annual); R.V.L. Walker Award (Annual); CVMA Humane Award (Annual); CVMA Student Leadership Award (Annual); CVMA Humane Award (Annual). **Geographic Preference:** National.

684 ■ Cornell Feline Health Center (FHC)
235 Hungerford Hill Rd.
 Ithaca, NY 14853
Ph: (607)253-3414
Co. E-mail: vet-hosp@cornell.edu
URL: http://www.vet.cornell.edu/departments-centers
 -and-institutes/cornell-feline-health-center
Contact: Dr. Bruce G. Kornreich, Director
Facebook: www.facebook.com/CornellFelineHeal
 thCenter
X (Twitter): x.com/cornellcats

Description: Professionals devoted to cats. Seeks to unravel the mysteries of feline health, nutrition, and behavior. Works to educate veterinarians and cat owners, and to aid veterinarians when new or unknown diseases occur. Provides educational programs. **Scope:** Basic and clinical research on diseases of domestic and non-domestic cats, designed to help prevent or cure cat diseases and to aid veterinarians when new or unknown diseases occur. Performs multidisciplinary studies on antiviral substances (including interferon); cardiovascular, respiratory, urinary tract, reproductive, nutritional, neurological, fungal, and hormonal diseases; infectious peritonitis; leukemia; panleukopenia (enteritis); feline immunodeficiency virus; and vaccines. **Founded:** 1974. **Holdings:** Articles; brochures; videos. **Publications:** *CatWatch* (Monthly); *Dog Watch*; *Pre-Vet* (Bimonthly); *Feline Health Topics*; *Cornell Feline Health Center Annual report* (Annual); *Feline Health Topics for Veterinarians*; *Feline Information Bulletin* (Periodic). **Geographic Preference:** National.

685 ■ *CVMA Source Guide and Directory*
339 Booth St.
 Ottawa, ON, Canada K1R 7K1
Ph: (613)236-1162
Free: 800-567-2862
Fax: (613)236-9681
Co. E-mail: admin@cvma-acmv.org
URL: http://www.canadianveterinarians.net
Contact: Dr. Trevor Lawson, President
URL(s): www.canadianveterinarians.net/veterinary
 -resources

Availability: Online.

686 ■ National Association for Black Veterinarians (NABV)
PO Box 84471
 Baton Rouge, LA 70884
Co. E-mail: info@nabvonline.org
URL: http://nabvonline.org
Contact: Dr. Stara Robertson, President
Facebook: www.facebook.com/nabvonline
X (Twitter): x.com/the_nabv
Instagram: www.instagram.com/the_nabv

Description: Works to build a network of individuals and organizations that advocate for blacks in veterinary medicine at every level and profession. **Founded:** 2016.

687 ■ Vaccine and Infectious Disease Organization - International Vaccine Centre - Library
University of Saskatchewan, 120 Veterinary Rd.
 Saskatoon, SK, Canada S7N 5E3
URL: http://www.vido.org/facilities/accessing-intervac

Description: Promotes animal health through diagnosis and prevention of production-limiting diseases. **Scope:** Genetically engineered novel live and bacterial vaccines, development of performance enhancement vaccines for growth and reproduction. **Founded:** 1975. **Holdings:** Figures not available. **Publications:** *VIDO Annual report* (Annual). **Geographic Preference:** Multinational.

688 ■ Veterinary Hospital Managers Association (VHMA)
PO Box 2280
 Alachua, FL 32616
Ph: (518)433-8911
Free: 888-795-4520
Co. E-mail: admin@vhma.org
URL: http://www.vhma.org/home
Contact: Jessica Speas, President
Facebook: www.facebook.com/veterinaryhospi
 talmanagersassociation
Linkedin: www.linkedin.com/company/vhma
X (Twitter): x.com/VHMAssoc

Description: Individuals involved in veterinary practice management. Seeks to advance the study, teaching, and practice of veterinary practice management. Serves as a forum for the exchange of information among members; sponsors continuing professional development courses; formulates standards of ethics and practice for veterinary medical managers. **Founded:** 1981. **Geographic Preference:** National.

REFERENCE WORKS

689 ■ "Best In Show" in Pet Product News (Vol. 64, November 2010, No. 11, pp. 20)

Ed: Lizett Bond. **Description:** Cherrybrook Premium Pet Supplies offers an expanded array of quality holistic products and is staffed by people who possess wide knowledge of these products. Aside from receiving the Outstanding Holistic Approach award, Cherrybrook has opened three stores in New Jersey. How a holistic approach to service kept customers coming back is discussed. **Availability:** Print; Online.

Small Business Profiles   Animal Clinic ■ 709

690 ■ "Ditch the Pet Store! MindJolt SGN and The Humane Society of the United States Unleash Fluff Friends Rescue" in Benzinga.com (January 4, 2012)
Pub: Benzinga.com
Contact: Jason Raznick, Founder
Ed: Aaron Wise. Description: The Humane Society of the United States has partnered with MindJolt SGN, a multiplatform game developer and distributor, to release a mobile game called Fluff Friends Rescue. The game introduces players to the real-world challenges of rescuing pets by nursing animals back to health while running their own animal shelter.

691 ■ "Experts Strive to Educate on Proper Pet Diets" in Pet Product News (Vol. 64, November 2010, No. 11, pp. 40)
Ed: Joan Hustace Walker. Description: Pet supply manufacturers have been bundling small mammal food and treats with educational sources to help retailers avoid customer misinformation. This action has been motivated by the customer's quest to seek proper nutritional advice for their small mammal pets. Availability: Online.

692 ■ "Food as Nature Intended" in Pet Product News (Vol. 64, November 2010, No. 11, pp. 30)
Ed: Nikki Moustaki. Description: Dog owners have been extending their health-consciousness to their pets by seeking natural products that will address their pets' raw food diet. Retailers response to this trend are outlined. Availability: Online.

693 ■ "People and Their Pets: Life Inside an Animal Clinic" in Midland Daily News (April 13, 2019)
URL(s): www.ourmidland.com/news/article/People-and-their-pets-13764789.php
Ed: Ashley Schafer. Released: April 19, 2019. Description: Profile of the Midland Animal Clinic in Michigan, which operates under some of the highest standards of care in the area. Certified by the American Animal Hospital Association,the Midland Animal Clinic must adhere to about 1,000 standards and recertify every three years. Animals receive the best care here, from checkups to dental work. Availability: Online.

694 ■ "PSCPets.com Gives Back to Support Military Working Dogs" in Pet Product News (Vol. 66, September 2012, No. 9, pp. 17)
Description: Menomonie, Wisconsin-based online pet health and wellness products supplier PSCPets.com donated on $26.99 bottle of PSCPets Joint Support Military Working Dogs for every $5 donation for the company's Rescue Outreach Program. Each month, PSCPets.com uses the program to benefit animal welfare causes. How the effort to assist military working dogs started is discussed. Availability: Online.

695 ■ "Quincy Veterinarian Advises That Pets as 'Young' as Seven Years Need Senior Care" in Benzinga.com (September 9, 2012)
Pub: Comtex News Network Inc.
Contact: Kan Devnani, President
Released: September 09, 2012. Description: Veterinarian advises pet owners to have their pets over seven years of age seen for regular senior office visits. That age in animals is equal to middle age of humans. At age 10, a pet is considered geriatric. Health conditions after age seven can include arthritis, heart disease, liver or kidney problems, and thyroid problems. Availability: Online.

696 ■ "Shelters Vie for $500,000 In Adoption Contest" in Pet Product News (Vol. 66, September 2012, No. 9, pp. 19)
Description: Fifty shelters across the US will vie for more than $500,000 in grants through the American Society for the Prevention of Cruelty to Animals' Rachael Ray $100K Challenge. The shelters will aspire to adopt out at least 300 more cats and dogs from August through October 2012 than they did during the period one year ago. Availability: Online.

697 ■ "Solutions for the Frustrating Feline" in Pet Product News (Vol. 64, November 2010, No. 11, pp. 46)
Ed: Lori Luechtefeld. Description: Products that can help customers deal with problematic cat behaviors, such as out-of-the-box urination and scratching are described. Information on such products including litter box deodorants and disposable scratchers is provided. Feline territorial behaviors can also be addressed by pheromone products that can calm hyperactive cats. Availability: Online.

698 ■ "Supplements Mix Nutrition With Convenience" in Pet Product News (Vol. 64, November 2010, No. 11, pp. 44)
Ed: Karen Shugart. Description: Pet supply manufacturers have been making supplements and enhanced foods that improve mineral consumption, boost bone density, and sharpen appetite in herps. Customers seem to enjoy the convenience as particular herps demands are being addressed by these offerings. Features of other supplements and enhanced foods for herps are described. Availability: Print; Online.

699 ■ "Tapping the 'Well' in Wellness" in Pet Product News (Vol. 64, November 2010, No. 11, pp. 1)
Ed: Wendy Bedwell-Wilson. Description: Healthy food and treats are among the leading wellness products being sought by customers from specialty retailers to keep their pets healthy. With this demand for pet wellness products, retailers suggest making sure that staff know key ingredients to emphasize to customers. Other insights into this trend and ways to engage customers are discussed. Availability: Online.

700 ■ Workforce Needs in Veterinary Medicine
Released: 2013. Description: Examines the changing societal needs and how it relates to the U.S. veterinary medical profession. Availability: Print.

TRADE PERIODICALS

701 ■ American Journal of Veterinary Research (AJVR)
Pub: American Veterinary Medical Association
Contact: Dr. Rena Carlson, President
URL(s): avmajournals.avma.org/loi/ajvr
Facebook: www.facebook.com/avmajournals/
X (Twitter): twitter.com/AVMAjournals
Released: Monthly Description: Peer-reviewed, open access, general science journal covering veterinary research on nutrition and diseases of domestic, wild, and furbearing animals. Availability: Online.

702 ■ Canadian Veterinary Journal (CVJ)
Pub: Canadian Veterinary Medical Association
Contact: Dr. Trevor Lawson, President
URL(s): www.canadianveterinarians.net/journals-and-classified-ads/the-canadian-veterinary-journal
Released: Monthly Price: $290, Individuals for print, foreign; $275, Individuals for print, Canada; $350, Institutions for print, Canada. Description: Peer-reviewed, scientific veterinary medicine journal serving the Canadian veterinary community. Publishes research articles, regular columns, news items, and business information. Availability: Print; PDF; Online.

703 ■ Humane News
Pub: Associated Humane Societies
Contact: Robert Baerenbach, President
URL(s): ahscares.org/category/humane-news
Description: Reports on news of the programs and activities of humane societies seeking to assist wild and domestic animals. Provides legislative updates on bills supporting animal welfare. Availability: PDF.

704 ■ Journal of the American Animal Hospital Association (JAAHA)
Pub: American Animal Hospital Association
Contact: Mark Thompson, President
URL(s): www.aaha.org/for-veterinary-professionals/publicationsmeridian.allenpress.com/jaaha
Released: Bimonthly Price: $650, Institutions for print and online, ROW; ams.aaha.org/eweb/dynamicpage.aspx?site=store&webcode=JAAHASubscriptions; $175, Nonmembers for print and online, US/Canada; $585, Institutions for print and online, US/Canada; $125, Nonmembers for print only, US/Canada; $185, Nonmembers for print and online, ROW; $55, Members for print, US/Canada; $135, Nonmembers for print only, ROW; $125, Nonmembers for online only; $540, Institutions for online only; $65, Members for print, ROW. Description: Includes advertisers' index. Availability: Print; PDF; Online.

705 ■ Trends® Magazine
Pub: American Animal Hospital Association
Contact: Mark Thompson, President
URL(s): www.aaha.org/publications/trends-magazine/#gsc.tab=0
Released= Monthly Price: $20, for single issue. Description: Professional magazine covering the management of small animal veterinary practices. Availability: Print; PDF; Download; Online.

706 ■ Veterinary Clinics of North America: Equine Practice
Pub: Elsevier Inc.
URL(s): www.vetequine.theclinics.com
X (Twitter): twitter.com/VetClinics
Ed: Thomas J Divers, DVM. Released: 3/year Price: $308, Individuals for online + print US; $351, Individuals for online + print Canada; $383, Individuals for online + print international; $355, Individuals for online only international; $276, Individuals for online Canada; $264, Individuals for online us. Description: Journal reviewing current techniques, drugs, and diagnostic and treatment techniques in equine veterinary medicine. Each issue covers a single topic in equine practice. Availability: Print; Download; PDF; Online.

TRADE SHOWS AND CONVENTIONS

707 ■ American Veterinary Medical Association Annual Convention
URL(s): www.atanet.org/events/index.php
Frequency: Annual. Description: Products, materials, equipment, data, and services for veterinary medicine. Audience: Veterinarians. Principal Exhibits: Products, materials, equipment, data, and services for veterinary medicine. Telecommunication Services: avma@wyndhamjade.com.

708 ■ Florida Veterinary Medical Association Annual Meeting
Florida Veterinary Medical Association (FVMA)
7207 Monetary Dr.
Orlando, FL 32809-5724
Ph: (407)851-3862
Free: 800-992-3862
Fax: (407)240-3710
Co. E-mail: info@fvma.org
URL: http://fvma.org
Contact: Marta P. Lista, President
URL(s): fvma.org/wp-content/uploads/2023/04/FVMA-Approved-Bylaws-2023.pdf
Frequency: Annual. Description: Scientific drugs and equipment related to veterinary medicine. Audience: Veterinarians, and technicians. Principal Exhibits: Scientific drugs and equipment related to veterinary medicine.

709 ■ Missouri Veterinary Medical Association Annual Convention
Missouri Veterinary Medical Association (MVMA)
2500 Country Club Dr.
Jefferson City, MO 65109
Ph: (573)636-8612
Fax: (573)659-7175
Co. E-mail: mvma@movma.org
URL: http://www.movma.org
Contact: Philip Brown, Vice Chairman of the Board
URL(s): www.movmaconvention.com

710 ■ Animal Clinic   Small Business Profiles

Frequency: Annual. **Description:** Veterinary instruments, surgical equipment, pharmaceuticals, dog food, publications, and animal care products. **Audience:** Members and their families. **Principal Exhibits:** Veterinary instruments, surgical equipment, pharmaceuticals, dog food, publications, and animal care products. Dates and Locations: 2025 Jan 30-Feb 02 Holiday Inn Executive Center, Columbia, MO. **Telecommunication Services:** mvma@movma.org.

710 ■ Ohio Veterinary Medical Association/ Midwest Veterinary Conference
Ohio Veterinary Medical Association (OVMA)
  1472 Manning Pky.
  Powell, OH 43065
Ph: (614)436-1300
Fax: (614)436-1301
Co. E-mail: ohiovma@ohiovma.org
URL: http://www.ohiovma.org
Contact: Dr. Ed Biggie, President
URL(s): www.mvcinfo.org
Facebook: www.facebook.com/mvcinfo
X (Twitter): twitter.com/mvcinfo

Price: $95, Members Early Bird; $105, Members Advance; $120, Onsite. **Frequency:** Annual. **Description:** Veterinary supplies and the latest advances in the field. **Audience:** Veterinarians, technicians, students, and suppliers of veterinary medicine, hospital staff, spouses, and hospital managers. **Principal Exhibits:** Veterinary supplies and the latest advances in the field. Dates and Locations: 2025 Feb 20-22. **Telecommunication Services:** info@mvcinfo.org.

711 ■ Wisconsin Veterinary Medical Association Annual Convention
Wisconsin Veterinary Medical Association (WVMA)
  4610 S Biltmore Ln., Ste. 107
  Madison, WI 53718
Ph: (608)257-3665
Co. E-mail: wvma@wvma.org
URL: http://wvma.org
Contact: Howard Ketover, President
URL(s): wvma.org/2020/07/farewell

Frequency: Annual. **Description:** Veterinary supplies, pharmaceuticals, pet food, business systems, and record-keeping equipment. **Audience:** Veterinarians, certified veterinary technicians, veterinary students, veterinary practice managers and spouses. **Principal Exhibits:** Veterinary supplies, pharmaceuticals, pet food, business systems, and record-keeping equipment.

712 ■ WVC Annual Conference (WVC)
Viticus Group
  2425 E Oquendo Rd.
  Las Vegas, NV 89120
Ph: (702)739-6698
Free: 866-800-7326
Fax: (702)739-6420
Co. E-mail: support@viticusgroup.org
URL: http://www.viticusgroup.org
Contact: Dr. Debbie White, President
URL(s): www.viticusgroup.org/wvc-conference

Frequency: Annual. **Description:** Veterinary equipment, supplies, and services, including drugs. **Audience:** Western Veterinarians. **Principal Exhibits:** Veterinary equipment, supplies, and services, including drugs. Dates and Locations: 2025 Mar 02-05, Mandalay Bay Convention Center, Las Vegas, NV. **Telecommunication Services:** support@viticusgroup.org.

CONSULTANTS

713 ■ Thinnes & Dutton P.C.
3515 Spring St., Ste. 5
  Davenport, IA 52807
Contact: Teresa A. Thinnes, Contact

Description: Provider of tax planning and preparation services.

LIBRARIES

714 ■ Animal Medical Center (AMC)
510 E 62nd St.
  New York, NY 10065
Ph: (212)838-8100
Fax: (212)752-2592
Co. E-mail: client.services@amcny.org
URL: http://www.amcny.org
Contact: Kathryn Coyne, President
Facebook: www.facebook.com/theanimalmedicalcenter
Linkedin: www.linkedin.com/company/the-animal-medical-center
X (Twitter): x.com/amcny
Instagram: www.instagram.com/amcny
YouTube: www.youtube.com/user/amcny510
Pinterest: www.pinterest.com/amcny1

Description: Provides quality medical and surgical care for small pets; conducts educational programs for veterinarians, students, and technicians; conducts clinical investigations in veterinary and comparative medicine. Sponsors charitable outreach programs including bereavement counseling, pet therapy, and subsidized care for indigent elderly pet owners and guide dog owners. **Founded:** 1910. **Geographic Preference:** National.

715 ■ Auburn University - Charles Allen Cary Veterinary Medical Library
231 Mell St.
  Auburn, AL 36849
Ph: (334)844-1749
Co. E-mail: vmedlib@auburn.edu
URL: http://www.lib.auburn.edu/vetmed/about.php
Contact: Kelly Weigand, Department Head
E-mail: kaj0050@auburn.edu

Scope: Veterinary medicine. **Services:** Interlibrary loan; copying; library open to the public. **Holdings:** 30,000 volumes; 120 papers; e-books; e-journals.

716 ■ Massachusetts Society for the Prevention of Cruelty to Animals - Angell Memorial Animal Hospital Veterinary Library
350 S Huntington Ave.
  Boston, MA 02130
Ph: (617)522-7282
Fax: (617)989-1635
URL: http://www.mspca.org
Contact: Neal Litvack, President

Scope: Veterinary medicine, conservation, zoology, pet care, humane education, animal welfare, animal rights. **Services:** Library open to the public by appointment. **Holdings:** 2,000 volumes.

717 ■ Ross University School of Veterinary Medicine - Stanley Mark Dennis Veterinary Library
630 US Hwy. 1, Ste. 2031
  North Brunswick, NJ 08902
Co. E-mail: sklibrarystaff@rossvet.edu.kn
URL: http://veterinary.rossu.edu/library
Contact: Grace Carr, Director, Library Services

Description: Offers access to a variety of library resources including the full library catalog, books, electronic databases and study spaces. It is open to both Ross Vet students and colleagues. **Scope:** Veterinary medicine. **Services:** Interlibrary loan; copying; library open to the public with restrictions (closed weekends and two weeks prior to finals). **Founded:** 1995. **Holdings:** Catalogs; books. **Subscriptions:** 107 journals and other serials.

718 ■ Voice for Animals, Inc. (VOICE) - Library
PO Box 120095
  San Antonio, TX 78212
Ph: (210)737-3138
Co. E-mail: voice@voiceforanimals.org
URL: http://www.voiceforanimals.org
Contact: Rachel Z. Wolf, Contact

Description: Individuals with an interest in animal rights. Seeks to raise public awareness of animal rights issues. Works to abolish "the systematic abuse of nonhuman animals." Conducts educational programs. **Scope:** Animal rights. **Founded:** 1987. **Holdings:** Figures not available. **Geographic Preference:** National.

RESEARCH CENTERS

719 ■ Cornell Feline Health Center (FHC)
235 Hungerford Hill Rd.
  Ithaca, NY 14853
Ph: (607)253-3414
Co. E-mail: vet-hosp@cornell.edu
URL: http://www.vet.cornell.edu/departments-centers-and-institutes/cornell-feline-health-center
Contact: Dr. Bruce G. Kornreich, Director
Facebook: www.facebook.com/CornellFelineHealthCenter
X (Twitter): x.com/cornellcats

Description: Professionals devoted to cats. Seeks to unravel the mysteries of feline health, nutrition, and behavior. Works to educate veterinarians and cat owners, and to aid veterinarians when new or unknown diseases occur. Provides educational programs. **Scope:** Basic and clinical research on diseases of domestic and non-domestic cats, designed to help prevent or cure cat diseases and to aid veterinarians when new or unknown diseases occur. Performs multidisciplinary studies on antiviral substances (including interferon); cardiovascular, respiratory, urinary tract, reproductive, nutritional, neurological, fungal, and hormonal diseases; infectious peritonitis; leukemia; panleukopenia (enteritis); feline immunodeficiency virus; and vaccines. **Founded:** 1974. **Holdings:** Articles; brochures; videos. **Publications:** *CatWatch* (Monthly); *Dog Watch*; *Pre-Vet* (Bimonthly); *Feline Health Topics*; *Cornell Feline Health Center Annual report* (Annual); *Feline Health Topics for Veterinarians*; *Feline Information Bulletin* (Periodic). **Geographic Preference:** National.

720 ■ Cornell University - Baker Institute for Animal Health
235 Hungerford Hill Rd.
  Ithaca, NY 14853
Ph: (607)256-5600
Fax: (607)256-5608
Co. E-mail: bakerinstitute@cornell.edu
URL: http://www.vet.cornell.edu/departments-centers-and-institutes/baker-institute
Contact: Dr. Gerlinde Van de Walle, Director (Acting)
E-mail: grv23@cornell.edu
Facebook: www.facebook.com/BakerInstituteCornell
X (Twitter): twitter.com/bakercornell

Description: Integral unit of Cornell University. **Scope:** Improvement of animal/human health through 2 major areas: 1. Immunology and Infectious Diseases; 2. Genetics and Reproduction. Research includes: infectious diseases, reproductive immunology, genetics/genomics, development, and reproductive and cancer biology with emphasis on the dog, cat and horse, often using a mouse model. **Founded:** 1950. **Publications:** *Baker Institute for Animal Health Annual report* (Annual); *Brochures on Research Topics* (Periodic).

721 ■ Iowa State University of Science and Technology - Institute for International Cooperation in Animal Biologics (IICAB)
Rm. 2160, Patterson Hall 1800 Christensen Dr.
  Ames, IA 50011
URL: http://www.cfsph.iastate.edu/IICAB
Contact: Dr. James A. Roth, Director
E-mail: jaroth@iastate.edu

Description: Integral unit of College of Veterinary Medicine, Iowa State University. Offers technology transfer from the Center to industry. **Scope:** Improvement of animal health and productivity through the effective use of biologics (vaccines) to control animal disease. **Founded:** 1995. **Publications:** *IICAB Annual Report* (Annual).

722 ■ Iowa State University of Science and Technology - Veterinary Diagnostic Laboratory (VDL)
1937 Christensen Dr.
  Ames, IA 50011-1100

Ph: (515)294-1950
Fax: (515)294-3564
Co. E-mail: isuvdl@iastate.edu
URL: http://vetmed.iastate.edu/vdl
Contact: Pat Halbur, Executive Director
E-mail: pghalbur@iastate.edu
Description: Integral unit of College of Veterinary Medicine at Iowa State University of Science and Technology. Diagnostic services and consultation available for livestock and pet owners. **Scope:** Characterizes infectious diseases as well as chemical toxicants by means of pathology, bacteriology, virology, serology, chemistry, and toxicology studies. Serves as a reference laboratory for veterinary diagnostic procedures. **Founded:** 1947. **Publications:** *VDL Annual Reports* (Annual); *Scientific journal articles*. **Educational Activities:** VDL Continuing education and scientific presentations, VDL Continuing education and research, development.

723 ■ University of California, Davis - School of Veterinary Medicine - Center for Companion Animal Health (CCAH)
One Shields Ave.
 Davis, CA 95616-8782
Ph: (530)752-7295
Fax: (530)752-7701
URL: http://ccah.vetmed.ucdavis.edu
Contact: Dr. Michael Kent, Director
Description: Integral unit of School of Veterinary Medicine. **Scope:** Health problems in companion animals, including studies on cancer, infectious diseases, congenital diseases, eye diseases, skin diseases, kidney diseases, animal population control, behavior problems, nutrition, medicine, and surgery (including laser surgery and therapies). **Founded:** 1992. **Educational Activities:** Annual Canine or Feline Health Seminars, To provide research and program support to improve the health and well-being of companion animals.; Research Educational Meeting, To provide research and program support to improve the health and well-being of companion animals.

724 ■ University of Wyoming - Wyoming State Veterinary Laboratory (WSVL)
1174 Snowy Range Rd.
 Laramie, WY 82070
Ph: (307)766-9925
Free: 800-442-8331
Fax: (307)721-2051
Co. E-mail: vetrec@uwyo.edu
URL: http://www.uwyo.edu/wyovet
Facebook: www.facebook.com/WyomingStateVetLab
Instagram: www.instagram.com/wystatevetlab
Description: Integral unit of University of Wyoming, functioning primarily as a diagnostic laboratory. **Scope:** Animal disease problems, including experimental control measures of animal diseases; etiology of animal diseases; and diseases of food-providing animals, wildlife, and companion animal species. **Founded:** 1947. **Publications:** *WSVL Annual report* (Annual); *WSVL Newsletter* (Irregular).

725 ■ Utah State University - Central Utah Veterinary Diagnostic Laboratory (UVDL)
514 West 3000 N
 Spanish Fork, UT 84660
URL: http://www.usu.edu/uvdl
Description: Integral unit of Utah Agricultural Experiment Station at Utah State University. **Scope:** Animal diseases and parasites. Conducts field experiments in support of studies conducted by members of the staff at the Experiment Station. **Founded:** 1944.

726 ■ Virginia Polytechnic Institute and State University - Virginia-Maryland Regional College of Veterinary Medicine - Marion DuPont Scott Equine
17690 Old Waterford Rd.
 Leesburg, VA 20176
Ph: (703)771-6800
URL: http://emc.vetmed.vt.edu
Contact: Stacey Ahner, Director
E-mail: smahner@vt.edu
Facebook: www.facebook.com/equinemedicalcenter
Description: Integral unit of Virginia/Maryland Regional College of Veterinary Medicine, Virginia Polytechnic Institute and State University. Offers clinical service to horses. **Scope:** Deals with equine research, including colic, shock, neurologic diseases, tendon and ligament injury and lameness. **Founded:** 1984. **Educational Activities:** Veterinary professional curriculum, residency training programs, graduate studies program; Equine Medical Center Tuesday Talks (Monthly), For research and education.

Antique Shop

START-UP INFORMATION

727 ■ *The Business of Antiques*
Ed: Wayne Jordan. **Released:** 2012. **Description:** A guide on running an antiques business. Includes sections about running a brick and mortar shop and an auction. **Availability:** E-book.

ASSOCIATIONS AND OTHER ORGANIZATIONS

728 ■ American Hatpin Society (AHS)
845 Sonoma Dr.
  Lake Arrowhead, CA 92352
Co. E-mail: americanhatpinsociety@aol.com
URL: http://www.americanhatpinsociety.com
Contact: Carla Walters, Editor
Description: Collectors of hatpins. Promotes collection, preservation, and restoration of hatpins and related fashion accessories. Serves as a clearinghouse on hatpins and their history; facilitates exchange of information among members; conducts educational programs. **Founded:** 1989. **Publications:** *American Hatpin Society Newsletter* (Quarterly). **Geographic Preference:** Multinational.

729 ■ Antiquarian Booksellers' Association of Canada (ABAC) [Association de la Librairie Ancienne du Canada (ALAC)]
c/o Karol Krysik Books
  491 Davenport Rd., 2nd Fl.
  Toronto, ON, Canada M4V 1B7
Co. E-mail: info@abac.org
URL: http://abac.org/wordpress/en
Contact: Robert Wright, President
Facebook: www.facebook.com/Antiquarian-Booksellers-Association-of-Canada-210124119032896
X (Twitter): x.com/A_B_A_C
Description: Bookselling firms and dealers in rare books and manuscripts. Promotes adherence to high standards of ethics and practice in the trade of antiquarian books. Serves as liaison between members and book collectors and as a clearinghouse on antiquarian books and their trade. **Founded:** 1966. **Geographic Preference:** National.

730 ■ Antiques and Collectibles National Association (ACNA) [Antiques & Collectibles Insurance Group]
20222 N Main St.
  Cornelius, NC 28031
Free: 800-287-7127
Fax: (704)895-0230
URL: http://aciginsurance.com
Contact: Angie Becker, President
E-mail: angie@acna.us
Description: Serves as a trade association in the antiques and collectibles industry. Provides benefit programs, information, educational opportunities and representation. Strives to create a public awareness and promotes professionalism. **Founded:** 1991. **Geographic Preference:** National.

731 ■ Appraisers Association of America (AAA)
212 W 35th St., 11th Fl. S
  New York, NY 10001
Ph: (212)889-5404
Fax: (212)889-5503
Co. E-mail: referrals@appraisersassociation.org
URL: http://www.appraisersassociation.org
Contact: Sharon Chrust, President
Facebook: www.facebook.com/appraisersassociation
X (Twitter): x.com/AppraisersAssoc
Description: Focus on the development of fine and decorative arts. **Founded:** 1949. **Publications:** *Find an Appraiser*; *The Appraiser* (Quarterly); *Appraisers Association of America--Membership Directory*. **Geographic Preference:** National.

732 ■ Art and Antique Dealers League of America (AADLA)
PO Box 2066
  New York, NY 10021
Ph: (212)879-7558
URL: http://aadla.com
Description: Represents retailers and wholesalers of antiques and art objects. **Founded:** 1926. **Geographic Preference:** National.

733 ■ Cracker Jack Collectors Association (CJCA)
c/o Fred Joyce, 415 Soft Shadow Ln.
  Debary, FL 32713-2343
Co. E-mail: brazeaufamily@charter.net
URL: http://www.crackerjackcollectors.com
Contact: Fred Joyce, Contact
Description: Collectors of Cracker Jack prizes and related items. Promotes collection and preservation of Cracker Jack memorabilia. Gathers and disseminates information on Cracker Jack collectibles and their availability; facilitates exchange of information and promotes good fellowship among members. **Founded:** 1994. **Geographic Preference:** National.

734 ■ The Fostoria Glass Society of America, Inc. (FGSA)
511 Tomlinson Ave.
  Moundsville, WV 26041
Ph: (304)845-9188
Co. E-mail: museum@fostoriaglass.org
URL: http://www.fostoriaglass.org
Contact: Jim Davis, President
Description: Represents Fostoria Glass collectors. Promotes interest in glass collecting. Offers referrals. **Founded:** 1988. **Educational Activities:** Annual F.G.S.A. Convention and Elegant Glass Show (Annual). **Geographic Preference:** National.

735 ■ Glass Paperweight Foundation
410 S Michigan Ave., Ste. 206
  Chicago, IL 60616
Ph: (312)419-0403
Co. E-mail: glasspaperweightfoundation@gmail.com
URL: http://www.glasspaperweightfoundation.com
Contact: Wes Clark, Contact
Description: Promotes paperweight collecting. Conducts educational programs. Runs a speakers' bureau. **Founded:** 1995. **Geographic Preference:** National.

736 ■ International League of Antiquarian Booksellers (ILAB)
First Floor
  21 John St.
  London WC1N 2BF, United Kingdom
Co. E-mail: info@pontesmaps.com
URL: http://ilab.org
Contact: Sally Burdon, President
E-mail: sally@asiabookroom.com
Facebook: www.facebook.com/ILABBooksellers
Instagram: www.instagram.com/ilab_booksellers_worldwide
Description: Represents national associations of antiquarian booksellers around the world. Organizes professional training courses for members. Sponsors book fairs. **Founded:** 1947. **Educational Activities:** ILAB Congress (Biennial). **Awards:** Breslauer Prize for Bibliography (Periodic). **Geographic Preference:** National.

737 ■ National Antique & Art Dealers Association of America (NAADAA)
220 E 57th St.
  New York, NY 10022
Co. E-mail: naadaa.antiques@gmail.com
URL: http://naadaa.org
Contact: James R. McConnaughy, President
Description: Art and antique dealers who handle antiques and works of art of the highest quality. Safeguards the interests of those who buy, sell, and collect antiques and works of art. Sponsors periodic exhibitions. **Founded:** 1954. **Publications:** *National Antique & Art Dealers Association of America--Membership Directory*. **Geographic Preference:** National.

REFERENCE WORKS

738 ■ *Appraisers Association of America--Membership Directory*
Pub: Appraisers Association of America
Contact: Sharon Chrust, President
URL(s): www.appraisersassociation.org/about-us
Description: Covers 800 member appraisers of fine art, antiques, and personal property. **Entries include:** Name, address, phone, specialties. **Arrangement:** Geographical. **Indexes:** Alphabetical, specialty. **Availability:** Print.

739 ■ *How to Buy and Sell Antiques*
Released: 3rd edition. **Description:** Fiona Shoop shares twenty years experience to train individuals to become successful antiques dealers. **Availability:** E-book.

740 ■ *"How Low Will Market for Antiques Actually Go?" in The New York Times (March 3, 2018)*
URL(s): www.nytimes.com/2018/03/03/style/how-low-will-market-for-antiques-actually-go.html

Released: March 03, 2018. Description: Examines the transition antique shops are implementing to include vintage items and contemporary design pieces. Changing tastes with the new generation of homeowners and new architecture in homebuilding are forces that are contributing to this trend. Availability: Print; Online.

741 ■ "Key Points You Must Know Before Buying an Existing Antiques Business" in Antique Trader (December 6, 2012)
URL(s): www.antiquetrader.com/articles/key-points-you-must-know-before-buying-an-existing-antiques-business/

Ed: Wayne Jordan. Released: December 06, 2012. Description: Practical advice on what to expect while navigating the purchase of an existing antiques store. Real estate, inventory, leasing, and negotiating the price are all discussed by a former store owner and business broker. Availability: Online.

742 ■ National Antique & Art Dealers Association of America--Membership Directory (Internet only)
Pub: National Antique & Art Dealers Association of America
Contact: James R. McConnaughy, President
URL(s): naadaa.org/about

Description: Covers 46 member dealers. Entries include: Firm name, address, phone, names of one or more principal executives, cable address, specialties, and areas of expertise. Arrangement: Alphabetical. Availability: Print.

743 ■ "New Beat for Marley's Daughter: Offspring of Reggae Royalty Opens Vintage Clothing Shop with Pal" in Los Angeles Business Journal (Vol. 34, March 12, 2012, No. 11, pp. 3)
Pub: CBJ L.P.
Contact: Laura Garrett, Vice President Publisher
E-mail: garrett@ocbj.com

Ed: Bethany Firnhaber. Description: Karen Marley, daughter of famous reggae musician Bob Marley, explains her passion for vintage clothing. Karen and her fried Monique Aquino have partnered to open a resale consignment store in Los Angeles selling designer and vintage clothing. Availability: Online.

TRADE PERIODICALS

744 ■ Antique Bottle & Glass Collector
Pub: Antique Bottle and Glass Collector
Contact: Jim Hagenbuch, Founder
URL(s): www.fohbc.org/bottles-extras

Released: Bimonthly Price: $145, for first class mail 3 years w/1 associate; $125, for standard mail 3 years w/1 Associate; $60, for first class mail w/1 associate; $45, for Standard Mail w/1 Associate; $125, for first class mail 3 years; $110, for standard mail 3 years; $55, U.S. for first class mail; $60, Canada for first Class Mail; $80, Other countries for first Class Mail; $40, for standard mail; $7, for sample issue. Description: Trade magazine for antique bottle and glass collectors. Availability: Print; PDF; Online.

745 ■ Antiques and the Arts Weekly
Pub: Bee Publishing Company Inc.
Contact: John Voket, Editor
URL(s): www.antiquesandthearts.com
Facebook: www.facebook.com/AntiquesAndTheArtsWeekly
X (Twitter): x.com/TheBeeAntiques
YouTube: www.youtube.com/@antiquesandthearts

Ed: Scudder R. Smith. Released: Weekly Price: $96, for per year; $425, for five years; $170, for two years; $70, for 6 months. Description: Magazine featuring antiques. Availability: Print; Online.

746 ■ Uncoverings
Pub: American Quilt Study Group
Contact: Jayne Steffens, President
URL(s): www.americanquiltstudygroup.org/content.aspx?page_id=22&club_id=267008&module_id=484671

Ed: Lynne Bassett. Released: Annual Price: $25, for vol 44. Description: Scholarly journal covering quilts, textiles and quilt makers. Availability: Print.

TRADE SHOWS AND CONVENTIONS

747 ■ National Antique Vintage Decoy & Sporting Collectibles Show
North American Decoy Collectors Association (MDCA)
c/o Matt Bryant
17114 Erskine St.
Omaha, NE 68116
Ph: (785)201-2923
Co. E-mail: matt.bryant@wilsonco.com
URL: http://nadecoycollectors.org
Contact: Rick Sandstrom, President
E-mail: sandstrom@nadecoycollectors.org
URL(s): nadecoycollectors.org/upcoming-events

Frequency: Annual. Description: Equipment, supplies, and services for the preservation of old decoys and for new decoy carving; other fishing and hunting collectibles. Audience: Decoy collectors and other sporting collectibles enthusiasts. Principal Exhibits: Equipment, supplies, and services for the preservation of old decoys and for new decoy carving; other fishing and hunting collectibles. Dates and Locations: 2025 Apr 22-26 Westin Chicago Lombard Hotel, Lombard, IL. Telecommunication Services: flyer180@gmail.com.

LIBRARIES

748 ■ California University of Pennsylvania - Louis L. Manderino Library - Special Collections
250 University Ave., Rm. 435
California, PA 15419
Ph: (724)938-5767
Co. E-mail: libraryarchives@calu.edu
URL: http://www.calu.edu/catalog/current/undergraduate/about/library.aspx
Contact: Daniel T. Zyglowicz, Library Technician
E-mail: zyglowicz@calu.edu
Facebook: www.facebook.com/PennWCalifornia
X (Twitter): twitter.com/i/flow/login?redirect_after_login=%2FPennWCalifornia
Instagram: www.instagram.com/PennWCalifornia/
YouTube: www.youtube.com/user/CalUofPA

Scope: History; the Civil War. Services: Interlibrary loan; library open to the public by appointment. Founded: 1852. Holdings: Journals; books; e-books; audiovisual materials.

749 ■ Dunham Tavern Museum Library
6709 Euclid Ave.
Cleveland, OH 44103
Ph: (216)431-1060
URL: http://dunhamtavern.org
Contact: James Edmonson, President

Scope: Cleveland history. Services: Library open to members only. Holdings: 1,000 books.

750 ■ Houston Museum of Decorative Arts Library
201 High St.
Chattanooga, TN 37403
Ph: (423)267-7176
Co. E-mail: houstonmuseumchattanooga@gmail.com
URL: http://www.thehoustonmuseum.org/#!location/csxp
Facebook: www.facebook.com/thehoustonmuseum
Instagram: www.instagram.com/thehoustonmuseum
YouTube: www.youtube.com/channel/UCOKjfCoYsDaQJzvA095VAmQ

Scope: Hand-blown antique glass; porcelain; pottery; ceramics; early American furniture; decorative art. Founded: 1961. Holdings: 300 books; 750 unbound reports; unbound periodical volumes; archival files of articles pertaining to the collection.

751 ■ Hunter Museum of American Art Library
10 Bluff View St.
Chattanooga, TN 37403
Ph: (423)267-0968
Co. E-mail: info@huntermuseum.org
URL: http://www.huntermuseum.org
Contact: Matthew Brock, Chairman of the Board

Scope: American art; antiques; architecture; biography; abstract art; arts and crafts. Services: Library not open to the public. Founded: 1958. Holdings: 800 books; 13 VF drawers of sales and auction catalogs; 17 VF drawers of museum and exhibition catalogs.

752 ■ Karpeles Manuscript Library
220 N St.
Buffalo, NY 14201
Co. E-mail: kmuseumsb@aol.com
URL: http://www.karpeles.com
Contact: Christopher Kelly, Director
E-mail: kmuseumbuf@aol.com
Linkedin: www.linkedin.com/company/karpelesmanuscriptlibrarymuseum
Instagram: www.instagram.com/karpelesmanuscriptlibrary

Description: Private holding of important original manuscripts & documents. Scope: Historical; literature, science; religion; political history; exploration; music; art rotates. Services: Open to public. Founded: 1983. Holdings: Books.

753 ■ Karpeles Manuscript Library - Buffalo Museum
220 N St.
Buffalo, NY 14201
Ph: (716)885-1986
Co. E-mail: kmuseumbuf@aol.com
URL: http://www.karpeles.com/visit/buffalo-new-york
Contact: Christopher Kelly, Director
Facebook: www.facebook.com/karpelesmanuscriptlibrarymuseum

Description: Contains reference materials, journals, books, online materials, and video and audio materials on historical studies. Scope: Literature; science; religion; political history; exploration; music. Services: Library open to the public. Founded: 2006. Holdings: Figures not available.

754 ■ Karpeles Manuscript Library - Charleston Museum
360 Meeting St.
Charleston, SC 29403
Ph: (843)722-2996
Co. E-mail: info@charlestonmuseum.org
URL: http://www.charlestonmuseum.org
Contact: Carl Borick, Director
E-mail: cborick@charlestonmuseum.org
Facebook: www.facebook.com/charlestonmuseum
X (Twitter): x.com/chasmuseum
Instagram: www.instagram.com/charlestonmuseum

Scope: Rare manuscripts; art. Services: Library open to the public. Founded: 1773. Holdings: Documents; manuscripts; photographs.

755 ■ Karpeles Manuscript Library - Santa Barbara Museum
21 W Anapamu St.
Santa Barbara, CA 93101
Ph: (805)962-5322
Co. E-mail: kmuseumsba@aol.com
URL: http://www.karpeles.com/visit/santa-barbara-california
Contact: Norm Cohan, Director

Description: Private holding of important original manuscripts & documents. Scope: Literature; science; religion; political history; exploration; music and art. Services: Library open to the public. Founded: 1986. Holdings: Documents.

756 ■ Karpeles Manuscript Library - Tacoma Museum
407 S G St.
Tacoma, WA 98405
Ph: (253)383-2575
Co. E-mail: kmuseumtaq@aol.com
URL: http://www.rain.org/~karpeles/taqfrm.html

Contact: Thomas M. Jutilla, Director
E-mail: kmuseumtaq@aol.com
Scope: Literature; science; religion; political history; exploration; music and art. **Services:** Library open to the public. **Founded:** 1991. **Holdings:** Figures not available.

757 ■ Kennett Library
216 E State St.
 Kennett Square, PA 19348
Ph: (610)444-2702
URL: http://kennettlibrary.org
Contact: Donna Murray, Director, Library Services
Facebook: www.facebook.com/KennettLibrary
X (Twitter): x.com/kennett_library
Instagram: www.instagram.com/kennett_library
YouTube: www.youtube.com/channel/UC0S-xIaN
 4XGo-oErL7XkVQA/videos
Scope: Education; entertainment. **Services:** Interlibrary loan; copying; open to the public. **Founded:** 1985. **Holdings:** Figures not available.

758 ■ Miami University - Southwest Ohio Regional Depository (SWORD)
4200 N University Blvd.
 Middletown, OH 45042
Ph: (513)727-3474
URL: http://www.lib.miamioh.edu/about/locations/
 regional/sword
Scope: Educational material. **Services:** Interlibrary loan; copying; library open to the public by appointment. **Holdings:** Figures not available.

759 ■ Niagara University Library's Rare Book Collection
4 Varsity Dr.
 Niagara University, NY 14109
URL: http://library.niagara.edu/research/special-collec
 tions/rare-book-collection
Contact: David Schoen, Director, Library Services
E-mail: schoen@niagara.edu
Description: Nigara university library. **Scope:** Educational material. **Founded:** 1850. **Holdings:** 400 books; manuscripts.

760 ■ Ohio Wesleyan University - L.A. Beeghly Library Archives/Special Collections
25 S Front St.
 Columbus, OH 43215
URL: http://www.ohiolink.edu/library-profiles/ohio
 _wesleyan_university_la_beeghly_library
Description: Ohio education department library. **Scope:** University history. **Services:** Interlibrary loan; library open to the public by appointment. **Founded:** 1842. **Holdings:** 550,000 volumes; manuscripts.

761 ■ Shelburne Museum Research Library
6000 Shelburne Rd.
 Shelburne, VT 05482
Ph: (802)985-3346
Co. E-mail: info@shelburnemuseum.org
URL: http://shelburnemuseum.org
Contact: D. Scott Wise, Chairman
Scope: American folk art; decorative arts; fine art; and design. **Services:** Copying; library open to the public by appointment. **Founded:** 1947. **Holdings:** 7,000 books; 400 lin.ft. archives; 450 manuscript items.

762 ■ Villanova University - Falvey Memorial Library Special Collections
Falvey Library Villanova University, 800 Lancaster Ave.
 Villanova, PA 19085
URL: http://library.villanova.edu/collections/distinctive/
 specialcollections
Contact: Michael P. Foight, Director, Collections
E-mail: michael.foight@villanova.edu
Scope: Educational material; local history. **Services:** Interlibrary loan; copying; library open to the public. **Holdings:** 500,000 volumes;35,000 electronic journals and 3,500 print journals.

763 ■ Western Maryland Regional Library (WMRL)
100 S Potomac St.
 Hagerstown, MD 21740
Ph: (301)739-3250
Co. E-mail: whilbr@washcolibrary.org
URL: http://www.wmrl.info
Contact: Jenny Bakos, Executive Director
E-mail: wcfl@washcolibrary.org
Facebook: www.facebook.com/whilbr
Scope: History. **Services:** Interlibrary loan; copying; library open to the public with restrictions. **Founded:** 1967. **Holdings:** Figures not available.

764 ■ Winfred L. and Elizabeth C. Post Foundation - Post Art Library
1901 E 20th St.
 Joplin, MO 64804
Ph: (417)623-7953
Co. E-mail: pal@postartlibrary.org
URL: http://www.postartlibrary.org
Contact: Sara Fisher, President
Facebook: www.facebook.com/postartlibrary
X (Twitter): x.com/postartlibrary
Pinterest: www.pinterest.com/postartlibrary
Description: Provides arts & cultural library exhibits, programming, resources, and services. **Scope:** Arts; architecture; historic preservation. **Founded:** 1981.

Apartment Locating Service

START-UP INFORMATION

765 ■ *"Costs to Starting and Operating an Apartment Locating Business" in Brokersponsorship (June 13, 2018)*
Ed: Bryan Bjerke. **Released:** June 13, 2018. **Description:** A breakdown of all of the costs associated with running an apartment locator business with tips on how to get started. **Availability:** Online.

REFERENCE WORKS

766 ■ *Airbnb for Dummies*
Pub: John Wiley & Sons, Inc.
Contact: Christina Van Tassell, Executive Vice President Chief Financial Officer
URL(s): www.wiley.com/en-us/Airbnb+For+Dummies%2C+2nd+Edition-p-9781394154630
Ed: Symon He, James Svetec. **Released:** 2nd edition. **Description:** This guide explains how to turn your rentable property into an Airbnb in order to earn an income. Tips on using the Airbnb website, navigating their policies, and even setting up your property to rent out are all included. **Availability:** paperback; Print.

767 ■ *"Are Apartment Finder Services a Scam?" in Spark Rental (April 19, 2017)*
URL(s): sparkrental.com/are-apartment-finder-services-scam/
Ed: Denise Supplee. **Released:** April 19, 2017. **Description:** Tips on what to look for when using an apartment locator service and if it's worth the risk of them being scammers or not. Details what an apartment locator service is and what they should be doing, versus using a real estate agent. **Availability:** Online.

768 ■ *"Hunt Valley Towne Center Gears Up for Growth; Ray Lewis Project Scrapped" in Baltimore Business Journal (Vol. 30, May 11, 2012, No. 1, pp. 1)*
Pub: American City Business Journals, Inc.
Contact: Mike Olivieri, Executive Vice President
Ed: James Briggs. **Description:** Greenberg Gibbons Commercial Corporation has plans for a 400-unit apartment complex and retail space at Hunt Valley Towne Centre in Baltimore, Maryland. The developer is also considering big-box stores to rent the vacant space that was supposed to be occupied by the failed bowling and entertainment venture MVP Lanes. **Availability:** Print; Online.

769 ■ *"Mechanic Theatre's Brutalist Style at Battle's Center" in Baltimore Business Journal (Vol. 30, May 11, 2012, No. 1, pp. 1)*
Pub: American City Business Journals, Inc.
Contact: Mike Olivieri, Executive Vice President
Ed: James Briggs. **Description:** David S. Brown Enterprises Ltd. plans to demolish the Morris A. Mechanic Theatre in Baltimore, Maryland and replace it with two 30-story towers that include 600 apartment units, retail, and parking spaces. The local chapter of the American Institute of Architects opposes the proposal and calls for the preservation of the former theatre's brutalist achitecture. **Availability:** Print; Online.

TRADE PERIODICALS

770 ■ *Apartment Management Magazine*
Pub: Apartment News Publications Inc.
Contact: Donn R. Smeallie, President
URL(s): www.aptmags.com
Ed: David Gale. **Released:** Monthly **Price:** $24, for California only; $72, Out of state; $40, for 2 years southern California only; $129, Out of state for 2 years. **Description:** Trade magazine serving owners, builders, and managers of apartment buildings. **Availability:** Print; Online.

771 ■ *Building Business & Apartment Management (BBAM)*
Pub: Home Builders Association of Southeastern Michigan
Contact: Michael Stoskopf, Executive Officer
E-mail: michaels@builders.org
Ed: Susan Adler Shanteau. **Released:** Monthly **Description:** Construction and apartment industry magazine. **Availability:** PDF.

TRADE SHOWS AND CONVENTIONS

772 ■ **American Real Estate Society Annual Meeting**
American Real Estate Society (ARES)
PO Box 500
Athens, OH 45701
Ph: (740)239-2737
Fax: (740)593-6758
Co. E-mail: membership@aresnet.org
URL: http://www.aresnet.org
Contact: Dr. Spenser J. Robinson, President
E-mail: s.robinson@cmich.edu
URL(s): www.ares.org/page/AnnConf
Frequency: Annual. **Description:** Exhibits relating to decision-making within real estate finance, real estate market analysis, investment, valuation, development, and other areas related to real estate in the private sector. Data providers, book publishers, etc. **Audience:** Industry Professionals. **Principal Exhibits:** Exhibits relating to decision-making within real estate finance, real estate market analysis, investment, valuation, development, and other areas related to real estate in the private sector. Data providers, book publishers, etc. Dates and Locations: 2025 Apr 08-12 Loews Ventana Canyon Resort, Tucson, AZ. **Telecommunication Services:** conference@aresnet.org.

773 ■ **Canadian Real Estate Association Annual Conference and Trade Show**
Description: Real Estate, financial, printing, and computer business equipment. **Audience:** Real estate professionals, brokers, managers, and corporate representatives from real estate boards across the country. **Principal Exhibits:** Real Estate, financial, printing, and computer business equipment.

774 ■ **South Dakota Association of Realtors Convention**
South Dakota Association of Realtors (SDAR)
2302 Patron Pwy.
Pierre, SD 57501
Ph: (605)224-0554
Free: 800-227-5877
Fax: (605)224-8975
Co. E-mail: sdar@sdrealtor.org
URL: http://www.sdrealtor.org
Contact: Kyle Lalim, Director
E-mail: soldbykyle@midco.net
URL(s): www.sdrealtor.org/events/realtor-convention-of-the-dakotas
Frequency: Annual. **Description:** Provide information, quality education, and political advocacy. **Audience:** Members and real estate professionals. **Principal Exhibits:** Provide information, quality education, and political advocacy. **Telecommunication Services:** robyn@ndrealtors.com.

775 ■ **Texas Apartment Association Annual Education Conference and Lone Star Expo**
Texas Apartment Association (TAA)
1011 San Jacinto Blvd., Ste. 600
Austin, TX 78701-1951
Ph: (512)479-6252
Fax: (512)479-6291
URL: http://taa.org
Contact: Clay Hicks, President
URL(s): www.taa.org/conference
Frequency: Annual. **Description:** Goods and services geared to multi-housing professionals, including software, soft goods, and property supplies. **Audience:** Owners and rental operators. **Principal Exhibits:** Goods and services geared to multi-housing professionals, including software, soft goods, and property supplies. Dates and Locations: 2025 May 07-09 Houston, TX. **Telecommunication Services:** conference@taa.org.

CONSULTANTS

776 ■ **Rental Relocation Inc. (RRI)**
535 Colonial Pk. Dr., Bldg. A
Roswell, GA 30075
Free: 844-737-0611
Co. E-mail: info@rentalrelocation.com
URL: http://www.rentalrelocation.com
Contact: James Bilderback, President
Facebook: www.facebook.com/RentalRelocationInc
Linkedin: www.linkedin.com/company/rental-relocation-inc.
YouTube: www.youtube.com/channel/UC3B3HJ4K3u_pZvNlT6omFXw
Description: Firm provides consulting services in corporate housing, rentals, locating free metro Atlanta apartment, property management, house and condo rental relocation tours. **Scope:** Firm provides consult-

ing services in corporate housing, rentals, locating free metro Atlanta apartment, property management, house and condo rental relocation tours. **Founded:** 1989.

COMPUTERIZED DATABASES

777 ■ *Colorado Economic Demographic Information System*
Colorado Department of Local Affairs
 1313 Sherman St., Ste. No. 518
 Denver, CO 80203
Ph: (303)864-7720
Fax: (303)353-0751
Co. E-mail: dola_web@state.co.us
URL: http://cdola.colorado.gov
Contact: Rick M. Garcia, Executive Director
URL(s): coloradodemography.github.io/demography/cedis
Availability: Online. **Type:** Time Series.

778 ■ *Psychoanalytic Dialogues*
Routledge, Taylor & Francis Group
 2-4 Park Sq., Oxfordshire
 Abingdon OX14 4RN, United Kingdom
URL: http://www.routledge.com
URL(s): www.tandfonline.com/journals/hpsd20
Released: 6/year **Price:** $223, Individuals for print and online; $954, Institutions for print and online; $188, Individuals for online only; $782, Institutions for online. **Availability:** Print; Download; PDF; Online. **Type:** Full-text.

RESEARCH CENTERS

779 ■ **Harvard University - Joint Center for Housing Studies (JCHS)**
1 Bow St., Ste. 400
 Cambridge, MA 02138
Ph: (617)495-7908
Fax: (617)496-9957
Co. E-mail: jchs@harvard.edu
URL: http://www.jchs.harvard.edu
Contact: David Luberoff, Director
Linkedin: www.linkedin.com/company/harvard-joint-center-for-housing-studies
X (Twitter): x.com/harvard_jchs
YouTube: www.youtube.com/channel/UCLQJRqIxAC2DdyzknJwi1kg
Description: Publishes reports, working papers, and a newsletter for professionals, academics, and interested laypeople. Research on housing and housing-related issues, broadly defined. Does not accept unsolicited manuscripts. **Scope:** Policy research in housing and construction, demographics, and related topics. Seeks to develop scholars, policy makers, and practitioners. Provides a forum for academics, business and labor leaders, and government officials. Conducts lectures. **Founded:** 1959. **Publications:** *Improving America's Housing* (Semiannual); *State of the Nation's Housing Report* (Annual). **Awards:** Edward M. Gramlich Fellowship in Community and Economic Development (Annual).

780 ■ **National Housing Law Project (NHLP)**
1663 Mission St Ste. 460
 San Francisco, CA 94103
Ph: (415)546-7000
Co. E-mail: nhlp@nhlp.org
URL: http://www.nhlp.org
Contact: Shamus Roller, Executive Director
E-mail: sroller@nhlp.org
Facebook: www.facebook.com/nationalhlp
X (Twitter): twitter.com/nhlp
Description: Provides back-up assistance, including research and litigation, to local legal services programs in areas of housing law such as landlord-tenant law, the Federal Community Development Block Grant program, displacement, public housing and Section 8, HUD subsidized multi-family housing, rural housing, single-family housing and state housing finance agencies. Maintains Washington, DC, office. **Scope:** Legal and policy research in area of low-income housing, including community development, displacement and relocation, landlord-tenant relationship, Housing and Urban Development-subsidized multifamily housing, rural housing, public housing and Section 8, single-family housing, state housing finance agencies, syndication, and housing management. **Founded:** 1968. **Publications:** *Farmers Home Administration Housing: Tenants' and Homeowners' Rights*; *Housing Law Bulletin* (10/year). **Educational Activities:** NHLP Conferences (Biennial), Exhibit relating to low-income housing issues. **Geographic Preference:** National.

781 ■ **San Francisco Planning and Urban Research Association (SPUR)**
654 Mission St.
 San Francisco, CA 94105-4015
Ph: (415)781-8726
Co. E-mail: info@spur.org
URL: http://www.spur.org
Contact: Alicia John-Baptiste, President
E-mail: ajohn-baptiste@spur.org
Facebook: www.facebook.com/SPUR.Urbanist
X (Twitter): x.com/SPUR_Urbanist
Instagram: www.instagram.com/spur_urbanist
Description: Citizens, businesses and government representatives; aims to develop balanced, informed and innovative solutions to urban problems, and promotes good government. **Scope:** Public policy issues of concern to San Francisco, including studies on housing, transportation, regional affairs, city planning, urban design and open space, city finance and operations. Recent activities include a study of an evaluation of how to improve service on the municipal railway and a ballot measure; a study of ways to increase housing supply in San Francisco and proposed legislation; car sharing; policy recommendation to improve operations of the city parks, and two proposed ballot measures; and ballot analysis of city propositions for each election. **Founded:** 1910. **Publications:** *SPUR Newsletter* (Monthly); *SPUR Newsletter*. **Educational Activities:** SPUR Annual conference, Offer exemplary teaching and training programs.; SPUR Forums, Offer exemplary teaching and training programs. **Awards:** Silver SPUR Awards (Annual); Silver SPUR Awards (Annual). **Geographic Preference:** Local.

782 ■ **University of California, Berkeley - Fisher Center for Real Estate and Urban Economics (FCREUE)**
2220 Piedmont Ave.
 Berkeley, CA 94720
Ph: (510)643-6105
Fax: (510)643-7357
Co. E-mail: creue@haas.berkeley.edu
URL: http://haas.berkeley.edu/RealEstate
Contact: Kenneth T. Rosen, Chairman
E-mail: krosen@haas.berkeley.edu
Facebook: www.facebook.com/FisherUCB
X (Twitter): x.com/FisherUCB
Description: Integral unit of University of California at Berkeley. **Scope:** Policy research in commercial real estate development and finance, housing finance and construction, and urban and regional development. Activities focus on improving understanding and encouraging innovation in the housing and mortgage finance systems and providing detailed study and analysis of the urban and regional economy of California, including studies on the demand for housing, affordability, alternative mortgage instruments, restructuring the housing finance system, land use regulations, property taxation and housing production, rental housing, housing revitalization and the change in national policy, housing and energy conservation, commercial real estate, real estate investment analysis, and international housing. Communicates research findings to both the public and private sectors, particularly to those concerned with allocation of urban land resources. **Founded:** 1950. **Publications:** *FCREUE Newsletter*; *Reprints*; *FCREUE Working papers*. **Educational Activities:** Executive education conferences, Offer exemplary teaching and training programs.; Professional conferences, Offer exemplary teaching and training programs.; FCREUE Public lectures, Offer exemplary teaching programs.; Real Estate Research Seminar (Weekly), Offer exemplary teaching programs.

Appliance Store

START-UP INFORMATION

783 ■ *"Stockerts Open Repair Business" in Dickinson Press (July 13, 2010)*
Pub: The Dickinson Press
Contact: Joy Schoch, Business Manager
Description: Ed Stockert is opening his new appliance repair firm in Dickinson, North Dakota with his wife Anna.

ASSOCIATIONS AND OTHER ORGANIZATIONS

784 ■ **Appliance Parts Distributors Association (APDA)**
PO Box 31816
Charlotte, NC 28231
URL: http://www.apda.com
Contact: Dave Cook, President
Facebook: www.facebook.com/AppliancePartsDistributorsAssociation
X (Twitter): x.com/APDA_News
Description: Represents wholesale distributors of appliance parts, supplies, and accessories. Promotes the sale of appliance parts through independent parts distributors. **Founded:** 1937. **Geographic Preference:** National.

785 ■ **Association of Home Appliance Manufacturers (AHAM)**
1111 19th St. NW, Ste. 402
Washington, DC 20036
Ph: (202)872-5955
Fax: (202)872-9354
Co. E-mail: info@aham.org
URL: http://www.aham.org
Contact: Joseph M. McGuire, President
E-mail: jmcguire@aham.org
Facebook: www.facebook.com/AHAMhome
Linkedin: www.linkedin.com/company/association-of-home-appliance-manufacturers-aham-
X (Twitter): x.com/AHAM_Voice
YouTube: www.youtube.com/user/AHAMMEdia
Description: Companies manufacturing major and portable appliances; supplier members provide products and services to the appliance industry. Major areas of activity include: market research and reporting of industry statistics; development of standard methods for measuring appliance performance and certification of certain characteristics of room air conditioners, refrigerators, freezers, humidifiers, dehumidifiers, and room air cleaners; public relations and press relations. Represents the appliance industry before government at the federal, state, and local levels. **Founded:** 1967. **Publications:** *AHAM Membership Directory* (Annual); *Directory of Certified Refrigerators and Freezers* (Semiannual); *Directory of Certified Dehumidifiers*; *Directory of Certified Humidifiers* (Semiannual); *Directory of Certified Room Air Conditioners* (Semiannual); *Association of Home Appliance Manufacturers--Directory of Certified* (Semiannual); *AHAM Verifide Database*. **Awards:** Home Appliance Industry Leadership Award (Annual). **Geographic Preference:** National.

786 ■ **International Housewares Association (IHA)**
6400 Shafer Ct., Ste. 650
Rosemont, IL 60018
Ph: (847)292-4200
Fax: (847)292-4211
Co. E-mail: sschatz@housewares.org
URL: http://www.housewares.org
Contact: Derek Miller, Director
E-mail: dmiller@housewares.org
Facebook: www.facebook.com/InternationalHousewaresAssociation
Instagram: www.instagram.com/theinspiredhomeshow
YouTube: www.youtube.com/housewaresShow
Description: Conducts annual market research survey of the housewares industry. Manages the international housewares show. **Founded:** 1906. **Publications:** *BusinessWatch* (Quarterly); *Housewares MarketWatch* (Quarterly); *IHA Reports* (Monthly); *January Exhibitors Directory* (Annual); *NHMA Reports Newsletter* (Bimonthly); *IHA Membership Directory* (Annual). **Educational Activities:** The Inspired Home Show (Annual); The Inspired Home Show (Annual). **Awards:** IHA Student Design Competition (Annual). **Geographic Preference:** National.

REFERENCE WORKS

787 ■ *"Abt Electronics and Appliances Announces the Second Annual Earth Day Recycle Drive" in Ecology, Environment & Conservation Business (May 3, 2014, pp. 3)*
Pub: NewsRX LLC.
Contact: Kalani Rosell, Contact
Description: Abt Electronics and Appliances is the largest independent, single-store appliance and electronics retailer in the U.S. In honor of Earth Day, Abt has partnered with the City of Chicago to help local residents recycle e-waste, such as electronics and appliances, in an environmentally friendly way for the second year in a row. **Availability:** Online.

788 ■ *"Cash for Appliances Targets HVAC Products, Water Heaters" in Contractor (Vol. 56, October 2009, No. 10, pp. 1)*
Ed: Candace Roulo. **Description:** States and territories would need to submit a full application that specifies their implementation plans if they are interested in joining the Cash for Appliances program funded by the American Recovery and Reinvestment Act. The Department of Energy urges states to focus on heating and cooling equipment, appliances and water heaters since these offer the greatest energy savings potential. **Availability:** Print; Online.

789 ■ *"Consumers Like Green, But Not Mandates" in Business Journal-Milwaukee (Vol. 28, December 10, 2010, No. 10, pp. A1)*
Pub: The Business Journal
Contact: Heather Ladage, President
E-mail: hladage@bizjournals.com
Ed: Sean Ryan. **Description:** Milwaukee, Wisconsin consumers are willing to spend more on green energy, a survey has revealed. Respondents also said they will pay more for efficient cars and appliances. Support for public incentives for homeowners and businesses that reduce energy use has also increased. **Availability:** Print; Online.

790 ■ *"First Sustainability Standard for Household Portable and Floor Care Appliances Developed to Identify Environmentally Responsible Products" in Ecology, Environment & Conservation Business (September 13, 2014, pp. 39)*
Pub: NewsRX LLC.
Contact: Kalani Rosell, Contact
Description: the Association of Home Appliance Manufacturers (AHAM), CSA Group, and the UL Environment released the AHAM 7002-2014/CSA SPE-7002-14/UL 7002, Sustainability Standard for Household Portable and Floor Care Appliances. This is the first voluntary sustainability standards for these appliances and is the third in a unit of product sustainability standards under development by the group. These standards are intended for use by manufacturers, governments, retailers, and others to identify products conforming to these standards in six key areas: materials, manufacturing and operations, energy consumption during use, end-of-life, consumables, and innovation. **Availability:** Online.

791 ■ *"Life's Work: James Dyson" in Harvard Business Review (Vol. 88, July-August 2010, No. 7-8, pp. 172)*
Pub: Harvard Business Publishing
Contact: Diane Belcher, Managing Director
Ed: Alison Beard. **Price:** $8.95. **Description:** The founder of appliance company Dyson Ltd. discusses the role of making mistakes in learning and innovation, and emphasizes the importance of hands-on involvement to make a company successful. **Availability:** Online; PDF.

792 ■ *"Men and Menu: A Switch in the Kitchen" in Barron's (Vol. 88, March 24, 2008, No. 12, pp. 17)*
Pub: Dow Jones & Company Inc.
Contact: Almar Latour, Chief Executive Officer
Ed: Robin Goldwyn Blumenthal. **Description:** Men are doing more kitchen duties, with 18 percent of meals at home being made by men in 2007 compared to 11 percent four years previously. Young wives, however, choose to forgo work and stay at home. **Availability:** Online.

793 ■ *"Sears, After Years of Closures, to Open Three Small-Format Stores" in The Wall Street Journal (April 4, 2019)*
URL(s): www.wsj.com/articles/sears-after-years-of-closures-is-opening-stores-again-11554379761
Ed: Suzanne Kapner. **Released:** April 04, 2019.
Description: After Sears closed hundreds of stores over the years, they are now planning on opening

three smaller stores with a focus on tools, appliances, and other hard goods. These smaller stores, called Sears Home & Life, will also sell mattresses and lawn and garden equipment. **Availability:** Print; Online.

794 ■ *"Truffles & Trifles' Marci Arthur Plans YouTube Channel, Cookbook" in Orlando Business Journal (Vol. 30, May 2, 2014, No. 45, pp. 3)*
Pub: American City Business Journals, Inc.
Contact: Mike Olivieri, Executive Vice President
Released: Weekly. **Price:** $8, introductory 4-week offer(Digital & Print). **Description:** Marci Arthur, founder of Truffles & Trifles Cooking School, plans to create a YouTube channel and publish a cookbook. Arthur believes that the survival of her business can be attributed to the devotion and integrity of her employees. Reports show that the school has been receiving donations from sponsors such as Wolf Appliances and Sub-Zero. **Availability:** Print; Online.

795 ■ *"War Veteran Hit Payoff with Repair Business" in Tulsa World (July 28, 2010)*
Pub: Tulsa World
Contact: Tim Chamberlin, Editor
E-mail: tim.chamberlin@tulsaworld.com
Ed: Tim Stanley. **Description:** Profile of Sam Melton, Korean War veteran and retired Air Force staff sergeant, launched appliance repair stores in the Tulsa, Oklahoma area 50 years ago. **Availability:** Print; Online.

796 ■ *"Whirlpool Virtual Showroom Opens for Business on Pinterest" in AdWeek (October 28, 2021)*
Ed: David Cohen. **Released:** October 28, 2021. **Description:** Whirlpool introduced a new showroom and it's all virtual on Pinterest. This format will give viewers the option to look at the set-up areas with a 360-degree view and will give them an opportunity to interact with new appliances. **Availability:** Online.

STATISTICAL SOURCES

797 ■ *Appliance Repair Industry in the US - Market Research Report*
URL(s): www.ibisworld.com/united-states/market-research-reports/appliance-repair-industry/
Price: $925. **Description:** Downloadable report analyzing data about the current and future trends in the appliance repair industry. **Availability:** Download.

798 ■ *Consumer Electronics & Appliances Rental Industry in the US - Market Research Report*
URL(s): www.ibisworld.com/united-states/market-research-reports/consumer-electronics-appliances-rental-industry/
Price: $925. **Description:** Downloadable report analyzing the current and future trends in the consumer electronics and appliance rental industries. **Availability:** Download.

799 ■ *RMA Annual Statement Studies*
Pub: Risk Management Association
Contact: Nancy Foster, President
Released: Annual. **Description:** Contains composite balance sheets and income statements for more than 360 industries, including the accounting, auditing, and bookkeeping industries. Also contains five years of comparative historical data for discerning trends. Includes 16 commonly used ratios, computed for most of the size groupings for nearly every industry.

800 ■ *Standard & Poor's Industry Surveys*
Pub: Standard And Poor's Financial Services LLC.
Contact: Douglas L. Peterson, President
Description: Two-volume book that examines the prospects for specific industries, including trucking. Also provides analyses of trends and problems, statistical tables and charts, and comparative company analyses.

TRADE PERIODICALS

801 ■ *Appliance Design*
Pub: BNP Media
Contact: Harper Henderson, Owner Co-Chief Executive Officer
URL(s): www.assemblymag.com/keywords/appliance%20design
Released: Monthly **Description:** Magazine on appliance technology, design for manufacturing, and design trends. **Availability:** Print; Online.

FRANCHISES AND BUSINESS OPPORTUNITIES

802 ■ Corbeil Appliances
2025 Rue Cunard
Laval, QC, Canada H7S 2N1
Free: 877-726-7234
Co. E-mail: service@corbeilelectro.com
URL: http://www.corbeilelectro.com
Facebook: www.facebook.com/CorbeilElectro
Instagram: www.instagram.com/corbeil.electro
Description: Retailer of refrigerators, cooking products, vacuum cleaner, dishwashers, wine coolers. **Founded:** 1949. **Training:** Provides 3 weeks training.

Appraisal Service

START-UP INFORMATION

803 ■ *How to Build an Appraisal Service Business: The Only Book You Need to Launch, Grow & Succeed*
Ed: T.K. Johnson. **Released:** 2015. **Description:** A guide on starting an appraisal service business. **Availability:** Print.

ASSOCIATIONS AND OTHER ORGANIZATIONS

804 ■ American Guild of Appraisers (AGA)
PO Box 553
 Spencerville, MD 20868
Ph: (301)377-0099
URL: http://www.appraisersguild.org
Contact: Mark Skapinetz, President
E-mail: markskap.aga@gmail.com
Facebook: www.facebook.com/American-Guild-of-Appraisers-184163251686836
X (Twitter): x.com/AGALocal44
Description: Union representing professional real estate appraisers.

805 ■ Appraisal Institute Education and Relief Foundation (AI) - Library
200 W Madison, Ste. 2000
 Chicago, IL 60606
Ph: (312)335-4133
Co. E-mail: aierf@appraisalinstitute.org
URL: http://www.aierf.org
Contact: Kelli Kline Mayhew, Chairman
Description: Supports and promotes the profession of real estate valuation and the individuals who comprise the profession. Administers and disburses funds for the purpose of improving, advancing, researching and teaching the techniques of real estate appraisal. **Scope:** Education; real estate. **Founded:** 1991. **Holdings:** Figures not available. **Publications:** *Directory of Members*; *Appraiser News in Brief* (8/year); *American Institute of Real Estate Appraisers--Directory of Members* (Annual); *Appraisal Institute--Directory of Designated Members*; *The Appraisal Journal* (Quarterly); *Valuation* (Quarterly). **Educational Activities:** ABA Real Estate Lending Conference; Appraisal Institute Annual Conference (Annual). **Awards:** AIERF College Scholarship (Annual); AIERF Candidate for Designation Course Scholarship (Quarterly); AIERF Minorities and Women AI Course Scholarship (Quarterly); AIERF Practicing Affiliate Course Scholarship (Quarterly); AIERF Minorities and Women College Scholarship (Annual). **Geographic Preference:** National.

806 ■ Appraisers Association of America (AAA)
212 W 35th St., 11th Fl. S
 New York, NY 10001
Ph: (212)889-5404
Fax: (212)889-5503
Co. E-mail: referrals@appraisersassociation.org
URL: http://www.appraisersassociation.org
Contact: Sharon Chrust, President
Facebook: www.facebook.com/appraisersassociation
X (Twitter): x.com/AppraisersAssoc
Description: Focus on the development of fine and decorative arts. **Founded:** 1949. **Publications:** *Find an Appraiser*; *The Appraiser* (Quarterly); *Appraisers Association of America--Membership Directory*. **Geographic Preference:** National.

807 ■ International Society of Appraisers (ISA)
225 W Wacker Dr., Ste. 650
 Chicago, IL 60606
Ph: (312)981-6778
Co. E-mail: isa@isa-appraisers.org
URL: http://www.isa-appraisers.org
Contact: Irene Szylinger, President
Facebook: www.facebook.com/ISAppraisers
Linkedin: www.linkedin.com/company/international-society-of-appraisers
X (Twitter): x.com/ISAppraisers
Instagram: www.instagram.com/internationalsocietyappraisers
Description: Seeks to provide the public with a network of appraisal specialists who have been pre-screened by ISA. Conducts educational opportunities for members, the consumer public and other affinity groups. **Founded:** 1979. **Publications:** *ISA Professional Appraisers Information Exchange*; *Find an Appraiser*; *ISA Membership Directory* (Annual). **Educational Activities:** ISA Annual Conference (Annual). **Geographic Preference:** National.

808 ■ Jewelers' Security Alliance (JSA)
6 E 45th St.
 New York, NY 10017
Free: 800-537-0067
Fax: (212)808-9168
Co. E-mail: jsa2@jewelerssecurity.org
URL: http://jewelerssecurity.org
Contact: John J. Kennedy, President
Linkedin: www.linkedin.com/in/jewelerssecurityalliance
Description: Advocates for crime prevention in the jewelry industry. Provides crime information and assistance to the jewelry industry and law enforcement. **Founded:** 1883. **Publications:** *Annual Report on Crime Against the Jewelry Industry in U.S.* (Annual); *JSA Manual of Jewelry Security*. **Educational Activities:** Security Seminar and Expo for Retail Jewelry Chains (Annual). **Geographic Preference:** National.

809 ■ National Association of Appraisers (NAA)
7113 San Pedro Ave., Ste. 508
 San Antonio, TX 78216
Ph: (210)570-4950
Co. E-mail: info@naappraisers.org
URL: http://naappraisers.org
Contact: Bryan S. Reynolds, President
Facebook: www.facebook.com/NAAppraisers
Linkedin: www.linkedin.com/company/national-association-of-appraisers
X (Twitter): x.com/NAAppraisers
Instagram: www.instagram.com/naappraisers
YouTube: www.youtube.com/channel/UC4JJPWVXBPwBe5J-7rqoY9w
Description: Works to unite those engaged in the appraisal profession for the purpose of exerting a beneficial influence upon the profession and to advocate appraiser interests, promote member awareness through education and information services, provide services as may be beneficial to the membership at a reasonable fee structure and promote high standards of conduct of members. **Founded:** 2010.

810 ■ National Association of Jewelry Appraisers (NAJP)
PO Box 18
 Rego Park, NY 11374-0018
Ph: (718)896-1536
Co. E-mail: office@najaappraisers.com
URL: http://najaappraisers.com
Contact: Gail Brett Levine, Executive Director
Description: Gem and jewelry appraisers, jewelers, importers, brokers, manufacturers, gemological students, and others professionally interested in jewelry appraisal. Seeks to recognize and make available to the public the services of highly qualified, experienced, independent, and reliable jewelry appraisers. **Founded:** 1981. **Publications:** *National Association of Jewelry Appraisers Membership Directory*; *The Jewelry Appraiser* (Quarterly). **Geographic Preference:** Multinational.

811 ■ National Association of Real Estate Appraisers (NAREA)
PO Box 879
 Palm Springs, CA 92263
Free: 877-743-6806
Co. E-mail: support@assoc-hdqts.org
URL: http://www.narea-assoc.org
Contact: Bill C. Merrell, Member
Description: Aims to make available the services of the most highly qualified real estate appraisers. Offers certification to members. Publishes directories. **Founded:** 1966. **Publications:** *National Association of Real Estate Appraisers--Database of Members*; *NAREA Real Estate Appraisal Newsletter* (Bimonthly). **Geographic Preference:** National.

REFERENCE WORKS

812 ■ *"The Appraisal Industry at the Crossroads of Change and Re-Invention"* in *MBA Insights (October 8, 2019)*
URL(s): www.mba.org/publications/insights/archive/mba-insights-archive/2019/the-appraisal-industry-at-the-crossroads-of-change-and-re-invention-x247556
Ed: Tony Pistilli. **Released:** January 28, 2019. **Description:** Comprehensive view of the changes coming along in the appraisal industry as it moves to have appraisers take on additional tasks and move towards a pay by the hour model. **Availability:** Online.

813 ■ Appraisal Service — Small Business Profiles

813 ■ Appraisers Association of America--Membership Directory
Pub: Appraisers Association of America
Contact: Sharon Chrust, President
URL(s): www.appraisersassociation.org/about-us
Description: Covers 800 member appraisers of fine art, antiques, and personal property. **Entries include:** Name, address, phone, specialties. **Arrangement:** Geographical. **Indexes:** Alphabetical, specialty. **Availability:** Print.

814 ■ "Reengineering the Appraisal Process, Revisited" in Appraisal Buzz (Fall 2016, No. 03, Year 2, pp. 51 - 54)
URL(s): cdn.coverstand.com/35955/346054/403e6dc31beb19800d2d401557433067b0d5abb0.1.pdf
Ed: Joan Trice. **Released:** 2016. **Description:** Discusses the consequences of the Home Valuation Code of Conduct upon Government Sponsored Enterprises. **Availability:** Print; Online.

815 ■ "Refinance: To Do Or Not To Do?" in Real Estate Review (Vol. 41, Spring 2012, No. 1, pp. 91)
Description: An author's experiences in home mortgage refinancing are presented. The author's encounter with home appraisers is mentioned. Special or streamlined loans can be secured by parties with existing conforming loans. **Availability:** Print; Online.

816 ■ "The Residential Appraisal Process Needs a New Standard" in Forbes (June 20, 2018)
URL(s): www.forbes.com/sites/forbesrealestatecouncil/2018/06/20/the-residential-appraisal-process-needs-a-new-standard/#7e7b010f7742
Ed: Jason Mitchell. **Released:** June 20, 2018. **Description:** Discusses the value of having an algorithm to assess a property's value, instead of relying solely on an assessor. A larger lender has already adopted this method, which could lead to massive savings in the industry and for the buyer. **Availability:** Online.

817 ■ "What You Should Know About Home Appraisals" in Investopedia (June 25, 2019)
URL(s): www.investopedia.com/articles/pf/12/home-appraisals.asp
Ed: Amy Fontinelle. **Released:** June 25, 2019. **Description:** Overview of the appraisal process for homes and other property during a new sale or a refinance situation. **Availability:** Online.

STATISTICAL SOURCES

818 ■ Credit Counselors, Surveyors & Appraisers Industry in the US - Market Research Report
URL(s): ibisworld.com/united-states/market-research-reports/credit-counselors-surveyors-appraisers-industry/
Price: $925. **Description:** Downloadable report analyzing the current and future trends in various industries that include credit counselors, surveyors, and appraisers. **Availability:** Download.

TRADE PERIODICALS

819 ■ The Appraisers Standard
Pub: New England Appraisers Association
URL(s): www.newenglandappraisers.org/membership/fees-for-membership
Description: Trade magazine for personal property appraisers. **Availability:** Online.

820 ■ Canadian Property Valuation
Pub: Appraisal Institute of Canada
Contact: Keith Lancastle, Chief Executive Officer
E-mail: keithl@aicanada.ca
URL(s): www.aicanada.ca/about-aic/canadian-property-valuation-magazine

Released: Quarterly **Price:** $40, for per year. **Description:** Magazine on the certification of real property appraisers and techniques regarding real estate appraising. **Availability:** Print; PDF; Download; Online.

TRADE SHOWS AND CONVENTIONS

821 ■ Appraisal Institute Annual Conference
Appraisal Institute Education and Relief Foundation (AI)
200 W Madison, Ste. 2000
Chicago, IL 60606
Ph: (312)335-4133
Co. E-mail: aierf@appraisalinstitute.org
URL: http://www.aierf.org
Contact: Kelli Kline Mayhew, Chairman
URL(s): ai.appraisalinstitute.org/eweb/DynamicPage.aspx?webcode=aiconfreglanding&evt_key=D2D766CF-3C68-4A48-AA83-B9EE093A2177
Frequency: Annual. **Description:** Exhibits of the latest cutting-edge valuation products and services. **Audience:** Appraisal services, government officials, or real estate industry leaders. **Principal Exhibits:** Exhibits of the latest cutting-edge valuation products and services. **Telecommunication Services:** lisa@norcal-ai.org.

822 ■ International Appraisers Conference
National Association of Independent Fee Appraisers (NAIFA)
330 N Wabash Ave., Ste. 2000
Chicago, IL 60611
Ph: (312)321-6830
Free: 800-272-8258
Fax: (312)673-6652
Co. E-mail: info@naifa.com
URL: http://www.naifa.com
Contact: Linda B. Trugman, President
URL(s): www.appraisers.org/Education/conferences
Frequency: Annual. **Description:** Offer exemplary teaching and training programs. **Audience:** Appraisal professionals. **Principal Exhibits:** Offer exemplary teaching and training programs. **Telecommunication Services:** asainfo@appraisers.org.

823 ■ ISA Annual Conference
International Society of Appraisers (ISA)
225 W Wacker Dr., Ste. 650
Chicago, IL 60606
Ph: (312)981-6778
Co. E-mail: isa@isa-appraisers.org
URL: http://www.isa-appraisers.org
Contact: Irene Szylinger, President
URL(s): www.isa-appraisers.org/annual-conference
Frequency: Annual. **Description:** Exhibits relating to materials and service pertaining to appraising. **Audience:** Professionals. **Principal Exhibits:** Exhibits relating to materials and service pertaining to appraising. Dates and Locations: 2025 Apr 02-05 The Ritz-Carlton Pentagon City hotel, Arlington, VA.

CONSULTANTS

824 ■ Artemis Inc.
7315 Wisconsin Ave., Ste. 242-W
Bethesda, MD 20814
Contact: Sheldon J. Singer, Contact
Description: Firm is a fine art appraiser who provides consultation on art purchases decoration, framing, and presentation and also provides auction services. **Scope:** Firm is a fine art appraiser who provides consultation on art purchases decoration, framing, and presentation and also provides auction services.

825 ■ Brian Kathenes Autographs & Collectibles
PO Box 341
Hope, NJ 07844
Ph: (908)256-6119
Co. E-mail: pbc@successfulteams.com
URL: http://www.pbcbiz.com
Contact: Brian Kathenes, President
E-mail: brian@nacvalue.com

Facebook: www.facebook.com/pages/Progressive-Business-Consultants/586310694783994
Linkedin: www.linkedin.com/profile/view
X (Twitter): x.com/pbc_biz
Description: Personal property appraisal consulting firm specializing in authentication and appraisal of antiques, collectibles, manuscripts, autographed documents and rare books and serves attorneys, trust officers, curators, archivists, museums, historical societies, accountants and government agencies worldwide and also provides expert witness in appraisal-related court cases. **Scope:** Personal property appraisal consulting firm specializing in authentication and appraisal of antiques, collectibles, manuscripts, autographed documents and rare books and serves attorneys, trust officers, curators, archivists, museums, historical societies, accountants and government agencies worldwide and also provides expert witness in appraisal-related court cases. **Publications:** "The Autograph Detective". **Training:** Beating the Bushes, Santa Fe, Apr, 2006; Authenticating and Appraising Autographed Material; How to Be an Autograph Detective; Using Your Writing Skills in a New Hobby; Appraising Historical Documents; A Selection of Customized Training for Changing Organizations; Critical Components of Highly Effective Teams and Teamwork; Negotiating Secrets Every Manager Needs to Know; Active Listening and Superb Communication; Identifying, Defining and Solving Problems; Through Effective Management and Supervision; Taking control of stress in business and in your life; Converting Conflict into a Positive Business Tool; Dealing with Challenging Situations and Difficult People; Everybody's a Leader; Motivating Your Staff and Yourself; How To Facilitate Experiential Learning and Team Building Activities.

FRANCHISES AND BUSINESS OPPORTUNITIES

826 ■ Auto Appraisal Network Inc. (AAN)
23986 Aliso Creek Rd., Ste. 204
Laguna Niguel, CA 92677
Ph: (949)387-7774
Free: 888-269-1120
Fax: (949)387-7775
Co. E-mail: info@autoappraisalnetwork.com
URL: http://autoappraisalnetwork.com
Contact: David Williams, Founder
Facebook: www.facebook.com/Auto-Appraisal-Network-Inc-319098384293
Linkedin: www.linkedin.com/company/autoappraisalnetwork
X (Twitter): x.com/AutoNetwork
Description: Firm provides vehicle appraisal reports. **Founded:** 1989. **Franchised:** 2007. **Financial Assistance:** Yes **Training:** Offers 5-6 days training at headquarters and ongoing support.

827 ■ Business America
555 Rte. Seventy Eight
Swanton, VT 05488
Ph: (802)868-7244
Co. E-mail: info@businessamerica1.com
URL: http://www.businessamerica1.com
Contact: Steve C. Selby, Contact
Description: Provider of payment solutions. **Founded:** 1997. **Franchised:** 1985. **Training:** Yes.

LIBRARIES

828 ■ Appraisal Institute Education and Relief Foundation (AI) - Library
200 W Madison, Ste. 2000
Chicago, IL 60606
Ph: (312)335-4133
Co. E-mail: aierf@appraisalinstitute.org
URL: http://www.aierf.org
Contact: Kelli Kline Mayhew, Chairman
Description: Supports and promotes the profession of real estate valuation and the individuals who comprise the profession. Administers and disburses funds for the purpose of improving, advancing, researching and teaching the techniques of real

estate appraisal. **Scope:** Education; real estate. **Founded:** 1991. **Holdings:** Figures not available. **Publications:** *Directory of Members*; *Appraiser News in Brief* (8/year); *American Institute of Real Estate Appraisers--Directory of Members* (Annual); *Appraisal Institute--Directory of Designated Members*; *The Appraisal Journal* (Quarterly); *Valuation* (Quarterly). **Educational Activities:** ABA Real Estate Lending Conference; Appraisal Institute Annual Conference (Annual). **Awards:** AIERF College Scholarship (Annual); AIERF Candidate for Designation Course Scholarship (Quarterly); AIERF Minorities and Women AI Course Scholarship (Quarterly); AIERF Practicing Affiliate Course Scholarship (Quarterly); AIERF Minorities and Women College Scholarship (Annual). **Geographic Preference:** National.

Aquarium Maintenance/Leasing Service

START-UP INFORMATION

829 ■ *"Add Aquatics to Boost Business"* in *Pet Product News (Vol. 64, December 2010, No. 12, pp. 20)*
Ed: David Lass. **Description:** Pet stores are encouraged to add aquatics departments to increase profitability through repeat sales. This goal can be realized by sourcing, displaying, and maintaining high quality live fish. Other tips regarding the challenges associated with setting up an aquatics department are presented. **Availability:** Online.

830 ■ *"Aquatic Medications Engender Good Health"* in *Pet Product News (Vol. 64, November 2010, No. 11, pp. 47)*
Ed: Madelaine Heleine. **Description:** Pet supply manufacturers and retailers have been exerting consumer education and preparedness efforts to help aquarium hobbyists in tackling ornamental fish disease problems. Aquarium hobbyists have been also assisted in choosing products that facilitate aquarium maintenance before disease attacks their pet fish. **Availability:** Online.

831 ■ *"Foods for Thought"* in *Pet Product News (Vol. 64, December 2010, No. 12, pp. 16)*
Ed: Maddy Heleine. **Description:** Manufacturers have been focused at developing species-specific fish foods due to consumer tendency to assess the benefits of the food they feed their fish. As retailers stock species-specific fish foods, manufacturers have provided in-store items and strategies to assist in efficiently selling these food products. Trends in fish food packaging and ingredients are also discussed. **Availability:** Online.

ASSOCIATIONS AND OTHER ORGANIZATIONS

832 ■ **American Pet Products Association (APPA)**
225 High Ridge Rd., Ste. W200
Stamford, CT 06905
Ph: (203)532-0000
Free: 800-452-1225
Fax: (203)532-0551
Co. E-mail: info@americanpetproducts.org
URL: http://www.americanpetproducts.org
Contact: Steve King, President
E-mail: sking@americanpetproducts.org
Facebook: www.facebook.com/AmericanPetProducts
Linkedin: www.linkedin.com/company/american-pet-products-association-appa
X (Twitter): x.com/APPAtweets
Instagram: www.instagram.com/americanpetproducts
YouTube: www.youtube.com/user/AmericanPetProducts
Description: U.S. Manufacturers and importers of pet products. Provides public relations program to promote pet ownership and pet care. Sponsors the association's annual National Pet Products Trade Show; publishes the National Pet Owner's Survey, the association's research study in the pet industry. **Founded:** 1958. **Publications:** *APPMA Advisor* (Quarterly). **Educational Activities:** Global Pet Expo (Annual). **Awards:** APPA New Product Showcase Awards (Annual). **Geographic Preference:** Multinational.

833 ■ **Aquarium and Zoo Facilities Association (AZFA)**
3900 Wildlife Way
Cleveland, OH 44109
URL: http://www.azfa.org
Contact: Trisha Crowe, President
Description: Seeks to increase understanding and appreciation of all life forms, with emphasis on conservation of all plants, animals, and natural resources. Fosters business and educational relations of its members. Engenders cooperation among the construction and maintenance staff members of zoos, parks, aquariums, and similar organizations. **Publications:** *The Outlet* (Quarterly). **Geographic Preference:** National.

834 ■ **Canadian Association of Aquarium Clubs (CAOAC)**
c/o Albert Van Montfort, Treasurer,
606 Stonebridge Ln.
Pickering, ON, Canada L1W 3B3
Co. E-mail: caoac1@gmail.com
URL: http://www.caoac.ca
Contact: Frank Aguirre, President
Facebook: www.facebook.com/CAOAC.RSAC
Description: Represents aquarium owners and other aquaculture hobbyists in Canada. Promotes effective care and breeding of aquatic plants and animals; encourages participation in the hobby of aquaculture. Conducts educational programs. **Founded:** 1959. **Publications:** *CAOAC Newsletter* (10/year). **Educational Activities:** Canadian Association of Aquarium Clubs Convention (Annual). **Awards:** CAOAC Breeders' Award (Annual); CAOAC Competition Awards (Annual); CAOAC Hobbyist of the Year (Annual); CAOAC Aquatic Horticulturist Award (Annual); CAOAC Junior Hobbyist of the Year (Annual); CAOAC Scientist Award (Annual). **Geographic Preference:** National.

835 ■ **World Pet Association (WPA) [American Pet Society (APS)]**
11801 Pierce St., Ste. 200
Riverside, CA 92505
Ph: (626)447-2222
Co. E-mail: info@wpamail.org
URL: http://www.worldpetassociation.org
Contact: Victor Mason, President
E-mail: vic.mason@wpamail.org
Linkedin: www.linkedin.com/in/world-pet-association-12700323
Description: Manufacturers, retailers and distributors of pet food and services and of avian, aquarium and companion animal care products, equipment and services. Seeks to advance the economic interests of members; promotes responsible pet ownership. Conducts trade shows, certificate training courses and seminars for pet shop retailers, grooming establishments and veterinary clinics. **Founded:** 1951. **Educational Activities:** Super Zoo (Annual); America's Family Pet Expo (Annual); WWPSA Annual Pet Industry Trade Show (Annual). **Geographic Preference:** National; Multinational.

REFERENCE WORKS

836 ■ *"Architect's Designs for Proposed Underwater Tennis Court Look Unreal"* in *Bleacher Report (May 16, 2015)*
URL(s): bleacherreport.com/articles/2466785-architect-wants-to-build-an-underwater-tennis-court-the-designs-look-unreal
Released: May 16, 2015. **Description:** Incredible underwater tennis court designs were unveiled by Polish architect Krysztof Kotala and his design firm, 8+8 Concept Studio. **Availability:** Online.

837 ■ *"Back To the Roots Puts a Hold On Bad Phone Music"* in *San Francisco Business Times (Vol. 28, February 21, 2014, No. 31, pp. 3)*
Pub: American City Business Journals, Inc.
Contact: Mike Olivieri, Executive Vice President
Released: Weekly. **Description:** Oakland, California-based Back to the Roots has changed its telephonehold music into a silly employee-produced tune. Former employee, Dennis Byrd, recorded the music that has a catchy beat, while the lyrics induce giggles from customers. The lyrics of the song are also presented. Back to the Roots sells aqua farm garden kits and mushroom kits. **Availability:** Print; Online.

838 ■ *"Ex-Im Bank Accepts $105 Million in Financing for Aquarium in Brazil"* in *Travel & Leisure Close-Up (October 8, 2012)*
Description: Export-Import Bank of the United States authorized a $105 million direct loan to the Brazilian state of Ceara to finance the export of American goods and services for the construction of an aquarium in Fortaleza, Brazil. This transaction will support 700 American jobs and at least 90 percent of the export contract value will be provided by U.S. small businesses. **Availability:** Print; Online.

839 ■ *"Faux Down Below"* in *Entrepreneur (May 2014)*
Pub: Entrepreneur Media Inc.
Contact: Dan Bova, Director
E-mail: dbova@entrepreneur.com
Description: Walter Marine of Orange Beach, Alabama has installed over 35,000 artificial reefs in waters in the U.S. and other countries to help prevent erosion and boost the tourism business. David Walter started his business in 1986 by sinking junk cars and items such as helicopters and kitchen sinks. Walter Marine is now focusing on custom-designed artificial reefs that are made of limestone and concrete. The company is hoping to increase its business by means of privately commissioned reefs. **Availability:** Print.

840 ■ "International Waters: Hawaii Aquarium Legislation Dead...Or Is It?" in Pet Product News (Vol. 66, September 2012, No. 9, pp. 76)
Ed: John Dawes. **Description:** SB 580 is deemed as one of the Hawaiin Senate bills that would lead to prohibition of, or heavy restrictions to, the collection of marine reef fish for home aquaria. Implications of these Senate bill on marine life conservation and stakeholder submissions are discussed. **Availability:** Online.

841 ■ "Invest in Energy-Efficient Equipment for Your Pet Store" in Pet Product News (Vol. 66, September 2012, No. 9, pp. 72)
Ed: Leila Meyer. **Description:** Aquatic retailers can achieve business growth by offering lighting products, pumps, heaters, filters, and other aquarium supplies that would help customers realize energy efficiency. Aside from offering an education in energy efficiency as a customer service opportunity, retailers are encouraged to determine what supplies are crucial in helping customers achieve energy usage goals. **Availability:** Online.

TRADE PERIODICALS

842 ■ *Tropical Fish Hobbyist*
Pub: T.F.H. Publications Inc.
URL(s): www.tfhmagazine.com
Facebook: www.facebook.com/TFHmagazine
X (Twitter): x.com/tfhmagazine
Instagram: www.instagram.com/tfhmag
Released: Bimonthly **Price:** $10, Individuals for back issues domestic, foreign and Canadian. **Description:** Tropical fish magazine for biologists, naturalists, schools, libraries, and commercial and non-commercial keepers and breeders of aquarium fish and plants. **Availability:** Print; Online.

RESEARCH CENTERS

843 ■ **Auburn University - College of Agriculture - School of Fisheries, Aquaculture and Aquatic Sciences - International Center for Aquaculture and Aquatic Environments (ICAAE) - Library**
Auburn, AL 36849
URL: http://aurora.auburn.edu/handle/11200/1127
Description: Integral unit of College of Agriculture, Auburn University. Provides information on relevant technical subjects. **Scope:** Provides technical assistance to developing countries on use of inland fisheries and aquaculture to enhance the production of food and income. Conducts in-country surveys, prepares project proposals for international funding agencies, helps establish pond culture research and development stations, and assists in the implementations of research, training, and extension programs in the following areas: aquacultural economics, aquacultural extension, inventory of fish species, fish taxonomy, fish nutrition and feeding, fish diseases, fish culture, hatchery management, chemical and biological aquatic weed control, limnological surveys, water pollution control and abatement, pond engineering and facility design, and fish technology, processing and preservation. **Founded:** 1991. **Holdings:** 2,500 books; annual reports of the Fisheries Resources Unit, 1936 to present; 10,000 slides and pictures; 250 dissertations; 550 theses. **Publications:** *ICAAE Abstracts*; *ICAAE Newsletter* (Quarterly).

Archery/Target/Shooting Range

ASSOCIATIONS AND OTHER ORGANIZATIONS

844 ■ Archery Range And Retailers' Organization, A Co-operative Association (ARRO)
516 Main St.
  Plattsmouth, NE 68048
Ph: (402)298-4700
Free: 800-234-7499
Fax: (402)298-4518
Co. E-mail: deb@archeryretailers.com
URL: http://archeryretailers.com
Contact: Martin Stubstad, President

Description: Owners of archery retail shops and/or indoor archery lanes. Functions as a cooperative buying group. Sanctions indoor archery leagues; provides national cash awards. **Founded:** 1981. **Geographic Preference:** National.

845 ■ National Field Archery Association (NFAA)
800 Archery Ln.
  Yankton, SD 57078
Ph: (605)260-9279
Fax: (605)260-9280
Co. E-mail: info@nfaausa.com
URL: http://www.nfaausa.com
Contact: Brian Sheffler, President
E-mail: lbsheff@comcast.net
Facebook: www.facebook.com/nfaausa
X (Twitter): x.com/NFAAUSA
Instagram: www.instagram.com/nfaausa
YouTube: www.youtube.com/user/NFAAUSA

Description: Field archers and bowhunters. Sponsors field archery schools, three national tournaments, and 16 sectional tournaments; works toward conservation of game and its natural habitat. **Founded:** 1939. **Publications:** *Archery* (Quarterly). **Educational Activities:** National Field Archery Association Conference. **Awards:** NFAA Bowfisher of the Year (Annual); NFAA Diamond Buck Award (Annual); NFAA Memorial Scholarship (Annual). **Geographic Preference:** National.

846 ■ National Sporting Clays Association (NSCA)
5931 Roft Rd.
  San Antonio, TX 78253
Ph: (210)688-3371
Free: 800-877-5338
Fax: (210)688-3014
Co. E-mail: nscrv@nssa-nsca.com
URL: http://nssa-nsca.org
Contact: Michael Hampton, Jr., Executive Director
E-mail: mhampton@nssa-nsca.com
Facebook: www.facebook.com/MyNSCA
X (Twitter): x.com/NationalSkeet
Instagram: www.instagram.com/nationalsportingclaysassoc
YouTube: www.youtube.com/channel/UChzKSrY8prE-u4yZQ2J-TyA

Description: Acts as the governing body of sporting clays and has an Advisory Council composed of range owners, shooters, and industry persons. Sanctions registered tournaments for member clubs, and uses registered scores to create an impartial classification system for competition. Operates national league and sweepstakes. Conducts championship competitions. Offers Instructor Certification Program to members. **Founded:** 1989. **Publications:** *Sporting Clays Magazine* (Quarterly). **Educational Activities:** National Delegate Meeting; National Sporting Clays Championships (Annual). **Geographic Preference:** National.

REFERENCE WORKS

847 ■ "Americans Spend $16.9 Billion on Target Shooting" in Shooting Illustrated (September 9, 2018)
URL(s): www.shootingillustrated.com/articles/2018/9/9/americans-spend-169-billion-on-target-shooting/
Ed: Guy J. Sagi. **Released:** September 09, 2018.
Description: Participation in the sport of target shooting is up 28% since 2001, which means more people are involved in this than other popular sports. Jobs are being created, leading to a higher GDP for the nation. **Availability:** Online.

848 ■ "Build Your Own Shooting Range" in RealTree (June 26, 2018)
URL(s): www.realtree.com/guns-and-shooting/articles/build-your-own-shooting-range
Released: June 26, 2018. **Description:** Outlines the advantages of building your own backyard shooting range and discusses visiting nearby ranges for practice. **Availability:** Online.

849 ■ Firearm Laws for Businesses and Their Customers
Ed: Gary Wells. **Released:** December 14, 2017.
Description: A guide on Texas firearm laws for businesses. **Availability:** Print.

850 ■ "How to Address a Negative Review on Social Media" in Archery Business (December 11, 2018)
URL(s): www.archerybusiness.com/address-negative-review-social-media
Ed: Michaelean Pike. **Released:** December 11, 2018.
Description: With the emergence of websites and social media that encourages leaving business reviews, how a business owner responds can either help or hurt the situation. Tips for writing a follow-up response are given, so that high customer service is maintained while keeping the integrity of the business intact. **Availability:** Online.

851 ■ "How to Keep Your Top Employees" in Archery Business (December 14, 2018)
URL(s): www.archerybusiness.com/keep-top-employees
Ed: Phillip M. Perry. **Released:** December 14, 2018.
Description: A guide on how to retain the best employees to help run your business. Gives tips on recognizing the top performers and how to compensate them so they stay, and points out how to create a respectful and supportive work environment. **Availability:** Online.

852 ■ "New Federal Law Will Promote Target Range Development on Public Lands" in NRA-ILA (May 24, 2019)
URL(s): nraila.org/articles/20190524/new-federal-law-will-promote-target-range-development-on-public-lands
Released: May 24, 2019. **Description:** The Target Practice and Marksmanship Training Support Act was signed into Law on May 10, 2019, which supports firearm safety and training. It allows for more federal funds to be used in the development and construction of public shooting ranges. **Availability:** Online.

TRADE PERIODICALS

853 ■ American Rifleman
Pub: National Rifle Association of America
URL(s): www.americanrifleman.org
Facebook: www.facebook.com/AmericanRifleman
X (Twitter): twitter.com/NRA_Rifleman
Instagram: www.instagram.com/americanriflemanmagazine

Description: Magazine covering firearms ownership and use. **Availability:** Online.

854 ■ Guns & Ammo
Pub: KSE Outdoor Sportsman Group LLC.
URL(s): www.gunsandammo.com
X (Twitter): x.com/GunsAndAmmoMag
Instagram: www.instagram.com/gunsandammomag
YouTube: www.youtube.com/user/GunsAndAmmoMag
Pinterest: www.pinterest.com/gunsandammomag

Released: Monthly **Price:** $15, for 1 year. **Description:** Magazine on firearms for beginners and experts. Features articles on target shooting, defensive techniques, plinking, hunting, law enforcement. **Availability:** Print; Online.

855 ■ Rifle: The Sporting Firearms Journal
Pub: Wolfe Publishing Company
Contact: Jeremiah Polacek, Manager
E-mail: jeremiah@wolfepub.com
URL(s): www.riflemagazine.com
Facebook: www.facebook.com/RifleMag

Ed: Dave Scovill. **Released:** Bimonthly; january-february, march-April, may-June, July-august, september-october, november-december. **Price:** $23.97, for digital only 1 year; $22.99, for print only 1 year; $10, Single issue; $39, U.S. for 2 years; $29, for foreign one year; $51, for foreign 2 years. **Description:** Covers all types of rifles-centerfires, rimfires, air rifles and muzzle loaders. **Availability:** Print; Online.

856 ■ Shooting Times
Pub: KSE Outdoor Sportsman Group LLC.
URL(s): www.shootingtimes.com

X (Twitter): x.com/ShootingTimesUS
Instagram: www.instagram.com/shootingtimesmag
Pinterest: www.pinterest.com/shootingtimesmag

Ed: Joel Hutchcroft. **Released:** Monthly **Price:** $15, for one year online only. **Description:** Magazine focusing on guns and shooting sports. **Availability:** Print; Online.

857 ■ *Skeet Shooting Review*
Pub: National Skeet Shooting Association
Contact: Michael Hampton, Executive Director
E-mail: mhampton@nssa-nsca.com
URL(s): nssansca.nssa-nsca.org/index.php/nssa
 -skeet-shooting/skeet-shooting-review

Released: Monthly **Description:** Magazine featuring shooting news, schedules of tournaments, shotgun tests and evaluations, shooting tips, new products, and coverage of major tournaments. **Availability:** Print; Online.

TRADE SHOWS AND CONVENTIONS

858 ■ Society for Range Management Annual Meeting
Society for Range Management (SRM)
 8918 W 21st St. N Ste. 200, No. 286
 Wichita, KS 67205
Ph: (303)986-3309
Fax: (303)986-3892
Co. E-mail: info@rangelands.org
URL: http://rangelands.org
Contact: Lia Biondo, Director
E-mail: policy@rangelands.org
URL(s): rangelands.org/annual-meeting-2025

Frequency: Annual. **Description:** Range management equipment and supplies. **Audience:** Land managers, scientists, educators, students, producers and conservationists. **Principal Exhibits:** Range management equipment and supplies. Dates and Locations: 2025 Feb 09-13 Spokane Convention Center, Spokane, WA. **Telecommunication Services:** specialsessions@rangelands.org.

LIBRARIES

859 ■ NRA Technical Library
National Rifle Association of America
 11250 Waples Mill Rd.
 Fairfax, VA 22030
Free: 800-672-3888
URL: http://contact.nra.org
Contact: Wayne LaPierre, Contact
Facebook: www.facebook.com/NRA
X (Twitter): x.com/nra
Instagram: www.instagram.com/NRA
YouTube: www.youtube.com/user/NRAVideos

Scope: Firearms; ammunition; military ordnance; antique arms; ballistics; handloading; collecting; history. **Services:** Library not open to the public. **Founded:** 1946. **Holdings:** 1,700 books. **Subscriptions:** 25 journals and other serials.

Architectural Restoration/Conservation

START-UP INFORMATION

860 ■ *"Staking Claim as Hub for Design"* in *Providence Business News (Vol. 28, March 17, 2014, No. 50, pp. 1)*
Pub: American City Business Journals, Inc.
Contact: Mike Olivieri, Executive Vice President
URL(s): pbn.com/staking-claim-as-hub-for-design95764

Description: Providence, Rhode Island is expected to have two startup accelerators in 2014, even though the city lacks a large technology and venture capital presence. The Providence Design Forward accelerator is a partnership with Rhode Island School of Design and will focus on architecture and interior design entrepreneurship. It is modeled after Boston's MassChallenge. **Availability:** Online.

ASSOCIATIONS AND OTHER ORGANIZATIONS

861 ■ Canadian Centre for Architecture (CCA) - Library [Centre Canadien d'Architecture; Centre Canadien d'Architecture - Bibliotheque]
1920, rue Baile Montréal
 Quebec, QC, Canada H3H 2S6
Ph: (514)939-7026
Co. E-mail: info@cca.qc.ca
URL: http://www.cca.qc.ca/en/about-research
Contact: Bruce Kuwabara, Partner
Facebook: www.facebook.com/cca.conversation
X (Twitter): x.com/ccawire
YouTube: www.youtube.com/user/CCAchannel

Description: Study center and museum devoted to the art of architecture, past and present. Provides access to research collections, exhibitions, publications, colloquial., educational and cultural programs, as well as family programs. **Scope:** Research institution operating from the fundamental premise that architecture is a public concern. **Services:** Copying; library open to the public by appointment. **Founded:** 1979. **Holdings:** 215,000 volumes; 5,000 periodicals; 100,000 reprints and drawings; 60,000 photographs.; . **Subscriptions:** ; 5,000 6,000 title reference collections; 1,500 bibliographies; 2,500 monographic titles; 200 dictionaries; almanacs; atlases; audio-visual materials; photocopies; newspapers. **Publications:** *Catalogues*; *CCA Monographs*; *Money Matters: A Critical Look at Bank Architecture*; *Sense of the City*. **Educational Activities:** CCA Architectural exhibitions (Continuous); Canadian Centre for Architecture Lectures. **Geographic Preference:** Multinational.

862 ■ Institut Royal d'Architecture du Canada (IRAC) [Royal Architectural Institute of Canada]
6118 James Bell Dr.
 Manotick, ON, Canada K4M 1B3
Ph: (613)241-3600
Free: 844-856-RAIC
Co. E-mail: info@raic.org
URL: http://raic.org
Contact: Jason Robbins, Co-President
E-mail: president@raic.org
Facebook: www.facebook.com/theraic.irac
Linkedin: www.linkedin.com/company/raic
X (Twitter): x.com/RAIC_IRAC
Instagram: www.instagram.com/raic_irac
YouTube: www.youtube.com/channel/UCNZQV0AnXh3LmLLETv0bEEw

Description: Registered architects in Canada united to further develop the quality of architecture. **Founded:** 1907. **Publications:** *RAIC Bulletin* (Bimonthly); *Update* (Bimonthly). **Educational Activities:** Royal Architectural Institute of Canada Conference (Annual). **Awards:** Andre Francou Legacy (Annual); Allied Arts Medal (Biennial); RAIC Gold Medal (Annual); RAIC Student Medal (Annual); Ernest Wilby Memorial Scholarship (Annual); Arthur Buckwell Memorial Scholarship (Annual). **Geographic Preference:** National.

863 ■ *Money Matters: A Critical Look at Bank Architecture*
1920, rue Baile Montréal
 Quebec, QC, Canada H3H 2S6
Ph: (514)939-7026
Co. E-mail: info@cca.qc.ca
URL: http://www.cca.qc.ca/en/about-research
Contact: Bruce Kuwabara, Partner
URL(s): www.cca.qc.ca/en/archives/502892/money-matters-exhibition-collection
Availability: Print.

864 ■ *RAIC Bulletin*
6118 James Bell Dr.
 Manotick, ON, Canada K4M 1B3
Ph: (613)241-3600
Free: 844-856-RAIC
Co. E-mail: info@raic.org
URL: http://raic.org
Contact: Jason Robbins, Co-President
E-mail: president@raic.org
URL(s): raic.org/raic/raic-bulletin
Released: Bimonthly **Availability:** Print; Online.

865 ■ Royal Oak Foundation (ROF)
20 W 44th St., Ste. 606
 New York, NY 10036-6603
Ph: (212)480-2889
Free: 800-913-6565
Fax: (212)764-7234
Co. E-mail: lectures@royal-oak.org
URL: http://www.royal-oak.org
Contact: Ian Murray, Executive Director
E-mail: imurray@royal-oak.org
Facebook: www.facebook.com/royaloakfoundation
Linkedin: www.linkedin.com/company/royal-oak-foundation
Instagram: www.instagram.com/theroyaloakfoundation

Description: Professionals, students, and laypeople who are interested in architecture, nature conservation, and historic preservation areas. Seeks to further the preservation and understanding of Anglo-American cultural and architectural heritage. Conducts symposia; presents lecture series and special lectures given by foreign speakers visiting the US.; sponsors exhibits emphasizing historic preservation. Maintains charitable program. **Founded:** 1973. **Geographic Preference:** National.

REFERENCE WORKS

866 ■ *"$100 Million Plan for Jefferson Arms"* in *Saint Louis Business Journal (Vol. 32, October 14, 2011, No. 7, pp. 1)*
Pub: Saint Louis Business Journal
Contact: Robert Bobroff, President
E-mail: rbobroff@bizjournals.com

Ed: Evan Binns. **Description:** Teach for America is planning a $100 million renovation project of the former Jefferson Arms hotel in St. Louis, Missouri. The organization has signed a letter of intent to occupy the space. Financing of the project will be mainly through tax credits. **Availability:** Print; Online.

867 ■ *"2010: Important Year Ahead for Waterfront"* in *Bellingham Business Journal (Vol. March 2010, pp. 2)*

Description: A tentative timeline has been established for the environmental impact statement (EIS) slated for completion in May 2010. The plan for the Waterfront District includes detailed economic and architectural analysis of the feasibility of reusing remaining structures and retaining some industrial icons. **Availability:** Print; Online.

868 ■ *"After 4 Decades, Claypool's Moving On"* in *Philadelphia Business Journal (Vol. 33, June 27, 2014, No. 20, pp. 8)*
Pub: American City Business Journals, Inc.
Contact: Mike Olivieri, Executive Vice President

Released: Weekly. **Price:** $4, Introductory 4-week offer(Digital only). **Description:** John Claypool, former executive director of the Philadelphia chapter of the American Institute of Architects (AIA) and its affiliated Center for Architecture, discusses the changes he has seen over the forty years of his association with the city's business community and government. Claypool reflects on his achievements during his tenure at AIA and the impact of the recession on the architectural industry. **Availability:** Print; Online.

869 ■ *"Annapolis Seeks City Market Vendors"* in *Boston Business Journal (Vol. 29, June 10, 2011, No. 5, pp. 3)*
Pub: Boston Business Journal
Contact: Carolyn M. Jones, President
E-mail: cmjones@bizjournals.com

Ed: Daniel J. Sernovitz. **Price:** $350. **Description:** The city of Annapolis, Maryland is planning to revive the historical landmark Market House and it is now accepting bids from vendors until June 10, 2011. The city hopes to reopen the facility by July 2011 for a six-month period after which it will undergo renovations. **Availability:** Print; Online.

870 ■ "Architects On Track for Ambitious Depot Renovation" in Sacramento Business Journal (Vol. 29, September 21, 2012, No. 30, pp. 1)
Pub: Baltimore Business Journal
Contact: Rhonda Pringle, President
E-mail: rpringle@bizjournals.com
Ed: Sanford Nax. Description: Page & Turnbull has set a plan to begin a major renovation of Sacramento Valley Station, a historic railroad depot in California and one of Amtrak's busiest stations. The city council has selected the Portland, Oregon-based Zimmer Gunsul Frasca Architects to lead the remodel and expects the construction to begin in fall 2013. Availability: Print; Online.

871 ■ "Architecture Panel Pushes Bozzuto" in Baltimore Business Journal (Vol. 31, March 21, 2014, No. 47, pp. 4)
Pub: American City Business Journals, Inc.
Contact: Mike Olivieri, Executive Vice President
Released: Weekly. Price: $4, introductory 4-week offer(Digital & Print). Description: The Bozzuto Group along with the Solstice Partners LLC, is developing its most ambitious $80 million Locust Point apartment project in Baltimore. Notorious for getting pretty tough with architects, the members of the city's Urban Design and Architecture Panel are highly focused on getting the building right. Designed in a unique S-shape, this building was approved by the UDARP panelists and they are planning to refine the details with the concerned architect within a week's time. Availability: Print; Online.

872 ■ "Bed and Breakfast Among Planned Uses for New Bohemia Properties" in Gazette (January 30, 2012)
Description: One of the buildings suffering flood damage in the middle of the New Bohemia district of Cedar Rapids, Iowa area will be converted into a one room bed and breakfast offering food catered by Parlor City. The two-story building will als house commercial business on the first floor and a two-bedroom apartment on the upper level. This concept follows the neighborhood's origins with shop owners living above their small business. Availability: Online.

873 ■ "'Better Together:' OCO LPA Executives Discuss Recent Merger" in San Antonio Business Journal (Vol. 28, July 4, 2014, No. 21, pp. 8)
Pub: American City Business Journals, Inc.
Contact: Mike Olivieri, Executive Vice President
Released: Weekly. Price: $4, introductory 4-week offer(Digital & Print). Description: Texas-based OCO Architects agreed to merge with LPA Inc. of Irvine, California effective July 1, 2014 and the local firm will initially operate as OCO LPA before it officially becomes LPA in January 2015. The merger is expected to keep OCO LPA relevant in the residential and commercial real estate sectors. Availability: Print; Online.

874 ■ "Brought To You By the Letter 'W'" in Washington Business Journal (Vol. 33, August 29, 2014, No. 19, pp. 6)
Pub: American City Business Journals, Inc.
Contact: Mike Olivieri, Executive Vice President
Released: Weekly. Price: $4, introductory 4-week offer(Digital & Print). Description: W Hotel, Washington DC's food and beverage spaces are undergoing renovations. Hotel guests will see a new roof and a more stylish, upscale restaurant. W Hotel's plan to offer a luxury experience is discussed. Availability: Print; Online.

875 ■ "C. Fla. Notches $5B in Real Estate Property Sales in Last 12 Months" in Orlando Business Journal (Vol. 31, July 4, 2014, No. 1, pp. 4)
Pub: American City Business Journals, Inc.
Contact: Mike Olivieri, Executive Vice President
Released: Weekly. Price: $8, Introductory 4-week offer(Digital & Print). Description: Real estate company Real Capital Analytics reports sales volumes totaling $5 billion in Central Florida's commercial real estate market between June 2013 and May 2014. Real estate deals in the region reflect investor interest in the Orlando market, as private equity and development firms renovate existing properties or build new construction projects, thus increasing property values, creating jobs and boosting the local economy. Availability: Print; Online.

876 ■ "Citrus Bowl Construction Bids Going Out This Year" in Orlando Business Journal (Vol. 29, June 29, 2012, No. 2, pp. 1)
Pub: Baltimore Business Journal
Contact: Rhonda Pringle, President
E-mail: rpringle@bizjournals.com
Description: The city of Orlando, Florida is expected to seek construction bids for the Florida Citrus Bowl's renovation in 2012. The project is estimated to cost $175 million. Availability: Print; Online.

877 ■ "Convention Ctr. Rehab To Impact Hotels, Eateries" in Silicon Valley/San Jose Business Journal (Vol. 30, May 18, 2012, No. 8, pp. 1)
Pub: Baltimore Business Journal
Contact: Rhonda Pringle, President
E-mail: rpringle@bizjournals.com
Description: The renovation of the San Jose McEnery Convention Center is seen to adversely impact businesses in the area. Contractors have already demolished the former Martin Luther King Jr. Main Library. Business sales in the area are expected to decline owing to the renovation.

878 ■ "Cradle of Commerce" in San Antonio Business Journal (Vol. 28, August 29, 2014, No. 29, pp. 4)
Pub: American City Business Journals, Inc.
Contact: Mike Olivieri, Executive Vice President
Description: Renewed interest in the Alamo is seen to boost tourism in San Antonio, Texas. The Alamo has been lagging behind other sites in terms of visitors. However, efforts to preserve and improve the grounds and visitor experience have heightened. Availability: Print; Online.

879 ■ "David Bugs Developer Goliaths" in Denver Business Journal (Vol. 64, August 17, 2012, No. 13, pp. 1)
Pub: Baltimore Business Journal
Contact: Rhonda Pringle, President
E-mail: rpringle@bizjournals.com
Description: The ordinance allowing citizens to file petitions for the declaration of some Denver buildings as historic is affecting real estate developers. Experts are concerned that these efforts for the preservation of abandoned facilities may become a trend that would hinder new land development projects. Changes in the ordinance are being suggested to ease the impact on developers. Availability: Print; Online.

880 ■ "Developers Tout Benefits of Federal Tax Breaks" in Business First of Buffalo (Vol. 30, March 14, 2014, No. 26, pp. 4)
Pub: American City Business Journals, Inc.
Contact: Mike Olivieri, Executive Vice President
Released: Weekly. Price: $140, Digital & Print; $115, Digital only. Description: President Obama has included a Federal tax credit program in the 2015 Federal budget that provides some relief to the local development community. Congressman Mark Higgins promised to support the program that offers tax breaks to urban developers who rehabilitate older buildings with new investments. The tax credit's economic benefits are also discussed. Availability: Print; Online.

881 ■ "Digging Dallas-Fort Worth: How Top 10 Major Construction Projects Will Change North Texas" in Dallas Business Journal (Vol. 37, May 23, 2014, No. 37, pp. 4)
Pub: American City Business Journals, Inc.
Contact: Mike Olivieri, Executive Vice President
Price: $4, print. Description: A list of the top ten largest construction projects in North Dallas in 2013 and their impact on local economies is presented. Included are the $303 million State Farm Insurance campus in Plano, $138.74 million termination renovation at Dallas-Fort Worth International Airport, and the $133.82 million Nebraska Furniture Mart in the Colony. Availability: Print; Online.

882 ■ "Fair or Foul? Ballparks and their Impact on Urban Revitalization" in Real Estate Review (Vol. 41, Spring 2012, No. 1, pp. 15)
Description: The influence of ballparks on urban renewal in the United States is examined. Cities have been using ballparks as a way to revitalize downtowns and redevelop/restore neighborhoods. Availability: Online.

883 ■ "Finally, New Life For Old IBM Offices" in Austin Business Journal (Vol. 34, June 6, 2014, No. 16, pp. A4)
Pub: American City Business Journals, Inc.
Contact: Mike Olivieri, Executive Vice President
Released: Weekly. Price: $4, introductory 4-week offer(Digital only). Description: Two nondescript, 1970s-style industrial buildings, occupied in the 1970s by IBM Corporation, were purchased by an Austin-based contracting and construction management company. Burt-Watts Industries, from Powell Austin Properties Ltd., a local family. The company spent $3 million to renovate all the spaces into attractive, contemporary offices. Tommy Burt, co-founder of Burt-Watts was helped in this endeavor by Clay Little, partner in NoackLittle Architecture & Interiors. Availability: Print; Online.

884 ■ "First, the Merger: Then, The Culture Clash. How To Fix the Little Things That Can Tear a Company Apart" in Inc. (January 2008)
Ed: Elaine Appleton Grant. Description: Ways three CEOs handled the culture classes that followed after company mergers; companies profiled include Fuel Outdoor, an outdoor advertising company; Nelson, an interior design and architecture firm; and Beber Silverstein, an ad agency. Availability: Online.

885 ■ "First Woman To Lead Builders Group" in Philadelphia Business Journal (Vol. 32, January 31, 2014, No. 51, pp. 8)
Pub: American City Business Journals, Inc.
Contact: Mike Olivieri, Executive Vice President
Released: Weekly. Price: $4, introductory 4-week offer(Digital & Print). Description: Anne Faldoun, president of the Building Industry Association of Philadelphia (BIA), reveals that she has always been interested in architecture. She shares that she worked at the Dorado Neighborhood Improvement Company after she attended graduate school. Her views about the BIA's policy on tax abatement are also discussed. Availability: Print; Online.

886 ■ "Flurry of Activity from Restaurant Groups as Industry Strengthens" in Wichita Business Journal (Vol. 27, February 17, 2012, No. 7, pp. 1)
Pub: Baltimore Business Journal
Contact: Rhonda Pringle, President
E-mail: rpringle@bizjournals.com
Description: Atlanta, Georgia-based Chick-fil-A chain is set to open two restaurants in Wichita, Kansas and those additions were highly anticipated. However, there were other local management groups and franchisees that are investing on new buildings and refurbishing stores. Insights on the increasing restaurant constructions are also given. Availability: Print; Online.

887 ■ "Former Prov. Mayor Sees Potential in Newport Grand" in Providence Business News (Vol. 29, July 21, 2014, No. 16, pp. 4)
Pub: American City Business Journals, Inc.
Contact: Mike Olivieri, Executive Vice President
URL(s): pbn.com/former-prov-mayor-sees-potential-in-newport-grand98638
Description: Joseph R. Paolino, Jr., managing partner at Paolino Properties and former Providence Mayor, believes introducing table games to Newport Grand can help the gambling casino generate needed revenues. Paolino notes that if voters approve a ballot referendum to authorize table games in November,

he and his partners will acquire and renovate Newport Grand as an entertainment center. **Telecommunication Services:** Daddona@pbn.com.

888 ■ *"Galveston Invests In Future as Major Cruise Destination"* in *Houston Business Journal (Vol. 44, February 28, 2014, No. 43, pp. 4)*
Pub: American City Business Journals, Inc.
Contact: Mike Olivieri, Executive Vice President
Released: Weekly. **Price:** $4, introductory 4-week offer(Digital only). **Description:** The Port of Galveston in Texas is planning to build a third cruise terminal to capitalize on the growing cruise industry as it faces new competition with the Bayport Cruise terminal of the Port of Houston Authority. Architecture firm McTigue of Los Angeles, California was commissioned to design the new terminal. **Availability:** Print; Online.

889 ■ *"Glenmede at Liberty To Show Off Space"* in *Philadelphia Business Journal (Vol. 32, January 24, 2014, No. 50, pp. 8)*
Pub: American City Business Journals, Inc.
Contact: Mike Olivieri, Executive Vice President
Released: Weekly. **Price:** $4, introductory 4-week offer(Digital & Print). **Description:** Glenmede Trust Company decided to undertake a full office renovation after renewing its lease at One Liberty Place. The investment company decided to replace drywall with glass and more informal meeting places were constructed. The firm, which focuses on employee engagement, aims to improve the work environment. **Availability:** Print; Online.

890 ■ *"Green Collar: Green Buildings Support Job Creation, Workforce Transformation and Economic Recovery"* in *Environmental Design and Construction (Vol. 15, July 2012, No. 7, pp. 31)*
Pub: BNP Media
Contact: Harper Henderson, Owner Co-Chief Executive Officer
Ed: Maggie Comstock. **Description:** Despite construction being at an all-time low, green building construction has maintained its hold on nonresidential buildings. It has even shown growth in some sectors and accounts for over one-third of all nonresidential design and construction jobs and is expected to show further growth through 2014. Statistical details included.

891 ■ *"'Groundhog Day' B&B Likely Will Be Converted Into One In Real Life"* in *Chicago Tribune (October 21, 2008)*
Pub: Tribune News Service
Contact: Jack Barry, Vice President, Operations
E-mail: jbarry@tribpub.com
Ed: Carolyn Starks. **Description:** Everton Martin and Karla Stewart Martin have purchased the Victorian house that was featured as a bed-and-breakfast in the 1993 hit move "Groundhog Day"; the couple was initially unaware of the structure's celebrity status when they purchased it with the hope of fulfilling their dream of owning a bed-and-breakfast. **Availability:** Print; Online.

892 ■ *"Healthcare Facilities Increasingly Embracing Dynamic Glass to Benefit Patients"* in *Ecology, Environment & Conservation Business (May 24, 2014)*
Pub: NewsRX LLC.
Contact: Kalani Rosell, Contact
Description: According to research, optimizing natural daylight and outdoor views in healthcare facilities helps to improve outcomes and shorter recovery times for patients. Therefore, a growing number of healthcare facilities are incorporating SageGlass(R) dynamic glass, a product of Saint-Gobain, into their new construction and remodeling/renovation designs. **Availability:** Online.

893 ■ *"Historic Is Hot, But Challenging, in Bham"* in *Birmingham Business Journal (Vol. 31, August 1, 2014, No. 31, pp. 10)*
Pub: American City Business Journals, Inc.
Contact: Mike Olivieri, Executive Vice President
Description: Birmingham, Alabama is witnessing a growing trend of restoring old and historic buildings for modern office spaces, driven by the new state credit for the projects. However, developers state that renovation projects present numerous challenges, including complying with current building codes and the use of energy-efficient innovation. **Availability:** Print; Online.

894 ■ *"Hunter Capital's Malone Relishes Role of Renovator"* in *Puget Sound Business Journal (Vol. 35, June 13, 2014, No. 8, pp. 9)*
Pub: American City Business Journals, Inc.
Contact: Mike Olivieri, Executive Vice President
Description: Hunter Capital's founder, Michael Malone, says Seattle, Washington's real estate development needs to be balanced. He also stated that his company is set to renovate the old Dunn Automotive Building. He added that his firm will continue with its construction restoration projects. **Availability:** Online.

895 ■ *"If They Build It, Will Customers Come?"* in *Business Journal Portland (Vol. 30, February 7, 2014, No. 49, pp. 7)*
Pub: American City Business Journals, Inc.
Contact: Mike Olivieri, Executive Vice President
Price: $4, Introductory 4-week offer(Digital & Print). **Description:** The Portland Trail Blazers partnered with Levy Restaurants to open a 10,000-square-foot restaurant at Moda Center in Oregon in spring 2014. GBD Architects and Lorentz Brunn Construction were enlisted for the project. **Availability:** Print; Online.

896 ■ *"Ihilani's New Day"* in *Pacific Business News (Vol. 26, August 22, 2014, No. 26, pp. 14)*
Pub: American City Business Journals, Inc.
Contact: Mike Olivieri, Executive Vice President
Description: JW Marriott Ihilani Resort and Spa is likely to be rebranded in 2014 as the Four Seasons Hotels and Resorts, making it the chain's fifth largest property in Hawaii. The implications of the hotel's renovation and rebranding for West Oahu's leisure and business travel sectors are discussed. **Availability:** Online.

897 ■ *"Innovation Can Be Imperative for Those in Hands-On Trades"* in *Crain's Cleveland Business (Vol. 28, November 12, 2007, No. 45)*
Pub: Crain Communications Inc.
Contact: K. C. Crain, President
Ed: Harriet Tramer. **Description:** Discusses the importance of networking and innovative marketing concerning those in art and restoration trades. **Availability:** Online.

898 ■ *"Investors Eye Old Buildings"* in *Business Journal-Portland (Vol. 24, October 19, 2007, No. 34, pp. 1)*
Pub: Portland Business Journal
Contact: Andy Giegerich, Managing Editor
E-mail: agiegerich@bizjournals.com
Ed: Wendy Culverwell. **Description:** Office vacancy rates in downtown Portland has dipped to around five percent, causing brokers and investors to search for older buildings in the Class B and Class C categories where the rent is also cheaper. Some notable older and cheaper buildings will be renovated for use. **Availability:** Print; Online.

899 ■ *"La Cantera Resort Expects to Benefit from Big Transformation"* in *San Antonio Business Journal (Vol. 28, July 18, 2014, No. 23, pp. 8)*
Pub: American City Business Journals, Inc.
Contact: Mike Olivieri, Executive Vice President
Released: Weekly. **Price:** $4, Introductory 4-week offer(Digital & Print). **Description:** La Cantera Hill County Resort in San Antonio, Texas is planning a multimillion dollar major renovation of the property and the addition of a spa. The resort announced the suspension of overnight accommodations and restaurant operations during the major phase of the construction from November 3, 2014 until early April 2015. **Availability:** Print; Online.

900 ■ *"Leadership in Architecture: My Passion in Life"*
Pub: AuthorHouse Inc.
Contact: William Elliott, President
Released: September 30, 2014. **Price:** $3.99, e-book; $27.99, hardcover; $3.99, E-Book. **Description:** MacDonal Becket, FAIA, profiles his career from the 1940s through the 1980s and his projects of Welton Becket and Associates and the Becket Group. His architecture firm is headquartered in Los Angeles, California and renovated the California State Capitol; Eisenhower Hall at West Point; Hyatt Reunion project in Dallas, Texas, the redevelopment of Boston Common; six buildings in Seoul, Korea; the Greet Wall Hotel in Beijing, China; and the World Trade Center in Moscow, USSR, and much more. **Availability:** E-book; Print.

901 ■ *"A Look Ahead at How Rail Could Change Ala Moana"* in *Pacific Business News (Vol. 52, August 22, 2014, No. 26, pp. 7)*
Pub: American City Business Journals, Inc.
Contact: Mike Olivieri, Executive Vice President
Released: August 22, 2014. **Price:** $4, Introductory 4-Week Offer(Digital & Print). **Description:** The City and County of Honolulu has hired Nate Cherry, vice president of California-based architectural firm RTKL, to create a new plan for Ala Moana in anticipation of the completed $5.16 billion Honolulu rail project. Cherry's plans for the neighborhood under the Transit Oriented Development project include better streets with wider sidewalks, wider tree canopies, bicycle trails and parks. **Availability:** Print; Online.

902 ■ *"Magellan Companies Establishes Century 21 Beachhead in Boise"* in *Idaho Business Review (September 15, 2014)*
Pub: BridgeTower Media
Contact: Adam Reinebach, President
Description: New Jersey-based Century 21, the largest real estate franchise worldwide, has entered the Idaho market under the name Century 21 Magellan Realty with five agents. Wesley Flacker, builder, home renovator, broker, and property manager purchased the franchise and expects to have 60 agents by 2015.

903 ■ *"Mall On a Mission: KOP to Get $150 Million Makeover"* in *Philadelphia Business Journal (Vol. 33, March 14, 2014, No. 5, pp. 6)*
Pub: American City Business Journals, Inc.
Contact: Mike Olivieri, Executive Vice President
Released: Weekly. **Price:** $4, introductory 4-week offer(Digital & Print). **Description:** Philadelphia, Pennsylvania-based King of Prussia Mall is set to undergo a $150 million renovation. The plan involves construction of about 250,000 square feet of space for retailers. Mall owner, Simon Property Group, has contracted IMC Construction to handle the project. **Availability:** Print; Online.

904 ■ *"Mechanic Theatre's Brutalist Style at Battle's Center"* in *Baltimore Business Journal (Vol. 30, May 11, 2012, No. 1, pp. 1)*
Pub: American City Business Journals, Inc.
Contact: Mike Olivieri, Executive Vice President
Ed: James Briggs. **Description:** David S. Brown Enterprises Ltd. plans to demolish the Morris A. Mechanic Theatre in Baltimore, Maryland and replace it with two 30-story towers that include 600 apartment units, retail, and parking spaces. The local chapter of the American Institute of Architects opposes the proposal and calls for the preservation of the former theatre's brutalist architecture. **Availability:** Print; Online.

905 ■ *"Muirhead Farmhouse B&B Owners Get Hospitality Wright"* in *Chicago Tribune (July 31, 2008)*
Pub: Tribune News Service
Contact: Jack Barry, Vice President, Operations
E-mail: jbarry@tribpub.com
Ed: Glenn Jeffers. **Description:** Profile of the Muirhead Farmhouse, a bed-and-breakfast owned by Mike Petersdorf and Sarah Muirhead Petersdorf; Frank Lloyd Wright designed the historic farmhouse

which blends farm life and history into a unique experience that is enhanced by the couple's hospitality. **Availability:** Online.

906 ■ *"New Ideas Urged for 'Superman' Reuse" in Providence Business News (Vol. 28, March 10, 2014, No. 49, pp. 1)*
Pub: American City Business Journals, Inc.
Contact: Mike Olivieri, Executive Vice President
Released: March 08, 2014. **Description:** High Rock Development is requesting help from the public to architecturally renovate the 'Superman Building', the tallest building in Providence, Rhode Island. High Rock, the owner of the building, started a lobbying and marketing campaign in February 2014 to garner support. **Availability:** Print; Online.

907 ■ *"New Law Regarding Notre Dame Says Restoration Must Preserve it's 'historic, artistic and architectural interest'" in The Art Newspaper (August 2, 2019)*
URL(s): www.theartnewspaper.com/analysis/it-s-official-the-new-notre-dame-will-look-like-the-old-notre-dame
Ed: Francesco Bandarin. **Released:** August 02, 2019. **Description:** After the massive fire that almost consumed Notre Dame in Paris, a new law was approved regarding it's restoration. When the cathedral is rebuilt it must "preserve the historic, artistic and architectural interest of the monument" and all of the funds given for the restoration will be managed by a new agency in charge of the project. **Availability:** Online.

908 ■ *"The Owyhee Is Filling Up Faster Than Expected" in Idaho Business Review (September 5, 2014)*
Pub: BridgeTower Media
Contact: Adam Reinebach, President
Description: Clay Carley discusses his idea to renovate the 104-year-old Owyhee Hotel into a modern office, residential and commercial center. He transformed the building's rooftop into an event space for weddings and other celebrations. Carley is the developer and part-owner of the property and reported 3,000 people attending its ribbon cutting. Retail and office space are filling faster than expected and the rooftop venue has already celebrated six weddings.

909 ■ *"Peabody Launching 464-Room Renovation" in Memphis Business Journal (Vol. 34, July 13, 2012, No. 13, pp. 1)*
Pub: Baltimore Business Journal
Contact: Rhonda Pringle, President
E-mail: rpringle@bizjournals.com
Ed: Michael Sheffield. **Description:** The Peabody Memphis has announced preparations for a massive renovation that will affect all 464 rooms of the hotel starting in November. Peabody Hotel Group, which manages the hotel fo rBelz Enterprises, has estimated the renovations to cost between $10 million and $20 million. **Availability:** Print; Online.

910 ■ *"Riverfront Revival in Pawtucket?" in Providence Business News (Vol. 28, March 17, 2014, No. 50, pp. 1)*
Pub: American City Business Journals, Inc.
Contact: Mike Olivieri, Executive Vice President
URL(s): pbn.com/Riverfront-revival-in-Pawtucket,95766
Description: Pawtucket, Rhode Island is focusing on riverfront redevelopment projects due to an improving economy. City planning director, Barney Heath, reveals that Tai-O Group, Peregrine Group and Apex Development Company have already responded to a request for qualifications to begin construction projects. **Availability:** Online. **Telecommunication Services:** Anderson@pbn.com.

911 ■ *"Six Arkansas Construction Projects Get LEED Certification" in Arkansas Business (Vol. 29, July 23, 2012, No. 30, pp. 19)*
Pub: Arkansas Business Publishing Group
Contact: Mitch Bettis, President
Ed: Lance Turner. **Description:** State of Arkansas has bestowed its Leadership in Energy and Environmental Design certification on 55 projects throughout the state. Six projects are identified and described. A list of all projects is included. **Availability:** Online.

912 ■ *"Stay In Your Home" in Consumer Reports Money (Vol. 9, May 20, 2012, No. 5, pp. 1)*
Pub: Consumer Reports Books
Contact: Marta L. Tellado, President
Description: Renovations to help the elderly remain in their homes are covered. **Availability:** Online.

913 ■ *"Sustainable Concept of Architectural Conservation" in IEREK (October 22, 2014)*
URL(s): www.ierek.com/news/index.php/2014/10/22/sustainable-concept-architectural-conservation/
Released: October 22, 2014. **Description:** Discusses Preventive Conservation and Curative Conservation in terms of protecting and maintaining historical sites. Also examines the various facets of being sustainable. **Availability:** Online.

914 ■ *"Top Architecture Firms" in South Florida Business Journal (Vol. 34, June 13, 2014, No. 47, pp. 13)*
Pub: American City Business Journals, Inc.
Contact: Mike Olivieri, Executive Vice President
Description: The top architectural firms in South Florida, as of June 13, 2014, ranked by gross billings are listed. AECOM Technology Corporation got the top spot, ADD Inc. ranked third. **Availability:** Print; Online.

915 ■ *"Top Stadium Builders Likely To Vie For Vikings Project" in Business Journal (Vol. 29, May 18, 2012, No. 51, pp. 1)*
Ed: John Vomhof Jr. **Description:** The $975 million Minnesota Vikings stadium project has been approved and is expected to attract big construction firms to bid for the project. A new Minnesota Sports Facility Authority will need to be appointed first, however, before actual selection of design-build team. Architecture firm Populous and contractor Mortenson Construction are among the frontrunners for the project. **Availability:** Print; Online.

916 ■ *"Trigate Rebrands Radisson at SMU to Holiday Inn" in Dallas Business Journal (Vol. 35, August 31, 2012, No. 51, pp. 1)*
Pub: Baltimore Business Journal
Contact: Rhonda Pringle, President
E-mail: rpringle@bizjournals.com
Description: Radisson Hotel, located near Southern Methodist University in Dallas, Texas, will soon be known as Holiday Inn Dallas Park Cities. Hotel owner Trigate Capital states that the rebranding is part of the hotel's renovation, which is expected to finish by the end of the year. The new name will take effect in October. **Availability:** Print; Online.

917 ■ *"USF Plans $30M Sports Complex" in Tampa Bay Business Journal (Vol. 29, October 23, 2009, No. 44, pp. 1)*
Pub: Tampa Bay Business Journal
Contact: Ian Anderson, President
E-mail: ianderson@bizjournals.com
Ed: Jane Meinhardt. **Description:** University of South Florida (USF) is going to build a new sports complex with the aid of a $30 million loan from BB&T. The project, which is also comprised of new and renovated athletic facilities on USF's Tampa campus, is projected to create more than $37 million in revenue in its first year. Revenues from the said facilities are expected to achieve an annual growth of at least four percent. **Availability:** Print; Online.

918 ■ *"Walnut Hill Sheds Its Past, Name" in Philadelphia Business Journal (Vol. 33, April 4, 2014, No. 8, pp. 8)*
Pub: American City Business Journals, Inc.
Contact: Mike Olivieri, Executive Vice President
Released: Weekly. **Price:** $4, introductory 4-week offer(Digital & Print). **Description:** Walnut Hill Plaza was bought by a fund comprised of Miller Investment Management and Hayden Real Estate at an auction in 2012 for $11 million and they spent $2 million in construction renovations. The property was also rebranded as 150 Walnut Warner and the once forlorn building is up to 100% leased space. The tenants renting space in the building are also highlighted. **Availability:** Print; Online.

919 ■ *"The Witte Museum to Undergo Major Makeover This Fall" in San Antonio Business Journal (Vol. 28, July 25, 2014, No. 24, pp. 7)*
Pub: American City Business Journals, Inc.
Contact: Mike Olivieri, Executive Vice President
Released: Weekly. **Price:** $4, introductory 4-week offer(Digital & Print). **Description:** The Witte Museum along Broadway in San Antonio, Texas is working on a $60 million expansion and renovation that will provide the 90-year-old institution with additional exhibition and activity space. Such construction improvements are expected to better connect the museum with the San Antonio River and the Broadway corridor. **Availability:** Print; Online.

TRADE PERIODICALS

920 ■ *Azure Magazine*
Pub: Azure Publishing Inc.
Contact: Jeffrey Bakazias, Manager, Accounting
E-mail: jeffrey@azureonline.com
URL(s): www.azuremagazine.com
Facebook: www.facebook.com/AzureMagazine
Linkedin: www.linkedin.com/company/azure-magazine
X (Twitter): x.com/AzureMagazine
Instagram: www.instagram.com/azuremagazine
YouTube: www.youtube.com/channel/UCvrVZE9TPyBGrqlB49F6JyQ
Pinterest: www.pinterest.ca/azuremagazine
Ed: Nelda Rodger. **Released:** 6/year **Price:** $49.95, for print + digital; $28.95, for digital only; $43.95, for print only; C$10.95, Single issue. **Description:** Trade magazine covering art, design and architecture. **Availability:** Print; Online.

921 ■ *Downtown Idea Exchange*
Pub: Alexander Communications Group Inc.
URL(s): ddc.downtowndevelopment.com/welcome-to-downtown-idea-exchange
Released: Monthly **Price:** $246, for online one year subscription. **Description:** Focuses on revitalizing central business districts, including planning, design, development, preservation, parking, transit, traffic, funding, and organization. **Availability:** Print; PDF; Download; Online.

922 ■ *Journal of the Society of Architectural Historians (JSAH)*
Pub: Society of Architectural Historians
Contact: Patricia A. Morton, President
E-mail: patricia.morton@ucr.edu
URL(s): www.sah.org/publications/jsah
Ed: Patricia Morton. **Released:** Quarterly; March, June, September, December. **Description:** Professional magazine devoted to architectural history. **Availability:** Print; PDF; Online.

923 ■ *Municipal Art Society Newsletter*
Pub: Municipal Art Society of New York
Contact: Elizabeth Goldstein, President
E-mail: egoldstein@mas.org
URL(s): www.mas.org/about-us
Released: Monthly **Description:** Provides updates on advocacy efforts, exhibitions, and programming on urban issues. Recurring features include a calendar of events and tour schedule. **Availability:** Print.

924 ■ *Timber Framing: Journal of the Timber Framers Guild*
Pub: Timber Framers Guild
Contact: Chris Koehn, President
E-mail: president@tfguild.org
URL(s): www.tfguild.org/store/timber-framing-journal
Ed: Ken Rower. **Released:** Quarterly; March, June, September, and December. **Price:** $115, for international; $75, U.S.; $85, Canada. **Description:** Trade

magazine covering timber frame design home construction, history, restoration, and preservation. **Availability:** Print; Online.

TRADE SHOWS AND CONVENTIONS

925 ■ Chicago Build
Frequency: Annual. **Description:** Provides networking, an exhibit hall, and key topic sessions about real estate, architecture, construction, and health and safety. **Audience:** Industry leaders in the building and construction trade. **Principal Exhibits:** Provides networking, an exhibit hall, and key topic sessions about real estate, architecture, construction, and health and safety.

926 ■ National Fall Conference
American Architectural Manufacturers Association (AAMA)
1900 E Golf Rd., Ste. 1250
Schaumburg, IL 60173
URL: http://fgiaonline.org
URL(s): fgiaonline.org/events/197/future-fgia-events
Frequency: Annual. **Description:** Exhibits relating to architecture, particularly window, door, skylight, curtain wall, and storefront products. **Audience:** Industry professionals. **Principal Exhibits:** Exhibits relating to architecture, particularly window, door, skylight, curtain wall, and storefront products.

CONSULTANTS

927 ■ ALSA Architecture L.L.C.
1430 Broadway, Ste. 1205
New York, NY 10018
Ph: (212)302-2180
Fax: (212)391-2148
Co. E-mail: mail@alsaarchitecture.com
URL: http://www.alsaarchitecture.com
Contact: Roy Sokoloski, President
Description: Architectural and engineering design Firm provides consulting expertise in construction contract documents, construction administration and facilities management. The firm serves various industries including academic, industrial, financial, government, health care, housing, corporate and retail.

928 ■ Beckett and Raeder Inc. (BRI)
535 W William St., Ste. 101
Ann Arbor, MI 48103
Ph: (734)663-2622
Fax: (734)663-6759
Co. E-mail: info@bria2.com
URL: http://www.bria2.com
Contact: Brian Barrick, Partner
Facebook: www.facebook.com/BECKETTRAEDER
Linkedin: www.linkedin.com/company/beckett-&-raeder-inc-
X (Twitter): x.com/BeckettRaeder
Instagram: www.instagram.com/beckettraeder
Description: Provides landscape architecture, planning, engineering and environmental aspects for clients and related services like designing, planning, and engineering. **Founded:** 1966.

929 ■ Brenda Spencer
10150 Onaga Rd.
Wamego, KS 66547
Ph: (785)456-9857
Co. E-mail: brenda@spencerpreservation.com
URL: http://spencerpreservation.com
Contact: Brenda Spencer, Founder
E-mail: brenda@spencerpreservation.com
Description: Firm is engaged in historic preservation and developing resources and provides consulting services such as planning and designing. **Founded:** 1994.

930 ■ Building Conservation Associates Inc. (BCA)
44 E 32nd St.
New York, NY 10016
Ph: (212)777-1300
Fax: (212)777-1606
Co. E-mail: info@bcausa.com
URL: http://www.bcausa.com
Contact: Raymond Pepi, President
E-mail: rpepi@bcausa.com
X (Twitter): x.com/bcanews
Description: A consulting firm that specializes in both the technical and historical aspects of restoring buildings and works of art. Assists clients in the preparation of federal rehabilitation tax credit applications. Combines field documentation, archival research, materials testing and scientific research. **Scope:** A consulting firm that specializes in both the technical and historical aspects of restoring buildings and works of art. Assists clients in the preparation of federal rehabilitation tax credit applications. Combines field documentation, archival research, materials testing and scientific research. **Founded:** 1985. **Publications:** "Journal of the American Institute for Conservation".

931 ■ Cox Graae + Spack Architects (CGS)
2909 M St. NW
Washington, DC 20007
Ph: (202)965-7070
Co. E-mail: info@cgsarchitects.com
URL: http://cgsarchitects.com
Contact: Joanna Schmickel, Principal
Facebook: www.facebook.com/CGS-Architects-103326828953980
Linkedin: www.linkedin.com/company/cgsarchitects
X (Twitter): x.com/CGSArchitects
Instagram: www.instagram.com/cgsarchitects
Description: Firm provides professional architectural services such as architectural and interior design, and much more. **Scope:** Firm provides professional architectural services such as architectural and interior design, and much more. **Founded:** 1981.

932 ■ Cropsey and Associates Inc.
230 W College St., Ste. A-2
Griffin, GA 30224
Contact: Paul A. Cropsey, Chief Executive Officer
Description: An architectural design firm is experienced in rehabilitating historic buildings in accordance with the secretary of the interiors guidelines for historic preservation and ISTEA funding. **Scope:** An architectural design firm is experienced in rehabilitating historic buildings in accordance with the secretary of the interiors guidelines for historic preservation and ISTEA funding.

933 ■ DANTH Inc.
83-85 116th St., Ste. 3D
Kew Gardens, NY 11418
Ph: (718)805-9507
Co. E-mail: danthinc@yahoo.com
URL: http://www.ndavidmilder.com
Contact: David N. Milder, Founder
X (Twitter): x.com/DANTHinc
Description: Provider of economic revitalization consulting to downtown, commercial district and local government organizations focused in the development of comprehensive retail and office revitalization policies and programs. **Scope:** Provider of economic revitalization consulting to downtown, commercial district and local government organizations focused in the development of comprehensive retail and office revitalization policies and programs. **Founded:** 1977. **Publications:** "MAKING MEMBERSHIP BUY-INS EASY," Downtown Idea Exchange, Oct, 2004. **Training:** Niche Development and Marketing; Reconnaissance and Action Plan; Retail Revitalization Strategy and Action Plan.

934 ■ DTAH
50 Park Rd.
Toronto, ON, Canada M4W 2N5
Ph: (416)968-9479
Fax: (416)968-0687
URL: http://www.dtah.com
Contact: Brent Raymond, Partner
Facebook: www.facebook.com/DTAHToronto
Linkedin: www.linkedin.com/company/dtah
X (Twitter): x.com/DTAHtoronto
Instagram: www.instagram.com/dtahtoronto
Description: Provider of planning and urban design services. **Scope:** Provider of planning and urban design services. **Founded:** 1975. **Publications:** "Designs for second Bow Bridge unveiled," Sep, 2009; "Waterfront on a roll with classy Wave Deck," Jun, 2009; "Skate parks, promenades and plazas," Jun, 2009; "Evergreen Brick Works"; "Toronto Central Waterfront".

935 ■ Halstead Architects
1139 Shelby St.
Indianapolis, IN 46203
Ph: (317)684-1431
URL: http://www.halstead-architects.com
Contact: Mike Halstead, President
E-mail: mikeh@halstead-architects.com
Facebook: www.facebook.com/HalsteadArch
Linkedin: www.linkedin.com/company/halstead-architects
Instagram: www.instagram.com/halsteadarchitects
Description: Offers architectural expertise in planning, libraries, community based projects, historic preservation, residential, entertainment, religious, educational and interiors in the United States. **Scope:** Offers architectural expertise in planning, libraries, community based projects, historic preservation, residential, entertainment, religious, educational and interiors in the United States. **Founded:** 1993. **Publications:** "Coffee, snacks ahead for canal walkers," Indianapolis Star, Oct, 2003; "Canal-side Church Building to Get Makeover," Indiana Business Journal.

936 ■ Hemmler + Camayd Architects
409 Lackawanna Ave.
Scranton, PA 18503-2062
Ph: (570)961-1302
Contact: Alex Camayd, President
E-mail: acamayd@hc-architects.com
Facebook: www.facebook.com/people/Hc-architects/100063468221485
Description: Provider of comprehensive architectural, interior design and planning services to corporate, government, education, health, elderly care and religious sectors. **Scope:** Provider of comprehensive architectural, interior design and planning services to corporate, government, education, health, elderly care and religious sectors. **Founded:** 1978.

937 ■ Historic Exterior Paint Colors Consulting
3661 Waldenwood Dr.
Ann Arbor, MI 48105
Ph: (734)668-0298
Co. E-mail: robs@umich.edu
URL: http://historichousecolors.com
Contact: Robert Schweitzer, Contact
Description: Provider of exterior paint color consulting services for historic, contemporary, and much more. **Scope:** Provider of exterior paint color consulting services for historic, contemporary, and much more. **Publications:** "Proof that Paint Color Lends Detail," Arts and Crafts Homes, 2006; "Bungalow Colors- Exteriors," Gibbs-Smith Publishers, 2002; "Color Scheming," Design NJ, 2002; "Colonial Revival Homes," Victorian Homes, Feb, 2003; "America's Favorite Homes"; "Color a New World," 60s Ranch Color Makeover, Romantic Homes, Aug, 2001; "How Shall I Paint my House," American Bungalow, 1999; "Color Concepts and Bungalow Basics," Cottages & Bungalows.

938 ■ Hoisington Koegler Group Inc. (HKGI)
800 Washington Ave. N, Ste. 103
Minneapolis, MN 55401
Ph: (612)338-0800
URL: http://www.hkgi.com
Contact: Paul Paige, President
E-mail: ppaige@hkgi.com
Description: Firm provides planning and landscape architecture, leadership and project management services. **Founded:** 1982.

939 ■ Howard L. Zimmerman Architects, P.C. (HLZA)
11 W 30th St.
New York, NY 10001
Ph: (212)564-9393

Co. E-mail: info@hlzimmerman.com
URL: http://www.hlzimmerman.com
Contact: Donna Singleton, Executive Director
Facebook: www.facebook.com/HLZimmerman
Linkedin: www.linkedin.com/company/howard-l-zimmerman-architects
YouTube: www.youtube.com/user/HLZimmerman
Description: Firm offers evaluation of building restoration and preventive maintenance to building owners, their services include exterior restoration, historic preservation, capital improvement, forensic investigation, and interior design services. **Scope:** Firm offers evaluation of building restoration and preventive maintenance to building owners, their services include exterior restoration, historic preservation, capital improvement, forensic investigation, and interior design services. **Founded:** 1981. **Publications:** "Forensic Architecture: The Art of Understanding a Buildings Unwritten History".

940 ■ Integrated Conservation Resources Inc. (ICR)
44-02 11th St., Ste. 604
  Long Island City, NY 11101
Ph: (212)947-4499
Fax: (212)947-7766
Co. E-mail: hello@icr-icc.com
URL: http://www.icr-icc.com
Contact: Norman R. Weiss, Director
Facebook: www.facebook.com/icricc
Instagram: www.instagram.com/icr_icc
Description: Firm assists design professionals by providing specialized expertise on historic building materials, their services span a full spectrum of architectural conservation services. **Scope:** Firm assists design professionals by providing specialized expertise on historic building materials, their services span a full spectrum of architectural conservation services. **Founded:** 1987.

941 ■ Jan Rubin Associates Inc.
2022-2024 Chancellor St.
  Philadelphia, PA 19103
Description: Firm engaged in structuring and developing low income housing and historic tax credits, HOPE VI, CDBG or HOME transactions for public and private organizations. **Scope:** Firm engaged in structuring and developing low income housing and historic tax credits, HOPE VI, CDBG or HOME transactions for public and private organizations.

942 ■ John Leeke
26 Higgins St.
  Portland, ME 04103
Ph: (207)773-2306
Co. E-mail: johnleeke@historichomeworks.com
URL: http://historichomeworks.com
Contact: John Leeke, Consultant
E-mail: johnleeke@historichomeworks.com
Description: Assists owners, trades people, contractors and professionals understand and maintain their historic and older buildings. **Scope:** Assists owners, trades people, contractors and professionals understand and maintain their historic and older buildings. **Publications:** "Window Restoration". **Training:** Save Your Wood Windows; Exterior Wood and Paint; Restore Omaha, Nov, 2006; The Business Side of Preservation Vermont, Nov, 2006; Save Your Wood Windows, May, 2007; Exterior Woodwork: Repairs and Painting, Jun, 2007; Windows: Small Shop Business, 2007. **Special Services:** Historic HomeWorks™.

943 ■ Karl Kardel Consultancy
4926 E 12th St.
  Oakland, CA 94601
Ph: (510)261-4149
Co. E-mail: karl@kardelconsultancy.com
URL: http://www.kardelcompany.com
Contact: Karl Kardel, Founder
E-mail: karl@kardelconsultancy.com
Facebook: www.facebook.com/Karl-Kardel-Company-153973817971189
Linkedin: www.linkedin.com/in/karl-kardel-46265519
Description: Provider of consultation in water invasion in windows, wall systems, and membranes, they offer problem resolution in finishes and coatings and forensic analysis in building failures and specializes in historic conservation, architectural finishes, water invasion, windows, curtain walls, and stucco, give analysis for managed case cost controls. **Scope:** Provider of consultation in water invasion in windows, wall systems, and membranes, they offer problem resolution in finishes and coatings and forensic analysis in building failures and specializes in historic conservation, architectural finishes, water invasion, windows, curtain walls, and stucco, give analysis for managed case cost controls. **Founded:** 1959.

944 ■ Karn Charuhas Chapman & Twohey (KCCT)
1350 Eye St. NW, Ste. 950
  Washington, DC 20005
Ph: (202)659-5600
Fax: (202)659-5605
Co. E-mail: info@kcct.com
URL: http://www.kcct.com
Contact: John W. Chapman, President
E-mail: jchapman@kcct.com
Linkedin: www.linkedin.com/company/kcct
X (Twitter): x.com/kcctarchitects
Instagram: www.instagram.com/kcctarchitects
Description: Firm provides architectural, planning and interior design related services. **Founded:** 1983.

945 ■ Leeds Clark Inc.
3010 Shady Grove Rd.
  Midlothian, TX 76065
Ph: (469)583-2236
Fax: (972)775-3263
Co. E-mail: info@leedsclark.com
URL: http://www.leedsclark.com
Contact: Thomas L. Clark, President
E-mail: tomclark@leedsclark.com
Facebook: www.facebook.com/Leeds-Clark-Inc-418959124879226
Description: Firm is engaged in the preservation of historic windows and provides historic window restoration, replication, surveys, mock-ups, restoration products, consulting and related services. **Founded:** 1978. **Training:** Historic Building Condition Assessment; Main Street Training and Lead Paint Abatement on Windows; Selecting and working with contractors; Specification writing and code compliance; Project planning.

946 ■ Shakespeare Composite Structures
19845 US Highway 76
  Newberry, SC 29108
Ph: (803)276-5504
Free: 800-800-9008
Fax: (803)276-8940
URL: http://www.skp-cs.com
Description: Manufacturer of fiberglass reinforced composites. **Scope:** Manufacturer of fiberglass reinforced composites. **Founded:** 1967.

947 ■ Uptown Shelby Association Inc. (USA)
211 S Trade St.
  Shelby, NC 28150
Ph: (704)484-3100
Co. E-mail: info@uptownshelby.com
URL: http://uptownshelby.com
Contact: Scott Sharp, President
Facebook: www.facebook.com/uptownshelby
X (Twitter): x.com/UptownShelby
Instagram: www.instagram.com/uptownshelby
Description: Firm provides economic vitality, historic preservation, promotion of uptown events, and working with other organizations to improve life and commerce in uptown area. **Founded:** 1982. **Publications:** "Help Save Historic Rogers Theatre".

948 ■ Vertical Systems Analysis Inc. (VSA)
307 W 36th St., 8th Fl.
  New York, NY 10018
Ph: (212)989-5525
Fax: (212)989-6860
URL: http://www.vsaconsulting.com
Contact: Ed Voll, Founder
Facebook: www.facebook.com/VerticalSystemsAnalysis
Linkedin: www.linkedin.com/company/vertical-systems-analysis
Description: Elevator and escalator engineering and consulting firm for residential and commercial buildings evaluate elevators and escalators for modernization and restoration projects and creates specs and plans an serves real estate, hospital, hotel, engineering, legal, universities and schools, cooperatives and condominiums, architectural and state facilities, and government agencies. **Scope:** Elevator and escalator engineering and consulting firm for residential and commercial buildings evaluate elevators and escalators for modernization and restoration projects and creates specs and plans an serves real estate, hospital, hotel, engineering, legal, universities and schools, cooperatives and condominiums, architectural and state facilities, and government agencies. **Founded:** 1986. **Publications:** "Owners Guide to Better Elevator Service".

949 ■ Walter Sedovic Architects
1 Union Sq., W
  New York, NY 10003
Ph: (914)591-1900
Co. E-mail: wsa@modernruins.com
URL: http://www.modernruins.nyc
Description: Firm provides performance diagnostics, planning, forensics and investigations, sustainable preservation and project development, new buildings and site design, grants and fund raising, and dream tree house. **Founded:** 1986. **Publications:** "What Replacement Windows Can't Replace," Association for Preservation Technology International, 2005; "Helping Main Street Thrive," Traditional Building, May, 2002; "Traditional Bldgs," Feb, 2002.

950 ■ W.J. Whatley Inc.
19845 US Hwy. 76
  Newberry, SC 29108
Ph: (803)276-5507
Free: 877-959-7678
Fax: (803)276-8940
URL: http://www.whatley.com
Description: Firm engineers and manufactures a variety of custom decorative lamp posts and light poles from various materials including steel, aluminum, stainless steel and other composites, used in a variety of applications, from infrastructure and urban redevelopments to suburban neighborhoods, shopping districts, recreational areas and higher education campuses. **Founded:** 1946. **Special Services:** XTREME.

LIBRARIES

951 ■ City College of City University of New York - Art Visual Resources Library
c/o Ching-Jung Chen, Librarian
  New York, NY 10031
Ph: (212)650-7607
Fax: (212)650-7604
Co. E-mail: cchen@ccny.cuny.edu
URL: http://www.adm.ccny.cuny.edu/v2/directory/dirfind.cfm?urltarget=Library
Contact: Ching-Jung Chen, Librarian
E-mail: cchen@ccny.cuny.edu
Description: New York-Art Visual Resources Library. **Scope:** Arts; education. **Holdings:** Figures not available.

952 ■ Tri-County Heritage Society Reference Library
4979 Twin Valley Rd.
  Elverson, PA 19520
Ph: (610)286-7477
Co. E-mail: tchs@dejazzd.com
URL: http://haycreek.org/tricounty-heritage-society
Scope: Local history; genealogy. **Services:** Library open to the public for reference use only. **Founded:** 1970. **Subscriptions:** magazines journals Maps; microfilm; photographs.

953 ■ University of Nevada, Las Vegas Architecture Studies Library
4505 S Maryland Pky.
  Las Vegas, NV 89154-4049
Ph: (702)895-1959
Co. E-mail: libasl@unlv.edu

URL: http://www.library.unlv.edu/arch
Contact: Richard Saladino, Librarian
E-mail: richard.saladino@unlv.edu
Scope: Architecture. **Services:** Interlibrary loan; Copying. **Founded:** 1997. **Holdings:** Books; journals.

RESEARCH CENTERS

954 ■ **College of William and Mary - Center for Archaeological Research (W&MCAR)**
308 Jamestown Rd.
Williamsburg, VA 23185
Ph: (757)221-2580
URL: http://www.wm.edu/sites/wmcar
Contact: David W. Lewes, Director (Acting)
E-mail: dwlewe@wm.edu
Facebook: www.facebook.com/williamandmary.car
Description: Integral unit of Department of Anthropology at College of William and Mary. Artifact identification and analysis, zooarchaeological analysis, and material excavation of archaeological ceramics; preparation of cultural resource planning overviews and reports for inclusion in Environmental Impact Statements; professional assistance to both public and private agencies and organizations in the area of cultural resource management; internships in public archaeology for graduate and undergraduate students of anthropology, history, and American studies.
Scope: Performs historic and prehistoric archaeological and architectural research services, including cultural resource management studies, archaeological testing and excavation of historic properties, architectural survey and evaluation, preservation planning, and historical research and interpretation.
Founded: 1988. **Publications:** *Occasional Papers in Archaeology*; *Technical Report Series*. **Awards:** CRM Internship.

955 ■ **Cornell University - International Studies in Planning Concentration**
106 W Sibley Hall
Ithaca, NY 14853
Ph: (607)255-4613
Fax: (607)255-1971
Co. E-mail: crpinfo@cornell.edu
URL: http://aap.cornell.edu/academics/crp/graduate/planning/mrp/concentrations/international-studies
Contact: Prof. Sophie Oldfield, Chairman
E-mail: sophie.oldfield@cornell.edu
Description: Integral unit of Department of City and Regional Planning, Cornell University, affiliated with the Center for International Studies. **Scope:** Analysis of the regional and spatial dimensions of development issues with a focus—although by no means exclusive—on the Third World, including political economy of regional and national development; planning and the global economy; critical development theory; project planning and administration; political ecology and international environmental planning; community economic development; gender and development; infrastructure; and NGOs and social movements. Areas of research include Latin America, Caribbean, Africa, Europe, and Southeast Asia. **Founded:** 1972.

956 ■ **Frank Lloyd Wright Trust Restoration Resource Center**
209 S LaSalle St., Ste. 118
Chicago, IL 60604
Co. E-mail: research@flwright.org
URL: http://flwright.org
Contact: John M. Rafkin, Chairman of the Board
Description: Independent, nonprofit organization. **Scope:** Frank Lloyd Wright, Prairie style of architecture, and architectural preservation and restoration. **Services:** Center open to the public by appointment. **Founded:** 1974. **Holdings:** 2,000 books; 89 lin.ft. of unbound periodical volumes; 300 videotapes; 90 sound recordings; 7 manuscripts; 1,000 drawings; clipping files; broadsides; 9,000 historic photographs; archives. **Publications:** *Frank Lloyd Wright Preservation Trust Research Center Journal* (Quarterly); *Frank Lloyd Wright Preservation Trust Research Center Newsletter* (Monthly).

957 ■ **Getty Conservation Institute (GCI) - Information Center**
1200 Getty Center Dr., Ste. 700
Los Angeles, CA 90049-1684
Ph: (310)440-7325
Fax: (310)440-7702
Co. E-mail: sgolfomitsou@getty.edu
URL: http://www.getty.edu/conservation
Contact: Cameron Trowbridge, Manager
E-mail: ctrowbridge@getty.edu
Facebook: www.facebook.com/GettyConservationInstitute
X (Twitter): x.com/gciconservation
YouTube: www.youtube.com/c/GettyConservationInstitute
Description: One of four programs of the J. Paul Getty Trust, a nonprofit organization. Other programs are the J. Paul Getty Museum, Getty Research Institute, and the Getty Foundation. **Scope:** Created to enhance the quality of conservation practice. Addresses the conservation needs of cultural property, including fine art collections, historic buildings and archeological sites. Also undertakes research in conservation and documentation methods and technologies. Maintains laboratories at the Getty Center in Los Angeles, where scientific research is conducted in the following areas: museum environment, conservation materials and techniques, analytical techniques, and archaeological and architectural conservation. **Services:** Customized research services; bibliographic management tools and training; reference assistance; facilitated access to conservation literature and related research resources visual resources management; guided development and growth of the Conservation Collection; library open to the public by appointment. **Founded:** 1985. **Holdings:** 50,000 titles; 400 serial subscriptions; 2000 titles of journals; print and online science resources; dictionaries; encyclopedias; scientific handbooks, GCI publications, print and online geographic resources including travel guides, maps and atlases; con. **Subscriptions:** 400 journals and other serials. **Publications:** *Provenance Index CD-ROM*; *Conservation Perspectives Newsletter* (Semiannual); *Research in Conservation Series*, *Tools for Conservation Series*; *Symposium proceedings and preprints*. **Educational Activities:** GCI Workshops.

958 ■ **Mississippi State University - Carl Small Town Center (CSTC)**
899 Collegeview St.
104 Giles Hall
Mississippi State, MS 39762
Ph: (662)325-2207
URL: http://smalltowncenter.wordpress.com
Contact: Leah Kemp, Director
E-mail: lkemp@caad.msstate.edu
Facebook: www.facebook.com/smalltowncenter
Linkedin: www.linkedin.com/company/small towncenter
X (Twitter): x.com/smalltowncenter
Instagram: www.instagram.com/smalltowncenter
Description: Research, teaching, and service component of the College of Architecture, Mississippi State University. **Scope:** Community design center in the College of Architecture, Art and Design at Mississippi State University. **Founded:** 1979.

959 ■ **University of Mary Washington - College of Arts and Sciences - Department of Historic Preservation - Center for Historic Preservation (CHP)**
1301 College Ave.
Fredericksburg, VA 22401
Ph: (540)654-1311
URL: http://cas.umw.edu/chp
Contact: Dr. Michael Spencer, Director
E-mail: mspen1bi@umw.edu
Description: Integral unit of Department of Historic Preservation, College of Arts and Sciences, University of Mary Washington. Cultural resource management. **Scope:** Archeological, architectural, and landscape studies focusing primarily on the Chesapeake region and Piedmont, Virginia from the 17th to the early 20th century. **Founded:** 1980. **Publications:** *Cultural resource management reports*; *Historic Preservation at Mary Washington College Newsletter* (Semiannual).

960 ■ **University of Texas at Austin - Center for American Architecture and Design (CAAD)**
310 Inner Campus Dr.
Austin, TX 78712-1009
Ph: (512)471-9890
Co. E-mail: caad@austin.utexas.edu
URL: http://soa.utexas.edu/libraries-centers/center-american-architecture-design
Contact: Michael Benedikt, Professor
E-mail: mbenedikt@utexas.edu
Description: Integral unit of School of Architecture at University of Texas at Austin, but operated under its own board of advisors. **Scope:** Architecture for the emerging American city, architectural history of all the Americas, historic preservation, design, work of twentieth century American architects, the dwelling, placemaking in American cities, and architecture and media. **Founded:** 1982. **Publications:** *CENTER: Architecture and Design in America*.

Art Gallery

ASSOCIATIONS AND OTHER ORGANIZATIONS

961 ■ Art Dealers Association of America, Inc. (ADAA)
205 Lexington Ave., Ste. 901
New York, NY 10016
Ph: (212)488-5550
Fax: (212)488-5539
Co. E-mail: adaa@artdealers.org
URL: http://artdealers.org
Contact: Anthony Meier, President
Facebook: www.facebook.com/ArtDealersAssociationofAmerica
X (Twitter): x.com/The_ADAA
Instagram: www.instagram.com/the_adaa
Pinterest: www.pinterest.com/The_ADAA

Description: Advocates on behalf of its member organizations regarding public policy issues and monitors any legislation that can have an effect on the fine arts community. Also conducts seminars to its members to keep them abreast of laws and regulations applicable to the business. **Founded:** 1962. **Publications:** *Art Dealers Association of America--Directory*. **Geographic Preference:** National.

962 ■ Association of International Photography Art Dealers (AIPAD)
41 E 11th St., 11th Fl.
New York, NY 10003
Ph: (609)799-4900
Co. E-mail: info@aipad.com
URL: http://www.aipad.com
Contact: Martijn van Pieterson, President
Facebook: www.facebook.com/AIPADphoto
Instagram: www.instagram.com/aipadphoto

Description: Involved in creating and maintaining high standards in the business of exhibiting, buying and selling photographs as art. **Founded:** 1979. **Publications:** *Association of International Photography Art Dealers Illustrated Annual Catalogue Directory* (Annual); *AIPAD Membership Directory and Illustrated Catalogue* (Annual); *On Collecting Photography*. **Educational Activities:** The Photography Show (Annual); The Photography Show (Annual). **Geographic Preference:** National.

963 ■ Inuit Art Foundation (IAF)
1655 Dupont St.
Toronto, ON, Canada M5T 2C7
Ph: (647)498-7717
URL: http://inuitartfoundation.org
Contact: Alysa Procida, Executive Director
X (Twitter): twitter.com/InuitArtFdn

Description: Offers professional development opportunities to Canadian Inuit artists. **Founded:** 1985. **Publications:** *Inuit Art Quarterly (IAQ)* (Quarterly); *Canadian Arctic Multimedia Information Kit*. **Geographic Preference:** National.

964 ■ Inuit Art Quarterly (IAQ)
1655 Dupont St.
Toronto, ON, Canada M5T 2C7
Ph: (647)498-7717
URL: http://inuitartfoundation.org
Contact: Alysa Procida, Executive Director
URL(s): www.inuitartfoundation.org/inuit-art-quarterly
Released: Quarterly **Price:** $33, Canada for 1 year 4 issues; $44, U.S. for 1 year 4 issues; $48, for 1 year 4 issues international; $50, Canada for 2 year 8 issues; $72, U.S. for 2 year 8 issues; $80, for 2 year 8 issues International; $17.95, Single issue for back-issue. **Description:** Consumer magazine covering Inuit art. **Availability:** Print; PDF; Online.

965 ■ Visual Artists and Galleries Association (VAGA)
111 Broadway, Ste. 1006
New York, NY 10006
Ph: (212)736-6666
Co. E-mail: admin@vagarights.com
URL: http://www.vagarights.com
Contact: Brian Johnson, Editor
E-mail: brian.johnson@vagarights.com

Description: Represents American and European artists, photographers, and art galleries. Allows members to control the reproduction of their works by arranging royalty agreements with the periodical, book, poster, and specialty publishing industries. Takes action on members' behalf against unauthorized reproductions of their works short of litigation; acts as a clearinghouse for licensing reproduction rights. Disseminates information about members and their works supplied by members themselves to users of art reproduction. Works to establish uniform art reproduction rights procedures throughout the industry. Offers protection against pirated art reproductions not only in the United States, but also throughout Europe and Japan its affiliation with other societies dealing with foreign artists' rights. Compiles statistics. **Founded:** 1975. **Geographic Preference:** National.

REFERENCE WORKS

966 ■ "5 Global Trends Affecting the Art Market This Fall" in Artsy (September 10, 2019)
Ed: Benjamin Sutton. **Released:** September 10, 2019. **Description:** An overview of five global, geopolitical, and industry trends influencing the current art market. Brexit and tariffs are mentioned along with the rise of the Paris art market. Mid-size galleries are following the trend of showcasing entire artists' estates, while Sotheby's is branching out by offering more objects with historical significance. **Availability:** Online.

967 ■ "Art Gallery Business Plan Template" in GrowThink
Ed: Dave Lavinsky. **Description:** Provides a link to filling out a business plan for an art gallery. Also discusses the sections that need to be filled out and gives out tips. **Availability:** Online.

968 ■ "Creative Cluster Paints Business Success" in Business Journal Serving Greater Tampa Bay (Vol. 30, October 29, 2010, No. 45, pp. 1)
Pub: Tampa Bay Business Journal
Contact: Ian Anderson, President
E-mail: ianderson@bizjournals.com
Ed: Jane Meinhardt. **Description:** How Tom Gaffney, a cofounder of the private equity firm The Anderson Group realized the great return on investment in the 600 block of Central Avenue in St. Petersburg, Florida is discussed. Focusing on long-term value rather than short-term profitability and exit, Gaffney purchased this block in 2008 for $2.3 million and cultivated arts businesses at tenants. **Availability:** Print; Online.

969 ■ "Economic Impact of the Arts: $125 Million" in Memphis Business Journal (Vol. 34, June 22, 2012, No. 10, pp. 1)
Pub: Baltimore Business Journal
Contact: Rhonda Pringle, President
E-mail: rpringle@bizjournals.com

Description: The culture industry in Memphis, Tennessee accounted for more than $125 million in combined spending from culturally-focused organizations and attendees in 2010 according to a study by the Americans for the Arts nonprofit group. Results indicate that the spending accounts form almost 4,000 jobs, over $100 million in household income and over $15 million in government revenue. **Availability:** Print; Online.

970 ■ "Gadget of the Week: the Age of iPhoneography" in Barron's (Vol. 92, August 25, 2012, No. 35, pp. 28)
Pub: Dow Jones & Company Inc.
Contact: Almar Latour, Chief Executive Officer
Ed: Nathaniel Wice. **Description:** Profile of iPhoneArt.com, the Website that allows enthusiasts to share photographic works and techniques with each other. The site is free but the Olloclip, a popular clip-on lense, costs $69.99. **Availability:** Online.

971 ■ Institute of Museum & Library Services--Annual Report
Pub: Institute of Museum & Library Services
Contact: Crosby Kemper, Director
URL(s): www.imls.gov/data/about-the-numbers

Released: Annual **Description:** Covers more than 1,000 museums and libraries receiving federal support. **Entries include:** Museum or library name, city, state, grant amount. **Arrangement:** Classified by type of funding received. **Indexes:** Institution name, museum discipline, size of budget. **Availability:** Print; Download; PDF.

972 ■ "Let the Light Shine" in Retail Merchandiser (Vol. 51, July-August 2011, No. 4, pp. 74)

Description: For over 25 years, The Thomas Kinkade Company has been producing art that is collected by both old and young, and is the only company that publishes Thomas Kinkade art. **Availability:** Print; Online.

973 ■ "Local Artists and Curators Offer Some Gallery Dos and Dont's" in Phoenix New Times (October 1, 2019)
URL(s): www.phoenixnewtimes.com/arts/gallery-dos-and-donts-11366381

Small Business Sourcebook • 42nd Edition

974 ■ Art Gallery   Small Business Profiles

Ed: Cody Fitzpatrick. **Released:** October 01, 2019. **Description:** Tips for visiting art galleries and how to get the most out of your experience are discussed. Gallery owners are trying to encourage more people to visit their events; beyond just opening night. **Availability:** Online.

974 ■ *"Seattle Art Gallery Upends Curatorial Norms and Centers Indigenous Viewpoints" in Nonprofit Quarterly (September 30, 2019)*
URL(s): nonprofitquarterly.org/seattle-art-gallery-upen ds-curatorial-norms-and-centers-indigenous -viewpoints/
Ed: Julie Euber. **Released:** September 30, 2019. **Description:** An exhibition at Seattle's King Street Station featured 200 artists who sought to exhibit their indigenous point of view through art. Satellite installations were also created, helping to create recognition of indigenous people. This fostered a Native-to-Native mentorship program in the area. **Availability:** Print; Online.

975 ■ *Seven Days in the Art World*
Pub: W.W. Norton & Company Ltd.
Contact: Stanley Kubrick, Director
Ed: Sarah Thornton. **Price:** $17.95, paperback. **Description:** A sociologist renders the interplay among buyers, critics, curators and makers of contemporary art. **Availability:** Print.

STATISTICAL SOURCES

976 ■ *Art Dealers Industry in the US - Market Research Report*
URL(s): www.ibisworld.com/united-states/market-re search-reports/art-dealers-industry/
Price: $925. **Description:** Downloadable report analyzing current and future trends in the art dealers industry. **Availability:** Online.

TRADE PERIODICALS

977 ■ *ARTnews Magazine*
Pub: ARTnews L.L.C.
Contact: Adeline Cippoletti-Saez, Manager, Production
URL(s): www.artnews.com
Facebook: www.facebook.com/artnewsmag
Linkedin: www.linkedin.com/company/artnewsmaga zine
X (Twitter): twitter.com/artnews
Instagram: www.instagram.com/artnews
Pinterest: www.pinterest.com/artnewsmag
Released: Bimonthly **Description:** News magazine reporting on art, personalities, issues, trends, and events that shape the international art world. **Availability:** Print; Online.

978 ■ *Azure Magazine*
Pub: Azure Publishing Inc.
Contact: Jeffrey Bakazias, Manager, Accounting
E-mail: jeffrey@azureonline.com
URL(s): www.azuremagazine.com
Facebook: www.facebook.com/AzureMagazine
Linkedin: www.linkedin.com/company/azure -magazine
X (Twitter): x.com/AzureMagazine
Instagram: www.instagram.com/azuremagazine
YouTube: www.youtube.com/channel/ UCvrVZE9TPyBGrqlB49F6JyQ
Pinterest: www.pinterest.ca/azuremagazine
Ed: Nelda Rodger. **Released:** 6/year **Price:** $49.95, for print + digital; $28.95, for digital only; $43.95, for print only; C$10.95, Single issue. **Description:** Trade magazine covering art, design and architecture. **Availability:** Print; Online.

979 ■ *CAA News*
Pub: College Art Association
Contact: Scott Gerhardt, Director
URL(s): www.collegeart.org/news-archive/news -archive
Released: Weekly **Description:** Features news of the Association as well as activities, achievements, funding opportunities, conferences, programs, exhibitions, and legislation in the arts field. Recurring features include news of research, a calendar of events, reports of meetings, news of educational opportunities, notices of publications available, and columns titled From the Executive Director, People in the News, Grants, Awards & Honors, Conferences & Symposia, and Opportunities. **Availability:** Print.

980 ■ *National Association of Women Artists, Inc. News*
Pub: National Association of Women Artists
Contact: Christie Devereaux, President
URL(s): thenawa.org/membership-benefits
Released: Weekly **Description:** Presents news of women in the art field. Recurring features include a calendar of events, news of educational opportunities, juried shows, workshops, exhibits, and a column titled President's Letter. (This is a members only newsletter). **Availability:** Print.

981 ■ *The Photograph Collector*
Pub: The Photograph Collector
URL(s): www.photoreview.org/collect.htm
Ed: Stephen Perloff. **Released:** Monthly **Price:** $149.95, Individuals for one year. **Description:** Carries in-depth coverage of topics such as print prices, archival techniques, dealer activities, major acquisitions, and the international photography market. Recurring features include statistics, book reviews, news of research, and columns titled Gallery Row, Auction News, and Publishers Row. **Availability:** Print; Online.

TRADE SHOWS AND CONVENTIONS

982 ■ **AIC Annual Meeting (Meeting)**
Gaylord Archival (GA)
PO Box 4901
Syracuse, NY 13221-4901
Free: 800-448-6160
Fax: (800)272-3412
Co. E-mail: customerservice@gaylord.com
URL: http://www.gaylord.com
URL(s): www.culturalheritage.org/events/annual-mee ting/current-meeting
Frequency: Annual. **Description:** Preserve cultural heritage collections. **Audience:** Conservators, educators, scientists, students, archivists, art historians, and conservation enthusiasts. **Principal Exhibits:** Preserve cultural heritage collections. Dates and Locations: 2025 May 27-Jun 01 Hyatt Regency, Minneapolis, MN; 2026 Apr 28-May 02 Montreal, QC. **Telecommunication Services:** meetings@cultural heritage.org.

983 ■ **LA Art Show**
The Agency
PO Box 139
Kings Park, NY 11754
Ph: (631)544-0705
Free: 800-296-5684
Fax: (631)544-0705
Co. E-mail: cooksreviews@optonline.net
Contact: Joel Cook, Author Editor
URL(s): www.laartshow.com/about-the-show
Frequency: Annual. **Description:** Art ranging from old masters to contemporary art, including photography, video, and print. **Audience:** Industry professionals. **Principal Exhibits:** Art ranging from old masters to contemporary art, including photography, video, and print. Dates and Locations: 2025 Feb 19-23 Los Angeles Convention Center, Los Angeles, CA. **Telecommunication Services:** info@laartshow.com.

PUBLICATIONS

984 ■ *Art Business News*
PO Box 360
Hinckley, OH 44233
Co. E-mail: info@redwoodmg.com
URL: http://www.redwoodmg.com
Contact: Eric Smith, President
E-mail: eric@redwoodmg.com
URL(s): artbusinessnews.com
Facebook: www.facebook.com/artbusinessnews
X (Twitter): x.com/ABNMag
Released: Quarterly **Description:** Trade magazine covering information, education, and marketing services for art and framing retailers, distributors, and wholesalers. **Availability:** Print; Download; Online. **Telecommunication Services:** Email: editor@art businessnews.com .

COMPUTERIZED DATABASES

985 ■ *Art on Screen Database™*
Program for Art on Film Inc.
c/o Pratt SILS, 200 Willoughby Ave.
Brooklyn, NY 11205
Ph: (718)399-4506
Fax: (718)399-4507
Co. E-mail: info@artfilm.org
URL: http://www.artfilm.org
Contact: J. Paul Getty Trust, Founder
URL(s): www.artfilm.org/aosdb.htm
Availability: CD-ROM; Online. **Type:** Directory.

986 ■ *Bibliography of the History of Art*
The J. Paul Getty Trust
1200 Getty Center Dr.
Los Angeles, CA 90049-1679
Ph: (310)440-7300
Co. E-mail: communications@getty.edu
URL: http://www.getty.edu
Contact: Katherine E. Fleming, President
URL(s): www.getty.edu/research/tools/bha
Availability: Online. **Type:** Bibliographic.

987 ■ *The Getty Provenance Index® Databases*
The J. Paul Getty Trust
1200 Getty Center Dr.
Los Angeles, CA 90049-1679
Ph: (310)440-7300
Co. E-mail: communications@getty.edu
URL: http://www.getty.edu
Contact: Katherine E. Fleming, President
URL(s): www.getty.edu/research/tools/provenance/ search.html
Availability: Download; Online. **Type:** Directory.

LIBRARIES

988 ■ **Allen Sapp Gallery (ASG)**
1 Railway Ave. E
North Battleford, SK, Canada S9A 2Y6
Ph: (306)445-1760
Fax: (306)445-1694
Co. E-mail: galleriesofnb@cityofnb.ca
URL: http://www.allensapp.com
Contact: Leah Garven, Manager
E-mail: lgarven@cityofnb.ca
Facebook: www.facebook.com/AllenSappGallery
YouTube: www.youtube.com/user/ASGallery
Description: Gallery with the Gonor collection. **Scope:** Local history. **Founded:** 1989.

989 ■ **Andy Warhol Museum Archives Study Center**
117 Sandusky St.
Pittsburgh, PA 15212
URL: http://www.warhol.org/research/archives-study -center/archives-collection-research-request-form
Description: Library of archiever collections. **Scope:** Museums collections. **Founded:** 1994. **Holdings:** Figures not available.

990 ■ **Art Gallery of Greater Victoria (AGGV)**
1040 Moss St.
Victoria, BC, Canada V8V 4P1
Ph: (250)384-4171
Fax: (250)361-3995
URL: http://aggv.ca
Contact: Chris Lawless, President
Facebook: www.facebook.com/artgalleryvictoria
Linkedin: www.linkedin.com/company/art-gallery-of -greater-victoria
X (Twitter): x.com/artgalleryvic
Instagram: www.instagram.com/artgalleryvic

Description: Publishes a newsletter and exhibit catalogs based on our collection of arts and crafts from Asia, Canada, Europe and America. Reaches market through the media, advertising, and direct mail. Does not accept unsolicited manuscripts. **Scope:** Art - Canadian, Asian; British Columbia artists. **Services:** Library currently only available to in-house staff and volunteers due to lack of staff. **Founded:** 1951. **Holdings:** 10,000 volumes.

991 ■ The Beaverbrook Art Gallery
703 Queen St.
  Fredericton, NB, Canada E3B 1C4
Ph: (506)458-2028
Co. E-mail: education@beaverbrookartgallery.org
URL: http://beaverbrookartgallery.org
Contact: Thomas Smart, Chief Executive Officer
E-mail: tsmart@beaverbrookartgallery.org
Facebook: www.facebook.com/BeaverbrookArtGallery
X (Twitter): x.com/BeaverbrookAG
Instagram: www.instagram.com/beaverbrook_ag
YouTube: www.youtube.com/channel/UCvTlz1T-BddhhHXMWKTmRrw
Description: Operator of an art gallery. **Founded:** 1959.

992 ■ California University of Pennsylvania - Louis L. Manderino Library - Special Collections
250 University Ave., Rm. 435
  California, PA 15419
Ph: (724)938-5767
Co. E-mail: libraryarchives@calu.edu
URL: http://www.calu.edu/catalog/current/undergraduate/about/library.aspx
Contact: Daniel T. Zyglowicz, Library Technician
E-mail: zyglowicz@calu.edu
Facebook: www.facebook.com/PennWCalifornia
X (Twitter): twitter.com/i/flow/login?redirect_after_login=%2FPennWCalifornia
Instagram: www.instagram.com/PennWCalifornia/
YouTube: www.youtube.com/user/CalUofPA
Scope: History; the Civil War. **Services:** Interlibrary loan; library open to the public by appointment. **Founded:** 1852. **Holdings:** Journals; books; e-books; audiovisual materials.

993 ■ Carnegie Library of Pittsburgh - Music Department
4400 Forbes Ave.
  Pittsburgh, PA 15213
Ph: (412)622-3114
Co. E-mail: musicdept@carnegielibrary.org
URL: http://www.carnegielibrary.org/services/music-resources
Scope: History; music. **Services:** Reference and reader's assistance; department open to the public. **Founded:** 1938. **Holdings:** 85,000 music books and scores; 28,000 sound recordings; 54,000 slides; 1,700 videos and DVDs; 400 periodical, newsletter and serial titles; mounted pictures.

994 ■ Colby College - Bixler Art and Music Library
5100 Mayflower Hill
  Waterville, ME 04901
URL: http://libraries.colby.edu
Description: Contains reference materials, journals, books, online materials, and video and audio materials on arts and musical studies. **Scope:** Art; music. **Services:** Interlibrary loan; copying; Apple computer lab; in-house listening and video viewing stations; library open to the public for reference use only. **Founded:** 1959. **Holdings:** 33,000 books and bound periodical volumes; 10,000 music scores; 11,000 sound recordings; 1,200 videos 450 CD-ROMs.

995 ■ Craigdarroch Castle - Library
1050 Joan Cres.
  Victoria, BC, Canada V8S 3L5
Ph: (250)592-5323
Fax: (250)592-1099
Co. E-mail: info@thecastle.ca
URL: http://thecastle.ca
Contact: John Hughes, Executive Director
X (Twitter): x.com/CraigdarrochC
YouTube: www.youtube.com/channel/UCFBwX9p05cn9G4_AScx6-g
Description: Craigdarroch Castle built between 1887 and 1890. **Scope:** History of craigdarroch castle. **Founded:** 1959. **Holdings:** Figures not available.

996 ■ Edinboro University - Baron-Forness Library Special Collections
200 Tartan Dr.
  Edinboro, PA 16444
URL: http://www.edinboro.edu/offices-services/library/index.php
Scope: Pennsylvania history; education. **Services:** Interlibrary loan;Tutoring. **Holdings:** 300,000 volumes;680,000 microform units;100 full-text journal databases; Reserve materials; software; equipment.

997 ■ Emmanuel College - Cardinal Cushing Library
400 The Fenway
  Boston, MA 02115
Ph: (617)655-7979
URL: http://learningcommons.emmanuel.edu/library
Contact: Diane Zydlewski, Associate Librarian
E-mail: zydlewsd@emmanuel.edu
Scope: Education; research; information literacy. **Services:** Open to Public, Interlibrary loan. **Founded:** 1964. **Holdings:** 250,000 print and e-Books; 3,600 print and electronic journal; 60 online subscription databases; 25,000 online streaming videos.

998 ■ Hardin-Simmons University (HSU) - Rupert and Pauline Richardson Library
2200 Hickory
  Abilene, TX 79698
URL: http://www.hsutx.edu/academics/library
Scope: Reference materials; circulating collections. **Services:** Library open to the public; interlibrary loan. **Founded:** 1891. **Holdings:** 400,000 items; 20,000 government publications; 48,000 periodicals.

999 ■ Hillwood Estate, Museum & Gardens Art Research Library
4155 Linnean Ave. NW
  Washington, DC 20008
Ph: (202)686-5807
URL: http://hillwoodmuseum.org
Contact: Kendall Aughenbaugh, Librarian, Digital Services
E-mail: kaughenbaugh@hillwoodmuseum.org
Description: Hillwood library-holdings reflect the museum's collection of imperial Russian and 18th-century French decorative arts within a broad social context. **Scope:** Art - decorative, French, Russian; Russian imperial history. **Services:** Copying; library open to the public by appointment. **Founded:** 1960. **Holdings:** 38,000 volumes; monographs; serials; annotated; early auction catalogues; and electronic resources; Marjorie Merriweather Post.

1000 ■ The Juilliard School - Lila Acheson Wallace Library
60 Lincoln Ctr Plz.
  New York, NY 10023
Ph: (212)799-5000
URL: http://www.juilliard.edu/admissions
Contact: Damian Woetzel, President
URL(s): www.juilliard.edu/student-life/library-archives
Facebook: www.facebook.com/TheJuilliardSchool
Linkedin: www.linkedin.com/school/19777
X (Twitter): x.com/juilliardschool
Instagram: www.instagram.com/juilliardschool
YouTube: www.youtube.com/juilliardschool
Pinterest: www.pinterest.com/juilliardschool
Description: The School offers miscellaneous educational services, such as dance and drama courses, as well as a variety of music courses including brass, guitar, harp, percussion, strings, piano, jazz studies, and opera. **Scope:** Music; dance; drama and general academic subjects. **Services:** Interlibrary loan; Open to scholars and researchers on an appointment basis. **Founded:** 1905. **Holdings:** 27,000 books; 25,000 sound recordings; 3,000 videos.

1001 ■ McCord Museum of Canadian History [Musee McCord d'Histoire Canadienne]
690 Sherbrooke St. W
  Montreal, QC, Canada H3A 1E9
URL: http://www.musee-mccord.qc.ca/en/privacy-policy
Description: Separately incorporated institution affiliated with McGill University and governed by a Board of Trustees; cafe, boutique. **Scope:** A research source of Canada's historical heritage, the Museum contains, preserves, and exhibits collections of Canadian ethnography, including exhibitions of paintings, prints, drawings, costumes, decorative and folk art, material cultures, and photography. **Services:** Copying; library open to the public by appointment. **Holdings:** 9,108 books; 2,000 rare books; 200 meters of archives; 95 reels of microfilm; 1 million photographs; electronic records; graphic materials; textual records. **Subscriptions:** 180 journals and other serials. **Publications:** Exhibition Catalogs; McCord Museum of Canadian History Monographs; McCord Museum of Canadian History Newsletter (Monthly). **Educational Activities:** McCord Research Associate Program.

1002 ■ Menil Collection Library
1533 Sul Ross St.
  Houston, TX 77006
Ph: (713)525-9400
Co. E-mail: info@menil.org
URL: http://www.menil.org/research/menil-library
Contact: Doug L. Lawing, President
Facebook: www.facebook.com/MenilCollection
X (Twitter): x.com/MenilCollection
Instagram: www.instagram.com/menilcollection
YouTube: www.youtube.com/user/themenilcollection
Description: The Library of the Menil Collection is the curatorial library of the museum. It supports the reference, research, and scholarly needs of the director's office and the curatorial, conservation, registration, archives, and publishing departments of the Menil Collection. **Scope:** Art; research. **Services:** Interlibrary loan; copying; library open to the public by appointment. **Founded:** 1987. **Holdings:** Figures not available.

1003 ■ St. Cloud State University - Learning Resources Services - University Archives and Special Collections
720 4th Ave. S
  Saint Cloud, MN 56301-4498
Ph: (320)308-4753
Co. E-mail: archives@stcloudstate.edu
URL: http://www.stcloudstate.edu/library/archives
Contact: Tom Steman, Professor
E-mail: tdsteman@stcloudstate.edu
Facebook: www.facebook.com/people/St-Cloud-State-University-Archives/100064673023103
Scope: Art; theater; literature; Sinclair Lewis. **Services:** Interlibrary loan; copying; archives open to the public. **Founded:** 1977. **Holdings:** 2.5 million items; 250,000 U.S. Government publications; Catalogs; SCSU publications; books (monographs); reference resources; journals, newspapers; videos; films; microforms. **Subscriptions:** 22000 periodicals (includes journals).

1004 ■ St. Norbert Arts Centre Archives (SNAC)
100 rue des Ruines du Monastere
  Winnipeg, MB, Canada R3V 1L6
Ph: (204)269-0564
Co. E-mail: snac@snac.mb.ca
URL: http://www.snac.mb.ca
Contact: Naomi Gerrard, Chairman of the Board
Facebook: www.facebook.com/StNorbertArtsCentre
YouTube: www.youtube.com/channel/UC2ylUhtsPQPin4LkfA86pqQ
Founded: 1991. **Holdings:** Figures not available.

1005 ■ San Francisco Public Library - Bernard Osher Foundation Art, Music & Recreation Center
100 Larkin St.
  San Francisco, CA 94102
Ph: (415)557-4525

Co. E-mail: artmusicrec@sfpl.org
URL: http://sfpl.org/locations/main-library/art-music
Scope: Visual arts; performing arts; music; sports and recreation. **Services:** Center open to the public. **Holdings:** Books; serials; scores; CD-ROMs; DVDs.

1006 ■ Santa Clara University - de Saisset Museum Library
500 El Camino Real
Santa Clara, CA 95053
Ph: (408)554-4528
Co. E-mail: desaissetmuseum@scu.edu
URL: http://www.scu.edu/desaisset
Facebook: www.facebook.com/deSaisset
Instagram: www.instagram.com/desaisset
Scope: California history; art history. **Services:** Library open to public by appointment. **Founded:** 1955. **Holdings:** 12,500 objects; 2,500 prints; photographs.

1007 ■ The Sculptors Society of Canada (SSC) - Canadian Sculpture Centre Archives
19 Mill St.
The Distillery District
Toronto, ON, Canada M5A 3R3
Ph: (647)435-5858
Co. E-mail: cansculpt@gmail.com
URL: http://www.sculptorssocietyofcanada.org
Contact: Judi Michelle Young, President
Facebook: www.facebook.com/sculptorssocietyofcanada
Description: Promotes Canadian sculpture through exhibition and education. Encourages the public and young talents to participate in raising the sculptures' standards. **Scope:** Sculpture. **Services:** Archives open to the public by appointment. **Founded:** 1928. **Holdings:** Photographs; slides; files. **Geographic Preference:** National.

1008 ■ Sweet Briar College - Martin C. Shallenberger Library
134 Chapel Rd.
Sweet Briar, VA 24595
Ph: (434)381-6138
Fax: (434)381-6173
URL: http://library.sbc.edu
Description: Sweet Briar College library. **Scope:** Rare books, college archives. **Services:** Interlibrary loan. **Founded:** 1901. **Holdings:** 5,000 volumes.; 400,000 microforms; 250,000 volumes; 8,000 audio-visual materials; 1,000 periodical titles.

1009 ■ Tom Thomson Art Gallery Archives
808 2nd Ave., E
Owen Sound, ON, Canada N4K 2H4
Ph: (519)376-1932
Co. E-mail: ttag@tomthomson.org
URL: http://www.owensound.ca/recreation-culture/arts-and-culture/tom-thomson-art-gallery
Contact: Aidan Ware, Director
E-mail: aware@tomthomson.org
Facebook: www.facebook.com/tomthomsonartgallery
X (Twitter): x.com/TheTomThomson
Scope: Arts; culture; heritage. **Founded:** 1967. **Holdings:** Papers, photographs, sculptures, textiles, installation pieces.

1010 ■ University of North Carolina School of the Arts - Semans Library
1533 S Main St.
Winston Salem, NC 27127-2738
Ph: (336)770-3399
URL: http://www.uncsa.edu/faculty-staff-hub/around-campus/facilities-maintenance/design-and-construction-projects/semans-renovation.aspx
Description: Library collects, organizes, describes and preserves access to records of permanent administrative, legal, fiscal and historical value. **Scope:** Art and design. **Services:** Interlibrary loan; library open to the public; copying; printing; scanning. **Founded:** 1965. **Holdings:** Books; periodicals; music and media.

1011 ■ Watkins College of Art, Design, & Film Library
1900 Belmont Blvd.
Nashville, TN 37212
Co. E-mail: librarian@watkins.edu
URL: http://www.watkins.edu
Description: Watkins Library is a comprehensive nerve center of resources for Watkins students, staff, and faculty. **Scope:** Film; fine arts; visual arts; graphic design; photography. **Services:** Interlibrary loan; library open to the public for reference use only. **Holdings:** Books; films.

RESEARCH CENTERS

1012 ■ New York University Graduate School of Arts and Science - Institute of Fine Arts - Conservation Center
Stephen Chan House
14 E 78th St.
New York, NY 10075
Ph: (212)992-5848
Fax: (212)992-5851
Co. E-mail: conservation.program@nyu.edu
URL: http://www.ifa.nyu.edu/conservation/index.htm
Contact: Michele D. Marincola, Chairman Professor
Description: Integral unit of Institute of Fine Arts in Graduate School of Arts and Science at New York University. Offers consultation: to museums. **Scope:** Deterioration, preservation, and restoration of works of art, including research and development of methods of examination to determine identity of materials and extent of alteration of works of art, preservation of stone, prevention of degradation, causes of deterioration in frescos, neutron activation analysis of art materials, and metal technology of antiquity. Conducts lectures. **Founded:** 1960. **Publications:** *Conservation Center Newsletter*. **Educational Activities:** Conservation Center Summer sessions, For museum professionals.; Conservation Center Time-Based Media Symposium; Conservation Center Workshops (Irregular).

Art Supplies Store

ASSOCIATIONS AND OTHER ORGANIZATIONS

1013 ■ Art and Creative Materials Institute (ACMI)
99 Derby St., Ste. 200
  Hingham, MA 02043
Ph: (781)556-1044
Fax: (781)207-5550
Co. E-mail: info@acmiart.org
URL: http://www.acmiart.org
Contact: Heather Trundle, President
Facebook: www.facebook.com/acmiart
Instagram: www.instagram.com/ACMIart
Pinterest: www.pinterest.com/artandcreativematerials

Description: Manufacturers of art and creative materials; sponsors certification program to ensure that art materials are non-toxic or affixed with health warning labels where appropriate. Works with ASTM International and the American National Standards Institute to develop and maintain chronic hazard labeling standards and performance standards. Sponsors annual Youth Art Month in March to emphasize the value of art education for all children and to encourage public support for quality school art programs; publicizes value of art and art education in newspapers and magazines. **Scope:** Reviews and tests the toxicity of art and craft materials. Conducts a certification program to ensure that art and craft materials are non-toxic or affixed with health warning labels where appropriate and meet voluntary standards of quality and performance. Products certified through the program bear the CP (Certified Product), AP (Approved Product), HL (Health Label) or CL (Cautionary Labeling) seal. **Founded:** 1940. **Publications:** *Institute Items Newsletter* (Monthly); *The Safe and Successful Use of Art Materials*; *What You Need to Know About the Safety of Art and Craft Materials*. **Educational Activities:** ACMI Seminars on the safe use of art materials. **Geographic Preference:** National.

1014 ■ NAMTA - The International Art Materials Association (NAMTA)
PO Box 3314
  Huntersville, NC 28070
Ph: (704)892-6244
Co. E-mail: kbrown@namta.org
URL: http://www.namta.org
Contact: Lawrence Hoffman, President
Facebook: www.facebook.com/internationalartmaterials
X (Twitter): x.com/namta
Instagram: www.instagram.com/namtaartmaterialsassociation

Description: Aims to provide art/creative materials industry members with the products, services and information needed to grow and prosper, and to be recognized as an international leader and unifying force in the support, sustainability and advocacy of art and the art/creative materials business. **Founded:** 1950. **Publications:** *National Art Materials Trade Association's Annual Convention Directory*; *Who's Who in Art Materials* (Annual); *NAMTA's Annual Convention Directory* (Annual); *National Art Materials Trade Association--News and Views* (Monthly). **Educational Activities:** NAMTAs Art Materials World Trade Show (Annual); Art Materials World Trade Show (Annual). **Geographic Preference:** Multinational.

REFERENCE WORKS

1015 ■ *"America's Oldest Art Supply Store Closes After 111 Years" in ArtnetNews (August 29, 2016)*
URL(s): news.artnet.com/art-world/oldest-art-supply-store-closes-623801
Ed: Rain Embuscado. **Released:** August 29, 2016. **Description:** New York Central Art Supply Inc, America's oldest art supply store, closed on September 2, 2016. Due to sagging retail sales, this store and others like it continue to close while larger chains and internet -based stores continue to thrive. **Availability:** Online.

1016 ■ *"Creative Cluster Paints Business Success" in Business Journal Serving Greater Tampa Bay (Vol. 30, October 29, 2010, No. 45, pp. 1)*
Pub: Tampa Bay Business Journal
Contact: Ian Anderson, President
E-mail: ianderson@bizjournals.com
Ed: Jane Meinhardt. **Description:** How Tom Gaffney, a cofounder of the private equity firm The Anderson Group realized the great return on investment in the 600 block of Central Avenue in St. Petersburg, Florida is discussed. Focusing on long-term value rather than short-term profitability and exit, Gaffney purchased this block in 2008 for $2.3 million and cultivated arts businesses at tenants. **Availability:** Print; Online.

1017 ■ *"New Biz Mixes Paint, Wine; Will It Yield Green?" in Crain's Detroit Business (Vol. 30, September 8, 2014, No. 36, pp. 6)*
Pub: Crain Communications Inc.
Contact: Barry Asin, President
Description: Profile of Leanna Haun, owner of Picasso's Grapevine in downtown Clarkston, Michigan. Haun describes her business as one part wine, one part paint, and one part entertainment. Sessions include as many as ten people who are given instruction to paint a picture while enjoying wine and conversation with others. **Availability:** Print; Online.

STATISTICAL SOURCES

1018 ■ *U.S. The Arts and Crafts Consumer Market Report 2021*
URL(s): store.mintel.com/report/us-the-arts-and-crafts-consumer-market-report
Price: $4,366.35. **Description:** Downloadable report discussing data about the arts and crafts industry and how US consumers are participating in that market. Report includes an executive summary, interactive databook, PowerPoint presentation, infographic overview, report PDF, and previous years data. **Availability:** PDF.

TRADE PERIODICALS

1019 ■ *Needlework Retailer*
Pub: Yarn Tree Design Inc.
URL(s): needleworkretailer.com
Facebook: www.facebook.com/NeedleworkRetailer
X (Twitter): x.com/NeedleworkRtlr
Instagram: www.instagram.com/needleworkretailer
YouTube: www.youtube.com/channel/UCv5g5swU2GJVz5arwkz7X9w
Pinterest: www.pinterest.com/NeedleworkRetailer
Ed: Megan Chriswisser. **Released:** Bimonthly **Price:** $14, for 6 issues US; $20, for 6 issues Canada; $43, for 6 issues other Countries; $28, Canada for 1 year; $17, U.S. for 1 year; $65, for overseas and Mexico. **Description:** Trade magazine for the needlework industry, especially small, independent needlework retailers. **Availability:** Print; Online.

Assisted Living Facilities

ASSOCIATIONS AND OTHER ORGANIZATIONS

1020 ■ American College of Health Care Administrators (ACHCA)
1101 Connecticut Ave. NW, Ste. 450
Washington, DC 20036
Free: 800-561-3148
Co. E-mail: info@achca.org
URL: http://www.achca.org
Contact: Amanda Charles, Business Manager
E-mail: acharles@achca.org
Facebook: www.facebook.com/pages/The-American-College-of-Health-Care-Administrators/326597784597
X (Twitter): x.com/ACHCA
Description: Persons actively engaged in the administration of long-term care facilities, such as nursing homes, retirement communities, assisted living facilities, and sub-acute care programs. Administers professional certification programs for assisted living, sub-acute and nursing home administrators. Works to elevate the standards in the field and to develop and promote a code of ethics and standards of education and training. Seeks to inform allied professions and the public that good administration of long-term care facilities calls for special formal academic training and experience. Encourages research in all aspects of geriatrics, the chronically ill, and administration. Maintains placement service. Holds special education programs; facilitates networking among administrators. **Founded:** 1962. **Publications:** *Continuum* (Quarterly); *Balance: The Source for Administrators in Long-Term Health Care* (8/year); *ACHCA E-News* (Bimonthly). **Educational Activities:** ACHCA Annual Winter Marketplace (Annual). **Awards:** New Administrator Award (Annual); ACHCA Education Award (Annual); ACHCA Journalism Award (Annual); W.Phillip McConnell Student Scholarship Fund (Irregular); Richard L. Thorpe Fellowship (Annual); ACHCA Distinguished Assisted Living Administrator Award (Annual); ACHCA Distinguished Nursing Home Administrator Award (Annual); ACHCA New Nursing Home Administrator Award (Annual). **Geographic Preference:** National.

1021 ■ American Health Care Association (AHCA)
1201 L St. NW
Washington, DC 20005
Ph: (202)842-4444
Fax: (202)842-3860
Co. E-mail: help@ltctrendtracker.com
URL: http://www.ahcancal.org/Pages/default.aspx
Contact: Mark Parkinson, President
Facebook: www.facebook.com/ahcancal
X (Twitter): x.com/ahcancal
YouTube: www.youtube.com/user/ahcancalstream
Description: Federation of state associations of long-term health care facilities. Promotes standards for professionals in long-term health care delivery and quality care for patients and residents in a safe environment. Focuses on issues of availability, quality, affordability, and fair payment. Operates as liaison with governmental agencies, Congress, and professional associations. Compiles statistics. American Health Care Association is an association of long term and post-acute care providers and advocates for quality care and services for frail, elderly and disabled Americans. **Founded:** 1949. **Publications:** *Focus* (Weekly); *Provider--LTC Buyers' Guide Issue* (Annual); *American Health Care Association: Provider* (Monthly); *Choosing a Nursing Home Pamphlet*; *Choosing An Assisted Living Residence: A Consumer's Guide*; *Having Your Say: Advance Directives Fact Sheet*; *Understanding Long Term Care Insurance Fact Sheet*; *Assisted Living State Regulatory Review* (Annual); *NCAL Connections* (Weekly); *Resident Assistant Newsletter*; *Assessing Your Needs: Consumer Guides to Nursing and Assisted Living Facilities*; *Caring for Someone with Alzheimer's Fact Sheet*; *Living in a Nursing Home: Myths and Realities Fact Sheet*; *Tips on Visiting Friends and Relatives Fact Sheet*; *Family Questions: The First Thirty Days Fact Sheet*; *Moving Into an Assisted Living Residence: Making a Successful Transition Fact Sheet*; *Making the Transition to Nursing Facility Life Fact Sheet*; *Paying for Long Term Care Pamphlet*; *Glossary of Terms Pamphlet*; *Advice for Families Pamphlet*; *Advance Preparation: Having the Conversation About Long Term Care Pamphlet*; *Coping with the Transition Pamphlet*; *Talking To Your Loved Ones About Their Care Pamphlet*; *Capitol Connection Newsletter* (Biweekly); *NCAL Focus Newsletter* (Monthly); *AHCA Notes* (Monthly); *Provider: For Long Term Care Professionals* (Monthly). **Educational Activities:** American Health Care Association Annual Convention and Exposition (Annual). **Awards:** AHCA/NCAL National Quality Award - Bronze Level (Annual); AHCA/NCAL Adult Volunteer of the Year (Annual); AHCA Group Volunteer of the Year (Annual); AHCA/NCAL Young Adult Volunteer of the Year Award (Annual); AHCA/NCAL National Quality Award - Silver Level (Annual); AHCA/NCAL National Quality Award - Gold Level (Annual). **Geographic Preference:** National.

1022 ■ Argentum
1650 King St.
Alexandria, VA 22314
Ph: (703)894-1805
Co. E-mail: info@argentum.org
URL: http://www.argentum.org
Contact: James Balda, President
E-mail: jbalda@argentum.org
Facebook: www.facebook.com/ArgentumSeniorLiving
Linkedin: www.linkedin.com/company/argentum1
X (Twitter): x.com/argentum
Instagram: www.instagram.com/argentumadvocates
YouTube: www.youtube.com/user/assistedlivingfed
Description: Promotes the interests of the assisted living industry and works to enhance the quality of life for the population it serves. **Founded:** 1990. **Publications:** *ALFA Alert* (Periodic); *Senior Housing Directory*; *Guide to Choosing an Assisted Living Residence*; *Senior Living Executive* (Bimonthly); *ALFA Public Policy Bulletins* (Monthly). **Awards:** Argentum Hero Awards (Annual). **Geographic Preference:** National.

REFERENCE WORKS

1023 ■ "Advancing the Ball" in Inside Healthcare (Vol. 6, December 2010, No. 7, pp. 31)
Description: Profile of Medicalodges an elder-care specialty company that provides both patient care and technology development. President and CEO of the firm believes that hiring good employees is key to growth for any small business. **Availability:** Online.

1024 ■ "Assisted Living Facility Faces Bankruptcy and Care Issues" in South Florida Business Journal (Vol. 33, August 17, 2012, No. 3, pp. 1)
Pub: Baltimore Business Journal
Contact: Rhonda Pringle, President
E-mail: rpringle@bizjournals.com
Description: FTMI Real Estate has filed for bankruptcy declaring a total debt of almost $29 million and assets of $19.6 million. The company owns The Lenox on the Lake, a 139-bed assisted living facility in Tamarac, which has at least one outstanding state complaint regarding patient care. **Availability:** Print; Online.

1025 ■ "CIT Serves as Sole Lead Arranger on $27.2 Million Financing for Texas Assisted Living Facilities" in Senior Living News (September 13, 2019)
URL(s): seniorlivingnews.com/cit-serves-as-sole-lead-arranger-on-27-2-million-financing-for-texas-assisted-living-facilities/
Released: September 13, 2019. **Description:** Two assisted living facilities in Texas received financing from CIT to cover closing costs and refinance existing debt. This move will enable the two facilities to maintain 154 units. **Availability:** Online.

1026 ■ "Communicating With Your Loved Ones in Long-Term Care Facilities During Disaster Situations" in Senior Living News (October 4, 2019)
URL(s): seniorlivingnews.com/communicating-with-your-loved-ones-in-long-term-care-facilities-during-disaster-situations/
Ed: Doug Wilcox. **Released:** October 04, 2019. **Description:** What do you do when disaster strikes and you need to reach a loved one in a care facility? The internet and social media can provide easy ways to monitor the situation around the facility instead of trying to repeatedly call, especially if the electricity is out. Asking in advance to put plans in place is also recommended. **Availability:** Online.

1027 ■ "Developer To Use New Owasso Senior Care Center as Template for More Services, Expansion" in Journal Record (May 23, 2012)
Description: A new $7.5 million senior care and rehabilitation center will be built in Owasso, Oklahoma. The builder, Steve Cox, is using his Senior

Small Business Profiles   Assisted Living Facilities ■ 1044

Suites of Owasso as his model. JRJ Construction of Weatherford, Texas will complete the 105-bed private-suite facility by spring 2013. **Availability:** Print; Online.

1028 ■ "Direct Care Workforce: LeadingAge Applauds New Legislation" in LeadingAge (September 24, 2019)
URL(s): www.leadingage.org/legislation/direct-care-workforce-leadingage-applauds-new-legislation
Ed: Barbara Gay. **Released:** September 24, 2019. **Description:** The U.S. Department of Labor is in charge of a new program that will recruit and train direct-care workers. In the next five years, the industry is expected to expand and there is a huge need to fill and retain employees who can provide caregiving. **Availability:** Online.

1029 ■ "Elder Care Costs Surge" in National Underwriter Life & Health (Vol. 114, November 8, 2020, No. 21, pp. 25)
Ed: Trevor Thomas. **Description:** Nursing home and assisted living rates rose from 2009 to 2010, according to MetLife Mature Market Institute. Statistical data included. **Availability:** Online.

1030 ■ "Elder Care, Rx Drug Reforms Top Zoeller's Agenda" in Times (December 21, 2010)
Pub: The Times
Ed: Sarah Tompkins. **Description:** Indiana Attorney General Greg Zoeller is hoping to develop a program in the state that will help regulate care for the elderly; freeze medical licenses for doctors involved in criminal investigations; address illegal drug use; and to establish a program to help individuals dispose of old prescription medications easily at pharmacies. **Availability:** Online.

1031 ■ "Elder-Care Seminar to Teach Ways to Avoid Falls" in Virginian-Pilot (November 25, 2010)
Pub: The Virginian-Pilot
Contact: Kevin Goyette, Director
E-mail: kgoyette@dailypress.com
Ed: Amy Jeter. **Description:** ResCare HomeCare, a home health services firm, offers free seminars on helping to make residences safer for seniors prone to falling. **Availability:** Print; Online.

1032 ■ "EVMS Gets Grant to Train Providers for Elder Care" in Virginian-Pilot (October 29, 2010)
Pub: The Virginian-Pilot
Contact: Kevin Goyette, Director
E-mail: kgoyette@dailypress.com
Ed: Elizabeth Simpson. **Description:** Eastern Virginia Medical School received a federal grant to train health providers in elder care. Details of the program are provided. **Availability:** Online.

1033 ■ "Ground Readied for Construction of $4.5 Million Senior Care Center in Crown Point" in Times (August 9, 2012)
Description: Bickford Senior Living will begin construction on a $4.5 million senior care center in Munster, Indiana. The facility will include assisted living apartments for seniors with various needs. Sixteen of the units will care for individuals with memory loss. Nurses and caregivers will be on staff 24 hours a day. **Availability:** Print; Online.

1034 ■ "Silver Dollars" in Small Business Opportunities (September 2008)
Description: Profile of Always Best Care Senior Services, a franchise created by Michael Newman, which offers non-medical In-Home Care, Personal Emergency Response Systems, and Assisted Living Placement Services to seniors; the company offers franchisees the opportunity to fill what is oftentimes a void for the seniors and their families in the community. **Availability:** Online.

1035 ■ "They've Fallen, But Can Senior-Housing Stocks Get Up" in Barron's (Vol. 88, March 10, 2008, No. 10, pp. 43)
Pub: Dow Jones & Company Inc.
Contact: Almar Latour, Chief Executive Officer

Ed: Kopin Tan. **Description:** Shares of senior housing companies present buying opportunities to investors because of their low prices. Companies such as Brookdale Senior Living are not as dependent on housing prices but have suffered declines in share prices. **Availability:** Online.

1036 ■ "When to Move from Independent Living to Assisted Living" in U.S.News & World Report (August 9, 2019)
URL(s): health.usnews.com/best-assisted-living/articles/when-to-move-from-independent-living-to-assisted-living
Ed: Elaine K. Howley. **Released:** August 09, 2019. **Description:** Defines assisted living and discusses when it could be time to move into such a facility. These include developing medical problems, memory loss, inability to care for oneself, and social isolation. **Availability:** Online.

TRADE PERIODICALS

1037 ■ Home Health Care Services Quarterly
Pub: Taylor And Francis Group
Contact: Annie Callanan, Chief Executive Officer
URL(s): www.tandfonline.com/journals/whhc20
Ed: Hongdao Meng. **Released:** Quarterly **Price:** $1,767, Institutions for print and online; $257, Individuals for print and online; $1,449, Institutions for online only; $237, Individuals for online only. **Description:** Professional journal. **Availability:** Print; Download; PDF; Online.

LIBRARIES

1038 ■ Albany Medical College - Schaffer Library of Health Sciences
43 New Scotland Ave.
 Albany, NY 12208
Ph: (518)262-5530
URL: http://www.amc.edu/academic/Schaffer/index.cfm

Scope: Medicine; health science. **Services:** Interlibrary loan; copying; document delivery; open to allied health personnel. **Founded:** 1928. **Holdings:** 150,000 volumes; 98,597 bound periodical volumes; 2,700 audio/visual programs.

1039 ■ American Association of Occupational Health Nurses, Inc. (AAOHN)
330 N Wabash Ave., Ste. 2000
 Chicago, IL 60611
Ph: (312)321-5173
Fax: (312)673-6719
Co. E-mail: info@aaohn.org
URL: http://www.aaohn.org
Contact: Kimberly Olszewski, President
E-mail: kimberly.olszewski@disa.com
Facebook: www.facebook.com/AAOHN
Linkedin: www.linkedin.com/company/american-association-of-occupational-health-nurses
X (Twitter): x.com/AAOHN

Description: Association of licensed nurses engaged in the practice of occupation and environmental health nursing. **Founded:** 1943. **Publications:** Foundation Blocks; Official Journal of the American Association of Occupational Health Nurses; AAOHN News (Monthly). **Educational Activities:** AAOHN National Conference (Annual); American Occupational Health Conference (AOHC) (Annual). **Awards:** AAOHN Chapter Communications Award (Annual); AAOHN Chapter Community Service Award (Annual); AAOHN Chapter Education Award - Best Short Activity (Annual); Mary Louise Brown Practice/Research Recognition Award; AAOHN Business Recognition Award (Annual); AAOHN Chapter of the Year Award (Annual); AAOHN Professional Development Scholarships - Academic Study (Annual); AAOHN Professional Development Scholarships - Continuing Education (Annual); AAOHN Nurse in Washington Internships (NIWI) (Annual); AAOHN Fellowship (Annual); AAOHN Chapter Education Award - Best One Day Activity (Annual); AAOHN Chapter Education Award - Best Multi-Day Activity (Annual); AAOHN Chapter Governmental Affairs Award (Annual). **Geographic Preference:** National.

1040 ■ American Nurses Association (ANA)
American Nurses Association (ANA)
8515 Georgia Ave. Ste. 400
 Silver Spring, MD 20910-3492
Ph: (301)628-5000
Free: 800-284-2378
Co. E-mail: customerservice@ana.org
URL: http://www.nursingworld.org
Contact: Dr. Jennifer S. Mensik Kennedy, President
Facebook: www.facebook.com/AmericanNursesAssociation
Linkedin: www.linkedin.com/company/american-nurses-association
X (Twitter): x.com/ANANursingWorld
YouTube: www.youtube.com/user/nursesmatter

Description: Empowers nurses within their professional sphere of activity and contributes to better patient outcome. **Founded:** 1990. **Publications:** The American Nurses Association Pamphlet; Directory of Accredited Organizations; National Directory of Nurse Practitioner Programs; Online Journal of Issues in Nursing; The American Nurse (TAN) (Monthly); Preventing Back Injuries: Safe Patient Handling and Movement Pamphlet; Preventing Needlestick Injuries: Safe Needles Save Lives Pamphlet; Preventing Transmission of Tuberculosis Pamphlet; Preventing Workplace Violence Pamphlet; Financial Aid for Nursing Education Pamphlet; Proceedings of the House of Delegates (Periodic); Credentialing News; Certification Review Products Catalogue (Annual); Directory of RN to BSN Programs; Facts About Needlestick Injury. **Educational Activities:** House of Delegates (Semiannual). **Geographic Preference:** National.

1041 ■ El Camino Hospital - The Health Library & Resource Center
2500 Grant Rd.
 Mountain View, CA 94040
Ph: (650)940-7000
URL: http://www.elcaminohealth.org
Contact: Andrew Cope, President
Facebook: www.facebook.com/elcaminohealth
Linkedin: www.linkedin.com/company/el-camino-health
Instagram: www.instagram.com/el.camino.health
YouTube: www.youtube.com/c/ElCaminoHealth

Scope: Medicine; nursing; healthcare administration. **Services:** Interlibrary loan; copying; library open to the public. **Founded:** 1958. **Holdings:** Books; DVDs, CD-ROMs; journals. **Subscriptions:** 150 journals and other serials. **Geographic Preference:** Local.

1042 ■ Kaiser-Permanente Medical Center Health Sciences Library
2500 Merced St.
 San Leandro, CA 94577
URL: http://healthy.kaiserpermanente.org/northern-california/facilities/san-leandro-medical-center-30
1981

Scope: Clinical medicine; healthcare management; nursing; consumer health; emergency medical services; geriatrics; quality improvement. **Founded:** 1985.

1043 ■ Loma Linda University - Del E. Webb Memorial Library
11072 Anderson St.
 Loma Linda, CA 92350
URL: http://library.llu.edu

Description: Seventh-day Adventist organization with more than 4,400 students located in Southern California. **Scope:** Educational materials. **Services:** Interlibrary loan; Photocopying. **Founded:** 1907. **Holdings:** Figures not available.

1044 ■ Los Angeles County/Harbor-UCLA Medical Center - A.F. Parlow Library of the Health Sciences
1000 W Carson St.
 Torrance, CA 90509-2910
Ph: (424)306-6100
Co. E-mail: libref@harbor-ucla.org

URL: http://library.harbor-ucla.org
Contact: Jenna Kim, Director
E-mail: jkim7@dhs.lacounty.gov
Scope: Medical and health science. **Services:** Interlibrary loan; copying; library open to the public with restrictions. **Founded:** 1946. **Holdings:** 8,000 e-books; 700 online journals; 700 journals.

1045 ■ McMaster University Health Sciences Library (HSL)
1280 Main St. W, HSC 2B
 Hamilton, ON, Canada L8S 4K1
Ph: (905)525-9140
Co. E-mail: hslib@mcmaster.ca
URL: http://hsl.mcmaster.ca
Contact: Jennifer McKinnell, Director
E-mail: mckinn@mcmaster.ca
Facebook: www.facebook.com/machealthscilibrary
X (Twitter): x.com/mcmasterhsl
Instagram: www.instagram.com/mcmasterhsl
YouTube: www.youtube.com/machealthscilibrary
Scope: Health and medicine history. **Services:** Interlibrary loan; copying; library open to the public for reference use only. **Founded:** 1967. **Holdings:** Figures not available.

1046 ■ Spectrum Health Libraries
100 Michigan St. NE
 Grand Rapids, MI 49503-2560
Free: 866-989-7999
Co. E-mail: socialmedia@spectrumhealth.org
Contact: Darryl Elmouchi, President
Facebook: www.facebook.com/spectrumhealth
Linkedin: www.linkedin.com/company/spectrum-health
X (Twitter): twitter.com/spectrumhealth
Instagram: www.instagram.com/spectrumhealth
YouTube: www.youtube.com/user/spectrumhealthtv
Pinterest: www.pinterest.com/spectrumhealth
Scope: Medicine; surgery; medical/surgical specialties; nursing. **Services:** Copying; document delivery; library open to the public. **Holdings:** 6,000 books; bound periodical volumes; audio and videocassettes; microfiche; microfilm.

Association Management Service

ASSOCIATIONS AND OTHER ORGANIZATIONS

1047 ■ AMC Institute (AMCI)
107 S W St., Ste. No. 481
Alexandria, VA 22314
Ph: (703)570-8955
Co. E-mail: info@amcinstitute.org
URL: http://www.amcinstitute.org
Contact: Tina Wehmeir, President
E-mail: twehmeir@amcinstitute.org
X (Twitter): x.com/AMCInstitute
YouTube: www.youtube.com/channel/UCz8mha00C5Jfc3uh5inkMcA

Description: Management companies serving a number of associations on a professional basis. Serves more than 1,800 associations with annual budgets exceeding $1.5 billion and serving nearly 1.7 million members. **Founded:** 1963. **Publications:** *Association Management Companies Institute--Membership Directory*. **Educational Activities:** AMC Institute Annual Meeting (Annual). **Geographic Preference:** National.

1048 ■ ANA Nonprofit Federation (DMANF)
Association of National Advertisers (ANA)
155 E 44th St.
New York, NY 10017
Ph: (212)697-5950
Fax: (212)687-7310
Co. E-mail: info@ana.net
URL: http://www.ana.net
Facebook: www.facebook.com/pages/Direct-Marketing-Association-DMA/60905377232

Description: Trade and lobbying group for non-profit organizations that use direct and online marketing to raise funds and communicate with members. Sponsors professional development conferences and seminars, lobbies on state and federal legislation, regulation, and standards related to direct marketing and related issues. Provides information about and participants in litigation affecting non-profits. Promotes the overall welfare of non-profits. Represents health care charities, social service agencies, religious groups, colleges and universities and fraternal organizations. **Founded:** 1982. **Publications:** *Journal of the DMA Nonprofit Federation* (3/year); *News Update* (Biweekly). **Educational Activities:** New York Nonprofit Conference (Annual); Washington Nonprofit Conference (Annual). **Awards:** Max Hart Nonprofit Achievement Award (Annual); DMA Nonprofit Organization of the Year (Annual). **Geographic Preference:** National.

1049 ■ ASAE: The Center for Association Leadership
1575 I St. NW
Washington, DC 20005
Ph: (202)626-2723
Free: 888-950-2723
Fax: (202)371-8315
Co. E-mail: asaeservice@asaecenter.org
URL: http://www.asaecenter.org
Contact: Michelle Mason, President
E-mail: mmason@asaecenter.org
Facebook: www.facebook.com/ASAEfan
Linkedin: www.linkedin.com/company/asae-the-center-for-association-leadership
X (Twitter): x.com/ASAEcenter
Instagram: www.instagram.com/asaecenter
YouTube: www.youtube.com/user/asaecenter

Description: Paid executives of international, national, state, and local trade, professional, and philanthropic associations. Educates association executives on management, including: the proper objectives, functions, and activities of associations; the basic principles of association management; the legal aspects of association activity; policies relating to association management; efficient methods, procedures, and techniques of association management; the responsibilities and professional standards of association executives. Conducts resume, guidance, and consultation services; compiles statistics in the form of reports, surveys, and studies; carries out research and education. **Scope:** Association management specialists providing training for those who manage nonprofit voluntary membership organizations. Typical client or target audience association executives and their staffs. **Founded:** 1920. **Publications:** "Guide to the Newest IRS Form 990"; "Spring 2009 Catalog"; "The Power of Partnership: Principles and Practices for Creating Strategic Relationships"; "Put Your Data to Work: 52 Tips and Techniques for Effectively Managing Your Database"; "Association Executive Compensation and Benefits Study"; "Turbulent Change: Every Working Person's Survival Guide"; "Reinventing Your Board: A Step-By-Step Guide to Implementing Policy Governance"; "International Legal Issues for Non-profit Organizations"; "Strategic Planning for Association Executives"; "Net Worth: Shaping Markets When Customers Make the Rules"; "1001 Ways to Market Your Books"; "199 Ideas: Membership Recruitment and Retention"; "2008-2009 Blue Chip Association Executive Compensation & Benefits Study"; "2009 Associations Now Volunteer Leadership Issue Magazine"; "2010-2011 Blue Chip Association Executive Compensation & Benefits Study"; "2010-2011GW Area & Nat'l Compensation & Benefits Study Set"; "50 Ways to Motivate Your Board: A Guide for Nonprofit Executives"; "7 Measures of Success Implementation Guide and Assessment Tool"; "70 Suggestions and More for a Shorter, Smarter Job Hunt"; "Achieving Goals: Making Your Mark as a Board Member". "Achieving Sponsorship Success". **Training:** Nation's Capital Distinguished Speakers Series. **Educational Activities:** ASAE Annual Meeting & Exposition (Annual); Xperience Design Project (XDP) (Annual). **Awards:** ASAE Key Award (Annual); ASAE Fellow (Annual); ASAE Academy of Leaders Award (Irregular); ASAE Gold Circle Awards (CGA) (Annual); Diversity Executive Leadership Program Scholarship (DELP) (Biennial); Power of A Awards (Annual); ASAE Sentinel Award (Annual). **Geographic Preference:** National.

1050 ■ *The Association Agenda*
2 Sheppard Ave. E, 20th Fl.
Toronto, ON, Canada M2N 5Y7
Ph: (416)363-3555
Free: 800-461-3608
Co. E-mail: info@csae.com
URL: http://csae.com
Contact: Tracy Folkes Hanson, President
URL(s): csae.com/news/the-association-agenda-see-whats-on-in-2022

Released: Semimonthly **Description:** Provides members with timely updates on advocacy issues and information on day-to-day association operations. **Availability:** Print.

1051 ■ Canadian Society of Association Executives (CSAE) [Société Canadienne des Directeurs d'Association (SCDA)]
2 Sheppard Ave. E, 20th Fl.
Toronto, ON, Canada M2N 5Y7
Ph: (416)363-3555
Free: 800-461-3608
Co. E-mail: info@csae.com
URL: http://csae.com
Contact: Tracy Folkes Hanson, President
Facebook: www.facebook.com/AssociationExecutives
Linkedin: www.linkedin.com/school/canadian-society-of-association-executives
X (Twitter): x.com/csaeconnect

Description: Promotes efficient operation of non-profit associations; facilitates continued professional advancement of members. **Founded:** 1951. **Publications:** *Association* (Bimonthly); *The Association Agenda* (Semimonthly). **Educational Activities:** CSAE National Conference & Showcase (Annual). **Awards:** CSAE Chapter of the Year Award (Annual); Donna Mary Shaw Award (Annual); John Griner Award (Annual); CSAE Pinnacle Award (Irregular). **Geographic Preference:** National.

1052 ■ Society for Nonprofit Organizations (SNPO)
PO Box 510354
Livonia, MI 48151
Ph: (734)451-3582
Fax: (734)451-5935
Co. E-mail: info@snpo.org
URL: http://www.snpo.org
Contact: Hannah Brazee Gregory, Contact
Facebook: www.facebook.com/snpo.org
X (Twitter): x.com/nonprofitworld

Description: Brings together those who serve in the nonprofit world in order to build a strong network of professionals throughout the country; provides a forum for the exchange of information, knowledge, and ideas for strengthening and increasing productivity within nonprofit organizations and among their leaders. Publishes Nonprofit World magazine, educational programs offered by the Learning Institute, and other communications with its members. **Founded:** 1983. **Publications:** *Nonprofit World Magazine* (Quarterly); *Nonprofit World--National Directory of Product and Service Providers*; *Funding Alert* (Monthly); *Resource Center Product Catalog*. **Geographic Preference:** Multinational.

REFERENCE WORKS

1053 ■ *Encyclopedia of Associations: National Organizations of the U.S.*
Pub: Gale, part of Cengage Group
Contact: Paul Gazzolo, General Manager Senior Vice President
URL(s): www.gale.com/intl/ebooks/9781414449821/encyclopedia-of-associations-national-organizations-of-the-u.s

Released: 46 edition. **Description:** Covers approximately 25,000 nonprofit U.S. Membership organizations of national scope divided into 18 classifications: trade, business, and commercial; environmental and agricultural; legal, governmental, public administration, and military; engineering, technological, and natural and social science; educational; cultural; social welfare; health and medical; public affairs; fraternal, nationality, and ethnic; religious organizations; veterans, hereditary, and patriotic; hobby and avocational; athletic and sports; labor unions, associations, and federations; chambers of commerce and trade and tourism; Greek and non-Greek letter societies, associations, and federations; fan clubs. **Entries include:** Organization name, address, phone, fax, name of executive officer, staff size, date founded, number of members, membership dues, annual budget, description of objectives, activities, committees, publications, computer and telecommunications services, historical information, convention dates and locations; publications, including title, description, ISSN, circulation, whether advertising is accepted, alternate formats, and former or alternate name(s) of publication. **Arrangement:** By subject keyword within classifications cited above. **Indexes:** Organization name/keyword (including references to organizations listed in International Organizations; also includes addresses and phone numbers after each association's primary reference); separate volume includes geographical and executive indexes (including organization name, address, phone, and name of chief executive in both arrangements). **Availability:** E-book. **Type:** Directory.

TRADE SHOWS AND CONVENTIONS

1054 ■ *ASAE Annual Meeting & Exposition*
ASAE: The Center for Association Leadership
1575 I St. NW
Washington, DC 20005
Ph: (202)626-2723
Free: 888-950-2723
Fax: (202)371-8315
Co. E-mail: asaeservice@asaecenter.org
URL: http://www.asaecenter.org
Contact: Michelle Mason, President
E-mail: mmason@asaecenter.org
URL(s): annual.asaecenter.org/about.cfm

Frequency: Annual. **Description:** With education sessions, countless networking opportunities, a bustling Expo Hall, and more. **Audience:** Association professionals and industry partners. **Principal Exhibits:** With education sessions, countless networking opportunities, a bustling Expo Hall, and more. Dates and Locations: 2025 Aug 09-12 Los Angeles Convention Center, Los Angeles, CA; 2026 Aug 15-18 Indiana Convention Center, Indianapolis, IN; 2027 Aug 07-10 Charlotte Convention Center, Charlotte, NC. **Telecommunication Services:** exhibit@asaecenter.org.

1055 ■ *Holiday Showcase*
Association Forum (AF)
10 S. Riverside Plaza, Ste. 800
Chicago, IL 60606
Ph: (312)924-7000
Co. E-mail: marketing@associationforum.org
URL: http://www.associationforum.org/homedec
Contact: Jed Mandel, Legal Counsel
URL(s): s6.goeshow.com/af/holidayshowcase/2024/proposal_submission.cfm?utm_source=af_home&utm_medium=calendar&utm_campaign=hs_cfp

Frequency: Annual. **Audience:** Association professionals and buyers. **Telecommunication Services:** membership@associationforum.org.

COMPUTERIZED DATABASES

1056 ■ *Associations Canada*
Grey House Publishing
3-1500 Upper Middle Rd.
Oakville, ON, Canada L6M 3H5
Ph: (416)644-6479
Free: 866-433-4739
Fax: (416)644-1904
Co. E-mail: info@greyhouse.ca
URL: http://greyhouse.ca
Contact: Stuart Paterson, Managing Editor
E-mail: spaterson@greyhouse.ca
URL(s): greyhouse.ca/assoc.htm

Released: Annual; print latest issue: 2024, 45th edition.; Monthly; online. **Price:** $499, for price. **Availability:** E-book; Print; Online. **Type:** Directory.

LIBRARIES

1057 ■ *ASAE: The Center for Association Leadership Knowledge Center*
1575 I St. NW
Washington, DC 20005
URL: http://www.asaecenter.orgwww.asaecenter.org/about-us/asae-staff-rosterresources
Contact: Jennifer Nelson, Director
E-mail: jnelson@asaecenter.org

Scope: Association management - law, communications, human resources, conventions, education, voluntarism, finance, membership promotion, government relations, international affair chapter relations, marketing. **Services:** Library open to the public by appointment. **Founded:** 1954. **Holdings:** 50,000 books; journals; media items; archival drawings.

Auctioneer/Broker

START-UP INFORMATION

1058 ■ *"Auction Company Grows with Much Smaller Sites" in Automotive News (Vol. 86, October 31, 2011, No. 6488, pp. 23)*
Pub: Crain Communications Inc.
Contact: Barry Asin, President
Ed: Arlena Sawyers. **Description:** Auction Broadcasting Company has launched auction sites and is expanding into new areas. The family-owned business will provide auctions half the size traditionally used. The firm reports that 40 percent of the General Motors factory-owned vehicles sold on consignment were purchased by online buyers, up 30 percent over 2010. **Availability:** Online.

1059 ■ *The Business of Antiques*
Ed: Wayne Jordan. **Released:** 2012. **Description:** A guide on running an antiques business. Includes sections about running a brick and mortar shop and an auction. **Availability:** E-book.

1060 ■ *The Complete Idiot's Guide to Starting an eBay® Business*
Pub: Penguin Publishing Group
Released: April 03, 2012. **Price:** $19.95, paperback; $12.99, e-book. **Description:** Guide for starting an eBay business includes information on products to sell, how to price merchandise, and details for working with services like PayPal, and how to organize fulfillment services. **Availability:** E-book; Print.

1061 ■ *eBay Business the Smart Way*
Released: 3rd edition. **Description:** eBay commands ninety percent of all online auction business. Computer and software expert and online entrepreneur shares information to help online sellers get started and move merchandise on eBay. Tips include the best ways to build credibility, find products to sell, manage inventory, create a storefront Website, and more. **Availability:** Print; PDF.

1062 ■ *The eBay Business Start-Up Kit: With 100s of Live Links to All the Information & Tools You Need*
Pub: Nolo
Contact: Chris Braun, President
Ed: Richard Stim. **Description:** Interactive kit that provides in-depth information and practical advice in launching an eBay business. **Availability:** Print.

1063 ■ *EBay Income: How ANYONE of Any Age, Location, and/or Background Can Build a Highly Profitable Online Business with eBay*
Pub: Atlantic Publishing Co.
Contact: Dr. Heather L. Johnson, Contact
Description: A complete overview of eBay is given and guides any small company through the entire process of creating the auction and auction strategies, photography, writing copy, text and formatting, multiple sales, programming tricks, PayPal, accounting, creating marketing, merchandising, managing email lists, advertising plans, taxes and sales tax, best time to list items and for how long, sniping programs, international customers, opening a storefront, electronic commerce, buy-it now pricing, keywords, Google marketing and eBay secrets.

ASSOCIATIONS AND OTHER ORGANIZATIONS

1064 ■ Livestock Marketing Association (LMA)
11501 Outlook St., Ste. 250
Overland Park, KS 66211-1811
Ph: (816)891-0502
Free: 800-821-2048
Fax: (816)891-7926
Co. E-mail: lrunft@lmaweb.com
URL: http://www.lmaweb.com
Contact: Mark Barnett, President
Facebook: www.facebook.com/auctionLMA
X (Twitter): x.com/sellatauction
Instagram: www.instagram.com/sellatauction
Description: Livestock marketing businesses and livestock dealers. Sponsors annual World Livestock Auctioneer Championships. Offers management and promotional services. **Founded:** 1947. **Geographic Preference:** National.

1065 ■ National Auctioneers Association (NAA)
8880 Ballentine St.
Overland Park, KS 66214
Ph: (913)541-8084
Fax: (913)894-5281
Co. E-mail: support@auctioneers.org
URL: http://www.auctioneers.org
Contact: Beth Rose, President
E-mail: beth@bethroseauction.com
Facebook: www.facebook.com/naaauctioneers
X (Twitter): x.com/naaauctioneers
YouTube: www.youtube.com/user/NAAAuctioneers
Description: Provides continuing education classes for auctioneers, promotes use of the auction method of marketing in both the private and public sectors. Encourages the highest ethical standards for the profession. **Founded:** 1949. **Publications:** *Auction E-News* (Bimonthly); *Find an NAA Auction Professional*; *Auctioneer* (Bimonthly); *Auctioneer--Directory Issue* (Annual). **Educational Activities:** NAA Conference and Show (Annual). **Awards:** NAA Marketing Competition Award (Annual); International Auctioneer Championship (IAC) (Annual); National Auctioneers Association Hall of Fame (Annual). **Geographic Preference:** Multinational.

1066 ■ National Auto Auction Association (NAAA)
5320 Spectrum Dr., Ste. D
Frederick, MD 21703
Ph: (301)696-0400
Fax: (301)631-1359
Co. E-mail: naaa@naaa.com
URL: http://www.naaa.com
Contact: Tricia Heon, Chief Executive Officer
E-mail: theon@naaa.com
Facebook: www.facebook.com/National-Auto-Auction-Association-35704747404
X (Twitter): x.com/NAutoAuctionAsn
Description: Owners/operators of wholesale automobile and truck auctions; associate members are car and truck manufacturers, insurers of checks and titles, car and truck rental companies, publishers of auto price guide books, and others connected with the industry. Maintains hall of fame. **Founded:** 1948. **Publications:** *National Auto Auction Association--Membership Directory* (Annual); *On the Block* (6/year). **Educational Activities:** NAAA Annual Convention (Annual); NAAA Annual Convention (Annual). **Awards:** NAAA Hall of Fame (Annual). **Geographic Preference:** National.

REFERENCE WORKS

1067 ■ *"5 Global Trends Affecting the Art Market This Fall" in Artsy (September 10, 2019)*
Ed: Benjamin Sutton. **Released:** September 10, 2019. **Description:** An overview of five global, geopolitical, and industry trends influencing the current art market. Brexit and tariffs are mentioned along with the rise of the Paris art market. Mid-size galleries are following the trend of showcasing entire artists' estates, while Sotheby's is branching out by offering more objects with historical significance. **Availability:** Online.

1068 ■ *"Auctions and Bidding: A Guide for Computer Scientists" in ACM Computing Surveys (Vol. 43, Summer 2011, No. 2, pp. 10)*
Pub: Association for Computing Machinery
Contact: Yannis Ioannidis, President
Ed: Simon Parsons, Juan A. Rodriguez-Aguilar, Mark Klein. **Released:** Volume 43 Issue 2. **Price:** $10, Members; $15, Nonmembers; $5, Students. **Description:** There are various actions: single dimensional, multi-dimensional, single-sided, double-sided, first-price, second-price, English, Dutch, Japanese, sealed-bid, and these have been extensively discussed and analyzed in economics literature. This literature is surveyed from a computer science perspective, primarily from the viewpoint of computer scientists who are interested in learning about auction theory, and to provide pointers into the economics literature for those who want a deeper technical understanding. In addition, since auctions are an increasingly important topic in computer science, the article also looks at work on auctions from the computer science literature. The aim is to identify what both bodies of work tell us about creating electronic auctions. **Availability:** Download; PDF.

1069 ■ *"B-N Pawn Shop Auctions Off Jimmy Hoffa's Rifle" in Pantagraph (September 14, 2010)*
Pub: The Pantagraph
Ed: Ryan Denham. **Description:** Midwest Exchange pawn shop located in IAA Drive in Bloomington, Illinois auctioned a rifle once belonging to Jimmy Hoffa. **Availability:** Print; Online.

1070 ■ *"Coin Toss? A Real Cartoon Caper"* in *Barron's* (Vol. 92, September 17, 2012, No. 38, pp. 17)
Description: An estimated $20,000 worth of coins bearing the likeness of cartoon character SpongeBob SquarePants are missing, according to Ira Bodenstein, the bankruptcy trustee of commodities futures broker Peregrine Financial. The coins were used by the company as a marketing tool and could rise in value if found and auctioned. **Availability:** Online.

1071 ■ *"Dollar General Selects GSI Commerce to Launch Its eCommerce Business"* in *Benzinga.com* (October 29, 2011)
Pub: Benzinga.com
Contact: Jason Raznick, Founder
Description: Dollar General Corporation chose GSI Commerce, a leading provider of ecommerce and interactive marketing solutions, to launch its online initiative. GSI Commerce is an eBay Inc. company. **Availability:** Online.

1072 ■ *"Fifty Percent of Global Online Retail Visits Were to Amazon, eBay and Alibaba in June 2011"* in *Benzinga.com* (October 29, 2011)
Pub: Benzinga.com
Contact: Jason Raznick, Founder
Description: Current statistics and future forecasts through the year 2015 for Amazon, eBay and Alibaba are explored. **Availability:** Online.

1073 ■ *"Former Schaefer & Strohminger Dealerships to Hit Auction Block"* in *Baltimore Business Journal* (Vol. 28, September 10, 2010)
Pub: Baltimore Business Journal
Contact: Rhonda Pringle, President
E-mail: rpringle@bizjournals.com
Ed: Gary Haber. **Description:** Maryland's real estate developers have a chance to vie for almost 11 acres of prime Baltimore County real estate that are on the auction block. The five properties were once home to Schaefer and Strohminger car dealerships and were located in the county's busiest areas. Other potential uses for the properties are also discussed.

1074 ■ *"I Brake for Yard Sales: And Flea Markets, Thrift Shops, Auctions, and the Occasional Dumpster"*
Released: April 01, 2012. **Price:** $24.95, Paperback.
Description: Lara Spencer, self-confessed frugalista and new correspondent, shares her passion for shopping at yard sales, consignment shops, and estate sales for decorating her home as well as her friend's homes. She shares her bargain hunting secrets and tells where to shop, what to look for, how to pay for sales, how to restore items, and how to decorate. **Availability:** E-book; Print.

1075 ■ *National Auto Auction Association--Membership Directory*
Pub: National Auto Auction Association
Contact: Tricia Heon, Chief Executive Officer
E-mail: theon@naaa.com
URL(s): www.naaa.com/member_directories/20 24_member_directory/index.html
Released: Annual **Description:** Covers 25,446 automobile auction firms. **Entries include:** Company name, address, names and phone numbers of auction personnel; pick up, delivery, and reconditioning services available. **Arrangement:** Geographical. **Availability:** Print; Online; PDF; Download.

1076 ■ *"The Open Mobile Summit Opens in San Francisco Today: John Donahoe CEO eBay to Keynote"* in *Benzinga.com* (November 2, 2011)
Pub: Benzinga.com
Contact: Jason Raznick, Founder
Description: eBay's CEO, John Donahoe was keynote speaker at the 4th Annual Open Mobile Summit held in San Francisco, California. eBay is one of the 130 companies participating as speakers at the event.

1077 ■ *"Points of Light Sells MissionFish to eBay"* in *Non-Profit Times* (Vol. 25, May 15, 2011, No. 7, pp. May 15, 2011)
Description: eBay purchased MissionFish, a subsidiary of Points of Light Institute for $4.5 million. MissionFish allows eBay sellers to give proceeds from sales to their favorite nonprofit organization and helps nonprofits raise funds by selling on eBay. **Availability:** Print; Online.

1078 ■ *"Pro Livestock Launches Most Comprehensive Virtual Sales Barn for Livestock and Breed Stock"* in *Benzinga.com* (October 29, 2011)
Description: Pro Livestock Marketing launched the first online sales portal for livestock and breed stock. The firm has designed a virtual sales barn allowing individuals to purchase and sell cattle, swine, sheep, goats, horses, rodeo stock, show animals, specialty animals, semen and embryos globally. It is like an eBay for livestock and will help ranchers and farmers grow. **Availability:** Print; PDF; Online.

1079 ■ *"RM Sotheby's Botched the $22 Million Sale of the 'First Porshe: Because Bidders Couldn't Understand the Auctioneer's Dutch Accent"* in *Artnet News* (August 19, 2019)
URL(s): news.artnet.com/market/botched-porsche-auction-1629727
Ed: Caroline Goldstein. **Released:** August 19, 2019.
Description: A recent auction of the 1939 Type 64 Porsche, billed as the "first" Porsche, was botched when the Dutch auctioneer had issues with audience understanding his accent. Confusion between what the auctioneer was saying versus the pricing on the screen led to the reserve price not being met and the car not selling at this auction. **Availability:** Online.

1080 ■ *Selling Online: Canada's Bestselling Guide to Becoming a Successful E-Commerce Merchant*
Description: Helps individuals build online retail enterprises; this updated version includes current tools, information and success strategies, how to launch an online storefront, security, marketing strategies, and mistakes to avoid. **Availability:** Online.

1081 ■ *"This is What the Hell Livestock Auctioneers are Actually Saying"* in *Vice* (August 23, 2018)
URL(s): www.vice.com/en_us/article/vbj878/this-is-what-the-hell-livestock-auctioneers-are-actually-saying
Ed: Oliver Noble, Michael Shade, Gabriel Connelly. **Description:** Goes behind the scenes to figure out what those fast-talking auctioneers are actually saying. The number being asked for in the bid should be dominant in the call, along with the auctioneer's own signature "chant" made up of filler words, which are often misheard.

1082 ■ *"Tim Tebow Foundation to Hold Pink 'Cleats for a Cure' Auction"* in *Travel & Leisure Close-Up* (October 20, 2011)
Pub: Close-Up Media Inc.
Contact: Caroline S. Moore, President
E-mail: cms@closeupmedia.com
Description: Tim Tebow Foundation partnered with XV Enterprises to hold the 'Cleats for a Cure' auction on eBay. Tebow is auctioning off a pair of pink cleans he wore during the Denver Broncos vs. Tennessee Titans game October 3, 2010. All funds will go toward finding a cure for breast cancer. **Availability:** Print; Online.

1083 ■ *"Why Your First Suitor Isn't Always the Best"* in *Business Journal Portland* (Vol. 30, January 24, 2014, No. 47, pp. 10)
Pub: American City Business Journals, Inc.
Contact: Mike Olivieri, Executive Vice President
Released: Weekly. **Price:** $4, Introductory 4-week offer(Digital & Print). **Description:** Norm Duffett of Orca Capital Securities offers tips on how business owners can avoid the downside of selling their business to the first buyer. An auction ensures the owners they got the best available deal. **Availability:** Print; Online.

1084 ■ *"Young Entrepreneur Gets Some Recognition and Some Help for College"* in *Philadelphia Inquirer* (August 30, 2010)
Pub: The Philadelphia Inquirer
Contact: Elizabeth H. Hughes, Chief Executive Officer
Ed: Susan Snyder. **Description:** Profile of Zachary Gosling, age 18, who launched an online auction Website from his bedroom, using advertising and sponsorship funds rather than charging fees to users.

TRADE PERIODICALS

1085 ■ *Auctioneer*
Pub: National Auctioneers Association
Contact: Beth Rose, President
E-mail: beth@bethroseauction.com
Released: Bimonthly; Dec/Jan, Feb/Mar, Apr/May, Jun/Jul, Aug/Sep, Oct/Nov. **Description:** Trade magazine for auctioneers. **Availability:** Print; Online.

TRADE SHOWS AND CONVENTIONS

1086 ■ *NAA Conference and Show*
National Auctioneers Association (NAA)
8880 Ballentine St.
Overland Park, KS 66214
Ph: (913)541-8084
Fax: (913)894-5281
Co. E-mail: support@auctioneers.org
URL: http://www.auctioneers.org
Contact: Beth Rose, President
E-mail: beth@bethroseauction.com
URL(s): auctioneers.org/cs2023
Frequency: Annual. **Description:** With networking opportunity and educational programs. **Audience:** Auction professionals. **Principal Exhibits:** With networking opportunity and educational programs. Dates and Locations: 2025 Jul 15-19 Schaumburg, IL. **Telecommunication Services:** registration@auctioneers.org.

Auto Supply Store

ASSOCIATIONS AND OTHER ORGANIZATIONS

1087 ■ Auto Suppliers Benchmarking Association (ASBA)
The Benchmarking Network
Houston, TX 77069-9949
Ph: (281)440-5044
URL: http://asbabenchmarking.com
Facebook: www.facebook.com/people/The-Benchmarking-Network/100075504566399
X (Twitter): twitter.com/benchmarkingnet
Description: Promotes the use of benchmarking, wherein businesses compare their processes with those of their competitors, as a means of improving corporate efficiency and profitability among automotive supplier firms; facilitates exchange of information among members; conducts target operations, procurement, development, and maintenance studies; and identifies model business practices. **Founded:** 1996. **Geographic Preference:** National.

1088 ■ Automotive Aftermarket Suppliers Association (AASA) - Brake Manufacturers Council (BMC)
79 TW Alexander Dr.
4501 Research Commons, Ste. 200
Research Triangle Park, NC 27709
URL: http://www.mema.org/networking-groups/brake-manufacturers-council
Contact: Ben Brucato, Contact
E-mail: bbrucato@mema.org
Description: Manufacturers of brake system parts who supply both the original equipment automotive market and the automotive replacement parts market. **Founded:** 1973. **Geographic Preference:** National.

1089 ■ Automotive Service Association (ASA) - Library
8209 Mid Cities Blvd., Ste. 100
North Richland Hills, TX 76182-4712
Ph: (817)514-2900
Co. E-mail: info@asashop.org
URL: http://www.asashop.org
Contact: Ray Fisher, Executive Director
E-mail: rayf@asashop.org
Facebook: www.facebook.com/ASAshop
Linkedin: www.linkedin.com/company/automotive-service-association
X (Twitter): x.com/asashop
Instagram: www.instagram.com/asa_national
YouTube: www.youtube.com/user/asawebops
Description: Serves the needs of mechanical, transmission, and collision shop owners through education and representation on legislation affecting the automotive service industry. **Scope:** Automobiles; repair. **Founded:** 1951. **Holdings:** Figures not available. **Publications:** AutoInc. (Bimonthly). **Educational Activities:** Congress of Automotive Repair and Service (CARS) (Annual); International Autobody Congress and Exposition - NACE (Annual). **Geographic Preference:** National.

1090 ■ Automotive Warehouse Distributors Association (AWDA)
7101 Wisconsin Ave., Ste. 1300
Bethesda, MD 20814-3415
URL: http://www.autocare.org/networking-and-development/communities/aftermarket-warehouse-distributors
Contact: Ryan Samuels, Chairman
Description: Warehouse distributors of automotive parts and supplies; manufacturers of automotive parts and suppliers; jobbers, business services, major program groups. **Publications:** APAA Who's Who (Annual); Foreign Buyers Directory (Annual); AAIA SmartBrief (Biweekly); Leadership Directory (Annual). **Awards:** AWDA Automotive Leader of the Year (Annual); AWDA Martin Fromm Lifetime Achievement Award (Annual); AWDA Art Fisher Memorial Scholarship Award (Annual); AWDA Pursuit of Excellence Awards (Annual). **Geographic Preference:** Multinational.

1091 ■ Import Vehicle Community
c/o Auto Care Association
7101 Wisconsin Ave., Ste. 1300
Bethesda, MD 20814
URL: http://www.autocare.org/networking-and-development/communities/import-vehicle-community
Contact: Steven Hughes, Contact
Description: Manufacturers/importers, distributors/retailers, subcontractors and manufacturers' representatives supporting the import automotive aftermarket products industry. Works to promote and protect the interests of the import auto and accessories industry. Offers Import Parts Specialist certification program for sales personnel. Produces annual AIA World Auto Parts Conference. Compiles statistics. **Founded:** 1981. **Publications:** AIA Facts (Biweekly). **Educational Activities:** Fabulous Networking Reception. **Geographic Preference:** National.

1092 ■ Motor and Equipment Manufacturers Association (MEMA)
79 TW Alexander Dr., 4501 Research Commons, Ste. 200
Research Triangle Park, NC 27709
Ph: (919)549-4800
Co. E-mail: info@mema.org
URL: http://www.mema.org
Description: Manufacturers of automotive and heavy-duty original equipment and aftermarket components, maintenance equipment, chemicals, accessories, refinishing supplies, tools, and service equipment united for research into all aspects of the automotive and heavy-duty markets. **Scope:** Supplies both the original equipment and aftermarket segments of the light vehicle (car and truck) and commercial vehicle (on- and off-road) industries. **Founded:** 1932. **Publications:** International Buyers Guide of U.S. Automotive and Heavy Duty Products for Export (Biennial); Automotive Industry Status Report (Annual); Car Maintenance in the U.S.A.; Credit and Sales Reference Directory (3/year); Market Analysis (Bimonthly; Monthly); Sales Force Compensation and Benefits Practice (Annual); Aftermarket Status Report (Annual); Truck Maintenance in the U.S.A. (Annual); World Automotive Market Report (Annual). **Awards:** MEMA Triangle Award (Annual). **Geographic Preference:** National.

1093 ■ National Truck Equipment Association (NTEA)
37400 Hills Tech Dr.
Farmington Hills, MI 48331-3414
Ph: (248)489-7090
Free: 800-441-6832
Fax: (248)489-8590
Co. E-mail: info@ntea.com
URL: http://www.ntea.com
Contact: Steve Carey, President
E-mail: steve@ntea.com
Facebook: www.facebook.com/NTEA.TheAssociationForTheWorkTruckIndustry
Linkedin: www.linkedin.com/company/239823
X (Twitter): x.com/nteanews
Instagram: www.instagram.com/the.ntea
YouTube: www.youtube.com/channel/UCQbxEMWDReFSIupUhoVLJsg
Description: Serves as a trade group for commercial truck, truck body, truck equipment, trailer and accessory manufacturers and distributors. Advises members of current federal regulations affecting the manufacturing and installation of truck bodies and equipment; works to enhance the professionalism of management and improve profitability in the truck equipment business. **Founded:** 1964. **Publications:** National Truck Equipment Association--Market Resource Guide (Annual); Excise Tax Bulletin (Periodic); Truck Equipment Handbook; NTEA Technical Report (Monthly); NTEA News ezine (Monthly). **Educational Activities:** The Work Truck Show (Annual). **Geographic Preference:** National.

1094 ■ Specialty Equipment Market Association (SEMA)
1575 S Valley Vista Dr.
Diamond Bar, CA 91765
Ph: (909)610-2030
Co. E-mail: research@sema.org
URL: http://www.sema.org
Contact: Mike Spagnola, President
Facebook: www.facebook.com/SEMA.org
Linkedin: www.linkedin.com/company/specialty-equipment-market-association-sema
X (Twitter): x.com/semamembers
YouTube: www.youtube.com/channel/UCfhmBjjzf8auV6zvt5mhGiA
Description: Manufacturers, retailers, sales representatives, distributors, motorsports sanctioning groups and other firms related to the automotive high performance and custom vehicle industry. Represents the industry to governmental agencies and consumer groups. Coordinates and conducts research; assists in writing of regulations and codes; collects and disseminates information; compiles statistics. **Founded:** 1963. **Publications:** SEMA Membership Directory (Annual); SEMA Fast Facts; SEMA News (Monthly). **Educational Activities:** SEMA Show (Annual); The

Hot Rod and Restoration Trade Show. **Awards:** SEMA Memorial Scholarships (Annual); SEMA Person of the Year (Annual); SEMA Hall of Fame (Annual); SEMA Warehouse Distributor of the Year (Annual); SEMA Scholarship and Loan Forgiveness (Annual); Specialty Equipment Market Association Scholarships (Annual). **Geographic Preference:** National.

REFERENCE WORKS

1095 ■ *"Auto Bankruptcies Could Weaken Defense"* in *Crain's Detroit Business (Vol. 25, June 8, 2009, No. 23, pp. 1)*
Pub: Crain Communications Inc.
Contact: Barry Asin, President
Ed: Chad Halcom. **Description:** Bankruptcy and supplier consolidation of General Motors Corporation and Chrysler LLC could interfere with the supply chains of some defense contractors, particularly makers of trucks and smaller vehicles. **Availability:** Print; Online.

1096 ■ *"AutoZone Revs Up Sales With Focus on Commercial Market"* in *Memphis Business Journal (Vol. 35, January 24, 2014, No. 42, pp. 4)*
Pub: American City Business Journals, Inc.
Contact: Mike Olivieri, Executive Vice President
Released: Weekly. **Price:** $4, introductory 4-week offer(Digital & Print). **Description:** Memphis, Tennessee-based automotive parts retailer AutoZone Inc. is focusing its growth on the commercial market after successfully dominating the retail division. The retailer is taking advantage of its strong supply chain to effectively deliver parts to its customers. **Availability:** Print; Online.

1097 ■ *"Baltimore Dealers Fear Shortages in Car Supply"* in *Boston Business Journal (Vol. 29, May 13, 2011, No. 1, pp. 1)*
Pub: Boston Business Journal
Contact: Carolyn M. Jones, President
E-mail: cmjones@bizjournals.com
Ed: Scott Dance. **Price:** $4, Introductory 4-Week Offer(Digital Only). **Description:** The earthquake and tsunami in Japan are seen to impact the automobile dealers in Baltimore, Maryland. Automobile supply in the area is seen to decrease dramatically during the summer sales season. Shortage of transmission parts and paint colors is also forecasted. **Availability:** Print; Online.

1098 ■ *"C-Class Could Boost Auto Suppliers"* in *Birmingham Business Journal (Vol. 31, June 27, 2014, No. 26, pp. 10)*
Pub: American City Business Journals, Inc.
Contact: Mike Olivieri, Executive Vice President
Released: June 27, 2014. **Description:** The 2014 model of the Mercedes-Benz C-Class will be the first to be built at the Vance, Alabama manufacturing plant, increasing business opportunities for auto suppliers in the region. Jason Hoff, president and CEO of Mercedes-Benz US International Inc. notes that the move will impact the local economy as several companies in the area expand their operations to meet the growing demand from Mercedes.

1099 ■ *"Car Parts Stocks are Down and for Once It's Not About Amazon"* in *Barron's (April 25, 2019)*
URL(s): www.barrons.com/articles/oreilly-automotive
-earnings-auto-parts-stocks-51556211277
Ed: Teresa Rivas. **Released:** April 25, 2019. **Description:** O'Reilly Automotive news is dragging down shares of other auto-parts companies. Revenue was lower than expected, but still has the possibility to rebound due to the large do-it-yourself market when it comes to car care and maintenance. **Availability:** Online.

1100 ■ *"Cars Get Stuck at U.S. Garages for Weeks in Spare-Parts Shortage"* in *Bloomberg (October 16, 2021)*
Ed: Michael Sasso. **Released:** October 16, 2021. **Description:** The world is experiencing a supply chain issue in many industries, particularly when it comes to auto parts. With the global semiconductor shortage, people are deciding to hold onto their older vehicles, which often need repairs.

1101 ■ *"GreenTech Gears Up for Production"* in *Memphis Business Journal (Vol. 33, April 6, 2012, No. 52, pp. 1)*
Pub: Baltimore Business Journal
Contact: Rhonda Pringle, President
E-mail: rpringle@bizjournals.com
Description: GreenTech Automotive has broken ground for construction of a new production facility in Tunica, Tennessee. The company will focus its manufacturing operations in the new facility. **Availability:** Print; Online.

1102 ■ *"Here's One Market Amazon Can't Easily Crack: Car Parts"* in *CNN (November 29, 2018)*
URL(s): www.cnn.com/2018/11/29/business/advance
-auto-parts-oreilly-autozone/index.html
Ed: Nathaniel Meyersohn. **Released:** November 29, 2018. **Description:** Amazon is trying to move into the car parts industry, but is hitting a snag due to smaller brick-and-mortar stores being able to provide customer service and helping to guide consumers through their purchases. Amazon is looking into partnering with other retail outlets, which may help their bottom line in this industry. **Availability:** Online.

1103 ■ *"Infrastructure Investment and Jobs Act Includes New Vehicle Safety Provisions"* in *Autobody News (November 19, 2021)*
Released: November 19, 2021. **Description:** The new Infrastructure bill signed by President Joe Biden into law includes some unconventional items that affect mechanical and collision repair shops. Included in the law are provisions for standardizing vehicle safety standards, electric vehicle charging stations, and to implement Advanced Driver-Assist Systems. **Availability:** Online.

1104 ■ *"Japan-Brand Shortages Will Linger Into '12"* in *Automotive News (Vol. 86, October 31, 2011, No. 6488, pp. 1)*
Pub: Crain Communications Inc.
Contact: Barry Asin, President
Ed: Amy Wilson, Mark Rechtin. **Description:** Floods in Thailand and the tsunami in Japan have caused shortages of Japanese-brand vehicle parts. These shortages are expected to linger into 2012. **Availability:** Online.

1105 ■ *"NKC Keeps Pace with Auto Industry"* in *Memphis Business Journal (Vol. 34, September 14, 2012, No. 22, pp. 1)*
Pub: Baltimore Business Journal
Contact: Rhonda Pringle, President
E-mail: rpringle@bizjournals.com
Ed: Michael Sheffield. **Description:** Memphis, Tennessee-based NKC of American Inc. has been expecting sales to increase to about $60 million for 2012 after its revenue dropped to about $20 million during the peak of the recession in 2008-2009. NKC's growth is being driven by new contracts with automotive manufacturers. **Availability:** Print; Online.

1106 ■ *"Outlook In Other Industries"* in *Crain's Detroit Business (Vol. 30, January 6, 2014, No. 1, pp. 3)*
Pub: Crain Communications Inc.
Contact: Barry Asin, President
Released: January 6, 2014. **Description:** Outlook for industries in the Detroit area are listed, including small business growth, restaurants, defense contracts, nonprofits, transportation, auto suppliers, healthcare, bankruptcy, and government. **Availability:** Print; PDF; Online.

1107 ■ *"Pep Boys to Pay $3.7M for Illegally Disposing of Hazardous Waste"* in *Waste Today (October 1, 2019)*
URL(s): www.wastetodaymagazine.com/article/pep
-boys-hazardous-waste-lawsuit
Ed: Adam Redling. **Released:** October 01, 2019. **Description:** After disposing toxic waste from automotive fluids into municipal landfills, Pep Boys must pay a $3.7 million settlement. This is based off of undercover inspections and charges were brought forth by the Alameda County District Attorney's Office Environmental Protection Unit. **Availability:** Online.

1108 ■ *"Recession Creating Surge in Business for Auto Recyclers"* in *Business Journal-Serving Phoenix & the Valley of the Sun (Vol. 31, November 12, 2010, No. 10, pp. 1)*
Pub: Phoenix Business Journal
Contact: Alex McAlister, Director
E-mail: amcalister@bizjournals.com
Ed: Patrick O'Grady. **Description:** Automotive parts recyclers in Arizona are benefiting from the challenging national economic conditions as well as from the green movement. Recyclers revealed that customers prefer recycled parts more because they are cheaper and are more environmentally friendly. Other information about the automotive parts recycling industry is presented. **Availability:** Print; Online.

1109 ■ *"Slimmer Interiors Make Small Cars Seem Big"* in *Automotive News (Vol. 86, October 31, 2011, No. 6488, pp. 16)*
Pub: Crain Communications Inc.
Contact: Barry Asin, President
Ed: David Sedgwick. **Description:** Cost-conscious buyers want luxury car amenities in their smaller vehicles, so automakers are rethinking interiors. Style, efficiency and value could be the next trend in vehicles. **Availability:** Print; Online.

1110 ■ *"Steering Toward Profitability"* in *Black Enterprise (Vol. 41, December 2010, No. 5, pp. 72)*
Pub: Earl G. Graves Ltd.
Contact: Earl Graves, Jr., President
Ed: Alan Hughes. **Description:** Systems Electro Coating LLC had to make quick adjustments when auto manufacturers were in a slump. The minority father-daughter team discuss their strategies during the auto industry collapse.

1111 ■ *"Suppliers May Follow Fiat: Local Group Says Italian Firms are Inquiring"* in *Crain's Detroit Business (Vol. 25, June 15, 2009, No. 24, pp. 1)*
Pub: Crain Communications Inc.
Contact: Barry Asin, President
Ed: Ryan Beene. **Description:** Italian suppliers to Fiat SpA are looking toward Detroit after the formation of Chrysler Group LLC, the Chrysler-Fiat partnership created from Chrysler's bankruptcy. The Italian American Alliance for Business and Technology is aware of two Italy-based powertrain component suppliers that are considering a move to Detroit. **Availability:** Online.

1112 ■ *"Supply-Chain Collaboration, Image of Industry are OESA Chief's Top Tasks; Q&A Julie Fream, Original Equipment Suppliers Association"* in *Crain's Detroit Business (Vol. 30, January 6, 2014, No. 1, pp. 4)*
Pub: Crain Communications Inc.
Contact: Barry Asin, President
Description: Julie Fream is the new CEO of the Original Equipment Suppliers Assocation. Fream is a former Visteon Corporation executive and has held numerous positions in automotive manufacturing, sales and marketing. She is committed to holding transparency and collaboration within the industry. **Availability:** Online.

1113 ■ *"Your Car Repair Handbook"* in *Consumer Reports (September 9, 2021)*
URL(s): www.consumerreports.org/car-repair/your
-car-repair-handbook
Ed: Benjamin Preston. **Released:** September 21, 2021. **Description:** Owning a vehicle can get expensive, especially if repairs are needed. Even regular maintenance can add up. A breakdown of what costs to expect when doing it yourself or taking it in to the shop is given. Repairs that should be handled at a dealership, such as airbag safety, is also discussed. **Availability:** Print; Online.

STATISTICAL SOURCES

1114 ■ *Auto Parts Stores Industry in the US - Market Research Report*
URL(s): www.ibisworld.com/united-states/market-research-reports/auto-parts-stores-industry/
Price: $925. **Description:** Downloadable report analyzing the current and future trends in the auto parts store industry. **Availability:** Online.

1115 ■ *RMA Annual Statement Studies*
Pub: Risk Management Association
Contact: Nancy Foster, President
Released: Annual. **Description:** Contains composite balance sheets and income statements for more than 360 industries, including the accounting, auditing, and bookkeeping industries. Also contains five years of comparative historical data for discerning trends. Includes 16 commonly used ratios, computed for most of the size groupings for nearly every industry.

1116 ■ *Standard & Poor's Industry Surveys*
Pub: Standard And Poor's Financial Services LLC.
Contact: Douglas L. Peterson, President
Description: Two-volume book that examines the prospects for specific industries, including trucking. Also provides analyses of trends and problems, statistical tables and charts, and comparative company analyses.

TRADE PERIODICALS

1117 ■ *Body Language*
Pub: Automotive Body Parts Association
Contact: Mike Dolabi, President
URL(s): www.autobpa.com/body-language
Description: Reports news impacting the aftermarket body parts industry, industry trends, and Association news. Recurring features include meeting reports and a calendar of events. **Availability:** Print; Online.

1118 ■ *Counterman*
Pub: Babcox Media Inc.
Contact: Bill Babcox, Chief Executive Officer
E-mail: bbabcox@babcox.com
URL(s): www.counterman.com
Facebook: www.facebook.com/CountermanMag
X (Twitter): x.com/countermanmag
Instagram: www.instagram.com/countermanmagazine
YouTube: www.youtube.com/channel/UCUWIRti-EtXnYcpwDekTEyA
Ed: Joshua Cable. **Released:** Monthly **Description:** Magazine devoted to improving the effectiveness of professional automotive parts counter-sales personnel. **Availability:** Print; Download; PDF; Online.

1119 ■ *ImportCar*
Pub: Babcox Media Inc.
Contact: Bill Babcox, Chief Executive Officer
E-mail: bbabcox@babcox.com
URL(s): www.import-car.combabcox.com/brand/importcar
Facebook: www.facebook.com/importcar
Linkedin: www.linkedin.com/showcase/importcar
X (Twitter): x.com/import_car
Instagram: www.instagram.com/importcarmag
YouTube: www.youtube.com/channel/UCsKI7G4mLNIeqierKaPo05g
Ed: Doug Kaufman. **Released:** Monthly **Price:** $89, for one year Canada; $69, for us one year. **Description:** Magazine focusing on import specialist repair shops that derive more than 50% of revenue from servicing import nameplates. **Availability:** Print; PDF; Download; Online.

1120 ■ *It Is Innovation*
Pub: Consumer Technology Association
Contact: Kinsey Fabrizio, President
URL(s): www.cta.tech/Resources/i3-Magazine/i3-Issues/2023/January-February
Released: Bimonthly **Price:** $24.99, for U.S. & Canada; $49.99, for Elsewhere; $39.99, for Mexico; $5, Single issue; $7.50, Single issue; $9, Single issue. **Description:** Provides news and information concerning mobile electronics, audio, radar, security, and cellular communications. Examines the manufacture, market trends, and installation of mobile electronics. Covers legislative and regulatory issues at the state and federal levels with particular emphasis on business, manufacturing, and insurance issues. Recurring features include a monthly series of retail management information and news of the Association. **Availability:** Print; Online.

1121 ■ *SEMA News*
Pub: Specialty Equipment Market Association
Contact: Mike Spagnola, President
URL(s): www.sema.org/news-media/magazine
Released: Monthly **Description:** Covers the automotive speciality, performance equipment, and accessory sectors. Recurring features include news of government and legislative actions, new products, international markets, and member and Association activities. **Availability:** Print; Online.

TRADE SHOWS AND CONVENTIONS

1122 ■ **APRA Big R Show**
Automotive Parts Remanufacturers Association (APRA)
1520 Belle View Blvd., 3097
Alexandria, VA 22307
Ph: (703)968-2772
Co. E-mail: info@apra.org
URL: http://www.apra.org/#/Home
Contact: Joe Kripli, President
E-mail: kripli@apra.org
URL(s): apra.org/page/2020BigR
Frequency: Annual. **Audience:** Automotive parts rebuilders, members.

1123 ■ **Brake Colloquium & Exhibition**
ITT Inc.
105 Commerce Way
Westminster, SC 29693
URL: http://www.itt.com
Contact: Luca Savi, President
URL(s): www.sae.org/attend/brake
Frequency: Annual. **Audience:** Brake professionals, engineers, executives, management and marketing professionals. Dates and Locations: 2025 Sep 21-24 Grand Rapids, MI; 2026 Sep 20-23 Palm Springs, CA; 2027 Oct 03-06 Orlando, FL. **Telecommunication Services:** melissa.jena@sae.org.

1124 ■ **Florida RV Supershow**
Florida RV Trade Association (FRVTA)
10510 Gibsonton Dr.
Riverview, FL 33578-5434
Ph: (813)741-0488
Fax: (813)741-0688
Co. E-mail: info@frvta.org
URL: http://www.frvta.org
Contact: Dave Kelly, Executive Director
URL(s): www.frvta.org/show/florida-rv-supershow
Price: $10, regular adult admission; free for children under 16. **Frequency:** Annual. **Description:** Exhibits related to recreational vehicle equipment, supplies and services. **Audience:** RV dealers and manufacturers, and general public. **Principal Exhibits:** Exhibits related to recreational vehicle equipment, supplies and services. **Telecommunication Services:** sales@eliteeventsandrentals.com.

1125 ■ **International Midas Dealers Association Annual Convention**
International Midas Dealers Association (IMDA)
4919 Lamar Ave.
Mission, KS 66202
Free: 877-543-6203
Co. E-mail: imda@dci-kansascity.com
URL: http://imda.today
Contact: Chery Whelan, Contact
URL(s): mda.today/convention-2/
Frequency: Annual. **Description:** Exhibits related to Midas equipment, supplies, and services. **Audience:** Members. **Principal Exhibits:** Exhibits related to Midas equipment, supplies, and services. Dates and Locations: 2025 Feb 23-25 ChampionsGate Resort, Orlando, FL. **Telecommunication Services:** imda@dci-kansascity.com.

1126 ■ **Noise and Vibration Conference and Exhibition**
SAE International (SAE)
400 Commonwealth Dr.
Warrendale, PA 15096
Ph: (724)776-4841
Free: 877-606-7323
Fax: (724)776-0790
Co. E-mail: customerservice@sae.org
URL: http://www.sae.org
Contact: David L. Schutt, Contact
URL(s): www.sae.org/attend/nvh
Frequency: Biennial. **Description:** Developments in vehicle and components noise and vibration cause, control, analysis, measurement, and evaluation. **Audience:** Automotive, commercial vehicle, and aerospace professionals. **Principal Exhibits:** Developments in vehicle and components noise and vibration cause, control, analysis, measurement, and evaluation. Dates and Locations: 2025 May 12-15 DeVos Place Convention Center, Grand Rapids, MI; 2027 May 10-13 DeVos Place Convention Center, Grand Rapids, MI; 2029 May 14-17 DeVos Place Convention Center, Grand Rapids, MI. **Telecommunication Services:** melissa.jena@sae.org.

1127 ■ **SAE International WCX World Congress Experience**
SAE International (SAE)
400 Commonwealth Dr.
Warrendale, PA 15096
Ph: (724)776-4841
Free: 877-606-7323
Fax: (724)776-0790
Co. E-mail: customerservice@sae.org
URL: http://www.sae.org
Contact: David L. Schutt, Contact
URL(s): wcx.sae.org.
Frequency: Annual. **Description:** Parts, components, systems, and materials related to the automotive industry. **Audience:** Automotive engineers and designers, engineering managers, industry executives, suppliers, academia, and government and military officials. **Principal Exhibits:** Parts, components, systems, and materials related to the automotive industry. Dates and Locations: 2025 Apr 08-10 Detroit, MI. **Telecommunication Services:** wcxtechsessions@sae.org.

1128 ■ **SSA Convention**
Service Specialists Association (SSA)
1531 Springside Pl.
Downers Grove, IL 60516
Ph: (224)990-1005
Co. E-mail: servicespecialists@outlook.com
URL: http://www.servicespecialistsassociation.com
Contact: Adm. (Ret.) Warren Wild, President
URL(s): www.servicespecialistsassociation.com/ssaconvention2024
Frequency: Annual. **Description:** Exhibits related to truck repair operations, equipment, supplies, and services. **Audience:** Members and industry professionals. **Principal Exhibits:** Exhibits related to truck repair operations, equipment, supplies, and services.

FRANCHISES AND BUSINESS OPPORTUNITIES

1129 ■ **Batteries Plus L.L.C.**
1325 Walnut Ridge Dr.
Hartland, WI 53029
Free: 800-677-8278
Co. E-mail: customercare@batteriesplus.com
URL: http://www.batteriesplus.com
Facebook: www.facebook.com/BatteriesPlus
Linkedin: www.linkedin.com/company/batteries-plus
X (Twitter): x.com/batteriesplus
Instagram: www.instagram.com/batteriesplus
YouTube: www.youtube.com/batteriesplus

Description: Manufacturer of batteries, light bulbs and accessories. **Founded:** 1988. **Training:** 3 weeks training at corporate headquarters plus 10 days at franchisee's store. Training covers successful company philosophies, store operations and product knowledge.

1130 ■ Top Value Car & Truck Service Centers
36887 Schoolcraft
Livonia, MI 48150
Ph: (734)462-3633
Co. E-mail: info@top-value.com
URL: http://www.top-value.com
Facebook: www.facebook.com/TopValueAuto
Description: Provider of automotive repair services. **Founded:** 1977. **Financial Assistance:** Yes **Training:** Yes.

COMPUTERIZED DATABASES

1131 ■ *Tire Business*
Crain Communications Inc.
1155 Gratiot Ave.
Detroit, MI 48207-2732
Ph: (313)446-6000
Co. E-mail: info@crain.com
URL: http://www.crain.com
Contact: Barry Asin, President
URL(s): www.tirebusiness.com
Facebook: www.facebook.com/TireBusinessCrain
Linkedin: www.linkedin.com/company/tire-business
X (Twitter): x.com/tirebusiness
Instagram: www.instagram.com/tirebusinesscrain

Released: Latest issue July 15, 2024. **Price:** $99, for digital only annual; $225, Other countries for Print + Digital; $119, for print+ digital. **Description:** Edited for independent tire retailers and wholesalers. **Availability:** Print; PDF; Download; Online. **Type:** Full-text; Numeric.

Automobile Detailing/Painting Service

ASSOCIATIONS AND OTHER ORGANIZATIONS

1132 ■ Auto Painters Association
PO Box 5
 Davis, CA 95617
Free: 866-809-6060
Fax: (866)863-8268
Co. E-mail: info@autopaintersassoc.com
URL: http://www.autopaintersassoc.com
Contact: Vin Pham, President
E-mail: vpham@autopaintersassoc.com
Facebook: www.facebook.com/wix
X (Twitter): x.com/wix

Description: Owners of Maaco franchises. Strives to provide owners of Maaco auto painting and collision repair shops with a voice in the franchise system, and to increase profitability throughout the Maaco system across the United States.

REFERENCE WORKS

1133 ■ *"Neighboring Auto Body Shops Merge as Parks Royal Body Works" in Idaho Business Review (August 26, 2014)*
Pub: BridgeTower Media
Contact: Adam Reinebach, President

Description: Parks Royal Body Works and Auto Body Specialists operated next door to each other and were rivals for many years. Ted Vinson, owner of Auto Body, recently sold his business to Ted Thornton's son, Matt in order for Parks Royal to expand. Thornton discusses his company's 13 percent growth in 2013. Details of the purchase are discussed.

STATISTICAL SOURCES

1134 ■ *Car Wash & Auto Detailing Industry in the US - Market Research Report*
URL(s): www.ibisworld.com/united-states/market-research-reports/car-wash-auto-detailing-industry/
Price: $925. **Description:** Downloadable report analyzing data about the current and future trends in the car wash and auto detailing industries. **Availability:** Download.

TRADE PERIODICALS

1135 ■ *ImportCar*
Pub: Babcox Media Inc.
Contact: Bill Babcox, Chief Executive Officer
E-mail: bbabcox@babcox.com
URL(s): www.import-car.combabcox.com/brand/importcar
Facebook: www.facebook.com/importcar
Linkedin: www.linkedin.com/showcase/importcar
X (Twitter): x.com/import_car
Instagram: www.instagram.com/importcarmag
YouTube: www.youtube.com/channel/UCsKI7G4mLNIeqierKaPo05g

Ed: Doug Kaufman. **Released:** Monthly **Price:** $89, for one year Canada; $69, for us one year. **Description:** Magazine focusing on import specialist repair shops that derive more than 50% of revenue from servicing import nameplates. **Availability:** Print; PDF; Download; Online.

1136 ■ *Underhood Service*
Pub: Babcox Media Inc.
Contact: Bill Babcox, Chief Executive Officer
E-mail: bbabcox@babcox.com
URL(s): www.underhoodservice.com
Facebook: www.facebook.com/UnderhoodService
Linkedin: www.linkedin.com/showcase/underhood-service
X (Twitter): x.com/UnderHoodServ
Instagram: www.instagram.com/babcox_underhood
YouTube: www.youtube.com/channel/UCA7Yzkz8Q55bfKSk9SnYPTw

Ed: Doug Kaufman. **Released:** Monthly **Description:** Magazine covering service and repair shops doing 50% or more of service underhood. **Availability:** PDF; Download; Online.

TRADE SHOWS AND CONVENTIONS

1137 ■ SSA Convention
Service Specialists Association (SSA)
 1531 Springside Pl.
 Downers Grove, IL 60516
Ph: (224)990-1005
Co. E-mail: servicespecialists@outlook.com
URL: http://www.servicespecialistsassociation.com
Contact: Adm. (Ret.) Warren Wild, President
URL(s): www.servicespecialistsassociation.com/ssaconvention2024

Frequency: Annual. **Description:** Exhibits related to truck repair operations, equipment, supplies, and services. **Audience:** Members and industry professionals. **Principal Exhibits:** Exhibits related to truck repair operations, equipment, supplies, and services.

FRANCHISES AND BUSINESS OPPORTUNITIES

1138 ■ CARSTAR Automotive Canada Inc.
Driven Brands Inc.
 77 Ferguson Ave. S
 Hamilton, ON, Canada L8N 3Z8
Ph: (704)377-8855
URL: http://www.drivenbrands.com
Facebook: www.facebook.com/carstarcanada
X (Twitter): x.com/carstarcanada
YouTube: www.youtube.com/channel/UCMDDuZ8Pf4SLvwJfSr8rsUw

Description: Provider of auto body repair services. **Founded:** 1989. **Training:** Full menu of support services.

1139 ■ Colors on Parade
125 Daytona St. Conway
 Myrtle Beach, SC 29572
Ph: (843)347-8818
Free: 866-756-4207
Co. E-mail: info@colorsonparade.com
URL: http://colorsonparade.com
Contact: Robert Lowery, Founder
Facebook: www.facebook.com/ColorsOnParade
X (Twitter): x.com/ColorsonParade
Instagram: www.instagram.com/colorsonparade
YouTube: www.youtube.com/channel/UCJBpIJMAN_I9eLdpby2aG5A

Description: Provider of automotive appearance technology field such as paint repair, interior repair. **No. of Franchise Units:** 260. **Founded:** 1988. **Financial Assistance:** Yes **Training:** Provides 2 weeks training at headquarters, 3 months at franchisee's location, and ongoing support.

1140 ■ The Ding King Training Institute Inc.
3186 Airway Ave., Bldg. L
 Costa Mesa, CA 92626
Free: 800-304-3464
Co. E-mail: info@thedingking.com
URL: http://thedingking.com
Contact: Todd Sudeck, Contact
Facebook: www.facebook.com/TheDingKingPaintlessDentRepairSchool
YouTube: www.youtube.com/channel/UCfyoVkbDuimHJQRPfOBvzkg

Description: Provider of educational courses on dent, paint, wheel, interior, windshield and headlight repair training. **No. of Franchise Units:** 1,345. **Founded:** 1991. **Franchised:** 1993. **Equity Capital Needed:** $100,000. **Franchise Fee:** None. **Financial Assistance:** Yes **Training:** Includes training at company headquarters and onsite with ongoing support.

1141 ■ Dr. Vinyl and Associates Ltd.
1350 SE Hamblen Rd.
 Lees Summit, MO 64081
Ph: (816)525-6060
Free: 800-531-6600
Fax: (816)525-6333
Co. E-mail: info@drvinyl.com
URL: http://www.drvinyl.com
Contact: Richard Reinders, Chief Executive Officer
E-mail: richard@drvinyl.com

Description: Mobile repair, reconditioning and aftermarket sales and services to auto dealers and other commercial accounts, such as vinyl, leather, velour, fabric, bumper, windshield, plastic and paint less dent repair, application of striping, body moldings, deck racks, graphics, gold plating, etc. **Founded:** 1972. **Financial Assistance:** Yes **Training:** (Missouri for combined classroom and field training and 4-5 days in franchisees territory). Training also available for franchisees employees or sub-contractors.

1142 ■ Fibrenew
101 & 105, 220 ae 3rd St., NE
 Diamond Valley, AB, Canada T0L 0H0

Ph: (403)278-7818
Free: 800-345-2951
Co. E-mail: info@fibrenew.com
URL: http://www.fibrenew.com
Contact: J. Jesse, President
Facebook: www.facebook.com/fibrenew
Linkedin: www.linkedin.com/company/fibrenew
X (Twitter): x.com/fibrenew_intl
Instagram: www.instagram.com/fibrenew
YouTube: www.youtube.com/channel/UCbKbFsVRsjYpY41Wa6aKWZA
Pinterest: www.pinterest.com/fibrenew

Description: Firm provides leather repair, plastic repair, franchise opportunities, mobile businesses. **No. of Franchise Units:** 230. **Founded:** 1985. **Training:** Yes.

1143 ■ Line-X Protective Coatings
301 James Record Rd., Ste. 250
Huntsville, AL 35824
Free: 877-330-1331
Co. E-mail: portalhelpcenter@linex.com
URL: http://www.linex.com
Contact: Blair H. Boggs, President
X (Twitter): x.com/linexprotects
Instagram: www.instagram.com/linexnorthamerica
YouTube: www.youtube.com/user/LINEXprotects

Description: Firm provides protective coatings and accessories for trucks. **Founded:** 1993. **Training:** Provides 3 weeks of in-house technical, business operations and onsite application training and onging training and support from Operations team.

1144 ■ Maaco Franchising Inc.
Driven Brands Inc.
440 S Church St., Ste. 700
Charlotte, NC 28202
Ph: (704)377-8855
URL: http://www.drivenbrands.com
Contact: John Wierman, Manager
URL(s): www.maaco.com
Facebook: www.facebook.com/MaacoFranchise

Description: Maaco Auto Painting & Bodyworks Centers are complete production auto paint and body repair centers. No prior automotive experience necessary. **No. of Franchise Units:** 459. **Founded:** 1972. **Franchised:** 1972. **Equity Capital Needed:** $90,000 minimum cash required. **Franchise Fee:** $40,000. **Financial Assistance:** Yes **Training:** 4 weeks formal training at corporate headquarters, continuing operational support thereafter. Assistance in financing, site selection and installation of equipment.

1145 ■ Maaco Franchising Inc.
ON, Canada
Free: 877-855-1180
URL: http://www.maaco.ca
Contact: Bo Durkop, Director
E-mail: bo.durkop@drivenbrands.com
Facebook: www.facebook.com/MAACOCA
X (Twitter): x.com/maaco
Instagram: www.instagram.com/maaconorthamerica
YouTube: www.youtube.com/user/MaacoAutoBodyShop

Description: Provider of auto painting and collision repair services including insurance claims, DRP, fleet and industrial services. **Founded:** 1972. **Training:** Provides 4 weeks in U.S. and 3 man weeks onsite with ongoing support.

1146 ■ The Shine Factory
170 Joseph Zatzman Dr.
Dartmouth, NS, Canada B3B 1L9
Ph: (902)407-4777
Fax: (902)407-4778
URL: http://www.shinefactory.com
Contact: Stephen Gaetz, President

Description: Firm provides automotive protection and detailing services. **Founded:** 2018. **Franchised:** 1986. **Equity Capital Needed:** Equity Capital depends upon area and facility size. **Franchise Fee:** Depending upon Market area and analysis. **Training:** Training conducted in Halifax, NS.

1147 ■ Ziebart International Corporation
1290 E Maple Rd.
Troy, MI 48083
Co. E-mail: info@ziebartworld.com
URL: http://www.ziebartworld.com
Contact: Thomas E. Wolfe, President
Linkedin: www.linkedin.com/company/ziebart-international
Instagram: www.instagram.com/ziebartinternational
YouTube: www.youtube.com/user/ziebartinternational

Description: Firm offers automobile detailing and automotive protection services. **No. of Franchise Units:** 400. **Founded:** 1959. **Franchised:** 1959. **Financial Assistance:** Yes **Training:** Yes.

Automobile/Truck Leasing Service

ASSOCIATIONS AND OTHER ORGANIZATIONS

1148 ■ American Automotive Leasing Association (AALA)
600 Pennsylvania Ave.SE
 Washington, DC 20003
Ph: (202)531-1398
URL: http://www.aalafleet.com
Contact: Mike Joyce, Executive Director
E-mail: joyce@aalafleet.com

Description: Represents the commercial automotive fleet leasing and management industry. **Founded:** 1955. **Geographic Preference:** National.

1149 ■ American Car Rental Association (ACRA)
PO Box 584
 Long Lake, NY 12847
Ph: (518)738-7381
Co. E-mail: sfaulkner@acraorg.com
URL: http://www.acraorg.com
Contact: Sharky Laguana, President

Description: Independent automobile and truck renting and leasing firms. Seeks to promote, improve, and enhance the vehicle rental industry. Facilitates communication and cooperation among members; represents members' commercial and regulatory interests. **Founded:** 1996. **Educational Activities:** International Car Rental Show (Annual). **Geographic Preference:** National.

1150 ■ Automotive Fleet and Leasing Association (AFLA)
N83 W13410 Leon Rd.
 Menomonee Falls, WI 53051
Ph: (414)386-0366
Fax: (414)359-1671
Co. E-mail: info@afla.org
URL: http://www.afla.org
Contact: Steve Bender, President
Facebook: www.facebook.com/AFLAFleet
Linkedin: www.linkedin.com/company/aflafleet

Description: New car dealers, fleet administrators, leasing companies, drive-away companies, auto manufacturers, and consultants. Provides a forum for the exchange of information between related segments of the fleet and leasing industry. Builds relationships with professionals in all phases of the industry, develop new ideas that will help the industry continue to grow, and help the industry find ways to operate more efficiently and profitably. **Founded:** 1969. **Publications:** *The Forum* (Quarterly). **Awards:** AFLA Professional Fleet Manager of the Year (Annual). **Geographic Preference:** National.

1151 ■ NAFA Fleet Management Association - Library
180 Talmadge R.d, IGO Bldg., Ste. 558
 Edison, NJ 08817
Ph: (609)720-0882
Fax: (609)452-8004
Co. E-mail: info@nafa.org
URL: http://www.nafa.org
Contact: Ray Brisby, President
Facebook: www.facebook.com/nafafleet
Linkedin: www.linkedin.com/company/nafa-fleet-management-association
X (Twitter): x.com/nafafleet
YouTube: www.youtube.com/user/nafafleetmanagement

Description: Persons responsible for the administration of a motor vehicle fleet of 25 or more units for a firm not commercially engaged in the sale, rental, or lease of motor vehicles. Compiles statistics. Maintains placement service and speaker's bureau; conducts research programs. Operates Fleet Information Resource Center. Sponsors professional Certified Automotive Fleet Manager certification. **Scope:** Motor vehicle fleets. **Founded:** 1957. **Holdings:** Figures not available. **Publications:** *FleetSolutions* (Bimonthly); *NAFA Annual Reference Book*; *National Association of Fleet Administrators--Annual Reference Book* (Annual); *NAFA Fleet Executive: The Magazine for Vehicle Management* (Monthly); *FleetFocus* (Biweekly); *NAFA Roster*. **Educational Activities:** NAFA Institute and Expo (NAFA I&E) (Annual). **Awards:** NAFA Distinguished Service Award (Annual); NAFA Excellence in Education Award (Irregular); Larry Goill Memorial Quality Fleet Management Idea Award (Annual); NAFA Outstanding Chapter Service Award (Annual). **Geographic Preference:** National.

1152 ■ National Vehicle Leasing Association (NVLA)
N83 W13410 Leon Rd.
 Menomonee Falls, WI 53051
Ph: (414)533-3300
Fax: (414)359-1671
Co. E-mail: info@nvla.org
URL: http://www.nvla.org
Contact: Ken Sopp, President

Description: Companies that lease vehicles. Provides education and information services. Lobbies on behalf of members. Maintains speakers' bureau; offers placement services; compiles statistics. **Founded:** 1968. **Publications:** *Lifeline* (Bimonthly); *Vehicle Leasing Today* (Bimonthly; Quarterly); *National Guide to Vehicle Leasing Suppliers and Services* (Annual). **Educational Activities:** NVLA Annual Conference (Annual). **Geographic Preference:** National.

1153 ■ NationaLease Inc. [NationaLease]
2651 Warrenville Rd., Ste. 560
 Downers Grove, IL 60515
Free: 800-729-6857
Co. E-mail: info@nationalease.com
URL: http://www.nationalease.com
Contact: Dave Renz, Chairman
Facebook: www.facebook.com/NationaLease
Linkedin: www.linkedin.com/company/nationalease
X (Twitter): x.com/NationaLease

Description: Franchiser of independent companies. Provides full-service truck leasing. Promotes simplification of operating practices. Sponsors seminars. **Founded:** 1944. **Publications:** *NationaLease Newsletter* (Weekly). **Educational Activities:** NationaLease Annual Meeting (Annual). **Geographic Preference:** National.

1154 ■ Recreation Vehicle Rental Association (RVRA)
3930 University Dr.
 Fairfax, VA 22030
Ph: (703)591-7130
Co. E-mail: info@rvda.org
URL: http://www.rvda.org/RVDA/Find_A_Dealer/About_RVRA.aspx
Contact: Phil Ingrassia, President
E-mail: pingrassia@rvda.org

Description: Represents dealers involved in the rental of recreation vehicles such as folding trailers, travel trailers, and motor homes. Works to improve the professionalism of the RV rental dealer through educational programs and promote the use of rentals by disseminating information. Compiles statistics; conducts seminars. **Founded:** 1982. **Geographic Preference:** National.

1155 ■ Truck Renting and Leasing Association (TRALA)
675 N Washington St., Ste. 410
 Alexandria, VA 22314
Ph: (703)299-9120
URL: http://www.trala.org
Contact: Jake Jacoby, President
E-mail: jjacoby@trala.org
Facebook: www.facebook.com/TRALAorg
Linkedin: www.linkedin.com/company/truck-renting-and-leasing-association
X (Twitter): x.com/TRALAorg

Description: Truck and trailer rental and leasing companies and systems; suppliers to the industry. Seeks to encourage and promote a favorable climate and sound environment conducive to the renting and leasing of trucks, tractors, and trailers, and dedicated contract carriage. Publishes on the truck renting and leasing industry. Offers membership directory and monthly bulletins for members. **Founded:** 1978. **Publications:** *The TRALA Vehicle* (Annual); *EnRoute* (Biweekly); *Inside TRALA* (Quarterly); *Truck Renting and Leasing Association--News Digest* (Quarterly); *Weekly Wire* (Weekly); *inside TRALA* (Quarterly). **Educational Activities:** National Leadership Conference (Annual). **Awards:** TRALA Industry Scholarship Awards (Annual). **Geographic Preference:** State; National.

REFERENCE WORKS

1156 ■ "Burger King Moves Forward on Commitment to Electric Vehicles" in *Bizwomen* (March 27, 2023)
URL(s): www.bizjournals.com/bizwomen/news/latest-news/2023/03/burger-king.html

Ed: Jasmine Floyd. **Released:** March 27, 2023. **Description:** Burger King parent company, Restaurant Brands International Inc., set goals on reducing

1157 ■ Automobile/Truck Leasing Service

greenhouse gas emissions from their businesses. To help achieve that, 31% of it's Burger King fleet has transitioned to electric vehicles. **Availability:** Online.

1157 ■ *"Enterprise Holdings Hires More Than 4,000 Military Veterans Since Joining 100,000 Jobs Mission Coalition" in Defense & Aerospace Business (September 3, 2014, pp. 9)*
Pub: NewsRX LLC.
Contact: Kalani Rosell, Contact
Description: Enterprise Holdings, which owns and operates the Enterprise Rent-A-Car, Alamo Rent A Car and National Car Rental brands has hired more than 4,000 military veterans since joining the 100,000 Jobs Mission coalition in 2012. The company is named after the USS Enterprise, an aircraft carrier, and its commitment to the military goes back almost sixty years. Their Website includes employment opportunities for transitioning military personnel, veterans, members of the National Guard and Reserve and their families. Enterprise Holdings has been designated a Top Veteran-Friendly Company by US Veterans Magazine. **Availability:** Online.

1158 ■ *"Hertz-Tesla Deal Signals Broad Shift to EVs for Rental-Car Companies" in The Wall Street Journal (November 27, 2021)*
Ed: Nora Naughton. **Released:** November 27, 2021. **Description:** As electric-vehicles (EVs) take up more and more market share in the auto industry, expect to see more of them next time you need to rent a car. Hertz, the car-rental company, has placed a large order for Teslas. **Availability:** Online.

1159 ■ *"Is B2B a New Growth Area for Car Rental?" in AutoRental News (November 6, 2019)*
URL(s): www.autorentalnews.com/344115/is-b2b-a-new-growth-area-for-car-rental
Ed: Chris Brown. **Released:** November 06, 2019. **Description:** After car rental agencies started to rent cares to Transportation Network Company drivers, they developed another business to business — last mile deliveries. **Availability:** Online.

1160 ■ *"With Car-Leasing Prices on the Rise, Here's What to Know Before You Sign on the Dotted Line" in CNBC (April 17, 2019)*
URL(s): www.cnbc.com/2019/04/17/with-car-leasing-prices-on-the-rise-heres-what-to-do-before-you-sign.html
Ed: Sarah O'Brien. **Released:** April 17, 2019. **Description:** Car-leasing prices are trending upwards, which is pricing some people out of the leasing game. Other options include purchasing a certified pre-owned car, extending their current lease, or purchasing the leased vehicle. **Availability:** Online.

STATISTICAL SOURCES

1161 ■ *Car Rental Industry in the US - Market Research Report*
URL(s): www.ibisworld.com/united-states/market-research-reports/car-rental-industry/
Price: $925. **Description:** Downloadable report analyzing the current and future trends in the car rental industry. **Availability:** Download.

1162 ■ *RMA Annual Statement Studies*
Pub: Risk Management Association
Contact: Nancy Foster, President
Released: Annual. **Description:** Contains composite balance sheets and income statements for more than 360 industries, including the accounting, auditing, and bookkeeping industries. Also contains five years of comparative historical data for discerning trends. Includes 16 commonly used ratios, computed for most of the size groupings for nearly every industry.

1163 ■ *Truck Rental Industry in the US - Market Research Report*
URL(s): www.ibisworld.com/united-states/market-research-reports/truck-rental-industry/

Price: $925. **Description:** Downloadable report analyzing the current and future trends in the truck rental industry. **Availability:** Download.

TRADE PERIODICALS

1164 ■ *Automotive Fleet*
Pub: Bobit Business Media
Contact: Derrick Beasley, Manager, Technical Services
URL(s): www.automotive-fleet.com
Facebook: www.facebook.com/AutomotiveFleet
Linkedin: www.linkedin.com/showcase/automotive-fleet-magazine
X (Twitter): twitter.com/AutomotiveFleet
YouTube: www.youtube.com/channel/UC1Kqlg9f0wQV_0rjzKEWs5g
Ed: Mike Antich. **Description:** Automotive magazine covering the car and light truck fleet market. **Availability:** Print; Online.

TRADE SHOWS AND CONVENTIONS

1165 ■ *International Car Rental Show*
Zurich
7045 College Blvd.
Overland Park, KS 66211-1523
Ph: (913)339-1000
Fax: (913)469-3776
Co. E-mail: zdm.management@zurichna.com
URL: http://NA
Contact: Michel M. Liès, Chairman of the Board
URL(s): www.internationalcarrentalshow.com
Facebook: www.facebook.com/AutoRentalNews
Frequency: Annual. **Audience:** Operators, manufacturers, and industry professionals. Dates and Locations: 2025 Apr 14-16 the Paris Las Vegas, Las Vegas, NV; 2025 Apr 14-16 Paris Las Vegas, Las Vegas, NV. **Telecommunication Services:** bobiteventregistration@bobit.com

1166 ■ *SSA Convention*
Service Specialists Association (SSA)
1531 Springside Pl.
Downers Grove, IL 60516
Ph: (224)990-1005
Co. E-mail: servicespecialists@outlook.com
URL: http://www.servicespecialistsassociation.com
Contact: Adm. (Ret.) Warren Wild, President
URL(s): www.servicespecialistsassociation.com/ssaconvention2024
Frequency: Annual. **Description:** Exhibits related to truck repair operations, equipment, supplies, and services. **Audience:** Members and industry professionals. **Principal Exhibits:** Exhibits related to truck repair operations, equipment, supplies, and services.

FRANCHISES AND BUSINESS OPPORTUNITIES

1167 ■ *Active Green + Ross*
580 Evans Ave.
Toronto, ON, Canada M8W 2W1
Ph: (416)255-5581
Fax: (416)255-4793
Co. E-mail: info@activegreenross.com
URL: http://www.activegreenross.com
Facebook: www.facebook.com/activegreenandrossontario
X (Twitter): x.com/TireExperts
Instagram: www.instagram.com/activegreenandross_official
YouTube: www.youtube.com/user/ActiveGreenRoss580
Description: Chain of tire and auto center. **Founded:** 1982. **Training:** Training provided for up to 2 months.

1168 ■ *Bates International Motor Home Rental Systems Inc.*
3430 E Flamingo Rd., Ste. 224
Las Vegas, NV 89121
Ph: (702)737-9050
Co. E-mail: headquarters@batesintl.com

Facebook: www.facebook.com/p/Bates-International-Motor-Home-Rental-Systems-Inc-100057432828708
Description: Firm provides RV rentals, franchises, revenue sharing management program services. **Founded:** 1973. **Training:** Yes.

1169 ■ *Budget Brake and Muffler Distributors Ltd.* (https://budgetbrake.com/company/contact-us/)
200-185 Golden Dr.
Coquitlam, BC, Canada V3K 6T1
Ph: (604)464-1239
Free: 800-746-9659
Fax: (604)648-8805
Co. E-mail: info2@budgetbrake.com
URL: http://budgetbrake.com
Contact: John Sinkie, Jr., Contact
Facebook: www.facebook.com/BudgetBrakeAuto
X (Twitter): x.com/BBMAOfficial
Instagram: www.instagram.com/budgetbrakeauto
YouTube: www.youtube.com/user/budgetbrakeauto
Description: Company provides car care advice and services. **No. of Franchise Units:** 30. **Founded:** 1972. **Training:** Provides 2 weeks.

1170 ■ *Dollar Rent A Car*
Description: Daily rental car. **No. of Franchise Units:** 1,300. **No. of Company-Owned Units:** 30. **Founded:** 1967. **Equity Capital Needed:** Dependent on fleet size. **Franchise Fee:** minimum $12,500. **Financial Assistance:** Yes **Training:** Yes.

1171 ■ *Eaglerider Motorcycle Rental*
11860 S La Cienega Blvd.
Hawthorne, CA 90250
Ph: (310)536-6777
Free: 800-501-8687
Fax: (310)536-6776
Co. E-mail: rent@eaglerider.com
URL: http://www.eaglerider.com
Contact: Chris McIntyre, Chief Executive Officer
Facebook: www.facebook.com/EagleRider
Instagram: www.instagram.com/eaglerider
YouTube: www.youtube.com/c/eaglerider
Description: Retailer of automobiles. **Founded:** 1992. **Equity Capital Needed:** Net worth $400,000. **Franchise Fee:** $30,000. **Royalty Fee:** 10% of Gross Rental Revenue and 5% of Gross Retail Revenue. **Financial Assistance:** Yes **Training:** Provides 6 days at headquarters, 2 days onsite, and ongoing support.

1172 ■ *Payless Car Rental System, Inc.*
Avalon Global Group Inc.
2501 N Hollywood Way
Burbank, CA 91505
Free: 800-729-5255
Description: Automobile rental and sales. **No. of Franchise Units:** 83. **Founded:** 1971. **Franchised:** 1971. **Equity Capital Needed:** Minimum $500,000 net worth. **Franchise Fee:** $20,000-$500,000. **Training:** Yes.

1173 ■ *Thrifty Rent-A-Car System, LLC*
The Hertz Corporation
The Hertz Corporation, c/o Customer Relations Department
PO Box 26120
Oklahoma City, OK 73126
Ph: (239)390-8380
Free: 800-654-4173
Co. E-mail: hertzracap@hertz.com
URL: http://www.hertz.com/rentacar/reservation
Facebook: www.facebook.com/ThriftyCarRental
X (Twitter): x.com/thriftycars
Instagram: www.instagram.com/thriftycarrental
YouTube: www.youtube.com/c/thriftycarrental
Description: Manufacturer of motor vehicles and car bodies. **Founded:** 1958.

COMPUTERIZED DATABASES

1174 ■ *Consumer InSite*
Type: Full-text.

LIBRARIES

1175 ■ Alabama Department of Transportation (ALDOT)
PO Box 303050
  Montgomery, AL 36130-3050
Ph: (334)353-6554
Co. E-mail: aldotinfo@dot.state.al.us
URL: http://www.dot.state.al.us
Contact: John Cooper, Director
E-mail: cooperjr@dot.state.al.us
Scope: Transportation. **Services:** Interlibrary loan; library not open to the public. **Founded:** 1953. **Holdings:** 1,000 books; 5,000 reports.

1176 ■ California State Department of Motor Vehicles - Licensing Operations Division - Research and Development Branch - Traffic Safety Research Library
1120 N St., Rm. 1430
  Sacramento, CA 95814
Ph: (914)654-4601
Co. E-mail: library@dot.ca.gov
URL: http://dot.ca.gov/programs/transportation-library
Scope: Automobile transportation. **Services:** Copying; library not open to the public. **Holdings:** 500 books; 10,000 bound periodical volumes; reports; manuscripts. **Subscriptions:** 20 journals and other serials.

1177 ■ Kansas Department of Transportation (KDOT) - Library
Dwight D. Eisenhower State Office Building 700 SW Harrison St.
  Topeka, KS 66603-3745
Ph: (785)296-3566
Fax: (785)368-7415
Co. E-mail: kdot#publicinfo@ks.gov
URL: http://www.ksdot.gov
Contact: Bob Brock, Director
Facebook: www.facebook.com/KSDOTHQ
X (Twitter): x.com/KDOTHQ
YouTube: www.youtube.com/user/kansastransportation
Pinterest: www.pinterest.com/kdothq
Description: Transportation: Local and suburban transit. **Scope:** Transportation. **Founded:** 1868. **Holdings:** Figures not available.

1178 ■ Missouri Department of Transportation-Division of Materials Library
Rm. 200 600 W Main St.
  Jefferson City, MO 65101
URL: http://www.modot.org
Scope: Transportation. **Services:** Library not open to the public. **Holdings:** Figures not available.

1179 ■ Montana Department of Transportation (MDT)
2701 Prospect Ave.
  Helena, MT 59601
Ph: (406)444-6200
Co. E-mail: mdtcommteam@mt.gov
Facebook: www.facebook.com/montanadot
Linkedin: www.linkedin.com/company/montana-department-of-transportation
Instagram: www.instagram.com/mtdot
YouTube: www.youtube.com/user/MontanaDOT
Description: Mission is to serve the public by providing a transportation system and services that emphasize quality, safety, cost effectiveness, economic vitality, and sensitivity to the environment. **Scope:** Transportation. **Services:** Interlibrary loan; copying. **Founded:** 1913. **Holdings:** 20,000 titles.

1180 ■ New Jersey Department of Transportation Research Library (NJDOT)
c/o David J. Goldberg Transportation Complex
  1035 Pky., Ave.
  Trenton, NJ 08625
Ph: (609)963-1982
URL: http://www.nj.gov/transportation/business/research/library
Contact: David J. Goldberg, Contact
Scope: Transportation. **Services:** Interlibrary loan; copying; library open to the public by appointment. **Founded:** 1962. **Holdings:** 300 books; 11,000 reports.

1181 ■ North Dakota Department of Transportation - Materials and Research Division - Library
608 East Blvd. Ave.
  Bismarck, ND 58505-0700
URL: http://www.dot.nd.gov/divisions/materials/materials.htm
Facebook: www.facebook.com/nddot
X (Twitter): x.com/NorthDakotaDOT
YouTube: www.youtube.com/user/NDDOTOnline
Description: Integral unit of North Dakota Department of Transportation. **Scope:** Transportation. **Services:** Library not open to the public. **Founded:** 1970. **Holdings:** 6,600 reports.

1182 ■ South Carolina Department of Transportation (SCDOT) - Library
955 Pk. St.
  Columbia, SC 29201-3959
Ph: (803)737-1200
Free: 855-467-2368
URL: http://www.scdot.org
Facebook: www.facebook.com/SCDOT
X (Twitter): x.com/SCDOTPress
YouTube: www.youtube.com/user/SCDOTconnectoronline
Scope: Transportation. **Founded:** 1998. **Holdings:** Figures not available.

1183 ■ University of Kentucky College of Engineering - Kentucky Transportation Center (KTC) - Library
176 Oliver H Raymond Bldg.
  Lexington, KY 40506
Ph: (859)257-4513
URL: http://ktc.uky.edu
URL(s): www.engr.uky.edu/research-faculty/departments/civil-engineering/kentucky-transportation-center
Facebook: www.facebook.com/KYTRANSPORTATION
Linkedin: www.linkedin.com/company/ktc-uky
X (Twitter): x.com/kytransport
YouTube: www.youtube.com/channel/UCCkzZxbfj-2ZzMKYgH6Jn5Q
Description: Integral unit of College of Engineering, University of Kentucky, operating under its own board of control. Offers technology transfer program, including transportation workshops, audiovisual and library materials, mail lists, and technical assistance. **Scope:** Highways; bridges; the environment; geotechnology; Intelligent Transportation Systems (ITS); pavements; traffic and safety; structures; construction management; transportation policy, planning, and finance. **Services:** Interlibrary loan; copying; library open to the public. **Founded:** 1981. **Holdings:** Books; Reports; Videotapes. **Subscriptions:** 300 journals and other serials. **Publications:** *The Link Technology Transfer Newsletter*. **Educational Activities:** Annual Transportation Forum, Cosponsored with the Advanced Institute for Transportation Systems Science.

Automotive Repair Shop

ASSOCIATIONS AND OTHER ORGANIZATIONS

1184 ■ Automatic Transmission Rebuilders Association (ATRA)
2400 Latigo Ave.
Oxnard, CA 93030
Ph: (805)604-2000
Free: 866-464-2872
Fax: (805)604-2003
Co. E-mail: membership@atra.com
URL: http://www.atra.com
Contact: Dennis Madden, Chief Executive Officer
E-mail: dmadden@atra.com
Facebook: www.facebook.com/transmissions
X (Twitter): x.com/ATRAHQ
YouTube: www.youtube.com/channel/UCAL16xvVtJ_QWkXejWQCHsA
Description: Provides a basis for cross-country guarantees among members; and formulates basic advertising format incorporating the association emblem and logo. Conducts automatic transmission service and repair clinics. **Founded:** 1954. **Publications:** *The Good Guys* (10/year); *Membership Roster*. **Geographic Preference:** National.

REFERENCE WORKS

1185 ■ "Auto Glass Shortage Requires Creativity to Persevere" in Autobody News (October 20, 2021)
Ed: Rebecca Barnabi. **Released:** October 20, 2021. **Description:** With the COVID-19 pandemic causing a glass shortage, auto glass shops are struggling to fill orders. However, manufacturers are trying to fulfill them as quickly as possible, but customers may still need to be patient and wait longer. **Availability:** Download.

1186 ■ Car Body Shops Industry in the US - Market Research Report
URL(s): www.ibisworld.com/united-states/market-research-reports/car-body-shops-industry/
Price: $925. **Description:** Downloadable report analyzing current and future trends in the car body shop industry. **Availability:** Download.

1187 ■ "Infrastructure Investment and Jobs Act Includes New Vehicle Safety Provisions" in Autobody News (November 19, 2021)
Released: November 19, 2021. **Description:** The new Infrastructure bill signed by President Joe Biden into law includes some unconventional items that affect mechanical and collision repair shops. Included in the law are provisions for standardizing vehicle safety standards, electric vehicle charging stations, and to implement Advanced Driver-Assist Systems. **Availability:** Online.

1188 ■ "These States are Where Auto Mechanics are in High Demand" in Small Business Trends (January 25, 2023)
URL(s): smallbiztrends.com/2023/01/states-where-auto-mechanics-are-in-high-demand.html
Ed: Gabrielle Pickard-Whitehead. **Released:** January 25, 2023. **Description:** Discusses where auto mechanics are in high demand and also the best states to work in that field. **Availability:** Online.

1189 ■ "Your Car Repair Handbook" in Consumer Reports (September 9, 2021)
URL(s): www.consumerreports.org/car-repair/your-car-repair-handbook
Ed: Benjamin Preston. **Released:** September 21, 2021. **Description:** Owning a vehicle can get expensive, especially if repairs are needed. Even regular maintenance can add up. A breakdown of what costs to expect when doing it yourself or taking it in to the shop is given. Repairs that should be handled at a dealership, such as airbag safety, is also discussed. **Availability:** Print; Online.

STATISTICAL SOURCES

1190 ■ Auto Windshield Repair Services Industry in the US - Market Research Report
URL(s): www.ibisworld.com/united-states/market-research-reports/auto-windshield-repair-services-industry/
Price: $925. **Description:** Downloadable report analyzing the current and future trends in the auto windshield repair industry. **Availability:** Download.

VIDEO/AUDIO MEDIA

1191 ■ The Solopreneur Hour: Ant Anstead of Wheeler Dealers/Master Mechanic - The Passion Behind the Work
URL(s): solopreneurhour.com/podcast/812-ant-anstead-of-wheeler-dealers-master-mechanic-the-passion-behind-the-work
Ed: Michael O'Neal. **Released:** May 27, 2020. **Description:** Podcast offers conversation with the host of car-centric TV shows.

Baby Store

REFERENCE WORKS

1192 ■ *"Baby's Room Franchisee Files Bankruptcy"* in *Crain's Detroit Business (Vol. 25, June 22, 2009, No. 25, pp. 15)*
Pub: Crain Communications Inc.
Contact: Barry Asin, President
Ed: Gabe Nelson. **Description:** Emery L, a franchisee of USA Baby Inc. and ran the franchised Baby's Room Nursery Furniture stores in the area has filed for bankruptcy. Details of the bankruptcy are included. **Availability:** Print; Online.

1193 ■ *"Borrow Baby Couture Launch Rocks Fasion World - Provides Couture Fashion for Girls"* in *Benzinga.com (June 18, 2012)*
Description: Borrow Baby Couture allows parents, family and friends to rent couture clothing by top fashion designers for girls ages 9 months to 4 years. The retailer has launched an online site. Purchases are wrapped in tissue arriving ready to wear and includes return shipping costs. **Availability:** Online.

1194 ■ *"Consignment Shop Offers Children's Clothes, Products"* in *Frederick News-Post (August 19, 2010)*
Pub: Federick News-Post
Contact: Connie Hastings, Director
E-mail: chastings@newspost.com
Ed: Ed Waters, Jr. **Description:** Sweet Pea Consignments for Children offers used items for newborns to pre-teens. The shop carries name brand clothing as well as toys, books and baby products. **Availability:** Print; Online.

1195 ■ *"King of the Crib: How Good Samaritan Became Ohio's Baby HQ"* in *Business Courier (Vol. 27, June 18, 2010, No. 7, pp. 1)*
Pub: Business Courier
Ed: James Ritchie. **Description:** Cincinnati's Good Samaritan hospital had 6,875 live births in 2009, which is more than any other hospital in Ohio. They specialize in the highest-risk pregnancies and deliveries and other hospitals are trying to grab Good Samaritan's share in this niche. **Availability:** Print; Online.

1196 ■ *"Necessity Mother of This Startup"* in *Providence Business News (Vol. 28, January 6, 2014, No. 40, pp. 1)*
Pub: American City Business Journals, Inc.
Contact: Mike Olivieri, Executive Vice President
URL(s): pbn.com/necessity-mother-of-this-startup94159
Description: Kailas Narendran, founder of kiinde LLC, invented a device that can quickly thaw breast milk to precisely the right temperature for feeding a baby without losing nutrients. Innovative products for mothers and babies are now being sold by kiine throughout the U.S., Canada and South Korea. New product development is discussed by Narendran. **Availability:** Online.

1197 ■ *"New Backers, New Products at Halo"* in *Business Journal (Vol. 32, July 18, 2014, No. 8, pp. 5)*
Pub: American City Business Journals, Inc.
Contact: Mike Olivieri, Executive Vice President
Released: Weekly. **Price:** $4, introductory 4-week offer(Digital only). **Description:** Minnetonka, Minnesota-based Halo Innovations Inc. announced the launch of its first baby bassinet. The product launch follows a recapitalization that allowed new backers, including Balance Point Capital Partners, to buy the stakes of long-time investors. The risk of suffocation in having babies sleep with parents is also discussed. **Availability:** Print; Online.

1198 ■ *"Toys R Us Tries for a Comeback a Year After Going Out of Business"* in *CNBC (February 11, 2019)*
URL(s): www.cnbc.com/2019/02/11/toys-r-us-executives-plot-retailers-comeback-with-tru-kids.html
Ed: Lauren Hirsch. **Released:** February 11, 2019. **Description:** The brand new company, Tru Kid, is a new concept developed to help bring back the Toys R Us brand, along with the Baby's R Us and Geoffrey brands. **Availability:** Online.

1199 ■ *"What's In That Diaper?"* in *Inc. (November 2007, pp. 126)*
Ed: Nitasha Tiku. **Description:** Profile of Jason and Kimberly Graham-Nye, inventors of the gDiaper, consisting of a washable cotton elastine outer pant and an insert made of fluffed wood pulp and viscose rayon, both harvested from trees certified by the Sustainable Forestry Initiative. **Availability:** Online.

SOURCES OF SUPPLY

1200 ■ *Toys & Games--Buyer's Guide Issue (Canada)*
Chelsie Communications Inc.
URL(s): toysandgamesmagazine.ca/about/2008_buyers_guide_sm-3/
Released: Annual; Latest edition 2008. **Description:** Publication includes list of about 400 Canadian manufacturers and distributors of toys and games for children; trade associations, trade show organizers, and licensors. **Entries include:** For manufacturers and distributors--Company name, address, phone, key officials, branches, name of firm represented, key to line of business. For associations--Name, address, phone, contact name, property/show represented. **Arrangement:** Alphabetical. **Indexes:** Product, brand name. **Availability:** Print.

TRADE SHOWS AND CONVENTIONS

1201 ■ **International Juvenile Product Show**
Juvenile Products Manufacturers Association (JPMA)
1120 Rte. 73, Ste. 200
Mount Laurel, NJ 08054
Ph: (856)638-0420
Co. E-mail: jpma@jpma.org
URL: http://www.jpma.org
Contact: Michael Dwyer, President
E-mail: mdwyer@jpma.org
URL(s): jpmashow.org
Description: Juvenile products, including furniture, toys, infant accessories, and soft goods. **Audience:** Industry professional. **Principal Exhibits:** Juvenile products, including furniture, toys, infant accessories, and soft goods. **Telecommunication Services:** sgargiulo@jpma.org.

FRANCHISES AND BUSINESS OPPORTUNITIES

1202 ■ **Children's Lighthouse Franchise Co. (CLFC)**
101 S Jennings Ave., Ste. 209
Fort Worth, TX 76104
Free: 888-338-4466
Fax: (817)338-2716
Co. E-mail: hello@childrenslighthouse.com
URL: http://childrenslighthouse.com
Contact: Michael Brown, President
Facebook: www.facebook.com/childrenslighthouse
Instagram: www.instagram.com/childrens_lighthouse
YouTube: www.youtube.com/channel/UCODzN_cwYIMMuvH9cQXfDvw
Description: School which provides values-based early childhood education. **Founded:** 1997. **Financial Assistance:** Yes **Training:** Available at headquarters for 4 weeks, 4 weeks at franchisee's location, unlimited training for the first year and unlimited support.

1203 ■ **Stork News**
1305 Hope Mills Rd.
Fayetteville, NC 28304
Ph: (910)461-5389
Co. E-mail: storknewsrental@gmail.com
URL: http://www.stork-news.com
Contact: Alexis Young, Contact
Facebook: www.facebook.com/StorkNewsofAmerica
Instagram: www.instagram.com/stork_news
Description: Firm provides announcement services to newborn. **Founded:** 1983. **Franchised:** 1985. **Training:** Yes.

LIBRARIES

1204 ■ **Fashion Institute of Design and Merchandising (FIDM) - Library**
919 S Grand Ave.
Los Angeles, CA 90015
Ph: (213)624-1200
Free: 800-624-1200
URL: http://fidm.edu
Contact: Tonian Hohberg, President
Facebook: www.facebook.com/FIDMCollege
Linkedin: www.linkedin.com/school/fidm
X (Twitter): x.com/FIDM
YouTube: www.youtube.com/fidm

Pinterest: www.pinterest.com/fidm
Scope: Textile design and research; fashion; business and marketing; interior design; retailing and costumes. **Services:** Copying; interlibrary loan. **Founded:** 1969. **Subscriptions:** 200 magazines Books; periodicals; publications; newspapers; DVDs; CDs.

1205 ■ State University of New York - Fashion Institute of Technology - Gladys Marcus Library
227 W 27th St.
  New York, NY 10001-5992
Ph: (212)217-7999
URL: http://www.fitnyc.edu/library/index.php

Description: Library supports the academic and research needs of the institute. **Scope:** Fashion, fashion history, textiles, fashion trend forecasting. **Services:** Interlibrary loan; library open by appointment. **Founded:** 1944. **Holdings:** 300,000 print, non-print, and electronic materials, including sketch collections, clipping files, and fashion show DVDs.

Bagel Shop

ASSOCIATIONS AND OTHER ORGANIZATIONS

1206 ■ American Bakers Association (ABA)
601 Pennsylvania Ave. NW, Ste. 230
 Washington, DC 20004
Ph: (202)789-0300
Fax: (202)898-1164
Co. E-mail: info@americanbakers.org
URL: http://americanbakers.org
Contact: Robb MacKie, President
Facebook: www.facebook.com/americanbakersassoc
Linkedin: www.linkedin.com/company/
 americanbakers
X (Twitter): x.com/AmericanBakers
Instagram: www.instagram.com/americanbakers
YouTube: www.youtube.com/user/americanbakers
Description: Manufacturers and wholesale distributors of bread, rolls, and pastry products; suppliers of goods and services to bakers. Conducts seminars and expositions. **Founded:** 1897. **Awards:** B&CMA Chairman's Award for Safety Excellence (Annual). **Geographic Preference:** National.

1207 ■ National Bagel Association (NBA)
425 N Broadway, No 700
 Jericho, NY 11753
Ph: (607)542-9365
Co. E-mail: info@bagels.org
URL: http://www.bagels.org
Contact: Andrew Hazen, Chief Executive Officer
Facebook: www.facebook.com/BagelsOrg
X (Twitter): x.com/bagelsorg
Instagram: www.instagram.com/bagelsorg
Pinterest: www.pinterest.com/bagelsorg
Description: Trade association promoting the consumption of bagels, and supporting bagel bakers and bagel store owners and operators. Organizes the annual National Bagel Eating Contest. **Founded:** 2012.

REFERENCE WORKS

1208 ■ "This Legendary New York Bagel Shop is Finally Going National" in Eat This, Not That (October 10, 2021)
Ed: Krissy Gasbarre. **Released:** October 10, 2021. **Description:** A famous New York City bagel shop, H&H Bagels, is heading out of its comfort zone and announcing franchise opportunities, as it tries to branch out into other states. **Availability:** Download.

1209 ■ "The Ultimate Vending Machine" in Benzinga.com (August 15, 2011)
Pub: Benzinga.com
Contact: Jason Raznick, Founder
Ed: Louis Bedigian. **Description:** Louis Hecht, a baker from Hombourg-Haut, France is selling fresh-baked bread in vending machines. Each machine holds 90 pre-cooked loaves which are warmed before being delivered to the customer. **Availability:** Online.

1210 ■ "You Don't Have to Go to New York City for an Excellent Bagel" in Houstonia (January 28, 2019)
URL(s): www.houstoniamag.com/articles/2019/1/28/
 best-bagels-in-houston
Ed: Timothy Malcolm. **Released:** January 28, 2019. **Description:** A former New Yorker living in Houston examines the best bagel shops in the area, where consumers can get authentic New York-style bagels. **Availability:** Online.

SOURCES OF SUPPLY

1211 ■ Baking/Snack Directory & Buyer's Guide
Sosland Publishing Co.
Contact: Joshua Sosland, President
URL(s): www.sosland.com/store
Price: $205, Single issue. **Description:** Covers wholesale bakers of bread, cake, cookies, crackers, pasta; manufacturers of snack foods, mixes, and frozen dough; licensors of proprietary brands; manufacturers of equipment and products and suppliers of services used in wholesale baking. For bakers--Company name, address, phone, principal headquarters and plant personnel, principal products, sales volume, production method, and number of employees. For manufacturers--Company name, address, phone, name and title of contact. **Entries include:** Company name, address, phone, executive name. **Arrangement:** Bakers are classified by product type; manufacturers are alphabetical. **Indexes:** Executive name, plant (bakers); product (manufacturers and suppliers). **Availability:** Print.

STATISTICAL SOURCES

1212 ■ Bagel Stores Industry in the US - Market Research Report
URL(s): www.ibisworld.com/united-states/market-re
 search-reports/bagel-stores-industry/
Price: $925. **Description:** Downloadable report analyzing the current and future trends in the bagel store industry. **Availability:** Download.

TRADE PERIODICALS

1213 ■ Bake
Pub: Sosland Publishing Co.
Contact: Joshua Sosland, President
URL(s): www.bakemag.com
Facebook: www.facebook.com/bakemagazine
Linkedin: www.linkedin.com/showcase/bake
 -magazine
X (Twitter): x.com/BakeMag
Ed: L. Joshua Sosland. **Released:** Bimonthly; Feb, Apr, Jun, Aug, Oct, and Dec. **Price:** $36, U.S. and Canada for per year print; $46, for print outside the U.S. and Canada. **Description:** Magazine for retail, in-store, foodservice, specialty, and wholesale bakers. **Availability:** Print; PDF; Download; Online.

1214 ■ Baking & Snack
Pub: Sosland Publishing Co.
Contact: Joshua Sosland, President
URL(s): www.bakingbusiness.com
Facebook: www.facebook.com/BakingandSnack
Linkedin: www.linkedin.com/showcase/baking&snack
 -magazine
X (Twitter): x.com/BakingSnackMag
Instagram: www.instagram.com/bakingandsnack
Ed: Dan Malovany. **Released:** Monthly **Description:** Equipment, engineering, production and formulating magazine for commercial manufacturers of baked and snack foods. **Availability:** Print; PDF; Online.

1215 ■ Milling & Baking News
Pub: Sosland Publishing Co.
Contact: Joshua Sosland, President
URL(s): www.bakingbusiness.comwww.sosland.com/
 milling-baking-news
Facebook: www.facebook.com/Millingan
 dBakingNews
Linkedin: www.linkedin.com/showcase/milling
 -&-baking-news
Ed: Joshua L. Sosland. **Released:** Weekly (Thurs.) **Description:** Trade magazine covering the grain-based food industries. **Availability:** Print; Online.

VIDEO/AUDIO MEDIA

1216 ■ Jamie Schrotberger CEO of Spread Bagelry
URL(s): restaurantunstoppable.com/jamie-schro
 tberger-spread-bagelry
Ed: Eric Cacciatore. **Released:** January 11, 2023. **Description:** Podcast discusses the fast casual concept along with growing too fast.

TRADE SHOWS AND CONVENTIONS

1217 ■ IDDBA Show
International Dairy-Deli-Bakery Association (IDDBA)
8317 Elderberry Rd.
 Madison, WI 53717-2603
Ph: (608)310-5000
Fax: (608)238-6330
Co. E-mail: iddba@iddba.org
URL: http://www.iddba.org
Contact: Mike Eardley, President
URL(s): www.iddba.org/iddba-show/about/iddba-2025
Frequency: Annual. **Description:** Topics include those related to the food industry. Event contains speakers, exhibitions, workshops, and entertainment. **Audience:** Buyers, bakers, merchandisers, and executives who have a shared passion for food and the industry. **Principal Exhibits:** Topics include those related to the food industry. Event contains speakers, exhibitions, workshops, and entertainment. Dates and Locations: 2025 Jun 01-3 Ernest N. Morial Convention Center, New Orleans, LA. **Telecommunication Services:** wisl@iddba.org.

FRANCHISES AND BUSINESS OPPORTUNITIES

1218 ■ Between Rounds Bakery Sandwich Cafe
Between Rounds Franchise Corp.
19 John Fitch Blvd., Rte. 5
South Windsor, CT 06074
Ph: (860)291-8780
URL: http://betweenroundsbagels.com
Contact: Jerry Puiia, Owner
Facebook: www.facebook.com/BetweenRoundsBakerySandwichCafe
X (Twitter): x.com/betweenroundsUS
Instagram: www.instagram.com/betweenroundsus
Description: Operator of restaurant. **Founded:** 1990. **Equity Capital Needed:** $300,000 liquid assets ; $1,000,000 net worth. **Franchise Fee:** $65,000 for a 3-unit Development ; $95,000 for a 5-unit Development ; $175,000 for a 10-unit Development. **Royalty Fee:** 5% of gross sales. **Financial Assistance:** No **Training:** Yes.

1219 ■ Big Apple Bagels (BAB)
500 Lake Cook Rd., Ste. 475
Deerfield, IL 60015
Free: 800-251-6101
Fax: (847)405-8140
Co. E-mail: info@babcorp.com
URL: http://www.babcorp.com
Contact: Michael W. Evans, President
Description: Operator of restaurant. **Founded:** 1993. **Franchised:** 1993. **Equity Capital Needed:** $294,700 - $398,100. **Franchise Fee:** $25,000. **Royalty Fee:** 5% of gross revenues – weekly. **Training:** Extensive training covers all aspects of operations and management, combines hands-on experience at our corporate store training facility with classroom presentations by management and key note vendors.

1220 ■ Big Town Hero (BTH)
1921 14th St. SE, D-405
Albany, OR 97321
Ph: (541)926-1880
Co. E-mail: franchise@bigtownhero.com
URL: http://bigtownhero.com
Contact: Christy Schaeffer, Owner
Facebook: www.facebook.com/BigTownHero
Linkedin: www.linkedin.com/company/big-town-hero-franchise
X (Twitter): x.com/bigtownhero
YouTube: www.youtube.com/channel/UCeZmUH9nljKghC9AlUHREqA
Description: Sandwiches, salads, soups, fresh bread and baked goods from scratch. Fast and friendly. **No. of Franchise Units:** 34. **Founded:** 1982. **Franchised:** 1989. **Equity Capital Needed:** $75,000-$175,000. **Franchise Fee:** $20,000. **Training:** Yes.

1221 ■ Blue Chip Cookies
5045 W 117th St.
Leawood, KS 66211
Ph: (913)663-1163
Co. E-mail: orders@bluechipcookies.com
URL: http://www.bluechipcookiesdirect.com
Facebook: www.facebook.com/BlueChipCookiesDirect
X (Twitter): x.com/bluechipcookies
Description: Cookies, bakery items, ice cream, coffees, depending on model and site. **No. of Franchise Units:** 5. **No. of Company-Owned Units:** 3. **Founded:** 1983. **Franchised:** 1986. **Equity Capital Needed:** $150,000-$250,000. **Franchise Fee:** $25,000. **Training:** Offers 2 weeks of training.

1222 ■ Breadsmith
409 E Silver Spring Dr.
Whitefish Bay, WI 53217
Ph: (414)962-1965
URL: http://www.breadsmith.com
Description: Producer of artisan breads and sweets. **Founded:** 1993. **Equity Capital Needed:** $354,250 – 399,900. **Royalty Fee:** 7% – 5%. **Training:** Yes.

1223 ■ Bruegger's Enterprises
8008 Cedar Springs Rd., LB 16
Dallas, TX 75235
Ph: (972)629-9255
URL: http://www.brueggers.com
Facebook: www.facebook.com/Brueggers
X (Twitter): x.com/Brueggers
Instagram: www.instagram.com/Brueggers
YouTube: www.youtube.com/brueggers
Pinterest: www.pinterest.com/BrueggersBagels
Description: Bakery style cafe serving bagels, sandwiches, breads, and fresh salads. **Founded:** 1983. **Training:** Up to 8 weeks of on-the-job training.

1224 ■ Canada Bread Company, Limited
Grupo Bimbo S.A.B. de C.V.
Etobicoke, ON, Canada
Ph: 52 55 526-866-00
URL: http://www.grupobimbo.com
Description: Producer and distributor of nutritious fresh bakery products including white, whole wheat, whole grain bread, rolls, bagels, English muffins and artisan breads. **No. of Franchise Units:** 985. **No. of Company-Owned Units:** 65. **Founded:** 1911. **Equity Capital Needed:** Initial investment ranges from $50,000-$200,000 Canadian. **Franchise Fee:** $5,000 Canadian. **Training:** Yes. **Educational Activities:** GSF West.

1225 ■ Einstein Bros. Bagels
555 Zang St., Ste. 300
Lakewood, CO 80228
Free: 800-BAG-ELME
URL: http://www.einsteinbros.com
Facebook: www.facebook.com/einsteinbros
X (Twitter): x.com/EinsteinBros
Instagram: www.instagram.com/einsteinbros
YouTube: www.youtube.com/user/EinsteinBrosBGL
Description: Chain of restaurants. **Founded:** 1992. **Franchised:** 2006. **Training:** Solid corporate infrastructure at headquarters, complete training materials, R&D and local support.

1226 ■ Perfecto's Caffe
79 N Main St.
Andover, MA 01810
Ph: (978)749-7022
URL: http://www.perfectoscaffe.com
Contact: Max Gabriello, Contact
Description: Operator of coffee restaurant. **Founded:** 1993. **Training:** Yes.

Bait and Tackle Shop

ASSOCIATIONS AND OTHER ORGANIZATIONS

1227 ■ American Fly Fishing Trade Association (AFFTA)
PO Box 5285
 Chico, CA 95927
Ph: (406)200-8398
Co. E-mail: info@affta.org
URL: http://affta.org
Contact: Jim Bartschi, Chairman
Facebook: www.facebook.com/AFFTA
X (Twitter): x.com/AFFTA
Instagram: www.instagram.com/_affta_
Description: Manufacturers and retailers of fly-fishing equipment. Promotes increased participation in fly-fishing; and seeks to advance members' commercial and regulatory interests. Represents members before government agencies and industrial organizations. **Publications:** *AFFTA Connects* (Bimonthly). **Geographic Preference:** National.

1228 ■ American Sportfishing Association (ASA)
1001 N Fairfax St., Ste. 501
 Alexandria, VA 22314
Ph: (703)519-9691
Fax: (703)519-1872
Co. E-mail: info@asafishing.org
URL: http://www.asafishing.org
Contact: Glenn Hughes, President
E-mail: ghughes@asafishing.org
Facebook: www.facebook.com/ASAfishing
Linkedin: www.linkedin.com/in/the-american-sportfishing-association-bbaba688
X (Twitter): x.com/asafishing
Instagram: www.instagram.com/explore/locations/125186299856/the-american-sportfishing-association
YouTube: www.youtube.com/user/ASAFishing
Description: Works to ensure healthy and sustainable fisheries resources and increase sportfishing participation through education, conservation, promotion and marketing. **Founded:** 1933. **Publications:** *American Sportfishing*; *American Sportfishing Association--Show Guide* (Annual). **Educational Activities:** International Convention of Allied Sportfishing Trade (ICAST) (Annual). **Geographic Preference:** National.

1229 ■ International Game Fish Association (IGFA) - E.K. Harry Library of Fishes
300 Gulf Stream Way, 3rd Fl.
 Dania Beach, FL 33004
Ph: (954)927-2628
Fax: (954)924-4299
Co. E-mail: hq@igfa.org
URL: http://igfa.org
Contact: Jason Schratwieser, President
Facebook: www.facebook.com/TheIGFA
X (Twitter): x.com/TheIGFA
Instagram: www.instagram.com/igfa_official
YouTube: www.youtube.com/user/IGFAHQ
Description: Represents freshwater and saltwater anglers, angling clubs, and others. Promotes the study of game fishes. Keeps the sport of game fishing ethical. Encourages this sport both as recreation and as a potential source of scientific data and to make this data available to all interested individuals. Keeps an attested and current chart of world record catches. Promotes conservation of fisheries and resources. Compiles and maintains freshwater, saltwater, and fly rod records. **Scope:** Fishing-related postage stamps. **Services:** Library open to the public. **Founded:** 1939. **Holdings:** 15,000 Books; Films; Videos; Vintage photographs; Artworks and artefacts; Newsletters; Postage stamps. **Subscriptions:** magazines. **Publications:** *International Angler* (Quarterly). **Educational Activities:** Annual IGFA International Auction & Banquet (Annual). **Geographic Preference:** Multinational.

1230 ■ National Marine Manufacturers Association (NMMA)
231 S LaSalle St., Ste. 2050
 Chicago, IL 60604
Ph: (312)946-6200
URL: http://www.nmma.org
Contact: Frank Hugelmeyer, President
E-mail: fhugelmeyer@nmma.org
Facebook: www.facebook.com/thenmma
Linkedin: www.linkedin.com/company/nmma
X (Twitter): x.com/therealnmma
YouTube: www.youtube.com/thenmma
Description: Manufacturers of pleasure boats, marine engines, outboard motors, and boating products. Advocates for and promotes marine manufacturing and the boating lifestyle. Compiles statistics and provides specialized training for designers of yachts. **Founded:** 1979. **Publications:** *Recreational Boating Facilities Directory of Architects, Engineers, and Consultants* (Biennial); *Inter/Port* (Monthly); *NMMA Currents* (Daily). **Educational Activities:** DesignBUILD (Annual); belektro Berlin: Specialist Electrical Engineering Fair (Biennial); Kansas Agri Business Expo (Annual); Northwest Sportshow (Annual); Atlantic City Boat Show (Annual); The International Boatbuilders Exhibition & Conference (IBEX) (Annual); Marine Equipment Trade Show (METS) (Annual); Nashville Boat Sports Show (Annual); Progressive Tampa Boat Show (Annual); New Orleans Boat Show; Atlanta Boat Show (Annual); Miami International Boat Show (Annual); Toronto International Boat Show (Annual); St. Louis Boat Sports Show (Annual); Kansas City Boat Sportshow (Annual); Minneapolis Boat Show (Annual); Annual Los Angeles Boat Show (Annual); Progressive Insurance Strictly Sail Long Beach; National Marine Manufacturers Association Conference (Annual). **Geographic Preference:** National.

REFERENCE WORKS

1231 ■ "Convictions Under the Fisheries Act" in Marketwired (May 16, 2007)
Pub: Comtex News Network Inc.
Contact: Kan Devnani, President
Description: Fisheries and Oceans Canada is mandated to protect and conserve marine resources and thus released a list of fishers fined for various offences under the Fisheries Act in March and April. **Availability:** Print; Online.

1232 ■ "Fishbrain Launches In-App Fishing Tackle Shop" in Fishing Tackle Retailer (October 10, 2019)
URL(s): fishingtackleretailer.com/fishbrain-launches-in-app-fishing-tackle-shop/
Released: October 10, 2019. **Description:** The popular social networking site for anglers, Fishbrain, launched it's own in-app marketplace after partnering with Marketplacer. Various categories of merchandise is available for so that users can easily locate what they need to purchase. **Availability:** Print; Online.

TRADE PERIODICALS

1233 ■ *Fishing Tackle Retailer (FTR)*
Contact: Ken Duke, Managing Editor
URL(s): fishingtackleretailer.comespn.go.com/outdoors/bassmaster/about/news/story?page=bass_media_fishing_tackle_retailer
Released: 7/year **Price:** $85, for foreign; $9.95, for single copy. **Description:** Magazine for the fishing tackle industry. **Availability:** Print; Online.

TRADE SHOWS AND CONVENTIONS

1234 ■ Detroit Boat Show
Michigan Boating Industries Association (MBIA)
8625 Richardson Rd.
 Commerce Township, MI 48390
Ph: (734)261-0123
Fax: (734)261-0880
Co. E-mail: boatmichigan@mbia.org
URL: http://www.mbia.org
Contact: Nicki Polan, Executive Director
E-mail: npolan@mbia.org
URL(s): boatmichigan.org/detroit-boat-show/#detroit-exhibitor-list
Facebook: www.facebook.com/DetroitBoatShow
Price: $12, adults. **Frequency:** Annual. **Description:** Boats, fishing equipment, boat-related accessories, charter rentals, nautical attire, trailer and outboard motors, and personal watercraft. **Audience:** Boat enthusiasts and manufacturers. **Principal Exhibits:** Boats, fishing equipment, boat-related accessories, charter rentals, nautical attire, trailer and outboard motors, and personal watercraft. Dates and Locations: 2025 Jan Huntington Place, Detroit, MI. **Telecommunication Services:** boatmichigan@mbia.org.

LIBRARIES

1235 ■ International Game Fish Association (IGFA) - E.K. Harry Library of Fishes
300 Gulf Stream Way, 3rd Fl.
 Dania Beach, FL 33004

Ph: (954)927-2628
Fax: (954)924-4299
Co. E-mail: hq@igfa.org
URL: http://igfa.org
Contact: Jason Schratwieser, President
Facebook: www.facebook.com/TheIGFA
X (Twitter): x.com/TheIGFA
Instagram: www.instagram.com/igfa_official
YouTube: www.youtube.com/user/IGFAHQ
Description: Represents freshwater and saltwater anglers, angling clubs, and others. Promotes the study of game fishes. Keeps the sport of game fishing ethical. Encourages this sport both as recreation and as a potential source of scientific data and to make this data available to all interested individuals. Keeps an attested and current chart of world record catches. Promotes conservation of fisheries and resources. Compiles and maintains freshwater, saltwater, and fly rod records. **Scope:** Fishing-related postage stamps. **Services:** Library open to the public. **Founded:** 1939. **Holdings:** 15,000 Books; Films; Videos; Vintage photographs; Artworks and artefacts; Newsletters; Postage stamps. **Subscriptions:** magazines. **Publications:** *International Angler* (Quarterly). **Educational Activities:** Annual IGFA International Auction & Banquet (Annual). **Geographic Preference:** Multinational.

1236 ■ Virginia Institute of Marine Science (VIMS) - William J. Hargis, Jr. Library
1208 Greate Rd.
Gloucester Point, VA 23062
Ph: (804)684-7116
URL: http://www.vims.edu/library/index.php
Facebook: www.facebook.com/hargislibrary
Scope: Biology; ecology; oceanography; physical sciences. **Services:** Interlibrary loan. **Founded:** 1947. **Holdings:** Articles; e-journals; books; reports; journals.

Bakery/Doughnut Shop

START-UP INFORMATION

1237 ■ *How to Open a Financially Successful Bakery: With a Companion CD-ROM*
Pub: Atlantic Publishing Co.
Contact: Dr. Heather L. Johnson, Contact
Ed: Sharon Fullen, Douglas R. Brown. **Released:** Revised second edition. **Price:** $29.95. **Description:** Expert tips, tricks and information are offered to help start and run a bakery. **Availability:** CD-ROM; Print.

1238 ■ *"A Messy Job" in Washington Business Journal (Vol. 33, May 30, 2014, No. 6, pp. 6)*
Pub: American City Business Journals, Inc.
Contact: Mike Olivieri, Executive Vice President
Description: Mess Hall founder, Al Goldberg, shares his views on business incubators for culinary entrepreneurs in District of Columbia. Goldberg says he expects to accommodate up to 100 members in the space of the former warehouse turned culinary center for entrepreneurs wishing to start restaurants, bakeries or bars. **Availability:** Print; Online.

1239 ■ *My Life From Scratch: A Sweet Journey of Starting Over, One Cake at a Time*
Pub: Broadway Business
Ed: Gesine Bullock-Prado. **Released:** June 08, 2010.
Price: $15, paperback; $10.99, e-book. **Description:** Lively account of Old World recipes, Bullock-Prado, a former Hollywood film developer and sister to actress Sandra Bullock, recounts the joys and heartbreak of running her own patisserie in Montpelier, Vermont. Having fled Los Angeles with her husband, Ray for the simpler pleasures of a small town near the Green Mountains, she opened her own bake shop, Gesine Confectionary in 2004, mostly on the fame of the macaroons she refashioned from her German mother's favorite almond treat, mandelhoernchen (and the casual mention of her sister in an interview). Her memoir follows one day in a busy baker's life, from waking at 3 a.m. to prepare the batter and bake her croissants, scones, and sticky buns, before opening her shop at 7 a.m., through the hectic lunch, and 3 p.m. tea time. **Availability:** E-book; Print.

ASSOCIATIONS AND OTHER ORGANIZATIONS

1240 ■ **AIB International**
1213 Bakers Way
 Manhattan, KS 66505-3999
Ph: (785)537-4750
Free: 800-633-5137
Fax: (785)537-1493
Co. E-mail: info@aibonline.org
URL: http://www.aibinternational.com
Contact: Dan Martin, President
Facebook: www.facebook.com/AIBInternational
Linkedin: www.linkedin.com/company/aib-international-inc
X (Twitter): x.com/AIBIntl
Description: Baking research and educational center. Conducts basic and applied research, educational and hands-on training, and in-plant sanitation and worker safety audits. Provides bibliographic and reference service. Serves as registrar for ISO-9000 quality certification. **Scope:** Offers consulting services in the fields of applied research and product development, food bakery plant equipment and engineering, food defense/security, food product nutritional labeling, bakery product nutrition, food safety audits, and general bakery production consultation. Also provides education, research, product development, technical assistance and management services to domestic and international food related industries. **Founded:** 1919. **Publications:** A technology and information transfer center for bakers and food processors. **Training:** Principles of Inspecting and Auditing Food Plants, Atlanta, Nov, 2009; Reportable Food Registry - An Executive Briefing and Discussion, Nov, 2009; Maintenance Management for Food Plants. **Awards:** Baking Science and Technology Resident Course (Annual). **Geographic Preference:** National.

1241 ■ **American Bakers Association (ABA)**
601 Pennsylvania Ave. NW, Ste. 230
 Washington, DC 20004
Ph: (202)789-0300
Fax: (202)898-1164
Co. E-mail: info@americanbakers.org
URL: http://americanbakers.org
Contact: Robb MacKie, President
Facebook: www.facebook.com/americanbakersassoc
Linkedin: www.linkedin.com/company/americanbakers
X (Twitter): x.com/AmericanBakers
Instagram: www.instagram.com/americanbakers
YouTube: www.youtube.com/user/americanbakers
Description: Manufacturers and wholesale distributors of bread, rolls, and pastry products; suppliers of goods and services to bakers. Conducts seminars and expositions. **Founded:** 1897. **Awards:** B&CMA Chairman's Award for Safety Excellence (Annual). **Geographic Preference:** National.

1242 ■ **American Society of Baking (ASB)**
7809 N Chestnut Ave.
 Kansas City, MO 64119
Free: 800-713-0462
Co. E-mail: info@asbe.org
URL: http://www.asbe.org
Contact: Kent van Amburg, Executive Director
E-mail: kvanamburg@asbe.org
Facebook: www.facebook.com/amsocbaking
X (Twitter): x.com/amsocbaking
Instagram: www.instagram.com/americansocietyofbaking
YouTube: www.youtube.com/channel/UC8DMICWyws1tR4DEdci5rxQ
Description: Professional organization of persons engaged in bakery production; chemists, production supervisors, engineers, technicians, and others from allied fields. Maintains information service and library references to baking and related subjects. **Founded:** 1924. **Publications:** *American Society of Baking Proceedings* (Annual). **Educational Activities:** BakingTECH (Annual). **Geographic Preference:** National.

1243 ■ **Baking Association of Canada (BAC) [Association Canadienne de la Boulangerie]**
4-2380 Wyecroft Rd.
 Oakville, ON, Canada L6L 6W1
Ph: (905)405-0288
Free: 888-674-2253
Co. E-mail: info@baking.ca
URL: http://baking.ca
Contact: Martin Barnett, Executive Director
E-mail: mbarnett@baking.ca
Description: Bakeries. Promotes growth and development of the domestic baking industries. Represents the interests of bakers (retail, wholesale, in-store, food service) before industrial and labor organizations, government agencies, and the public. **Founded:** 1997. **Publications:** *The Bulletin* (10/year). **Educational Activities:** Bakery Showcase (Annual). **Geographic Preference:** National.

1244 ■ **Independent Bakers Association (IBA)**
529 14th St. NW, Ste. 1112A
 Washington, DC 20045
Ph: (202)333-8190
URL: http://www.ibabaker.com
Contact: Nicholas Pyle, President
E-mail: nick@ibabaker.com
X (Twitter): x.com/indeptbakers
Description: Trade association representing small-medium wholesale bakers and allied trade members. Represents independent wholesale bakers on federal legislative and regulatory issues. Offers annual Smith-Schaus-Smith internships. **Founded:** 1968. **Publications:** *The Independent* (Annual); *News Release* (Biweekly). **Educational Activities:** Independent Bakers Association Fall Membership Meeting (Annual). **Geographic Preference:** National.

1245 ■ **Retail Bakers of America (RBA)**
15941 Harlem Ave., No. 347
 Tinley Park, IL 60477
Free: 800-638-0924
Co. E-mail: info@retailbakersofamerica.org
URL: http://www.retailbakersofamerica.org
Contact: Scott Calvert, President
Facebook: www.facebook.com/retailbakersofamerica
X (Twitter): x.com/RetailBakers
Description: Independent and in-store bakeries, food service, specialty bakeries, suppliers of ingredients, tools and equipment; other. Provides information, management, production, merchandising and small business services. **Founded:** 1918. **Publications:** *The Business Owner* (Bimonthly). **Educational Activities:** The Retailer's Bakery Association Marketplace (Annual). **Geographic Preference:** National.

REFERENCE WORKS

1246 ■ *"Bakeries Turn to Automation to Tackle Warehouse Woes" in BakingBusiness.com (November 18, 2021)*
Ed: Dan Malovany. **Released:** November 18, 2021.
Description: The COVID-19 pandemic has caused a

labor shortage in the baking business and in order to compensate, bakeries are now implementing some automation solutions to help with production issues. **Availability:** Online.

1247 ■ *"Blue Hill Tavern to Host Baltimore's First Cupcake Camp"* in *Daily Record* (August 10, 2011)
Pub: BridgeTower Media
Contact: Adam Reinebach, President

Ed: Rachel Bernstein. **Description:** Cities joining the trend to host cupcake camps are listed. The camps are open to all individuals wishing to share and eat cupcakes in an open environment.

1248 ■ *"Canada's Largest Bakery Officially Opened Today"* in *Ecology,Environment & Conservation Business* (October 15, 2011, pp. 7)

Description: Maple Leaf Foods opened Canada's largest commercial bakery in Hamilton, Ontario. The firm's 385,000 square foot Trillium bakery benefits from efficient design flow and best-in-class technologies. **Availability:** Print; Online.

1249 ■ *"Cold Stone Creamery Offers New Eight-Layer Ice Cream Cakes"* in *Ice Cream Reporter* (Vol. 23, October 20, 2010, No. 11, pp. 2)

Description: Cold Stone Creamery is introducing a new line of eight-layer ice cream cakes, which are crafted with three layers of ice cream, three layers of cake and two mid-layers of mix-ins and finished with frosting and a creative design. **Availability:** Print; Online.

1250 ■ *"Corner Bakery Readies Its Recipes for Growth"* in *Dallas Business Journal* (Vol. 35, February 17, 2012, No. 23, pp. 1)
Pub: Baltimore Business Journal
Contact: Rhonda Pringle, President
E-mail: rpringle@bizjournals.com

Description: Corner Bakery Cafe is planning to add 10 corporate locations and 15-20 franchise locations in 2012. The company was acquired by Roark Capital. **Availability:** Print; Online.

1251 ■ *"Cupcake Maker Explains Tricks of the Trade"* in *Chattanooga Times/Free Press* (September 6, 2011)
Pub: Chattanooga Publishing Company Inc.

Ed: Holly Leber. **Description:** Sunny Burden, head baker at Whipped Cupcakes in Chattanooga, Tennessee creates themed cupcakes as well as traditional ones. Burden finds baking therapeutic. **Availability:** Online.

1252 ■ *"Dunkin' Donuts Franchise Looking Possible for 2011"* in *Messenger-Inquirer* (January 2, 2010)

Description: Dunkin' Donuts has approved expansion of their franchises in the Owensboro, Kentucky region.

1253 ■ *"Entenmann's Brings Back Classic Packaging after Rampant Customer Complaints"* in *Small Business Trends* (March 12, 2023)
URL(s): smallbiztrends.com/2023/03/entenmanns-brings-back-classic-packaging.html

Ed: Joshua Sophy. **Released:** March 12, 2023. **Description:** After receiving negative feedback about their new windowless packaging, Entenmann's has reverted back to their classic design so consumers can see the products before making a purchase. **Availability:** Online.

1254 ■ *"Evolution of the Cookie"* in *Women in Business* (Vol. 65, Winter 2013, No. 3, pp. 10)

Description: The history of the cookie is presented and its background as a festive food item is presented in view of its role in human celebrations. The cookie continues to play a role in bringing family and friends together and helps strengthen bonds that support a common identity among groups of people. **Availability:** Print; Online.

1255 ■ *"Hostess Names $10,000 Grand Prize Winner of its 'CupCake Jackpot' Promotion"* in *Entertainment Close-Up* (August 19, 2011)
Pub: Close-Up Media Inc.
Contact: Caroline S. Moore, President
E-mail: cms@closeupmedia.com

Description: Tricia Botbyl was the grand prize winner of the Hostess 'CupCake Jackpot' promotion that asked consumers to 'spin' online to win $10,000. Consumers were asked to vote for their favorite Hostess Brand cupcake flavor. **Availability:** Online.

1256 ■ *"How I... Operate a Food Truck on the Streets of Honolulu"* in *Pacific Business News* (Vol. 21, July 18, 2014, No. 21, pp. 19)
Pub: American City Business Journals, Inc.
Contact: Mike Olivieri, Executive Vice President

Released: Weekly. **Price:** $4, Introductory 4-week offer(Digital only). **Description:** Jennifer Hino, co-owner of The Girls Who Bake Next Door, believes that social media is important as it helps create and reach a wider customer base for her business, which she runs out of a food truck in Honolulu. She also posts photos on the site, which helps reinforce her brand. **Availability:** Print; Online.

1257 ■ *"It's Good To Be King"* in *South Florida Business Journal* (Vol. 35, August 29, 2014, No. 5, pp. 12)

Released: December 01, 2013. **Description:** The $11.4 billion deal that will create a new holding company for Burger King Worldwide and Tim Hortons will be based in Oakville, Ontario, Canada and was met with public outrage. Burger King declares that the merger with the Canadian coffee and doughnut franchise chain was about global growth, not a strategy to avoid millions of dollars in corporate income tax payments to the U.S. government. **Availability:** Print; Online.

1258 ■ *"Katie's Cupcakes to Celebrate One-Year Anniversary"* in *Bellingham Business Journal* (Vol. March 2010, pp. 3)
Pub: Sound Publishing Inc.
Contact: Josh O'Connor, President

Ed: Lance Henderson. **Description:** Katie Swanson, owner of Katie's Cupcakes, celebrated her firm's one-year anniversary with a fundraiser for the Whatcom Humane Society by offering free specialty cupcakes and other special events to the public. The specialty cupcakes will feature either a paw or bone and will be available throughout the month of March.

1259 ■ *"Lux Coffees, Breads Push Chains to React"* in *Advertising Age* (Vol. 77, June 26, 2006, No. 26, pp. S14)
Pub: Crain Communications, Inc.
Contact: Jessica Botos, Manager, Marketing
E-mail: jessica.botos@crainsnewyork.com

Ed: Kate MacArthur. **Description:** Fast-food giants such as McDonald's, Burger King, Dunkin' Donuts and Subway have adjusted their menus in order to become more competitive with gourmet coffee shops and bakeries like Panera Bread and Starbucks which have taken a large share in the market. Statistical data included. **Availability:** Online.

1260 ■ *"New Zealand Natural Co-Branding with Mrs. Fields"* in *Ice Cream Reporter* (Vol. 23, November 20, 2010, No. 12, pp. 2)

Description: Mrs. Fields has partnered with a New Zealand firm to co-brand ice cream and cookies in Australian markets. **Availability:** Print; Online.

1261 ■ *"Nothing Says Celebration Like Cake"* in *BakingBusiness.com* (November 18, 2021)
URL(s): www.bakingbusiness.com/articles/55168-nothing-says-celebration-like-cake

Ed: Michelle Smith. **Released:** November 18, 2021. **Description:** Discusses cakes and snack cakes sales in the US. **Availability:** Online.

1262 ■ *"One of Dallas' Best Bread Geniuses Announces Plans for a New Storefront Bakery"* in *The Dallas Morning News* (July 5, 2019)
URL(s): www.dallasnews.com/food/cooking/2019/07/05/one-of-dallas-best-bread-geniuses-announces-plans-for-a-new-storefront-bakery/

Ed: Tina Danzel. **Released:** July 05, 2019. **Description:** A popular staple at the Saint Michael's Farmers Market, Bresnan Bread and Pastry, is obtaining a permanent retail space for its customers. **Availability:** Print; Online.

1263 ■ *"Panera Breadwinner Tries on Tattu Designer Jeans"* in *Houston Business Journal* (Vol. 40, December 18, 2009, No. 32, pp. 1)
Pub: Houston Business Journal
Contact: Bob Charlet, President
E-mail: bcharlet@bizjournals.com

Ed: Allison Wollam. **Description:** Chuck Cain, the franchisee who introduced Panera Bread to Houston, Texas has partnered with tax accountant Jim Jacobsen to introduce custom-make Tattu Jeans. As more Tattu Jeans outlets are being planned, Cain is using entrepreneurial lessons learned from Panera Bread in the new venture. Both Panera Bread and Tattu Jeans were opened by Cain during economic downturns. **Availability:** Print; Online.

1264 ■ *"Panera Opens First Next-Generation Bakery-Cafe"* in *BakingBusiness.com* (November 18.2021)
URL(s): www.bakingbusiness.com/articles/55172-panera-opens-first-next-generation-bakery-cafe

Ed: Jeff Gelski. **Released:** November 18, 2021. **Description:** Featuring a new double lane drive-thru and digital-ordering options, a new Panera in Ballwin, MO opened. A new brand logo is also in play and baking ovens are in full view of customers. **Availability:** Online.

1265 ■ *"Red Light's Green Light"* in *Washington Business Journal* (Vol. 32, April 11, 2014, No. 52, pp. 6)
Pub: American City Business Journals, Inc.
Contact: Mike Olivieri, Executive Vice President

Released: Weekly. **Price:** $4, introductory 4-week offer(Digital & Print). **Description:** Restaurateur, Aaron Gordon, is opening his dessert and cocktail bar called Red Light in Washington DC on April 10, 2014. Gorden envisions Red Light as a destination and a before- or after-dinner stop for patrons wanting drinks and dessert along the hottest dining corridor of the city. Specialty drinks and baked goods are described. **Availability:** Print; Online.

1266 ■ *"Red Velvet Cupcake Bites"* in *CandyIndustry* (Vol. 176, September 2011, No. 9, pp. RC4)
Pub: BNP Media
Contact: Harper Henderson, Owner Co-Chief Executive Officer

Description: Taste of Nature's Cookie Dough Bites has launched a new candy called, Red Velvet Cupcake Bites. The new product will feature a cupcake center covered in red frosting; ingredients are listed.

1267 ■ *"The South Looks Yummy to Tastykakes"* in *Philadelphia Business Journal* (Vol. 31, March 30, 2012, No. 7, pp. 1)
Pub: Baltimore Business Journal
Contact: Rhonda Pringle, President
E-mail: rpringle@bizjournals.com

Description: Tasty Baking Company owner, Flowers Foods, is planning to increase the number of stores selling Tastykake. Sales of Tastykake is expected to grow to as much as $225 million. **Availability:** Print; Online.

1268 ■ *"Two Local Bakers Winners of TV's 'Cupcake Wars"* in *Toledo Blade* (July 6, 2011)

Description: Winners of cable network Food Channel's Cupcake Wars, Lori Jacobs and Dana Iliev own Cake in a Cup in Toledo, Ohio. The partners shop features creative cupcakes with names such as Monkey Business, Pretty in Pink, and Tropical Getaway. **Availability:** Print; Online.

Small Business Profiles • Bakery/Doughnut Shop ■ 1287

1269 ■ *"The Ultimate Vending Machine"* in Benzinga.com (August 15, 2011)
Pub: Benzinga.com
Contact: Jason Raznick, Founder

Ed: Louis Bedigian. **Description:** Louis Hecht, a baker from Hombourg-Haut, France is selling fresh-baked bread in vending machines. Each machine holds 90 pre-cooked loaves which are warmed before being delivered to the customer. **Availability:** Online.

1270 ■ *"US Firm The Bakery Companies Gets Fresh Investment"* in Just-Food (October 9, 2019)
URL(s): just-food.com/news/us-firm-the-bakery-companies-gets-fresh-investment_id142378.aspx

Ed: Dean Best. **Released:** October 09, 2019. **Description:** Private-equity firm Arbor Investments is now investing in The Bakery Companies, which is a supplier of fresh and frozen baked goods. **Availability:** Online.

1271 ■ *"Want to Open A Bakery? Keep These Expert Tips in Mind"* in Entrepreneur (September 8, 2016)
URL(s): www.entrepreneur.com/article/281005

Ed: Ashlea Halpern. **Released:** September 08, 2016. **Description:** Practical tips from experts in the industry on what to expect when opening a bakery. Obtaining a license, renting space, and some tricks of the trade are discussed. Also included is a state-by-state guide on the average salary a baker makes in each state. **Availability:** Print; Online.

1272 ■ *"Wolferman's Bakery Introduces New Brand Positioning"* in Snack Food & Wholesale Bakery Magazine (October 3, 2019)
URL(s): www.snackandbakery.com/articles/93542-wolfermans-bakery-introduces-new-brand-positioning

Released: October 03, 2019. **Description:** Wolferman's is introducing a new brand positioning to help consumers be aware they sell more than just English Muffins. They have a full online bakery, which complements it's partnership with Harry & David and 1-800-FLOWERS.COM Inc. **Availability:** Print; Online.

1273 ■ *"Woof Gang Bakery & Grooming Claws Through Recession"* in Orlando Business Journal (Vol. 29, July 6, 2012, No. 3, pp. 1)
Pub: Baltimore Business Journal
Contact: Rhonda Pringle, President
E-mail: rpringle@bizjournals.com

Ed: Anjali Fluker. **Description:** Woof Gang Bakery and Grooming has reported increased sales des;pite the economic crisis. The company is set to open its 30th store by the end of 2012. **Availability:** Print; Online.

STATISTICAL SOURCES

1274 ■ Coffee & Snack Shops Industry in the US - Market Research Report
URL(s): www.ibisworld.com/united-states/market-research-reports/coffee-snack-shops-industry/

Price: $925. **Description:** Downloadable report analyzing the coffee and snack shop industry and projecting growth through the year 2026. Delivers key concepts and industry outlooks. **Availability:** Download.

1275 ■ RMA Annual Statement Studies
Pub: Risk Management Association
Contact: Nancy Foster, President

Released: Annual. **Description:** Contains composite balance sheets and income statements for more than 360 industries, including the accounting, auditing, and bookkeeping industries. Also contains five years of comparative historical data for discerning trends. Includes 16 commonly used ratios, computed for most of the size groupings for nearly every industry.

TRADE PERIODICALS

1276 ■ Baking & Snack
Pub: Sosland Publishing Co.
Contact: Joshua Sosland, President
URL(s): www.bakingbusiness.com
Facebook: www.facebook.com/BakingandSnack
Linkedin: www.linkedin.com/showcase/baking&snack-magazine
X (Twitter): x.com/BakingSnackMag
Instagram: www.instagram.com/bakingandsnack

Ed: Dan Malovany. **Released:** Monthly **Description:** Equipment, engineering, production and formulating magazine for commercial manufacturers of baked and snack foods. **Availability:** Print; PDF; Online.

1277 ■ Milling & Baking News
Pub: Sosland Publishing Co.
Contact: Joshua Sosland, President
URL(s): www.bakingbusiness.comwww.sosland.com/milling-baking-news
Facebook: www.facebook.com/MillingandBakingNews
Linkedin: www.linkedin.com/showcase/milling-&-baking-news

Ed: Joshua L. Sosland. **Released:** Weekly (Thurs.) **Description:** Trade magazine covering the grain-based food industries. **Availability:** Print; Online.

VIDEO/AUDIO MEDIA

1278 ■ The How of Business: Candace Nelson - Sweet Success
URL(s): www.thehowofbusiness.com/447-candace-nelson-sweet-success

Ed: Henry Lopez. **Released:** November 07, 2022. **Description:** Podcast offers a conversation with Candace Nelson, founder of the Sprinkles cupcake bakery.

1279 ■ How I Built This: Tate's Bake Shop: Kathleen King
URL(s): www.npr.org/2021/12/15/1064659311/tates-bake-shop-kathleen-king-2019

Ed: Guy Raz. **Released:** December 27, 2021. **Description:** Podcast reflects on starting--and re-starting--a cookie brand.

1280 ■ How I Built This: The Cronut and Dominique Ansel Bakery
URL(s): wondery.com/shows/how-i-built-this/episode/10386-the-cronut-and-dominique-ansel-bakery-dominique-ansel

Ed: Guy Raz. **Released:** June 17, 2024. **Description:** Podcast offers a conversation with the founder of the Cronut who found an entrepreneurial sweet spot with both brick-and-mortar locations and a ail-order business.

1281 ■ Main Street Business Insights: Nicole Fleetwood and McKinzie Hodges, Scratch Made Bakery
URL(s): mainstreet.org/resources/knowledge-hub/podcast/nicole-fleetwood-and-mckinzie-hodges-scratch-made-bakery

Ed: Matt Wagner. **Released:** March 21, 2024. **Description:** Podcast features a conversation with the co-owners of a bakery, in which they discuss their path to entrepreneurship, supporting each other, and navigating change.

1282 ■ Marketplace: Time Again for Home-Based Utah Baker to "Fly the Coop" for a Commercial Space
URL(s): www.marketplace.org/2023/07/24/utah-baker-is-opening-commercial-kitchen-after-9-years-working-at-home

Ed: Andie Corban. **Released:** July 24, 2023. **Description:** Podcast discusses how a home-based baker decide to rent commerical space,.

TRADE SHOWS AND CONVENTIONS

1283 ■ IDDBA Show
International Dairy-Deli-Bakery Association (IDDBA)
8317 Elderberry Rd.
Madison, WI 53717-2603
Ph: (608)310-5000
Fax: (608)238-6330
Co. E-mail: iddba@iddba.org
URL: http://www.iddba.org
Contact: Mike Eardley, President
URL(s): www.iddba.org/iddba-show/about/iddba-2025

Frequency: Annual. **Description:** Topics include those related to the food industry. Event contains speakers, exhibitions, workshops, and entertainment. **Audience:** Buyers, bakers, merchandisers, and executives who have a shared passion for food and the industry. **Principal Exhibits:** Topics include those related to the food industry. Event contains speakers, exhibitions, workshops, and entertainment. Dates and Locations: 2025 Jun 01-3 Ernest N. Morial Convention Center, New Orleans, LA. **Telecommunication Services:** wisl@iddba.org.

1284 ■ International Artisan Bakery Expo
Frequency: Annual. **Description:** Includes educational sessions and demonstrations plus an expo with new products, equipment, and service. **Principal Exhibits:** Includes educational sessions and demonstrations plus an expo with new products, equipment, and service.

1285 ■ Sweets & Snacks Expo
National Confectioners Association (NCA)
1101 30th St. NW, Ste. 200
Washington, DC 20007
Ph: (202)534-1440
Co. E-mail: info@candyusa.com
URL: http://candyusa.com
Contact: John H. Downs, President
E-mail: john.downs@candyusa.com
URL(s): sweetsandsnacks.com
Facebook: www.facebook.com/SWEETSandSNACKS

Frequency: Annual. **Description:** Showcases new products in the sweets and snacks industry. **Audience:** Buyers, merchandisers, operations managers, executives and store owners from supermarkets, convenience stores, warehouse clubs, mass and dollar merchants, drug stores, vending, wholesalers, theaters, specialty and department stores, confectionery and snack professionals. **Principal Exhibits:** Showcases new products in the sweets and snacks industry. Dates and Locations: 2025 May 13-15 Indiana Convention Center, Indianapolis, IN; 2026 May 19-21 Las Vegas Convention Center, Las Vegas, NV; 2027 May 18-20 Indiana Convention Center, Indianapolis, IN; 2028 May 16-18 Indiana Convention Center, Indianapolis, IN; 2029 May 15-17 Las Vegas Convention Center, Las Vegas, NV; 2030 May 14-16 Indiana Convention Center, Indianapolis, IN; 2031 May 13-15 Indiana Convention Center, Indianapolis, IN; 2032 May 18-20 Las Vegas Convention Center, Las Vegas, NV. **Telecommunication Services:** attendeehelp@sweetsandsnacks.com.

1286 ■ Tortilla Industry Association Convention & Trade Exposition
URL(s): www.tortilla-info.com

Frequency: Annual. **Description:** Networking and education for bakers who would like to learn more about tortillas. Product booths are also featured. **Principal Exhibits:** Networking and education for bakers who would like to learn more about tortillas. Product booths are also featured.

FRANCHISES AND BUSINESS OPPORTUNITIES

1287 ■ Atlanta Bread Company International
4490 S Cobb Dr. SE
Smyrna, GA 30080
Ph: (770)438-6800
Co. E-mail: abc@atlantabread.com

URL: http://atlantabread.com
Facebook: www.facebook.com/atlantabreadco
X (Twitter): x.com/atlantabread
Instagram: www.instagram.com/atlantabread
Description: Producer of sandwiches, salads, soups and pastries. **Founded:** 1993. **Training:** Sandwich cafe in Atlanta.

1288 ■ Blue Chip Cookies
5045 W 117th St.
Leawood, KS 66211
Ph: (913)663-1163
Co. E-mail: orders@bluechipcookies.com
URL: http://www.bluechipcookiesdirect.com
Facebook: www.facebook.com/BlueChipCookiesDirect
X (Twitter): x.com/bluechipcookies
Description: Cookies, bakery items, ice cream, coffees, depending on model and site. **No. of Franchise Units:** 5. **No. of Company-Owned Units:** 3. **Founded:** 1983. **Franchised:** 1986. **Equity Capital Needed:** $150,000-$250,000. **Franchise Fee:** $25,000. **Training:** Offers 2 weeks of training.

1289 ■ Bojangles', Inc. [Bojangles' Famous Chicken 'n Biscuits]
9432 S Pine Blvd.
Charlotte, NC 28273
Ph: (704)527-2675
Co. E-mail: copyright@bojangles.com
URL: http://www.bojangles.com
Contact: Brian Unger, Chief Operating Officer
Facebook: www.facebook.com/Bojangles
X (Twitter): x.com/bojangles
Instagram: www.instagram.com/bojangles
YouTube: www.youtube.com/ItsBoTime
Description: Chain of fast food restaurants serving chicken and biscuits. **Founded:** 1977. **Franchise Fee:** $25,000. **Managerial Assistance:** Ongoing training, marketing and Operations is part of the franchise support. **Training:** Offers an 5 week training program at as well as a one week training program at Bojangles University.

1290 ■ Breadsmith
409 E Silver Spring Dr.
Whitefish Bay, WI 53217
Ph: (414)962-1965
URL: http://www.breadsmith.com
Description: Producer of artisan breads and sweets. **Founded:** 1993. **Equity Capital Needed:** $354,250 – 399,900. **Royalty Fee:** 7% – 5%. **Training:** Yes.

1291 ■ Cinnzeo
4280 23rd St., NE
Calgary, AB, Canada T2E 8G8
Ph: (403)255-4556
Fax: (403)259-5124
Co. E-mail: info@cinnzeo.com
URL: http://cinnzeo.com
Facebook: www.facebook.com/Cinnzeo
Linkedin: www.linkedin.com/company/cinnzeo
X (Twitter): x.com/cinnzeo
Instagram: www.instagram.com/cinnzeobakerycafe
Description: Quick service cinnamon roll bakery. **No. of Franchise Units:** 20. **No. of Company-Owned Units:** 4. **Founded:** 1987. **Franchised:** 1998. **Equity Capital Needed:** $214,00-$621,000. **Franchise Fee:** $15,000. **Royalty Fee:** 7%. **Training:** Offers 3 weeks at headquarters, 2 weeks at franchise's location with ongoing support.

1292 ■ Coffee Time Donuts Inc.
2195 Midland Ave.
Scarborough, ON, Canada M1P 3E7
Ph: (647)351-8463
URL: http://coffeetime.com
Description: Chain of coffee shops. **Founded:** 1982. **Training:** Yes.

1293 ■ Fuddruckers Inc. [Luby's Fuddruckers Restaurants, LLC]
415 W Slaughter Ln.
Austin, TX 78748
Ph: (512)590-7540
Co. E-mail: comments@fuddruckers.com
URL: http://www.fuddruckers.com

Facebook: www.facebook.com/fuddruckers
X (Twitter): x.com/fuddruckers
Instagram: www.instagram.com/fuddruckers
Description: A franchised restaurant chain specializing in hamburgers. **Founded:** 1980. **Financial Assistance:** Yes

1294 ■ Great Harvest Franchising Inc.
28 S Montana St.
Dillon, MT 59725
Ph: (406)683-6842
Free: 800-442-0424
URL: http://www.greatharvest.com
Contact: Eric Keshin, President
Facebook: www.facebook.com/GreatHarvestBreadCo
Linkedin: www.linkedin.com/company/great-harvest-bread-co.
X (Twitter): x.com/GreatHarvest
Instagram: www.instagram.com/greatharvest
Description: Retail premium bread bakeries, specializing in whole wheat products. **Founded:** 1976. **Franchised:** 1978. **Equity Capital Needed:** $192,411- $482,776. **Franchise Fee:** $38,000. **Royalty Fee:** 7% gross sales. **Financial Assistance:** No **Training:** Yes.

1295 ■ House of Bread, Inc.
299 Marsh St.
San Luis Obispo, CA 93401
Ph: (805)542-0255
Co. E-mail: bread@houseofbread.com
URL: http://www.houseofbread.com
Contact: Sheila McCann, Founder Owner
Facebook: www.facebook.com/HOBBakeryCafe
Linkedin: www.linkedin.com/company/house-of-bread
Instagram: www.instagram.com/house_of_bread
YouTube: www.youtube.com/channel/UCXH5NgT8vpnAuSuZN5AxEQQ
Description: Specialty bread bakery. **Founded:** 1996. **Franchised:** 2000. **Equity Capital Needed:** $125,000. **Franchise Fee:** $35,000. **Royalty Fee:** 0.06. **Financial Assistance:** No **Training:** Offers 3 weeks of hands-on training and ongoing support.

1296 ■ Insomnia Cookies Franchising, LLC - 14th Street New York City
304 W 14th St.
New York, NY 10014
Ph: (646)762-9313
Co. E-mail: customerservice@insomniacookies.com
URL: http://insomniacookies.com
Facebook: www.facebook.com/insomniacookies
X (Twitter): twitter.com/insomniacookies
Instagram: www.instagram.com/insomniacookies
Description: Chain of cookies shops. **No. of Company-Owned Units:** 14. **Founded:** 2003. **Franchised:** 2006. **Equity Capital Needed:** $65,600-$111,400. **Franchise Fee:** $25,000. **Royalty Fee:** 6%. **Training:** Offer 2-3 weeks training at headquarters, 2-3 weeks at franchisee's location, at other franchisee/corporate locations as needed and ongoing support.

1297 ■ Joe To Go Coffee [Groundwork Coffee Co]
1501 N Cahuenga Blvd.
Hollywood, CA 90028
Ph: (818)762-9189
Co. E-mail: customerservice@groundworkcoffee.com
Facebook: www.facebook.com/joetogocoffee
Description: Producer and distributor of coffee roster. **Founded:** 1995. **Franchised:** 2001. **Financial Assistance:** Yes **Training:** Provides 1 week at headquarters, 1 week at franchisee's location, 1 week at a corporate store and ongoing support.

1298 ■ Kolache Factory Inc. (KF)
23240 Westheimer Pky., Ste. C
Katy, TX 77494
Ph: (281)347-2253
Co. E-mail: shipping@kolachefactory.com
URL: http://kolachefactory.com
Contact: Jerri Banks, Co-Founder
X (Twitter): x.com/kolachefactory
Pinterest: www.pinterest.com/kolachefactory

Description: Producer and retailer of traditional pastries such as cinnamon rolls, croissants, strudel. **Founded:** 1982.

1299 ■ Lamar's Donuts
Donut Holdings, Inc.
3600 S Yosemite St., Ste. 750
Denver, CO 80237
Ph: (402)420-0203
Free: 800-533-7489
Fax: (402)420-0209
Contact: Ray LaMar, Contact
Facebook: www.facebook.com/LaMarsDonuts
X (Twitter): x.com/LamarsDonuts
Description: Donuts, specialties and gourmet coffee. **No. of Franchise Units:** 28. **No. of Company-Owned Units:** 4. **Founded:** 1933. **Franchised:** 1993. **Equity Capital Needed:** $290,000-$390,000. **Franchise Fee:** $28,500. **Training:** Yes.

1300 ■ Michel's Bakery Cafe
55 Administration Rd., Ste. 37
Vaughan, ON, Canada L4K 4G9
Ph: (905)482-7300
Free: 855-869-3217
URL: http://michelsbakerycafe.com
Description: Retailer of sandwiches, salads, baked breads and pastries. **Training:** Provides 3 week training program.

1301 ■ Mrs. Fields' Original Cookies, Inc. [Taste of Nature, Inc.]
8001 Arista Pl., Ste. 600
Broomfield, CO 80021
Co. E-mail: support@mrsfields.com
Facebook: www.facebook.com/mrsfieldscookies
X (Twitter): x.com/mrsfields
Pinterest: www.pinterest.com/mrsfields
Description: Fresh baked cookies and more. **Founded:** 1977. **Training:** Yes.

1302 ■ PJ's Coffee of New Orleans
4480 LA 22, Ste. 2
Mandeville, LA 70471
Ph: (985)792-7999
Co. E-mail: info@pjscoffee.com
URL: http://www.pjscoffee.com
Contact: David Mesa, Chief Development Officer
Facebook: www.facebook.com/pjscoffee
X (Twitter): x.com/pjscoffee
Instagram: www.instagram.com/pjscoffee
Pinterest: www.pinterest.com/pjscoffee
Description: Chain of retail coffee houses. **Founded:** 1978. **Training:** Raving Brands University classroom and onsite training provided. From register operation to food preparation, from hiring staff to accounting procedures, you'll improve your management skills, setup your back office and develop an airtight sales and marketing plan.

1303 ■ Robin's Donuts
77 Progress Ave.
Toronto, ON, Canada M1P 2Y7
Co. E-mail: social@robinsdonuts.com
URL: http://robinsdonuts.com
Facebook: www.facebook.com/RobinsDonutsCAN
Linkedin: www.linkedin.com/company/robinsdonuts
X (Twitter): x.com/RobinsDonutsCAN
Description: Chain of fast food restaurants. **Founded:** 1975. **Franchised:** 1975. **Equity Capital Needed:** $365,000-$405,000. **Franchise Fee:** $25,000. **Royalty Fee:** 5% of gross sales. **Training:** Yes.

1304 ■ Southern Maid Donuts
3615 Cavalier Dr.
Garland, TX 75042-7504
Contact: Les Franklin, President
Description: Makes and sells donuts, muffins and other delectable items, as well as coffee, juices and soda drinks. **Founded:** 1937. **Training:** Yes.

LIBRARIES

1305 ■ Food Institute (FI)
330 Changebridge Rd., Ste. 101
Pine Brook, NJ 07058

Ph: (201)791-5570
Free: 855-791-5570
Co. E-mail: questions@foodinstitute.com
URL: http://www.foodinstitute.com
Contact: Anika Wilson, Contact
E-mail: anika.wilson@foodinstitute.com
Facebook: www.facebook.com/foodinstitutenj
Linkedin: www.linkedin.com/company/the-food-institute
X (Twitter): x.com/FoodInstitute
Instagram: www.instagram.com/foodinstitute
YouTube: www.youtube.com/channel/UCYAPI0TXNtJa04aQre4h4pA
Description: Strives to provide food industry-related information to its members. **Scope:** The food industry. **Services:** Center open to the public on fee basis. **Founded:** 1928. **Holdings:** Figures not available. **Publications:** *Today in Food*; *Get It Out, Get It Right, Get It Over! Avoiding Food Product Recalls*; *The Food Institute* (Weekly); *Almanac of the Canning, Freezing, Preserving Industries* (Annual); *Food Business Mergers and Acquisitions*; *OSHA Inspection Manual*; *Regulatory Directory* (Periodic); *Food Business Mergers & Acquisitions*. **Geographic Preference:** Multinational.

RESEARCH CENTERS

1306 ■ American Institute of Baking (AIB)
1213 Bakers Way
  Manhattan, KS 66505-3999
Ph: (785)537-4750
Free: 800-633-5137
Fax: (785)537-1493
Co. E-mail: info@aibonline.org
URL: http://www.aibinternational.com
Contact: Dan Martin, President
Facebook: www.facebook.com/AIBInternational
Linkedin: www.linkedin.com/company/aibint
X (Twitter): x.com/aibintl
Description: Independent, nonprofit research and educational organization for the food industry. Offers food safety/security audits and consulting, as well as ISO 9000 registration. **Scope:** Researches on nutrition, including effects of ingredients, processing, and baked products on physiological responses in humans; and cereal science, particularly applied technology. Contract research projects include performance characteristics of new and improved ingredients for the baking industry and product and process development utilizing laboratory and pilot bakeries. **Founded:** 1919. **Publications:** *American Institute of Baking Technical Bulletin*; *Maintenance Engineering Bulletins* (Bimonthly); *AIB Update* (Bimonthly); *AIB Newsletter* (Monthly).

Bar/Nightclub

START-UP INFORMATION

1307 ■ *"Kitchen Aid: D.C. Food Incubator Turns Growth Tactics Inward"* in *Washington Business Journal (Vol. 32, February 28, 2014, No. 46, pp. 6)*
Pub: American City Business Journals, Inc.
Contact: Mike Olivieri, Executive Vice President
Released: Weekly. **Price:** $4, introductory 4-week offer(Digital only). **Description:** The founders of the 14-month-old food business incubator, Union Kitchen, are considering their own growth strategies as they open up a second space for small business owners. The incubator has 55 members that pay monthly fees from $800 to $1,000, focusing on bar services and fine dining opportunities. **Availability:** Print; Online.

1308 ■ *"A Messy Job"* in *Washington Business Journal (Vol. 33, May 30, 2014, No. 6, pp. 6)*
Pub: American City Business Journals, Inc.
Contact: Mike Olivieri, Executive Vice President
Description: Mess Hall founder, Al Goldberg, shares his views on business incubators for culinary entrepreneurs in District of Columbia. Goldberg says he expects to accommodate up to 100 members in the space of the former warehouse turned culinary center for entrepreneurs wishing to start restaurants, bakeries or bars. **Availability:** Print; Online.

1309 ■ *"Thirsty Lion Cooks Up Big Expansion Plan"* in *Business Journal Portland (Vol. 27, November 5, 2010, No. 36, pp. 1)*
Pub: Portland Business Journal
Contact: Andy Giegerich, Managing Editor
E-mail: agiegerich@bizjournals.com
Ed: Wendy Culverwell. **Description:** Concept Entertainment Inc.'s impending launch of the Thirsty Lion Pub and Grill at the Washington Square in downtown Portland, Oregon is part of its West Coast expansion plan. A discussion of the planning involved in realizing Thirsty Lion is discussed, along with pub offerings that are expected to be enjoyed by customers. **Availability:** Print; Online.

ASSOCIATIONS AND OTHER ORGANIZATIONS

1310 ■ **American Nightlife Association (ANA)**
712 H St. NE, Ste. 1013
Washington, DC 20002
Ph: (202)670-9079
URL: http://www.nightlifeassociation.org
Contact: J. C. Diaz, President
E-mail: jc@nightlifeassociation.org
Facebook: www.facebook.com/americannightlifeassociation
Linkedin: www.linkedin.com/company/american-nightlife-association
X (Twitter): x.com/nightlife_assoc
Instagram: www.instagram.com/american_nightlife_association
YouTube: www.youtube.com/channel/UCgqp7gWYL1ODyE-qMxIE_rA
Description: Represents the interests of DJs, clubs, promoters, record companies, producers, suppliers, manufacturers and service providers. Promotes the club and electronic music industry. Serves as the national governing body of the club industry. **Founded:** 1989. **Geographic Preference:** National.

1311 ■ **Distilled Spirits Council of the United States (DISCUS)**
101 Constitution Ave., NW, Ste. 350 W
Washington, DC 20001
Ph: (202)628-3544
Co. E-mail: membership@distilledspirits.org
URL: http://www.distilledspirits.org
Contact: Chris R. Swonger, President
Facebook: www.facebook.com/DistilledSpiritsCouncilUS
X (Twitter): x.com/DistilledSpirit
Description: Producers and marketers of distilled spirits sold in the U.S. Provides statistical and legal data for industry and the public and serves as public information source; conducts educational programs. **Founded:** 1973. **Publications:** *Distilled Spirit, Wine and Beer Directories* (Biennial); *Summary of State Laws and Regulations Relating to Distilled Spirits*. **Geographic Preference:** National.

REFERENCE WORKS

1312 ■ *"50 Years of Wings Big Business for Anchor Bar"* in *Business First of Buffalo (Vol. 30, March 7, 2014, No. 25, pp. 4)*
Pub: American City Business Journals, Inc.
Contact: Mike Olivieri, Executive Vice President
Released: Weekly. **Price:** $140, Digital & Print; $115, Digital only. **Description:** The Anchor Bar and restaurant in Buffalo, New York has celebrated its 50th anniversary. The restaurant is known for its Buffalo-style chicken wings. A brief history of the restaurant is presented. **Availability:** Print; Online.

1313 ■ *"$100M Complex To Be Built on Purple People Bridge"* in *Business Courier (Vol. 27, November 12, 2010, No. 28, pp. 1)*
Pub: Business Courier
Ed: Lucy May. **Description:** A development firm closed a deal with the Newport Southbank Bridge Company for a $100M entertainment complex that will be built on top of the Purple People Bridge. The proposed project will cover 150,000 square feet with attractions such as restaurants, a boutique hotel, and pubs. **Availability:** Print; Online.

1314 ■ *"Alamo Beer Tapping Into New Momentum on East Side"* in *San Antonio Business Journal (Vol. 28, July 4, 2014, No. 21, pp. 7)*
Pub: American City Business Journals, Inc.
Contact: Mike Olivieri, Executive Vice President
Released: July 04, 2014. **Description:** Alamo Beer is working on completing the $8 million brewery and beer garden in San Antonio, Texas by the later part of 2014. Company founder, Eugene Simor, says other development activity in the area emerged because of the brewery. **Availability:** Print; Online.

1315 ■ *"Baldor Specialty Foods, Bronx Brewery Release Beer to Benefit Brownsville Community Center"* in *Brewbound (September 18, 2019)*
URL(s): www.brewbound.com/news/baldor-specialty-foods-bronx-brewery-release-beer-to-benefit-brownsville-community-culinary-center
Released: September 18, 2019. **Description:** The Brownsville Community Culinary Center is set to benefit from sales of a new beer from the joint efforts of Baldor Specialty Foods, The Bronx Brewery, and Union Beer Distributors. B-Note will be sold in the Bronx Brewery Taproom and in select stores. **Availability:** Online.

1316 ■ *"Bars, Restaurants to Change Game for Baltimore Grand Prix Patrons"* in *Baltimore Business Journal (Vol. 29, July 22, 2011, No. 11, pp. 1)*
Pub: Boston Business Journal
Contact: Carolyn M. Jones, President
E-mail: cmjones@bizjournals.com
Ed: Alexander Jackson. **Description:** Restaurants and bar owners in Baltimore, Maryland have changed the way they do business as the Baltimore Grand Prix approaches. Owners have gone so far as to offering new services or renting out their entire restaurants to companies for the three-day event in September. **Availability:** Print; Online.

1317 ■ *"Bars See Green, Neighbors In Red Over Strolls"* in *Baltimore Business Journal (Vol. 31, February 28, 2014, No. 44, pp. 7)*
Pub: American City Business Journals, Inc.
Contact: Mike Olivieri, Executive Vice President
Released: Weekly. **Price:** $4, introductory 4-week offer(Digital & Print). **Description:** Baltimore, Maryland-based bars are preparing for the St. Patrick's Day celebrations. The event is the first business boost of the year for the City. Local government officials have signed a memorandum of understanding with local bar owners to help prevent violence during the celebrations. **Availability:** Print; Online.

1318 ■ *"The Best Bar in N.J. is a Semi-Swanky Cocktail Lounge That Serves Some of the Best Food in the Region"* in *NJ.com (June 27. 2019)*
URL(s): www.nj.com/entertainment/2019/06/the-best-bar-in-nj-is-a-semi-swanky-cocktail-lounge-that-serves-some-of-the-best-food-in-the-region.html
Ed: Peter Genovese. **Released:** June 27, 2019. **Description:** Profile of Verve, voted as the best bar in New Jersey. What made this bar stand out from the rest was the food, which rivals it's cocktails in quality. **Availability:** Online.

1319 ■ *"The Best Bars in America, 2019"* in *Esquire (June 6, 2019)*
URL(s): www.esquire.com/food-drink/bars/a274539
19/best-bars-america-2019/
Released: June 06, 2019. **Description:** The atmosphere and type of bars are gradually changing in America, with wine bars and alcohol-free options on the rise. Here are profiles of some of the best bars that provide not only quality beverages, but a great space that all can enjoy. **Availability:** Print; Online.

1320 ■ *"Big Gains Brewing at Anheuser-Busch InBev"* in *Barron's (Vol. 90, August 30, 2010, No. 35, pp. 34)*
Pub: Barron's Editorial & Corporate Headquarters
Ed: Christopher C. Williams. **Description:** Anheuser-Busch InBev is realizing cost synergies and it posted better than expected returns two years after the merger that formed the company. One analyst believes its American depositary receipt could be worth as much as 72 in a year. **Availability:** Online.

1321 ■ *"Canada's New Government Introduces Amendments to Deny Work Permits to Foreign Strippers"* in *Marketwired (May 16, 2007)*
Pub: Comtex News Network Inc.
Contact: Kan Devnani, President
Description: Honourable Diane Finley, Minister of Citizenship and Immigration, introduced amendments to the Immigration and Refugee Protection Act (IRPA) to help prevent the exploitation and abuse of vulnerable foreign workers, such as strippers. **Availability:** Print.

1322 ■ *"Closures Pop Cork on Wine Bar Sector Consolidation"* in *Houston Business Journal (Vol. 40, January 22, 2010, No. 37, pp. A2)*
Pub: Houston Business Journal
Contact: Bob Charlet, President
E-mail: bcharlet@bizjournals.com
Ed: Allison Wollam. **Description:** Wine bar market in Houston, Texas is in the midst of a major shift and heads toward further consolidation due to the closure of pioneering wine bars that opened in the past decade. The Corkscrew owner, Andrew Adams, has blamed the creation of competitive establishments to the closure which helped wear out his concept. **Availability:** Print; Online.

1323 ■ *"Co-Working Space by Day, Cocktail Lounge by Night"* in *OakPark.com (July 16, 2019)*
URL(s): www.oakpark.com/News/Articles/7-16-2019/
Co_working-space-by-day,-cocktail-lounge-by-night/
Released: July 16, 2019. **Description:** Flourish Lounge, which operates as a bar in the evening, also functions as a co-working space during the day hours. Typical office space, conference rooms, and breakout rooms are available and later the area turns into a self-pour lounge. **Availability:** Online.

1324 ■ *"Counting on Cornhole: Popular Bean Bag Game Brings Crowds to Bars"* in *Baltimore Business Journal (Vol. 29, July 15, 2011, No. 10, pp. 1)*
Pub: Boston Business Journal
Contact: Carolyn M. Jones, President
E-mail: cmjones@bizjournals.com
Ed: Alexander Jackson. **Description:** Cornhole game is being used by bars to spur business as the games hikes beer and food sales on slow weekdays. The game is played with two cornhole boards facing each other and is played with one or two people on one team who try to place a bag on the board. **Availability:** Print; Online.

1325 ■ *"Craft Brewers Want 20 Percent of U.S. Market"* in *Denver Business Journal (Vol. 65, April 18, 2014, No. 49, pp. A8)*
Pub: American City Business Journals, Inc.
Contact: Mike Olivieri, Executive Vice President
Description: The United States Brewers Association aims to increase the national craft brewing industry's share of beer sales to 20 percent by 2020. However, the industry will need to take more of the market from large domestic beer manufacturers. Reports show that beer sales in smaller breweries have reached 14.3 percent in 2014. **Availability:** Print; Online.

1326 ■ *"Crystal Hotel Resumes Construction"* in *Business Journal Portland (Vol. 27, December 31, 2010, No. 44, pp. 1)*
Pub: Portland Business Journal
Contact: Andy Giegerich, Managing Editor
E-mail: agiegerich@bizjournals.com
Ed: Wendy Culverwell. **Description:** McMenamins Pubs and Breweries has resumed construction of its Crystal Hotel project. The company has been working to convert a former bath house into a 51-room hotel. The hotel is expected to open in 2011. **Availability:** Print; Online.

1327 ■ *"Discount Beers Take Fizz Out Of Molson"* in *Globe & Mail (February 10, 2006, pp. B3)*
Description: The reasons behind the decline in profits by 60 percent for Molson Coors Brewing Co., during fourth quarter 2005, are presented. **Availability:** Online.

1328 ■ *"Downtown: Grunnah Trades Homes for a Shot at Warehouse District"* in *Austin Business Journal (Vol. 34, February 28, 2014, No. 2, pp. 8)*
Pub: American City Business Journals, Inc.
Contact: Mike Olivieri, Executive Vice President
Released: Weekly. **Price:** $4, Introductory 4-week offer(Digital only). **Description:** Real estate developer Robert Grunnah is set to open the Highland Club bar in Austin, Texas. Grunnah has invested about $1.5 million on the bar's interior design. **Availability:** Print; Online.

1329 ■ *"Drinking Buddies: S.F.'s New Round of Barkeeps"* in *San Francisco Business Times (Vol. 28, January 17, 2014, No. 26, pp. 4)*
Pub: American City Business Journals, Inc.
Contact: Mike Olivieri, Executive Vice President
Released: Weekly. **Price:** $4, Introductory 4-week offer(Digital & Print). **Description:** The influx of young workers in San Francisco, California contributed to the growth of the city's bar industry. Ben Bleiman of the tonic Nightlife Group reveals that his bars are doing well because of a rebound in the U.S. economy. Reports also show that smaller groups are now opening multiple drinking establishments across San Francisco. **Availability:** Print; Online.

1330 ■ *"Executive Decision: Damn the Profit Margins, Sleeman Declares War on Buck-a-Beer Foes"* in *Globe & Mail (January 28, 2006, pp. B3)*
Description: The cost savings plans of chief executive officer John Sleeman of Sleeman Breweries Ltd. are presented. **Availability:** Online.

1331 ■ *Find. Build. Sell.: How I Turned a $100 Backyard Bar into a $100 Million Pub Empire*
URL(s): www.wiley.com/en-us/Find+Build+Sell+%3A
+How+I+Turned+a+%24100+Backyard+Bar+into+a
+%24100+Million+Pub+Empire-p-9780730399865
Ed: Stepehn J. Hunt. **Released:** February 2022.
Price: $13, e-book; $22, paperback. **Description:** Stephen J. Hunt tells the story of how he turned his backyard beer garden into a huge pub industry. Learn about developing your passion into a business. **Availability:** E-book; Print.

1332 ■ *"Fines Can't Snuff Out Hookah Sales"* in *Providence Business News (Vol. 28, March 3, 2014, No. 48, pp. 1)*
Pub: American City Business Journals, Inc.
Contact: Mike Olivieri, Executive Vice President
Released: March 01, 2014. **Description:** The City of Providence, Rhode Island initiated a crackdown on bars and restaurants serving Middle Eastern-style water pipes, known as hookahs in violation of state anti-smoking laws. Gianfranco Marrocco, owner of several Federal Hill nightspots, believes that many bar owners will just pay the fine because hookah lounges are a good revenue source. **Availability:** Print; Online.

1333 ■ *"Hi-Fi Cocktail Bars Aren't Just for Tokyo Anymore"* in *Bloomberg (April 11, 2019)*
URL(s): www.bloomberg.com/news/features/2019-0
4-11/hi-fi-listening-bars-eclectic-music-epic-sound-a
t-cocktail-hour
Ed: Matthew Kronsberg. **Released:** April 11, 2019.
Description: Bars are serving up not only delicious drinks, but providing a dedicated space for music lovers to simply sit and listen to music played on superior sound-systems. These "listening rooms" are increasing in popularity and owners are investing into high-end equipment. **Availability:** Online.

1334 ■ *"Hike in Md.'s Alcohol Tax May Be Hard For Lawmakers to Swallow"* in *Baltimore Business Journal (Vol. 28, November 19, 2010, No. 28)*
Pub: Baltimore Business Journal
Contact: Rhonda Pringle, President
E-mail: rpringle@bizjournals.com
Ed: Emily Mullin. **Description:** Maryland's General Assembly has been reluctant to support a dime-per-drink increase in alcohol tax that was drafted in the 2009 bill if the tax revenue goes into a separate fund. The alcohol tax increase is considered unnecessary by some lawmakers and business leaders due to impending federal spending boosts. **Availability:** Print; Online.

1335 ■ *"Homes, Not Bars, Stay Well Tended"* in *Advertising Age (Vol. 79, January 28, 2008, No. 4, pp. 8)*
Pub: Crain Communications, Inc.
Contact: Jessica Botos, Manager, Marketing
E-mail: jessica.botos@crainsnewyork.com
Ed: Jeremy Mullman. **Description:** Due to the downturn in the economy, consumers are drinking less at bars and restaurants; however, according to the Distilled Spirits Council of the United States, they are still purchasing expensive liquor to keep in their homes. **Availability:** Online.

1336 ■ *"I Love L.A."* in *Canadian Business (Vol. 81, December 8, 2008, No. 21, pp. S22)*
Description: Los Angeles-based Standard Downtown, which was built in the 1950s, has a bar that remains popular to Hollywood celebrities. The Standard L.A., which used to house the former headquarters of Superior Oil, offers Devon's Bourbon Sour.

1337 ■ *"Imports Frothing Up Beer Market"* in *Globe & Mail (February 16, 2006, pp. B4)*
Ed: Andy Hoffman. **Description:** The reasons behind the rise in market share of beer imports, in Canada, are presented. **Availability:** Online.

1338 ■ *"It's 4:30 p.m. Do You Know Where Your Staff Is?"* in *Canadian Business (Vol. 85, August 13, 2012, No. 13, pp. 62)*
Ed: Chris Johns, Courtney Shea. **Description:** Some of the best business patios in Canada are recommended. They include the Terrase Place D'Armes in Montreal, Quebec; West Restaurant and Bar in Calgary, Alberta; and Earl's Kitchen and Bar in Toronto, Ontario. **Availability:** Online.

1339 ■ *"Labatt to Swallow Lakeport"* in *Globe & Mail (February 2, 2007, pp. B1)*
Ed: Keith McArthur. **Description:** The decision of Labatt Brewing Company Ltd. to acquire Lakeport Brewing Income Fund for $201.4 million is discussed. **Availability:** Print; Online.

1340 ■ *"Law Firms Cash In On Alcohol"* in *Business Journal Portland (Vol. 27, November 19, 2010, No. 38, pp. 1)*
Pub: Portland Business Journal
Contact: Andy Giegerich, Managing Editor
E-mail: agiegerich@bizjournals.com

Ed: Andy Giegerich. **Description:** Oregon-based law firms have continued to corner big business on the state's growing alcohol industry as demand for their services increased. Lawyers, who represent wine, beer and liquor distillery interests, have seen their workload increased by 20 to 30 percent in 2009. **Availability:** Print; Online.

1341 ■ *"Lee's Launches With Focus on Liqueur-based Ice Creams" in Ice Cream Reporter (Vol. 23, August 20, 2010, No. 9, pp. 6)*

Description: Lee's Cream Liqueur Ice Cream Parlors launched their grand opening in Old Town Scottsdale in July, featuring premium liqueurs to create adult-only ice creams that can be served on their own or blended into exotic drinks. **Availability:** Print; Online.

1342 ■ *"Little Cheer in Holiday Forecast for Champagne" in Advertising Age (Vol. 88, November 17, 2008, No. 43, pp. 6)*
Pub: Crain Communications, Inc.
Contact: Jessica Botos, Manager, Marketing
E-mail: jessica.botos@crainsnewyork.com

Ed: Jeremy Mullman. **Description:** Due to a weak economy that has forced consumers to trade down from the most expensive alcoholic beverages as well as a weak U.S. dollar that has driven already lofty Champagne prices higher, makers of the French sparkling wine are anticipating a brutally slow holiday season. **Availability:** Online.

1343 ■ *"Minnesota State Fair Vendors Accept Big Risks for Big Rewards" in Business Journal (Vol. 32, August 22, 2014, No. 13, pp. 10)*
Pub: American City Business Journals, Inc.
Contact: Mike Olivieri, Executive Vice President

Released: Weekly. **Price:** $4, introductory 4-week offer(Digital & Print). **Description:** Food and beverage concessionaires compete for booths at the Minnesota State Fair and there are many vendors that wait for years to get one, especially a large booth with room for tables and a beer garden. The State Fair has been a good business opportunity and a family bonding experience for most of the vendors. **Availability:** Video; Print; Online.

1344 ■ *National Conference of State Liquor Administrators--Official Directory*
Pub: National Conference of State Liquor Administrators
Contact: Pamela Frantz, Executive Director
URL(s): www.ncsla.org/State-Officials.html

Released: Annual **Description:** Covers state alcohol beverage control administrators in 36 jurisdictions in the United States, Puerto Rico, District of Columbia, and Guam. **Entries include:** Name, office address and phone. **Arrangement:** Geographical. **Availability:** Print; Online.

1345 ■ *"A New Flavor for Second Street: Lamberts Chef Backs New Restaurant" in Austin Business JournalInc. (Vol. 28, January 2, 2009)*

Description: Chef Larry McGuire has teamed up with the Icon Group to develop the La Condesa restaurant and the Malverde lounge in the Second Street district. The La Condesa restaurant will be a Mexico City-inspired restaurant, while the Malverde lounge atop the La Condesa will host DJs and live music. **Availability:** Print; Online.

1346 ■ *"Nighttime Shuttle to Connect Detroit, Ferndale, Royal Oak" in Crain's Detroit Business (Vol. 24, October 6, 2008, No. 40, pp. 24)*
Pub: Crain Communications Inc.
Contact: Barry Asin, President

Ed: Nancy Kaffer. **Description:** With hopes of bridging the social gap between the cities and suburbs, Chris Ramos has launched The Night Move, a new shuttle service that will ferry passengers between Royal Oak, Ferndale and downtown Detroit. The cost for a round trip ticket is $12. **Availability:** Online.

1347 ■ *"Nine Things You're Doing Wrong in a Cocktail Bar" in Bloomburg (March 9, 2017)*
URL(s): www.bloomberg.com/news/articles/2017-03-09/nine-things-you-re-doing-wrong-in-a-cocktail-bar

Ed: Kate Krader. **Released:** March 09, 2017. **Description:** A top-rated bar owner gives nine tips to help consumers make the most of their experiences at bars and cocktail lounges. **Availability:** Online.

1348 ■ *"Plan B Saloon Opens New Year's Eve" in Bellingham Business Journal (Vol. February 2010, pp. 7)*
Pub: Sound Publishing Inc.
Contact: Josh O'Connor, President

Ed: Isaac Bonnell. **Description:** Plan B Saloon, located in Bellingham, Washington, opened New Year's Eve 2010. The bar/restaurant will feature classic American food consisting of sandwiches and burgers and will host local musicians on Friday and Saturday nights.

1349 ■ *"Red Light's Green Light" in Washington Business Journal (Vol. 32, April 11, 2014, No. 52, pp. 6)*
Pub: American City Business Journals, Inc.
Contact: Mike Olivieri, Executive Vice President

Released: Weekly. **Price:** $4, introductory 4-week offer(Digital & Print). **Description:** Restaurateur, Aaron Gordon, is opening his dessert and cocktail bar called Red Light in Washington DC on April 10, 2014. Gorden envisions Red Light as a destination and a before- or after-dinner stop for patrons wanting drinks and dessert along the hottest dining corridor of the city. Specialty drinks and baked goods are described. **Availability:** Print; Online.

1350 ■ *"Seahawks' Win? A Seattle Windfall" in Puget Sound Business Journal (Vol. 34, January 10, 2014, No. 39, pp. 3)*
Pub: American City Business Journals, Inc.
Contact: Mike Olivieri, Executive Vice President

Released: Weekly. **Price:** $4, introductory 4-week offer(Digital & Print). **Description:** Seattle, Washington is anticipating a windfall from the Seattle Seahawks' ninth game of the season. The sold-out CenturyLink Field can hold 67,000 spectators, who are potential customers outside the stadium at restaurants, bars, hotels and attractions. The economic benefits of hosting a high-profile sports event are explored. **Availability:** Print; Online.

1351 ■ *So! You Want to Own a Bar: An Insider's Guide to Bar Ownership*
URL(s): www.barnesandnoble.com/w/so-you-want-to-own-a-bar-jasmine-mancos/1141772717?ean=2940186670384

Ed: Jasmine Mancos. **Released:** April 22, 2022. **Price:** $12, e-book; $15, paperback. **Description:** Breaks down the myths surrounding bar ownership and gives a true look at what it really takes to own a bar and run it successfully. **Availability:** E-book; Print.

1352 ■ *"Strange Brew" in Canadian Business (Vol. 85, June 11, 2012, No. 10, pp. 52)*

Ed: Paul Brent. **Description:** Molson Coors is launching the Coors Light Iced T beer in summer 2012 as part of its effort to improve weak sales in North America. The new product is aimed at female drinkers and is part of an effort to win back sales from wine and spirits. **Availability:** Print; Online.

1353 ■ *"To Live and Thrive in L.A." in Canadian Business (Vol. 81, October 13, 2008, No. 17, pp. 78)*

Description: Toronto entrepreneur Shereen Arazm thrived in Los Angeles, California as the queen of nightlife. Arazm holds or has held ownership stakes in bars, nightspots and restaurants that include the Geisha House, Concorde, Shag, Parc and Central, and Terroni L.A. **Availability:** Online.

1354 ■ *"The Traveling Godfather: Beam Global Spirits & Wine Inc." in Canadian Business (Vol. 81, October 13, 2008, No. 17, pp. S10)*

Description: Dan Tullio, director of Canadian Club, is seen as a godfather because he gets to be asked a lot of favors. Tullio gets to immerse himself into other cultures because of his employment as global ambassador of Beam Global Spirits & Wine Inc. Tullio's views, as well as information about him are presented.

1355 ■ *"Uneven But Imaginative, Union Sushi & Barbecue Bar Works" in Crain's Chicago Business (Vol. 34, September 12, 2011, No. 37, pp. 30)*
Pub: Crain Communications Inc.
Contact: Barry Asin, President

Ed: Alison Neumer Lara. **Description:** Japanese restaurant, Union Sushi & Barbecue Bar opened in Chicago this year. Union is a hip and urban place for business and leisure diners. **Availability:** Online.

STATISTICAL SOURCES

1356 ■ *Bars & Nightclubs Industry in the US - Market Research Report*
URL(s): www.ibisworld.com/united-states/market-research-reports/bars-nightclubs-industry/

Price: $925. **Availability:** Download.

1357 ■ *Brewery Tours Industry in the US - Market Research Report*
URL(s): www.ibisworld.com/united-states/market-research-reports/brewery-tours-industry/

Price: $925. **Description:** Downloadable report analyzing the current and future trends in the brewery tours industry. **Availability:** Download.

1358 ■ *Karaoke Bars Industry in the US - Market Research Report*
URL(s): www.ibisworld.com/united-states/market-research-reports/karaoke-bars-industry/

Price: $925. **Description:** Downloadable report analyzing the current and future trends in the karaoke bar industry. **Availability:** Download.

1359 ■ *RMA Annual Statement Studies*
Pub: Risk Management Association
Contact: Nancy Foster, President

Released: Annual. **Description:** Contains composite balance sheets and income statements for more than 360 industries, including the accounting, auditing, and bookkeeping industries. Also contains five years of comparative historical data for discerning trends. Includes 16 commonly used ratios, computed for most of the size groupings for nearly every industry.

1360 ■ *US Alcoholic Beverages Online Market Report 2021*
URL(s): store.mintel.com/report/us-alcoholic-beverages-online-market-report

Price: $4,366.35. **Description:** When the Covid-19 pandemic hit, online alcoholic beverage sales went up, due to people not wanting to shop instore. This downloadable report covers the reasons online sources are used to purchase alcohol, barriers to doing so, and consumer behavior trends. Included are an executive summary, interactive databook, PowerPoint presentation, infographic overview, report PDF, and previous years data. **Availability:** PDF.

TRADE PERIODICALS

1361 ■ *Cocktails Magazine*
Pub: Destiny Productions for Print, Radio and Cable Promotions
URL(s): www.cocktail.com/

Released: Monthly **Description:** Trade magazine for the alcohol service industry. **Availability:** Print.

1362 ■ *Modern Brewery Age*
Contact: Peter V.K. Reid, Publisher
E-mail: pete@breweryage.com

Released: Bimonthly **Price:** $95, U.S. and other countries 52 PDF weekly tabloids via email & delivery of quarterly magazine. **Description:** Magazine for the wholesale and brewing industry. **Availability:** Print; Online.

VIDEO/AUDIO MEDIA

1363 ■ *Gary Crunkleton Owner of The Crunkleton*
URL(s): restaurantunstoppable.libsyn.com/1012-gary-crunkleton-owner-of-the-crunkleton
Ed: Eric Cacciatore. **Released:** July 27, 2023. **Description:** Podcast offers a conversation with a bartender who began with one bar specializing in antique drinks but is now involved in six.

1364 ■ *The How of Business: Matt Grech-Smith - Swingers Crazy Golf*
URL(s): www.thehowofbusiness.com/459-matt-grech-smith-swingers-crazy-golf
Ed: Henry Lopez. **Released:** February 13, 2023. **Description:** Podcast discusses the opening of Crazy Swingers, where mini golf meets cocktails.

TRADE SHOWS AND CONVENTIONS

1365 ■ Bar Convent Brooklyn
URL(s): www.barconventbrooklyn.com
Facebook: www.facebook.com/barconventbrooklyn
Linkedin: www.linkedin.com/company/barconventbrooklyn
X (Twitter): twitter.com/bcbrooklyn
Instagram: www.instagram.com/barconventbrooklyn
YouTube: www.youtube.com/channel/UCgdehC_nQiZyXAgS6yfObtw
Frequency: Annual. **Description:** Provides demonstrations, keynote talks, and panel discussions about the latest trends in the bar and beverage industry. **Principal Exhibits:** Provides demonstrations, keynote talks, and panel discussions about the latest trends in the bar and beverage industry. **Telecommunication Services:** inquiry@barconventbrooklyn.com.

FRANCHISES AND BUSINESS OPPORTUNITIES

1366 ■ Bridge Business and Property Brokers Inc.
300 W Main St.
Smithtown, NY 11787
Free: 866-948-3330
Co. E-mail: info@bridgebrokers.com
URL: http://bridgebrokers.com
Linkedin: www.linkedin.com/in/bridgebrokers
Description: Services: Business and property brokers. **Founded:** 2004. **Training:** Offers training program designed to expedite the process of making your employees proficient in the art of business brokering.

1367 ■ Cartoon Cuts
927 N University Dr.
Coral Springs, FL 33071
URL: http://cartooncuts.com
X (Twitter): x.com/cartooncuts
Instagram: www.instagram.com/cartooncuts
Description: Hair salons for children. **Founded:** 1991. **Training:** Yes.

1368 ■ Dooley's Inc.
463 Elmwood Dr.
Moncton, NB, Canada E1A 2X2
Ph: (506)857-8050
Co. E-mail: info@doolys.ca
URL: http://www.doolys.ca
Contact: Pierre Lariviere, President
Facebook: www.facebook.com/doolys.billiards
Description: Entertainment firm provides billiards and video games for social gatherings. **Founded:** 1993. **Equity Capital Needed:** $100,000-$150,000. **Franchise Fee:** 25000. **Training:** Extensive training, both in operations and marketing are provided. Field representatives will help with hiring and training your manager and staff with ongoing training and support through workshops and annual meetings.

1369 ■ Old Chicago Pizza & Taproom
SPB Hospitality
3550 S Wadsworth Blvd.
Lakewood, CO 80235
URL: http://www.spbhospitality.com
Facebook: www.facebook.com/OCLakewood
Instagram: www.instagram.com/oldchicago
Description: Restaurant offering craft beer, pizza. **Founded:** 1976. **Training:** Yes.

1370 ■ Sculpture Hospitality
601-505 Consumers Rd.
Toronto, ON, Canada M2J 4V8
Ph: (512)572-6123
Free: 888-238-4626
Co. E-mail: info@sculpturehospitality.com
URL: http://www.sculpturehospitality.com
Contact: Vanessa De Caria, President
Facebook: www.facebook.com/sculpturehospitality
Linkedin: www.linkedin.com/company/sculpturehospitality
X (Twitter): x.com/sculptureHQ
Instagram: www.instagram.com/sculpture.hospitality
YouTube: www.youtube.com/channel/UCMzz-FD7WmK2W4FGI41O-BQ
Description: Firm provides technology solutions and services to bar and restaurant operators. **Founded:** 1987. **Financial Assistance:** Yes **Training:** 7 days corporate training in Toronto, 5-10 days regional training with state master franchise.

INTERNET DATABASES

1371 ■ *Alcoholic Beverage Industry*
URL(s): guides.loc.gov/alcoholic-beverage-industry
Description: A guide on the various alcoholic beverages made and sold in the United States. Contains market information and trade literature. Also includes a section on the Temperance Movement and Prohibition. **Availability:** Online.

LIBRARIES

1372 ■ Anheuser-Busch Companies, LLC (ABC) - Library
Anheuser-Busch InBev SA/NV
1 Busch Pl.
Saint Louis, MO 63118
Ph: 32 16 276 111
Co. E-mail: glass-help@ab-inbev.com
URL: http://www.ab-inbev.com
Contact: Andy Thomas, President
URL(s): www.tapintoyourbeer.com
Facebook: www.facebook.com/AnheuserBusch
Linkedin: www.linkedin.com/company/anheuser-busch
X (Twitter): x.com/AnheuserBusch
Instagram: www.instagram.com/anheuserbusch
YouTube: www.youtube.com/user/ABInBevNews
Description: Operator of bars offering beer. **Scope:** Beer. **Founded:** 1852. **Holdings:** Figures not available. **Educational Activities:** Chain Operators Exchange (COEX) (Annual); FMI Midwinter Executive Conference (Annual).

1373 ■ The Coca-Cola Company
The Coca-Cola Company
1 Coca-Cola Plz.
Atlanta, GA 30313
Ph: (404)676-2121
Free: 800-438-2653
Co. E-mail: press@coca-cola.com
URL: http://www.coca-colacompany.com
Contact: John Murphy, President
Facebook: www.facebook.com/TheCocaColaCo
Linkedin: www.linkedin.com/company/the-coca-cola-company
X (Twitter): twitter.com/CocaCola
Instagram: www.instagram.com/cocacola
YouTube: www.youtube.com/user/CocaColaCo
Description: Producer and distributor of non-alcoholic beverages such as juices, ready-to-drink teas and coffees, sport, dairy and energy drinks. **Founded:** 1886. **Educational Activities:** GSF West; Sunshine Expo (Annual); Big Iron Farm Show and Exhibition (Annual).

1374 ■ Distilled Spirits Council of the United States (DISCUS)
101 Constitution Ave., NW, Ste. 350 W
Washington, DC 20001
Ph: (202)628-3544
Co. E-mail: membership@distilledspirits.org
URL: http://www.distilledspirits.org
Contact: Chris R. Swonger, President
Facebook: www.facebook.com/DistilledSpiritsCouncilUS
X (Twitter): x.com/DistilledSpirit
Description: Producers and marketers of distilled spirits sold in the U.S. Provides statistical and legal data for industry and the public and serves as public information source; conducts educational programs. **Founded:** 1973. **Publications:** *Distilled Spirit, Wine and Beer Directories* (Biennial); *Summary of State Laws and Regulations Relating to Distilled Spirits*. **Geographic Preference:** National.

Beauty Salon/Day Spa

REFERENCE WORKS

1375 ■ *Building a Wellness Business That Lasts: How to Make a Great Living Doing What You Love*
URL(s): www.wiley.com/en-us/Building+a+Wellness
+Business+That+Lasts%3A+How+to+Make+a
+Great+Living+Doing+What+You+Love-p-9781119
679066
Ed: Rick Stollmeyer. **Released:** October 2020. **Price:** $17, e-book; $28, hardcover. **Description:** There are a lot of business opportunities to bring wellness into the community, through gyms, spas, salons, etc. This book will help guide you on starting your own wellness small business. **Availability:** E-book; Print.

STATISTICAL SOURCES

1376 ■ *Online Beauty Retailing - US - 2021*
URL(s): store.mintel.com/report/online-beauty-retailing-us-2021

Price: $4,366.35. **Description:** A downloadable report with insights on how the Covid-19 pandemic affected consumers and the way they shop. However, people still bought beauty products and this report gives the reasons, methods, considerations, and attitudes towards these purchases. The full report includes an executive summary, interactive databook, PowerPoint presentation, infographic overview, report PDF, and previous years data. **Availability:** PDF.

1377 ■ *US Gen Z Beauty Consumer Market Report 2021*
URL(s): store.mintel.com/report/us-gen-z-beauty-consumer-market-report

Price: $4,366.35. **Description:** Downloadable report detailing the shopping habits of Generation Z as they purchase beauty products. Report includes executive summary, interactive databook, PowerPoint presentation, infographic overview, report pdf, and previous years data. **Availability:** PDF.

INTERNET DATABASES

1378 ■ *African Americans in Business and Entrepreneurship: A Resource Guide*
URL(s): guides.loc.gov/african-americans-in-business

Description: A guide providing key topics on the history of African Americans in various business industries. **Availability:** Online.

1379 ■ *Business of Beauty: A Resource Guide*
URL(s): guides.loc.gov/business-of-beauty

Description: This online resource contains links to further resources on the history of the beauty business. Also contains links to current practices; retail, wholesale, and manufacturing; trade data, and print and electronic sources. **Availability:** Online.

Beauty Supply Center

ASSOCIATIONS AND OTHER ORGANIZATIONS

1380 ■ Cosmetic Industry Buyers and Suppliers (CIBS)
740 Blue Point Rd.
  Holtsville, NY 11742
Ph: (631)758-4200
URL: http://www.cibsonline.com
Contact: Veronica Cruz, President
Facebook: www.facebook.com/CIBSOnlineOfficial
Linkedin: www.linkedin.com/company/cosmetic-industry-buyers-&-suppliers
X (Twitter): x.com/cibs_online
Instagram: www.instagram.com/cibs_online
Description: Buyers and suppliers of essential oils, chemicals, packaging, and finished goods relative to the cosmetic industry. Enhances growth, stability, prosperity, and protection of the American cosmetic industry through close personal contact and the exchange of ideas and experiences. **Founded:** 1948. **Geographic Preference:** National.

1381 ■ International Aloe Science Council (IASC)
8630 Fenton St., Ste. 918
  Silver Spring, MD 20910
Ph: (734)476-9690
Co. E-mail: info@iasc.org
URL: http://www.iasc.org
Contact: Jane Wilson, Executive Director
E-mail: jwilson@iasc.org
X (Twitter): x.com/AloeCouncil
Instagram: www.instagram.com/iasc_1980
Description: Manufacturers and marketers of foods, drugs and cosmetics containing gel of the aloe vera plant. Aims to provide scientific research for support of product claims. Educates members on the plant and its products and uses. Acts as a liaison for government agency regulations on aloe vera business. **Awards:** Yun Ho Lee Scientific Award (Annual). **Geographic Preference:** Multinational.

1382 ■ National Association of General Merchandise Representatives (NAGMR)
1305 Thorndale Ave.
  Elk Grove Village, IL 60007
Free: 877-377-8322
URL: http://nagmr.com
Description: Consumer products brokers specializing in selling drug, health, beauty aids, and nonfood products to food chains and the same products and grocery items to the nonfood market. **Founded:** 1948. **Educational Activities:** NAGMR Convention; National Association of General Merchandise Representatives Annual Convention. **Geographic Preference:** National.

1383 ■ Personal Care Product Council
1620 L St. NW, Ste. 1200
  Washington, DC 20036
Ph: (202)331-1770
Fax: (202)331-1969
Co. E-mail: membership@personalcarecouncil.org
URL: http://www.personalcarecouncil.org
Contact: Lezlee Westine, President
Facebook: www.facebook.com/Personal-Care-Products-Council-1443878795835012
Linkedin: www.linkedin.com/company/464630
X (Twitter): x.com/PCPC_News
YouTube: www.youtube.com/user/PersonalCareCouncil
Description: Manufacturers and distributors of finished cosmetics, fragrances, and personal care products; suppliers of raw materials and services. Provides scientific, legal, regulatory, and legislative services. Coordinates public service, educational, and public affairs activities. **Founded:** 1894. **Publications:** *Member Directory*; *Executive Update*; *International Cosmetic Legal & Regulatory Database (IRDB)* (Annual); *On-Line INFOBASE*; *CTFA News* (Biweekly); *International Color Handbook*; *International Resource Manual*. **Geographic Preference:** National.

1384 ■ Professional Beauty Association (PBA)
7755 E Gray Rd.
  Scottsdale, AZ 85260-3459
Ph: (480)281-0424
Free: 800-468-2274
Co. E-mail: info@probeauty.org
URL: http://www.probeauty.org
Contact: Nina Daily, Executive Director
Facebook: www.facebook.com/professionalbeautyassociation
Linkedin: www.linkedin.com/company/professional-beauty-association
X (Twitter): x.com/probeautyassoc
Instagram: www.instagram.com/probeautyassoc
YouTube: www.youtube.com/user/professionalbeauty
Description: Manufacturer of beauty and barber products, cosmetics, equipment, and supplies used in or resold by beauty salons or barbershops. **Founded:** 1985. **Publications:** *American Salon Magazine* (Quarterly); *PBA Progress*. **Educational Activities:** Professional Beauty Africa (Annual); National Beauty Show - HAIRWORLD (Annual); Cosmoprof North America (CPNA) (Annual); International Salon & Spa Expo (Annual). **Awards:** Sally Beauty Scholarships for High School Graduates (Annual). **Geographic Preference:** National.

REFERENCE WORKS

1385 ■ *"1st Black-Owned Beauty Supply Store in Nashville Made $50,000 In it's First 3 Hours of Opening!"* in *Soultanicals (March 4, 2019)*
URL(s): soultanicals.com/blogs/news/1st-black-owned-beauty-supply-store-in-nashville-made-50-000-in-its-first-3-hours-of-opening
Ed: Ayo Ogun. **Released:** March 04, 2019. **Description:** Roots Beauty Supply, the first Black-owned beauty supply store in Nashville had a fantastic opening day by taking in $50,000 within the first three hours of being open. **Availability:** Online.

1386 ■ *"Amazon Targets Denton-Based Sally Beauty's Professional Salon Customers"* in *The Dallas Morning News (June 24, 2019)*
URL(s): www.dallasnews.com/business/retail/2019/06/24/amazon-targets-denton-based-sally-beauty-s-professional-salon-customers/
Ed: Maria Halkias. **Released:** June 24, 2019. **Description:** Amazon launched a beauty store for salon professionals, which is in direct competition with Denton-based Sally Beauty Supply, which has been a staple in the industry for decades. Amazon is now selling online, what Sally's carries inside their stores, which is going to make Sally's add new products and improve their own technology in order to remain competitive. **Availability:** Print; Online.

1387 ■ *"avVaa World Health Care Products Rolls Out Internet Marketing Program"* in *Health and Beauty Close-Up (September 18, 2009)*
Description: avVaa World Health Care Products, Inc., a biotechnology company, manufacturer and distributor of nationally branded therapeutic, natural health care and skin products, has signed an agreement with Online Performance Marketing to launch of an Internet marketing campaign in order to broaden its presence online. The impact of advertising on the Internet to generate an increase in sales is explored. **Availability:** Online.

1388 ■ *"Cross Atlantic Commodities Launches National Internet Marketing Programs"* in *Manufacturing Close-Up (September 8, 2009)*
Description: Profile of the Internet campaign recently launched by Cross Atlantic Commodities, Inc., a manufacturer of specialty beauty and health products. **Availability:** Print; Online.

1389 ■ *"In the Raw: Karyn Calabrese Brings Healthy Dining to a New Sophisticated Level"* in *Black Enterprise (Vol. 41, September 2010)*
Pub: Earl G. Graves Ltd.
Contact: Earl Graves, Jr., President
Ed: Sonia Alleyne. **Description:** Profile of Karyn Calabrese whose businesses are based in Chicago, Illinois. Calabrese has launched a complete line of products (vitamins and beauty items), services (spa, chiropractic, and acupuncture treatments), and restaurants to bring healthy dining and lifestyles to a better level. **Availability:** Online.

1390 ■ *"Mother and Daughter Create Tool to Unbraid 8 Braids at One Time"* in *Black Enterprise(February 25, 2023)*
URL(s): www.blackenterprise.com/mother-and-daughter-create-tool-to-unbraid-8-braids-at-one-time/
Released: February 25, 2023. **Description:** A mother and daughter duo launched a company to develop and create The Original Unbraider, which is being used in salons and sold at hair shows. **Availability:** Online.

1391 ■ Beauty Supply Center

1391 ■ *"Sally Beauty: What the Company Must Do Now"* **in Forbes (October 21, 2018)**
URL(s): www.forbes.com/sites/brittainladd/2018/10/21/sally-beauty-supply-what-the-company-must-do-now/#3df62ec5024d
Ed: Brittain Ladd. **Released:** October 21, 2018.
Description: With increased competition from from high-end cosmetics and beauty chains, the real competitors of Sally's are Amazon, Walmart, and CVS. Streamlining operations, improving efficiencies, and improving inventory management are all in the plan to keep Sally's as a main force in the industry. **Availability:** Online.

1392 ■ *"Sally Beauty's Plans Highlight Hair Color"* **in BizWomen (February 7, 2019)**
URL(s): www.bizjournals.com/bizwomen/news/latest-news/2019/02/sally-beautys-plans-highlight-hair-color.html?page=all
Ed: Anne Stych. **Released:** February 07, 2019.
Description: Sally Beauty Holdings is looking at reorganizing it's distrubution system while moving to digital platforms and at the same time will be focusing on increasing it's presence in the hair color industry. **Availability:** Online.

1393 ■ *"Sisters Partner to Open Beauty Supply Store"* **in The Philadelphia Tribune (August 27, 2019)**
URL(s): www.phillytrib.com/news/business/sisters-partner-to-open-beauty-supply-store/article_51b223fd-401c-5c44-ae7b-8086d8802161.html
Ed: Ayana Jones. **Released:** August 27, 2019.
Description: Two sisters with extensive backgrounds in cosmetology are opening a new beauty supply store in an area where independent shops like this are owned by Korean Americans. This store will serve the Black community and give back to the area. **Availability:** Online.

STATISTICAL SOURCES

1394 ■ *Online Beauty Retailing - US - 2021*
URL(s): store.mintel.com/report/online-beauty-retailing-us-2021
Price: $4,366.35. **Description:** A downloadable report with insights on how the Covid-19 pandemic affected consumers and the way they shop. However, people still bought beauty products and this report gives the reasons, methods, considerations, and attitudes towards these purchases. The full report includes an executive summary, interactive databook, PowerPoint presentation, infographic overview, report PDF, and previous years data. **Availability:** PDF.

1395 ■ *RMA Annual Statement Studies*
Pub: Risk Management Association
Contact: Nancy Foster, President
Released: Annual. **Description:** Contains composite balance sheets and income statements for more than 360 industries, including the accounting, auditing, and bookkeeping industries. Also contains five years of comparative historical data for discerning trends. Includes 16 commonly used ratios, computed for most of the size groupings for nearly every industry.

1396 ■ *Standard & Poor's Industry Surveys*
Pub: Standard And Poor's Financial Services LLC.
Contact: Douglas L. Peterson, President
Description: Two-volume book that examines the prospects for specific industries, including trucking. Also provides analyses of trends and problems, statistical tables and charts, and comparative company analyses.

1397 ■ *US Gen Z Beauty Consumer Market Report 2021*
URL(s): store.mintel.com/report/us-gen-z-beauty-consumer-market-report
Price: $4,366.35. **Description:** Downloadable report detailing the shopping habits of Generation Z as they purchase beauty products. Report includes executive summary, interactive databook, PowerPoint presentation, infographic overview, report pdf, and previous years data. **Availability:** PDF.

TRADE PERIODICALS

1398 ■ *Cosmetics & Toiletries: The International Magazine of Cosmetic Technology*
Pub: Allured Business Media
Contact: Janet Ludwig, President
E-mail: jludwig@allured.com
URL(s): www.cosmeticsandtoiletries.com
Facebook: www.facebook.com/CandTmagazine
Linkedin: www.linkedin.com/company/cosmeticsandtoiletries
Instagram: www.instagram.com/cosmeticsandtoiletries
Released: 10/year; Jan., Feb., March, April, May, June, July/Aug., Sept., Oct. and Nov./Dec. **Price:** $199, for print. **Description:** Trade magazine on cosmetic and toiletries manufacturing with an emphasis on product research and development issues. **Availability:** Print; PDF; Online.

1399 ■ *Skin Inc.: Professional Skin Care*
Contact: Katie Anderson, Managing Editor
E-mail: kanderson@allured.com
URL(s): www.skininc.com
Facebook: www.facebook.com/SkinInc
X (Twitter): twitter.com/SkinIncMagazine
Released: Monthly **Description:** The complete business guide for face and body care. **Availability:** Print; PDF; Online.

TRADE SHOWS AND CONVENTIONS

1400 ■ *AACS Annual Convention & Expo*
American Association of Cosmetology Schools (AACS)
20 F St., NW, Ste. 700
Washington, DC 20001
Ph: (202)963-5730
Co. E-mail: info@beautyschools.org
URL: http://myaacs.org
Contact: Cecil Kidd, Executive Director
E-mail: cecil@myaacs.org
URL(s): myaacs.org/annual-conference
Frequency: Annual. **Description:** Exhibits related to beauty supplies and products, and cosmetology services. **Audience:** Industry professionals. **Principal Exhibits:** Exhibits related to beauty supplies and products, and cosmetology services. **Telecommunication Services:** kimber@myaacs.org.

1401 ■ *International Beauty Exposition*
URL(s): www.internationalbeautyexposition.com
Frequency: Annual. **Description:** Showcases the newest beauty products and provides networking opportunities between manufacturers and store owners. **Audience:** Professional beauty distributors and OTC stores. **Principal Exhibits:** Showcases the newest beauty products and provides networking opportunities between manufacturers and store owners.

FRANCHISES AND BUSINESS OPPORTUNITIES

1402 ■ Beauty Supply Outlet
2090 Hurontario St.
Mississauga, ON, Canada L5B 1M8
Ph: (905)275-6202
Co. E-mail: bso@thebsoonline.com
URL: http://thebsoonline.com
Facebook: www.facebook.com/BeautySupplyOutlet
Description: Distributor and retailer of professional salon products and appliances. **Founded:** 1993. **Training:** New franchisee training and ongoing support.

1403 ■ Chatters Salon
271 Burnt Park Dr.
Red Deer County, AB, Canada T4S 0K7
Ph: (403)356-2734
Free: 877-820-9365
Co. E-mail: customerservice@chatters.ca
URL: http://chatters.ca
Facebook: www.facebook.com/ChattersHairSalon
X (Twitter): x.com/ChattersHair
Instagram: www.instagram.com/chattershairsalon
YouTube: www.youtube.com/channel/UCRF3o5RcvXz0x0plSdCkAsQ
Pinterest: www.pinterest.ca/ChattersSalons
Description: Provider of salon services such as hair cuts, lashes, brows, waxing, perms, colors and other services for men, women and children. **Founded:** 1991.

1404 ■ Facelogic [Emerald Lotus Massage & Spa]
3525 G. Longmire Dr.
College Station, TX 77845
Ph: (979)693-2600
Co. E-mail: info@emeraldlotusspa.com
URL: http://emeraldlotusspa.com
Description: Operator of spa. **Founded:** 2005. **Franchised:** 2005. **Training:** 3 days training provided at headquarters, 5 days onsite and ongoing support.

1405 ■ The Woodhouse Spas Corp. (WH) [The Woodhouse Day Spa]
609 N Wheeler St.
Victoria, TX 77901
Free: 877-570-7772
Co. E-mail: info@woodhousespas.com
URL: http://www.woodhousespas.com
Facebook: www.facebook.com/WoodhouseSpas
X (Twitter): x.com/thewoodhousespa
Instagram: www.instagram.com/woodhouse_spa_
Pinterest: www.pinterest.com/woodhousespas
Description: Provides day spa services, bath and body retail products. **Founded:** 2001. **Franchised:** 2003. **Equity Capital Needed:** net worth of $750,000; liquid capital of $250,000. **Franchise Fee:** $48,000. **Financial Assistance:** No **Training:** Offers 2-3 weeks training and an additional 1-2 days with ongoing support.

LIBRARIES

1406 ■ Mary Kay Inc. Information Resources
16251 N Dallas Pky.
Addison, TX 75001
URL: http://www.marykay.com
Scope: Cosmetics; dermatology; toxicology; chemistry; business; marketing. **Services:** Interlibrary loan. **Holdings:** 2000 books; 500 bound periodical volumes.

Bed and Breakfast Operation

REFERENCE WORKS

1407 ■ *"8 Bed-And-Breakfasts Perfect For a Romantic Getaway"* in USA Today (April 16, 2019)
URL(s): www.usatoday.com/story/travel/hotels/2019/04/16/bed-and-breakfasts-romantic-getaway/3378134002/
Ed: Jean Chen Smith. **Released:** April 16, 2019. **Description:** Overview of eight bed and breakfast operations, which highlight what makes each space unique and special for their guests. **Availability:** Online.

1408 ■ *"30 Charming Bed-and-Breakfasts Across America"* in U.S. News & World Report (September 10, 2018)
URL(s): travel.usnews.com/gallery/30-charming-bed-and-breakfasts-across-america
Ed: Gwen Pratesi. **Released:** September 10, 2018. **Description:** Showcases 30 extraordinary bed and breakfasts to visit across America. **Availability:** Online.

1409 ■ *"B&B Hopes to Appeal to Fiat Execs"* in Crain's Detroit Business (Vol. 25, June 15, 2009, No. 24, pp. 21)
Pub: Crain Communications Inc.
Contact: Barry Asin, President
Ed: Daniel Duggan. **Description:** Cobblestone Manor, a ten-room bed and breakfast in Auburn Hills, Michigan is hoping to provide rooms for Fiat executives. The owners have been working with travel organizations to promote the castle-like bed and breakfast which appeals to European visitors. **Availability:** Online.

1410 ■ *"Bed and Breakfast Among Planned Uses for New Bohemia Properties"* in Gazette (January 30, 2012)
Description: One of the buildings suffering flood damage in the middle of the New Bohemia district of Cedar Rapids, Iowa area will be converted into a one room bed and breakfast offering food catered by Parlor City. The two-story building will als house commercial business on the first floor and a two-bedroom apartment on the upper level. This concept follows the neighborhood's origins with shop owners living above their small business. **Availability:** Online.

1411 ■ *"Bed and Breakfast Inspired by 'The Waltons' Set to Open in Virginia"* in WSLS.com (October 10, 2019)
URL: www.wsls.com/news/virginia/nelson/bed-and-breakfast-inspired-by-the-waltons-set-to-open-in-virginia
Ed: Jeff Williamson. **Released:** October 10, 2019. **Description:** A new five-bedroom, five-bathroom bed and breakfast inspired by the popular TV show, The Waltons, is set to open. Some of the original cast is due to make an appearance as well. **Availability:** Online.

1412 ■ *"Bedandbreakfast.eu: Bed & Breakfast Emerging in Europe"* in Travel & Leisure Close-Up (January 11, 2012)
Pub: Close-Up Media Inc.
Contact: Caroline S. Moore, President
E-mail: cms@closeupmedia.com
Description: According to experts, only 15 percent of all bed and breakfast operations in Europe were launched before the year 2000, with the majority opening after 2005. Reports show approximately 2,400 new operations opening on a monthly basis. Bedandbreakfast.eu offer current offerings for vacationers interested in staying at a bed and breakfast while visiting Europe. **Availability:** Online.

1413 ■ *Buying and Running a Guesthouse or Small Hotel*
Released: Second edition. **Description:** Teaches how to build and enjoy a lifestyle while running a guesthouse or small hotel.

1414 ■ *"Five Myths About Bed and Breakfasts"* and USA Today (December 29, 2015)
URL(s): www.usatoday.com/story/travel/destinations/2015/12/29/bed-and-breakfast/77976168/
Released: December 29, 2015. **Description:** Five myths about bed and breakfasts are discussed and debunked. Issues about privacy, bathrooms, and price are explored. **Availability:** Online.

1415 ■ *"'Groundhog Day' B&B Likely Will Be Converted Into One In Real Life"* in Chicago Tribune (October 21, 2008)
Pub: Tribune News Service
Contact: Jack Barry, Vice President, Operations
E-mail: jbarry@tribpub.com
Ed: Carolyn Starks. **Description:** Everton Martin and Karla Stewart Martin have purchased the Victorian house that was featured as a bed-and-breakfast in the 1993 hit move "Groundhog Day"; the couple was initially unaware of the structure's celebrity status when they purchased it with the hope of fulfilling their dream of owning a bed-and-breakfast. **Availability:** Print; Online.

1416 ■ *How to Open and Operate a Bed & Breakfast*
Ed: Jan Stankus. **Released:** December 20, 2011. **Price:** $21.95, paperback(£14.95); $20.99, e-book(-£13.95); paperback, softback. **Description:** Handbook outlines how to set up and run a bed and breakfast, whether using a spare room of a home or a small inn. **Availability:** E-book; Print.

1417 ■ *"How to... Harness Green Power"* in The Caterer (July 20, 2012, No. 325)
Pub: LNRS Data Services Limited
Contact: Mark Vickers Kelsey, Director
Description: Roger and Emma Stevens discuss their success as at winning the Considerate Hoteliers Association's award for Best Green Marketing Initiative. The couple discusses their restaurant and its partnership with tow nearby guesthouses. **Availability:** Online.

1418 ■ *INNside Scoop: Everything You Ever Wanted to Know About Bed & Breakfast Inns*
Pub: The B&B and Country Inn Marketplace
Contact: Mariette Gagne, Contact
E-mail: mariettehnc@gmail.com
Ed: Maxine Pinson. **Price:** $14.95, Free. **Description:** Guide for running a successful bread and breakfast inn. **Availability:** Print.

1419 ■ *"Muirhead Farmhouse B&B Owners Get Hospitality Wright"* in Chicago Tribune (July 31, 2008)
Pub: Tribune News Service
Contact: Jack Barry, Vice President, Operations
E-mail: jbarry@tribpub.com
Ed: Glenn Jeffers. **Description:** Profile of the Muirhead Farmhouse, a bed-and-breakfast owned by Mike Petersdorf and Sarah Muirhead Petersdorf; Frank Lloyd Wright designed the historic farmhouse which blends farm life and history into a unique experience that is enhanced by the couple's hospitality. **Availability:** Online.

1420 ■ *"A New Breed of Innkeepers for the Airbnb Era"* in The Wall Street Journal (November 8, 2018)
URL(s): www.wsj.com/articles/a-new-breed-of-innkeepers-for-the-airbnb-era-1541691939
Ed: Amy Gamerman. **Released:** November 08, 2018. **Description:** Traditional bed and breakfasts are upgrading in order to attract guests away from Airbnb style getaways. This includes installing free Wi-Fi, providing more vegan options for breakfast, and even advertising on Airbnb. **Availability:** Online.

1421 ■ *"Realtors Irate Over Tax Plan"* in Providence Business News (Vol. 26, March 26, 2012, No. 51, pp. 1)
Pub: American City Business Journals, Inc.
Contact: Mike Olivieri, Executive Vice President
URL(s): pbn.com/realtors-irate-over-tax-plan66344
Ed: Kelly L. Anderson. **Description:** Rhode Island realtors are criticizing Governor Lincoln D. Chafee's plan to tax vacation rentals and bed and breakfast operations. The plan is in line with the state's efforts to balance the 2013 budget. Comments from executives are included.

1422 ■ *"Sleep It Off In a Silo B&B"* in Chicago Tribune (December 14, 2008)
Pub: Tribune News Service
Contact: Jack Barry, Vice President, Operations
E-mail: jbarry@tribpub.com
Ed: Bill Daley. **Description:** Profile of Oregon's Abbey Road Farm bed-and-breakfast which is located on an 82-acre working farm; guests stay in shiny metal farm silos which have been converted into luxury rooms with views of the farm.

1423 ■ *"South Lake Tahoe B&B Blocks Out Nevada's Neon"* in Chicago Tribune (May 18, 2008)
Pub: Tribune News Service
Contact: Jack Barry, Vice President, Operations

E-mail: jbarry@tribpub.com
Ed: Randall Weissman. **Description:** Profile of the Black Bear Inn, a small bed-and-breakfast in South Lake Tahoe owned by Jerry Birdwell and Kevin Chandler; the welcoming ambience is a delightful departure from ski resort hotel rooms. Pricing and further details of the various rooms are described. **Availability:** Print; Online.

1424 ■ *Starting a Bed and Breakfast: Bite Sized Interviews with Successful B&B's on Building a Brand That Lasts*
Ed: Jon Nelson. **Released:** October 19, 2021. **Description:** Owners of bed and breakfast establishments throughout the country share their experiences of running this niche business. Answers to questions, such as: what time do you need to wake up? Do you need to be a good cook? Plus many others are answered to help give potential new owners an idea of what to expect while running a bed and breakfast. **Availability:** E-book.

1425 ■ *"West Palm Beach Bed and Breakfast is a Labor of Love" in Palm Beach Post (April 7, 2012)*
Pub: McClatchy Tribune Information Services
Contact: Patrick J. Talamantes, President
Ed: Susan Salisbury. **Released:** April 07, 2012. **Description:** Profile of Cheryl and Kirk Grantham, husband and wife team who run a bed and breakfast in West Palm Beach, Florida. The couple discusses their move to the community and why they decided to open their inn. Their property offers five bed and breakfast guest suites along with another five suites in an Art Deco building. Cheryl talks about her love for entertaining along with the four diamond rating of their establishment. **Availability:** Print; Online.

STATISTICAL SOURCES

1426 ■ *Bed & Breakfast & Hostel Accommodations Industry in the US - Market Research Report*
URL(s): www.ibisworld.com/united-states/market-research-reports/bed-breakfast-hostel-accommodations-industry/
Price: $925. **Description:** Downloadable report analyzing the trends and future outlook for the bed and breakfast and hostel industries. **Availability:** Download.

COMPUTERIZED DATABASES

1427 ■ *FDA Food Code*
URL(s): www.fda.gov/food/retail-food-protection/fda-food-code
Released: Semiannual **Availability:** PDF. **Type:** Full-text.

Beekeeping

ASSOCIATIONS AND OTHER ORGANIZATIONS

1428 ■ American Beekeeping Federation (ABF)
136 Everett Rd.
Albany, NY 12205
Ph: (518)694-9793
Co. E-mail: info@abfnet.org
URL: http://www.abfnet.org
Contact: Dan Winter, President
Facebook: www.facebook.com/AmericanBeekeepingFederation
Instagram: www.instagram.com/americanbeekeepingfederation
YouTube: www.youtube.com/channel/UCpf26uL2FYrjnbnxUYTY_dA
Description: Commercial and avocational beekeepers, suppliers, bottlers, packers, and others affiliated with the honey industry. Promotes the industry and serves as an representative before legislative bodies; makes recommendations and helps secure appropriations for research programs. Operates the Honey Defense Fund, which works to insure the purity of honey marketed in the US. Sponsors American Honey Queen Program. **Founded:** 1943. **Publications:** *Bee Culture* (Quarterly); *ABF E-Buzz* (Monthly). **Educational Activities:** American Beekeeping Federation Conference & Tradeshow (Annual). **Awards:** ABF President's Award (Annual). **Geographic Preference:** National.

1429 ■ American Honey Producers Association (AHPA)
PO Box 12
Grand Haven, MI 49417
Ph: (281)900-9740
Co. E-mail: cassie@ahpanet.com
URL: http://ahpanet.com
Contact: Adm. (Ret.) Chris Hiatt, President
E-mail: chrishiatt@ahpanet.com
Facebook: www.facebook.com/AmericanHoneyProducersAssociation
Instagram: www.instagram.com/americanhoneyproducersassoc
Description: Commercial and avocational beekeepers. Represents the interests of beekeepers in agricultural research programs and before legislative bodies, and marketing. **Founded:** 1969. **Geographic Preference:** National.

1430 ■ Apiary Inspectors of America (AIA)
PO Box 1163
Richmond, VA 23218
Ph: (804)786-3515
URL: http://apiaryinspectors.org
Contact: Natasha Garcia-Andersen, President
E-mail: president@apiaryinspectors.org
Description: State and provincial apiarists; individuals interested in beekeeping and bee research are associate members. Seeks to promote and protect the beekeeping industry of North America. Participates in research meetings at United States Department of Agriculture-Science and Educational Administration laboratories. **Geographic Preference:** National.

1431 ■ The Beekeepers of Indiana
7784 N Sanctuary Ln.
Mooresville, IN 46158
Ph: (317)432-9578
Co. E-mail: beekeepers.indiana@yahoo.com
URL: http://indianabeekeeper.com
Contact: John Schellenberger, President
Facebook: www.facebook.com/beekeepersofindiana
X (Twitter): x.com/BeekeepersIn
Description: Represents all beekeepers in Indiana from hobbyists to commercial.

1432 ■ Bees in the D
200 River Pl. Dr.
Detroit, MI 48207
Ph: (313)462-9624
URL: http://beesinthed.com
Contact: Brian Peterson-Roest, Founder
Facebook: www.facebook.com/BeesInTheD
Instagram: www.instagram.com/beesinthed
Description: Organization educates the public on the importance of honeybees and other pollinators while creating a network of urban hives.

1433 ■ Connecticut Beekeepers Association (CBA)
c/o Mark Creighton
123 Huntington Ave.
New Haven, CT 06504
Ph: (203)530-5743
Co. E-mail: mark.creighton@ct.gov
URL: http://www.ctbees.org
Contact: Bill Hesbach, President
Facebook: www.facebook.com/ConnecticutBeekeepers
YouTube: www.youtube.com/channel/UCkNud2h_wiR_Cmo2IA3j_ng
Description: Promotes and supports all beekeepers with the goal of providing a common forum for the beekeepers of Connecticut to come together to share information and ideas.

1434 ■ Detroit Hives (DH)
9336 E Warren Ave.
Detroit, MI 48214
Ph: (248)808-8467
Co. E-mail: info@detroithives.org
URL: http://detroithives.org
Contact: Timothy Paule Jackson, Contact
Description: Nonprofit organization transforming empty lots in Detroit into bee hive farms to support the community and teach the importance of bees. **Founded:** 2018.

1435 ■ Eastern Apicultural Society of North America (EAS)
c/o David Morris, President
9309 Montpelier Dr.
Laurel, MD 20708-2553
URL: http://easternapiculture.org
Contact: Lou Naylor, Chairman of the Board
E-mail: chairman@easternapiculture.org
Facebook: www.facebook.com/easternapiculture
X (Twitter): x.com/easternapicult1
Description: Hobbyist beekeepers and producers of honey; supporting members are manufacturers of beekeeping equipment and packers of honey. Provides an educational program for hobbyist beekeepers and the public on the science of apiculture (beekeeping). **Founded:** 1955. **Awards:** Charles and Evelyn Divelbiss Education Award (Annual); EAS Student Apiculture Award (Annual); James I. Hambleton Award (Annual); J. I. Hambleton Award (Annual); Roger A. Morse Outstanding Teaching/Extension Service/Regulatory Award (Annual). **Geographic Preference:** National.

1436 ■ Empire State Honey Producers Association
5550 Eddy Ridge Rd.
Marion, NY 14505
Ph: (315)576-1930
URL: http://eshpa.org
Contact: Kim Ess, Treasurer
E-mail: treasurer@eshpa.org
Facebook: www.facebook.com/EmpireStateHoneyProducers
Description: Statewide beekeeping organization representing the needs of beekeepers in New York.

1437 ■ Georgia Beekeepers Association (GBA)
1917 Rock Springs Rd.
Lavonia, GA 30553
Co. E-mail: georgiabeekeepersfacebook@gmail.com
URL: http://gabeekeeping.com
Contact: Gina Gallucci, President
E-mail: president@gabeekeeping.com
Facebook: www.facebook.com/georgiabeeclub
X (Twitter): x.com/GeorgiaBeekeep3
Description: Advances beekeeping and interests of beekeepers in Georgia. Provides information and resources to youth members and beginners. Supports honey bee research and activities that further beekeeping industry. **Founded:** 1920. **Geographic Preference:** State.

1438 ■ Heartland Apicultural Society (HAS)
2713 State Hwy. 14
Mulkeytown, IL 62865
Ph: (618)724-2786
Co. E-mail: info@heartlandbees.org
URL: http://www.heartlandbees.org
Contact: Jennifer Tsuruda, Chairman of the Board
Facebook: www.facebook.com/HAS.Beekeeping
Description: A non-profit that brings scientific beekeeping research, beginning beekeeping classes, and advanced beekeeping classes to beekeepers.

1439 ■ Illinois State Beekeepers Association
PO Box 21094
Springfield, IL 62708
Ph: (217)638-7891
URL: http://www.ilsba.com

1440 ■ Beekeeping

Contact: Rose Leedle, President
Facebook: www.facebook.com/illinois.state.beekeepers

Description: Association supporting beekeepers in Illinois. Works to promote interest in honeybees and beekeeping by encouraging responsible beekeeping. **Founded:** 1891.

1440 ■ Maine State Beekeepers Association (MSBA)
ME
Co. E-mail: info@mainebeekeepers.org
URL: http://mainebeekeepers.org
Contact: Beth Goodwin, President
E-mail: goodwin.elizabeth@gmail.com
URL(s): simmonslis.libguides.com/beginnerbeekeeping/associations
Facebook: www.facebook.com/mainebeekeepers

Description: Promotes beekeeping in Maine. Provides information and resources on topics relating to honey bees and beekeeping practices. Informs members and the public of latest development in bee research. **Founded:** 1976. **Geographic Preference:** State.

1441 ■ Maryland State Beekeepers Association Inc. (MSBA)
c/o Robert Crouse, Treasurer
1606 Dogwood Ln.
Bel Air, MD 21015-2502
Ph: (410)638-0105
Co. E-mail: rlcrouse@qis.net
URL: http://mdbeekeepers.org
Contact: Robert Crouse, Treasurer
E-mail: rlcrouse@qis.net

Description: Focuses on educating and supporting its members in all aspects of beekeeping. Supports honey bee research and activities that further beekeeping industry and protection of honey bees. **Founded:** 1908. **Geographic Preference:** State.

1442 ■ Massachusetts Beekeepers Association (MBA)
425 N Ave.
Weston, MA 02493
URL: http://www.massbee.org
Contact: Mary Duane, President
E-mail: president@massbee.org

Description: Works to promote education in matters relating to honeybees and beekeeping in the state of Massachusetts.

1443 ■ Michigan Beekeepers Association (MBA)
17 Millenium Dr.
Muskegon, MI 49442
Co. E-mail: president@mba-bees.org
URL: http://www.michiganbees.org
Contact: Rich Wieske, President
E-mail: richwieske@icloud.com
Facebook: www.facebook.com/michiganbees

Description: Supports Michigan bees and beekeepers. **Founded:** 1865.

1444 ■ National Honey Packers and Dealers Association (NHPDA)
3301 Rte. 66
Bldg. C, Ste. 205
Neptune, NJ 07753
Ph: (732)922-3008
Fax: (732)922-3590
Co. E-mail: info@nhpda.org
URL: http://www.nhpda.org

Description: Represents cooperative and independent processors, packers, and dealers of honey at either the wholesale or retail level. Offers members information on testing facilities for honey analysis. Consults with Department of Agriculture on research programs in the field of honey marketing. **Geographic Preference:** National.

1445 ■ New Hampshire Beekeepers Association (NHBA)
99 Foster Rd.
Canterbury, NH 03224
URL: http://www.nhbeekeepers.org
Contact: Mary Ellen McKeen, President
Facebook: www.facebook.com/NHBeekeepers

Description: A non-profit organization dedicated to the advancement and study of bees, beekeeping, and the economic importance of apiculture in the state of New Hampshire. **Founded:** 1977.

1446 ■ New Jersey Beekeepers Association (NJBA)
NJ
Co. E-mail: info@njbeekeepers.org
URL: http://www.njbeekeepers.org
Contact: Dave Elkner, President
E-mail: president@njbeekeepers.org

Description: A not-for-profit, all-volunteer organization dedicated to the promotion and support of all aspects of beekeeping in New Jersey. **Founded:** 1902.

1447 ■ North Carolina State Beekeepers Association (NCSBA)
PO Box 99
Hurdle Mills, NC 27541
URL: http://www.ncbeekeepers.org
Contact: Rick Coor, President
E-mail: president@ncbeekeepers.org
Facebook: www.facebook.com/ncbeekeepers
X (Twitter): x.com/ncbeekeepers
Instagram: www.instagram.com/ncbeekeepers

Description: Represents beekeepers of North Carolina. Promotes cooperation, relations among beekeeping advocates, and markets for beekeeping products. **Geographic Preference:** State.

1448 ■ Ohio State Beekeepers Association (OSBA)
330 N Sunderland Rd.
Delphos, OH 45833
URL: http://ohiostatebeekeepers.org
Contact: Peggy Garnes, President
Facebook: www.facebook.com/OhioStateBeekeepers

Description: Serves and supports beekeepers in Ohio.

1449 ■ Pennsylvania State Beekeepers Association (PSBA)
c/o Bob Tatro, Treasurer
110 Holly Hill Dr.
Oakdale, PA 15071
Ph: (412)508-0820
Co. E-mail: beehelp@pastatebeekeepers.org
URL: http://www.pastatebeekeepers.org
Contact: Mark Gingrich, President
E-mail: president@pastatebeekeepers.org
Facebook: www.facebook.com/pastatebeekeepers
X (Twitter): x.com/PABeekeepers

Description: Supports beekeepers in Pennsylvania through advocacy, research and education. Promotes scientific study of honeybees and honey production by working on the proposed legislation that may effect apiculture or honey production throughout the state. **Founded:** 1904. **Geographic Preference:** State.

1450 ■ Rhode Island Beekeepers Association (RIBA)
PO Box 61
East Greenwich, RI 02818
Co. E-mail: ribeekeeper@ribeekeeper.org
URL: http://ribeekeeper.org
Contact: Sara Michaud, Co-President

Description: Provides support to beekeepers in Rhode Island. **Founded:** 1917.

1451 ■ South Carolina State Beekeepers Association (SCBA)
1437 Jessamine Rd.
Lexington, SC 29073
Ph: (803)981-2495
Co. E-mail: info@scstatebeekeepers.com
URL: http://scstatebeekeepers.com
Contact: Cynthia Robinson, Secretary
Facebook: www.facebook.com/SouthCarolinaBeekeepers
X (Twitter): x.com/scbeekepers

Description: A private non-profit organization dedicated to education and advocacy for South Carolina beekeepers. Works to ensure that local beekeepers have the information and tools they need to meet the challenges of modern beekeeping.

1452 ■ Tennessee Beekeepers Association (TBA)
c/o David Hale, President
PO Box 33
Drummonds, TN 38023
Co. E-mail: info@tnbeekeepers.org
URL: http://tnbeekeepers.org
Contact: A. C. Mann, Director
Facebook: www.facebook.com/TNBeekeepersAssoc

Description: Provides information and support for all registered beekeepers in Tennessee. Promotes programs and meetings about beekeeper assistance. **Geographic Preference:** State.

1453 ■ Treasure Valley Beekeepers Club (TVBC)
PO Box 5066
Boise, ID 83705-0066
Co. E-mail: tvbeekeepers@gmail.com
URL: http://www.idabees.org
Contact: Marc von Huene, President
Facebook: www.facebook.com/groups/Treasure.Valley.Beekeepers
YouTube: www.youtube.com/channel/UCl1nzbCyyW2tnqR5ZyHVBzA/about

Description: Fosters camaraderie and enjoyment of beekeeping among members. Offers workshops and classes to beginners and enthusiasts. **Geographic Preference:** Local.

1454 ■ Vermont Beekeepers Association (VBA)
PO Box 764
Burlington, VT 05402-0764
URL: http://www.vermontbeekeepers.org
Contact: Richard Roy, Treasurer
Facebook: www.facebook.com/VermontBeekeepersAssociation
Instagram: www.instagram.com/vermontbeekeepers

Description: Provides information and support for all registered beekeepers and hobbyists. Promotes the general welfare of Vermont's Honey Industry through education, programs and meetings about beekeeping. **Founded:** 1986. **Geographic Preference:** State.

1455 ■ Virginia State Beekeepers Association (VSBA)
c/o Scott Polling, Treasurer
201 Bluebird Ln.
Charlotte Court House, VA 23923
Ph: (434)823-8600
Co. E-mail: membershipvsba@virginiabeekeepers.org
URL: http://www.virginiabeekeepers.org
Contact: Scott Poling, Treasurer
E-mail: treasurer@virginiabeekeepers.org
Facebook: www.facebook.com/VirginaStateBeekeepers
X (Twitter): x.com/VABeekeepers
Instagram: www.instagram.com/virginia_beekeepers
YouTube: www.youtube.com/channel/UCDfydmBoa-F_Na5BfXRQW8A

Description: Represents beekeepers and those people interested in beekeeping in the state of Virginia. Promotes advancing beekeeping throughout the state. **Founded:** 1918. **Geographic Preference:** State.

1456 ■ Western Apicultural Society (WAS)
PO Box 5274
Twin Falls, ID 83303
Co. E-mail: westernapiculturalsociety@gmail.com
URL: http://www.westernapiculturalsociety.org
Contact: Etienne Tardif, President
Facebook: www.facebook.com/WesternApiculturalSociety
X (Twitter): x.com/WestApiculture
Instagram: www.instagram.com/westernapiculturalsociety
YouTube: www.youtube.com/channel/UClxcdLsc9Eu_lyD5ZNZ5rmg

Description: A non-profit educational beekeeping organization for the benefit and enjoyment of all beekeepers designed specifically to meet the educational needs of beekeepers from the states of Alaska, Arizona, California, Colorado, Hawaii, Idaho, Montana, Nevada, New Mexico, Oregon, Utah, Washington, and Wyoming; the provinces of Alberta, British Columbia, Saskatchewan, and the Yukon; and the states of northern Mexico. **Founded:** 1978.

REFERENCE WORKS

1457 ■ *American Bee Journal*
URL(s): americanbeejournal.com
Released: Monthly. **Description:** Publication on bees that provides beekeepers with scores of interesting and informative articles to make beekeeping more fun and profitable. Includes monthly crop and market information, practical information, scientific and experimental reports, industry news, and display and classified ads. **Availability:** Print; Electronic publishing. **Telecommunication Services:** info@americanbeejournal.com.

1458 ■ *The Backyard Beekeeper*
Ed: Kim Flottum. **Released:** January 02, 2018. **Price:** $11.99 e-textbook; $14.56 paperback. **Description:** For backyard beekeepers of all skill levels, this illustrated book provides information on equipment, seasonal duties, and much more specific to small apiaries. **Availability:** E-book; Print.

1459 ■ *Bee Culture*
URL(s): www.beeculture.com
Facebook: www.facebook.com/BeeCultureMagazine
X (Twitter): twitter.com/beeculture
Instagram: www.instagram.com/beeculturemag/
Description: Magazine designed for beginning, sideline, and commercial beekeepers who want the latest information on keeping bees. **Availability:** Print; Online. **Telecommunication Services:** info@beeculture.com.

1460 ■ *"Bee Mindful: NY Lawmakers Want to Preserve, Relocate Pesky Hives"* in *TimesUnion (October 10, 2019)*
URL(s): www.timesunion.com/news/article/Bee-min
dful-State-lawmakers-want-to-preserve-and-145039
33.php
Ed: Cayla Harris. **Released:** October 10, 2019. **Description:** A new bill is being proposed to help preserve honey bee colonies in New York. This bill would require people to contact the state's Division of Plant Industry about pesky bee colonies so they be removed and relocated, inside of destroyed. **Availability:** Online.

1461 ■ *The Beekeeper's Bible: Bees, Honey, Recipes & Other Home Uses*
Ed: Richard Jones. **Released:** April 01, 2011. **Price:** $30.99. **Description:** Part history book, part handbook, and part cookbook, this illustrated guide covers every facet of the ancient hobby of beekeeping, from how to manage hives safely to harvesting one's own honey, and ideas for how to use honey and beeswax. **Availability:** Print.

1462 ■ *The Beekeeper's Handbook*
Ed: Diana Sammataro, Alphonse Avitabile. **Released:** April 15, 2021. **Price:** $26.68. **Description:** Provides step-by-step instructions for setting up an apiary, handling bees, and working throughout the season to maintain a healthy colony and a generous supply of honey. **Availability:** Print.

1463 ■ *The Beekeeper's Problem Solver*
Ed: James Tew. **Released:** February 15, 2015. **Description:** Explains 100 common problems faced by beekeepers including their underlying problems and how to solve them. **Availability:** E-book; Print.

1464 ■ *"Beekeepers Seek to Save Honeybees From a Colony-Invading Pest"* in *Smithsonian (September 30, 2019)*
URL(s): www.smithsonianmag.com/science-nature/
beekeepers-seek-save-honeybees-colony-invading
-pest-180973241/
Ed: Paige Embry. **Released:** September 30, 2019. **Description:** A parasitic Asian mite, Varroa destructor, is wreaking havoc on bee colonies across the nation. Several solutions are presented as beekeepers scramble to keep their colonies flourishing. **Availability:** Online.

1465 ■ *"Beekeeping 101: Should You Raise Honey Bees? The Pros and Cons of Keeping Bees"* in *The Old Farmer's Almanac (July 24, 2019)*
URL(s): www.almanac.com/news/beekeeping/
beekeeping-101-why-raise-honeybees
Released: July 24, 2019. **Description:** Explores the pros and cons of beekeeping. Issues from cost to the benefits of the end product are discussed. **Availability:** Print; Online.

1466 ■ *Beekeeping: For Beginners and Backyard Business People*
Ed: Sarah Jacobs. **Released:** August 06, 2020. **Description:** Guides the reader into learning about setting up a beekeeping and honey business and taking a hobby and turning it into something that turns a profit. **Availability:** E-book.

1467 ■ *Beekeeping For Beginners: How to Raise Your First Bee Colonies*
Ed: Amber Bradshaw. **Released:** June 25, 2019. **Price:** $13.99 paperback. **Description:** A simple, step-by-step guide that covers the fundamentals of modern beekeeping, from picking the right hive and bringing bees home to surviving winter and collecting honey. **Availability:** E-book; Print.

1468 ■ *Beekeeping For Dummies*
Ed: Howland Blackiston. **Released:** January 17, 2017. **Description:** A hands-on guide providing all the tools, tips, tricks, and techniques needed to become a backyard beekeeper, stressing the importance of both tradition and individuality within beekeeping. **Availability:** Print.

1469 ■ *Beekeeping: Growing a Backyard Business with Bees*
Ed: Sarah Jacobs. **Released:** August 06, 2020. **Description:** A two-book set discussing setting up a beekeeping business. The first book discusses the various types of bees and how to set up your own hive. The second book focuses on the practical aspects of beekeeping as a business. **Availability:** E-book.

1470 ■ *Beekeeping: Planning, Managing, and Keeping Bees*
Ed: Sarah Jacobs. **Released:** August 06, 2020. **Description:** A general guide to beekeeping and tips for running your own hives as a small business. **Availability:** E-book.

1471 ■ *Beekeeping: The Business, Care, and Specifics of Handling Bees*
Ed: Sarah Jacobs. **Released:** August 06, 2020. **Description:** A guide to setting up a beekeeping business. Includes a business plan, practical information about bees, and a guide about the honey side of the business. **Availability:** E-book.

1472 ■ *Beekeeping: The Techniques, Benefits, and Drawbacks of Beekeeping Explained*
Ed: Sarah Jacobs. **Released:** August 06, 2020. **Description:** A practical guide to all aspects of beekeeping, so the reader can make an informed decision about turning this hobby into a business. **Availability:** E-book.

1473 ■ *Beekeeping: The Ultimate Beginner's Guide to Learn Managing Bees*
Ed: Sarah Jacobs. **Released:** August 06, 2020. **Description:** A three-book set explaining all there is to know about beekeeping, how to harvest honey, and how to set up your own beekeeping business. **Availability:** E-book.

1474 ■ *Beekeeping: Understanding the Opportunities and Dangers of Keeping Bees*
Ed: Sarah Jacobs. **Released:** August 06, 2020. **Description:** This two-book set discusses setting up a beekeeping enterprise as a hobby and then moving into setting it up as a business. **Availability:** E-book.

1475 ■ *"Bees & Beekeeping: Past & Present"* in *American Bee Journal (November 1, 2021)*
Released: November 01, 2021. **Description:** An overview of beekeeping and hives, noting what could go wrong with the queen and the workers.

1476 ■ *Beginning Beekeeping: Everything You Need to Make Your Hive Thrive!*
Ed: Tanya Phillips. **Released:** March 14, 2017. **Description:** Teaches beginning beekeepers how to foster and maintain healthy, vibrant colonies as well as how to harvest honey and how to keep your bees healthy and happy. Illustrated. **Availability:** E-book; Print.

1477 ■ *Build Your Own Beekeeping Equipment*
Ed: Tony Pisano. **Released:** April 23, 2013. **Price:** $11.99 e-book; $16.29 paperback. **Description:** Practical guide to building beekeeping equipment. **Availability:** E-book; Print.

1478 ■ *"Buzz Kill"* in *Canadian Business (Vol. 83, August 17, 2010, No. 13-14, pp. 24)*
Description: Beekeeping industry has been plagued by a massive wave of honeybee deaths since 2006, which pushed upward the cost of per hive-rental. The death of honeybees has put the food supply at risk since it jeopardized the growth of pumpkins, as well as other crops in large acreage. Insights on the Colony Collapse Disorder are outlined. **Availability:** Online.

1479 ■ *The Complete Idiot's Guide to Beekeeping*
Ed: Dean Stiglitz, Laura Herboldsheimer. **Released:** May 04, 2010. **Price:** $7.99 e-book; $15.35 paperback. **Description:** Covers all of the information a beginning beekeeper needs to start a hive and keep it buzzing. **Availability:** E-book; Print.

1480 ■ *Honey Bee Biology and Beekeeping*
Ed: Dewey Caron. **Released:** June 28, 2013. **Price:** $77.65. **Description:** The standard beekeeping (apiculture) textbook used to teach college students and beekeepers the science and practice of bees and beekeeping. This book concentrates on the 'why','how' and 'when' of beekeeping. **Availability:** Print.

1481 ■ *Langstroth's Hive and the Honey-Bee: The Classic Beekeeper's Manual*
Ed: L.L. Langstroth. **Released:** February 20, 2004. **Description:** A classic manual representing beekeeping history. This book illustrates techniques still employed 150 years later after its first publication, including the author's patented invention, a movable frame hive that quickly spread into common use around the world. **Availability:** E-book; Print.

1482 ■ *"Local Couple Pushes for Change to Waco Beekeeping Ordinance"* in *Waco Tribune-Herald (May 31, 2019)*
URL(s): www.wacotrib.com/news/government/local
-couple-pushes-for-change-to-waco-beekeeping-or
dinance/article_d8e9559e-13dc-5634-92ab-d22fc
d898aec.html
Released: May 31, 2019. **Description:** Due to an ordinance that requires beekeepers to obtain permission from everyone who lives in a 300-foot radius of the hive, a local beekeeper had to give up her hives. This spurred the beekeeper into action, hoping to get the ordinance changed so that more people can easily keep bees and help the ecosystem. **Availability:** Online.

1483 ■ *"Massive Loss of Thousands of Hives Afflicts Orchard Growers and Beekeepers"* in *NPR (February 18, 2019)*
URL(s): www.npr.org/sections/thesalt/2019/02/18/69
4301239/massive-loss-of-thousands-of-hives-afflic
ts-orchard-growers-and-beekeepers

Ed: Anna King. **Released:** February 18, 2019. **Description:** A 40 percent loss of bees is becoming common for beekeepers across the nation, which is having a huge negative impact on orchards and farming. Honey bees are susceptible to chemicals, bad nutrition, viruses, parasites, and even a loss of wildflowers and climate change. **Availability:** Online.

1484 ■ *Natural Beekeeping: Organic Approaches to Modern Apiculture*

Ed: Ross Conrad. **Released:** March 08, 2013. **Price:** $26.08 Paperback; $24.78 e-book. **Description:** Offers holistic, sensible alternatives to conventional chemical beekeeping practices with a program of natural hive management. Provides "do no harm" strategies for keeping honeybees healthy and productive with nontoxic methods of controlling mites; eliminating American foulbrood disease without the use of antibiotics; selective breeding for naturally resistant bees; and many other detailed management techniques, which are covered in a thoughtful, matter-of-fact way. **Availability:** E-book; Print.

1485 ■ *"Nearly 40% Decline in Honey Bee Popularion Last Winter 'Unsustainable,' Experts Say" in ABC News (July 9, 2019)*

URL(s): abcnews.go.com/US/40-decline-honey-bee-population-winter-unsustainable-experts/story?id=64191609

Ed: Julia Jacobo. **Released:** July 09, 2019. **Description:** With honeybees being one of the most important agricultural commodities, bringing in $170 billion in crops worldwide, the decline in their populations has scientists and farmers concerned. Bee-friendly options in pesticides are being explored. **Availability:** Online.

1486 ■ *QueenSpotting*

Ed: Hilary Kearney. **Released:** April 30, 2019. **Description:** A practical guide to queen bee management as well as a compelling book of interest to anyone who is interested in the lives of queen bees. **Availability:** E-book; Print.

1487 ■ *Storey's Guide to Keeping Honey Bees*

Ed: Malcolm Sanford, Richard Bonney. **Released:** July 10, 2018. **Description:** Handbook for novice and seasoned beekeepers featuring color photos and graphics as well as information on honey bee health. This reference presents comprehensive yet accessible information on everything from planning hives and installing a colony to preventing disease and managing productive hives that will bear bountiful honey harvests year after year. **Availability:** E-book; Print.

1488 ■ *Top-Bar Beekeeping*

Ed: Les Crowder, Heather Harrell. **Released:** August 31, 2012. **Price:** $21.15 e-book; $22.26 paperback. **Description:** Designed to encourage beekeepers around the world to keep bees naturally by providing beekeeping basics, hive management, and the utilization of top-bar hives. **Availability:** E-book; Print.

1489 ■ *"Urban Beekeeping Raises Southern California Concerns" in The Sacramento Bee (October 13, 2019)*

URL(s): www.sacbee.com/news/california/article10312841.html

Released: October 13, 2019. **Description:** In Southern California, legislators and beekeepers are struggling to find a balance between raising bees and keeping the human population safe from any aggressive bee species. **Availability:** Online.

STATISTICAL SOURCES

1490 ■ *Beekeeping Industry in the US - Market Research Report*

URL(s): www.ibisworld.com/united-states/market-research-reports/beekeeping-industry/

Price: $925. **Description:** Downloadable report analyzing current and future trends in the beekeeping industry. **Availability:** Download.

1491 ■ *Beekeeping in the US - Industry Market Research Report*

URL(s): www.marketresearch.com/IBISWorld-v2487/Beekeeping-Research-31870659/

Price: $1,020. **Description:** Report covering the scope, size, disposition and growth of the U.S. beekeeping industry including the key sensitivities and success factors. Also included are five-year industry forecasts, growth rates and an analysis of the industry key players and their market shares. **Availability:** Download.

TRADE PERIODICALS

1492 ■ *ABF E-Buzz*

Pub: American Beekeeping Federation
Contact: Dan Winter, President
URL(s): abfnet.org

Released: Monthly **Description:** Discusses Federation activities and national problems of the beekeeping industry. Also covers related legislation, regulations, and marketing and production information. Recurring features include news of research, book reviews, and columns titled President's Page, Washington Update, and Honey Queen Program Activities. **Availability:** PDF.

1493 ■ *American Bee Journal*

Pub: Dadant and Sons Inc.
URL(s): americanbeejournal.com
Facebook: www.facebook.com/AmericanBeeJournal
X (Twitter): x.com/beejournal

Ed: Kirsten Traynor, Joe Graham. **Released:** Monthly **Price:** $32, for 1 year us; $58, for 2 year us; $81, for 3 year us; $6.50, for issue 1 - 5 years us; $5, for single issue back issue us; $14.95, for single issue back issue us Canada foreign; $7.95, for journal issue us Canada foreign; $81, for 1 year Canada airmail; $53, for 1 year Canada surface; $152, for 1 year Canada airmail; $98, for 1 year Canada airmail; $106, for 1 year foreign airmail foreign; $63, for 1 year foreign surface foreign; $201, for 2 year foreign airmail foreign; $113, for 1 year foreign surface foreign. **Description:** Magazine for hobbyist and professional beekeepers. Covers hive management, honey handling, disease control, honey markets, foreign beekeeping, beekeeping history, bee laws, honey plants, marketing, and government beekeeping research. **Availability:** Print; Online.

1494 ■ *HiveLights*

Pub: Canadian Honey Council
Contact: Rod Scarlett, Executive Director
URL(s): honeycouncil.ca/educationresources/hivelights-newsletter-archive

Ed: Heather Clay. **Released:** Quarterly **Price:** $25, for per year; $50, for Canadian. **Description:** Cover topics related to the beekeeping and honey industry. Recurring features include letters to the editor, news of research, a calendar of events, reports of meetings, news of educational opportunities, and job listings. **Availability:** Print.

TRADE SHOWS AND CONVENTIONS

1495 ■ *American Beekeeping Federation Conference & Tradeshow*

American Beekeeping Federation (ABF)
136 Everett Rd.
Albany, NY 12205
Ph: (518)694-9793
Co. E-mail: info@abfnet.org
URL: http://www.abfnet.org
Contact: Dan Winter, President
URL(s): abfnet.org/2025-abf-conference

Frequency: Annual; held in January. **Description:** Exhibits related to beekeeping industry latest products and services. **Audience:** Beekeepers and general public. **Principal Exhibits:** Exhibits related to beekeeping industry latest products and services. **Telecommunication Services:** abfnet.org@gmail.com.

CONSULTANTS

1496 ■ Bee-Craft Consult
350 W Lucy Ave.
Salt Lake City, UT 84101
Ph: (801)462-5901
Co. E-mail: oduntan@beecraftconsult.tech
URL: http://beecraftconsult.tech
Contact: Adesina Daniel Oduntan, Chief Executive Officer
Facebook: www.facebook.com/honeybeesgold
Instagram: www.instagram.com/Beecraftconsult
Description: A one-stop-shop beekeeping consulting firm that produces high-quality natural honey and other beehive products. The consultants work with other beekeepers in doing the same. **Founded:** 1993.

1497 ■ Bee2Bee Honey Collective
1613 Branard St.
Houston, TX 77006
Ph: (281)845-4069
Co. E-mail: info@bee2beehoney.com
URL: http://bee2beehoney.com
Facebook: www.facebook.com/bee2beehoneytx
X (Twitter): x.com/bee2beehoneytx
Instagram: www.instagram.com/bee2beehoney
Description: Provides local honey, beekeeping classes, and beekeeping services. Specializes in small-batch neighborhood honeys, honey infusions and products of the beehive. **Founded:** 2016.

1498 ■ BeeHively Group
129 E St., D3
Davis, CA 95616
Free: 888-851-4879
Co. E-mail: support@beehively.com
URL: http://www.beehively.com
Facebook: www.facebook.com/beehivelearning
Linkedin: www.linkedin.com/company/beehively
Instagram: www.instagram.com/beehivelybees
Description: Offers software to educational institutions.

1499 ■ Bonnie Bee and Company
CA
URL: http://bonniebeecompany.com/wp/classes
Description: Offers consulting services for beekeepers. Services include private lessons, hive management, and honey extraction.

1500 ■ Foxhound Bee Company
424 9th St. N
Birmingham, AL 35203
Ph: (205)670-1337
URL: http://www.foxhoundbeecompany.com
Contact: Adam Hickman, Owner
Facebook: www.facebook.com/foxhoundbeeco
X (Twitter): x.com/foxhoundbeeco
Instagram: www.instagram.com/foxhoundbeeco
Description: Full-service beekeeping supply company helping beekeepers with all aspects of beekeeping. **Founded:** 2014.

1501 ■ Hansen Honey Farm LLC
3279 Hwy. 8 E
Rhinelander, WI 54501
Ph: (715)369-0383
URL: http://hansenhoneyfarm.com/beekeeping-consulting
Facebook: www.facebook.com/Keepnbees
Instagram: www.instagram.com/hansenhoneyfarmllc
Description: Offers consulting and maintenance services to help beekeepers care for their bees. Services include colony and equipment evaluation, queen evaluation, and varroa mite testing.

1502 ■ Honeysuckle Nectary Apiary and Gardens LLC
Howell, NJ
Ph: (908)652-6130
Co. E-mail: honeysucklenectary@gmail.com
URL: http://www.honeysucklenectary.com
Facebook: www.facebook.com/honeysucklenectary
Instagram: www.instagram.com/honeysucklenectary
Description: Offers expertise to help new beekeepers better understand how to handle different situations they may face with beekeeping.

1503 ■ Keystone Wildflowers
675 Hill Rd.
  Robesonia, PA 19551
Ph: (610)750-4186
Co. E-mail: bill@keystonewildflowers.com
URL: http://www.keystonewildflowers.com
Contact: Bill Hofmann, Owner
Facebook: www.facebook.com/KeystoneWildflowers
Linkedin: www.linkedin.com/company/keystone-wildflowers
Instagram: www.instagram.com/keystone.wildflowers
Description: Provides landscape and beekeeping consulting services. **Founded:** 2000.

LIBRARIES

1504 ■ Florida Department of Agriculture and Consumer Services - Division of Plant Industry Library
Doyle Conner Bldg., 1911 SW 34th St.
  Gainesville, FL 32608-1268
Fax: (352)395-4614
Co. E-mail: dpi-library@fdacs.gov
URL: http://www.fdacs.gov/Divisions-Offices/Plant-Industry/Division-of-Plant-Industry-Library
Contact: Jeff Eby, Librarian
E-mail: jeffrey.eby@fdacs.gov
Scope: Research associates; uf entomology; nematology department. **Services:** Interlibrary loan; copying; library open to the public for reference use only; scanning. **Founded:** 1915. **Holdings:** Photographs; clippings; maps; manuscripts; books; journals; documents; DVDs; videos; theses and dissertations; microforms; government reports; articles; archives materials.

1505 ■ Michigan State University - Special Collections Library
366 W Cir., Dr.
  East Lansing, MI 48824
Ph: (517)884-6471
Co. E-mail: spc@lib.msu.edu
URL: http://lib.msu.edu/MurrayHongSPC
Contact: Stephen O. Murray, Librarian
Scope: European history and culture; Italian Risorgimento; European criminology; French monarchy; radicalism; cookery; comic art. **Services:** Interlibrary loan; Library open to the public with required identification. **Founded:** 1962. **Holdings:** 450,000 Printed works; Numerous manuscript; Archival collections; Extensive collection of ephemera.

1506 ■ University of California, Davis - Archives and Special Collections
Shields Library, 100 NW Quad
  Davis, CA 95616
Ph: (530)752-1621
Co. E-mail: speccoll@ucdavis.edu
URL: http://library.ucdavis.edu/archives-and-special-collections
Contact: William Garrity, Head Librarian
E-mail: wfgarrity@ucdavis.edu
Scope: Agriculture; American; British literature; apiculture; botany; British history; entomology; religion; viticulture; enology and zoology. **Services:** Copying; collections open to the public for reference use only. **Founded:** 1966. **Holdings:** 183,000 volumes; 17,000 lin.ft. of archives and manuscripts; books; rare books; pamphlets; articles; journals.

Beeper/Paging Service

ASSOCIATIONS AND OTHER ORGANIZATIONS

1507 ■ *Advisor*
22 Spiral Dr.
Florence, KY 41042
Ph: (859)283-1885
Fax: (859)283-8178
Co. E-mail: info@nkadd.org
URL: http://nkadd.org
URL(s): us7.campaign-archive.com/home/?u=bb379
4330c2da62b5d8595091&id=78ba71998a
Released: Monthly; last update, April 2023. **Availability:** Print.

1508 ■ Canadian Call Management Association (CAM-X)
24 Olive St., Unit No 10
Grimsby, ON, Canada L3M 2B6
Ph: (905)309-0224
Free: 800-896-1054
Fax: (905)309-0225
Co. E-mail: info@camx.ca
URL: http://www.camx.ca
Contact: Linda Osip, Executive Director
E-mail: linda@camx.ca
Facebook: www.facebook.com/people/CAM-X/1000
57082765650
Linkedin: www.linkedin.com/company/cam-x-cana
dian-call-management-association
Description: Facilitates technical advancement in the field of telecommunications. **Founded:** 1964. **Publications:** *Advisor* (Monthly). **Awards:** CAM-X Award of Excellence (Annual); CAM-X Call Centre Award of Distinction (Annual). **Geographic Preference:** National.

1509 ■ Wireless Infrastructure Association (WIA) - Library
211 Wilson Blvd., Ste. 210
Arlington, VA 22201
Ph: (703)739-0300
Free: 800-759-0300
Fax: (703)836-1608
URL: http://wia.org
Contact: Jonathan Adelstein, President
Facebook: www.facebook.com/Wireless-Infrastruc
ture-Association-37483328338
Linkedin: www.linkedin.com/company/wireless-infras
tructure-association
X (Twitter): x.com/wiaorg
Description: Represents the companies that make up the wireless infrastructure ecosystem in the United States, including wireless carriers, infrastructure providers, and professional services firms that own and operate telecommunications facilities. Aims to support the wireless infrastructure through public affairs and advocacy efforts on the local, state and federal level. **Scope:** The wireless infrastructure ecosystem in the United States. **Holdings:** Figures not available. **Publications:** *The Bulletin* (Bimonthly); *PICA Bulletin: News and Analysis for the Personal Communication Industry*. **Educational Activities:** PCIA Wireless Infrastructure Show (Annual). **Geographic Preference:** Multinational.

REFERENCE WORKS

1510 ■ *"Why the Hospital Pager Withstood the Test of Time" in Health Tech (June 21, 2019)*
Ed: Jen A. Miller. **Released:** June 21, 2019. **Description:** Pagers are alive and well — in the healthcare industry. Pagers are still used in hospitals because they do not experience cellular and Wi-Fi dead zones, which means better response times from doctors and staff. Other advantages are discussed, with a brief history of the pager. **Availability:** Print; Online.

Bicycle Shop

ASSOCIATIONS AND OTHER ORGANIZATIONS

1511 ■ Adventure Cycling Association
150 E Pine St.
  Missoula, MT 59807
Ph: (406)721-1776
Free: 800-755-2453
Fax: (406)721-8754
Co. E-mail: info@adventurecycling.org
URL: http://www.adventurecycling.org
Contact: Joyce Casey, President
Facebook: www.facebook.com/adventurecycling
X (Twitter): x.com/advcyclingassoc
YouTube: www.youtube.com/user/AdvCyclingAssoc
Description: Originally founded to develop the TransAmerica Coast-to-Coast Bicycle Trail (4450 miles) that was inaugurated in 1976 during the 200th birthday celebration of the U.S. Focuses on the research, maintenance, and mapping of over 20,000 miles of bicycle touring and mountain biking routes. Efforts are aimed at promoting bicycle adventure travel and educating the public in bicycle usage and safety. **Publications:** *Adventure Cyclist* (6/year); *Cyclists' Yellow Pages* (Annual). **Geographic Preference:** National; Local.

1512 ■ League of American Bicyclists
1612 K St. NW, Ste. 1102
  Washington, DC 20006
Ph: (202)822-1333
Co. E-mail: bikeleague@bikeleague.org
URL: http://www.bikeleague.org
Contact: Bill Nesper, Executive Director
E-mail: bill@bikeleague.org
Facebook: www.facebook.com/
  leagueamericanbicyclists
X (Twitter): x.com/BikeLeague
YouTube: www.youtube.com/user/bikeleaguevideo
Description: Bicyclists and bicycle clubs. Promotes bicycling for fun, fitness, and transportation, and works through advocacy and education for a bicycle-friendly America. Represents members' interests. Seeks to bring better bicycling to all communities. **Founded:** 1880. **Publications:** *American Bicyclist* (Semiannual); *Almanac, Tour Finder, and Ride Guide: Tour Finder and Ride Guide* (Annual); *TourFinder: Almanac of Cyclists, Tourfinder, and Ride Guide* (Annual); *BikeLeague News* (Biweekly). **Educational Activities:** National Bike Summit (Annual). **Awards:** Dr. Paul Dudley White Award (Annual). **Geographic Preference:** National.

1513 ■ National Bicycle Dealers Association (NBDA)
3972 Barranca Pkwy., Ste. J-423
  Irvine, CA 92606
Ph: (949)540-8020
Co. E-mail: info@nbda.com
URL: http://nbda.com/#!event-list
Contact: Heather Mason, President
Linkedin: www.linkedin.com/company/national-bicycle
  -dealers-association
X (Twitter): x.com/NBDARetailers
Instagram: www.instagram.com/nationalbicycle
  dealersassoc
YouTube: www.youtube.com/channel/
  UCLxefr7FABBBTvSFEEInfFw
Description: Represents independent retail dealers who sell and service bicycles. Sponsors workshops and provides programs. **Founded:** 1946. **Publications:** *Outspokin'* (Weekly); *Outspokin'* (Weekly). **Geographic Preference:** National.

1514 ■ National Center for Bicycling and Walking (NCBW) [Pro Bike]
1612 K St. NW, Ste. 802
  Washington, DC 20006
Ph: (202)223-3621
Co. E-mail: mark@bikewalk.org
URL: http://ecologycenter.org/directory/directory-en
  tries/national-center-for-bicycling-and-walking-ncbw
Description: Promotes bicycling for transportation and recreation; encourages increased quality and number of local bicycling programs; facilitates communication within the bicycle community. **Founded:** 1977. **Publications:** *NCBW Forum* (Quarterly); *NCBW Pro Bike Directory* (Periodic); *Pro Bike News* (Monthly); *Pro Bike Proceedings* (Biennial). **Geographic Preference:** National.

1515 ■ USA Cycling
210 USA Cycling Pt., Ste. 100
  Colorado Springs, CO 80919
Ph: (719)434-4200
Co. E-mail: membership@usacycling.org
URL: http://www.usacycling.org
Contact: Rob Demartini, President
E-mail: robd@usacycling.org
Facebook: www.facebook.com/usacycling
X (Twitter): x.com/usacycling
Instagram: www.instagram.com/usacycling
YouTube: www.youtube.com/user/USACyclingOrg
Description: Conducts development camps, coaching education, mechanics and officials training. **Founded:** 1921. **Publications:** *USA Cycling Magazine* (Bimonthly); *NORBA Newsletter* (Periodic); *Take the Lead*. **Awards:** USA Cycling National Championships (Annual). **Geographic Preference:** National.

REFERENCE WORKS

1516 ■ "Adapt or Die: How Local Bike Shops Are Evolving to Stay Alive" in Gear Junkie (November 16, 2018)
Ed: Robert Annis. **Released:** November 16, 2018. **Description:** Describes how bike shops are evolving as they try to stay afloat in the digital age. From bikes and brews to at-home repair, bike shop owners are coming up with creative endeavors to maintain relevance. **Availability:** Online.

1517 ■ "B&B Bicycles Named Best Bicycle Shop" in Focus Daily News (July 28, 2019)
URL(s): www.focusdailynews.com/bb-bicycles-name
  d-best-bicycle-shop/
Ed: Jo Ann Holt. **Released:** July 28, 2019. **Description:** Profile of Reader's Choice Awards winner for Best Bicycle Shop, B&B Bicycles. **Availability:** Online.

1518 ■ *Best Small Business Ideas for Bike Shops*
Released: August 06, 2018. **Description:** Bike shops are an excellent small business idea and can be revamped in plenty of ways to enter, occupy, and ultimately take over a niche market waiting to be filled. This article details a variety of services or specialties for your bike shop to ensure you successfully fulfill the need in your community. **Availability:** Online.

1519 ■ "Bike Company Sharing More Than Pedal Power: Long Beach To Get Some of Bike Nation's Profits; L.A. Might, Too" in Los Angeles Business Journal (Vol. 34, September 3, 2012, No. 36, pp. 12)
Pub: CBJ L.P.
Contact: Terri Cunningham, Contact
Ed: James Rufus Koren. **Description:** Bike Nation USA plans to have up to 250 kiosks so customers can pay to borrow specially equipped bikes for rides in town. They hope to eventually have 400 kiosks installed in the Los Angeles, California area. Details of the plans are outlined. **Availability:** Online.

1520 ■ "The Death of the Local Bike Shop" in Outside (November 2, 2016)
URL(s): www.outsideonline.com/2126741/death-local
  -bike-shop
Ed: Robbie Carver. **Released:** November 02, 2016. **Description:** With the advent of popular bike brands Trek and Giant moving to an online sales model, the decline of the local bike shop is explored. **Availability:** Online.

1521 ■ "Hey, Bike Shops: Stop Treating Cusotmers Like Garbage" in Bicycling (June 12, 2019)
URL(s): www.bicycling.com/culture/a27496999/bike
  -shops-need-change/
Ed: Gloria Liu. **Released:** June 12, 2019. **Description:** Poor customer service within bike shops has been well-documented with the advent of social media reviews. Females, overweight people, and older people are more likely to feel these negative effects and shop anecdotes are discussed in this article. Some solutions are also presented. **Availability:** Online.

1522 ■ "How to Start a Bike Shop" in Outspokin'
Description: Covers 11 key steps to follow to be sure you have a solid foundation for your bike shop including business planning, marketing, location, product lineup, hiring, customer acquisition and retention, and building a brand in your community. **Availability:** Online.

1523 ■ *"Lincoln Park to Lose Longtime Bike Shop after 73 Years as it Consolidates to Woodhaven Location"* in *News-Herald (July 15, 2019)*
URL(s): www.thenewsherald.com/news/lincoln-park
-to-lose-longtime-bike-shop-after-years-as/article
_180577fe-a74d-11e9-85c9-132af1fc3108.html
Ed: Colin Maloney. **Released:** July 15, 2019. **Description:** Long-time staple in the Downriver community of Metro Detroit, Al Petri & Sons Bicyles is closing up shop. Any leftover merchandise will be transferred to their Woodhaven location. **Availability:** Online.

1524 ■ *"Opening a Bike Shop: Advice, Common Pitfalls and Money Saving Tips from Those Who Have Done It"* in *Cycling Industry News (July 5, 2016)*
Ed: Mark Sutton. **Released:** July 05, 2016. **Description:** Provides first-hand experience from real-world bike shop owners about common mistakes, money saving tips, and often overlooked costs associated with running a bike shop. **Availability:** Online.

1525 ■ *"Pandemic Leads to a Bicycle Boom, and Shortage, around World"* in *AP NEws (June 14, 2020)*
Ed: David Sharp, Kelvin Chan. **Released:** June 14, 2020. **Description:** Bicycle shops are booming during the pandemic as more people are staying home and looking for a recreational outlet, creating a huge demand and a shortage of affordable bikes that isn't slowing down.

1526 ■ *"Riding High"* in *Small Business Opportunities (November 2008)*
Description: Profile of David Sanborn who found a way to turn his passion for biking into a moneymaking opportunity by opening his own bicycle shops; Sanborn's goal is to become the largest independent bike retailer in the United States.

1527 ■ *"ROI for a Profitable Small Business and Bike Shop"* in *Bike Shop Girl blog (October 9, 2020)*
Ed: Arleigh Greenwald. **Released:** October 09, 2020. **Description:** Making your small business profitable is the most important aspect of owning a small business. This article discusses key performance indicators held by a bike shop owner and why locally owned bike shops and small businesses need to think about these indicators. **Availability:** Online.

1528 ■ *"South-Side Bicycle Shop Set to Close After Nearly a Century"* in *Indianpolis Business Journal (June 4, 2019)*
URL(s): www.ibj.com/articles/74033-south-side-bi-cycle-shop-set-to-close-after-nearly-a-century
Ed: Susan Orr. **Released:** June 04, 2019. **Description:** Circle City Bicycles, which has been in business for 100 years in Indianapolis, announced this week it is closing. Declining sales are a factor for the close. **Availability:** Online.

1529 ■ *"Ten of the World's Coolest Bike Shops: 2018 Edition"* in *CyclingTips (November 7, 2018)*
URL(s): cyclingtips.com/2018/11/ten-of-the-worlds
-coolest-bike-shops-2018-edition/
Released: November 07, 2018. **Description:** Even with online sales taking up a bigger chunk of bike sales there is still a lot of value in visiting and buying from a local brick-and-mortar shop. Discussed are ten of the coolest bike shops in the world — a completely subjective analysis but also based on the opinions of people who visited these places and had a positive experience. **Availability:** Online.

STATISTICAL SOURCES

1530 ■ *RMA Annual Statement Studies*
Pub: Risk Management Association
Contact: Nancy Foster, President

Released: Annual. **Description:** Contains composite balance sheets and income statements for more than 360 industries, including the accounting, auditing, and bookkeeping industries. Also contains five years of comparative historical data for discerning trends. Includes 16 commonly used ratios, computed for most of the size groupings for nearly every industry.

TRADE PERIODICALS

1531 ■ *Adventure Cyclist*
Pub: Adventure Cycling Association
Contact: Joyce Casey, President
URL(s): www.adventurecycling.org/adventure-cyclist/
adventure-cyclist-online

Ed: Michael Deme. **Released:** 6/year; January/February, March/April, May/June, July/August, September/October, and November/December. **Price:** $5, Single issue for back issues. **Description:** Magazine for members of Adventure Cycling Assn. **Availability:** Print; Download; PDF; Online.

Billiards Hall

START-UP INFORMATION

1532 ■ *"Business for Sale: Pocket Change?" in Inc. (Vol. 30, December 2008, No. 12, pp. 28)*
Pub: Mansueto Ventures L.L.C.
Contact: Stephanie Mehta, Chief Executive Officer
Ed: Ryan McCarthy. **Description:** Owner of a chain of nine retail billiard showrooms grew his business by starting to deliver pool tables for Sears. The company, consisting of seven retail locations and two warehouses, is now for sale. Details are included. **Availability:** Online.

ASSOCIATIONS AND OTHER ORGANIZATIONS

1533 ■ **Billiard and Bowling Institute of America (BBIA)**
621 Six Flags Dr.
Arlington, TX 76011
Ph: (817)385-8441
Co. E-mail: bill@ibpsia.com
URL: http://billiardandbowling.org
Contact: Andy Brenneman, President
E-mail: andy@bowlerssupply.com

Description: Represents distributors and manufacturers of billiard and bowling equipment. **Founded:** 1940. **Publications:** *BBIA enews* (Monthly); *BBIA Membership and Product Information Guide* (Annual). **Educational Activities:** BBIA Convention (Annual); BBIA Convention (Annual). **Awards:** BBIA Industry Service Award (Annual). **Geographic Preference:** National.

1534 ■ **Billiard Congress of America (BCA)**
500 Discovery Pkwy, Ste. 125
Superior, CO 80027
Ph: (303)243-5070
URL: http://bca-pool.com
Contact: Rob Johnson, Chief Executive Officer

Description: Develops rules for pocket billiards. Serves as national clearinghouse for billiard activities. Compiles statistics. **Founded:** 1948. **Publications:** *Official Billiard Rules*; *BCA Break and BCA Open Table* (Quarterly). **Educational Activities:** BCA Expo (Annual). **Awards:** BCA Hall of Fame (Annual). **Geographic Preference:** National.

REFERENCE WORKS

1535 ■ *"Breaking Bad? This New Everett Pool Hall Can Help Your Shot" in HeraldNet (August 5, 2019)*
URL(s): www.heraldnet.com/business/breaking-ba d-this-new-everett-pool-ace-can-help-your-shot/
Released: August 05, 2019. **Description:** Profile of Golden Fleece Billiards, which moved from Seattle to Everett. The business hosts international tournaments and traveling teams, along with having professional billiards player Kim Jones give lessons. **Availability:** Online.

1536 ■ *"Cones and Cues Closes After Decades-Long Run" in The Monroe News (August 24, 2019)*
URL(s): www.monroenews.com/news/20190824/ cones-and-cues-closes-after-decades-long-run
Released: August 24, 2019. **Description:** History of Metro Detroit downriver business Cones and Cues is given, which is closing after 33 years in business. **Availability:** Online.

1537 ■ *"A Day in the Life of an Albany Pool Hall" in Spotlightnews.com (April 4, 2018)*
URL(s): spotlightnews.com/news/2018/04/04/a-day -in-the-life-of-an-albany-pool-hall/
Ed: Sean Stone. **Released:** April 04, 2018. **Description:** Profile of the Golden Cue billiard lounge, which thrives despite many pool halls closing over the years due to a decline in popularity with the sport. **Availability:** Online.

1538 ■ *"The Life and Death of the American Pool Hall" in Punch (January 23, 2015)*
URL(s): punchdrink.com/articles/the-life-and-death-of -the-american-pool-hall/
Ed: Sarah Baird. **Released:** January 23, 2015. **Description:** Explores the history of the American pool hall and the way pool halls have morphed from hot beds of debauchery to a place where first dates take place and staples of friendly neighborhoods. **Availability:** Online.

1539 ■ *"Nine-Year-Old Turning Heads at Englewood Pool Hall" in 9News.com (June 9, 2019)*
URL(s): www.9news.com/article/news/nine-year-ol d-turning-heads-at-englewood-pool-hall/73-307420 3b-5752-4686-9271-899fc1c88991
Ed: Bryan Wendland. **Released:** June 09, 2019. **Description:** Nine-year-old Jin Powell is using his billiard's skill to beat any adult player that takes on the challenge of opposing him. Powell is gearing up to participate in national billiards tournaments. **Availability:** Online.

TRADE PERIODICALS

1540 ■ **Billiards Digest**
Pub: Luby Publishing Inc.
Contact: Keith Hamilton, President
E-mail: keithh@lubypublishing.com
URL(s): www.billiardsdigest.com
YouTube: www.youtube.com/@BilliardsDigest
Ed: Gianmarc Manzione. **Released:** Monthly **Price:** $32, U.S. for 1 year; $28, U.S. for annual; $9, for back issue January 2006 - present; $15, for back issue before January 2006; $62, for 1 year international; $53, for international. **Description:** Billiards industry magazine. **Availability:** Online.

TRADE SHOWS AND CONVENTIONS

1541 ■ **BCA Expo**
Billiard Congress of America (BCA)
500 Discovery Pkwy, Ste. 125
Superior, CO 80027
Ph: (303)243-5070
URL: http://bca-pool.com
Contact: Rob Johnson, Chief Executive Officer
URL(s): bcaexpo.com
Frequency: Annual. **Description:** Exhibits related to billiards and pocket billiards equipment, supplies, and services. **Audience:** Players, retailers and manufacturers. **Principal Exhibits:** Exhibits related to billiards and pocket billiards equipment, supplies, and services. Dates and Locations: 2025 Mar 19-20 Las Vegas Convention Center, Las Vegas, NV. **Telecommunication Services:** rob@bca-pool.com.

FRANCHISES AND BUSINESS OPPORTUNITIES

1542 ■ **Canadian Poolplayers Association (CPA) [American Poolplayers Association (APA)]**
1000 Lake St. Louis Blvd., Ste. 325
Lake Saint Louis, MO 63367
Ph: (636)625-8611
Free: 888-327-8752
Fax: (636)265-6556
URL: http://poolplayers.com/canada
Contact: Larry Hubbart, Founder
Facebook: www.facebook.com/poolplayers
Linkedin: www.linkedin.com/company/236406
X (Twitter): x.com/poolplayers
Instagram: www.instagram.com/poolplayers
YouTube: www.youtube.com/apaleagues

Description: Oversees and provides ongoing support to recreational pool league operators. **No. of Franchise Units:** 17. **No. of Company-Owned Units:** 5. **Founded:** 1979. **Franchised:** 1989. **Equity Capital Needed:** $17,080-$24,150. **Franchise Fee:** $5,000. **Royalty Fee:** $2.50 plus/team/wk. **Geographic Preference:** National.

1543 ■ **Dooley's Inc.**
463 Elmwood Dr.
Moncton, NB, Canada E1A 2X2
Ph: (506)857-8050
Co. E-mail: info@doolys.ca
URL: http://www.doolys.ca
Contact: Pierre Lariviere, President
Facebook: www.facebook.com/doolys.billiards

Description: Entertainment firm provides billiards and video games for social gatherings. **Founded:** 1993. **Equity Capital Needed:** $100,000-$150,000. **Franchise Fee:** 25000. **Training:** Extensive training, both in operations and marketing are provided. Field representatives will help with hiring and training your manager and staff with ongoing training and support through workshops and annual meetings.

1544 ■ **West Side Charlies**
428 Torbay Rd.
Saint John's, NL, Canada A1A 5J3
Ph: (709)579-2601
Co. E-mail: feedback@westsidecharlies.com
URL: http://westsidecharlies.com
Contact: Fabian Power, Contact
E-mail: fabian@westsidecharlies.com
Facebook: www.facebook.com/WestSideCharlies
Description: Operator of pool halls. **Founded:** 1996. **Training:** Offers 1 week and ongoing support.

Blacktop Surfacing Business

ASSOCIATIONS AND OTHER ORGANIZATIONS

1545 ■ American Concrete Pavement Association (ACPA)
9450 W Bryn Mawr Ave., Ste. 150
Rosemont, IL 60018
Ph: (847)966-2272
Co. E-mail: acpa@acpa.org
URL: http://www.acpa.org
Contact: Laura O'Neill Kaumo, President
Facebook: www.facebook.com/paveconcrete63
Linkedin: www.linkedin.com/company/american-concrete-pavement-association
X (Twitter): x.com/PaveConcrete
Instagram: www.instagram.com/Concrete_Pavement_Association
YouTube: www.youtube.com/user/ConcretePavements
Description: Contractors, cement companies, equipment manufacturers, material service suppliers, ready mixed concrete producers, consultants, trucking companies/material haulers and others allied with the concrete pavement industry. Advocates the use of concrete pavement for highways, airports, streets, and roads. **Founded:** 1963. **Educational Activities:** World of Concrete (WOC) (Annual); American Concrete Pavement Association Annual Conference (Annual). **Awards:** ACPA Excellence in Concrete Pavements Awards (Annual). **Geographic Preference:** National.

1546 ■ Asphalt Institute
2696 Research Park Dr.
Lexington, KY 40511-8480
Ph: (859)288-4960
Free: 866-540-9577
Fax: (859)288-4999
Co. E-mail: info@asphaltinstitute.org
URL: http://www.asphaltinstitute.org
Contact: Peter T. Grass, President
Facebook: www.facebook.com/asphaltinstitute
Description: Promotes the use, benefits, and quality performance of petroleum asphalt through environmental marketing, research, engineering, and technical development, and through the resolution of issues affecting the industry. **Scope:** Asphalt, including Superpave asphalt binder and mixture technology, Superpave gyratory compaction procedure, and hot-mix asphalt overlays. **Founded:** 1919. **Publications:** Asphalt (3/year); Catalog of Asphalt Institute Publications (Annual); MS-4: The Asphalt Handbook. **Geographic Preference:** Multinational.

1547 ■ International Slurry Surfacing Association (ISSA)
800 Roosevelt Rd., Bldg. C-312
Glen Ellyn, IL 60137
Ph: (630)942-6577
Fax: (630)790-3095
Co. E-mail: annew@cmservices.com
URL: http://www.slurry.org
Contact: Ali Mostardo, Officer
E-mail: alim@cmservices.com
Facebook: www.facebook.com/issa.social
Linkedin: www.linkedin.com/company/international-slurry-surfacing-association
X (Twitter): x.com/ISSAhq
Description: Resource for promotion, training, education and best practices of our pavement preservation technologies. **Founded:** 1963. **Educational Activities:** ISSA World Congress (Annual); AEMA-ARRA-ISSA Annual Meeting (Annual). **Awards:** ISSA President's Award for Excellence (Annual). **Geographic Preference:** Multinational.

1548 ■ National Asphalt Pavement Association (NAPA)
6406 Ivy Ln., Ste. 350
Greenbelt, MD 20770-1441
Ph: (301)731-4748
Free: 888-468-6499
Fax: (301)731-4621
URL: http://www.asphaltpavement.org
Contact: Audrey Copeland, President
X (Twitter): x.com/NAPATweets
YouTube: www.youtube.com/channel/UCDroWs5yMvWHi1mEjHPOAlw
Description: Manufacturers and producers of scientifically proportioned Hot Mix Asphalt for use in all paving, including highways, airfields, and environmental usages. Membership includes hot mix producers, paving contractors, equipment manufacturers, engineering consultants, and others. **Founded:** 1955. **Publications:** National Asphalt Pavement Association--Publications Catalog (Annual); Asphalt Pavement. **Educational Activities:** Yarmouth Clam Festival (Annual); World of Asphalt Show & Conference (Annual). **Awards:** NAPA Community Involvement Awards (Annual); Asphalt Pavement Hall of Fame (Annual); Sheldon G. Hayes Award (Annual); Quality in Construction Awards (QIC) (Annual). **Geographic Preference:** National.

1549 ■ Virginia Asphalt Association (VAA)
7814 Carousel Ln., Ste. 310
Richmond, VA 23294
Ph: (804)288-3169
Fax: (804)288-4551
Co. E-mail: cfahed@vaasphalt.com
URL: http://vaasphalt.org
Contact: Trenton M. Clark, President
E-mail: tclark@vaasphalt.com
Facebook: www.facebook.com/Virginia-Asphalt-Association-762145360498284
YouTube: www.youtube.com/channel/UCRpnWK5sMqeDyhq5wfUy1VA
Description: Promotes the increased use and quality of asphalt for the paving of highways and streets in Virginia. Offers information and consulting services to governmental and private bodies interested in paving. **Founded:** 1952. **Publications:** VAA Asphalt News (Monthly). **Geographic Preference:** State.

REFERENCE WORKS

1550 ■ Asphalt Emulsion Manufacturers Association--Membership Directory
Pub: Asphalt Emulsion Manufacturers Association
Contact: Dan Koeninger, President
URL(s): www.aema.org/page/Membership
Ed: Michael R. Krissoff. **Description:** Covers about 100 member manufacturers and their plants and suppliers to the industry; international coverage. **Entries include:** Company name, address, phone, names and titles of representatives. Plant listings include address and phone. **Arrangement:** Classified by membership type, then alphabetical. Plants are geographical. **Indexes:** Personal name, company name. **Availability:** Print.

1551 ■ Asphalt Paving Technologists
Pub: Association of Asphalt Paving Technologists
Contact: Eileen Soler, Manager
URL(s): www.asphalttechnology.org/site_page.cfm?pk_association_webpage_menu=9169&pk_association_webpage=19109
Ed: Eugene L. Skok, Jr. **Released:** Annual **Description:** Covers about 850 member engineers and chemists engaged in paving or related fields, such as paving materials and construction equipment; international coverage. **Entries include:** Name, affiliation, address, phone. **Arrangement:** Alphabetical. **Availability:** Print.

1552 ■ Asphalt Recycling & Reclaiming Association--Membership Directory
Pub: Asphalt Recycling and Reclaiming Association
Contact: Kimbel Stokes, President
URL(s): www.arra.org/page/ContractorBenefits
Description: Covers about 200 contractors, manufacturers, consulting engineers, and public works officials involved in asphalt reclaiming and recycling. **Entries include:** Name of company, address, phone; key personnel; type of organization or company; product line, or contact person. **Arrangement:** By type of membership, then alphabetical. **Indexes:** Personal name, geographical. **Availability:** Online.

1553 ■ "Braves' Parking Pitch Fails to Connect With Property Owners" in Atlanta Business Chronicle (June 27, 2014, pp. 1)
Pub: American City Business Journals, Inc.
Contact: Mike Olivieri, Executive Vice President
Released: June 27, 2014. **Price:** $4, introductory 4-week offer(Digital only). **Description:** A new $672 million ballpark plan of the Atlanta Braves was given the green light by Cobb County Commissioners recently. However, the Braves are facing a new hurdle for securing parking spaces in the office complexes around the proposed ballpark site. The stadium itself will have more than 6,000 parking spots, but the Braves also want an additional 4,000 to 5,000 spaces, and although the Braves are said to be offering building owners around the stadium up to $100 per space, the owners have not been swayed to give access to their parking. **Availability:** Print; Mailing list; Online.

1554 ■ "Bridging the Bay" in Business Journal Serving Greater Tampa Bay (Vol. 30, November 5, 2010, No. 46, pp. 1)
Pub: Tampa Bay Business Journal
Contact: Ian Anderson, President

E-mail: ianderson@bizjournals.com
Ed: Mark Holan. **Description:** The Florida Department of Transportation has launched a study to design the proposed addition to the Howard Frankland Bridge. The bridge would be designed to accommodate more than personal vehicles. **Availability:** Print; Online.

1555 ■ *"Downtown Light Rail Plans Up in the Air" in Business Journal Serving Greater Tampa Bay (Vol. 30, October 22, 2010, No. 44, pp. 1)*
Pub: Tampa Bay Business Journal
Contact: Ian Anderson, President
E-mail: ianderson@bizjournals.com
Ed: Mark Holan. **Description:** Construction of Tampa's $2 billion light rail transit is suspended pending the result of the November 2, 2010 referendum. The routes, usage, and financing of the light rail project will be decided on the referendum. Whether the light rail will be elevated is also discussed. **Availability:** Print; Online.

1556 ■ *"Giant Garages Could Rise Up in Downtown Cincinnati" in Business Courier (Vol. 27, October 22, 2010, No. 25, pp. 1)*
Pub: Business Courier
Ed: Dan Monk. **Description:** More than 2,500 new parking spaces could rise up to the eastern edge of downtown Cincinnati, Ohio as public and private investors collect resources for new garage projects. These projects are expected to accommodate almost 1,500 monthly parkers who will lose access at Broadway Commons due to the construction of Harrah's casino. **Availability:** Print; Mailing list; Online.

1557 ■ *"A Second Chance at Road Dollars" in Orlando Business Journal (Vol. 26, February 5, 2010, No. 36, pp. 1)*
Pub: Orlando Business Journal
Contact: Julie Swyers, Director
E-mail: jswyers@bizjournals.com
Description: Nearly $10 million worth of construction projects in Central Florida would give construction companies that missed the initial round of federal stimulus-funded local road building projects another opportunity. Cost savings in the initial round of road projects enabled Orange, Osceola, and Seminole Counties to secure additional projects. **Availability:** Print; Online.

TRADE PERIODICALS

1558 ■ *Asphalt Contractor*
Pub: The Asphalt Contractor
Contact: Brandon Noel, Editor
E-mail: bnoel@acbusinessmedia.com
URL(s): www.forconstructionpros.com/magazinewww.asphalt.com
Facebook: www.facebook.com/Asphalt.Contractor
X (Twitter): x.com/AsphaltContrctr
Ed: Lisa Cleaver. **Released:** 10/year **Description:** Trade journal for asphalt contractors, asphalt producers, and public work specifiers. **Availability:** Print; Online.

TRADE SHOWS AND CONVENTIONS

1559 ■ **AEMA-ARRA-ISSA Annual Meeting**
International Slurry Surfacing Association (ISSA)
800 Roosevelt Rd., Bldg. C-312
Glen Ellyn, IL 60137
Ph: (630)942-6577
Fax: (630)790-3095
Co. E-mail: annew@cmservices.com
URL: http://www.slurry.org
Contact: Ali Mostardo, Officer
E-mail: alim@cmservices.com
URL(s): www.aema.org/mpage/2023AnnualMeeting
Frequency: Annual. **Description:** Exhibits relating to slurry surfacing, including heavy paving machinery. **Audience:** Slurry surfacing professionals. **Principal Exhibits:** Exhibits relating to slurry surfacing, including heavy paving machinery. **Dates and Locations:** 2025 Mar 03-07 The Westin Rancho Mirage Golf Resort & Spa, Rancho Mirage, CA. **Telecommunication Services:** alim@cmservices.com.

CONSULTANTS

1560 ■ **Asphalt Consultants L.L.C.**
PO Box 306
New Holland, PA 17557
Ph: (717)278-0388
Co. E-mail: mikeb@asphaltconsultants.net
URL: http://www.asphaltconsultants.net
Facebook: www.facebook.com/asphaltconsultants
Description: Provides consulting services for the asphalt paving industry.

LIBRARIES

1561 ■ **National Asphalt Pavement Association (NAPA)**
6406 Ivy Ln., Ste. 350
Greenbelt, MD 20770-1441
Ph: (301)731-4748
Free: 888-468-6499
Fax: (301)731-4621
URL: http://www.asphaltpavement.org
Contact: Audrey Copeland, President
X (Twitter): x.com/NAPATweets
YouTube: www.youtube.com/channel/UCDroWs5yMvWHi1mEjHPOAIw
Description: Manufacturers and producers of scientifically proportioned Hot Mix Asphalt for use in all paving, including highways, airfields, and environmental usages. Membership includes hot mix producers, paving contractors, equipment manufacturers, engineering consultants, and others. **Founded:** 1955. **Publications:** *National Asphalt Pavement Association--Publications Catalog* (Annual); *Asphalt Pavement*. **Educational Activities:** Yarmouth Clam Festival (Annual); World of Asphalt Show & Conference (Annual). **Awards:** NAPA Community Involvement Awards (Annual); Asphalt Pavement Hall of Fame (Annual); Sheldon G. Hayes Award (Annual); Quality in Construction Awards (QIC) (Annual). **Geographic Preference:** National.

1562 ■ **U.S. Army Corps of Engineers - Engineer Research and Development Center Research Library (ERDC)**
3909 Halls Ferry Rd.
Vicksburg, MS 39180-6199
Ph: (601)634-2355
Free: 866-362-3732
Co. E-mail: erdclibrary@chat.libraryh3lp.com
URL: http://www.erdc.usace.army.mil/Library
Scope: Mission-related research; scientists and engineers. **Services:** Interlibrary loan. **Holdings:** 300,000 items; 34,000 e-books and reports; 28,000 journals.

1563 ■ **U.S. Army Engineer Research and Development Center - Geotechnical and Structures Laboratory (GSL) - Airfields, Pavements, and Mobility Information Analysis Center**
3909 Halls Ferry Rd.
Vicksburg, MS 39180-6199
URL: http://www.erdc.usace.army.mil
Contact: Bartley P. Durst, Director
Scope: Soil trafficability; mobility; pavements; terrain evaluation. **Services:** Interlibrary loan; copying.

RESEARCH CENTERS

1564 ■ **Auburn University - National Center for Asphalt Technology (NCAT)**
277 Technology Pky.
Auburn, AL 36830
Ph: (334)844-6228
Fax: (334)844-6248
URL: http://www.eng.auburn.edu/research/centers/ncat
Contact: Ron Sines, Vice President
Facebook: www.facebook.com/NCATAuburn
Linkedin: www.linkedin.com/company/ncatauburn
X (Twitter): x.com/pavetrack
YouTube: www.youtube.com/channel/UC5grTAnUU_oE9F2FPpEdgJw
Description: Integral unit of Auburn University. **Scope:** Asphalt technology, including asphalt mixture design and characterization, and asphalt chemistry and material properties. **Founded:** 1986. **Educational Activities:** NCAT Asphalt Technology, Training course covering asphalt mix design, production and control, construction, pavement design.

1565 ■ **Oregon State University - College of Engineering - Department of Civil and Construction Engineering - Kiewit Center for Infrastructure and Transportation**
1491 SW Campus Way
Corvallis, OR 97331
Co. E-mail: jason.weiss@oregonstate.edu
URL: http://cce.oregonstate.edu/research
Contact: Jason Weiss, Director
E-mail: jason.weiss@oregonstate.edu
URL(s): research.engr.oregonstate.edu/weiss/kiewit-center
Description: Integral unit of Oregon State University. **Scope:** Transportation system economics, regulations, and management; geotechnical engineering and materials testing; transportation system planning, operations, and safety; facility design, construction, and maintenance; transportation for resource development; transportation for persons with disabilities; social impacts of transportation; and environment and energy, including studies on transportation materials and applications of microcomputers. Transportation materials research concerns include alternate surfacings for temporary or intermittent use roads; effect of moisture, aging, and thermal changes on asphalt pavements; modified asphalt; slope stability; and asphalt properties. Microcomputer applications studies include collection and use of data from high-speed traffic monitoring systems, pavement analysis, design, and evaluation with microcomputers, the use of microcomputers to analyze and evaluate traffic operation and safety, the economic feasibility of alternate surfacings, and the performance of Portland cement concrete pavements. **Founded:** 1962. **Publications:** *Biennial report*. **Educational Activities:** Northwest Transportation Conference (Biennial); Kiewit Center for Infrastructure and Transportation Short courses, As part of a continuing education program sponsored by the Oregon Traffic Safety Division.; Kiewit Center for Infrastructure and Transportation Seminars. **Awards:** Kiewit Center for Infrastructure and Transportation Fellowships (Annual).

1566 ■ **Texas A&M University System - Texas A&M Transportation Institute (TTI) - Library**
3135 TAMU
College Station, TX 77843-3135
Ph: (979)317-2000
Co. E-mail: media@tti.tamu.edu
URL: http://tti.tamu.edu
Contact: Gregory D. Winfree, Chief Executive Officer
E-mail: g-winfree@tti.tamu.edu
Facebook: www.facebook.com/ttitamu
Linkedin: www.linkedin.com/company/texasa-m transportationinstitute
X (Twitter): x.com/TTITAMU
Instagram: www.instagram.com/ttitamu
YouTube: www.youtube.com/ttitamu
Description: Integral unit of Texas A&M University System, operating as an official research arm of the Texas Department of Transportation, and the Railroad Commission of Texas. Contributes to the Texas Transportation Technology Transfer Program. **Scope:** Researches on all modes of transportation, including highways, airports, pipelines, waterways, and rail systems. Research areas include all aspects of transportation. **Founded:** 1950. **Subscriptions:** 10,000 volumes. **Publications:** *Texas Transportation Researcher* (Quarterly).

1567 ■ **University of Texas at Austin - Center for Transportation Research (CTR)**
3925 W Braker Ln., Ste. No.4 11080
Austin, TX 78759

Ph: (512)232-3100
Co. E-mail: ctrlib@austin.utexas.edu
URL: http://ctr.utexas.edu
Contact: Michael Morris, Director
Facebook: www.facebook.com/CTRUTAustin
X (Twitter): x.com/CTRUTAustin
YouTube: www.youtube.com/channel/UCTeKQ191ip5j6ki1qRF4u7Q

Description: Separately incorporated research unit affiliated with College of Engineering at University of Texas at Austin. **Scope:** Coordinates and develops highway, air, rail, pipeline, waterway, intermodal and transportation policy, and mass transportation research activities at the University. Emphasizes improvement of local and state transportation, including studies on optimizing traffic flow, transportation planning and policy, computer methods of structural design, foundation design, alternative fuels, multimodal transportation investment, pavement design, drainage, dynamics of highway loading, safety, and highway structures. Operates a cooperative research program with the Texas Department of Transportation. **Publications:** *CTR Annual report* (Annual). **Educational Activities:** Annual Symposium (Annual), To bring together research being conducted as part of the Data Supported Transportation Operations and Planning.

1568 ■ Western Research Institute (WRI)

3474 N 3rd St.
  Laramie, WY 82072
Ph: (307)721-2011
Free: 888-463-6974
URL: http://www.westernresearch.org
Contact: Dr. Jean-Pascal Planche, Chief Executive Officer
E-mail: jplanche@uwyo.edu

Description: Separately incorporated, contract-based research organization, affiliated with University of Wyoming. **Scope:** Energy recovery and utilization technology, including engineering research, kinetics and thermodynamics, environmental monitoring, environmental control technology, fossil and alternative fuel technology. Also conducts research on asphalt. **Founded:** 1983. **Educational Activities:** Petersen Asphalt Research Conference (Annual); WRI Annual Asphalt Meeting (Annual), Energy recovery and utilization technology, including engineering research, kinetics and thermodynamics, environmental monitoring, environmental control technology, fossil and alternative fuel technology.

Blind Cleaning/Installation

ASSOCIATIONS AND OTHER ORGANIZATIONS

1569 ■ Home Fashion Products Association (HFPA)
National Press Bldg., 529 14th St. NW, No. 1280
  Washington, DC 20045
Ph: (212)297-2189
URL: http://homefashionproducts.com
Contact: Charles Gaenslen, President
Linkedin: www.linkedin.com/company/home-fashion-products

Description: Manufacturers of curtains, draperies, bedding, rugs, and related products. Sponsors annual scholarship for students attending accredited schools in home textiles. **Founded:** 1968. **Awards:** HFPA Scholarships. **Geographic Preference:** National.

1570 ■ International Furnishings and Design Association (IFDA)
610 Freedom Business Ctr., Ste. 110
  King of Prussia, PA 19406
Ph: (610)992-0011
Fax: (610)992-0021
Co. E-mail: info@ifda.com
URL: http://ifda.com
Contact: Dawn Brinson, President
Facebook: www.facebook.com/IFDAssociation
Linkedin: www.linkedin.com/in/ifda-association-9
  4332a32

Description: Represents individuals in design, production, distribution, education, promotion and editorial phases of the interior furnishings industry and related fields. Founded IFDA Educational Foundation in 1968. Conducts charitable programs. **Founded:** 1947. **Publications:** *IFDA Directory* (Annual); *IFDA Network* (Quarterly). **Awards:** IFDA Student Member Scholarship (Annual); International Furnishings and Design Association Part-time Student Scholarship (Annual); IFDA Fellow (Annual); IFDA Honorary Recognition Award (Annual); IFDA Trailblazer Award (Annual). **Geographic Preference:** National.

1571 ■ Window Covering Manufacturers Association (WCMA)
355 Lexington Ave. 15th Flr.
  New York, NY 10017
Ph: (212)297-2122
Co. E-mail: contact@wcmanet.org
URL: http://wcmanet.com

Description: Represents corporations engaged in the manufacture or assembly of Venetian blinds, vertical blinds, pleated shades, or their components. Promotes the use, utility, image, and attractiveness of the products and services offered by the window covering industry. **Founded:** 1950. **Geographic Preference:** National.

FRANCHISES AND BUSINESS OPPORTUNITIES

1572 ■ Blind Man of America
Keller Corp.
  606 Fremont Cir.
  Colorado Springs, CO 80919
Free: 800-547-9889
Fax: (719)272-4105
Facebook: www.facebook.com/The-Blind-Man-of
  -America-1927177524179237
X (Twitter): twitter.com/TheblindmanofUS

Description: Mobile window coverings. **No. of Franchise Units:** 9. **No. of Company-Owned Units:** 1. **Founded:** 1991. **Franchised:** 1996. **Equity Capital Needed:** $45,500-$69,100. **Franchise Fee:** $15,000. **Royalty Fee:** 4.3%. **Training:** Provides 2 weeks at headquarters with ongoing support.

1573 ■ Budget Blinds, LLC (BB)
Home Franchise Concepts Inc. (HFC)
  19000 MacArthur Blvd., Ste. 100
  Irvine, CA 92612
Ph: (949)404-1100
Free: 866-388-3432
Co. E-mail: info@homefranchiseconcepts.com
URL: http://www.homefranchiseconcepts.com
Facebook: www.facebook.com/budgetblinds
X (Twitter): x.com/budgetblinds
Instagram: www.instagram.com/budget_blinds_official
YouTube: www.youtube.com/budgetblinds
Pinterest: www.pinterest.com/budgetblinds

Description: Custom window coverings. **No. of Franchise Units:** 710. **No. of Operating Units:** 794. **Founded:** 1992. **Franchised:** 1994. **Equity Capital Needed:** $89,240-$174,070. **Franchise Fee:** $14,950. **Royalty Fee:** Varies. **Training:** Provides 2 weeks at headquarters and ongoing training and support.

1574 ■ Coit Services Inc. [Coit Cleaning and Restoration]
897 Hinckley Rd.
  Burlingame, CA 94010
Free: 800-367-2648
Co. E-mail: info@coit.com
URL: http://www.coit.com
Facebook: www.facebook.com/COITClean
Linkedin: www.linkedin.com/company/coit-services
X (Twitter): x.com/coitclean
Instagram: www.instagram.com/coitclean

Description: Provides cleaning services in upholstery, draperies, carpeting and other flooring surfaces. **No. of Franchise Units:** 42. **No. of Company-Owned Units:** 8. **Founded:** 1950. **Franchised:** 1962. **Equity Capital Needed:** $50,000-$145,000. **Franchise Fee:** $24,000-$40,000. **Financial Assistance:** Yes **Training:** Includes 10 days in corporate office.

LIBRARIES

1575 ■ Arizona State University Architectural and Environmental Design Library
300 E Orange Mall
  Tempe, AZ 85281
Ph: (480)965-6400
URL: http://lib.asu.edu/design/collections/caed
Contact: Debra Riley-Huff, Department Head
E-mail: debra.riley-huff@asu.edu

Scope: Architecture; landscape architecture; industrial; interior; urban and visual communication design. **Services:** Interlibrary loan; copying; printing; scanning; open to the public. **Holdings:** 50,000 books; journals; media items; textual records; project files.

Body Care Shop

START-UP INFORMATION

1576 ■ *"Franchises with an Eye on Chicago"* **in Crain's Chicago Business (Vol. 34, March 14, 2011, No. 11, pp. 20)**
Pub: Crain Communications Inc.
Contact: Barry Asin, President
Ed: Kevin McKeough. **Description:** Profiles of franchise companies seeking franchisees for the Chicago area include: Extreme Pita, a sandwich shop; Hand and Stone, offering massage, facial and waxing services; Molly Maid, home-cleaning service; Primrose Schools, private accredited schools for children 6 months to 6 hears and after-school programs; Protect Painters, residential and light-commercial painting contractor; and Wingstop, a restaurant offering chicken wings in nine flavors, fries and side dishes. **Availability:** Online.

ASSOCIATIONS AND OTHER ORGANIZATIONS

1577 ■ **Cosmetic Industry Buyers and Suppliers (CIBS)**
740 Blue Point Rd.
Holtsville, NY 11742
Ph: (631)758-4200
URL: http://www.cibsonline.com
Contact: Veronica Cruz, President
Facebook: www.facebook.com/CIBSOnlineOfficial
Linkedin: www.linkedin.com/company/cosmetic-industry-buyers-&-suppliers
X (Twitter): x.com/cibs_online
Instagram: www.instagram.com/cibs_online
Description: Buyers and suppliers of essential oils, chemicals, packaging, and finished goods relative to the cosmetic industry. Enhances growth, stability, prosperity, and protection of the American cosmetic industry through close personal contact and the exchange of ideas and experiences. **Founded:** 1948. **Geographic Preference:** National.

1578 ■ **International Spa Association (ISPA)**
2365 Harrodsburg Rd., Ste. A325
Lexington, KY 40504
Contact: Lynne Walker McNees, President
Description: Raises awareness of the spa industry and educates the public and industry professionals about the benefits of the spa experience. **Publications:** *Pulse* (8/year); *LiveSpa*. **Educational Activities:** ISPA Conference & Expo (Annual). **Awards:** ISPA Foundation Mary Tabacchi Scholarship (Annual). **Geographic Preference:** Multinational.

1579 ■ **Personal Care Product Council**
1620 L St. NW, Ste. 1200
Washington, DC 20036
Ph: (202)331-1770
Fax: (202)331-1969
Co. E-mail: membership@personalcarecouncil.org
URL: http://www.personalcarecouncil.org
Contact: Lezlee Westine, President
Facebook: www.facebook.com/Personal-Care-Products-Council-1443878795835012
Linkedin: www.linkedin.com/company/464630
X (Twitter): x.com/PCPC_News
YouTube: www.youtube.com/user/PersonalCareCouncil
Description: Manufacturers and distributors of finished cosmetics, fragrances, and personal care products; suppliers of raw materials and services. Provides scientific, legal, regulatory, and legislative services. Coordinates public service, educational, and public affairs activities. **Founded:** 1894. **Publications:** *Member Directory*; *Executive Update*; *International Cosmetic Legal & Regulatory Database (IRDB)* (Annual); *On-Line INFOBASE*; *CTFA News* (Biweekly); *International Color Handbook*; *International Resource Manual*. **Geographic Preference:** National.

REFERENCE WORKS

1580 ■ *"The Body Shop: What Went Wrong?"* **in BBC (February 9, 2017)**
URL(s): www.bbc.com/news/business-38905530
Ed: Katie Hope. **Released:** February 09, 2017. **Description:** Explores the decisions that led to the demise of the once-popular The Body Shop. **Availability:** Online.

1581 ■ *Business as Usual*
Description: Founder of The Body Shop shares her story and gives her opinion on everything from cynical cosmetic companies to destructive consultants.

1582 ■ *Cosmetics & Toiletries--Cosmetic Bench Reference*
Contact: Janet Ludwig, President
URL(s): store.yahoo.com/allured/itoma.htmlwww.allured.com/ct; allured.stores.yahoo.net/cobere20.html
Ed: Linda Knott. **Released:** Annual **Price:** $199, Individuals. **Description:** Publication includes list of cosmetic ingredient suppliers. **Entries include:** Supplier name, address, phone, fax, chemicals, trade names. Principal content of publication is data on cosmetic ingredients, with label names, trade names, functions, EINECS, INCI names, and CAS numbers. **Arrangement:** Alphabetical by chemical name (includes trade names). **Availability:** Microfiche; Print; Online.

1583 ■ *"How I Did It: Bobbi Brown, Founder and CEO, Bobbi Brown Cosmetics"* **in Inc. (November 2007, pp. 110-112)**
Ed: Athena Schindelheim. **Description:** Profile of Bobbi Brown, CEO and founder of Bobbi Brown Cosmetics, designed to highlight a woman's natural look. Brown opened her first freestanding retail store recently that houses a makeup artistry school in the back. **Availability:** Online.

1584 ■ *"In the Raw: Karyn Calabrese Brings Healthy Dining to a New Sophisticated Level"* **in Black Enterprise (Vol. 41, September 2010)**
Pub: Earl G. Graves Ltd.
Contact: Earl Graves, Jr., President
Ed: Sonia Alleyne. **Description:** Profile of Karyn Calabrese whose businesses are based in Chicago, Illinois. Calabrese has launched a complete line of products (vitamins and beauty items), services (spa, chiropractic, and acupuncture treatments), and restaurants to bring health dining and lifestyles to a better level. **Availability:** Online.

1585 ■ *"Longtime Advocacy for Green Skin Care Is Paying Off"* **in Providence Business News (Vol. 29, June 2, 2014, No. 9, pp. 24)**
Pub: American City Business Journals, Inc.
Contact: Mike Olivieri, Executive Vice President
Released: February 01, 2014. **Description:** Brenda Brock, entrepreneur and founder of Farmaesthetics, achieved success with her line of green, sustainable skin care products. She is now expanding her business to start new outlets. **Availability:** Print; Online.

1586 ■ *"New Year's Resolutions: How Three Companies Came Up With Their 2008 Growth Strategies"* **in Inc. (January 2008, pp. 47-49)**
Ed: Martha C. White. **Description:** Three companies share 2008 growth strategies; companies include a candle company, a voice mail and text messaging marketer, and hotel supplier of soap and shampoo. **Availability:** Online.

1587 ■ *"Old Spice Guy (Feb.-July 2010)"* **in Canadian Business (Vol. 83, August 17, 2010, No. 13-14, pp. 23)**
Pub: Rogers Media Inc.
Contact: Neil Spivak, Chief Executive Officer
Ed: Andrew Potter. **Description:** Old Spice Guy was played by ex-football player and actor Isaiah Mustafa who made the debut in the ad for Old Spice Red Zone body wash that was broadcast during Super Bowl XLIV in February 2010. Old Spice Guy has become one of social marketing success but was cancelled in July when online viewership started to wane. **Availability:** Print; Online.

1588 ■ *"Owner of Skin Care Business Offers Westfield State Scholarships If Ex-President Drops Lawsuit"* **in Boston Business Journal (Vol. 34, April 25, 2014, No. 12, pp. 5)**
Pub: American City Business Journals, Inc.
Contact: Mike Olivieri, Executive Vice President
Description: John Walsh, CEO of Elizabeth Grady Company, has offered $100,000 in scholarships if Westfield State University President, Evan Dobelle, drops his lawsuits against the university. Dobelle decided to sue the school after he was placed on paid leave by three trustees. **Availability:** Print; Online.

1589 ■ *"Private Equity Firm Links First Arizona Deal"* **in Business Journal-Serving Phoenix and the Valley of the Sun (November 2, 2007)**
Description: Pacific Investment Partners and Your Source Financial launched a $10 million fund and signed their first deal. The two companies acquires a

minority stake in Dreambrands Inc. for $3 million. Dreambrands is using the capital to market its personal lubricant product Carrageenana.

1590 ■ *"Quintessential Gentleman: Going Old-School on Calvert"* in Baltimore Business Journal (Vol. 31, February 7, 2014, No. 41, pp. 6)
Pub: American City Business Journals, Inc.
Contact: Mike Olivieri, Executive Vice President
Description: Quintessential Gentleman owner, Craig Martin shares his vintage idea in the expansion of his men's barbershop, spa, and tailor business in the Jewelers Building at South Calvert Street in downtown Baltimore, Maryland. Martin says his idea is to bring back tradition combined with modern amenities. He also shares his plan to model the business on a department store. **Availability:** Print; Online.

1591 ■ *"To Catch Up, Colgate May Ratchet Up Its Ad Spending"* in Advertising Age (Vol. 81, December 6, 2010, No. 43, pp. 1)
Pub: Crain Communications, Inc.
Contact: Jessica Botos, Manager, Marketing
E-mail: jessica.botos@crainsnewyork.com
Ed: Jack Neff. **Description:** Colgate-Palmolive Company has been losing market share in the categories of toothpaste, deodorant, body wash, dish soap and pet food. **Availability:** Online.

1592 ■ *"Vitabath: Sweet Smell of Success"* in Retail Merchandiser (Vol. 51, September-October 2011, No. 5, pp. 82)
Pub: Phoenix Media Corp.
Description: After taking over at Vitabath, Rich Brands developed new scents and products and while discovering new channels to distribute these items. **Availability:** PDF; Online.

1593 ■ *"What's Behind the Rise of G-Beauty"* in The New York Times (April 10, 2019)
URL(s): www.nytimes.com/2019/04/10/style/german-beauty.html
Ed: Bee Shapiro. **Released:** April 10, 2019. **Description:** The rise in popularity of German beauty products is investigated. With it's minimalist packaging and lack of toxins, these products are gaining control of the market share. **Availability:** Online.

TRADE PERIODICALS

1594 ■ *Cosmetics & Toiletries: The International Magazine of Cosmetic Technology*
Pub: Allured Business Media
Contact: Janet Ludwig, President
E-mail: jludwig@allured.com
URL(s): www.cosmeticsandtoiletries.com
Facebook: www.facebook.com/CandTmagazine
Linkedin: www.linkedin.com/company/cosmeticsandtoiletries
Instagram: www.instagram.com/cosmeticsandtoiletries
Released: 10/year; Jan., Feb., March, April, May, June, July/Aug., Sept., Oct. and Nov./Dec. **Price:** $199, for print. **Description:** Trade magazine on cosmetic and toiletries manufacturing with an emphasis on product research and development issues. **Availability:** Print; PDF; Online.

1595 ■ *Flavour and Fragrance Journal*
Pub: John Wiley & Sons Ltd.
Contact: Matthew Kissner, Chief Executive Officer
URL(s): onlinelibrary.wiley.com/journal/10991026
Released: Bimonthly **Price:** $4,483, Institutions for print and online US, Canada; $3,992, Institutions for online only US, Canada; $4,483, Institutions for print and online Japan; $3,992, Institutions for online only Japan; $4,164, Institutions for print US, Canada; $4,164, Institutions for print Japan. **Description:** International, multidisciplinary scientific journal covering all aspects of flavor and fragrance. **Availability:** Print; PDF; Download; Online.

1596 ■ *Skin Inc.: Professional Skin Care*
Contact: Katie Anderson, Managing Editor
E-mail: kanderson@allured.com
URL(s): www.skininc.com
Facebook: www.facebook.com/SkinInc
X (Twitter): twitter.com/SkinIncMagazine
Released: Monthly **Description:** The complete business guide for face and body care. **Availability:** Print; PDF; Online.

FRANCHISES AND BUSINESS OPPORTUNITIES

1597 ■ **Fruits & Passion**
FiberLink Inc
5500 Trans-Canada Hwy.
Pointe-Claire, QC, Canada H9R 1B6
Facebook: www.facebook.com/FruitsPassionEN
Instagram: www.instagram.com/fruits_passion
Pinterest: www.pinterest.com/fruitspassion
Description: Manufacturer and retailer of fragrance, body care, ambiance products and much more. **Founded:** 1992. **Training:** Initial and ongoing.

1598 ■ **Women's Health Boutique (WHB)**
605 N 6th St.
Longview, TX 75601
Ph: (903)758-9904
Free: 800-525-2420
Fax: (903)236-9786
Co. E-mail: info@whblongview.com
URL: http://www.mywhb.com
Contact: Vicki Jones, President
Facebook: www.facebook.com/womenshealthboutique
X (Twitter): x.com/WHBgirls
Pinterest: www.pinterest.com/whbladies
Description: Products and services related to pre and postnatal care, post-mastectomy, compression therapy, hair loss, incontinence, and skin care. **No. of Franchise Units:** 13. **Founded:** 1991. **Franchised:** 1994. **Equity Capital Needed:** $49,000 minimum start-up cash. **Training:** Yes.

COMPUTERIZED DATABASES

1599 ■ *Pharmaceutical News Index®*
ProQuest LLC
789 E Eisenhower Pky.
Ann Arbor, MI 48108
Ph: (734)761-4700
Free: 800-521-0600
URL: http://www.proquest.com
Contact: Matti Shem Tov, Chief Executive Officer
URL(s): about.proquest.com/en/customer-care/title-lists
Availability: Print. **Type:** Bibliographic; Full-text.

LIBRARIES

1600 ■ **Colgate-Palmolive Company - Library**
Colgate-Palmolive Company
300 Park Ave.
New York, NY 10022
Ph: (212)310-2000
Free: 800-468-6502
Fax: (212)310-3745
Co. E-mail: ethics@colpal.com
URL: http://www.colgatepalmolive.com
Contact: Noel Wallace, President
Linkedin: www.linkedin.com/company/colgate-palmolive
X (Twitter): twitter.com/cp_news
YouTube: www.youtube.com/user/colgatepalmolive
Description: Global manufacturer and distributor of consumer oral care, personal care, home care, pet nutrition products, and pharmaceutical products for dentists and other oral health professionals. **Scope:** Health; hygiene. **Founded:** 1806. **Holdings:** Figures not available. **Educational Activities:** Business Today International Conference (Annual). **Awards:** ACS Award in Colloid Chemistry (Annual); Make the U (Annual).

1601 ■ **Mary Kay Inc. Information Resources**
16251 N Dallas Pky.
Addison, TX 75001
URL: http://www.marykay.com
Scope: Cosmetics; dermatology; toxicology; chemistry; business; marketing. **Services:** Interlibrary loan. **Holdings:** 2000 books; 500 bound periodical volumes.

Book Publishing

START-UP INFORMATION

1602 ■ *"9 Strategies to BUILD and GROW Your Author Platform: A Step-by-Step Book Marketing Plan to Get More Exposure and Sales"*

Released: May 04, 2016. **Description:** A nine-step formula for marketing self-published books is presented. The author has sold over 103,000 books using this method since 2008 and continues to grow her customer base through email and followers. **Availability:** Print.

1603 ■ *"Legal Matters: 'Crowdfunding' a Boon for Entrepreneurs, If They Clear Regulatory Hurdles" in Finance and Commerce (July 17, 2012)*

Pub: BridgeTower Media
Contact: Adam Reinebach, President

Ed: Dan Heilman. **Description:** Part of the Jumpstart Our Business Startups Act (JOBS) is crowdfunding, which allows the funding of a company by selling small parts of equity to a group of investors. Kickstarter, a Website for raising funds for business entitites, is primarily used for film and book projects. Most businesses cannot adopt Kickstarter's model because of the legality of receiving investor funds without offering security.

ASSOCIATIONS AND OTHER ORGANIZATIONS

1604 ■ **About Books (ABI)**
502 N 31st St.
  Colorado Springs, CO 80904
Ph: (719)440-8932
URL: http://about-books.com
Contact: Scott Flora, Contact
E-mail: scott@about-books.com

Description: Information clearinghouse on self-publishing and marketing of books. Provides educational programs; maintains speakers' bureau. Provides audiotape programs and books on the subject. **Scope:** Full service writing and publishing consultants organized to assist corporations, organizations and individuals in the writing, editing, producing and marketing of books. Also develop sponsored and premium books. **Publications:** "Molding Young Athletes," Purington Press. **Geographic Preference:** National.

1605 ■ **ACP Update**
401 Richmond St. W Studio 257A
  Toronto, ON, Canada M5V 3A8
Ph: (416)487-6116
Co. E-mail: admin@canbook.org
URL: http://publishers.ca
Contact: Kate Edwards, Executive Director
E-mail: kate_edwards@canbook.org
URL(s): publishers.ca/about

Released: Biweekly **Description:** Includes information for The Association of Canadian Publishers members. **Availability:** Online.

1606 ■ **American Book Producers Association (ABPA)**
23 Waverly Pl., Ste. 6B
  New York, NY 10003
Co. E-mail: office@abpaonline.org
URL: http://abpaonline.org
Facebook: www.facebook.com/ABPAbooks
Linkedin: www.linkedin.com/company/abpabooks
X (Twitter): x.com/abpabooks
Instagram: www.instagram.com/abpabooks

Description: Aims to increase the book industry's awareness of members' capabilities and the state of the book producers' art. Facilitates exchange of information for the purpose of improving business and establishing trade standards. **Founded:** 1980. **Publications:** *American Book Producers Association--Newsletter* (Bimonthly). **Geographic Preference:** National.

1607 ■ **Association of American Publishers (AAP)**
455 Massachusetts Ave. NW, Ste. 700
  Washington, DC 20001
Ph: (202)347-3375
Fax: (202)347-3690
Co. E-mail: info@publishers.org
URL: http://www.publishers.org
Contact: Maria A. Pallante, President
X (Twitter): x.com/AmericanPublish

Description: Represents the major commercial publishers in the United States as well as smaller and non-profit publishers, university presses and scholarly societies. Helps in the protection of intellectual property rights in all media. Promotes reading and literacy and the freedom to publish at home and abroad. Conducts seminars and workshops on various publishing topics including rights and permission, sales, and educational publishing. Compiles statistics. **Founded:** 1970. **Publications:** *Who's Who (Internationally) at American Booksellers Association Annual Convention*; *Exhibits Directory*; *AAP Monthly Report* (Monthly). **Awards:** AAP Honors (Annual); Association of American Publishers Golden Lamp Awards (Annual); Mary McNulty Award (Periodic); R.R. Hawkins Award (Annual); Jeri Laber International Freedom to Publish Award (Annual). **Geographic Preference:** National.

1608 ■ **Association of American University Presses (AAUP)**
1412 Bwdy., ste. 2135
  New York, NY 10018
Ph: (212)989-1010
Fax: (212)989-0275
Co. E-mail: info@aaupnet.org
URL: http://aupresses.org
Contact: Peter Berkery, Executive Director
E-mail: pberkery@aupresses.org
Facebook: www.facebook.com/universitypresses
X (Twitter): x.com/aupresses

Description: Helps university presses do their work more economically, creatively, and effectively through its own activities in education-training, fundraising and development, statistical research and analysis, and community and institutional relations. **Founded:** 1937. **Publications:** *Advertising and Publicity Resources for Scholarly Books*; *AAUP Directory* (Annual); *Association of American University Presses--Directory* (Annual); *Exchange* (Quarterly). **Educational Activities:** Association of American University Presses Annual Meeting (Annual). **Awards:** AAUP Constituency Award (Annual); AAUP Book, Jacket, and Journal Show (Annual). **Geographic Preference:** Multinational.

1609 ■ **Association of Canadian Publishers (ACP)**
401 Richmond St. W Studio 257A
  Toronto, ON, Canada M5V 3A8
Ph: (416)487-6116
Co. E-mail: admin@canbook.org
URL: http://publishers.ca
Contact: Kate Edwards, Executive Director
E-mail: kate_edwards@canbook.org
X (Twitter): x.com/cdnpublishers

Description: Conducts industry research, including salary surveys, book sales analyses, and accounting modifications; facilitates communication among members; makes available promotion, public relations, and marketing services. **Founded:** 1971. **Publications:** *Directory of Canadian Media*; *Association of Canadian Publishers--Directory*; *ACP Update* (Biweekly). **Geographic Preference:** National.

1610 ■ **Association of Catholic Publishers (ACP)**
4725 Dorsey Hall Dr., Ste. A
  Ellicott City, MD 21042
Ph: (410)988-2926
Fax: (410)571-4946
Co. E-mail: info@catholicpublishers.org
URL: http://www.catholicpublishers.org
Contact: Joellyn Cicciarelli, President
Facebook: www.facebook.com/CatholicPublishers
Linkedin: www.linkedin.com/company/association-of-catholic-publishers
X (Twitter): x.com/catholicpubs
YouTube: www.youtube.com/channel/UCQtS-RoGA95dsaYiJbX2PMw

Description: Facilitates the sharing of professional information, networking, cooperation, and friendship among those involved in Catholic publishing in the United States and abroad. **Founded:** 1992. **Publications:** *The Catholic Book Publishers Association Directory*; *CBPA Newsletter*; *The Spirit of Books* (Semiannual). **Awards:** ACP Outstanding Service Award (Annual). **Geographic Preference:** Multinational.

1611 ■ **Association of Publishers for Special Sales (APSS)**
c/o Kaye Krasner
  PO Box 9725
  Colorado Springs, CO 80932-0725

Ph: (719)924-5534
Fax: (719)213-2602
URL: http://community.bookapss.org
Contact: Brian Jud, Executive Director
E-mail: brianjud@bookapss.org
Facebook: www.facebook.com/bookapss
X (Twitter): x.com/APSSBrianJud
Description: For self-publishers, authors and small presses. Works to advance the image and profits of independent publishers through education and marketing. Offers continuing education, co-op buying power and sales and networking opportunities, plus discounts on many products and services. Publishes monthly newsletter. **Founded:** 1996. **Geographic Preference:** National.

1612 ■ Bay Area Independent Publishers Association (BAIPA)
369-B 3rd St., Ste. 422
San Rafael, CA 94901
Co. E-mail: valpub@yahoo.com
URL: http://baipa.org
Contact: Becky Parker Geist, President
E-mail: becky@proaudiovoices.com
Facebook: www.facebook.com/pg/baipa.org
X (Twitter): x.com/BAIPA
Description: Promotes authors interested in independent publishing as an alternative to the commercial publishing system; printers, artists, typists, and others in allied fields. Aims to become a comprehensive source of self-publishing information and to develop knowledge and expertise to better assist members in promoting, marketing, and publishing their works. Acts as a liaison and clearinghouse of information and provides guidance in all aspects of self-publishing, including copy preparation, book production, and marketing and sales. **Founded:** 1979. **Publications:** *SPEX* (Monthly); *SPEX*. **Geographic Preference:** National.

1613 ■ *Best Books for Kids and Teens (BBKT)*
500-30 Wellington Street West
Toronto, ON, Canada M5V 3C1
Ph: (416)975-0010
Co. E-mail: info@bookcentre.ca
URL: http://bookcentre.ca
Contact: Urve Tamberg, President
URL(s): bookcentre.ca/best-books-for-kids-and-teens
Released: Semiannual **Price:** $64.95, for international annual; $2.95, for fall or spring 2022; $29.95, for price annual; $6.95, for spring 2024; $5.95, for fall 2023. **Description:** Serves as a guide to the best new Canadian children's books, magazines, audio and video. **Availability:** Print; PDF; Online.

1614 ■ Book Industry Study Group (BISG)
232 Madison Ave., Ste. 1400
New York, NY 10016
Ph: (646)336-7141
Co. E-mail: info@bisg.org
URL: http://www.bisg.org
Contact: Brian O'Leary, Executive Director
E-mail: brian@bisg.org
Linkedin: www.linkedin.com/company/book-industry-study-group
X (Twitter): x.com/BISG
Description: Maintains and implements standardized best practices. BISG also develops and shares leading-edge research and information and creates education and events that help our membership and the industry better understand market trends and issues. **Scope:** Facilitates connections and conversations to solve common problems, advance new ideas, and more profitably bring published content to readers. **Founded:** 1976. **Publications:** *BISG Research Reports* (Quarterly); *Student Attitudes Toward Content in Higher Education*; *Trends Update*; *Book Industry TRENDS* (Annual). **Educational Activities:** BISG Seminars and conferences, For discussion of implications of statistical information on the book industry. **Geographic Preference:** Multinational.

1615 ■ Book Manufacturers Institute, Inc. (BMI)
7282 55th Ave. E, Ste. 147
Bradenton, FL 34203
Ph: (386)986-4552
URL: http://www.bmibook.com
Contact: Jim Fetherston, President
Linkedin: www.linkedin.com/company/bmibook
X (Twitter): x.com/bmibook
YouTube: www.youtube.com/channel/UCRxDyN0mq_yII6vah5XbCeA
Description: Represents the trade association for manufacturers of books. **Founded:** 1933. **Awards:** BMI Gutenberg Award (Annual); BMI Distinguished Master Bookman Award (Irregular); BMI Signature Award (Annual). **Geographic Preference:** National.

1616 ■ Book and Periodical Council (BPC)
192 Spadina Ave., Ste. 107
Toronto, ON, Canada M5T 2C2
Ph: (416)975-9366
Co. E-mail: info@thebpc.ca
URL: http://www.thebpc.ca
Contact: Anne McClelland, Executive Director
Facebook: www.facebook.com/BookandPeriodicalCouncil
X (Twitter): x.com/intent/follow
Description: Associations representing writers, editors, and publishers of books and periodicals and manufacturers, distributors, and sellers and lenders of printed materials. **Geographic Preference:** National.

1617 ■ Canadian Children's Book Centre (CCBC) - Library
500-30 Wellington Street West
Toronto, ON, Canada M5V 3C1
Ph: (416)975-0010
Co. E-mail: info@bookcentre.ca
URL: http://bookcentre.ca
Contact: Urve Tamberg, President
Facebook: www.facebook.com/kidsbookcentre
X (Twitter): x.com/kidsbookcentre
Instagram: www.instagram.com/kidsbookcentre
Description: Promotes the reading, writing, illustrating and publishing of Canadian books for young readers. **Scope:** Canadian children's book. **Services:** Non-circulating; open to visitors. **Founded:** 1976. **Holdings:** Books. **Publications:** *Chirp*; *Canadian Children's Book News* (Quarterly); *Best Books for Kids and Teens (BBKT)* (Semiannual). **Awards:** Geoffrey Bilson Award for Historical Fiction for Young People (Annual); Norma Fleck Award for Canadian Children's Non-Fiction (Annual); TD Canadian Children's Literature Award (Annual). **Geographic Preference:** National.

1618 ■ *Canadian Children's Book News*
500-30 Wellington Street West
Toronto, ON, Canada M5V 3C1
Ph: (416)975-0010
Co. E-mail: info@bookcentre.ca
URL: http://bookcentre.ca
Contact: Urve Tamberg, President
URL(s): bookcentre.ca/canadian-childrens-book-news
Released: Quarterly **Price:** $26.95, Single issue. **Description:** Magazine covering various topics related to children's book publishing in Canada. **Availability:** Print; Online.

1619 ■ Canadian Copyright Institute (CCI)
192 Spadina Ave., Ste. 107
Toronto, ON, Canada M5T 2C2
Ph: (416)975-9366
Co. E-mail: info@thecci.ca
URL: http://thecci.ca/default.html
Contact: Anne McClelland, Administrator
Description: Creators, producers, and distributors of copyrighted works. Encourages a more complete understanding of copyright laws among members and the public. Consults with government and judicial bodies regarding reform of copyright laws. Conducts and sponsors research on copyright laws worldwide. Works with organizations pursuing similar goals to improve copyright legislation and enforcement. **Founded:** 1965. **Publications:** *Copyright Reform Legislation Reporting Service* (Periodic). **Geographic Preference:** National.

1620 ■ Canadian Publishers' Council (CPC)
3080 Yonge St., Ste. 6060
Toronto, ON, Canada M4N 3N1
Ph: (647)255-8880
URL: http://pubcouncil.ca
Contact: David Swail, President
E-mail: dswail@pubcouncil.ca
X (Twitter): x.com/pubcouncil_ca
Description: English-language publishers. Seeks to advance the domestic book publishing industry; encourages publication of Canadian authors. Facilitates communication and cooperation among members; represents members' interests before trade organizations, government agencies, and the public. **Founded:** 1910. **Geographic Preference:** National.

1621 ■ Center for the Book in the Library of Congress (LOC)
101 Independence Ave. SE
Washington, DC 20540
Ph: (202)707-5000
URL: http://www.loc.gov
Contact: John van Oudenaren, Director
URL(s): read.gov/cfb
Facebook: www.facebook.com/libraryofcongress
X (Twitter): x.com/librarycongress
Instagram: www.instagram.com/librarycongress
YouTube: www.youtube.com/c/loc
Pinterest: www.pinterest.com/LibraryCongress
Description: Uses resources and prestige of Library of Congress to stimulate public interest in books, reading, literacy, and libraries, and encourage the study of books and the printed word. **Founded:** 1977. **Publications:** *Community of the Book: A Directory of Organizations and Programs*. **Geographic Preference:** National.

1622 ■ Evangelical Christian Publishers Association (ECPA)
5801 S McClintock Dr., Ste. 104
Tempe, AZ 85283
Co. E-mail: info@ecpa.org
URL: http://www.ecpa.org
Contact: Jeff Crosby, President
E-mail: jcrosby@ecpa.org
Facebook: www.facebook.com/ECPA.org
X (Twitter): x.com/ecpa
Description: Companies that primarily publish Christian religious literature. Conducts annual sales and operation survey, and a series of educational seminars and trade shows. **Founded:** 1974. **Publications:** *Evangelical Christian Publishers Association--Membership Directory*; *Monday Rush* (Weekly). **Awards:** Gold Book Award (Annual); Platinum Book Award (Annual); ECPA Christian Book of the Year Award (Annual); ECPA Top Shelf Book Cover Awards (Annual); ECPA Christian Book Awards - Bibles (Annual); Book Cover Award (Annual); Jordon Lifetime Achievement Award (Annual); ECPA Diamond Book Awards (Irregular). **Geographic Preference:** Multinational.

1623 ■ Independent Book Publishers Association (IBPA)
1020 Manhattan Beach Blvd., Ste. 204
Manhattan Beach, CA 90266
Ph: (310)546-1818
Co. E-mail: info@ibpa-online.org
URL: http://www.ibpa-online.org
Contact: Andrea Fleck-Nisbet, Chief Executive Officer
E-mail: andrea@ibpa-online.org
Facebook: www.facebook.com/IBPAonline
X (Twitter): x.com/ibpa
Instagram: www.instagram.com/ibpalovesindies
YouTube: www.youtube.com/user/ibpavideo
Description: Entrepreneurial publishers of trade books and video and audio cassette tapes. Aims to assist independent publishers in the marketing and sale of their titles to bookstores, libraries, and specialty markets. Holds marketing and educational programs. **Founded:** 1983. **Publications:** *Independent Publishing Now eNewsletter* (Monthly); *PMA Resource Directory* (Annual). **Awards:** IBPA Book Award (Annual). **Geographic Preference:** National.

1624 ■ Literary Press Group of Canada (LPG)
234 Eglinton Ave. E, Ste. 401
Toronto, ON, Canada M4P 1K5
Ph: (416)483-1321
Fax: (416)483-2510
URL: http://www.lpg.ca
Contact: Laura Rock Gaughan, Executive Director
E-mail: laurag@lpg.ca
Facebook: www.facebook.com/lpgcanada
X (Twitter): x.com/LPGCanada
Description: Canadian owned and controlled literary book publishers. Promotes growth and development of members. Makes available cooperative sales and marketing services. **Founded:** 1975. **Geographic Preference:** National.

1625 ■ Livres Canada Books
1 Nicholas St., Ste. 504
Ottawa, ON, Canada K1N 7B7
Ph: (613)562-2324
Fax: (613)562-2329
Co. E-mail: info@livrescanadabooks.com
URL: http://www.livrescanadabooks.com/en
Contact: François Charette, Executive Director
E-mail: fcharette@livrescanadabooks.com
Facebook: www.facebook.com/LivresCanadaBooks
Linkedin: www.linkedin.com/company/livres-canada-books
X (Twitter): x.com/livresCAbooks
Instagram: www.instagram.com/livrescanadabooks
YouTube: www.youtube.com/channel/UCRmaaNmT_0_ZqG77r2EVuVA
Description: Helps Canadian publishers develop foreign markets and promote export sales of books. Provides financial assistance and market intelligence. Organizes collective Canada stands at major international book fairs. **Founded:** 1972. **Publications:** *Livres Canada Books News* (Monthly); *Rights Canada* (Annual); *Books on Canada* (Annual). **Geographic Preference:** National.

1626 ■ *Livres Canada Books News*
1 Nicholas St., Ste. 504
Ottawa, ON, Canada K1N 7B7
Ph: (613)562-2324
Fax: (613)562-2329
Co. E-mail: info@livrescanadabooks.com
URL: http://www.livrescanadabooks.com/en
Contact: François Charette, Executive Director
E-mail: fcharette@livrescanadabooks.com
URL(s): www.livrescanadabooks.com/Newsletter-Archive
Released: Monthly **Description:** Features programs and services updates, latest export expertise, news of funding, fairs and other business opportunities. **Availability:** Print.

1627 ■ National Information Standards Organization (NISO)
3600 Clipper Mill Rd., Ste. 302
Baltimore, MD 21211-1948
Ph: (301)654-2512
Fax: (410)685-5278
Co. E-mail: nisohq@niso.org
URL: http://www.niso.org
Contact: Todd Carpenter, Executive Director
Description: Identifies, develops, maintains, and publishes technical standards to manage information in the changing environment used by libraries, publishers, and information services. Supports open access to NISO standards. Standards available at website. **Founded:** 1939. **Publications:** *Newsline* (Monthly); *Newsline* (Semiannual); *Information Standards Quarterly (ISQ)* (Quarterly); *Technical Report*. **Geographic Preference:** National.

1628 ■ *Rights Canada*
1 Nicholas St., Ste. 504
Ottawa, ON, Canada K1N 7B7
Ph: (613)562-2324
Fax: (613)562-2329
Co. E-mail: info@livrescanadabooks.com
URL: http://www.livrescanadabooks.com/en
Contact: François Charette, Executive Director
E-mail: fcharette@livrescanadabooks.com
URL(s): www.livrescanadabooks.com/Catalogues/Rights-Canada/Rights-Canada
Released: Annual **Description:** Includes articles concerning collective rights. **Availability:** Print; PDF.

1629 ■ Society for Scholarly Publishing (SSP)
1120 Rte. 73, Ste. 200
Mount Laurel, NJ 08054
Ph: (856)439-1385
Fax: (856)439-0525
Co. E-mail: info@sspnet.org
URL: http://www.sspnet.org
Contact: Alice Meadows, President
Facebook: www.facebook.com/SocietyforScholarlyPublishing
X (Twitter): x.com/ScholarlyPub
Description: A non-profit organization formed to promote and advance communication among all sectors of the scholarly publication community including publishers, printers, e-products developers, technical service providers, librarians and editors, through networking, information dissemination, collaboration and facilitation of new developments in the field. **Founded:** 1978. **Publications:** *Society for Scholarly Publishing--Membership Directory* (Annual). **Educational Activities:** Society for Scholarly Publishing Seminar (Annual). **Geographic Preference:** National.

1630 ■ Special Libraries Association (SLA)
1120 Rte. 73, Ste. 200
Mount Laurel, NJ 08054
Ph: (703)647-4900
Co. E-mail: membership@sla.org
URL: http://sla.org
Contact: John Digilio, President
E-mail: jdigilio@gmail.com
Facebook: www.facebook.com/SpecialLibrariesAssociation
Linkedin: www.linkedin.com/company/sla
X (Twitter): x.com/slahq
Description: International association of information professionals who work in specialized information environments such as business, research, government, universities, newspapers, museums, and institutions. Seeks to advance the leadership role of information professionals through learning, networking and advocacy. Offers consulting services to organizations that wish to establish or expand a library. Conducts strategic learning and development courses, public relations, and government relations programs. Provides employment services. Operates knowledge exchange on topics pertaining to the development and management of special libraries. **Scope:** Libraries. **Founded:** 1909. **Holdings:** Figures not available. **Publications:** *Information Outlook* (Bimonthly); *Business and Finance Division Bulletin* (Quarterly); *Directory of Catalogers in the Special Libraries Association*; *Information Outlook: The Monthly Magazine of the Special Libraries Association* (Bimonthly); *Who's Who in Special Libraries* (Annual); *SLA Annual Salary Survey* (Annual); *SLA Connections* (Continuous); *Physics-Astronomy-Mathematics Division--Membership Directory* (Annual); *SpeciaList* (Monthly); *Insurance and Employee Benefits Literature*. **Educational Activities:** The Library Innovation Conference (Annual). **Awards:** Fellows of SLA (Annual); SLA Hall of Fame (Annual); John Cotton Dana Award (Irregular); H. W. Wilson Company Award (Irregular); SLA Diversity Leadership Development Program Award (Annual); SLA Presidential Citations. **Geographic Preference:** National.

1631 ■ Women's National Book Association (WNBA)
PO Box 237, FDR Sta.
New York, NY 10150
Free: 866-610-9622
Co. E-mail: info@wnba-books.org
URL: http://wnba-books.org
Contact: Natalie Obando-Desai, President
Facebook: www.facebook.com/WomensNationalBookAssociation
X (Twitter): x.com/WNBA_National
Instagram: www.instagram.com/wnba_books
YouTube: www.youtube.com/channel/UCFQ-43NoUKQwM6fPJpzzLtg
Description: Women and men who work with and value books. Exists to promote reading and to support the role of women in the book community. **Founded:** 1917. **Publications:** *The Bookwoman* (Monthly); *The Bookwoman* (Monthly). **Awards:** WNBA Pannell Award (Annual); WNBA Eastman Grant (Annual); The WNBA Award (Annual); WNBA Eastman Grants (Annual). **Geographic Preference:** National.

EDUCATIONAL PROGRAMS

1632 ■ EEI Communications Managing the Publications Department
URL(s): www.eeicom.com
Description: Covers the role of the publications manager, techniques for managing multiple projects, standardizing and organizing the publications process, creating productivity standards and quality control procedures, using new technology, and working effectively with peers, subordinates, and superiors. **Audience:** Writers, editors, designers, proofreaders, and publication specialists. **Principal Exhibits:** Covers the role of the publications manager, techniques for managing multiple projects, standardizing and organizing the publications process, creating productivity standards and quality control procedures, using new technology, and working effectively with peers, subordinates, and superiors. **Telecommunication Services:** train@eeicom.com.

1633 ■ EEI Communications Production Techniques and Technology
URL(s): www.eeicom.com
Description: Covers the print production process within the publishing industry, including processes and principles of graphic production, pre-press, and printing; basics of design, typography, and layout; electronic advances on the desktop and in the printing plant; working with vendors; and the basics of scheduling, estimating, and quality control. **Audience:** Writers, editors, designers, proofreaders, and publication specialists. **Principal Exhibits:** Covers the print production process within the publishing industry, including processes and principles of graphic production, pre-press, and printing; basics of design, typography, and layout; electronic advances on the desktop and in the printing plant; working with vendors; and the basics of scheduling, estimating, and quality control. **Telecommunication Services:** train@eeicom.com.

1634 ■ EEI Communications Quality Control in Publications
URL(s): www.eeicom.com
Description: Covers the process of publication, including planning and quality control systems, error detection processes, effectively using software, and dealing with print vendors. **Audience:** Content creators, editors, proofers, graphic designers, specialists, desktop publishers, recruiters, and sales team. **Principal Exhibits:** Covers the process of publication, including planning and quality control systems, error detection processes, effectively using software, and dealing with print vendors. **Telecommunication Services:** train@eeicom.com.

REFERENCE WORKS

1635 ■ "3 Big Trends in 2019 Indie Books, According to Publishing Startup Reedsy's CEO" in Forbes (March 4, 2019)
URL(s): www.forbes.com/sites/adamrowe1/2019/03/04/3-big-trends-in-2019-indie-books-according-to-publishing-startup-reedsys-ceo/#1e8e8af4700f
Ed: Adam Rowe. **Released:** March 04, 2019. **Description:** Profile of Reedsy Discovery, a new online service aimes at independently published books. This platform is capitalizing on the trend of authors who prefer to independently publish instead of using traditional publishing houses. **Availability:** Online.

1636 ■ "5 Book Genre Trends We Predict for 2019" in Mythos & Ink (January 3, 2019)
URL(s): www.mythosink.com/2019-genre-predictions/

Ed: Kyle Rudge. **Released:** January 03, 2019. **Description:** Five possible book genre trends are discussed, based on growth patterns in the industry. Urban Fantasy, Science Fantasy, Utopian with a Post-Apocalyptic Origin, Diversity in Fantasy and Sci-Fi, and Cyberpunk are all genres that may be the next big thing in publishing. **Availability:** Online.

1637 ■ *"Africa Rising" in Harvard Business Review (Vol. 86, September 2008, No. 9, pp. 36)*
Pub: Harvard Business Review Press
Contact: Moderna V. Pfizer, Contact

Ed: Vijay Mahajan. **Description:** Review of the book entitled, "Africa Rising: How 900 Million African Consumers Offer More Than You Think" provides advice for marketing to those on the African continent. **Availability:** Print; Online.

1638 ■ *"ALA: Hot Topics for Librarianship" in Information Today (Vol. 28, September 2011, No. 8, pp. 17)*
Pub: Information Today Inc.
Contact: Thomas H. Hogan, President

Ed: Barbara Brynko. **Description:** Highlights from the American Library Association Annual Conference and Exhibition are listed. Thousands of attendees sought out services, displays, demos, new product rollouts, and freebies. Emerging technology for librarians, staff development, gray literature, interlibrary loans, and next-generation interfaces were among the topics discussed.

1639 ■ *Association of American University Presses--Directory*
Pub: Association of American University Presses
Contact: Peter Berkery, Executive Director
E-mail: pberkery@aupresses.org
URL(s): aupresses.org/membership/annual-directory

Released: Annual **Price:** $9, for online 30 day; $30, Individuals for print or PDF; $30, for pdf. **Description:** Covers 124 presses and affiliates worldwide. **Entries include:** Press name, address, phone, e-mail, URL; titles and names of complete editorial and managerial staffs; editorial program; mailing, warehouse, printing, and/or customer service addresses; other details. **Arrangement:** Classified by press affiliation, alphabetical by press name. **Indexes:** Personal name. **Availability:** Print; PDF; Online.

1640 ■ *"Bad Reviews Can Boost Sales. Here's Why" in Harvard Business Review (Vol. 90, April 2012, No. 4, pp. 28)*
Pub: Harvard Business Review Press
Contact: Moderna V. Pfizer, Contact

Ed: Jonah Berger. **Price:** $6. **Description:** Research on positive and negative book reviews found that sales increased for books with bad reviews, as the review itself made people aware of a work they would not have otherwise known about. **Availability:** Online; PDF.

1641 ■ *"Because Kids Need To Be Heard: Tina Wells: Buzz Marketing Group: Voorhees, New Jersey" in Inc. (Volume 32, December 2010)*
Pub: Mansueto Ventures L.L.C.
Contact: Stephanie Mehta, Chief Executive Officer

Ed: Tamara Schweitzer. **Released:** December 01, 2010. **Description:** Profile of Tina Wells, founder and CEO of Buzz Marketing Group, who writes a tween book series called Mackenzie Blue to reach young girls. **Availability:** Online.

1642 ■ *"Book Industry Supply Chain Delays to Impact Holiday Season" in American Booksellers Association (August 19, 2021)*

Ed: Emily Behnke. **Released:** August 19, 2021. **Description:** It takes many steps and adjacent industries to get books on shelves, such as trucking and warehousing. Expect delays in the book supply chain as the COVID-19 pandemic rages on and disruptions are common. **Availability:** Online.

1643 ■ *"The Book On Indigo" in Canadian Business (Vol. 81, July 22, 2008, No. 12-13, pp. 29)*

Description: Indigo Books & Music Inc. reported record sales of $922 million resulting in a record net profit of $52.8 million for the 2008 fiscal year ended March 29, 2008. Earnings per share were $2.13, greater than Standard & Poor's expected $1.70 per share. Additional information concerning Indigo Books is presented.

1644 ■ *"Book Publishing is Growing" in Information Today (Vol. 28, October 2011, No. 9, pp. 10)*
Pub: Information Today Inc.
Contact: Thomas H. Hogan, President

Ed: Paula J. Hane. **Description:** U.S. book publishing industry is reporting growth in its sector, despite the poor economy. BookStats, a comprehensive statistical survey conducted on the modern publishing industry in the U.S. reported Americans are reading in all print and digital formats. In 2011, 114 million ebooks were sold and now account for 13.6 percent of revenue from adult fiction. In contrast, 603 million trade hardcover books (fiction and nonfiction) were sold in 2011, a 5.8 percent increase over 2008.

1645 ■ *"Bridging the Worlds" in Academy of Management Journal (Vol. 50, No. 5, October 1, 2007, pp. 1043)*
Pub: Academy of Management
Contact: Sharon Alvarez, President

Ed: Lise Saari. **Description:** Need to transfer human resource research information published in journals to practitioners and organizations is investigated, along with suggestions on ways of achieving this goal. **Availability:** Electronic publishing; PDF; Download; Online.

1646 ■ *"Cancer Survivor Becomes Marathoner, Author" in Business Journal-Serving Phoenix & the Valley of the Sun (Vol. 30, August 20, 2010, No. 50, pp. 1)*
Pub: Phoenix Business Journal
Contact: Alex McAlister, Director
E-mail: amcalister@bizjournals.com

Ed: Angela Gonzales. **Description:** Cancer survivor Helene Neville has finished a record-breaking 2,520-mile run in 93 days and then celebrated her 50th birthday despite being diagnosed with Hodgkins' lymphoma in 1991. Neveille, who is also a Phoenix area registered nurse, made stops along the way to promote her book, 'Nurses in Shape'. Neville also discusses how she fought her cancer through running. **Availability:** Print; Online.

1647 ■ *"Cengage Learning Makes Boston Its Headquarters" in Boston Business Journal (Vol. 34, April 25, 2014, No. 12, pp. 6)*
Pub: American City Business Journals, Inc.
Contact: Mike Olivieri, Executive Vice President

Released: April 14, 2014. **Description:** Cengage Learning's office in Boston, Massachusetts will become the company's new corporate headquarters. The educational publishing firm, which has more than 400 employees in Boston, is also expected to develop new digital products for higher education. **Availability:** Print; Mailing list; Online.

1648 ■ *Children's Books in Print*
Pub: R.R. Bowker L.L.C.
URL(s): www.greyhouse.com/Childrens-Books-In-Print

Price: $990, for Softcover. **Entries include:** Book entries--Title, subtitle, author(s), editor(s), illustrator(s), publishing date, edition, price, binding, ISBN, LC number, publisher; Publisher entries--Name, address, phone, ISBN prefix. The material in "Children's Books in Print" is also available in subject-classified form in "Subject Guide to Children's Books in Print," also published in December. **Arrangement:** Alphabetical within each index. **Indexes:** Author, title, illustrator, award or prize, publisher. **Availability:** Print; PDF; Online.

1649 ■ *"Copyright Clearance Center (CCC) Partnered with cSubs" in Information Today (Vol. 28, November 2011, No. 10, pp. 14)*

Description: Copyright Clearance Center (CCC) partnered with cSubs to integrate CCC's point-of-content licensing solution RightsLink Basic directly into cSubs workflow. The partnership will allow cSubs' customers a user-friendly process for obtaining permissions. Csubs is a corporate subscription management service for books, newspapers, and econtent. **Availability:** Online.

1650 ■ *"The Day That Apple Called" in Business Journal Portland (Vol. 31, March 28, 2014, No. 4, pp. 9)*
Pub: American City Business Journals, Inc.
Contact: Mike Olivieri, Executive Vice President

Description: Cathy Filgas recalls the time when she became part of Dilithium Press, a textbook publisher based in Beaverton, Oregon that developed a how-to book for Apple in 1984 to help launch the Macintosh computer. Filgas says Dilithium grew too fast and closed a few years after working with Apple. **Availability:** Print; Online.

1651 ■ *Directory of Small Press/Magazine Editors & Publishers*
Pub: Dustbooks
URL(s): www.dustbooks.com/de.htm

Ed: Len Fulton. **Released:** Annual; latest edition 2017-2018. **Description:** Covers about 7,500 publishers and editors. **Entries include:** Individual name, title of press or magazine, address and phone number. **Arrangement:** Alphabetical. **Availability:** Print.

1652 ■ *"Etextbook Space Heats Up" in Information Today (Vol. 28, November 2011, No. 10, pp. 10)*
Pub: Information Today Inc.
Contact: Thomas H. Hogan, President

Ed: Paula J. Hane. **Description:** The use of etextbooks is expected to grow with the use of mobile devices and tablets. A new group of activists is asking students, faculty members and others to sign a petition urging higher education leaders to prioritize affordable textbooks or free ebooks over the traditional, expensive new books required for classes.

1653 ■ *"Etextbooks: Coming of Age" in Information Today (Vol. 28, September 2011, No. 8, pp. 1)*
Pub: Information Today Inc.
Contact: Thomas H. Hogan, President

Ed: Amanda Mulvihill. **Description:** National average for textbooks costs was estimated at $1,137 annually at a 4-year public college for the 2010-2011 school year. Amazon reported selling 105 etextbooks for every 100 print books, while Barnes and Noble announced that their etextbooks were outselling print 3 to 1.

1654 ■ *"Ex-MP? Ex-con? Exactly!" in Canadian Business (Vol. 83, October 12, 2010, No. 17, pp. 16)*

Description: British author Jeffrey Archer's novels could be made into movies. Archer sold 250 million books in 63 countries, which include political thrillers, spy novels, and crime capers. **Availability:** Print; Online.

1655 ■ *"Facebook Purchased Push Pop Press" in Information Today (Vol. 28, October 2011, No. 9, pp. 12)*

Description: Facebook purchased Push Pop Press, a digital publishing company that developed a multi-touch interface for ebook publishing on the iPad.

1656 ■ *"Gadget of the Week: Espresso Book Machine" in Barron's (Vol. 92, September 15, 2012, No. 38, pp. 27)*
Pub: Dow Jones & Company Inc.
Contact: Almar Latour, Chief Executive Officer

Ed: Crystal Kim. **Description:** The Espresso Book Machine from Demand Books can print custom-make and out-of-copyright books within minutes. The set up costs up to $349 while each book costs $7 to bind and $0.03/page to print. **Availability:** Online.

1657 ■ *"A Good Book Is Worth a Thousand Blogs" in Barron's (Vol. 88, July 14, 2008, No. 28, pp. 42)*
Pub: Dow Jones & Company Inc.
Contact: Almar Latour, Chief Executive Officer
Ed: Gene Epstein. **Description:** Nine summer book suggestions on economics are presented. The list includes 'The Revolution' by Ron Paul, 'The Forgotten Man' by Amity Shales, 'The Commitments of Traders Bible' by Stephen Briese, and 'Economic Facts and Fallacies' by Thomas Sowell. **Availability:** Online.

1658 ■ *"Hard-To-Read Fonts Promote Better Recall" in Harvard Business Review (Vol. 90, April 2012, No. 4, pp. 32)*
Pub: Harvard Business Review Press
Contact: Moderna V. Pfizer, Contact
Ed: Daniel Oppenheimer. **Price:** $6, hardcover. **Description:** Elaborate fonts have been found to boost reading comprehension because they make text harder to skim. However, because elaborate fonts are more difficult to read, it raises the likelihood that individuals might simply stop reading. **Availability:** PDF; Online.

1659 ■ *How to Start a Publishing Company: Turn Your Passion into Profit Using This Comprehensive Publishing Business Blueprint*
Released: March 28, 2020. **Description:** Explains how to set up and run a small publishing company to publish your own or others' books. **Availability:** Print.

1660 ■ *The International Directory of Little Magazines & Small Presses*
Pub: Dustbooks
URL(s): www.dustbooks.com/d.htm
Ed: Len Fulton. **Released:** Annual **Description:** Covers over 4,000 small, independent magazines, presses, and papers. **Entries include:** Name, address, size, circulation, frequency, price, type of material used, number of issues or books published annually, and other pertinent data. **Arrangement:** Alphabetical. **Indexes:** Subject, regional.

1661 ■ *The Library and Book Trade Almanac*
Pub: Information Today Inc.
Contact: Thomas H. Hogan, President
URL(s): store.infotoday.com/product/the-library-an
d-book-trade-almanac
Released: Annual; latest edition 68th; 2023. **Price:** $339.50, U.S.; $371.50, for outside north America; $361.50, for Canada or Mexico; $339.50, for annual. **Description:** Publication includes lists of accredited library schools; scholarships for education in library science; library organizations; library statistics; publishing and bookselling organizations. Includes lists of notable books, best-sellers, literary prize winners; library and trade statistics; calendar of events. **Entries include:** Directory listings give name of institution, address, phone, fax, name of officer or contact, publications; scholarship listings include requirements, value of grant, contact name. Principal content is articles and special reports on topics of interest to those in library/information science and publishers; international reports; annual reports from federal agencies and libraries and from national associations; information on legislation, funding, etc. **Arrangement:** Topical. **Indexes:** Organization; subject. **Availability:** Print; Online.

1662 ■ *Literary Market Place: The Directory of the American Book Publishing Industry*
Pub: Information Today Inc.
Contact: Thomas H. Hogan, President
URL(s): store.infotoday.com/product/literary-marke
t-place
Released: Latest edition 84th Edition 2024. **Price:** $539.50, for outside North America; $529.50, for Canada or Mexico; $507.50, Individuals. **Description:** Covers over 12,500 firms or organizations offering services related to the publishing industry, including book publishers in the United States and Canada who issued three or more books during the preceding year, plus a small press section of publishers who publish less than three titles per year or those who are self-published. Also included: book printers and binders; book clubs; book trade and literary associations; selected syndicates, newspapers, periodicals, and radio and TV programs that use book reviews or book publishing news; translators and literary agents. **Entries include:** For publishers--Company name, address, phone, address for orders, principal executives, editorial directors, and managers, date founded, number of titles in previous year, number of backlist titles in print, types of books published, ISBN prefixes, representatives, imprints, and affiliations. For suppliers, etc.--Listings usually show firm name, address, phone, executives, services, etc. **Arrangement:** Classified by line of business. **Indexes:** Principal index is 35,000-item combined index of publishers, publications, and personnel; several sections have geographical and/or subject indexes; translators are indexed by source and target language. **Availability:** Print; Online.

1663 ■ *"Major Publishers Are Selling a Ton of Ebooks in 2021" in Good E-Reader (May 7, 2021)*
URL(s): goodereader.com/blog/e-book-news/major
-publishers-are-selling-a-ton-of-ebooks-in-2021
Ed: Michael Kozlowski. **Released:** May 07, 2021. **Description:** Ebook and audiobooks sales are doing quite well in 2021, which is due mainly to people staying home and not shopping at bookstores. Harpercollins, S&S, and Hachette had increased sales. **Availability:** Download.

1664 ■ *"Negotiating Tips" in Black Enterprise (Vol. 37, December 2006, No. 5, pp. 70)*
Pub: Earl G. Graves Ltd.
Contact: Earl Graves, Jr., President
Ed: Marcia A. Reed-Woodard. **Description:** Sekou Kaalund, head of strategy, mergers & acquisitions at Citigroup Securities & Fund Services, states that "Negotiation skills are paramount to success in a business environment because of client, employee, and shareholder relationships". He discusses how the book by George Kohlrieser, Hostage at the Table: How Leaders Can Overcome Conflict, Influence Others, and Raise Performance, has helped him negotiate more powerfully and enhance his skills at conflict-resolution. **Availability:** Online.

1665 ■ *"New Approach to Mechanical Binding" in American Printer (Vol. 128, July 1, 2011, No. 7)*
Description: EcoBinder coil binding system from Kugler-Womako eliminates traditional plastic combs or wire spiral with the use of 22-mm wide printable paper rings. **Availability:** Online.

1666 ■ *"New Book Takes Alternate View on Ontario's Wind Industry" in CNW Group (September 19, 2011)*
Pub: CNW Group Ltd.
Description: Dirty Business: The Reality Behind Ontario's Rush to Wind Power, was written by editor and health care writer Jane Wilson of Ottawa, Ontario, Canada along with contributing editor Parker Gallant. The book contains articles and papers on the wind business, including information on illnesses caused from the environmental noise. **Availability:** Print; Online.

1667 ■ *"Online Book Sales Surpass Bookstores" in Information Today (Vol. 28, September 2011, No. 8, pp. 11)*
Pub: Information Today Inc.
Contact: Thomas H. Hogan, President
Ed: Cindy Martine. **Description:** Online book sales outpaced bookstore purchases in the United States, signaling a shift in the US book industry. Statistical data included.

1668 ■ *"PrintCity Shares Guide for Carbon Footprinting" in American Printer (Vol. 128, June 1, 2011, No. 6)*
Description: PrintCity Alliance published its new report, 'Carbon Footprint & Energy Reduction for Graphic Industry Value Chain.' The report aims to help improve the environmental performance of printers, converters, publishers, brand owners and their suppliers. **Availability:** Online.

1669 ■ *Publishers Directory*
Pub: Gale, part of Cengage Group
Contact: Paul Gazzolo, General Manager Senior Vice President
URL(s): www.gale.com/ebooks/9780028670133/pub
lishers-directory
Description: Covers over 20,000 new and established, commercial and nonprofit, private and alternative, corporate and association, government and institution publishing programs and their distributors; includes producers of books, classroom materials, prints, reports, and databases. **Entries include:** Firm name, address, phone, fax, company e-mail address, URL, year founded, ISBN prefix, Standard Address Number, whether firm participates in the Cataloging in Publication program of the Library of Congress, names of principal executives, personal e-mail addresses, number of titles in print, description of firm and its main subject interests, discount and returns policies, affiliated and parent companies, mergers and amalgamations, principal markets, imprints and divisions, alternate formats products are offered; distributors also list firms for which they distribute, special services, terms to publishers and regional offices. **Arrangement:** Alphabetical; distributors listed separately. **Indexes:** Subject, geographical, publisher, imprints, and distributor. **Availability:** Large print; CD-ROM; E-book; Online; DVD; Download. **Type:** Directory.

1670 ■ *Publishers, Distributors, and Wholesalers of the United States*
Pub: R.R. Bowker L.L.C.
URL(s): www.greyhouse.com/Publishers-Distributors
-and-Wholesalers-of-the-United-States
Price: $995, Individuals. **Description:** Covers over 196,066 publishers, distributors, and wholesalers; includes associations, museums, software producers and manufacturers, and others not included in 'Books in Print'. **Entries include:** Publisher name, editorial and ordering addresses, e-mail, websites, phone, Standard Address Numbers (SANs), International Standard Book Number prefix. **Arrangement:** Alphabetical; distributors and wholesalers are listed separately. **Indexes:** ISBN prefix, abbreviation, type of business, imprint name, geographical, inactive and out of business company name, toll-free phone and fax, wholesaler and distributor. **Availability:** Print; PDF.

1671 ■ *"Publishing: Art or Science? Reflections from an Editorial Perspective" in Accounting and Finance (Vol. 52, June 2012, No. 2, pp. 359)*
Released: February 01, 2012. **Description:** Insights into the 'journal process' is shared by an experienced editor. Three basics messages emerge from the discussion. First, if a study is to be successful, it must address an interesting and important topic to investigate; secondly, the study must be communicated in a transparent and accessible way so the work can be critically evaluated; finally, authors are advised to subject their work to external scrutiny before submitting for peer review. **Availability:** Print; PDF; Online.

1672 ■ *"Q&A: Chuck Hughes, Celebrity Chef" in Canadian Business (Vol. 85, July 16, 2012, No. 11-12, pp. 65)*
Ed: Nancy Won. **Description:** Celebrity chef Chuck Hughes feels blessed for the opportunity to work on a new cookbook based on the 'Chuck's Day Off' series and to start filming for a new U.S. show called 'Chuck Eats the Street'. For Hughes, cooking at the restaurant is the most rewarding and fulfilling job of all the things he does. **Availability:** Print; Online.

Small Business Profiles　　　　　　　　　　　　　　　　　　　　　　　　　　　　　　　　　　Book Publishing ■ 1693

1673 ■ "Reducing the Book's Carbon Footprint" in American Printer (Vol. 128, July 1, 2011, No. 7)
Description: Green Press Initiative's Book Industry Environmental Council is working to achieve a 20 percent reduction in the book industry's carbon footprint by 2020. The Council is made up of publishers, printers, paper suppliers, and non-governmental organizations. Availability: Online.

1674 ■ "Savvy Solutions" in Black Enterprise (Vol. 41, November 2010, No. 4, pp. 42)
Description: Society of Children's Book Writers and Illustrators offers members many benefits, including directories of agencies looking for new writers of books. Availability: Online.

1675 ■ "Scientific American Builds Novel Blog Network" in Information Today (Vol. 28, September 2011, No. 8, pp. 12)
Pub: Information Today Inc.
Contact: Thomas H. Hogan, President
Ed: Kurt Schiller. Description: Scientific American launched a new blog network that joins a diverse lineup of bloggers cover various scientific topics under one banner. The blog network includes 60 bloggers providing insights into the ever-changing world of science and technology.

1676 ■ Self-Publishing for Dummies
Pub: John Wiley & Sons, Inc.
Contact: Christina Van Tassell, Executive Vice President Chief Financial Officer
URL(s): www.wiley.com/en-us/Self+Publishing+For+Dummies%2C+2nd+Edition-p-9781394201273
Ed: Jason R. Rich. Released: 2nd edition. Price: $24.99, paperback. Description: Learn the latest updates in the self-publishing world and get your book out to the market. This guide will take the reader through the initial process of writing all the way to generating publicity for your work. Availability: Print.

1677 ■ "A Skimmer's Guide to the Latest Business Books" in Inc. (Volume 32, December 2010, No. 10, pp. 34)
Pub: Inc. Magazine
Description: A list of new books published covering all aspects of small business is offered. Availability: Online.

1678 ■ "Top 7 Free Online Publishing Platforms For New Writers" in Just Publishing Advice (October 13, 2019)
URL(s): justpublishingadvice.com/top-7-free-publishing-platforms-for-new-writers/
Released: October 13, 2019. Description: In these modern times, most people prefer to publish online instead of pursuring print options. This article explores the seven best platforms new writers can use to get their work published online. Availability: Online.

1679 ■ "Top Ten Publishing Industry Trends Every Author Needs to Know in 2019" in Written Word Media (January 3, 2019)
URL(s): writtenwordmedia.com/top-ten-publishing-industry-trends-every-author-needs-to-know-in-2019/
Ed: Ricci Wolman. Released: January 03, 2019. Description: Based upon reader polls, industry leaders, and the publication's own thoughts, the top 2019 industry trends in publishing are explored. Availability: Online.

1680 ■ "Truffles & Trifles' Marci Arthur Plans YouTube Channel, Cookbook" in Orlando Business Journal (Vol. 30, May 2, 2014, No. 45, pp. 3)
Pub: American City Business Journals, Inc.
Contact: Mike Olivieri, Executive Vice President
Released: Weekly. Price: $8, introductory 4-week offer(Digital & Print). Description: Marci Arthur, founder of Truffles & Trifles Cooking School, plans to create a YouTube channel and publish a cookbook. Arthur believes that the survival of her business can be attributed to the devotion and integrity of her employees. Reports show that the school has been receiving donations from sponsors such as Wolf Appliances and Sub-Zero. Availability: Print; Online.

1681 ■ "Why You Don't Get Published: An Editor's View" in Accounting and Finance (Vol. 52, June 2012, No. 2, pp. 343)
Ed: Michael E. Bradbury. Released: March 12, 2012. Description: This paper uses content analysis to examine 66 reviews on 33 manuscripts submitted to 'Accounting and Finance'. Selected extracts from reviews are provided to illustrate the issues considered important to reviewers. The main message is that papers need to be work-shopped and more care taken over editorial matters. A checklist for prospective authors is provided. Availability: Print; Online.

1682 ■ "Women Prefer Cookbooks Over Word-Of-Mouth for Recipe Suggestions" in Marketing to Women (Vol. 23, November 2010, No. 11, pp. 6)
Pub: EPM Communications Inc.
Contact: Ira Mayer, Chief Executive Officer
Description: Sixty-five percent of women surveyed enjoy a sit-down dinner at least five times a week according to Martha Steward Omni-media. Cookbooks, recipe Websites, food-focused magazines, and TV cooking shows are their primary source for new recipes. Availability: Print; Online.

1683 ■ "Wondering Where Publishing Is Headed? Ask Its Future Leaders" in Publishers Weekly (January 4, 2019)
URL(s): www.publishersweekly.com/pw/by-topic/industry-news/publisher-news/article/78932-wondering-where-publishing-is-headed-ask-its-future-leaders.html
Ed: John Maher. Released: January 04, 2019. Description: Explores what publishing looks like in this day and age. Two book topics have helped changed the modern publishing landscape: politcs and TV. More diverse voices are also explored. Availability: Online.

STATISTICAL SOURCES

1684 ■ Book Publishing Industry in the US - Market Research Report
URL(s): www.ibisworld.com/united-states/market-research-reports/book-publishing-industry/
Price: $925. Description: Downloadable report analyzing the current and future trends in book publishing. Availability: Download.

1685 ■ E-Book Publishing Industry in the US - Market Research Report
URL(s): www.ibisworld.com/united-states/market-research-reports/e-book-publishing-industry/
Price: $925. Description: Downloadable report analyzing the current and future trends of e-book publishing. Availability: Download.

1686 ■ RMA Annual Statement Studies
Pub: Risk Management Association
Contact: Nancy Foster, President
Released: Annual. Description: Contains composite balance sheets and income statements for more than 360 industries, including the accounting, auditing, and bookkeeping industries. Also contains five years of comparative historical data for discerning trends. Includes 16 commonly used ratios, computed for most of the size groupings for nearly every industry.

1687 ■ Standard & Poor's Industry Surveys
Pub: Standard And Poor's Financial Services LLC.
Contact: Douglas L. Peterson, President
Description: Two-volume book that examines the prospects for specific industries, including trucking. Also provides analyses of trends and problems, statistical tables and charts, and comparative company analyses.

TRADE PERIODICALS

1688 ■ Guild of Book Workers Newsletter
Pub: Guild of Book Workers
Contact: Bexx Caswell, President
E-mail: president@guildofbookworkers.org
URL(s): guildofbookworkers.org/newsletter
Released: 6/year Description: Covers issues in book arts, binding, book conservation, calligraphy, and printing. Recurring features include letters to the editor, interviews, news of research, a calendar of events, reports of meetings, news of educational opportunities, job listings, book reviews, and notices of publications available. Availability: PDF; Online.

1689 ■ The Horn Book Magazine: About Books for Children and Young Adults
Pub: The Horn Book Inc.
Contact: Etienne Veber, President
URL(s): www.hbook.com/page/horn-book-magazine-2
Facebook: www.facebook.com/TheHornBook
X (Twitter): x.com/HornBook
Instagram: www.instagram.com/thehornbook
Pinterest: www.pinterest.com/thehornbook
Released: 6/year Price: $120, for print and online single-user yearly; $72, for online single-user year. Description: Journal devoted to children's and young adult literature. Availability: Print; Online.

1690 ■ Independent Publishing Now eNewsletter
Pub: Independent Book Publishers Association
Contact: Andrea Fleck-Nisbet, Chief Executive Officer
E-mail: andrea@ibpa-online.org
URL(s): www.ibpa-online.org/page/enewsletter
Released: Monthly Description: Informs member entrepreneurial book publishers about upcoming marketing programs and other Association activities aimed at helping independent publishers succeed. Also carries articles on topics such as desktop publishing and typesetting systems. Recurring features include member, committee, and research news, notices of educational and cooperative marketing opportunities, a calendar of events, and columns titled News from the "Net" and From the Director's Desk. Availability: Online.

1691 ■ Journal of Scholarly Publishing
Pub: University of Toronto Press Journals Division
Contact: Antonia Pop, Vice President
E-mail: apop@utpress.utoronto.ca
URL(s): utpjournals.press/loi/jsp
Released: Quarterly Price: $126, Individuals for 1 year print and online; $2,675, Institutions for online Volumes 20-54; $245, Institutions for print and online; $7,236.69, Institutions for print and online; $80, Individuals for 1 year online; $170, Institutions for online; $5,831.04, Institutions for online; $105, Individuals for print; $221, Institutions for print. Description: Journal covering scholarly publishing from writer to reader. Availability: Print; PDF; Online.

1692 ■ Kirkus Reviews
URL(s): www.kirkusreviews.com
Released: Monthly Price: $199, Individuals print and digital; $299, Other countries print and digital. Description: Publishes book reviews on current titles of both fiction and nonfiction for adults and children. Also provides author, publisher, price, and page count. Availability: Print; Online.

1693 ■ Publishers Weekly: The International voice for Book Publishing and Bookselling
Pub: Publishers Weekly
Contact: George Slowik, Jr., President
URL(s): www.publishersweekly.com/pw/corp/aboutus.html
Facebook: www.facebook.com/pubweekly
Linkedin: www.linkedin.com/company/publishers-weekly
X (Twitter): x.com/PublishersWkly
Instagram: www.instagram.com/pwpics
Ed: Michael Coffey. Released: Weekly Price: $199, for print and online; $169, for online and digital; $9.99, for back issues; $15, for online and digital monthly; $20, for print and online monthly. Description: Magazine for publishers. Availability: Print; Online.

VIDEO/AUDIO MEDIA

1694 ■ *Side Hustle to Small Business: Nick Courtright's Shift from Academia to Entrepreneurship*
URL(s): www.hiscox.com/side-hustle-to-small-business/nick-courtright-atmosphere-press-podcast-season-4
Ed: Sanjay Parekh. **Released:** July 24, 2024. **Description:** Podcast features an author-forward publishing company.

TRADE SHOWS AND CONVENTIONS

1695 ■ Special Libraries Association Information Revolution
URL(s): www.sla.org
Description: Library equipment, supplies, and services, including computers and software, Database information. **Audience:** Industry professionals. **Principal Exhibits:** Library equipment, supplies, and services, including computers and software, Database information.

CONSULTANTS

1696 ■ About Books (ABI)
502 N 31st St.
Colorado Springs, CO 80904
Ph: (719)440-8932
URL: http://about-books.com
Contact: Scott Flora, Contact
E-mail: scott@about-books.com

Description: Information clearinghouse on self-publishing and marketing of books. Provides educational programs; maintains speakers' bureau. Provides audiotape programs and books on the subject. **Scope:** Full service writing and publishing consultants organized to assist corporations, organizations and individuals in the writing, editing, producing and marketing of books. Also develop sponsored and premium books. **Publications:** "Molding Young Athletes," Purington Press. **Geographic Preference:** National.

1697 ■ Cohesion Consulting L.L.C.
300 Brickstone Sq., Ste. 201
Andover, MA 01810
Ph: (781)273-6300
URL: http://www.nsightworks.com
Contact: Tess Kastning, Chief Executive Officer
E-mail: tkastning@nsightworks.com
Facebook: www.facebook.com/cohesionit
Linkedin: www.linkedin.com/company/1536016
X (Twitter): twitter.com/cohesion

Founded: 1982. **Training:** Business Writing: Grammar and Usage; XML: An Introduction; XML: DTD Design; Writing and Editing for the Web; Writing for Public Relations; Editing for an International Audience; Creating Effective PowerPoint Presentations; Instructional Design for Blended Learning: A Practical Approach, Apr, 2008; Project Management for Publishing Writers and Editors, Mar, 2008; Online Editing with MS Word and Adobe Acrobat, Mar, 2008; Copyediting for Technical Documentation, Mar, 2008; Advanced Copyediting for Technical Documentation, Mar, 2008; Business Writing: Grammar and Usage, Mar, 2008; Copyediting for BioTech/Medical Documentation, Feb, 2008; Copyediting Fundamentals, Feb, 2008; Editing International Documents, Feb, 2008; Creating Corporate Style Guides, Feb, 2008; Creating a Web Content Style Guide, Feb, 2008; Design for Non-Designers, Feb, 2008; HTML 4.01 Web Authoring Basic, Jan, 2008; Indexing Technical Documentation, Jan, 2008; Polishing Your Writing through Self-Editing, Jan, 2008; Proofreading essentials, Jan, 2008; Substantive and Developmental Editing, Jan, 2008. **Special Services:** EDIT EXPRESS™.

1698 ■ Editorial Code and Data Inc. (ECDI)
814 Wolverine Dr., Ste. 2
Wolverine Lake, MI 48390
Ph: (248)245-4500
Co. E-mail: monique.magee@gmail.com
URL: http://www.marketsize.com
Contact: Arsen J. Darnay, Editor
Facebook: www.facebook.com/EditorialCodeAndData

Description: Developer of statistical publishing and software development services. **Scope:** Developer of statistical publishing and software development services. **Founded:** 1990. **Holdings:** ECDI has wide holdings of U.S. government data in print and electronic format. **Publications:** "Market Share Reporter"; "Encyclopedia of Products & Industries"; "Economic Indicators Handbook"; "American Salaries and Wages Survey"; "Dun and Bradstreet & Gale: Industrial Handbook"; "Reference American Cost of Living Survey".

1699 ■ Heidelberg Graphics (HG)
2 Stansbury Ct.
Chico, CA 95928
Ph: (530)342-6582
Fax: (530)342-6582
Co. E-mail: service@heidelberggraphics.com
URL: http://www.heidelberggraphics.com
Contact: Larry S. Jackson, Owner

Description: Publisher of books and also provides publishing, layout, printing and e-Book solutions. **Founded:** 1972. **Publications:** "Chronicles of the Clandestine Knights: Hyacinth Blue," 2003; "A Book of Thoughts II," 2001; "Historic Shot Glasses: The pre-Prohibition," 1992; "After the War," 1981; "Phantasm," 1980.

1700 ■ J. S. Eliezer Associates Inc. (JSEA)
300 Atlantic St.
Stamford, CT 06902
Contact: Peter M. Harding, Chief Executive Officer

Description: Management and market research consultants offering design and implementation of manufacturing strategy, feasibility analysis, and systems analysis, as well as management information systems and prepress systems, manufacturing proposals analysis, negotiations and contracts, paper purchasing strategy and contract negotiations, and catalog distribution effectiveness analysis and serves the publishing and catalog industries. **Scope:** Management and market research consultants offering design and implementation of manufacturing strategy, feasibility analysis, and systems analysis, as well as management information systems and prepress systems, manufacturing proposals analysis, negotiations and contracts, paper purchasing strategy and contract negotiations, and catalog distribution effectiveness analysis and serves the publishing and catalog industries.

1701 ■ The Live Oak Press L.L.C.
PO Box 60036
Palo Alto, CA 94306
URL: http://liveoakpress.com
Contact: David M. Hamilton, Publisher

Description: Manages design and implementation of publishing programs. Also offers complete book and magazine preparation and publishing consulting, including web resources, advertising, concept development, manuscript, design, development and production through finished product. Specializes in high-technology clients and electronic publishing. **Scope:** Manages design and implementation of publishing programs. Also offers complete book and magazine preparation and publishing consulting, including web resources, advertising, concept development, manuscript, design, development and production through finished product. Specializes in high-technology clients and electronic publishing. **Founded:** 1970. **Publications:** "The Tools of My Trade"; "To the Yukon with Jack London"; "Earthquakes and Young Volcanoes"; "The Lost Cement Mine"; "Inner Voyage"; "Studies in the Development of Consciousness"; "Dialectical Realism: Studies on a Philosophy of Growth"; "Mammoth Lakes Sierra"; "Deepest Valley"; "Mammoth Gold"; "Old Mammoth". **Training:** Internet publishing Seminar.

1702 ■ Martin Cook Associates Ltd.
148 W 24th St.
New York, NY 10011
Contact: Martin Cook, Chief Executive Officer

Description: Provider of book and print production and design management to publishers, foundations and corporations. Offers allied graphic services, including copy editing, proofreading, design and typography of books, jackets and print materials, typesetting, color separations, printing, binding, warehousing and distribution. **Scope:** Provider of book and print production and design management to publishers, foundations and corporations. Offers allied graphic services, including copy editing, proofreading, design and typography of books, jackets and print materials, typesetting, color separations, printing, binding, warehousing and distribution.

FRANCHISES AND BUSINESS OPPORTUNITIES

1703 ■ FinderBinder/SourceBook Directories
5173 Waring Rd., Ste. 8
San Diego, CA 92120
Ph: (619)582-8500
Co. E-mail: info@finderbindersd.com
URL: http://www.finderbindersd.com
Contact: Kathy Zwolinski, Contact
E-mail: kzwolinski@yahoo.com

Description: Publisher of electronic databases and newsletters. **Training:** Franchisor provides a field representative to assist franchise for a minimum of 8 hours and for further time as deemed necessary by the franchisor. Supervisory assistance is available at the discretion of the franchisor.

1704 ■ The Little Black Book For Every Busy Woman
PO Box 21466
Charleston, SC 29413
Ph: (843)958-8600
Co. E-mail: betty@everybusywoman.com
URL: http://www.everybusywoman.com
Facebook: www.facebook.com/everybusywoman
Linkedin: www.linkedin.com/company/the-little-black-book-for-every-busy-woman
X (Twitter): twitter.com/everybusywoman
Instagram: www.instagram.com/everybusywoman

Description: Publishes a directory for women. **Founded:** 1999. **Training:** Yes.

COMPUTERIZED DATABASES

1705 ■ *Book Review Index (BRI)*
URL(s): www.cengage.com/search/productOverview.do?Ntt=Book+Review+Index+Online|8908020 35159688936219142254912483759 77&N=197&Nr=197&Ntk=APG%7CP_EPI&Ntx=mode+matchallpartial

Released: Annual; latest 2017 edition. **Price:** $685, for paperback. **Availability:** Print. **Type:** Bibliographic.

LIBRARIES

1706 ■ Cleveland Public Library Literature Department
Main Bldg., 2nd Fl.
325 Superior Ave.
Cleveland, OH 44114
Ph: (216)623-2881
Co. E-mail: literature@cpl.org
URL: http://cpl.org/aboutthelibrary/subjectscollections/literature
Contact: Donald Boozer, Manager

Scope: World Literature and Criticism; Fiction; Poetry; Drama and Theater; Film; Television and Radio and much more. **Services:** Department open to the public; Interlibrary loan. **Founded:** 1869. **Holdings:** 500,000 volumes.

Small Business Profiles   Book Publishing ■ 1710

1707 ■ Free Library of Philadelphia-Social Science & History Department
1901 Vine St., Rm 201
Philadelphia, PA 19103
Ph: (215)686-5396
URL: http://libwww.freelibrary.org/locations/departments/social-science-and-history-department
Scope: History; biography; social sciences; law; travels and geography; archaeology; anthropology; sports; criminology. **Services:** Interlibrary loan. **Founded:** 1953. **Holdings:** Books; pamphlets; newspapers; government documents; ephemera; 414,000 biographies.

1708 ■ Grolier Club of New York Library
47 E 60th St.
New York, NY 10022
Ph: (212)838-6690
Fax: (212)838-2445
Co. E-mail: assistantlibrarian@grolierclub.org
URL: http://www.grolierclub.org/Default.aspx?p=DynamicModule&pageid=384831&ssid=322452&vnf=1
Contact: Meghan Constantinou, Librarian
E-mail: mconstantinou@grolierclub.org
Facebook: www.facebook.com/grolierclub
X (Twitter): x.com/GrolierClub
Instagram: www.instagram.com/grolierclub
Scope: Art and history; literature. **Services:** Library open to the public with restrictions. **Founded:** 1884. **Holdings:** 100,000 volumes; 5,000 prints and portraits; bookplates. **Subscriptions:** 100 journals and other serials.

1709 ■ Houghton Mifflin Company - School Division Research Center - Library
125 High Str.
Boston, MA 02110
URL: http://www.hmhco.com
Contact: John Lynch, President
Scope: Publishing, education, textbooks. **Services:** Interlibrary loan; research. **Founded:** 1966. **Holdings:** 8000 books.

1710 ■ John Wiley & Sons, Inc. - Information Center
John Wiley & Sons, Inc.
111 River St.
Hoboken, NJ 07030-5774
Ph: (201)748-6000
Fax: (410)955-0298
Co. E-mail: cs-journals@wiley.com
URL: http://www.wiley.com/en-us
Contact: Christina Van Tassell, Executive Vice President Chief Financial Officer
Description: Develops digital education, certification, learning, and assessment solutions for universities, businesses, and individuals. **Scope:** Publishing; business and management; higher education. **Services:** Center not open to the public. **Founded:** 1807. **Holdings:** Data bases are maintained in machine-readable form.; 200 books; 9 VF drawers of clippings. **Subscriptions:** ; 25 journals and other serials. **Publications:** *Ground Water Monitoring & Remediation* (Quarterly); *The Southern Journal of Philosophy* (Quarterly); *Microbiology and Immunology* (Monthly); *Journal of Surfactants and Detergents (JSD)* (6/year); *Journal of the American Oil Chemists' Society (JAOCS)* (Monthly); *Applied Vegetation Science* (Quarterly); *Journal of Theoretical Social Psychology (JTSP)*; *Journal of the World Aquaculture Society (JWAS)* (Bimonthly); *Veterinary Radiology & Ultrasound* (Bimonthly); *The Developing Economies* (Quarterly); *Veterinary Ophthalmology* (Bimonthly); *Journal of SID (JSID)* (Monthly); *Journal of the American Ceramic Society (JACerS)* (Monthly); *BioFactors* (Bimonthly); *Australian Dental Journal (ADJ)* (Quarterly); *Journal of Accounting Research (JAR)* (5/year); *Legislative Studies Quarterly (LSQ)* (Quarterly); *Obesity: A Research Journal* (Monthly); *Anthropology of Consciousness* (Semiannual); *Dyslexia* (Continuous); *Asian Journal of Control* (Bimonthly); *Journal of Intellectual Disability Research (JIDR)* (Monthly); *Journal of Inherited Metabolic Disease (JIMD)* (6/year); *United European Gastroenterology Journal* (10/year); *Resource Geology* (Continuous); *Stahlbau* (Monthly); *International Journal of Psychology (IJP)* (6/year); *Annals of Neurology* (Monthly); *Presidential Studies Quarterly (PSQ)* (Quarterly); *Meteoritics and Planetary Science* (Monthly); *Arthritis & Rheumatism*; *American Institute of Chemical Engineers Journal* (Monthly); *International Review of Mission (IRM)* (Semiannual); *Wildlife Society Bulletin* (Quarterly); *Criminology* (Quarterly); *British Educational Research Journal (BERJ)* (6/year); *Presidential Studies Quarterly* (Quarterly); *Agricultural & Environmental Letters (A&EL)* (Semiannual); *Agrosystems, Geosciences & Environment (AGE)* (Quarterly); *Crops & Soils* (6/year); *Food and Energy Security (FES)*; *Journal of Plant Nutrition and Soil Science (JPNSS)* (6/year); *Plants, People, Planet (PPP)* (6/year); *Cardiovascular Therapeutics* (Monthly); *Equine Veterinary Journal (EVJ)* (Bimonthly); *Journal of Economic and Social Geography* (5/year); *Ethnographic Praxis in Industry Conference Proceedings* (Annual); *Nutrition in Clinical Practice (NCP)* (6/year); *Public Administration Review (PAR)* (Bimonthly); *Journal of Genetic Counseling (JOGC)* (6/year); *Lipids* (6/year); *Anatomical Sciences Education* (6/year); *International Journal of Auditing (IJA)* (Quarterly); *Cognitive Science: A Multidisciplinary Journal* (Monthly); *Children & Society* (Bimonthly); *International Journal of Mental Health Nursing (IJMHN)* (Bimonthly); *Public Budgeting & Finance* (Quarterly); *Journal of Diabetes (JDB)* (Monthly); *Canadian Journal of Administrative Sciences (CJAS)* (Quarterly); *Journal of Operations Management (JOM)* (8/year); *Methods and Molecular and Cellular Biology* (Bimonthly); *Litigation Services: Information Sources for Export Witnesses* (Annual); *Business Evaluation Systems*; *Cochrane Collection Plus*; *Wiley Database of Polymer Properties*; *Evolution* (Monthly); *The Brown University Geriatric Psycopharmacology Update* (Monthly); *Brown University Child and Adolescent Psychopharmacology Update* (Monthly); *The Brown University Psychopharmacology Update* (Monthly); *Genetic Technology News*; *Directory of Business Information*; *Frommer's Best RV and Tent Campgrounds in the U.S.A.: 3rd Edition*; *The Unofficial Guide to Cruises: 11th Edition*; *Marathon Training for Dummies*; *The Unofficial Guide to Florida with Kids: 4th Edition*; *The Unofficial Guide to Las Vegas: 2012 Edition*; *The Unofficial Guide to Disneyland: 2012 Edition* (Annual); *The Unofficial Guide to Walt Disney World: 2012 Edition*; *The Unofficial Guide to Central Italy: Florence, Rome, Tuscany & Umbria*; *The Unofficial Guide to New York City: 7th Edition*; *The Unofficial Guide to San Francisco: 7th Edition*; *The Unofficial Guide to Florida*; *The Unofficial Guide to London: 5th Edition*; *The Unofficial Guide to Paris: 6th Edition*; *Mini Las Vegas: The Pocket-Sized Unofficial Guide to Las Vegas*; *The Unofficial Guide to England: 3rd Edition*; *The Unofficial Guide to Skiing & Snowboarding in the West: 1st Edition*; *Mini Mickey: The Pocket-Sized Unofficial Guide to Walt Disney World*; *The Unofficial Guide to Walt Disney World for Grown-Ups: 6th Edition*; *The Unofficial Guide to Walt Disney World with Kids: 2012 Edition*; *The Unofficial Guide to New Orleans: 6th Edition*; *Beyond Disney: The Unofficial Guide to Universal, SeaWorld & the Best of Central Florida*; *The Unofficial Guide to Maui: 4th Edition*; *The Unofficial Guide to Mexico's Best Beach Resorts: 4th Edition*; *The Unofficial Guide to Washington, D.C.: 11th Edition*; *The Unofficial Guide to California with Kids: 7th Edition*; *The Unofficial Guide to the Best RV and Tent Campgrounds in the Mid-Atlantic States: 1st Edition*; *Frommer's Portable London 2004* (Annual); *Frommer's Portable Acapulco, Ixtapa & Zihuatanejo: 6th Edition*; *Frommer's Portable San Francisco: 7th Edition*; *Frommer's Portable New York City: 2009 Edition* (Annual); *Frommer's Portable Cancun: 4th Edition*; *Frommer's Portable Puerto Vallarta, Manzanillo & Guadalajara: 8th Edition*; *Frommer's Portable Los Cabos & Baja: 4th Edition*; *Frommer's Portable Dominican Republic: 4th Edition*; *Frommer's Portable Washington, D.C.: 7th Edition*; *Frommer's Portable Cayman Islands: 5th Edition*; *Frommer's Portable San Diego: 5th Edition*; *Frommer's Portable Rio de Janeiro: 4th Edition*; *Frommer's Portable Portland: 6th Edition*; *Frommer's Portable Paris: 2011 Edition* (Annual); *Frommer's Portable Los Angeles: 2nd Edition* (Annual); *Frommer's Portable Big Island of Hawaii: 7th Edition*; *Frommer's Portable Phoenix and Scottsdale: 2nd Edition*; *Frommer's Portable Nantucket and Martha's Vineyard: 2nd Edition*; *Frommer's Portable Maui: 5th Edition*; *Frommer's Portable California Wine Country: 6th Edition*; *Frommer's Portable Boston: 5th Edition*; *Frommer's Portable Australia's Great Barrier Reef: 4th Edition*; *Frommer's Portable Virgin Islands: 5th Edition*; *Movement Disorders: Official Journal of the Movement Disorder Society* (Monthly); *Clinical Neuroscience: Topical Reviews on Research and Treatment* (Bimonthly); *Competitive Intelligence Review* (Quarterly); *Depression* (Bimonthly); *Diabetes Prevention and Therapy* (Quarterly); *English Audio Reviews: The Biomedical Sciences Wiley Professional Language Training* (Bimonthly); *Environmental Law & Management* (6/year); *Heterogeneous Chemistry Reviews: The Review Journal Devoted to Heterogeneous Catalysis and to the Chemistry and Molecular Physics of Surfaces and Materials* (Quarterly); *Infectious Diseases in Obstetrics and Gynecology*; *Integrated Computer-Aided Engineering* (Quarterly); *Geriatric Psychiatry: A Journal of the Psychiatry of Late Life and Allied Sciences* (Monthly); *Methods in Psychiatric Research (MPR)* (Quarterly); *Journal of the Clinical Orthopaedic Society* (Bimonthly); *The Journal of Trace Elements in Experimental Medicine: The Official Publication of the International Society for Trace Element Research in Humans* (Quarterly); *Prenatal Diagnosis*; *Journal of Chemical Technology and Biotechnology (JCTB)* (Monthly); *Radiation Oncology Investigations: Clinical and Basic Research* (Bimonthly); *Talking Medicine: Wiley Professional Language Training* (Bimonthly); *Behavioral Interventions* (Quarterly); *Changes: An International Journal of Psychology & Psychotherapy* (Quarterly); *European Journal of Personality* (6/year); *Perspectives on science and practice* (Quarterly); *Banks in Insurance Report*; *International Review of Strategic Management* (Annual); *Inflammatory Bowel Diseases* (Monthly); *e-EROS: Encyclopedia of Reagents for Organic Synthesis*; *Polymer International*; *CTBUH special annual edition of the Wiley Journal "The Structural Design of Tall and Special Buildings"* (8/year); *Frommer's Budapest Day by Day*; *Frommer's Cancun & the Yucatan Day by Day*; *Frommer's Chicago Day by Day*; *Frommer's Edinburgh & Glasgow Day by Day*; *Frommer's Florence & Tuscany Day by Day*; *Frommer's Hong Kong Day by Day*; *Frommer's Honolulu & Oahu Day by Day*; *Frommer's Krakow Day by Day*; *Frommer's Las Vegas Day by Day*; *Frommer's London Day by Day*; *Frommer's Los Angeles Day by Day*; *Frommer's Madrid Day by Day*; *Frommer's Maui Day by Day*; *Frommer's Montreal Day by Day*; *Frommer's Moscow Day by Day*; *Frommer's New York City Day by Day*; *Frommer's Paris Day by Day*; *Frommer's Prague Day by Day*; *Frommer's Provence & the Riviera Day by Day*; *Frommer's Rome Day by Day*; *Frommer's San Diego Day by Day*; *Frommer's San Francisco Day by Day*; *Frommer's Seattle Day by Day*; *Frommer's Shanghai Day by Day*; *Frommer's Stockholm Day by Day*; *Biometrical Journal* (Continuous; Continuous); *Zeitschrift fur Angewandte Mathematik und Mechanik (ZAMM)* (Monthly); *Ethnobiology and the Science of Humankind: Journal of the Royal Anthropological Institute*; *Evidence-Based Child Health: A Cochrane Review Journal* (6/year); *Mitteilungen der Fachgruppe Umweltchemie und Okotoxikologie* (Quarterly); *Gleditschia*; *Geowissenschaftliche Reihe* (Annual); *Physik Journal* (Monthly; 6/year); *Biotechnology Journal (BTJ)* (Monthly); *Teratology: The Journal of Abnormal Development* (Monthly); *Working Solo Sourcebook: Essential Resources for Independent Entrepreneurs*; *Working Solo: The Real Guide to Freedom & Financial Success with Your Own Business, 2nd Edition*; *International Journal of Fluids Mechanics Research* (6/year); *Journal of Electron Microscopy Technique* (Monthly); *The Journal of Futures Markets: Futures, Options, and other Derivative Products* (Monthly); *Journal of Leukocyte Biology (JLB)* (Monthly); *Climate and Energy* (Monthly); *Naval Research Logistics: An International Journal* (8/year); *Population and Development Review* (Quarterly); *Frommer's Portable Turks & Caicos*; *Directory of Global Professional Accounting and Business Certifications*; *Online Shopping Directory for Dummies*; *Regulated Chemicals Directory*; *Food Professional's*

Guide: The James Beard Foundation Directory of People, Products, and Services; *Software Directory for Retailers: 5th Edition*; *Complete Cyberspace Reference and Directory: An Addressing and Utilization Guide to Internet, Electronic Mail Systems, and Bulletin Board Systems*; *Directory of Business Information*; *Frommer's Chicago: 2011 Edition*; *Frommer's Bermuda: 2012 Edition*; *Non-Linear Finite Element Analysis of Solids and Structures: Volume 2, Advanced Topics*; *Handbook of Animal Lectins: Properties and Biomedical Applications*; *Frommer's Rome: 20th Edition*; *Frommer's Washington, D.C. day by day*; *Frommer's London day by day*; *Frommer's Amsterdam day by day*; *Blogging for Dummies*; *Frommer's Cape Cod, Nantucket, and Martha's Vineyard*; *Search Engine Optimization for Dummies: 5th Edition*; *Frommer's Vancouver and Victoria*; *Handbook of Plastic Compounds, Elastomers, and Resins: An International Guide By Category, Tradename, Composition, and Supplier*; *How to Start, Run, and Stay in Business: The Nuts-and-Bolts Guide to Turning Your Business Dream into a Reality*; *Frommer's Arizona and the Grand Canyon: 2012* (Annual); *Broadband Bible: Desktop Edition*; *Frommer's Caribbean*; *Frommer's Mexico*; *Black Book of Outsourcing: How to Manage the Changes, Challenges, and Opportunities*; *Furniture and Architecture*; *Free Software for Dummies*; *Preservation Yellow Pages: The Complete Information Source for Homeowners, Communities, and Professionals*; *International Environmental Consulting Practice: How and Where to Take Advantage of Global Opportunities*; *Frommer's South Florida: 7th Edition*; *Frommer's Florida: 2011 Edition*; *Frommer's Los Angeles: 2011 Edition*; *Frommer's EasyGuide to San Francisco*; *Frommer's Ireland* (Annual); *Nonprofit Guide to the Internet: How to Survive and Thrive*; *Frommer's Hawaii* (Annual); *Frommer's Cancun, Cozumel and the Yucatan*; *Researching Online for Dummies*; *Starting an Online Business for Dummies*; *Comprehensive Tumour Terminology Handbook*; *Home Business Bible: Everything You Need to Know to Start and Run Your Successful Home-Based Business*; *Wetland Restoration, Flood Pulsing, and Disturbance Dynamics*; *Frommer's Great Britain*; *Geografiska Annaler: Series B, Human Geography* (Quarterly); *Public Budgeting & Finance* (Quarterly); *The Brown University Child and Adolescent Behavior Letter* (Monthly); *Journal of Community & Applied Social Psychology* (6/year); *Journal of Oral Rehabilitation* (Monthly); *Wiley Not-For-Profit Accounting Field Guide* (Annual); *Portable petswelcome.com: The Complete Guide to Traveling with Your Pet*; *Protein Science* (Monthly); *International Journal of Human Factors in Manufacturing* (Quarterly); *International Journal of Numerical Methods for Heat & Fluid Flow* (Monthly); *Journal of Communications Technology and Electronics* (Monthly); *Russian Journal of Computational Mechanics*; *Shock and Vibration* (Continuous); *Visualization of Engineering Research: An International Journal on CD-ROM* (Semiannual); *Environmental Manager: Environmental Solutions that Make Good Business Sense* (Monthly); *Federal Facilities Environmental Journal* (Quarterly); *Journal of Environmental Permitting* (Quarterly); *Land Degradation & Rehabilitation: Management of Terrestrial Environments* (Quarterly); *Natural Gas: The Monthly Journal for Producers, Marketers, Pipelines, Distributors and End Users*; *North Sea Monitor* (Quarterly); *Pollution Prevention Review* (Quarterly); *Total Quality Environmental Management* (Quarterly); *Fund-Raising Regulation Report* (Bimonthly); *Letters of Credit Report* (Bimonthly); *Loan Officer's Legal Alert* (Monthly); *The Nonprofit Counsel* (Monthly); *Utilities Law Review*; *The Journal of Water Law* (6/year); *Cell Biochemistry and Function: Cellular Biochemistry and Its Modulation by Active Agents or Disease* (8/year); *Developmental Dynamics* (Monthly); *Mental Retardation and Developmental Disabilities Research Reviews: The Official Journal of the Society for Developmental Pediatrics* (Quarterly); *Natural Toxins* (Bimonthly); *Neuroscience Research Communications* (Bimonthly); *Applied Stochastic Models in Business and Industry* (Bimonthly); *Cultural Diversity and Mental Health* (3/year); *Concepts in Magnetic Resonance* (10/year); *Environmental Regulation and Permitting* (Quarterly); *Heteroatom Chemistry*; *Infrastructure* (Quarterly); *In Session: Psychotherapy in Practice* (Quarterly); *Laboratory Robotics and Automation* (Bimonthly); *Current Protocols in Molecular Biology (CPMB)*; *Current Protocols in Protein Science*; *Human Communication Research (HCR)*; *Dialysis & Transplantation* (Monthly); *SpecInfo on the Internet*; *Arthritis and Rheumatism: The Official Journal of the American College of Rheumatology*; *The National Trust Guide to Historic Bed and Breakfasts, Inns, and Small Hotels* (Biennial); *The International Business Dictionary and Reference*; *Regulated Chemical Directory* (Annual); *Journal of Magnetic Resonance Imaging (JMRI)* (Monthly); *Wilmott Magazine* (6/year); *Knowledge and Process Management: The Journal of Corporate Transformation* (Quarterly); *Mergent's Handbook of NASDAQ Stocks* (Quarterly); *Quality Assurance Journal*; *Journal of Separation Science (JSS)* (Continuous); *Process Safety Progress* (Quarterly); *Chemistry - A European Journal* (Weekly); *Chemistry and Biodiversity* (Annual); *Electroanalysis: An International Journal Devoted to Electroanalysis Sensors and Bioelectronic Devices* (Monthly); *Fuel Cells: From Fundamentals to Systems* (6/year); *Helvetica Chimica Acta* (Monthly); *The Chemical Record (TCR)* (6/year); *European Journal of Inorganic Chemistry*; *European Journal of Organic Chemistry*; *Bauen mit Textilien*; *Pharmazie in unserer Zeit* (6/year); *Bell Labs Technical Journal* (Quarterly); *Assessment Update* (6/year); *Progress in Structural Engineering and Materials* (Quarterly); *Wireless Communications and Mobile Computing*; *Advanced Synthesis & Catalysis (ASC)*; *C++ Scientific Programming: Computational Recipes at a Higher Level*; *Eco-Management and Auditing* (6/year); *Leadership in Action* (Bimonthly; Semimonthly); *Mergent's Dividend Achievers* (Quarterly); *Heat Transfer Soviet Research* (Bimonthly); *Science Education* (Bimonthly); *Seminars in Surgical Oncology* (Bimonthly); *Journal of Research in Science Teaching (JRST)* (10/year); *Design Computing* (Quarterly); *Genesis: The Journal of Genetics and Development*; *The Young Women's Guide to the Top Colleges: What You Need to Know to Make the Best Choice*; *Paleontological Journal* (Monthly); *Journal of Microcolumn Separations*; *Biochemistry and Molecular Biology Education* (Bimonthly); *British Journal of Psychotherapy (BJP)* (Quarterly); *The Brown University Digest of Addiction Theory and Application*; *The Brown University Geriatric Psychopharmacology Update* (Monthly); *Bruce R. Hopkins' Nonprofit Counsel* (Monthly); *Development and Alumni Relations Report* (Monthly); *Future Prescriber* (Quarterly); *General Anthropology* (Semiannual); *HEPATOLOGY: Journal of the American Association for the Study of Liver Disease* (Monthly); *Higher Education FERPA Bulletin*; *human_ontogenetics*; *IEEJ Transactions on Electrical and Electronic Engineering (TEEE)* (Monthly); *International Statistical Review (ISI)* (3/year); *Performance Improvement Quarterly (PIQ)* (Quarterly); *Performance Improvement* (10/year); *Pharmaceutical Formulation & Quality*; *Quality Assurance and Safety of Crops & Foods*; *Security and Communication Networks*; *Strategic Entrepreneurship Journal (SEJ)* (Quarterly); *The Hospitalist* (Monthly); *The Australian Journal of Agricultural and Resource Economics (AJARE)* (Quarterly); *Complete Cyberspace Reference and Directory: An Addressing and Utilization Guide to the Internet, Electronic Mail Systems, and Bulletin Board Systems*; *Who's Who in Venture Capital*; *Australian and New Zealand Journal of Family Therapy* (Quarterly); *New Directions for Institutional Research* (Quarterly); *Kirk-Othmer Encyclopedia of Chemical Technology Online*; *Registry of Mass Spectral Data*; *The Brown University Digest of Addiction Theory and Application Newsletter* (Monthly); *Practitioner's Guide to GAAS*; *Health Economic Evaluations Database (HEED)*; *The Mother of All Toddler Books: An All-Canadian Guide to Your Child's Second and Third Years*; *The Mother of All Pregnancy Books: An All-Canadian Guide to Conception, Birth & Everything in Between*; *The Mother of All Parenting Books: The Ultimate Guide to Raising a Happy, Healthy Child from Preschool through the Preteens*; *The Mother of All Pregnancy Books: An All-Canadian Guide to Conception, Birth & Everything in Between*; *Directory of Venture Capital: 2nd Edition*; *The Everyday Internet All-In-One Desk Reference for Dummies*; *So You're Having a Heart Cath and Angioplasty*; *International Architecture Centres*; *The Unofficial Guide to Bed & Breakfasts and Country Inns in the Mid-Atlantic: 1st Edition*; *So You're Having Heart Bypass Surgery*; *So You're Having Prostate Surgery*; *Canadian Wine for Dummies*; *SBA Loans: A Step-by-Step Guide*; *The 50 Best Global Stocks for Canadians* (Annual); *The 50 Best Science & Technology Stocks for Canadians* (Annual); *The 50 Best Stocks for Canadians* (Annual); *Mutual Funds for Canadians for Dummies: 2nd Edition*; *The Children's Hospital of Philadelphia Guide to Asthma: How to Help Your Child Live a Healthier Life*; *The Fathers Book: Being a Good Dad in the 21st Century*; *The Unofficial Guide to Homeschooling*; *The Unofficial Guide to the Best RV & Tent Campgrounds, California & the West: 1st Edition*; *Infant Mental Health Journal (IMHJ)* (Bimonthly); *Frommer's Portable Vancouver Island, the Gulf Islands and San Juan Islands: 3rd Edition*; *Frommer's Portable Puerto Rico: 5th Edition*; *Frommer's Portable Frankfurt: 2nd Edition*; *Frommer's Portable Paris from $90 a Day: 1st Edition*; *Frommer's Portable Miami: 2nd Edition*; *Frommer's Portable Florence: 4th Edition*; *Frommer's Portable Aruba, Bonaire and Curacao: 6th Edition*; *Frommer's Portable Whistler*; *Frommer's Portable Venice: 7th Edition*; *Frommer's Portable Vancouver: 3rd Edition*; *Frommer's Portable Savannah: 5th Edition*; *Frommer's Portable New York City from $90 a Day: 2nd Edition*; *Frommer's Portable New Orleans: 8th Edition*; *Frommer's Portable Maine Coast: 4th Edition*; *Frommer's Portable London from $90 a Day: 2nd Edition*; *Frommer's Portable Las Vegas: 9th Edition*; *Frommer's Portable Las Vegas for Non-Gamblers: 4th Edition*; *Frommer's Portable Hong Kong: 2nd Edition*; *Frommer's Portable Dublin*; *Frommer's Portable Disneyland: 2nd Edition*; *Frommer's Portable Chicago: 6th Edition*; *Frommer's Portable Charleston: 5th Edition*; *Frommer's Portable Bahamas: 8th Edition*; *Frommer's Portable Amsterdam: 3rd Edition*; *System Dynamics Review: The Journal of the System Dynamics Society* (Quarterly); *Strategic Management Journal (SMJ)*; *Journal of Quaternary Science (JQS)* (8/year); *Journal of Physical Organic Chemistry (JPOC)* (Monthly); *Regulated Rivers: Research and Management: An International Journal Dedicated to River Research and Management* (Quarterly); *Regional Immunology* (Bimonthly); *Rapid Communications in Mass Spectrometry*; *Journal of Organizational Behavior* (9/year); *Journal of Molecular Recognition (JMR)* (Monthly); *Phytochemical Analysis* (8/year); *Journal of Maternal Fetal Medicine* (Bimonthly); *Packaging Technology and Science: An International Journal* (8/year); *Journal of Labelled Compounds and Radiopharmaceuticals (JLCR)*; *Journal of International Development (JID)* (8/year); *Journal of Intelligent & Fuzzy Systems: Applications in Engineering and Technology* (Monthly); *Journal of Forecasting* (8/year); *Journal of Direct and Interactive Marketing: A Publication of the Direct Marketing Educational Foundation, Inc* (Quarterly); *Journal of Chemometrics* (Monthly); *Biomedical Chromatography* (Monthly); *Journal of Chemical Neuroanatomy* (8/year); *International Video Journal of Engineering Research*; *Electronic Publishing: Origination, Dissemination and Design* (Quarterly); *Congestive Heart Failure* (Bimonthly); *Mathematical Methods in the Applied Sciences*; *Mathematical Modeling and Computational Experiment*; *Employment Relations Today*; *Human Resource Management*; *International Journal of Intelligent Systems*; *Knowledge and Process Management: The Journal of Corporate Transformation*; *Managerial and Decision Economics*; *Psychology & Marketing*; *Public Administration and Development*; *Strategic Change* (8/year); *Strategic Management Journal*; *System Dynamics Review*; *Systems Research and Behavioral Science* (Bimonthly); *Archives of Insect Biochemistry and Physiology*; *Biomedical Chromatography*; *Biopharmaceutics & Drug Disposition*; *Biopolymers*; *Cell Biochemistry and Function*; *Biotechnology & Bioengineering*; *Encyclopedia of Life Sciences*; *Hepatology*; *Liver Transplantation*; *Kirk-Othmer Encyclopedia of Chemical Technology*; *Landmark Yellow Pages: All the Names, Addresses, Facts and Figures You Need in Preservation: National Trust for Historic Preservation* (Irregular); *Frommer's 500 Places for Food & Wine Lovers*; *Frommer's Athens Day by Day*; *From-*

mer's Barcelona Day by Day; *Frommer's Beijing Day by Day: Official U.S.O.C. Edition*; *Frommer's Berlin Day by Day*; *Chemical Engineering & Technology (CET)* (Monthly); *Macromolecular Reaction Engineering* (6/year); *Journal of Philanthropy and Marketing* (Quarterly); *Headache Currents* (10/year); *Systems Research and Behavioral Science* (Bimonthly); *Chinese Journal of Chemistry (CJC)*; *Berichte zur Wissenschaftsgeschichte* (Quarterly); *Forschungsberichte aus Technik und Naturwissenschaften* (Quarterly); *Atmospheric Science Letters (ASL)* (Monthly); *Environmental Toxicology* (Bimonthly); *german research* (3/year); *Journal of Basic Microbiology (JBM)* (Monthly); *Comparative and Functional Genomics* (Bimonthly); *Systems and Computers in Japan*; *Telecommunications & Radio Engineering* (Monthly); *Birth Defects Research Part B: Developmental and Reproductive Toxicology* (Bimonthly); *Pediatric Blood & Cancer*, *Entomological Review* (9/year); *Environmental and Molecular Mutagenesis (EMM)* (9/year); *Ashgate Handbook of Antineoplastic Agents*; *Journal of the Association for Information Science and Technology (JASIST)* (Monthly); *Journal of Biomedical Materials Research: An Official Journal of the Society for Biomaterials and the Japanese Society for Biomaterials* (8/year); *Plant Biology* (Bimonthly); *Wallpapers for Historic Buildings* (Irregular); *New Management* (Quarterly); *Journal of Energetics & Fluids Engineering* (Bimonthly); *Marketing on a Shoestring: Low-Cost Tips for Marketing Your Products and Services* (Irregular); *Passport to Europe's Small Hotels and Inns* (Irregular); *Applied Geographic Studies* (Quarterly); *National Civic Review* (Quarterly); *AORN Journal: The Official Voice of Perioperative Nursing* (Monthly); *SEO Search Engine Optimization Bible*; *The Little Black Book of Online Business: 1001 Insider Resources Every Business Owner Needs*; *Mechanics of Cohesive-frictional Materials*; *Free Money from the Federal Government for Small Businesses and Entrepreneurs*; *Guide to New York City Landmarks*; *Wright Sites: A Guide to Frank Lloyd Wright Public Places*; *Great American Ships*; *Great American Bridges and Dams*; *Sustainable Development Policy Directory*; *Journal of Interior Design (JID)* (Quarterly); *Journal of Environmental Regulation* (Quarterly); *Meteorological Applications* (Monthly); *Journal of International Management (JIM)* (6/year); *Journal of Strategic Change* (Bimonthly); *Talking Business* (Bimonthly); *Biospectroscopy* (Bimonthly); *X-Ray Spectrometry* (Bimonthly); *Internetworking: Research and Experience* (Quarterly); *Journal of Software Maintenance and Evolution: Research and Practice*; *Journal of Software: Evolution and Process* (8/year); *Theory and Practice of Object Systems* (Quarterly); *Tranputer Communications* (Quarterly); *International Journal of Climatology*; *International Petroleum Abstracts: Incorporating Offshore Abstracts* (Quarterly); *International Journal of Tourism Research* (Bimonthly); *Engineering Design and Automation*; *International Journal of Adaptive Control and Signal Processing* (Monthly); *International Journal of Circuit Theory and Applications* (Monthly); *Wiley IFRS: Interpretation and Application for International Accounting and Financial Reporting Standards*; *HPLC Methods for Pharmaceutical Analysis, Volumes 1-4*; *Encyclopedia of Inorganic and Bioinorganic Chemistry (EIBC)*; *Comprehensive Organic Transformations on CD-ROM: A Guide to Functional Group Preparations*; *Environmental Endocrine Disruptors: A Handbook of Property Data*; *Current Protocols in Human Genetics*; *Current Protocols in Immunology* (Quarterly); *Current Protocols in Cytometry*; *Current Protocols in Neuroscience (CPN)*; *Current Protocols in Toxicology*; *Current Protocols in Pharmacology*; *Current Protocols in Cell Biology*; *Nutrition Reviews* (Monthly); *Clinical Psychology: Science and Practice* (Quarterly); *Communication Theory*; *Contemporary Economic Policy (CEP)*; *International Nursing Review: The Official Journal of the International Council of Nurses* (Quarterly); *American Journal of Community Psychology (AJCP)* (Quarterly); *International Journal of Cancer (IJC)* (Semimonthly); *Journal of Leadership Studies: Expanding Interdisciplinary Discourse* (Quarterly); *Journal of Traumatic Stress* (Bimonthly); *Russian Journal of Mathematical Physics* (Quarterly); *Southern Economic Journal (SEJ)* (Quarterly); *Journal of Prosthodontics--Clinical Journal* (9/year); *Circulatory Shock* (6/year); *Color Research and Application* (Bimonthly); *Geochemistry International*; *Marketing for Dummies*; *The Anatomical Record: Advances in Integrative Anatomy and Evolutionary Biology* (Monthly); *Developmental Neurobiology*; *Journal of Pascal, ADA and Modula-2* (Bimonthly); *Journal of Policy Analysis and Management (JPAM)* (Quarterly); *Journal of Polymer Science*; *Cytometry, Part A: Journal of Quantitative Cell Science* (Monthly); *Human Communication Research* (Quarterly); *Asia-Pacific Psychiatry*; *Reviews in Aquaculture* (Quarterly); *Industrial Relations: A Journal of Economy and Society* (Quarterly); *The Rheumatologist* (Monthly); *World's Futures and Options Markets*; *Freshney's Culture of Animal Cells: A Manual of Basic Technique*; *Chemist's Companion: A Handbook of Practical Data, Techniques, and References*; *Go It Alone: The Streetwise Secrets of Self Employment*; *Management Consulting: A Complete Guide to the Industry*; *Veterinary Drugs: Synonyms & Properties*; *Audel Basic Electronics*; *Official Scrabble Word-Finder*; *Industrial Relations: A Journal of Economy and Society* (Quarterly); *Faith-Based Marketing: The Guide to Reaching 140 million Christian Consumers*; *Journal of Applied Entomology* (10/year); *International Affairs* (Bimonthly); *Cooper's Comprehensive Environmental Desk Reference*; *Van Nostrand's Scientific Encyclopedia*; *Irrigation and Drainage* (5/year); *European Journal of Immunology (EJI)* (Monthly); *Review of Financial Markets*; *GPS Solutions: The Journal of Global Navigation Satellite Systems* (Quarterly); *Field Analytical Chemistry and Technology*; *Asian Case Research Journal* (Semiannual); *International Journal of Nautical Archaeology*; *Environmental Progress & Sustainable Energy* (Quarterly); *P2: Pollution Prevention Review* (Quarterly); *Electrophoresis* (Semimonthly); *Proteomics: Proteomics and Systems Biology*; *Engineering in Life Sciences (ELS)* (Monthly); *European Journal of Lipid Science and Technology (EJSLT)* (Monthly); *Lebensmittelchemie* (Bimonthly); *Birth Defects Research Part A: Clinical and Molecular Teratology*; *genesis: The Journal of Genetics and Development* (Continuous); *Food Service Technology* (Quarterly); *Ultrasound in Obstetrics and Gynecology (UOG)* (Monthly); *Cancer* (Biweekly); *Laser Physics Letters* (Monthly); *Journal of Vinyl and Additive Technology* (Quarterly); *Polymer Composites (PC)* (Monthly); *Developmental Disabilities Research Reviews* (Quarterly); *European Journal of Social Psychology (EJSP)* (7/year); *Mergent's Handbook of Common Stocks* (Quarterly); *New Directions for Philanthropic Fundraising* (Quarterly); *ChemBioChem*; *National Civic Review* (Quarterly); *Behavioral Residential Treatment*; *Behavioral Sciences & the Law* (Bimonthly); *Bioelectromagnetics: Journal of the Bioelectromagnetics Society and the Society for Physical Regulation in Biology and Medicine* (8/year); *Soviet Journal of Automation and Information Sciences* (Bimonthly); *Journal of Communications Technology & Electronics* (6/year); *Urasian Soil Science* (Bimonthly); *Employment Relations Today (ERT)* (Quarterly); *International Journal of Short-Term Psychotherapy* (Quarterly); *The Journal of Wildlife Management* (8/year); *Project Management Journal® (PMJ)* (Bimonthly; 6/year); *Asia-Pacific Journal of Chemical Engineering* (Bimonthly); *Contrast Media & Molecular Imaging (CMMI)* (Bimonthly); *Drug Testing and Analysis* (Monthly); *Geomechanics and Tunnelling* (Bimonthly); *Laser Technik Journal* (5/year); *Spectroscopy Asia* (6/year). **Managerial Assistance:** Founded in 1809, John Wiley & Sons, Inc. is a publicly traded publishing company headquartered in Hoboken, New Jersey, primarily focused on educational materials Specializing in academic, scientific, technical, and professional literature, the company produces a diverse range of books, journals, and online content spanning various fields, including science, engineering, technology, healthcare, business, and finance. John Wiley & Sons, provides educational resources to students, instructors, and institutions through traditional print formats and digital platforms, encompassing textbooks, online courses, and learning management systems. Moreover, it plays a crucial role in academic and scientific research by publishing numerous peer-reviewed journals and research articles, facilitating the widespread dissemination of new knowledge and discoveries. **Educational Activities:** BERA Annual Conference (Annual). **Awards:** R.H. Gallagher Young Investigator Award (Biennial); William H. Walker Award for Excellence in Contributions to Chemical Engineering Literature (Annual). **Geographic Preference:** Multinational.

1711 ■ Omohundro Institute of Early American History and Culture (OIEAHC)

400 Landrum Dr.
Williamsburg, VA 23185
Ph: (757)221-1114
Fax: (757)221-1047
Co. E-mail: oieahc@wm.edu
URL: http://oieahc.wm.edu
Contact: Catherine E. Kelly, Executive Director
E-mail: cekelly01@wm.edu
Linkedin: www.linkedin.com/company/omohundro-institute
X (Twitter): x.com/OIEAHC

Description: Seeks to further the study, research and publication about American history to the year 1815. Covers geographical scope of interest that reaches back into European and African origins and influences and also includes the imperial domains in North America. Awards postdoctoral fellowships. Sponsors and cosponsors conferences on early American history. Cosponsored by The Colonial Williamsburg Foundation and the College of William and Mary, Williamsburg, VA. **Scope:** History and culture of mainland North America to 1815 and the related histories of Africa, the British Isles, the Caribbean, Europe, and Latin America. **Founded:** 1943. **Holdings:** 8,650 books; 942 bound periodical volumes; 2,000 reels of microfilm; 7,480 books; maps; monographs; periodicals; papers. **Subscriptions:** 54 journals and other serials. **Publications:** *Scholarly books* (Periodic); *Uncommon Sense* (Semiannual); *William & Mary Quarterly* (Quarterly). **Educational Activities:** Annual OI Conference (Annual), New ideas and interpretations over well-worn topics.; OIEAHC Colloquium (Irregular), Meets up to six times per semester.; OIEAHC Thematic Conferences. **Awards:** Douglass Adair Memorial Award (Biennial); Omohundro Institute-NEH Postdoctoral Fellowships (Annual); Lester J. Cappon Prize (Annual); Andrew W. Mellon Postdoctoral Research Fellowship (Annual); Institute/NEH Postdoctoral Fellowship (Annual); Jamestown Prize (Biennial); Richard L. Morton Prize (Annual); Ronald Hoffman Fund Postdoctoral Research Fellowship (Annual); Institute Andrew W. Mellon Postdoctoral Research Fellowships (Annual). **Geographic Preference:** Multinational.

1712 ■ S&P Global Inc.

S&P Global Inc.
55 Water St.
New York, NY 10041
Ph: (212)438-1000
Co. E-mail: index_services@spglobal.com
URL: http://www.spglobal.com
Contact: Douglas L. Peterson, President
Facebook: www.facebook.com/sandpglobal
Linkedin: www.linkedin.com/company/2934
X (Twitter): twitter.com/SPGlobal
Instagram: www.instagram.com/sp_global/
YouTube: www.youtube.com/c/spglobal

Description: Provides independent ratings, benchmarks, analytics, and data to the capital and commodity markets worldwide. **Founded:** 1888. **Publications:** *Metals Daily* (Daily); *Science Navigator*, *McGraw-Hill Publications Online*; *Aviation Week Online*; *Metals Week*; *Compustat*; *Aerospace Daily*; *The Top 500 Design Firms Sourcebook* (Annual); *ENR Top 400 Contractors* (Annual); *ENR-Top International Design Firms* (Annual); *The McGraw-Hill Companies Publications Online*; *Mastering Auscultation: An Audio Tour to Cardiac Diagnosis*; *Basic & Clinical Pharmacology*; *Current Critical Care Diagnosis & Treatment*; *Current Diagnosis & Treatment in Cardiology*; *Current Diagnosis & Treatment in Orthopedics*; *Current Obstetric & Gynecologic Diagnosis and Treatment*; *DeGowin's Diagnostic Examination*; *Review of Medical Physiology*; *Smith's General Urology*; *Williams Obstetrics*; *NTC's American English*

Learner's Dictionary; Harrison's Principles of Internal Medicine; tele.com (Monthly); Business Week; Business Week China (Bimonthly); Standard & Poor's SmallCap 600 Guide; CreditWire; Multimedia Encyclopedia of Mammalian Biology; AccessScience; International Private Power Quarterly (Quarterly); Business Forms and Agreements; Entourage on CD: A Clip Art Resource for Architects & Designers; Essential Internet Starter Kit; McGraw-Hill Multimedia Encyclopedia of Science and Technology; Energy Services and Telecom Report; U.S. Nursing Homes and Nursing Home Chains; A/C Flyer: Best Read Resale Magazine Worldwide; Kitchen & Bath Sourcebook (Annual); The Electronic Giecks' Engineering Formulas; Modern Plastics Encyclopedia (Annual); Standard Handbook for Civil Engineers; Hurst's the Heart Online; ENR: Connecting the Industry Worldwide; Complete Guide to Your Real Estate Closing: Answers to All Your Questions from Opening Escrow to Negotiating Fees to Signing Closing Papers.

1713 ■ Simmons College Graduate School of Library and Information Science Library (SLIS)
300 The Fenway
Boston, MA 02115
Ph: (617)521-2000
URL: http://www.simmons.edu/academics/colleges-schools-departments/schools-departments/slis
Contact: Dr. Lynn Perry Wooten, President
Description: This library consists of collections, books, reference materials, journals, and audio-visual materials on medical education. **Scope:** Cultural heritage informatics; information science and technology. **Services:** Interlibrary loan; copying; library open to the public for reference use only by appointment. **Founded:** 1902. **Holdings:** 24,258 books; 7,537 bound periodical volumes; 4,935 microfiche; 911 reels of microfilm; 34 VF drawers; School of Library Science doctoral field studies; information files on 100 library-related subjects; doctoral dissertations on microfilm.

RESEARCH CENTERS

1714 ■ Simon Fraser University - Canadian Institute for Studies in Publishing (CISP)
515 W Hastings St.
Vancouver, BC, Canada V6B 5K3
URL: http://publishing.sfu.ca/research-2
Description: Integral unit of Simon Fraser University. Consulting: for specialized professional development. **Scope:** Role of publishing and the dynamics of information in society. **Publications:** *CCSP Articles* (Occasionally); *CISP Books*; *Canadian Journal of Communication* (Quarterly); *CISP Reports* (Occasionally); *Scholarly and Research Communication* (3/year). **Educational Activities:** CCSP Master of Publishing Program, Attended by graduate students from Canada and around the world.; CCSP Seminars and conferences; CCSP Summer Publishing Workshops; CCSP Writing and Publishing Program, For specialized professional development.

Bookbinder

ASSOCIATIONS AND OTHER ORGANIZATIONS

1715 ■ Binding Industries Association (BIA)
301 Brush Creek Rd.
 Warrendale, PA 15086
Free: 800-910-2311
Fax: (412)741-2311
Co. E-mail: info@printing.org
URL: http://www.printing.org/programs/groups/bia
Description: Represents trade binders and loose-leaf manufacturers united to conduct seminars, hold conventions, and formulate and maintain standards. **Founded:** 1955. **Publications:** Binders Bulletin (Monthly). **Awards:** Product of Excellence (Annual). **Geographic Preference:** Multinational.

1716 ■ Book Manufacturers Institute, Inc. (BMI)
7282 55th Ave. E, Ste. 147
 Bradenton, FL 34203
Ph: (386)986-4552
URL: http://www.bmibook.com
Contact: Jim Fetherston, President
Linkedin: www.linkedin.com/company/bmibook
X (Twitter): x.com/bmibook
YouTube: www.youtube.com/channel/UCRxDyN0mq_yIl6vah5XbCeA
Description: Represents the trade association for manufacturers of books. **Founded:** 1933. **Awards:** BMI Gutenberg Award (Annual); BMI Distinguished Master Bookman Award (Irregular); BMI Signature Award (Annual). **Geographic Preference:** National.

1717 ■ Center for Book Arts (CBA)
28 W 27th St., 3rd Fl.
 New York, NY 10001
Ph: (212)481-0295
Co. E-mail: info@centerforbookarts.org
URL: http://centerforbookarts.org
Contact: Corina Reynolds, Executive Director
E-mail: corina@centerforbookarts.org
Facebook: www.facebook.com/center4bookarts
Linkedin: www.linkedin.com/company/center-for-book-arts
X (Twitter): x.com/center4bookarts
Instagram: www.instagram.com/centerforbookarts
YouTube: www.youtube.com/channel/UCMAt94lZJDyeDQCJ_YQ6kxg
Description: Dedicated to the preservation of the traditional crafts of bookmaking, as well as encouraging contemporary interpretations of the book as an art object. Organizes exhibitions related to the art of the book and offers an extensive selection of educational courses, workshops and seminars in traditional and contemporary bookbinding, letterpress printing, fine press publishing, and other associated arts. Other programs include Artist-in-Residence, Broadsides Reading Series, and the Poetry Chapbook Competition. Supported by local businesses, various foundations including the Lenrow Fund, the Milton and Sally Avery Arts Foundation, the NY State Council on the Arts, the National Endowment for the Arts, and its members. **Founded:** 1974. **Awards:** Artist-in-Residence Workspace Grant (Annual); Center for Book Arts Poetry Chapbook Competition (Annual). **Geographic Preference:** National.

1718 ■ Guild of Book Workers (GBW) - Library
521 5th Ave.
 New York, NY 10175
Co. E-mail: communications@guildofbookworkers.org
URL: http://guildofbookworkers.org
Contact: Bexx Caswell, President
E-mail: president@guildofbookworkers.org
X (Twitter): x.com/bookworkers
Description: Works to improve standards by the sponsorship of exhibitions, field trips, lectures, workshops, and discussion groups, as well as to broaden public awareness of the handbook arts, to stimulate commissions of fine bindings, and to stress the need for sound book conservation and restoration. **Scope:** Calligraphy; printing; papermaking; decorated papers and conservation. **Founded:** 1906. **Holdings:** 1200 books; 700 monographs; 300 items; journals; videos. **Publications:** Supply Directory; Directory of Study Opportunities; Guild of BookWorkers--Study Opportunities List; Guild of Book Workers--Membership Directory; Guild of Book Workers--Membership List (Annual); Guild of Book Workers--Supplies and Services Directory; Guild of Book Workers Newsletter (6/year). **Geographic Preference:** Multinational.

REFERENCE WORKS

1719 ■ "Bookbinder Restores Pages From the Past" in The Dallas Morning News (February 24, 2012)
URL(s): www.dallasnews.com/arts-entertainment/2012/02/25/bookbinder-restores-pages-from-the-past/
Released: February 24, 2012. **Description:** Catherine Burkhard, and East Dallas bookbinder, talks about restoring priceless books for the Dallas Museum of Art's reference library and the Dallas Woman's Club. **Availability:** Online.

1720 ■ "A Bookbinding Bonanza" in The Harvard Gazette (September 22, 2014)
URL(s): news.harvard.edu/gazette/story/2014/09/a-bookbinding-bonanza/
Ed: Kate Kondayen. **Released:** September 22, 2014. **Description:** The show "InsideOUT: Contemporary Bindings of Private Press Books" displays artistic and innovative approaches to the traditional craft of bookbinding. These pieces have transcended the practical uses of bookbinding to become art pieces. **Availability:** Online.

1721 ■ "Educator Makes It Her Business to Bring Books Back to Life" in U.S. News & World Report (January 27, 2019)
URL(s): www.usnews.com/news/best-states/west-virginia/articles/2019-01-27/educator-makes-it-her-business-to-bring-books-back-to-life
Ed: Paul LaPann. **Released:** January 27, 2019. **Description:** Interview with Heather Royer, owner of A Stitch in Time Bookbindery who repairs Bibles and other books special to people. **Availability:** Online.

1722 ■ "Famous For Its Bookies, New Jersey Keeps a Different Type Of Bookmaker in Business" in Northjersey.com (April 16, 2018)
URL(s): www.northjersey.com/story/news/columnists/christopher-maag/2018/04/16/book-binding-ancient-craft-kept-alive-bookmaker-nj/444160002/
Ed: Christopher Maag. **Released:** April 16, 2018. **Description:** Interview with Michael LoGatto, who is a second-generation bookbinder in North Jersey who started his trade at the age of eight. **Availability:** Online.

1723 ■ "Gadget of the Week: Espresso Book Machine" in Barron's (Vol. 92, September 15, 2012, No. 38, pp. 27)
Pub: Dow Jones & Company Inc.
Contact: Almar Latour, Chief Executive Officer
Ed: Crystal Kim. **Description:** The Espresso Book Machine from Demand Books can print custom-make and out-of-copyright books within minutes. The set up costs up to $349 while each book costs $7 to bind and $0.03/page to print. **Availability:** Online.

1724 ■ Guild of BookWorkers--Study Opportunities List
Pub: Guild of Book Workers
Contact: Bexx Caswell, President
E-mail: president@guildofbookworkers.org
URL(s): guildofbookworkers.org/content/study-opportunities
Description: Covers about 130 teachers, schools, and centers offering hand bookbinding and calligraphic services; international coverage. **Entries include:** Craftsperson's name, address, special interests, source of expertise, whether apprentices are desired; also includes (for schools and other centers) names and addresses of instructors and courses offered. **Arrangement:** Geographical. **Availability:** Online.

1725 ■ "He Fixes the Cracked Spines of Books, Without an Understudy" in The New York Times (January 6, 2017)
URL(s): www.nytimes.com/2017/01/06/us/donald-vass-book-repair-seattle-library.html
Ed: Kirk Johnson. **Released:** January 06, 2017. **Description:** Donald Vass, a bookbinder at the King County Public Library system, talks about his craft and how he may be the last bookbinder in the area. **Availability:** Online.

TRADE PERIODICALS

1726 ■ Guild of Book Workers Newsletter
Pub: Guild of Book Workers
Contact: Bexx Caswell, President
E-mail: president@guildofbookworkers.org
URL(s): guildofbookworkers.org/newsletter

Released: 6/year **Description:** Covers issues in book arts, binding, book conservation, calligraphy, and printing. Recurring features include letters to the editor, interviews, news of research, a calendar of events, reports of meetings, news of educational opportunities, job listings, book reviews, and notices of publications available. **Availability:** PDF; Online.

1727 ■ MCBA Newsletter
Pub: Minnesota Center for Book Arts
Contact: Anna Bredeson, Director, Education
URL(s): www.mnbookarts.org/news
Released: Biweekly **Description:** Focuses on the field of book arts, including letterpress printing, bookbinding, and papermaking. Reviews current and future Center exhibitions and announces classes available at the Center. Recurring features include book reviews and news of educational opportunities. **Availability:** Online.

LIBRARIES

1728 ■ Book Club of California - Albert Sperisen Library
312 Sutter St., Ste. 500
San Francisco, CA 94108
Ph: (415)781-7532
Co. E-mail: info@bccbooks.org
URL: http://www.bccbooks.org
Contact: Kevin Kosik, Executive Director
E-mail: kevin@bccbooks.org
Facebook: www.facebook.com/pages/The-Book-Club-of-California/114655099741
Description: Supports book making, fine printing, design, typography, illustration, literature, and scholarship related to the history and literature of California and the western US. **Scope:** History and literature of California and West. **Services:** Library open to the public by appointment. **Founded:** 1912. **Holdings:** 10,000 volumes; books; ephemera. **Subscriptions:** 10 journals and other serials.

1729 ■ Canadian Bookbinders and Book Artists Guild (CBBAG) [la Guilde canadienne des relieurs et des artistes du livre]
82809 - 467 Parliament St.
Toronto, ON, Canada M5A 3Y2
Co. E-mail: cbbag@cbbag.ca
URL: http://www.cbbag.ca
Contact: Christine McNair, President
E-mail: president@cbbag.ca
Facebook: www.facebook.com/CanadianBookbindersandBookArtistsGuild
Description: Seeks to insure excellence in the book arts; conducts educational programs; sponsors competitions. **Founded:** 1983. **Publications:** Book Arts arts du livre Canada (Semiannual); Exhibition Catalogue; Suppliers List (Periodic). **Awards:** CBBAG Exhibition Awards (Quinquennial). **Geographic Preference:** National.

1730 ■ Grolier Club of New York Library
47 E 60th St.
New York, NY 10022
Ph: (212)838-6690
Fax: (212)838-2445
Co. E-mail: assistantlibrarian@grolierclub.org
URL: http://www.grolierclub.org/Default.aspx?p=DynamicModule&pageid=384831&ssid=322452&vnf=1
Contact: Meghan Constantinou, Librarian
E-mail: mconstantinou@grolierclub.org
Facebook: www.facebook.com/grolierclub
X (Twitter): x.com/GrolierClub
Instagram: www.instagram.com/grolierclub
Scope: Art and history; literature. **Services:** Library open to the public with restrictions. **Founded:** 1884. **Holdings:** 100,000 volumes; 5,000 prints and portraits; bookplates. **Subscriptions:** 100 journals and other serials.

1731 ■ Guild of Book Workers (GBW) - Library
521 5th Ave.
New York, NY 10175
Co. E-mail: communications@guildofbookworkers.org
URL: http://guildofbookworkers.org
Contact: Bexx Caswell, President
E-mail: president@guildofbookworkers.org
X (Twitter): x.com/bookworkers
Description: Works to improve standards by the sponsorship of exhibitions, field trips, lectures, workshops, and discussion groups, as well as to broaden public awareness of the handbook arts, to stimulate commissions of fine bindings, and to stress the need for sound book conservation and restoration. **Scope:** Calligraphy; printing; papermaking; decorated papers and conservation. **Founded:** 1906. **Holdings:** 1200 books; 700 monographs; 300 items; journals; videos. **Publications:** Supply Directory; Directory of Study Opportunities; Guild of BookWorkers--Study Opportunities List; Guild of Book Workers--Membership Directory; Guild of Book Workers--Membership List (Annual); Guild of Book Workers--Supplies and Services Directory; Guild of Book Workers Newsletter (6/year). **Geographic Preference:** Multinational.

1732 ■ Mills College - F.W. Olin Library - Special Collections
5000 MacArthur Blvd.
Oakland, CA 94613
Ph: (510)430-2047
Co. E-mail: specialcollections-oak@northeastern.edu
URL: http://library.northeastern.edu/oakland_campus/about-the-f-w-olin-library/special-collections
Scope: Education materials. **Services:** Interlibrary Loan; Copying; collections open to the public for reference use only. **Founded:** 1852.

1733 ■ Newark Public Library - Special Collections Division
5 Washington St.
Newark, NJ 07102
Ph: (973)733-7745
Fax: (973)733-5648
Co. E-mail: specialcollections@npl.org
URL: http://www.npl.org/special-collections
Facebook: www.facebook.com/special.collections.at.npl
X (Twitter): twitter.com/npl_scd
Instagram: www.instagram.com/newarkpl_specialcollections
Scope: History of the graphic arts business. **Services:** Interlibrary loan; copying; library open to the public. **Founded:** 1889. **Holdings:** E-books; audiobooks; posters; autographs; cards; drawings.

1734 ■ Rochester Institute of Technology - Melbert B. Cary, Jr. Graphic Arts Collection
90 Lomb Memorial Dr.
Rochester, NY 14623
URL: http://archivesspace.rit.edu/repositories/2/resources/235
Scope: Graphic art. **Holdings:** 45,000 volumes.

1735 ■ Yale University - Robert B. Haas Family Arts Library Special Collections
190 York St.
New Haven, CT 06520
Ph: (203)432-2645
Co. E-mail: artds.library@yale.edu
URL: http://web.library.yale.edu/arts/special-collections
Facebook: www.facebook.com/YaleHaasArtsLib
X (Twitter): twitter.com/YaleHaasArtsLib
Instagram: www.instagram.com/YaleHaasArtsLib/
Description: The collection includes contemporary catalogue raisonnes, 18th- and 19th-century works on artists and architecture, a wide selection of fine press and artists' books, rare research stuff in support of these subject areas, and the Faber Birren collection on color. **Scope:** Art history; drama. **Services:** Collection open to the public. **Founded:** 1967. **Holdings:** 125,000 volumes; prints and broadsides; type specimens; archive of student printing, including masters' theses from School of Graphic Design and School of Photography at Yale; 1 million bookplates; Japanese prints; stage and costume designs.

Bookkeeping

START-UP INFORMATION

1736 ■ *Bookkeeping: A Beginner's Guide to Accounting and Bookkeeping for Small Businesses*
Ed: Michael Kane. **Released:** March 05, 2021. **Description:** Tips on how to set up a virtual work-at-home bookkeeping business. **Availability:** E-book.

ASSOCIATIONS AND OTHER ORGANIZATIONS

1737 ■ **Canadian Institute of Quantity Surveyors (CIQS) [Institut Canadien des Economistes en Construction]**
90 Nolan Ct., Unit 19
Markham, ON, Canada L3R 4L9
Ph: (905)477-0008
Free: 866-345-1168
Fax: (905)477-6774
Co. E-mail: info@ciqs.org
URL: http://ciqs.org
Contact: Sheila Lennon, Chief Executive Officer
E-mail: ceo@ciqs.org
Facebook: www.facebook.com/canadianinstitu teofquantitysurveyors
Linkedin: www.linkedin.com/company/ciqs
X (Twitter): x.com/ciqs_official
YouTube: www.youtube.com/channel/UC5l 59C8R7cQN0Ngq-FvjS7g
Description: Establishes and maintains standards for certification and provides through advice to members relating to construction costs, management and administration of construction projects. **Founded:** 1959. **Publications:** *The Construction Economist* (Quarterly). **Awards:** Buster Vermeulen Memorial Award (Annual); Frank Helyar Memorial Award (Annual). **Geographic Preference:** National.

1738 ■ **Chartered Professional Accountants of Canada (CPA CANADA) - Library**
277 Wellington St., W
Toronto, ON, Canada M5V 3H2
Ph: (416)977-3222
Free: 800-268-3793
Fax: (416)977-8585
Co. E-mail: member.services@cpacanada.ca
URL: http://www.cpacanada.ca
Contact: Pamela Steer, President
Facebook: www.facebook.com/CPACanada
Linkedin: www.linkedin.com/company/cpa-canada
X (Twitter): x.com/CPAcanada
Instagram: www.instagram.com/cpa.canada
YouTube: www.youtube.com/cpacanada
Description: Aims to represent professional accountants in Canada by providing the highest standards of accounting, ethics, and best business practices. **Scope:** Accounting. **Founded:** 2013. **Holdings:** Figures not available. **Publications:** *CA Magazine: For Canada's Chartered Accountants*; *Directory of Canadian Chartered Accountants* (Periodic; Biennial); *CMA Magazine* (6/year). **Geographic Preference:** National.

1739 ■ **The Construction Economist**
90 Nolan Ct., Unit 19
Markham, ON, Canada L3R 4L9
Ph: (905)477-0008
Free: 866-345-1168
Fax: (905)477-6774
Co. E-mail: info@ciqs.org
URL: http://ciqs.org
Contact: Sheila Lennon, Chief Executive Officer
E-mail: ceo@ciqs.org
URL(s): ciqs.org/web/08-News-Announcements -Pages/Construction-Economist-Journal.aspx
Released: Quarterly; Spring, Summer, Fall, Winter. **Description:** Provides up-to-date information on the Institute, technical articles and information on past and upcoming events. **Availability:** Print; PDF; Online.

1740 ■ **National Association of Certified Public Bookkeepers, LLC (NACPB)**
1838 N 1075 W, Ste. 300
Farmington, UT 84025
Free: 844-249-3551
Fax: (801)513-5361
Co. E-mail: info@nacpb.org
URL: http://certifiedpublicbookkeeper.org
Description: Aims to protect the public interest by ensuring that only qualified individuals provide public bookkeeping services. Fosters the professional development of public bookkeepers. Offers certification programs in bookkeeping. **Geographic Preference:** National.

1741 ■ **Society of Professional Accountants of Canada (SPAC) [La societe des comptables professionnels du Canada; RPA Canada]**
48 Village Ctr. Pl., Ste., 100
Mississauga, ON, Canada L4Z 1V9
Ph: (416)350-8145
Free: 877-515-4447
Co. E-mail: info@rpacanada.org
URL: http://rpacanada.org
Contact: Zubair Choudhry, President
Facebook: www.facebook.com/Registere dProfessionalAccountants
Linkedin: www.linkedin.com/in/registered-professional -accountant-555378190
X (Twitter): x.com/rpacanada
YouTube: www.youtube.com/channel/UCqo7eFpci_fk tegT5vwjB8A
Description: Professional accountants and individuals working to pass qualifying accountancy examinations. Promotes ongoing professional education among accountants; encourages students to enter the accounting field; works to advance the profession of accounting. Gathers and disseminates information on accounting; sponsors educational programs; conducts professional accountancy qualifying examinations. **Founded:** 1978. **Publications:** *Professional Accountant* (Quarterly). **Geographic Preference:** National.

REFERENCE WORKS

1742 ■ *"6 Lessons from Audit Experts Who Adopted AI Early" in Journal of Accountancy (November 23, 2021)*
Ed: Andrew Kenney. **Released:** November 23, 2021. **Description:** With the advance of AI, the best thing those in the accountancy industries can do is learn about various AI platforms and how to incorporate them into their businesses. The technology is still evolving, but tips are given on how to use AI to benefit customers. **Availability:** Online.

1743 ■ *"2011 Tax Information of Interest" in Business Owner (Vol. 35, November-December 2011, No. 6, pp. 10)*
Description: Compilation of 2011 tax information to help small business take advantage of all tax incentives. **Availability:** Print; Online.

1744 ■ *"Accrual vs. Cash Accounting, Explained" in Business Owner (Vol. 35, July-August 2011, No. 4, pp. 13)*
Description: Cash method versus accrual accounting methods are examined, using hypothetical situations.

1745 ■ *"Bookkeeping For Dummies"*
Pub: For Dummies
Released: 2nd edition. **Description:** Because accurate and concise bookkeeping is critical to any small business, information for managing finances to save money while growing your business is offered. The guide covers the basics of bookkeeping, from recording transactions to producing balance sheets and year-end reports. **Availability:** Print; Online.

1746 ■ *"Bookkeeping Options for Time-Starved Startups" in Legal Zoom (February 21, 2023)*
URL(s): www.legalzoom.com/articles/bookkeeping-op tions-for-time-starved-startups
Ed: Sandra Beckwith. **Released:** February 21, 2023. **Description:** Bookkeeping is an essential part of any business and not everyone has the skills to manage the books. Listed are several options that would work well with startups. **Availability:** Online.

1747 ■ *"Cautions on Loans with Your Business" in Business Owner (Vol. 35, July-August 2011, No. 4, pp. 5)*
Description: Caution must be used when borrowing from or lending to any small business. Tax guidelines for the borrowing and lending practice are also included. **Availability:** Print; Online.

1748 ■ *"Changing the Rules of the Accounting Game" in Canadian Business (Vol. 81, December 8, 2008, No. 21, pp. 19)*
Description: Interference from world politicians in developing accounting standards is believed to have resulted in untested rules that are inferior to current

standards. European lawmakers have recently asked to change International Financial Reporting Standards. **Availability:** Online.

1749 ■ *"Column: It's Time to Take Full Responsibility" in Harvard Business Review (Vol. 88, October 2010, No. 10, pp. 42)*
Pub: Harvard Business Publishing
Contact: Diane Belcher, Managing Director

Ed: Rosabeth Moss Kanter. **Price:** $6, PDF. **Description:** A case for corporate responsibility is cited, focusing on long-term impact and the effects of public accountability. **Availability:** Online; PDF.

1750 ■ *"Convergence Collaboration: Revising Revenue Recognition" in Management Accounting Quarterly (Vol. 12, Spring 2011, No. 3, pp. 18)*
Pub: Management Accounting Quarterly
Contact: Mike DePrisco, President

Ed: Jack T. Ciesielski, Thomas R. Weirich. **Description:** While revenue recognition is critical, regulations have been developed on an ad hoc basis until now. The joint FASB/IASB proposed accounting standard on revenue recognition is a meaningful convergence of standards that will require a major adjustment for financial statement preparers. The proposal is a radical departure from the way revenue has been recognized by the U.S. GAAP. For industries such as consulting, engineering, construction, and technology, it could dramatically change revenue recognition, impacting the top line. The new proposed standard, its potential impact, and the critical role that contracts play is examined thoroughly. **Availability:** PDF; Online.

1751 ■ *"Crucible: Battling Back from Betrayal" in Harvard Business Review (Vol. 88, December 2010, No. 12, pp. 130)*
Pub: Harvard Business Publishing
Contact: Diane Belcher, Managing Director

Ed: Daniel McGinn. **Price:** $8.95, PDF. **Description:** Stephen Greer's scrap metal firm, Hartwell Pacific, lost several million dollars due to a lack of efficient and appropriate inventory audits, accounting procedures, and new-hire reference checks for his foreign operations. Greer believes that balancing growth with control is a key component of success. **Availability:** Print; PDF.

1752 ■ *Deduct It! Lower Your Small Business Taxes*
Pub: Nolo
Contact: Chris Braun, President

Ed: Stephen Fishman. **Released:** 19th edition. **Price:** $17.99, e-book; $19.99, book and e-book; $17.99, E-Book; $19.99, book and e-book; $17.99, e-book. **Description:** Information is provided to help small companies maximize taxable deductions. **Availability:** Handheld; E-book; Print; Electronic publishing; PDF.

1753 ■ *"Do Fair Value Adjustments Influence Dividend Policy?" in Accounting and Business Research (Vol. 41, Spring 2011, No. 2, pp. 51)*

Ed: Igor Goncharov, Sander van Triest. **Description:** The impact of positive fair value adjustments on corporate distributions is examined using a Russian setting that requires disclosure of unrealized fair value adjustments in income. It was found that there is no rise in dividends due to positive fair value adjustments and that on the contrary, a negative relationship exists between adjustments and dividend changes.

1754 ■ *"Economic Crisis and Accounting Evolution" in Accounting and Business Research (Vol. 41, Summer 2011, No. 3, pp. 2159)*
Pub: Routledge, Taylor & Francis Group

Ed: Gregory Waymire, Sudipta Basu. **Description:** Financial reporting changes at the face of economic crises are studied using a punctuated equilibrium evolution. Findings show that financial reporting has a minor impact but may amplify economic crises. Attempts to enhance accounting and economic crises may not be as beneficial as planned. **Availability:** PDF; Online; Download.

1755 ■ *"Family Child Care Record-Keeping Guide, Ninth Edition (Redleaf Business Series)"*
Pub: Redleaf Press
Contact: Barbara Yates, President

Released: 9th edition. **Price:** $21.95, soft bound. **Description:** Writer, trainer, lawyer, and consultant provides concise information for home-based family child care (day care) providers. The book covers tracking expenses, being profitable, filing taxes, and meeting government regulations. This resources covers the process of accurate bookkeeping and record-keeping to take advantage of all allowable tax deductions. Changes in depreciation rules, adjustments to food and mileage rates, and clarifications on how to calculate the Time-Space percentage are defined. **Availability:** Print.

1756 ■ *"Feds Finalize I-9 Form Rules Allowing Electronic Storage" in HR Specialist (Vol. 8, September 2010, No. 9, pp. 5)*
Pub: Capitol Information Group Inc.
Contact: Allie Ash, Chief Executive Officer

Description: U.S. Department of Homeland Security issued regulations that give employers more flexibility to electronically sing and store I-9 employee verification forms. **Availability:** Print; PDF; Online.

1757 ■ *Finance & Accounting: How to Keep Your Books and Manage Your Finances with an MBA, a CPA, or a Ph.D*

1758 ■ *"Furniture Making May Come Back--Literally" in Business North Carolina (Vol. 28, March 2008, No. 3, pp. 32)*
Pub: Business North Carolina
Contact: Peggy Knaack, Manager
E-mail: pknaack@businessnc.com

Description: Due to the weak U.S. dollar and the fact that lumber processors never left the country, foreign furniture manufacturers are becoming interested in moving manufacturing plants to the U.S. **Availability:** Online.

1759 ■ *How to Start an Internet Sales Business Without Making the Government Mad*
Pub: Lulu Press Inc.

Ed: Dan Davis. **Released:** October 01, 2011. **Price:** $19.95, paperback; $14.38, PDF; $14.38, e-book. **Description:** Small business guide for launching an Internet sales company. Topics include business structure, licenses, and taxes. **Availability:** E-book; Print; PDF.

1760 ■ *"How To: Manage Your Cash Better" in Inc. (Volume 32, December 2010, No. 10, pp. 69)*
Pub: Mansueto Ventures L.L.C.
Contact: Stephanie Mehta, Chief Executive Officer

Released: December 01, 2010. **Description:** A monthly guide to policies, procedures and practices for managing cash for a small business. **Availability:** Online.

1761 ■ *"Inesoft Cash Organizer Desktop: A New Approach to Personal Accounts Bookkeeping" in America's Intelligence Wire (August 7, 2012)*

Description: Inesoft Cash Organizer Desktop application is offering a new product for financial management on a home PC and mobile devices. The program supports the classification of money transactions by category, sub-category, project, sub-project, budget planning, and world currencies (including current exchange rates), credit calculators, special reports, and more. Multiple users in the family can use the appllication. Details of the program are outlined. **Availability:** Online.

1762 ■ *"IRS Announces New Standards for Tax Preparers" in Bellingham Business Journal (Vol. February 2010, pp. 9)*
Pub: Sound Publishing Inc.
Contact: Josh O'Connor, President

Ed: Isaac Bonnell. **Description:** A new oversight plan was announced by the Internal Revenue Services (IRS) that will require tax professionals to pass a competency test and register with the government in order to ensure greater accountability in the industry.

1763 ■ *"Is the Death Knell Upon Bookkeepers in 2019?" in AccountantsDaily (February 13, 2019)*
URL(s): www.accountantsdaily.com.au/columns/
12642-is-the-death-knell-upon-bookkeepers-in
-2019

Ed: Mel Power. **Released:** February 13, 2019. **Description:** Discusses how bookkeepers need to incorporate technology into their work, but still retain human relationships with their clients. The business model needs to change in order for the industry to survive with how business is currently done. **Availability:** Online.

1764 ■ *"Kaboom!" in Canadian Business (Vol. 81, November 10, 2008, No. 19, pp. 18)*

Description: International Financial Reporting Standards (IFRS) is a good idea in theory but was implemented in a hurry and had poor quality standards from the beginning. **Availability:** Print; Online.

1765 ■ *"Living in a 'Goldfish Bowl'" in WorkingUSA (Vol. 11, June 2008, No. 2, pp. 277)*

Description: Recent changes in laws, regulations and even the reporting format of labor organization annual financial reports in both the U.S. and Australia have received surprisingly little attention, yet they have significantly increased the amount of information available both to union members and the public in general, as reports in both countries are available via government Websites. While such financial reporting laws are extremely rare in European countries, with the exception of the UK and Ireland, the U.S. and Australian reporting systems have become among the most detailed in the world. After reviewing these changes in financial reporting and the availability of these reports, as well as comparing and contrasting the specific reporting requirements of each country, this paper then examines the cost-benefit impact of more detailed financial reporting. **Availability:** Print; Online.

1766 ■ *"My Favorite Tool for Managing Expenses" in Inc. (Volume 32, December 2010, No. 10, pp. 60)*
Pub: Inc. Magazine

Ed: J.J. McCorvey. **Description:** Web-based service called Expensify is outlined. The service allows companies to log expenses while away from the office using the service's iPhone application. **Availability:** Online.

1767 ■ *"A Necessary Balancing Act: Bookkeeping" in Contractor (Vol. 56, November 2009, No. 11, pp. 22)*

Ed: Al Schwartz. **Description:** Pros and cons of getting a bookkeeper or a certified public accountant for the subcontractor are discussed. A bookkeeper can help a subcontractor get new accounting software up and running while an accountant will more than likely keep after the books at regular intervals throughout the year. **Availability:** Print; Online.

1768 ■ *"New Institutional Accounting and IFRS" in Accounting and Business Research (Vol. 41, Summer 2011, No. 3, pp. 309)*
Pub: Routledge, Taylor & Francis Group

Ed: Peter Wysocki. **Description:** A new framework for institutional accounting research is presented. It has five fundamental components: efficient versus inefficient results, interdependencies, causation, level of analysis, and institutional structure. The use of the framework for evaluation accounting institutions such as the international financial reports standards (IFRS) is discussed. **Availability:** PDF; Online; Download.

1769 ■ *"Privacy Concern: Are 'Group' Time Sheets Legal?" in HR Specialist (Vol. 8, September 2010, No. 9, pp. 4)*

Pub: Capitol Information Group Inc.
Contact: Allie Ash, Chief Executive Officer

Description: Under the Fair Labor Standards Act (FLSA) employers are required to maintain and preserve payroll or other records, including the number of hours worked, but it does not prescribe a particular order or form in which these records must be kept. **Availability:** PDF; Online.

1770 ■ *"Proposed Accounting Changes Could Complicate Tenants' Leases" in Baltimore Business Journal (Vol. 28, July 2, 2010, No. 8, pp. 1)*

Pub: Baltimore Business Journal
Contact: Rhonda Pringle, President
E-mail: rpringle@bizjournals.com

Ed: Daniel J. Sernovitz. **Description:** The Financial Accounting Standards Board has proposed that companies must indicate the value of real estate leases as assets and liabilities on balance sheets instead of expenses. The proposals could cause some companies to document millions of dollars in charges on their books or find difficulty in getting loans. **Availability:** Print.

1771 ■ *Reading Financial Reports for Dummies*

Pub: John Wiley & Sons, Inc.
Contact: Christina Van Tassell, Executive Vice President Chief Financial Officer
URL(s): www.amazon.com/gp/product/1119871360/ref=as_li_tl?ie=UTF8&tag=wiley01-20

Ed: Lita Epstein. **Released:** 4th Edition. **Price:** $27.18, paperback; $18, e-book. **Description:** The fourth edition contains more new and updated information. This book is meant as a guide to help the reader interpret and understand financial reports, annual reports, balance sheets, income statements, statements of cash flow and consolidated statements. Real-world examples are given. . **Availability:** E-book; Print.

1772 ■ *Self-Employed Tax Solutions: Quick, Simple, Money-Saving, Audit-Proof Tax and Recordkeeping Basics*

Released: Second edition. **Description:** A simple system for maintaining tax records and filing tax forms for any small business is explored.

1773 ■ *The Small Business Bible: Everything You Need to Know to Succeed in Your Small Business*

Pub: John Wiley & Sons, Inc.
Contact: Christina Van Tassell, Executive Vice President Chief Financial Officer

Ed: Steven D. Strauss. **Released:** Third edition. **Price:** $22.95, paperback; $14.99, E-book. **Description:** Comprehensive guide to starting and running a successful small business. Topics include bookkeeping and financial management, marketing, publicity, and advertising. **Availability:** E-book; Print.

1774 ■ *"Surviving an IRS Audit: Tips for Small Businesses" in Agency Sales Magazine (Vol. 39, July 2009, No. 7, pp. 52)*

Description: It is a good idea to enlist the services of a tax professional even if an audit is expected to go smoothly since the IRS is likely to scrutinize the unreported income and personal as well as business expenses of a small business during an audit. **Availability:** Online.

1775 ■ *"Throughput Metrics Meet Six Sigma" in Management Accounting Quarterly (Vol. 12, Spring 2011, No. 3, pp. 12)*

Pub: Management Accounting Quarterly
Contact: Mike DePrisco, President

Ed: Shaun Aghili. **Description:** Throughput accounting (TA) metrics can be combined with six sigma's DMAIC methodology and various time-tested analysis and measurement tools for added effectiveness in resolving resource constraint issues. The goal is to optimize not only the output of a specific department but that of the entire system, by implementing a cost accounting system that is conducive to system optimization while increasing product quality, process integrity, or ideally, both. **Availability:** Print; PDF; Online.

STATISTICAL SOURCES

1776 ■ *Payroll & Bookkeeping Services Industry in the US - Market Research Report*
URL(s): www.ibisworld.com/united-states/market-research-reports/payroll-bookkeeping-services-industry/

Price: $925. **Description:** Downloadable report analyzing the current and future trends in the payroll and bookkeeping industries. **Availability:** Download.

VIDEO/AUDIO MEDIA

1777 ■ *Getting Paid on Past Due Invoices*
URL(s): bizchix.com/584-getting-paid-on-past-due-invoices

Ed: Natalie Eckdahl. **Released:** July 23, 2023. **Description:** Podcast discusses blocks and boundaries to getting paid, tactics to get paid, and how to prevent unpaid invoices in the future.

1778 ■ *How to Master Your Monthly Bookkeeping*
URL(s): omny.fm/shows/startup-hustle/how-to-master-your-monthly-bookkeeping

Ed: Andrew Morgans. **Released:** August 29, 2023. **Description:** Podcast discusses how to perfect your bookkeeping. Features Nathan Hirsch, co-founder of EcomBalance.

TRADE SHOWS AND CONVENTIONS

1779 ■ **IME Annual Conference & Expo**
Institute of Management Accountants (IMA)
10 Paragon Dr., Ste. 1
Montvale, NJ 07645-1760
Ph: (201)573-9000
Free: 800-638-4427
Fax: (201)474-1600
URL: http://in.imanet.org
Contact: Mike DePrisco, President
URL(s): www.imaconference.org/event/0d81b1ed-896a-492b-9bd5-450d7913d3da/summary?_ga=2.252859721.1593101258.1628525610-648749330.1628525610

Frequency: Annual. **Description:** Management accounting equipment, supplies, and services. Review courses, shipping companies, software companies, and risk management consultants. **Audience:** Accountants, auditors, and financial professionals. **Principal Exhibits:** Management accounting equipment, supplies, and services. Review courses, shipping companies, software companies, and risk management consultants.

1780 ■ **New Jersey Accounting, Business & Technology Show & Conference**
New Jersey Society of Certified Public Accountants (NJCPA)
105 Eisenhower Pky., Ste. 300
Roseland, NJ 07068
Ph: (973)226-4494
Co. E-mail: njcpa@njcpa.org
URL: http://njcpa.org
Contact: Kathleen F. Powers, President
URL(s): www.flaggmgmt.com/nj

Description: Information and technology, financial and business services, computer accounting systems, software, tax preparation, accounting, audit, practice management software - windows, and computer and business systems. Banking, insurance, financial and business software. Internet, online systems and middle market software and investment services. **Audience:** CPAs, accounting professionals, business and financial executives of New Jersey, Fortune 1000 corporations, business owners and managers, and IT managers. **Principal Exhibits:** Information and technology, financial and business services, computer accounting systems, software, tax preparation, accounting, audit, practice management software - windows, and computer and business systems. Banking, insurance, financial and business software. Internet, online systems and middle market software and investment services.

CONSULTANTS

1781 ■ **A Bigger Bottom Line LLC**
4470 W Sunset Blvd., Unit No 90599
Los Angeles, CA 90027
Free: 855-752-6886
Co. E-mail: info@abiggerbottom-line.com
URL: http://www.abiggerbottomline.com
Contact: Sandra Menjivar, Contact
Facebook: www.facebook.com/abiggerbottomline
Linkedin: www.linkedin.com/in/andria-radmacher-68612b95
Instagram: www.instagram.com/abiggerbottomline

Description: Provides a variety of business services including bookkeeping and accounting, payables and receivables, payroll support, cash flow forecasting, Quickbooks setup/training, system integration, remote working, tax planning, start-up consulting, business consulting, forensic accounting, and PPP and bank loans. **Scope:** Provides a variety of business services including bookkeeping and accounting, payables and receivables, payroll support, cash flow forecasting, Quickbooks setup/training, system integration, remote working, tax planning, start-up consulting, business consulting, forensic accounting, and PPP and bank loans.

1782 ■ **Fischer Kraker Miscelli Inc.**
10 E 40 th St.
New York, NY 10016

Description: Business consultants specializing in bookkeeping and accounting services for advertising agencies. **Scope:** Business consultants specializing in bookkeeping and accounting services for advertising agencies.

1783 ■ **On-Q Software Inc.**
13764 SW 11 St.
Miami, FL 33184
URL: http://www.on-qsoftware.com
Contact: Teresita Cajigas, President

Description: Developer of computer software solutions. **Scope:** Developer of computer software solutions. **Founded:** 1987.

1784 ■ **Southern Business Services**
7109 Airline Dr.
Houston, TX 77076
Contact: S. A. Landry, Contact

Description: Offers hourly bookkeeping and secretarial services, preliminary employee screening and interviewing services, business manuals and reminder services. **Scope:** Offers hourly bookkeeping and secretarial services, preliminary employee screening and interviewing services, business manuals and reminder services.

1785 ■ Bookkeeping

1785 ■ Tax Preparations Etc. Inc.
77 Remsen Rd.
Yonkers, NY 10710
Contact: Anna Faustini, Chief Executive Officer
Description: Provider of payroll, tax preparation, and bookkeeping services. **Scope:** Provider of payroll, tax preparation, and bookkeeping services.

FRANCHISES AND BUSINESS OPPORTUNITIES

1786 ■ Ledgers Professional Services
26 Wilstead Dr.
Newmarket, ON, Canada L3Y 4T9
Free: 855-LED-GERS
Co. E-mail: clientcare@ledgers.com
URL: http://ledgers.com
Contact: Savio Goveas, Contact
Facebook: www.facebook.com/LedgersCanada
X (Twitter): x.com/ledgerscanada
Description: Provider of accounting, bookkeeping and financial statement preparation services for small businesses. **Founded:** 1994. **Training:** Provides 5 days training.

LIBRARIES

1787 ■ Deloitte Services LLP Information Center
50 S 6th St., Ste. 2800
Minneapolis, MN 55402-1844
Ph: (612)397-4000
Fax: (612)397-4450
URL: http://www2.deloitte.com/us/en.html
Facebook: www.facebook.com/DeloitteUS
Linkedin: www.linkedin.com/company/deloitte
X (Twitter): twitter.com/deloitteus
Instagram: www.instagram.com/lifeatdeloitteus
YouTube: www.youtube.com/user/DeloitteLLP
Description: A brand under which tens of thousands of dedicated professionals in independent firms throughout the world collaborate to provide audit, consulting, financial advisory, risk advisory, tax and related services to select clients. Mainly focusses on the US region. **Scope:** Accounting, auditing, taxation, healthcare, consulting. **Services:** Library not open to the public. **Founded:** 1976. **Holdings:** 3,000 books; 178 bound periodical volumes.

1788 ■ Deloitte & Touche - Research Center
111 S Wacker Dr., Ste. 1800
Chicago, IL 60606-4301
URL: http://www2.deloitte.com/us/en/pages/energy-and-resources/articles/deloitte-research-center-energy-industrials.html
Contact: Kate Hardin, Executive Director
E-mail: khardin@deloitte.com
Scope: Accounting; auditing; taxation; business and finance; management; electronic data processing; information technology. **Services:** Interlibrary loan; library open to the public by appointment. **Holdings:** 2,500 books.

1789 ■ Howard University - School of Business Library (HUSBL)
2600 Sixth St., NW
Washington, DC 20059
Ph: (202)806-1560
Co. E-mail: ab_coleman@howard.edu
URL: http://businesslibrary.howard.edu
Contact: Rossini Clark, Librarian
E-mail: rcclark@howard.edu
Scope: Business.; Small Business; accounting; finance; international business; information systems and decision sciences; marketing; management; supply-chain management and much more. **Services:** Interlibrary loan; library open to the public. **Founded:** 1964. **Holdings:** Figures not available.

1790 ■ KPMG L.L.P., Library
550 S Hope St., Ste. 1500
Los Angeles, CA 90071-1568
URL: http://kpmg.com/us/en.html
Scope: Accounting; taxation; business management; auditing; economics. **Services:** Interlibrary loan; library open to the public. **Holdings:** Figures not available.

1791 ■ KPMG - Research Centre
777 Dunsmuir St., 11 Fl.
Vancouver, BC, Canada V7Y 1K3
Ph: (604)691-3000
Fax: (604)691-3031
URL: http://home.kpmg/ca/en/home.html
Scope: Tax; general business; stocks. **Founded:** 1982. **Subscriptions:** journals Figures not available.

1792 ■ PricewaterhouseCoopers - North Toronto Research Centre [PwC - Toronto - Metro North]
18 York St., Ste. 2600
Toronto, ON, Canada M5J 0B2
Ph: (416)863-1133
Fax: (416)365-8215
URL: http://www.pwc.com/ca/en/about-us/our-organization/office-location.html
Contact: Nicolas Marcoux, Chief Executive Officer
Scope: Taxation, GST/Commodity tax, real estate, estate administration, tax law. **Services:** Interlibrary loan; centre not open to the public. **Founded:** 1995. **Holdings:** 1,200 books. **Subscriptions:** 100 journals and other serials; 3 newspapers.

RESEARCH CENTERS

1793 ■ Credit Research Foundation (CRF) - Library
1812 Baltimore Blvd., Ste. H
Westminster, MD 21157
Ph: (443)821-3000
Fax: (443)821-3627
URL: http://www.crfonline.org
Contact: Bill Balduino, President
Linkedin: www.linkedin.com/company/credit-research-foundation
YouTube: www.youtube.com/channel/UCl3ulPzpwNOPvHq2nOMDtsg
Description: Represents credit, financial, and working capital executives of manufacturing and banking concerns. Aims to create a better understanding of the impact of credit on the economy. Plans, supervises, and administers research and educational programs. Conducts surveys on economic conditions, trends, policies, practices, theory, systems, and methodology. Sponsors formal educational programs in credit and financial management. Maintains library on credit, collections, and management. **Scope:** Financial management, including management theory, electronic data processing, human resources management, business practices and techniques, economic impact of business credit, credit and receivables management, working capital management, international credit and finance, and related subjects. **Services:** Library open to the public; copying. **Founded:** 1949. **Holdings:** 500 articles; books; Cds. **Publications:** Credit Professional's Handbook; Perspective by CRF (Quarterly); National Summary of Domestic Trade Receivables (Quarterly); Annual Collection Productivity Report; Credit Executives Handbook; Net Bad-Debt Writeoffs and Allowance for Uncollectibles (Annual); Credit and Financial Management Review (Quarterly). **Educational Activities:** CRF Credit and Accounts Receivable Open Forums (Irregular). **Geographic Preference:** National.

1794 ■ Financial Executives Research Foundation (FERF) - Library
1250 Headquarters Plz., 7th Fl.
Morristown, NJ 07960
Fax: (973)765-1018
Co. E-mail: membership@financialexecutives.org
URL: http://www.financialexecutives.org/Research.aspx
Contact: Andrej Suskavcevic, President
E-mail: andrej@financialexecutives.org
Facebook: www.facebook.com/financialexecutivesinternational
Linkedin: www.linkedin.com/company/financial-executives-international
X (Twitter): x.com/feinews
YouTube: www.youtube.com/user/FEITVOnDemand
Description: Publishes research in business management, with emphasis on corporate financial management issues. Maintains inquiry services. **Scope:** Business management, with particular emphasis on principles and practices of financial management and their evolving role in the management of business. **Founded:** 1931. **Holdings:** Figures not available. **Publications:** Issue alerts (Quarterly); FERF Newsletters (Quarterly). **Geographic Preference:** National.

1795 ■ New York University - Leonard N. Stern School of Business - Salomon Center for the Study of Financial Institutions
44 W 4th St., Ste. 9-160
New York, NY 10012
Ph: (212)998-0700
Fax: (212)995-4220
Co. E-mail: salomon@stern.nyu.edu
URL: http://www.stern.nyu.edu/experience-stern/about/departments-centers-initiatives/centers-of-research/salomon-center-for-the-study-of-financial-institutions
Contact: Matthew Richardson, Director
Description: Publishes books in the field of financial economics. Research findings are disseminated in published form. Does not accept unsolicited manuscripts. **Scope:** Evaluates changing structure of financial instruments and markets and the use of these instruments and markets in financial intermediation and the management of risk by financial institutions and business corporations. Recent projects include modern portfolio management and the prudent man rule, role of financial futures and options in large financial institutions' investment portfolios, information and stock market efficiency, composition of individual investment portfolios, hedging and trading performance of new financial futures and options, new financial instruments, reforming Japan's financial markets, reconfiguration of the insurance industry, and restructuring the U.S. financial and insurance sectors. Produces working paper series, occasional papers in business and finance, workshops, forums, and conferences. **Founded:** 1972. **Publications:** Instruments and Markets (5/year); The Journal of Derivatives (JOD) (Quarterly); Journal of Financial Institutions; Journal of International Financial Management and Accounting (JIFMA) (3/year); Salomon Center for the Study of Financial Institutions Newsletter (Annual).

1796 ■ Shippensburg University of Pennsylvania - Office of Professional, Continuing and Distance Education
1871 Old Main Dr., Horton Hall, Rm. 116
Shippensburg, PA 17257
Ph: (717)477-1502
Fax: (717)477-4050
Co. E-mail: pcde@ship.edu
URL: http://www.ship.edu/PCDE
Contact: Mark Chimel, Director
E-mail: mschimel@ship.edu
Facebook: www.facebook.com/ShipPCDE
X (Twitter): twitter.com/ShipPCDE
Instagram: www.instagram.com/shippcde/
Description: Research, data collection, teaching and consulting center at Shippensburg University of Pennsylvania. Provides speakers for professional meetings; research and data collection services.

Scope: Research focuses on personnel development programs and problem-solving in organizational function, including accounting, finance, marketing, management, sales, advertising, training, and taxes. **Founded:** 1976. **Publications:** *Working Paper Series*. **Educational Activities:** Office of Professional, Continuing and Distance Education Annual Small Business Management Series, Open to small business owners or managers.; Tax Institute Small Business Management Seminar.

1797 ■ University of Iowa - Henry B. Tippie College of Business - McGladrey Institute of Accounting Education and Research
108 John Pappajohn Business Bldg.
Iowa City, IA 52242-1994
URL: http://tippie.uiowa.edu/175

Description: Integral unit of Henry B. Tippie College of Business, University of Iowa. **Scope:** Accounting, auditing, and financial reporting by public and private organizations. **Founded:** 1984. **Publications:** *RSM McGladrey Institute of Accounting Education and Research Working papers* (Occasionally). **Educational Activities:** National Speaker Series (Annual), Offer exemplary teaching programs.; PriceWaterhouseCoopers Accounting Research Workshop, Offer exemplary teaching and training programs.; Sidney G. Winter Lecture Series, Offer exemplary teaching programs.

1798 ■ University of Rhode Island - Research Center in Business and Economics (RCBE)
Ballentine Hall
7 Lippitt Rd. Ballentine Hall
Kingston, RI 02881

URL: http://www.uri.edu/about/history/detailed-history
Contact: Dr. David M. Dooley, President

Description: Integral unit of College of Business Administration at University of Rhode Island. **Scope:** Services research activities of faculty members of the College in fields of accounting, business law, economics, finance, insurance, management, marketing, and quantitative analysis. Conducts survey research, economic analyses, and business-related research projects on a contract basis.

Bookstore

START-UP INFORMATION

1799 ■ *How to Open and Operate a Financially Successful Bookstore on Amazon and Other Web Sites: With Companion CD-ROM*
Pub: Atlantic Publishing Co.
Contact: Dr. Heather L. Johnson, Contact
Description: This book was written for every used book aficionado and bookstore owner who currently wants to take advantage of the massive collection of online resources available to start and run your own online bookstore business.

ASSOCIATIONS AND OTHER ORGANIZATIONS

1800 ■ **Antiquarian Booksellers Association of America (ABAA)**
20 W 44th St., Ste. 507
New York, NY 10036-6604
Ph: (212)944-8291
Co. E-mail: hq@abaa.org
URL: http://www.abaa.org
Contact: Sheryl Jaeger, President
Facebook: www.facebook.com/ABAARareBooks
X (Twitter): x.com/ABAA49
Description: Promotes ethical standards in the industry. Sponsors educational programs for members, librarians, archivists, and the public. Administers the Antiquarian Booksellers' Benevolent Fund. **Founded:** 1949. **Publications:** *ABAA Membership Directory* (Annual); *International Directory of Antiquarian Booksellers* (Irregular); *Antiquarian Booksellers' Association of America--Membership Directory* (Annual). **Geographic Preference:** National.

1801 ■ **Antiquarian Booksellers' Association of Canada (ABAC) [Association de la Librairie Ancienne du Canada (ALAC)]**
c/o Karol Krysik Books
491 Davenport Rd., 2nd Fl.
Toronto, ON, Canada M4V 1B7
Co. E-mail: info@abac.org
URL: http://abac.org/wordpress/en
Contact: Robert Wright, President
Facebook: www.facebook.com/Antiquarian-Booksellers-Association-of-Canada-210124119032896
X (Twitter): x.com/A_B_A_C
Description: Bookselling firms and dealers in rare books and manuscripts. Promotes adherence to high standards of ethics and practice in the trade of antiquarian books. Serves as liaison between members and book collectors and as a clearinghouse on antiquarian books and their trade. **Founded:** 1966. **Geographic Preference:** National.

1802 ■ **Book Industry Study Group (BISG)**
232 Madison Ave., Ste. 1400
New York, NY 10016
Ph: (646)336-7141
Co. E-mail: info@bisg.org
URL: http://www.bisg.org
Contact: Brian O'Leary, Executive Director
E-mail: brian@bisg.org
Linkedin: www.linkedin.com/company/book-industry-study-group
X (Twitter): x.com/BISG
Description: Maintains and implements standardized best practices. BISG also develops and shares leading-edge research and information and creates education and events that help our membership and the industry better understand market trends and issues. **Scope:** Facilitates connections and conversations to solve common problems, advance new ideas, and more profitably bring published content to readers. **Founded:** 1976. **Publications:** *BISG Research Reports* (Quarterly); *Student Attitudes Toward Content in Higher Education*; *Trends Update*; *Book Industry TRENDS* (Annual). **Educational Activities:** BISG Seminars and conferences, For discussion of implications of statistical information on the book industry. **Geographic Preference:** Multinational.

1803 ■ **CBA: The Association for Christian Retail (CBA)**
1365 Garden of the Gods Rd., Ste. 105
Colorado Springs, CO 80907
URL: http://cbaonline.org
Instagram: www.instagram.com/cbaretail
Description: Trade association for retail stores selling Christian books, Bibles, gifts, and Sunday school and church supplies. Compiles statistics; conducts specialized education programs. **Founded:** 1950. **Publications:** *CBA International Market Directory*; *Christian Booksellers Association--Suppliers Directory* (Annual); *Christian Market* (Monthly); *Current Christian Books* (Annual). **Educational Activities:** Christian Booksellers Association International Convention (Annual); International Christian Retail Show.

1804 ■ **Great Lakes Independent Booksellers Association (GLiBA) [Great Lakes Booksellers Association]**
3123 Andrea Ct.
Woodridge, IL 60517
Ph: (630)841-8129
URL: http://www.gliba.org
Contact: Lynn Mooney, President
Facebook: www.facebook.com/glibabooksellers
YouTube: www.youtube.com/channel/UC3EjWgxicToWB5Ipgo6Hgkw
Description: Promotes excellence in publishing, distribution, promotion and selling of books. Provides a forum for information exchange; fosters a sense of community among booksellers; provides information and services for the advancement of members; promotes literacy; and supports the First Amendment rights of members. **Founded:** 1989. **Publications:** *Books for Holiday Giving* (Annual); *Great Lakes Bookseller* (Weekly); *Directory and Handbook* (Annual). **Geographic Preference:** National.

1805 ■ **Independent College Bookstore Association (ICBA)**
134 N LaSalle St., Ste. 225
Chicago, IL 60602
Free: 800-888-9222
Co. E-mail: office@icbainc.com
URL: http://icbainc.com
Contact: Ann Floresca, President
E-mail: floresca@union.edu
Facebook: www.facebook.com/ICBAinc
Linkedin: www.linkedin.com/company/independent-college-bookstore-association
Instagram: www.instagram.com/icbainc
Pinterest: www.pinterest.com/icbainc
Description: Provides education, networking, and vendor programs for owners of independent college bookstores. Hosts an annual conference. **Founded:** 1927.

1806 ■ **Institute of Communication Agencies (ICA)**
2300 Yonge St., Ste. 3002
Toronto, ON, Canada M4P 1E4
Ph: (437)351-0585
Co. E-mail: ica@icacanada.ca
URL: http://theica.ca
Contact: Scott Knox, President
E-mail: scott@theica.ca
Linkedin: www.linkedin.com/company/institute-of-canadian-agencies
X (Twitter): x.com/icacanada
Instagram: www.instagram.com/theicacanada
YouTube: www.youtube.com/user/TheICAcanada
Description: Aims to represent advertising agencies in a wide variety of beneficial activities. **Founded:** 1905. **Geographic Preference:** National.

1807 ■ **International League of Antiquarian Booksellers (ILAB)**
First Floor
21 John St.
London WC1N 2BF, United Kingdom
Co. E-mail: info@pontesmaps.com
URL: http://ilab.org
Contact: Sally Burdon, President
E-mail: sally@asiabookroom.com
Facebook: www.facebook.com/ILABBooksellers
Instagram: www.instagram.com/ilab_booksellers_worldwide
Description: Represents national associations of antiquarian booksellers around the world. Organizes professional training courses for members. Sponsors book fairs. **Founded:** 1947. **Educational Activities:** ILAB Congress (Biennial). **Awards:** Breslauer Prize for Bibliography (Periodic). **Geographic Preference:** National.

1808 ■ **National Association of College Stores (NACS)**
National Association of College Stores (NACS)
500 E Lorain St.
Oberlin, OH 44074
Free: 800-622-7498
Co. E-mail: info@nacs.org
URL: http://www.nacs.org
Contact: Andy Dunn, President
E-mail: andy.dunn@gcu.edu
Facebook: www.facebook.com/NACSorg

Linkedin: www.linkedin.com/company/national
-association-of-college-stores
X (Twitter): x.com/nacsorg
Description: Association that provides goods and services to campus stores. **Founded:** 1923. **Publications:** *Campus Marketplace* (Weekly); *The College Store (CS)* (Bimonthly); *NACS Directory of Colleges and College Stores* (Annual); *NACS Directory of Publishers* (Biennial); *Instructional Resources for Faculty* (Biennial); *The College Store--Buyers' Guide Issue* (Annual); *NACS Book Buyers Manual* (Annual); *Schedule of College and University Dates* (Annual). **Educational Activities:** CAMEX (Annual); NACS Campus Market Expo (NACS CAMEX) (Annual). **Geographic Preference:** National.

1809 ■ **Women's National Book Association (WNBA)**
PO Box 237, FDR Sta.
New York, NY 10150
Free: 866-610-9622
Co. E-mail: info@wnba-books.org
URL: http://wnba-books.org
Contact: Natalie Obando-Desai, President
Facebook: www.facebook.com/WomensNa
  tionalBookAssociation
X (Twitter): x.com/WNBA_National
Instagram: www.instagram.com/wnba_books
YouTube: www.youtube.com/channel/UCFQ
  -43NoUKQwM6fPJpzzLtg
Description: Women and men who work with and value books. Exists to promote reading and to support the role of women in the book community. **Founded:** 1917. **Publications:** *The Bookwoman* (Monthly); *The Bookwoman* (Monthly). **Awards:** WNBA Pannell Award (Annual); WNBA Eastman Grant (Annual); The WNBA Award (Annual); WNBA Eastman Grants (Annual). **Geographic Preference:** National.

REFERENCE WORKS

1810 ■ *"Africa Rising" in Harvard Business Review (Vol. 86, September 2008, No. 9, pp. 36)*
Pub: Harvard Business Review Press
Contact: Moderna V. Pfizer, Contact
Ed: Vijay Mahajan. **Description:** Review of the book entitled, "Africa Rising: How 900 Million African Consumers Offer More Than You Think" provides advice for marketing to those on the African continent. **Availability:** Print; Online.

1811 ■ *"Amazon Was Supposed to Have Crushed Bookstores. So Why Are Indie Bookshops Booming in D.C.?" in wamu.org (July 6, 2017)*
Ed: Ally Schweitzer. **Released:** July 06, 2017. **Description:** Examines why Amazon isn't doing as well as they should in the bookselling industry, and how indie bookstores are filling that void. **Availability:** Online.

1812 ■ *"Assessing the Health of Independent Bookshops" in The New York Times (February 25, 2015)*
URL(s): www.nytimes.com/2015/02/26/arts/interna
  tional/assessing-the-health-of-independent-book-
  shops.html
Ed: Stephen Heyman. **Released:** February 25, 2015. **Description:** The health of indie bookstores varies from one country to the next, with some showing growth while others have a decline. Some stores in Europe have remained constant due to a law that fixes the prices of all new books, regardless of who sells it. That keeps large chains from offering deep discounts and forcing small stores out of business. Across the pond in America, indie booksellers are filling the void left by the big box chains once they went bust. **Availability:** Online.

1813 ■ *"Bad Reviews Can Boost Sales. Here's Why" in Harvard Business Review (Vol. 90, April 2012, No. 4, pp. 28)*
Pub: Harvard Business Review Press
Contact: Moderna V. Pfizer, Contact
Ed: Jonah Berger. **Price:** $6. **Description:** Research on positive and negative book reviews found that sales increased for books with bad reviews, as the review itself made people aware of a work they would not have otherwise known about. **Availability:** Online; PDF.

1814 ■ *"Book Industry Supply Chain Delays to Impact Holiday Season" in American Booksellers Association (August 19, 2021)*
Ed: Emily Behnke. **Released:** August 19, 2021. **Description:** It takes many steps and adjacent industries to get books on shelves, such as trucking and warehousing. Expect delays in the book supply chain as the COVID-19 pandemic rages on and disruptions are common. **Availability:** Online.

1815 ■ *"The Book On Indigo" in Canadian Business (Vol. 81, July 22, 2008, No. 12-13, pp. 29)*
Description: Indigo Books & Music Inc. reported record sales of $922 million resulting in a record net profit of $52.8 million for the 2008 fiscal year ended March 29, 2008. Earnings per share were $2.13, greater than Standard & Poor's expected $1.70 per share. Additional information concerning Indigo Books is presented.

1816 ■ *"Book Publishing is Growing" in Information Today (Vol. 28, October 2011, No. 9, pp. 10)*
Pub: Information Today Inc.
Contact: Thomas H. Hogan, President
Ed: Paula J. Hane. **Description:** U.S. book publishing industry is reporting growth in its sector, despite the poor economy. BookStats, a comprehensive statistical survey conducted on the modern publishing industry in the U.S. reported Americans are reading in all print and digital formats. In 2011, 114 million ebooks were sold and now account for 13.6 percent of revenue from adult fiction. In contrast, 603 million trade hardcover books (fiction and nonfiction) were sold in 2011, a 5.8 percent increase over 2008.

1817 ■ *"Book Sales Are Up This Year Over Last Year, and Physical Books Are Thriving" in Quartz (December 28, 2018)*
URL(s): qz.com/1510303/book-sales/
Ed: Natasha Frost. **Released:** December 28, 2018. **Description:** Contrary to what most people expect, indie bookstores are doing very well. More physical books are being bought and the between 2009 and 2015, the number of these stores grew by 35%. **Availability:** Online.

1818 ■ *"Bookstores Find Growth as 'Anchors of Authenticity'" in The New York Times (June 23, 2019)*
URL(s): www.nytimes.com/2019/06/23/business/in
  dependent-bookstores.html
Ed: Andria Cheng. **Released:** June 23, 2019. **Description:** Independent bookstores are fighting back against online bookstores by offering consumers something their electronic counterparts cannot: community. Author talks, open mic nights, and even cafes are helping owners keep the doors open and the lights on. **Availability:** Online.

1819 ■ *"Bookworms, Rejoice: Shakespeare & Co. Returns to the Upper West Side" in News 1 NY (November 28, 2018)*
URL(s): www.ny1.com/nyc/manhattan/news/2018/11/
  28/bookworms--rejoice--shakespeare---co--returns
  -to-the-upper-west-side#
Ed: Michael Scotto. **Released:** November 28, 2018. **Description:** After a big-chain bookstore forced it's closure, the small indie bookstore Shakespeare & Co. has made a comeback to the neighborhood. This is due to consumers choosing to buy physical books and and preferring to shop in a store rather than online. **Availability:** Online.

1820 ■ *"Boom and Bust in the Book Biz" in Canadian Business (Vol. 83, August 17, 2010, No. 13-14, pp. 16)*
Pub: Rogers Media Inc.
Contact: Neil Spivak, Chief Executive Officer
Ed: Jordan Timm. **Description:** Electronic book marketplace is booming with Amazon.com's e-book sales for the Kindle e-reader exceeding the hardcover sales. Kobo Inc. has registered early success with its Kobo e-reader and has partnered with Hong Kong telecom giant on an e-book store. **Availability:** Print; Online.

1821 ■ *Children's Books in Print*
Pub: R.R. Bowker L.L.C.
URL(s): www.greyhouse.com/Childrens-Books-In
  -Print
Price: $990, for Softcover. **Entries include:** Book entries--Title, subtitle, author(s), editor(s), illustrator(-s), publishing date, edition, price, binding, ISBN, LC number, publisher; Publisher entries--Name, address, phone, ISBN prefix. The material in "Children's Books in Print" is also available in subject-classified form in "Subject Guide to Children's Books in Print," also published in December. **Arrangement:** Alphabetical within each index. **Indexes:** Author, title, illustrator, award or prize, publisher. **Availability:** Print; PDF; Online.

1822 ■ *"Consignment Shop Offers Children's Clothes, Products" in Frederick News-Post (August 19, 2010)*
Pub: Frederick News-Post
Contact: Connie Hastings, Director
E-mail: chastings@newspost.com
Ed: Ed Waters, Jr. **Description:** Sweet Pea Consignments for Children offers used items for newborns to pre-teens. The shop carries name brand clothing as well as toys, books and baby products. **Availability:** Print; Online.

1823 ■ *"Copyright Clearance Center (CCC) Partnered with cSubs" in Information Today (Vol. 28, November 2011, No. 10, pp. 14)*
Description: Copyright Clearance Center (CCC) partnered with cSubs to integrate CCC's point-of-content licensing solution RightsLink Basic directly into cSubs workflow. The partnership will allow cSubs' customers a user-friendly process for obtaining permissions. Csubs is a corporate subscription management service for books, newspapers, and econtent. **Availability:** Online.

1824 ■ *The Everything Store: Jeff Bezos and the Age of Amazon*
Pub: Little, Brown and Company
Contact: Judy Clain, Editor-in-Chief
Released: October 15, 2013. **Price:** $28, hardcover; $30, audiobook CD; $24.98, audiobook downloadable; $12.99, e-book; $18, paperback; $30, hardcover(large print); $28. **Description:** Amazon.com started as a bookseller, a company delivering books through the mail. Today, the online store, offers a limitless selection of goods at competitively low prices. Profile of entrepreneur Jeff Bezos that outlines his endless pursuit of new markets and risky new ventures to transform retail. **Availability:** audiobook; CD-ROM; E-book; Print.

1825 ■ *"Gadget Makers Aim for New Chapter in Reading" in Crain's Cleveland Business (Vol. 28, October 22, 2007, No. 42, pp. 20)*
Pub: Crain Communications Inc.
Contact: K. C. Crain, President
Ed: Jennifer McKevitt. **Description:** Although e-books and e-audiobooks are becoming more popular, e-readers, devices that display digital books, still haven't caught on with the public. Experts feel that consumers, many of whom have to look at a computer screen all day for work, still like the feel of a real book in their hands. **Availability:** Online.

1826 ■ *"A Good Book Is Worth a Thousand Blogs" in Barron's (Vol. 88, July 14, 2008, No. 28, pp. 42)*
Pub: Dow Jones & Company Inc.
Contact: Almar Latour, Chief Executive Officer
Ed: Gene Epstein. **Description:** Nine summer book suggestions on economics are presented. The list includes 'The Revolution' by Ron Paul, 'The Forgot-

ten Man' by Amity Shales, 'The Commitments of Traders Bible' by Stephen Briese, and 'Economic Facts and Fallacies' by Thomas Sowell. **Availability:** Online.

1827 ■ *"A Gripping Read: Bargains & Noble"* *in Barron's (Vol. 88, March 17, 2008, No. 11, pp. 20)*

Pub: Dow Jones & Company Inc.

Contact: Almar Latour, Chief Executive Officer

Ed: Jonathan R. Laing. **Description:** Barnes & Noble's earnings forecast for the fiscal year ending in January, 2008 to be $1.70 to $1.90 per share which is way lower than the $2.12 analyst consensus. The company also said that sales at stores one-year old or older dropped 0.5 percent in the fourth quarter. However, the shares are now cheap at 4.9 times enterprise value with some analysts putting a price target of 41 per share. **Availability:** Online.

1828 ■ *"Indie Bookstores Flourish in an Amazon World" in Axios (January 12, 2019)*

URL(s): www.axios.com/what-amazon-could-learn -from-local-bookstores-0bf14ed9-32a7-4cbd-b5a7 -8ade3575998d.html

Released: January 12, 2019. **Description:** Independent bookstores have been secretly thriving, even when online retailers took over the industry. Print sales continue to rise, and e-book sales are dropping. Indie bookstores offer experiences, events, and a rich environment that people cannot find online.

1829 ■ *"Interactive Stores a Big Part of Borders' Turnaround Plan" in Crain's Detroit Business (Vol. 24, February 18, 2008, No. 7, pp. 4)*

Pub: Crain Communications Inc.

Contact: Barry Asin, President

Ed: Nathan Skid. **Description:** Borders Group Inc. is using digital technology and interactive media as a part of the firm's turnaround plan. The digital store will allow shoppers to create CDs, download audio books, publish their own works, print photos and search family genealogy. **Availability:** Online.

1830 ■ *The Library and Book Trade Almanac*

Pub: Information Today Inc.

Contact: Thomas H. Hogan, President

URL(s): store.infotoday.com/product/the-library-an d-book-trade-almanac

Released: Annual; latest edition 68th; 2023. **Price:** $339.50, U.S.; $371.50, for outside north America; $361.50, for Canada or Mexico; $339.50, for annual. **Description:** Publication includes lists of accredited library schools; scholarships for education in library science; library organizations; library statistics; publishing and bookselling organizations. Includes lists of notable books, best-sellers, literary prize winners; library and trade statistics; calendar of events. **Entries include:** Directory listings give name of institution, address, phone, fax, name of officer or contact, publications; scholarship listings include requirements, value of grant, contact name. Principal content is articles and special reports on topics of interest to those in library/information science and publishers; international reports; annual reports from federal agencies and libraries and from national associations; information on legislation, funding, etc. **Arrangement:** Topical. **Indexes:** Organization; subject. **Availability:** Print; Online.

1831 ■ *"Literati Bookstore Marks a New Chapter for Ann Arbor" in Forbes (February 6, 2018)*

URL(s): www.forbes.com/sites/rebeccalerner/2018/0 2/06/literati-bookstore-marks-a-new-chapter-for-ann -arbor/#53eda6264335

Ed: Rebecca Lerner. **Released:** February 06, 2018. **Description:** Profile of Literati, a small indie bookstore that opened in 2013 in Ann Arbor. The success of the store is based on not only a personal connection with its customers, but an online one as well. **Availability:** Online.

1832 ■ *"Local Independent Bookstore Owners Find Success With Author Events, Personal Touch" in Crain's Detroit Business (January 22, 2017)*

Released: January 22, 2017. **Description:** A tour of several small independent bookstores operating within Detroit. Defying online retailers and big chains, these stores are thriving in local neighborhoods and helping to stitch together a community with local events and supporting local authors. **Availability:** Online.

1833 ■ *"Negotiating Tips" in Black Enterprise (Vol. 37, December 2006, No. 5, pp. 70)*

Pub: Earl G. Graves Ltd.

Contact: Earl Graves, Jr., President

Ed: Marcia A. Reed-Woodard. **Description:** Sekou Kaalund, head of strategy, mergers & acquisitions at Citigroup Securities & Fund Services, states that "Negotiation skills are paramount to success in a business environment because of client, employee, and shareholder relationships". He discusses how the book by George Kohlrieser, Hostage at the Table: How Leaders Can Overcome Conflict, Influence Others, and Raise Performance, has helped him negotiate more powerfully and enhance his skills at conflict-resolution. **Availability:** Online.

1834 ■ *"New Book Takes Alternate View on Ontario's Wind Industry" in CNW Group (September 19, 2011)*

Pub: CNW Group Ltd.

Description: Dirty Business: The Reality Behind Ontario's Rush to Wind Power, was written by editor and health care writer Jane Wilson of Ottawa, Ontario, Canada along with contributing editor Parker Gallant. The book contains articles and papers on the wind business, including information on illnesses caused from the environmental noise. **Availability:** Print; Online.

1835 ■ *"Online Book Sales Surpass Bookstores" in Information Today (Vol. 28, September 2011, No. 8, pp. 11)*

Pub: Information Today Inc.

Contact: Thomas H. Hogan, President

Ed: Cindy Martine. **Description:** Online book sales outpaced bookstore purchases in the United States, signaling a shift in the US book industry. Statistical data included.

1836 ■ *Publishers Directory*

Pub: Gale, part of Cengage Group

Contact: Paul Gazzolo, General Manager Senior Vice President

URL(s): www.gale.com/ebooks/9780028670133/pub lishers-directory

Description: Covers over 20,000 new and established, commercial and nonprofit, private and alternative, corporate and association, government and institution publishing programs and their distributors; includes producers of books, classroom materials, prints, reports, and databases. **Entries include:** Firm name, address, phone, fax, company e-mail address, URL, year founded, ISBN prefix, Standard Address Number, whether firm participates in the Cataloging in Publication program of the Library of Congress, names of principal executives, personal e-mail addresses, number of titles in print, description of firm and its main subject interests, discount and returns policies, affiliated and parent companies, mergers and amalgamations, principal markets, imprints and divisions, alternate formats products are offered; distributors also list firms for which they distribute, special services, terms to publishers and regional offices. **Arrangement:** Alphabetical; distributors listed separately. **Indexes:** Subject, geographical, publisher, imprints, and distributor. **Availability:** Large print; CD-ROM; E-book; Online; DVD; Download. **Type:** Directory.

1837 ■ *"Scarsdale's Bronx River Books the Latest in Independent Bookstore Comeback" in Westchester Journal News (December 6, 2018)*

URL(s): www.lohud.com/story/news/local/westches ter/scarsdale/2018/12/06/bronx-river-books-scars dale-new-independent-bookstore-westchester/2160 552002/

Ed: Jason Chirevas. **Released:** December 06, 2018. **Description:** Profile of Bronx River Books, which recently opened in Scarsdale, and filling a void left by the last bookstore when it closed eight years ago. Owners Mark Fowler and Jessica Kaplan put in a lot of effort and time to create this indie bookstore and to make it a success. **Availability:** Online.

1838 ■ *"School Uses Book Vending Machine to Get Kids Reading" in U.S. News & World Report (November 23, 2019)*

URL(s): www.usnews.com/news/best-states/south -dakota/articles/2019-11-23/school-uses-book-ven ding-machine-to-get-kids-reading

Ed: Shelly Conlon. **Released:** November 23, 2019. **Description:** An innovative new vending machine is a big hit with kids, not because it is dispensing candy but because it is dispensing books. Inchy, the Bookwarm Vending Machine, was installed in the John Harris Elementary school and doesn't take money, but does uses special coins that kids use when they earned a good deed award at school. It's led to a higher interest in reading and the students are excited to be part of something new and unique. **Availability:** Online.

1839 ■ *"Web Tax Holiday About to End" in Silicon Valley/San Jose Business Journal (Vol. 30, September 7, 2012, No. 24, pp. 1)*

Pub: Baltimore Business Journal

Contact: Rhonda Pringle, President

E-mail: rpringle@bizjournals.com

Description: Retailers outside California will be required to charge sales tax to customers in the state making online purchases. It is believed that the sales tax will provide an additional boost for independent booksellers. These sellers claim that they have been at a disadvantage becazuse they were required to automatically charge customers with an 8.375 percent tax. **Availability:** Print; Mailing list; Online.

1840 ■ *"What Slump? Davis Likely to Fill Borders Gap Quickly" in Sacramento Business Journal (Vol. 28, July 29, 2011, No. 22, pp. 1)*

Pub: Sacramento Business Journal

Contact: Stephanie Fretwell, Director

E-mail: sfretwell@bizjournals.com

Ed: Kelly Johnson. **Description:** The nationwide shutdown of Borders bookstores worry most cities, but not Davis, California, which is experiencing a relatively low retail vacancy rate of 6.3 percent. **Availability:** Online.

STATISTICAL SOURCES

1841 ■ *Book Stores Industry in the US - Market Research Report*

URL(s): www.ibisworld.com/united-states/market-re search-reports/book-stores-industry/

Price: $925. **Description:** Downloadable report analyzing the current and future trends in the book store industry. **Availability:** Download.

1842 ■ *RMA Annual Statement Studies*

Pub: Risk Management Association

Contact: Nancy Foster, President

Released: Annual. **Description:** Contains composite balance sheets and income statements for more than 360 industries, including the accounting, auditing, and bookkeeping industries. Also contains five years of comparative historical data for discerning trends. Includes 16 commonly used ratios, computed for most of the size groupings for nearly every industry.

TRADE PERIODICALS

1843 ■ *Forecast*

Pub: Baker & Taylor, Inc.

Contact: Amandeep Kochar, President

URL(s): cloud.e.baker-taylor.com/subscription-center

Ed: Charles Pizar. **Description:** Prepublication announcement magazine for booksellers and librarians containing bibliographic data and descriptions for new and forthcoming adult hardcover books. **Availability:** Online.

1844 ■ Publishers Weekly: The International voice for Book Publishing and Bookselling
Pub: Publishers Weekly
Contact: George Slowik, Jr., President
URL(s): www.publishersweekly.com/pw/corp/aboutus.html
Facebook: www.facebook.com/pubweekly
Linkedin: www.linkedin.com/company/publishers-weekly
X (Twitter): x.com/PublishersWkly
Instagram: www.instagram.com/pwpics
Ed: Michael Coffey. **Released:** Weekly **Price:** $199, for print and online; $169, for online and digital; $9.99, for back issues; $15, for online and digital monthly; $20, for print and online monthly. **Description:** Magazine for publishers. **Availability:** Print; Online.

VIDEO/AUDIO MEDIA

1845 ■ Main Street Business Insights: Katie Pinard and Michael Macomber, Elements: Coffee Books Beer
URL(s): mainstreet.org/resources/knowledge-hub/podcast/katie-pinard-and-michael-macomber-elements-coffee-books-beer
Ed: Matt Wagner. **Released:** June 19, 2024. **Description:** Podcast discusses the impact of business on community, staff management, and small business grants.

TRADE SHOWS AND CONVENTIONS

1846 ■ BookExpo America
American Booksellers Association, Inc. (ABA)
333 Westchester Ave., Ste. S202
White Plains, NY 10604
Free: 800-637-0037
Fax: (914)417-4013
Co. E-mail: info@bookweb.org
URL: http://www.bookweb.org
Contact: Bradley Graham, President
URL(s): www.bookweb.org/events
Facebook: www.facebook.com/bookexpoamerica
X (Twitter): twitter.com/BookExpoAmerica
Frequency: Annual. **Description:** For bookseller members with exhibit portion owned and managed by Reed Expositions. **Audience:** Publishers, librarians, retailers, booksellers, digital content creators, traditional and self-published authors, media, rights, professionals, and movie and television executives. **Principal Exhibits:** For bookseller members with exhibit portion owned and managed by Reed Expositions.

1847 ■ Boston International Antiquarian Book Fair
Antiquarian Booksellers Association of the United Kingdom (ABA)
First Fl., 21 John St.
London WC1N 2BF, United Kingdom
Ph: 44 20 8004 9512
Co. E-mail: admin@aba.org.uk
URL: http://aba.org.uk
Contact: Pom Harrington, President
URL(s): aba.org/bostonbookfair
Facebook: www.facebook.com/BostonBookFair
Frequency: Annual. **Description:** Rare books, collectibles, modern first editions, autographs, maps, atlases, manuscripts, and related articles. **Audience:** Book lovers and collectors. **Principal Exhibits:** Rare books, collectibles, modern first editions, autographs, maps, atlases, manuscripts, and related articles.

1848 ■ Christian Booksellers Association International Convention
CBA: The Association for Christian Retail (CBA)
1365 Garden of the Gods Rd., Ste. 105
Colorado Springs, CO 80907
URL: http://cbaonline.org
URL(s): cbaunite.com
Frequency: Annual. **Description:** Christian bookstore merchandise, including literature, music, gifts, cards, jewelry, and curricula. **Audience:** Industry professionals. **Principal Exhibits:** Christian bookstore merchandise, including literature, music, gifts, cards, jewelry, and curricula.

1849 ■ ICBA Conference & PRIMEtime
URL(s): icbainc.com/conference
Frequency: Annual. **Description:** Offers professional development, networking, plus buyer an vendor meetings for independent college bookstore owners. **Principal Exhibits:** Offers professional development, networking, plus buyer an vendor meetings for independent college bookstore owners. **Telecommunication Services:** Office@ICBAinc.com.

PUBLICATIONS

1850 ■ Book Business
1500 Spring Garden St., Ste. 1200
Philadelphia, PA 19130
Ph: (215)238-5300
Free: 800-627-2689
Co. E-mail: customerservice@napco.com
URL: http://www.napco.com
Contact: Mark J. Subers, President
E-mail: msubers@napco.com
URL(s): www.bookbusinessmag.com
X (Twitter): twitter.com/BookBusinessmag
Description: Magazine publishing information about book production and manufacturing. **Availability:** Print; Online. **Type:** Full-text; Directory; Numeric.

COMPUTERIZED DATABASES

1851 ■ The Title Source™ III
Baker & Taylor, Inc.
2810 Coliseum Ctr. Dr., Ste. 300
Charlotte, NC 28217
Ph: (704)998-3100
Free: 800-775-1800
Co. E-mail: btinfo@baker-taylor.com
URL: http://www.baker-taylor.com
Contact: Amandeep Kochar, President
URL(s): www.baker-taylor.com/library-solutions/books-av-content/axis-360
Availability: Online. **Type:** Bibliographic; Numeric.

LIBRARIES

1852 ■ Grolier Club of New York Library
47 E 60th St.
New York, NY 10022
Ph: (212)838-6690
Fax: (212)838-2445
Co. E-mail: assistantlibrarian@grolierclub.org
URL: http://www.grolierclub.org/Default.aspx?p=DynamicModule&pageid=384831&ssid=322452&vnf=1
Contact: Meghan Constantinou, Librarian
E-mail: mconstantinou@grolierclub.org
Facebook: www.facebook.com/grolierclub
X (Twitter): x.com/GrolierClub
Instagram: www.instagram.com/grolierclub
Scope: Art and history; literature. **Services:** Library open to the public with restrictions. **Founded:** 1884. **Holdings:** 100,000 volumes; 5,000 prints and portraits; bookplates. **Subscriptions:** 100 journals and other serials.

1853 ■ Villanova University - Falvey Memorial Library Special Collections
Falvey Library Villanova University, 800 Lancaster Ave.
Villanova, PA 19085
URL: http://library.villanova.edu/collections/distinctive/specialcollections
Contact: Michael P. Foight, Director, Collections
E-mail: michael.foight@villanova.edu
Scope: Educational material; local history. **Services:** Interlibrary loan; copying; library open to the public. **Holdings:** 500,000 volumes;35,000 electronic journals and 3,500 print journals.

Bottled Water Service

ASSOCIATIONS AND OTHER ORGANIZATIONS

1854 ■ **International Bottled Water Association (IBWA)**
1700 Diagonal Rd., Ste. 650
Alexandria, VA 22314
Ph: (703)683-5213
Free: 800-WAT-ER11
Co. E-mail: ibwainfo@bottledwater.org
URL: http://www.bottledwater.org
Contact: Joseph Doss, President
Facebook: www.facebook.com/bottledwatermatters
X (Twitter): x.com/BottledWaterOrg
Instagram: www.instagram.com/bottledwatermatters
YouTube: www.youtube.com/user/BottledWaterMatters
Pinterest: www.pinterest.com/luvbottledwater
Description: Unifies the bottled water industry and represents uncompromising commitment to the safety and availability of bottled water worldwide. **Founded:** 1958. **Publications:** Bottled Water Reporter (Bimonthly); International Bottled Water Association--Membership Directory; IBWA Audit Handbook; IBWA Membership Roster (Annual). **Educational Activities:** IBWA Convention & Tradeshow (Annual). **Awards:** IBWA Aqua Awards (Annual); Bottled Water Hall of Fame (Annual). **Geographic Preference:** Multinational.

REFERENCE WORKS

1855 ■ *"12 Facts That Show Shy Bottled Water Is One of the Biggest Scams of the Century" in Business Insider (March 20, 2019)*
URL(s): www.businessinsider.com/bottled-water-facts-science-healthy-2017-4
Ed: Erin Brodwin, Aylin Woodward. **Released:** March 20, 2019. **Description:** Examines the cost of using bottled water, not only for consumers but for the environment. With millions of people worldwide who do not have access to clean water, do we really need to use bottled water when 99.2% of us have access to clean tap water?. **Availability:** Online.

1856 ■ *"Agana To Bottle Rain for Whole Foods" in Austin Business Journal (Vol. 32, March 30, 2012, No. 4, pp. 1)*
Pub: American City Business Journals, Inc.
Contact: Mike Olivieri, Executive Vice President
Ed: Vicky Garza. **Description:** Agana Rainwater has signed a deal to bottle rainwater for Whole Foods Market Inc. Rainwater bottling is seen as a conservation tools as it does not deplete the lake or aquifier. **Availability:** Online.

1857 ■ *"Arsenic in Some Bottled Water Brands at Unsafe Levels, Consumer Reports Say" in Consumer Reports (June 28, 2019)*
URL(s): www.consumerreports.org/water-quality/arsenic-in-some-bottled-water-brands-at-unsafe-levels/
Ed: Ryan Felton. **Released:** June 28, 2019. **Description:** Investigation of bottled water, which should be cleaner than tap water, but after reviewing public records and test reports it was found that several popular brands sell bottled water with worrisome arsenic levels. **Availability:** Online.

1858 ■ *"Eco-Preneuring" in Small Business Opportunities (Feb. 6, 2012)*
Pub: Harris Publishing, Inc.
Contact: Janet Chase, Contact
Description: Iceland Naturally is a joint marketing effort among tourism and business interests hoping to increase demand for Icelandic products including frozen seafood, bottled water, agriculture, and tourism in North America.

1859 ■ *"Nestlé Makes Billions Bottling Water It Pays Nearly Nothing For" in Bloomberg (September 27, 2017)*
Ed: Caroline Winter. **Released:** September 22, 2017. **Description:** Examines how Néstle, the world's largest food and beverage company, has come to dominate the bottled water industry. Seeking out areas with lax water regulations, it pumps water from local watersheds and wells to bottle. Controversy is rising in Michigan, as Néstle applies for a permit to more than double its pumping rate. **Availability:** Online.

1860 ■ *"Newark Phasing Out Bottled Water in Wake of Filter Tests" in The New York Times (October 4, 2019)*
URL(s): www.nytimes.com/aponline/2019/10/04/us/ap-us-newark-lead-in-water.html
Released: October 04, 2019. **Description:** Residents in Neward received bottled water starting in August after lead tested high with homes with lead pipes. After extensive testing of the city-issued filters, the lead levels have dropped. **Availability:** Online.

1861 ■ *"Plastic Particles Found in Bottled Water" in BBC (March 15, 2018)*
URL(s): www.bbc.com/news/science-environment-43388870
Ed: David Shukman. **Released:** March 15, 2018. **Description:** A professor of chemistry at the State University of New York in Fredonia, Sherri Mason, conducted a test on 250 bottles of water from nine countries and found an average of 10 plastic participles per liter. While the effects of ingesting plastic are not fully known, plastic use and waste has become a big issue as pollution concerns continue to rise. **Availability:** Online.

1862 ■ *"A Precious Resource: Investing In the Fate of Fresh Water" in Black Enterprise (Vol. 38, February 2008, No. 7, pp. 44)*
Pub: Earl G. Graves Ltd.
Contact: Earl Graves, Jr., President
Ed: Charles Keenan. **Description:** Despite rising oil prices, water may become the most precious commodity in years to come because the world's supply of drinkable water is dwindling. **Availability:** Online.

1863 ■ *"Thirsty? Now There's a Water Cooler to Suit Every Taste" in Inc. (Vol. 33, October 2011, No. 8, pp. 43)*
Description: Brita's Hydration Station is a wall-mounted unit with a touch-free sensor for dispensing water. This water cooler cuts down on landfill waste and offers special features. **Availability:** Print; Online.

STATISTICAL SOURCES

1864 ■ *The Bottled Water Market*
Description: An in-depth examination of the size and projected growth (to 2014) of the bottled water market, covering both domestic and imported products. **Availability:** Online.

TRADE PERIODICALS

1865 ■ *Bottled Water Reporter*
Pub: International Bottled Water Association
Contact: Joseph Doss, President
URL(s): bottledwater.org/ibwa-history
Released: Bimonthly **Description:** Magazine for bottled water industry. **Availability:** Print; Online.

TRADE SHOWS AND CONVENTIONS

1866 ■ **IBWA Convention & Tradeshow**
International Bottled Water Association (IBWA)
1700 Diagonal Rd., Ste. 650
Alexandria, VA 22314
Ph: (703)683-5213
Free: 800-WAT-ER11
Co. E-mail: ibwainfo@bottledwater.org
URL: http://www.bottledwater.org
Contact: Joseph Doss, President
URL(s): conference.bottledwater.org
Frequency: Annual. **Description:** Bottled water industry supplies and equipment. **Audience:** Bottled water company executives and industry professionals. **Principal Exhibits:** Bottled water industry supplies and equipment. **Telecommunication Services:** conferenceinfo@bottledwater.org.

FRANCHISES AND BUSINESS OPPORTUNITIES

1867 ■ **Water Depot (WD)**
92 Commerce Pk. Dr., Unit 2
Barrie, ON, Canada L4N 8W8
Ph: (705)735-6642
Co. E-mail: info@waterdepotinc.com
URL: http://waterdepot.com
Facebook: www.facebook.com/waterdepot
Linkedin: www.linkedin.com/in/water-depot-6551571a3
YouTube: www.youtube.com/channel/UCPZmtXGLkqsbE9N2RpDIF0g

Description: To provide safe drinking water in Ontario. **Founded:** 1989. **Franchise Fee:** $25,000. **Training:** Ongoing Water Depot College and University courses, seminars, question and answer Sessions and events.

1868 ■ World of Water International Ltd.
326 Keewatin St.
  Winnipeg, MB, Canada R2X 2R9
Ph: (204)774-7770
Free: 866-749-1146
Fax: (204)772-5051
Co. E-mail: info@worldofwater.ca
URL: http://www.worldofwater.ca
Contact: Ken Mittelstadt, President

Facebook: www.facebook.com/WorldofWater
Instagram: www.instagram.com/worldofwaterwpg
Description: Retailer of bottled water. **Founded:** 1976. **Training:** Yes.

LIBRARIES

1869 ■ The Coca-Cola Company
The Coca-Cola Company
  1 Coca-Cola Plz.
  Atlanta, GA 30313
Ph: (404)676-2121
Free: 800-438-2653
Co. E-mail: press@coca-cola.com
URL: http://www.coca-colacompany.com
Contact: John Murphy, President
Facebook: www.facebook.com/TheCocaColaCo
Linkedin: www.linkedin.com/company/the-coca-cola
  -company
X (Twitter): twitter.com/CocaCola
Instagram: www.instagram.com/cocacola
YouTube: www.youtube.com/user/CocaColaCo

Description: Producer and distributor of non-alcoholic beverages such as juices, ready-to-drink teas and coffees, sport, dairy and energy drinks. **Founded:** 1886. **Educational Activities:** GSF West; Sunshine Expo (Annual); Big Iron Farm Show and Exhibition (Annual).

Bowling Alley

ASSOCIATIONS AND OTHER ORGANIZATIONS

1870 ■ Billiard and Bowling Institute of America (BBIA)
621 Six Flags Dr.
  Arlington, TX 76011
Ph: (817)385-8441
Co. E-mail: bill@ibpsia.com
URL: http://billiardandbowling.org
Contact: Andy Brenneman, President
E-mail: andy@bowlerssupply.com
Description: Represents distributors and manufacturers of billiard and bowling equipment. **Founded:** 1940. **Publications:** *BBIA enews* (Monthly); *BBIA Membership and Product Information Guide* (Annual). **Educational Activities:** BBIA Convention (Annual); BBIA Convention (Annual). **Awards:** BBIA Industry Service Award (Annual). **Geographic Preference:** National.

1871 ■ Bowl Canada
1845 Sandstone Manor, Unit 13
  Pickering, ON, Canada L1W 3X9
Ph: (905)479-1560
Fax: (905)479-8613
Co. E-mail: info@bowlcanada.ca
URL: http://bowlcanada.ca
Contact: Ray Brittain, President
E-mail: ray@bowlcanada.ca
Facebook: www.facebook.com/Bowl-Canada-70 3790949700789
X (Twitter): x.com/bowlcanada
Instagram: www.instagram.com/bowlcanada
YouTube: www.youtube.com/bowlcanada
Pinterest: www.pinterest.com/bowlcanada
Description: Owners of bowling alleys. Promotes increased participation in recreational and competitive bowling. Represents members' interests before business and labor organizations, government agencies, and the public. Conducts promotional activities. **Geographic Preference:** National.

1872 ■ Bowling Proprietors Association of America (BPAA)
621 Six Flags Dr.
  Arlington, TX 76011
Free: 800-343-1329
Co. E-mail: answer@bpaa.com
URL: http://bpaa.com
Contact: Kevin Krauss, President
E-mail: kevin@seminolelanes.com
Facebook: www.facebook.com/bowling.proprietors
X (Twitter): x.com/bowlexpo
Description: Firm represents proprietors of bowling establishments. **Founded:** 1932. **Publications:** *Bowling Proprietor* (Bimonthly); *Talking Human Resources*; *Bowling Center Management* (Monthly). **Educational Activities:** International Bowl Expo (Annual). **Awards:** V. A. Wapensky Award (Annual); Victor Lerner Memorial Medal (Annual); BPAA President's Medal (Annual). **Geographic Preference:** National.

1873 ■ The National Bowling Association Inc. (TNBA)
9944 Reading Rd.
  Evendale, OH 45241-3106
Ph: (513)769-1985
Fax: (513)769-3596
Co. E-mail: nationaloffice@tnbainc.org
URL: http://tnbainc.org
Contact: Dewann G. Clark, President
E-mail: dewann.clark@tnbainc.org
Description: Seeks to foster good sportsmanship, fellowship, and friendship; increase the interests, talents, and skills of adult and youth bowlers; create national awareness and interest in civic and community programs. Promotes bowling tournaments and other activities. Sponsors fundraising programs for sickle cell anemia and the United Negro College Fund. **Founded:** 1939. **Publications:** *Souvenir Yearbook* (Annual); *Bowler* (3/year). **Geographic Preference:** National.

1874 ■ Professional Bowlers Association of America (PBA)
7313 Bell Creek
  Mechanicsville, VA 23111
URL: http://www.pba.com
Description: Professional bowlers. Promotes the status of the qualified bowler to the rank of professional and bowling as a major sport. **Founded:** 1958. **Awards:** Chris Schenkel PBA Player of the Year Award (Annual); PBA Hall of Fame (Annual); Harry Golden PBA Rookie of the Year Award (Annual); PBA50 Player of the Year Award (Annual); PBA50 Rookie of the Year Award (Annual). **Geographic Preference:** National.

1875 ■ United States Bowling Congress (USBC)
621 Six Flags Dr.
  Arlington, TX 76011
Free: 800-514-2695
Fax: (817)385-8260
Co. E-mail: bowlinfo@bowl.com
URL: http://www.bowl.com
Contact: Melissa Mcdaniel, President
E-mail: melissa.mcdaniel@bowl.com
Facebook: www.facebook.com/usbc
Instagram: www.instagram.com/usbowlingcongress
YouTube: www.youtube.com/BowlTV
Description: Aims to be the unified organization of choice focused on the growth of bowling. Ensures the integrity and protects the future of the sport, provides programs and services and enhances the bowling experience. **Publications:** *Bowling Magazine: Official Publication of American Bowling Congress* (Bimonthly); *US Bowler* (Monthly). **Awards:** USBC Writing Competition (Annual). **Geographic Preference:** National.

EDUCATIONAL PROGRAMS

1876 ■ Vincennes University (VU) - Byron R. Lewis Historical Collection Library
1002 N First St.
  Vincennes, IN 47591
Ph: (812)888-8888
Free: 800-742-9198
Co. E-mail: ithelpdesk@vinu.edu
URL: http://www.vinu.edu
Facebook: www.facebook.com/vincennesuniversity
Linkedin: www.linkedin.com/school/30770
X (Twitter): x.com/vincennesu
Instagram: www.instagram.com/vincennesu
YouTube: www.youtube.com/user/vinu1801
Description: Two-year college offering a program in business administration; small business management classes; and bowling lane management and technology. **Scope:** Governmental; business; genealogy. **Founded:** 1801. **Holdings:** Books; pamphlets; newspapers; art; artifacts; papers; records; photographs.

REFERENCE WORKS

1877 ■ "Hunt Valley Towne Center Gears Up for Growth; Ray Lewis Project Scrapped" in *Baltimore Business Journal* (Vol. 30, May 11, 2012, No. 1, pp. 1)
Pub: American City Business Journals, Inc.
Contact: Mike Olivieri, Executive Vice President
Ed: James Briggs. **Description:** Greenberg Gibbons Commercial Corporation has plans for a 400-unit apartment complex and retail space at Hunt Valley Towne Centre in Baltimore, Maryland. The developer is also considering big-box stores to rent the vacant space that was supposed to be occupied by the failed bowling and entertainment venture MVP Lanes. **Availability:** Print; Online.

1878 ■ "Is Bowling in Its Final Frames or Will It Roll On?" in *USA Today* (March 10, 2015)
URL(s): www.usatoday.com/story/money/business/20 15/05/10/bowling-final-frames-roll/27070351/
Released: May 10, 2015. **Description:** Examines what steps bowling alleys need to take in order to stay open and thrive. Newer alleys not only feature bowling, but also offer dining, bars, and other sources of entertainment. Older lanes are often being demolished as once-popular bowling leagues get smaller, but there's hope for newer lanes who establish themselves with catering to the walk-in bowler. **Availability:** Online.

1879 ■ "The Lost Art of Duckpin Bowling" in *The New York Times* (May 26, 2016)
URL(s): www.nytimes.com/2016/05/29/sports/duckpin-bowling.html
Ed: Dan Barry. **Released:** May 26, 2016. **Description:** Profile of duckpin bowling, a sport similar to regular bowling but the ball weighs less than four pounds and has no finger holes, and the pins are also smaller than traditional bowling pins. Most alleys for this game are closed, but Bisson Sykes, the women's top player, is still touring with the Duckpin women's league. **Availability:** Online.

1880 ■ *"No. 423: How a Date Led To al Bowling Juggernaut" in Inc. (Vol. 36, September 2014, No. 7, pp. 42)*
Pub: Mansueto Ventures L.L.C.
Contact: Stephanie Mehta, Chief Executive Officer

Released: September 2014. **Description:** Profile of Tom Shannon, entrepreneur who got the idea to buy a bowling alley following a date with a girl. The New York City-based Bowlmor is a 262-location bowling and entertainment venue that recently became an AMF bowling company. **Availability:** Print; Online.

STATISTICAL SOURCES

1881 ■ *RMA Annual Statement Studies*
Pub: Risk Management Association
Contact: Nancy Foster, President

Released: Annual. **Description:** Contains composite balance sheets and income statements for more than 360 industries, including the accounting, auditing, and bookkeeping industries. Also contains five years of comparative historical data for discerning trends. Includes 16 commonly used ratios, computed for most of the size groupings for nearly every industry.

TRADE PERIODICALS

1882 ■ *Bowlers Journal International (BJI)*
Pub: Luby Publishing Inc.
Contact: Keith Hamilton, President
E-mail: keithh@lubypublishing.com
URL(s): bowl.com/bowlers-journal-international
Facebook: www.facebook.com/BowlersJournal
X (Twitter): x.com/BowlersJournal
YouTube: www.youtube.com/channel/UCuT_RnhTcmlzOBOhLhPKnrg

Released: Monthly **Price:** $36, for print 1 year US or digital subscription only; $44, for print + online US 1 year; $54, for print 2 year US or digital subscription only; $61, for print 1 year international; $69, for print + online international; $70, for print 3 year US or digital subscription only; $70, for print + online US 2 year; $94, for print + online US 3 year; $104, for print 2 year international; $120, for print + online international; $145, for print 3 year international; $169, for print + online international. **Description:** Sports magazine - bowling's premier magazine. **Availability:** Print; Online.

TRADE SHOWS AND CONVENTIONS

1883 ■ **Bowling Proprietors Association of America International Bowl Expo**
URL(s): bpaa.com/bowlexpo
Facebook: www.facebook.com/bowlexpo
X (Twitter): twitter.com/bowlexpo
Instagram: www.instagram.com/bowlexpo

Frequency: Annual. **Description:** Tradeshow featuring products and services used in the bowling alley industry. Seminars provide education and useful information on how to run a bowling alley business. **Audience:** Bowling alley owners, arcade owners, and billiard hall owners. **Principal Exhibits:** Tradeshow featuring products and services used in the bowling alley industry. Seminars provide education and useful information on how to run a bowling alley business.

1884 ■ **International Bowl Expo**
Brunswick Bowling Products, LLC
525 W Laketon Ave.
Muskegon, MI 49441-2601
Ph: (231)725-4966
Free: 800-937-2695
Co. E-mail: inquiries@brunbowl.com
URL: http://www.brunswickbowling.com
URL(s): bpaa.com/bowlexpo
Facebook: www.facebook.com/bowlexpo
X (Twitter): twitter.com/bowlexpo
Instagram: www.instagram.com/bowlexpo

Frequency: Annual. **Description:** Equipment, supplies, and services for the bowling industry, Awards and Promotional Products, Financial and Insurance Services, Redemption Products. **Audience:** Industry Professionals. **Principal Exhibits:** Equipment, supplies, and services for the bowling industry, Awards and Promotional Products, Financial and Insurance Services, Redemption Products. Dates and Locations: 2025 Jun 29-Jul 03 Sheraton Washington, Washington, DC; 2025 Jun 29-Jul 03 Gaylord Rockies Resort & Convention Center, Denver, CO. **Telecommunication Services:** expo@bpaa.com.

Brewpub and Microbrewery

START-UP INFORMATION

1885 ■ *Brewing Up a Business: Adventures in Beer from the Founder of Dogfish Head Craft Brewery*
Pub: John Wiley & Sons, Inc.
Contact: Christina Van Tassell, Executive Vice President Chief Financial Officer
Ed: Sam Calagione. **Released:** 2nd Edition. **Price:** $18.95, paperback; $12.99, E-book. **Description:** Author shares nontraditional success secrets. Calgione began his business with a home brewing kit and grew it into Dogfish Head Craft Beer, the leading craft brewery in the U.S. **Availability:** E-book; Print.

ASSOCIATIONS AND OTHER ORGANIZATIONS

1886 ■ **American Beverage Institute (ABI)**
1090 Vermont Ave., NW
Washington, DC 20005
Ph: (202)463-7110
Co. E-mail: info@abionline.org
URL: http://abionline.org
Contact: Jackson Shedelbower, Contact
E-mail: shedelbower@abionline.org
Facebook: www.facebook.com/AmericanBeverageInstitute
Linkedin: www.linkedin.com/company/american-beverage-institute
Description: Provides public information regarding the consumption of adult beverages. Offers research and educational programs. **Founded:** 1991. **Geographic Preference:** National.

1887 ■ **American Breweriana Association Inc. (ABA) - Lending library**
PO Box 269
Manitowish Waters, WI 54545-0269
Ph: (715)604-2774
Co. E-mail: director@americanbreweriana.org
URL: http://www.americanbreweriana.org
Contact: Darrell Smith, Executive Director
E-mail: director@americanbreweriana.org
Facebook: www.facebook.com/groups/41311150282
Description: Promotes the interest of collectors of brewery advertising and antiques, brewery historians, breweries, beer distributors and retailers, industrial workers, and beer workers. Promotes public knowledge of brewing history. **Scope:** U. S. breweries. **Services:** Library open to the public. **Founded:** 1982. **Holdings:** Articles; videos; rare books; films; audio archives. **Publications:** *American Breweriana* (Bimonthly); *Directory of the American Breweriana Association* (Bimonthly). **Educational Activities:** American Breweriana Association Convention (Annual). **Geographic Preference:** National.

1888 ■ **Beer Canada - Library**
PO Box 654
Stittsville, ON, Canada K2S 1A7
Co. E-mail: cheers@beercanada.com
URL: http://www.beercanada.com
Contact: Roger Mittag, Contact
Facebook: www.facebook.com/BeerCanadaCheers
Linkedin: www.linkedin.com/company/beer-canada
X (Twitter): x.com/BeerCanada
Instagram: www.instagram.com/beercanadacheers
YouTube: www.youtube.com/channel/UCJY_Lw8 t5-Ru9NyHjbsp-TQ
Description: Promotes operation of microbreweries; seeks growth and development of the brewing industry. **Scope:** Beer; food; recipes. **Founded:** 1943. **Holdings:** Figures not available. **Publications:** *On Tap* (Bimonthly); *Statistical Bulletin* (Annual). **Geographic Preference:** National.

1889 ■ **Beer Institute**
440 1st. St. NW, Ste. 350
Washington, DC 20001
Ph: (202)737-2337
Free: 800-379-2739
Fax: (202)737-7004
Co. E-mail: info@beerinstitute.org
URL: http://www.beerinstitute.org
Contact: Jim McGreevy, President
E-mail: jmcgreevy@beerinstitute.org
Facebook: www.facebook.com/BeerInstitute
X (Twitter): x.com/beerinstitute
Instagram: www.instagram.com/beerinstitute
YouTube: www.youtube.com/channel/UCOx 5NuR8ZUL0K9QS2dvJJvQ
Description: Brewers, importers, and suppliers to the industry. Committed to the development of public policy and to the values of civic duty and personal responsibility. **Founded:** 1986. **Publications:** *Membership*; *Brewers Almanac* (Annual); *Beer Institute Bulletin* (Quarterly); *Brewing Industry in the U.S.: Brewers Almanac* (Annual). **Geographic Preference:** National.

1890 ■ **Brewers Association (BA)**
1327 Spruce St.
Boulder, CO 80302
Ph: (303)447-0816
Free: 888-822-6273
Co. E-mail: info@brewersassociation.org
URL: http://www.brewersassociation.org
Contact: Bob Pease, President
Facebook: www.facebook.com/BrewersAssoc
Linkedin: www.linkedin.com/company/brewers-association
X (Twitter): x.com/BrewersAssoc
Instagram: www.instagram.com/brewersassoc
YouTube: www.youtube.com/user/BrewersAssociation
Description: Represents micro and regional brewers of beer. Aims to promote and protect American Craft Beer and American Craft Brewers and the community of brewing enthusiasts. **Founded:** 1942. **Publications:** *Breweries Directory*; *The New Brewer* (Bimonthly); *Commercial Brewing Suppliers*; *Beer Distributors*; *Craft Beer Retailers*; *Brewers Resource Directory* (Annual); *BAA Bulletin* (8/year). **Educational Activities:** Craft-Brewers Conference Brew-Expo America (Annual). **Geographic Preference:** National.

1891 ■ **Brewers Association of Maryland (BAM)**
1783 Forest Dr., Ste. 343
Annapolis, MD 21401
Ph: (410)252-9463
Co. E-mail: info@marylandbeer.org
URL: http://marylandbeer.org
Contact: Brett Snyder, President
Facebook: www.facebook.com/BrewersAssocMD
X (Twitter): x.com/MDBrewers
Description: Promotes the hobby and enjoyment of brewing. Encourages sound brewing practices and advocates proper brewing techniques. Engages in social activities focused on home brewing. Promotes the responsible use of alcoholic beverages. **Founded:** 1996. **Geographic Preference:** State.

1892 ■ **Brewing and Malting Barley Research Institute - Library [BMBRI]**
c/o Gina Feist, Executive Director
PO Box 39120
Saskatoon, MB, Canada S7V 0A9
Ph: (306)370-1787
Co. E-mail: gfeist@bmbri.ca
URL: http://bmbri.ca
Contact: Gina Feist, Executive Director
E-mail: gfeist@bmbri.ca
Description: Supports the development and evaluation of new malting barley varieties in Canada on behalf of member companies. **Scope:** Barley and malt research institute. **Services:** Library not open to the public. **Founded:** 1948. **Holdings:** Archival materials and periodicals. **Publications:** *BMBRI Annual report*. **Awards:** BMBRI Grants (Annual). **Geographic Preference:** National.

1893 ■ **Master Brewers Association of the Americas (MBAA)**
3285 Northwood Cir., Ste. 100
Saint Paul, MN 55121
Ph: (651)454-7250
Fax: (651)454-0766
Co. E-mail: mbaa@mbaa.com
URL: http://www.mbaa.com/pages/default.aspx
Contact: Andy Tveekrem, President
Facebook: www.facebook.com/MasterBrewers
Linkedin: www.linkedin.com/company/masterbrewers
X (Twitter): x.com/MasterBrewers
Instagram: www.instagram.com/masterbrewers
YouTube: www.youtube.com/channel/UCs 4HlhhNnIcU1Od9ep94SLw
Description: Provides opportunity for brewing professionals to interact with other fermentation industry professionals and to learn practical solutions, resourceful safeguards, and innovative technologies. **Founded:** 1887. **Publications:** *MBAA Technical Quarterly* (Quarterly); *Communicator* (Monthly). **Educational Activities:** Master Brewers Conference (Annual). **Geographic Preference:** National.

INCUBATORS/RESEARCH AND TECHNOLOGY PARKS

1894 ■ **Pilot Project Brewing**
2140 N Milwaukee Ave.
Chicago, IL 60647

Ph: (773)270-5995
Co. E-mail: hello@pilotprojectbrewing.com
URL: http://www.pilotprojectbrewing.com
Facebook: www.facebook.com/pilotprojectbrewing
Instagram: www.instagram.com/pilotprojectbrewing
Description: Business incubator for breweries, offering assistance with recipes, business development, production, marketing, etc. Includes a tasting room and cafe.

REFERENCE WORKS

1895 ■ *"9 Tips for Marketing Your Craft Brewery"* in TripleSeat blog (August 26, 2020)
Released: August 26, 2020. Description: With the brewing industry landscape's popularity, marketing is a tried-and-true way to make your brewery stand out. This article provides nine tips to help you develop a strong marketing strategy, no matter your budget. Availability: Online.

1896 ■ *"11 Creative Craft Brewery Marketing Tips (+5 Examples)"* in 2ndKitchen.com (February 27, 2020)
Released: February 27, 2020. Description: Discusses creative marketing tips for your craft brewery, how much a brewery marketing strategy costs, and examples of creative brewery marketing campaigns. Availability: Online.

1897 ■ *"20 Beer Packaging Innovations"* in TrendHunter (March 20, 2019)
Ed: Jana Pijak. Released: March 20, 2019. Description: From edible beer labels to compostable beer can holders, beer packaging has come a long way toward sustainability. This article discusses environmentally friendly beer packaging innovations you should know about. Availability: Online.

1898 ■ *"$100M Merger Stalled"* in Philadelphia Business Journal (Vol. 31, February 17, 2012, No. 1, pp. 1)
Description: The $100 million merger between Origlio Beverage and All Star Beverage has been delayed by lawsuits. The merger will create an entity to distribute Yuengling Beer. But Yuengling and Son Inc. has sued All Star for breach of contract.

1899 ■ *"Airport Adds More Detroit Flavor; Local Brands Bolster Metro Dining, Retail"* in Crain's Detroit Business (Vol. 30, July 28, 2014, No. 30, pp. 3)
Pub: Crain Communications Inc.
Contact: Barry Asin, President
Description: Gayle's Chocolates, Hockeytown Café, and National Coney Island have operated at the Detroit Metropolitan Airport for years. Soon new Detroit favorites will be joining the lineup for the enjoyment of both business and leisure travelers with a food court offering local foods and beverages, including wine and 18 craft brewery beers. There will also be a self-serve kiosk where travelers can buy items to take with them. Availability: Print; Online.

1900 ■ *"Alamo Beer Tapping Into New Momentum on East Side"* in San Antonio Business Journal (Vol. 28, July 4, 2014, No. 21, pp. 7)
Pub: American City Business Journals, Inc.
Contact: Mike Olivieri, Executive Vice President
Released: July 04, 2014. Description: Alamo Beer is working on completing the $8 million brewery and beer garden in San Antonio, Texas by the later part of 2014. Company founder, Eugene Simor, says other development activity in the area emerged because of the brewery. Availability: Print; Online.

1901 ■ *"Ale for One, One for Ale: DC's Beer Industry Collects Behind a New Brewers' Guild"* in Washington Business Journal (Vol. 33, August 15, 2014, No. 17, pp. 6)
Pub: American City Business Journals, Inc.
Contact: Mike Olivieri, Executive Vice President
Released: Weekly. Price: $4, introductory 4-week offer(Digital & Print). Description: Washington DC's growing brewery industry launched the District of Columbia Brewers Guild. The Guild is composed of a group of women who helped launch the professional guild by convening all the major DC breweries and forming a steering committee. Availability: Print; Online.

1902 ■ *"Baldor Specialty Foods, Bronx Brewery Release Beer to Benefit Brownsville Community Center"* in Brewbound (September 18, 2019)
URL(s): www.brewbound.com/news/baldor-specialty-foods-bronx-brewery-release-beer-to-benefit-brownsville-community-culinary-center
Released: September 18, 2019. Description: The Brownsville Community Culinary Center is set to benefit from sales of a new beer from the joint efforts of Baldor Specialty Foods, The Bronx Brewery, and Union Beer Distributors. B-Note will be sold in the Bronx Brewery Taproom and in select stores. Availability: Online.

1903 ■ *"Beermakers Are Experimenting With New - and Sustainable - Six-Pack Designs"* in Fortune (September 2, 2019)
Ed: John Kell. Released: September 02, 2019. Description: Discusses the importance of sustainability in packaging and how breweries are moving away from single-use, plastic beer rings and moving toward sustainable packaging. Availability: Online.

1904 ■ *"Big Gains Brewing at Anheuser-Busch InBev"* in Barron's (Vol. 90, August 30, 2010, No. 35, pp. 34)
Pub: Barron's Editorial & Corporate Headquarters
Ed: Christopher C. Williams. Description: Anheuser-Busch InBev is realizing cost synergies and it posted better than expected returns two years after the merger that formed the company. One analyst believes its American depositary receipt could be worth as much as 72 in a year. Availability: Online.

1905 ■ *"Brewers Association: US Craft Brewing Industry Contributes $79 Billion to US Economy"* in Brewbound (September 30, 2019)
URL(s): www.brewbound.com/news/brewers-association-us-craft-brewing-industry-contributes-79-billion-to-us-economy
Ed: Justin Kendall. Released: September 30, 2019. Description: The Brewer's Association, located in Boulder, shared that $79.1 billion has been added to the US economy from the craft beer industry. That is 0.4 percent of the GDP. Small craft brewers also added 559,545 jobs. Breweries continue to attract consumers, with more opening every year. Availability: Online.

1906 ■ *"Brewpub and Taproom Safety Tips"* in Brewers Association (October 6, 2020)
Released: October 06, 2020. Description: A safe brewpub or taproom will provide necessary tools to help your staff fully serve your patrons. This article provides advice on creating a safety culture in your brewpub or taproom as it applies to front-of-house operations. Availability: Online.

1907 ■ *"Buffalo, Barrels, & Bourbon: The Story of How Buffalo Trace Distillery Became The World's Most Awarded Distillery*
Pub: John Wiley & Sons, Inc.
Contact: Christina Van Tassell, Executive Vice President Chief Financial Officer
URL(s): www.wiley.com/en-us/Buffalo%2C+Barrels%2C+%26+Bourbon%3A+The+Story+of+How+Buffalo+Trace+Distillery+Became+The+World%27s+Most+Awarded+Distillery-p-9781119599913
Ed: F. Paul Pacult. Released: September 2021. Price: $16, e-book; $27, hardcover. Description: Conveys the history of Buffalo Trace Distillery and how the brand was developed and grown. Availability: E-book; Print.

1908 ■ *"Business Briefs: Alcoholic Beverage Manufacturing Is Big Business In Idaho"* in Idaho Business Review (August 19, 2014)
Pub: BridgeTower Media
Contact: Adam Reinebach, President
Description: Idaho's alcoholic beverage manufacturing industry is growing at a steady pace, reporting an $8.7 million payroll in 2013. Breweries, as well as wineries and distilleries are also strong. Statistical data included.

1909 ■ *"Colorado's Oldest Craft Brewery is Downsizing, Ending Distribution and Laying Off 21 Employees"* in The Denver Post (October 10, 2019)
URL(s): www.denverpost.com/2019/10/10/boulder-beer-co-downsizing/
Ed: Josie Sexton. Released: October 10, 2019. Description: Boulder Beer Company, Colorado's first craft brewery is downsizing by shrinking its operations and laying off 21 employees. It's brew will only be available in its taproom, Wilderness Place, which is located outside of Boulder. Too much competition in the local brew industry is causing these changes, but the company hopes that by cutting back it can still survive. Availability: Online.

1910 ■ *"Craft Beers without the Buzz: Brewing New Options for the 'Sober Curious"* in NPR (June 20, 2019)
URL(s): www.npr.org/sections/thesalt/2019/06/20/733476733/craft-beers-without-the-buzz-brewing-new-options-for-the-sober-curious
Ed: Allison Aubrey. Released: June 20, 2019. Description: With a large nation-wide demand for nonalcoholic brews, small craft breweries are working to fill that void. Millennials are drinking less and people in general are looking for non-alcoholic alternatives, but still crave that craft beer taste. Availability: Online.

1911 ■ *"Craft Brewers Want 20 Percent of U.S. Market"* in Denver Business Journal (Vol. 65, April 18, 2014, No. 49, pp. A8)
Pub: American City Business Journals, Inc.
Contact: Mike Olivieri, Executive Vice President
Description: The United States Brewers Association aims to increase the national craft brewing industry's share of beer sales to 20 percent by 2020. However, the industry will need to take more of the market from large domestic beer manufacturers. Reports show that beer sales in smaller breweries have reached 14.3 percent in 2014. Availability: Print; Online.

1912 ■ *"Craft-Spirits Maker Brings Art of Distilling to SoFlo Area"* in San Antonio Business Journal (Vol. 28, March 7, 2014, No. 4, pp. 5)
Pub: American City Business Journals, Inc.
Contact: Mike Olivieri, Executive Vice President
Released: Weekly. Price: $4, Introductory 4-week offer(Digital only). Description: Chris Mobley and Boyan Kolusevic established Dorcol Distilling Company in the SoFlo area of San Antonio, Texas. Kolusevic reveals that the growth of San Antonio's craft spirits/brewery industry has been evident in recent years. Dorcol has been described as an urban, boutique craft distillery. Availability: Print; Online.

1913 ■ *"Crystal Hotel Resumes Construction"* in Business Journal Portland (Vol. 27, December 31, 2010, No. 44, pp. 1)
Pub: Portland Business Journal
Contact: Andy Giegerich, Managing Editor
E-mail: agiegerich@bizjournals.com
Ed: Wendy Culverwell. Description: McMenamins Pubs and Breweries has resumed construction of its Crystal Hotel project. The company has been working to convert a former bath house into a 51-room hotel. The hotel is expected to open in 2011. Availability: Print; Online.

1914 ■ *"Going Green: How Can Craft Brewers Improve Sustainability"* in Beverage Daily (April 23, 2019)
Ed: Beth Newhart. Released: April 23, 2019. Description: Discusses the three pillars of sustainability that brewers should follow: social, environmental, and economic. Availability: Online.

1915 ■ Good News for 'Green' Brews: Consumers Say They'll Pay More for Sustainable Beer
Ed: Rachel D. Cohen. **Released:** October 13, 2018. **Description:** Discusses the importance of sustainability and reports on breweries can incorporate sustainable business practices and the willingness of customers to pay more for products that come from green businesses. **Availability:** Online.

1916 ■ "Harpoon Brewery Wins Boston Green Business Award for Sustainability and EnerNOC Energy Management Programs" in Investment Weekly News (May 12, 2012, No. 543)
Description: Harpoon Brewery was awarded a 2012 Boston Green Business Award by Mayor Thomas Menino of Boston, Massachusetts. The brewery was cited for having an exceptional sustainability program that includes waste reduction, responsible chemical usage, and operational efficiency measures combined with energy management initiatives with EnerNOC. EnerNOC is a leading provider of energy management applications for commercial, industrial, and institutional energy users, including Harpoon. **Availability:** Online.

1917 ■ "The Hawaiian Philosophy Making Craft Beer More Sustainable" in Vinepair (October 3, 2019)
URL(s): vinepair.com/articles/craft-beer-sustainability-hawaii/
Ed: Jeremy Storton. **Released:** October 03, 2019. **Description:** Hawaii is leading the way in sustainable efforts to create craft beer, with respect to the land and to the community. Craft beer is becoming a bigger industry in the Hawaiian Islands, and it's important for local brewers to incorporate the spirit of Hawaii in all they do. **Availability:** Online.

1918 ■ "How Beer Brewers Are Embracing Sustainability" in SevenFiftyDaily (May 11, 2020)
Ed: Nickolaus Hines. **Released:** May 11, 2020. **Description:** From new energy sources to landfill diversion, craft beer is transforming into an environmentally-friendly industry. This article discusses how breweries can incorporate sustainability practices into their workflows. **Availability:** Online.

1919 ■ How to Open a Brewpub or Microbrewery
Ed: Bobbye Alley. **Description:** Discusses what it takes to open a brewpub or microbrewery including planning, organization, and a substantial capital investment. **Availability:** Online.

1920 ■ "How to Start a Brewery in 6 Steps" in JustBusiness (October 22, 2020)
Ed: Vivian Giang. **Released:** October 22, 2020. **Description:** If you're considering how to start a brewery, it's definitely an industry with potential. This article provides things to consider so you can turn your passion project into a real business. **Availability:** Online.

1921 ■ How to Start a Brewery Business
Description: A simple guide to starting a successful brewery business from highlighting important facts to validating your ideas, and from choosing the right structure to learning your options for managing and running your business. **Availability:** Online.

1922 ■ How to Start a Brewery Business in 2020: The Complete 9 Step Guide
Ed: Katie Lundin. **Released:** January 07, 2020. **Description:** If you're passionate about beer, and you're ready to join the craft beer community, this guide provides information on how to start a brewery business in 9 steps. **Availability:** Online.

1923 ■ The King of Vodka: The Story of Pyotr Smirnov and the Upheaval of an Empire
Pub: HarperCollins Publishers L.L.C.
Contact: Brian Murray, President
Ed: Linda Himelstein. **Released:** November 30, 2010. **Price:** $15.99, paperback. **Description:** Biography of Pyotr Smirnov and how his determination took him from serf to the head of Smirnov Vodka. Smirnov's marketing techniques are defined and show how he expanded the drink worldwide. **Availability:** E-book; Print; Online.

1924 ■ "Kokanee Films World's Longest Beer Commercial: Ready for a 90-Minute Feature Starring the Cast of Kokanee?" in Canadian Business (Vol. 85, July 16, 2012, No. 11-12, pp. 11)
Ed: Jeff Beer. **Description:** Labatt Brewing Company and advertising agency Grip Ltd. produced a feature-length commercial for the Kokanee beer entitled, "The Movie Out Here", which centers on the reunion of friends in a ski town. As part of the marketing campaign, consumers can submit suggestions for props and set locations, audition for parts and vote online for the soundtrack. **Availability:** Online.

1925 ■ "Law Firms Cash In On Alcohol" in Business Journal Portland (Vol. 27, November 19, 2010, No. 38, pp. 1)
Pub: Portland Business Journal
Contact: Andy Giegerich, Managing Editor
E-mail: agiegerich@bizjournals.com
Ed: Andy Giegerich. **Description:** Oregon-based law firms have continued to corner big business on the state's growing alcohol industry as demand for their services increased. Lawyers, who represent wine, beer and liquor distillery interests, have seen their workload increased by 20 to 30 percent in 2009. **Availability:** Print; Online.

1926 ■ "Legislative Changes Providing Boost to San Antonio Distillers" in San Antonio Business Journal (Vol. 28, March 7, 2014, No. 4, pp. 4)
Pub: American City Business Journals, Inc.
Contact: Mike Olivieri, Executive Vice President
Released: Weekly. **Price:** $4, Introductory 4-week offer(Digital only). **Description:** Lawmakers in Texas have implemented legislative changes that will provide financial flexibility to brew pubs and breweries. Distilleries in the state are now allowed to sell their products directly to food companies. The growth in San Antonio, Texas' craft spirits industry is also discussed. **Availability:** Print; Online.

1927 ■ "Leinenkugel's Looks Beyond Honey Weiss To Stay Relevant" in Business Journal (Vol. 31, January 3, 2014, No. 32, pp. 4)
Pub: American City Business Journals, Inc.
Contact: Mike Olivieri, Executive Vice President
Description: Jacob Leinenkugel Brewing Company president, Jake Leinenkugel, shares his views about the changes at the brewery and in the beer industry. Leinenkugel believes hop-forward beer has a good niche within the American beer drinkers market and they started getting into this market with the Hoppin' Helles. Minneapolis-St. Paul shares about 15 percent share of the craft beer market. **Availability:** Online.

1928 ■ "Local Brewers Hop Onboard Craft-Beer Train" in Providence Business News (Vol. 29, April 14, 2014, No. 2, pp. 1)
Pub: American City Business Journals, Inc.
Contact: Mike Olivieri, Executive Vice President
Released: April 12, 2014. **Description:** Rhode Island has become a home to more than a dozen breweries for craft beers. The state's craft brewers plan to create the infrastructure for a thriving, self-sustaining local brewing ecosystem and two groups in Providence announced separate plans for larger breweries capable of boosting more-established labels to larger markets. The growth of craft brewing is discussed. **Availability:** Print; Online.

1929 ■ "Meet the Maker: Sean Dempsey, Dempsey's Brewery Restaurant & Pub, SD" in Pizza Today (October 24, 2019)
URL(s): www.pizzatoday.com/news/pizza-headlines/meet-the-maker-sean-dempsey-dempseys-brewery-restaurant-pub-sd/
Ed: Denise Greer. **Released:** October 24, 2019. **Description:** An interview of Sean Dempsey, the owner of Dempsey's Brewery Restaurant & Pub in Watertown, South Dakota about his pizzeria. **Availability:** Online.

1930 ■ "Microbrewery Aims Big with New Facility" in Business Journal (Vol. 31, May 9, 2014, No. 50, pp. 6)
Pub: American City Business Journals, Inc.
Contact: Mike Olivieri, Executive Vice President
Released: Weekly. **Description:** Insight Brewing Company is opening an unusually large production brewery with a tap room in Northeast Minneapolis, Minnesota in fall 2014. The company purchased equipment with annual production capacity of up to 5,400 barrels of beer and should the business continue to grow, the large building will allow the firm to brew up to 40,000 barrels annually. **Availability:** Print; Online.

1931 ■ "New Brewpub Includes a Manapua Shop" in Pacific Business News (Vol. 52, March 14, 2014, No. 3, pp. 2)
Pub: American City Business Journals, Inc.
Contact: Mike Olivieri, Executive Vice President
Released: March 14, 2014. **Price:** $4, Introductory 4-Week Offer(Digital & Print). **Description:** Hoku Brewing Company is set to open a brewery restaurant in Hawaii. The new restaurant will be built on the site of the former Aloha Beer Company restaurant. The project is a joint venture between Hoku and restaurateur Dave Campbell. **Availability:** Print; Online.

1932 ■ "Real Estate Reinventions: Black Lotus Brewing Co." in Crain's Detroit Business (Vol. 23, October 1, 2007, No. 40, pp. 13)
Pub: Crain Communications Inc.
Contact: Barry Asin, President
Ed: Leah Boyd. **Description:** Profile of Black Lotus Brewing Company and owner, Mike Allan who converted a drug store location into a brewery while restoring the building's original architecture. **Availability:** Print; Online.

1933 ■ "San Antonio's Craft-Brewing Industry is Gearing Up to Make More Suds" in San Antonio Business Journal (Vol. 26, August 3, 2012, No. 27, pp. 1)
Pub: Baltimore Business Journal
Contact: Rhonda Pringle, President
E-mail: rpringle@bizjournals.com
Description: Craft brewery projects are underway in San Antonio, Texas as more companies look to take advantage of craft beer's growing market. Texas craft breweries registered over $75 million in sales and could have an economic impact of $6 billion by 2020. **Availability:** Print; Online.

1934 ■ "So You Want to Start a Brewery? The Lagunitas Story"
Pub: Chicago Review Press Inc.
Contact: Cynthia Sherry, Publisher
E-mail: csherry@chicagoreviewpress.com
Released: October 01, 2014. **Price:** $17.95, trade paper, estimate shipping and sales tax; C$21.95, trade paper, estimate shipping and sales tax; $12.99, pdf, estimate shipping and sales tax; C$17.99, pdf, estimate shipping and sales tax; $12.99, epub, estimate shipping and sales tax; C$17.99, epub, estimate shipping and sales tax; $12.99, mob. **Description:** Profile of Tony Magee, who founded a brewery in 1993, based in Petaluma, California. The entrepreneur describes the business story of his firm, Lagunitas Brewing Company that makes craft bee that he says defies categorization. **Availability:** E-book; Print; Electronic publishing; PDF; Online.

1935 ■ "South Park Draws Brewers, Vintners" in Puget Sound Business Journal (Vol. 29, August 29, 2008, No. 19, pp. 1)
Description: Craft breweries and wineries are moving into Seattle, Washington's South Park neighborhood due to the area's low rents, convenience, and ample equipment space. These industries bring a

more upscale flavor to the heavily industrial area and the tastings and festivals draw people from throughout the Seattle region. **Availability:** Print; Online.

1936 ■ *"Strange Brew" in Canadian Business (Vol. 85, June 11, 2012, No. 10, pp. 52)*
Ed: Paul Brent. **Description:** Molson Coors is launching the Coors Light Iced T beer in summer 2012 as part of its effort to improve weak sales in North America. The new product is aimed at female drinkers and is part of an effort to win back sales from wine and spirits. **Availability:** Print; Online.

1937 ■ *"The Traveling Godfather: Beam Global Spirits & Wine Inc." in Canadian Business (Vol. 81, October 13, 2008, No. 17, pp. S10)*
Description: Dan Tullio, director of Canadian Club, is seen as a godfather because he gets to be asked a lot of favors. Tullio gets to immerse himself into other cultures because of his employment as global ambassador of Beam Global Spirits & Wine Inc. Tullio's views, as well as information about him are presented.

1938 ■ *"Tsingtao's Chairman On Jump-Starting a Sluggish Company" in Harvard Business Review (Vol. 90, April 2012, No. 4, pp. 41)*
Pub: Harvard Business Review Press
Contact: Moderna V. Pfizer, Contact
Ed: Jin Zhiguo. **Description:** The key challenge Tsingtao Brewery Company Ltd. faced was the focus on pleasing corporate superiors, rather than the firm's customers. By inventing a new model, the brewery was able to boost both employee productivity and product quality. First half profits and revenue for 2011 grew more than 20 percent over the previous year.

1939 ■ *"Urban Organics Launches Aquaponic Farm in Old Hamm's Brewery" in Business Journal (Vol. 31, April 11, 2014, No. 46, pp. 4)*
Pub: American City Business Journals, Inc.
Contact: Mike Olivieri, Executive Vice President
Price: $4, Introductory 4-Week Offer(Digital & Print).
Description: Urban Organics launched its new aquaponics farm at the old site of Hamm's Brewery in St. Paul, Minnesota. The facility has four 3,000 gallon fish tanks that hold 1,000 fish which Urban Organics uses to grow fresh and healthy tilapia and vegetable produce. **Availability:** Print; Online.

1940 ■ *"Victory Not Resting On Its Laurels" in Philadelphia Business Journal (Vol. 33, April 11, 2014, No. 9, pp. 6)*
Pub: American City Business Journals, Inc.
Contact: Mike Olivieri, Executive Vice President
Description: Downingtown, Pennsylvania-based Victory Brewing Company co-founder, Bill Covaleski, shares his views on the industry's rapid growth. Cavaleski says he got complacent with the brands while building their second brewery so they added three new brews in 2013. He says they are looking for better market penetration in the mid-Atlantic and Philadelphia markets. **Availability:** Online.

1941 ■ *"Water Woes Force Big Brewers to Tighten the Tap" in Idaho Business Review (June 11, 2014)*
Pub: BridgeTower Media
Contact: Adam Reinebach, President
Description: As drought or wildfires threated watersheds, large brewers across the nation are seeking to reduce their water-to-beer ratio in order to conserve the nation's water supply. Craft beer makers have expanded to its highest level since the 1870s. Statistical data included.

1942 ■ *"We Asked 10 Brewers: What's the Most Underrated Brewery?" in Vinepair (September 26, 2019)*
URL(s): vinepair.com/articles/10-best-underrated-breweries-2019/
Ed: Matt Osgood. **Released:** September 26, 2019.
Description: The brewery community has a prolific presence on social media message boards, and very often, only the most popular breweries get notice. In this article, ten brewers were asked to discuss their favorite underrated brewery. **Availability:** Online.

1943 ■ *"We Have Surpassed Our Early Goals...Everything Else Is a Bonus" in Business Journal (Vol. 32, June 6, 2014, No. 2, pp. 13)*
Pub: American City Business Journals, Inc.
Contact: Mike Olivieri, Executive Vice President
Released: June 2014. **Description:** Lift Bridge Brewing Company co-founder and president, Dan Schwarz, shares his views about making the transition into a regional player. Schwarz discusses the quality of their beer as the main reason for their relevance to beer drinkers in Minnesota. The firm plans to become a regional brewery and distributor of beer across the nation. **Availability:** Print; Online.

STATISTICAL SOURCES

1944 ■ *Brewery Tours Industry in the US - Market Research Report*
URL(s): www.ibisworld.com/united-states/market-research-reports/brewery-tours-industry/
Price: $925. **Description:** Downloadable report analyzing the current and future trends in the brewery tours industry. **Availability:** Download.

1945 ■ *Online Beer, Wine & Liquor Sales Industry in the US - Market Research Report*
URL(s): www.ibisworld.com/united-states/market-research-reports/online-beer-wine-liquor-sales-industry/
Price: $925. **Description:** Downloadable report analyzing the online beer, wine, and liquor retail industry. **Availability:** Online.

1946 ■ *Outlook for the American Beer Market*
Released: 2004-2005. **Price:** $1,895. **Description:** Analyzes the U.S. beer market. Covers the influence of new imports and the Canadian beer market through 1991. Profiles companies such as Anheuser-Busch, Coors, Heilemann, Philip Morris, and Stroh. Profiles include financial news, marketing strategies, and brand performance.

1947 ■ *Standard & Poor's Industry Surveys*
Pub: Standard And Poor's Financial Services LLC.
Contact: Douglas L. Peterson, President
Description: Two-volume book that examines the prospects for specific industries, including trucking. Also provides analyses of trends and problems, statistical tables and charts, and comparative company analyses.

TRADE PERIODICALS

1948 ■ *Cocktails Magazine*
Pub: Destiny Productions for Print, Radio and Cable Promotions
URL(s): www.cocktail.com/
Released: Monthly **Description:** Trade magazine for the alcohol service industry. **Availability:** Print.

1949 ■ *Modern Brewery Age*
Contact: Peter V.K. Reid, Publisher
E-mail: pete@breweryage.com
Released: Bimonthly **Price:** $95, U.S. and other countries 52 PDF weekly tabloids via email & delivery of quarterly magazine. **Description:** Magazine for the wholesale and brewing industry. **Availability:** Print; Online.

VIDEO/AUDIO MEDIA

1950 ■ *Scott Shor Managing Partner at Edmund's Oast*
URL(s): restaurantunstoppable.libsyn.com/981-scott-shor-managing-partner-at-edmunds-oast
Ed: Eric Cacciatore. **Released:** April 10, 2023.
Description: Podcast offers a conversation with a brewery owner.

TRADE SHOWS AND CONVENTIONS

1951 ■ NBWA Annual Convention & Trade show
BMO Harris Bank N.A.
111 W Monroe St.
Chicago, IL 60603
Free: 888-340-2265
URL: http://www.bmoharris.com
Contact: David Casper, President
URL(s): nbwa.org/event/annual-convention-product-showcase
Description: Brewery software and hardware, trucking, beer cleaning equipment, and related equipment, supplies, and services. Includes education seminars and exhibits. **Audience:** Beer distributors and wholesalers, and the public. **Principal Exhibits:** Brewery software and hardware, trucking, beer cleaning equipment, and related equipment, supplies, and services. Includes education seminars and exhibits. **Telecommunication Services:** gmoery@nbwa.com.

1952 ■ WSWA Annual Convention & Exposition
Wine and Spirits Wholesalers of America (WSWA)
805 15th St. NW, Ste. 1120
Washington, DC 20005
Ph: (202)371-9792
Fax: (202)789-2405
Co. E-mail: info@wswa.org
URL: http://www.wswa.org
Contact: Michelle L. Korsmo, President
URL(s): accesslive.wswa.org
Facebook: www.facebook.com/WSWAConvention
Frequency: Annual. **Description:** Producers of spirits, wine, beer, mixes, bottled water; freight routing/forwarding companies; computer hardware/software; point of sale products vendors; warehouse equipment producers; forklifts, security systems, conveyor and packing systems; scanners. **Audience:** Wine spirits wholesales. **Principal Exhibits:** Producers of spirits, wine, beer, mixes, bottled water; freight routing/forwarding companies; computer hardware/software; point of sale products vendors; warehouse equipment producers; forklifts, security systems, conveyor and packing systems; scanners. Dates and Locations: 2025 Feb 02-04 Gaylord Rockies Resort & Convention Center, Aurora, CO. **Telecommunication Services:** registrations@wswa.org.

CONSULTANTS

1953 ■ Bio-Technical Resources L.P. (BTR)
1035 S 7th St.
Manitowoc, WI 54220-5301
Ph: (920)684-5518
Fax: (920)684-5519
Co. E-mail: info@biotechresources.com
URL: http://www.biotechresources.com
Contact: Reinhardt A. Rosson, President
Description: Firm provides research and development of industrial fermentation processes service. **Scope:** Services include strain improvement, process development and metabolic engineering. **Founded:** 1962. **Publications:** "A Novel Fungus for the Production of Efficient Cellulases and Hemi-Cellulases," Jun, 2009; "Linoleic Acid Isomerase from Propionibacterium acnes: Purification, Characterization, Molecular Cloning, and Heterologous Expression," 2007; "Purification and Characterization of a Membrane-Bound Linoleic Acid Isomerase from Clostridium sporogenes," 2007; "Metabolic Engineering of Sesquiterpene Metabolism in Yeast," 2007; "Purification and Characterization of a Membrane-Bound Linoleic AcidIsomerase from Clostridium sporogenes," 2007. **Training:** Metabolic Engineering for Industrial Production of Glucosamine and N-Acetylglucosamine, Aug, 2003; Metabolic Engineering of E. coli for the Industrial Production of Glucosamine, Apr, 2003.

LIBRARIES

1954 ■ Anheuser-Busch Companies, LLC (ABC) - Library
Anheuser-Busch InBev SA/NV
1 Busch Pl.
Saint Louis, MO 63118

Ph: 32 16 276 111
Co. E-mail: glass-help@ab-inbev.com
URL: http://www.ab-inbev.com
Contact: Andy Thomas, President
URL(s): www.tapintoyourbeer.com
Facebook: www.facebook.com/AnheuserBusch
Linkedin: www.linkedin.com/company/anheuser
 -busch
X (Twitter): x.com/AnheuserBusch
Instagram: www.instagram.com/anheuserbusch
YouTube: www.youtube.com/user/ABInBevNews

Description: Operator of bars offering beer. **Scope:** Beer. **Founded:** 1852. **Holdings:** Figures not available. **Educational Activities:** Chain Operators Exchange (COEX) (Annual); FMI Midwinter Executive Conference (Annual).

1955 ■ Beer Canada - Library
PO Box 654
 Stittsville, ON, Canada K2S1A7
Co. E-mail: cheers@beercanada.com
URL: http://www.beercanada.com
Contact: Roger Mittag, Contact
Facebook: www.facebook.com/BeerCanadaCheers
Linkedin: www.linkedin.com/company/beer-canada
X (Twitter): x.com/BeerCanada
Instagram: www.instagram.com/beercanadacheers
YouTube: www.youtube.com/channel/UCJY_Lw8
 t5-Ru9NyHjbsp-TQ

Description: Promotes operation of microbreweries; seeks growth and development of the brewing industry. **Scope:** Beer; food; recipes. **Founded:** 1943. **Holdings:** Figures not available. **Publications:** *On Tap* (Bimonthly); *Statistical Bulletin* (Annual). **Geographic Preference:** National.

1956 ■ University of California, Davis - Archives and Special Collections
Shields Library, 100 NW Quad
 Davis, CA 95616
Ph: (530)752-1621
Co. E-mail: speccoll@ucdavis.edu
URL: http://library.ucdavis.edu/archives-and-special
 -collections
Contact: William Garrity, Head Librarian
E-mail: wfgarrity@ucdavis.edu

Scope: Agriculture; American; British literature; apiculture; botany; British history; entomology; religion; viticulture; enology and zoology. **Services:** Copying; collections open to the public for reference use only. **Founded:** 1966. **Holdings:** 183,000 volumes; 17,000 lin.ft. of archives and manuscripts; books; rare books; pamphlets; articles; journals.

Bridal Shop/Bridal Consultant

START-UP INFORMATION

1957 ■ *"Event-Planning Startup Extends Its Reach"* in *Indianapolis Business Journal (Vol. 33, June 18, 2012, No. 16, pp. 2A)*
Description: Snappening.com offers a searchable database of central Indiana event venues ad professional planners and is expanding its service to four new markets. **Availability:** Print; Online.

1958 ■ *Start Your Own Wedding Consultant Business*
Pub: Entrepreneur Media Inc.
Contact: Dan Bova, Director
E-mail: dbova@entrepreneur.com
Ed: Eileen Figure Sandlin. **Released:** Third edition.
Description: Advice for starting and running a wedding consulting business.

ASSOCIATIONS AND OTHER ORGANIZATIONS

1959 ■ **Association of Bridal Consultants (ABC)**
632 Federal Rd., Ste. 2
 Brookfield, CT 06804
Ph: (860)355-7000
Fax: (203)775-0037
Co. E-mail: info@bridalassn.com
URL: http://bridalassn.com
Contact: David M. Wood, III, President
Facebook: www.facebook.com/AssocBridalConsultants
YouTube: www.youtube.com/channel/UC77N7hfAwxl4k6sAiD72O6Q
Description: Represents independent bridal and wedding consultants; persons employed by companies in wedding-related businesses and novices looking to get into the business. Strives to improve professionalism and recognition of bridal and wedding consultants. Offers professional development program, startup manual and seminars. Provides advertising, publicity, referrals and information services. Operates speakers' bureau; compiles statistics. **Founded:** 1955. **Publications:** *Association of Bridal Consultants--Retail Resource Directory* (Semiannual); *ABC Dialogue* (6/year); *Ethnic and Specialty by Wedding Guide* (Periodic); *Retail Resource Directory* (Semiannual); *Weddings As A Business*. **Educational Activities:** Business of Brides Annual Conference (Annual). **Geographic Preference:** Multinational.

1960 ■ **Association for Wedding Professionals International (AFWPI)**
2929 35th St., Ste. 5598.
 Sacramento, CA 95817
Ph: (916)392-5000
Fax: (916)392-5222
Co. E-mail: richard@afwpi.com
URL: http://afwpi.com
Contact: Richard Markel, Associate Director
E-mail: richard@afwpi.com
Facebook: www.facebook.com/afwpiFans
Linkedin: www.linkedin.com/in/afwpi
X (Twitter): x.com/afwpi
YouTube: www.youtube.com/user/afwpi
Description: Professionals working in the wedding industry. Promotes adherence to high standards of ethics and practice by members; seeks to advance members' professional standing. Serves as a network linking members; offers member discounts on business services, insurance, and advertising; sponsors educational programs. **Founded:** 1995. **Educational Activities:** Harrogate Gown Market Show; Christmas Party; Monthly Networking Mixer (Monthly). **Geographic Preference:** Multinational.

1961 ■ **Bridal Association of America (BAOA)**
5630 District Blvd., Ste. 120
 Bakersfield, CA 93313-2182
Ph: (661)633-9200
Free: 866-MYW-EDDING
URL: http://www.bridalassociationofamerica.com
Contact: Kyle Brown, Member
Description: Provides free and accessible information on wedding planning and on how to adjust on living life as a couple. Provides a forum for wedding professionals to express their own approaches and styles when it comes to their own wedding products and services. Acts as a forum for wedding professionals. **Founded:** 1999. **Geographic Preference:** National.

1962 ■ **Wedding and Event Videographers Association International (WEVA)**
5020 Clark Rd., No. 345
 Sarasota, FL 34233
Co. E-mail: info@weva.com
URL: http://www.weva.com/index.shtml
Contact: Roy Chapman, President
Description: Represents professional wedding and event videographers worldwide, providing resources in technical training, marketing, and networking. **Publications:** *Wedding & Event Videography Resource Guide* (Quarterly). **Awards:** WEVA Creative Excellence Award (Annual). **Geographic Preference:** Multinational.

1963 ■ **Wedding and Portrait Photographers International (WPPI)**
Las Vegas, NV
Co. E-mail: info@wppievents.com
URL: http://wppiexpo.com
Facebook: www.facebook.com/wppievents
X (Twitter): x.com/RfWPPI
Instagram: www.instagram.com/wppievents
YouTube: www.youtube.com/user/rfwppi
Description: Represents wedding portrait and digital photographers and photographers employed at general photography studios. Promotes high artistic and technical standards in wedding photography. **Publications:** *Wedding Photography Monthly* (Monthly); *Marketing and Technical Manual* (Quarterly); *Rangefinder* (Monthly); *Wedding Photographer* (Monthly); *WPPI Photography Monthly* (Monthly). **Educational Activities:** Wedding and Portrait Photographers International Competition (Semiannual). **Awards:** Honors of excellence Award (Annual). **Geographic Preference:** Multinational.

REFERENCE WORKS

1964 ■ *"Bridal Chain Files for Bankruptcy, Leaving Brides Frantic Over Gowns"* in *Charlotte Business Journal (July 17, 2017)*
URL(s): www.bizjournals.com/charlotte/news/2017/07/17/bridal-chain-files-for-bankruptcy-leaving-brides.html
Ed: Brian Bandell. **Released:** July 17, 2017. **Description:** The bridal chain Alfred Angelo abruptly closed it's doors to all 61 of its locations after filing for bankruptcy. Brides across the nation are in a panic since they do not know the status of their dresses and whether or not they will ever receive them. In the meantime, David's Bridal is offering a discounted replacement dress to these brides. **Availability:** Online.

1965 ■ *"Carnival Cruise Lines Hosts First-Ever Wedding at Charleston's Annual 10K Cooper River Bridge Run"* in *Benzinga.com (April 4, 2011)*
Pub: PR Newswire Association LLC.
Description: Carnival Cruise Lines hosted a post-race wedding ceremony after the Cooper River Bridge Run in South Carolina.

1966 ■ *"Chesapeake Beach Resort and Spa Announces Dream Waterfront Wedding Giveaway"* in *Benzinga.com (October 29, 2011)*
Description: Chesapeake Beach Resort and Spa will give away a Dream Waterfront Wedding to a lucky bride and groom in order to promote their resort as a wedding venue. **Availability:** Print; Online.

1967 ■ *"Consultant Helps Brides Choose the Best Dress for the Special Day"* in *The Oakland Press (February 18, 2019)*
URL(s): www.theoaklandpress.com/lifestyles/consultant-helps-brides-choose-the-best-dress-for-the-special/article_5b3c10ec-2bf5-11e9-a64c-bfa2c5baf2f6.html
Ed: Susan Kirwan. **Released:** February 18, 2019. **Description:** Profile of Hannah Abboud, owner of l'Amour Bridal Boutique, who helps brides choose the perfect dress for their special day. **Availability:** Online.

1968 ■ *"CPI Corp. Acquires Assets of Bella Pictures"* in *Benzinga.com (January 28, 2011)*
Pub: PR Newswire Association LLC.
Description: CPI Corporation acquired assets of Bella Pictures Inc., a leading provider of branded wedding photography services. Details of the acquisition are explained. **Availability:** Online.

1969 ■ *"Destination Wedding Giveaway: A Custom Instagram Book"* in *Benzinga.com (October 29, 2011)*
Pub: Benzinga.com
Contact: Jason Raznick, Founder

1970 ■ Bridal Shop/Bridal Consultant

Description: Eden Condominiums in Perdido Key, Florida will award a beach wedding to a couple in 2012. The event is a marketing tool to draw attention brides as a perfect wedding venue. **Availability:** Print; Online.

1970 ■ *"Discover the Wedding Location of Your Dreams"* in Benzinga.com (December 24, 2011)

Description: Ritz Carlton Hotel Company helps couples choose from their 70 wedding locations worldwide with wedding advisors to assist in planning. **Availability:** Online.

1971 ■ *"Esencia Estate to Host 'The Esencia Experience for Upscale Wedding Planners' to Re-Introduce the Estate as a Premier Wedding Venue"* in Benzinga.com (October 29, 2011)

Description: Esencia Estate located in the Riviera Maya, Mexico is reintroducing the estate as a premier wedding venue. They are hosting an event to help wedding planners envision plans at the estate. **Availability:** Print; Online.

1972 ■ *"Food Truck Weddings Gain Popularity, Buck Tradition"* in Tampa Tribune (June 24, 2012)

Ed: Jeff Houck. **Description:** A new trend crossing the nation is the use of a food truck for feeding guests as wedddding receptions. Food trucks allow the bride and groom to provide a more casual atmosphere for their wedding party and is less expensive than a formal dinner. **Availability:** Print; Online.

1973 ■ *"Fort Lauderdale Hotel's Service, Facilities Honored at 'Bride's Choice' by WeddingWire"* in Internet Wire (February 10, 2012)

Pub: Comtex News Network Inc.
Contact: Kan Devnani, President

Description: Harbor Beach Marriott Resort & Spa was awarded the WeddingWire's Bride's Choice Awards for excellence in quality, service, responsiveness and professionalism. More than 200,000 wedding professionals are members of WeddingWire, which brings couples and wedding professionals together in an all-in-one marketing platform. **Availability:** Print; Online.

1974 ■ *"Freelance Writer Creates LI Bridal Blog"* in Long Island Business News (September 10, 2010)

Pub: BridgeTower Media
Contact: Adam Reinebach, President

Ed: Gregory Zeller. **Description:** Profile of Claudia Copquin, freelance journalist who created a blog for brides on the Internet. **Availability:** Online; Audio.

1975 ■ *"Gowns Ready to Go"* in Houston Chronicle (June 3, 2010)

Pub: Houston Chronicle

Ed: Molly Glentzer. **Description:** Wedding gowns with slender silhouettes travel well for destination weddings. Amsale, Oscar del la Renta and Monique Lhuillier dresses are highlighted. **Availability:** Online.

1976 ■ *"Host Your Dream Wedding at the Minneapolis Marriott Southwest"* in Benzinga.com (June 6, 2011)

Description: Minneapolis Marriott Southwest is helping engaged couples plan their wedding destination at their property. Details of wedding reception options are outlined. **Availability:** Online.

1977 ■ *"The Life of a Bridal Consultant"* in Levittown Tribune (July 25, 2016)

URL(s): levittown-tribune.com/2016/07/25/the-life-of-a-bridal-consultant/

Ed: Jennifer Fauci. **Released:** July 25, 2016. **Description:** Explores the day-to-day activities of a bridal consultant, from creating displays to helping brides choose the best dress for their special day. **Availability:** Online.

1978 ■ *"Markel American Insurance Company Announces Wedding and Special Event Insurance for Consumers"* in Benzinga.com (February 16, 2011)

Pub: Benzinga.com
Contact: Jason Raznick, Founder

Description: Markel American Insurance Company, headquartered in Waukesha, Wisconsin has launched its new special event insurance and wedding insurance to protect both liabilities and cancellations associated with these events. **Availability:** Print; Online.

1979 ■ *"Memphis Marriott Downtown Offers Wedding Reception Discounts to Soon-To-Be Newlyweds"* in Benzinga.com (June 23, 2011)

Pub: PR Newswire Association LLC.

Description: Memphis Marriott Downtown in Memphis, Tennessee is offering wedding reception discounts to couples planning their weddings.

1980 ■ *"Military Brides Can Get Free Wedding Gowns"* in Virginian-Pilot (November 10, 2010)

Pub: The Virginian-Pilot
Contact: Kevin Goyette, Director
E-mail: kgoyette@dailypress.com

Ed: Jamesetta M. Walker. **Description:** Seventy-five designer wedding gowns will be given to military brides on a first-come, first-served basis at Maya Couture through the Brides Across America's wedding gown giveaway program. Gowns are valued between $500 to $3,000 and are donated by designers Maggie Sottero, Pronovias and Essense of Australia. **Availability:** Online.

1981 ■ *"Modern Bride Unveiled Exclusively at JCPenney"* in Benzinga.com (February 3, 2011)

Pub: PR Newswire Association LLC.

Description: JCPenney created its new Modern Bride concept in its bridal find jewelry departments. The new shopping experience is a collaboration between the retailer and Conde Nast catering to the bridal customer. **Availability:** Online.

1982 ■ *"More Brides, Grooms Say 'I Do' to Interracial Marriage"* in Black Enterprise (Vol. 41, August 2010, No. 1, pp. 36)

Pub: Earl G. Graves Ltd.
Contact: Earl Graves, Jr., President

Description: According to a recent survey conducted by Pew Research Center, a record 14.6 percent of all new marriages in the U.S. in 2008 were interracial. Statistical data included.

1983 ■ *"New York City-Based New Street Realty Advisors has Secured a New Flagship for David's Bridal"* in Chain Store Age (August 2008)

Description: New York City-based New Street Realty Advisors secured a new flagship store for David's Bridal in the Chelsea district of Manhattan. David's Bridal will occupy 12,800 square feet on two floors in a retail condominium development. **Availability:** PDF; Online.

1984 ■ *"On Your Marks, American Airlines, Now Vote! Contest Creating Possibilities and Opportunities for Delray Beach Wedding Planner"* in Benzinga.com (2011)

Pub: Benzinga.com
Contact: Jason Raznick, Founder

Description: Wedding planner, Aviva Samuels, owner of Kiss the Planner boutique wedding and event planning agency in Florida, says that winning this contest would help her increase her knowledge base and provide in-depth, personal experience offering more destination wedding destinations.

1985 ■ *"Online Security Crackdown"* in Chain Store Age (Vol. 84, July 2008, No. 7, pp. 46)

Ed: Samantha Murphy. **Description:** Online retailers are beefing up security on their Websites. Cyber thieves use retail systems in order to gain entry to consumer data. David's Bridal operates over 275 bridal showrooms in the U.S. and has a one-stop wedding resource for new brides planning weddings. **Availability:** Online.

1986 ■ *"The Owyhee Is Filling Up Faster Than Expected"* in Idaho Business Review (September 5, 2014)

Pub: BridgeTower Media
Contact: Adam Reinebach, President

Description: Clay Carley discusses his idea to renovate the 104-year-old Owyhee Hotel into a modern office, residential and commercial center. He transformed the building's rooftop into an event space for weddings and other celebrations. Carley is the developer and part-owner of the property and reported 3,000 people attending its ribbon cutting. Retail and office space are filling faster than expected and the rooftop venue has already celebrated six weddings.

1987 ■ *"Paradise Banquet Hall of Toronto: Breaking Traditions Can Keep a Wedding Budget Intact"* in Internet Wire (June 12, 2012)

Description: Average wedding costs can reach nearly $27,000 and that amount does not inclue honeymoon, wedding shower, engagement party, or bachelor/bachelorette parties. Paradise Banquet Hall of Toronto uses Donna Freedman's approach to planning a wedding on a budget. Details are included. **Availability:** Print; Online.

1988 ■ *"Person To Watch: Wedding Planner Brings Energy to Her Job"* in Chattanooga Times/Free Press (April 24, 2012)

Ed: Karen Nazor Hill. **Description:** Profile of Morgan Holland, 28-year-old founder of Soirees of Chattanooga. Weddings are a large part of Holland's event planning business, with parties for nonprofits, birthday parties, and private parties making up the other 15 percent. **Availability:** Print; Online.

1989 ■ *"Plan Your Next Event at Newport News Marriott at City Center"* in Benzinga.com (July 29, 2011)

Pub: PR Newswire Association LLC.

Description: Newport News Marriott at City Center is promoting itself as the premier venue for business meetings, conventions and weddings.

1990 ■ *"Plan Your Wedding with Cleveland Airport Marriott's Certified Event Planners"* in Benzinga.com (February 2, 2011)

Description: Cleveland's Airport Marriott makes wedding planning easy with its venue spaces and a full team of wedding planners. **Availability:** Print; Online.

1991 ■ *"Planning a Wedding Fit for a Royal? Read This First, Urge Legal & General"* in Marketwired (April 21, 2011)

Released: April 21, 2011. **Description:** When planning a wedding, the author suggests checking life insurance to be sure you are covered for any situations that may arise. **Availability:** Print; Online.

1992 ■ *"Renren Partners With Recruit to Launch Social Wedding Services"* in Benzinga.com (June 7, 2011)

Pub: PR Newswire Association LLC.

Description: Renren Inc., the leading real name social networking Internet platform in China has partnered with Recruit Company Limited, Japan's largest human resource and classified media group to form a joint venture to build a wedding social media catering to the needs of engaged couples and newlyweds in China.

1993 ■ *"Say Yes to the New Wedding Collection from Pinhole Press"* in Benzinga.com (May 1, 2012)

Pub: Benzinga.com
Contact: Jason Raznick, Founder

Ed: Aaron Wise. **Description:** Online retailer, Pinhole Press, providing personalized photo gifts has introduced a new Edding Collection that includes wedding invitations, save the dates, bridal shower sets, wedding gifts and more. Further details of the new wedding collection are included. **Availability:** Online.

1994 ■ *"Social Work Professor's Bridal Shop Helps Those Living With Cancer"* **in The University Record (August 13, 2018)**
URL(s): record.umich.edu/articles/social-work-professors-bridal-shop-helps-those-living-cancer/
Ed: Safiya Merchant. **Released:** August 13, 2018. **Description:** The Brides Project in Ann Arbor collects donated wedding dresses and at a discount, sells them to brides. Even better, the proceeds all goes towards people suffering from Cancer and their caregivers. **Availability:** Online.

1995 ■ *"Sylvie Collection Offers a Feminine Perspective and Voice in Male Dominated Bridal Industry"* **in Benzinga.com (October 29, 2011)**
Description: Bridal jewelry designer Sylvie Levine has created over 1,000 customizable styles of engagement rings and wedding bands and is reaching out to prospective new brides through a new Website, interactive social media campaign and monthly trunk show appearances. **Availability:** Online.

1996 ■ *"TLC's 'Jumping the Broom' Red Carpet Wedding Contest"* **in Benzinga.com (March 30, 2011)**
Pub: Benzinga.com
Contact: Jason Raznick, Founder
Description: The Learning Channel's 'Jumping the Broom' Red Carpet Wedding Contest provides couples the chance to marry or renew vows at the star-studded Hollywood premier of the new film. **Availability:** Print; Online.

1997 ■ *"TripIt Itineraries Show Labor Day is the Most Popular Weekend for Wedding Travel"* **in Benzinga.com (August 26, 2011)**
Pub: Benzinga.com
Contact: Jason Raznick, Founder
Description: According to TripIt, the leading mobile trip organizer, Labor Day is the most popular weekend to travel for weddings between the months of April and August. **Availability:** Online.

1998 ■ *"Trousseaus of Memories Trail Behind Wedding Gowns"* **in Oregonian (September 4, 2010)**
Pub: The Oregonian
Contact: John Maher, President
Ed: Anne Saker. **Description:** Readers are asked to share stories about their wedding gowns and what that garment meant to them at the time and now. **Availability:** Online.

1999 ■ *"Wedding Bells on a Budget: Cash Saving Tips for the Big Day"* **in Benzinga.com (June 11, 2011)**
Pub: Benzinga.com
Contact: Jason Raznick, Founder

Description: Typical American weddings cost about $24,000 with most couples spending between $18,000 to $30,000; a checklist and budget are critical. Nine ideas to help couples plan for their big day are outlined. **Availability:** Online.

2000 ■ *"Wedding Present Shopping - What to Get the Couple Who Have Everything"* **in Benzinga.com (April 19, 2011)**
Released: April 19, 2011. **Description:** Tips for purchasing the perfect wedding gift are outlined. **Availability:** Online.

2001 ■ *"WeddingChannel.com Reviews Tops More than 200,000 Wedding Reviews"* **in Benzinga.com (June 23, 2011)**
Description: WeddingChannel.com is the leading wedding and gift registry Website for soon-to-be brides with search and review information on over 130,000 of the wedding industry's top vendors and even allows vendors to interact with the prospective brides. **Availability:** Print; Online.

2002 ■ *"Where to Find Bridesmaid Dresses for Less"* **in The New York Times (July 4, 2018)**
URL(s): www.nytimes.com/2018/07/04/fashion/weddings/where-to-find-bridesmaid-dresses-for-less.html
Ed: Marianne Rohrlich. **Released:** July 04, 2018. **Description:** With bridesmaids dresses, and alterations, costing much more than the average bridesmaid wants to spend, there are several good alternatives to the standard dress shop. Several clothes shops are highlighted, along with eBay, where dresses can be found for a fraction of the price. **Availability:** Online.

STATISTICAL SOURCES

2003 ■ *Lingerie, Swimwear & Bridal Stores Industry in the US - Market Research Report*
URL(s): www.ibisworld.com/united-states/market-research-reports/lingerie-swimwear-bridal-stores-industry/
Price: $925. **Description:** Downloadable report analyzing the current and future trends in the lingerie, swimwear, and bridal store industries. **Availability:** Download.

TRADE PERIODICALS

2004 ■ *ABC Dialogue*
Pub: Association of Bridal Consultants
Contact: David M. Wood, III, President
Released: 6/year **Price:** $24, Members for 1 yr associate. **Description:** Explores the various aspects of wedding consulting, including bridal attire, jewelry, food, photography, and business management and advertising. Recurring features include business tips and profiles of members. **Availability:** Print.

2005 ■ *Bridal Guide*
Pub: RFP Corp.

Contact: Rita Sadowski, Vice President, Creative Development
URL(s): www.bridalguide.com
Facebook: www.facebook.com/bridalguide
Linkedin: www.linkedin.com/company-beta/57909
X (Twitter): Twitter.com/bridalguidemag
Instagram: www.instagram.com/bridalguide
YouTube: www.youtube.com/@BridalGuideMagazine
Pinterest: www.pinterest.com/bridalguide
Released: Bimonthly **Price:** $9.95, for one year. **Description:** Magazine. **Availability:** Print; Online.

2006 ■ *MunaLuchi Bride*
Pub: MunaLuchi
URL(s): www.munaluchibridal.com
Linkedin: www.linkedin.com/company/munaluchi
X (Twitter): twitter.com/munaluchibride
Instagram: www.instagram.com/munaluchibride
YouTube: www.youtube.com/channel/UCT08xk5dHp6iVXTvSM25zqA
Pinterest: www.pinterest.com/munaluchibride
Released: Quarterly **Price:** $22.75, Single issue for Issue No. 29 - Summer 2023 (PRE-ORDER). **Description:** Wedding publication that caters to women of color. **Availability:** Print; Online.

2007 ■ *Vows: The Bridal and Wedding Business Journal*
Pub: Grimes and Associates Inc.
Contact: Karl Nazarro, Creative Director
E-mail: karl@vowsmagazine.com
URL(s): www.vowsmagazine.com/home
Facebook: www.facebook.com/VOWSMAGAZINE
Ed: Shannon Hurd. **Released:** Bimonthly **Price:** $30, for 1 year 6 issues; $52, for 2 years 12 issues; $89, Canada for 2 years 12 issue; $55, Canada for 1 year 6 issues; $139, for 2 year international surface; $89, for 1 year international surface; $199, for 2 years international air; $129, for 1 year international air. **Description:** Trade journal for bridal and wedding professionals. **Availability:** Print; Online.

TRADE SHOWS AND CONVENTIONS

2008 ■ *Business of Brides Annual Conference*
Association of Bridal Consultants (ABC)
632 Federal Rd., Ste. 2
Brookfield, CT 06804
Ph: (860)355-7000
Fax: (203)775-0037
Co. E-mail: info@bridalassn.com
URL: http://bridalassn.com
Contact: David M. Wood, III, President
URL(s): www.abcweddingplanners.com/2024wow
Frequency: Annual. **Description:** Bridal and wedding consulting equipment, supplies, and services. **Audience:** Wedding professionals. **Principal Exhibits:** Bridal and wedding consulting equipment, supplies, and services. Dates and Locations: 2025. **Telecommunication Services:** education@abcweddingplanners.com.

Building/Home Inspection Service

START-UP INFORMATION

2009 ■ *"WIN Home Inspection Garners Recognition as 2012 Military Friendly Franchise by G.I. Jobs Magazine"* in *Entertainment Close-Up (May 21, 2012)*
Description: G.I. Jobs Magazine ranked WIN Home Inspection in the top ten franchises thoughout the United States on its 2012 Military Friendly Franchises. Veterans represent 1/4 of the firm's franchisee base, offering realistic opportunities for vets to become successful. Details of the training and skills involved and what it takes to be selected to launch a WIN franchise are included. **Availability:** Print; Online.

ASSOCIATIONS AND OTHER ORGANIZATIONS

2010 ■ **American Institute of Inspectors (AII)**
PO Box 7243
South Lake Tahoe, CA 96158
Free: 800-877-4770
Co. E-mail: info@inspection.org
URL: http://www.inspection.org
Contact: Perry Hawkins, Chairman of the Board
Description: Certified home inspectors. Works to set standards for impartial evaluations of residential properties. Certifies members in four areas: residential homes, mobile homes, mechanics, and earthquake hazard reduction. Maintains speakers' bureau. **Founded:** 1989. **Geographic Preference:** National.

2011 ■ **Canadian Association of Home and Property Inspectors (CAHPI)**
832 March Rd.
Ottawa, ON, Canada K2W 0E1
Ph: (613)227-3919
Co. E-mail: info@cahpi.ca
URL: http://www.cahpi.ca/en
Contact: Peter Weeks, President
E-mail: president@cahpi.ca
Facebook: www.facebook.com/Canadian-Association
-of-Home-Property-Inspectors-560275667458106
Linkedin: www.linkedin.com/company/canadian
-association-of-home-property-inspectors-cahpi
Description: Seeks to insure adherence to high standards of ethics and practice among Canadian home inspectors. Represents members' collective interests. **Founded:** 1982. **Publications:** *The Canadian Home Inspector* (Semiannual). **Awards:** CAHPI President's Award (Annual); Stephen Greenford Award (Annual). **Geographic Preference:** National.

2012 ■ *The Canadian Home Inspector*
832 March Rd.
Ottawa, ON, Canada K2W 0E1
Ph: (613)227-3919
Co. E-mail: info@cahpi.ca
URL: http://www.cahpi.ca/en
Contact: Peter Weeks, President
E-mail: president@cahpi.ca
URL(s): www.cahpi.ca/fr/255-francais/chi-magazine
Released: Semiannual **Availability:** Print; Online.

2013 ■ *Construction Canada*
15 Wertheim Ct., Ste. 710
Richmond Hill, ON, Canada L4B 3H7
Ph: (905)771-7333
Free: 800-409-8688
Fax: (905)771-7336
Co. E-mail: sales@kenilworth.com
URL: http://www.kenilworth.com
Contact: Erik Tolles, Chief Executive Officer
URL(s): www.constructioncanada.net
X (Twitter): x.com/constructCanMag
Instagram: www.instagram.com/constructcanmag
Released: 9/year **Price:** $120, for 1 year foreign; $88, U.S. for 1 year; $56, Canada. **Description:** Magazine covers architecture and engineering construction. **Availability:** Print; Online.

2014 ■ **Construction Specifications Canada (CSC)**
120 Carlton St., Ste. 312
Toronto, ON, Canada 652452
Ph: (416)777-2198
Fax: (416)777-2197
Co. E-mail: info@csc-dcc.ca
URL: http://www.csc-dcc.ca
Contact: Kimberly Tompkins, President
E-mail: kim@tecagencies.com
Facebook: www.facebook.com/CSCDCC
Linkedin: www.linkedin.com/company/construction
-specifications-canada
X (Twitter): x.com/csc_dcc
Instagram: www.instagram.com/csc_dcc
Description: Seeks to insure adherence to high standards of practice in the building industries. **Founded:** 1954. **Publications:** *Construction Canada* (9/year); *National Master Specification (NMS)*; *Construction Specifications Canada--Directory of Members* (Annual); *Chapter Specifiers* (10/year); *CSC News in Brief* (Bimonthly). **Awards:** CSC Chapter Award of Merit (Annual); Lloyd Boddy Chapter of the Year Award (Annual); CSC-DCC President's Award (Periodic). **Geographic Preference:** National.

INCUBATORS/RESEARCH AND TECHNOLOGY PARKS

2015 ■ **Builder Incubator**
PO Box 3335
Plant City, FL 33566
Ph: (813)626-8778
URL: http://www.builderincubator.com
Facebook: www.facebook.com/BuilderIncubator
Linkedin: www.linkedin.com/company/builder
-incubator
X (Twitter): x.com/buildrincubator
Description: Provides home builders of all sizes, and in particular entry-level home builders, a fully integrated system of services designed specifically for their industry at significant cost savings.

REFERENCE WORKS

2016 ■ *"4 Signs You Hired a Bad Home Inspector"* in *U.S.News & World Report (August 28, 2015)*
URL(s): realestate.usnews.com/real-estate/articles/
signs-you-hired-a-bad-home-inspector
Ed: Geoff Williams. **Released:** August 28, 2015. **Description:** Investigates four signs that the home inspector you hired isn't up to par with the job you need done. Bringing in a second inspector is an option for many who suspect their original inspector is not up to the job. **Availability:** Online.

2017 ■ *"April is National Home Inspection Month"* in *Internet Wire (April 27, 2012)*
Pub: Comtex News Network Inc.
Contact: Kan Devnani, President
Description: The month of April has been designated National Home Inspection Month. The importance of a home inspection when buying or selling a home is stressed. A home inspector checks for structural and safety issues, check the foundation, as well as safety hazards. **Availability:** Online.

2018 ■ *"Builder Confidence Continues Cautious Increase"* in *Small Business Trends (March 16, 2023).*
URL(s): smallbiztrends.com/2023/03/builder-confi
dence-continues-cautious-increase.html
Released: March 16, 2023. **Description:** The National Association of Home Builders (NAHB) announced builders confidence is up to 44%, which is a slight raise. Contains an explanation of how the number is calculated. **Availability:** Online.

TRADE PERIODICALS

2019 ■ *The Appraisers Standard*
Pub: New England Appraisers Association
URL(s): www.newenglandappraisers.org/
membership/fees-for-membership
Description: Trade magazine for personal property appraisers. **Availability:** Online.

2020 ■ *The Construction Specifier*
Pub: Construction Specifications Institute
Contact: Mark Dorsey, Chief Executive Officer
E-mail: ceo@csinet.org
URL(s): www.constructionspecifier.com
X (Twitter): x.com/specifiermagcsi
Released: Monthly **Description:** Provides architects, engineers, specifiers, contractors, and others with technical information on construction materials, methods, and products. **Availability:** Print; Online.

CONSULTANTS

2021 ■ **Applied Fire Protection Engineering, Inc.**
14401 Sweitzer Ln., Ste. 40
Laurel, MD 20707
Ph: (301)595-5558

URL: http://afpe.us

Description: Provider of comprehensive consulting services in the field of fire protection as well as annual testing and maintenance of fire alarm systems, fire pumps and sprinkler systems. **Scope:** Provider of comprehensive consulting services in the field of fire protection as well as annual testing and maintenance of fire alarm systems, fire pumps and sprinkler systems.

2022 ■ Breen & Associates Inc.
161 Great Frontier Dr.
 Georgetown, TX 78633-4595
Contact: James E. Breen, President
Description: Firm provides structural, foundation and drainage evaluation services.

2023 ■ Foit-Albert Associates, Architecture, Engineering and Surveying, P.C.
295 Main St., Ste. 200
 Buffalo, NY 14203
Ph: (716)856-3933
Fax: (716)856-3961
Co. E-mail: info@foit-albert.com
URL: http://foit-albert.com
Contact: Gregory R. Carballada, President
E-mail: gcarballada@foit-albert.com
Facebook: www.facebook.com/foitalbertassociates
Linkedin: www.linkedin.com/company/foit-albert-associates
X (Twitter): x.com/foitalbert
Description: Provider of architecture, engineering and land surveying solutions. **Founded:** 1977.

2024 ■ InspectAmerica Engineering P.C.
3 School St.
 White Plains, NY 10606
Ph: (914)682-9090
URL: http://www.inspectamerica.com
Contact: E. M. Frank, President
Description: Provider of engineering inspection services for pre-purchase purposes, condominium and cooperative conversions and inspections to analyze and design remedies for problems in homes and buildings and their services include commercial and residential properties and serves real estate, lawyers, bankers, property management, landlords, investors and government agencies. **Scope:** Provider of engineering inspection services for pre-purchase purposes, condominium and cooperative conversions and inspections to analyze and design remedies for problems in homes and buildings and their services include commercial and residential properties and serves real estate, lawyers, bankers, property management, landlords, investors and government agencies. **Founded:** 1974. **Publications:** "Home Inspectors Check for Termites"; "Structural Inspection"; "Healthy Home Inspection". **Special Services:** Home Inspection SuperSite™; Home Inspection TechTalk™; InspectAmerica®.

2025 ■ Kohn Engineering
4220 Mountain Rd.
 Macungie, PA 18062
Ph: (610)967-4766
Co. E-mail: kohnengineering@ptd.net
URL: http://www.kohnengineering.com
Contact: Don Kohn, Contact
Description: Provider of fire protection engineering services. **Scope:** Provider of fire protection engineering services. **Founded:** 1995. **Training:** Fire Protection in Nuclear Power Plants.

2026 ■ Middle Department Inspection Agency, Inc. (MDIA)
Route 19
 Wexford, PA 15090
Contact: Glenn G. Beave, President
Description: Firm offers code inspections, periodic inspections, plan reviews and various other inspection related services. **Founded:** 1883. **Special Services:** IBC®; IRC®; ICC®; CABO®; BOCA®.

2027 ■ N.R. Goldstein and Associates
1200 Rte. 130
 Robbinsville, NJ 08691
Ph: (609)426-1888

Co. E-mail: mail@lawdiary.com
URL: http://www.lawdiary.com
Description: Provider of forensic safety services regarding slips and falls, machine guarding, construction and building codes and primarily serves attorneys and insurance carriers. **Scope:** Provider of forensic safety services regarding slips and falls, machine guarding, construction and building codes and primarily serves attorneys and insurance carriers. **Founded:** 1987.

2028 ■ Professional Engineering Inspections Inc.
PO Box 859
 Friendswood, TX 77549
Ph: (713)664-1264
URL: http://profengineering.com
Contact: Edward G. Robinson, President
Facebook: www.facebook.com/Professional.Engineering.Inspections
X (Twitter): x.com/profengineering
Description: Firm provides residential and commercial inspection and consulting services. **Scope:** Firm provides residential and commercial inspection and consulting services.

2029 ■ Trendzitions Inc.
25691 Atlantic Ocean, Dr. No. B13
 Lake Forest, CA 92630
Ph: (949)727-9100
URL: http://www.trendzitions.com
Contact: Chris Tooker, President
E-mail: ctooker@trendzitions.com
X (Twitter): x.com/trendzitions
Instagram: www.instagram.com/trendzitions
Description: Provider of services in the areas of communications consulting, project management, construction management, and furniture procurement. Offers information on spatial uses, building codes, ADA compliance and city ordinances. Also offers budget projections. **Scope:** Provider of services in the areas of communications consulting, project management, construction management, and furniture procurement. Offers information on spatial uses, building codes, ADA compliance and city ordinances. Also offers budget projections. **Founded:** 1986.

FRANCHISES AND BUSINESS OPPORTUNITIES

2030 ■ AmeriSpec Inspection Service
5462 Timberlea Blvd.
 Mississauga, ON, Canada L4W 2T7
Ph: (416)410-0909
Free: 866-284-6010
Co. E-mail: info@amerispec.ca
URL: http://www.amerispec.ca
Facebook: www.facebook.com/amerispeccanada
X (Twitter): x.com/amerispeccanada
Description: Home inspection franchise in North America. **Founded:** 1987. **Training:** Yes.

2031 ■ The BrickKicker
849 N Ellsworth St.
 Naperville, IL 60563
Free: 800-821-1820
Fax: (630)420-2270
Co. E-mail: request@brickkicker.com
URL: http://www.brickkicker.com
Contact: Ron Ewald, Co-Founder
Facebook: www.facebook.com/The.BrickKicker
X (Twitter): x.com/BrickKickerHQ
Description: Building inspection service. **No. of Franchise Units:** 152. **Founded:** 1989. **Franchised:** 1995. **Equity Capital Needed:** $15,000-$40,000. **Franchise Fee:** $9,000-$40,000. **Financial Assistance:** Yes **Training:** Yes.

2032 ■ The Hometeam Inspection Services Inc.
575 Chamber Dr.
 Milford, OH 45150
Free: 800-755-4847
Co. E-mail: info@hometeam.com
URL: http://www.hometeam.com

Facebook: www.facebook.com/HomeTeamInspectionFans
Linkedin: www.linkedin.com/company/hometeam-inspection-service
X (Twitter): x.com/HomeTeamInspect
Instagram: www.instagram.com/hometeaminspectionservice
YouTube: www.youtube.com/channel/UCmY-2CwaQsEafz67RywHBrg
Description: Provider of home inspection services for home buyers and home sellers. **Founded:** 1998. **Financial Assistance:** Yes **Training:** 14 day comprehensive training program at corporate office.

2033 ■ Housemaster, Home Inspections, Done Right
92 E Main St., Ste. 301
 Somerville, NJ 08876
Free: 800-526-3939
Co. E-mail: dw.sales@housemaster.com
URL: http://housemaster.com
Facebook: www.facebook.com/HouseMasterHomeInspections
Linkedin: www.linkedin.com/company/housemaster
X (Twitter): x.com/housemaster
Description: Home inspections for home buyers and sellers. **Founded:** 1971. **Training:** Offers 2-5 weeks of initial training.

2034 ■ ImageOne Janitorial Service Inc.
658 Douglas Ave., Ste. 1110
 Altamonte Springs, FL 32714
Ph: (407)862-8300
Co. E-mail: customerservice@imageonejanitorial.com
URL: http://www.imageonejanitorial.com
Contact: Jeff Hiers, President
Description: Provides Customized Commercial Cleaning Services. **Founded:** 2001.

2035 ■ Inspect-It 1st L.L.C.
446 E Meadow Ave., Ste. 238
 East Meadow, NY 11554
Ph: (516)662-1746
Co. E-mail: info@inspectit1stny.com
URL: http://www.inspectit1st.com
Facebook: www.facebook.com/inspectit1st.home.inspectors
Linkedin: www.linkedin.com/company/inspect-it-1st
X (Twitter): x.com/Inspect_It_1st
Description: Provider of professional home and building inspection services. **Founded:** 1991. **Equity Capital Needed:** Minimum investment of $30,000. **Financial Assistance:** Yes **Training:** Provides 10 days in Phoenix with ongoing support.

2036 ■ Lighthouse Inspections Canada
6-2400 Dundas St. W, Ste. 731
 Mississauga, ON, Canada L5K 2R8
Ph: (905)822-7889
Free: 888-505-7887
Co. E-mail: info@lighthouseinspections.com
URL: http://lighthouseinspections.com
Facebook: www.facebook.com/lighthousehomeinspections
Description: Provider of home inspection services. **Founded:** 1999. **Franchise Fee:** $20,000. **Training:** Minimum 3 weeks initial training, ongoing support, seminars and re-certification.

2037 ■ National Property Inspections (NPI)
9375 Burt St., Ste. 201
 Omaha, NE 68114
Free: 800-333-9807
Co. E-mail: info@npiweb.com
URL: http://www.npiweb.com
Contact: Roland Bates, Founder
Facebook: www.facebook.com/npifranchise
Linkedin: www.linkedin.com/company/national-property-inspections-inc
X (Twitter): x.com/NPIFranchise

Founded: 1987. **Financial Assistance:** Yes **Training:** 2 weeks of training at our home office, plus a third optional week in the field with a veteran NPI inspector in our mentor program.

2038 ■ Pillar to Post Inc. (PTP)
FirstService Brands
　14502 N Dale Mabry Hwy., Ste. 200
　Tampa, FL 33618
Free: 866-366-0420
Fax: (601)549-7973
URL: http://www.fsvbrands.com
Contact: Dan Steward, President
Facebook: www.facebook.com/pillartopost
Linkedin: www.linkedin.com/company/pillar-to-post
X (Twitter): x.com/pillartopost
Description: Provider of home inspection services including franchises, training and investment services. **No. of Franchise Units:** 450. **Founded:** 1994. **Franchised:** 1994. **Training:** Yes.

2039 ■ Pillar to Post Inc.
Mississauga, ON, Canada
Free: 800-294-5591
Co. E-mail: marketing@pillartopost.com
URL: http://pillartopost.com
Contact: Dan Steward, President
Facebook: www.facebook.com/pillartopost
Linkedin: www.linkedin.com/company/pillar-to-post
X (Twitter): x.com/pillartopost
Description: Provider of home inspection services including franchises, training and investment services. **Royalty Fee:** 7%. **Financial Assistance:** Yes **Training:** Offers 2 weeks of training and ongoing support.

2040 ■ Sharkey's Cuts For Kids
37 Highland Rd.
　Westport, CT 06880
Ph: (203)637-8911
Co. E-mail: info@sharkeyscutsforkids.com
URL: http://sharkeyscutsforkids.com
Contact: Scott Sharkey, Contact
Facebook: www.facebook.com/SharkeysFranchise
Linkedin: www.linkedin.com/in/scottsharkeys
X (Twitter): x.com/SharkeysHair
Description: Kids' salon, including Flat Screen/Fun Chairs/PS2, Gamecube, X-box/Rides/Pinball/Glamour Parties/Party Favors, and Karaoke Parties for Moms. **Founded:** 2002. **Equity Capital Needed:** $114,920 to $150,495. **Financial Assistance:** Yes **Training:** Yes.

2041 ■ The Snip-Its Corp.
211 River Ridge Cir. S, No. 100
　Burnsville, MN 55337
Free: 877-SNI-PITS
Co. E-mail: products@snipits.com
URL: http://www.snipits.com
Facebook: www.facebook.com/snipitssalons
X (Twitter): x.com/SnipitsSalons
Instagram: www.instagram.com/snipitssalons
YouTube: www.youtube.com/user/SnipitsSalons
Pinterest: www.pinterest.com/snipitssalons
Description: Firm provides kids salon services. **Founded:** 1993.

2042 ■ WIN Home Inspection
Madison, AL
Free: 800-309-6753
Co. E-mail: info@wini.com
URL: http://wini.com
Facebook: www.facebook.com/WINHomeInspection
Linkedin: www.linkedin.com/company/winhomeinspection
X (Twitter): x.com/winhomeinspect
Instagram: www.instagram.com/winhomeinspection
Description: Firm provides home and property inspection services for home buyers, home sellers, home owners and real estate professionals. **Founded:** 1993. **Training:** Yes.

Building Maintenance/Custodial Service

START-UP INFORMATION

2043 ■ *"Cleaning Service Companies in Oklahoma Find Green Market Niche" in Journal Record (April 19, 2012)*
Pub: BridgeTower Media
Contact: Adam Reinebach, President
Ed: Brianna Bailey. **Description:** Well Maid was launched in 2010 when owner, Candace Lockett, grew frustrated with trying to find a cleaning service that refrained from using harsh chemicals. Her service uses common household products such as olive oil and baking soda in order to environmentally responsible. Well Maid's green philosophy is helping to grow the new firm.

2044 ■ *"Fast-Growing Office Pride Franchise Targets Louisville For Expansion" in Internet Wire (September 9, 2014)*
Pub: Comtex News Network Inc.
Contact: Kan Devnani, President
Description: Office Pride is a commercial cleaning service that is built on principles that include: honesty, trustworthy service, excellence, and treating everyone with dignity and respect. The commercial cleaning franchise is seeking a developer to help expand its business in Louisville, Kentucky. **Availability:** Online.

2045 ■ *"Nude Maid Service Could Face Fines" in UPI NewsTrack (April 10, 2012)*
Pub: United Press International Inc.
Contact: Nicholas Chiaia, President
Description: Lubbock Fantasy Maid Service, located in Texas, is facing fines because it is operating without a permit. The cleaning service provides maids dresses in lingerie, topless or nude. Without the permit, the firm could face fines of $2,000 daily. The company reports it is doing nothing illegally. **Availability:** Online.

ASSOCIATIONS AND OTHER ORGANIZATIONS

2046 ■ **Building Service Contractors Association International (BSCAI)**
330 N Wabash Ave., Ste. 2000
Chicago, IL 60611
Ph: (312)321-5167
Free: 800-368-3414
Fax: (312)673-6735
Co. E-mail: info@bscai.org
URL: http://www.bscai.org
Contact: Eric Luke, President
Linkedin: www.linkedin.com/company/building-service-contractors-association-international
X (Twitter): x.com/BSCAI
YouTube: www.youtube.com/user/BSCAI
Description: Seeks to provide a unified voice for building service contractors and to promote increased recognition by government, property owners and the general business and professional public. **Founded:** 1965. **Publications:** *Who's Who in Building Service Contracting* (Annual); *Contractor Connections*; *Services: The Magazine for the Building Service Contracting Industry* (Bimonthly). **Awards:** BSCAI Awards and Recognition (Annual). **Geographic Preference:** Multinational.

2047 ■ **Canadian Association of Environmental Management (CAEM) [Association Canadienne de Gestion Environnementale]**
Canada
URL: http://www.caenvironmentalmanagement.com
Description: Seeks to advance the environmental profession; promotes adherence to high standards of ethics and practice by members. **Founded:** 1972. **Publications:** *The Quarterly* (Quarterly). **Awards:** CAEM CEH Certification (Annual). **Geographic Preference:** National.

2048 ■ **Cleaning Management Institute (CMI)**
3300 Dundee Rd.
Northbrook, IL 60062
Ph: (847)982-0800
Free: 800-225-4772
Co. E-mail: membership@issa.com
URL: http://cmi.issa.com
Contact: Brant Insero, Director
Description: Represents individuals and organizations active in cleaning maintenance and management, including contract cleaner firms. Develops home study educational courses and publications to promote professional certification, self-improvement, and efficient work methods. **Founded:** 1964. **Publications:** *Cleaning and Maintenance Management (CMM)* (Bimonthly). **Geographic Preference:** National.

2049 ■ **International Facility Management Association - Toronto Chapter (IFMA)**
7398 Yonge St, 6D
Thornhill, ON, Canada L4J 8J2
Ph: (416)346-4729
Fax: (866)461-6469
Co. E-mail: admin@ifma-toronto.org
URL: http://ifma-toronto.org
Contact: Stuart James Ross, President
Facebook: www.facebook.com/ifmatoronto1
Linkedin: www.linkedin.com/company/ifmatoronto1
X (Twitter): x.com/IFMAToronto1
Instagram: www.instagram.com/ifmatoronto1
Description: Promotes professionalism in the practice of facilities management; encourages professional advancement of members. **Founded:** 1982. **Publications:** *Facility Management Journal (FMJ)* (Bimonthly); *IFMA Membership Services Directory* (Periodic); *IFMA News* (Weekly); *Toronto News*. **Educational Activities:** IFMA's World Workplace Conference & Expo (Annual). **Geographic Preference:** Multinational.

2050 ■ **International Sanitary Supply Association (ISSA) - Reference Library**
10275 W. Higgins Rd., Ste. 280
Rosemont, IL 60018
Ph: (847)982-0800
Free: 800-225-4772
Fax: (847)982-1012
Co. E-mail: membership@issa.com
URL: http://www.issa.com
Facebook: www.facebook.com/issaworldwide
Linkedin: www.linkedin.com/company/issaworldwide
X (Twitter): x.com/issaworldwide
Instagram: www.instagram.com/issaworldwide
Description: Manufacturers, distributors, wholesalers, manufacturer representatives, publishers, and associate members of cleaning and maintenance supplies, chemicals, and equipment used by janitors, custodians, and maintenance workers in all types of industrial, commercial, and institutional buildings. Represents members in 83 countries. Offers specialized education seminars. **Scope:** Information to facilitate your compliance with various rules and regulations that are of particular relevance to the cleaning industry. **Founded:** 1923. **Holdings:** Figures not available. **Publications:** *ISSA Today* (Bimonthly); *Legislative and Regulatory Roundup* (Irregular). **Awards:** International Sanitary Supply Association Foundation Scholarships (Annual). **Geographic Preference:** Multinational.

2051 ■ **Sanitary Supply Wholesaling Association (SSWA)**
1432 Riverwalk Ct.
Waterville, OH 43566
Ph: (419)878-2787
Co. E-mail: dfrendt@sswa.com
URL: http://sswa.com
Contact: Chris Ford, President
Linkedin: www.linkedin.com/company/sanitary-supply-wholesalers-association
Description: Wholesalers and manufacturers of janitorial supplies and/or paper products. Seeks to create integrity and recognition of wholesale distribution in the sanitary supply industry. **Founded:** 1980. **Awards:** Stanley E. Friedman Award of Merit (Periodic). **Geographic Preference:** National.

EDUCATIONAL PROGRAMS

2052 ■ **Air Conditioning and Refrigeration (Onsite)**
TPC Trainco Inc.
225 E Robinson St., Ste. 570
Orlando, FL 32801
Free: 877-978-7246
Co. E-mail: sales@tpctraining.com
URL: http://live.tpctraining.com
URL(s): live.tpctraining.com/public-seminars/hvac-training/air-conditioning-refrigeration
Description: A two-day course for building, plant, and facility maintenance personnel. Covers understanding principles, components and systems, maintenance, troubleshooting, and operating efficiency. **Audience:** Air conditioning and refrigeration professionals. **Principal Exhibits:** A two-day course for building, plant, and facility maintenance person-

nel. Covers understanding principles, components and systems, maintenance, troubleshooting, and operating efficiency.

2053 ■ Basic Electricity for the Non Electrician
TPC Trainco Inc.
  225 E Robinson St., Ste. 570
  Orlando, FL 32801
Free: 877-978-7246
Co. E-mail: sales@tpctraining.com
URL: http://live.tpctraining.com
URL(s): live.tpctraining.com/public-seminars/electrical-training/fundamentals/basic-electrical-training
Description: A two-day, in-house, hands-on training course for building, plant, and facility maintenance personnel. **Audience:** Building, plant and facility maintenance professionals. **Principal Exhibits:** A two-day, in-house, hands-on training course for building, plant, and facility maintenance personnel.

2054 ■ Boiler Operation, Maintenance and Safety
TPC Trainco Inc.
  225 E Robinson St., Ste. 570
  Orlando, FL 32801
Free: 877-978-7246
Co. E-mail: sales@tpctraining.com
URL: http://live.tpctraining.com
URL(s): live.tpctraining.com/public-seminars/hvac-training/boiler-operation-maintenance-safety-training
Description: A two-day in-house training course for everyday building, plant, and facility maintenance. **Audience:** Industry professionals. **Principal Exhibits:** A two-day in-house training course for everyday building, plant, and facility maintenance.

2055 ■ Electric Motors, Drives and Control Circuits
TPC Trainco Inc.
  225 E Robinson St., Ste. 570
  Orlando, FL 32801
Free: 877-978-7246
Co. E-mail: sales@tpctraining.com
URL: http://live.tpctraining.com
URL(s): live.tpctraining.com/public-seminars/electrical-training/electrical-controls/electric-motors-and-motor-control-circuits
Description: A practical in-house course for maintenance personnel working in industrial plants, public facilities, and commercial buildings. **Audience:** Technicians and industry professionals. **Principal Exhibits:** A practical in-house course for maintenance personnel working in industrial plants, public facilities, and commercial buildings.

2056 ■ HVAC Controls and Air Distribution (Onsite)
TPC Trainco Inc.
  225 E Robinson St., Ste. 570
  Orlando, FL 32801
Free: 877-978-7246
Co. E-mail: sales@tpctraining.com
URL: http://live.tpctraining.com
URL(s): live.tpctraining.com/public-seminars/hvac-training/hvac-electrical-controls-air-distribution
Description: A two-day course that teaches how to maximize HVAC comfort and efficiency. **Audience:** Building maintenance technicians, supervisors, building owners, managers, engineers and industry professionals. **Principal Exhibits:** A two-day course that teaches how to maximize HVAC comfort and efficiency.

2057 ■ Maintenance Welding (Onsite)
TPC Trainco Inc.
  225 E Robinson St., Ste. 570
  Orlando, FL 32801
Free: 877-978-7246
Co. E-mail: sales@tpctraining.com
URL: http://live.tpctraining.com
URL(s): www.seminarinformation.com/qqbtyt/maintenance-welding
Description: Covers the fundamental, practical applications, and best practices of maintenance welding. **Audience:** Welders, maintenance and repair personnel, multi-craft technicians, fabricators, maintenance supervisors and managers and inspectors. **Principal Exhibits:** Covers the fundamental, practical applications, and best practices of maintenance welding.

2058 ■ Total Productive Maintenance and 5S
TPC Trainco Inc.
  225 E Robinson St., Ste. 570
  Orlando, FL 32801
Free: 877-978-7246
Co. E-mail: sales@tpctraining.com
URL: http://live.tpctraining.com
URL(s): live.tpctraining.com/public-seminars/plant-management/total-productive-maintenance-tpm-training
Description: A two-day in-house seminar designed to help reduce breakdowns, stoppages, and lower costs. **Audience:** Industry professionals. **Principal Exhibits:** A two-day in-house seminar designed to help reduce breakdowns, stoppages, and lower costs.

2059 ■ Troubleshooting Mechanical Drive Systems and Rotating Equipment (Onsite)
TPC Trainco Inc.
  225 E Robinson St., Ste. 570
  Orlando, FL 32801
Free: 877-978-7246
Co. E-mail: sales@tpctraining.com
URL: http://live.tpctraining.com
URL(s): live.tpctraining.com/on-site-training/specialty-on-site-training-topics/troubleshooting-mechanical-drive-systems-rotating-equipment
Description: A practical course designed for building facility and industrial plant maintenance technicians. **Audience:** Maintenance technicians, apprentices, mechanics, electricians, engineers and HVAC technicians. **Principal Exhibits:** A practical course designed for building facility and industrial plant maintenance technicians.

2060 ■ Understanding and Troubleshooting Hydraulics (Onsite)
TPC Trainco Inc.
  225 E Robinson St., Ste. 570
  Orlando, FL 32801
Free: 877-978-7246
Co. E-mail: sales@tpctraining.com
URL: http://live.tpctraining.com
URL(s): live.tpctraining.com/public-seminars/mechanical-and-industrial-training/understanding-troubleshooting-hydraulics
Description: A two-day training course for everyday building, plant, and facility maintenance, including systems and components and identifying and fixing common problems. **Audience:** Mechanics, machine operator, plant and facility managers, and hydraulics professionals. **Principal Exhibits:** A two-day training course for everyday building, plant, and facility maintenance, including systems and components and identifying and fixing common problems.

REFERENCE WORKS

2061 ■ "ABM Janitorial Services Receives Service Excellence Award from Jones Lang LaSalle" in Investment Weekly News (July 16, 2011, pp. 75)
Description: ABM Janitorial Services was awarded the 2010 Jones Lang LaSalle Distinction award in the category of Service Excellence. LaSalle is a leading financial and professional services firm that specializes in real estate services and investment management. The program recognizes supplier partners who play a vital role in LaSalle's aim to provide the highest quality of services, value and innovation to clients. **Availability:** PDF; Online.

2062 ■ "Brief: Janitorial Company Must Pay Back Wages" in Buffalo News (September 24, 2011)
Description: Knights Facilities Management, located in Michigan, provides grounds maintenance and janitorial services at the Ralph Wilson Stadium in Buffalo, New York. The US Department of Labor ordered the firm to pay $22,000 in back wages and damages to 26 employees for overtime and minimum wage compensation. Details of the company's violation of the Fair Labor Standards Act are included. **Availability:** Online.

2063 ■ "Bringing Charities More Bang for Their Buck" in Crain's Chicago Business (Vol. 34, May 23, 2011, No. 21, pp. 31)
Pub: Crain Communications Inc.
Contact: Barry Asin, President
Ed: Lisa Bertagnoli. **Description:** Marcy-Newberry Association connects charities with manufacturers in order to use excess items such as clothing, janitorial and office supplies. **Availability:** Online.

2064 ■ "Butane Heated Pressure Washer Offers Diverse Cleaning Options" in Product News Network (March 8, 2011)
Description: Profile of the Super Max (TM) 6000B power sprayer the can clean with cold or heated water and wet steam. Daimer Industries, provider of janitorial supplies, announced the availability of the machine that offers a variety of cleaning options for a range of applications. **Availability:** Online.

2065 ■ "Dirty Schools the Norm Since Privatizing Custodians: Principals" in Chicago Reporter (September 8, 2014)
URL(s): www.chicagoreporter.com/dirty-schools-norm-privatizing-custodians-principals/
Ed: Sarah Karp. **Released:** September 08, 2014. **Description:** A survey from AAPPLE has found that with the privatization of the custodian industry in public schools, these buildings are not as clean as they used to be, and principals have to take time out of their days to go over their buildings to make sure it is clean. Schools were also forced to downsize their custodial staff, making it harder to maintain high standards and forcing more to work harder with less. **Availability:** Online.

2066 ■ "Elevating the Vital Role of the Custodian" in Cleaning & Maintenance Management (June 1, 2015)
URL(s): www.cmmonline.com/articles/elevating-the-vital-role-of-the-custodian
Ed: Nicole Bowman. **Released:** June 01, 2016. **Description:** Even though maintaining a clean space if vital, custodians are often perceived in a negative light. Companies nowadays are giving their janitors training and promoting recognition and praise, in order to instill the ability for their workers to see the bigger picture of what they are doing. It's for the success of the whole, rather than just cleaning one particular space. **Availability:** Online.

2067 ■ "Is Maid Service Right For Your Home?" in Internet Wire (April 18, 2012)
Pub: Comtex News Network Inc.
Contact: Kan Devnani, President
Description: Merry Maids service fanchise is discussed. The article helps individuals looking for a cleaning service to investigate the wide range of services offered by each company. **Availability:** Print; Online.

2068 ■ "IU Health Bloomington's Contract with Local Cleaning Service Set to Expire" in Herald-Times (March 16, 2012)
Pub: McClatchy Tribune Information Services
Contact: Patrick J. Talamantes, President
Ed: Dann Denny. **Description:** Groff Enterprises, a building maintenace firm in Monroe and other surrounding counties of Indiana. The firm will have to let go some 20 or so employees due to the loss of its contract to provide services to IU Health in Bloomington. IU Health Bloomington Hospital sent out a request for proposals from cleaning companies that could provide services to off-site locations that were comparable to those of the in-house staff working at the hospital. **Availability:** Print; Online.

2069 ■ "Jacksonville-based Interline Expanding in Janitorial-Sanitation Market" in Florida Times-Union (May 10, 2011)
Pub: Florida Times-Union

Ed: Mark Basch. **Description:** Interline Brands Inc., located in Jacksonville, Florida, aims to grow its business with two recent acquisitions of firms that distribute janitorial and sanitation products. Interline markets and distributes maintenance, repair and operations products. **Availability:** Online.

2070 ■ *"Janitorial Equipment and Supplies US Market"* in PR Newswire (October 24, 2011)

Description: United States demand for janitorial equipment and supplies (excluding chemical products) is predicted to rise 2.4 percent per year to $7.6 billion in 2013. New product development will lead to increased sales of higher-value goods in the industry. **Availability:** Print; Online.

2071 ■ *"Knox County Schools Debate Outsourcing Janitorial Services"* in (March 29, 2011)

Description: Custodial services of Knox County Schools in Tennessee may be outsourced in move to save money for the school district. Details of the proposed program are included. **Availability:** Print; Online.

2072 ■ *"Koneco Building Services Inc. to Add Theme Park Division"* in Orlando Business Journal (Vol. 30, April 25, 2014, No. 44, pp. 3)
Pub: American City Business Journals, Inc.
Contact: Mike Olivieri, Executive Vice President
Released: Weekly. **Price:** $8, introductory 4-week offer(Digital & Print). **Description:** Koneco Building Services Inc. operations director, Ernie Falco and sales director Wolf Adler, discuss plans to add a theme park division to the Florida-based facility maintenance firm. They offer advice to other entrepreneurs and share the sacrifices they made as their business was growing. **Availability:** Print; Online.

2073 ■ *"Prepare for Your Fourth of July Party With a Maid Service"* in Internet Wire (July 3, 2012)
Pub: Comtex News Network Inc.
Contact: Kan Devnani, President
Description: Merry Maids will assist in preparing a house for special occasions and holiday parties. The firm still specializes in house cleaning, but has expanded its services. Details of services offered are included. **Availability:** Print; Online.

2074 ■ *"Pride Lands Janitorial Work at New Terminal"* in Sacramento Business Journal (Vol. 28, June 10, 2011, No. 15, pp. 1)
Pub: Sacramento Business Journal
Contact: Stephanie Fretwell, Director
E-mail: sfretwell@bizjournals.com
Ed: Kelly Johnson. **Description:** Pride Industries Inc. won the five-year $9.4 million contract to clean the Sacramento International Airport's new Terminal B, which will open in fall 2011. The nonprofit organization posts a revenue of $191 million for 2011 and currently employs more than 2,400 people with disabilities. The contract is expected to provide savings of over $3 million a year to the airport. **Availability:** Online.

2075 ■ *"Rebrand, Rebuild, and Recharge Your Business: How This BE 100s CEO Got a New Lease On Life With a Frozen Yogurt Café"* in Black Enterprise (Vol. 44, March 2014, No. 7, pp. 11)
Pub: Earl G. Graves Ltd.
Contact: Earl Graves, Jr., President
Description: Profile of Rumia Ambrose-Burbank, chief executive of one of the country's largest minority-owned businesses. Her Troy, Michigan-based firm ranks number 51 on the magazine's 100 Industrial/Service companies and focuses on the maintenance, repair, and operations (MRO) supply side. Ambrose-Burbank opened Sol De Frio, in 2013, a self-serve frozen yogurt dessert shop.

2076 ■ *"These Custodians are Cleaning Up in More Ways Than One"* in New York Post (June 3, 2017)
URL(s): nypost.com/2017/06/03/these-custodians-are-cleaning-up-in-more-ways-than-one/
Ed: Susan Edelman, Dean Balsamini. **Released:** June 03, 2017. **Description:** Three "custodian engineers" in the Department of Education are making more than $200,000 a year while others are pulling in more than $100,000. These custodians are in charge of large school campuses and have to keep them not only clean, but safe. **Availability:** Online.

2077 ■ *"What to Expect from a Home Inspection"* in The New York Times (March 23, 2018)
URL(s): www.nytimes.com/2018/03/23/realestate/home-inspection.html
Ed: Megan Wild. **Released:** March 23, 2018. **Description:** General tips on what a first-time homebuyer should look for with a home inspection. Includes specific systems the inspector should be noting, and what steps the buyer needs to take in order to successfully complete this task. **Availability:** Online.

STATISTICAL SOURCES

2078 ■ *RMA Annual Statement Studies*
Pub: Risk Management Association
Contact: Nancy Foster, President
Released: Annual. **Description:** Contains composite balance sheets and income statements for more than 360 industries, including the accounting, auditing, and bookkeeping industries. Also contains five years of comparative historical data for discerning trends. Includes 16 commonly used ratios, computed for most of the size groupings for nearly every industry.

TRADE PERIODICALS

2079 ■ *American Window Cleaner Magazine: The Voice of the Professional Window Cleaner*
Pub: American Window Cleaner Magazine
Facebook: www.facebook.com/AWCmag
Instagram: www.instagram.com/awcmag
YouTube: www.youtube.com/channel/UCChFzBXvD_BffB5vNT6nmpQ
Released: Monthly **Price:** $69, for one year; $99, for Canada one year; $199, for international; $4.99, for per months; $6.99, for months; $8.99, for months. **Description:** Designed to make professional window cleaners work faster, safer and more profitably. **Availability:** Print; Online.

2080 ■ *Contracting Profits*
Pub: Trade Press Media Group Inc.
Contact: Kimberly Reed, Manager
E-mail: kimberly.reed@tradepress.com
URL(s): www.cleanlink.com/cp/default.aspx
Released: Bimonthly; January / February , March / April , May / June, July / August , September / October and November / December. **Description:** Trade magazine covering business and operations management issues for commercial and institutional building cleaning service contractors. **Availability:** Print; Online.

TRADE SHOWS AND CONVENTIONS

2081 ■ *Facilities Maintenance Expo*
Frequency: Annual. **Description:** Expo featuring products for plant engineers and building maintenance professionals. **Principal Exhibits:** Expo featuring products for plant engineers and building maintenance professionals.

2082 ■ *Hawaii Buildings, Facilities, and Property Management Expo*
Frequency: Annual. **Description:** Tradeshow featuring products and services geared towards the operation, renovation, maintenance, and sustainability needs of buildings on the islands of Hawaii. Seminars are also presented. **Principal Exhibits:** Tradeshow featuring products and services geared towards the operation, renovation, maintenance, and sustainability needs of buildings on the islands of Hawaii. Seminars are also presented.

2083 ■ *National Facilities Management and Technology Conference and Expo*
URL(s): www.nfmt.com/baltimore/default.aspx
Frequency: Annual. **Description:** Offers key topic sessions, free education, networking, and a product exhibit for those in the facilities management industry. **Principal Exhibits:** Offers key topic sessions, free education, networking, and a product exhibit for those in the facilities management industry.

CONSULTANTS

2084 ■ *Cleaning Consultant Services Inc. (CCS)*
PO Box 98757
Seattle, WA 98198
URL: http://www.cleaningbusiness.com
Contact: Bill Griffin, Founder
Description: Firm provides engineering and consulting services and deals with claim and dispute resolution, program and material development and cleaning services and also offers business solutions and support services for cleaning professionals, and publishes books on various areas of the cleaning industry. **Scope:** Firm provides engineering and consulting services and deals with claim and dispute resolution, program and material development and cleaning services and also offers business solutions and support services for cleaning professionals, and publishes books on various areas of the cleaning industry. **Founded:** 1973. **Publications:** "Raising the Bar with Science, Training and Upward Mobility," Jan, 2010; "Technology Revolutionizes the Cleaning Process "Cleaning for Health" is the New Mantra," Distribution Sales and Management Magazine, May, 2003; "Bill Griffin's Crystal Balls-Cleaning Trends in the Usa 2001," Floor Care is Hot in 2001," Mar, 2001; "Inclean Magazine (Australia), Feb, 2001; "Maintaining Swimming Pools, Spas, Whirlpool Tubs and Saunas," Executive House keeping, Feb, 2001; "Whats New with Floor Care," 2001. **Training:** Publisher of books and magazines.

FRANCHISES AND BUSINESS OPPORTUNITIES

2085 ■ *1-800-Got-Junk L.L.C.*
301-887 Great Northern Way
Vancouver, BC, Canada V5T 4T5
Free: 800-468-5865
URL: http://www.1800gotjunk.com/ca_en
Contact: Erik Church, President
Facebook: www.facebook.com/1800GOTJUNK
Linkedin: www.linkedin.com/company/1-800-got-junk
X (Twitter): x.com/1800gotjunk
Instagram: www.instagram.com/1800gotjunk
YouTube: www.youtube.com/1800gotjunk
Description: Junk removal service. **Founded:** 1989. **Financial Assistance:** Yes **Training:** Yes.

2086 ■ *360Clean*
National Support Ctr., 2265 Clements Ferry Rd., Ste. 309
Charleston, SC 29492
Ph: (843)552-0116
URL: http://360cleanfranchise.com
Contact: Barry Bodiford, Chief Executive Officer
URL(s): 360clean.com
X (Twitter): x.com/360clean
Description: Provider of janitorial services for medical offices and other facilities. **Founded:** 2005. **Financial Assistance:** Yes **Training:** Yes.

2087 ■ *AAAC Wildlife Removal (AAAC)*
Dunbar, WV
Ph: (281)688-2435
Co. E-mail: wildlifecareer@aallanimalcontrol.com
URL: http://aallanimalcontrol.com
Facebook: www.facebook.com/AAACWildlifeRemovalOfHouston
Pinterest: www.pinterest.com/aallanimal

Description: Providing wildlife, animal, and pest control services and removal for residential, industrial and commercial clients. **Founded:** 1995. **Training:** Extensive 5 day training program includes operations, marketing, sales and field experience followed by ongoing monthly webinars and an Annual Franchise Owners Convention.

2088 ■ Aire-Master of America Inc.
1821 N Hwy. CC
Nixa, MO 65714
Ph: (417)725-2691
Free: 800-525-0957
Fax: (417)725-5737
URL: http://www.airemaster.com
Contact: Douglas McCauley, Chief Executive Officer
Description: Room deodorizing, restroom deodorizing and disinfecting service. **Founded:** 1958. **Financial Assistance:** Yes **Training:** Yes.

2089 ■ American Restoration Services
22 Rutgers Rd.
Pittsburgh, PA 15205
Ph: (412)921-4000
URL: http://www.americanrestoration.com
Contact: Russell Case, Contact
Description: Firm provides restoration services for architects, engineers, property managers and property owners. **Founded:** 1970. **Financial Assistance:** Yes **Training:** Yes.

2090 ■ Anago Franchising Inc.
Anago Cleaning Systems Inc. (ACS)
20 SW 27th Ave., Ste. No., 100
Pompano Beach, FL 33069
Ph: (954)289-6250
Free: 800-956-8532
Co. E-mail: contactus@anagocleaning.com
URL: http://www.anagocleaning.com
Contact: Adam Povlitz, President
Facebook: www.facebook.com/AnagoCleaning
Linkedin: www.linkedin.com/company/anago-cleaning-systems
X (Twitter): x.com/AnagoCleaning
Instagram: www.instagram.com/anagocleaning
YouTube: www.youtube.com/AnagoCleaning
Description: Provider of commercial cleaning, cleaning business and janitorial services for office buildings, schools, health care sectors. **Founded:** 1989. **Training:** Yes.

2091 ■ Bonus Building Care
PO Box 300
Indianola, OK 74442
Free: 800-931-1102
Fax: (918)823-4994
Co. E-mail: contact@bonusbuildingcare.com
URL: http://www.bonusbuildingcare.com
Contact: Arleen Cavanaugh, Founder
Description: Firm provides commercial janitorial services and office cleaning services. **Founded:** 1996. **Franchise Fee:** Financing guaranteed. A down payment of $1,000 starts your business and guarantees financing of the franchise fee, equipment, supplies and growth. **Financial Assistance:** Yes **Training:** Intensive initial training, extended training and special services training all included at no additional cost. Flexible, onsite training coupled with comprehensive written guides gets you up and running.

2092 ■ BuildingStars International
33 Worthington Access Dr.
Maryland Heights, MO 63043
Ph: (314)991-3256
Co. E-mail: info@buildingstars.com
URL: http://www.buildingstars.com
Contact: Chris Hogg, Contact
Facebook: www.facebook.com/buildingstarsIntl
Description: Commercial cleaning services. **Founded:** 1994. **Financial Assistance:** Yes **Training:** 1 week at corporate headquarters with ongoing support.

2093 ■ CertaPro Painters Ltd.
FirstService Brands
2621 Van Buren Ave., Ste. 550A
Audubon, PA 19403
Free: 866-366-0420
Fax: (601)549-7973
URL: http://www.fsvbrands.com
Contact: Michael Stone, President
URL(s): www.fsvbrands.com/our_companies/certa_pro_painters.html
Facebook: www.facebook.com/certapropainters
Linkedin: www.linkedin.com/company/certapro-painters
X (Twitter): x.com/CertaPro
Instagram: www.instagram.com/certapro
YouTube: www.youtube.com/user/certaproyt
Pinterest: www.pinterest.com/certapro
Description: Provider of residential and commercial building painting services. **Founded:** 1992.

2094 ■ ChemStation International Inc.
3400 Encrete Ln.
Dayton, OH 45439
Ph: (937)294-8265
Free: 800-554-8265
Co. E-mail: information@chemstation.com
URL: http://chemstation.com
Contact: Chas Quatman, President
Facebook: www.facebook.com/chemstationhq
Linkedin: www.linkedin.com/company/chemstation
X (Twitter): x.com/chemstationhq
Instagram: www.instagram.com/chemstationhq
YouTube: www.youtube.com/channel/UCJwzEEUNr_zAl1CVin3CLEA
Description: Manufactures and distributes detergents in bulk. **No. of Franchise Units:** 48. **No. of Company-Owned Units:** 8. **No. of Operating Units:** 56. **Founded:** 1977. **Franchised:** 1977. **Equity Capital Needed:** $205,000 - $295,000. **Financial Assistance:** Yes **Training:** Yes.

2095 ■ City Wide Maintenance Company Inc.
15230 W 105th Ter.
Lenexa, KS 66219
Ph: (913)888-5700
Free: 855-879-2937
URL: http://gocitywide.com
Contact: Jeff Oddo, President
Facebook: www.facebook.com/CityWideFacilitySolutionsKC
X (Twitter): x.com/CityWide_KC
Instagram: www.instagram.com/citywidekc
YouTube: www.youtube.com/c/CityWideFacilitySolutions
Description: Maintenance services. **Founded:** 1961. **Franchised:** 2001. **Financial Assistance:** Yes **Training:** Offers 2 weeks at headquarters, 2 weeks at franchisee's location, annual training meeting with ongoing support.

2096 ■ Clean and Happy Windows
PO Box 1545
Gig Harbor, WA 98335
Ph: (206)762-7617
Fax: (206)762-7637
Co. E-mail: cleanhappy@cleanhappy.com
URL: http://www.cleanhappy.com
Description: Franchise offers maintenance and cleaning of windows. **Founded:** 1990. **Franchised:** 1999. **Training:** Yes.

2097 ■ Clean Living Specialists Inc.
Orleans, ON, Canada K1E 3V7
Ph: (613)673-2445
Co. E-mail: sales@cleanliving.net
URL: http://cleanliving.net
Contact: Deanna Twerd, President
Facebook: www.facebook.com/Clean-Living-Specialists-Inc-1291936554250471
Description: Provider of housecleaning services such as floors washed, baseboards washed, furniture moved, pictures dusted and personalized service tailored. **Founded:** 1988. **Training:** Provides 2 weeks in Kanata, Ontario, 1 month in new business, followed by ongoing support.

2098 ■ The Cleaning Authority (TCA)
Authority Brands
7085 Samuel Morse Dr., Ste. 105
Columbia, MD 21046
Free: 800-496-9019
URL: http://www.authoritybrands.com
Contact: Tim Evankovich, President
Facebook: www.facebook.com/thecleaningauthority
Linkedin: www.linkedin.com/company/the-cleaning-authority
X (Twitter): x.com/livelifeweclean
Instagram: www.instagram.com/the_cleaning_authority
YouTube: www.youtube.com/user/thecleaningauthority
Pinterest: www.pinterest.com/tcauthority
Description: Provider of home cleaning services. **Founded:** 1977. **Training:** 2 week home office training; on-site visits, quarterly newsletter, ongoing training sessions.

2099 ■ Cleaning Consultant Services Inc. (CCS)
PO Box 98757
Seattle, WA 98198
URL: http://www.cleaningbusiness.com
Contact: Bill Griffin, Founder
Description: Firm provides engineering and consulting services and deals with claim and dispute resolution, program and material development and cleaning services and also offers business solutions and support services for cleaning professionals, and publishes books on various areas of the cleaning industry. **Scope:** Firm provides engineering and consulting services and deals with claim and dispute resolution, program and material development and cleaning services and also offers business solutions and support services for cleaning professionals, and publishes books on various areas of the cleaning industry. **Founded:** 1973. **Publications:** "Raising the Bar with Science, Training and Upward Mobility," Jan, 2010; "Technology Revolutionizes the Cleaning Process "Cleaning for Health" is the New Mantra," Distribution Sales and Management Magazine, May, 2003; "Bill Griffin's Crystal Balls-Cleaning Trends in the Usa 2001," Floor Care is Hot in 2001," Mar, 2001; "Inclean Magazine (Australia), Feb, 2001; "Maintaining Swimming Pools, Spas, Whirlpool Tubs and Saunas," Executive House keeping, Feb, 2001; "Whats New with Floor Care," 2001. **Training:** Publisher of books and magazines.

2100 ■ CleanNet USA, Inc.
8300 Boone Blvd., Ste. 500
Vienna, VA 22182
Free: 800-735-8838
Co. E-mail: info@cleannetusa.com
URL: http://www.cleannetusa.com
Description: Firm provides cleaning services. **Founded:** 1987. **Training:** Yes.

2101 ■ Clintar Groundskeeping Services
200 Cachet Woods Ct., Unit 119
Markham, ON, Canada L6C 0Z8
Free: 800-361-3542
Co. E-mail: info@clintar.com
URL: http://www.clintar.com
Contact: Rob Gannett, Chief Executive Officer
Description: Firm provides commercial landscape services such as parking lot maintenance, water management. **No. of Franchise Units:** 23. **Founded:** 1973. **Equity Capital Needed:** Approximately $100,000-$150,000 to start. **Royalty Fee:** 8%. **Training:** Yes.

2102 ■ Coverall Health-Based Cleaning System
350 SW 12th Ave.
Deerfield Beach, FL 33442
URL: http://www.coverall.com
Description: One of the nation's leading commercial cleaning franchise companies with more than 9,000 Franchise Owners worldwide. Franchisees are provided with training, equipment, billing and collection services, a quality control program, and a customer base. Ranked as the fastest growing commercial cleaning franchise in the nation by Entrepreneur's 22nd Annual 'Franchise 500'. **No. of Franchise Units:** 9,137. **Founded:** 1985. **Franchised:** 1985. **Equity Capital Needed:** $12,683-$37,160. **Franchise Fee:** $9,120-$30,643. **Training:** Coverall

supports its Franchise Owners through comprehensive training, an initial customer base, billing and collection, services and a global network of 90 Support Centers, plus the unique benefits of the Health-Based Cleaning System Program.

2103 ▪ Fish Window Cleaning Services Inc.
200 Enchanted Pky.
 Manchester, MO 63021
Ph: (636)779-1500
URL: http://www.fishwindowcleaning.com
Contact: Mike Merrick, Founder
Facebook: www.facebook.com/FishWindowCleaning
Linkedin: www.linkedin.com/company/fish-window-cleaning
X (Twitter): x.com/fishwindowclean
Instagram: www.instagram.com/fishwindowclean
YouTube: www.youtube.com/user/fishwindowcleaning
Description: Firm provides window washing and cleaning service in the United States. **Founded:** 1978. **Financial Assistance:** Yes **Training:** Intensive 10 day training in St. Louis followed by 4 days in franchisee territory. On-going support included.

2104 ▪ Goodbye Graffiti Inc.
950 Powell St., No. 206
 Vancouver, BC, Canada V6A 1H9
Free: 877-684-4747
Co. E-mail: customercarecentre@goodbyegraffiti.com
URL: http://goodbyegraffiti.com
Contact: Kendra Klemke, Contact
E-mail: kklemke@goodbyegraffiti.com
Facebook: www.facebook.com/goodbyegraffitiinc
X (Twitter): x.com/goodbyegraffiti
Instagram: www.instagram.com/goodbyegraffitiinc
YouTube: www.youtube.com/channel/UCrtEtjSFDVv_rpOJCcWTV5A
Description: The company is into graffiti removal and abatement franchises. Specializes in environmentally friendly graffiti removal from all surfaces and long-term maintenance. **No. of Franchise Units:** 11. **Founded:** 1997. **Franchised:** 2000. **Equity Capital Needed:** $60-$100,000. **Franchise Fee:** $27,000. **Training:** 2 weeks and ongoing support provided.

2105 ▪ Jani-King International Inc.
16885 Dallas Pky.
 Addison, TX 75001
Ph: (972)991-0900
Free: 800-JAN-IKING
Co. E-mail: info@janiking.com
URL: http://www.janiking.com
Contact: James A. Cavanaugh, Jr., Director
Facebook: www.facebook.com/janikinginternational
Linkedin: www.linkedin.com/company/janikinginternational
X (Twitter): x.com/JaniKingClean
Instagram: www.instagram.com/janikinginternational
YouTube: www.youtube.com/user/JaniKingUSA
Description: Provider of commercial cleaning services. **Founded:** 1969. **Training:** Training covers cleaning, personnel, client relations, proposals and sales. **Educational Activities:** IFA Annual Convention (Annual); International Franchise Expo (IFE) (Annual).

2106 ▪ Jantize America
5555 Concord Pkwy S, Ste. 336
 Concord, NC 28027
Ph: (704)503-7141
Free: 888-540-0001
Co. E-mail: info@jantize.com
URL: http://www.jantize.com
Facebook: www.facebook.com/JantizeAmerica
X (Twitter): x.com/jantize
Description: Company provides commercial cleaning services. **Royalty Fee:** 4%. **Financial Assistance:** Yes **Training:** Includes 3 days training at headquarters, 2 days at franchisee's location and ongoing support.

2107 ▪ JDI Cleaning Systems Inc.
3380 S Service Rd., Ste. 108
 Burlington, ON, Canada L7N 3J5
Ph: (905)634-5228
Free: 800-567-5091
Fax: (905)634-8790
URL: http://jdicleaning.com
Contact: Jonathan Draycott, President
Facebook: www.facebook.com/jdicleangreen
X (Twitter): x.com/jdicleaning
YouTube: www.youtube.com/user/jdicleaning
Description: Provider of cleaning services such as cleaning and maintenance programs, green cleaning, carpet care programs, strip, seal and waxing floors and window cleaning for office. **Founded:** 1992. **Training:** 5 days and on the job training provided.

2108 ▪ Jhn Inc. [Coustic-Glo]
950 Enchanted Way, Ste. 109
 Simi Valley, CA 93065
URL: http://www.cousticglo.net
Contact: Richard Read, Chief Executive Officer
Description: Plastering, drywall, and insulation. **Founded:** 1985.

2109 ▪ Master Care
Unit B 555 Ardersier Rd.
 Victoria, BC, Canada V8Z 1C8
Ph: (250)590-5970
Free: 800-889-2799
Co. E-mail: info@mastercare.com
URL: http://www.mastercare.com
Linkedin: www.linkedin.com/company/master-care-janitorial-and-facility-services
X (Twitter): twitter.com/mastercareclean
Instagram: www.instagram.com/mastercarejanitorial
Description: Provider of cleaning services such as green cleaning, carpet and floor cleaning, building maintenance, janitorial services and more. **Founded:** 1986. **Training:** Provides 3 weeks training and ongoing support.

2110 ▪ Octoclean
1695 Spruce St., Ste. 100
 Riverside, CA 92507
Ph: (951)683-5859
Free: 888-540-0828
Co. E-mail: info@octoclean.com
URL: http://octoclean.com
Contact: Yvonne Stowe, President
Facebook: www.facebook.com/OctoClean
Linkedin: www.linkedin.com/company/octoclean
X (Twitter): x.com/octoclean
Instagram: www.instagram.com/octoclean
YouTube: www.youtube.com/user/OctoCleanHQ
Description: Firm is a provider of commercial cleaning and janitorial services. **Founded:** 2000. **Financial Assistance:** Yes **Training:** Provides hands on training and ongoing support.

2111 ▪ Office Pride Commercial Cleaning Services
3450 E Lake Rd., Ste. 200
 Palm Harbor, FL 34685
Free: 888-641-2310
Co. E-mail: communications@officepride.com
URL: http://officepride.com
Contact: Todd Hopkins, Chief Executive Officer
Facebook: www.facebook.com/OfficePride
Linkedin: www.linkedin.com/company/office-pride-commercial-cleaning-services
X (Twitter): x.com/officepride
Description: Provider of commercial cleaning services. **Founded:** 1992. **Financial Assistance:** Yes **Training:** 5 days of classroom training at corporate headquarters, follow-up training and ongoing support.

2112 ▪ Omex Office Maintenance Experts
205 House Ave.
 Camp Hill, PA 17011
Ph: (717)737-7311
Free: 800-827-6639
Co. E-mail: info@omexcorp.com
URL: http://www.omexcorp.com
Contact: Gerald Boarman, President
Description: Firm provides commercial cleaning and office maintenance services. **Founded:** 1979. **Franchised:** 1994. **Training:** Yes.

2113 ▪ Openworks
2355 E Camelback Rd., Ste. 600
 Phoenix, AZ 85016
Ph: (602)224-0440
Free: 800-777-6736
Fax: (602)468-3788
Co. E-mail: marketing@openworksweb.com
URL: http://www.openworksweb.com
Contact: Eric Roudi, Chief Executive Officer
Facebook: www.facebook.com/openworksaz
Linkedin: www.linkedin.com/company/openworks
X (Twitter): x.com/OpenWorksAZ
Instagram: www.instagram.com/openworksfranchise
Description: Firm engages in providing maintenance and cleaning services. **Founded:** 1983. **Financial Assistance:** Yes **Training:** Offers training at headquarters and 2 weeks at franchisee's location and ongoing support.

2114 ▪ Scrubway Wash And Lube
12715 Boudreaux Rd.
 Tomball, TX 77375
Ph: (832)698-5285
URL: http://www.scrubwaywashandlube.com
Contact: Ben Johnson, Director, Operations
Facebook: www.facebook.com/scrubwayhouston
Description: Commercial restroom hygiene franchise. **No. of Franchise Units:** 6. **No. of Company-Owned Units:** 1. **Founded:** 1994. **Franchised:** 1994. **Equity Capital Needed:** $50,000-$75,000. **Franchise Fee:** $25,000-$35,000. **Training:** Yes.

2115 ▪ Service-Tech Corp. (STC)
7589 First Pl
 Cleveland, OH 44146
Ph: (440)735-1505
Co. E-mail: info@service-techcorp.com
URL: http://www.service-techcorp.com
Contact: Gabriel S. Chick, President
E-mail: gchick@service-techcorp.com
Facebook: www.facebook.com/servicetechcorp
Linkedin: www.linkedin.com/company/service-tech-corporation
X (Twitter): x.com/ServiceTechOH
Description: Indoor air quality remediation and industrial cleaning services. The list of cleaning services offered includes air duct systems, industrial exhaust systems, industrial ovens, overhead structural steel and restaurant hood exhaust systems. **Founded:** 1960. **Training:** 14 days training schedule conducted at the corporate training center, with hands-on field instruction at job sites. Training in marketing, sales, field operations, accounting, personnel and management trainings.

2116 ▪ Steamatic Inc.
BMS Enterprises Inc.
4909 Blue Mound Rd.
 Fort Worth, TX 76106
Contact: W. G. Blackmon, Contact
YouTube: www.youtube.com/channel/UCAQN5uk3cigGmOWVayCs8DQ
Description: Provides water, fire and storm insurance restoration (disaster recovery services); indoor environmental services, air duct and coil cleaning; carpet cleaning; furniture cleaning; drapery cleaning; deodorizing; wood restoration; document restoration; corrosion control; ceiling and wall cleaning. and 24-hour toll-free numbers. **Founded:** 1948. **Training:** Yes.

2117 ▪ System4 Facility Services
4700 Rockside Rd., Ste. 610
 Independence, OH 44131
Ph: (216)524-6100
URL: http://system4.com
Contact: Phillip W. Kubec, Contact
Description: Firm is a provider of commercial cleaning services, hard floor care, window cleaning, commercial landscaping, parking lot services, lighting maintenance. **Founded:** 2004. **Franchised:** 2003. **Franchise Fee:** $1,400. **Royalty Fee:** Mothly 5%. **Financial Assistance:** Yes **Training:** Training includes 3 days at franchisees location, 1 day each seminars and ongoing support.

2118 ▪ Vanguard Cleaning Systems, Inc. (VCS)
655 Mariners Island Blvd., Ste. 303
 San Mateo, CA 94404

URL: http://www.vanguardcleaning.com
Contact: Raymond Chang Lee, Chief Executive Officer
Facebook: www.facebook.com/vanguardcleaning
Linkedin: www.linkedin.com/company/vanguard-cleaning-systems
X (Twitter): x.com/vanguardclean
Description: Franchisor of janitorial service providers in the United States and Canada. **Founded:** 1984. **Franchised:** 1984. **Franchise Fee:** $100,000 – $350,000. **Financial Assistance:** Yes **Training:** Initial training at headquarters followed by onsite training.

2119 ■ Window Genie (WG)
Neighborly
40 W Crescentville Rd.
Cincinnati, OH 45246
Free: 800-490-7501
Fax: (877)496-2356
URL: http://www.neighborlybrands.com
Contact: John Marshall, Contact
Facebook: www.facebook.com/windowgenie
Linkedin: www.linkedin.com/company/window-genie
X (Twitter): twitter.com/thewindowgenie
Instagram: www.instagram.com/windowgenie
YouTube: www.youtube.com/channel/UC8CEiBA9H-Dj6B1BQOZlpYQ
Pinterest: www.pinterest.com/windowgenie
Description: Provider of window cleaning, window tinting, pressure washing, gutter cleaning services. **Founded:** 1994. **Franchised:** 1998. **Equity Capital Needed:** $80,000 - $150,000. **Franchise Fee:** $32,000-$57,000,. **Financial Assistance:** Yes **Training:** Offers 5 days at headquarters, 5 days at franchisees location with ongoing support.

Bulletin Board Service

REFERENCE WORKS

2120 ■ *"7 Modern BBSes Worth Calling Today"* in PCMag (December 26, 2017)
URL(s): www.pcmag.com/feature/358037/7-modern-bbses-worth-calling-today
Ed: Benj Edwards. **Released:** December 26, 2017.
Description: Discusses the hobby of using old pre-internet Bulletin Board Systems (BBS), which are barely existing today. After a quick tutorial on how to connect to these, the author gives his seven best sites to visit. **Availability:** Online.

2121 ■ *"The Lost Civilization of Dial-Up Bulletin Board Systems"* in The Atlantic (November 4, 2016)
URL(s): www.theatlantic.com/technology/archive/2016/11/the-lost-civilization-of-dial-up-bulletin-board-systems/506465/
Ed: Benj Edwards. **Released:** November 04, 2016.
Description: A Bulletin Board System (BBS) is a 1990s-era text-based service that pre-dated the internet. All it took was a basic phone modem to connect personal computers with the dial-in system, and users would be able to message each other. The author visits an old BBS still up and running and discusses what and who he finds lurking in these old systems. **Availability:** Online.

TRADE PERIODICALS

2122 ■ *DCL News*
Pub: Data Conversion Laboratory
Contact: Mark Gross, President
URL(s): www.dataconversionlaboratory.com/newsletter
Released: Monthly **Description:** E-journal providing you insider information on XML and SGML, along with the latest technology and e-publishing news.
Availability: Online.

CONSULTANTS

2123 ■ Law Offices of Robert J. Keller P.C.
PO Box 33428 - Farragut Sta.
Washington, DC 20033-3428
Ph: (202)656-8490
Fax: (202)223-2121
Co. E-mail: rjk@telcomlaw.com
URL: http://www.telcomlaw.com
Contact: Robert J. Keller, Contact
E-mail: rjk@telcomlaw.com
Description: Law firm specializes in federal telecommunications law provides legal services for wireless telecommunications, new and emerging technologies. **Founded:** 1994.

LIBRARIES

2124 ■ Gartner IRC - Research Library
56 Top Gallant Rd.
Stamford, CT 06902
Ph: (203)964-0096
Co. E-mail: inquiry@gartner.com
URL: http://www.gartner.com/en
Contact: Eugene A. Hall, Chief Executive Officer
Facebook: www.facebook.com/Gartne
Linkedin: www.linkedin.com/company/gartner
X (Twitter): x.com/Gartner_inc
Instagram: www.instagram.com/gartner_inc
YouTube: www.youtube.com/user/Gartnervideo
Description: Research and advisory company.
Scope: Information technology. **Services:** SDI; center not open to the public (client research only). **Founded:** 1979. **Holdings:** 3,000 items.

2125 ■ International Data Group, Inc. (IDC) - Library
140 Kendrick St., Bldg. B
Needham, MA 02494
Ph: (508)872-8200
Co. E-mail: leads@idc.com
URL: http://www.idc.com
Contact: Crawford del Prete, President
Linkedin: www.linkedin.com/company/idc
X (Twitter): x.com/IDC
Description: Provides market intelligence, advisory services, and events for the information technology, telecommunications, and consumer technology markets. **Scope:** Information technology; telecommunications; advisory services. **Founded:** 1964. **Holdings:** Figures not available. **Publications:** *Computerworld*; *The Standard*; *Macworld*; *IDG.net*; *WebSolutionsWorld Newsletter Online*; *E-Commerce Newsletter Online*; *Security-Informer Newsletter Online*; *TechInformer Newsletter Online*; *dummies.com*; *cliffsnotes.com*; *Arthur Frommer's Budget Travel Online*; *Network World, Inc.*; *CIO Online*; *Computerworld Online*; *Darwin Magazine Online*; *JavaWorld Online*; *LinuxWorld.com*; *InfoWorld.com*; *NetworkWorld.com*; *SunWorld Magazine Online*; *GamePro.com*; *MacWorld Online* (Monthly); *Publish.com*; *Financial News Channel*; *International News Channel*; *E-Commerce News Channel*; *Enterprise News Channel*; *Personal Computing News Channel*; *How-To & Advice News Channel*; *Multimedia & Leisure News Channel*; *Telecom & Connectivity News Channel*; *Security News Channel*; *Networking & Systems News Channel*; *Technical Development News Channel*; *IDC Research*; *ExecuTrain Corporation*; *China Network World* (Weekly); *Network World*; *IT Forecaster* (Biweekly).

RESEARCH CENTERS

2126 ■ University of Minnesota - Charles Babbage Institute for Computing, Information, and Culture - Erwin Tomash Library
University of Minnesota, Charles Babbage Institute
211 Andersen Library
222 21st Ave. S
Minneapolis, MN 55455
Co. E-mail: cbi@umn.edu
URL: http://cse.umn.edu/cbi
Contact: Dr. Jeffrey R. Yost, Professor
E-mail: yostx003@umn.edu
Facebook: www.facebook.com/babbageinstitute
X (Twitter): x.com/BabbageInst
Description: Facilitates, fosters, and conducts research to advance the understanding of computing, information, and culture. Studies the development of information processing, including technical and socioeconomic aspects, and works to promote increased awareness of the impact of that development on society. Provides counsel and research assistance to other scholars in the field. Maintains archives, including 320 oral histories of computing pioneers. **Scope:** History of information science and technology, including development of computer technology, applications of information processing techniques ranging from banking to science research, automation techniques in archival development and historical database generation, history and social impacts of the information processing field, and entrepreneurial activity of the information industry. Identifies and makes accessible important letters, diaries, manuscripts, unpublished reports, industry records, financial information, interviews, and photographs that document and interpret the information revolution. Acts as a clearinghouse on the location of historical material. **Services:** Copying; collection open to researchers. **Founded:** 1979. **Holdings:** Corporate records; manuscript materials; records of professional associations; oral history interviews; trade publications; periodicals; photographs; films; videos; and reference materials.; 550 photos; 40 videos; 100,000 photographs depicts books; journals.; . **Subscriptions:** ; books. **Publications:** *Iterations: Interdisciplinary Journal of Software History*; *Charles Babbage Institute Newsletter* (Semiannual). **Educational Activities:** CBI Lecture series. **Awards:** Arthur L. Norberg Travel Fund (Annual); Arthur L. Norberg Travel Fund (Annual); The Adelle and Erwin Tomash Fellowship in the History of Information Technology (Annual). **Geographic Preference:** National.

Business Broker Service

START-UP INFORMATION

2127 ■ The eBay Business Start-Up Kit: With 100s of Live Links to All the Information & Tools You Need
Pub: Nolo
Contact: Chris Braun, President
Ed: Richard Stim. **Description:** Interactive kit that provides in-depth information and practical advice in launching an eBay business. **Availability:** Print.

ASSOCIATIONS AND OTHER ORGANIZATIONS

2128 ■ Arizona Business Brokers Association (AZBBA)
PO Box 6046
Scottsdale, AZ 85261
Free: 855-442-9222
URL: http://azbba.org
Contact: Shaun Rudgear, President
E-mail: shaun@arizonamedicalbrokers.com
Description: Represents and supports professional business brokers and intermediaries in the state of Arizona.

2129 ■ Business Brokers of Florida (BBF)
6122 US Hwy. 98
Sebring, FL 33876
Ph: (863)655-3085
Fax: (863)655-2670
Co. E-mail: support@bbms.biz
URL: http://www.bbfmls.com
Contact: Joe Shemansky, President
Description: Represents professionals and firms in business brokerage, mergers and acquisitions. Provides business brokers education, conferences, professional designations, and networking opportunities in Florida. Works to become a leader in the exchange of business referrals, and to create professional relationships with successful business transaction advisors. **Founded:** 1985. **Geographic Preference:** State.

2130 ■ California Association of Business Brokers (CABB)
4747 N 1st St., Ste. 140
Fresno, CA 93726
Free: 866-972-2220
Fax: (559)227-1463
Co. E-mail: info@cabb.org
URL: http://www.cabb.org
Contact: Randy Katz, President
Facebook: www.facebook.com/CABB.org
Linkedin: www.linkedin.com/company/cabborg
X (Twitter): x.com/cabborg
Description: Represents professionals and firms in business brokerage, mergers and acquisitions. Provides business brokers education, conferences, professional designations, and networking opportunities in California. Works to become a leader in the exchange of business referrals, and to create professional relationships with successful business transaction advisors. **Founded:** 1986. **Geographic Preference:** State.

2131 ■ Carolinas - Virginia Business Brokers Association (CVBBA)
10911 Raven Ridge Rd., Ste. 103-80
Raleigh, NC 27614
Ph: (646)573-7014
Co. E-mail: admin1@cvbba.com
URL: http://www.cvbba.com
Contact: Joe Santora, President
Facebook: www.facebook.com/carolinasvirginiabba
Description: Represents professionals and firms in business brokerage, mergers and acquisitions. Provides business brokers education, conferences, professional designations, and networking opportunities in North and South Carolina and Virginia. Works to become a leader in the exchange of business referrals, and to create professional relationships with successful business transaction advisors. **Founded:** 2005. **Geographic Preference:** Regional.

2132 ■ Franchise Brokers Association (FBA)
3751 Maguire Blvd., Ste. .,115
Orlando, FL 32803
Free: 866-515-8814
Fax: (407)856-0616
Co. E-mail: info@franchiseba.com
URL: http://www.franchiseba.com
Contact: Chris Wall, Officer
Facebook: www.facebook.com/franchiseba
Linkedin: www.linkedin.com/company/franchise-brokers-association
X (Twitter): x.com/franchiseba
Instagram: www.instagram.com/franchiseba
YouTube: www.youtube.com/franchiseba
Description: Provides access to brokers for prospective franchisees. **Founded:** 2008.

2133 ■ Georgia Association of Business Brokers (GABB)
4780 Ashford Dunwoody Rd., Ste. A-241.
Atlanta, GA 30338-5564
Ph: (770)744-3639
Co. E-mail: georgiabusinessbrokers@gmail.com
URL: http://www.gabb.org
Contact: Judy J. Mims, President
E-mail: judy@childcare.properties
Facebook: www.facebook.com/GeorgiaAssociationBusinessBrokersGABB
Linkedin: www.linkedin.com/company/georgia-association-of-business-brokers
X (Twitter): x.com/GABB_Brokers
Description: Represents professionals and firms in business brokerage, mergers and acquisitions. Provides business brokers education, conferences, professional designations, and networking opportunities in Georgia. Works to become a leader in the exchange of business referrals, and to create professional relationships with successful business transaction advisors. **Founded:** 1986. **Geographic Preference:** State.

2134 ■ International Business Brokers Association (IBBA)
7100 E Pleasant Valley Rd., Ste. 160
Independence, OH 44131
Free: 888-686-4222
Fax: (800)630-2380
Co. E-mail: admin@ibba.org
URL: http://www.ibba.org
Contact: Kate Stretar, Director, Operations
E-mail: kstretar@ibba.org
Facebook: www.facebook.com/ibbaorg
X (Twitter): x.com/IBBAHQ
YouTube: www.youtube.com/user/IBBABrokers
Description: Serves the interests of brokers and brokerages whose specialty is bringing together the buyers and sellers of businesses. Encourages growth of sales; assists in new industry developments. Represents members in legislative matters and lobbies for recognition of the industry. Coordinates activity among business brokerages and cooperates with other types of brokerages. Conducts educational and promotional programs for members. Maintains library on legal aspects of business brokerage. **Founded:** 1984. **Geographic Preference:** Multinational.

2135 ■ Michigan Business Brokers Association (MBBA)
4418 Penny Ln., SW
Grandville, MI 49418
Free: 800-988-8850
URL: http://www.mbba.org
Contact: Brad Scoffin, President
Description: Provides education, professional designations, and networking opportunities to further growth and development of professionals engaged in business brokerage, mergers, and acquisitions. **Founded:** 1983. **Geographic Preference:** State.

2136 ■ Mid-Atlantic Business Brokers Association (MABBA)
715 Periwinkle Ln.
Wynnewood, PA 19096
Ph: (610)825-7777
Fax: (484)270-8702
Co. E-mail: info@mabba.net
URL: http://www.mabba.net
Contact: Francis L. Serafin, President
E-mail: gary@hershassociates.com
Description: Provides education, professional designations, and networking opportunities to further growth and development of professionals engaged in business brokerage, mergers, and acquisitions. **Geographic Preference:** Regional.

2137 ■ Midwest Business Brokers and Intermediaries (MBBI)
1018 W Madison Ave., Ste. 9
Chicago, IL 60607
Ph: (847)847-7703
URL: http://www.mbbi.org
Contact: Raymond Horn, III, Contact
E-mail: rhorn@mpslaw.com
Facebook: www.facebook.com/MBBIAssociation
Linkedin: www.linkedin.com/company/mbbi

X (Twitter): x.com/MBBIAssociation
YouTube: www.youtube.com/channel/UCzO7uJf15eX5difyTCyguKg
Description: Represents industry leaders involved in the buying, funding, and selling of small businesses. **Geographic Preference:** Regional.

2138 ■ National Association of General Merchandise Representatives (NAGMR)
1305 Thorndale Ave.
Elk Grove Village, IL 60007
Free: 877-377-8322
URL: http://nagmr.com
Description: Consumer products brokers specializing in selling drug, health, beauty aids, and nonfood products to food chains and the same products and grocery items to the nonfood market. **Founded:** 1948. **Educational Activities:** NAGMR Convention; National Association of General Merchandise Representatives Annual Convention. **Geographic Preference:** National.

2139 ■ National Customs Brokers and Forwarders Association of America, Inc. (NCBFAA)
1200 18th St. NW, Ste. 901
Washington, DC 20036
Ph: (202)466-0222
Fax: (202)466-0226
Co. E-mail: development@ncbfaa.org
URL: http://www.ncbfaa.org
Contact: Jose D. Gonzalez, President
Facebook: www.facebook.com/NCBFAAFacebook
Linkedin: www.linkedin.com/company/national-customs-brokers-&-forwarders-association-of-america-inc-
X (Twitter): x.com/NCBFAA
Instagram: www.instagram.com/ncbfaa
Description: Treasury-licensed customs brokers, FMC-licensed independent ocean freight forwarders, and CNS-registered air cargo agents; associate members in 25 foreign countries. Seeks to maintain high standards of business practice throughout the industry. Monitors legislative and regulatory issues affecting customs brokers and forwarders. **Founded:** 1897. **Publications:** *Membership Directory*; *National Customs Brokers and Forwarders Association of America Membership Directory* (Annual); *NCBFAA Membership Directory: The Who's Who of American Customs Brokers and International Freight Forwarders* (Annual); *National Customs Brokers & Forwarders Association of America--Membership Directory* (Annual). **Educational Activities:** Government Affairs Conference (GAC) (Annual). **Geographic Preference:** National.

2140 ■ Nevada Business Brokers Association (NBBA)
2190 E Pebble Rd., Ste. 260
Las Vegas, NV 89123
URL: http://www.ibba.org/about/affiliates
Description: Provides education, professional designations, and networking opportunities to further growth and development of professionals engaged in business brokerage, mergers, and acquisitions. **Geographic Preference:** State.

2141 ■ New England Business Brokers Association (NEBBA)
11 Robert Toner Blvd.
Sute 5, PMB 233
North Attleboro, MA 02760
Ph: (978)263-5559
Co. E-mail: administrator@nebba.com
URL: http://www.nebba.com
Contact: Jennife Fox, President
E-mail: jfox@tworldma.com
Description: Disseminates industry information; encourages growth of sales; assists in new industry developments. Represents members in legislative matters and lobbies for recognition of the industry. Coordinates activity among business brokerages and cooperates with other types of brokerages. Conducts educational and promotional programs for members. **Founded:** 1993. **Geographic Preference:** Regional.

2142 ■ New York Association of Business Brokers (NYABB)
c/o Anthony Citrolo/President
25 Melville Pk. Rd., Ste. 216
Melville, NY 11747
Ph: (516)346-5272
Co. E-mail: anthony@nybbinc.com
URL: http://nyabb.org
Contact: Anthony Citrolo, Co-President
E-mail: anthony@nybbinc.com
X (Twitter): x.com/NYABizBrokers
Description: Represents professionals and firms in business brokerage, mergers and acquisitions. Provides business brokers education, conferences, professional designations, and networking opportunities in New York. Works to become a leader in the exchange of business referrals, and to create professional relationships with successful business transaction advisors. **Founded:** 1993. **Geographic Preference:** State.

2143 ■ Pennsylvania Business Brokers Association (PBBA)
c/o Michael Meyer, President
308 Lakeside Pk.
Southampton, PA 18966
Ph: (215)357-9694
Co. E-mail: mmeyer@benjaminrossgroup.com
URL: http://www.pennbba.com
Contact: Michael Meyer, President
E-mail: mmeyer@benjaminrossgroup.com
Description: Represents professionals and firms in business brokerage, mergers and acquisitions. Provides business brokers education, conferences, professional designations, and networking opportunities in Pennsylvania. Works to become a leader in the exchange of business referrals, and to create professional relationships with successful business transaction advisors. **Founded:** 2000. **Geographic Preference:** State.

2144 ■ Printing Brokerage/Buyers Association International (PB/BA) - Library
1530 Locust St., Mezzanine 124
Philadelphia, PA 19102
Ph: (215)821-6581
URL: http://pbba.org
Description: Promotes understanding, cooperation, and interaction among members while obtaining the highest standard of professionalism in the graphic arts industry. **Scope:** Printing and publishing marketing and corporate development specialists, whose services include start ups, joint ventures, acquisitions, mergers, contract negotiation, international trade, seminars, workshops, facilities planning, and cost reduction programs. Serves private industries as well as government agencies. **Founded:** 1985. **Holdings:** Figures not available. **Publications:** "Hot Markets for 2007-2008," Jan, 2005. **Training:** How to Sell Printing Effectively; Sales Compensation and Management; How to Buy Printing Effectively; Hot Markets; International Priority Commerce. **Awards:** PBBA Printing Broker Reseller of the Year (Annual). **Geographic Preference:** Multinational. **Special Services:** Findprint®; Salesort®.

2145 ■ Texas Association of Business Brokers (TABB)
909 Lake Carolyn Pky., Ste. 320
Irving, TX 75039
Ph: (214)445-6395
URL: http://www.tabb.org
Contact: David Sweeten, President
Description: Disseminates industry information; encourages growth of sales; assists in new industry developments. Represents members in legislative matters and lobbies for recognition of the industry. Coordinates activity among business brokerages and cooperates with other types of brokerages. Conducts educational and promotional programs for members. **Geographic Preference:** State.

REFERENCE WORKS

2146 ■ "Bartering Takes Businesses Back to Basics" in Buffalo News (July 9, 2010)
Pub: The Buffalo News, Inc.
Contact: Tom Wiley, President
E-mail: twiley@buffnews.com
Ed: Dino Grandoni. **Description:** Bartering clubs can help small businesses reach new customers and to expand their business. **Availability:** Print; Online.

2147 ■ "The Neighborhood Watch" in Hawaii Business (Vol. 53, March 2008, No. 9, pp. 36)
Pub: PacificBasin Communications
Contact: Chuck Tindle, Director
E-mail: chuckt@pacificbasin.net
Ed: David K. Choo. **Description:** OahuRe.com offers information on Hawaii real estate market, with spreadsheets and comparative market analysis page, which shows properties that are active, sold, or in escrow. Other details about OahuRe.com are discussed. A list of other top real estate websites in Hawaii and in the U.S. in general is provided.

TRADE PERIODICALS

2148 ■ Barron's
Pub: Dow Jones & Company Inc.
Contact: Almar Latour, Chief Executive Officer
URL(s): www.dowjones.com/products/barrons
Released: Weekly **Price:** $4, for 2 / 4 weeks 1 year. **Description:** Business and finance magazine. **Availability:** Print; Online.

2149 ■ Better Investing
Pub: National Association of Investors Corp.
Contact: John Gannon, Secretary
URL(s): www.betterinvesting.org/learn-about-investing/betterinvesting-magazine
Ed: Adam Ritt. **Released:** Weekly **Description:** Magazine focusing on investing in long-term common stock. **Availability:** Print; Online.

2150 ■ Computerized Investing
Pub: American Association of Individual Investors
Contact: Raymond Rondeau, President
URL(s): www.aaii.com/journal/category/Computerized-Investing
Ed: Andrew Lautner, Wayne A. Thorp. **Released:** Quarterly **Description:** Magazine covering the use of computers for investment analysis. **Availability:** Print.

2151 ■ Dow Theory Forecasts
Pub: Horizon Publishing Company LLC.
Contact: Robert T. Evans, Chairman
URL(s): dtf.horizonpublishing.com
Facebook: www.facebook.com/dowtheoryforecasts
Ed: Richard Moroney, CFA. **Released:** Weekly **Price:** $10, for back issues; $289, for per year. **Description:** Financial magazine. **Availability:** Print; PDF.

2152 ■ Investment Advisor Magazine
Contact: Danielle Andrus, Managing Editor
E-mail: dandrus@summitpronets.com
URL(s): www.thinkadvisor.com/investment-advisor?ref=nav
X (Twitter): twitter.com/InvestAdvMag
Released: Monthly **Description:** Investment magazine for financial professionals. Includes coverage of mutual funds, insurance products and partnerships combined with feature articles for financial planners. **Availability:** Print; PDF; Online.

2153 ■ Money
Pub: Dotdash Meredith
Contact: Neil Vogel, Chief Executive Officer
URL(s): money.com
Facebook: www.facebook.com/MoneyMagazine
X (Twitter): x.com/money
Instagram: www.instagram.com/moneymag
YouTube: www.youtube.com/channel/UCGFBKGwap9wa9npMd1n-1Vw
Released: Bimonthly **Description:** Magazine focusing on personal and family finance. **Availability:** Print; PDF; Online.

2154 ■ Official Summary of Security Transactions and Holdings
Pub: U.S. Government Publishing Office
URL(s): bookstore.gpo.gov/products/official-summary-security-transactions-and-holdings-v-62-no-6-period-june-11-1996-thru-july

Price: $42, Other countries; $30, U.S. **Description:** Journal reporting securities holdings figures and transactions by owner. **Availability:** Print.

VIDEO/AUDIO MEDIA

2155 ■ *How I Built My Small Business: Loren Vandegrift - Insights from Business Exits Broker on Sales, Values, and Trends*
URL(s): www.annemcginty.com/transcripts/lorenvandegrift
Released: March 26, 2024. **Description:** Podcast offers a conversation with a business broker about sales, values, and industry trends.

CONSULTANTS

2156 ■ **Associated Management Systems Inc.**
2995 Woodside Rd., Ste. 400-188
Woodside, CA 94062
Contact: Adil Khan, Chief Executive Officer
Description: Consulting firm is engaged in entrepreneurial and professional expertise includes corporate management, investment banking, finance, strategic planning, risk evaluation, due diligence studies and management audits and also assists with mergers and acquisitions and provides management for turnaround situations and undertakes project packaging, plant relocations, capital restructuring and funding. **Scope:** Consulting firm is engaged in entrepreneurial and professional expertise includes corporate management, investment banking, finance, strategic planning, risk evaluation, due diligence studies and management audits and also assists with mergers and acquisitions and provides management for turnaround situations and undertakes project packaging, plant relocations, capital restructuring and funding.

2157 ■ **Business Brokers Hawaii L.L.C. (BBH)**
4473 Pahee St. Unit Q
Lihue, HI 96766
Contact: James Mayfield, Contact

2158 ■ **Business Team (BT)**
1475 S Bascom Ave., Ste. 113
Campbell, CA 95008
Ph: (408)246-1102
Fax: (408)246-2219
Co. E-mail: sanjose@business-team.com
URL: http://www.business-team.com
Contact: Armstrong Wong, Officer
E-mail: armstrong@business-team.com
Description: A business brokerage firm that specializes in merger, acquisition, and divestiture services for privately held, mid-sized companies. The company's value-added services include business valuation, pre-marketing consultation, and exit strategy planning. **Founded:** 1981. **Training:** Business Valuation Enhancing the Value of Your Company.

FRANCHISES AND BUSINESS OPPORTUNITIES

2159 ■ **Business America**
555 Rte. Seventy Eight
Swanton, VT 05488
Ph: (802)868-7244
Co. E-mail: info@businessamerica1.com
URL: http://www.businessamerica1.com
Contact: Steve C. Selby, Contact
Description: Provider of payment solutions. **Founded:** 1997. **Franchised:** 1985. **Training:** Yes.

2160 ■ **Empire Business Brokers**
257 Elmwood Ave.
Buffalo, NY 14222
Ph: (716)240-2544
Co. E-mail: info@empirebb.com
URL: http://empirebb.com
Contact: Nick Gugliuzza, President
E-mail: nickgug1@gmail.com
Description: Assist sellers of existing business opportunities in finding buyers. **Founded:** 1981. **Franchised:** 1989. **Training:** 5 days at company Headquarters by the country's foremost business broker, ongoing Seminars and conventions. Manuals, forms and tapes provided.

2161 ■ **The Entrepreneur's Source (TES)**
900 Main St. S, Bldg. 2
Southbury, CT 06488
Free: 800-289-0086
Co. E-mail: information@franchisesource.com
URL: http://esourcecoach.com
Contact: Terry Powell, Founder
Facebook: www.facebook.com/TheEntrepreneursSource
Linkedin: www.linkedin.com/company/the-entrepreneur's-source
YouTube: www.youtube.com/user/EntrepreneursSource
Description: Business and franchise consulting organization, specializes in coaching and placement services for people exploring options in business ownership. **Scope:** Business and franchise consulting organization, specializes in coaching and placement services for people exploring options in business ownership. **Founded:** 1984. **Publications:** "E-Myth and Franchise source Brands Create the Largest Franchise Network"; "Women in Franchising," Black Enterprise Magazine, Sep, 2006; "Make it a Success with Entrepreneur's Source," Work Magazine, Aug, 2006; "Retirement Not the Goal," the Journal News, Jan, 2006. **Training:** Initial and ongoing.

2162 ■ **Murphy Business and Financial Corp.**
407 N Belcher Rd.
Clearwater, FL 33765
Ph: (727)725-7090
Free: 888-561-3243
Fax: (727)725-8090
URL: http://murphybusiness.com
Contact: Wayne Quilitz, President
Facebook: www.facebook.com/MurphyBusiness
X (Twitter): x.com/murphybiz
YouTube: www.youtube.com/user/murphybusinesscorp/videos
Description: Firm engages in business valuations, machinery, equipment appraisals, commercial real estate and business consulting services. **Founded:** 1994. **Financial Assistance:** Yes

2163 ■ **Realty World (RW)**
1101 Dove St., Ste. 228
Newport Beach, CA 92660
Ph: (714)436-9009
Free: 800-685-4984
Co. E-mail: corporate@realtyworldhq.com
URL: http://www.realtyworld.com
Contact: Andrew Cimerman, Chief Executive Officer
Facebook: www.facebook.com/corporaterealtyworld
Linkedin: www.linkedin.com/company/lucasgroup123
X (Twitter): x.com/realtyworldinc
Instagram: www.instagram.com/realtyworld
YouTube: www.youtube.com/channel/UCdv9qyi7QU_GU-JQo_DRE_A
Description: Firm engages in development of residential, commercial and retail properties. **Founded:** 1973.

2164 ■ **Sunbelt Business Brokers Ottawa [Sunbelt Ottawa]**
2821 Riverside Dr.
Ottawa, ON, Canada K1V 8N4
Ph: (613)731-9140
Free: 800-905-3557
Co. E-mail: ottawa@sunbeltcanada.com
URL: http://www.sunbeltcanada.com/ottawa
Contact: Gregory Kells, President
E-mail: gregkells@sunbeltcanada.com
Description: Business brokerage company. **No. of Franchise Units:** 29. **Founded:** 2002. **Franchised:** 2002. **Equity Capital Needed:** $100,000. **Franchise Fee:** $25,000. **Training:** Provides training and ongoing support.

COMPUTERIZED DATABASES

2165 ■ *ABI/INFORM*
ProQuest LLC
789 E Eisenhower Pky.
Ann Arbor, MI 48108
Ph: (734)761-4700
Free: 800-521-0600
URL: http://www.proquest.com
Contact: Matti Shem Tov, Chief Executive Officer
URL(s): about.proquest.com/en/products-services/abi_inform_complete
Availability: Online. **Type:** Full-text; Bibliographic; Image.

2166 ■ *Best's Statement File - Life/Health - United States*
A.M. Best Company Inc.
1 Ambest Rd.
Oldwick, NJ 08858-0700
Ph: (908)438-2200
Free: 800-424-2378
Co. E-mail: customer_support@ambest.com
URL: http://web.ambest.com
Availability: PDF; Online. **Type:** Numeric.

Business Consulting Service

START-UP INFORMATION

2167 ■ *How to Start a Home-Based Consulting Business: Define Your Specialty Build a Client Base Make Yourself Indispensable*
Ed: Bert Holtje. **Released:** January 06, 2010. **Price:** Paperback. **Description:** Everything needed for starting and running a successful consulting business from home. **Availability:** Print.

2168 ■ *Starting Up On Your Own: How to Succeed as an Independent Consultant or Freelance*
Ed: Mike Johnson. **Released:** 2012. **Price:** $27.99, e-book; $55.98, book plus e-book bundle. **Description:** Concise guide for anyone wanting to start their own consulting firm is provided. **Availability:** E-book.

ASSOCIATIONS AND OTHER ORGANIZATIONS

2169 ■ **Association of Consulting Engineering Companies - Canada (ACEC)**
130 Albert St., Ste. 420
Ottawa, ON, Canada K1P 5G4
Ph: (613)236-0569
Free: 800-565-0569
Fax: (613)236-6193
Co. E-mail: info@acec.ca
URL: http://www.acec.ca
Contact: John D. Gamble, President
E-mail: jgamble@acec.ca
Linkedin: www.linkedin.com/company/association-of
 -consulting-engineering-companies-canada
X (Twitter): x.com/aceccanada
Description: Promotes the interests of independent consulting engineers; represents electrical, civil, environmental, geotechnical, metallurgical, cultural, and other engineering fields. **Scope:** Promotes and safeguards the business and professional interests of the Canadian consulting engineering industry in Canada and abroad. **Founded:** 1925. **Publications:** "There is a Best Practice for Hiring Engineering Firms"; "The Budget 2009 Infrastructure Stimulus Package: Maximizing Benefits to Canadians"; "Foreign Policy Statement: A Ray of Hope for Infrastructure Investments"; "Infrastructure Recovery: National Planning and the Right Engineering Needed". **Training:** Understanding Public Private Partnerships in Canada. **Awards:** Beaubien Award (Annual); ACEC Awards of Excellence (Annual); Schreyer Award (Annual). **Geographic Preference:** National.

2170 ■ **Association for Corporate Growth - Toronto Chapter (ACG) [Canadian Angus Association]**
411 Richmond St. E, Ste. 200
Toronto, ON, Canada M5A 3S5
Ph: (416)868-1881
Fax: (416)929-5256
Co. E-mail: toronto@acg.org
URL: http://www.acg.org/toronto
Contact: Mike Fenton, President
Linkedin: www.linkedin.com/company/association-for
 -corporate-growth-toronto-chapter
X (Twitter): x.com/ACGGlobal
Description: Professionals with a leadership role in strategic corporate growth. Seeks to facilitate the professional advancement of members, and the practice of corporate growth management. Fosters communication and cooperation among members; conducts continuing professional education programs. **Founded:** 1954. **Educational Activities:** Annual Capital Connection Conference (Annual). **Geographic Preference:** National.

2171 ■ **Canadian Association of International Development Professionals (CAIDP) [Regroupement des consultants canadiens en developpement internationale]**
Ottawa, ON, Canada 516 555
Co. E-mail: caidprpcdi@gmail.com
URL: http://www.caidp-rpcdi.ca
Contact: Abbas Sumar, Member
Facebook: www.facebook.com/caidprpcdi
X (Twitter): x.com/CAIDP_RPCDI
YouTube: www.youtube.com/channel/UC
 -PGLvYZy9rTh944EatSrbg
Description: Aims to provide services for, and to represent the interests of, Canadian international development consultants. **Founded:** 1993. **Geographic Preference:** Multinational.

2172 ■ *Canadian Consulting Engineer*
111 Gordon Baker Rd., Ste. 400
Toronto, ON, Canada M2H 3R1
Ph: (416)442-5600
Free: 800-268-7742
Fax: (416)510-5134
Co. E-mail: apotal@annexbusinessmedia.com
URL: http://www.mromagazine.com
Contact: Beata Olechnowicz, Manager
E-mail: bolechnowicz@annexbusinessmedia.com
URL(s): www.canadianconsultingengineer.com
Facebook: www.facebook.com/CanadianConsul
 tingEngineer
Linkedin: www.linkedin.com/company/canadian
 -consulting-engineer-magazine
X (Twitter): x.com/CdnConsultEng
Ed: Bronwen Parsons. **Released:** 6/year **Description:** Magazine providing professional engineers in consulting engineering and architectural practice. **Availability:** Print; PDF; Download; Online.

2173 ■ **International Association of Professional Business Consultants (IAPO)**
167 Midland Pl. SE
Calgary, AB, Canada T2X 1N1
URL: http://www.iapcollege.com/program/member
 ship-business-consultants
Description: Provides business development and education services to professional business consultants and students.

2174 ■ **International Association for Time Use Research (IATUR)**
Brussels, Belgium
URL: http://www.iatur.org
Contact: Theun Pieter van Tienoven, Treasurer
E-mail: t.p.van.tienoven@vub.be
Description: Facilitates exchange of ideas, methodology, and data collection techniques among researchers and compilers of official statistics on the patterns of daily activities and changes in people's behaviours over time. **Founded:** 1970. **Publications:** *The Journal of Time Use Research (eIJTUR)* (Annual); *Fifteenth Reunion of the International Association for Time Use Research Amsterdam* (Periodic); *Time Use Methodology: Towards Consensus*. **Geographic Preference:** Multinational.

2175 ■ *The Journal of Time Use Research (eIJTUR)*
Brussels, Belgium
URL: http://www.iatur.org
Contact: Theun Pieter van Tienoven, Treasurer
E-mail: t.p.van.tienoven@vub.be
URL(s): jtur.iatur.org
X (Twitter): x.com/journaltur
Ed: Prof. Jonathan Gershuny, Prof. Andrew S. Harvey. **Released:** Annual **Availability:** Print; Download; Online.

2176 ■ *Thrive-on-Line*
145 Thornway Ave.
Thornhill, ON, Canada L4J 7Z3
Ph: (416)410-8163
URL: http://www.aiconsult.ca/en
Price: free for members. **Availability:** Print; Online.

REFERENCE WORKS

2177 ■ *"Altegrity Acquires John D. Cohen, Inc." in (November 19, 2009, pp. 14)*
Pub: Investment Weekly News
Description: John D. Cohen, Inc., a contract provider of national security policy guidance and counsel to the federal government, was acquired by Altegrity, Inc., a global screening and security solutions provider; the company will become part of US Investigations Services, LLC and operate under the auspices of Altegrity's new business, Altegrity Security Consulting. **Availability:** Print; Online.

2178 ■ *"The Art of War for Women" in Hawaii Business (Vol. 54, July 2008, No. 1, pp. 23)*
Pub: PacificBasin Communications
Contact: Chuck Tindle, Director
E-mail: chuckt@pacificbasin.net
Ed: Chin-Ning Chu. **Description:** Business consultant Chi-Ning Chu talks about her new book 'The Art of War for Women: Sun Tzu's Ancient Strategies and Wisdom for Winning at Work', which discusses how women can more effectively win in business. She also shares her thoughts about the advantages that women have, which they can use in businesses decisions.

2179 ■ "BDC Launches New Online Business Advice Centre" in Marketwired (July 13, 2010)
Pub: Comtex News Network Inc.
Contact: Kan Devnani, President
Description: The Business Development Bank of Canada (BDC) offers entrepreneurs the chance to use their new online BDC Advice Centre in order to seek advice regarding the challenges of entrepreneurship. Free online business tools and information to help both startups and established firms are also provided. **Availability:** Print; Online.

2180 ■ "Best Foot Forward" in Canadian Business (Vol. 80, October 22, 2007, No. 21, pp. 115)
Description: Jeremy Shinewald's mbaMission admissions consulting business helps prospective MBA students with essay writing, mock interview preparation and school selection. The consulting fee for application to one school is $2,250. Details of the business schools' MBA programs and tuition fees are explored. **Availability:** Online.

2181 ■ "Brite-Strike Tactical Launches New Internet Marketing Initiatives" in Marketwired (September 15, 2009)
Pub: Comtex News Network Inc.
Contact: Kan Devnani, President
Description: Brite-Strike Tactical Illumination Products, Inc. has enlisted the expertise of Internet marketing guru Thomas J. McCarthy to help revamp the company's Internet campaign. An outline of the Internet marketing strategy is provided. **Availability:** Print; Online.

2182 ■ Business Consulting: Insane But True Facts About Consulting
Ed: Michael Motes. **Released:** January 15, 2019.
Description: Encourages the reader to explore the options available to become a business consultant based upon their own passions and interests. **Availability:** E-book.

2183 ■ "The Consulting Business Booms Just as Consultants Disappear" in Bloomberg (July 29, 2021)
URL(s): www.bloomberg.com/news/articles/2021-07-29/the-consulting-business-booms-just-as-consultants-disappear
Ed: Matthew Boyle. **Released:** July 29, 2021.
Description: During these pandemic times, a lot of employees in consulting are making decisions to leave their current industries and look for work in other sectors. Often times poached by other companies or tired of the constant travel, these employees are often settling down for new work from home positions or joining high-interest fields. **Availability:** Online.

2184 ■ "The Couch in the Corner Office: Surveying the Landscape of the CEO Psyche" in Inc. (January 2008, pp. 33-34)
Description: Profile of Leslie G. Mayer, founder of the Leadership Group, a firm that provides assistance to CEOs of firms by offering a deep understanding of the relationships, insecurities, and blind spots that can weaken strong leadership. **Availability:** Online.

2185 ■ "The End of Clock-Punching" in Canadian Business (Vol. 83, September 14, 2010, No. 15, pp. 96)
Pub: Rogers Media Inc.
Contact: Neil Spivak, Chief Executive Officer
Ed: Lyndsie Bourgon. **Description:** Workplace consultant Peter Hadwen is pushing for the transformation of Canada's government departments into results-only work environments (ROWE). ROWE does not require employees to show up to work at a certain time as long as they are meeting goals and achieving results in their jobs. Details of studies regarding ROWE in US companies are examined. **Availability:** Online.

2186 ■ "Fail Forward's Ashley Good on How to Screw Up in the Best Possible Way" in Canadian Business (Vol. 87, October 2014, No. 10, pp. 47)
Pub: American City Business Journals, Inc.
Contact: Mike Olivieri, Executive Vice President
Description: Ashley Good, founder and CEO of Toronto, Ontario-based consultancy firm, Fail Forward, offers advice on ways to recover from a business failure. The best way to separate from the failure is to share the story and get other people's perspectives. **Availability:** Online.

2187 ■ "The Firm: The Story of McKinsey and Its Secret Influence on American Business"
Pub: Simon & Schuster Adult Publishing Group
Contact: Jonathan Karp, President
Released: September 30, 2014. **Price:** $20, paperback, plus $1.55 shipping charges. **Description:** Profile of McKinsey & Company, the most influential and controversial business consulting firm in the United States. McKinsey consultants have ushered in waves of structural, financial, and technological change to America's best organizations; they've reorganized the power structure within the White House; and they have revolutionized business schools. **Availability:** E-book; Print.

2188 ■ "Gen Z-Led Executive Communications and Strategic Engagement Agency Launches in DC" in Minority Business Entrepreneur (March 17, 2023)
URL(s): mbemag.com/articles/gen-z-led-executive-communications-and-strategic-engagement-agency-launches-in-dc/
Ed: Gaby M. Rojas. **Description:** One of the first Black, Queer, and Gen Z-led agencies was launched by Words Normalize Behavior, which is a company dedicated to communications, coalition-building, and advice. **Availability:** Online.

2189 ■ Heart: Building a Great Brand in the Digital Age
Pub: CreateSpace
Released: September 29, 2014. **Price:** $3.70, paperback. **Description:** Business leader and consultant who works with designers, contractors and service providers in the green industry helps business owners develop and implement company systems and increase revenue. His is a third-generation horticulturist and small business owner and share the challenges of being an entrepreneur. **Availability:** Print.

2190 ■ "Innovate or Stagnate: How Doing Things Differently Helps Business" in South Florida Business Journal (Vol. 34, January 10, 2014, No. 25, pp. 10)
Pub: American City Business Journals, Inc.
Contact: Mike Olivieri, Executive Vice President
Released: Weekly. **Price:** $8, Introductory 4-week offer(Digital & Print). **Description:** Business enterprises can drive growth by focusing on innovations. Companies are advised to consider radical ideas, invent different ways of working and avoid bureaucracy. Peter Drucker, a management consultant, believes that business has two functions: marketing and innovation. **Availability:** Print; Online.

2191 ■ "Into the Groove: Fine-Tune Your Biz By Getting Into the Good Habit Groove" in Small Business Opportunities (Spring 2008)
Description: Profile of Ty Freyvogel and his consulting firm Freyvogel Communications. Freyvogel serves the telecommunications need of Fortune 500 and mid-sized businesses.

2192 ■ "'I've Always Been an Entrepreneur" in South Florida Business Journal (Vol. 34, June 13, 2014, No. 47, pp. 11)
Pub: American City Business Journals, Inc.
Contact: Mike Olivieri, Executive Vice President
Released: June 13, 2014. **Price:** $4, Introductory 4-Week Offer(Digital & Print). **Description:** Modernizing Medicine CEO, Daniel Cane, says he started doing business at age six when he opened a lemonade stand. His firm helps physicians increase efficiencies in their practices while improving both business and treatment outcomes. He surrounds himself with talented people, which is what he likes most about his job. Cane added that dividing time between work and family is difficult for entrepreneurs. **Availability:** Print; Online.

2193 ■ "The Leadership Equation: 10 Practices That Build Trust, Spark Innovation, and Create High-Performing Organizations"
Pub: Greenleaf Book Group Press
Contact: Tanya Hall, Chief Executive Officer
Released: September 30, 2014. **Price:** $18.95, U.S., paperback. **Description:** Entrepreneur and business consultant draws upon his work with corporations, government agencies, and nonprofit organizations and their human resource departments to explain the workings of high-performing organizations with his equation: Trust + Spark = Leadership Culture. He describes the ten more important practices for building trust and spark that improves team performance, the business unit, and the entire organization. **Availability:** Print.

2194 ■ "Managing the Facebookers; Business" in The Economist (Vol. 390, January 3, 2009, No. 8612, pp. 10)
Pub: Economist Newspaper Ltd.
Contact: Lara Boro, Chief Executive Officer
Description: According to a report from PricewaterhouseCoopers, a business consultancy, workers from Generation Y, also known as the Net Generation, are more difficult to recruit and integrate into companies that practice traditional business acumen. 61 percent of chief executive managers say that they have trouble with younger employees who tend to be more narcissistic and more interested in personal fulfillment with a need for frequent feedback and an over-precise set of objectives on the path to promotion which can be hard for managers who are used to a different relationship with their subordinates. Older bosses should prepare to make some concessions to their younger talent since some of the issues that make them happy include cheaper online ways to communicate and additional coaching, both of which are good for business. **Availability:** Online.

2195 ■ "MBAs for Hire, By the Hour" in Entrepreneur (August 2014)
Pub: Entrepreneur Media Inc.
Contact: Dan Bova, Director
E-mail: dbova@entrepreneur.com
Description: HourlyNerd started from a classroom project by Pat Petitti and Rob Biederman at Harvard Business School in Boston, Massachusetts in 2003. the temporary-staffing firm recruits business students to act as consultants to small businesses that hire them. Consultants must come from one of the top 40 Master of Business Administration Programs in the U.S. in order to bid on a project. The firm receives 15 percent of the project fee from the hiring company while the business consultants pay 5 percent to the company. **Availability:** Online.

2196 ■ The Mirror Test: Is Your Business Really Breathing?
Pub: Grand Central Publishing
Contact: Michael Pietsch, Chairman
Ed: Jeffrey W. Hayzlett. **Released:** May 05, 2010. **Price:** $9.99, e-book. **Description:** Consultant and author, Jeffrey Hayzlett, explains why a business is not doing well and asks the questions that most business managers are afraid to ask. **Availability:** E-book; Print.

2197 ■ "Montgomery & Barnes: a Service-Disabled, Veteran-Owned Small Business" in Underground Construction (Vol. 65, October 2010, No. 10)
Description: Gary Montgomery, chairman of Montgomery and Barnes announced that President Wendell (Buddy) Barnes is now majority owner, thus making the Houston-based civil engineering and consulting services firm, eligible to quality as a Service-Disabled Veteran-Owned Small Business (SDVOSB). **Availability:** Online.

2198 ■ The New Business of Consulting: The Basics and Beyond
Ed: Elaine Biech. **Released:** April 30, 2019. **Description:** A guide for entrepreneurs who are venturing out into the consulting industry. **Availability:** E-book.

2199 ■ *"Pay Heed to 'Smack Stack" in Puget Sound Business Journal* (Vol. 35, May 16, 2014, No. 4, pp. 6)
Pub: American City Business Journals, Inc.
Contact: Mike Olivieri, Executive Vice President
Description: Technology consultant, Geoffrey Moore, discloses the topics he plans to discuss at the annual State of Technology Luncheon held in Washington on May 19, 2014. He will explore the impact of technology and business trends on public-policy making and regulations. **Availability:** Online.

2200 ■ *"Plan Your Next Event at Newport News Marriott at City Center"* in *Benzinga.com* (July 29, 2011)
Pub: PR Newswire Association LLC.
Description: Newport News Marriott at City Center is promoting itself as the premier venue for business meetings, conventions and weddings.

2201 ■ *PPC's Guide to Small Business Consulting Engagements*
Released: Annual. **Price:** $365, book; $280, online.
Description: Technical guide for conducting consulting engagements for small business. **Availability:** Print; Online.

2202 ■ *"Sleeping with Your Smartphone: How to Break the 24/7 Habit and Change the Way You Work"*
Pub: Harvard Business Review Press
Contact: Moderna V. Pfizer, Contact
Released: May 29, 2012. **Price:** $30, Hardcover/Hardcopy. **Description:** Harvard Business School professor, Leslie Perlow, reveals ways to become more productive after disconnecting from your smartphone. A six-person team was used in an experiment at The Boston Consulting Group, an elite management consulting firm, where teams changed the way they worked and became more efficient and effective by disconnecting. The team was better able to perform and recruit new talent. A step-by-step guide is offered to change your team. **Availability:** E-book; Print.

2203 ■ *"Teksapiens, A Leading SEO Company, Offers Free SEO Consulting Services to Dallas Businesses"* in *Wireless News* (March 29, 2012)
Description: Dallas-based Web design firm, Teksapiens, offers free search engine optimization to Dallas businesess signing up at DallasBestSEO.com. The free service provides tips to outperform competition when marketing on the Internet. **Availability:** Print; Online.

2204 ■ *"Think Disruptive! How to Manage In a New Era of Innovation"* in *Strategy & Leadership* (Vol. 38, July-August 2010, No. 4, pp. 5-10)
Pub: Emerald Inc.
Ed: Brian Leavy, John Sterling. **Price:** $32, online only 30 days. **Description:** The views expressed by Scott Anthony, president of an innovation consultancy Innosight, on the need for corporate leaders to apply disruptive innovation in a recessionary environment are presented. His suggestion that disruptive innovation is the only way to survive during the economic crisis is discussed. **Availability:** Online; PDF.

CONSULTANTS

2205 ■ **4aBetterBusiness, Inc.**
1417 Main St.
Evanston, IL 60202
Ph: (847)606-2605
URL: http://4abetterbusiness.com
Contact: Paul Vragel, President
E-mail: pvragel@4abetterbusiness.com
Description: Provider of professional solutions to help businesses. **Scope:** Provider of professional solutions to help businesses. **Founded:** 1989. **Training:** Achieving Breakthrough Results, No Capital Investment Required, Apr, 2006; Manufacturing and Economic Recovery Conference, Apr, 2006; Achieving Breakthrough Results, No Capital Investment Required, 2005; Improving Productivity - NOW!, 2004; Make Your Processes Yield Higher Productivity, 2003. **Special Services:** QlikView.

2206 ■ **ABONAR Business Consultants Ltd.**
3110 8th St. E, Ste. 8B-376
Saskatoon, SK, Canada S7H 0W2
Co. E-mail: info@abonarconsultants.com
URL: http://www.abonarconsultants.com
Contact: Sean McAlpine, P. Eng., MBA, Contact
E-mail: sean.mcalpine@abonarconsultants.com
X (Twitter): x.com/abonarbusiness
Description: Provider of business plans, financial and operations management, and strategic management business consulting services. **Scope:** Provider of business plans, financial and operations management, and strategic management business consulting services. **Founded:** 2006.

2207 ■ **Advanced Business Learning Inc. (ABL)**
125 S 52nd St.
Tempe, AZ 85281
Ph: (480)222-7507
Co. E-mail: info@advancedbusinesslearning.com
URL: http://www.advancedbusinesslearning.com
Contact: Susan Morris, President
E-mail: susan@advancedbusinesslearning.com
Description: Firm provides sales effectiveness, IT training and leadership, professional development program services, and much more. **Scope:** Firm provides sales effectiveness, IT training and leadership, professional development program services, and much more. **Publications:** "Leading Effectively from a Distance"; "Building Extended Learning Systems That Deliver"; "How to Manage Virtual Teams," 2009; "Collaboration Rules," Aug, 2005. **Training:** Project Management; Critical Thinking; Consulting Skills for Knowledge Workers; Organizational Ethics; Innovator Sessions of Wilson Learning; Visioning; Strategic Thinking; Work Culture Analysis; HR Planning; Meeting Leadership Challenges; Creating an Empowering Environment; Working Styles: Working with People Effectively.

2208 ■ **Advantage Business Concepts (ABC)**
PO Box 512
Batavia, IL 60510
Ph: (630)879-6511
URL: http://advantage-biz.com
Contact: Ellen Huxtable, Contact
Facebook: www.facebook.com/AdvantageBusinessConcepts
Description: Firm is engaged in business consulting services such as team facilitation and consultative services to the small businesses. **Scope:** Firm is engaged in business consulting services such as team facilitation and consultative services to the small businesses.

2209 ■ **The Alliance Management Group Inc.**
38 Old Chester Rd., Ste. 300
Gladstone, NJ 07934
Ph: (908)234-2344
Fax: (908)234-0638
URL: http://www.strategicalliance.com
Contact: Dr. Gene Slowinski, Director
Description: Firm is engaged in business management consultant such as integration, technology management and related services. **Scope:** Firm is engaged in business management consultant such as integration, technology management and related services. **Publications:** "Effective Practices For Sourcing Innovation," Jan-Feb, 2009; "Intellectual Property Issues in Collaborative Research Agreements," Nov-Dec, 2008; "Building University Relationships in China," Sep-Oct, 2008; "Reinventing Corporate Growth: Implementing the Transformational Growth Model"; "The Strongest Link"; "Allocating Patent Rights in Collaborative Research Agreements"; "Protecting Know-how and Trade Secrets in Collaborative Research Agreements," Aug, 2006; "Sourcing External Technology for Innovation," Jun, 2006. **Special Services:** "Want, Find, Get, Manage" Model®; "Want, Find, Get, Manage" Framework®; WFGM Framework®; The Alliance Implementation Program®; WFGM Paradigm®; WFGM Model®; "Want, Find, Get, Manage" Paradigm®, Transformational Growth®; T-growth®.

2210 ■ **Alliance Management International Ltd.**
6200 Rockside Rd.
Cleveland, OH 44131
Contact: Carolyn K. Matheson, Contact
Description: A consulting company that helps to form national and international strategic alliances. Handles alliances between companies forming joint ventures. Staff specialized in small company-large company alliance, alliance assessment and analysis and alliance strategic planning. **Scope:** A consulting company that helps to form national and international strategic alliances. Handles alliances between companies forming joint ventures. Staff specialized in small company-large company alliance, alliance assessment and analysis and alliance strategic planning. **Training:** Joint Business Planning; Developing a Shared Vision; Current and New/Prospective Partner Assessment; Customer Service; Sales Training; Leader and Management Skills.

2211 ■ **Alternative Services Inc. (ASI)**
32625 W 7 Mile Rd., Ste. 11
Livonia, MI 48152
Ph: (248)471-4880
URL: http://www.asi-mi.org
Contact: Jenny Bhaskaran, Executive Director
E-mail: jbhaskaran@asi-mi.org
Description: Services: Developmental disabilities training. **Scope:** Services: Developmental disabilities training. **Founded:** 1978.

2212 ■ **Ambler Growth Strategy Consultants Inc.**
3432 Reading Ave.
Hammonton, NJ 08037-8008
Fax: (609)567-3810
Description: Growth strategies, strategic assessments, CEO coaching. **Scope:** Growth strategies, strategic assessments, CEO coaching. **Founded:** 1979. **Publications:** "A joint venture can deliver more than growth"; "Achieving competitive advantage"; "Achieving resilience for your business during difficult times"; "Achieving resilient growth during challenging times"; "Acquisitions: A growth strategy to consider"; "Attracting and retaining longterm corporate sponsors"; "Celebrate Selling: The Consultative Relationship Way"; "A Joint Venture Can Deliver More Than Growth"; "Achieving Competitive Advantage"; "Achieving Resilience for Your Business During Difficult Times"; "Balancing Revenue Growth with Growth of a Business"; "Capture Your Competitive Advantage"; "Ease Succession Planning"; "Games Employees Play"; "How to Spark Innovation in an Existing Company"; "Managers demands must change with growth"; "Motivating Generation employees"; "Knowing when to hire ratios provide answers"; "Better customer service can bring black ink". **Training:** Strategic Leadership; Managing Innovation; Breaking Through Classic Barriers to Growth; Energize Your Enterprise; Capture Your Competitive Advantage; Four Entrepreneurial Styles; Perservance and Resilience; Real-Time Strategic Planning/RO1. **Special Services:** The Growth Strategist™.

2213 ■ **American English Academy (AEA) [American English College]**
111 N Atlantic Blvd., Ste. 112
Monterey Park, CA 91754
Ph: (626)457-2800
Fax: (626)457-2808
Co. E-mail: info@aec.edu
URL: http://www.aec.edu
Facebook: www.facebook.com/americanenglishcollege
Linkedin: www.linkedin.com/company/american-english-college
Instagram: www.instagram.com/americanenglishcollege
YouTube: www.youtube.com/channel/UC6eS1MpXLDagYdZVZWWJO6A

Description: Specializes in providing on-site English language and communication development for corporations and individuals. Also develops and delivers training in speaking, writing, pronunciation, grammar, and idioms with an emphasis on business communication. Offers individual, small group, intensive, and long-distance learning. Programs tailor-made for each client. **Scope:** Specializes in providing on-site English language and communication development for corporations and individuals. Also develops and delivers training in speaking, writing, pronunciation, grammar, and idioms with an emphasis on business communication. Offers individual, small group, intensive, and long-distance learning. Programs tailor-made for each client. **Founded:** 1983.

2214 ■ ARAMARK Business & Industry, LLC
ARAMARK Corporation
2400 Market St.
Philadelphia, PA 19103
Ph: (215)238-3000
Free: 800-388-3300
Co. E-mail: aramark-cares@aramark.com
URL: http://www.aramark.com

Description: Provider of technical services, energy management, and building commissioning and also physical plant, grounds and performance management. **Scope:** Provider of technical services, energy management, and building commissioning and also physical plant, grounds and performance management.

2215 ■ Aspire Business Development Inc.
10955 Lowell Ave., Ste. 400
Overland Park, KS 66210
Ph: (913)660-9400
Co. E-mail: info@aspirekc
URL: http://aspirekc.com
Contact: Shawn Kinkade, President
E-mail: skinkade@aspirekc.com

Description: Firm provides business management consulting services, business aspirations models, business effectiveness analysis, and much more services. **Scope:** Firm provides business management consulting services, business aspirations models, business effectiveness analysis, and much more services.

2216 ■ Aurora Management Partners Inc.
1201 Peachtree St., Ste. 1570
Atlanta, GA 30361
Ph: (704)377-6010
Co. E-mail: info@auroramp.com
URL: http://www.auroramp.com
Contact: David Baker, CTP, Managing Partner
Linkedin: www.linkedin.com/company/aurora-management-partners/about

Description: Specializes in turnaround management and reorganization consulting, the company develops strategic initiatives, organize and analyze solutions, deal with creditor issues, review organizational structures and develop time frames for decision making. **Founded:** 2000. **Publications:** "TMA Turnaround of the Year Award, Small Company, Honorable Mention," Nov, 2005; "Back From The Brink - Bland Farms," Progressive Farmer, Oct, 2004; "New Breed of Turnaround Managers," Catalyst Magazine, Aug, 2004; "Key Performance Drivers - Bland Farms," The Produce News, Apr, 2004; "Corporate Governance: Averting Crisis's Before They Happen," ABJ journal, Feb, 2004.

2217 ■ Beacon Management-Management Consultants
Pompano Beach, FL 33069
Co. E-mail: md@beaconmgmt.com
URL: http://www.beaconmgmt.com
Contact: Michael J. Donnelly, Consultant Managing Director Principal

Description: Provider of management consulting services such as strategic and business planning, market intelligence, decision support services, corporate finance, and much more. **Scope:** Provider of management consulting services such as strategic and business planning, market intelligence, decision support services, corporate finance, and much more. **Founded:** 1985. **Publications:** "Sun-Sentinel Article," Oct, 2012.

2218 ■ Bimen Business Consultants Ltd.
365 Evans Ave., Ste. L10
Toronto, ON, Canada M8Z 1K2
Co. E-mail: info@bimenbusiness.com
URL: http://test.bimenbusiness.com
Contact: Tom Caringi, President

Description: Firm provides business consulting and technical services and much more. **Scope:** Firm provides business consulting and technical services and much more. **Founded:** 1987. **Publications:** "Return of the King!," Apr, 2005.

2219 ■ Bio-Technical Resources L.P. (BTR)
1035 S 7th St.
Manitowoc, WI 54220-5301
Ph: (920)684-5518
Fax: (920)684-5519
Co. E-mail: info@biotechresources.com
URL: http://www.biotechresources.com
Contact: Reinhardt A. Rosson, President

Description: Firm provides research and development of industrial fermentation processes service. **Scope:** Services include strain improvement, process development and metabolic engineering. **Founded:** 1962. **Publications:** "A Novel Fungus for the Production of Efficient Cellulases and Hemi-Cellulases," Jun, 2009; "Linoleic Acid Isomerase from Propionibacterium acnes: Purification, Characterization, Molecular Cloning, and Heterologous Expression," 2007; "Purification and Characterization of a Membrane-Bound Linoleic Acid Isomerase from Clostridium sporogenes," 2007; "Metabolic Engineering of Sesquiterpene Metabolism in Yeast," 2007; "Purification and Characterization of a Membrane-Bound Linoleic AcidIsomerase from Clostridium sporogenes," 2007. **Training:** Metabolic Engineering for Industrial Production of Glucosamine and N-Acetylglucosamine, Aug, 2003; Metabolic Engineering of E. coli for the Industrial Production of Glucosamine, Apr, 2003.

2220 ■ BioChem Technology Inc.
1004 9th Ave., Ste. 230
King of Prussia, PA 19406
Ph: (610)768-9360
Co. E-mail: sales@biochemtech.com
URL: http://www.biochemtech.com/about

Description: Firm engages in construction of monitoring, optimization, control of waste water treatment processes, technological optimization services and much more. **Scope:** Firm engages in construction of monitoring, optimization, control of waste water treatment processes, technological optimization services and much more. **Founded:** 1979. **Publications:** "Process Evaluation Provides Optimization and Energy Reduction"; "Effect of Ionic Strength on Ion Selective Electrodes in the Activated Sludge Process". **Training:** A Five Year Case Study of a Feed Forward Nitrogen Reduction Process Control System, Jun, 2009; Alternate DO Control Based on On-line Ammonia Measurement, Jun, 2009.

2221 ■ BioSciCon, Inc. [Biomedical Science Consulting Company, Inc.]
14905 Forest Landing Cir.
Rockville, MD 20850
Ph: (301)610-9130
Fax: (301)610-7662
Co. E-mail: info@bioscicon.com
URL: http://www.bioscicon.com
Contact: Dr. Nenad Markovic, President

Description: Provider of biomedical science consulting and also a developer of biotechnology products. **Scope:** Provider of biomedical science consulting and also a developer of biotechnology products. **Founded:** 1996. **Publications:** "Cervical Acid Phosphates: A Biomarker of Cervical Dysplasia and Potential Surrogate Endpoint for Colposcopy," 2004; "Enhancing Pap test with a new biological marker of cervical dysplasia," 2004; "A cytoplasmic biomarker for liquid-based Pap," The FACEB Journal Experimental Biology, 2004; "Pap test and new biomarker-based technology for enhancing visibility of abnormal cells," 2004. **Special Services:** MarkPap®; PreservCyt®.

2222 ■ Birchfield Jacobs Foodsystems Inc.
519 N Charles St.
Baltimore, MD 21201
Contact: John C. Birchfield, Jr., Contact
E-mail: jbirchfield@birchfieldjacobs.com

Description: Firm provides foodservice consulting services.

2223 ■ Black Sheep Business Consulting Corp. (BSBCON)
1771 Robson St., Ste. 247
Vancouver, BC, Canada V6G 1C9
Ph: (604)690-7113
Free: 888-880-1898
Co. E-mail: info@bsbcon.com
URL: http://www.bsbcon.com
Contact: Kevin Foreman, President
Facebook: www.facebook.com/blacksheepbusinessconsulting
Linkedin: www.linkedin.com/company/bsbcon
X (Twitter): x.com/BSBCON
Instagram: www.instagram.com/bsbcon

Description: A team of experienced business consultants that work with SMEs to break through the barriers of their industry. **Scope:** A team of experienced business consultants that work with SMEs to break through the barriers of their industry.

2224 ■ Brandywine Business Advisory L.L.C. (BBA)
2 Camp David Rd.
Wilmington, DE 19810
URL: http://www.bb-advisory.com
Contact: Arun Jain, President
E-mail: arun.jain@bb-advisory.com

Description: Partners with business owners to help them increase productivity and quality and to enhance customer satisfaction. Services include operations consulting, strategic planning and process improvement services. **Scope:** Partners with business owners to help them increase productivity and quality and to enhance customer satisfaction. Services include operations consulting, strategic planning and process improvement services. **Founded:** 2010.

2225 ■ Business Advancement Inc. (BAI)
178 Sycamore Ter.
Glen Rock, NJ 07452
Ph: (201)612-1228
URL: http://businessadvance.com
Contact: Pamela S. Harper, Chief Executive Officer
E-mail: harper@businessadvance.com
Facebook: www.facebook.com/businessadvancementinc
Linkedin: www.linkedin.com/company/business-advancement-inc.

Description: Firm provides business management consulting services for entrepreneurs, private companies, and government corporations. **Scope:** Firm provides business management consulting services for entrepreneurs, private companies, and government corporations. **Founded:** 1991. **Publications:** "Four Steps to Making Strategic Alliances Work"; "The Key to Aligning Strategy with Execution"; "Grow Your Business by Finding Your Hidden Organization"; "How Boards Can Support Organizational Transformation"; "Uncover the Assumptions that Stall Business Growth"; "Help Your Business Get Out of Its Own Way"; "How to Keep From Getting Blindsided by Your Organizations Reality"; "How to Keep Your Organizational Reality from Sabotaging Your Outsource Strategy". **Special Services:** QuickConsult™.

2226 ■ Business Automation Specialists of Minnesota Inc. (BASM)
300 Coon Rapids Blvd. NW, Ste. 100
Minneapolis, MN 55433-5644
Ph: (763)571-8580
Free: 877-571-8580
Fax: (763)571-5504
Co. E-mail: sales@bautomation.com
URL: http://bautomation.com

Contact: Ron Ketterling, President
Description: Firm is engaged in business automation solutions, project management, system integration, implementation, training and much more. **Scope:** Firm is engaged in business automation solutions, project management, system integration, implementation, training and much more. **Founded:** 1985. **Publications:** "FDA Requires Faster Food Safety Reporting," Sep, 2009; "How Do You Have a Good Year in a Downturn," Jun, 2009; "Behind the Scenes With Barb and Sharon of Business Automation Specialists," May, 2009; "Being Self-Sufficient vs. Knowing When to Ask for Help," Apr, 2009; "How to Make Business Intelligence Pay," Apr, 2009; "A Day With An Automation Systems Specialist," Mar, 2009. **Special Services:** Sage PRO; Sage CRM; Sage WMS; Radio Beacon warehouse Automation.

2227 ■ Business Consultants Network Inc. (NYBC)
405 Lexington Ave.
New York, NY 10174
Free: 888-201-9524
Fax: (888)201-9524
Co. E-mail: info@newyorkbusinessconsultants.com
URL: http://www.newyorkbusinessconsultants.com/index.html
Contact: Malko Ebers, Chief Executive Officer
Facebook: www.facebook.com/NYConsultant
Linkedin: www.linkedin.com/company/new-york-business-consultants
Founded: 2011.

2228 ■ Business Consulting Services
720 Highpoint Dr.
Wexford, PA 15090
Contact: Reed Powell, Owner
Description: Management consulting organization dedicated to providing professional services to the business, government and non-profit communities and specializes in the two key areas of business performance improvement and information technology consulting and specifically for small business owners. **Scope:** Management consulting organization dedicated to providing professional services to the business, government and non-profit communities and specializes in the two key areas of business performance improvement and information technology consulting and specifically for small business owners. **Publications:** "If You Fail To Plan"; "The True Cost Of Technology"; "Why Projects Fail"; "Planning For A Business Disruption". **Training:** How To Select, Manage and Contract Consultants, and Other Resources; How To Market Professional Services; Introduction To Management Consulting.

2229 ■ Business Development International Corp.
522 fifth Ave.
New York, NY 10036
Contact: Maged F. Riad, Contact
Description: Specializing in the business side of chemical, plastics and related industries-international technology transfer, licensing, acquisitions, divestitures, mergers, joint ventures, evaluating, due diligence, trouble-shooting, marketing research, plastics flame retardant and recycling. **Scope:** Specializing in the business side of chemical, plastics and related industries-international technology transfer, licensing, acquisitions, divestitures, mergers, joint ventures, evaluating, due diligence, trouble-shooting, marketing research, plastics flame retardant and recycling.

2230 ■ Business Enterprise Mapping Inc. (BEM)
13835 N Northsight Blvd., Ste. 100
Scottsdale, AZ 85260
Ph: (480)515-9001
Co. E-mail: info@businessmapping.com
URL: http://www.businessmapping.com
Contact: Joe Bockerstette, Partner
Linkedin: www.linkedin.com/company/business-enterprise-mapping-inc-

Description: Firm provides business process management services. **Scope:** Firm provides business process management services. **Founded:** 1993. **Publications:** "Mapping A Path to Quality Systems," Jun, 2008. **Training:** Strategic Process Management for Executives, Feb, 2010; Mastery of Process Mapping, Oct, 2009; The Power of Process Mapping, Sep, 2009; Public and On site Training Courses; Seven Steps to Problem Solving; Auditing Process Based Systems; Process Mapping Using Visio; Process Management for Executives.

2231 ■ Business Forecast Systems Inc.
465 Waverley Oaks Rd., Ste. 318
Waltham, MA 02452
Ph: (617)484-5050
Co. E-mail: info@forecastpro.com
URL: http://www.forecastpro.com
Contact: Eric Stellwagen, Chief Executive Officer
Linkedin: www.linkedin.com/company/business-forecast-systems
YouTube: www.youtube.com/channel/UCukxfvd1ba5N62I5g9xD5tw
Description: Developer of business forecasting software. **Scope:** Specializes in developing easy-to-use forecasting software for business professionals in sales, marketing, manufacturing and finance. **Founded:** 1986. **Publications:** "Improving Your Forecasting with Top-down Models"; "Forecast Projects in Forecast Pro Unlimited and Forecast Pro Unlimited Collaborator". **Training:** Business Forecasting: Techniques, Applications, and Experiences; Forecast Pro XE Training Class; Basics of Time Series Forecasting; Change Management: Key to Effective S and OP Implementation. **Special Services:** Forecast Pro Trac.

2232 ■ Business & Government Continuity Services Inc.
13404 Princeton Ln.
Edmond, OK 73013
Ph: (405)286-1649
Fax: (405)286-1649
Co. E-mail: lrsbgcs@aol.com
URL: http://businesscontinuity.info
Description: Provider of disaster prevention training and services to organizations. **Scope:** Provider of disaster prevention training and services to organizations. **Founded:** 1960. **Training:** Compelling Case for Business/Government Continuity and Recovery Planning; Critical Functions and Significant Responsibilities; Executive Liabilities and Recovery Considerations; Business and Mission Continuity Planning Issues; Implementing Business/Mission Recovery Planning Steps; Quality Benefits; Obtaining Approval and Gaining Support; Selecting Recovery Teams; Types of Recovery Teams, Duties & Functions; Project Management and Continuity Planning; Personal and Home Disaster Recovery Planning; A Cost Saving Software Option; Plan Structure and Formats.

2233 ■ Business Improvement Architects (BIA)
633 Lakelands Ave.
Innisfil, ON, Canada L9S 4E5
Co. E-mail: info@bia.ca
URL: http://bia.ca
Contact: Rowena Lamy, Consultant
E-mail: rlamy@bia.ca
Facebook: www.facebook.com/BusinessImprovementArchitects
Linkedin: www.linkedin.com/company/business-improvement-architects
Description: Provider of the following services, strategic planning, leadership development, innovation and project and quality management. Specialize in strategic planning, change management, leadership assessment and development of skills. **Scope:** Provider of the following services, strategic planning, leadership development, innovation and project and quality management. Specialize in strategic planning, change management, leadership assessment and development of skills. **Founded:** 1989. **Publications:** "Avoiding Pit falls to Innovation"; "Create a New Dimension of Performance with Innovation"; "The Power of Appreciation in Leadership"; "Why It Makes Sense To Have a Strategic Enterprise Office"; "Burning Rubber at the Start of Your Project"; "Accounting for Quality"; "How Pareto Charts Can Help You Improve the Quality of Business Processes"; "Managing Resistance to Change". **Training:** The Innovation Process From Vision to Reality, San Diego, Oct, 2007; Critical Thinking, Kuala Lumpor, Sep, 2007; Critical Thinking, Brunei, Sep, 2007; Delivering Project Assurance, Auckland, Jun, 2007; From Crisis to Control: A New Era in Strategic Project Management, Prague, May, 2007; What Project Leaders Need to Know to Help Them Sleep Better At Night, London, May, 2007; Innovation Process. From Vision To Reality, Orlando, Apr, 2007. **Special Services:** Project Planning Tool™.

2234 ■ Business Performance Associates Inc. (BPA)
10658 La Roda Dr.
Cupertino, CA 95014
Contact: Timothy R. Stein, Chief Executive Officer
E-mail: tstein@bpaconsultants.com
Description: Firm assists companies in improving their business performance, their services include biomedical quality systems, software validation, ISO 13485 2003 conversions, ISO implementation, documentation management and continuous improvement. **Scope:** Firm assists companies in improving their business performance, their services include biomedical quality systems, software validation, ISO 13485 2003 conversions, ISO implementation, documentation management and continuous improvement. **Publications:** "The Computer System Risk Management and Validation Life Cycle," Paton Press, 2006; "Minimizing Failures of Purchased Computer Systems," Quality Digest, Mar, 2005. **Training:** Practical Methods for Complying with the ISO 13485 Software Validation Requirements, 2005; Practical and Compliant Electronic Records, 2003; Putting Software Validation into Practice, 2002; Understanding ISO 9001: 2000 and How It Applies to You; Implementing ISO 9001: Establishing and Managing Quality Systems; Internal Auditing for Medical Device Companies; Achieving Compliance with Part 11; Computer System Validation for Business Applications; Managing for Continuous Improvement; Validating Computer Systems for Business Applications. **Special Services:** RiskVal Life Cycle; RiskVal Services.

2235 ■ Business Process Consulting Group (BPCG)
166 Willowleaf Dr.
Littleton, CO 80127-3574
Ph: (720)981-1111
URL: http://theprocessconsultant.com
Linkedin: www.linkedin.com/in/ianjamestheprocessconsultant
X (Twitter): twitter.com/fixesprocess
Description: A provider of training, consulting services, kaizen and software solutions in flow and lean manufacturing and Kanban techniques, as they apply to the factory and the office. Consultants have implemented the flow methodologies in factories and offices throughout the world. **Scope:** A provider of training, consulting services, kaizen and software solutions in flow and lean manufacturing and Kanban techniques, as they apply to the factory and the office. Consultants have implemented the flow methodologies in factories and offices throughout the world. **Founded:** 1999. **Publications:** "Leaning Out Health Care: A How-To Manual for the Optimization of Health Care Processes"; "Flow White Paper"; "Flow Processing in at Medical Device Manufacturer"; "Operational Savings Choices"; "Sky Radio™; Soundtrack - Gerard Leone"; "Advanced Manufacturing Magazine: When to Train your Employees," Nov, 2002. **Special Services:** Administrative Flow™; Flow Processing Advantage®.

2236 ■ Business and Quality Process Management L.L.C. (BQPM)
26925 Reiling Ave.
Monroe, OR 97456
Ph: (541)288-0079
Co. E-mail: info@bqpm.com
URL: http://bqpm.com

Contact: Stanley H. Salot, President
Description: Provider of consulting, training and software tools to help companies create leaner effective organizations. **Scope:** Provider of consulting, training and software tools to help companies create leaner effective organizations. **Publications:** "IEC-IECQ Hazardous Substance Free Process Management Certification Assessment Training"; "IEC-IECQ Launches Hazardous Substance Free Process Management Certification System"; "Zhu Zhu Pets and Hazardous Substance Process Management - Quality Digest". **Special Services:** BQPM; QMX Software Support; ISO-XPRESS™.

2237 ■ Business Spotlight Inc.
8075 Wycliffe Dr.
  Cincinnati, OH 45244
Contact: Christopher S. Allen, Contact
Description: Focuses on sales, time issues, team development and exit strategies. **Scope:** Focuses on sales, time issues, team development and exit strategies.

2238 ■ ByrneMRG Corp.
5459 Rinker Cir.
  Doylestown, PA 18902
Ph: (215)630-7411
Co. E-mail: info@byrnemrg.com
URL: http://www.byrnemrg.com
Contact: Patrick Boyle, Founder Consultant
E-mail: pjboyle@byrnemrg.com
Description: Services: Management consulting. **Scope:** Services: Management consulting. **Founded:** 1972. **Publications:** "Implementing Solutions to Everyday Issues".

2239 ■ Capital Business Solutions (CBS)
3725 National Dr., Ste. 160
  Raleigh, NC 27612
Ph: (843)249-6008
Free: 888-249-6008
Co. E-mail: info@capitalbusiness.net
URL: http://www.capitalbusiness.net
Contact: Bob Schilling, Director
E-mail: bschilling@capitalbusiness.net
Facebook: www.facebook.com/CapitalBusinessSolutions
Linkedin: www.linkedin.com/company/capital-business-solutions-cbs
X (Twitter): twitter.com/CapitalBusiness
Description: Firm provides integrated financial, fundraising software solutions, software implementation, and much more. **Scope:** Firm provides integrated financial, fundraising software solutions, software implementation, and much more. **Founded:** 1997. **Financial Assistance:** Yes

2240 ■ Cartesian, Inc.
6405 Metcalf Ave., Ste. 417
  Overland Park, KS 66202
Fax: (913)273-1395
URL: http://www.cartesian.com
Contact: Dale Reynolds, Vice President
Facebook: www.facebook.com/cartesian
Linkedin: www.linkedin.com/company/cartesian
X (Twitter): x.com/cartesiantweets
Description: Firm provides strategy, management consulting and managed solutions for the communication, media and entertainment sectors. **Founded:** 1990. **Special Services:** Lexicon™; QBC™; QSA™.

2241 ■ CBIZ, Inc.
CBIZ, Inc.
  5959 Rockside Woods Blvd. N, Ste. 600
  Independence, OH 44131
Ph: (216)447-9000
Fax: (216)447-9007
Co. E-mail: cbizwomensadvantage@cbiz.com
URL: http://www.cbiz.com
Contact: Jerome P. Grisko, Jr., President
Facebook: facebook.com/cbizmhmcareers
Linkedin: www.linkedin.com/company/cbiz
X (Twitter): twitter.com/cbz
YouTube: www.youtube.com/user/CBIZSolutions
Description: Diversified services company is engaged in providing an array of professional business services which include accounting and tax, healthcare and health benefits consulting, financial advisory, valuation, risk and advisory services, payroll, property and casualty insurance, retirement planning, managed networking and hardware services primarily to small and medium-sized businesses, as well as individuals, government agencies, and not-for-profit enterprises. **Founded:** 1996. **Training:** Health Care - What the Future Holds; Consumer Driven Health Plans; Executive Plans; Health Savings Accounts; Healthy Wealthy and Wise; Legislative Update; Medicare Part D; Retirement Plans.

2242 ■ Center for Lifestyle Enhancement-Columbia Medical Center of Plano
3901 West 15th St
  Plano, TX 75075
Ph: (972)596-6800
Fax: (972)519-1299
URL: http://medicalcityplano.com
Contact: Erol R. Akdamar, President
Facebook: www.facebook.com/medicalcityplano
X (Twitter): twitter.com/MedCityPlano
Description: Firm provides professional health counseling in the areas of general nutrition for weight management, eating disorders, diabetic education, cholesterol reduction and adolescent weight management. Offers work site health promotion and preventive services. Also coordinates speaker's bureau, cooking classes and physician referrals. **Scope:** Firm provides professional health counseling in the areas of general nutrition for weight management, eating disorders, diabetic education, cholesterol reduction and adolescent weight management. Offers work site health promotion and preventive services. Also coordinates speaker's bureau, cooking classes and physician referrals. **Founded:** 1975. **Training:** Rx Diet and Exercise; Smoking Cessation; Stress Management; Health Fairs; Fitness Screenings; Body Composition; Nutrition Analysis; Exercise Classes; Prenatal Nutrition; SHAPEDOWN; Successfully Managing Diabetes; Gourmet Foods for Your Heart; The Aging Heart; Heart Smart Saturday featuring Day of Dance; Weight-Loss Management Seminars; The Right Stroke for Men; Peripheral Artery Disease Screening; Menstruation: The Cycle Begins; Boot Camp for New Dads; Grand parenting 101: Caring for Kids Today; Teddy Bear C New Baby Day C Safe Sitter Babysitting Class.

2243 ■ The Center for Organizational Excellence, Inc. (COE)
15204 Omega Dr., Ste. 300
  Rockville, MD 20850
Contact: Stephen P. Goodrich, Contact
E-mail: sgoodrich@center4oe.com
Description: Firm provides consulting services such as designing and delivering consulting solutions in the areas of organizational effectiveness, human capital, information technology, and data management. **Scope:** Firm provides consulting services such as designing and delivering consulting solutions in the areas of organizational effectiveness, human capital, information technology, and data management. **Founded:** 1984.

2244 ■ CEO Advisors
848 Brickell Ave., Ste. 603
  Miami, FL 33131
Ph: (305)371-8560
URL: http://www.ceoadvisors.us
Contact: Roberto Arguello, Jr., President
Facebook: www.facebook.com/CEOAdvisors9
Linkedin: www.linkedin.com/company/wix-com
Description: Provider of clients services in strategy, mergers and acquisitions, corporate finance and advisory, supply chain management, government relations and public affairs. **Scope:** Provider of clients services in strategy, mergers and acquisitions, corporate finance and advisory, supply chain management, government relations and public affairs. **Founded:** 1989. **Preferred Investment Size:** $300,000 to $500,000. **Industry Preferences:** Communications and media, computer hardware and software, semiconductors and other electronics, biotechnology, medical and health, consumer related.

2245 ■ CES Business Consultants
514 Old Hickory Ln.
  Ringgold, GA 30736
Ph: (428)580-0093
URL: http://marniekuhns.com/privacy-policy
Description: Firm provides civil engineering, construction management, structural engineering, program management and many more. **Scope:** Firm provides civil engineering, construction management, structural engineering, program management and many more. **Founded:** 1990. **Publications:** "Bullet-Proof Your Business with Multiple Income Streams"; "A Christian's Guide to Surviving a Home Business"; "How to Get and Keep Customers for Your Computer-Based Business". **Training:** Faith Precedes the Miracle: Develop Your Own Mountain-Moving Faith.

2246 ■ Chartered Management Co.
100 Saunders Rd., Ste. 150
  Lake Forest, IL 60045
Contact: William B. Avellone, President
Description: Operations improvement consultants. Specializes in strategic planning, feasibility studies, management audits and reports, profit enhancement, start-up businesses, mergers and acquisitions, joint ventures, divestitures, interim management, crisis management, turnarounds, business process re-engineering, venture capital and due diligence. **Scope:** Operations improvement consultants. Specializes in strategic planning, feasibility studies, management audits and reports, profit enhancement, start-up businesses, mergers and acquisitions, joint ventures, divestitures, interim management, crisis management, turnarounds, business process re-engineering, venture capital and due diligence. **Founded:** 1985.

2247 ■ Children's Psychological Health Center, Inc. (CPHC)
2105 Divisadero St.
  San Francisco, CA 94115
Ph: (415)292-7119
Fax: (415)749-2802
URL: http://www.childrenspsychologicalhealthcenter.org
Contact: Jessie Rios, Executive Director
E-mail: jessie.rios@expertchildpsychiatry.org
Linkedin: www.linkedin.com/in/childrenspsychological
Description: Treats those with psychological trauma claimed from stressors including institutional negligence, vehicular and aviation accidents, wrongful death in the family, rape, molestation, fire, explosion, flood, earthquake, loss of parents, terrorism, kidnapping, disfiguring events, emotional damage from social work, medical malpractice or defective products. **Scope:** Treats those with psychological trauma claimed from stressors including institutional negligence, vehicular and aviation accidents, wrongful death in the family, rape, molestation, fire, explosion, flood, earthquake, loss of parents, terrorism, kidnapping, disfiguring events, emotional damage from social work, medical malpractice or defective products. **Founded:** 1992. **Publications:** "My Personal Story About Tropical Storm Stan," Feb, 2006; "My Personal Story About Hurricanes Katrina and Rita: A guided activity workbook to help coping, learning and Healthy expression," Sep, 2005; "Helping Patients and their Families Cope in a National Disaster," Jan, 2002; "The practice of behavioral treatment in the acute rehabilitation setting".

2248 ■ Comer & Associates L.L.C. (CA)
5255 Holmes Pl.
  Boulder, CO 80303
Ph: (303)786-7986
URL: http://www.comerassociates.com
Contact: Gerald Comer, Contact
Description: Specialize in developing markets and businesses. Marketing support includes developing and writing strategic and tactical business plans, developing and writing focused, effective market plans, researching market potential and competition, implementing targeted marketing tactics to achieve

company objectives, conducting customer surveys to determine satisfaction and attitudes toward client. **Scope:** Specialize in developing markets and businesses. Marketing support includes developing and writing strategic and tactical business plans, developing and writing focused, effective market plans, researching market potential and competition, implementing targeted marketing tactics to achieve company objectives, conducting customer surveys to determine satisfaction and attitudes toward client. **Training:** Developing a Strategic Market Plan; Market Research: Defining Your Opportunity; Management and Leadership Effectiveness; Team Building; Developing a Business Plan; How to Close; Using Questions to Sell; Sales System Elements and Checklist; Working With Independent Reps; Features vs. Benefits; Overcoming Objections; Sales Force Automation.

2249 ■ Compleat Business Solutions
Calgary, AB, Canada
Ph: (403)286-3978
Co. E-mail: cbsolutions@lycos.com
URL: http://cbsolutions.tripod.com
Contact: Kenneth Fung, Contact
E-mail: kenneth_fung@canada.com
Description: Firm provides project and knowledge management and information systems consulting, custom training and facilitating, and much more. **Scope:** Firm provides project and knowledge management and information systems consulting, custom training and facilitating, and much more.

2250 ■ Consulting & Conciliation Service (CCS)
Sacramento, CA
Ph: (916)396-0480
URL: http://conciliation.org
Contact: Jane McCluskey, Contact
E-mail: jane@conciliation.org
Description: Firm offers consulting and conciliation services, they provide pre-mediation counseling, training and research on preparing for a peaceful society, mediation and facilitation, preparation for shifts in structure, policy, and personnel, it offers sliding scale business rates and free individual consultation. **Scope:** Firm offers consulting and conciliation services, they provide pre-mediation counseling, training and research on preparing for a peaceful society, mediation and facilitation, preparation for shifts in structure, policy, and personnel, it offers sliding scale business rates and free individual consultation. **Publications:** "Native America and Tracking Shifts in US Policy"; "Biogenesis: A Discussion of Basic Social Needs and the Significance of Hope". **Training:** Positive Approaches to Violence Prevention: Peace building in Schools and Communities.

2251 ■ Corporate Consulting, Inc.
100 Fillmore St.
Denver, CO 80206
Contact: Devereux C. Josephs, Contact
Description: Engaged in feasibility studies, organizational development, small business management, mergers and acquisitions, joint ventures, divestitures, interim management, crisis management, turnarounds, financing, appraisals valuations and due diligence studies. **Scope:** Engaged in feasibility studies, organizational development, small business management, mergers and acquisitions, joint ventures, divestitures, interim management, crisis management, turnarounds, financing, appraisals valuations and due diligence studies.

2252 ■ Culture Solutions Group
1610 Little Raven St., Unit PH3
Denver, CO 80202
Ph: (970)390-9420
Co. E-mail: info@culturesolutionsgroup.com
URL: http://culturesolutionsgroup.com
Contact: Caroline Fisher, Principal
Facebook: www.facebook.com/culturesolutionsgroup
Linkedin: www.linkedin.com/company/culture-solutions-group
X (Twitter): x.com/CSG_Culture

Description: Works to transform business culture through targeted training, facilitation, and leadership development.

2253 ■ Daugherty Business Solutions
3 Cityplace Dr., Ste. 400
Saint Louis, MO 63141
Free: 800-737-8200
URL: http://www.daugherty.com
Contact: Ron Daugherty, President
Linkedin: www.linkedin.com/company/daugherty-business-solutions
YouTube: www.youtube.com/c/Daugherty
Description: Provider of business consulting services.

2254 ■ De Bellas & Co.
7700 Irvine Ctr. Dr., Ste. 800
Irvine, CA 92618
URL: http://debellas.com
Contact: Alfred F. De Bellas, Jr., President
E-mail: adebellas@debellas.com
Description: Finance: Investment banking firm. **Scope:** Finance: Investment banking firm. **Founded:** 1983. **Publications:** "Tools to Take Advantage of the Current IT Staffing M and A Market," 2005; "Healthcare Staffing: Buy, Sell or Build," 2005.

2255 ■ DenMark Business Solutions Inc.
587 Old York Rd., Ste. 1
Etters, PA 17319
Ph: (717)932-4757
Co. E-mail: denmark@denmarkbusinesssolutions.com
URL: http://denmarkbusinesssolutions.com
Contact: Mark Dixon, President
Facebook: www.facebook.com/DenMarkTelecom
Linkedin: www.linkedin.com/in/denmarktelecom
X (Twitter): twitter.com/denmark_telecom
Instagram: www.instagram.com/denmark_business_solutions
Description: Provider of consulting services that helps businesses understand and control their telecommunications costs. **Scope:** Provider of consulting services that helps businesses understand and control their telecommunications costs. **Founded:** 2002.

2256 ■ Diversified Health Resources Inc.
1209 N Astor St., No. 2N
Chicago, IL 60610-2655
Contact: Andrea Rice Rozran, President
Description: Offers health care consulting for hospitals, nursing homes including homes for the aged and other health related facilities and companies. Specializes in planning and marketing. Also conducts executive searches for top level health care administrative positions. Serves private industries as well as government agencies. **Scope:** Offers health care consulting for hospitals, nursing homes including homes for the aged and other health related facilities and companies. Specializes in planning and marketing. Also conducts executive searches for top level health care administrative positions. Serves private industries as well as government agencies. **Publications:** "City Finance".

2257 ■ Eastern Point Consulting Group Inc.
75 Oak St.
Newton, MA 02465
Ph: (617)965-4141
URL: http://www.eastpt.com
Contact: Katherine Herzog, President
Description: Firm specializes in bringing practical solutions to complex challenges and provides consulting and training in managing diversity, comprehensive sexual-harassment policies and programs, organizational development, benchmarks 360-degree skills assessment, executive coaching, strategic human resource planning, team building, leadership development for women, mentoring programs, and gender issues in the workplace. **Scope:** Firm specializes in bringing practical solutions to complex challenges and provides consulting and training in managing diversity, comprehensive sexual-harassment policies and programs, organizational development, benchmarks 360-degree skills assessment, executive coaching, strategic human resource planning, team building, leadership development for women, mentoring programs, and gender issues in the workplace. **Training:** Leadership Development for Women.

2258 ■ Education Development Center Inc. (EDC)
300 Fifth Ave., Ste. 2010
Waltham, MA 02451
Ph: (617)969-7100
Fax: (617)969-5979
Co. E-mail: contact@edc.org
URL: http://www.edc.org
Contact: Siobhan Murphy, Chief Executive Officer
Facebook: www.facebook.com/edc.worldwide
Linkedin: www.linkedin.com/company/education-development-center
X (Twitter): x.com/EDCtweets
YouTube: www.youtube.com/edcworldwide
Description: Delivers programs to address early childhood development, youth workforce development, and suicide prevention. Creates curricula and online courses and conducts surveys. **Scope:** Serves to design, deliver and evaluate innovative programs to address some of the world's most urgent challenges in education, health, and economic opportunity. Renders services to US. and foreign government agencies, private foundations, healthcare sectors, educational institutions, nonprofit organizations, universities, and corporations. **Founded:** 1958. **Publications:** "A Call to Action: HIV/AIDS, Health, Safety, and the Youth Employment Summit"; "A Case Against "Binge" as the Term of Choice: How to Get College Students to Personalize Messages about Dangerous Drinking"; "A Description of Foundation Skills Interventions for Struggling Middle-Grade Readers in Four Urban Northeast and Islands Region School Districts"; "A Guide to Facilitating Cases in Education"; "A Look at Social, Emotional, and Behavioral Screening Tools for Head Start and Early Head Start"; "A Multifaceted Social Norms Approach to Reduce High-Risk Drinking: Lessons from Hobart and William Smith Colleges"; "The New Media Literacy Handbook"; "Helping Children Outgrow War"; "Worms, Shadows, and Whirlpools: Science in the Early Childhood Classroom"; "Teacher Leadership in Mathematics and Science Casebook and Facilitator's Guide"; "Teachers' Professional Development and the Elementary Mathematics Classroom: Bringing Understandings to Light". **Training:** Designed to Introduce the Materials; To Guide Schools Through the Issues. **Geographic Preference:** Multinational.

2259 ■ Effective Compensation Inc. (ECI)
5856 S Lowell Blvd., Ste. 32 No 322
Littleton, CO 80123
Ph: (303)854-1000
Co. E-mail: eci@effectivecompensation.com
URL: http://www.effectivecompensation.com
Contact: Terry Isselhardt, President
Description: Independent compensation consulting firm specializing in working with clients on a collaborative basis to improve their organization's efficiency through competitive, focused total compensation processes. Helps organizations determine how to competitively pay their employees. Provides quality, culture sensitive, compensation consulting assistance to all types of employers. **Scope:** Independent compensation consulting firm specializing in working with clients on a collaborative basis to improve their organization's efficiency through competitive, focused total compensation processes. Helps organizations determine how to competitively pay their employees. Provides quality, culture sensitive, compensation consulting assistance to all types of employers. **Founded:** 1991. **Publications:** "Alternative Job Evaluation Approaches"; "Broad Banding: A Management Overview"; "Job Evaluation: Understanding the Issues"; "Industry Compensation Surveys"; "Skill Based Pay"; "Four Levels of Team Membership"; "Factors in Designing an Incentive Plan"; "Key Stock Allocation Issues"; "Stock Plans Primer". **Training:** Alternative Job Evaluation Approaches; Broad Banding: A Management Overview; Skill Based Pay; Job Evaluation: Understanding the

Issues; Designing Compensation Programs that Motivate Employees; Master the Compensation Maze; Base Salary Administration Manual.

2260 ■ Effectiveness Resource Group Inc.
2215 2nd Ave. N
Seattle, WA 98109-2318
Contact: Donald Swartz, Governor
Description: Provider of problem solving help to client organizations in public and private sectors so they can release and mobilize the full potential of their personnel to achieve productive and satisfying results. **Scope:** Provider of problem solving help to client organizations in public and private sectors so they can release and mobilize the full potential of their personnel to achieve productive and satisfying results. **Training:** Life/Work Goals Exploration; Influencing Change Thru Consultation; Designing and Leading Participative Meetings; Designing, Leading and Managing Change; Project Management and Leadership; Performance Management; Productive Management of Differences; Performance Correction.

2261 ■ Environmental Business International Inc. (EBI)
4452 Pk. Blvd., Ste. 306
San Diego, CA 92116
Ph: (619)295-7685
Fax: (619)295-5743
Co. E-mail: info@ebionline.org
URL: http://ebiusa.com
Contact: Grant Ferrier, President
Linkedin: www.linkedin.com/company/environmental-business-international
Description: Publisher of business periodicals. Services: Environmental consulting and research firm. **Scope:** Offers a variety of research and professional services to deliver the market information and business intelligence required for growth and profit in today's rapidly changing business climate. **Founded:** 1988. **Publications:** "Water view Report: Water & Wastewater Markets," Dec, 2006; "Report 2020 the U.S. Environmental Industry & Global Markets"; "Mergers & Acquisitions in the Environmental Industry".

2262 ■ Family Business Institute Inc. (FBI)
3520 Ridge View Ct.
Marietta, GA 30068
Ph: (770)952-4085
URL: http://www.family-business-experts.com
Contact: Don A. Schwerzler, Founder
Description: Firm engages in business consulting and professional services. **Scope:** Assists families in business to achieve personal, family and organizational goals. **Founded:** 1995. **Publications:** "Professional Intervention in the Family Owned Business"; "Building Consensus in a Family Business"; "Professionalizing Family Business Management".

2263 ■ Family Resource Center on Disabilities (FRCD)
11 E Adams St., Ste. 1002
Chicago, IL 60603
Ph: (312)939-3513
Fax: (312)854-8980
Co. E-mail: info@frcd.org
URL: http://frcd.org
Contact: Michelle Phillips, Contact
X (Twitter): x.com/FRCDPTI
YouTube: www.youtube.com/user/frcd1231
Pinterest: www.pinterest.com/frcdpti
Description: Parents, professionals, and volunteers seeking to improve services for all children with disabilities. Organized as a result of the 1969 Illinois law mandating the education of all children with disabilities and operates as a coalition to inform and activate parents. Provides information and referral services, individualized support services for low-income Chicago families, transition services, and special education rights training. **Scope:** Provider of consulting services to advocacy groups and individuals seeking support for children with disabilities. **Founded:** 1969. **Publications:** "How to Get Services By Being Assertive"; "How to Organize an Effective Parent/Advocacy Group and Move Bureaucracies"; "Main roads Travel to Tomorrow - a Road Map for the Future"; "Does Your Child Have Special Education Needs"; "How to Prepare for a Successful Due Process Hearing"; "How to Participate Effectively in Your Child's IEP Meeting"; "Tax Guide for Parents". **Training:** How to Support Parents as Effective Advocates; How to Get Services by Being Assertive; How to Develop an Awareness Program for Nondisabled Children; How to Organize a Parent Support Group; How to Move Bureaucratic Mountains; How to Raise Money Painlessly through Publishing; How to Use Humor in Public Presentations. **Geographic Preference:** National.

2264 ■ Flett Research Ltd.
440 DeSalaberry Ave.
Winnipeg, MB, Canada R2L 0Y7
Ph: (204)667-2505
Fax: (204)667-2505
Co. E-mail: flett@flettresearch.ca
URL: http://www.flettresearch.ca
Contact: Dawn Gilbert, Coordinator
Description: Provider of environmental audits and assessments. Offers contract research and consultation on environmental topics, specializes in limnology, with emphasis in microbiology, bio-geo chemistry and radio-chemistry. **Scope:** Provider of environmental audits and assessments. Offers contract research and consultation on environmental topics, specializes in limnology, with emphasis in microbiology, bio-geo chemistry and radio-chemistry. **Founded:** 1978. **Training:** Comparison of Two Methods for the Measurement of Methyl Mercury Concentrations in Penobscot River Sediments.

2265 ■ Forum Business Advisors
383 E Main St.
Centerport, NY 11721
Free: 800-433-7002
Co. E-mail: info@forumba.com
URL: http://www.forumba.com
Contact: Martin B. Stevens, Director
Description: Firm is engaged in business of solutions such as general business, marketing, sales and much more. **Scope:** Firm is engaged in business of solutions such as general business, marketing, sales and much more.

2266 ■ Franchise Consulting Group (FCG)
1801 Century Pk. E, Ste. 2400
Los Angeles, CA 90067
Ph: (310)552-2901
URL: http://franchiseconsulting.com
Contact: Edward Kushell, President
Description: Firm provides consulting services in new business startup and company expansion programs and performs analysis, research, planning and development of product service distribution systems. **Founded:** 1978.

2267 ■ Freese & Associates Inc. (F&A)
16105 Lucky Bell Ln.
Newbury, OH 44065
Ph: (440)487-4509
URL: http://www.freeseinc.com
Contact: Thomas L. Freese, Principal
E-mail: tfreese@freeseinc.com
Description: Provider of supply chain management and logistics consulting services such as customer service, material management, transportation, and much more. **Scope:** Provider of supply chain management and logistics consulting services such as customer service, material management, transportation, and much more. **Founded:** 1987. **Publications:** "Building Relationships is Key to Motivation," Distribution Center Management, Apr, 2006; "Getting Maximum Results from Performance Reviews," WERC Sheet, Oct, 2003; "SCM: Making the Vision a Reality," Supply Chain Management Review, Oct, 2003; "Contents Under Pressure," DC Velocity, Aug, 2003; "When Considering Outsourcing, It's Really a Financial Decision," Inventory Management Report, Mar, 2003. **Training:** WERC/CAWS Warehousing in China Conference, Sep, 2008; CSCMP Annual Conference, Denver, Oct, 2008; Keys to Retaining and Motivating Your Associates, Dallas, Mar, 2006; The Value and Challenges of Supply Chain Management, Dubai, Feb, 2006; Best Practices in Logistics in China, Jun, 2005; Keys to Motivating Associates, Dallas, May, 2005; The Goal and the Way of International Cooperation in Logistics, Jenobuk, Apr, 2005.

2268 ■ Full Voice
9912B Holmes Rd., Ste. 237
Kansas City, MO 64131-4206
Description: Vocal performance training firm offering consulting services and personal training sessions in the implementation of effective vocal communication techniques for the development of business relationships and career enhancement. **Scope:** Vocal performance training firm offering consulting services and personal training sessions in the implementation of effective vocal communication techniques for the development of business relationships and career enhancement. **Publications:** "You Can Sound Like You Know What You're Saying". **Training:** You Can Sound Like You Know What You're Saying; The Psychology of Vocal Performance; Security. . .the Ability to Accept Change; Knowing. . .the Key to Relaxed Public Communication; The Effective Voice for Customer Service Enhancement; You Can Speak With Conviction; How To Make Yours a Championship Team; Functional English For Foreign Trade. **Special Services:** FULL VOICE™.

2269 ■ Global Technology Transfer L.L.C.
1500 Dixie Hwy.
Park Hills, KY 41011
Contact: Anthony R. Zembrodt, Sr., Member
Description: Firm specializes in product development, quality assurance, new product development, and total quality management focusing on household chemical specialties, especially air fresheners. Utilizes latest technology from global resources. Specializes in enhancement products for home and automobile. **Scope:** Firm specializes in product development, quality assurance, new product development, and total quality management focusing on household chemical specialties, especially air fresheners. Utilizes latest technology from global resources. Specializes in enhancement products for home and automobile.

2270 ■ Go Business Plans
6581 W Manchester Ave.
Los Angeles, CA 90045
URL: http://www.gobusinessplans.com
Contact: Phil Chau, Managing Partner
Facebook: www.facebook.com/GoBusinessPlans
Linkedin: www.linkedin.com/company/gobusinessplans
X (Twitter): x.com/gobusinessplans
Description: A strategic business planning and consulting firm that works with early stage ventures, mid-market companies, and enterprise level corporations to start or grow their businesses through our suite of business consulting services including business plans, financial models, strategic planning, investor presentations, feasibility studies, and valuation analyses. **Scope:** A strategic business planning and consulting firm that works with early stage ventures, mid-market companies, and enterprise level corporations to start or grow their businesses through our suite of business consulting services including business plans, financial models, strategic planning, investor presentations, feasibility studies, and valuation analyses.

2271 ■ Hardy Stevenson and Associates Ltd.
364 Davenport Rd., Ste. 1
Toronto, ON, Canada M5R 2Y4
Ph: (416)944-8444
Free: 877-267-7794
Co. E-mail: info@hardystevenson.com
URL: http://www.hardystevenson.com
Contact: Dave Hardy, Contact
Facebook: www.facebook.com/HardyStevensonandAssociatesLimited
Linkedin: www.linkedin.com/company/hardy-stevenson-and-associates-limited
X (Twitter): x.com/HardyStevenson
Description: Offers environmental planning, assessment, facilitation, conflict resolution community relations, strategic planning and project management

consulting. **Scope:** Offers environmental planning, assessment, facilitation, conflict resolution community relations, strategic planning and project management consulting. **Founded:** 1990.

2272 ■ Harvey A. Meier Co. (HAM)
410 W Nevada St.
Ashland, OR 97520-1043
Ph: (509)458-3210
Fax: (541)488-7905
Co. E-mail: harvey@harveymeier.com
URL: http://www.harveymeier.com
Contact: Dr. Harvey A. Meier, President
E-mail: harvey@harveymeier.com
Description: Services: Management consulting. **Scope:** Services: Management consulting. **Publications:** "The D'Artagnan Way".

2273 ■ Hewitt Development Enterprises (HDE)
1717 N Bayshore Dr., Ste. 2154
Miami, FL 33132
Ph: (305)372-0941
Fax: (305)372-0941
Co. E-mail: info@hewittdevelopment.com
URL: http://www.hewittdevelopment.com
Contact: Robert G. Hewitt, Contact
E-mail: bob@hewittdevelopment.com
Description: Firm specializes in strategic planning, profit enhancement, startup businesses, interim and crisis management, turnarounds, production planning, just-in-time inventory and project management, serves senior management and acquirers of distressed businesses. **Scope:** Firm specializes in strategic planning, profit enhancement, startup businesses, interim and crisis management, turnarounds, production planning, just-in-time inventory and project management, serves senior management and acquirers of distressed businesses. **Founded:** 1985.

2274 ■ Hybrid Business Advisors
309 Fellowship Rd., Ste. 200
Mount Laurel, NJ 08054
Ph: (856)533-2344
URL: http://www.hybridbizadvisors.com
Contact: Joan Nowak, Founder
E-mail: jnowak@hybridbizadvisors.com
Facebook: www.facebook.com/HybridBusinessAdvisors
Description: Business coaching and consulting practice that combines innovation with practical strategies and support to help business owners build profit and reach new levels of success. **Scope:** Business coaching and consulting practice that combines innovation with practical strategies and support to help business owners build profit and reach new levels of success.

2275 ■ Impact Business Network Ltd.
3098 Midland Rd.
Victoria, BC, Canada V8R 6P2
Ph: (250)812-6771
Co. E-mail: victoria@impact-ltd.ca
URL: http://www.impact-ltd.ca
Contact: Sandra Birrell, President
E-mail: sandra@impact-ltd.ca
Description: Provider of project management and business consulting services including training development, communications assessment and development for government and corporate organizations. **Scope:** Provider of project management and business consulting services including training development, communications assessment and development for government and corporate organizations.

2276 ■ In Plain English
14501 Antigone Dr.
Gaithersburg, MD 20878-2484
Ph: (301)340-2821
Free: 800-274-9645
Fax: (301)279-0115
URL: http://www.inplainenglish.com
Description: Management consultants helping government and businesses research, design, write and produce user oriented management information for human resources, employee benefits, business process, corporate and marketing needs. Services include: GSA mob is schedule for consulting to the government; employee benefit communications, plain English business writing workshops for print and electronic media; communicating strategy and tactics; marketing research, business planning and communications; readability testing; usability testing and monitoring strategy. **Scope:** Management consultants helping government and businesses research, design, write and produce user oriented management information for human resources, employee benefits, business process, corporate and marketing needs. Services include: GSA mob is schedule for consulting to the government; employee benefit communications, plain English business writing workshops for print and electronic media; communicating strategy and tactics; marketing research, business planning and communications; readability testing; usability testing and monitoring strategy. **Founded:** 1977. **Publications:** "The Benefits Communication"; "The Employee Benefits Communication ToolKit," Commerce Clearinghouse; "Benefits Communication," Business and Legal Reports. **Training:** Plain English Writing Training; Summary Plan Description Compliance workshops; Re-Humanizing the Corporation, Human Resources and Employee Benefits Communication Workshop; 21 Writing Tips for the 21st Century; Make the Write Impression; Writing to Inform and Instruct; The Dreaded Nuts and Bolts; Writing to Persuade; Writing Policy and Procedure Manuals In Plain English; Writing for Accountants and Auditors In Plain English. **Special Services:** In Plain English®.

2277 ■ Institute for Management Excellence
Trabuco Canyon, CA 92679
Ph: (949)667-1012
URL: http://www.itstime.com
Contact: Barbara Taylor, Executive Director
Description: Consulting firm and training focuses on improving productivity, using practices and creative techniques. **Scope:** Consulting firm and training focuses on improving productivity, using practices and creative techniques. **Founded:** 1995. **Publications:** "Income Without a Job," 2008; "The Other Side of Midnight, 2000: An Executive Guide to the Year 2000 Problem"; "Concordance to the Michael Teachings"; "Handbook of Small Business Advertising"; "The Personality Game"; "How to Market Yourself for Success". **Training:** The Personality Game; Power Path Seminars; Productivity Plus; Sexual Harassment and Discrimination Prevention; Worker's Comp Cost Reduction; Americans with Disabilities Act; In Search of Identify: Clarifying Corporate Culture.

2278 ■ Interminds & Federer Resources Inc.
PO Box 438
Pasadena, CA 91102
Ph: (512)261-0761
Co. E-mail: yesyoucan@interminds.com
URL: http://www.interminds.com
Description: Firm specializes in feasibility studies, startup businesses, small business management, mergers and acquisitions, joint ventures, divestitures, interim and crisis management, turnarounds, production planning, team building, appraisals, and valuations. **Scope:** Firm specializes in feasibility studies, startup businesses, small business management, mergers and acquisitions, joint ventures, divestitures, interim and crisis management, turnarounds, production planning, team building, appraisals, and valuations. **Founded:** 1985. **Publications:** "Yes You Can: How To Be A Success No Matter Who You Are Or Where You're From".

2279 ■ International Business Strategies Inc. (IBS)
632 Industrial Way
Los Gatos, CA 95030
Ph: (408)395-9585
Co. E-mail: info@ibs-inc.net
URL: http://www.ibs-inc.net
Contact: Dr. Handel H. Jones, Chief Executive Officer
Linkedin: www.linkedin.com/company/international-business-strategies
Description: Business consulting firm that provides management consulting, strategy development, market research, technology assessment, financial investments and global decision processes. **Scope:** Business consulting firm that provides management consulting, strategy development, market research, technology assessment, financial investments and global decision processes. **Founded:** 1988. **Training:** Return on Investment in Simulink for Electronic System Design, Apr, 2005.

2280 ■ International Business & Technical Consultants Inc. (IBTCI)
8618 Westwood Center Dr., Ste. 400
Vienna, VA 22182
Ph: (703)749-0100
Fax: (703)749-0110
URL: http://www.ibtci.com
Contact: Ajay S. Kalotra, President
Facebook: www.facebook.com/IBTCIfb
Linkedin: www.linkedin.com/company/ibtci
X (Twitter): x.com/ibtci
Instagram: www.instagram.com/ibtciimages
Description: Firm provides quality monitoring, evaluation, learning, capacity building, training, knowledge management, communications and outreach services. **Scope:** Firm provides quality monitoring, evaluation, learning, capacity building, training, knowledge management, communications and outreach services. **Founded:** 1987. **Training:** Procurement Management; financial Restructuring Technical Assistance; External Debt Management Project; Financial Restructuring Technical Assistance; Public Education and Information.

2281 ■ International Immigration and Business Consulting (IIBC)
250-15 Innovation Blvd.
Saskatoon, SK, Canada S7N 0X8
Ph: (306)805-0113
Co. E-mail: contact@immigrate.biz
URL: http://iibc.ca
Contact: Dirk Propp, Owner
E-mail: dirk@iibc.ca
Facebook: www.facebook.com/IIBC-International-Immigration-and-Business-Consulting-240805969598562
Linkedin: www.linkedin.com/company/iibc---international-immigration-and-business-consulting
Description: An immigration and business consulting firm. Specializes in providing growth, hiring, immigration, relocation and retention strategies for growing businesses requiring foreign workers. Also provides consulting services for all types of Federal immigration applications and Saskatchewan Immigration Nominee Program applications through a streamlined approach. **Scope:** An immigration and business consulting firm. Specializes in providing growth, hiring, immigration, relocation and retention strategies for growing businesses requiring foreign workers. Also provides consulting services for all types of Federal immigration applications and Saskatchewan Immigration Nominee Program applications through a streamlined approach. **Founded:** 2009.

2282 ■ Johnston Co.
78 Bedford St.
Lexington, MA 02420
Ph: (781)862-7595
Fax: (781)862-9066
Co. E-mail: info@johnstoncompany.com
URL: http://www.johnstoncompany.com
Contact: Jim Johnston, Chief Executive Officer
E-mail: jimj@johnstoncompany.com
Description: Firm provides consulting on environmental and workplace services such as LSRP service, property acquisition and redevelopment, engineering and site remediation. **Scope:** Firm provides consulting on environmental and workplace services such as LSRP service, property acquisition and redevelopment, engineering and site remediation. **Publications:** "Why are board meetings such a waste of time," Boston Business Journal, Apr, 2004.

2283 ■ Kaufman Global
160 W Carmel Dr., Ste. 180
Carmel, IN 46032

Ph: (317)818-2430
Fax: (317)818-2434
Co. E-mail: marketing@kaufmanglobal.com
URL: http://www.kaufmanglobal.com
Contact: Jerry Timpson, President
Linkedin: www.linkedin.com/company/kaufman-global
Description: Firm provides capital analysis and implementation services. **Scope:** Firm provides capital analysis and implementation services. **Founded:** 1995. **Publications:** "What You Do Not Know Can Hurt You," Aug, 2012; "The Small Stuff is the Big Stuff," May, 2012; "Understanding the Value of Information as a Corporate Asset," Jul, 2012; "Do Not Waste Your Time with Marketing," Jun, 2012; "ArvinMeritor: A Lean Culture"; "The Struggle to Get Lean"; "The Missing Link of Lean Success"; "Using a Full-Court Press to Transform a Business"; "Managing Growth - BD Finds Success Integrating Lean and Six Sigma". **Training:** Conducting Office Rapid Improvement Events; Developing Lasting Capability Inside the Organization; Building Sustainable Solutions; A Structured and Proven Process for Engaging the Organization and Delivering Results. **Special Services:** Lean Leadership®; SLIM-IT®; Lean Daily Management System LDMS®; 20 Keys®; WIn-Lean®; Lean Six Sigma.

2284 ■ Liberty Business Strategies Ltd.
329 S 16th
 Philadelphia, PA 19102
Ph: (267)858-4021
Co. E-mail: info@libertystrategies.com
URL: http://libertystrategies.com
Contact: Emmy Miller, President
Linkedin: www.linkedin.com/company/525207
X (Twitter): x.com/LibertyBusiness
Description: Management consulting firm provides executive coaching, strategic alignment, succession planning such as healthcare, consumer products, technology, and much more. **Scope:** Management consulting firm provides executive coaching, strategic alignment, succession planning such as healthcare, consumer products, technology, and much more. **Founded:** 1980. **Training:** Winning with Talent, Morison Annual Conference, Jul, 2009.

2285 ■ Linda Lipsky Restaurant Consultants Inc.
216 Foxcroft Rd.
 Broomall, PA 19008
Ph: (610)325-3663
Co. E-mail: lipsky@restaurantconsult.com
URL: http://restaurantconsult.com
Contact: Linda Lipsky, Founder
E-mail: lipsky@restaurantconsult.com
Description: Provider of marketing and survey solutions such as management training, evaluation programs, recipe documentation, cost analysis and bridge management services for restaurants. **Scope:** Provider of marketing and survey solutions such as management training, evaluation programs, recipe documentation, cost analysis and bridge management services for restaurants. **Founded:** 1988. **Training:** Designing Menus for Maximum Sales and Profits; How to Maximize Your Check Average.

2286 ■ Mankind Research Unlimited (MRU) [Mankind Research Foundation]
1315 Apple Ave.
 Silver Spring, MD 20910
URL: http://mankindresearchunlimited.weebly.com
Description: Publishes monographs, books, bibliographies and technical reports on health, education and energy resources. **Scope:** Firm provide an organization for scientific development and application of technology that could have positive impact on the health, education, and welfare of mankind. Provide solution to seek and apply futuristic solutions to current problems. Provides services in the areas of advanced sciences, biotechnical, bionic, biocybernetic, biomedical, holistic health, bio immunology, solar energy, accelerated learning, and sensory aids for handicapped. Current specific activities involve research in AIDS, drug abuse, affordable housing, food for the hungry, and literacy and remedial education. **Founded:** 1966.

2287 ■ McMann & Ransford
2950 N Loop. W Ste. 500
 Houston, TX 77092
Ph: (713)730-7519
URL: http://mcmannransford.com
Contact: Dean McMann, Chief Executive Officer
Linkedin: www.linkedin.com/company/mcmann-&-ransford_2
Description: Firm provides management consulting, training, executive recruiting, market research services, and specializes in the professional services industry. **Scope:** Firm provides management consulting, training, executive recruiting, market research services, and specializes in the professional services industry.

2288 ■ McShane Group L.L.C.
2119 E Franklin St.
 Richmond, VA 23223
URL: http://www.mcshanegroup.com
Contact: Jim L. Huitt, Jr., Principal
E-mail: jhuitt@mcshanegroup.com
Description: Firm provides diligence services, interim management, strategic business realignments, marketing, and much more. **Scope:** Firm provides diligence services, interim management, strategic business realignments, marketing, and much more. **Founded:** 1987.

2289 ■ Medical Imaging Consultants Inc. (MIC)
1037 US Hwy. 46, Ste. G-2
 Clifton, NJ 07013-2445
Ph: (973)574-8000
Free: 800-589-5685
Fax: (973)574-8001
Co. E-mail: info@micinfo.com
URL: http://www.micinfo.com
Contact: Philip A. Femano, President
Description: Provider of professional support services in radiology management and comprehensive continuing education programs for radiologic technologists such as professional educators, life scientists, biomedical engineers, and much more. **Scope:** Provider of professional support services in radiology management and comprehensive continuing education programs for radiologic technologists such as professional educators, life scientists, biomedical engineers, and much more. **Founded:** 1991. **Training:** Sectional Anatomy and Imaging Strategies; CT Cross-Trainer; CT Registry Review Program; MR Cross Trainer; MRI Registry Review Program; Digital Mammography Essentials for Technologists; Radiology Trends for Technologists.

2290 ■ Medical Outcomes Management Inc. (MOM)
15 S Main St., Ste. 208
 Sharon, MA 02067
Ph: (781)806-0275
URL: http://www.mom-inc.us
Contact: Dr. Alan Kaul, Chief Executive Officer
E-mail: alan@mom-inc.us
Facebook: www.facebook.com/akaul2019
Linkedin: www.linkedin.com/company/medical-outcomes-management
Description: Management and technology consulting firm providing a specially focused group of services such as disease management programs and pharmacoeconomic studies. Services include clinical and educational projects, medical writing and editing, marketing and sales projects, disease registries, educational seminars, strategic planning projects, managed care organizations and pharmaceutical and biotechnology companies. **Scope:** Management and technology consulting firm providing a specially focused group of services such as disease management programs and pharmacoeconomic studies. Services include clinical and educational projects, medical writing and editing, marketing and sales projects, disease registries, educational seminars, strategic planning projects, managed care organizations and pharmaceutical and biotechnology companies. **Founded:** 1991. **Publications:** "Treatment of acute exacerbation's of chronic bronchitis in patients with chronic obstructive pulmonary disease: A retrospective cohort analysis logarithmically extended release vs. Azithromycin," 2003; "A retrospective analysis of cyclooxygenase-II inhibitor response patterns," 2002; "DUE criteria for use of regional urokinase infusion for deep vein thrombosis,"2002; "The formulary management system and decision-making process at Horizon Blue Cross Blue Shield of New Jersey," Pharmaco therapy, 2001. **Training:** Economic Modeling as a Disease Management Tool, Academy of Managed Care Pharmacy, Apr, 2005; Integrating Disease State Management and Economics, Academy of Managed Care Pharmacy, Oct, 2004; Clinical and economic outcomes in the treatment of peripheral occlusive diseases, Mar, 2003.

2291 ■ Mefford, Knutson & Associates Inc. (MKA)
6437 Lyndale Ave. S
 Richfield, MN 55423
Co. E-mail: info@mkcconsulting.com
URL: http://mkaconsulting.com
Contact: Jeanette Mefford, Co-Founder
Description: Provider of consulting services to home health and related sectors. **Scope:** Provider of consulting services to home health and related sectors. **Founded:** 1990.

2292 ■ Midwest Computer Group L.L.C. (MCG)
6060 Franks Rd.
 House Springs, MO 63051
Contact: Leon Sanford, Jr., Contact
Description: Specializes in helping businesses create accounting, marketing and business information systems, software development and database design and management. **Scope:** Specializes in helping businesses create accounting, marketing and business information systems, software development and database design and management.

2293 ■ Midwest Research Institute (MRI) - Patterson Library
425 Dr. Martin Luther King, Jr Blvd.
 Kansas City, MO 64110
Co. E-mail: info@mriglobal.org
URL: http://www.mriglobal.org
Contact: Martin Nevshemal, Chief Financial Officer
Facebook: www.facebook.com/MRIGlobalResearch
Linkedin: www.linkedin.com/company/mriglobal
X (Twitter): x.com/mriglobal_news
Description: Nonprofit research institute offers scientific services in the areas of national defense, health sciences, agriculture and food safety, engineering, energy, and infrastructure. **Scope:** Nonprofit research institute offers scientific services in the areas of national defense, health sciences, agriculture and food safety, engineering, energy, and infrastructure. **Services:** Interlibrary loan; copying; center open to the public for reference use only and by appointment. **Founded:** 1944. **Holdings:** 22,000 volumes. **Subscriptions:** 100 journals and other serials. **Publications:** Innovations; Midwest Research Institute Annual Report (Annual).

2294 ■ Miller, Leiby & Associates P.C.
32 Broadway, 13th Fl.
 New York, NY 10004
Ph: (212)227-4200
Fax: (212)504-8369
URL: http://www.millerleiby.com
Contact: Doron Leiby, Partner
Facebook: www.facebook.com/MillerLeibyAssociatesPc
Linkedin: www.linkedin.com/company/1269719
Instagram: www.instagram.com/millerleiby
Description: Firm is engaged in legal counsel for individuals and businesses. **Scope:** Firm is engaged in legal counsel for individuals and businesses. **Training:** Objectives and standards/recruiting for boards of directors.

2295 ■ Momentum Business Consulting L.L.C.
2335 Andrew Dr.
 Superior, CO 80027
Ph: (303)946-9533
Co. E-mail: info@momentumbc.com

URL: http://momentumbc.com
Contact: Maureen Kanwischer, Contact
E-mail: mo@momentumbc.com

Description: Firm provides business development and marketing consulting for small and mid-size technology firms. **Scope:** Firm provides business development and marketing consulting for small and mid-size technology firms. **Founded:** 2004. **Publications:** "Don't Listen to Your Mother - Talk to Strangers"; "Motivating the Motivating Factor - Your Sales Team"; "A Time for Marketing"; "Build a Bridge and Get Over It"; "Laughing on the Job"; "What is a Peer Advisory Board?".

2296 ■ Murray Dropkin & Associates
390 George St.
  New Brunswick, NJ 08901
URL: http://dropkin.com
Contact: Murray Dropkin, Contact

Description: Firm specializes in feasibility studies, business management, business process reengineering, team building, healthcare, and housing. **Scope:** Firm specializes in feasibility studies, business management, business process reengineering, team building, healthcare, and housing. **Publications:** "Bookkeeping for Nonprofits," Jossey Bass, 2005; "Guide to Audits of Nonprofit Organizations," PPC; "The Nonprofit Report," Warren, Gorham & Lamont; "The Budget Building Book for Nonprofits," Jossey-Bass; "The Cash Flow Management Book for Nonprofits," Jossey-Bass.

2297 ■ National Center for Public Policy Research (NCPPR)
2005 Massachusetts Ave. NW
  Washington, DC 20036
Ph: (202)507-6398
Co. E-mail: info@nationalcenter.org
URL: http://nationalcenter.org
Contact: David A. Ridenour, President
E-mail: dridenour@nationalcenter.org
Facebook: www.facebook.com/NCPPR
X (Twitter): x.com/NationalCenter
YouTube: www.youtube.com/channel/UCFrg
  tYxKOBuDqXavBuK0FFA

Description: Educates the public about public policy issues. Conducts research; distributes national policy analysis papers, memorandums, brochures, newsletters, article reprints, and other materials to the public, libraries, and the media. **Scope:** A communications and research nonprofit organization offering advice and information on international affairs and United States domestic affairs. Sponsors Project 21. Gives special emphasis an environmental and regulatory issues and civil rights issues. **Founded:** 1982. **Publications:** "National Policy Analysis"; "Legal Briefs"; "White Paper: National Policy Analysis 523"; "Shattered Dreams: One Hundred Stories of Government Abuse"; "Shattered Lives: 100 Victims of Government Health Care". **Awards:** National Center for Public Policy Research Paid Internships. **Geographic Preference:** National.

2298 ■ Nexus Business Solutions
350 E Michigan Ave., Ste. 400
  Kalamazoo, MI 49007
Ph: (269)373-1500
Co. E-mail: info@nexusbusiness.com
URL: http://nexusbusiness.com
Contact: David Bowman, Consultant

Description: Provider of organizational consultation through the entrepreneurial operating system, a comprehensive business system with a set of simple business tools and a proven process. **Scope:** Provider of organizational consultation through the entrepreneurial operating system, a comprehensive business system with a set of simple business tools and a proven process. **Founded:** 2004.

2299 ■ Nightingale Associates
7445 Setting Sun Way
  Columbia, MD 21046
Ph: (410)381-4280
URL: http://www.nightingaleassociates.net
Contact: Frederick C. Nightingale, Managing Director
E-mail: fredericknightingale@nightingaleassociates
  .net

X (Twitter): x.com/FCNightingale

Description: Management training and consulting firm offering the following skills productivity and accomplishment, leadership skills for the experienced manager, management skills for the new manager, leadership and teambuilding, supervisory development, creative problem solving, real strategic planning. **Scope:** Management training and consulting firm offering the following skills productivity and accomplishment, leadership skills for the experienced manager, management skills for the new manager, leadership and teambuilding, supervisory development, creative problem solving, real strategic planning. **Founded:** 1984. **Training:** Productivity and Accomplishment Management Skills for the New Manager; Leadership and Team building; Advanced Management; Business Process Re engineering; Strategic Thinking; Creative Problem Solving; Customer Service; International Purchasing and Materials Management; Fundamentals of Purchasing; Negotiation Skills Development; Providing superior customer service; Leadership skills for the experienced manager.

2300 ■ North Carolina Fair Share CDC
3509 Haworth Dr., Ste. 303
  Raleigh, NC 27609
Contact: Akiba H. Byrd, Sr., Contact

Description: Social services firm consults on community organizing and lobbying for health issues. **Scope:** Social services firm consults on community organizing and lobbying for health issues.

2301 ■ Occupational & Environmental Health Consulting Services Inc. (OEHCS)
6877 Bonillo Dr.
  Las Vegas, NV 89103
Ph: (630)325-2083
URL: http://www.oehcs.com

Description: Provider of consulting services such as regulatory, safety, industrial hygiene and environmental engineering, and much more. **Scope:** Provider of consulting services such as regulatory, safety, industrial hygiene and environmental engineering, and much more. **Founded:** 1984. **Publications:** "Worldwide Exposure Standards for Mold and Bacteria"; "Global Occupational Exposure Limits for Over 5000 Specific Chemicals"; "Post-Remediation Verification and Clearance Testing for Mold and Bacteria Risk Based Levels of Cleanliness". **Training:** Right-To-Know Compliance; Setting Internal Exposure Standards; Hospital Right-to-Know and Contingency Response; Ethylene Oxide Control; Industrial Hygiene Training; Asbestos Worker Training; Biosafety; Asbestos Operations and Maintenance. **Special Services:** Safety Software Program, Audiogram Analysis, First Report of Injury Form, Human Resources Database, Material Safety Data Sheet (MSDS); NPDES Monthly Reports; Lockout/Tagout (LOTO) Procedure Software; VOC Usage Tracking and Reporting Software, Medical Department Patient Records Database, Pictorial Labels for Chemical Containers, TIER II Hazardous Material Inventory Form & Database.

2302 ■ Optial UK Ltd.
1 Red Pl.
  London W1K 6PL, United Kingdom
Ph: 44 20 7247 7673
Co. E-mail: request@optial.com
URL: http://www.optial.com
Contact: Chris O'Brien, Chief Executive Officer

Description: Firm provides consulting services such as web-based governance, audit, software solutions, and much more. **Scope:** Firm provides consulting services such as web-based governance, audit, software solutions, and much more. **Founded:** 2000. **Publications:** "Optial OpRisk on Demand," May, 2010; "Operational Risk," May, 2010; "Making Room for Treasury," May, 2010; "Tackling Operational Risk in a Sub-prime World," May, 2010; "Operational risk concerns concentrate on due diligence," May, 2010; "Cultural aspects of Operational risk," May, 2010. **Special Services:** Optial™.

2303 ■ Optimus I SBR
33 Yonge St., Ste. 900
  Toronto, ON, Canada M5E 1G4
Ph: (416)649-6000
Co. E-mail: info@optimussbr.com
URL: http://www.optimussbr.com
Contact: Kevin Gauci, Chief Executive Officer
YouTube: www.youtube.com/channel/UCO1Dh
  1VZyNDpm2dQ_CTcyUA

Description: Firm provides strategy, process and project management advisory services. **Scope:** Firm provides strategy, process and project management advisory services. **Founded:** 1979. **Training:** Electronic counter measures; Strategic planning; Project management.

2304 ■ PBC Advisors L.L.C.
903 Commerce Dr., Ste. 333
  Oak Brook, IL 60523
Ph: (630)571-6770
Fax: (630)571-8810
Co. E-mail: info@pbcgroup.com
URL: http://www.pbcgroup.com
Contact: Steve Blohm, Partner
Facebook: www.facebook.com/PBC-Advisors-LLC
  -520676794749915

Description: Firm provides accounting, financial, retirement, estate and tax planning, employment agreements, pension profit sharing administration, practice management, surveys, mergers, acquisitions, sales, and liquidation. **Scope:** Firm provides accounting, financial, retirement, estate and tax planning, employment agreements, pension profit sharing administration, practice management, surveys, mergers, acquisitions, sales, and liquidation. **Founded:** 1986.

2305 ■ Performance Consultants Group, Inc. (PCG)
1 Innovation Way., Ste. 400
  Newark, DE 19711
Ph: (302)738-7532
Free: 888-724-3578
URL: http://www.pcgius.com

Description: Firm provides consulting services in the areas of strategic planning, profit enhancement, product development, and production planning. **Scope:** Firm provides consulting services in the areas of strategic planning, profit enhancement, product development, and production planning. **Founded:** 1988.

2306 ■ Performance Consulting Associates, Inc. (PCA)
3700 Crestwood Pky., Ste. 100
  Duluth, GA 30096
Ph: (770)717-2737
Co. E-mail: info@pcaconsulting.com
URL: http://pcaconsulting.com
Contact: Richard deFazio, President
Linkedin: www.linkedin.com/company/pcaconsulting

Description: Firm provides asset management solutions, business process optimization, and much more. **Scope:** Firm provides asset management solutions, business process optimization, and much more. **Founded:** 1976. **Publications:** "Does Planning Pay," Plant Services, Nov, 2000; "Asset Reliability Coordinator," Maintenance Technology, Oct, 2000; "Know What it is You Have to Maintain," Maintenance Technology, May, 2000; "Does Maintenance Planning Pay," Maintenance Technology, Nov, 2000.; "What is Asset Management?"; "Implementing Best Business Practices".

2307 ■ Performance Dynamics Group L.L.C.
50 Virginia Key Dr.
  Union Hall, VA 24176
Ph: (732)537-0381
URL: http://mark-green.com
Contact: Mark Green, Contact

Description: Provider of strategic advisors for top level people in businesses and coaches for executive team development and related services such as technology, professional, strategic and business planning, sales force hiring education and development, and much more. **Scope:** Provider of strategic advisors for top level people in businesses and coaches for executive team development and related services such as technology, professional, strategic and business planning, sales force hiring education and development, and much more. **Founded:** 2003. **Training:** Accelerated Approach to Change; Commitment to Quality; Managing Cultural Diversity; The Corporate Energizer; The Power Pole Experience; Team Assessment; Self-Directed Work Teams.

2308 ■ Pinpoint Tactics Business Consulting
5525 West Blvd.
  Vancouver, BC, Canada V6M 3W6
Ph: (604)263-4698
Co. E-mail: info@pinpointtactics.com
URL: http://www.pinpointtactics.com
Contact: Sandy Huang, President
Facebook: www.facebook.com/PinpointTactics
X (Twitter): x.com/pinpointtactics

Description: Firm provides business consulting services such as marketing programs, small business launch program, strategic business program, market research, and much more. **Scope:** Firm provides business consulting services such as marketing programs, small business launch program, strategic business program, market research, and much more.

2309 ■ Practice Development Counsel
New York, NY
Ph: (212)593-1549
URL: http://www.pdcounsel.com
Contact: Phyllis Weiss Haserot, President
E-mail: pwhaserot@pdcounsel.com

Description: Firm is engaged in business development, organizational consulting and coaching. **Founded:** 1983. **Publications:** "The Rainmaking Machine: Marketing Planning, Strategy and Management For Law Firms"; "The Marketer's Handbook of Tips and Checklists"; "Venturesome Questions: The Law Firms Guide to Developing a New Business Venture"; "Navigating the Whitewater of Internal Politics"; "Changing Attitudes on Firm Flexibility"; "Transition Planning: A Looming Challenge"; "Don't You Think the Solution Is to Bring In a Good Rainmaker?"; "Aligning Firm Culture with the Needs of the Times"; "What New Partners Need to Know"; "Dangers of Lack of Diversity"; "Learn to Respect Emotion in Business"; "What New Partners Need to Know"; "Taking Responsibility: Implementing Personal Marketing Plans"; "How to Change Unwritten Rules"; "Mentoring and Networking Converge"; "Integrating a New Practice into the Firm"; "Using Conflict Resolution Skills for Marketing Success"; "Sports Team Models for Law Firm Management". **Training:** Managing Work Expectations; Effective Coaching Skills; Service Quality; End-Running the Resistance Professionals Have to Getting Client Input; Ancillary Business Activities; Marketing for Professional Firms; Marketing Ethics; Business Development Training; Trends in Professional Services Marketing; Client Relationship Management; Collaborative Culture; Reaching Consensus; Conflict Resolution; Work life Balance; Generational Issues; Preparing New Partners; Becoming the Employer of Choice; A Marketing Approach to Recruiting; Implementing Workplace Flexibility; The Business Case for Flexible Work Arrangements.

2310 ■ Public Sector Consultants Inc. (PSC)
230 N Washington Sq., Ste. 300
  Lansing, MI 48933
Ph: (517)484-4954
Fax: (517)484-6549
Co. E-mail: psc@publicsectorconsultants.com
URL: http://publicsectorconsultants.com
Contact: Jonathon Beard, Director
E-mail: jbeard@publicsectorconsultants.com
Facebook: www.facebook.com/PublicSectorConsultants
X (Twitter): x.com/pscmichigan
YouTube: www.youtube.com/channel/UCjoEsgFvA7ks_46qrf-pYqQ

Description: Offers policy research expertise, specializing in opinion polling, public relations, conference planning, and legislative and economic analysis. Industries served: Associations, education, environment, health-care, and public finance. **Scope:** Offers policy research expertise, specializing in opinion polling, public relations, conference planning, and legislative and economic analysis. Industries served: Associations, education, environment, health-care, and public finance. **Founded:** 1980. **Publications:** "The New Landscape of Civic Business: How Business Leadership Is Influencing Civic Progress in Our Metropolitan Regions Today," Feb, 2012; "Saginaw Bay Watershed and Area of Concern," Mar, 2012; "Michigan Public School Employees Retirement System: Major Changes in Recent Years and More Changes to Come," May, 2012; "Saginaw River/Bay Area of Concern: Restoration Plan for the Habitat and Populations BUIs," Sep, 2012; "Proposal 3: Key Questions and Answers," Sep, 2012; "Final Report of the Michigan State Park and Recreation Blue Ribbon Panel," Oct, 2012; "The Impact of Reducing PIP Coverage in Michigan," Sep, 2011; "Michigan Sales Tax Collection and the Internet: A Need for Fairness," Sep, 2011; "Ingham Community Voices Final Evaluation Report," Nov, 2008; "First Class Schools Analysis," Aug, 2008; "Opportunities for Achieving Efficiency in the Aging, Community Mental Health, Local Public Health, and Substance Abuse Coordinating Agency Networks," Aug, 2008; "Saginaw River Bay Area of Concern," Jun, 2008; "Portage Lake Water shed Forever Plan," May, 2008; "Smoke Free Workplaces," Apr, 2008; "Protecting and Restoring the Upper Looking Glass River," Feb, 2008; "Market Structures and the 21st Century Energy Plan," Sep, 2007; "The Growing Crisis of Aging Dams," Apr, 2007; "Financing Community Health Workers Why and How," Jan, 2007; "Hastings Area: Inter local Approaches to Growth Management," Jan, 2007; "Michigan's Part 201 Environmental Remediation Program Review," Jan, 2007.

2311 ■ Quality Business Consulting Inc. (QBCI)
8405 Pershing Dr., Ste. 404
  Playa del Rey, CA 90293
Ph: (310)822-9008
Free: 866-636-5666
Fax: (310)822-9009
Co. E-mail: info@qbconsulting.com
URL: http://www.qbconsulting.com
Contact: Jean-Paul Issock, Contact

Description: Technology consulting firm specializing in the implementation, support and engineering of construction management and accounting systems. Offers services to heavy construction, marine salvage, property development/management, law firms and general and specialty contractors. **Scope:** Technology consulting firm specializing in the implementation, support and engineering of construction management and accounting systems. Offers services to heavy construction, marine salvage, property development/management, law firms and general and specialty contractors. **Founded:** 1987. **Special Services:** LIBRA Signature; StarBid; StarViewer; StarProject; ToolBox; ProEst.

2312 ■ Queen's Business Consulting (QBC)
Queen's University
  Stephen J. R. Smith School of Business
  Goodes Hall, Rm. LL201
  Kingston, ON, Canada K7L 3N6
Ph: (613)893-2327
Co. E-mail: sbc@queensu.ca
URL: http://smith.queensu.ca/index.php
Contact: Charlie Mignault, Director
E-mail: cem10@queensu.ca

Description: Provider of management consulting services such as strategy, sales, marketing, data analysis, and operational planning. **Scope:** Provider of management consulting services such as strategy, sales, marketing, data analysis, and operational planning. **Founded:** 1973. **Publications:** "Information technology, network structure and competitive action. Information Systems Research," 2010; "The role of dominance in the appeal of violent media depictions. Journal of Advertising," 2010; "Great expectations and broken promises: Misleading claims, product failure, expectancy disconfirmation and consumer distrust. Journal of the Academy of Marketing Science," 2010; "Development and psychometric properties of the Transformational Teaching Questionnaire. Journal of Health Psychology," 2010; ". Predicting workplace aggression: myths, realities, and remaining questions," 2009; "The Inconvenient Truth about Improving Vehicle Fuel Efficiency: An MultiAttribute Analysis of the Efficient Frontier of the U.S. Automobile Industry, Transportation Research-Part," 2009; "Fraud in Canadian Nonprofit Organizations as Seen through the Eyes of Canadian Newspapers," 2009; "Disentangling the Indirect Links between SES and Health: The Dynamic Roles of Work Stressors and Personal Contro," 2009; "The strong situation hypothesis. Personality and Social Psychology Review," 2009; " Planning Your Next Crisis Decisively and Effectively. Ivey Business Journal," 2009. **Training:** Enabling Innovation Discussion Highlights, 2011; Intellectual Capital, 2010; On the diffusion of knowledge inside the organization, 2010; A model of the tacit knowledge lifecycle for decision-making: From creation to utilization, 2010; Individual, group, and organizational learning; A knowledge management perspective, 2009; Political economies of knowledge, with an example, 2009; The alignment of business and knowledge strategies and structures, 2009; Using IT To Support the Discovery of Novel Knowledge in Organizations, 2008; Leadership: Knowledge Management by a New Name?, 2007; Every User Tells a Story, 2007.

2313 ■ R. Miller Hicks & Co.
2404 Enfield Rd.
  Austin, TX 78703-3228
Contact: R. Miller Hicks, President

Description: Services: Business development and consulting in many fields of commerce and industry worldwide. **Scope:** Services: Business development and consulting in many fields of commerce and industry worldwide. **Publications:** "Failures are Not Fatal-And Other Experiences of a Two Score and Five Year Professional Entrepreneur".

2314 ■ Rental Relocation Inc. (RRI)
535 Colonial Pk. Dr., Bldg. A
  Roswell, GA 30075
Free: 844-737-0611
Co. E-mail: info@rentalrelocation.com
URL: http://www.rentalrelocation.com
Contact: James Bilderback, President
Facebook: www.facebook.com/RentalRelocationInc
Linkedin: www.linkedin.com/company/rental-relocation-inc
YouTube: www.youtube.com/channel/UC3B3HJ4K3u_pZvNIT6omFXw

Description: Firm provides consulting services in corporate housing, rentals, locating free metro Atlanta apartment, property management, house and condo rental relocation tours. **Scope:** Firm provides consulting services in corporate housing, rentals, locating free metro Atlanta apartment, property management, house and condo rental relocation tours. **Founded:** 1989.

2315 ■ Rose & Crangle Ltd.
102 E Lincoln Ave.
  Lincoln, KS 67455
Contact: S. Jeanne Crangle, Contact

Description: Provider of evaluation, planning and policy analyzes for universities, associations, foundations, governmental agencies and private companies engaged in scientific, technological or educational activities. Special expertise in the development of new institutions. Special skills in providing planning and related group facilitation workshops. **Scope:** Provider of evaluation, planning and policy analyzes for universities, associations, foundations, governmental agencies and private companies engaged in scientific, technological or educational activities. Special expertise in the development of new institutions. Special skills in providing planning and related group facilitation workshops. **Publications:** "Preface to Bulgarian Integration Into Europe and NATO: Issues of Science Policy And research Evaluation Practice," Ios Press, 2006; "Allocating Limited National Resources for Fundamental Research," 2005.

2316 ■ Schneider Consulting Group Inc.
2801 E 4th Ave.
  Denver, CO 80206
Contact: Frank S. Schneider, Contact
Description: Firm assists family-owned and privately-held business transition to the next generation and or to a more professionally managed company, turn around consulting for small and medium-sized companies. **Scope:** Firm assists family-owned and privately-held business transition to the next generation and or to a more professionally managed company, turn around consulting for small and medium-sized companies. **Founded:** 1987. **Training:** Family Business Council; Impact of the Energy Renaissance.

2317 ■ Strategic Business Planning Co. (SBP)
1702 N Woodland Blvd., Ste. 116167
  Deland, FL 32720
Ph: (954)704-9100
Free: 888-704-9100
Co. E-mail: info@sbplan.com
URL: http://www.ipplan.com
Contact: Elmer Hall, President
Description: Provider of business expansion, import and export feasibility analysis, strategic plans, marketing plans and strategic planning workshop consulting services to the clients. **Scope:** Provider of business expansion, import and export feasibility analysis, strategic plans, marketing plans and strategic planning workshop consulting services to the clients. **Founded:** 1995. **Publications:** "Strategic Planning and Patent Commercialization". **Training:** Strategic Planning; Intellectual Property and New Product Development; Horizon/Scenario planning.

2318 ■ Strategic Business Services Inc. (SBS)
19710 S Governors Hwy., Ste. 1
  Flossmoor, IL 60422
Ph: (708)957-0022
Fax: (708)957-0002
Co. E-mail: lorine@sbsbusiness.com
URL: http://www.sbsbusiness.com
Contact: Lorine S. Samuels, President
E-mail: lorine@sbsbusiness.com
Description: Firm provides financial and management consulting services such as business planning, service management studies, project administration, contract monitoring, cash management, human resource planning, market surveys, seminars, and workshops. **Founded:** 1985. **Training:** Effective Budgeting Procedures; Accounts Receivable/Credit Collections: Improve Your Cash Flow; Managing for Profitability: The Bottom Line is Planning and Controlling; Preparing to Use Consultants: Strategies for Success; Board Responsibility in Nonprofit Organizations; The Business Plan: A Plan for Action.

2319 ■ Suiter Business Builders
27055 W 102nd St.
  Olathe, KS 66061
Ph: (415)884-0288
Co. E-mail: vicki@suiterbusinessbuilders.com
URL: http://suiterbusinessbuilders.com
Contact: Vicki Suiter, President
E-mail: vicki@suiterbusinessbuilders.com
Facebook: www.facebook.com/SuiterBusinessBuilders
Description: Provider of financial services. **Scope:** Provider of financial services. **Founded:** 1990. **Publications:** "Help Employees Step Up to the Plate and Transform Your Business"; "Outlast and Outshine the Competition!"; "Breaking the Sales Elephant Into Bite-sized Pieces"; "Five Critical Steps to Business Success"; "5 Critical Steps to Contractors Success". **Training:** Vicki Suiter's Business Builder; Business Boot Camp; Increase Your Cash Flow NOW!; One-Minute Budget; Master Builder - The Next Level.

2320 ■ Sunday Business Systems (SBS)
7960 B Soquel Dr., Ste. 109
  Aptos, CA 95003
Ph: (408)217-9680
Co. E-mail: support@sundaybizsys.com
URL: http://sundaybizsys.com
Contact: Andrew P. Stack, Chief Executive Officer
Facebook: www.facebook.com/SundayBusinessSystems
Linkedin: www.linkedin.com/company/sunday-business-systems
Description: Firm provides software solutions, consulting, and training to help improve business performance, offers consulting services in custom database solutions, quality systems consulting, and shop floor control solutions. **Scope:** Firm provides software solutions, consulting, and training to help improve business performance, offers consulting services in custom database solutions, quality systems consulting, and shop floor control solutions. **Founded:** 2004.

2321 ■ Synergistic Business Solutions Group L.L.C. (SBSG)
18 Park Ln.
  Fair Haven, NJ 07704-3514
Co. E-mail: info@sbs-corp.com
URL: http://www.sbs-corp.com
Description: Provider of financial services including rent-a-CFO, accounting systems selection, tailoring, business formation services and more. **Scope:** Provider of financial services including rent-a-CFO, accounting systems selection, tailoring, business formation services and more.

2322 ■ Think Creative Collective LLC
1915 NW Fawn Dr.
  Blue Springs, MO 64015-1727
URL: http://bossproject.com
Contact: Abagail Pumphrey, Chief Financial Officer
E-mail: cfo@bossproject.com
Linkedin: www.linkedin.com/company/boss-project
Instagram: www.instagram.com/bossproject
Pinterest: www.pinterest.com/bossprojecthq
Description: Offers strategic tools and resources for small businesses.

2323 ■ Total Business Care, L.L.C. (TBC)
39500 Stevenson Pl., Ste. 210
  Fremont, CA 94539
Ph: (510)797-8375
Fax: (510)797-9503
Co. E-mail: info@totalbizcare.com
URL: http://www.totalbizcare.com
Contact: Elise Berticevich, Office Manager
Facebook: www.facebook.com/totalbizcare
Linkedin: www.linkedin.com/company/totalbusinesscarellc
Description: Services: Management consulting, accounting, tax preparation, franchise development, marketing management, operational analysis, management training and more. **Scope:** Services: Management consulting, accounting, tax preparation, franchise development, marketing management, operational analysis, management training and more. **Founded:** 1985. **Special Services:** ProAdvisors®; QuickBooks®.

2324 ■ Total Business Services Inc. (TBSI)
7215 Bosque Blvd., No. 113
  Waco, TX 76710-4020
Contact: Billy D. Richardson, President
E-mail: brichardson@tbsi.consulting
Description: Firm provides business consulting services. **Scope:** Firm provides strategic and operational analysis and planning services to a variety of businesses.

2325 ■ Trendzitions Inc.
25691 Atlantic Ocean, Dr. No. B13
  Lake Forest, CA 92630
Ph: (949)727-9100
URL: http://www.trendzitions.com
Contact: Chris Tooker, President
E-mail: ctooker@trendzitions.com
X (Twitter): x.com/trendzitions
Instagram: www.instagram.com/trendzitions
Description: Provider of services in the areas of communications consulting, project management, construction management, and furniture procurement. Offers information on spatial uses, building codes, ADA compliance and city ordinances. Also offers budget projections. **Scope:** Provider of services in the areas of communications consulting, project management, construction management, and furniture procurement. Offers information on spatial uses, building codes, ADA compliance and city ordinances. Also offers budget projections. **Founded:** 1986.

2326 ■ The Walk The Talk Co.
PO Box 480
  Youngsville, LA 70592
Free: 800-888-2811
Fax: (972)899-9291
Co. E-mail: info@walkthetalk.com
URL: http://www.walkthetalk.com
Contact: Eric Harvey, Founder
Facebook: www.facebook.com/WalkTheTalk.LPDC
X (Twitter): x.com/WalkTheTalk_com
YouTube: www.youtube.com/user/WalkTheTalkCompany
Description: Firm engages in performance management system developed by individual responsibility and decision-making instead of disciplinary penalties. **Scope:** Firm engages in performance management system developed by individual responsibility and decision-making instead of disciplinary penalties. **Founded:** 1978. **Publications:** "Positive Discipline"; "Leadership Secrets of Santa Claus"; "Start Right-Stay Right"; "Walk Awhile in My Shoes"; "Listen Up, Leader!"; "Five Star Teamwork"; "Ethics4Everyone"; "Leadership Courage"; "The Manager's Communication Handbook"; "180 Ways to Walk the Recognition Talk"; "The Manager's Coaching Handbook"; "The Best Leadership Advice I Ever Got"; "Power Exchange". **Training:** Walk the Talk; Coaching for Continuous Improvement; Managing Employee Performance; Customized Management Development Forums; Keynote presentations; Leadership Development Workshops; Consulting Services and Publications; Customer service training; Ethics and Values training.

2327 ■ Western Business Services Ltd. (WBS)
1269 Lindsay St.
  Regina, SK, Canada S4N 3B4
Ph: (306)522-1493
Fax: (306)522-9076
Co. E-mail: wbs@myaccess.ca
URL: http://business.accesscomm.ca/wbs
Contact: O'Neil A. Zuck, President
Description: Provides advice and assistance to organizations on administrative management issues. **Scope:** Provides advice and assistance to organizations on administrative management issues. **Founded:** 1992.

2328 ■ ZS Engineering P.C. (ZSE)
99 Tulip Ave., Ste. 102
  Floral Park, NY 11001
Ph: (516)328-3200
Fax: (516)328-6195
Co. E-mail: office@zsengineering.com
URL: http://zsengineering.com/index.html
Contact: Zygmunt Staszewski, President
E-mail: staszewski@zsengineering.com
Description: Offers engineering consulting services to building owners, building managers and contractors. Specializes in design and inspections of fire alarm systems, sprinkler systems, smoke control systems, building evaluations for fire code compliance, violations removal. **Scope:** Offers engineering consulting services to building owners, building managers and contractors. Specializes in design and inspections of fire alarm systems, sprinkler systems, smoke control systems, building evaluations for fire code compliance, violations removal. **Founded:** 1989. **Training:** Fire protection courses for contractors and building management.

FRANCHISES AND BUSINESS OPPORTUNITIES

2329 ■ ActionCOACH
5781 S Fort Apache Rd.
  Las Vegas, NV 89148
Ph: (702)795-3188
Free: 888-483-2828

Co. E-mail: info@actioncoach.com
URL: http://www.actioncoach.com
Contact: Ken Zelazny, Chief Executive Officer
Facebook: www.facebook.com/Ac
tionCOACHBusinessCoaching
Linkedin: www.linkedin.com/company/actioncoach
X (Twitter): x.com/ActionCOACH
YouTube: www.youtube.com/user/actioncoachtv
Description: Business consulting and coaching service. **Scope:** Firm provides coaching, business coach, mentoring, accountability coach, executive coaching, consultant, executive leadership coach and small business coaching. **No. of Operating Units:** 1000. **Founded:** 1993. **Franchised:** 1997. **Royalty Fee:** 5% Marketing Fund fee. **Publications:** "The Business Coach"; "Instant Cashflow"; "Billionaire In Training"; "Instant Systems"; "Instant Team Building"; "Instant Profit"; "Instant Leads"; "Instant Sales"; "Instant Repeat Business"; "Instant Referrals"; "Instant Promotions" "Instant Advertising"; "Successful Franchising"; "The Real Estate Coach". **Financial Assistance:** Yes **Training:** Offers 10 days at headquarters, 10 days at various locations with ongoing support.

2330 ■ Alliance Cost Containment L.L.C. (ACC)
802 E Main St., Ste. 200
Louisville, KY 40206
Ph: (502)805-0975
Co. E-mail: info@alliancecost.com
URL: http://alliancecost.com
Contact: Miles Lee, President
E-mail: mlee@alliancecost.com
Facebook: www.facebook.com/alliancecost
Linkedin: www.linkedin.com/company/alliance-cos
t-containment
X (Twitter): x.com/alliancecost
Instagram: www.instagram.com/alliancecost
Description: Firm provides cost reduction services. **Founded:** 1992. **Training:** Training includes 3-4 days at headquarters, 3 days at annual conference and ongoing support.

2331 ■ Alpha Legal Forms & More Inc.
1830 E Broadway Blvd., Ste. 124
Tucson, AZ 85719
Contact: Kermit Burton, President
Description: Legal forms. **Founded:** 1976.

2332 ■ The Alternative Board (TAB)
11031 Sheridan Blvd.
Westminster, CO 80020
Ph: (303)839-1200
Free: 800-727-0126
Fax: (303)839-0012
Co. E-mail: contactus@thealternativeboard.com
URL: http://www.thealternativeboard.com
Contact: Jason P. Zickerman, President
E-mail: jpolino@thealternativeboard.com
Facebook: www.facebook.com/TheAlternativeBoard
Linkedin: www.linkedin.com/company/the-alternative
-board-worldwide-
X (Twitter): x.com/TAB_Boards
Instagram: www.instagram.com/thealterna
tiveboardsa
YouTube: www.youtube.com/user/TheAlterna
tiveBoard
Description: Firm provides coaching and advisory board services. **Founded:** 1990. **Training:** Training available at headquarters for 6 days and 4 weeks onsite with monthly/quarterly conference calls.

2333 ■ Arch Franchise Consultants
Wentzville, MO
Ph: (636)262-8317
Co. E-mail: info@archfranchises.com
URL: http://archfranchises.com
Contact: Robert Barclay, President
Facebook: www.facebook.com/ArchFranchiseConsul
tants
Linkedin: www.linkedin.com/company/arch-franchise
-consultants/
Description: A franchise consulting company dedicated to matching you with an established franchise or business opportunity that best fits your goals and objectives.

2334 ■ The Crestcom International L.L.C.
6900 E Belleview Ave., Ste. No.100
Greenwood Village, CO 80111
Ph: (303)267-8200
URL: http://crestcom.com
Contact: Douglas R. Ferguson, Contact
Facebook: www.facebook.com/crestcomleadership
Linkedin: www.linkedin.com/company/crestcom-in
ternational-llc
YouTube: www.youtube.com/user/CrestcomGlobal
Description: Business centers around marketing and conducting video-based management and sales training. Training is a combination of video instruction, featuring renowned business and management personalities, and hands-on monthly seminars. Training is currently used by many leading organizations throughout the world. **Scope:** Provides video based, live facilitated management, sales and office personnel training. **Founded:** 1987. **Financial Assistance:** Yes **Training:** Initial classroom and field training, ongoing training, a lead assistance program.

2335 ■ Criterium Engineers
5 Depot St., Ste. 23
Freeport, ME 04032
Free: 800-242-1969
URL: http://criterium-engineers.com
Contact: David Leopold, Co-President
E-mail: dleopold@criterium-engineers.com
Facebook: www.facebook.com/criteriumengineers
Linkedin: www.linkedin.com/company/criterium
-engineers
Instagram: www.instagram.com/criteriumengineers
YouTube: www.youtube.com/user/CriteriumEngineers
Description: Nationwide network of registered professional engineers, specializing in buildings and related consulting services. **Founded:** 1957. **Franchise Fee:** $34,500. **Royalty Fee:** 6% of your gross receipt. **Financial Assistance:** Yes **Training:** Yes.

2336 ■ Days Inns Canada
2151 Kingston Rd.
Toronto, ON, Canada M1N 1T5
Free: 800-329-7466
URL: http://www.wyndhamhotels.com/en-ca/days-inn
Facebook: www.facebook.com/daysinncanada
X (Twitter): x.com/daysinncanada
Description: Chain of hotels. **Founded:** 1992. **Training:** Training provided at opening and ongoing. Site selection and advisory council are provided.

2337 ■ Expense Reduction Analysts Inc. (ERA)
16415 Addison Rd., Ste. 410
Addison, TX 75001
Free: 877-299-7801
Co. E-mail: info@expensereduction.com
URL: http://us.expensereduction.com
Contact: Fred Marfleet, Founder Executive Chairman of the Board
X (Twitter): x.com/expenseredux
Description: Firm provides cost management consulting services. **Founded:** 1992. **Training:** Yes.

2338 ■ Focal Point Business Coaching
462 Stevens Ave., Ste. 202
Solana Beach, CA 92075
Free: 877-433-6225
Co. E-mail: info@focalpointcoaching.com
URL: http://www.focalpointcoaching.com
Contact: Steve Thompson, President
Linkedin: www.linkedin.com/company/focalpoint
X (Twitter): twitter.com/FPBusinessCoach
Instagram: www.instagram.com/focalpointcoaching
YouTube: www.youtube.com/c/FocalPoin
tBusinessCoaching
Description: Business coaching and consulting. **Founded:** 1999. **Franchised:** 2005. **Training:** Provides 1 week at headquarters, 2 months at franchisee's location, virtual training and ongoing support.

2339 ■ Franchise Compliance Inc.
487 E 520 S
Smithfield, UT 84335
Contact: Adam Valdez, Contact
Description: Provider of franchise services and mystery shopping.

2340 ■ Franchise Development International
6278 N Federal Hwy., Ste. 382
Fort Lauderdale, FL 33308
Contact: Linda D. Biciocchi, President
Description: Franchise development and marketing. **Founded:** 1991.

2341 ■ Franchise Developments Inc.
5840 Aylesboro Ave.
Pittsburgh, PA 15217
Description: Franchise consultants that offer clients full development services for the purpose of designing and implementing a total franchise program. **Publications:** "Franchising Your Business," May/Jun, 2003; "Female Entrepreneur," May/Jun, 2003; "Franchising World," May/Jun, 2003; "Canadian Business Franchise," Jul/Aug, 2000. **Training:** Has presented franchising seminars under auspices of American Management Association, Management Center Europe and International Franchise Association. Recent programs include Expanding Your Business by Franchising; Writing Effective Franchise Operations Manuals. Also has franchise seminar on Prodigy.

2342 ■ Franchise Foundations (FF)
San Francisco, CA
Ph: (415)225-3010
Co. E-mail: franchise888@gmail.com
URL: http://www.franchisefoundations.com
Contact: Kevin B. Murphy, Contact
Facebook: www.facebook.com/franchisefoundations
Linkedin: www.linkedin.com/company/franchise-foun
dations
X (Twitter): x.com/KevinB_Murphy
Pinterest: www.pinterest.com/franchisefoundations
Description: Firm provides franchise consulting services. **Founded:** 1980.

2343 ■ The Franchise Maker
1880 Camino De La Reina, Ste. 1051
San Diego, CA 92108
Free: 877-615-5177
URL: http://www.thefranchisemaker.com
Contact: David Waldman, President
Description: Takes business owners through a step-by-step process to franchise your business. **Founded:** 2005.

2344 ■ Franchise Marketing Systems
6110 McFarland Station Dr., Unit 105
Alpharetta, GA 30004
Free: 800-610-0292
Co. E-mail: info@franchisemarketingsystems.com
URL: http://www.fmsfranchise.com
Contact: Chris Conner, President
Facebook: www.facebook.com/FranchiseMarke
tingSystems
Linkedin: www.linkedin.com/company/fmsfranchise
X (Twitter): x.com/FranchiseMkting
Instagram: www.instagram.com/fmsfranchise
YouTube: www.youtube.com/user/FranchiseMarke
ting1/videos
Description: Full service franchise consulting agency offering marketing and sales support to its clients. **Scope:** Full service franchise consulting agency offering marketing and sales support to its clients.

2345 ■ Franchise Opportunity Consultants
2000 Mallory Ln., Ste. 130-253
Franklin, TN 37067
Ph: (615)908-5002
Co. E-mail: info@franchiseoc.com
URL: http://franchiseopportunityconsultants.com
Contact: Kevin Bauerle, President
Description: Franchise consultants that help organize your business into a franchise system, outsource franchise development services, and create structured guidance to grow a successful franchise system.

2346 ■ Franchise Search Inc.
48 Burd St., Ste. 101
Nyack, NY 10960-3226

Contact: Douglas Todd Kushell, Chief Executive Officer
E-mail: dkushell@franchise-search.com
Description: International executive search firm for franchisers. **Scope:** An international search firm specializing in executive searching for franchisers. Works exclusively for franchise organizations that need experienced franchise specialists in President, CEO, COO, Sales, Operations, Training, Marketing and Advertising, Legal, Finance, Real Estate and Construction and International Development. **Founded:** 1982.

2347 ■ Franchise Selection Specialists Inc.
633 Lander Dr.
  Highland Heights, OH 44143
Ph: (216)831-2610
URL: http://www.thefranchiseking.com
Contact: Joel Libava, Contact
Linkedin: www.linkedin.com/company/thefranchiseking
Description: Provider of franchise related advice and consulting services. **Founded:** 1990.

2348 ■ Franchise Specialists
2988 Silver Springs Blvd., Unit. 209
  Coquitlam, BC, Canada V3E 3R6
Ph: (604)941-4361
URL: http://www.franchisespecialists.com
Contact: Wayne Maillet, Consultant
E-mail: wmaillet@franchisespecialists.com
Description: Firm provides franchise development and management such as operation manuals, strategic planning, franchise recruitment, and business coaching. **Scope:** Firm provides franchise development and management such as operation manuals, strategic planning, franchise recruitment, and business coaching. **Founded:** 1997. **Publications:** "Do you have what it takes to succeed as a franchisee?"; "Intro to Franchising," Franchise Canada Magazine, Feb, 2008; "Franchise Tutorial," Franchise Canada Magazine, Apr, 2008; "Is My Business Franchisable," Canadian Business Franchise, 2003; "Understanding Franchising"; "Do you have what it takes".

2349 ■ Franchise Specialists Inc.
801 E 2120 Greentree Rd.
  Pittsburgh, PA 15220
Contact: William F. Repack, President
Description: Firm is engaged in professional franchise development and sales. **Founded:** 1978.

2350 ■ FranchiseKnowHow L.L.C.
76 Manchester Ln.
  Stony Brook, NY 11790
Contact: Edward Teixeira, Contact
Description: Franchise consulting service. **Scope:** Firm provides a full range of services to companies who desire to begin a franchise operation. Other areas of expertise include international franchising. **Publications:** "Flame"; "Franchising From the Inside Out"; "The Benefits of Acquiring an Existing Franchise Business"; "Meeting the Franchisor"; "Negotiating the Franchise Agreement," Franchise Trade; "Franchising Your Company," Franchise Trade; "How Franchisees Can Promote Positive Franchise Relations," Franchise Trade; "Meeting the Franchisor," Fracnhisehandbook.Com; "Franchising an Independent Business," Franchise Trade; "Key Factors in Evaluating and Operating a Franchise"; "Understanding the Chinese Market"; "Utilizing Your Franchise Attorney to Maintain and Promote Positive"; "Going International"; "Establishing a Franchise Program". **Training:** Meeting the Franchisor. **Special Services:** FLAME®.

2351 ■ FranchiseMart
2121 Vista Pky.
  West Palm Beach, FL 33411
URL: http://unitedfranchisegroup.com
Contact: A. J. Titus, President
Description: Provider of franchising information and consulting services. **Franchised:** 2007. **Financial Assistance:** Yes **Training:** Yes.

2352 ■ FranServe, Inc.
345 Rte. 17 S, Ste. 48
  Upper Saddle River, NJ 07458
Free: 800-206-5454
URL: http://franserve.com
Facebook: www.facebook.com/franserveinc
Linkedin: www.linkedin.com/company/franserve-inc-
Instagram: www.instagram.com/franserveinc
YouTube: www.youtube.com/channel/UCKXT9EVxogLevFd-3N8hlyQ
Description: Franchise consulting and expansion firm that works to connect entrepreneurs to franchise opportunities.

2353 ■ Global Recruiters Network - GRN (GRN)
200 S Wacker Dr., No. 1300
  Chicago, IL 60606
URL: http://www.grncorp.net
Contact: Brad Baiocchi, Chief Executive Officer
Facebook: www.facebook.com/grncorp
Linkedin: www.linkedin.com/company/global-recruiters-network
Description: Firm provides management, technical, professional and executive search services to the corporate community. **Founded:** 2003. **Franchised:** 2003. **Franchise Fee:** $89,000. **Financial Assistance:** Yes **Training:** Offers management, technical, professional and executive search services.

2354 ■ The Growth Coach
4755 Lake Forest Dr., Ste. 100
  Blue Ash, OH 45242
Ph: (513)999-9928
Free: 877-498-3626
Co. E-mail: operations@thegrowthcoach.com
URL: http://www.thegrowthcoach.com
Contact: Daniel Murphy, Chief Executive Officer
Description: Provider of small business and self-employed coaching. **Founded:** 2003. **Equity Capital Needed:** $52,125 - $82,025. **Financial Assistance:** Yes **Training:** Yes.

2355 ■ The iFranchise Group Inc.
905 W 175th St., 2nd Fl.
  Homewood, IL 60430
URL: http://www.ifranchisegroup.com
Contact: David E. Hood, President
Linkedin: www.linkedin.com/company/ifranchise-group
X (Twitter): x.com/ifranchisegroup
Instagram: www.instagram.com/ifranchisegroup
Description: Firm provides franchise consulting, development and marketing services. **Scope:** Firm provides franchise consulting, development and marketing services. **Founded:** 1998. **Publications:** "Is Your Business Franchisable?"; "The Right Marketing Materials". **Training:** Franchise Sales and Marketing Techniques; Minimizing Franchise Litigation; How to Franchise a Business; Developing and Maintaining Good Franchisee Relations.

2356 ■ "Know the Difference Between a Franchise Advisor, Consultant & Broker?" in The Franchise Maker website
URL(s): www.thefranchisemaker.com/learningcenter/what-is-the-difference-between-a-franchise-consultant-franchise-advisor-franchise-broker-franchise-developer/
Description: Breaks down players in the franchising industry that are often co-mingled and poorly defined. Describes franchise consultants, franchise advisors, franchise brokers, and franchise developers. **Availability:** Online.

2357 ■ The Lease Coach
127 St NWUnit 1083
  Edmonton, AB, Canada T6V 1M2
Ph: (780)448-2645
Free: 800-738-9202
URL: http://www.theleasecoach.com
Contact: Dale Willerton, Founder
E-mail: dalewillerton@theleasecoach.com
Description: Involves in commercial lease negotiating for retail, professional, franchise and office tenants. **Founded:** 1993. **Royalty Fee:** $2,200-$3,200/month. **Training:** Includes 1 week training at headquarters and ongoing training via teleconference/webconference.

2358 ■ MoreSALES
250 Dundas St. S, Ste. 236
  Cambridge, ON, Canada N1R 8A8
Ph: (519)620-8127
Free: 855-735-9861
Co. E-mail: info@moresales.ca
URL: http://www.moresales.ca
Contact: Mike Jennings, President
X (Twitter): x.com/MoreSALES_CAMB
YouTube: www.youtube.com/channel/UCz5xxa2c19-7CBwkEwSa6yw
Description: Sales and marketing firm provides market research, sales strategies, website design, marketing communication and much more. **Founded:** 2005. **Training:** 5-part training program included in franchise fee.

2359 ■ National Franchise Associates, Inc. (NFA)
240 Lake View Ct.
  Lavonia, GA 30553
Ph: (706)356-5637
Fax: (706)356-5180
URL: http://www.nationalfranchise.com
Contact: Stephen S. Raines, Consultant
Description: Full service consulting and developmental firm with expertise in feasibility studies, Franchise agreements and UFOC's, advertising and public relations campaigns, operations and training manuals, franchise sales programs, and ongoing franchise consulting. **Scope:** Firm provides franchise consulting services including feasibility studies, franchise plans, venture capital, franchise agreement, FTC disclosure document, state registration applications, operations manuals, training materials, advertising and public relations, computer software programs, sales and marketing of franchises for businesses, public and private sector. **Founded:** 1981. **Publications:** "Keys To Successful Franchising: Franchise Marketing Reflections Of A Franchise Consultant"; "Keys To A Successful Franchise Training"; "Keys To Successful Franchise Development: Will The Franchise Generate Sufficient Money? Reflections Of A Franchise Consultant"; "Focus on Operations Manuals & Marketing"; "Keys To Successful Franchising: Will Your Franchise Program Make Enough Money?"; "Keys To Successful Franchise Planning: Selecting The Right Franchisees"; "DePalma's expanding into Asia"; "Spirit Of Ingenuity"; "Why a Franchise Consultant Can Be Helpful". **Training:** Franchise Training Program.

2360 ■ Osler, Hoskin & Harcourt L.L.P.
First Canadian Pl.
  100 King St. W
  Toronto, ON, Canada M5X 1B8
Ph: (416)362-2111
Fax: (416)862-6666
Co. E-mail: info@osler.com
URL: http://www.osler.com/en
Contact: Shahir Guindi, Co-Chairman of the Board
E-mail: sguindi@osler.com
Linkedin: www.linkedin.com/company/osler-hoskin-&-harcourt-llp
X (Twitter): x.com/osler_law
Instagram: www.instagram.com/osler_law
YouTube: www.youtube.com/c/osler
Description: Law firm provides legal services. **Founded:** 1862.

2361 ■ "Partner" On-Call Network L.L.C. (POCN)
730 Sandy Point Ln.
  North Palm Beach, FL 33410
URL: http://partneroncall.com
Contact: Ted J. Leverette, Founder
E-mail: tedjleverette@partneroncall.com
Description: Provider of management and business consulting services. **Founded:** 2005. **Franchised:** 2006. **Financial Assistance:** Yes **Managerial Assistance:** CDs, DVDs and numerous how-to manuals and books. **Training:** 10 day home study, plus 5

days at headquarters and 3 days on-call via telephone and fax, conferences and proactive training & mentoring from a consultant seasoned in our business.

2362 ■ Performance Group Ltd. (TPG)
122 St. Albans Ln., Ste. D
Davidson, NC 28036
URL: http://www.samfrowine.com
Contact: Sam Frowine, Chief Executive Officer
Description: Group company engages in healthcare, business ownership optimization and industrial consulting services. **Founded:** 1995.

2363 ■ Pinnacle Franchise Development
10302 Brookridge Village Blvd., Ste. 201
Louisville, KY 40291
Ph: (954)205-3855
Co. E-mail: lory@pinnaclefd.com
URL: http://www.pinnaclefd.com
Linkedin: www.linkedin.com/company/pinnacle-franchise-development
Description: Franchise development firm serving emerging brands as well as established brands. **Founded:** 2015.

2364 ■ President's Resource Organization (PRO)
Ph: (312)593-5133
URL: http://peeradvisoryboard.com/online-peer-board
Contact: Ray Silverstein, President
Description: Facilitate peer advisory boards. **No. of Franchise Units:** 3. **No. of Company-Owned Units:** 2. **Founded:** 1993. **Franchised:** 1999. **Equity Capital Needed:** $12,000-$40,000. **Franchise Fee:** $8,500-$36,000. **Financial Assistance:** Yes **Training:** Yes.

2365 ■ Red Wheel
16 S 15th St.
Council Bluffs, IA 51501
Free: 800-659-6478
Co. E-mail: rwfr@redwheelfundraising.com
URL: http://redwheelfundraising.com
Description: Manufacturer and distributor of frozen foods. **Founded:** 1982. **Franchised:** 1988. **Training:** Yes.

2366 ■ Renaissance Executive Forums Inc. (REF)
2810 N Church St.
Wilmington, DE 19802-4447
Co. E-mail: contact@executiveforums.com
URL: http://executiveforums.com
Facebook: www.facebook.com/renaissanceexecutiveforums
Linkedin: www.linkedin.com/company/executiveforums
Description: Interactive peer review forums for business professionals. **Scope:** Firm is engaged in conducting business forum meetings, executive coaching programs, and workshops. **Founded:** 1994. **Publications:** "10 Reasons Why Your Sales Team Needs a Systematic Approach to Managing Key Accounts"; "Advanced Referral Marketing"; "Attract Clients with Your Business Card"; "Audit Your Marketing"; "Beware the Subtle Signs of Brand Decay"; "Building a Database - An Overlooked, Easy Marketing Step". **Training:** Offers business related training, including: One-on-One Coaching; Strategies for Success Planning Retreat; Business Improvement Group.

2367 ■ Signature Franchising Inc.
PO Box 149
Islamorada, FL 33036
Free: 800-343-3213
URL: http://signaturefranchising.com
Description: Developer of franchise software. **Founded:** 1980.

2368 ■ Summa Franchise Consulting
15051 N Kierland Blvd., Ste. 300
Scottsdale, AZ 85254
Ph: (623)999-1727
Co. E-mail: info@summafranchise.com
URL: http://summafranchise.com
Contact: Robert Stidham, Chief Executive Officer
Facebook: www.facebook.com/SummaFranchise
X (Twitter): x.com/SummaFranchise
Instagram: www.instagram.com/summafranchise
Description: Franchise consulting company specializing in advising franchising companies of all types at every step along the process, from emerging concept to sustainable success.

2369 ■ Sunbelt Business Brokers
7100 E Pleasant Valley Rd., Ste. 300
Independence, OH 44131
Ph: (216)674-0645
Fax: (216)674-0650
URL: http://www.sunbeltnetwork.com
Contact: Brian Knoderer, President
Facebook: www.facebook.com/sunbeltnetwork
Linkedin: www.linkedin.com/company/sunbelt-business-brokers
X (Twitter): x.com/SunbeltCorp
Description: Firm provides business brokerage services such as buying and selling advisory services for main street and middle market businesses. **Founded:** 1979.

2370 ■ Turbo Leadership Systems Ltd. (TLS)
36280 NE Willsonville Rd.
Newberg, OR 97132
Free: 800-574-4373
Fax: (503)625-2699
Co. E-mail: turbo@turbols.com
URL: http://turboleadershipsystems.com
Contact: Larry W. Dennis, President
E-mail: larry@turbols.com
Description: Management training and team building training. **Scope:** Provider of improvement programs that creates synergistic teamwork, impacts culture, and much more. **Founded:** 1985. **Publications:** "Empowering Leadership"; "How to Turbo Charge You"; "Repeat Business"; "Making Moments Matter, Information"; "The Turbo Charger"; "15 Leadership Principles and Ronald Reagan"; "Motorcycle Meditations"; "Repeat Business"; "Empowering Leadership"; "Communication For Results"; "The Great Baseball Cap". **Training:** Yes.

2371 ■ Upside Group Franchise Consulting Corp.
11445 E Via Linda, Ste. 2-495
Scottsdale, AZ 85259
Free: 888-445-2882
Co. E-mail: info@upsidefc.com
URL: http://upsidefranchiseconsulting.com
Contact: Mario Altiery, President
Description: Firm engages in full franchise consulting sales development. **Founded:** 2000. **Training:** Yes.

2372 ■ Venture Marketing Associates L.L.C.
800 Palisade Ave., Ste. 907
Fort Lee, NJ 07024
Ph: (201)924-7435
Co. E-mail: venturemkt@aol.com
URL: http://www.venturemarketingassociates.com
Contact: Shep Altshuler, Contact
Description: Business development/franchise consultants. **Scope:** Firm provides business development services for startups or multi-unit operations. **Founded:** 1976. **Training:** Franchise Your Business; How to Research a Franchise Services.

2373 ■ West Coast Commercial Credit
16787 Bernardo Center Dr., Ste. 11A
San Diego, CA 92128
Contact: Edward Spooner, Manager
Description: Nationwide commercial financing. **Founded:** 1987.

COMPUTERIZED DATABASES

2374 ■ *ABI/INFORM*
ProQuest LLC
789 E Eisenhower Pky.
Ann Arbor, MI 48108
Ph: (734)761-4700
Free: 800-521-0600
URL: http://www.proquest.com
Contact: Matti Shem Tov, Chief Executive Officer
URL(s): about.proquest.com/en/products-services/abi_inform_complete

Availability: Online. **Type:** Full-text; Bibliographic; Image.

LIBRARIES

2375 ■ Alameda Business Library
2400 Stevenson Blvd.
Fremont, CA 94538
Ph: (510)745-1400
Co. E-mail: fremont@aclibrary.org
URL: http://aclibrary.org
Contact: Jane Carr, Manager

Scope: Starting and managing a business; small business; investments; real estate; International business; management and personnel planning; career planning; San Francisco Bay area business. **Services:** Interlibrary loan; copying; library open to the public. **Holdings:** 18,000 books; 300 audiocassettes; 100 videocassettes.

2376 ■ Association for Talent Development (ATD) - Library
1640 King St.
Alexandria, VA 22313-1443
Ph: (703)683-8100
Free: 800-628-2783
Fax: (703)683-1523
Co. E-mail: customercare@td.org
URL: http://www.td.org
Contact: Tony Bingham, President
Facebook: www.facebook.com/ATD
Linkedin: www.linkedin.com/company/15989
X (Twitter): x.com/ATD
Instagram: www.instagram.com/atdnational
Pinterest: www.pinterest.com/ATDofficial

Description: Supports the talent development profession by providing trusted content in the form of research, books, webcasts, events, and education programs. **Scope:** Management; leadership. **Services:** Library open to members only. **Founded:** 1943. **Holdings:** 170 monographs; 100 books; 100 newspapers. **Publications:** *American Society Training and Development Buyer's Guide and Consultant Directory* (Annual); *Technical Training Basics*; *ASTD Buyer's Guide & Consultant Directory* (Annual); *TD at Work* (Monthly); *Learning Circuits* (Monthly); *TD Magazine* (Monthly); *Member Information Exchange (MIX)*; *TRAINET*; *ATD Buyer's Guide*; *ATD Buyer's Guide*; *American Society for Training and Development--Training Video Directory*; *Who's Who in Training and Development* (Annual). **Educational Activities:** ATD International Conference and Exposition (Annual); ATD TechKnowledge Conference (Annual); TechKnowledge Conference and Exposition (Annual). **Awards:** ATD BEST Award (Annual); Awards in the Advancing Workplace Learning and Performance; ATD Excellence in Practice Awards (Annual); Gordon M. Bliss Memorial Award (Annual); ATD Dissertation Award (Annual); ASTD Talent Development Thought Leader Award (Annual); ATD Torch Award (Annual). **Geographic Preference:** Multinational.

Business Services Operation

ASSOCIATIONS AND OTHER ORGANIZATIONS

2377 ■ Business Council (BC)
1901 Pennsylvania Ave. NW, Ste. 307
Washington, DC 20006
Ph: (202)298-7650
Fax: (202)785-0296
URL: http://businesscouncil.com
Contact: Marlene M. Colucci, Co-Chief Executive Officer
E-mail: mcolucci@businesscouncil.com
Description: Represents business executives. Aims to serve the national interest, with the primary objectives of developing a constructive point of view on matters of public policy affecting the business interests of the country and by providing a medium for a better understanding of government problems by business. Members are former and present chief executive officers of corporations. **Founded:** 1933. **Geographic Preference:** National.

REFERENCE WORKS

2378 ■ "France Telecom Takes Minitel Offline" in Canadian Business (Vol. 85, August 13, 2012, No. 13, pp. 12)
Ed: Matthew McClearn. **Description:** The Minitel online service was developed to reduce the costs of printing phone directories in the French postal and telecommunications ministry in 1978 and became popular in Paris in 1982. With its user-based halved annually and services declining in its waning years, France Telecom opted to terminate the service on June 30, 2012. **Availability:** Print; Online.

2379 ■ "Is Maid Service Right For Your Home?" in Internet Wire (April 18, 2012)
Pub: Comtex News Network Inc.
Contact: Kan Devnani, President
Description: Merry Maids service fanchise is discussed. The article helps individuals looking for a cleaning service to investigate the wide range of services offered by each company. **Availability:** Print; Online.

STATISTICAL SOURCES

2380 ■ Document Preparation Services Industry in the US - Market Research Report
URL(s): www.ibisworld.com/united-states/market-research-reports/document-preparation-services-industry/
Price: $925. **Description:** Downloadable report analyzing data about the document preparation industry and the competition it faces from other similar industries. **Availability:** Download.

CONSULTANTS

2381 ■ Bengston Business Forms Inc.
9201 Shore Blvd.
Brooklyn, NY 11209
Contact: Carl B. Bengston, Chief Executive Officer

Description: Services: Designing and layout of all kinds of business forms. **Scope:** Services: Designing and layout of all kinds of business forms.

2382 ■ BioSciCon, Inc. [Biomedical Science Consulting Company, Inc.]
14905 Forest Landing Cir.
Rockville, MD 20850
Ph: (301)610-9130
Fax: (301)610-7662
Co. E-mail: info@bioscicon.com
URL: http://www.bioscicon.com
Contact: Dr. Nenad Markovic, President
Description: Provider of biomedical science consulting and also a developer of biotechnology products. **Scope:** Provider of biomedical science consulting and also a developer of biotechnology products. **Founded:** 1996. **Publications:** "Cervical Acid Phosphates: A Biomarker of Cervical Dysplasia and Potential Surrogate Endpoint for Colposcopy," 2004; "Enhancing Pap test with a new biological marker of cervical dysplasia," 2004; "A cytoplasmic biomarker for liquid-based Pap," The FACEB Journal Experimental Biology, 2004; "Pap test and new biomarker-based technology for enhancing visibility of abnormal cells," 2004. **Special Services:** MarkPap®; PreservCyt®.

2383 ■ Business Planning Inc. (BPI)
2075 Columbiana Rd., Ste. 1
Birmingham, AL 35216
Ph: (205)824-8969
Free: 800-239-5135
Fax: (205)824-8939
URL: http://www.businessplanninginc.com
Contact: Scott Sutton, Contact
E-mail: scott@businessplanninginc.com
Description: Firm provides personalized planning, installation, administration, corporate retirement planning, and much more services. **Scope:** Firm provides personalized planning, installation, administration, corporate retirement planning, and much more services. **Founded:** 1974.

2384 ■ David G. Schantz
29 Wood Run Cir.
Rochester, NY 14612-2271
Ph: (716)723-0760
Fax: (716)723-8724
Co. E-mail: daveschantz@yahoo.com
URL: http://www.daveschantz.freeservers.com
Description: Provider of industrial engineering services for photo finishing labs, including amateur-wholesale, professional, commercial, school and package. **Scope:** Provider of industrial engineering services for photo finishing labs, including amateur-wholesale, professional, commercial, school and package.

2385 ■ DRI Consulting Inc. (DRIC)
Two Otter Ln.
Saint Paul, MN 55127
Ph: (651)415-1400
Co. E-mail: dric@dric.com
URL: http://www.dric.com

Contact: Dr. John Fennig, Director
Description: Provides high-quality, research-based services and training in leadership, team processes, supervision, and management, and organizational development, clients with direct and substantial impact on individual and team performance and on organizational success through proven processes for selecting, developing and deploying leaders. **Scope:** Provides high-quality, research-based services and training in leadership, team processes, supervision, and management, and organizational development, clients with direct and substantial impact on individual and team performance and on organizational success through proven processes for selecting, developing and deploying leaders. **Founded:** 1991.

2386 ■ Family Business Institute Inc. (FBI)
3520 Ridge View Ct.
Marietta, GA 30068
Ph: (770)952-4085
URL: http://www.family-business-experts.com
Contact: Don A. Schwerzler, Founder
Description: Firm engages in business consulting and professional services. **Scope:** Assists families in business to achieve personal, family and organizational goals. **Founded:** 1995. **Publications:** "Professional Intervention in the Family Owned Business"; "Building Consensus in a Family Business"; "Professionalizing Family Business Management".

2387 ■ First Strike Management Consulting Inc. (FSMC)
PO Box 1188
Little River, SC 29566-1188
Ph: (843)385-6338
Co. E-mail: info@fsmc.com
URL: http://www.fsmc.com
Description: Offers proposal management and program management services. Specializes in enterprise systems, management systems, and staff augmentation. Serves the following industries: Nuclear/Fossil Power, Petro-Chemical, Aerospace and Defense, Telecommunications, Engineering and Construction, Information Technology, Golf Course Construction/Management, Utility Engineering/Construction, Civil Works, and Housing Development. **Scope:** Offers proposal management and program management services. Specializes in enterprise systems, management systems, and staff augmentation. Serves the following industries: Nuclear/Fossil Power, Petro-Chemical, Aerospace and Defense, Telecommunications, Engineering and Construction, Information Technology, Golf Course Construction/Management, Utility Engineering/Construction, Civil Works, and Housing Development. **Founded:** 1991. **Publications:** "Project Management for Executives"; "Project Risk Management"; "Project Communications Management"; "Winning Proposals, Four Computer Based Training (CBT) courses"; "Principles of Program Management". **Training:** Preparing Winning Proposals in Response to Government RFPs.

2388 ■ Full Voice
9912B Holmes Rd., Ste. 237
Kansas City, MO 64131-4206

Description: Vocal performance training firm offering consulting services and personal training sessions in the implementation of effective vocal communication techniques for the development of business relationships and career enhancement. **Scope:** Vocal performance training firm offering consulting services and personal training sessions in the implementation of effective vocal communication techniques for the development of business relationships and career enhancement. **Publications:** "You Can Sound Like You Know What You're Saying". **Training:** You Can Sound Like You Know What You're Saying; The Psychology of Vocal Performance; Security. . .the Ability to Accept Change; Knowing. . .the Key to Relaxed Public Communication; The Effective Voice for Customer Service Enhancement; You Can Speak With Conviction; How To Make Yours a Championship Team; Functional English For Foreign Trade. **Special Services:** FULL VOICE™.

2389 ■ Institute for Management Excellence
Trabuco Canyon, CA 92679
Ph: (949)667-1012
URL: http://www.itstime.com
Contact: Barbara Taylor, Executive Director

Description: Consulting firm and training focuses on improving productivity, using practices and creative techniques. **Scope:** Consulting firm and training focuses on improving productivity, using practices and creative techniques. **Founded:** 1995. **Publications:** "Income Without a Job," 2008; "The Other Side of Midnight; 2000: An Executive Guide to the Year 2000 Problem"; "Concordance to the Michael Teachings"; "Handbook of Small Business Advertising"; "The Personality Game"; "How to Market Yourself for Success". **Training:** The Personality Game; Power Path Seminars; Productivity Plus; Sexual Harassment and Discrimination Prevention; Worker's Comp Cost Reduction; Americans with Disabilities Act; In Search of Identify: Clarifying Corporate Culture.

2390 ■ On-Q Software Inc.
13764 SW 11 St.
Miami, FL 33184
URL: http://www.on-qsoftware.com
Contact: Teresita Cajigas, President

Description: Developer of computer software solutions. **Scope:** Developer of computer software solutions. **Founded:** 1987.

2391 ■ Rose & Crangle Ltd.
102 E Lincoln Ave.
Lincoln, KS 67455
Contact: S. Jeanne Crangle, Contact

Description: Provider of evaluation, planning and policy analyzes for universities, associations, foundations, governmental agencies and private companies engaged in scientific, technological or educational activities. Special expertise in the development of new institutions. Special skills in providing planning and related group facilitation workshops. **Scope:** Provider of evaluation, planning and policy analyzes for universities, associations, foundations, governmental agencies and private companies engaged in scientific, technological or educational activities. Special expertise in the development of new institutions. Special skills in providing planning and related group facilitation workshops. **Publications:** "Preface to Bulgarian Integration Into Europe and NATO: Issues of Science Policy And research Evaluation Practice," Ios Press, 2006; "Allocating Limited National Resources for Fundamental Research," 2005.

2392 ■ Schneider Consulting Group Inc.
2801 E 4th Ave.
Denver, CO 80206
Contact: Frank S. Schneider, Contact

Description: Firm assists family-owned and privately-held business transition to the next generation and or to a more professionally managed company, turn around consulting for small and medium-sized companies. **Scope:** Firm assists family-owned and privately-held business transition to the next generation and or to a more professionally managed company, turn around consulting for small and medium-sized companies. **Founded:** 1987. **Training:** Family Business Council; Impact of the Energy Renaissance.

2393 ■ Trendzitions Inc.
25691 Atlantic Ocean, Dr. No. B13
Lake Forest, CA 92630
Ph: (949)727-9100
URL: http://www.trendzitions.com
Contact: Chris Tooker, President
E-mail: ctooker@trendzitions.com
X (Twitter): x.com/trendzitions
Instagram: www.instagram.com/trendzitions

Description: Provider of services in the areas of communications consulting, project management, construction management, and furniture procurement. Offers information on spatial uses, building codes, ADA compliance and city ordinances. Also offers budget projections. **Scope:** Provider of services in the areas of communications consulting, project management, construction management, and furniture procurement. Offers information on spatial uses, building codes, ADA compliance and city ordinances. Also offers budget projections. **Founded:** 1986.

2394 ■ Xerox Business Research Group
80 State St.
Albany, NY 12207
URL: http://www.xerox.com
Contact: Steve Bandrowczak, President
Linkedin: www.linkedin.com/company/xerox
X (Twitter): twitter.com/Xerox
Instagram: www.instagram.com/xerox

Description: Firm is engaged in providing document management, business processing, legal services and much more. **Founded:** 1906.

2395 ■ Zaetric Business Solutions L.L.C.
27350 Blueberry Hill Dr., No 14
Conroe, TX 77385
Ph: (281)298-1878
Co. E-mail: inquries@zaetric.com
URL: http://zaetric.com
Contact: David L. Woody, Owner Founder
Linkedin: www.linkedin.com/company/zaetric-business-solutions-llc

Description: Firm provides services such as technical writing, business management systems support, printing and binding. **Founded:** 2000. **Publications:** "Earned Value Management System". **Special Services:** ZAETRIC®.

FRANCHISES AND BUSINESS OPPORTUNITIES

2396 ■ Alpha Legal Forms & More Inc.
1830 E Broadway Blvd., Ste. 124
Tucson, AZ 85719
Contact: Kermit Burton, President

Description: Legal forms. **Founded:** 1976.

2397 ■ AmSpirit Business Connections
AmSpirit Business Connections
158 W Johnstown Rd.
Columbus, OH 43230
Ph: (614)476-5540
Free: 888-509-5323
URL: http://www.amspirit.com
Contact: Frank Agin, Chief Executive Officer
E-mail: frankagin@amspirit.com
Facebook: www.facebook.com/amspiritbusinessconnections

Description: Establish and support networking groups. **Founded:** 1997. **Training:** Yes.

2398 ■ A Day to Cherish Wedding Videos
10174 S Memorial Dr.
South Jordan, UT 84095
Contact: Murry L. Dalton, Contact

Description: Wedding and special occasion videos. **Founded:** 2004. **Training:** Provides 6 days at headquarters and 2 days at franchisee's location with ongoing support.

2399 ■ Decorating Elves (DE)
13670 Roosevelt Blvd.
Clearwater, FL 33762
Ph: (727)474-2628
Free: 800-MYL-ITES
Co. E-mail: office@decoratingelves.com
URL: http://www.decoratingelves.com
Contact: Nick Schriver, Contact
Facebook: www.facebook.com/DecoratingElvesLighting
Linkedin: www.linkedin.com/in/decoratingelves
YouTube: www.youtube.com/channel/UC8NcvFBg-M5fKFDBZwhLPHQ

Description: Provider of outdoor lighting and landscape lighting services. **Founded:** 2006. **Financial Assistance:** Yes **Training:** Yes.

2400 ■ Franchise Search Inc.
48 Burd St., Ste. 101
Nyack, NY 10960-3226
Contact: Douglas Todd Kushell, Chief Executive Officer
E-mail: dkushell@franchise-search.com

Description: International executive search firm for franchisers. **Scope:** An international search firm specializing in executive searching for franchisers. Works exclusively for franchise organizations that need experienced franchise specialists in President, CEO, COO, Sales, Operations, Training, Marketing and Advertising, Legal, Finance, Real Estate and Construction and International Development. **Founded:** 1982.

2401 ■ Goin' Postal
4941 4th St.
Zephyrhills, FL 33542
Ph: (813)782-1500
Free: 800-504-6040
Fax: (813)782-1599
Co. E-mail: info@goinpostal.com
URL: http://goinpostal.com
Contact: Marcus Price, Founder
Facebook: www.facebook.com/gpcorp

Description: Operator of packers and movers. **Founded:** 2001. **Equity Capital Needed:** $48,865 - $139,500. **Franchise Fee:** $15,000. **Royalty Fee:** $440. **Financial Assistance:** Yes **Training:** 1 week training at headquarters, 1 week at franchisee's location, refresher training at corporate location throughout term of the franchise and ongoing support.

2402 ■ Handyman-Network Franchise Systems LLC
4381 Broadway, Ste. 105
American Canyon, CA 94503
Ph: (415)884-2360
Co. E-mail: info@l3wconstruction.com
URL: http://handyman-network.com

Description: Provides homeowners with service, people, systems, and technology. **No. of Franchise Units:** 5. **Founded:** 2000. **Franchised:** 2002. **Equity Capital Needed:** $67,388-$107,044 total start-up, including franchise fee. **Franchise Fee:** $30,000. **Royalty Fee:** 6%. **Training:** Start-up program is an extensive 3 module training program. Includes 2 weeks of on the job training at headquarters, and 4 days of onsite training. Each module is supported with manuals with ongoing support.

2403 ■ Liberty Tax Service, Inc.
Franchise Group, Inc. (FRG)
110 Riviera Dr., Unit 16
Markham, ON, Canada L3R 5M1
Ph: (740)363-2222
Free: 800-790-3863
Fax: (800)880-6432
URL: http://www.franchisegrp.com
Facebook: www.facebook.com/libertytaxCA
X (Twitter): x.com/libtaxcanada

Description: Provider of tax preparation, tax returns and tax filling services, tax courses, small business accounting. **Founded:** 1997. **Training:** Provides 5 days training.

2404 ■ Lord and Partners Ltd.
9-741 Muskoka Rd., Ste. 3 N
Huntsville, ON, Canada P1H 2L3

Description: Manufacturer and distributor of solvents, cleaners and specialty products for industries, automotive, aviation, government and others. **Training:** Provides 29 days training on the proven proprietary business, marketing systems, a demo "showroom on wheels," with ongoing support for a protected territory.

2405 ■ Luxury Bath Systems
Glendale Heights, IL 60139
Free: 800-822-7905
URL: http://www.luxurybath.com
Facebook: www.facebook.com/LuxuryBathInc
X (Twitter): x.com/luxurybathinc
Instagram: www.instagram.com/luxurybathcorp
Pinterest: www.pinterest.com/luxurybathinc
Description: Retailer of bathroom remodeling products. **Founded:** 1994. **Training:** 5 days covering marketing, installation and support and 3 days at franchisee's location with ongoing support.

2406 ■ Mail Boxes Etc. - MBEC Communications, Inc.
1115 N Service Rd., Unit 1
Oakville, ON, Canada L6M 2V9
Ph: (905)338-9754
URL: http://www.theupsstore.ca
Contact: David Druker, President
Facebook: www.facebook.com/TheUPSStoreCA
Linkedin: www.linkedin.com/company/the-ups-store-canada
X (Twitter): x.com/theupsstore_can
Instagram: www.instagram.com/theupsstoreca
YouTube: www.youtube.com/user/TheUPSStoreCanada
Description: With over 4,000 locations worldwide and over 260 centers operating in Canada, MBE is one of the largest and fastest growing business and communications service franchise. Services include expert packing services, shipping, worldwide courier services, black and white and color photocopies, electronic document services, digital color printing, fax sending and receiving, computer rental, word processing, Internet/email access and mail receiving services. **No. of Franchise Units:** 351. **Founded:** 1990. **Franchised:** 1991. **Equity Capital Needed:** $146,150-$179,550 plus working capital. **Franchise Fee:** $35,900. **Royalty Fee:** 6% of gross. **Training:** Complete pre-opening support provided, including site selection, lease negotiation, design and construction, training, marketing, as well as ongoing operational and marketing field support.

2407 ■ Padgett Business Services (PBS)
555 High St., Ste. 102
Westwood, MA 02090
Ph: (781)219-0395
URL: http://www.padgettadvisors.com
Contact: John Barucci, Contact
Facebook: www.facebook.com/PadgettBusiness
X (Twitter): x.com/PadgettBusSvcs
Description: Padgett provides an array of services to small businesses, such as consulting, financial reporting, government compliance, payroll and tax preparation services. Padgett also offers credit card processing, pension and 125 plan administration, equipment financing and workers' compensation payment service. **Founded:** 1993. **Training:** Initial training 12 days field visits, covering marketing, operations, and software. Ongoing training and support is provided through regular seminars in marketing, operations, tax, etc. Support is delivered through toll-free telephone and a wide range of information and material is provided via the company's web site.

2408 ■ Padgett Business Services
1200 Speers Rd., Unit 22
Oakville, ON, Canada L6L 2X4
Ph: (905)842-5812
Fax: (905)842-8366
URL: http://smallbizpros.ca
Contact: Alphonse Nachla, Owner
E-mail: anachla@cogeco.net
Description: Provider of business advice and consultation, tax preparation, government compliance, financial reporting, complete payroll services and other services. **No. of Franchise Units:** 120.

Founded: 1966. **Franchised:** 1975. **Equity Capital Needed:** $42,500-$50,000. **Franchise Fee:** $25,000. **Training:** Complete program of training and support.

2409 ■ Pro Fleet Care Franchising Inc.
Brantford, ON, Canada
Ph: (905)667-8595
Free: 866-787-8645
Co. E-mail: info@profleetcare.com
URL: http://profleetcare.com
Description: Provider of mobile rust control services. **Founded:** 1984. **Training:** Provides 2 weeks training, including technical and operational and ongoing.

2410 ■ The UPS Store Inc.
United Parcel Service, Inc. (UPS)
6060 Cornerstone Ct. W
San Diego, CA 92121-3795
Ph: (404)828-4147
Free: 800-742-5877
Co. E-mail: custsvcgben@ups.com
URL: http://www.ups.com
Contact: Sarah Casalan Bittle, President
URL(s): www.ups.com
Facebook: www.facebook.com/theupsstore
Linkedin: www.linkedin.com/company/201257
X (Twitter): x.com/theupsstore
Instagram: www.instagram.com/theupsstore
YouTube: www.youtube.com/user/theupsstore
Description: Firm provides trucking and transportation services. **Founded:** 1980.

PUBLICATIONS

2411 ■ *BizTech*
URL(s): biztechmagazine.com
X (Twitter): twitter.com/BizTechMagazine
Released: Quarterly **Description:** Provides insightful articles on various technology and business topics. **Availability:** Print; Online.

COMPUTERIZED DATABASES

2412 ■ *Florida Trend*
Trend Magazines Inc.
490 First Ave. S, Eighth Fl.
Saint Petersburg, FL 33701
Ph: (727)821-5800
Fax: (727)822-5083
URL: http://www.floridatrend.com
Contact: John Annunziata, Managing Editor
E-mail: jannunziata@floridatrend.com
URL(s): www.floridatrend.com
Facebook: www.facebook.com/floridatrend
Linkedin: www.linkedin.com/company/floridatrend
X (Twitter): twitter.com/FloridaTrend
YouTube: www.youtube.com/user/FloridaTrendVideo?reload=9
Released: Monthly **Price:** $24.98, for print and online one year; $14.98, for print or online 1 year. **Description:** Business. **Availability:** Print; Online. **Type:** Full-text.

INTERNET DATABASES

2413 ■ *Business History: A Resource Guide*
101 Independence Ave., SE
Washington, DC 20540
Ph: (202)707-9779
Co. E-mail: visit@loc.gov
URL: http://www.loc.gov
Contact: Carla Hayden, Librarian
URL(s): guides.loc.gov/business-history-research
Description: An online resource that contains links for resources in American business, industries, companies, and business leaders. Links to periodicals, internet resources, and databases are included. **Availability:** Print.

2414 ■ *Business and Labor History: Primary Sources at the Library of Congress*
URL(s): guides.loc.gov/business-and-labor-history

Description: An online resource providing links to key topics to business and labor history. Contains links to company records, presidential papers, government agencies, judicial papers, and primary sources. **Availability:** Online.

LIBRARIES

2415 ■ Alabama A & M University - J.F. Drake Memorial Learning Resources Center
4900 Meridian St. N
Normal, AL 35762
Ph: (256)372-4725
URL: http://alabamam.ent.sirsi.net/client/en_US/default
Contact: Linda McClellan, Coordinator
Scope: Arts; sciences; business; engineering; education; agriculture and technology. **Services:** Interlibrary loan; copying; media services; Center open to the public (courtesy card must be purchased for check out of materials by persons not enrolled at the university or at one of the cooperating institutions). **Founded:** 1875. **Holdings:** 236,147 books; 25,517 bound periodical volumes; 5,044 AV programs; 20,869 periodicals on microfilm; 1,053 college catalogs; various telephone directories; 16,166 ERIC microfiche; 141,376 government documents; Wall Street Journal on microfiche (11,643); 359 microfilm subscriptions. **Subscriptions:** 1,657 journals and other serials; 93 newspapers.

2416 ■ Alameda Business Library
2400 Stevenson Blvd.
Fremont, CA 94538
Ph: (510)745-1400
Co. E-mail: fremont@aclibrary.org
URL: http://aclibrary.org
Contact: Jane Carr, Manager
Scope: Starting and managing a business; small business; investments; real estate; International business; management and personnel planning; career planning; San Francisco Bay area business. **Services:** Interlibrary loan; copying; library open to the public. **Holdings:** 18,000 books; 300 audiocassettes; 100 videocassettes.

2417 ■ Balch & Bingham LLP (B&B) - Library
1901 6th Ave. N, Ste. 1500
Birmingham, AL 35203-4642
Ph: (205)251-8100
Free: 888-254-2466
Co. E-mail: info@balch.com
URL: http://www.balch.com
Contact: M. Stanford Blanton, Managing Partner
E-mail: sblanton@balch.com
Facebook: www.facebook.com/balchbingham
Linkedin: www.linkedin.com/company/balchbingham
X (Twitter): x.com/BalchBingham
Instagram: www.instagram.com/balchbingham
YouTube: www.youtube.com/channel/UCACznFBHonqlqEKylvblVbg
Description: Corporate law firm with offices in Alabama, Florida, Georgia, Mississippi, and Washington DC. **Scope:** Law; business. **Services:** Interlibrary loan; library not open to the public. **Founded:** 1922. **Holdings:** 35,000 volumes; legislative and government documents.

2418 ■ Boston Consulting Group - Chicago Information and Research Group
300 N La Salle Dr.
Chicago, IL 60654
Ph: (312)993-3300
Fax: (312)876-0771
URL: http://www.bcg.com/en-in/offices/chicago/default
Contact: Brad Martens, Senior Managing Director Partner
Description: Aims to bring the right people together to challenge established thinking and drive transformation. **Scope:** Statistics, finance, industry. **Services:** Interlibrary loan; library not open to the public. **Founded:** 1979. **Holdings:** 4,500 books; 3,000 Annual reports; 21 lin.ft. of microfiche; 84 reels of microfilm.

2419 ■ Business Services Operation

2419 ■ California Polytechnic State University - Robert F. Kennedy Library - Government Documents and Map Department - Diablo Canyon Power Plant Depository Library
1 Grand Ave., Bldg. 35
San Luis Obispo, CA 93407
URL: http://lib.calpoly.edu
Contact: Mark Bieraugel, Librarian
E-mail: mbieraug@calpoly.edu
Scope: Nuclear power plants. **Services:** Interlibrary loan; copying; Wi-Fi access; library open to the public. **Founded:** 1901. **Holdings:** Figures not available.

2420 ■ Golden Gate University - University Library
536 Mission St.
San Francisco, CA 94105-2968
URL: http://www.ggu.edu/libraries
Scope: Business; public administration; information systems; telecommunications. **Services:** Interlibrary loan; libraries open to the public on Annual fee basis. **Founded:** 1901. **Holdings:** 90,000 volumes; 264 microfiche; 435 microfilms. **Subscriptions:** 3000 journals and other serials.

2421 ■ Kearney Inc. - Collection
Kearney Holdings Limited
227 W Monroe St.
Chicago, IL 60606
Ph: 44 20 7468 8000
Contact: Alex Liu, Chairman Managing Partner
Facebook: www.facebook.com/ATKearney
Linkedin: www.linkedin.com/company/kearney
X (Twitter): twitter.com/atkearney
Instagram: www.instagram.com/kearneyofficial
YouTube: www.youtube.com/kearneyofficial
Description: Global management consulting firm which focuses on strategic and operational corporate-level agenda issues facing businesses, governments, and institutions in a wide array of industries, its services include analytics, mergers and acquisitions, strategic information technology, digital business, operations, strategy, innovation, organization and transformation, sustainability, marketing and sales, and procurement. **Scope:** Strategic and operational corporate-level agenda issues facing businesses, governments, and institutions. **Founded:** 1926. **Holdings:** Figures not available.

2422 ■ McKinsey & Company Inc. - Resource Library
110 Charles St., W
Toronto, ON, Canada M5S 1K9
URL: http://www.mckinsey.com/industries/healthcare-systems-and-services/our-insights/patients-struggle-with-unmet-basic-needs-medical-providers-can-help
Description: Accelerates transformations by unlocking the potential of people. **Services:** Members can access. **Founded:** 1969. **Holdings:** Figures not available.

2423 ■ Towers Watson Information Center
1800 McGill College Ave., 22nd Fl., Ste. 2200
Montreal, QC, Canada H3A 3J6
Ph: (514)982-9411
URL: http://www.willistowerswatson.com/en-GB
Scope: Employee benefits, compensation, actuarial science, taxation, labor, social security, employee communications, insurance, human resource management. **Founded:** 1976. **Holdings:** Figures not available.

Butcher Shop

START-UP INFORMATION

2424 ■ *"Aubry & Kale Walch, Herbivorous Butcher"* in *Business Journal (Vol. 32, August 29, 2014, No. 14, pp. 6)*
Pub: American City Business Journals, Inc.
Contact: Mike Olivieri, Executive Vice President
Released: August 29, 2014. **Description:** Kale and Aubry Walch, founders of family-owned The Herbivorous Butcher, reveal that the process of formulating recipes for their shop took years. Aubry said that she and her brother used to make fake meats for themselves. Their plan to open a full-scale vegan butcher shop is also discussed. **Availability:** Print; Online.

ASSOCIATIONS AND OTHER ORGANIZATIONS

2425 ■ **American Association of Meat Processors (AAMP)**
1 Meating Pl.
Elizabethtown, PA 17022
Ph: (717)367-1168
URL: http://www.aamp.com
Contact: Darla Kiesel, President
Facebook: www.facebook.com/AAMP1939
Linkedin: www.linkedin.com/company/american
 -association-of-meat-processors
X (Twitter): x.com/aampnews
Instagram: www.instagram.com/aampmeat
YouTube: www.youtube.com/AampVideo%E
 2%80%8B
Description: Represents small and mid-sized packers, processors, wholesalers, home food service businesses, meat retailers, deli, mail order businesses and catering operators and their suppliers. Represents its members at the federal level of government. Provides education, insurance options and business management assistance to the independent segment of the meat industry. **Founded:** 1939. **Publications:** *Membership Directory and Buyers Guide of the American Association of Meat Processors* (Irregular); *AAMPlifier* (Semimonthly); *Capitol Line-Up* (Semimonthly). **Educational Activities:** American Convention of Meat Processors and Suppliers' Tradeshow (Annual). **Awards:** AAMP Achievement Award (Annual); Cured Meats Hall of Fame (Annual); AAMP Accomplishment Award (Annual); F. W. Witt Supplier of the Year Award (Annual); Clarence Knebel Best of Show Memorial Award (Annual); AAMP Golden Cleaver Trophy (Annual); Best Booth Awards (Annual); AAMP Outstanding Service Award (Annual); American Cured Meat Championship Awards (Annual); AAMP Package Wrapping Award (Annual); Stephen Krut Scholarship Award (Annual). **Geographic Preference:** National; Local.

2426 ■ **Canadian Meat Council (CMC) [Conseil des Viandes du Canada (CVC)]**
220 Laurier Ave. W, Ste. 930
Ottawa, ON, Canada K1P 5Z9
Ph: (613)729-3911
Fax: (613)729-4997
Co. E-mail: info@cmc-cvc.com
URL: http://cmc-cvc.com
Contact: Chris White, President
E-mail: chris@cmc-cvc.com
Facebook: www.facebook.com/cmccvc
Linkedin: www.linkedin.com/company/canadian-mea
 t-council
X (Twitter): x.com/cmccvc
Description: Meat packers and distributors. Promotes the development of the meat industries. Sponsors promotional campaigns. **Founded:** 1919. **Publications:** *Food Service Meat Manual*. **Geographic Preference:** National.

2427 ■ **National Cattlemen's Beef Association (NCBA) - Library**
9110 E Nichols Ave., Ste. 300
Centennial, CO 80112
Ph: (303)694-0305
Fax: (303)694-2851
URL: http://www.ncba.org
Contact: Todd Wilkinson, President
Facebook: www.facebook.com/BeefUSA
X (Twitter): x.com/BeefUSA
YouTube: www.youtube.com/user/Cattlementoca
 ttlemen
Description: Represents 149 organizations of livestock marketers, growers, meat packers, food retailers, and food service firms. Conducts extensive program of promotion, education and information about beef, veal, and associated meat products. Conducts projects such as recipe testing and development, food demonstrations, food photography, educational service to colleges, experimental meat cutting methods, merchandising programs, and preparation of materials for newspapers, magazines, radio, and television. **Scope:** Cattle farmers. **Founded:** 1898. **Holdings:** Figures not available. **Publications:** *National Cattlemen Magazine* (Monthly). **Educational Activities:** Cattle Industry Convention & NCBA Trade Show (Annual). **Geographic Preference:** National.

2428 ■ **North American Meat Institute (NAMI)**
1150 Connecticut Ave. NW, 12th Fl.
Washington, DC 20036
Ph: (202)587-4200
Fax: (202)587-4300
Co. E-mail: info@meatinstitute.org
URL: http://www.meatinstitute.org
Contact: Julie Anna Potts, President
Facebook: www.facebook.com/NorthAmericanMea
 tInstitute
Linkedin: www.linkedin.com/company/american-mea
 t-institute
X (Twitter): x.com/MeatInstitute
YouTube: www.youtube.com/user/meatnewsnetwork
Pinterest: www.pinterest.com/NorthAmericanMeatIns
 titute
Description: Represents the interests of packers and processors of beef, pork, lamb, veal, and turkey products and their suppliers throughout North America. Provides legislative, regulatory, and public relations services. Conducts scientific research. Offers marketing and technical assistance. Sponsors educational programs. **Founded:** 1919. **Publications:** *North American Meat Association-- Membership Directory*. **Educational Activities:** The NGA Show; International Production & Processing Expo (IPPE) (Annual); AMI - International Meat Industry Convention and Exposition; Worldwide Food Expo; Animal Care and Handling Conference (Annual). **Awards:** Edward C. Jones Community Service Award (Annual); NAMI Industry Advancement Award (Annual); NAMI Supplier of the Year Award (Annual). **Geographic Preference:** National.

REFERENCE WORKS

2429 ■ *"Small Butcher Shops Are in 'A Renaissance.' How Did They Survive the Supermarket Offensive?'* in *Miami Herald (July 2, 2018).*
URL(s): www.miamiherald.com/news/business/article
 213600564.html
Ed: Dylan Jackson. **Released:** July 02, 2018. **Description:** Explores the rising popularity of specialty butcher shops due to more people wanting to know where their meat comes from and how and where it's raised. Personalized service is also responsible for their come-back and several owners are interviewed to explain how they created a niche in this market. **Availability:** Print; Online.

2430 ■ *"Uptown Goes Local To Fill Final Entertainment District Vacancy"* in *Birmingham Business Journal (Vol. 31, May 9, 2014, No. 19, pp. 8)*
Pub: American City Business Journals, Inc.
Contact: Mike Olivieri, Executive Vice President
Released: Weekly. **Price:** $4, introductory 4-week offer(Digital & Print). **Description:** A new butcher, beer and wine shop called Bottle & Bone will become the final tenant for the new Uptown entertainment district in Birmingham, Alabama, slated to open by fall 2014. The shop is owned by Freshfully founder Jen Barnett and will focus on local offerings, particularly fresh meats, wine and beer. **Availability:** Print; Online.

2431 ■ *"USDA Invests $270 Million to Assist Meat, Poultry Producers"* in *Meat+Poultry (November 24, 2021)*
Ed: Erica Shaffer. **Released:** November 24, 2021. **Description:** Due to the COVID-19 pandemic, some contract producers of livestock and poultry experienced some revenue declines and the Consolidated Appropriations Act is giving some relief in the form of direct checks.

2432 ■ *"The Vegetarians Who Turned Into Butchers"* in *The New York Times (August 6, 2019)*
URL(s): www.nytimes.com/2019/08/06/dining/bu
 tchers-meat-vegetarian-vegan.html

Ed: Melissa Clark. **Released:** August 06, 2019. **Description:** Former vegetarians and vegans who became butchers with the goal of becoming ethical butchers. Animal well-being, environmental conservation, and minimal waste are their primary concerns in an industry that has become full of waste and known for it's overuse of antibiotics. **Availability:** Print; Online.

STATISTICAL SOURCES

2433 ■ *Meat Markets Industry in the US - Market Research Report*
URL(s): www.ibisworld.com/united-states/market-research-reports/meat-markets-industry/
Price: $925. **Description:** Downloadable report analyzing the current and future trends in the meat market industry. **Availability:** Online.

TRADE PERIODICALS

2434 ■ *Iowa Grocer*
Pub: Iowa Grocery Industry Association
Contact: Michelle Hurd, President
E-mail: mhurd@iowagrocers.com
URL(s): www.iowagrocers.com/iowa-grocer-magazine.html
Released: Quarterly **Description:** Magazine for grocery industry - retail and supply. **Availability:** Online.

2435 ■ *Lean Trimmings*
URL(s): meatinstitute.org
Released: Weekly **Price:** Included in membership. **Description:** Deals with the latest regulatory and business news on the meat industry. Recurring features include news of research, a calendar of events, reports of meetings, job listings, and sections on members, labor relations, and marketing trends. Remarks: Also available via e-mail. **Availability:** Print.

2436 ■ *Meat + Poultry: The Business Journal of the Meat & Poultry Industry*
Pub: Sosland Publishing Co.
Contact: Joshua Sosland, President
URL(s): www.meatpoultry.com
Facebook: www.facebook.com/MeatPoultry
Linkedin: www.linkedin.com/company/meat-poultry
X (Twitter): x.com/meatpoultry
Instagram: www.instagram.com/meatpoultry
Released: Monthly **Price:** $85, for print outside the united states and Canada. **Description:** Magazine serving the meat and poultry processing, distributing, and wholesaling industries in the U.S. and Canada. **Availability:** Print; Online.

TRADE SHOWS AND CONVENTIONS

2437 ■ *American Convention of Meat Processors and Suppliers' Tradeshow*
American Association of Meat Processors (AAMP)
1 Meating Pl.
Elizabethtown, PA 17022
Ph: (717)367-1168
URL: http://www.aamp.com
Contact: Darla Kiesel, President
URL(s): www.aamp.com/ev_calendar_day.asp?date=8/1/2024&eventid=9
Price: $545, Members; $845, Non-members. **Frequency:** Annual. **Description:** Poultry and food business. **Audience:** Meat, poultry and seafood processors, wholesalers, retailers, catering and deli operators/owners and public. **Principal Exhibits:** Poultry and food business. Dates and Locations: 2025 Jul 24-26 Kansas City, MO; 2026 Jul 09-11 Milwaukee, WI. **Telecommunication Services:** niki@aamp.com.

FRANCHISES AND BUSINESS OPPORTUNITIES

2438 ■ *Logan Farms Honey Glazed Hams*
10950 Westheimer Rd.
Houston, TX 77042
URL: http://www.loganfarms.com
Description: Gourmet meat stores, specializing in the sale of honey-glazed, spiral-sliced hams. Also sells gourmet rib eye roast, pork loins, chicken breast, smoked turkeys, spiral-sliced boneless hams, spiral-sliced honey-glazed turkey breast, smoked sausage, bacon, cheesecakes and a variety of honey mustard and preserves. **Founded:** 1984. **Franchise Fee:** $30,000. **Royalty Fee:** 4% of the gross sales. **Training:** 2 weeks on procedures and techniques in manufacturing and marketing the products, manuals for advertising and market programs, record-keeping and inventory control.

2439 ■ *M & M Meat Shops Ltd.*
100-2240 Argentia Rd.
Mississauga, ON, Canada L5N 2K7
Free: 800-461-0171
URL: http://www.mmfoodmarket.com
Description: Retailer of frozen foods, desserts, party foods and much more. **Founded:** 1980. **Equity Capital Needed:** Approximately $400,000-$450,000. **Royalty Fee:** 3%. **Training:** Provides 2 weeks at headquarters, 2 days at franchisees location with ongoing support.

LIBRARIES

2440 ■ *National Cattlemen's Beef Association (NCBA) - Library*
9110 E Nichols Ave., Ste. 300
Centennial, CO 80112
Ph: (303)694-0305
Fax: (303)694-2851
URL: http://www.ncba.org
Contact: Todd Wilkinson, President
Facebook: www.facebook.com/BeefUSA
X (Twitter): x.com/BeefUSA
YouTube: www.youtube.com/user/Cattlementocattlemen
Description: Represents 149 organizations of livestock marketers, growers, meat packers, food retailers, and food service firms. Conducts extensive program of promotion, education and information about beef, veal, and associated meat products. Conducts projects such as recipe testing and development, food demonstrations, food photography, educational service to colleges, experimental meat cutting methods, merchandising programs, and preparation of materials for newspapers, magazines, radio, and television. **Scope:** Cattle farmers. **Founded:** 1898. **Holdings:** Figures not available. **Publications:** *National Cattlemen Magazine* (Monthly). **Educational Activities:** Cattle Industry Convention & NCBA Trade Show (Annual). **Geographic Preference:** National.

Cable Network

START-UP INFORMATION

2441 ■ *"Former WCVB Anchor Bianca De la Garza Discusses the Launch of Her New Media Venture" in Boston Business Journal (Vol. 34, June 6, 2014, No. 18, pp. 4)*
Pub: American City Business Journals, Inc.
Contact: Mike Olivieri, Executive Vice President
Released: June 02, 2014. **Description:** News anchor, Bianca de la Garza says career advancement prompted her to form Lucky Gal Productions LLC. She said her entrepreneurial pursuit will develop a television show focusing on lifestyle and entertainment. De la Garza admits she will miss her co-anchor job at WCVB-TV's morning show, 'EyeOpener'. **Availability:** Print; Online.

ASSOCIATIONS AND OTHER ORGANIZATIONS

2442 ■ **CTAM: Cable and Telecommunications Association for Marketing (CTAM)**
120 Waterfront St., Ste. 200
 National Harbor, MD 20745
Ph: (301)485-8900
Fax: (304)485-8898
Co. E-mail: info@ctam.com
URL: http://www.ctam.com
Contact: Vicki Lins, President
Linkedin: www.linkedin.com/company/ctam
X (Twitter): x.com/ctam
Description: Network of cable and telecommunications professionals dedicated to the pursuit of marketing excellence. Provides its members with competitive marketing resources including education, research, networking and leadership opportunities. **Founded:** 1982. **Publications:** *CTAM Quarterly Journal* (Quarterly). **Awards:** CTAM TAMI Awards (Irregular). **Geographic Preference:** National.

2443 ■ **Jones NCTI**
6855 S Havana St., Ste. 300
 Centennial, CO 80112
Free: 866-575-7206
Co. E-mail: customercare@ncti.com
URL: http://ncti.com
Contact: Stacey Slaughter, Chief Executive Officer
Facebook: www.facebook.com/NCTITraining
Linkedin: www.linkedin.com/company/jonesncti/
 mycompany
X (Twitter): x.com/NCTItraining
YouTube: www.youtube.com/channel/UCIDTzvLtv7
 5BxeqZBGke9iw
Description: Firm provides learning solutions to nurture committed employees, supporting their education and career goals. **Founded:** 1968. **Geographic Preference:** National.

2444 ■ **National Cable and Telecommunications Association (NCTA)**
25 Massachusetts Ave. NW, Ste. 100
 Washington, DC 20001
Ph: (202)222-2300
Co. E-mail: info@ncta.com
URL: http://www.ncta.com
Contact: Michael Powell, President
Facebook: www.facebook.com/NCTAitv
Linkedin: www.linkedin.com/company/ncta
X (Twitter): x.com/NCTAitv
Description: A trade association of the cable industry in the United States whose mission is to provide its members with a strong national presence by providing a single, unified voice on issues affecting the cable and telecommunications industry. Publishes cable television-related directories. **Founded:** 1952. **Publications:** *Cable Industry Overview* (Semiannual). **Awards:** NCTA Distinguished Vanguard Awards for Leadership (Annual); NCTA Vanguard Award for Cable Operations Management (Annual). **Geographic Preference:** National.

2445 ■ **Society of Cable Telecommunications Engineers (SCTE)**
140 Philips Rd.
 Exton, PA 19341
Ph: (610)363-6888
Free: 800-542-5040
Fax: (610)884-7237
Co. E-mail: info@scte.org
URL: http://www.scte.org
Contact: Guy McCormick, Vice Chairman of the Board
Facebook: www.facebook.com/TheSCTE
X (Twitter): x.com/SCTE
YouTube: www.youtube.com/user/sctevideo
Description: Persons engaged in engineering, construction, installation, technical direction, management, or administration of cable telecommunications and broadband communications technologies. **Publications:** *Cable Telecommunications Engineering* (Quarterly); *Society of Cable Telecommunications Engineers--Membership Directory*; *Communications Technology* (Monthly); *Interval* (Quarterly). **Educational Activities:** SCTE® Cable-Tec Expo® (Annual); Mid-America Cable Telecommunications Association Meeting & Show (Annual); Society of Cable Telecommunication Engineers Lecture. **Awards:** SCTE Member of the Year (Annual); SCTE Chairman's Award (Annual).

2446 ■ **Women in Cable Telecommunications (WICT)**
2000 K St. NW, Ste. 350
 Washington, DC 20006
Ph: (202)827-4794
Fax: (202)450-5596
Co. E-mail: membership@wict.org
URL: http://www.wict.org
Contact: Maria E. Brennan, President
Facebook: www.facebook.com/WICTHQ
X (Twitter): x.com/wicthq
Instagram: www.instagram.com/wicthq
Description: Empowers women to achieve their professional goals by providing opportunities for leadership, networking and advocacy. **Founded:** 1979. **Publications:** *The Catalyst* (Monthly); *WICT Wire* (Monthly). **Educational Activities:** The WICT Network Leadership Conference (Annual). **Awards:** Woman of the Year (Annual); PAR Forerunner Accolades Best Companies for Women in Cable (Annual); WICT Woman to Watch Award (Annual); Woman of the Year Award (Annual). **Geographic Preference:** National.

REFERENCE WORKS

2447 ■ *"Branded Entertainment: Dealmaking Strategies & Techniques for Industry Professionals"*
Pub: J. Ross Publishing Inc.
Contact: Stephen Buda, President
Released: October 01, 2014. **Price:** $39.95, hardcover, plus shipping charge extra. FL sale tax $3.36. **Description:** Branded entertainment, also known as branded content or advertisment, is an entertainment-based method that is funded by and complementary to a brand's marketing strategy. These projects are usually a partnership between brands, television or radio producers, and broadcasters. **Availability:** E-book; Print; Download.

2448 ■ *"Cable TV News Viewership Slows in July, Fox News Keeps Lead" in MediaPost (August 1, 2019)*
URL(s): www.mediapost.com/publications/article/
 338827/cable-tv-news-viewership-slows-in-july-fox
 -news-k.html
Ed: Wayne Friedman. **Released:** August 01, 2019. **Description:** Cable TV news networks continued to experience a decline in viewership in July, with Fox News still in the lead over other networks. **Availability:** Online.

2449 ■ *"Cincinnati Reds Hit Ratings Homer" in Business Courier (Vol. 27, July 30, 2010, No. 13, pp. 1)*
Pub: Business Courier
Ed: Steve Watkins, John Ourand. **Description:** Cincinnati Reds fans have tuned in to their TVs and radios as their team made a hottest start to a season. The Reds TV ratings have increased 49 percent during the first six months of 2010 and continued to rise while the Reds' games broadcast on WLW-AM reported the highest average audience share per game of any Major League Baseball team. **Availability:** Print; Online.

2450 ■ *"Comcast Corp. Enters Home Security Business" in Record (May 27, 2012)*
Ed: Reed Fujii. **Description:** Comcast and Verizon are offering home security products to consumers. AT&T will launch their home security products soon. Details of the home security systems offered are provided. **Availability:** Online.

2451 ■ *"Comcast Launches New Home Security Service, Developed in Portland" in The Oregonian (June 7, 2011)*
Pub: McClatchy-Tribune Regional News

Ed: Mike Rogoway. **Description:** Comcast introduced its new high-end home security system that provides 24-hour monitoring and control of homes and utilities, along with Web and mobile access. **Availability:** Print; Online.

2452 ▪ *"Davis Family Expands Cable Empire"* in St. Louis Business Journal (Vol. 32, June 15, 2012, No. 43, pp. 1)
Pub: Baltimore Business Journal
Contact: Rhonda Pringle, President
E-mail: rpringle@bizjournals.com

Description: Missouri-based Fidelity Communications has become a standout in the $98 billion cable industry through low-profile management of the Davis family, with the help of John Colbert. Fidelity has made five acquisitions since 1992 and has grown its subscriber base to more than 115,000 customers or revenue generating units. **Availability:** Print; Online.

2453 ▪ *"Defend Your Research: Commercials Make Us Like TV More"* in Harvard Business Review (Vol. 88, October 2010, No. 10, pp. 36)
Pub: Harvard Business Publishing
Contact: Diane Belcher, Managing Director

Ed: Leif Nelson. **Price:** $6, PDF. **Description:** Research indicates that people prefer commercial interruption over uninterrupted shows due to the break creating a reactivation of the initial pleasure when beginning a desirable activity. **Availability:** Online; PDF.

2454 ▪ *"Dish's Charlie Ergen Sees Nothing Good in Comcast-Time Warner Merger"* in Denver Business Journal (Vol. 65, February 21, 2014, No. 41)
Pub: American City Business Journals, Inc.
Contact: Mike Olivieri, Executive Vice President

Released: Weekly. **Description:** The co-founder and CEO of Dish Network, Charlie Ergen, is against the proposed $45.2 billion merger of Comcast and Time Warner. Ergen feels that his satellite TV company and others in the broadband and TV industries will be put in an unfair situation if the two companies are allowed to combine. **Availability:** Print; Online.

2455 ▪ *"Don't' Hate the Cable Guy"* in Saint Louis Business Journal (Vol. 31, August 5, 2011, No. 50, pp. 1)
Pub: Saint Louis Business Journal
Contact: Robert Bobroff, President
E-mail: rbobroff@bizjournals.com

Ed: Angela Mueller. **Description:** Charter Communications named John Birrer as senior vice president of customer experience. The company experienced problems with its customer services. **Availability:** Print; Online.

2456 ▪ *"For Apple, It's Showtime Again"* in Barron's (Vol. 90, August 30, 2010, No. 35, pp. 29)
Pub: Barron's Editorial & Corporate Headquarters

Ed: Eric J. Savitz. **Description:** Speculations on what Apple Inc. will unveil at its product launch event are presented. These products include a possible new iPhone Nano, a new update to its Apple TV, and possibly a deal with the Beatles to distribute their songs over iTunes. **Availability:** Online.

2457 ▪ *"Game Changing"* in Business Strategy Review (Vol. 23, Spring 2012, No. 1, pp. 26)

Released: Spring 2012. **Description:** Barney Francis is Managing Director of Sky Sports. In a television career spanning 18 years, he has worked in the multichannel terrestrial and independent sectors. At Sky, he was executive producer for cricket, leading his team through two ICC World Cups, two Ashes Tours, England tours to nine nations, and the first Twenty20 Cup. In 2007, he became executive producer for Sky's Premier league football and in 2008 executive producer for the UEFA Champions League.

2458 ▪ *"KXAN Seeks Larger Studio, Office Space in Austin"* in Austin Business Journal (Vol. 31, May 27, 2011, No. 12, pp. A1)
Pub: Austin Business Journal
Contact: Rachel McGrath, Director
E-mail: rmcgrath@bizjournals.com

Ed: Cody Lyon. **Description:** Austin NBC affiliate KXAN Television is opting to sell its property north of downtown and relocate to another site. The station is now inspecting possible sites to house its broadcasting facility and employees totaling as many as 200 people. Estimated cost of the construction of the studios and offices is $13 million plus another million in moving the equipment. **Availability:** Print; Online.

2459 ▪ *"Liberty Media Pushes to Close on Sirius XM While Cable Deals Wait"* in Denver Business Journal (Vol. 65, February 28, 2014, No. 42)
Pub: American City Business Journals, Inc.
Contact: Mike Olivieri, Executive Vice President

Released: Weekly. **Description:** Liberty Media Corporation CEO, Greg Maffei, notes that various cable TV mergers are on hold while everyone awaits the decision if Comcast and Time Warner will be allowed to go through with their $45.2 billion merger. Liberty Media had supported Charter Communications plans to buy Time Warner for cash and stock. That deal was pushed aside when Comcast came along with a larger, all-stock offer. **Availability:** Print; Online.

2460 ▪ *"Local Film Industry Stands To Lose Jobs, Millions of Dollars Unless Florida Expands"* in Orlando Business Journal (Vol. 30, March 14, 2014, No. 38, pp. 4)
Pub: American City Business Journals, Inc.
Contact: Mike Olivieri, Executive Vice President

Released: Weekly. **Price:** $8, introductory 4-week offer(Digital & Print). **Description:** Central Florida's motion picture and TV production industries are in need of more government incentives. Many TV programs have been cancelled due to lack of this funding. Meanwhile, members of the sectors are set to lobby legislature to pass a $1.2 billion incentive package. **Availability:** Print; Online.

2461 ▪ *"Local TV Hits Media Radar Screen"* in Business Courier (Vol. 27, July 2, 2010, No. 9, pp. 1)
Pub: Business Courier

Ed: Dan Monk. **Description:** Fort Wright, Kentucky-based broadcasting company Local TV LLC has acquired 18 television stations since its founding in 2007, potentially boosting its chances of becoming a media empire. In the last twelve months that ended in March 2010, Local TV LLC has posted total revenues of $415 million. How Local TV LLC has entered into cost-sharing deals with other stations is also discussed. **Availability:** Print; Online.

2462 ▪ *"Loonies Buy U.S. Cable"* in Canadian Business (Vol. 85, September 17, 2012, No. 14, pp. 8)

Ed: Jeff Beer. **Description:** The move by two Canadian companies to invest in the U.S. cable industry get mixed reactions from analyst and observers. Cogeco Cable purchased Atlantic Broadband for $1.36 billion while the Canada Pension Plan Investment Board announced its partnership with European private equity firm BC Partners to acquire Suddenlink Communications for $6.6 billion. **Availability:** Online.

2463 ▪ *"Md.'s Film Industry Professionals have to Leave the State to Find Work: Exiting Stage Left"* in Baltimore Business Journal (Vol. 28, June 18, 2010, No. 6, pp. 1)
Pub: Baltimore Business Journal
Contact: Rhonda Pringle, President
E-mail: rpringle@bizjournals.com

Ed: Scott Dance. **Released:** Weekly. **Description:** Film professionals including crew members and actors have been leaving Maryland to find work in other states such as Michigan, Louisiana, and Georgia where bigger budgets and film production incentives are given. Other consequences of this trend in local TV and film production are discussed. **Availability:** Print.

2464 ▪ *Media, Organizations and Identity*
Pub: Palgrave Macmillan

Released: First edition. **Description:** The mass media, press, and television are essential in the formation of corporate identity and the promotion of business image and reputation. This book offers a new perspective into the interrelationships between media and organizations over three dimensions: media as business, media in business and business in the media.

2465 ▪ *"Merger Expected to Bring New Player to TV Market"* in Providence Business News (Vol. 28, March 31, 2014, No. 52, pp. 1)
Pub: American City Business Journals, Inc.
Contact: Mike Olivieri, Executive Vice President
URL(s): pbn.com/merger-expected-to-bring-new-player-to-tv-market96073

Description: The proposed merger of Media General and Providence, Rhode Island-based LIN Media LLC has the potential to change the TV landscape in the state. The two media companies' TV stations overlap in five markets and ownership at one of the stations is expected to change due to federal regulations regarding TV station ownership. The two TV stations are outlined.

2466 ▪ *"No. 82: a Few Good Apps"* in Inc. (Vol. 36, September 2014, No. 7, pp. 103)
Pub: Mansueto Ventures L.L.C.
Contact: Stephanie Mehta, Chief Executive Officer

Description: Alan S. Knitowski, former U.S. Army Captain, and his Austin, Texas-based mobile-focused development company is profiled. Phunware, creates apps for clients like ESPN, Cisco, Noscar, WWE, and NBC Sports. The firm won awards for its MythBusters app. **Availability:** Online.

2467 ▪ *"On Comcast, Sarge, Wheels and the Big Price"* in Philadelphia Business Journal (Vol. 32, February 7, 2014, No. 52, pp. 4)
Pub: American City Business Journals, Inc.
Contact: Mike Olivieri, Executive Vice President

Released: Weekly. **Price:** $4, introductory 4-week offer(Digital & Print). **Description:** In an interview with David Montgomery, president and CEO of the Philadelphia Phillies team, he shares his views on the upcoming baseball season, the tremendous fan support the team is receiving, and the marketability of the team, with a special focus on their association with Comcast SportsNet as a broadcast producer. He also disclosed the league's plans for spending the new incoming TV money and said they will try to deliver the best product using the available resources. **Availability:** Print; Online.

2468 ▪ *"Ready, Aim, (Cool) Fire"* in Saint Louis Business Journal (Vol. 32, September 2, 2011, No. 1, pp. 1)
Pub: Saint Louis Business Journal
Contact: Robert Bobroff, President
E-mail: rbobroff@bizjournals.com

Ed: E.B. Solomont. **Description:** Coolfire Originals' CEO Jeff Keane is co-producing 'Welcome Sweetie Pie's' with Los Angeles, California-based Pilgrims Films and Television Films for the Oprah Winfrey Network. The reality show focuses on restaurant owner Robbie Montgomery of Sweetie Pie's in St. Louis, Missouri. **Availability:** Print; Online.

2469 ▪ *"Recovery on Tap for 2010?"* in Orlando Business Journal (Vol. 26, January 1, 2010, No. 31, pp. 1)
Pub: Orlando Business Journal
Contact: Julie Swyers, Director
E-mail: jswyers@bizjournals.com

Ed: Melanie Stawicki Azam, Richard Bilbao, Christopher Boyd, Anjali Fluker. **Description:** Economic forecasts for Central Florida's leading business sectors in 2010 are presented. These sectors include housing, film and TV, sports business, law, restaurants, aviation, tourism and hospitality, banking and finance, commercial real estate, retail, health care, insurance, higher education, and manufacturing. According to some local executives, Central Florida's economy will slowly recover in 2010. **Availability:** Online.

2470 ■ *"What We Know - And What We Don't - About Apple TV' in Barron's (Vol. 92, August 25, 2012, No. 38, pp. 27)*
Pub: Dow Jones & Company Inc.
Contact: Almar Latour, Chief Executive Officer
Ed: Alexander Eule. **Description:** Apple Inc.'s entry into the television market is not likely to involve an introduction of disruptive technologies. Cable companies are the most likely partners of Apple as it seeks to enter the televisiion broadcasting market. **Availability:** Online.

SOURCES OF SUPPLY

2471 ■ *FINDERBINDER--Oklahoma (Media)*
FINDERBINDER of Oklahoma
URL(s): www.finderbinderok.com
Released: Annual **Price:** $175, online; $200, print; plus $10 for shipping and handling fee. **Description:** 'FINDERBINDER' directories are loose-leaf directories of broadcast and print media covering states or smaller areas published by companies, usually advertising and public relations firms, licensed to use the name and format by Finderbinder (see entry for 'FINDERBINDER--San Diego'). Types of media covered include daily and weekly local and outstate newspapers; religious, ethnic, and labor papers; business, trade, sports, recreation, and general interest publications; college papers; and radio and television stations in Oklahoma. **Entries include:** Publication or station name, names of management, editorial, and advertising personnel, deadlines, frequency or circulation as appropriate, and other data; cable TV listings show homes served. **Arrangement:** Classified by type of medium. **Indexes:** Publication or station name. **Availability:** Print; Online.

TRADE PERIODICALS

2472 ■ *TelevisionWeek*
Pub: Crain Communications Inc.
Contact: Barry Asin, President
URL(s): www.tvweek.com
Released: Daily **Description:** Newspaper covering management, programming, cable and trends in the television and the media industry. **Availability:** Print.

TRADE SHOWS AND CONVENTIONS

2473 ■ **MFM Annual conference**
Media Financial Management Association (MFM)
2365 Harrodsburg Rd., Ste. A325
Lexington, KY 40504
Ph: (847)716-7000
Fax: (847)784-8059
Co. E-mail: info@mediafinance.org
URL: http://www.mediafinance.org
Contact: Joseph J. Annotti, President
E-mail: joe.annotti@mediafinance.org
URL(s): www.mediafinance.org/annual-conference
Frequency: Annual. **Description:** Exhibits relating to the financial management of radio, television, and cable television operations, including issues such as industry - specific software, collection agencies, insurance, investments, banking, accounting firms and music licensing. **Audience:** Financial professionals for media industry. **Principal Exhibits:** Exhibits relating to the financial management of radio, television, and cable television operations, including issues such as industry - specific software, collection agencies, insurance, investments, banking, accounting firms and music licensing. Dates and Locations: 2025 May 18-21 Crystal Gateway Marriott, Arlington, VA. **Telecommunication Services:** info@mediafinance.org.

LIBRARIES

2474 ■ **Alliance for Community Media (ACM) - Library**
4248 Pk. Glen Rd.
Minneapolis, MN 55416
Ph: (952)928-4643
Co. E-mail: info@allcommunitymedia.org
URL: http://www.allcommunitymedia.org
Contact: Mike Wassenaar, President
Facebook: www.facebook.com/AllianceforCommunityMedia
X (Twitter): x.com/alliancecm
YouTube: www.youtube.com/user/ACMNational
Description: Individual access producers, community producers, public access organizations, public access professionals, cable television firms, cable regulators, and other interested organizations and individuals. **Scope:** Cable television - community access, local origination, legislation, industry, franchising; public television; educational television; governmental access television. **Services:** Library not open to the public. **Founded:** 1976. **Holdings:** 6 books; 1 bound periodical volume. **Publications:** *Community Media Review* (Quarterly). **Awards:** Hometown Media Awards (Annual); Buske Leadership Award (Annual); Dirk Koning-George Stoney Humanistic Communication Award (Annual); Jewell Ryan-White Award for Cultural Diversity (Annual). **Geographic Preference:** National.

2475 ■ **American Film Institute (AFI) - Louis B. Mayer Library**
2021 N W Ave.
Los Angeles, CA 90027-1657
Ph: (323)856-7600
Fax: (323)467-4578
Co. E-mail: information@afi.com
URL: http://www.afi.com
Contact: Bob Gazzale, President
X (Twitter): x.com/americanfilm
YouTube: www.youtube.com/AFI
Description: Preserves the nation's artistic and cultural resources in film and video. Catalogs and preserves America's film heritage. Acts as a bridge between learning a craft and practicing a profession, through an intensive two-year course in filmmaking and film theory. Promotes the study of film as an art form with its own aesthetics, history, and techniques, through seminars for film teachers and special materials. Brings outstanding classic and contemporary films to public attention at a national film theater through The American Film Institute Theatre in the Kennedy Center in Washington, DC. **Scope:** Filmmaking; movie history; theory and criticism. **Services:** Open to the public by appointment; Scanning; Printing. **Founded:** 1967. **Holdings:** Books; DVDs; films; documentary; photography; scripts. **Publications:** *Catalog of Feature Films*; *Catalog of Motion Pictures Produced in the United States*; *National Moving Image Database (NAMID)*. **Awards:** AFI Movies of the Year (Annual); AFI TV Programs of the Year (Annual); AFI Life Achievement Award (Annual). **Geographic Preference:** National.

Calligraphy Service

ASSOCIATIONS AND OTHER ORGANIZATIONS

2476 ■ International Association of Master Penmen, Engrossers, and Teachers of Handwriting (IAMPETH)
1213 W Morehead St., Ste. 500
Charlotte, NC 28208
Free: 866-457-2582
Co. E-mail: privacy@clubexpress.com
URL: http://www.iampeth.com
Contact: Christen Turney, President
Facebook: www.facebook.com/iampethofficial
Instagram: www.instagram.com/iampethofficial

Description: Promotes the preservation of the arts of calligraphy, engrossing, and fine penmanship. Encourages the restoration of teaching penmanship in schools. **Founded:** 1949. **Geographic Preference:** Multinational.

2477 ■ Michigan Association of Calligraphers (MAC)
PO Box 2229
Birmingham, MI 48012-2229
Co. E-mail: hello@michigancalligraphy.org
URL: http://www.michigancalligraphy.org/contact
Contact: Leah Sachs, President

Description: Promotes the study, teaching and practice of calligraphy and related disciplines. Fosters exchange of information and ideas about calligraphy. **Founded:** 1978. **Geographic Preference:** State.

2478 ■ Society of Scribes (SOS)
PO Box 933
New York, NY 10150
Ph: (212)452-0139
Co. E-mail: info@societyofscribes.org
URL: http://societyofscribes.org
Contact: Chi Nguyen, Co-President
Facebook: www.facebook.com/societyofscribes
X (Twitter): x.com/scribesnyc
Instagram: www.instagram.com/societyofscribes

Description: Calligraphers, bookbinders, lettering artists, and individuals with an interest in book arts. Promotes calligraphy and related lettering arts. Collects and disseminates information. Conducts exhibitions, workshops, lecturers, programs, and publications. **Founded:** 1974. **Publications:** *Letters from New York* (Annual); *SoS* (Semiannual); *Classes and Workshops*. **Educational Activities:** Society of Scribes Holiday Fair (Annual); Holiday Fair (Annual). **Geographic Preference:** National.

2479 ■ Washington Calligraphers Guild (WCG) - Library
PO Box 3688
Merrifield, VA 22116
Co. E-mail: wash.calligraphers@gmail.com
URL: http://www.calligraphersguild.org
Contact: Marilyn Davis, President
E-mail: president@calligraphersguild.org
Facebook: www.facebook.com/Washington-Calligraphers-Guild-233445036701381
Instagram: www.instagram.com/wcguild

Description: Calligraphers and individuals interested in calligraphy. Promotes the appreciation of calligraphy and its applications and history. Seeks to foster a greater understanding of calligraphy as an art. Conducts studies on calligraphy; sponsors charitable and educational programs. **Scope:** Advertising; alphabets; american calligraphy; ampersands; asian calligraphy; bible passages; bibliography; biography; black letter, gothic; arts; brush lettering; business; children calligraphy; capital ventures; celtic arts and calligraphy; folk art; isl. **Services:** Open to the public by appointment. **Founded:** 1976. **Holdings:** 700 titles – books; slides; videos; CDs; DVDs; pamphlets; journals; manuscripts. **Publications:** *Scripsit* (Semiannual). **Educational Activities:** Art Exhibit (Irregular); Letterforum (Periodic). **Awards:** Hermann Zapf Education Fund (HZEF) (Annual). **Geographic Preference:** Multinational.

REFERENCE WORKS

2480 ■ "The Art of Calligraphy" in The Guardian (February 19, 2010)
URL(s): www.theguardian.com/money/2010/feb/20/disappearing-acts-calligraphy
Ed: Jon Henley. **Released:** February 19, 2010. **Description:** Profile of Paul Antonio, a calligrapher with private and business clients and a lecturer on the subject. **Availability:** Online.

2481 ■ *Society for Calligraphy--Membership Directory*
Pub: Society for Calligraphy
Contact: Eva-Lynn Diesenhaus, President
E-mail: president@societyforcalligraphy.org
URL(s): societyforcalligraphy.org/Contacts

Released: Annual **Description:** Covers about 1,200 members and societies interested in calligraphy, including calligraphers, illustrators, graphic artists, and curators; international coverage. **Entries include:** For individual members--Name, address, phone, title. For societies--Contact name, address, phone; committee members. **Arrangement:** Alphabetical. **Indexes:** Personal name. **Availability:** Print.

2482 ■ "Today's Calligraphers Are Inkstagram-Worthy" in YoungPost (April 5, 2017)
URL(s): yp.scmp.com/news/features/article/105955/today%E2%80%99s-calligraphers-are-inkstagram-worthy
Ed: Pauline Wong. **Released:** April 05, 2017. **Description:** Calligraphy has taken on a new life with the help of Instagram. Artists use the social media platform to receive feedback on their work and to keep track of what they were able to create over time. The younger generation has embraced this old tradition as people look to include personal touches in their everyday lives. **Availability:** Online.

TRADE PERIODICALS

2483 ■ *Colorado Calligraphers' Guild Newsletter*
Pub: Colorado Calligraphers' Guild
Contact: Margaret Stookesberry, Contact
URL(s): www.coloradocalligraphers.com/category/newsletter

Released: Latest Edition 2018. **Description:** Reports the business of the Guild. Supplies tips on techniques and materials used by calligraphers, and news of other calligraphic organizations. Recurring features include book reviews, workshop reprints, and listings of educational opportunities. **Availability:** Print; Download; PDF.

2484 ■ *Guild of Book Workers Newsletter*
Pub: Guild of Book Workers
Contact: Bexx Caswell, President
E-mail: president@guildofbookworkers.org
URL(s): guildofbookworkers.org/newsletter

Released: 6/year **Description:** Covers issues in book arts, binding, book conservation, calligraphy, and printing. Recurring features include letters to the editor, interviews, news of research, a calendar of events, reports of meetings, news of educational opportunities, job listings, book reviews, and notices of publications available. **Availability:** PDF; Online.

2485 ■ *Valley Calligraphy Guild Newsletter*
Pub: Valley Calligraphy Guild
Contact: Judith Bailey, Treasurer
E-mail: bailey8860@comcast.net
URL(s): valleycalligraphyguild.com/membership.html

Description: Dedicated to preserving the art of calligraphy. Contains tips and techniques on lettering, italic handwriting, design, color use, and such crafts as papermaking, bookmaking, and bookbinding. Offers articles on workshop reviews, supplies, projects, artists, and activities of the Guild. Recurring features include schedules of classes, meetings, workshops, shows, and news of the activities of other societies of interest. Remarks: Newsletter text is primarily handwritten in calligraphy. **Availability:** Print; Online; PDF.

LIBRARIES

2486 ■ Long Beach Public Library - Performing Arts Department
200 W Broadway
Long Beach, CA 90802
URL: http://www.longbeach.gov/library

Scope: Art history and techniques, music history and scores, dance, flower arranging, antiques, theater, moving pictures, sports. **Services:** Interlibrary loan; department open to the public with restrictions. **Founded:** 1926. **Holdings:** 34,103 books; 8,624 bound scores; 7,099 pieces of sheet music; 91,043 mounted pictures; 9,000 videocassettes; 10,000 phonograph records; 5,000 cassettes; 5,500 CDs.

2487 ■ Rochester Institute of Technology - Melbert B. Cary, Jr. Graphic Arts Collection
90 Lomb Memorial Dr.
Rochester, NY 14623
URL: http://archivesspace.rit.edu/repositories/2/resources/235

Scope: Graphic art. **Holdings:** 45,000 volumes.

2488 ■ Society for Calligraphy (SfC)
PO Box 64174
  Los Angeles, CA 90064-0174
URL: http://www.societyforcalligraphy.org
Contact: Eva-Lynn Diesenhaus, President
E-mail: president@societyforcalligraphy.org
Facebook: www.facebook.com/societyforcalligraphy
Instagram: www.instagram.com/societyforcalligraphy

Description: Promotes the study and practice of calligraphy; fosters exchange of information and ideas about calligraphy. **Founded:** 1974. **Publications:** *The Calligraph*; *Society for Calligraphy--Membership Directory* (Annual). **Educational Activities:** International Calligraphy Conference. **Geographic Preference:** National.

2489 ■ Yale University - Robert B. Haas Family Arts Library Special Collections
190 York St.
  New Haven, CT 06520
Ph: (203)432-2645
Co. E-mail: artds.library@yale.edu
URL: http://web.library.yale.edu/arts/special-collections
Facebook: www.facebook.com/YaleHaasArtsLib
X (Twitter): twitter.com/YaleHaasArtsLib
Instagram: www.instagram.com/YaleHaasArtsLib/

Description: The collection includes contemporary catalogue raisonnes, 18th- and 19th-century works on artists and architecture, a wide selection of fine press and artists' books, rare research stuff in support of these subject areas, and the Faber Birren collection on color. **Scope:** Art history; drama. **Services:** Collection open to the public. **Founded:** 1967. **Holdings:** 125,000 volumes; prints and broadsides; type specimens; archive of student printing, including masters' theses from School of Graphic Design and School of Photography at Yale; 1 million bookplates; Japanese prints; stage and costume designs.

Camera Shop

START-UP INFORMATION

2490 ■ *"Picture Perfect: Startup Ships Camera Products After Kickstarter Campaign" in Austin Business Journal (Vol. 34, June 6, 2014, No. 16, pp. A12)*
Pub: American City Business Journals, Inc.
Contact: Mike Olivieri, Executive Vice President
Released: Weekly. **Description:** The nearly three-year-old Austin camera technology startup Cinetics of Texas LLC has begun shipping its latest modular product the Axis360. The shipping began after a successful Kickstarter marketing campaign whereby Cinetics founder and CEO, Justin Jensen, raised more than $1.1 million. All products of Cinetics are built and tested in Austin, Texas. **Availability:** Print; Online.

ASSOCIATIONS AND OTHER ORGANIZATIONS

2491 ■ **The Imaging Alliance**
7600 Jericho Tpke., Ste. 301
Woodbury, NY 11797
Ph: (516)802-0895
Fax: (516)364-0140
Co. E-mail: info@theimagingalliance.com
URL: http://www.theimagingalliance.com
Contact: Jerry Grossman, Executive Director
Linkedin: www.linkedin.com/company/the-imaging-alliance
Instagram: www.instagram.com/theimagingalliance
Description: Represents manufacturers, wholesalers, distributors, and importers of photographic equipment. Holds lecture meetings presenting programs on topics facing the photographic industry. Helps to further the consumer's interest in photography through its website and a traveling information booth. **Founded:** 1939. **Publications:** *Photographic Manufacturers & Distributors Association--Membership Directory* (Annual). **Awards:** PMDA Person of the Year Award (Annual); Professional Photographer Award (Annual); Technical Achievement Award (Annual). **Geographic Preference:** National.

2492 ■ **Photographic Society of America (PSA)**
8241 S Walker Ave., Ste. 104
Oklahoma City, OK 73139
Ph: (405)843-1437
Free: 855-772-4636
URL: http://psa-photo.org
Contact: J. R. Schnelzer, President
E-mail: prespsa@psa-photo.org
X (Twitter): x.com/PSA_Photo
Instagram: www.instagram.com/photographicsocietyofamerica
Description: Camera clubs; amateur, advanced amateur photographers. Sponsors competitions. Conducts slide and print contests, provides instruction slide sets, slide analysis, print portfolios, and other technical services. **Founded:** 1919. **Publications:** *PSA Journal* (Monthly). **Geographic Preference:** National.

REFERENCE WORKS

2493 ■ *"Gadget of the Week: Easy as a Snap" in Barron's (Vol. 90, September 13, 2010, No. 37, pp. 35)*
Pub: Barron's Editorial & Corporate Headquarters
Ed: Jay Palmer. **Description:** SanMyPhotos.com offers a service whereby people can receive an empty box they can fill with photos then send back to the company to be stored digitally. The photos are returned to the customer with a disc containing the digital photographs. The service costs $150 for one box and $300 for three boxes. **Availability:** Online.

2494 ■ *"KEH is Opening a Brick-and-Mortar Location in Atlanta" in PetaPixel (November 4, 2021)*
Ed: David Crewe. **Released:** November 04, 2021. **Description:** The popular reseller of camera parts, KEH, is opening a store in the Atlanta area, while still maintaining its online presence. **Availability:** Online.

2495 ■ *"Looking for the Best Camera Stores in the World?" in Format (June 21, 2019)*
URL(s): www.format.com/magazine/resources/photography/camera-stores
Released: June 21, 2019. **Description:** Compilation of the best online and brick-and-mortar camera stores in the world. **Availability:** Online.

2496 ■ *"Olympus is Urged to Revise Board" in Wall Street Journal Eastern Edition (November 28, 2011, pp. B3)*
Pub: Dow Jones & Company Inc.
Contact: Almar Latour, Chief Executive Officer
Ed: Phred Dvorak. **Description:** Koji Miyata, once a director on the board of troubled Japanese photographic equipment company, is urging the company to reorganize its board, saying the present group should resign their board seats but keep their management positions. The company has come under scrutiny for its accounting practices and costly acquisitions. **Availability:** Online.

2497 ■ *"Play By Play: These Video Products Can Add New Life to a Stagnant Website" in Black Enterprise (Vol. 41, December 2010, No. 5)*
Pub: Earl G. Graves Ltd.
Contact: Earl Graves, Jr., President
Ed: Marcia Wade Talbert. **Description:** Web Visible, provider of online marketing products and services, cites video capability as the fastest-growing Website feature for small business advertisers. Profiles of various devices for adding video to a Website are included. **Availability:** Online.

STATISTICAL SOURCES

2498 ■ *Camera Stores Industry in the US - Market Research Report*
URL(s): www.ibisworld.com/united-states/market-research-reports/camera-stores-industry/
Price: $925. **Description:** Downloadable report analyzing the current and future trends of the camera store industry. **Availability:** Online.

2499 ■ *RMA Annual Statement Studies*
Pub: Risk Management Association
Contact: Nancy Foster, President
Released: Annual. **Description:** Contains composite balance sheets and income statements for more than 360 industries, including the accounting, auditing, and bookkeeping industries. Also contains five years of comparative historical data for discerning trends. Includes 16 commonly used ratios, computed for most of the size groupings for nearly every industry.

TRADE SHOWS AND CONVENTIONS

2500 ■ **Photo Marketing Association International Annual Convention and Trade Show (PMA)**
Professional School Photographers Association International (PSPA)
3000 Picture Pl.
Jackson, MI 49201
Ph: (517)788-8100
Free: 800-762-9287
Fax: (517)788-8371
URL: http://www.pmai.org
URL(s): www.pmai.org
Description: Profile of exhibitors: film, cameras and photo accessory manufacturers and distributors, photo processing equipment and materials suppliers, digital imaging hardware and software marketers, studio imaging equipment distributors, and original equipment manufacturers (OEMs). **Audience:** Photography and digital imaging professionals. **Principal Exhibits:** Profile of exhibitors: film, cameras and photo accessory manufacturers and distributors, photo processing equipment and materials suppliers, digital imaging hardware and software marketers, studio imaging equipment distributors, and original equipment manufacturers (OEMs). **Telecommunication Services:** pmaces@pmai.org.

Campground Management

ASSOCIATIONS AND OTHER ORGANIZATIONS

2501 ■ American Camp Association (ACA)
5000 State Rd. 67 N
 Martinsville, IN 46151-7902
Ph: (765)342-8456
Free: 800-428-2267
Fax: (765)342-2065
URL: http://www.acacamps.org
Contact: Tom Rosenberg, President
E-mail: trosenberg@acacamps.org
Facebook: www.facebook.com/ACACamps
Linkedin: www.linkedin.com/company/american-camp
 -association
X (Twitter): x.com/acacamps
YouTube: www.youtube.com/user/
 AmericanCampAssoc
Description: Camp owners, directors, program directors, businesses, and students interested in resident and day camp programming for youth and adults. **Founded:** 1910. **Publications:** *Find a Camp*; *Camping Magazine* (Bimonthly); *ACA Buyer's Guide*; *Accreditation Process Guide* (Annual); *Guide to ACA-Accredited Camps*. **Awards:** National Honor Award (Annual); Hedley S. Dimock Award (Irregular); ACA Distinguished Service Award (Annual); ACA National Honor Award (Annual); ACA Special Recognition Award (Annual); Eleanor P. Eells Award for Program Excellence (Annual). **Geographic Preference:** National.

2502 ■ Canadian Camping Association (CCA)
BC, Canada
Ph: (541)909-1141
Co. E-mail: info@bccamping.org
URL: http://ccamping.org
Contact: Claire Friedrich, Administrator
X (Twitter): x.com/ccampingorg
Instagram: www.instagram.com/ccampingorg
Description: Commercial camps and nonprofit organizations and individuals with an interest in camping. Promotes the "growth and development of organized camping for all populations in Canada." Furthers the interests and welfare of children, youth and adults through camping. Functions as a coordinating body for organized camping nationwide. Develops and enforces standards of practice and facilities among commercial camps; provides guidance, advocacy, and resources for camping leaders. Offers services to members including discount insurance, credit card, and online programs. Compiles industry statistics; operates bookstore. **Founded:** 1936. **Awards:** Ron Johnstone Lifetime Achievement Award (Periodic); Jack Pearse Award of Honour. **Geographic Preference:** National.

2503 ■ Christian Camp and Conference Association (CCCA)
PO Box 62189
 Colorado Springs, CO 80962-2189
Ph: (719)260-9400
Free: 888-922-2287
Fax: (719)260-6398
Co. E-mail: support@ccca.org
URL: http://www.ccca.org/ccca/default.asp
Contact: Gregg Hunter, President
Facebook: www.facebook.com/cccaorgconnect
X (Twitter): x.com/cccaorg
Pinterest: www.pinterest.com/christiancamp
Description: Exists to proclaim the power of the Christian camp and conference experience and to interpret its benefits to the Church and the public at large; and to provide leaders at member organizations with ongoing encouragement, professional training, and timely resources. **Publications:** *Executive Briefing* (Monthly); *InSite* (Bimonthly); *CCI/USA Membership Directory* (Annual). **Educational Activities:** CCCA National Conference (Annual). **Geographic Preference:** National.

2504 ■ Family Campers and RVers (FCRV)
Bldg. 2
 4804 Transit Rd.
 Depew, NY 14043
Ph: (716)668-6242
Free: 800-245-9755
Co. E-mail: fcrvnat@verizon.net
URL: http://www.fcrv.org
Contact: Gerry Pfirsch, President
E-mail: fcrvnd@yahoo.com
X (Twitter): x.com/FCRV_Official
YouTube: www.youtube.com/channel/
 UCeJEe0XGXFu6EdXnpZ5GOIQ
Description: Family campers and hikers; others interested in outdoor activities. Promotes and enhances the experience of "family" style camping/RVing. **Publications:** *Camping Today* (Monthly). **Educational Activities:** Campvention (Annual). **Geographic Preference:** Multinational.

2505 ■ KampGround Owners Association (KOA)
N26676 Hwy. 53
 Ettrick, WI 54627
Co. E-mail: info@koaowners.org
Facebook: www.facebook.com/KOAOwners
Description: Represents KOA franchisees. Offers seminars and workshops. Compiles statistics; maintains speakers' bureau, charitable program, and several committees. **Founded:** 1964. **Geographic Preference:** National.

2506 ■ National Association of RV Parks & Campgrounds (ARVC)
9085 E Mineral Cir., Ste. 200
 Centennial, CO 80112
Ph: (303)681-0401
Fax: (303)681-0426
Co. E-mail: info@arvc.org
URL: http://www.arvc.org
Contact: Paul Bambei, President
E-mail: pbambei@arvc.org
Facebook: www.facebook.com/arvc.updates
X (Twitter): x.com/MyARVC
Instagram: www.instagram.com/gocampingamerica
Description: Regular members are commercial campground owners and operators; associate members are manufacturers and suppliers of campground products and services. Promotes the interests of the commercial campground industry, with government officials and agencies, campers, the press and the general public. Represents the campground industry in contact with RV manufacturers, RV dealers and other branches of the camping business. **Founded:** 1966. **Publications:** *Michigan Campground Directory* (Annual); *Direct Line* (Monthly); *ARVC Report* (Monthly); *National Association of RV Parks & Campgrounds--Buyers Guide and Membership Directory* (Annual). **Educational Activities:** ARVC Outdoor Hospitality Conference & Expo (OHCE) (Annual). **Awards:** ARVC Parks of the Year (Annual); ARVC State Executive of the Year (Annual); Stan Martin Memorial Award (Annual). **Geographic Preference:** National.

2507 ■ National Forest Recreation Association (NFRA)
PO Box 488
 Woodlake, CA 93286
Ph: (559)564-2365
Fax: (559)564-2048
Co. E-mail: info@nfra.org
URL: http://nfra.org
Contact: Warren Meyer, President
E-mail: warren@camprrm.com
Description: Owners and operators of resorts, winter sports areas, marinas, campgrounds, stores, river trip outfitters, packer-outfitters, restaurants, and motels located on or adjacent to federal land. Participates in trade and public relations matters that is of interest to members, including legislation and relationships with U.S. agencies; state and local officials in matters of taxation, insurance, finance, health, and building requirements; and employment. **Founded:** 1948. **Awards:** NFRA Ranger of the Year Award (Annual). **Geographic Preference:** National.

2508 ■ North American Family Campers Association (NAFCA)
PO Box 345
 Billerica, MA 01821
Co. E-mail: linandjimo@verizon.net
URL: http://www.nafca.org
Contact: Jim Ostiguy, President
Facebook: www.facebook.com/NAFCACampers
X (Twitter): x.com/NAFCACampers
Description: Works to improve camping conditions, inform members about camping areas, equipment, and techniques, promote good camping manners, and foster fellowship among family campers. **Founded:** 1957. **Publications:** *Campfire Chatter* (Monthly). **Educational Activities:** NAFA Spring Safari (Annual). **Geographic Preference:** National.

REFERENCE WORKS

2509 ■ *7 Best Free and Open Source Campground Management Software*
Description: The changing requirements of campers have compelled businesses to change the technol-

ogy that they have been using for managing their campground operations. Many campground owners now use campground management software to ease their everyday business operations. This article details why campground owners should use campground management software. **Availability:** Online.

2510 ■ *7 Steps to a Multi-Million Dollar Campground*
Description: Details seven ways to increase the value of your campground, RV park, or vacation cabins, and fetch top dollar when you're ready to sell. **Availability:** Online.

2511 ■ *9 Ways to Market Your Campground: A Guide for Campgrounds and RV Parks*
Description: Marketing your campground is a tough task. Not only do you have to make yourself known to campers and RVers near and far, you also have to distinguish what makes you a must-visit spot. This article discusses how to develop the most effective marketing campaign to set your campground apart. **Availability:** Online.

2512 ■ *ACA Buyer's Guide*
Pub: American Camp Association
Contact: Tom Rosenberg, President
E-mail: trosenberg@acacamps.org
URL(s): www.acacamps.org/callout-buyers-guide
Description: Publication includes list of over 200 firms providing sporting equipment, food, infirmary supplies, etc. For children's and other organized camps. **Entries include:** Company name, address, product or service provided. **Arrangement:** Alphabetical. **Indexes:** Product. **Availability:** Online.

2513 ■ *"Draft Recommendations Call for Making National Park Campgrounds More Accommodating" in National Parks Traveler (October 13, 2019)*
URL(s): www.nationalparkstraveler.org/2019/10/draft-recommendations-call-making-national-park-campgrounds-more-accommodating
Ed: Kurt Repanshek. **Released:** October 13, 2019. **Description:** A two-page list of recommended improvements to park campgrounds has been sent to Interior Secretary David Bernhardt. Many of the suggested improvements are for more amenities such as cleaner bathrooms, wi-fi, and the ability to bring a long RV with a car, but there is debate on how this will be paid for — through private investors is one option but not everyone is on board with that idea. **Availability:** Online.

2514 ■ *"Hosts Provide Vital Services Helping Maintain Lake Mitchell Campground" in The Daily Republic (August 28, 2019)*
URL(s): www.mitchellrepublic.com/lifestyle/4633808-Hosts-provide-vital-services-helping-maintain-Lake-Mitchell-Campground
Ed: Sam Fosness. **Released:** August 28, 2019. **Description:** Willie and Yvonne Karl, who work as Lake Mitchell Campground host managers, spend their summers with another couple cleaning the sites and overseeing the day-to-day operations. This has worked well for the campsite now that the city is running it and needed a small team to help with the daily operations. **Availability:** Online.

2515 ■ *How to Start a Successful Campground Business*
Description: Starting a camping business requires a solid business plan and a good understanding of the management principle, execution strategy, and the drive to go a step beyond your business potential. This article enables you to understand how to get started with your campground business. **Availability:** Online.

2516 ■ *"Is Owning a Campground Profitable?" in Outdoor Command (March 16, 2020)*
Ed: Riley Draper. **Released:** March 16, 2020. **Description:** While location, business experience of the owners, and timing are just a few of the factors that affect the profitability of a campground, it is possible to get a general sense of the potential profitability of owning a campground. This article evaluates costs and factors that influence success. **Availability:** Online.

2517 ■ *"Learn How To Start a Campground From Someone Who Did It" in Small Business Trends (June 18, 2015)*
Ed: Julie Fidler. **Released:** June 18, 2015. **Description:** This article provides information from Andrea Steele, co-owner of Camper's Paradise in Sigel, Pennsylvania. Steele details what it was like to give up everything to spend time with her family and teach her children the value of hard work and determination. Steele discusses the importance of understanding location, infrastructure, lodging, licensing and permits, and the ultimate payoff of running your own campground. **Availability:** Online.

2518 ■ *"Managing a Campground as a Business" in Financial Buzz (December 19, 2018)*
Released: December 19, 2018. **Description:** Discusses the necessities involved in managing a campground as a business. **Availability:** Online.

2519 ■ *New York/New England & Eastern Canada Campground Guide*
Released: Annual; Latest edition 2012. **Price:** $10.95, retail price; $4.95, discounted price. **Description:** Covers campground site listings for New England states, including Maine, Connecticut, Massachusetts, New Hampshire, New York, Rhode Island, Vermont, and Ontario. **Entries include:** Site name, address, phone, facility description, driving directions, camping fees, attractions and seasonal events. **Availability:** Print.

2520 ■ *"Rich in Surprises and Secretes, There's a State Park Waiting for You" in The New York Times (July 29, 2019)*
URL(s): www.nytimes.com/2019/07/29/travel/state-parks-western-united-states.html
Ed: Peter Kujawinski. **Released:** July 29, 2019. **Description:** Every state park has unique aspects, so a visit to a new park will be a brand-new experience. President Lincoln was one of the first who thought that all citizens should have access to nature and signed Yosemite Valley over to the state of California in 1864. Ever since then, America has embraced it's state parks and the author takes us on his journey to the parks he visited. **Availability:** Online.

2521 ■ *Running an RV Park: Tips, Benefits and Business Models*
Ed: Bruce Hakutizwi. **Description:** An RV park can be a stable and lucrative investment with plenty of scope for growth. This article describes the benefits of owning an RV park, the main types of business models, and how to maximize your chances of success. **Availability:** Online.

2522 ■ *RV Park Model - 20 Ways RV Park Owners Make Money*
Ed: Ejike Cynthia. **Description:** A guide to help you understand the RV park business model plus 20 smart ways RV park owners make money. **Availability:** Online.

2523 ■ *"Survey Reveals RV Owners' Internet Needs" in RV News (November 24, 2021)*
Released: November 24, 2021. **Description:** Even though many campers hit the road to leave behind their hectic lives for awhile, having a good Internet connection is become more and more vital for RV owners. Discusses the various needs for Internet and full results of the survey. **Availability:** Online.

2524 ■ *Woodall's Great Lakes Campground Guide*
Released: Annual; Latest edition 2012. **Price:** $4.95, Individuals; $10.95, Individuals retail price. **Description:** Covers campground site listings for Great Lakes states, including Illinois, Indiana, Iowa, Michigan, Minnesota, Ohio, and Wisconsin. **Entries include:** Site name, address, phone, facility description, driving directions, camping fees, attractions and seasonal events. **Availability:** Print.

STATISTICAL SOURCES

2525 ■ *Campgrounds & RV Parks Industry in the US - Market Research Report*
URL(s): www.ibisworld.com/united-states/market-research-reports/campgrounds-rv-parks-industry/
Price: $925. **Description:** Downloadable report analyzing data about campgrounds and RV parks and how the industry has been impacted by COVID-19. **Availability:** Download.

TRADE PERIODICALS

2526 ■ *Camping Magazine*
Pub: American Camp Association
Contact: Tom Rosenberg, President
E-mail: trosenberg@acacamps.org
URL(s): www.acacamps.org/resources/camping-magazine
Released: Bimonthly **Price:** $104, Other countries for 2 year; $29.95, U.S. for 1 year; $56, U.S. for 2 year; $48, Canada and Mexico for 1 year(Alaska, Hawaii, Puerto Rico); $92, Canada and Mexico for 2 year(Alaska, Hawaii, Puerto Rico); $54, Other countries for 1 year; $6, for back issues. **Description:** Magazine on organized camp management. **Availability:** Print; PDF; Download; Online.

2527 ■ *InSite*
Pub: Christian Camp and Conference Association
Contact: Gregg Hunter, President
URL(s): www.ccca.org/ccca/Publications.asp
X (Twitter): x.com/Rockinsite
Released: Bimonthly **Price:** $29.95, Nonmembers; $39.95, for foreign; $4.99, Single issue. **Description:** Religious magazine covering Christian camps and conferences. **Availability:** Print; Download; PDF; Online.

TRADE SHOWS AND CONVENTIONS

2528 ■ *ACA National Conference*
URL(s): www.acacamps.org/conference/exhibithall
Frequency: Annual. **Description:** National conference for camp owners to have an opportunity to network and engage in professional development. **Principal Exhibits:** National conference for camp owners to have an opportunity to network and engage in professional development.

2529 ■ *American Camping Association Conference & Exhibits*
Markel Corporation
4521 Highwoods Pky.
Glen Allen, VA 23060
Free: 800-446-6671
Co. E-mail: information@markelcorp.com
URL: http://www.markel.com
Contact: Jeremy Noble, President
URL(s): www.acacamps.org/conference
Frequency: Annual. **Description:** Offers a mobile app to enhance the experience of the event. **Audience:** Camp directors, counselors, and exhibitors. **Principal Exhibits:** Offers a mobile app to enhance the experience of the event.

2530 ■ *Tri-State CAMP Conference*
URL(s): www.acanynj.org/tri-state-camp-conference
Facebook: www.facebook.com/acanynj
X (Twitter): twitter.com/SummerCamp411
Instagram: www.instagram.com/acanynj
YouTube: www.youtube.com/channel/UCUVWyCUXODstYo3IIacaiCw
Description: Provides education and networking for summer camp owners. Also features new products and services in the exhibit hall. **Audience:** Summer camp for children owners. **Principal Exhibits:**

Small Business Profiles

Provides education and networking for summer camp owners. Also features new products and services in the exhibit hall.

FRANCHISES AND BUSINESS OPPORTUNITIES

2531 ■ **Kampgrounds of America Inc. (KOA)**
PO Box 30558
  Billings, MT 59114
Free: 888-562-0000
URL: http://koa.com
Contact: Toby O'Rourke, President
Facebook: www.facebook.com/KOAKampgrounds
X (Twitter): x.com/KOAKampgrounds
YouTube: www.youtube.com/user/KOAKampgrounds
Pinterest: www.pinterest.com/KOAKampgrounds
Description: Franchisor of campgrounds. **Founded:** 1962. **Publications:** *KOA Directory*. **Training:** Publisher of directories.

2532 ■ **Yogi Bear's Jellystone Park Camp-Resorts**
502 TechneCenter Dr., Ste. D
  Milford, OH 45150
URL: http://www.campjellystone.com
Facebook: www.facebook.com/campjellystone
X (Twitter): x.com/campjellystone
Instagram: www.instagram.com/campjellystone
Pinterest: www.pinterest.com/campjellystone
Description: Firm holds an exclusive license to franchise Yogi Bear's resorts in the US and Canada. Presently, there are 70 units in the U.S. and 3 in Canada. **Founded:** 1969. **Franchised:** 1971. **Royalty Fee:** 6% of gross revenues. **Financial Assistance:** Yes **Training:** Franchisee's are required to attend a 5 day training program held at the home office in Cincinnati, OH. Additional onsite training is also conducted for a period of 2-3 days.

LIBRARIES

2533 ■ **American Camp Association (ACA)**
5000 State Rd. 67 N
  Martinsville, IN 46151-7902
Ph: (765)342-8456
Free: 800-428-2267
Fax: (765)342-2065
URL: http://www.acacamps.org
Contact: Tom Rosenberg, President
E-mail: trosenberg@acacamps.org
Facebook: www.facebook.com/ACACamps
Linkedin: www.linkedin.com/company/american-camp-association
X (Twitter): x.com/acacamps
YouTube: www.youtube.com/user/AmericanCampAssoc
Description: Camp owners, directors, program directors, businesses, and students interested in resident and day camp programming for youth and adults. **Founded:** 1910. **Publications:** *Find a Camp*; *Camping Magazine* (Bimonthly); *ACA Buyer's Guide*; *Accreditation Process Guide* (Annual); *Guide to ACA-Accredited Camps*. **Awards:** National Honor Award (Annual); Hedley S. Dimock Award (Irregular); ACA Distinguished Service Award (Annual); ACA National Honor Award (Annual); ACA Special Recognition Award (Annual); Eleanor P. Eells Award for Program Excellence (Annual). **Geographic Preference:** National.

Candy/Chocolate Shop

ASSOCIATIONS AND OTHER ORGANIZATIONS

2534 ■ American Association of Candy Technologists (AACT)
711 W Water St.
　Princeton, WI 54968
Ph: (920)295-6959
Fax: (920)295-6843
Co. E-mail: aactinfo@gomc.com
URL: http://www.aactcandy.org
Contact: Michelle Schwenk, President
E-mail: michelle@bellissolutions.com
Description: Candy technologists who seek to further the education of the technical community of the confectionery industry. **Founded:** 1947. **Awards:** Stroud Jordan Award (Annual); AACT John Kitt Memorial Scholarship (Annual). **Geographic Preference:** National.

2535 ■ Convenience Distribution Association (CDA)
11250 Roger Bacon Dr. 8
　Reston, VA 20190
Ph: (703)208-3358
Free: 800-482-2962
Fax: (703)573-5738
Co. E-mail: info@cdaweb.net
URL: http://www.cdaweb.net
Contact: Kimberly Bolin, President
E-mail: kimberlyb@cdaweb.net
Facebook: www.facebook.com/conveniencedistribution
X (Twitter): x.com/CDA_01
Description: Represents the interests of distributors of convenience-related products. Its members include wholesalers, retailers, manufacturers, brokers and allied organizations from across the US. and abroad. Programs include strong legislative representation in Washington and a broad spectrum of targeted education, business and information services. Sponsors the country's largest show for candy and convenience related products in conjunction with its semi-annual convention. **Founded:** 1945. **Publications:** *Convenience Distribution: AWMA's Magazine for Candy, Tobacco, Grocery, Foodservice and General Merchandiser Marketers* (Monthly); *Quick Topics Newsletter*; *Convenience Distribution* (Bimonthly); *Buying Guide and AWMA Directory* (Annual); *Buying Guide and Membership Directory*. **Educational Activities:** University of Innovative Distribution (Annual); Convenience Distribution Marketplace (Annual); Convenience Distribution Business Exchange (CDBX) (Annual); Summit and Business Exchange (Annual). **Awards:** CDA's Hall of Fame Award (Annual). **Geographic Preference:** National.

2536 ■ National Confectionery Association (NCA)
1101 30th St. NW, Ste. 200
　Washington, DC 20007
Ph: (202)534-1440
Co. E-mail: info@candyusa.com
URL: http://candyusa.com
Contact: John H. Downs, President
E-mail: john.downs@candyusa.com
Facebook: www.facebook.com/NationalConfectionersAssociation
X (Twitter): x.com/CandyUSA
Instagram: www.instagram.com/CandyUSA
Description: Represents manufacturers of confectionery products and suppliers to the industry. Conducts research and technical and governmental services; provides information to the public; conducts annual confectionery technology course at the University of Wisconsin, Madison; gathers statistics on the industry. **Founded:** 1884. **Publications:** *The Sweet Journal*; *A Year of Confectionery* (Annual). **Educational Activities:** NBWA Annual Convention & Trade show; Sweets Snacks Expo (Annual); Chocolate Manufacturers Association of the U.S.A. Conference; Sweets & Snacks Expo (Annual). **Geographic Preference:** National.

2537 ■ National Confectionery Sales Association (NCSA)
3135 Berea Rd.
　Cleveland, OH 44111
Ph: (216)631-8200
Co. E-mail: info@candyhalloffame.org
URL: http://www.candyhalloffame.org
Contact: Joseph Melville, President
Facebook: www.facebook.com/candyhalloffame
X (Twitter): x.com/candyhalloffame
Description: Salespersons, brokers, sales managers, wholesalers, and manufacturers in the candy industry. Maintains Candy Hall of Fame. **Founded:** 1899. **Publications:** *National Confectionery Sales Association of America-Journal* (Annual). **Educational Activities:** National Confectionery Sales Association Meeting (Annual). **Awards:** Candy Hall of Fame Award (Annual). **Geographic Preference:** National.

2538 ■ Professional Manufacturing Confectioners Association (PMCA) - Lending Library
2980 Linden St., Ste. E3
　Bethlehem, PA 18017
Ph: (610)625-4655
Co. E-mail: info@pmca.com
URL: http://pmca.com
Contact: Yvette Thomas, Chief Operating Officer
Facebook: www.facebook.com/ProfessionalManufacturingConfectionersAssociation
Linkedin: www.linkedin.com/company/pmca
YouTube: www.youtube.com/channel/UCM61Y9U1W8qYILxd67e3R8g
Description: Manufacturers and suppliers of confectionery and chocolate products. Conducts research and educational programs. **Scope:** Confectionery industry studies. **Services:** Open to the members by appointment. **Founded:** 1907. **Holdings:** Books; reports; CDs; articles; abstracts; newsletters. **Publications:** *Proceedings of Annual Production Conference* (Annual); *PMCA News Update* (Quarterly). **Educational Activities:** PMCA Annual Production Conference (Annual). **Awards:** Allen Allured Fellowship (Annual). **Geographic Preference:** Multinational; State.

2539 ■ Retail Confectioners International (RCI)
3029 E Sunshine St., Ste. A
　Springfield, MO 65804
Ph: (417)883-2775
Free: 800-545-5381
Co. E-mail: info@retailconfectioners.org
URL: http://www.retailconfectioners.org
Contact: Jeffery Smith, President
Facebook: www.facebook.com/RetailConfectioners
X (Twitter): x.com/RCIchocolate
YouTube: www.youtube.com/user/RetailConfectioners
Description: Manufacturing retail confectioners who make and sell their own candies through directly-owned retail candy shops; associates are suppliers to the industry. Provides education, promotion, and legislative and information service. Monitors legislative activities that affect the industry at state and national levels. Holds comprehensive two-week course and one-week specialized course on retail candy making biennially. **Founded:** 1917. **Educational Activities:** Retail Confectioners International Fall Regional Conference (Annual). **Geographic Preference:** National.

REFERENCE WORKS

2540 ■ "Airport Adds More Detroit Flavor; Local Brands Bolster Metro Dining, Retail" in Crain's Detroit Business (Vol. 30, July 28, 2014, No. 30, pp. 3)
Pub: Crain Communications Inc.
Contact: Barry Asin, President
Description: Gayle's Chocolates, Hockeytown Café, and National Coney Island have operated at the Detroit Metropolitan Airport for years. Soon new Detroit favorites will be joining the lineup for the enjoyment of both business and leisure travelers with a food court offering local foods and beverages, including wine and 18 craft brewery beers. There will also be a self-serve kiosk where travelers can buy items to take with them. **Availability:** Print; Online.

2541 ■ "The Best Candy Store in Every State" in Insider (August 9, 2019)
URL(s): www.insider.com/best-candy-shop-every-state-2019-8
Ed: Darcy Schild. **Released:** September 09, 2019.
Description: Using data from Yelp, a list of the best candy shops in each state are featured. Links are given to the individual Yelp pages and a description of each store is given. **Availability:** Online.

2542 ■ *Candy Industry Buyer's Guide*
Pub: BNP Media
Contact: Harper Henderson, Owner Co-Chief Executive Officer

URL(s): www.snackandbakery.com/directories/13430-candy-industry-buyers-guide
Description: Publication includes list of approximately 682 suppliers of ingredients, equipment, and services to the candy industry. **Entries include:** Company name, address, phone. **Arrangement:** Alphabetical. **Indexes:** Product. **Availability:** Online.

2543 ■ "Cold Stone in Licensing Agreement with Turin Chocolates" in Ice Cream Reporter (Vol. 22, December 20, 2008, No. 1, pp. 2)
Description: Cold Stone Creamery and Turin Chocolatier are teaming up to offer a new line of chocolate truffles under the Cold Stone label. The treats will feature four the most popular Cold Stone flavors: Coffee Lovers Only, Chocolate Devotion, Our Strawberry Blonde, and Peanut Butter Cup Perfection. **Availability:** Print; Online.

2544 ■ Directory of Ingredients, Equipment and Packaging
Pub: Manufacturing Confectioner Publishing Corp.
URL(s): gomc.com/index.php/product-category/directory-of-suppliers
Ed: Kate Allured. **Released:** Annual **Price:** $50, Single issue. **Description:** Publication includes suppliers of machinery, equipment, raw materials, and supplies to the confectionery industry; laboratory instrumentation and services. **Entries include:** Company name, address, phone, telex, fax. **Arrangement:** Separate alphabetical sections for raw materials, equipment, agents, packaging, laboratory instrumentation, and services. **Indexes:** Product, trade name. **Availability:** Online.

2545 ■ "New Meridian Candy Shop Hires People with Special Needs" in KTVB.com (February 1, 2019)
URL(s): www.ktvb.com/article/news/new-meridian-candy-shop-hires-people-with-special-needs/277-2f09495d-619b-417f-9d18-e38ead5ad83b
Ed: Maggie O'Mara. **Released:** February 01, 2019. **Description:** Sweet Zola's Candy Shop is focusing on hiring people with special needs. Owner Cyndy Radovich explains how she wants to give these people opportunities that they may not have anywhere else and is hoping to inspire other business owners. **Availability:** Online.

2546 ■ Progressive Grocer's Marketing Guidebook: The Comprehensive Source for Grocery, Drug and Mass Merchant Insights
URL(s): retailbuyers.net/custom-retail-database-solutions/marketing-guidebook
Released: Annual; latest edition 2015. **Price:** $1,085, Individuals ADVANTAGE (Includes more than 10,500 personal e-Mail addresses); $685, Individuals (Personal e-Mail addresses not included). **Description:** Covers over 2,800 U.S. and Canadian supermarket chains, large independents and wholesalers; also includes 350 specialty distributors include smaller food wholesalers, food brokers, non-food distributors, and candy/tobacco/media distributors and over 24,800 key executives and buyers. **Entries include:** For retailers and wholesalers--Company name, address, phone, email and websites, number of stores operated or served, areas of operation, major grocery supplier, three-year financial summary, buying policies, private label information, lists of executives, buyers, and merchandisers. For specialty distributors--Name, address, phone, list of key personnel including buyers' categories, list of items handled, URL. **Arrangement:** Alphabetical by hierarchy, geographical by eight regions and 50 market areas. **Indexes:** Grocery related organizations, chain and wholesalers, state index, store operating name/parent company reference. **Availability:** CD-ROM; Print.

2547 ■ "Shari's Berries Founder Shuts Last Store" in Sacramento Business Journal (Vol. 28, September 2, 2011, No. 27, pp. 1)
Pub: Sacramento Business Journal
Contact: Stephanie Fretwell, Director
E-mail: sfretwell@bizjournals.com
Ed: Kelly Johnson. **Description:** Sacramento, California-based Shari's Berries owner Shari Fitzpatrick closed the company's last three stores called The Berry Factory. Fitzpatrick also filed for business bankruptcy protection. The weak economy is blamed for the company's failure. **Availability:** Online.

2548 ■ "The Sky's the Limit" in Retail Merchandiser (Vol. 51, July-August 2011, No. 4, pp. 64)
Description: Mars Retail Group (MRG) is the licensing division handling M&M's Brand Candies. Since taking over the brand they have expanded from 12 licensees to 50 licensees with new offerings. **Availability:** Online.

2549 ■ "Swedish Candy Shop Adds Frozen Treats" in The New York Times (May 28, 2019)
URL(s): www.nytimes.com/2019/05/28/dining/bonbon-swedish-candy-soft-serve.html
Ed: Florence Fabricant. **Released:** May 28, 2019. **Description:** The candy store BonBon, which sells Swedish confections, has decided to add soft-serve ice cream. The toppings are a Swedish import, even if the ice cream isn't. **Availability:** Online.

TRADE PERIODICALS

2550 ■ Candy Industry: The Global Magazine of Chocolate Confectionery
Pub: BNP Media
Contact: Harper Henderson, Owner Co-Chief Executive Officer
URL(s): www.snackandbakery.com/candy-industry
Facebook: www.facebook.com/CandyIndustry
Linkedin: www.linkedin.com/company/candy-industry
X (Twitter): twitter.com/CandyIndustry
Instagram: www.instagram.com/candyindustrymag
YouTube: www.youtube.com/c/Candyindustry
Released: Irregular **Description:** Magazine serving candy industry management. **Availability:** Print.

2551 ■ Convenience Distribution: AWMA's Magazine for Candy, Tobacco, Grocery, Foodservice and General Merchandiser Marketers
Pub: Convenience Distribution Association
Contact: Kimberly Bolin, President
E-mail: kimberlyb@cdaweb.net
URL(s): www.cdaweb.net/Resources/Magazine
Ed: Lisa White, Bob Gatty. **Released:** Monthly; latest edition Sprint 2024. **Description:** For service based distributors marketing to the retail trade. **Availability:** Online.

TRADE SHOWS AND CONVENTIONS

2552 ■ Specialty Food Association Winter Fancy Food Show
Specialty Food Association Inc.
136 Madison Ave., 12th Fl.
New York, NY 10016-6788
Ph: (212)482-6440
Fax: (212)482-6459
URL: http://www.specialtyfood.com
Contact: Phil Kafarakis, President
URL(s): www.specialtyfood.com/fancy-food-shows/winter
Price: $60, Onsite. **Frequency:** Annual. **Description:** Exhibits relating to international specialty food and dessert. **Audience:** Retailers, the educational sector, buyers from various food businesses, manufacturers, the press, and other industry professionals. **Principal Exhibits:** Exhibits relating to international specialty food and dessert. Dates and Locations: 2025 Jan 19-21 Las Vegas Convention Center, Las Vegas, NV. **Telecommunication Services:** mboulefrakh@specialtyfood.com.

2553 ■ Western Candy Conference
URL(s): westerncandyconference.org
Description: Tradeshow for the candy and sweets industry. **Audience:** Candy manufacturers, suppliers, and distributors. **Principal Exhibits:** Tradeshow for the candy and sweets industry.

FRANCHISES AND BUSINESS OPPORTUNITIES

2554 ■ AmeriCandy Retail Interactive Kiosk (AIRK)
3618 St. Germaine Ct.
Louisville, KY 40207
Ph: (502)583-1776
Fax: (502)583-1776
Co. E-mail: omar@americandybar.com
URL: http://americandybar.com
Contact: Omar L. Tatum, Founder
Facebook: www.facebook.com/AmeriCandyBar
X (Twitter): twitter.com/AmeriCandyBar
Description: Distributor and retailer of candies, chocolates and much more. **Financial Assistance:** Yes **Training:** Yes.

2555 ■ Candy Bouquet International (CBI)
4100 Milam St.
Houston, TX 77006
Free: 877-226-3901
URL: http://www.candybouquet.com
Contact: Margaret McEntire, Founder
Description: Retailer of candies and chocolates. **Founded:** 1989. **Training:** Yes.

2556 ■ Kilwin's Chocolates and Ice Cream
Kilwins Chocolates Franchise Inc.
1050 Bay View Rd.
Petoskey, MI 49770
Ph: (231)758-3901
Free: 888-454-5946
Fax: (231)347-6951
URL: http://www.kilwins.com
Contact: Donald McCarty, President
Facebook: www.facebook.com/KilwinsChocolateKitchenPetoskey
Description: Producer and distributor of chocolates, fudges, brittles, truffles, tattles. **No. of Franchise Units:** 100. **Founded:** 1947. **Franchised:** 1982. **Equity Capital Needed:** $125,000 and a minimum net worth of $500,000. **Franchise Fee:** $40,000. **Royalty Fee:** 5% Of Gross Sales. **Financial Assistance:** No **Training:** Online gift and cakes restaurant.

2557 ■ Powell's Sweet Shoppe
Description: Candy, gelato, and nostalgic toys. **No. of Franchise Units:** 8. **No. of Company-Owned Units:** 1. **Founded:** 2003. **Franchised:** 2005. **Equity Capital Needed:** $370,000-$440,000. **Franchise Fee:** $30,000. **Royalty Fee:** 6%.

2558 ■ Rocky Mountain Chocolate Factory, Inc. (RMCF)
Rocky Mountain Chocolate Factory, Inc. (RMCF)
265 Turner Dr.
Durango, CO 81303
Ph: (970)259-0554
Fax: (970)259-6102
Co. E-mail: customerservice@rmcf.net
URL: http://www.rmcf.com
Contact: Robert Sarlls, Chief Executive Officer
Facebook: www.facebook.com/myrmcf
X (Twitter): twitter.com/rockymtnchocinc
Instagram: www.instagram.com/rockymountain.chocolatefactory
Pinterest: www.pinterest.com/rmcfinc
Description: Manufacturer and retailer of confectionary products such as chocolate candies, clusters, caramels, creams, mints, and truffles. **No. of Franchise Units:** 400.0. **Founded:** 1982. **Franchised:** 1982. **Training:** Training provided in customer service, record keeping, merchandising, inventory control and marketing during 10 day program at corporate headquarters, in addition to several days onsite for store opening.

2559 ■ Schakolad Chocolate Factory
53 Boone Village
Zionsville, IN 46077
Ph: (317)872-9000
Co. E-mail: indianapolis@schakolad.com
URL: http://www.schakolad.com
Facebook: www.facebook.com/SchakoladIndy
Description: Producer of fine chocolate. **Founded:** 1995. **Equity Capital Needed:** $130,000-$170,000. **Franchise Fee:** $39,500. **Financial Assistance:** Yes **Training:** Offers 1-2 weeks at headquarters and 1-2 weeks at franchisee's location and ongoing support.

2560 ■ The South Bend Chocolate Company Inc.
3300 W Sample St.
South Bend, IN 46619
Free: 800-301-4961
Co. E-mail: orders@sbchocolate.com
URL: http://sbchocolate.com
Contact: Mark Tarner, President
X (Twitter): x.com/chocolatebend
Description: Gourmet chocolate and confectionery manufacturer. **No. of Franchise Units:** 4.0. **No. of Company-Owned Units:** 13. **Founded:** 1991. **Training:** Offers 10 days at headquarters, 80 hours at franchisees location with ongoing support.

LIBRARIES

2561 ■ Professional Manufacturing Confectioners Association (PMCA) - Lending Library
2980 Linden St., Ste. E3
Bethlehem, PA 18017
Ph: (610)625-4655
Co. E-mail: info@pmca.com
URL: http://pmca.com
Contact: Yvette Thomas, Chief Operating Officer
Facebook: www.facebook.com/ProfessionalManufacturingConfectionersAssociation
Linkedin: www.linkedin.com/company/pmca
YouTube: www.youtube.com/channel/UCM61Y9U1W8qYlLxd67e3R8g
Description: Manufacturers and suppliers of confectionery and chocolate products. Conducts research and educational programs. **Scope:** Confectionery industry studies. **Services:** Open to the members by appointment. **Founded:** 1907. **Holdings:** Books; reports; CDs; articles; abstracts; newsletters. **Publications:** *Proceedings of Annual Production Conference* (Annual); *PMCA News Update* (Quarterly). **Educational Activities:** PMCA Annual Production Conference (Annual). **Awards:** Allen Allured Fellowship (Annual). **Geographic Preference:** Multinational; State.

Car Alarm and Stereo Store

ASSOCIATIONS AND OTHER ORGANIZATIONS

2562 ■ International Auto Sound Challenge Association (IASCA)
2400 S Ridgewood Ave. Unit 55
South Daytona, FL 32119
URL: http://iasca.com
Contact: Travis Chin, President
E-mail: travis@iasca.com
Description: Manufacturers, retailers, and representatives/distributors of auto stereos; other interested individuals. Promotes the automotive stereo industry; holds sound quality and security contests; conducts consumer education. **Founded:** 1987. **Educational Activities:** Consumer Electronics Show (CES); International Electronics Expo. **Geographic Preference:** National.

2563 ■ Mobile Electronics Association (MEA)
85 Flagship Dr., Ste. F
North Andover, MA 01845
Free: 800-949-6372
Co. E-mail: info@mobile-electronics.com
URL: http://mobile-electronics.com
Facebook: www.facebook.com/Knowledgefest
X (Twitter): x.com/MobileE_Group
YouTube: www.youtube.com/channel/UCdZfhpfXTMaoEV7v16DKIbQ
Description: Retailers, manufacturers, distributors, manufacturers' representatives, and others related to the mobile electronics industry in the United States. Provides members with education, marketing, and business resources to advance the professionalism and profitability of the mobile electronics industry. **Founded:** 1992.

2564 ■ Mobile Electronics Competition Association (MECA)
235 Flamingo Dr.
Louisville, KY 40218
Ph: (615)851-7428
Co. E-mail: mecacaraudio@comcast.net
URL: http://mecacaraudio.com
Facebook: www.facebook.com/mecacaraudio
X (Twitter): x.com/mecacaraudio1
Instagram: www.instagram.com/mecacaraudio
YouTube: www.youtube.com/channel/UCMmKGkg6d_1WEgvVahLvC_Q
Description: Organizes car shows with contests for mobile electronics. **Founded:** 1990.

REFERENCE WORKS

2565 ■ "Car Audio Is Second-Fastest-Declining Profession in U.S." in CEPro (March 30, 2017)
URL(s): www.cepro.com/news/car_audio_installation_decline/
Ed: Jason Knott. **Released:** March 30, 2017. **Description:** It seems that the audio installation industry is on the decline, with expected projections of a 50% loss of jobs by 2024. **Availability:** Online.

TRADE PERIODICALS

2566 ■ *It Is Innovation*
Pub: Consumer Technology Association
Contact: Kinsey Fabrizio, President
URL(s): www.cta.tech/Resources/i3-Magazine/i3-Issues/2023/January-February
Released: Bimonthly **Price:** $24.99, for U.S. & Canada; $49.99, for Elsewhere; $39.99, for Mexico; $5, Single issue; $7.50, Single issue; $9, Single issue. **Description:** Provides news and information concerning mobile electronics, audio, radar, security, and cellular communications. Examines the manufacture, market trends, and installation of mobile electronics. Covers legislative and regulatory issues at the state and federal levels with particular emphasis on business, manufacturing, and insurance issues. Recurring features include a monthly series of retail management information and news of the Association. **Availability:** Print; Online.

FRANCHISES AND BUSINESS OPPORTUNITIES

2567 ■ Alta Mere
11524 W 183rd Pl.
Orland Park, IL 60467
Free: 888-227-8468
Fax: (708)389-9882
Co. E-mail: info@altamere.com
URL: http://altamere.com
Facebook: www.facebook.com/altamere
Linkedin: www.linkedin.com/company/alta-mere
X (Twitter): twitter.com/alta_mere
Description: Manufacturer of automotive outfitters such as window films, paint protection film, alarm systems, backup cameras and much more. **Founded:** 1987. **Financial Assistance:** Yes **Training:** Provides 1 week training at headquarters, 3 weeks at franchisee's location with ongoing support.

2568 ■ Ziebart International Corporation
1290 E Maple Rd.
Troy, MI 48083
Co. E-mail: info@ziebartworld.com
URL: http://www.ziebartworld.com
Contact: Thomas E. Wolfe, President
Linkedin: www.linkedin.com/company/ziebart-international
Instagram: www.instagram.com/ziebartinternational
YouTube: www.youtube.com/user/ziebartinternational
Description: Firm offers automobile detailing and automotive protection services. **No. of Franchise Units:** 400. **Founded:** 1959. **Franchised:** 1959. **Financial Assistance:** Yes **Training:** Yes.

Car Inspection Service

REFERENCE WORKS

2569 ■ *"Are Vehicle Inspections Really About Safety?" in The Zebra (July 18, 2016)*
URL(s): www.thezebra.com/insurance-news/3175/vehicle-inspections-really-safety/
Ed: Julia Eddington. **Released:** July 18, 2016.
Description: Explores why only some states require vehicle inspections and whether or not they make us safer. **Availability:** Online.

2570 ■ *"On-Site Used-Car Inspections Better the Odds in Buying Used" in Autotrader (September, 2012)*
Ed: Russ Heaps. **Released:** September 2012.
Description: If you're in the market for a used car, it would be in your best interest to have a vehicle inspection completed. All too often, the online history report doesn't tell the complete story of the car, but an on-site inspection can make sure the car's current condition is in line with what you are paying. **Availability:** Online.

2571 ■ *"Safelite Auto-Glass Replacement Practice Challenged by Glass-Repair Resin Maker" in The Columbus Dispatch (February 13, 2018)*
URL(s): www.dispatch.com/business/20180213/safelite-auto-glass-replacement-practice-challenged-by-glass-repair-resin-maker
Ed: Dan Gearino. **Released:** February 13, 2018.
Description: Discusses the lawsuit against Safelite, the nation's largest retailer of auto glass products, as they defend claims that it is not spreading lies about the "six-inch" or "dollar-bill" rule for repairing windshields. **Availability:** Online.

2572 ■ *"When the Windshield Helps Drive the Car, a Repair Isn't So Simple" in The New York Times (February 7, 2019)*
URL(s): www.nytimes.com/2019/02/07/business/windshield-repairs.html
Released: February 07, 2019. **Description:** Today's newer vehicles come equipped with high-tech driver assistance features that are embedded into windshields, making any repairs difficult, time-consuming, and expensive. As drivers are depending more and more on these systems, making sure they are properly repaired is crucial for the safety of everyone driving in the car. **Availability:** Online.

2573 ■ *"Where Should I Take a Used Car for Inspection?" in Autolist (December 18. 2018)*
URL(s): www.autolist.com/guides/where-to-take-a-used-car-for-inspection
Released: December 28, 2018. **Description:** Tips for where to take your car, or the used car you are about to purchase, for an inspection. Also includes what to expect when the report the completed. **Availability:** Online.

2574 ■ *"Your Car Repair Handbook" in Consumer Reports (September 9, 2021)*
URL(s): www.consumerreports.org/car-repair/your-car-repair-handbook
Ed: Benjamin Preston. **Released:** September 21, 2021. **Description:** Owning a vehicle can get expensive, especially if repairs are needed. Even regular maintenance can add up. A breakdown of what costs to expect when doing it yourself or taking it in to the shop is given. Repairs that should be handled at a dealership, such as airbag safety, is also discussed. **Availability:** Print; Online.

FRANCHISES AND BUSINESS OPPORTUNITIES

2575 ■ **Snap-On Tools of Canada Ltd.**
Snap-on Incorporated
6500 Millcreek Dr.
Mississauga, ON, Canada L5N 2W6
Ph: (262)656-5200
Free: 877-762-7664
Co. E-mail: questions@snapon.com
URL: http://www.snapon.com
Contact: Nicholas T. Pinchuk, Chief Executive Officer
Facebook: www.facebook.com/SnaponTools
Linkedin: www.linkedin.com/company/snap-on-inc
X (Twitter): x.com/Snapon_Tools
YouTube: www.youtube.com/user/snaponscanner

Description: Manufacturer and distributor of shop equipment products, automotive diagnostic tools and repair information solutions for vehicle dealerships, repair centers, aerospace, agriculture, construction and government. **Founded:** 1931. **Training:** Initial training and ongoing.

Car Towing Service

ASSOCIATIONS AND OTHER ORGANIZATIONS

2576 ■ Towing and Recovery Association of America, Inc. (TRAA)
700 12th St. NW, Ste. 700
Washington, DC 20005
Free: 888-392-9300
Fax: (888)392-9300
Co. E-mail: contact@traaonline.com
URL: http://traaonline.com
Contact: Joanne Blyton, President
Facebook: www.facebook.com/TRAAOnline

Description: Tow truck owners or operators; associate members are wrecker and accessory manufacturers and vendors. Aims to upgrade and promote the industry. Promotes uniform legislation; offers specialized education and National Driver Certification Program. **Founded:** 1979. **Publications:** *TRAA Membership Directory* (Annual); *TRAA National Towing E-News* (Bimonthly). **Educational Activities:** Towing and Recovery Association of America Annual Trade Show. **Geographic Preference:** National.

REFERENCE WORKS

2577 ■ "Vehicle Towing and Recovery - Expert Article" in Robson Forensic (July 9, 2013)
URL(s): www.robsonforensic.com/articles/vehicle-towing-and-recovery-expert-article/
Ed: Douglas J. Rowland. **Released:** July 09, 2013. **Description:** Provides an overview of the responsibilities tow companies must provide in order to maintain safety in a crash site. The driver along with everyone else at the scene, including by-standers, need to be protected from hazards, and the vehicle being towed must also be protected in order to not cause further damage. **Availability:** Online.

TRADE PERIODICALS

2578 ■ *TRAA National Towing E-News*
Pub: Towing and Recovery Association of America, Inc.
Contact: Joanne Blyton, President
URL(s): traaonline.com/membership

Released: Bimonthly **Description:** Gives news of the Association. Recurring features include a column titled From the State Line. **Availability:** Print.

Car Wash

ASSOCIATIONS AND OTHER ORGANIZATIONS

2579 ■ Canadian Carwash Association (CCA)
3228 Service Rd., Ste. 109
Burlington, ON, Canada L7N 3H8
Ph: (905)331-1768
Co. E-mail: office@canadiancarwash.ca
URL: http://www.canadiancarwash.ca
Contact: Karen Smith, President
Linkedin: www.linkedin.com/company/canadian-carwash-association
Description: Promotes growth and development of the car wash industry. Provides benefits to members including discount insurance programs and customer handouts. **Founded:** 1960. **Publications:** *Wash-Word* (Quarterly). **Geographic Preference:** National.

2580 ■ International Carwash Association (ICA)
350 N Orleans St., Ste. 9000N
Chicago, IL 60654
Free: 888-422-8422
Co. E-mail: info@carwash.org
URL: http://www.carwash.org
Contact: Robert Dubinsky, President
Facebook: www.facebook.com/carwashorg
X (Twitter): x.com/carwashorg
Instagram: www.instagram.com/carwashorg
Description: The association promotes car wash industry. It provides educational opportunities to members by producing car wash trade show and conventions, publishing car wash magazine, and hosts a variety of educational and networking events. **Founded:** 1995. **Publications:** *International Carwash Association--Member Directory and Buyers Guide* (Annual); *ICA Directory and Buyer's Guide* (Annual); *ICA News* (Weekly). **Educational Activities:** International Carwash Association Annual Convention and Exhibition (Annual); The Car Wash Show (Annual). **Awards:** Brian Campbell Leadership in Innovation Award (Annual); ICA Car Wash Hall of Fame Award (Annual); Car Wash Environmental Leadership Award (Annual). **Geographic Preference:** Multinational.

STATISTICAL SOURCES

2581 ■ *Car Wash & Auto Detailing Industry in the US - Market Research Report*
URL(s): www.ibisworld.com/united-states/market-research-reports/car-wash-auto-detailing-industry/
Price: $925. **Description:** Downloadable report analyzing data about the current and future trends in the car wash and auto detailing industries. **Availability:** Download.

2582 ■ *RMA Annual Statement Studies*
Pub: Risk Management Association
Contact: Nancy Foster, President
Released: Annual. **Description:** Contains composite balance sheets and income statements for more than 360 industries, including the accounting, auditing, and bookkeeping industries. Also contains five years of comparative historical data for discerning trends. Includes 16 commonly used ratios, computed for most of the size groupings for nearly every industry.

TRADE SHOWS AND CONVENTIONS

2583 ■ Southwest Car Wash Association Convention and Expo
URL(s): wcarwash.org
Frequency: Annual. **Description:** Education, talks, and networking for car wash owners. Features an exhibit show with the latest products and services. **Audience:** Car wash owners. **Principal Exhibits:** Education, talks, and networking for car wash owners. Features an exhibit show with the latest products and services.

FRANCHISES AND BUSINESS OPPORTUNITIES

2584 ■ Cactus Car Wash
4216 Roswell Rd.
Marietta, GA 30062
Ph: (678)500-1492
Co. E-mail: cactusmarietta@gmail.com
Facebook: www.facebook.com/CactusCarWashMarietta
X (Twitter): x.com/ccwmarietta
Description: Provider of car washing services. **Founded:** 1996. **Equity Capital Needed:** $2,370,000 – $3,805,000. **Franchise Fee:** $45,000. **Royalty Fee:** 5.5%. **Training:** Offers 2 weeks at headquarters, 2 weeks onsite and ongoing support.

2585 ■ Fine Details Inc.
187 Cross Ave., Unit 1
Oakville, ON, Canada L6J 2W7
Description: Provider of car cleaning services such as hand wash and vacuum, fabric protection, leather treatment and interior shampoo and detailing. **Founded:** 1995. **Equity Capital Needed:** 110000. **Franchise Fee:** $30,000. **Royalty Fee:** $150 per week. **Training:** 2 weeks training with ongoing operational and marketing support.

2586 ■ The Shine Factory
170 Joseph Zatzman Dr.
Dartmouth, NS, Canada B3B 1L9
Ph: (902)407-4777
Fax: (902)407-4778
URL: http://www.shinefactory.com
Contact: Stephen Gaetz, President
Description: Firm provides automotive protection and detailing services. **Founded:** 2018. **Franchised:** 1986. **Equity Capital Needed:** Equity Capital depends upon area and facility size. **Franchise Fee:** Depending upon Market area and analysis. **Training:** Training conducted in Halifax, NS.

2587 ■ Super Wash Inc.
707 W Lincolnway
Morrison, IL 61270
Ph: (815)772-2111
Co. E-mail: info@superwash.com
URL: http://www.superwash.com
Contact: Robert D. Black, President
Facebook: www.facebook.com/SuperWashUSA
Description: Franchisor of car washes. **No. of Operating Units:** 270. **Founded:** 1982. **Franchised:** 2002. **Financial Assistance:** Yes **Training:** Training available at headquarters, onsite and ongoing support provided.

Career Counseling

ASSOCIATIONS AND OTHER ORGANIZATIONS

2588 ■ American Counseling Association (ACA)
PO Box 31110
Alexandria, VA 22310-9998
Ph: (703)823-9800
Free: 800-347-6647
Fax: (800)473-2329
Co. E-mail: acamemberservices@counseling.org
URL: http://www.counseling.org/#
Contact: Dr. Kent S. Butler, President
Facebook: www.facebook.com/American.Counseling.Association
Linkedin: www.linkedin.com/company/american-counseling-association
X (Twitter): x.com/CounselingViews
Instagram: www.instagram.com/americancounselingassociation
Description: Counseling professionals in elementary and secondary schools, higher education, community agencies and organizations, rehabilitation programs, government, industry, business, private practice, career counseling, and mental health counseling. Conducts professional development institutes and provides liability insurance. Maintains Counseling and Human Development Foundation to fund counseling projects. Continuing education specialists in the areas of counseling, guidance and human resource development. The organization is committed to the principle that continuing education is a paramount service obligation. **Founded:** 1952. **Subscriptions:** journals. **Publications:** *Adultspan Journal* (Semiannual); *The Journal of Humanistic Counseling (JHC)* (Semiannual; 3/year); *Journal of Employment Counseling (JEC)* (Quarterly); *Counseling Today* (Monthly); *Journal of Counseling & Development (JCD)* (Quarterly; Quarterly); *The Career Development Quarterly (CDQ)* (Quarterly); *ACA Journal of College Counseling* (Quarterly); *Journal of Multicultural Counseling and Development (JMCD)* (Quarterly); *Measurement and Evaluation in Counseling and Development*; *ACAeNews for Counselor Educators* (3/year); *Counselor Education and Supervision* (Quarterly); *The School Counselor*; *Journal of Addictions & Offender Counseling (JAOC)* (Semiannual); *American Counselor* (Quarterly); *Counseling and Values* (Semiannual); *Government Relations Update* (Quarterly). **Educational Activities:** ACA Conference & Expo (Annual). **Awards:** ACA Research Award (Annual); Kitty Cole Human Rights Award (Annual); Ross Trust Future School Counselors Essay Competition (Annual); ACA Extended Research Award (Annual); ACA Federal Legislative Service Award (Annual); ACA Professional Development Award (Annual); Ralph F. Berdie Memorial Research Award (Annual); Arthur A. Hitchcock Distinguished Professional Service Award (Annual); Glen E. Hubele National Graduate Student Award (Annual); Gilbert and Kathleen Wrenn Award for a Humanitarian and Caring Person (Annual); Carl D. Perkins Government Relations Award (Annual); David K. Brooks, Jr. Distinguished Mentor Award (Annual); Don Dinkmeyer Social Interest Award (Annual); Courtland C. Lee Multicultural Excellence Scholarship Award (Annual); ACA Best Practices Award (Annual); Robert H. Rencken Emerging Professional Leader Award (Annual); ACA Counselor Educator Advocacy Award (Annual). **Geographic Preference:** National.

2589 ■ American Indian Sciences and Engineering Society (AISES)
6321 Riverside Plz. Ln. NW, Unit A
Albuquerque, NM 87120
Ph: (505)765-1052
Co. E-mail: info@aises.org
URL: http://www.aises.org
Contact: Sarah EchoHawk, Chief Executive Officer
Facebook: www.facebook.com/aises.org
Linkedin: www.linkedin.com/company/aiseshq
X (Twitter): x.com/AISES
Instagram: www.instagram.com/aises_hq
YouTube: www.youtube.com/user/aiseshq
Description: A national nonprofit organization focused on increasing the representation of Indigenous peoples of North America and the Pacific Islands in science, technology, engineering, and math (STEM) studies and careers. **Founded:** 1977.

2590 ■ Association Nationale des Enterprises en Recrutement et Placement de Personnel (ACSESS) [Association of Canadian Search, Employment and Staffing Services (ACSESS)]
7145 W Credit Ave., Bldg. 2, Ste. 201
Mississauga, ON, Canada L5N 6J7
Ph: (905)826-6869
Free: 888-232-4962
Fax: (905)826-4873
Co. E-mail: acsess@acsess.org
URL: http://acsess.org
Contact: Mary McIninch, Executive Director
E-mail: mmcininch@acsess.org
X (Twitter): x.com/ACSESSCanada
YouTube: www.youtube.com/channel/UCi4MEqDWZtDDstt93HSlUMw
Description: Represents the employment, recruitment, and staffing services industry in Canada, including direct-hire and executive search services, and temporary and contract staffing services. Promotes best industry practices and adherence to employment legislation and regulations. **Founded:** 1998. **Publications:** *Dialogue* (3/year). **Geographic Preference:** National.

2591 ■ Career Directors International (CDI)
1665 Clover Cir.
Melbourne, FL 32935
Ph: (321)752-0442
Co. E-mail: info@careerdirectors.com
URL: http://careerdirectors.com
Contact: Laura DeCarlo, President
E-mail: laura@careerdirectors.com
Facebook: www.facebook.com/CareerDirectors
Linkedin: www.linkedin.com/company/career-directors-international
X (Twitter): x.com/careerdirectors
Instagram: www.instagram.com/careerdirectorsintl
YouTube: www.youtube.com/user/careerdirectors
Description: Global careers membership association for coaches, resume writers, recruiters, and human resources professionals.

2592 ■ Career Planning and Adult Development Network (CPADN)
1401 21ST St., Ste. R
Sacramento, CA 95811
Contact: Rich Feller, Chief Executive Officer
Description: Non-profit association of career practitioners who work with youth and adults in job or career transition. **Founded:** 1979. **Publications:** *Career Planning & Adult Development Network Newsletter* (Bimonthly). **Geographic Preference:** National.

2593 ■ International Association of Counseling Services (IACS)
101 S Whiting St., Ste. 211
Alexandria, VA 22304
Ph: (703)823-9840
Co. E-mail: admin@iacsinc.org
URL: http://iacsinc.org
Contact: Paul Galvinhill, President
Description: Represents accredited university and four-year college counseling services in the U.S., Canada, and Australia. Fosters communications and cooperation among counseling services. **Publications:** *Directory of Accredited Counseling Services* (Annual); *National Survey of Counseling Center Directors*. **Geographic Preference:** Multinational.

2594 ■ National Board for Certified Counselors, Inc. and Affiliates (NBCC)
3 Ter. Way
Greensboro, NC 27403
Ph: (336)547-0607
Fax: (336)547-0017
Co. E-mail: nbcc@nbcc.org
URL: http://www.nbcc.org
Contact: Kylie P. Dotson-Blake, President
Facebook: www.facebook.com/NBCCandAffiliates
Linkedin: www.linkedin.com/company/the-national-board-for-certified-counselors
Description: Establishes and monitors professional credentialing standards for counselors. Identifies individuals who have obtained voluntary certification as a National Certified Counselor, one who assists persons with aging, vocational development, adolescence, family, and marital concerns, or a National Certified School Counselor, one who specializes in counseling within the school setting, or a Certified Clinical Mental Health Counselor, one who specializes in working in clinical settings, or a Master Addictions Counselor, one who specializes in addictions counseling. Maintains a database of nearly 65,000 certified counselors. **Founded:** 1982. **Publications:** *National Directory of Certified Counselors* (Irregular); *NBCC Visions* (Monthly); *National Counselor Exami-*

nation for Licensure and Certification. **Educational Activities:** ACA Conference & Expo (Annual). **Geographic Preference:** National.

2595 ■ National Career Development Association (NCDA)
305 N Beech Cir.
Broken Arrow, OK 74012
Ph: (918)663-7060
Fax: (918)663-7058
Co. E-mail: info@ncda.org
URL: http://www.ncda.org/aws/ncda/pt/sp/home_page
Contact: Dr. Sharon Givens, President
E-mail: sgivens62@gmail.com
Facebook: www.facebook.com/NCDACareer
X (Twitter): x.com/ncdaCareer
Instagram: www.instagram.com/NCDACareer
Description: Represents professionals and others interested in career development in various work environments. Provides consulting and education opportunities. **Founded:** 1913. **Publications:** *The Career Development Quarterly (CDQ)* (Quarterly). **Geographic Preference:** National.

2596 ■ National Employment Counseling Association (NECA)
TX
Co. E-mail: employmentcounseling@gmail.com
URL: http://www.employmentcounseling.org
Contact: Carolyn Greer, President
Facebook: www.facebook.com/GCDFOnLine
Description: Serves as a division of the American Counseling Association. Represents individuals who are engaged in employment counseling, counselor education, research, administration or supervision in business and industry, colleges and universities, and federal and state governments; students. Offers professional leadership and development services; provides opportunities for professional growth through workshops and special projects. **Founded:** 1964. **Publications:** *Journal of Employment Counseling (JEC)* (Quarterly). **Geographic Preference:** National.

REFERENCE WORKS

2597 ■ "Career Guidance Helps Students Figure Out Their Paths" in EdSource (May 26, 2015)
URL(s): edsource.org/2015/career-guidance-helps-students-figure-out-their-paths/80474
Ed: Michelle Maitre. **Released:** May 26, 2015. **Description:** With the advent of high-stakes testing in public schools, career counseling fell out of favor, which was detrimental to the graduating students. Now, these opportunities are back and it's helping give students an edge when it comes to career development. **Availability:** Online.

2598 ■ "Design program in Athletic Footwear" in Occupational Outlook Quarterly (Vol. 55, Fall 2011, No. 3, pp. 21)
Description: The Fashion Institute of Technology offers the only certificate program in performance athletic footwear design in the U.S. The program focuses on conceptualizing and sketching shoe designs and covers ergonomic, anatomical, and material considerations for athletic footwear design. **Availability:** Print; Online.

2599 ■ "Encouraging Study in Critical Languages" in Occupational Outlook Quarterly (Vol. 55, Summer 2011, No. 2, pp. 23)
Description: Proficiency in particular foreign languages is vital to the defense, diplomacy, and security of the United States. Several federal programs provide scholarships and other funding to encourage high school and college students to learn languages of the Middle East, China, and Russia. **Availability:** Print; Online.

2600 ■ "Finishing High School Leads to Better Employment Prospects" in Occupational Outlook Quarterly (Vol. 55, Summer 2011, No. 2, pp. 36)
Pub: U.S. Department of Labor Bureau of Labor Statistics
Contact: Amrit Kohli, Director
E-mail: kohli.amrit@bls.gov
Description: Students who drop out of high school are more likely to face unemployment than those who finish. Statistical data included. **Availability:** PDF; Online.

2601 ■ "Genetic Counselor" in Occupational Outlook Quarterly (Vol. 55, Summer 2011, No. 2, pp. 34)
Pub: U.S. Department of Labor Bureau of Labor Statistics
Contact: Amrit Kohli, Director
E-mail: kohli.amrit@bls.gov
Ed: John Mullins. **Description:** Genetic counseling involves the practice of informing clients about genetic disorders and to help them understand and manage a disorder. There are approximately 2,400 certified genetic counselors in the U.S. and earn a median annual salary of about $63,000, according to the American Board of Genetic Counseling. The US Bureau of Labor Statistics does not have data on employment or wages for genetic counselors. **Availability:** PDF; Online.

2602 ■ "How to Get the Most Value From a Career Counselor" in Time (November 17, 2014)
URL(s): time.com/3590683/how-to-get-the-most-value-from-a-career-counselor/
Ed: Marty Nemko. **Released:** November 17, 2014. **Description:** Instead of listing the help of a career counselor to find a job, it may be better to utilize that time towards having the counselor assist in some key areas. After a job is found, a career counselor can help with communication skills, time management, organization, and management and leadership. Landing the job is the first part, but keep the job and advancing in a career are also crucial to success. **Availability:** Online.

2603 ■ "Paid to Persuade: Careers in Sales" in Occupational Outlook Quarterly (Vol. 55, Summer 2011, No. 2, pp. 24)
Pub: U.S. Department of Labor Bureau of Labor Statistics
Contact: Amrit Kohli, Director
E-mail: kohli.amrit@bls.gov
Ed: Ilka Maria Torpey. **Description:** Sales workers are paid to persuade others to buy goods and services. There were over 13 million wage and salary sales workers in the US in 2010. Wages in sales careers can vary and some become lucrative, lifelong career positions. Seven sales occupations with annual wages higher than $33,000 are profiled. **Availability:** Online; PDF.

2604 ■ "Physics for Females" in Occupational Outlook Quarterly (Vol. 55, Summer 2011, No. 2, pp. 22)
Description: Free resources to help females investigate careers in medical physics and health physics are available from the American Physical Society. The booklet is designed for girls in middle and high school and describes the work of 15 women who use physics to solve medical mysteries, discover planets, research new materials, and more. **Availability:** Print; Online.

2605 ■ "Plan Your Future with My Next Move" in Occupational Outlook Quarterly (Vol. 55, Summer 2011, No. 2, pp. 22)
Description: My Next Move, an online tool offering a variety of user-friendly ways to browse more than 900 occupations was created by the National Center for O NET Development for the US Department of Labor's Employment and Training Administration. Clicking on an occupation presents a one-page profile summarizing key information for specific careers. **Availability:** Print; Online.

2606 ■ "Schools Start Early with Career Counseling" in U.S. News & World Report (September 6, 2018)
URL(s): www.usnews.com/news/education-news/articles/2018-09-06/colleges-welcome-first-year-students-with-career-counseling
Released: September 06, 2018. **Description:** Colleges and universities are beginning to start career counseling with students before classes start. The goal is to help guide the students into a satisfying career path and help them gain a competitive edge in the job market. **Availability:** Online.

2607 ■ "Work for Play: Careers in Video Game Development" in Occupational Outlook Quarterly (Vol. 55, Fall 2011, No. 3, pp. 2)
Pub: U.S. Department of Labor Bureau of Labor Statistics
Contact: Amrit Kohli, Director
E-mail: kohli.amrit@bls.gov
Ed: Drew Liming, Dennis Vilorio. **Description:** Game developers make a living creating the games the public enjoys playing. The video gaming industry reported sales over $10 billion in 2009 and employed 32,000 people in 34 states. Career options in video game development are featured. **Availability:** PDF; Online.

STATISTICAL SOURCES

2608 ■ Job Training and Career Counseling - 2022 U.S. Market Research Report with Updated Forecasts
URL(s): www.marketresearch.com/Kentley-Insights-v4035/Job-Training-Career-Counseling-Research-32203844/
Price: $295. **Description:** Comprehensive and in-depth assessments of the job training and career counseling industry in the United States with over 100 data sets covering 2013-2026. The report includes historical and forecasted market size, product lines, profitability, financial ratios, BCG matrix, statistics by state, operating expense details, organizational breakdown, consolidation analysis, employee productivity, price inflation, pay bands for the top 20 industry jobs, trend analysis and forecasts on companies, locations, employees, and payroll. **Availability:** Download.

2609 ■ Job Training & Career Counseling in the US - Industry Market Research Report
URL(s): www.marketresearch.com/IBISWorld-v2487/Job-Training-Career-Counseling-Research-32175372/
Price: $1,020. **Description:** Report covering the scope, size, disposition and growth of the job training and career counseling industry including the key sensitivities and success factors. Also included are five-year industry forecasts, growth rates and an analysis of the industry key players and their market shares. **Availability:** Download.

TRADE PERIODICALS

2610 ■ The Career Development Quarterly (CDQ)
Pub: Wiley-Blackwell
URL: www.ncda.org/aws/NCDA/pt/sp/cdquarterlywww.counseling.org/publications/counseling-journals
Ed: Mei Tang. **Released:** Quarterly; September - December - March - June. **Price:** $326, Institutions for online only US , IN , CA; $367, Institutions for print and online US , IN , CA; $341, Institutions for print US , IN , CA. **Description:** Journal focused on the design and use of career interventions, covering career counseling and development, work, leisure, career education, and coaching and management. Official journal of the National Career Development Association (NCDA), a division of the American Counseling Association. **Availability:** Print; Download; PDF; Online.

2611 ■ Changing Course
Contact: Valerie Young, Editor
URL(s): changingcourse.com/ezine-subscribe
Ed: Valerie Young. **Released:** Bimonthly **Price:** Free. **Description:** Contains inspiration and information on creating more satisfying work lives outside the 9-to-5 job world. Recurring features include letters to the editor, interviews, book reviews, and columns titled

Opportunities Knock: Creative Alternatives to Working 9-5, Resources for a Change, and Dollar/Sense. **Availability:** Online.

2612 ■ *Journal of Employment Counseling (JEC)*
Pub: American Counseling Association
Contact: Dr. Kent S. Butler, President
URL(s): www.counseling.org/publications/counseling
-journals/employment-counseling#onlinelibrary
.wiley.com/journal/21611920
Ed: Rebecca Michel. **Released:** Quarterly **Price:** $245, Institutions for online only US, Canada, India; $275, Institutions for print and online US, Canada, India; $256, Institutions for print only US, Canada, India; $275, Institutions for print and online; C$275, Institutions for print and online; $245, Institutions for online only; C$245, Institutions for online only; $256, Institutions for print Only; C$256, Institutions for print Only. **Description:** Peer-reviewed journal focused on theory and practice in employment counseling, including professional experimentation and research, current client vocational problems, and professional concerns of counselors. Official journal of the National Employment Counseling Association (NECA), a division of the American Counseling Association. **Availability:** Print; PDF; Download; Online.

CONSULTANTS

2613 ■ Career Dimensions Inc.
6535 Southpoint Dr.
Dallas, TX 75248
Contact: Taunee S. Besson, President
E-mail: tauneeb@careerdimensions-dfw.com
Description: Firm provides consulting in career change such as job search, executive, small business and life coaching, talent management and related services. **Scope:** Firm provides consulting in career change such as job search, executive, small business and life coaching, talent management and related services. **Publications:** "What Do I Say When I Don't Know What Career to Pursue?"; "How Do I Choose a College Major?"; "The National Business Employment Weekly's Premier Guide to Resumes"; "The National Business Employment Weekly's Premier Guide to Cover Letters"; "Ten Common Interview Mistakes and How to Avoid Them"; "Eating Your Way Through an Interview"; "How to Respond to 'Tell Me About Yourself'"; "Interview to Stand Out From the Crowd". **Training:** What Do I Do When I am Bored With My Job?.

2614 ■ Jobs In Horticulture Inc.
PO Box 521731
Longwood, FL 32752-1731
Free: 800-428-2474
Fax: (800)884-5198
Co. E-mail: info@hortjobs.com
URL: http://www.hortjobs.com
Contact: Armand Pichardo, Manager
X (Twitter): x.com/hortjobs
Description: Firm provides staffing and recruitment services. **Scope:** Firm provides staffing and recruitment services. **Founded:** 1993.

FRANCHISES AND BUSINESS OPPORTUNITIES

2615 ■ AAA Franchise Legal Help advice hotline
San Francisco, CA
Ph: (415)225-3010
Free: 800-942-4402
URL: http://www.franchisefoundations.com
Contact: Kevin B. Murphy, Contact
Description: Firm providing strategic franchise planning services. **Founded:** 1980.

2616 ■ Huck Bouma Pc. Attorneys at Law
1755 S Naperville Rd., Ste. 200
Wheaton, IL 60189
Ph: (630)221-1755
Co. E-mail: attorneys@huckbouma.com
URL: http://www.huckbouma.com

Contact: William J. Strons, Managing Partner
E-mail: wstrons@huckbouma.com
Facebook: www.facebook.com/HuckBoumaPC
Linkedin: www.linkedin.com/company/huck-bouma-pc
X (Twitter): x.com/huckboumapc
Description: Assist start-up franchisees and franchisors. **Scope:** Firm provides legal services for franchisors, sub franchisors, master franchisees, and area developers such as franchise agreements, state franchise registrations, and much more. **Founded:** 1991. **Training:** Franchise Law Compliance Attorneys.

PUBLICATIONS

2617 ■ *Careers in Focus--Business*
132 W 31st., 16 Fl.
New York, NY 10001
Ph: (212)896-4268
Free: 800-322-8755
Fax: (800)678-3633
Co. E-mail: info@infobase.com
URL: http://www.infobase.com
Contact: Paul Skordilis, President
URL(s): www.infobasepublishing.com/Bookdetail
.aspx?ISBN=081608016X&eBooks=0
Released: Latest edition 3rd; Published May, 2010. **Price:** $35, for hardcover. **Description:** Covers an overview of business, followed by a selection of jobs profiled in detail, including the nature of the job, earnings, prospects for employment, what kind of training and skills it requires, and sources for further information. **Availability:** Print; Online.

2618 ■ *Careers in Focus--Business Managers*
132 W 31st., 16 Fl.
New York, NY 10001
Ph: (212)896-4268
Free: 800-322-8755
Fax: (800)678-3633
Co. E-mail: info@infobase.com
URL: http://www.infobase.com
Contact: Paul Skordilis, President
URL(s): www.infobasepublishing.com/Bookdetail
.aspx?ISBN=0816072965&Ebooks=0
Released: Latest edition 2nd; Published January, 2009. **Price:** $35, for hardcover. **Description:** Covers an overview of business managers, followed by a selection of jobs profiled in detail, including the nature of the job, earnings, prospects for employment, what kind of training and skills it requires, and sources for further information. Includes black and white photographs. **Availability:** Print.

COMPUTERIZED DATABASES

2619 ■ *Oregon Career Information System*
Oregon Career Information System
328 E Broadway
Eugene, OR 97401
Ph: (541)346-3872
Free: 800-495-1266
Fax: (541)346-3823
Co. E-mail: cisservice@uoregon.edu
URL: http://oregoncis.uoregon.edu/Portal.aspx
Contact: Tom Goodhue, Executive Director
E-mail: tgoodhue@obcweb.com
URL(s): oregoncis.uoregon.edu/portal/org/AboutUs
.aspx
Price: $19.95, for print three months. **Availability:** Print. **Type:** Directory.

LIBRARIES

2620 ■ Chicago Public Library Central Library - Business/Science/Technology Division
400 S State St.
Chicago, IL 60605
URL: http://www.chipublib.org/resources/science
-technology

Scope: Small business; marketing; technology; sciences; computer science; careers and environmental information. **Services:** Interlibrary loan; library open to the public. **Founded:** 1977. **Holdings:** Figures not available.

2621 ■ Eureka, The California Career Information System Library
PO Box 687
Pinole, CA 94564-0687
Ph: (510)669-0996
Free: 888-463-2247
Fax: (510)669-0992
Co. E-mail: support@eureka.org
URL: http://www.eureka.org
Contact: M. Sumyyah Bilal, Executive Director
Facebook: www.facebook.com/EUREKA-the-Career
-Information-System-106353826112810
Scope: Career exploration; California and National occupational and school information; international occupational information; job search and financial aid; programs of study and training; skills assessment. **Services:** Copying. **Founded:** 1976. **Holdings:** Figures not available.

2622 ■ Florida State University - Career Center Library
100 S Woodward Ave.
Tallahassee, FL 32306-4162
Ph: (850)644-6431
Fax: (850)644-3273
URL: http://career.fsu.edu/resources/career-center
-library
Contact: Myrna Hoover, Director
E-mail: mhoover@fsu.edu
Facebook: www.facebook.com/fsucareercenter
Linkedin: www.linkedin.com/company/
fsucareercenter
X (Twitter): x.com/fsucareercenter
Instagram: www.instagram.com/fsucareercenter
YouTube: www.youtube.com/user/FSUCareerCenter
Pinterest: www.pinterest.com/fsucareercenter
Scope: Career planning; planning; occupations; education; experience; preparation; opportunities; training. **Services:** Library open to the public. **Founded:** 1975. **Holdings:** 1,000 books; 600 occupational files; 44 VF drawers; 100 videotapes; 66 CD-ROMs.

2623 ■ Indian River Area Library (IRAL)
3546 S Straits Hwy.
Indian River, MI 49749
Ph: (231)238-8581
Co. E-mail: info@indianriverlibrary.org
URL: http://www.indianriverlibrary.org
Contact: Kelsey Rutkowski, Director
Facebook: www.facebook.com/IndianRiverLibrary
Instagram: www.instagram.com/indianriverarealibrary
Scope: Local history. **Services:** Photocopy; Printer & Copier; Laminating; Faxing; Reciprocal Borrowing Agreement. **Founded:** 1976. **Holdings:** Figures not available.

2624 ■ Kershaw County Applied Technology Education Campus - Vocational-Technical Library
70 Innovation Way
Camden, SC 29020
URL: http://www.kcsdschools.net/Domain/26
Contact: Gordon Morris, Director
E-mail: william.morris@kcsdschools.net
Description: Kershaw County applied technology education Campus vocational-technical library. **Scope:** Vocational education. **Services:** Library open to the public. **Founded:** 1970. **Holdings:** 5,000 books.

2625 ■ Lee Hecht Harrison L.L.C. - Library
Lee Hecht Harrison L.L.C.
140 E Ridgewood Ave.
Paramus, NJ 07652
Ph: (201)930-9333
URL: http://lhh.com/us/en
X (Twitter): twitter.com/lhh_global
Description: Provider of outplacement, career development, and customized re-deployment services. **Scope:** A global career services firm special-

izing in out placement, leadership development, coaching and career development. Services include individual and group career consulting, career center management, dual career relocation assistance, executive coaching and career planning programs for employees and their managers. Out placement consulting expertise is provided to organizations planning a restructuring, downsizing or corporate relocation. **Founded:** 1974. **Holdings:** Figures not available. **Publications:** "Severance and Separation Benefits Study and Other Research Downsizing and Retention". **Training:** Out placement/Career Transition Services; Career Development Seminars; Change Seminars; Resilience Workshops; Executive Coaching; Dual Career Relocation Assistance.

2626 ■ National Association of Colleges and Employers (NACE) - Library
62 Highland Ave.
  Bethlehem, PA 18017
Ph: (610)868-1421
Co. E-mail: customerservice@naceweb.org
URL: http://www.naceweb.org
Contact: Marilyn Mackes, Executive Director
E-mail: mmackes@naceweb.org
Facebook: www.facebook.com/NACEOrg
Linkedin: www.linkedin.com/company/nationalassociationofcollegesandemployers
X (Twitter): x.com/naceorg
Instagram: www.instagram.com/NACEOrg
Pinterest: www.pinterest.com/naceorg

Description: Connects more than 5,200 college career services professionals at nearly 2,000 college and universities nationwide, and more than 3,000 HR/staffing professionals focused on college relations and recruiting. Forecasts trends in the job market; tracks legal issues in employment, the job search, and hiring practices; and provides college and employer professionals with benchmarks for their work. **Scope:** College; employment. **Founded:** 1956. **Holdings:** Figures not available. **Publications:** *CPC Career & Job Fair Finder*; *NACE Directory: Who's Who in Career Services and HR/Staffing* (Annual); *Directory: Who's Who in Career Services & HR/Staffing* (Annual); *NACE Journal* (Quarterly); *Job Choices*; *Job Choices for Business & Liberal Arts Students* (Annual); *Job Choices in Business and Liberal Arts Students* (Annual); *NACE--Salary Survey* (Semiannual). **Educational Activities:** NACE National Meeting (Annual). **Awards:** NACE Recruiting Excellence Award (Annual); NACE Diversity and Inclusion Excellence Award (Irregular); NACE Technology Excellence Award (Annual); NACE Innovation Excellence Awards (Annual); Kauffman Award (Annual); NACE Academy of Fellows (Annual); NACE/Chevron Award (Annual); NACE Career Services Excellence Awards (Irregular). **Geographic Preference:** National.

2627 ■ Ohio State University - Career Connection - Library
281 W Ln., Ave.
  Columbus, OH 43210
URL: http://exploration.osu.edu/careers

Scope: Personal and career self-assessment; career exploration; training opportunities; job search resources. **Services:** Interlibrary Loan ; Copying; center open to the public for reference use only. **Holdings:** Figures not available.

2628 ■ University of South Carolina Career Center Library
Thomas Cooper Library, Level 5
1322 Greene St.
  Columbia, SC 29208
Ph: (803)777-7280
Co. E-mail: career@sc.edu
URL: http://sc.edu/about/offices_and_divisions/career_center/index.php
Contact: Helen Powers, Director
E-mail: hefields@mailbox.sc.edu
Facebook: www.facebook.com/UofSCCareers
X (Twitter): x.com/UofSCCareers
Instagram: www.instagram.com/uofsccareers

Scope: Career development; self-assessment; career planning; job searching. **Holdings:** Figures not available.

2629 ■ YWCA Resource Center Library
2222 14th St.
  Boulder, CO 80302
Ph: (303)443-0419
Fax: (303)443-5098
Co. E-mail: frontdesk@ywcaboulder.org
URL: http://www.ywcaboulder.org
Contact: Angelique Espinoza, Chairman
Facebook: www.facebook.com/ywcaboulder
X (Twitter): twitter.com/ywcaboulder
YouTube: www.youtube.com/channel/UCFL00QSX3q1xLLsl3Smn3xw

Scope: Careers; job searching; educational resources; parenting; divorce; women's literature. **Services:** Copying; library open to the public. **Founded:** 1988. **Holdings:** 550 books.

Carpentry Service

ASSOCIATIONS AND OTHER ORGANIZATIONS

2630 ■ **Architectural Woodwork Institute (AWI) - Library**
46179 Westlake Dr., Ste. 120
  Potomac Falls, VA 20165
Ph: (571)323-3636
Co. E-mail: info@awinet.org
URL: http://www.awinet.org
Contact: Doug Hague, Chief Executive Officer
E-mail: dhague@awinet.org
Linkedin: www.linkedin.com/company/architectural
  -woodwork-institute
Instagram: www.instagram.com/awi_national
Description: Manufacturers of architectural woodwork products (casework, fixtures, and paneling) and associated suppliers of equipment and materials. Works to: raise industry standards; research new and improved materials and methods; publish technical data helpful in the design and use of architectural woodwork. Conducts seminars and training course. **Scope:** Architectural woodwork. **Founded:** 1953. **Holdings:** Figures not available. **Publications:** *Architectural Woodwork Institute--Source Book*. **Educational Activities:** AWI Annual Convention (Annual). **Awards:** AWI Standard of Excellence Award (Annual). **Geographic Preference:** National.

2631 ■ **Moulding and Millwork Producers Association (MMPA)**
1282 Stabler Ln., Ste. 630 No. 146
  Yuba City, CA 95993-2625
Ph: (530)661-9591
Co. E-mail: info@wmmpa.com
URL: http://wmmpa.com
Contact: Matt Weaber, President
Facebook: www.facebook.com/people/Moulding
  -Millwork-Producers-Association/100092533911079
X (Twitter): x.com/WMmoulding
Instagram: www.instagram.com/wmmpa
Description: Represents manufacturers of wood mouldings and millwork. Provides promotion, standardization and marketing information services. **Founded:** 1963. **Publications:** *Case 'n Base News* (Monthly); *Wood Moulding and Millwork Producers Association--Products and Services Membership Directory*. **Geographic Preference:** Multinational.

2632 ■ **Window and Door Manufacturers Association (WDMA)**
330 N Wabash Ave., Ste. 2000
  Chicago, IL 60611
Ph: (312)321-6802
Co. E-mail: membersupport@wdma.com
URL: http://www.wdma.com
Contact: Michael O'Brien, President
Linkedin: www.linkedin.com/company/window-&-door
  -manufacturers-association-wdma-
Description: Fosters, promotes, and protects members' interests; encourages product use. Establishes quality and performance standards; conducts research in all areas of door and window manufacture. Issues seals of approval for wood preservative treatment, hardwood doors, and window unit manufacture. **Founded:** 1927. **Publications:** *WDMA Newsletter*; *Window and Door Manufacturers Association-- Membership and Product Directory* (Annual); *Window and Door Manufacturers Association--Member & Product Directory* (Annual). **Geographic Preference:** National.

2633 ■ **World Millwork Alliance (WMA)**
10047 Robert Trent Jones Pky.
  New Port Richey, FL 34655-4649
Ph: (727)372-3665
Fax: (727)372-2879
Co. E-mail: mail@worldmillwrkalliance.com
URL: http://worldmillworkalliance.com
Contact: Rosalie Leone, President
E-mail: rleone@worldmillworkalliance.com
Facebook: www.facebook.com/WorldMillworkAlliance
X (Twitter): x.com/WMAmillwork
Instagram: www.instagram.com/worldmillworkalliance
Description: Wholesale distributors of windows, door, millwork and related products. Conducts research and statistical studies. Offers millwork home study course and audiovisual program dealing with product knowledge; furnishes group insurance. Compiles statistics. **Founded:** 1963. **Publications:** *Furniture Manufacturing Management* (Monthly); *AMD Newsletter*; *AMD News* (Monthly); *Membership Directory and Products' Guide* (Annual); *AMD Newsletter* (Monthly); *National Sash & Door Jobbers Association--Membership Directory* (Annual). **Educational Activities:** World Millwork Alliance Annual Convention & Tradeshow (Annual). **Geographic Preference:** National.

REFERENCE WORKS

2634 ■ *"5 Tips for Starting a Carpentry Business" in Woodworking Network (November 28, 2018)*
URL(s): www.woodworkingnetwork.com/best-prac
  tices-guide/components-hardware-assembly/5-tips
  -starting-carpentry-business
Released: November 28, 2018. **Description:** If you ever wanted to start your own carpentry business, these five tips will help you get started. A discussion of what to include in a business plan, to creating a brand, and even getting insured. **Availability:** Online.

2635 ■ *"Carpenters Picket to Highlight Wage Theft Laws; Contractors Targeted Dispute Claims" in Twin Cities Pioneer Press (August 2, 2019)*
URL(s): www.twincities.com/2019/08/02/unfair-to
  -workers-or-just-competitive-wage-theft-law-promp
  ts-picket-debate/
Ed: Christopher Magan. **Released:** August 02, 2019. **Description:** Carpenters union members took to the picket lines outside of construction sites in the Twin Cities to draw attention to unfair wages. They claim contractors are violating the recent wage theft laws and driving down wages, while leaders of the firms allege they are following state laws and paying fair wages. **Availability:** Online.

2636 ■ *"'Climate Positive Now' a Welcome Message of Sustainability" in Woodworking Network (November 19, 2021)*
URL(s): www.woodworkingnetwork.com/news/woo
  dworking-industry-news/climate-positive-now-wel
  come-message-sustainability
Ed: Larry Adams. **Released:** November 19, 2021. **Description:** A positive trend of using sustainable wood materials is being voiced by consumers and designers. Furniture makers are listening and looking for leads on materials that are branded as climate positive.

2637 ■ *"Del Mar's Free Carpentry Classes to Expand in Corpus Christi" in Corpus Christi Business News (September 6. 2019)*
URL(s): www.ccbiznews.com/news/del-mar-free
  -carpentry-classes-expand-in-corpus-christi
Ed: Suzanne Freeman. **Released:** September 06, 2019. **Description:** The need for skilled labor is high and a free 10-week carpentry program at Del Mar College in Corpus Christi is helping to fill that void. It's so successful that two additional locations for the classes are being added in Sinton and Refugio. Demand is high for trained workers due to the devastation that hit the area during Hurricane Harvey and the need to rebuild. **Availability:** Online.

2638 ■ *"Home Improvement Service Chain Had to Fix Its Own House" in Crain's Detroit Business (Vol. 30, October 13, 2014, No. 41, pp. 15)*
Pub: Crain Communications Inc.
Contact: Barry Asin, President
Description: Mr. Handyman International LLC is the franchising arm for the Mr. Handyman home improvement service chain. The franchises provide smaller home repair and improvement projects, mostly residential with only 15 percent of the jobs being commercial. Statistical data included. **Availability:** Online.

2639 ■ *"Job Program is 'Giving People Dignity" in Forest Park Review (September 17, 2019)*
URL(s): www.forestparkreview.com/News/Articles/9
  -17-2019/Job-program-is-'giving-people-dignity'/
Released: September 17, 2019. **Description:** Revolution Workshop in Chicago is a woodworking shop that trains people with few to no skills in carpentry and construction. People who have been affected by drugs, crime, trauma, homelessness, and jail often come here to learn a trade and change their lives. Official certification can be earned, and it's all free. **Availability:** Online.

2640 ■ *"What Goes into a Good Cabinet?" in Woodshop News (September 1, 2021)*
Ed: John English. **Released:** September 01, 2021. **Description:** Discusses the design, hardware, wood needed to produce quality cabinets. **Availability:** Online.

2641 ■ Carpentry Service

2641 ■ "Yes They Can! Program Boosts Number of Women Construction Workers" in The Wall Street Journal (February 12, 2019)
URL(s): www.wsj.com/articles/yes-they-can-program-boosts-number-of-women-construction-workers-11549983600
Ed: Anne Kadet. **Released:** February 12, 2019.
Description: The Nontraditional Employment for Women (NEW) recruits and trains around 225 women a year for the purpose of entering New York City's apprentice construction programs. With this effort well under way, women represent more than 6% of construction workers in the city. These jobs have higher pay and benefits than traditional jobs held by women and are helping women sustain their families.
Availability: Online.

STATISTICAL SOURCES

2642 ■ Cabinet & Vanity Manufacturing Industry in the US - Market Research Report
URL(s): www.ibisworld.com/united-states/market-research-reports/cabinet-vanity-manufacturing-industry/
Price: $925. **Description:** Downloadable report analyzing the current and future trends in the cabinet and vanity manufacturing industry. **Availability:** Download.

2643 ■ Carpenters Industry in the US - Market Research Report
URL(s): www.ibisworld.com/united-states/market-research-reports/carpenters-industry/
Price: $925. **Description:** Downloadable report analyzing the current and future trends in the carpentry industry. **Availability:** Download.

2644 ■ RMA Annual Statement Studies
Pub: Risk Management Association
Contact: Nancy Foster, President
Released: Annual. **Description:** Contains composite balance sheets and income statements for more than 360 industries, including the accounting, auditing, and bookkeeping industries. Also contains five years of comparative historical data for discerning trends. Includes 16 commonly used ratios, computed for most of the size groupings for nearly every industry.

TRADE PERIODICALS

2645 ■ Wood Digest: Productivity Solutions for Manufacturers of Furniture, Cabinets, Millworks and Speciality Wood Products
Pub: NueMedia L.L.C.
Description: Manufactures of wood products trade magazine. **Availability:** Print.

2646 ■ Woodshop News: The News Magazine for Professional Woodworkers
Pub: Cruz Bay Publishing Inc.
Contact: Andrew W. Clurman, President
E-mail: aclurman@aimmedia.com
URL(s): www.woodshopnews.com
Linkedin: www.linkedin.com/company/woodshop-news
X (Twitter): x.com/woodshopnews
Ed: Tod Riggio. **Released:** Monthly **Price:** $10, for 1 year (12 issues); $18, Two years for (24 issues).
Description: Newspaper (tabloid) focusing on people and businesses involved in woodworking. **Availability:** Print; PDF; Online.

FRANCHISES AND BUSINESS OPPORTUNITIES

2647 ■ Archadeck
2924 Emerywood Pkwy., Ste. 101
Richmond, VA 23294
Ph: (804)374-4717
URL: http://www.archadeck.com
Description: Custom design deck franchise. When a deck design is chosen, franchisees send preliminary sketches to the company's drafting division which will supply full construction plans with complete material layouts and specifications. Subcontracted Archadeck-trained carpenters will usually build the deck in 2-3 days. **No. of Franchise Units:** 75. **Founded:** 1980. **Franchised:** 1984. **Equity Capital Needed:** $69,000-$102,900. **Franchise Fee:** $49,500. **Financial Assistance:** Yes **Training:** Yes.

2648 ■ Dollar Castle Inc.
7031 Orchard Lake Rd., Ste. 201A
West Bloomfield, MI 48322
Ph: (248)539-3100
URL: http://dollarcastle.com
Contact: Eddie Denha, Chief Executive Officer
Facebook: www.facebook.com/dollarcastlestores
Instagram: www.instagram.com/dollarcastle
Description: Retailer of brand products, food, cleaning and party supplies in outlets. **Founded:** 1992. **Franchised:** 1992. **Training:** Yes.

2649 ■ DreamMaker Bath & Kitchen
4710 W Waco Dr.
Waco, TX 76710
Ph: (254)277-2202
Free: 833-569-1386
Co. E-mail: marketing@dreammakerbk.com
URL: http://www.dreammaker-remodel.com
Contact: Doug Dwyer, President
URL(s): www.dreammakerfranchise.com
Facebook: www.facebook.com/DreamMakerRemodel
X (Twitter): x.com/dmbkremodel
Instagram: www.instagram.com/dreammakerremodel
YouTube: www.youtube.com/user/DreamMakerRemodeling
Pinterest: www.pinterest.com/dreammakerbk
Description: Specializes in bath and kitchen remodeling options. **No. of Franchise Units:** 38.0. **Founded:** 1988. **Franchised:** 1971. **Equity Capital Needed:** Net Worth $100,000 to $400,000 ; Liquid Capital $50,000 to $80,000. **Franchise Fee:** $37,000 to $44,000 plus $185 per 1,000 additional population over the minimum. **Royalty Fee:** 3% to 6%, of gross sales. **Financial Assistance:** No **Training:** Extensive business, marketing and management training provided including team training conferences, an annual convention (Reunion) offers networking opportunities with other DreamMaker Bath & Kitchen franchisees, and continuous training.

2650 ■ Exovations
1550-A Oak Industrial Ln.
Cumming, GA 30041
Free: 877-396-8632
Co. E-mail: customerservice@exovations.com
URL: http://exovations.com
Contact: Roone Unger, Chief Executive Officer
Facebook: www.facebook.com/EXOVATIONS
Linkedin: www.linkedin.com/company/exovations
X (Twitter): x.com/exovations
YouTube: www.youtube.com/user/TheEXOVATIONS
Pinterest: www.pinterest.com/exovations
Description: Provider of home exterior remodeling services. **Founded:** 1996. **Financial Assistance:** Yes **Training:** Offers 2 weeks at headquarters, 2 weeks at franchisee's location and ongoing support.

2651 ■ Garagetek
206 Bethpage-Sweet Hollow Rd.
Old Bethpage, NY 11804
Free: 866-664-2724
Co. E-mail: hq@garagetek.com
URL: http://www.garagetek.com
Contact: Marc Shuman, President
Facebook: www.facebook.com/GarageTek
Instagram: www.instagram.com/garagetek
Pinterest: www.pinterest.com/garagetek
Description: Firm provides garage storage solutions. **Founded:** 2000. **Training:** Provides 2 weeks at corporate and ongoing field support.

2652 ■ Granite Transformations
1565 NW 36th St.
Miami, FL 33142
Ph: (954)435-5538
Co. E-mail: rsgmarketing@trend-group.com
URL: http://www.granitetransformations.com
X (Twitter): x.com/granite_trans
Instagram: www.instagram.com/granitetrendtransformations
YouTube: www.youtube.com/user/GraniteTrans
Pinterest: www.pinterest.com/granitetrans
Description: Provider of Construction, remodeling and bath and closets services. **Founded:** 1996. **Training:** Training program consists of operations, installations, and sales training. Each training module is supported with training material. Training facility is an actual working location allowing trainees to evaluate, test, and see results. Grand opening supported by sales manager onsite and ongoing support.

2653 ■ House Doctors Handyman Service
400 Techne Center Dr., Ste. 101
Milford, OH 45150
Free: 800-319-3359
Co. E-mail: info@housedoctors.com
URL: http://housedoctors.com
Description: Firm provides home repair and light remodeling services. **Founded:** 1994. **Financial Assistance:** Yes **Training:** 5 days of training includes marketing, technical knowledge, and business procedures.

2654 ■ Kitchen Solvers
301 Fourth St. S
Onalaska, WI 54650
Ph: (608)784-2855
Free: 800-845-6779
Co. E-mail: info@kitchensolvers.com
URL: http://www.kitchensolvers.com
Facebook: www.facebook.com/kitchensolversfranchise
X (Twitter): x.com/KitchenSolvers
Instagram: www.instagram.com/kitchensolvers
YouTube: www.youtube.com/KitchenSolversLLC
Pinterest: www.pinterest.com/kitchensolv0036
Description: Firm provides kitchen remodeling, kitchen cabinet refacing, storage solutions, kitchen design. **Founded:** 1982. **Financial Assistance:** Yes **Training:** Yes.

2655 ■ Kitchen Tune-Up
813 Cir., Dr.
Aberdeen, SD 57401
Free: 800-333-6385
URL: http://kitchentuneup.com
Contact: Heidi Morrissey, President
Linkedin: www.linkedin.com/company/kitchen-tune-up-franchise-system
Instagram: www.instagram.com/kitchentuneup
YouTube: www.youtube.com/channel/UCD5S3Upl_ACJYLoBp6vTSYg
Pinterest: www.pinterest.com/ktuofficial
Description: Provides inexpensive wood care services to both the residential homeowner and the commercial property owner. Also offers door replacement materials. This is a home-based, no-inventory, high-profit margin business. Offers potential franchise owners the unique opportunity to attend training and evaluate the franchise before signing the franchise agreement. **No. of Franchise Units:** 204. **Founded:** 1975. **Franchised:** 1988. **Equity Capital Needed:** $58,000- $66,000 or $22,000-$25,000 for Express. **Franchise Fee:** $25,000 or $10,000 for Kitchen Tune-Up Express. **Financial Assistance:** Yes **Training:** Initial training and ongoing support.

2656 ■ Ready Decks Franchise Systems Inc.
1250 New Natchitoches Rd.
West Monroe, LA 71292
Free: 888-Dec-ks50
URL: http://www.readydecks.com
Contact: Bradley W. Johns, Contact
Facebook: www.facebook.com/ReadyDecksInc
X (Twitter): x.com/readydecks
YouTube: www.youtube.com/user/readydecks
Pinterest: www.pinterest.com/readydecks
Description: Builder of decks, pool decks, steps, porches, wheel chair ramps and car ports. **Founded:** 2001. **Financial Assistance:** Yes **Training:** Offers 2 weeks at headquarters, 1 week onsite and ongoing support.

2657 ■ RENOCanada-Bathroom and Kitchen Makeover Specialists
3301 Uplands Dr.
  Ottawa, ON, Canada K1V 9V8
Ph: (613)850-7738
Co. E-mail: renocanadainc@hotmail.com
URL: http://www.renocanada.net
Facebook: www.facebook.com/people/GA-Renocanada-Inc/100090930280692
Linkedin: www.linkedin.com/company/g-a-renocanada-inc
Instagram: www.instagram.com/garenocanadainc

Description: New concept in home renovation where home improvement is not about the house, it's about self-improvement (lifestyle) and that bathrooms and kitchens are personal. **Founded:** 2023. **Training:** Intensive franchisee training at Head Office, in-store, pre-opening and grand opening assistance with ongoing support.

2658 ■ United States Seamless
474 45th St. S
  Fargo, ND 58103
Free: 888-743-3632
URL: http://www.usseamless.com
Contact: Michael J. Bullinger, Contact
Linkedin: www.linkedin.com/company/united-states-seamless
X (Twitter): x.com/USSeamless
Instagram: www.instagram.com/usseamless

Description: Manufacturer of seamless steel siding. **Founded:** 1992. **Financial Assistance:** Yes **Training:** Available unlimited at headquarters, annual training, and ongoing support.

Catering Service

START-UP INFORMATION

2659 ■ *Culinary Careers: How to Get Your Dream Job in Food with Advice from Top Culinary Professionals*
Pub: Clarkson Potter
Ed: Rick Smilow, Anne E. McBride. **Released:** May 04, 2010. **Price:** $23.99, paperback. **Description:** Top culinary experts offer advice for working in or owning a food service firm. **Availability:** E-book; Print.

2660 ■ *How to Start a Home-Based Catering Business*
Ed: Denise Vivaldo. **Released:** January 06, 2010. **Price:** $19.95, paperback; $18.99, e-book; Paperback. **Availability:** E-book; Print.

2661 ■ *How to Start a Home-Based Personal Chef Business*
Ed: Denise Vivaldo. **Released:** January 04, 2011. **Price:** paperback/softback. **Description:** Everything needed to know to start a personal chef business is featured. **Availability:** E-book; Print.

2662 ■ *Start and Run a Home-Based Food Business*
Pub: Self-Counsel Press Inc.
Contact: Diana Douglas, Governor
Ed: Mimi Shortland Fix. **Price:** C$23.95; C$23.95, E pub; $12.99. **Description:** Information is shared to help start and run a home-based food business, selling your own homemade foods. **Availability:** Electronic publishing; PDF.

ASSOCIATIONS AND OTHER ORGANIZATIONS

2663 ■ **Association of Club Catering Professionals (ACCP)**
PO Box 800266
Santa Clarita, CA 91380-0266
Ph: (805)338-7640
Co. E-mail: lynne@theaccp.com
URL: http://www.theaccp.com
Contact: Lynne LaFond DeLuca, Contact
E-mail: lynne@theaccp.com
Description: Supports catering professionals at private clubs through education, training, and certification.

2664 ■ **International Caterers Association (ICA)**
3601 E Joppa Rd.
Baltimore, MD 21234
Fax: (410)931-8111
Co. E-mail: info@internationalcaterers.org
URL: http://www.internationalcaterers.org
Contact: Steve Sanchez, President
Instagram: www.instagram.com/icacater
Description: Caterers and vendors. Strives to educate and raise the level of awareness about the catering industry. Sponsors the annual Art of Catering Food conference. **Founded:** 1981. **Publications:** *International Caterers Association Membership Directory*. **Geographic Preference:** Multinational.

2665 ■ **National Association for Catering and Events (NACE)**
10440 Little Patuxent Pky., Ste. 300
Columbia, MD 21044
Ph: (410)290-5410
Fax: (410)630-5768
Co. E-mail: info@nace.net
URL: http://www.nace.net
Contact: James Filtz, President
Facebook: www.facebook.com/NACENatl
Linkedin: www.linkedin.com/company/national-association-for-catering-and-events
X (Twitter): x.com/nacenational
Instagram: www.instagram.com/nacenational
YouTube: www.youtube.com/c/NationalAssociationforCateringandEventsNACE
Description: Addresses banquet facilities, off-premise, country club, military and resort catering. Provides continuing education, certification, networking and career support. **Founded:** 1958. **Publications:** *How To Get 5 Star Reviews*; *Legal Moves for a Successful 2022*; *Brand Authenticity Webinar*; *No Dozing on the Closing: 4 Tips to Win the Sale*; *5 Ways to Streamline Your Digital Marketing Webinar*; *Communication is Key: How to Communicate and Show Gratitude Effectively Amongst Colleagues*; *Don't Overlook the Obvious: Safety & Site Selection*; *Cultivating Comfort: The Key to Impeccable Client Experience*; *Prep, Reset & Revive for the New Year Webinar Series*; *Secrets of Highly Effective Networking to Build Brand Equity*; *Sorry, Not Sorry — How to Stop Over Apologizing and Feeling Guilty in Your Business*; *Uncovering Innovation in Events in 2022*; *Culture Eats Strategy for Breakfast*; *The Conversion Factor: How to Turn Inquiries into Bookings*; *Marketing Health Check: How to Know What Works and What Doesn't in Your Marketing Mix*; *The Impact of Operation on Your Business Longevity*; *The Wedding Roller Coaster and the Client Experience*; *Five Steps to Strategically Position Yourself in the Wedding Marketplace*; *A Look at Weddings in the New World: How Couples are Planning Weddings in the COVID Era*; *The Power of Language in Your Business*; *Beyond the Gram - Why Networking is Still the Most Powerful Marketing Tool*; *Springing into Sustainability: The What, Where, How, Why and Who of Food and Beverage Sustainability Part 1*; *Springing into Sustainability: The What, Where, How, Why and Who of Food and Beverage Sustainability Part 3*; *Stopping Business Takeover, Enslavement to Empowerment: How African Americans Molded Today's Catering Industry and It's Continued Evolution*; *NACE News Network* (Monthly); *Professional Caterer* (Quarterly). **Educational Activities:** National Association of Catering and Events Education Conference. **Awards:** NACE Chapter of the Year Award (Annual); George Zell Spirit of NACE Award (Annual). **Geographic Preference:** Multinational.

2666 ■ **National Barbecue & Grilling Association (NBBQA)**
500 NE 23rd St.
Fort Worth, TX 76135
Co. E-mail: admin@nbbqa.org
URL: http://www.nbbqa.org
Contact: Barbara Latimer, President
Facebook: www.facebook.com/NBBQA
Linkedin: www.linkedin.com/company/nbbqa
X (Twitter): x.com/NBBQA
Instagram: www.instagram.com/nbbqa
Description: Industry professionals and barbecue enthusiasts including restaurants, caterers, specialty equipment retailers, grill manufacturers and distributors, smoker manufacturers and distributors, food product suppliers and distributors, sauces and spice distributors, backyard hobbyists. **Founded:** 1991. **Publications:** *National Barbecue News* (Bimonthly); *NBBQA Barbecue Buyers' Guide* (Annual). **Awards:** NBBQA Award of Excellence (Annual). **Geographic Preference:** National.

2667 ■ **Restaurants Canada - Library**
1155 Queen St. W
Toronto, ON, Canada M6J 1J4
Ph: (416)923-8416
Free: 800-387-5649
Fax: (416)923-1450
Co. E-mail: info@restaurantscanada.org
URL: http://www.restaurantscanada.org
Contact: Christian Buhagiar, Co-Chief Executive Officer Co-President
Facebook: www.facebook.com/RestaurantsCanada
Linkedin: www.linkedin.com/company/restaurants-canada
X (Twitter): x.com/RestaurantsCA
Instagram: www.instagram.com/RestaurantsCanada
YouTube: www.youtube.com/channel/UCxVckfCBIISII9LOuflNX8w
Description: Restaurant and food service corporations, hotels, caterers, and food service suppliers and educators, seeks to create a favorable business environment for members. **Scope:** Food service; quantity cooking; legislation; administration; management; statistics; training; customer attitude surveys. **Services:** Copying; open to the public on fee basis. **Founded:** 1944. **Publications:** *CRFA National Hospitality News*; *Canadian Foodservice Industry Operations Report* (Biennial); *Foodservice Facts* (Annual); *Legislation Guide* (Quarterly). **Educational Activities:** Restaurants Canada Show (Annual); ApEx. **Geographic Preference:** National.

REFERENCE WORKS

2668 ■ *"As the Supply Chain Slows, Demand for Aftermarket Equipment Takes Off' in Restaurant Business (November 17, 2021)*
URL(s): www.restaurantbusinessonline.com/financing/supply-chain-slows-demand-aftermarket-equipment-takes
Ed: Jonathan Maze. **Released:** November 18, 2021. **Description:** Since Covid put in a dent in the global supply chain, restaurants have taken a second look at used equipment in order to stock their kitchens. **Availability:** Online.

Small Business Profiles

2669 ■ "Best Places to Work; No. 2 Tasty Catering Inc." in Crain's Chicago Business (Vole 35, April 2, 2012, No. 14, pp. 18)
Pub: Crain Communications Inc.
Contact: Barry Asin, President
Ed: Sachiko Yoshitsugu. Description: Tasty Catering Inc., located in Elk Grove Village, Illinois was rated Number 2 in Crain's Best Places to Work category. The event planning and catering firm offers a family style lunch to employees weekly. CEO Tom Walters enjoys this meal with his workers. The company offers an educational program called Tasty Catering University that provides up to 30 hours of paid class time in courses ranging from English to business. Availability: Online.

2670 ■ "The Caterer Interview - Patrick Harbour and Nathan Jones" in Caterer & Hotelkeeper (October 28, 2011, No. 288)
Description: Profiles of Patrick Harbour and Nathan Jones who quit their jobs to start their own catering business. The partners discuss their business strategy when launching their boutique catering firm and ways they are adapting to the slow economy in order to remain successful. Availability: Print; Mailing list; Online.

2671 ■ "Chef Revelations - Derek Johnstone" in Caterer & Hotelkeeper (October 28, 2011, No. 288)
Description: Profile of Derek Johnstone, head chef at Greywalls Hotel and Chez Roux and his love for catering. Availability: Print; Online.

2672 ■ "Edible Endeavors" in Black Enterprise (March 1, 2008)
Pub: Earl G. Graves Ltd.
Contact: Earl Graves, Jr., President
Ed: Carolyn M. Brown. Description: Profile of Jacqueline Frazer, woman entrepreneur who turned her love for cooking into a catering business. She is chef and owner of Command Performance in New York City. The firm works with more than 50 clients annually and generates annual revenues of about $350,000. Availability: Online.

2673 ■ Foodservice Consultants Society International--Membership Directory
Pub: Foodservice Consultants Society International
Contact: Nick Vaccaro, Executive
E-mail: nick@fcsi.org
URL(s): www.fcsi.org/about-fcsi/divisions/the-americas/membership
Description: Covers about 1,400 members who design and advise on management and other aspects of food service operations. Entries include: Name, company name, address, business phone, home phone (if available), fax, e-mail, areas of specialty. Arrangement: Classified by membership type. Indexes: Geographical, company name. Availability: Print; Online.

2674 ■ "Grazing Tables Are Suddenly Everywhere —And Nobody Knows How to Use Them" in The Wall Street Journal (October 14, 2019)
URL(s): www.wsj.com/articles/grazing-tables-are-suddenly-everywhere-and-nobody-knows-how-to-use-them-11571065282
Ed: Alina Dizik. Released: October 14, 2019. Description: Caters are embracing the new trend of providing tables piled with food, instead of appetizers presented on traditional trays. This less formal set-up may be the hottest new thing but it does confuse guests and creates some health and hygiene issues. Availability: Online.

2675 ■ "Meeting and Banquet Venues" in Business Review Albany (Vol. 41, August 8, 2014, No. 20, pp. 6)
Released: Weekly. Price: $25, download. Description: The top 25 meeting and banquet venues in Albany, New York in 2013 are ranked by number of banquets hosted. The Desmond Hotel and Conference Center hold the top spot. The Otesega Resort Hotel ranked second. Availability: Print; Online.

2676 ■ "NACE Becomes the National Association for Catering and Events" in Entertainment Close-Up (July 29, 2012)
Pub: Close-Up Media Inc.
Contact: Caroline S. Moore, President
E-mail: cms@closeupmedia.com
Description: National Association for Catering and Events (NACE) is committed to event and catering professionals seeking the highest training in all aspects of event planning, design and execution. In a recent survey, NACE reports that 44 percent of its members chose catering and event planning as a second career. Availability: Online.

2677 ■ "Professional Help: Cross That Off Your To-Do List" in Inc. (November 2007, pp. 89-90, 92)
Ed: Alison Stein Wellner. Description: Small business owners are finding that it pays to hire someone to takeover the personal tasks of daily living, including hiring a personal assistant, chauffeur, chef, stylist, pet caregiver, or concierge service. Availability: Online.

2678 ■ "Q&A: Chuck Hughes, Celebrity Chef" in Canadian Business (Vol. 85, July 16, 2012, No. 11-12, pp. 65)
Ed: Nancy Won. Description: Celebrity chef Chuck Hughes feels blessed for the opportunity to work on a new cookbook based on the 'Chuck's Day Off' series and to start filming for a new U.S. show called 'Chuck Eats the Street'. For Hughes, cooking at the restaurant is the most rewarding and fulfilling job of all the things he does. Availability: Print; Online.

2679 ■ "Savvy Solutions" in Black Enterprise (Vol. 41, November 2010, No. 4, pp. 42)
Description: Society of Children's Book Writers and Illustrators offers members many benefits, including directories of agencies looking for new writers of books. Availability: Online.

2680 ■ "Supersized: Delaware North Ready to Feed 80,000 NFL Fans" in Business First of Buffalo (Vol. 30, January 31, 2014, No. 20, pp. 3)
Pub: American City Business Journals, Inc.
Contact: Mike Olivieri, Executive Vice President
Released: January 31, 2014. Description: Delaware North is set to cater the food, retailing and beverage needs of 80,000 football fans at the Super Bowl games in New York. The company will bring 80 top venue managers and 30 high-level executive sous chefs to the event. Menu for the event is presented.

2681 ■ "To-Go Packaging, Streamlined Menus Remain Big in 2022" in Restaurant Business (November 16, 2021)
URL(s): www.restaurantbusinessonline.com/food/go-packaging-streamlined-menus-remain-big-2022
Ed: Patricia Cobe. Released: November 16, 2021. Description: The National Restaurant Association's "What's Hot" report lists the number one trend in the industry is packaging for food. More people are still ordering to-go and getting the right type of packaging to keep the food hot and tasty is a priority for at least the next year. Availability: Online.

2682 ■ "Transparency Tops Tate & Lyle's List of Trends" in Food Business News (November 18,2021)
URL(s): www.foodbusinessnews.net/articles/20075-transparency-tops-tate-and-lyles-list-of-trends
Ed: Jeff Gelski. Released: November 18, 2021. Description: Six trends in the food and beverage industry are driving the needs of consumers. The top one, transparency, is based on customers wanting to know what the products they are eating and drinking are made of. Availability: Online.

2683 ■ "Unconventional Success: The Story of Naomi Ariel Catering and Event Planning" in The Southern (October 13, 2019)
URL(s): thesouthern.com/business/local/unconventional-success-the-story-of-naomi-ariel-catering-and-event/article_6d74983e-529b-51bb-a7de-c28c5aadaf9e.html
Ed: Les O'Dell. Released: October 13, 2019. Description: Profile of Carla Childs and her business, Naomi Ariel Catering and Event Planning. Childs discusses her path to success and how she grew her business from the ground up into the area's fastest growing catering business. Availability: Online.

2684 ■ Wholesale Grocer & Foodservice Distributor Leads
Pub: Chain Store Guide
Contact: Kaitlyn Toner, Account Manager
URL(s): www.chainstoreguide.com/c-88-wholesale-grocer-foodservice-distributor-leads-plus.aspx
Description: Covers about 4,700 companies in the United States and Canada with at least $500,000 in sales to foodservice companies. Included companies must distribute more than one product line and obtain no more than 95% of its total sales volume from self-manufactured merchandise. Entries include: Company name, address, phone and fax numbers, e-mail and web addresses; Internet order processing indicator and sales percentage; total sales; foodservice and wholesale sales; product lines; total units served; foodservice accounts served; trading areas; distribution center locations; markets served; buying/marketing group name and location; subsidiaries names and locations; divisional, regional and branch office locations; year founded; public company indicator; key personnel with titles; 21,700 foodservice distribution contacts; 9,642 Name, address, phone, fax. Arrangement: Geographical. Indexes: Product lines, alphabetical, exclusions. Availability: Download; Online.

STATISTICAL SOURCES

2685 ■ Caterers Industry in the US - Market Research Report
URL(s): www.ibisworld.com/united-states/market-research-reports/caterers-industry/
Price: $925. Description: Downloadable report detailing the data from the catering industry and future outlook concerning the affects of COVID-19. Availability: Download.

TRADE PERIODICALS

2686 ■ Cooking for Profit
Released: Monthly Description: Food service trade publication for owners/operators of food service businesses. Profiles successful operations, offers management tips, recipes with photos and step-by-step instructions, new and improved uses and maintenance of gas equipment. Availability: Print; Online.

2687 ■ The National Culinary Review (NCR)
Pub: American Culinary Federation
Contact: Kimberly Brock Brown, President
E-mail: chefkbb@acfchefs.org
URL(s): www.acfchefs.org/ACF/About/Media/Publications/ACF/About/Media/Publications
Ed: Kay Orde. Released: 6/year Price: $140, for online; $40, for domestic; $200, for international; $140, for online and print. Description: Trade magazine covering food and cooking. Includes articles on food, drink, and menu trends; recipes; personal and professional development; and management. Availability: Print; PDF; Online.

VIDEO/AUDIO MEDIA

2688 ■ Matt Lombardo Chef/Owner Pink Door Catering + Market
URL(s): restaurantunstoppable.libsyn.com/1023-matt-lombardo-chefowner-pink-door-catering-market
Ed: Eric Cacciatore. Released: September 04, 2023. Description: Podcast offers a conversation with the owner of Pink Door Catering + Market.

2689 ■ Sandy Korem Founder and CEO at Festive Kitchen
URL(s): restaurantunstoppable.com/sandy-korem-festive-kitchen

Ed: Eric Cacciatore. **Released:** February 01, 2023. **Description:** Podcast discusses starting with no experience (and first experiences), starting small, and budgeting in the catering industry.

TRADE SHOWS AND CONVENTIONS

2690 ■ ApEx
Restaurants Canada
1155 Queen St. W
Toronto, ON, Canada M6J 1J4
Ph: (416)923-8416
Free: 800-387-5649
Fax: (416)923-1450
Co. E-mail: info@restaurantscanada.org
URL: http://www.restaurantscanada.org
Contact: Christian Buhagiar, Co-Chief Executive Officer Co-President
URL(s): www.apextradeshow.ca
Description: Products and services for the restaurant and hospitality industry, as well as institutions, convenience stores, delis and bakeries. **Audience:** Industry professionals. **Principal Exhibits:** Products and services for the restaurant and hospitality industry, as well as institutions, convenience stores, delis and bakeries. **Telecommunication Services:** chuckn@mediaedge.ca.

CONSULTANTS

2691 ■ Cini-Little International Inc.
20251 Century Blvd., Ste. 375
Germantown, MD 20874
Ph: (301)528-9700
Co. E-mail: kheld@cinilittle.com
URL: http://cinilittle.com
Contact: Kathleen M. Held, Chief Executive Officer
E-mail: kheld@cinilittle.com
Facebook: www.facebook.com/CiniLittle
Linkedin: www.linkedin.com/company/cini-little-international
X (Twitter): x.com/cinilittle
Pinterest: www.pinterest.com/cinilittle
Description: Firm provides planning, operational consulting and designing service. **Founded:** 1968.

FRANCHISES AND BUSINESS OPPORTUNITIES

2692 ■ City Kitchen
670 S Santa Fe Ave.
Los Angeles, CA 90021
Ph: (213)236-4995
Free: 800-704-2070
Fax: (213)236-0951
Co. E-mail: infola@citykitchen.com
URL: http://www.citykitchen.com
Contact: Ken Brown, Executive
Description: Firm provides catering services for meetings, parties and special events.

2693 ■ Corporate Caterers
10631 N Kendall Dr., Ste. 220
Miami, FL 33176
Ph: (305)223-1230
Co. E-mail: corpcaterers@corpcaterers.com
URL: http://www.corporatecaterers.com/franchising/resources/food-for-thought
Contact: Greg Halton, President
Facebook: www.facebook.com/CorpCaterers
Linkedin: www.linkedin.com/company/corporate-caterers
X (Twitter): x.com/corpcaterers
YouTube: www.youtube.com/user/corpcaterersusa
Description: Firm provides catering services for professional offices and business events. **Founded:** 1997. **Franchised:** 2008. **Training:** Offers corporate catering services.

2694 ■ Steak-Out Charbroiled Delivery
2300 Holcomb Bridge Rd., Ste. 103-363
Roswell, GA 30076
Free: 877-878-3257
Co. E-mail: info@steakout.com
URL: http://steakout.com
Facebook: www.facebook.com/savorthesizzle
X (Twitter): x.com/SteakOutUSA
Description: Full meal delivery chain featuring charbroiled steaks, chicken, seafood, burgers, chef salads and deserts. **Founded:** 1986. **Financial Assistance:** Yes **Training:** Training is 4 weeks in the store and at headquarters for 3 to 4 management employees. Complete support in site finding, store opening, marketing and ongoing.

LIBRARIES

2695 ■ City College of San Francisco (CCSF) - Culinary Arts and Hospitality Studies - Alice Statler Library
50 Frida Kahlo Way
Statler Wing, Rm. 10
San Francisco, CA 94112
Ph: (415)239-3460
URL: http://library.ccsf.edu/locations/statler
Scope: Culinary arts and hospitality study; historical menus; notable titles; local chefs, restaurateurs, hoteliers and entrepreneurs in the industry. **Services:** Copying; Wi-Fi; library open to the public for reference use only. **Founded:** 1964. **Holdings:** Books; menus; archives; monographs; periodicals; DVDs.

2696 ■ Culinary Institute of America - Conrad N. Hilton Library
1946 Campus Dr.
Hyde Park, NY 12538-1430
Ph: (845)451-1747
Co. E-mail: library@culinary.edu
URL: http://library.culinary.edu/index
Contact: Jon Grennan, Director
E-mail: j_grenna@culinary.edu
Scope: Arts materials. **Services:** Interlibrary loan; copying; library open to the public by appointment. **Founded:** 1946. **Holdings:** 86,000 volumes; 30,000 menus; 4,500 DVDs and videos. **Subscriptions:** 280 journals and other serials.

2697 ■ Food Institute (FI)
330 Changebridge Rd., Ste. 101
Pine Brook, NJ 07058
Ph: (201)791-5570
Free: 855-791-5570
Co. E-mail: questions@foodinstitute.com
URL: http://www.foodinstitute.com
Contact: Anika Wilson, Contact
E-mail: anika.wilson@foodinstitute.com
Facebook: www.facebook.com/foodinstitutenj
Linkedin: www.linkedin.com/company/the-food-institute
X (Twitter): x.com/FoodInstitute
Instagram: www.instagram.com/foodinstitute
YouTube: www.youtube.com/channel/UCYAPI0TXNtJa04aQre4h4pA
Description: Strives to provide food industry-related information to its members. **Scope:** The food industry. **Services:** Center open to the public on fee basis. **Founded:** 1928. **Holdings:** Figures not available. **Publications:** *Today in Food*; *Get It Out, Get It Right, Get It Over! Avoiding Food Product Recalls*; *The Food Institute* (Weekly); *Almanac of the Canning, Freezing, Preserving Industries* (Annual); *Food Business Mergers and Acquisitions*; *OSHA Inspection Manual*; *Regulatory Directory* (Periodic); *Food Business Mergers & Acquisitions*. **Geographic Preference:** Multinational.

2698 ■ Johnson & Wales University-Harborside Culinary Library (JWU)
321 Harborside Blvd.
Providence, RI 02905
Ph: (401)598-1466
Co. E-mail: ask@jwu-ri.libanswers.com
URL: http://pvd.library.jwu.edu/lticulinary
Contact: Lisa Spicola, Librarian
E-mail: lisa.helwigpayne@jwu.edu
X (Twitter): x.com/jwulibrary
YouTube: www.youtube.com/user/JWULibraryPVD
Scope: Food service; menu planning; nutrition; professional management; catering and banquets; household manuals; canning; preserving and freezing; hotel and motel management. **Services:** Copying; Library open to the public. **Founded:** 1979.

Cellular Phone/Telephone Business

START-UP INFORMATION

2699 ■ *"'Entrepreneurial Spirit' Leads Executives to Form New Tower Company"* in *South Florida Business Journal (Vol. 34, February 21, 2014, No. 31, pp. 6)*
Pub: American City Business Journals, Inc.
Contact: Mike Olivieri, Executive Vice President
Released: Weekly. **Price:** $8, Introductory 4-week offer(Digital & Print). **Description:** Phoenix Tower International is a new company in Boca Raton, Florida formed by the former executives of Global Tower Partners, a multibillion-dollar company that was sold in October 2013. Phoenix is self-funded and will focused on owning, leasing, and managing cellular phone service towers. **Availability:** Print; Online.

ASSOCIATIONS AND OTHER ORGANIZATIONS

2700 ■ **Canadian Telecommunications Association (CWTA)**
180 Elgin St., Ste. 1100
Ottawa, ON, Canada K2P 2K3
Ph: (613)233-4888
Fax: (613)233-2032
Co. E-mail: info@canadatelecoms.ca
URL: http://canadatelecoms.ca
Contact: Robert Ghiz, President
Linkedin: www.linkedin.com/company/canadian-telecommunications-association
Description: Promotes the wireless communications industry in Canada in order to create and maintain a positive economic environment; encourages further investment by the industry to improve the delivery of existing services and create further innovation. **Founded:** 1969. **Publications:** *CWTA Membership - Products and Services Directory*; *Wireless Telecom* (3/year); *Wireless Telecom*. **Geographic Preference:** National.

2701 ■ **Communications Marketing Association (CMA)**
204 S Shaffer Dr.
New Freedom, PA 17349
Free: 844-262-2625
Co. E-mail: cmaexecdirector@gmail.com
URL: http://cma-cmc.org
Contact: Jeff Hall, President
Description: Manufacturers, independent manufacturers' representatives, and distributors who deal in two-way radio and wireless communication equipment and associated products. Promotes effective marketing and ensures professional industry standards. **Founded:** 1973. **Publications:** *CMA Newsletter* (Quarterly). **Educational Activities:** Communications Marketing Conference (CMC) (Annual). **Geographic Preference:** National.

2702 ■ **CTIA - The Wireless Association**
1400 16th St. NW, Ste. 600
Washington, DC 20036
Ph: (202)736-3200
URL: http://www.ctia.org
Contact: Meredith Attwell Baker, President
Description: Represents the U.S. wireless communications industry. **Founded:** 1984. **Publications:** *Cellular Technology Report* (Monthly); *Industry Data Survey* (Semiannual). **Educational Activities:** Cellular Telecommunications Industry Association Winter Meeting (CTIA) (Semiannual). **Geographic Preference:** National.

2703 ■ **Telecommunications Industry Association (TIA)**
1310 N Courthouse Rd., Ste. 890
Arlington, VA 22201
Ph: (703)907-7700
Fax: (703)907-7727
URL: http://tiaonline.org
Contact: Doug Moore, President
Facebook: www.facebook.com/TIAEvents
X (Twitter): x.com/TIAonline
YouTube: www.youtube.com/c/TIANOW/featured
Description: Serves the communications and IT industry, with proven strengths in standards development, domestic and international public policy, and trade shows. Facilitates business development and opportunities and a competitive market environment; provides a forum for member companies, the manufacturers and suppliers of products and services used in global communications. **Founded:** 1988. **Publications:** *TIA Directory and Desk Reference*; *Industry Pulse*; *Channel Intelligence Report*; *Industry Beat* (Weekly); *PulseOnline* (Monthly); *TIA Network* (Weekly). **Educational Activities:** Network of the Future (Annual). **Geographic Preference:** National.

2704 ■ **Wireless Infrastructure Association (WIA) - Library**
211 Wilson Blvd., Ste. 210
Arlington, VA 22201
Ph: (703)739-0300
Free: 800-759-0300
Fax: (703)836-1608
URL: http://wia.org
Contact: Jonathan Adelstein, President
Facebook: www.facebook.com/Wireless-Infrastructure-Association-37483328338
Linkedin: www.linkedin.com/company/wireless-infrastructure-association
X (Twitter): x.com/wiaorg
Description: Represents the companies that make up the wireless infrastructure ecosystem in the United States, including wireless carriers, infrastructure providers, and professional services firms that own and operate telecommunications facilities. Aims to support the wireless infrastructure through public affairs and advocacy efforts on the local, state and federal level. **Scope:** The wireless infrastructure ecosystem in the United States. **Holdings:** Figures not available. **Publications:** *The Bulletin* (Bimonthly); *PICA Bulletin: News and Analysis for the Personal Communication Industry*. **Educational Activities:** PCIA Wireless Infrastructure Show (Annual). **Geographic Preference:** Multinational.

REFERENCE WORKS

2705 ■ *"7 Trends Affecting the Security Technology Business"* in *IP SecurityWatch.com (March 2012)*
Ed: Geoff Kohl. **Description:** Scott Harkins, president of Honeywell Security Products for the Americas, outlines the seven trends affecting the security technology business. He covers smart phones and tablets, home automation, interctive services, integration beyond security systems, cloud services, standards, and apps. **Availability:** Online.

2706 ■ *"Acacia Subsidiary Acquires Patents Related to Shared Memory for Multimedia Processing from a Major Corporation"* in *Economics & Business Week (April 26, 2014, pp. 5)*
Pub: NewsRX LLC.
Contact: Kalani Rosell, Contact
Description: Acacia Research Corporation that a subsidiary has acquired U.S. patents and foreign counterparts related to the use of shared memory in multimedia processing systems such as mobile phones, tablets and other consumer electronic devices. **Availability:** Online.

2707 ■ *"Actiontec and Verizon Team Up for a Smarter Home"* in *Ecology,Environment & Conservation Business (November 5, 2011, pp. 3)*
Pub: Comtex News Network Inc.
Contact: Kan Devnani, President
Description: Verizon is implementing Actiontec Electronics' SG200 Service Gateway as a basic component of its Home Monitoring and Control service. This new smart home service allows customers to remotely check their homes, control locks and appliances, view home-energy use and more using a smartphone, PC, or FiOS TV. **Availability:** Online.

2708 ■ *"Agricharts Launches New Mobile App for Ag Market"* in *Farm Industry News (December 1, 2011)*
Pub: Informa Business Media, Inc.
Contact: Charlie McCurdy, President
Description: AgriCharts provides market data, agribusiness Website hosting and technology solutions for the agricultural industry. AgriCharts is a division of Barchart.com Inc. and announced the release of a new mobile applications that offers real-time or delayed platform for viewing quotes, charts and analysis of grains, livestock and other commodity markets. **Availability:** Print; Online.

2709 ■ *"All Those Applications, and Phone Users Just Want to Talk"* in *Advertising Age (Vol. 79, August 11, 2008, No. 31, pp. 18)*
Pub: Crain Communications, Inc.
Contact: Jessica Botos, Manager, Marketing
E-mail: jessica.botos@crainsnewyork.com
Ed: Mike Vorhaus. **Description:** Although consumers are slowly coming to text messaging and other data applications, a majority of those Americans surveyed

stated that they simply want to use their cell phones to talk and do not care about other activities. Statistical data included. **Availability:** Online.

2710 ■ *"Amazing Apple Does It Again"* in *Barron's (Vol. 92, September 15, 2012, No. 38, pp. 26)*
Pub: Dow Jones & Company Inc.
Contact: Almar Latour, Chief Executive Officer
Ed: Tiernan Ray. **Description:** The introduction of the Apple iPhone 5 lacked the flair of previous product introductions by the company. New chief executive officer Tim Cook has been criticized for this lack of flair for marketing, although pre-orders for the iPhone 5 remain high. **Availability:** Online.

2711 ■ *"Android Users Can Now Manage Life On-the-Go With New AboutOne Family Organizer Companion Application"* in *PR Newswire (August 1, 2012)*
Pub: PR Newswire Association LLC.
Description: AboutOne Family Organizer allows customers to handle family memories and paperwork using android and iPhone mobile phones. The Family Organizer app allows users to organize all household information and is password protected. Details of the app are included. **Availability:** Online.

2712 ■ *"App Brings Real-Time Personal Security, Company Says"* in *Philadelphia Business Journal (Vol. 33, July 4, 2014, No. 21, pp. 11)*
Pub: American City Business Journals, Inc.
Contact: Mike Olivieri, Executive Vice President
Released: Weekly. **Price:** $4, Introductory 4-week offer(Digital & Print). **Description:** EmergenSee, which is a mobile technology that transforms smartphones or tablets into personal security systems by downloading the app. It has the ability to stream live video and audio. **Availability:** Print; Online.

2713 ■ *"App Maker Thinks He Has the Ticket: But Denver Is Balking At Alternative To Parking Fines"* in *Denver Business Journal (Vol. 65, April 25, 2014, No. 50, pp. A10)*
Pub: American City Business Journals, Inc.
Contact: Mike Olivieri, Executive Vice President
Released: Weekly. **Price:** $4, introductory 4-week offer(Digital & Print). **Description:** Taylor Linnell started Ticket Cricket LLC with partner, Jeff Valdez, to make parking tickets obsolete in Denver, Colorado by using two smartphone applications, One, Ticket Cricket and 5 for 5. The Department of Public Works rejected Linnell's proposal; he was encouraged to try it with the city's parking system technology vendor, Xerox. **Availability:** Print; Online.

2714 ■ *"Apps For Anybody With an Idea"* in *Advertising Age (Vol. 79, October 17, 2008, No. 39, pp. 29)*
Pub: Crain Communications, Inc.
Contact: Jessica Botos, Manager, Marketing
E-mail: jessica.botos@crainsnewyork.com
Ed: Beth Snyder Bulik. **Description:** Apple's new online App Store is open to anyone with an idea and the ability to write code and many of these developers are not only finding a sense of community through this venue but are also making money since the sales are split with Apple, 30/70 in the developer's favor. **Availability:** Online.

2715 ■ *"As Traditional Web Site Adoption Slows, Facebook and Other Social Networks Become Key Platforms for Home-Based Business Promotional and Commercial Activity Online"* in *Marketing Weekly News (June 16, 2012)*
Description: Websites have provided an inexpensive means for businesses to market their products and services. However, home-based businesses are using social networking, email marketing, search engine optimization, search engine marketing, Website optimization for mobile devices, banner advertisements, and the use of ecommerce platforms such as eBay, Craigs list, and Amazon. **Availability:** Print; Online.

2716 ■ *"AT&T Spend Nears $2 Billion in California With Minority, Women and Disabled Veteran-Owned Businesses in 2011"* in *Engineering Business Journal (March 21, 2012)*
Description: AT&T reported $2 billion working with diverse suppliers in 2011, representing a consistent annual increase working with minority, women and disabled veteran owned businesses in California. AT&T prides itself on its 44 years leading the way by including minority, women and disabled veteran owned businesses to its supply chain. **Availability:** Print; Online.

2717 ■ *"Bank of America Fights To Keep Top Spot in Mobile Banking"* in *Charlotte Business Journal (Vol. 27, June 15, 2012, No. 13, pp. 1)*
Pub: American City Business Journals, Inc.
Contact: Mike Olivieri, Executive Vice President
Released: Weekly. **Price:** $20, Introductory 12-week offer(Digital & Print). **Description:** Bank of America has been fighting to maintain its lead in mobile banking services. Financial institutions, payment processors and e-commerce firms have started offering mobile banking services. **Availability:** Print; Online.

2718 ■ *"Big Trouble at Sony Ericsson"* in *Barron's (Vol. 88, March 24, 2008, No. 12, pp. M9)*
Pub: Dow Jones & Company Inc.
Contact: Almar Latour, Chief Executive Officer
Ed: Angelo Franchini. **Description:** Sony Ericsson is facing trouble as it warned that its sales and net income before taxes will fall by nearly half for the first quarter of 2008. The joint venture of Sony and Ericsson has a global mobile phone market share of nine percent as of 2007, fourth largest in the world. **Availability:** Online.

2719 ■ *"BlackBerry 10 Unlikely to Save RIM. RIM Has Few Options. Staying the Course Isn't One of Them"* in *Canadian Business (Vol. 85, July 16, 2012, No. 11-12, pp. 12)*
Ed: Joe Castaldo. **Description:** Research in Motion (RIM) plans to launch a new line of Blackberry 10 Smartphones in 2012 as part of a strategy to stay in business despite expected operating loss in the first quarter and strong competition. Other options for RIM include a sale, opening its network to offer added security and data compression services, or reinventing itself as a niche handset provider. **Availability:** Print; Online.

2720 ■ *"Blog Buzz Heralds Arrival of iPhone 2.0"* in *Advertising Age (Vol. 79, June 9, 2008, No. 40, pp. 8)*
Pub: Crain Communications, Inc.
Contact: Jessica Botos, Manager, Marketing
E-mail: jessica.botos@crainsnewyork.com
Ed: Abbey Klaassen. **Description:** Predictions concerning the next version of the iPhone include a global-positioning-system technology as well as a configuration to run on a faster, 3G network. **Availability:** Online.

2721 ■ *Buyology: Truth and Lies About Why We Buy*
Pub: Doubleday
Ed: Martin Lindstrom. **Released:** February 02, 2010. **Price:** $15, paperback. **Description:** Marketers study brain scans to determine how consumers rate Nokia, Coke, and Ford products. **Availability:** Print.

2722 ■ *"Can You Hear Them Now?"* in *Hawaii Business (Vol. 54, August 2008, No. 2, pp. 48)*
Description: Coral Wireless LLC (dba Mobi PCS) is ranked 237 in Hawaii Business' list of the state's top 250 companies for 2008. The company is a local wireless phone provider, which has expanded its market to Oahu, Maui and the Big Island since opening in 2006, offering 13 phones and unlimited texts and calls. Details on the company's sales are provided. **Availability:** Print; Online.

2723 ■ *"Cash for Kiosks: EcoATM Pulls in Series B Funding"* in *San Diego Business Journal (Vol. 33, May 7, 2012, No. 19, pp. 10)*
Pub: CBJ L.P.
Contact: Terri Cunningham, Contact
Ed: Brad Graves. **Description:** EcoATM received $17 million in Series B venture funds as well as a $1 million grant from the National Science Foundation. The Series B funds will be used to install mall kiosks that offer cash for used cellphones and other small electronic devices. **Availability:** Online.

2724 ■ *"Clearwire Struggling, Banks on Deals with Competitors"* in *Puget Sound Business Journal (Vol. 33, August 24, 2012, No. 18, pp. 1)*
Pub: Baltimore Business Journal
Contact: Rhonda Pringle, President
E-mail: rpringle@bizjournals.com
Ed: Emily Parkhurst, Alyson Raletz. **Description:** Clearwire Corporation's chief executive, Erik Prusch, is planning to lease the wireless spectrum of the company to major mobile providers that run out of their own supply. At issue is whether the Bellevue, Washington-based telecommunication company can manage its $4 billion debt and maximize the value of its technology while managing its partners all at the same time. **Availability:** Print; Online.

2725 ■ *"Comcast Launches New Home Security Service, Developed in Portland"* in *The Oregonian (June 7, 2011)*
Pub: McClatchy-Tribune Regional News
Ed: Mike Rogoway. **Description:** Comcast introduced its new high-end home security system that provides 24-hour monitoring and control of homes and utilities, along with Web and mobile access. **Availability:** Print; Online.

2726 ■ *"Consumer Startup Hub Set for Downtown"* in *Atlanta Business Chronicle (June 13, 2014, pp. 3A)*
Pub: American City Business Journals, Inc.
Contact: Mike Olivieri, Executive Vice President
Description: Michael Tavani, co-founder of Scoutmob, believes that Atlanta is fast becoming the hub for consumer- and design-focused startups. He is planning to locate his consumer-focused startup, Switchyards, in a 1920s building downtown, which will become a hive for mobile app, media, and ecommerce startups. **Availability:** Print; Online.

2727 ■ *"Cox Opens Norfolk Mall Kiosk; Wireless Service Not Ready"* in *Virginian-Pilot (September 20, 2010)*
Pub: The Virginian-Pilot
Contact: Kevin Goyette, Director
E-mail: kgoyette@dailypress.com
Ed: Carolyn Shapiro. **Description:** Cox Communications opened a kiosk at MacArthur Center that will sell wireless telephone devices and plans. **Availability:** Print; Online.

2728 ■ *"Death of the PC"* in *Canadian Business (Vol. 83, October 12, 2010, No. 17, pp. 44)*
Description: The future of the personal computer (PC) is looking bleak as consumers are relying more on new mobile devices instead of their PC. A 'Wall Street Journal' article published in September 2010 reported that the iPad had cannibalized sales of laptops by as much as 50 percent. The emergence of tablet computers running alternative operating systems is also explained. **Availability:** Print; Online.

2729 ■ *"Defense Mobile Joins Forces with RadioShack to launch New Military Focuses Mobile Service this Fall"* in *Defense & Aerospace Business (September 10, 2014, pp. 7)*
Pub: NewsRX LLC.
Contact: Kalani Rosell, Contact
Description: RadioShack and Defense Mobile Corporation have partnered for RadioShack to be the exclusive national retailer for Defense Mobile's new nationwide 4G LTE mobile services. Defense Mobile

was launched by veterans and supported by a 100 percent veteran-staffed Member Service organization and its mobile services are designed to benefit, honor and reward active U.S. military and veterans for their commitment and service. **Availability:** Online.

2730 ■ *"Developer Plans to Build Verizon Store in Woodstock" in Northwest Herald (July 20, 2019)*
URL(s): www.nwherald.com/2019/07/19/developer-plans-to-build-verizon-store-in-woodstock/a1h6sj9/
Ed: Brittany Keeperman. **Released:** July 20, 2019. **Description:** The Woodstock City Council approved plans for a new Verizon store in Woodstock. Idaho-based Hawkins Company LLC will oversee the development, which when completed will be the home of Cellular Sales of Knoxville, and authorized Verizon dealer. **Availability:** Online.

2731 ■ *"Don't Hang Up On FairPoint" in Barron's (Vol. 88, July 7, 2008, No. 27, pp. M5)*
Description: Shares of FairPoint Communications, priced at $6.63 each, are undervalued and should be worth over $12 each. The company increased its size by more than five times by acquiring Verizon's local telephone operations in Vermont, New Hampshire, and Maine, but must switch customers in those areas into their system by the end of September 2007. **Availability:** Online.

2732 ■ *"Don't' Hate the Cable Guy" in Saint Louis Business Journal (Vol. 31, August 5, 2011, No. 50, pp. 1)*
Pub: Saint Louis Business Journal
Contact: Robert Bobroff, President
E-mail: rbobroff@bizjournals.com
Ed: Angela Mueller. **Description:** Charter Communications named John Birrer as senior vice president of customer experience. The company experienced problems with its customer services. **Availability:** Print; Online.

2733 ■ *Electronic Commerce*
Ed: Gary P. Schneider, Bryant Chrzan, Charles McCormick. **Released:** 12th edition. **Price:** $29.49, e-book. **Description:** E-commerce can open the door to more opportunities than ever before for small business. Packed with real-world examples and cases, the book delivers comprehensive coverage of emerging online technologies and trends and their influence on the electronic marketplace. It details how the landscape of online commerce is evolving, reflecting changes in the economy and how business and society are responding to those changes. Balancing technological issues with the strategic business aspects of successful e-commerce, the new edition includes expanded coverage of international issues, social networking, mobile commerce, Web 2.0 technologies, and updates on spam, phishing, and identity theft. **Availability:** Print.

2734 ■ *"Etextbook Space Heats Up" in Information Today (Vol. 28, November 2011, No. 10, pp. 10)*
Pub: Information Today Inc.
Contact: Thomas H. Hogan, President
Ed: Paula J. Hane. **Description:** The use of etextbooks is expected to grow with the use of mobile devices and tablets. A new group of activists is asking students, faculty members and others to sign a petition urging higher education leaders to prioritize affordable textbooks or free ebooks over the traditional, expensive new books required for classes.

2735 ■ *"Executive Decision: To Make Inroads Against RIM, Palm Steals Its Strategy" in Globe & Mail (March 25, 2006, pp. B3)*
Ed: Simon Avery. **Description:** The Palm Inc., global leader in portable device manufacturing, is looking forward to improve its sales of Palm Treos, a wireless portable device that connects to internet and email. Palm is also planning to build partnerships, under the efficient management of Michael Moskowitz, general manager and vice-president of Palm Inc., with the other companies to increase the sales of its wireless devices.

2736 ■ *"Firm Restricts Cellphone Use While Driving" in Globe & Mail (January 30, 2006, pp. B3)*
Description: The details on AMEC Plc, which adopted cellphone-free driving policy, are presented. **Availability:** Online.

2737 ■ *"Firms Bet On Games To Hike Wellness" in Business Journal (Vol. 30, June 1, 2012, No. 1, pp. 1)*
Pub: American City Business Journals, Inc.
Contact: Mike Olivieri, Executive Vice President
Ed: Katharine Grayson. **Released:** Weekly. **Price:** $4, introductory 4-week offer(Digital only). **Description:** Twin Cities-based firms providing corporate wellness services are integrating games into these programs. These games include friendly competitions between work teams or high-tech smartphone applications. **Availability:** Print; Online.

2738 ■ *"For Apple, It's Showtime Again" in Barron's (Vol. 90, August 30, 2010, No. 35, pp. 29)*
Pub: Barron's Editorial & Corporate Headquarters
Ed: Eric J. Savitz. **Description:** Speculations on what Apple Inc. will unveil at its product launch event are presented. These products include a possible new iPhone Nano, a new update to its Apple TV, and possibly a deal with the Beatles to distribute their songs over iTunes. **Availability:** Online.

2739 ■ *"For Retailers, the Smartphone is Future of Store Experience" in The Associated Press (December 12, 2018)*
URL(s): www.apnews.com/4949636dcced43f899 12dfc2d71b54bb
Ed: Anne D'Innocenzio. **Released:** December 12, 2018. **Description:** Shoppers are increasingly using their smartphones to shop and make purchases online, so brick-and-mortar stores are capitalizing on that trend by introducing ways for shoppers to use their phones to make purchases within a store. Mobile checkout is rising in popularity but stores have to work out issues such as increasing their Wi-Fi to make this work. **Availability:** Online.

2740 ■ *"France Telecom Takes Minitel Offline" in Canadian Business (Vol. 85, August 13, 2012, No. 13, pp. 12)*
Ed: Matthew McClearn. **Description:** The Minitel online service was developed to reduce the costs of printing phone directories in the French postal and telecommunications ministry in 1978 and became popular in Paris in 1982. With its user-based halved annually and services declining in its waning years, France Telecom opted to terminate the service on June 30, 2012. **Availability:** Print; Online.

2741 ■ *"Gadget of the Week: the Age of iPhoneography" in Barron's (Vol. 92, August 25, 2012, No. 35, pp. 28)*
Pub: Dow Jones & Company Inc.
Contact: Almar Latour, Chief Executive Officer
Ed: Nathaniel Wice. **Description:** Profile of iPhoneArt.com, the Website that allows enthusiasts to share photographic works and techniques with each other. The site is free but the Olloclip, a popular clip-on lense, costs $69.99. **Availability:** Online.

2742 ■ *"Gartner Says Global Smartphone Sales Declined 6.8% in Third Quarter of 2021" in Gartner.com (November 23, 2021)*
Released: November 23, 2021. **Description:** Due to supply chain issues of critical components, smartphone sales were down in the third quarter of 2021, since consumers had limited choices at retail stores and online. **Availability:** Online.

2743 ■ *"Generation Y Chooses the Mobile Web" in PR Newswire (November 24, 2010)*
Pub: PR Newswire Association LLC.
Description: Generation Y individuals between the ages of 18 - 27 use their mobile phones to browse the Internet more often than a desktop or laptop computer, according to a survey conducted by Opera, a Web browser company. **Availability:** Print; Online.

2744 ■ *"GIV Mobile Announces New Partnership with American Forests, the Oldest National Nonprofit Conservation Organization in the Country" in Ecology, Environment & Conservation Business (January 25, 2014, pp. 34)*
Pub: PR Newswire Association LLC.
Description: GIV Mobile has partnered with American Forests to restore and protect urban and rural forests in the nation. GIV is the first consumer conscious wireless network and operates on the 4G network of T-Mobile USA cellular service. **Availability:** Online.

2745 ■ *"Google Places a Call to Bargain Hunters" in Advertising Age (Vol. 79, September 29, 2008, No. 36, pp. 13)*
Pub: Crain Communications, Inc.
Contact: Jessica Botos, Manager, Marketing
E-mail: jessica.botos@crainsnewyork.com
Ed: Abbey Klaassen. **Description:** Google highlighted application developers who have created tools for its Android mobile phone in the device's unveiling; applications such as ShopSavvy and CompareEverywhere help shoppers to find bargains by allowing them to compare prices in their local areas and across the web. **Availability:** Online.

2746 ■ *"HatchedIt.com Social Organizer for Families Launches New Phone App at BlogHer '12" in PR Newswire (August 3, 2012)*
Pub: PR Newswire Association LLC.
Description: HatchedIt.com is a free social organizer for families. The new phone app includes two new updates: shareable to do lists and an inbox for members to accept or decline invitations for events or to connect with members.

2747 ■ *"Horse Race: Putting the App in Apple" in Inc. (Vol. 30, November 2008, No. 11)*
Pub: Mansueto Ventures L.L.C.
Contact: Stephanie Mehta, Chief Executive Officer
Ed: Nitasha Tiku. **Description:** Aftermarket companies are scrambling to develop games and widgets for Apple's iPhone. Apple launched a kit for developers interested in creating iPhone-specific software along with the App Store, and an iTunes spinoff. Profiles of various software programs that may be used on the iPhone are given. **Availability:** Online.

2748 ■ *"How to Play the Tech Mergers" in Barron's (Vol. 90, August 30, 2010, No. 35, pp. 18)*
Pub: Barron's Editorial & Corporate Headquarters
Ed: Tiernan Ray. **Description:** The intense bidding by Hewlett-Packard and Dell for 3Par was foreseen in a previous Barron's cover story and 3Par's stock has nearly tripled since reported. Other possible acquisition targets in the tech industry include Brocade Communication Systems, NetApp, Xyratex, and Isilon Systems. **Availability:** Online.

2749 ■ *"How to Reuse Or Recycle Your Old Tech: eWaste Is on the Rise but You Can Help Combat It By Using Old PCs and Electronics in Different Ways" in PC Magazine (Vol. 31, February 2012, No. 2, pp. 108)*
Description: US recycling businesses employ 30,000 workers to recycle 3.5 million tons of electronic waste, that does not include the number of devices that go to landfills. Simple and cheap ways to recycle or put old electronics to work are examined. **Availability:** Online.

2750 ■ *"The Intel Trinity: How Robert Noyce, Gordon Moore, and Andy Grove Built the World's Most Important Company"*
Pub: Harper Business
Contact: Hollis Heimbouch, Senior Vice President Publisher
Released: July 15, 2014. **Price:** $34.99, hardcover; $11.74, e-book; $4.34, kindle; $19.42, hardcover; $4.30, hardcover(69 used from $4.30); $15.17, hardcover(56 new from $15.17); $19.99, hardcover(1 collectible from $19.99); $31.74, paperback; $22.95,

paperback(10 used from $22.95); $19.13, paperback(4 new from $19.13). **Description:** A complete history of Intel Corporation, the essential company of the digital age, is presented. After over four decades Intel remains the most important company in the world, a defining company of the global digital economy. The inventors of the microprocessor that powers nearly every intelligent electronic device worldwide are profiled. These entrepreneurs made the personal computer, Internet, telecommunications, and personal electronics all possible. The challenges and successes of the company and its ability to maintain its dominance, its culture and its legacy are examined. **Availability:** E-book; Print; Online.

2751 ■ *"Into the Groove: Fine-Tune Your Biz By Getting Into the Good Habit Groove" in Small Business Opportunities (Spring 2008)*
Description: Profile of Ty Freyvogel and his consulting firm Freyvogel Communications. Freyvogel serves the telecommunications need of Fortune 500 and mid-sized businesses.

2752 ■ *"IP Transition Is Unlikely To Make Waves In R.I." in Providence Business News (Vol. 28, January 13, 2014, No. 41, pp. 1)*
Pub: American City Business Journals, Inc.
Contact: Mike Olivieri, Executive Vice President
Released: January 13, 2014. **Description:** The transition from copper and circuit switches to fiber and Internet Protocol is changing the telecommunications landscape across the U.S. The Rhode Island General Assembly passed a bill that deregulates wireless communications systems, which means that the growth of wireless in the area previously held by landlines will not change its status for now. **Availability:** Print; Online.

2753 ■ *"Is Your Smartphone Disaster Proof? If Not, These Rugged Cases Could Help: After Shelling Out a Couple of Hundred Dollars for a New Smartphone, You Don't Want to Worry About Breaking It" in Inc. (Vol. 34, September 2012, No. 7, pp. 48)*
Pub: Mansueto Ventures L.L.C.
Contact: Stephanie Mehta, Chief Executive Officer
Ed: Jennifer Alsever. **Description:** Profiles of cellular phone cases that keep them safe include: Otterbox Defender Series, Ballistic Hard Core Case, and Tank by Case-Mate. **Availability:** Online.

2754 ■ *"Israeli Spam Law May Have Global Impact" in Information Today (Vol. 26, February 2009, No. 2, pp. 28)*
Pub: Information Today Inc.
Contact: Thomas H. Hogan, President
Ed: David Mirchin. **Description:** Israels new law, called Amendment 40 of the Communications Law, will regulate commercial solicitations including those sent without permission via email, fax, automatic phone dialing systems, or short messaging technologies. **Availability:** PDF; Online.

2755 ■ *"It Was a Very Good Year..To Be Ted Rogers" in Canadian Business (Vol. 80, Winter 2007, No. 24, pp. 121)*
Description: Ted Rogers had a banner year in 2007 as Rogers Communications Inc. (RCI) took in huge profits from its phone and wireless business and his personal wealth grew sixty-seven percent to $7.6 billion. Rogers has record of betting on technologies that get the best returns relative to the investment in the marketplace such as its use of the GSM network and its cable hybrid fiber coaxial network.

2756 ■ *"Jab, Jab, Jab, Right Hook: How to Tell Your Story in a Noisy Social World"*
Pub: Harper Business
Contact: Hollis Heimbouch, Senior Vice President Publisher
Released: November 26, 2013. **Price:** $23.99, hardcover. **Description:** Author and social media expert shares advice on ways to connect with customers and beat the competition. Social media strategies for marketers and managers need to convert Internet traffic to sales. Communication is the key to online sales that are adapted to high quality social media platforms and mobile devices. **Availability:** E-book; Print.

2757 ■ *"Last Call?" in Puget Sound Business Journal (Vol. .35, August 8, 2014, No. 16, pp. 12)*
Pub: American City Business Journals, Inc.
Contact: Mike Olivieri, Executive Vice President
Description: T-Mobile US cellular phone service is targeted for acquisition by large firms, but so far no deals have materialized. Analysts believe a deal will emerge soon as T-Mobile's parent company is seeking suitable bidders. The impact of a merger on Puget Sound's economy is viewed. **Availability:** Online.

2758 ■ *"Lawsuits Claim Coke Sent Illegal Ad Texts" in Atlanta Business Chronicle (June 13, 2014, pp. 4A)*
Pub: American City Business Journals, Inc.
Contact: Mike Olivieri, Executive Vice President
Description: Coca-Cola Company is facing lawsuits in San Diego and California from consumers who claim to have received unsolicited ads to their wireless phones, thus putting Coke in violation of the Federal law, called the Telephone Consumer Protection Act. The plaintiff of the California lawsuit is seeking damages amounting to $1,500 for each text message sent. **Availability:** Print; Online.

2759 ■ *"Look, No Hands!" in Inc. (Vol. 33, September 2011, No. 7, pp. 52)*
Description: The Jabra Freeway, a small Bluetooth speakerphone clips to a car visor and allows the user to place, answer and ignore calls by speaking commands. **Availability:** Print; Online.

2760 ■ *"Marketers Push for Mobile Tuesday as the New Black Friday" in Advertising Age (Vol. 79, December 1, 2008, No. 44, pp. 21)*
Pub: Crain Communications, Inc.
Contact: Jessica Botos, Manager, Marketing
E-mail: jessica.botos@crainsnewyork.com
Ed: Natalie Zmuda. **Description:** Marketers are using an innovative approach in an attempt to stimulate business on the Tuesday following Thanksgiving by utilizing consumer's cell phones to alert them of sales or present them with coupons for this typically slow retail business day; with this campaign both advertisers and retailers are hoping to start Mobile Tuesday, another profitable shopping day in line with Black Friday and Cyber Monday. **Availability:** Online.

2761 ■ *"MBlox, Which Sends Coupons to Phones and Tables, Raises $43.5M" in Atlanta Business Chronicle (July 11, 2014, pp. 12A)*
Pub: American City Business Journals, Inc.
Contact: Mike Olivieri, Executive Vice President
Released: Weekly. **Price:** $4, introductory 4-week offer(Digital only). **Description:** mBlox, the mobile technology firm that sends coupons to hphones and tablets has managed to successfully raise $43.5 million to undertake global expansion. **Availability:** Print; Online.

2762 ■ *"Microsoft Partners With Good Technology to Provide Enterprise-Class Security for Business Customers on Windows Phone Devices" in Benzinga.com (February 27, 2012)*
Pub: PR Newswire Association LLC.
Description: Microsoft has partnered with Good Technology in order to provide its Windows Phone 7.5 Preferred Partner Solution for secured encrypted mobile mail services. Details of the strategic partnership are outlined.

2763 ■ *"Mobile Marketing Grows With Size of Cell Phone Screens" in Crain's Detroit Business (Vol. 24, January 14, 2008, No. 2, pp. 13)*
Pub: Crain Communications Inc.
Contact: Barry Asin, President
Ed: Bill Shea. **Description:** Experts are predicting increased marketing for cell phones with the inception of larger screens and improved technology.

2764 ■ *Mobile Office: The Essential Small Business Guide to Office Technology*
Released: September 1, 2009. **Price:** $6.95. **Description:** Essential pocket guide for startup businesses and entrepreneurs which provides information to create a mobile office in order to maximize business potential while using current technologies.

2765 ■ *"The Mobility Imperative" in Business Strategy Review (Vol. 23, Spring 2012, No. 1, pp. 70)*
Description: The founder of Sutton Trust, Sir Peter Lampl, explains his passion for social mobility. **Availability:** Print; Online.

2766 ■ *"My Favorite Tool for Managing Expenses" in Inc. (Volume 32, December 2010, No. 10, pp. 60)*
Pub: Inc. Magazine
Ed: J.J. McCorvey. **Description:** Web-based service called Expensify is outlined. The service allows companies to log expenses while away from the office using the service's iPhone application. **Availability:** Online.

2767 ■ *"My Favorite Tool for Organizing Data" in Inc. (Vol. 33, November 2011, No. 9, pp. 46)*
Pub: Inc. Magazine
Ed: Abram Brown. **Description:** Intelligence software firm uses Roambi, a Web-based service that turns spreadsheet data into interactive files for iPhones and iPads. **Availability:** Online.

2768 ■ *"MyWireless.org Commends Arizona Congressman Trent Franks for Committing to Wireless Tax Relief for American Consumers and Businesses" in PR Newswire (September 21, 2012)*
Pub: PR Newswire Association LLC.
Description: MyWireless.org presented Congressman Trent Franks from Arizona with the 2012 Wireless Consumer Hero Award for his work on wireless tax relief for American consumers and businesses. Franks' 'Wireless Tax Fairness Act' (HR 1002) promotes access to wireless networks as a key ingredient of millions of Americans' livelihoods, whether phone, broadband Internet necessary to run a small business. **Availability:** Print; Online.

2769 ■ *"A New Cloud-Based Phone System Is Installed Remotely for North Carolina Senior Care Council" in Information Technology Business (June 19, 2012)*
Description: North Carolina Senior Care Council (NcSCC) has partnered with VoxNet to provide long-term care for Cloud-based PBX to help NcSCC manage their system that assists seniors. **Availability:** Online.

2770 ■ *"New IPhone Also Brings New Way of Mobile Marketing" in Advertising Age (Vol. 79, June 16, 2008, No. 24, pp. 23)*
Pub: Crain Communications, Inc.
Contact: Jessica Botos, Manager, Marketing
E-mail: jessica.botos@crainsnewyork.com
Ed: Abbey Klaassen. **Description:** Currently there are two kinds of applications for the iPhone and other mobile devices: native applications that allow for richer experiences and take advantage of features that are built into a phone and web applications, those that allow access to the web through specific platforms. Marketers are interested in creating useful experiences for customers and opening up the platforms which will allow them to do this. **Availability:** Online.

2771 ■ *"New Sprint Phone Whets Appetite for Applications, Brings Revenue for Handmark" in The Business Journal-Serving Metropolitan Kansas City (Vol. 26, July 25, 2008)*
Description: Firms supporting the applications of the new Samsung Instinct, which was introduced by Sprint Nextel Corp. in June 2008, have reported usage rates increase for their products. Handmark, whose mobile services Pocket Express comes loaded

with Instinct, has redirected employees to meet the rising demand for the services. Other views and information on Instinct, are presented. **Availability:** Print; Online.

2772 ■ *"New Year's Resolutions: How Three Companies Came Up With Their 2008 Growth Strategies"* in Inc. (January 2008, pp. 47-49)
Ed: Martha C. White. **Description:** Three companies share 2008 growth strategies; companies include a candle company, a voice mail and text messaging marketer, and hotel supplier of soap and shampoo. **Availability:** Online.

2773 ■ *"The Next Frontier"* in San Francisco Business Times (Vol. 28, February 28, 2014, No. 32, pp. 4)
Pub: American City Business Journals, Inc.
Contact: Mike Olivieri, Executive Vice President
Description: The growth of the electronic payments business in San Francisco, California has captured the interest of venture capitalists, entrepreneurs, and other investors. Social media companies like Facebook and Google are expected to expand into electronic payments. Telecommunication companies are also investing in promising startups and joint ventures. **Availability:** Print; Online.

2774 ■ *The Nokia Revolution: The Story of an Extraordinary Company That Transformed an Industry*
Description: Profile of Nokia, the world's largest wireless communications company. Nokia started in 1865 in rural Finland and merged its rubber company and a cabling firm to form the corporation around 1965. The firm's corporate strategy in the mobile communications industry is highlighted. **Availability:** E-book; Print.

2775 ■ *"NY: T-Mobile's Metro Stores Sold Used Phones as New to Consumers"* in PCMag (September 6, 2019)
URL(s): www.pcmag.com/news/370609/ny-t-mobiles-metro-stores-sold-used-phones-as-new-to-consu
Ed: Michael Kan. **Released:** September 06, 2019. **Description:** New York City's Department of Consumer and Worker Protection announed that more than 50 official "Metro by T-Mobile" dealers were selling used phones as new. T-Mobile is investigating these illegal tactics. **Availability:** Online.

2776 ■ *"Online Translation Service Aids Battlefield Troops"* in Product News Network (August 30, 2011)
Pub: Thomas Publishing Company
Contact: Tony Uphoff, President
E-mail: tuphoff@thomaspublishing.com
Description: Linquist online service, LinGo Link provides real-time interpreter support to military troops overseas. Interpreters skilled in multiple languages and dialects are used in various areas and in multiple instances without requiring physical presence. The service is available through commercial cellular or WiFi services or tactical communications network. The system accommodates exchange of audio, video, photos, and text during conversations via smartphones and mobile peripheral devices. **Availability:** Online.

2777 ■ *"The Perils of Popularity"* in Business Strategy Review (Vol. 23, Spring 2012, No. 1, pp. 51)
Description: The iPhone's worldwide success would seem to be an unqualified win-win for Apple and the mobile operators that sell it. Not so, explains Marco Bertini and Ricardo Cabornero, as mobile operators they must maintain a delicate balance between winning new customers and retaining existing ones. This task is made more difficult when their own brands can actually be diminished by selling the competitor's iPhone. **Availability:** Print; Online.

2778 ■ *"Play By Play: These Video Products Can Add New Life to a Stagnant Website"* in Black Enterprise (Vol. 41, December 2010, No. 5)
Pub: Earl G. Graves Ltd.
Contact: Earl Graves, Jr., President

Ed: Marcia Wade Talbert. **Description:** Web Visible, provider of online marketing products and services, cites video capability as the fastest-growing Website feature for small business advertisers. Profiles of various devices for adding video to a Website are included. **Availability:** Online.

2779 ■ *"Prepaid Phones Surge in Bad Economy"* in Advertising Age (Vol. 79, November 17, 2008, No. 43, pp. 6)
Pub: Crain Communications, Inc.
Contact: Jessica Botos, Manager, Marketing
E-mail: jessica.botos@crainsnewyork.com
Ed: Rita Chang. **Description:** Prepay cell phone offerings are becoming increasingly competitive amid a greater choice of plans and handsets. In an economic environment in which many consumers are unable to pass the credit checks required for traditional cell phone plans, the prepay market is surging.

2780 ■ *"Presidential Address: Innovation in Retrospect and Prospect"* in Canadian Journal of Electronics (Vol. 43, November 2010, No. 4)
Pub: Journal of the Canadian Economics Association
Ed: James A. Brander. **Description:** Has innovation slowed in recent decades? While there has been progress in information and communications technology, the recent record of innovation in agriculture, energy, transportation and healthcare sectors is cause for concern. **Availability:** PDF; Online.

2781 ■ *"Q&A with Google's Patrick Pichette"* in Canadian Business (Vol. 81, October 13, 2008, No. 17, pp. 6)
Description: Patrick Pichette finds challenge in taking over the finances of an Internet company that has a market cap of about $140 billion. He feels, however, that serving as Google's chief financial officer is nothing compared to running Bell Canada Enterprises (BCE). Pichette's other views on Google and BCE are presented. **Availability:** Print; Online.

2782 ■ *"Racing to Beam Electricity to Devices Wirelessly"* in San Francisco Business Times (Vol. 28, April 11, 2014, No. 38, pp. 6)
Pub: American City Business Journals, Inc.
Contact: Mike Olivieri, Executive Vice President
Description: Pleasanton, California-based Energous Corporation has developed a technology that safely converts radio waves into electrical current. The innovation makes it possible to charge multiple/cellular mobile phones or other electrical devices from a distance of 15 feet. The prototype of Energous founder, Michael Leabman's invention is also outlined. **Availability:** Print; Online.

2783 ■ *"Recycling Old Cellphones"* in San Jose Mercury News (September 26, 2012)
Description: Gazelle.com buys old gadgets, including mobile phones, on its Website. The firm either resells the gadgets through retail channels such as eBy or turns them over to wholesalers. Recycling electronic waste information is provided. **Availability:** Online.

2784 ■ *"Repairing - Not Recycling - Is the First Step to Tackling E-Waste From Smartphones. Here's Why."* in World Economic Forum (July 19, 2021)
Ed: Mo Chatterji. **Released:** July 19, 2021. **Description:** While smartphones have gained popularity throughout the years, so has the electronic waste from these devices. Recycling may not be the only answer unless the phone has truly reached the end of usefulness. Instead, repairing smartphones is making more sense because the process doesn't produce as much carbon emissions as recycling, and is therefore more environmentally friendly.

2785 ■ *"Research and Markets Adds Report: The U.S. Mobile Web Market"* in Entertainment Close-Up (December 10, 2009)
Description: Highlights of the new Research and Markets report "The U.S. Mobile Web Market: Taking Advantage of the iPhone Phenomenon" include: mobile Internet marketing strategies; the growth of mobile web usage; the growth of revenue in the mobile web market; and a look at Internet business communications, social media and networking. **Availability:** Print; Online.

2786 ■ *"Retailers at the Ready to Adopt Mobile Pay Options"* in Dallas Business Journal (Vol. 35, August 24, 2012, No. 50, pp. 1)
Pub: Baltimore Business Journal
Contact: Rhonda Pringle, President
E-mail: rpringle@bizjournals.com
Ed: Steven R. Thompson. **Description:** Dallas-Fort Worth-based major retailers have been looking for ways to integrate the apps and mobile technology into their customer experience. The retailers formed the Irving, Texas-based Merchant Customer Exchange to develop mobile payment technology. **Availability:** Print; Online.

2787 ■ *"RIM Opts to Be Less Open"* in Canadian Business (Vol. 83, October 12, 2010, No. 17, pp. 13)
Pub: Rogers Media Inc.
Contact: Neil Spivak, Chief Executive Officer
Ed: Joe Castaldo. **Description:** RIM is planning to stop releasing quarterly subscriber updates. However, some analysts are skeptical about the change due to the previous drop in company subscribers. The company also decided to stop reporting the average selling price of the BlackBerry, which analysts have also scrutinized. **Availability:** Online.

2788 ■ *"RIM's Demise Stems from Arrogance: It Didn't Have To Come To This"* in Canadian Business (Vol. 85, August 13, 2012, No. 13, pp. 4)
Ed: James Cowan. **Description:** The business collapse of Research in Motion (RIM) was blamed on the management's arrogance in terms of recognizing that Apple's iPhone is dominating the consumer market and that corporate customers would remain loyal despite the emergence of better smartphones. It is speculated that the failure of RIM could lead to at least 5,000 job losses. **Availability:** Online.

2789 ■ *"Samsung's Metamorphosis in Austin"* in Austin Business Journal (Vol. 31, May 20, 2011, No. 11, pp. 1)
Pub: Austin Business Journal
Contact: Rachel McGrath, Director
E-mail: rmcgrath@bizjournals.com
Ed: Christopher Calnan. **Description:** Samsung Austin Semiconductor LP, a developer of semiconductors for smartphones and tablet computers, plans to diversify its offerings to include niche products: flash memory devices and microprocessing devices. In light of this strategy, Samsung Austin will be hiring 300 engineers as part of a $3.6 billion expansion of its plant. **Availability:** Print; Online.

2790 ■ *"Skype Ltd. Acquired GroupMe"* in Information Today (Vol. 28, October 2011, No. 9, pp. 12)
Description: Skype Ltd. acquired GroupMe, a group messaging company that allows users to form impromptu groups where they can text message, share data, and make conference calls for free and is supported on Android, iPhone, BlackBerry, and Windows phones. **Availability:** Print; Online.

2791 ■ *"Sleeping with Your Smartphone: How to Break the 24/7 Habit and Change the Way You Work"*
Pub: Harvard Business Review Press
Contact: Moderna V. Pfizer, Contact

Released: May 29, 2012. **Price:** $30, Hardcover/ Hardcopy. **Description:** Harvard Business School professor, Leslie Perlow, reveals ways to become more productive after disconnecting from your smartphone. A six-person team was used in an experiment at The Boston Consulting Group, an elite management consulting firm, where teams changed the way they worked and became more efficient and effective by disconnecting. The team was better able to perform and recruit new talent. A step-by-step guide is offered to change your team. **Availability:** E-book; Print.

2792 ■ *"Social Apps, Business Style: Savvy App Makers Bring Consumer Features to the Enterprise"* in *Silicon Valley/San Jose Business Journal (Vol. 30, September 28, 2012, No. 27, pp. 1)*
Pub: Baltimore Business Journal
Contact: Rhonda Pringle, President
E-mail: rpringle@bizjournals.com
Description: Companies like Good Technology Inc. and Socialtext Inc. are developing mobile apps software for business enterprises with consumer features such as photo sharing and location check-ins. Consumer tendencies have influenced the growth of the enterprise mobiel apps market, which is predicted to reach $11.5 billion by 2004. **Availability:** Print; Online.

2793 ■ *"A Socko Payout Menu: Rural Phone Carrier Plots to Supercharge Its Shares"* in *Barron's (Vol. 88, June 30, 2008, No. 26, pp. M5)*
Description: CenturyTel boosted its quarterly common payout to 70 cents from 6.75 cents per share die to its strong cash flows and solid balance sheet. Eastman Kodak's plan for a buyback will be partially funded by its $581 million tax refund. CME Group will buyback stocks through 2009 worth $1.1 billion. **Availability:** Online.

2794 ■ *"A Survey of Smart Data Pricing: Past Proposals, Current Plans, and Future Trends"* in *ACM Computing Surveys (Vol. 46, Summer 2014, No. 2, pp. 15)*
Pub: Association for Computing Machinery - University of Wyoming
Contact: Ed Seidel, President
E-mail: uwpres@uwyo.edu
Price: $15, Nonmembers; $42, Students. **Description:** Traditionally, network operators have used simple flat-rate broadband data plans for both wired and wireless network access. But today, with the popularity of mobile devices and exponential growth of apps, videos, and clouds, service providers are gradually moving toward more sophisticated pricing schemes. The benefits and challenges or pricing data are examined. **Availability:** PDF; Online.

2795 ■ *"T-Mobile's Risky Strategy Aims to Get iPhone Owners to Switch"* in *Puget Sound Business Journal (Vol. 33, September 7, 2012, No. 20, pp. 1)*
Pub: Baltimore Business Journal
Contact: Rhonda Pringle, President
E-mail: rpringle@bizjournals.com
Description: Bellevue, Washington-based T-Mobile has offered unlimited data to customers in a risky strategy to attract competitor iPhone customers withoutoffering an iPhone on its own. T-Mobile is also encouraging existing iPhone user to unlock their phones and then switch to T-Mobile service. **Availability:** Print; Online.

2796 ■ *"Taking on 911 - and Making a New Tech Biz In the Process"* in *Orlando Business Journal (Vol. 30, January 24, 2014, No. 31, pp. 3)*
Pub: American City Business Journals, Inc.
Contact: Mike Olivieri, Executive Vice President
Released: Weekly. **Price:** $8, introductory 4-week offer(Digital & Print). **Description:** Central Florida-based TapShield LLC is on the path to growth. The firm has developed a mobile application that enables University of Florida students to coordinate with police. Meanwhile, TapShield is in negotiations with large companies for similar deals. **Availability:** Print; Online.

2797 ■ *"Taking a Leap With Mobile Wi-Fi"* in *Austin Business Journal (Vol. 34, July 25, 2014, No. 23, pp. 10)*
Pub: American City Business Journals, Inc.
Contact: Mike Olivieri, Executive Vice President
Released: July 25, 2014. **Price:** $4, introductory 4-week offer(Digital only). **Description:** Austin-based semi-conductor design company Nitero Inc.'s recent release of its Wi-Fi chip, Nietero's key rival Wilocity Ltd.'s acquisition by a tech giant, pushing demand for semiconductors; thus spurring growth for Nitero. It's Wi-Fi's system for mobile platforms will enable users to do more things on their Smartphones, thus converging more devices into one. **Availability:** Print; Online.

2798 ■ *"Tale of the Tape: IPhone Vs. G1"* in *Advertising Age (Vol. 79, October 27, 2008, No. 40, pp. 6)*
Pub: Crain Communications, Inc.
Contact: Jessica Botos, Manager, Marketing
E-mail: jessica.botos@crainsnewyork.com
Ed: Rita Chang. **Description:** T-Mobile's G1 has been positioned as the first serious competitor to Apple's iPhone. G1 is the first mobile phone to run on the Google-backed, open-source platform Android.

2799 ■ *"Tech Jobs Rebound from Downturn"* in *Denver Business Journal (Vol. 65, March 7, 2014, No. 43, pp. A9)*
Pub: American City Business Journals, Inc.
Contact: Mike Olivieri, Executive Vice President
Released: Weekly. **Price:** $4, Introductory 4-week offer(Digital & Print). **Description:** Denver, Colorado's employment in core technology industries has returned from pre-Great Recession figures. The computer software industry's surging job growth and the slight increase in the broadcasts and telecommunications industry offset the job losses in biotechnology and private aerospace industry from 2008 through 2013. The growth in specific industries is also discussed. **Availability:** Print; Online.

2800 ■ *"Technology: Elder Care Enters the Digital Age: Wireless Companies Devise Ways to Aid Home Health, Let People Stay in Homes"* in *Atlanta Journal-Constitution (April 29, 2012, pp. D1)*
Description: Mobile phone industry is actually helping families keep aging loved one in their homes. The home healthcare industry is adding technology, telecommunications, smartphone applications and other devices to make it easier for seniors to remain in their homes. Details on this growing industry are included along with statistical data. **Availability:** Online.

2801 ■ *"Titan to Become New York's Largest Provider of Phone Kiosk Advertising"* in *Marketing Weekly News (September 11, 2010, pp. 150)*
Pub: VerticalNews
Description: Titan will acquire from Verizon 1,900 payphones at 1,300 phone kiosk locations in New York City, New York. This transaction will triple the firm's inventory of New York Phone Kiosk media to over 5,000 advertising faces. Details are included. **Availability:** Print; Online.

2802 ■ *"Total Defense Launches Mobile Security for Business"* in *Benzinga.com (August 1, 2012)*
Pub: Benzinga.com
Contact: Jason Raznick, Founder
Ed: Aaron Wise. **Description:** Total Defense Inc. launched its Total Defense Mobile Secuirty Suite, a cloud-based solution for business that secures and manages mobile devices. Total Defense is a leading provider of malware protection against cybercrime. **Availability:** Online.

2803 ■ *"Travel Tech: 4 Gadgets for Running Your Business on the Fly"* in *Entrepreneur (May 2014)*
Pub: Entrepreneur Media Inc.
Contact: Dan Bova, Director
E-mail: dbova@entrepreneur.com
Description: The Goal Zero Sherpa 100 Power Pack includes two USB ports, a 12-volt plug and a proprietary laptop port that can fill a MacBook Air's battery faster on a single charge. The Nomad ChargeKey is lightweight, flexible and allows users to connect their spent smartphones to any full-size USB outlet. The Jawbone Era Bluetooth headset features a sleek carrying case that also functions as a battery-powered charger. The Belkin WeMo Insight Switch is a mobile wall plug that connects to a Wi-Fi and links to smartphones through an application. **Availability:** Online.

2804 ■ *"Trusted Choice: Mobile App"* in *Best's Review (Vol. 113, September 2012, No. 5, pp. 14)*
Description: Profile of Trusted Choice, the new mobile app launched in March 2012 for use on smartphones and tablet computers. The app helps clients contact their independent insurance agent. Consumers can keep an inventory of insured personal possessions, document a car accident with photos, read insurance tips, communicate with Trusted Choice agent and ask insurance-related questions. **Availability:** Online.

2805 ■ *"Verizon Loses Wireless Phone Customers"* in *The Wall Street Journal (April 23, 2019)*
URL(s): www.wsj.com/articles/verizon-loses-wireless -phone-customers-11556020514
Ed: Sarah Krouse. **Released:** April 23, 2019. **Description:** While upgrading to a faster 5G network, Verizon decided to offer fewer promotions which led to a decline in customers. Competitors in a crowded market offered deals to consumers, causing some to switch and others to not even consider Verizon as a carrier. **Availability:** Online.

2806 ■ *"Verizon, Union Dispute is a Vestige of the Past"* in *Philadelphia Business Journal (Vol. 30, August 26, 2011, No. 28, pp. 1)*
Pub: Philadelphia Business Journal
Contact: Sierra Quinn, Director
E-mail: squinn@bizjournals.com
Ed: Peter Key. **Description:** Verizon is arguing that some of the provisions of its unionized workers' contracts date back to the days before AT&T was forced to spin off its local phone-service providers in 1984. The evolution of Verizon through the years and its relations with its unions are discussed. **Availability:** Online.

2807 ■ *"Weightplan.com Launches 'Gymcodes' the Virtual Personal Trainer - Scan QR Codes on Gym Equipment for on the Spot Exercise Tuition"* in *America's Intelligence Wire (June 11, 2012)*
Description: The Weightplan.com iPhone app provides instant gym tuition simply by scanning QR codes on pieces of gym equipment. Details of the 'Gymcode' program are provided. **Availability:** Print; Online.

2808 ■ *"What the T-Mobile Takeover of Sprint Means for Your Wireless Bill"* in *The Wall Street Journal (August 1, 2019)*
URL(s): www.wsj.com/articles/what-the-t-mobile -takeover-of-sprint-means-for-your-wireless-bill -11564156044
Ed: Sarah Krouse. **Released:** August 01, 2019. **Description:** Discusses the impact the merger between T-Mobile and Sprint will have on consumers. The majority of Sprint customers will be rolled into the T-Mobile plan while the rest who use pay-as-you-go will be using the Dish, which is selling wireless service for the first time. **Availability:** Online.

2809 ■ *"Will mCommerce Make Black Friday Green?"* in *Retail Merchandiser (Vol. 51, September-October 2011, No. 5, pp. 8)*
Description: Retailers speculate the possibilities of mobile commerce and are implementing strategies at their stores. Consumers using mobile devices accounted for only 0.1 percent of visits to retail Websites on Black Friday 2009 and rose to 5.6 percent in 2010; numbers are expected to rise for 2011. **Availability:** Print; Online.

2810 ■ *"Will Mobile's Massive Growth Ever Equal Real Revenue?"* in *Advertising Age (Vol. 83, October 1, 2012, No. 35, pp. 18)*
Pub: Crain Communications Inc.
Contact: Barry Asin, President

Ed: Jason Del Rey. **Description:** Media companies are concerned over the return on investment when advertising on mobile applications. Firms lament that these ads are worth less to a small business than offline marketing programs. **Availability:** Online.

2811 ■ "Who's On Top in the Telecom Turf Fight" in Dallas Business Journal (Vol. 37, April 25, 2014, No. 33, pp. 4)
Pub: American City Business Journals, Inc.
Contact: Mike Olivieri, Executive Vice President
Released: Weekly. **Price:** $4, introductory 4-week offer(Digital & Print). **Description:** The four major wireless providers in the U.S. are competing for customers in North Texas and around the country. Experts say AT&T, Verizon, Sprint and T-Mobile have to offer better quality services, faster service and lower pricing to win customers from each other. **Availability:** Print; Online.

2812 ■ "Words at Work" in Information Today (Vol. 26, February 2009, No. 2, pp. 25)
Description: Current new buzzwords include the following: digital amnesia, or overload by availability, speed and volume of digital information; maternal profiling, a form a discrimination against women; recipe malpractice, a reminder that just because you can turn on a stove it doesn't make you a chef; ringxiety, the act when everyone reaches for their cell phone when one rings; verbing, the practice of turning good nouns into verbs. **Availability:** Print; Online.

STATISTICAL SOURCES

2813 ■ Cell Phone Recycling Industry in the US - Market Research Report
URL(s): www.ibisworld.com/united-states/market-research-reports/cell-phone-recycling-industry/
Price: $925. **Description:** Downloadable report analyzing the current and future trends in the cell phone recycling industry. **Availability:** Download.

2814 ■ The Retail Market for Smartphones Industry in the US - Market Research Report
URL(s): www.ibisworld.com/united-states/market-research-reports/the-retail-market-for-smartphones-industry/
Price: $925. **Description:** Downloadable report analyzing the current and future trends of the smartphone retail market. **Availability:** Online.

2815 ■ RMA Annual Statement Studies
Pub: Risk Management Association
Contact: Nancy Foster, President
Released: Annual. **Description:** Contains composite balance sheets and income statements for more than 360 industries, including the accounting, auditing, and bookkeeping industries. Also contains five years of comparative historical data for discerning trends. Includes 16 commonly used ratios, computed for most of the size groupings for nearly every industry.

2816 ■ Standard & Poor's Industry Surveys
Pub: Standard And Poor's Financial Services LLC.
Contact: Douglas L. Peterson, President
Description: Two-volume book that examines the prospects for specific industries, including trucking. Also provides analyses of trends and problems, statistical tables and charts, and comparative company analyses.

TRADE PERIODICALS

2817 ■ Green Data Centers and Internet Business
Pub: Information Gatekeepers Inc.
Contact: Will Ashley, Manager
E-mail: washley@igigroup.com
URL(s): www.igigroup.com/nl/pages/business.html
Ed: Tony Carmona. **Released:** Monthly; 12 issues / year. **Price:** $695, U.S. and Canada for print 1 year; $695, Individuals for pdf - 1 user 1 year; $745, for print overseas 1 year; $2,500, Individuals for pdf - 2 to 10 users; $4,000, Individuals for pdf - 11 to 20 users; $7,500, Individuals for pdf - 21 to 50 users; $10,000, Individuals for pdf - 50+ users. **Description:** Provides marketing and technology information on new developments in the internet telephone industry on a worldwide basis. **Availability:** Print; Online; PDF.

2818 ■ Sound & Communications Magazine
Pub: Testa Communications
URL(s): www.soundandcommunications.com
Facebook: www.facebook.com/SoundandComms
Linkedin: www.linkedin.com/showcase/soundandcomms
X (Twitter): twitter.com/soundandcomms
YouTube: www.youtube.com/channel/UCxY_fXRFKIFBHf_I7YoBoFA
Ed: David A. Silverman. **Released:** Monthly; last edition September 2021. **Description:** Magazine focusing on sound and communications systems equipment, installations, and technology. **Availability:** Print; Online.

2819 ■ Urgent Communications: Technical Information for Paging, Trunking and Private Wireless Networks
Contact: Greg Herring, President
E-mail: gregg.herring@penton.com
URL(s): urgentcomm.com
Facebook: www.facebook.com/UrgentCommunications
Linkedin: www.linkedin.com/company/iwce%27s-urgent-communications
X (Twitter): twitter.com/UrgentComm
Ed: Donny Jackson. **Description:** Technical magazine for the mobile communications industry. **Availability:** Print; Online.

2820 ■ Wireless Cellular / WiMAX
Pub: Information Gatekeepers Inc.
Contact: Will Ashley, Manager
E-mail: washley@igigroup.com
URL(s): www.igigroup.com/nl/pages/fixed.html
Released: Monthly **Price:** $745, Other countries for print one year; $695, U.S. and Canada for PDF; $695, U.S. and Canada for U.S and Canada (print) one year; $2,500, for 2-10 users; $7,500, for 21-50 users; $4,000, for 11-20 users; $10,000, for 50 users. **Description:** Covers international developments in the wireless cellular industry, including new products, market opportunities and forecasts, regulations and standards, procurements, mergers and acquisitions, and applications. **Availability:** Print; Online; PDF.

TRADE SHOWS AND CONVENTIONS

2821 ■ Wireless
URL(s): www.ctia.org/ctia-show
Description: Cellular and wireless equipment and support services. **Audience:** Wireless carriers, suppliers, providers and manufacturers. **Principal Exhibits:** Cellular and wireless equipment and support services.

CONSULTANTS

2822 ■ AECOM - Library
AECOM
13355 Noel Rd., Ste. 400
Dallas, TX 75240
Ph: (972)788-1000
Co. E-mail: info@aecom.com
URL: http://www.aecom.com
Contact: Lara Poloni, President
Facebook: www.facebook.com/AecomTechnologyCorporation
Linkedin: www.linkedin.com/company/aecom
X (Twitter): twitter.com/AECOM
Instagram: www.instagram.com/aecom
YouTube: www.youtube.com/user/AECOMTechnologyCorp
Description: Fully integrated provider of planning, consultation, architectural, and engineering design and construction services. **Scope:** Environment; air quality; hazardous waste. **Services:** Interlibrary loan; library not open to the public. **Founded:** 1990. **Holdings:** 5,000 books; technical and government reports; government agency rules and regulations. **Publications:** "Global Perspectives"; "Asia Beyond Growth"; "Climate Design"; "Water Reuse: Issues, Technologies, Applications"; "Wastewater Engineering: Treatment and Reuse"; "The Bigger Picture". **Educational Activities:** Air & Waste Management Association Annual Conference & Exhibition (ACE) (Annual); CoreNet Global Symposium (Irregular); American Planning Association Conference (APA) (Annual); IFMA's World Workplace Conference & Expo (Annual); ACENZ Annual Conference (Annual); ASFPM Annual National Conference (Annual); Airports Council International - Asia-Pacific Regional Assembly, Conference & Exhibition (Annual).

2823 ■ Trott Communications Group, Inc.
1303 W Walnut Hill Ln., Ste. 300
Irving, TX 75038
Ph: (972)518-1811
URL: http://www.trottgroup.com
Contact: Roxanne Trott, President
Description: Firm provides wireless engineering and consulting services. **Founded:** 1978.

FRANCHISES AND BUSINESS OPPORTUNITIES

2824 ■ Worldwide Wireless
Worldwide Wireless Franchise Services L.L.C.
Dlouha 38
110 00 Prague, Czech Republic
Free: 877-346-3999
Contact: Barry M. Gilbert, Director General
Description: Exclusive Sprint dealership. **Founded:** 1999. **Franchised:** 2006. **Equity Capital Needed:** $75,000-$150,000. **Franchise Fee:** $30,000. **Financial Assistance:** Yes **Training:** Yes.

LIBRARIES

2825 ■ U.S. Federal Communications Commission (FCC)
45 L St. NE
Washington, DC 20554
Free: 888-225-5322
Fax: (866)418-0232
URL: http://www.fcc.gov
Contact: Jessica Rosenworcel, Chairperson
E-mail: jessica.rosenworcel@fcc.gov
Facebook: www.facebook.com/FCC
X (Twitter): x.com/fcc
Instagram: www.instagram.com/fcc
YouTube: www.youtube.com/fcc
Description: An independent government agency engaged in the regulation of interstate and international communications by radio, television, wire, satellite and cable. The commission serves as the primary authority for communications law, regulation and technology innovation in the United States. **Founded:** 1934. **Publications:** AM Radio Database Query (AMQ); FCC Amateur License Data Search; FM Radio Database Query (FMQ); FCC Universal Licensing System (ULS); FCC Antenna Structure Registration (ASR); AM/FM Broadcast Financial Data/TV Broadcast Financial Data; TV Database Query (TVQ); Universal Licensing System License Search; Universal Licensing System Aircraft License Search; Universal Licensing System Commercial/Restricted Permits License Search; Universal Licensing System General Mobile Radio License Search (GMRS); Universal Licensing System Ship License Search; Universal Licensing System Geographic Search; Universal Licensing System Market Based License Search; Filed Comments Search; Equipment Authorization System Generic Search; Electronic Document Management System Search (EDOCS); Part 68 Registration Search; Station Search; Application Search; EEO Filing Search - Broadcast; Ownership Report Search (Continuous); Antenna Search.

Charter Boat Service

ASSOCIATIONS AND OTHER ORGANIZATIONS

2826 ■ Boat Owners Association of the United States [BoatUS]
5323 Port Royal Rd.
Springfield, VA 22151
Free: 800-937-3300
URL: http://www.boatus.com
Contact: Tammy Moore, President
Facebook: www.facebook.com/BoatUS
Linkedin: www.linkedin.com/company/boatus
X (Twitter): x.com/boatus
Instagram: www.instagram.com/boatus
YouTube: www.youtube.com/boatus
Description: Represents owners or prospective owners of recreational boats. Independent, consumer service organization offering representation, benefits, and programs for boat owners. **Founded:** 1966. **Publications:** *BOAT U.S. Magazine* (5/year); *Boat U.S. Trailering Magazine* (Bimonthly); *Equipment Catalog* (Annual); *Seaworthy*; *Boater's Source Directory* (Semiannual). **Geographic Preference:** National.

2827 ■ Michigan Charter Boat Association (MCBA)
c/o John Giszczak, Secretary
9760 Judd
Willis, MI 48191
Free: 800-622-2971
Co. E-mail: straycat@straycatsportfishingcharters.com
URL: http://www.michigancharterboats.com
Contact: Bill Winowiecki, President
E-mail: charterfishing@wattabite.com
Facebook: www.facebook.com/michigancharterboats
X (Twitter): x.com/michiganfishing
Description: Promotes fishing, diving, duck hunting, cruises, and excursions in the state of Michigan. **Founded:** 1971. **Geographic Preference:** State.

2828 ■ National Women's Sailing Association (NWSA)
PO Box 588
Marblehead, MA 01945
Ph: (985)247-8919
Co. E-mail: wsf@womensailing.org
URL: http://womensailing.org
Contact: Elise Read, President
Facebook: www.facebook.com/nationalwomenssailingassociation
X (Twitter): x.com/WomenSail
Description: Works to enhance the lives of women and girls through education and access to the sport of sailing. **Founded:** 1990. **Publications:** *Women's Sailing Resource* (Biennial). **Educational Activities:** Sail Expo (Annual); Pacific Sail Expo (Annual); Sail Boat Show (Annual). **Geographic Preference:** National.

2829 ■ Passenger Vessel Association (PVA)
103 Oronoco St., Ste. 200
Alexandria, VA 22314
Ph: (703)518-5005
Co. E-mail: pvainfo@passengervessel.com
URL: http://www.passengervessel.com
Contact: Bob Bijur, President
Facebook: www.facebook.com/passengervesselassociation
Linkedin: www.linkedin.com/company/passengervesselassociation
Description: Monitors and disseminates information on current and proposed federal regulation and legislation affecting passenger ship owners. Represents the industry's views to legislative and regulatory bodies. **Founded:** 1971. **Publications:** *Foghorn* (11/year). **Geographic Preference:** National; Regional.

2830 ■ States Organization for Boating Access (SOBA)
1020 Monarch St., Ste. 200
Lexington, KY 40513
URL: http://www.sobaus.org/home
Contact: B. Todd Mize, President
Linkedin: www.linkedin.com/company/states-organization-for-boating-access-soba
Description: Provides information regarding the construction, maintenance, financing and administration of recreational boating facilities to state program administrators charged with their management. **Founded:** 1986. **Publications:** *Design Handbook and Operations and Maintenance Guidelines*. **Educational Activities:** States Organization for Boating Access Annual Conference (Annual). **Awards:** SOBA Outstanding Project Awards (Annual); SOBA Outstanding Service Award (Annual); SOBA Professional Service Award (Annual); SOBA Special Recognition Award (Annual); SOBA Program Excellence Award (Annual); SOBA State Clean Vessel Act (CVA) Program Excellence Award (Annual); William H. Ivers Award (Annual); SOBA Meritorious Service Award (Annual). **Geographic Preference:** National.

REFERENCE WORKS

2831 ■ *Atlantic Boating Almanac*
Pub: Atlantic Boating Almanac
URL(s): www.prostarpublications.com/b1/product_info.php?products_id=57
Released: Annual; Latest edition 2006. **Price:** $24.95, Individuals. **Description:** Covers listings on coast piloting, electronics, GPS by Gordon West, first aid, weather, facilities and fuel docks. There are four separate regional editions: Florida & Bahamas; North & South Carolina and Georgia; Massachusetts, Rhode Island, Connecticut and Long Island; and Maine, New Hampshire & Massachusetts. Includes tide and current tables; maps and fishing charts; navigation and star charts; first aid; US coast pilot. **Arrangement:** Geographical. **Availability:** Print.

2832 ■ "*Macomb County Man Accused of Illegally Operating Charter Boat*" in *Macomb Daily* (July 7, 2019)
URL(s): www.macombdaily.com/news/copscourts/macomb-county-man-accused-of-illegally-operating-charter-boat/article_90caddc0-9df0-11e9-9f19-6ba1eed2ca26.html
Ed: Mitch Hotts. **Released:** July 07, 2019. **Description:** A 33-year-old Macomb County man is being charged with running an illegal charter boat operation, which operated in the Chicago area. The man and his vessels have not been certified by the US Coast Guard, putting clients at risk. **Availability:** Print; Online.

TRADE PERIODICALS

2833 ■ *NMMA Currents*
Pub: Ormazabal Y Cia S.L.U
URL(s): www.nmma.org/currents
Released: Daily **Description:** Reviews boat shows. Reports industry trends. Offers trade and consumer show advice. Recurring features include interviews, a calendar of events, and reports of meetings. **Availability:** Online.

2834 ■ *Seaworthy*
Pub: Boat Owners Association of the United States
Contact: Tammy Moore, President
URL(s): www.boatus.com/expert-advice/expert-advice-archive/2021/june/where-to-anchor
Ed: Beth A. Leonard, Charles Fort. **Description:** Seeks to help boaters avoid accidents or problems by listing actual insurance claims. Includes case studies that provide insight in to how to avoid accidents, breakdowns, injuries, and other "unexpected" circumstances that can jeopardize the safety of their boat, themselves, and guests. **Availability:** Print.

FRANCHISES AND BUSINESS OPPORTUNITIES

2835 ■ The Cruising Club Fractional Boat Ownership
Ph: (954)397-1185
Co. E-mail: carlton@thecruisingclub.com
URL: http://www.thecruisingclub.com
Facebook: www.facebook.com/The-Cruising-Club-Fractional-Boat-Ownership-174126792201
X (Twitter): twitter.com/CruisingClubUSA
Description: Fractional boat ownership. **No. of Franchise Units:** 6. **No. of Company-Owned Units:** 5. **Founded:** 1998. **Franchised:** 2004. **Equity Capital Needed:** Varies, $35,000-$500,000. **Franchise Fee:** $25,000-$100,000. **Training:** Yes.

Check Cashing Service

REFERENCE WORKS

2836 ■ *"Do Check-Cashing Services Provide a Banking Alternative?" in The Simple Dollar (March 11, 2019)*
URL(s): www.thesimpledollar.com/banking/blog/a-deeper-look-at-check-cashing-services-do-they-really-provide-an-alternative-banking-opportunity/
Ed: Trent Hamm. **Released:** March 11, 2019. **Description:** Explores the rise of check cashing outlets and why people choose them over traditional banks. Even though there is a cost associated with these services, they are upfront about the cost, transparent, and provide great service. Banks often hide their fees and unlike check cashing outlets, the consumer doesn't always receive their money right away because the check needs to be deposited. **Availability:** Online.

2837 ■ *"Inside the World of Check-Cashing Outlets" in Dollars&Sense (January/February 2015)*
URL(s): dollarsandsense.org/archives/2015/0115barr-figart.html
Ed: Deborah M. Figart, Thomas Barr. **Released:** January 2015. **Description:** About 35 million people in the US use a check cashing outlet, and these businesses are growing due to the repercussions of income inequality and the financial Great Recession. These businesses provide a vital service, which is cashing checks for people that are turned down by banks. Some states are cracking down on regulations and are insisting on capped, low check-cashing fees for paychecks, which is helping consumers. **Availability:** Online.

2838 ■ *"The Unbanking of America"*
Ed: Lisa Servon. **Released:** January 10, 2017. **Price:** $15.99, hardcover; $9.99, e-book. **Description:** With nearly half of Americans living paycheck to paycheck, consumers are finding alternatives to traditional banking. Banks often have high monthly fees and overdraft charges are pushing more and more to seek out check-cashers, payday lenders, and even informal lending clubs. This book examines how middle class Americans are operating without banks. **Availability:** E-book; Print.

FRANCHISES AND BUSINESS OPPORTUNITIES

2839 ■ **Cash Plus Inc. (CP)**
PO Box 2185
 Anaheim, CA 92814
Ph: (714)731-2274
Free: 877-227-4758
Fax: (714)731-2099
Co. E-mail: cpcorp@cashplusinc.com
URL: http://cashplusinc.com
Contact: Craig Wells, President
Description: Provider of financial services. **Founded:** 1984. **Training:** Provides training including easy-to-run computerized operating system, promotions and check verification and payday advance process.

2840 ■ **Family Financial Centers (FFC)**
2801 E Rd.
 Willow Grove, PA 19090
Ph: (215)675-7033
URL: http://www.familyfinancialcenters.com
Description: Provider of check cashing and other financial services. **Founded:** 2004. **Equity Capital Needed:** $148,000- $149,000. **Franchise Fee:** $36,500. **Financial Assistance:** Yes **Training:** Offers 1 week training at headquarters, 1 week field training and ongoing support.

2841 ■ **United Check Cashing**
United Financial Services Group Inc. (UFSG)
 1123 S Broad St.
 Philadelphia, PA 19147
Ph: (215)238-0300
Free: 800-626-0787
Fax: (215)238-9056
Co. E-mail: info@unitedfsg.com
URL: http://www.unitedcheckcashing.com
Contact: Anjali Patel, Contact
Description: Firm provides check cashing services, money orders, wire transfer, bill payment, prepaid debit cards and much more. **Founded:** 1977. **Financial Assistance:** Yes **Training:** Receive training in customer servicing, sales, human resources, loss prevention and risk management.

Children's Apparel Shop

START-UP INFORMATION

2842 ■ *"Mount Laurel Woman Launches Venture Into Children's Used Clothing"* in *Philadelphia Inquirer (September 17, 2010)*
Pub: The Philadelphia Inquirer
Contact: Elizabeth H. Hughes, Chief Executive Officer

Ed: Maria Panaritis. **Description:** Profile of Jennifer Frisch, stay-at-home mom turned entrepreneur. Frisch started a used-clothing store Once Upon a Child after opening her franchised Plato's Closet, selling unwanted and used baby clothing and accessories at her new shop, while offering used merchandise to teens at Plato's Closet.

ASSOCIATIONS AND OTHER ORGANIZATIONS

2843 ■ **American Apparel and Footwear Association (AAFA)**
740 6th St., NW
  Washington, DC 20001
Ph: (202)853-9080
Co. E-mail: membership@aafaglobal.org
URL: http://www.aafaglobal.org
Contact: Stephen Lamar, President
E-mail: slamar@apparelandfootwear.org
Facebook: www.facebook.com/apparelandfootwear
Linkedin: www.linkedin.com/company/aafa
X (Twitter): x.com/apparelfootwear
Instagram: www.instagram.com/apparelandfootwear
YouTube: www.youtube.com/user/apparelandfootwear

Description: Manufacturers of infants', children's, boys', girls', juniors', men's, and women's wearing apparel; associate members are suppliers of fabrics, equipment, accessories, and services to the apparel industry. Operates the Apparel Foundation; offers placement service through newsletter. **Founded:** 2000. **Publications:** *AAFA Directory of Members and Associate Members* (Annual); *Technical Advisory Committee Bulletin* (Periodic); *SoleSource: The Footwear Industry Directory* (Annual); *SoleSource: The footwear industry reserviece directory* (Annual). **Geographic Preference:** National.

REFERENCE WORKS

2844 ■ *"Best Baby Clothing Stores of 2019"* in *Babylist (January 1, 2019)*
URL(s): www.babylist.com/hello-baby/best-baby-clothing-stores

Released: January 01, 2019. **Description:** Top online places to shop for baby clothes. Some offer either instore or online deals, so it may be best to check both if you are looking for a steal. **Availability:** Online.

2845 ■ *"Borrow Baby Couture Launch Rocks Fasion World - Provides Couture Fashion for Girls"* in *Benzinga.com (June 18, 2012)*
Description: Borrow Baby Couture allows parents, family and friends to rent couture clothing by top fashion designers for girls ages 9 months to 4 years. The retailer has launched an online site. Purchases are wrapped in tissue arriving ready to wear and includes return shipping costs. **Availability:** Online.

2846 ■ *"Consignment Shop Offers Children's Clothes, Products"* in *Frederick News-Post (August 19, 2010)*
Pub: Frederick News-Post
Contact: Connie Hastings, Director
E-mail: chastings@newspost.com

Ed: Ed Waters, Jr. **Description:** Sweet Pea Consignments for Children offers used items for newborns to pre-teens. The shop carries name brand clothing as well as toys, books and baby products. **Availability:** Print; Online.

2847 ■ *"Consignment Shops Form Friendly Alliance in Eagle Plaza"* in *Mail Tribune (August 7, 2012)*
Ed: Greg Stiles. **Description:** Loren Clear was concerned about opening his men's only consignment shop in a plaza already housing three other consignment stores. However, all four retailers have found it to be an asset, each having their own specialty. Along with Clear's men's clothing consignment, there is a children's store, a plus-size shop, and a women's clothing and accessory business. Clear said there are few men's consignment stores and it is an answer for the businessman to purchase better quality clothing and suits at better prices., Loren Clear thought opening his men's only consignment shop in the same plaza shared with three other consignment stores might be a bad idea. However, all three retailers have found it to be an asset. Along with Clear's men's only shop called Men's Hangups, there is a plus-size shop, a women's store, and a children's store. **Availability:** Online.

2848 ■ *"The Cutest Houston-Made Kids' Clothes Will Soon Come in Mom Versions"* in *Houstonia (August 7, 2019)*
URL(s): www.houstoniamag.com/articles/2019/8/7/bee-and-birdie-kids-clothes-etsy-shop

Ed: Abby Ledoux. **Released:** August 07, 2019. **Description:** The small online shop, Bee + Birdie has made a name for itself selling affordable toddler clothing that has a more subdued aesthetic instead of the in-your-face fashion that most stores carry. With its current success, the brand is now launching "mom" versions of their fashions. **Availability:** Online.

2849 ■ *Directory of Apparel Specialty Stores*
Pub: Chain Store Guide
Contact: Kaitlyn Toner, Account Manager
URL(s): www.chainstoreguide.com/c-75-apparel-specialty-store-leads.aspx

Released: Annual **Price:** $1,850, for plus one year subscription. **Description:** Covers 5,040 apparel and sporting goods specialty retailers in the United States and Canada, operating more than 70,700 stores. Apparel retailers must have annual retail sales of at least $500,000; sporting goods specialty retailers must also have $500,000 in annual sales, with the condition that at least 20% of product sales are from sporting goods equipment. **Entries include:** Company name, phone, and fax numbers; physical and mailing addresses; company e-mail and web addresses; Internet order processing indicator; percentage of Internet sales; type of business; listing type; product lines; total, industry, and product group sales; total selling square footage; store prototype sizes; total stores; trading areas; projected openings and remodeling; units by trade name; distribution center locations; resident buyer's name and location; mail order indicator; percentage of mail order sales; catalog names; private label indicator; private label credit card indicator; apparel price lines; average number of checkouts; year founded; public company indicator; parent company name and location; and key personnel with titles; 7,200 personnel email addresses. **Arrangement:** Geographical. **Indexes:** Alphabetical, product lines, exclusions. **Availability:** Online.

2850 ■ *"Green It Like You Mean It"* in *Special Events Magazine (Vol. 28, February 1, 2009, No. 2)*
Description: Eco-friendly party planners offer advice for planning and hosting green parties or events. Tips include information for using recycled paper products, organic food and drinks. The Eco Nouveau Fashion Show held by Serene Star Productions reused old garments to create new fashions as well as art pieces from discarded doors and window frames for the show; eco-friendly treats and gift bags were highlighted at the event.

2851 ■ *"Intrepid Souls: Meet a Few Who've Made the Big Leap"* in *Crain's Chicago Business (Vol. 31, November 10, 2008, No. 45, pp. 26)*
Description: Advice is given from entrepreneurs who have launched businesses in the last year despite the economic crisis. Among the types of businesses featured are a cooking school, a child day-care center, a children's clothing store and an Internet-based company. **Availability:** Online.

2852 ■ *"The Nation's #1 Children's Shoe Retailer, Payless ShoeSource(R), Launches Hassle-Free Back-to-School Shoe Shopping"* in *Benzinga.com (July 25, 2012)*
Pub: PR Newswire Association LLC.
Description: Nation's largest shoe retailer, Payless ShoeSource(R), is offering a Happiness Guarantee for back-to-school shoe shopping. The firm's goal is to make shoppers happy and keep them returning to purchase shoes during the rest of the year.

2853 ■ *"The Smartest Ways to Shop for Kids Clothes Without Breaking the Bank: A Guide"* in *SlickDeals.net (July 1, 2019)*
URL(s): slickdeals.net/article/buying-guide/shopping-guide-for-kids-clothes/

Ed: Ashley Eneriz. **Released:** July 01, 2019. **Description:** A guide to shopping for children's clothes from babies to pre-teens. Discusses which stores have the best deals and guarantees and tells the consumer which price points to aim for. **Availability:** Online.

2854 ■ "SPOILED! Children's Consignment Boutique Now Collecting Donations To Support Baby2Baby & Help Children In Need" in Benzinga.com (July 30, 2012)
Pub: Benzinga.com
Contact: Jason Raznick, Founder

Ed: Aaron Wise. **Description:** CeCe Hendriks opened her high-end children's consignment store in response to wanting to provide quality clothing for her son. Because children outgrow their clothing so fast, she decided a consignment shop is what all mom's needed. Hendriks offers a 50 percent consignment to donors and if the item isn't sold in 90 days, the consignee can choos to have the item returned or donate it to Baby2Baby. Hendriks also gives 10 percent of proceeds from sales to Baby2Baby, a nonprofit that works with homeles and domestic violence shelters. **Availability:** Online.

2855 ■ "ThredUP Launches Online Concierge Service to Compete With Children's Consignment" in Benzinga.com (January 25, 2012)
Description: Concierge is a new service offered by thredUP, the top online site for used children's clothing. Concierge simplifies the process of recycling children's clothing. Users sign up at the Website and request a prepaid, ready to ship recycling bag. After filling the bag, it is placed on the doorstep, and thredUp takes it from there. After consignors inspect the items, senders are given rewards up to $5 per piece, based on quality and quantity of items shipped. The received items are then sold on thredUP's online shop.

STATISTICAL SOURCES

2856 ■ U.S. Children's Clothing Market Report 2021
URL(s): store.mintel.com/report/us-childrens-clothing-market-report
Price: $4,366.35. **Description:** Downloadable report covering data analysis of parents and how and why they shop for their children's clothing. Report includes an executive summary, interactive databook, PowerPoint presentation, infographic overview, report PDF, and previous years data. **Availability:** PDF.

TRADE PERIODICALS

2857 ■ California Apparel News
Pub: Apparel News Group
URL(s): www.apparelnews.net
Facebook: www.facebook.com/ApparelNews
Instagram: www.instagram.com/apparelnews
Ed: Terry Martinez, Deborah Belgum, Alison A. Nieder. **Released:** Biweekly **Price:** $180, for 1 year foreign print and all access online; $79.95, for 2 Years print and all access online; $49.95, for 1 Year print and all access online; $135, for 1 Year Canada print and all access online. **Description:** Weekly newspaper covering the apparel industry and providing information about textiles, trimmings, fashion trends, retailing and business. **Availability:** Print; Online; PDF.

TRADE SHOWS AND CONVENTIONS

2858 ■ Trendz Show
Florida Fashion Focus, Inc.
URL(s): www.trendzshow.com/show-dates
Frequency: Irregular. **Description:** Ladies ready-to-wear clothing, handbags, jewelry, and accessories. Order-writing for future delivery. **Audience:** Industry professionals. **Principal Exhibits:** Ladies ready-to-wear clothing, handbags, jewelry, and accessories. Order-writing for future delivery. Dates and Locations: Palm Beach County Convention Center, Palm Beach, FL.

FRANCHISES AND BUSINESS OPPORTUNITIES

2859 ■ Children's Orchard (CO)
13625 Grove Dr.
Maple Grove, MN 55311
Ph: (952)232-5603
Co. E-mail: maplegrove@childrensorchard.com
URL: http://www.childrensorchard.com
Facebook: www.facebook.com/ChildOrchard
Instagram: www.instagram.com/childrensorchard

Description: Children's upscale/resale retail store. **No. of Franchise Units:** 93. **No. of Company-Owned Units:** 1. **Founded:** 1980. **Franchised:** 1985. **Equity Capital Needed:** $115,600-$197,000. **Franchise Fee:** $25,000. **Royalty Fee:** 5%. **Training:** Provides 12 days training at headquarters, 3 days onsite and ongoing support.

2860 ■ Educational Outfitters Group L.L.C.
1601 Gulf St., Ste. 200
Chattanooga, TN 37408
Ph: (423)465-4444
Free: 877-814-1222
Co. E-mail: info@educationaloutfitters.com
URL: http://educationaloutfitters.com
Contact: John Clark, Contact

Description: Franchise of school uniforms and dress-code apparel for schools. **Founded:** 1999. **Training:** initial training at store, additional training at the franchisees location along with on-going support.

RESEARCH CENTERS

2861 ■ Texas A&M University - Mays Business School - Center for Retailing Studies
4113 TAMU
College Station, TX 77843-4113
Co. E-mail: crs@mays.tamu.edu
URL: http://mays.tamu.edu/center-for-retailing-studies
Facebook: www.facebook.com/TAMURetail
Linkedin: www.linkedin.com/company/tamuretail
X (Twitter): twitter.com/TAMURetail
YouTube: www.youtube.com/channel/UC8fGvvvhoeTL4S619OVdDCA

Description: Integral unit of Texas A&M University, operated with industry advisory board. **Scope:** Business school and center for retailing studies. **Founded:** 1983. **Publications:** *Faculty retailing research Papers*; *Retailing Issues Letter* (Quarterly). **Educational Activities:** Center for Retailing Studies Retailing Summit (Annual), Held in September for retailing executives and academics.; Center for Retailing Studies Thought Leadership Conference (Annual), Brings together academic scholars and industry professionals from around the globe to develop position papers on retailing research issues.

Children's Day Care Center

START-UP INFORMATION

2862 ■ *"Franchises with an Eye on Chicago"* **in Crain's Chicago Business (Vol. 34, March 14, 2011, No. 11, pp. 20)**
Pub: Crain Communications Inc.
Contact: Barry Asin, President
Ed: Kevin McKeough. **Description:** Profiles of franchise companies seeking franchisees for the Chicago area include: Extreme Pita, a sandwich shop; Hand and Stone, offering massage, facial and waxing services; Molly Maid, home-cleaning service; Primrose Schools, private accredited schools for children 6 months to 6 hears and after-school programs; Protect Painters, residential and light-commercial painting contractor; and Wingstop, a restaurant offering chicken wings in nine flavors, fries and side dishes. **Availability:** Online.

2863 ■ *"Making Money Is Child's Play With This Retailer"* **in Small Business Opportunities (March 1, 2008)**
Pub: Harris Publishing, Inc.
Contact: Janet Chase, Contact
Description: Proven system helps launch a successful child care business. **Availability:** Print; Online.

ASSOCIATIONS AND OTHER ORGANIZATIONS

2864 ■ **American Montessori Society (AMS) - Montessori Research Library**
211 E 43rd St., 7th Fl., No.262
New York, NY 10017
Ph: (212)358-1250
Fax: (212)358-1256
Co. E-mail: ams@amshq.org
URL: http://amshq.org
Contact: Munir Shivji, Executive Director
E-mail: mshivji@amshq.org
Facebook: www.facebook.com/AmericanMontessoriSociety
X (Twitter): x.com/amshq
Instagram: www.instagram.com/americanmontessori
YouTube: www.youtube.com/channel/UC3_iLp2TLe0ZlsXwj-aTMMA
Description: School affiliates and teacher training affiliates; heads of schools, teachers, parents, non-Montessori educators, and other interested individuals dedicated to stimulating the use of the Montessori teaching approach and promoting better education for all children. Seeks to meet demands of growing interest in the Montessori approach to early learning. Assists in establishing schools; supplies information and limited services to member schools in other countries. Maintains school consultation and accreditation service; provides information service; assists research and gathers statistical data; offers placement service. **Scope:** Montessori education. **Founded:** 1960. **Holdings:** Dissertations; theses; journal articles; papers. **Publications:** *Montessori Life* (Quarterly); *School Directory*; *American Montessori Society School Directory*. **Awards:** AMS Teacher Education Scholarships (Annual); Teacher Education Scholarship (Annual); American Montessori Society Dissertation and Thesis Awards (Annual). **Geographic Preference:** National.

2865 ■ **Association for Early Learning Leaders (AELL)**
1250 S Capital of Texas Hwy., Bldg. 3, Ste. 400
Austin, TX 78746
Free: 800-537-1118
Co. E-mail: info@earlylearningleaders.org
URL: http://www.earlylearningleaders.org
Contact: Lori Buxton, Contact
Facebook: www.facebook.com/EarlyLearningLeaders
Linkedin: www.linkedin.com/company/association-for-early-learning-leaders
X (Twitter): x.com/aelleaders
Description: Child care supervisors and individuals involved in decision-making at a child care facility. Offers networking opportunities and support services to child care professionals. Dedicated to the professional development of child care directors. Conducts educational programs. **Founded:** 1984. **Publications:** *Caring for Your Children* (Quarterly); *Immunizing Children Against Disease: A Guide For Child Care Providers*; *Professional Connections* (Quarterly); *Team Work* (Quarterly). **Educational Activities:** How Successful Directors Lead National Conference (Annual). **Awards:** AELL Director of the Year Award (Annual). **Geographic Preference:** National.

2866 ■ **Child Welfare League of America (CWLA) - Library**
727 15th St. NW Ste. 1200
Washington, DC 20005
Ph: (202)688-4200
Co. E-mail: cwla@cwla.org
URL: http://www.cwla.org
Contact: Ray Bierria, Chief Financial Officer
E-mail: rbierria@cwla.org
Facebook: www.facebook.com/CWLAUpdates
X (Twitter): x.com/CWLAofficial
Description: Works to improve care and services for abused, dependent, or neglected children, youth, and their families. Provides training and consultation; conducts research; maintains information service and develops standards for child welfare practice. **Scope:** Policy and practice issues related to child welfare such as family preservation, child abuse and neglect, adoption, foster care, teenage pregnancy, child rearing by young parents and protectors, chemical dependency, runaway youth, and management and administration of child welfare services. **Founded:** 1920. **Holdings:** Figures not available. **Publications:** *Child Welfare League of America--Directory of Member Agencies* (Biennial); *Children's Voice*; *Child Welfare League of America--Guide to Adoption Agencies: A National Directory of Adoption Agencies and Adoption Resources*; *Child Welfare: Journal of Policy, Practice, and Program (CWJ)* (Bimonthly); *Child Abuse and Neglect, A Look at the States: The 1997 Child Welfare Stat Book*; *CWLA 1997 Salary Study*. **Awards:** CWLA Corporate Advocate of the Year Award (Annual); Anna Quindlen Award for Excellence in Journalism (Irregular); CWLA Corporate Friend of Children Awards (Annual). **Geographic Preference:** National.

2867 ■ **Childhood Education International (ACEI)**
1100 15th St. NW 10th Fl.
Washington, DC 20005
Ph: (202)372-9986
Free: 800-423-3563
Co. E-mail: headquarters@ceinternational1892.org
URL: http://ceinternational1892.org
Contact: Diane Whitehead, President
E-mail: dwhitehead@acei.org
Facebook: www.facebook.com/ChildhoodEducationIntl
Linkedin: www.linkedin.com/company/childhood-education-international
X (Twitter): x.com/ChildhoodEdIntl
Description: Promotes a flexible, child-centered approach to education. Conducts advocacy through a variety of public forums and major coalitions for children and education. **Founded:** 1892. **Publications:** *Childhood Education: Infancy Through Early Adolescence* (Bimonthly); *ACEI Innovation Exchange*; *Childhood Education* (Bimonthly); *Focus on Elementary* (Quarterly); *Journal of Research in Childhood Education (JRCE)* (Quarterly). **Geographic Preference:** National.

2868 ■ **Children's Defense Fund (CDF)**
840 First St. NE, Ste. 300
Washington, DC 20002
Ph: (202)628-8787
Co. E-mail: cdfinfo@childrensdefense.org
URL: http://www.childrensdefense.org
Contact: Dr. Starsky Wilson, President
Facebook: www.facebook.com/childrensdefensefund
Linkedin: www.linkedin.com/company/children%27s-defense-fund
X (Twitter): x.com/ChildDefender
Instagram: www.instagram.com/childdefender1973
YouTube: www.youtube.com/childrensdefense
Description: Advocates: access to existing programs and services; creation of new programs and services where necessary; consistent emphasis on prevention; enforcement of civil rights laws; program accountability; strong parent and community role in decision-making; adequate funding for essential programs for children. **Founded:** 1973. **Publications:** *America's Cradle to Prison Pipeline*. **Awards:** Beat the Odds Award. **Geographic Preference:** National.

2869 ■ **National Association for the Education of Young Children (NAEYC) - Library**
1401 H St. NW Ste. 600
Washington, DC 20005
Ph: (202)232-8777
Free: 800-424-2460
Fax: (202)328-1846
Co. E-mail: help@naeyc.org

URL: http://www.naeyc.org
Contact: Michelle Kang, Chief Executive Officer
Facebook: www.facebook.com/NAEYC
Linkedin: www.linkedin.com/company/naeyc
X (Twitter): x.com/naeyc
YouTube: www.youtube.com/channel/UCoqygeWY9lnViJE5bGSE_eg
Description: Teachers and directors of preschool and primary schools, kindergartens, child care centers, and early other learning programs for young childhood; early childhood education and child development educators, trainers, and researchers and other professionals dedicated to young children's healthy development. Promotes quality early learning for children from birth to age 8. **Scope:** Early Childhood; Professional development. **Founded:** 1926. **Holdings:** Books. **Publications:** *GOAL ONE Resource Directory* (Irregular); *Young Children: The Journal of the National Association for the Education of Young Children* (5/year). **Educational Activities:** National Association for the Education of Young Children Annual Conference (Annual). **Geographic Preference:** National.

2870 ■ National Black Child Development Institute (NBCDI)
8455 Colesville Rd. Ste. 910
Silver Spring, MD 20910
Ph: (202)833-2220
Free: 800-556-2234
Co. E-mail: moreinfo@nbcdi.org
URL: http://www.nbcdi.org
Contact: Dr. Leah Austin, President
Facebook: www.facebook.com/nbcdi
Linkedin: www.linkedin.com/company/national-black-child-development-institute
X (Twitter): x.com/nbcdi
Instagram: www.instagram.com/nbcdi_
YouTube: www.youtube.com/channel/UCtuX7K_9l_FVXK6uT-X1qJQ
Pinterest: www.pinterest.com/nbcdi
Description: Aims to improving the quality of life for African American children and youth. Conducts direct services and advocacy campaigns aimed at both national and local public policies focusing on issues of health, child welfare, education, and child care. **Scope:** Policy issues affecting black children, with emphasis on child care, child welfare, health, and education. Studies foster care and tutoring/mentoring programs, include after-school care, teenage pregnancy, health care policy, and juvenile justice. **Founded:** 1970. **Publications:** *Black Child Advocate* (Quarterly); *Child Health Talk (CHT)* (3/year). **Educational Activities:** NBCDI Conference (Annual), Offer exemplary teaching and training programs.; NBCDI Forums, Offer exemplary teaching programs. **Geographic Preference:** National.

2871 ■ National Coalition for Campus Children's Centers (NCCCC)
188 Front St., Ste. 116-104
Franklin, TN 37064
Ph: (615)614-3723
Co. E-mail: info@campuschildren.org
URL: http://www.campuschildren.org
Contact: Daniela Baca, President
E-mail: danielah@unm.edu
Facebook: www.facebook.com/NationalCoalitionforCampusChildrensCenters
Description: Promotes child care centers on college campuses and provides information on organizing and operating these centers. Believes that campus child care programs should be an integral part of higher education systems and should provide safe and healthy environments for children, developmentally sound educational programs, and services to both parents and campus programs. **Founded:** 1970. **Geographic Preference:** National.

2872 ■ National Head Start Association (NHSA)
1651 Prince St.
Alexandria, VA 22314
Ph: (703)739-0875
Free: 866-677-8724
Co. E-mail: info@nhsa.org

URL: http://nhsa.org
Contact: Damon Carson, Chairman
Facebook: www.facebook.com/NatlHeadStart
Linkedin: www.linkedin.com/company/national-head-start-association
X (Twitter): x.com/natlheadstart
Instagram: www.instagram.com/natlheadstart
YouTube: www.youtube.com/user/nationalheadstart
Description: Members of National Head Start Parent Association, National Head Start Directors Association, National Head Start Staff Association, National Head Start Friends Association, and others interested in the Head Start Program. Upgrades the quality and quantity of Head Start Program services. Integrates the activities of the 4 divisions to present cohesive policies, positions, and statements. Conducts seminars and training sessions in early childhood education. Maintains speakers' bureau. **Founded:** 1974. **Publications:** *Children and Families: Magazine of the National Head Start Association* (3/year); *Children and Families* (Quarterly); *NHSA Newsletter* (Monthly). **Educational Activities:** National Head Start Association Conference (Annual); Annual National Head StartConference & Expo (Annual); Parent and Family Engagement Conference (Annual). **Geographic Preference:** National.

2873 ■ National Resource Center for Health and Safety in Child Care and Early Education (NRC)
13120 E 19th Ave.
Aurora, CO 80045
Free: 888-227-5125
Co. E-mail: health@ecetta.info
URL: http://nrckids.org
Contact: Marilyn J. Krajicek, EdD, Director
Description: Seeks to enhance the quality of child care and early education by supporting state and local health departments, child care regulatory agencies, child care providers/teachers, and parents/guardians in their effort to promote health and safety in child care and early education. Provides information services and technical assistance. **Founded:** 1995. **Geographic Preference:** National.

2874 ■ Southern Early Childhood Association (SECA)
1123 S University Ave.
Little Rock, AR 72204
Ph: (501)221-1648
Co. E-mail: info@seca.info
URL: http://www.seca.info
Contact: Judy Whitesell, President
Facebook: www.facebook.com/4SECA
X (Twitter): x.com/secatweets
Pinterest: www.pinterest.com/seca1948
Description: Early childhood educators, day care providers, program administrators, researchers, teacher trainers, and parents from the U.S. and abroad who share a common concern for the wellbeing of young children. Provides a unified voice on vital local, state, and federal issues affecting young children. Exchanges information and ideas through conferences and workshops. Explores contemporary issues in child development and early education through publications. **Founded:** 1948. **Publications:** *Dimensions of Early Childhood* (3/year). **Educational Activities:** Southern Early Childhood Association Annual Conference (Annual). **Awards:** SECA Friend of Children (Annual); Marian B. Hamilton Memorial Award (Annual). **Geographic Preference:** National.

2875 ■ USA Toy Library Association (USA-TLA)
2719 Broadway Ave.
Evanston, IL 60201
Ph: (847)612-6966
Fax: (847)864-8473
Co. E-mail: usatla@gmail.com
URL: http://usatla.org
Contact: Judith Iacuzzi, Executive Director
Facebook: www.facebook.com/USA-Toy-Library-Association-118012331559912
Description: Child care professionals, parents, and others interested in the role of toys and play in child development. Promotes the importance of play and the development of toy libraries in public and school libraries, hospitals, day care centers, and mobile collections. Seeks to broaden understanding of how toys can educate, increase parent-child interaction, and aid in development and therapy of disabled children. **Founded:** 1984. **Geographic Preference:** National.

2876 ■ World Organization for Early Childhood Education - Canada [Organisation Mondiale pour l'Education Prescolaire - Canada (OMEP)]
390 Grande Allee ouest, app. 33
Quebec, QC, Canada G1S 1B6
Co. E-mail: omep-canada@videotron.ca
Facebook: www.facebook.com/people/OMEP-CANADA-Organisation-Mondiale-pour-l%C3%89ducation-Pr%C3%A9scolaire/100064846806200
Description: Organizations and individuals in 72 countries concerned with the health, education, and welfare of children. Promotes greater understanding of children from birth to age 8. Facilitates international exchange of research experience and knowledge on topics including child psychology, toys and play materials, living conditions of families with young children, preschool education and care, and other issues in education. Members promote research on early childhood education, conduct surveys of nursery schools and teacher training, and encourage parent education. Maintains speakers' bureau; conducts seminars and forums. **Founded:** 1958. **Geographic Preference:** Multinational.

REFERENCE WORKS

2877 ■ "Can Day Care Help a Child Succeed in School?" in VeryWellFamily (September 30, 2019)
URL(s): www.verywellfamily.com/the-great-day-care-debate-616852
Ed: Robin McClure. **Released:** September 30, 2019. **Description:** With many parents placing their children in day care before they are old enough for school, a study found that there are some pros and cons that parents should expect. Children who spent time in high-quality centers did develop a more complex vocabulary and were better socialized. However, behavior issues were a concern along with the amount of illnesses a child could contract. **Availability:** Online.

2878 ■ Child Care Millionaire: Secrets to Building a Profitable 7 or 8 Figure Child Care Business
Ed: Brian Duprey. **Released:** October 08, 2018. **Price:** $21.99, Paperback; $9.99, E-Book. **Description:** A guide for existing early childhood business owners to grow their current business into a large or multiple daycare center. **Availability:** E-book; Print.

2879 ■ "Child-Care Policy and the Labor Supply of Mothers with Young Children: A Natural Experiment from Canada" in University of Chicago Press (Vol. 26, July 2008, No. 3)
Description: In 1997, the provincial government of Quebec, the second most populous province in Canada, initiated a new childcare policy. Licensed childcare service providers began offering day care spaces at the reduced fee of $5 per day per child for children aged four. By 2000, the policy applied to all children not in kindergarten. Using annual data (1993-2002) drawn from Statistics Canada's Survey of Labour and Income Dynamics, the results show that the policy had a large and statistically significant impact on the labor supply of mothers with preschool children. **Availability:** PDF.

2880 ■ "Day-Care Center Owner to Argue Against Liquor Store Opening Nearby" in Chicago Tribune (March 13, 2008)
Pub: Tribune News Service
Contact: Jack Barry, Vice President, Operations
E-mail: jbarry@tribpub.com

Ed: Matthew Walberg. **Description:** NDLC's owner feels that Greenwood Liquors should not be granted its liquor license due to the claim that the NDLC is not only a day-care center but also a school that employs state-certified teachers. **Availability:** Print; Online.

2881 ■ "Day Care Directors Are Playing Doctor, and Parents Suffer" in The New York Times (September 16, 2019)
URL(s): www.nytimes.com/2019/09/16/upshot/day-care-pink-eye-parents.html
Ed: Aaron E. Carroll. **Released:** September 16, 2019. **Description:** Discusses how day cares, in an effort to protect the health of all children within the facility, may actually be doing more harm than good. With strict policies in place for minor childhood illnesses needing to be fully treated before the child can be readmitted, this has put a large burden on working parents, their bank accounts, and the health of the sick child who may be receiving antibiotics with limited effects. **Availability:** Online.

2882 ■ "Family Child Care Record-Keeping Guide, Ninth Edition (Redleaf Business Series)"
Pub: Redleaf Press
Contact: Barbara Yates, President
Released: 9th edition. **Price:** $21.95, soft bound. **Description:** Writer, trainer, lawyer, and consultant provides concise information for home-based family child care (day care) providers. The book covers tracking expenses, being profitable, filing taxes, and meeting government regulations. This resources covers the process of accurate bookkeeping and record-keeping to take advantage of all allowable tax deductions. Changes in depreciation rules, adjustments to food and mileage rates, and clarifications on how to calculate the Time-Space percentage are defined. **Availability:** Print.

2883 ■ "Five Myths About Child Care" in The Washington Post (November 5, 2021)
URL(s): www.washingtonpost.com/outlook/five-myths/five-myths-child-care/2021/11/05/3266114e-3d9b-11ec-8ee9-4f14a26749d1_story.html
Ed: Elliot Haspel. **Released:** November 05, 2021. **Description:** Breaks down and discusses misconceptions about child-care in the US from a political viewpoint. **Availability:** Print; Online.

2884 ■ "Intrepid Souls: Meet a Few Who've Made the Big Leap" in Crain's Chicago Business (Vol. 31, November 10, 2008, No. 45, pp. 26)
Description: Advice is given from entrepreneurs who have launched businesses in the last year despite the economic crisis. Among the types of businesses featured are a cooking school, a child day-care center, a children's clothing store and an Internet-based company. **Availability:** Online.

2885 ■ "State Moves to Improve Child Care" in Providence Business News (Vol. 29, April 7, 2014, No. 1, pp. 1)
Pub: American City Business Journals, Inc.
Contact: Mike Olivieri, Executive Vice President
URL(s): pbn.com/state-moves-to-improve-child-care96248
Description: Rhode Island Department of Human Services has been helping to administer BrightStars contracts to child care centers, home-based providers and educational programs to help ensure the availability of high quality child care to the workforce. Part of the BrightStars funding came from the $50 million Race to the Top grant. Insights on BrightStars rating systems are also given.

2886 ■ "Susan Leger Ferraro Built a $7.2 Million Day Care Business: Now She Wants To Expand-And Cash Out" in Inc. (January 2008, pp. 50-53)
Ed: Dalia Fahmy. **Description:** Profile of Susan Leger Ferraro who wants to expand her chain of day care centers into Florida and California and sell part of her 87 percent stake to reduce financial risk. **Availability:** Online.

STATISTICAL SOURCES

2887 ■ *RMA Annual Statement Studies*
Pub: Risk Management Association
Contact: Nancy Foster, President
Released: Annual. **Description:** Contains composite balance sheets and income statements for more than 360 industries, including the accounting, auditing, and bookkeeping industries. Also contains five years of comparative historical data for discerning trends. Includes 16 commonly used ratios, computed for most of the size groupings for nearly every industry.

TRADE PERIODICALS

2888 ■ *Child Care Bridges*
Pub: Manitoba Child Care Association
Contact: Lynda Raible, President
URL(s): mccahouse.org/child-care-bridges
Released: Quarterly **Description:** Advocates for a quality system of child care, to advance early childhood education as a profession, and to provide services to our members. **Availability:** Print; Electronic publishing.

2889 ■ *Child Welfare: Journal of Policy, Practice, and Program (CWJ)*
Pub: Child Welfare League of America
Contact: Ray Bierria, Chief Financial Officer
E-mail: rbierria@cwla.org
URL(s): www.cwla.org/child-welfare-journal
Released: Bimonthly **Price:** $145, Individuals for 1 year; $210, Institutions for 1 year; $215, Individuals for international 1 year; $275, Institutions for international 1 year; $35, for pdf. **Description:** Journal publishing articles on child welfare services. **Availability:** Print; Online.

2890 ■ *Young Children: The Journal of the National Association for the Education of Young Children*
Pub: National Association for the Education of Young Children
Contact: Michelle Kang, Chief Executive Officer
URL(s): www.naeyc.org/resources/pubs/yc
Released: 5/year **Price:** $30, Members for add on print; $70, Nonmembers for print; $120, Institutions for print. **Description:** Peer-reviewed professional journal focusing on issues in the field of early childhood education. **Availability:** Print; Online.

TRADE SHOWS AND CONVENTIONS

2891 ■ Association for Childhood Education International Annual International Conference & Exhibition
URL(s): www.acei.org
Description: Commercial and educational exhibits of interest to teachers, teacher educators, college students, daycare personnel and other care givers. **Audience:** Teachers, educators and day-care personnel. **Principal Exhibits:** Commercial and educational exhibits of interest to teachers, teacher educators, college students, daycare personnel and other care givers.

2892 ■ National Association for the Education of Young Children Annual Conference
National Association for the Education of Young Children (NAEYC)
1401 H St. NW Ste. 600
Washington, DC 20005
Ph: (202)232-8777
Free: 800-424-2460
Fax: (202)328-1846
Co. E-mail: help@naeyc.org
URL: http://www.naeyc.org
Contact: Michelle Kang, Chief Executive Officer
URL(s): www.naeyc.org/events/annual
Frequency: Annual. **Description:** Educational materials and equipment designed for children ages birth through eight years old. **Audience:** Early childhood professionals. **Principal Exhibits:** Educational materials and equipment designed for children ages birth through eight years old. **Telecommunication Services:** conference@naeyc.org.

FRANCHISES AND BUSINESS OPPORTUNITIES

2893 ■ Baby Power / Forever Kids (BPFK)
15 Midvale Dr.
Pittstown, NJ 08867
Ph: (908)507-3857
Co. E-mail: info@babypower.com
URL: http://babypower.com
Contact: Linda Searles, President
Facebook: www.facebook.com/babypowerinternational
YouTube: www.youtube.com/channel/UC-5J2cO5QsbtkBQSJkVY5iQ
Description: Provider of parent and child fun play and educational programs. **Founded:** 1984. **Training:** Yes.

2894 ■ Cardiac Carr Co.
5568-A Bramble Ct.
Willoughby, OH 44094
Contact: Robert E. Carr, Jr., Contact
Description: Services: Children fitness programs. **Founded:** 1986. **Financial Assistance:** No

2895 ■ Children's Lighthouse Franchise Co. (CLFC)
101 S Jennings Ave., Ste. 209
Fort Worth, TX 76104
Free: 888-338-4466
Fax: (817)338-2716
Co. E-mail: hello@childrenslighthouse.com
URL: http://childrenslighthouse.com
Contact: Michael Brown, President
Facebook: www.facebook.com/childrenslighthouse
Instagram: www.instagram.com/childrens_lighthouse
YouTube: www.youtube.com/channel/UCODzN_cwYlMMuvH9cQXfDvw
Description: School which provides values-based early childhood education. **Founded:** 1997. **Financial Assistance:** Yes **Training:** Available at headquarters for 4 weeks, 4 weeks at franchisee's location, unlimited training for the first year and unlimited support.

2896 ■ CLIX
3 Townline Cir., Ste. 5
Rochester, NY 14623
Ph: (585)338-2521
URL: http://clixrochester.com
Contact: Austin Haines, President
Description: Dedicated to creating a digital portrait experience like no other. With the latest in technology, a proprietary proven system and focus on service and our customer's experience. Offering a unique multifaceted business opportunity. **Founded:** 1999. **Training:** Training includes pre-opening, store set-up and onsite training.

2897 ■ Creative World School Franchising
25110 Bernwood Dr., Ste. 104
Bonita Springs, FL 34135
Ph: (239)947-6177
Free: 800-362-5940
Co. E-mail: info@creativeworldschool.com
URL: http://creativeworldschool.com
Contact: Billie McCabe, Co-Founder
Linkedin: www.linkedin.com/company/creative-world-schools-franchising-company-inc.
Description: Academic institution provides childcare, preschool, early childhood education, summer camp services. **Founded:** 1970. **Training:** Extensive training at our facility and onsite staff training at your location with ongoing support.

2898 ■ Gymboree Play & Music
1503A Sloat Blvd.
San Francisco, CA 94132
Ph: (415)604-3094
URL: http://www.gymboreeclasses.com
Contact: Joan Barnes, Founder

Facebook: www.facebook.com/gymboreeclasses
Instagram: www.instagram.com/gymboreeplayan dmusic
YouTube: www.youtube.com/channel/UCu7GV9 dXvirjXomsXNWmt9Q

Description: Parent and child participation play and music program. Specialized equipment, songs and games. Classes offered for children-newborn through 5 years of age. **Founded:** 1976. **Franchised:** 1978. **Training:** Offers initial training and also regional training. Franchises receive continued support in programming, operations, and marketing.

2899 ■ Kid to Kid
BaseCamp Franchising L.L.C.
39 E Eagle Ridge Dr., Ste. 100
North Salt Lake, UT 84054
Ph: (801)359-0071
URL: http://uptowncheapskatefranchise.com
Contact: Shauna Sloan, Founder
Facebook: www.facebook.com/KidtoKid
X (Twitter): x.com/kidtokid
Instagram: www.instagram.com/kidtokid
YouTube: www.youtube.com/channel/UCwggT 17IyJaP86na96n0kSw
Pinterest: www.pinterest.com/kidtokid

Description: Resale store for children's clothing and toys. **No. of Franchise Units:** 72. **No. of Company-Owned Units:** 1. **Founded:** 1992. **Franchised:** 1994. **Equity Capital Needed:** $196,028-$272,718. **Franchise Fee:** $25,000. **Royalty Fee:** 5%. **Financial Assistance:** Yes **Training:** Offers 10 days at headquarters, 3 days at franchisee's location, 5 days at existing location, and ongoing support.

2900 ■ Kiddie Academy Child Care Learning Centers
3415 Box Hill Corporate Center Dr.
Abingdon, MD 21009
Ph: (410)515-0788
Free: 800-554-3343
Co. E-mail: ka@kiddieacademy.com
URL: http://kiddieacademy.com
Contact: Josh Frick, President
Facebook: www.facebook.com/KiddieAcademy
Linkedin: www.linkedin.com/company/kiddie-aca demy
X (Twitter): x.com/kiddieacademy
Instagram: www.instagram.com/kiddieacademyhq
YouTube: www.youtube.com/user/Communi tyBeginsHere
Pinterest: www.pinterest.com/kiddieacademy

Description: Firm operates, and franchises chain of education-based child daycare preschools in the United States. **Founded:** 1981.

2901 ■ Kidokinetics
Broward, Miami-Dade
Weston, FL 33326
Ph: (954)385-8511
Co. E-mail: sef@kidokinetics.com
URL: http://kidokinetics.com
Contact: Terri Braun, Founder
Facebook: www.facebook.com/kidokinetics
X (Twitter): x.com/kidokinetics
Instagram: www.instagram.com/kidokineticssefl
Pinterest: www.pinterest.com/kidokinetics

Description: Firm provides sports and fitness programs for children. **Founded:** 1995. **Equity Capital Needed:** $42,900 to $57,000. **Franchise Fee:** $30,000. **Royalty Fee:** 7%. **Training:** Yes.

2902 ■ Kidspark Inc.
820 S Winchester Blvd.,No., 120
San Jose, CA 95128
Ph: (408)985-2599
Co. E-mail: kidpark@kidspark.com
URL: http://kidspark.com
Contact: Debbie Milner, Chief Executive Officer
Facebook: www.facebook.com/KidsPark
Instagram: www.instagram.com/kidsparkinc
YouTube: www.youtube.com/channel/UCTol t1xQWobfbOEm3HbadrA
Pinterest: www.pinterest.com/kidsparkinc

Description: Provider of childcare services such as games, arts and crafts, stories, music, snacks and meals. **Founded:** 1988. **Equity Capital Needed:** $185,000-$340,000. **Training:** Owns and operates parks for kids.

2903 ■ Kinderdance International Inc.
Roanoke
Roanoke, VA 24015
Ph: (504)904-2595
Free: 800-554-2334
Fax: (540)904-2506
Co. E-mail: kindercorp@kinderdance.com
URL: http://www.kinderdance.com
Contact: Carol Kay Harsell, Founder
Facebook: www.facebook.com/Kinderdance
X (Twitter): x.com/Kinderdance
Instagram: www.instagram.com/kinderdance_interna tional
YouTube: www.youtube.com/user/Kinderdance

Description: If you enjoy children and have high energy, you can qualify to join in the quality preschool education through dance, gymnastics and creative movement. No studio required. The program has been taught to thousands of children in hundreds of child-care centers since 1979. Enjoy flexible hours, fulfilling work and adorable customers. Rated one of the top 15 franchises for women by Working Woman Magazine. 24-hours a day, an operations manual, newsletters and active franchisee advisory counsel. **No. of Franchise Units:** 131. **No. of Company-Owned Units:** 2. **Founded:** 1979. **Franchised:** 1985. **Equity Capital Needed:** $14,950-$46,100, including franchise fee. **Franchise Fee:** $12,000-$40,000. **Financial Assistance:** Yes **Training:** 1 week training class, field support, ongoing support and an annual training conference provides continuing education.

2904 ■ The Little Gym
7001 N Scottsdale Rd., Ste. 1050
Scottsdale, AZ 85253
Co. E-mail: marketing@thelittlegym.com
URL: http://www.thelittlegym.com
Facebook: www.facebook.com/thelittlegym
Linkedin: www.linkedin.com/company/thelittlegym
X (Twitter): x.com/thelittlegym
YouTube: www.youtube.com/officialthelittlegym
Pinterest: www.pinterest.com/thelittlegym

Description: Operator of children gym provides activities for kids including parent and child classes, kids dance, gymnastics, sports skills and karate. **Founded:** 1976. **Financial Assistance:** Yes **Training:** Yes.

2905 ■ Little Scientists
25 Higgins Dr.
Milford, CT 06460
Ph: (203)783-1114
Free: 800-322-8386
Co. E-mail: info@little-scientists.com
URL: http://littletogreatscientists.com
Contact: Dr. Heidi Gold-Dworkin, Founder Member
Facebook: www.facebook.com/LittleScientistsUSA
X (Twitter): x.com/LScientists
Instagram: www.instagram.com/greatscientists

Description: Hands-on science education for children. **No. of Franchise Units:** 20. **No. of Company-Owned Units:** 2. **Franchised:** 1996. **Equity Capital Needed:** $25,000-$50,000. **Franchise Fee:** $25,000. **Training:** Aims to empower students & teachers, through the highest quality of hands-on learning, to participate in science in the classroom and beyond.

2906 ■ Oxford Learning Centers Inc.
747 Hyde Park Rd., Ste. 230
London, ON, Canada N6H 3S3
Ph: (226)646-9422
Co. E-mail: info@oxfordlearning.com
URL: http://www.oxfordlearning.com
Contact: Kala Challis, Manager
Facebook: www.facebook.com/OxfordLearning
X (Twitter): x.com/oxfordlearning
Instagram: www.instagram.com/oxfordlearningcen tres
YouTube: www.youtube.com/user/OxfordLearning

Description: Provider of supplemental education and tutoring services. **Founded:** 1984. **Equity Capital Needed:** 50000. **Franchise Fee:** $109,600-$243,000. **Royalty Fee:** 0.1. **Training:** Provides 2 weeks training and ongoing support.

2907 ■ Primrose School Franchising Company Inc.
3200 Windy Hill Rd. SE, Ste. 1200E
Atlanta, GA 30339
Ph: (770)529-4100
Free: 800-774-6767
Fax: (770)529-1551
URL: http://www.primroseschools.com
Contact: Steve Clemente, President
URL(s): franchise.primroseschools.com
Linkedin: www.linkedin.com/showcase/primrose -schools-franchise-investments

Description: Quality educational childcare, with proven, traditional curriculum for infants through 4/5 kindergarten, after-school explorers club ages 5-12 years, Spanish, computer intergenerational program and strong parental communication. Programs develop positive self-esteem and a joy of learning. ongoing after opening. **Founded:** 1982. **Training:** Initial training and ongoing support.

2908 ■ Pump It Up - The Inflatable Party Zone
1325 W Auto Dr., Ste. 101
Tempe, AZ 85284
Ph: (480)940-7867
URL: http://www.pumpitupparty.com
Contact: A. Helen, Manager

Description: Firm is engaged in organizing children birthday parties, group events and much more. **Founded:** 2000. **Franchised:** 2002. **Equity Capital Needed:** net worth of $500,000 ; $200,000 in liquid funds. **Franchise Fee:** $30,000. **Royalty Fee:** 6% of Gross Sales. **Training:** Training both onsite and at our main offices. Training includes logistics, sales, marketing and more. Ongoing phone support is provided.

2909 ■ Reading Friends Forth Worth
5228 Pershing Ave.
Fort Worth, TX 76107
Ph: (817)738-9430
Co. E-mail: office@readingfriends.org
URL: http://readingfriendsaledo.com
Contact: Nancy Thompson Spencer, Founder

Description: Preschool for children. **No. of Franchise Units:** 4. **No. of Company-Owned Units:** 1. **Founded:** 1980. **Franchised:** 2002. **Equity Capital Needed:** $119,000-$325,000. **Franchise Fee:** $35,000. **Training:** Focuses on creating an environment that fosters not only reading skills but also a love for learning.

2910 ■ Sunbrook Academy at Legacy Park
Sunbrook Academy
3871 Jiles Rd.
Kennesaw, GA 30144
Ph: (770)794-0234
Co. E-mail: stilesboro@sunbrookacademy.com
URL: http://www.cadence-education.com

Description: Provider of childcare programs. **No. of Franchise Units:** 8. **No. of Company-Owned Units:** 3. **Founded:** 1984. **Franchised:** 1999. **Equity Capital Needed:** $250,000-$450,000. **Franchise Fee:** $55,000. **Training:** 21 day training program prior to opening, and 30 days onsite training with ongoing assistance after opening.

2911 ■ Tumbles
1221 Encinitas Blvd.
Encinitas, CA 92024
Ph: (760)942-7411
Co. E-mail: encinitas@tumbles.net
URL: http://encinitas.tumbles.net
Facebook: www.facebook.com/TEncinitas
Instagram: www.instagram.com/tumblesgym

Description: Provider of physical activities and growth development classes to motor skills, spatial awareness, coordination, balance, agility, flexibility and sports preparation for children. **Founded:** 1985. **Training:** Yes.

LIBRARIES

2912 ■ BOCES Putnam/Northern Westchester - BOCES Professional Library
200 Boces Dr.
Yorktown Heights, NY 10598
Ph: (914)248-2391
URL: http://www.pnwboces.org/library/Home.aspx
Contact: Joseph Mannozzi, Coordinator
E-mail: jmannozzi@pnwboces.org
Scope: Education. **Services:** Interlibrary loan; copying; library open to the public with restrictions (reference use only for those not residing or working in the 18 school districts). **Founded:** 1965. **Holdings:** 8,000 books; 16,000 bound periodical volumes; 300,000 nonbook items; DVDs.

2913 ■ Georgetown University - Maternal and Child Health Library (NCEMCH)
2115 Wisconsin Ave. NW, Ste. 601
Washington, DC 20007
URL: http://www.mchlibrary.org
Contact: John Richards, Leader
E-mail: jrichards@ncemch.org
Scope: Health care; medical care. **Services:** Library open to the public. **Founded:** 1982. **Holdings:** E-newsletter; posters; historical documents; reports.

2914 ■ Illinois Early Childhood Intervention Clearinghouse Library
Children's Research Ctr., Rm. 20
51 Gerty Dr.
Champaign, IL 61820-7469
Free: 877-275-3227
Co. E-mail: illinois-eic@illinois.edu
URL: http://eiclearinghouse.org/library/library-policies
Scope: Early childhood; parenting; young children. **Services:** Interlibrary loan; copying; clearinghouse open to Illinois residents. **Founded:** 1986. **Holdings:** Figures not available.

RESEARCH CENTERS

2915 ■ Arizona State University - Child Development Laboratory (CDL)
T. Denny Sanford School of Social & Family Dynamics, PO Box 873701
Tempe, AZ 85287-3701
Ph: (480)965-7257
Co. E-mail: cdlapplications@asu.edu
URL: http://thesanfordschool.asu.edu/cdl
Contact: Courtney Romley, Program Manager
E-mail: clromle@asu.edu
Description: Integral unit of Department of Family Resource and Human Development at Arizona State University. **Scope:** Child development industry deals with Children and their families, including emotional development, sex-role development, parent-child interaction, and children and television. **Educational Activities:** CDL Parent Education Seminars.

2916 ■ Arizona State University - Child Study Laboratory (CSL)
950 S McAllister
Tempe, AZ 85287-1104
Ph: (480)965-5320
Fax: (480)965-8544
URL: http://psychology.asu.edu/childstudylab
Contact: Anne Kupfer, Director
E-mail: anne.kupfer@asu.edu
Facebook: www.facebook.com/Child-Study-Lab-107400805980546
Description: Research activity and preschool service unit of Psychology Department in College of Liberal Arts at Arizona State University. **Scope:** Children and, in some studies, their parents. Conducts a preschool program for children from Tempe and surrounding communities who are 15 months through five years of age. **Founded:** 1972.

2917 ■ Jewish Board of Family and Children's Services Child Development Center
255 E 98th St.
Brooklyn, NY 11212
Ph: (718)881-1524
URL: http://jewishboard.org/program-directory/brownsville-child-development-center
Description: Integral unit of Jewish Board of Family and Children's Services Inc. **Scope:** Therapeutic and educational techniques for emotionally disturbed, language-impaired, and central nervous system-impaired children; development of criteria for assessment and monitoring; and onsite group treatment of preschool children in daycare centers. **Founded:** 1874. **Educational Activities:** Early Childhood Workshops, Offers exemplary teaching and training programs.

2918 ■ University of Georgia - Institute for Behavioral Research - Center for Family Research (CFR)
1095 College Station Rd.
Athens, GA 30602
Ph: (706)425-2992
Co. E-mail: cfruga@uga.edu
URL: http://cfr.uga.edu
Contact: Dr. Gene Brody, Founder
E-mail: gbrody@uga.edu
Facebook: www.facebook.com/CFRatUGA
Linkedin: www.linkedin.com/company/center-for-family-research
X (Twitter): x.com/uga_cfr
YouTube: www.youtube.com/channel/UCiUZyvbbdXRQOnwZl3ON49Q
Description: Integral unit of Institute for Behavioral Research of University of Georgia. **Scope:** Family study, including topics such as divorce rates, women entering the work force, isolation of the family, child abuse and incest, governmental family welfare programs, daycare, and family care for elderly parents. **Founded:** 1985.

Chimney Sweeping Business

ASSOCIATIONS AND OTHER ORGANIZATIONS

2919 ■ National Chimney Sweep Guild (NCSG)
1255 SW Prairie Trl., Pky.
  Ankeny, IA 50023
Ph: (317)837-1500
Co. E-mail: office@ncsg.org
URL: http://www.ncsg.org
Contact: Thomas Hunkele, President
Facebook: www.facebook.com/na
  tionalchimneysweepguild
X (Twitter): x.com/NCSG
YouTube: www.youtube.com/channel/UCk
  2xxSZljLDKn1toxEQWwAA

Description: Individuals in the chimney service profession. Provides an opportunity for chimney service professionals to learn about technical aspects of trade and new equipment, and to share ideas for building strong businesses and promoting chimney safety. Conducts training and certification seminars. **Founded:** 1977. **Publications:** *Newslink* (Monthly); *Sweeping: The Journal of Chimney and Venting Technology* (11/year). **Educational Activities:** NCSG National Convention (Annual); NCSG National Convention & Tradeshow (Annual). **Geographic Preference:** National.

REFERENCE WORKS

2920 ■ "The Disappearing Chimney Sweeps of Paris" in The New York Times (February 18, 2019)
URL(s): www.nytimes.com/2019/02/18/lens/the
  -disappearing-chimney-sweeps-of-paris.html
Ed: Evelyn Nieves. **Released:** February 18, 2019. **Description:** A freelance photographer, Pete Hawk, talks about his fascination of chimney sweeps in Paris and the steps he took to document them while they work. With less wood-burning in chimneys these days, the job is slowly becoming obsolete. **Availability:** Online.

TRADE SHOWS AND CONVENTIONS

2921 ■ National Chimney Sweep Guild Conference and Expo
URL(s): www.ncsgconvention.org
Description: Provides education and key topic sessions for those in the chimney sweep industry. **Principal Exhibits:** Provides education and key topic sessions for those in the chimney sweep industry. **Telecommunication Services:** office@ncsg.org.

2922 ■ NCSG National Convention & Tradeshow
National Chimney Sweep Guild (NCSG)
  1255 SW Prairie Trl., Pky.
  Ankeny, IA 50023
Ph: (317)837-1500
Co. E-mail: office@ncsg.org
URL: http://www.ncsg.org
Contact: Thomas Hunkele, President
URL(s): na.eventscloud.com/website/60807

Frequency: Annual. **Audience:** Chimney and hearth industry professionals. Dates and Locations: 2025 Mar 05-08 Northern Kentucky Convention Center, Covington, KY; 2025 Mar 05-08 Cincinnati, OH. **Telecommunication Services:** bburton@ncsg.org.

Christmas Decoration Store

REFERENCE WORKS

2923 ■ *"If Palmer's Is Your Go-To Place to Cut a Christmas Tree, You're Out of Luck This Year" in Statesman Journal (October 13, 2019)*
URL(s): www.statesmanjournal.com/story/news/local/mid-valley/2019/10/13/palmers-christmas-tree-farm-closes-after-51-years-family-tradition/3912218002/
Ed: Capi Lynn. **Released:** October 13, 2018. **Description:** Palmer's Christmas Tree Farm is closing after being in business since 1967. **Availability:** Online.

2924 ■ *"Selfridges Has Already Opened Its Christmas Shop - and There's Still Five Months to Go" in House Beautiful (July 29, 2019)*
URL(s): www.housebeautiful.com/uk/lifestyle/shopping/a28543649/selfridges-christmas-shop-opens-early-july/
Ed: Olivia Heath. **Released:** July 29, 2019. **Description:** Famed London department store Selfridges is getting a jump on the Christmas season — five months before the holiday actually arrives. With many people on holiday from all over the world, it's the perfect chance for visitors to snap up some decorations as a souvenirs to bring home. **Availability:** Online.

2925 ■ *"Why Do Stores Put Christmas Decorations Out So Early?" in CheatSheet (October 24, 2018)*
URL(s): www.cheatsheet.com/culture/why-do-stores-put-christmas-decorations-out-so-early.html
Ed: Chelena Goldman. **Released:** October 04, 2018. **Description:** The "Christmas Creep" originated in the mid-80s and describes how stores sneak their Christmas merchandise onto the shelves earlier in the year. The reason why is simple: competition. Everyone is trying to get a jump on the next store to get consumers' dollars. **Availability:** Online.

STATISTICAL SOURCES

2926 ■ *RMA Annual Statement Studies*
Pub: Risk Management Association
Contact: Nancy Foster, President
Released: Annual. **Description:** Contains composite balance sheets and income statements for more than 360 industries, including the accounting, auditing, and bookkeeping industries. Also contains five years of comparative historical data for discerning trends. Includes 16 commonly used ratios, computed for most of the size groupings for nearly every industry.

FRANCHISES AND BUSINESS OPPORTUNITIES

2927 ■ **Christmas Decor Inc.**
2301 Crown Crt.
Irving, TX 75038
Ph: (806)722-1225
URL: http://www.christmasdecor.net
Facebook: www.facebook.com/ChristmasDecor
X (Twitter): x.com/ChristmasDecor_

Description: Distributor of holiday and event decorations. **Founded:** 1986. **Training:** 4 day quick start training at headquarters, 4 days at regional locations and ongoing support.

Christmas Tree Farm

ASSOCIATIONS AND OTHER ORGANIZATIONS

2928 ■ National Christmas Tree Association (NCTA)
PO Box 3609
Littleton, CO 80161
Free: 800-975-5920
Fax: (303)374-6594
Co. E-mail: info@realchristmastrees.org
URL: http://realchristmastrees.org
Contact: Dugald Kell, Jr., President
Facebook: www.facebook.com/ChristmasTreesandWreaths
Description: Exists to promote the use of real Christmas trees and support the industry that provides them. Includes grower-wholesalers, grower-retailers, and all other retailers that sell real Christmas trees and related green products. Sponsors National Christmas Tree Contest. Maintains information and referral service and provides the option of liability insurance for retailers, and choose and cut growers. **Founded:** 1955. **Publications:** *American Christmas Tree Journal*. **Geographic Preference:** National.

2929 ■ Pacific Northwest Christmas Tree Association (PNWCTA)
PO Box 660
Molalla, OR 97038
Ph: (503)364-2942
Fax: (971)314-4703
Co. E-mail: pnwchristmastrees@gmail.com
URL: http://www.nwchristmastrees.org
Contact: Jan Hupp, Contact
Description: Provides guidance and assistance to Christmas tree growers in the Northwest. Promotes, assists and engages in research of value to all members. **Founded:** 1955. **Publications:** *Pacific Northwest Christmas Tree Association Buy-Sell Directory* (Annual); *Buy-Sell Directory* (Annual); *Christmas Tree Lookout*. **Educational Activities:** Summer Meeting & Farm Tour (Annual); PNWCTA Tree Fair and Trade Show (Annual). **Geographic Preference:** National; Regional.

2930 ■ Sheerlund Products LLC
740 Corporate Dr.
Reading, PA 19605
Free: 800-233-2958
Co. E-mail: sales@sheerlundproducts.com
URL: http://www.sheerlundproducts.com/christmas/tree-lot-supplies
Contact: Margaret S. McShane, Owner
Facebook: www.facebook.com/Sheerlund
Description: Provider of supplies for Christmas tree lots.

REFERENCE WORKS

2931 ■ *21 Tips for Starting & Running a Successful Christmas Tree Farm*
URL(s): oolipo.com/start-run-christmas-tree-farm/
Ed: Liz Garcia. **Released:** July 19, 2021. **Description:** Whether you already own acreage or plan to buy land, the Christmas tree business holds significant potential for profitability and success. This article includes 21 tips to help you start and flourish a Christmas tree farm. **Availability:** Online.

2932 ■ *45 Marketing Ideas for a Christmas Tree Farm*
URL(s): www.starterstory.com/ideas/christmas-tree-farm/marketing-ideas
Ed: Pat Walls. **Released:** October 20, 2022. **Description:** Details a variety of marketing ideas to promote your Christmas tree farm. Includes information on content marketing, relationship marketing, sales, email marketing, organic social media marketing, affiliate marketing, word-of-mouth marketing, search engine optimization, paid social media marketing, buzz marketing, print and traditional marketing, automated marketing, and influencer marketing. **Availability:** Online.

2933 ■ *"Christmas Tree Farmers Rapidly Abandoning the Industry"* in York Dispatch (Dec. 4, 2019)
URL(s): www.yorkdispatch.com/story/money/business/2019/12/04/christmas-tree-farmers-rapidly-abandoning-industry/40762125/
Ed: Abdel Jimeniz. **Released:** December 04, 2019. **Description:** Discusses the challenges that Christmas tree farmers face and presents information on why some farmers are leaving the business. **Availability:** Online.

2934 ■ *"Christmas Trees Are a Big Small Business"* in Business News Daily (June 29, 2022)
URL(s): www.businessnewsdaily.com/1775-christmas-tree-farming-big-small-business.html
Ed: Ned Smith. **Released:** June 29, 2022. **Description:** The Christmas tree business is big, but most Christmas tree farms are actually family-owned. This article presents information on the business of Christmas tree farming. **Availability:** Online.

2935 ■ *"Christmas Trees Keep Giving in St. Louis Area"* in St. Louis Post-Dispatch (January 11, 2012)
Pub: Tribune News Service
Contact: Jack Barry, Vice President, Operations
E-mail: jbarry@tribpub.com
Ed: Jonah Newman. **Description:** Missouri state law prohibiting disposing of Christmas trees into area lakes has forced citizens to find new ways to use their old trees. Saint Louis and other municipalities offers ways to recycle Christmas trees while creating a good habitat for fish. Cities have sunk a portion of the trees, then created mulch and is offered free to residents. **Availability:** Online.

2936 ■ *Digital Marketing for Christmas Tree Farms: 4 Online Growth Strategies*
URL(s): www.webfx.com/industries/industrial/farms/digital-marketing-for-christmas-tree-farms/
Description: Provides four of the best digital marketing strategies for your Christmas tree farm. **Availability:** Online.

2937 ■ *"The Economics of Christmas Trees"* in The Hustle (Dec. 5, 2020)
URL(s): thehustle.co/the-economics-of-christmas-trees/
Ed: Zachary Crockett. **Released:** December 05, 2020. **Description:** Presents information from Christmas tree farm owners, ecologists, and representatives from the real and artificial tree markets on the economics of the Christmas tree business. **Availability:** Online.

2938 ■ *Four Lessons from COVID-19 for the Future of Christmas Tree Marketing*
URL(s): www.canr.msu.edu/news/four-lessons-from-covid-19-for-the-future-of-christmas-tree-marketing
Ed: Bridget Behe. **Released:** June 28, 2021. **Description:** A study detailing the state of the Christmas tree shopping environment. **Availability:** Online.

2939 ■ *"Groups Seek Donations to Recycle Christmas Trees"* in The Register-Guard (January 7, 2012, pp. B11)
Description: Groups wishing to recycle used Christmas trees in the Eugene, Oregon area are listed. Some of the groups offer incentives as well as free pickup. Contact information for each group is provided. **Availability:** Print; Online.

2940 ■ *Growing Christmas Trees*
Ed: Patrick White. **Released:** February 24, 2015. **Price:** $8.69. **Description:** From selecting a site and planting the right species to marketing and selling trees, this guide shows you how to build and maintain your own small tree nursery. **Availability:** Online.

2941 ■ *"Here's Why Your Family's Christmas Tree Is So Expensive"* in USA Today (November 30, 2018)
Ed: Dalvin Brown. **Released:** November 29, 2018. **Description:** A national shortage on firs, spruces, and pines is causing an increase in Christmas tree prices. The shortage started in 2008 when farmers decided not to plant as many trees due to the Great Recession and people not spending money on a tree. Now that the recession has dwindled, the trees that should have been there are not. Also, recent wildfires and hurricanes have played a role in diminishing the tree supply. **Availability:** Online.

2942 ■ *How Much Money Does a Christmas Tree Farm Make? A Breakdown*
URL(s): grocycle.com/how-much-money-does-a-christmas-tree-farm-make/
Description: Presents information on the amount of money you can expect to make selling Christmas trees. Includes information on start-up costs, location, time, pros and cons, and marketing. **Availability:** Online.

2943 ■ "How to Start a Christmas Tree Farm" in Part-Time Money (March 29, 2022)
URL(s): ptmoney.com/start-christmas-tree-farm/
Ed: Phillip Taylor. **Released:** March 29, 2022. **Description:** Provides tips for anyone interested in starting their own Christmas tree business from a 40-year veteran in the business. Includes a list of seven important things to consider as you start your business. **Availability:** Online.

2944 ■ "How to Start a Christmas Tree Farm" in AG America Lending Blog (June 21, 2022)
URL(s): agamerica.com/blog/tips-from-the-land-lenders-on-starting-a-christmas-tree-farm/startingyourbusiness.com/how-to-start-a-christmas-tree-farm/
Released: June 21, 2022. **Description:** Provides information on how starting a Christmas tree farm can provide ample opportunity for additional income and environmental stewardship. Includes industry facts and figures as well as factors to consider when starting your own Christmas tree farm. **Availability:** Online.

2945 ■ How to Start a Christmas Tree Farm Business in 23 Steps
URL(s): www.profitableventure.com/starting-a-christmas-tree-farm/
Description: A guide to starting a Christmas tree farm from scratch with little money and no experience. Includes a sample Christmas tree farming business plan template. **Availability:** Online.

2946 ■ "How to Start a Tree Farm" in Small Business Trends (Dec. 18, 2019)
URL(s): smallbiztrends.com/2019/12/how-to-start-a-tree-farm.html
Ed: Rob Starr. **Released:** December 18, 2019. **Description:** Provides information on how to start a tree farm, how to start a nursery, what types of trees to sell, how to care for your trees, how to market your trees, what type of equipment you need, and certifications needed for Christmas tree farming. **Availability:** Online.

2947 ■ Pacific Northwest Christmas Tree Association Buy-Sell Directory
Pub: Pacific Northwest Christmas Tree Association
Contact: Jan Hupp, Contact
URL(s): www.pnwcta.org/content.aspx?page_id=22&club_id=43779&module_id=416760
Released: Annual **Description:** Covers christmas tree sellers and buyers in Washington, Oregon, California, Idaho, and southwestern Canada. Includes list of trucking companies and nurseries, with name, address, phone, fax, type of truck, number of units, geographical area served, dates available, and required lead time. **Entries include:** For sellers--Farm or company name, address, phone, name and title of contact, number of acres, year established, number of trees for sale by species. For buyers--Company or individual name, address, phone, name and title of contact, number of trees to be purchased by species. **Arrangement:** Separate alphabetical seller and buyer sections. **Availability:** Print.

2948 ■ Start A Christmas Tree Farm - Business Ideas
URL(s): www.starterstory.com/ideas/christmas-tree-farm
Ed: Pat Walls. **Released:** September 15, 2022. **Description:** Starting a Christmas tree farm requires a great deal of effort, dedication, and passion. This guide provides information on all you need to know to get started selling Christmas trees. Includes startup costs, success stories, pros and cons, and marketing ideas. **Availability:** Online.

STATISTICAL SOURCES

2949 ■ North America Christmas Tree Market - Growth, Trends, COVID-19 Impact, and Forecasts (2022 - 2027)
URL(s): www.marketresearch.com/Mordor-Intelligence-LLP-v4018/North-America-Christmas-Tree-Growth-30766179/
Price: $4,750. **Description:** Report covers the Christmas tree market in North America. Includes growth, trends, COVID-19 impact, and forecasts. **Availability:** PDF.

TRADE PERIODICALS

2950 ■ American Christmas Tree Journal
Pub: National Christmas Tree Association
Contact: Dugald Kell, Jr., President
URL(s): realchristmastrees.org/education/tree-varieties/grand-fir
Ed: Dennis Tompkins. **Description:** Christmas tree industry trade magazine covering growing, harvesting, and retailing. **Availability:** Print.

CONSULTANTS

2951 ■ American Christmas Tree Association (ACTA)
8605 Santa Monica Blvd., Ste. 1189
West Hollywood, CA 90069
URL: http://www.christmastreeassociation.org
Contact: Jami Warner Goldstene, Contact
Facebook: www.facebook.com/AmericanChristmasTreeAssociation
Linkedin: www.linkedin.com/company/american-christmas-tree-association-acta
X (Twitter): x.com/americantrees
Instagram: www.instagram.com/americanchristmastrees
Description: A non-profit organization that serves as a resource for media and consumers seeking information and education on the Christmas tree industry.

2952 ■ Brown's Tree Farm
230 Stan Warn Rd.
Muncy, PA 17756
Ph: (570)546-2200
Free: 888-384-8733
Fax: (570)546-3111
URL: http://brownstreefarm.com/services/christmas-tree-sales-consulting
Contact: Bill Brown, Contact
Description: Christmas tree farm owner offering consulting services to those who run their own Christmas tree stands.

2953 ■ Connwood Foresters Inc.
39 Cherry Hill Rd.
Rockfall, CT 06481
Ph: (860)349-9910
Co. E-mail: info@connwood.com
URL: http://www.connwood.com
Contact: Nathaniel Gosselin, President
Description: Provider of forestry and forest management services, including consultation on Christmas tree farming.

2954 ■ High Ground Tree Farm
N2521 Barnes Crk. Ave.
Merrill, WI 54452
Ph: (715)536-6048
Co. E-mail: highground1@frontier.com
URL: http://www.highgroundtreefarm.com
Description: More than just a Christmas tree farm, High Ground offers custom tree planting for private landowners and other agencies. Offers site preparation, discing, mowing, and spraying. Also provides custom pesticide applications. **Founded:** 1967.

2955 ■ Hutchison Forestry Inc. [Mount Pleasant Sugarworks]
2668 Rte. 7
Leicester, VT 05733
Ph: (802)247-3117
Co. E-mail: mountpleasantmaple@gmail.com
URL: http://www.mountpleasantmaple.com
Contact: Andrew G. Hutchison, President
Facebook: www.facebook.com/mtpleasantsugarworks
Description: Consulting forester offering counsel on timber and woodland management and Christmas tree management. Serves private industries as well as government agencies. **Scope:** Consulting forester offering counsel on timber and woodland management and Christmas tree management. Serves private industries as well as government agencies. **Founded:** 1987.

2956 ■ Kavanagh Christmas Trees
Wicklow Farm
Glendarragh
Newtown Mount A63 E270, Dublin, Ireland
Ph: 353 87 797 4521
URL: http://kavanaghchristmastrees.ie
Facebook: www.facebook.com/KavanaghChristmasTrees
YouTube: www.youtube.com/channel/UCgj4OU9S1XQsH8OB5uFp78Q
Description: Christmas tree growing consultancy providing a fully-fledged demonstration and guidance on growing techniques and nutrition advice. **Founded:** 1952.

2957 ■ Steigerwaldt Tree Farms
856 N Fourth St.
Tomahawk, WI 54487
Ph: (715)453-3274
Co. E-mail: stf@steigerwaldttreefarms.com
URL: http://steigerwaldttreefarms.com
Contact: Lee Ann Steigerwaldt, President
Description: Expert Christmas tree farmers offering the products and services customers desire as well as accurate retail sales advice. **Founded:** 1957.

FRANCHISES AND BUSINESS OPPORTUNITIES

2958 ■ Christmas Decor Inc.
2301 Crown Crt.
Irving, TX 75038
Ph: (806)722-1225
URL: http://www.christmasdecor.net
Facebook: www.facebook.com/ChristmasDecor
X (Twitter): x.com/ChristmasDecor_
Description: Distributor of holiday and event decorations. **Founded:** 1986. **Training:** 4 day quick start training at headquarters, 4 days at regional locations and ongoing support.

RESEARCH CENTERS

2959 ■ Purdue University - College of Agriculture - Southeast-Purdue Agricultural Center (SEPAC)
c/o Joel Wahlman, Superintendent
4425 E 350 N
Butlerville, IN 47223
Ph: (812)458-6977
Co. E-mail: jwahlman@purdue.edu
URL: http://ag.purdue.edu/department/arge/PACs/sepac/index.html
Contact: Joel Wahlman, Superintendent
E-mail: jwahlman@purdue.edu
URL(s): ag.purdue.edu/department/arge/PACs/sepac/hunting-policy.html
Description: Integral unit of Purdue University. **Scope:** Soils and crops, including soil drainage, water quality, tillage, fertility, varieties, insects, diseases, and weeds. Forestry research includes studies on Christmas trees, walnuts, and oaks. **Founded:** 1977. **Educational Activities:** SEPAC Field and Research Report Days, Offer exemplary teaching and training programs.

2960 ■ Texas A&M Forest Service (TFS)
200 Technology Way, Ste. 1281
College Station, TX 77845
Ph: (979)458-6600
Co. E-mail: support@tfs.tamu.edu
URL: http://tfsweb.tamu.edu
Contact: Thomas G. Boggus, Director
E-mail: tboggus@tfs.tamu.edu
Facebook: www.facebook.com/texasforestservice
X (Twitter): x.com/TXForestService
Instagram: www.instagram.com/texasforestservice
YouTube: www.youtube.com/user/TexasForestService

Description: Integral unit of Agricultural Research and Extension Center, Texas A&M University. **Scope:** Tree production. **Founded:** 1915.

2961 ■ University of Wisconsin, Madison College of Agricultural and Life Sciences - Hancock Agricultural Research Station (HARS)
N3909 County Rd V
Hancock, WI 54943
Ph: (715)249-5961
Co. E-mail: hancock@cals.wisc.edu
URL: http://hancock.ars.wisc.edu
Contact: Troy Fishler, Superintendent
E-mail: troy.fishler@wisc.edu

Description: Off-campus research unit of Wisconsin Agricultural Research Stations at College of Agricultural and Life Sciences, University of Wisconsin, Madison, located 80 miles north of Madison. **Scope:** Potato, vegetable, and fruit production under irrigation. Integrated efforts are directed at refining cultural practices to control wind erosion and eliminate groundwater contamination. **Founded:** 1916.

Cleaning Service

START-UP INFORMATION

2962 ■ *Cleanlots: America's Simplest Business, A Parking Lot Litter Removal Business You Can Be Proud Of*
Ed: Brian Winch. **Released:** August 03, 2018. **Description:** A guide on how to set up a simple parking lot cleaning business. **Availability:** Print.

ASSOCIATIONS AND OTHER ORGANIZATIONS

2963 ■ **American Association of Cleaning Professionals (AACP)**
7549 W 99th Pl.
Bridgeview, IL 60455
Ph: (815)485-8800
URL: http://cleaningprofessionalsassoc.com
Contact: Wayne Baxtrom, President
E-mail: baxtromwayne@aol.com
Description: Trade association for small and medium-sized cleaning contractors. Provides training and certification.

2964 ■ **American Cleaning Institute (ACI)**
1401 H St. NW, Ste. 700
Washington, DC 20005
Ph: (202)347-2900
Fax: (202)347-4110
Co. E-mail: info@cleaninginstitute.org
URL: http://www.cleaninginstitute.org
Contact: Melissa Hockstad, President
E-mail: mhockstad@cleaninginstitute.org
Facebook: www.facebook.com/AmericanCleaningIns titute
X (Twitter): x.com/CleanInstitute
Instagram: www.instagram.com/americancleaningins titute
Pinterest: www.pinterest.com/americancleaninginsti tute
Description: Manufacturers of household, industrial and institutional cleaning products, their ingredients and finished packaging and oleochemical producers. Advances the public understanding of the safety and benefits of cleaning products and protecting the ability of its members to formulate products that best meet consumer needs. **Founded:** 1926. **Awards:** Clean and Healthy Families & Communities Award (Annual); ACI Distinguished Paper Award (Annual); Elva Walker Spillane Distinguished Service Award (Annual); ACI/NBB Glycerine Innovation Award (Annual). **Geographic Preference:** National.

2965 ■ **American House Cleaners Association (AHCA)**
103 E Main St., Ste. 204B
Walla Walla, WA 99362
Ph: (503)398-9194
Co. E-mail: info@theahca.org
URL: http://www.theahca.org
Contact: Kevin Reynolds, Founder
Facebook: www.facebook.com/TheAHCA
X (Twitter): x.com/theahca
Description: Seeks to elevate respect, recognition, and awareness for the profession of cleaning as a skilled trade. Provides members support, tools, and education, including the Professional Cleaning Provider certification.

2966 ■ **Association of Residential Cleaning Services International (ARCSI)**
7870 Olentangy River Rd., Ste. 301
Columbus, OH 43235
Ph: (614)547-0887
Fax: (614)505-7136
URL: http://issa-canada.com/fr/issa-canada-fr/organisations-affili%C3%A9es
Contact: Erin Lasch, Contact
E-mail: erin@issa.com
Description: Represents residential cleaning service owners and professionals. Advances and improves the residential cleaning industry. Shares knowledge and information to ensure the growth and development of cleaning service businesses. **Founded:** 2003. **Publications:** *Residential Cleaning Connection* (Biweekly). **Educational Activities:** Executive Leadership Conference. **Awards:** ARCSI Professional Image Awards (Annual); ARCSI President's Award (Annual); ARCSI Seal of Excellence (Annual); ARCSI Professional Cleaner of the Year (Annual). **Geographic Preference:** Multinational.

2967 ■ **Cleaning and Restoration Association (CRA)**
3284 Ramos Cir.
Sacramento, CA 95827
URL: http://www.scrt.org
Contact: Dick Wagner, President
E-mail: dick@thecrestnetwork.com
Description: Seeks to promote and support firms engaged in the cleaning and restoration industry in the western United States.

2968 ■ **Midwest Cleaning and Restoration Association (MCRA)**
PO Box 14182
Madison, WI 53708-0182
Co. E-mail: info@mcraonline.org
URL: http://www.mcraonline.org
Facebook: www.facebook.com/MCRAonline
Linkedin: www.linkedin.com/in/midwest-cleaning-an d-restoration-association-398923121
Description: Promotes the use of professional cleaning contractors by the general public, through marketing and public relation efforts. **Geographic Preference:** State.

REFERENCE WORKS

2969 ■ *"BBB Tips: 7 Tips for Hiring a Cleaning Service"* in International Association of Better Business Bureaus (April 28, 2020)
Released: April 28, 2020. **Description:** Provides tips on what customers are looking for when hiring cleaning services for their homes, home offices, and businesses. **Availability:** Online.

2970 ■ *"Can You Make a Million Bucks in the House Cleaning Business?"* in Cleaning Business Today (July 13, 2016)
Ed: Terry Sambrowski. **Released:** July 13, 2016. **Description:** Discusses seven steps that control the costs that affect gross income potential of your cleaning business. **Availability:** Online.

2971 ■ *"Green Cleaning - It's Your Business"* in Cleaning Business Today (April 3, 2019)
Ed: Cloud Conrad. **Released:** April 03, 2019. **Description:** Information on how to run an environmentally friendly green cleaning business. **Availability:** Online.

2972 ■ *"How to Attract Clients for Your Residential and Office Cleaning Business"* in Chron (March 12, 2019)
Ed: Tracey Sandilands. **Released:** March 12, 2019. **Description:** Provides information on effectively marketing home and office cleaning services to attract clients. **Availability:** Online.

2973 ■ *"How to get Commercial Cleaning Clients without Appearing Desperate"* in Marketing Systems by Design (July 3, 2019)
Ed: Jean Hanson. **Released:** July 03, 2019. **Description:** Details information on how to gain commercial cleaning clients for your cleaning business. **Availability:** Online.

2974 ■ *"How to Get More Clients for Your Cleaning Business"* in insureon Small Business Blog (January 6, 2020)
Released: January 06, 2020. **Description:** Provides information on tactics to use to attract and keep clients for your cleaning business. **Availability:** Online.

2975 ■ *"How to Make my House Cleaning Service Business Unique"* in A Janitor's Story
Ed: Stacy Freeman. **Description:** Information on how to make your house cleaning business unique. **Availability:** Online.

2976 ■ *"How to Start a Cleaning Business"* in Entrepreneur (June 14, 2003)
Released: June 14, 2003. **Description:** Information on how to start a successful cleaning business. Topics include target market, location, pricing, marketing, and resources. **Availability:** Online.

2977 ■ *How to Start a Cleaning Business*
Ed: Maxwell Rotheray. **Released:** January 22, 2020. **Description:** Explores the commercial cleaning industry and gives steps on how to start your own business. **Availability:** Print.

2978 ■ *"How to Start a Cleaning Business in 7 Steps"* in JustBusiness (September 15, 2020)
Ed: Meredith Wood. **Released:** September 15, 2020. **Description:** Provides practical steps for starting a cleaning business including funding, marketing, business planning and budgeting, registering, and finding and maintaining clients. **Availability:** Online.

2979 ■ *How to Start Your Very Own Cleaning Business: Houses and Apartments Plus Much More*
Ed: J.M. Norman, M.R. Norman. **Released:** September 23, 2021. **Description:** An in-depth guide to starting a cleaning business from the ground up. Includes discussions on setting up financing, managing employees, and acquiring new business. **Availability:** Print.

2980 ■ *"What Is the Profit Potential with a New Cleaning Business?" on The Maid Coach (November 8, 2019)*
Ed: Debbie Sardone. **Released:** November 08, 2019. **Description:** Describes the profit potential of a cleaning business based on the work put into the business, business expenses, number of employees and quality of employees. **Availability:** Online.

2981 ■ *"While Tech Threatens Jobs, Janitorial Industry Continues to Flourish" in Services (November 21, 2021)*
Released: November 21, 2021. **Description:** Janitorial jobs are on the rise even when automation replaces skilled workers in other industries.

STATISTICAL SOURCES

2982 ■ *Carpet Cleaning Industry in the US - Market Research Report*
URL(s): www.ibisworld.com/united-states/market-research-reports/carpet-cleaning-industry/
Price: $925. **Description:** Downloadable report analyzing data about the current and future trends in the carpet cleaning industry. **Availability:** Download.

2983 ■ *Contract Cleaning Services*
URL(s): www.marketresearch.com/Global-Industry-Analysts-v1039/Contract-Cleaning-Services-32280806/
Price: $5,450. **Description:** Report covering the contract cleaning services industry. Includes market overview, market trends and drivers, global market perspective, and market analysis. **Availability:** PDF.

2984 ■ *Global Business Cleaning Services Market Growth (Status and Outlook) 2022-2028*
URL(s): www.marketresearch.com/LP-Information-Inc-v4134/Global-Business-Cleaning-Services-Growth-32228986/
Price: $3,660. **Description:** Report provides a comprehensive picture of the global business cleaning services market with both quantitative and qualitative data to help readers understand how the market scenario changed across the globe during the pandemic and Russia-Ukraine War. The base year considered for analyses is 2021, while the market estimates and forecasts are given from 2022 to 2028. **Availability:** PDF.

2985 ■ *Global Healthy Cleaning Services Market Growth (Status and Outlook) 2022-2028*
URL(s): www.marketresearch.com/LP-Information-Inc-v4134/Global-Healthy-Cleaning-Services-Growth-32228982/
Price: $3,660. **Description:** Report provides a comprehensive picture of the global Healthy Cleaning Services market, with both quantitative and qualitative data, to help readers understand how the Healthy Cleaning Services market scenario changed across the globe during the pandemic and Russia-Ukraine War. The base year considered for analyses is 2021, while the market estimates and forecasts are given from 2022 to 2028. **Availability:** PDF.

2986 ■ *Global Industrial Cleaning Services Market 2022-2026*
URL(s): www.marketresearch.com/Infiniti-Research-Limited-v2680/Global-Industrial-Cleaning-Services-31538903/
Price: $2,500. **Description:** Report offering an up-to-date analysis regarding the current global market scenario, latest trends and drivers, and the overall market environment. The market is driven by rising awareness about workplace wellness and sustainability, the growing number of office spaces, and the increasing demand for less toxic substances for industrial cleaning. **Availability:** Download.

2987 ■ *Home Cleaning Services*
URL(s): www.marketresearch.com/Global-Industry-Analysts-v1039/Home-Cleaning-Services-32281648/
Price: $5,600. **Description:** Report covers the home cleaning services industry and includes a market overview, market trends and drivers, global market perspective, and market analysis. **Availability:** PDF.

2988 ■ *Janitorial Services Industry in the US - Market Research Report*
URL(s): www.ibisworld.com/united-states/market-research-reports/janitorial-services-industry/
Price: $925. **Description:** Downloadable report analyzing data about the current and future trends in the janitorial services industry. **Availability:** Download.

2989 ■ *Maids, Nannies & Gardeners Industry in the US - Market Research Report*
URL(s): www.ibisworld.com/united-states/market-research-reports/maids-nannies-gardeners-industry/
Price: $925. **Description:** Downloadable report analyzing current and future trends in the domestic help industries. **Availability:** Download.

VIDEO/AUDIO MEDIA

2990 ■ *Side Hustle to Small Business: Turning a Pandemic Passion Project into a Full-Time Business*
URL(s): www.hiscox.com/side-hustle-to-small-business/paige-stuart-neat-organizing-podcast-season-4
Ed: Sanjay Parekh. **Released:** July 31, 2024. **Description:** Podcast features an entrepreneur who turned cleaning out a storage locker into an organizing business.

TRADE SHOWS AND CONVENTIONS

2991 ■ *Experience Conference & Exhibition*
URL(s): experiencetheevents.com/texp_conf.html
Frequency: Annual. **Description:** Seminars and presentations about the latest technology available in the cleaning and restoration industry. Also includes a tradeshow exhibit. **Principal Exhibits:** Seminars and presentations about the latest technology available in the cleaning and restoration industry. Also includes a tradeshow exhibit.

PUBLICATIONS

2992 ■ *Cleaning Business: Published for Self-Employed Cleaning Professionals*
PO Box 98757
Seattle, WA 98198
URL: http://www.cleaningbusiness.com
Contact: Bill Griffin, Founder
URL(s): www.cleaningbusiness.com
Released: Monthly; last Update 2017. **Price:** $119, for print. **Description:** Magazine providing technical and management information for self-employed cleaning businesses such as janitorial services, carpet cleaners, water & odor damage restorers, window washers, and maid services. **Availability:** Print; Online.

Clipping Service

REFERENCE WORKS

2993 ■ *SRDS International Media Guides: Newspapers Worldwide*
Pub: SRDS
URL(s): srds.com/international-media-guides
Description: Covers approximately 20,000 newspapers and color newspaper magazines/supplements from 200 countries, including the United States. **Entries include:** Publication name; publisher name, address, phone, fax, e-mail, URL, names of editor, advertising manager, and representatives in the United States and worldwide; advertising rates in U.S. dollars and/or local currency, circulation, mechanical data, ad closing, readership description, etc. **Arrangement:** Geographical. **Availability:** Print.

COMPUTERIZED DATABASES

2994 ■ *Business Periodicals Index Retrospective™: 1913-1982*
EBSCO Information Services
  10 Estes St.
  Ipswich, MA 01938
Ph: (978)356-6500
Free: 800-653-2726
Co. E-mail: information@ebsco.com
URL: http://www.ebsco.com
Contact: Tim Collins, Chief Executive Officer
URL(s): www.ebsco.com/products/digital-archives/retrospective-indexes/business-periodicals-index-retrospective
Description: Contains citations to more than 2.5 million articles and book reviews in more than 1000 general business periodicals and trade journals. **Availability:** Online. **Type:** Bibliographic; Full-text.

Clothing Designer

START-UP INFORMATION

2995 ■ *"Do Cool Sh*t: Quit Your Day Job, Start Your Own Business, and Live Happily Ever After"*
Pub: Harper Business
Contact: Hollis Heimbouch, Senior Vice President Publisher

Released: January 20, 2015. **Price:** $16.61, hardcover; $11.97, paperback; $11.49, e-book; $3.13, kindle; $0.05, hardcover(99 used from $0.05); $8, hardcover(44 new from $8.00); $2, paperback(76 used from $2.00); $5.47, paperback(64 new from $5.47). **Description:** Serial social entrepreneur, angel investor, and woman business leader, Miki Agrawal, teaches how to start and run a successful new business. She covers all issues from brainstorming, to raising money to getting press without any connections, and still have time to enjoy life. She created WILD, a farm-to-table pizzeria in New York City and Las Vegas. She also partnered in a children's multimedia company called Super Sprowtz--a story-driven nutrition program for children, and she launched a patented high-tech underware business called THINX. Agrawal also discusses the growth in her businesses. **Availability:** E-book; Print.

2996 ■ *"Etsy: Etsy Business for Beginners! Master Etsy and Build a Profitable Business In No Time"*
Released: December 23, 2014. **Price:** $6.99, regular price is $13.99. **Description:** Craft artisans take note: information is offered to start an online business through Etsy. Whether handmade home accessories, clothing, or knick-knacks, Etsy is the perfect option for artists and crafters to start a home-based, online retail operation. **Availability:** Print; Download.

2997 ■ *Start Your Own Fashion Accessories Business*
Pub: Entrepreneur Media Inc.
Contact: Dan Bova, Director
E-mail: dbova@entrepreneur.com

Ed: Eileen Figure Sandlin. **Released:** Second edition. **Description:** Entrepreneurs wishing to start a fashion accessories business will find important information for setting up a home workshop and office, exploring the market, managing finances, publicizing and advertising the business and more.

2998 ■ *"Upscale Consignment Shop Opens In Brandon"* in *Tampa Tribune (January 25, 2012)*
Ed: Yvette C. Hammett. **Description:** Agape Chic Consignment Boutique opened February 4, 2012. The owners, Dena Ham and Stacy Ulrey Regan became friends working on their children's school PTA. Their business partnership hopes that people walking into their new shop will feel as if they are walking into an upscale boutique. The store offers designer labels in sizes 2-20. **Availability:** Print; Online.

ASSOCIATIONS AND OTHER ORGANIZATIONS

2999 ■ **Association of Sewing and Design Professionals (ASDP)**
2885 Sanford Ave. SW, Ste. 19588
Grandville, MI 49418
Free: 877-755-0303
Co. E-mail: communications@sewingprofessionals.com
URL: http://sewingprofessionals.com
Contact: Bonny Carmicino, President
E-mail: president@sewingprofessionals.com
Facebook: www.facebook.com/ASDPglobal
Linkedin: www.linkedin.com/company/association-of-sewing-and-design-professionals-asdp
Instagram: www.instagram.com/asdpglobal
Description: Encourages the interchange of ideas among individuals involved in the sewing and design fields. Promotes professions in the industry; represents members' interests. Conducts educational and training programs. **Founded:** 1991. **Geographic Preference:** National.

3000 ■ **CFDA Foundation [Council of Fashion Designers of America (CFDA)]**
1350 Avenue of the Americas, 2nd Fl.
New York, NY 10019
Ph: (212)302-1821
Co. E-mail: info@cfda.com
URL: http://cfda.com/philanthropy/foundation
Facebook: www.facebook.com/cfda
X (Twitter): x.com/CFDA
Instagram: www.instagram.com/cfda
Description: Seeks "to further the position of fashion design as a recognized branch of American art and culture, to advance its artistic and professional standards, to establish and maintain a code of ethics and practices of mutual benefit in professional, public, and trade relations, and to promote and improve public understanding and appreciation of the fashion arts through leadership in quality and taste". **Founded:** 1962. **Awards:** CFDA Fashion Awards (Annual). **Geographic Preference:** National.

3001 ■ **Custom Tailors and Designers Association (CTDA)**
1392 E Ridge Rd.
Rochester, NY 14621
Ph: (585)342-5886
Free: 888-248-2832
Fax: (866)661-1240
Co. E-mail: info@ctda.com
URL: http://www.ctda.com
Contact: Peter A. Roberti, President
Facebook: www.facebook.com/CustomTailorsDesignersAssociation
X (Twitter): x.com/CTDA_USA
Description: Designers and makers of men's custom tailored outerwear and clothing. **Founded:** 1880. **Publications:** *The Custom Tailor* (3/year). **Geographic Preference:** National.

3002 ■ *On The Button*
979, av. Bourgogne, Ste. 570
Montreal, QC, Canada G1W 2L4
Ph: (418)652-7682
Co. E-mail: amiq@macten.net
Contact: Alain Plourde, Executive Director
Released: Quarterly **Availability:** Print.

3003 ■ **Organization of Black Designers (OBD)**
300 M St. SW, Ste. N110
Washington, DC 20024
Ph: (937)837-6319
Co. E-mail: orgblackdesigners@gmail.com
URL: http://obd.org
Contact: Michael Chabbi, President
Facebook: www.facebook.com/groups/OrganizationBlackDesigners
Description: Black designers involved in graphic design, animation, Web design, film/video, illustration, user interface design, or mobile app design. Strives to support black designers through program development, business opportunities, scholarly pursuit, and continuing education. **Founded:** 1968. **Publications:** *DesigNation* (Biennial); *OBData* (Weekly). **Educational Activities:** DesigNation. **Geographic Preference:** National; Multinational.

REFERENCE WORKS

3004 ■ *"11 Minutes That Rocked the Sneaker World"* in *Business Journal Portland (Vol. 30, February 14, 2014, No. 50, pp. 8)*
Pub: American City Business Journals, Inc.
Contact: Mike Olivieri, Executive Vice President

Released: Weekly. **Price:** $4, Introductory 4-week offer(Digital & Print). **Description:** The sale of the Nike Air Yeezy 2, the latest shoes from a partnership with artist Kanye West, sparked a social media debate on the importance of limited edition shoes for the Nike brand. The shoes sold out in 11 minutes and made their way to eBay for as much as $10,000. **Availability:** Print; Online.

3005 ■ *"100 Brilliant Companies"* in *Entrepreneur (May 2014)*
Pub: Entrepreneur Media Inc.
Contact: Dan Bova, Director
E-mail: dbova@entrepreneur.com

Description: Entrepreneur magazine annually selects 100 companies, ideas, innovations and applications which the editors feel offer unique, simple and high-tech solutions to various everyday problems. These may include design developments, innovations in wearable gadgets, travel applications and other new ideas which represent 21st Century breakthroughs and thinking outside the box. The list is divided into ten categories, including Fashion, The Human Factor, and Travel and Transportation. **Availability:** Online.

3006 ■ *Alex James: Slowing Down Fast Fashion*
Released: 2016. **Description:** A critical look at the fashion industry and the impact it has had on society and the environment. **Availability:** Streaming.

3007 ■ *"American Apparel: When Dov Cries" in Canadian Business (Vol. 83, June 15, 2010, No. 10, pp. 71)*
Pub: Rogers Media Inc.
Contact: Neil Spivak, Chief Executive Officer
Ed: Joe Castaldo. **Description:** American Apparel disclosed that they will have problems meeting one of its debt covenants which could trigger a chain reaction that could lead to bankruptcy. The prospects look bleak, but eccentric company founder Dov Charney, has always defied expectations. **Availability:** Online.

3008 ■ *"Betsey Johnson Falls Out of Fashion" in Canadian Business (Vol. 85, June 11, 2012, No. 10, pp. 14)*
Ed: Sarah Barmak. **Description:** Fashion label Betsey Johnson LLC filed for Chapter 11 bankruptcy protection in April 2012 that would result in 350 layoffs and closure of most of its 63 stores. The company cited severe liquidity constraints and $4.1 million in outstanding unsecured obligations to creditors in its filing. **Availability:** Print; Online.

3009 ■ *"Borrow Baby Couture Launch Rocks Fasion World - Provides Couture Fashion for Girls" In Benzinga.com (June 18, 2012)*
Description: Borrow Baby Couture allows parents, family and friends to rent couture clothing by top fashion designers for girls ages 9 months to 4 years. The retailer has launched an online site. Purchases are wrapped in tissue arriving ready to wear and includes return shipping costs. **Availability:** Online.

3010 ■ *"The Bottom Line" in Retail Merchandiser (Vol. 51, July-August 2011, No. 4, pp. 60)*
Description: Hanky Panky believes that comfort and style don't have to be mutually exclusive when designing their line of intimate apparel for women. The lingerie retailer was launched in 1977. **Availability:** Print; PDF; Online.

3011 ■ *"Bringing Charities More Bang for Their Buck" in Crain's Chicago Business (Vol. 34, May 23, 2011, No. 21, pp. 31)*
Pub: Crain Communications Inc.
Contact: Barry Asin, President
Ed: Lisa Bertagnoli. **Description:** Marcy-Newberry Association connects charities with manufacturers in order to use excess items such as clothing, janitorial and office supplies. **Availability:** Online.

3012 ■ *"A Change Would Do You Good" in Canadian Business (Vol. 80, November 19, 2007, No. 23, pp. 15)*
Description: Western Glove Works will be manufacturing clothing offshore, including Sheryl Crow's jeans collection, in countries such as China and the Philippines. The company decided to operate offshore after 86 years of existence due to the high price of manufacturing jeans in Canada. Western Glove's focus on producing celebrity-endorsed goods is discussed. **Availability:** Print; Online.

3013 ■ *Clothing Poverty: The Hidden World of Fast Fashion and Second-Hand Clothes*
Ed: Andrew Brooks. **Released:** March 15, 2015. **Price:** $21.95, Paperback; $14.95, E-Book. **Description:** A journey around the world exploring where our clothes come from and how the fashion industry perpetuates poverty around the world. **Availability:** E-book; Print.

3014 ■ *"Consignment Shop Offers Children's Clothes, Products" in Frederick News-Post (August 19, 2010)*
Pub: Federick News-Post
Contact: Connie Hastings, Director
E-mail: chastings@newspost.com
Ed: Ed Waters, Jr. **Description:** Sweet Pea Consignments for Children offers used items for newborns to pre-teens. The shop carries name brand clothing as well as toys, books and baby products. **Availability:** Print; Online.

3015 ■ *"ConsignPro Elevates Nature of Consignment Business, Encourages Designer Resale" in Internet Wire (May 15, 2012)*
Description: Forbes magazine recently highlighted an article on an upscale thrift store located in New York called Designer Resale. The shop features fashion-forward retail merchandies sold on consignment. These new boutique-type resale shops are growing in popularity across the country. **Availability:** Print; Online.

3016 ■ *"Design '07 (Fashion): Haute Flyers" in Canadian Business (Vol. 80, November 19, 2007, No. 23, pp. 68)*
Pub: Rogers Media Inc.
Contact: Neil Spivak, Chief Executive Officer
Ed: Rachel Pulfer. **Description:** Duckie Brown has been nominated by the Council of Fashion Designers of America as best menswear designer in the U.S. for 2007, along with leaders Calvin Klein and Ralph Lauren. The New York-based company was formed the day after September 11, 2001, but the timing did not hamper its growth. The works and plans of owners Steven Cox and Daniel Silver are described. **Availability:** Online.

3017 ■ *"Design program in Athletic Footwear" in Occupational Outlook Quarterly (Vol. 55, Fall 2011, No. 3, pp. 21)*
Description: The Fashion Institute of Technology offers the only certificate program in performance athletic footwear design in the U.S. The program focuses on conceptualizing and sketching shoe designs and covers ergonomic, anatomical, and material considerations for athletic footwear design. **Availability:** Print; Online.

3018 ■ *The Designer's Guide to Marketing and Pricing: How to Win Clients and What to Charge Them*
Released: First edition. **Description:** Guide to running a creative services business teaches designers how to be more effective, attract new clients, wages, and how to accurately estimate a project.

3019 ■ *"Empreinte Enters the Activewear Market with IN-PULSE" in The Lingerie Journal (November 5, 2019)*
URL(s): thelingeriejournal.com/empreinte-enters-the-activewear-market-with-in-pulse/
Ed: Estelle Puleston. **Released:** November 05, 2019. **Description:** French lingerie brand Empreinte launched its first activewear line, IN-PULSE to meet demand of women who want function and fashion in the undergarments. **Availability:** Online.

3020 ■ *"Fall Fever" in Canadian Business (Vol. 81, October 13, 2008, No. 17, pp. S12)*
Description: Buyer's guide of men's suits and jackets for fall are presented, including a suit by Boss Hugo Boss recommended for fun in the city after finishing work. Designers Ermenegildo, Michael Kors, and Arnold Brant are also highlighted. **Availability:** Print; Online.

3021 ■ *Fashion Calendar*
Contact: Ruth Finley, Founder
URL(s): fashioncalendar.com
Released: Biweekly; Latest edition 2016. **Price:** $925, Individuals; $395, Individuals. **Description:** Covers events of interest to the fashion industry, including private and public fashion openings, and important events in other fields which are scheduled for principal fashion cities; coverage is heavily New York City, but major cities worldwide are also covered. **Entries include:** For openings--Event name, date, address, phone. For other events--Event name, date, time, location, phone. **Arrangement:** Openings are alphabetical; events are chronological. **Availability:** Print; Online.

3022 ■ *"Fashionistas Weigh in on the Super-Thin" in Charlotte Observer (February 7, 2007)*
Description: Council of Fashion Designers of America held a panel discussion regarding the weight and ages of models used to highlight clothing. **Availability:** Online.

3023 ■ *Fashionopolis: The Price of Fast Fashion and the Future of Clothes*
Ed: Dana Thomas. **Released:** September 03, 2019. **Price:** $22.49, Hardcover; $14.99, E-Book. **Description:** Investigates the impact the fashion and clothing industry has had on the environment and in society. Also studies companies and people who are leading the way in producing sustainable clothing. **Availability:** E-book; Print.

3024 ■ *"Fight Ensues Over Irreplaceable Princess Diana Gowns" in Tampa Bay Business Journal (Vol. 30, January 15, 2010, No. 4, pp. 1)*
Pub: Tampa Bay Business Journal
Contact: Ian Anderson, President
E-mail: ianderson@bizjournals.com
Ed: Janet Leiser. **Description:** People's Princess Charitable Foundation Inc. founder Maureen Rorech Dunkel has sought Chapter 11 bankruptcy protection before a state court decides on the fate of the five of 13 Princess Diana Gowns. Dunkel and the nonprofit were sued by Patricia Sullivan of HRH Venture LLC who claimed they defaulted on $1.5 million in loans. **Availability:** Print; Online.

3025 ■ *"Fledgling Brands May Take the Fall With Steve & Barry's" in Advertising Age (Vol. 79, July 7, 2008, No. 26, pp. 6)*
Pub: Crain Communications, Inc.
Contact: Jessica Botos, Manager, Marketing
E-mail: jessica.botos@crainsnewyork.com
Ed: Natalie Zmuda. **Description:** Steve & Barry's, a retailer that holds licensing deals with a number of designers and celebrities, may have to declare bankruptcy; this leaves the fate of the retailer's hundreds of licensing deals and exclusive celebrity lines in question. **Availability:** Online.

3026 ■ *"From Rapper to Fashion Designer, Philly 12-Year-Old Builds Brand Using Instagram" in WHYY (December 19, 2018)*
URL(s): whyy.org/articles/from-rapper-to-fashion-designer-philly-12-year-old-builds-his-brand-using-instagram/
Ed: Unique Ratcliff. **Released:** December 19, 2018. **Description:** Trey Brown is a 12-year-old fashion designer, motivational speaker, and Instagram influencer residing in Philadelphia. His clothing brand is SPERGO, which ships around the world, and is successful in part due to his ability to use Intagram. **Availability:** Online.

3027 ■ *"Going Western with a Touch of Style" in Women In Business (Vol. 63, Summer 2011, No. 2, pp. 8)*
Pub: American Business Women's Association
Contact: Rene Street, Executive Director
Ed: Maureen Sullivan. **Released:** June 22, 2011. **Description:** Tips on ways women should dress up in Western style are presented. The wearing of Western-style denims is recommended. Use of accessories such as belt buckles, boots and hats is also encouraged. **Availability:** Print; Online.

3028 ■ *"Gowns Ready to Go" in Houston Chronicle (June 3, 2010)*
Pub: Houston Chronicle
Ed: Molly Glentzer. **Description:** Wedding gowns with slender silhouettes travel well for destination weddings. Amsale, Oscar del la Renta and Monique Lhuillier dresses are highlighted. **Availability:** Online.

3029 ■ *"H&M Offers a Dress for Less" in Canadian Business (Vol. 83, September 14, 2010, No. 15, pp. 20)*
Pub: Rogers Media Inc.
Contact: Neil Spivak, Chief Executive Officer

Ed: Laura Cameron. Description: Swedish clothing company H&M has implemented loss leader strategy by pricing some dresses at extremely low prices. The economy has forced retailers to keep prices down despite the increasing cost of manufacturing, partly due to Chinese labor becoming more expensive. How the trend will affect apparel companies is discussed. Availability: Print; Online.

3030 ■ *"Helping Apple Go Wearable"* in *Austin Business Journal (Vol. 34, July 4, 2014, No. 20, pp. 13)*
Pub: American City Business Journals, Inc.
Contact: Mike Olivieri, Executive Vice President
Released: July 04, 2014. Price: $4, introductory 4-week offer(Digital only). Description: Andrew Hamra, CEO and designer at Red Street Ventures will launch the Runnur Hands Free iPad Clip and Carry Case across the U.S. in July 2014 following the success of his flagship product the Hands Free Carry-All. Hamra builds and designs the products and controls startup costs by outsourcing most of the production to China's Xiamen Uptex Industrial Company Ltd. Availability: Print; Online.

3031 ■ *"The High Price of Fast Fashion"* in *The Wall Street Journal (August 29, 2019)*
URL(s): www.wsj.com/articles/the-high-price-of-fast-fashion-11567096637
Ed: Dana Thomas. Released: August 29, 2019. Description: Examines the impact fast fashion has on the environment and in society. Fast fashion comes from designers who steal ideas from fashion runways and "reinterpret" the piece and product it as cheap as possible. To do this, the poorest labor in third-world countries is used, which is a problem due to labor-rights violations. Clothes that do not sell are discarded into the environment, and since many of these items are synthetic, they are not biodegradable. Availability: Online.

3032 ■ *If You Have to Cry, Go Outside: And Other Things Your Mother Never Told You*
Pub: HarperCollins Publishers L.L.C.
Contact: Brian Murray, President
Ed: Kelly Cutrone, Meredith Bryan. Released: February 02, 2010. Price: $10.99, e-book; $7.24, e-book. Description: Women's mentor advices on how to make it in one of the most competitive industries in the world, fashion. She has kicked people out of fashion shows, forced some of reality television's shiny start to fire their friends, and built her own company which is one of the most powerful public relations firms in the fashion business. Availability: E-book; Print.

3033 ■ *"Image Consultants"* in *Entrepreneur (June 2014)*
Pub: Entrepreneur Media Inc.
Contact: Dan Bova, Director
E-mail: dbova@entrepreneur.com
Description: The ASAP54 mobile application, created by a company of the same name, uses visual recognition technology to help users determine the name of the designer or retailer of a clothing item using photographs. The company has compiled a database consisting of more than 1 million products from its retail partners. It claims an average of 5 percent commission on purchases completed through the application. Other useful wearable gadgets include Nymi, which authenticates identities based on cardiac rhythms, and Netatmo, a bracelet that measures daily sun exposure. Availability: Online.

3034 ■ *International Textile & Apparel Association--Membership Directory*
Pub: International Textile and Apparel Association
Contact: Dr. Jung Ha-Brookshire, President
URL(s): itaaonline.org/page/Benefits
Description: Covers about 1,000 college professors of clothing and textile studies. Entries include: Name, address, phone, academic credentials. Arrangement: Alphabetical; geographical by zip code. Availability: Print; PDF.

3035 ■ *"It's So You! Consignment Shop Owner Thrilled to See Vision Come to Fruition"* in *News-Herald (August 27, 2010)*
Pub: The News Herald
Contact: Tricia Ambrose, Executive Editor
E-mail: tambrose@news-herald.com
Ed: Brandon C. Baker. Description: Profile of Laurel Howes and her It's So You! Boutique. The consignment shop is located in Willoughby's Pine Ride Plaza in Ohio. The shop targets all women, but particularly those who are not that comfortable with shopping consignment. Availability: Online.

3036 ■ *"Jordan Still Soaring"* in *Business Journal Portland (Vol. 30, January 17, 2014, No. 46, pp. 7)*
Pub: American City Business Journals, Inc.
Contact: Mike Olivieri, Executive Vice President
Released: Weekly. Price: $4, introductory 4-week offer(Digital only). Description: Nike Inc. is planning to open retail stores that will exclusively sell Jordan Brand merchandise. The company is seeking to grow its direct-to-consumer sales to $8 billion by 2017. Nike's capital spending is also expected to increase by 3 to 4 percent. Availability: Print; Online.

3037 ■ *"Juicy Couture (1997-2014) Couldn't Evolve When Its Cachet Dried Up"* in *Canadian Business (Vol. 87, July 2014, No. 7, pp. 16)*
Description: Fashion brand Juicy Couture was started by Pamela Skaist-Ley and Gela Nash-Taylor in Los Angeles, California in 1997 and was acquired by Fifth & Pacific Companies in 2003. Fifth & Pacific put Juicy Couture up for sale in fall 2013, with Authentic Brands Group owning the rights to the brand name for $195 million. The last of the Canadian outlets will close June 30, 2014. Availability: Online.

3038 ■ *"Karl Lagerfeld, Pioneering Fashion Designer, Has Died"* in *CNN (February 20, 2019)*
URL(s): www.cnn.com/style/article/karl-lagerfeld-dead-intl/index.html
Ed: Tara John. Released: February 20, 2019. Description: Famous German fashion designer, Karl Lagerfeld, died in Paris at the age of 85. Availability: Online.

3039 ■ *"Life's Work: Manolo Blahnik"* in *Harvard Business Review (Vol. 88, December 2010, No. 12, pp. 144)*
Pub: Harvard Business Publishing
Contact: Diane Belcher, Managing Director
Ed: Alison Beard. Price: $8.95, PDF. Description: Shoe designer Manolo Blahnik recounts his beginnings in the shoe industry and the influence art has had on his work, as well as balancing art and commerce. He also discusses the importance of quality materials and craftsmanship and the benefits of managing an independent, family-owned business. Availability: Online; PDF.

3040 ■ *"Making It Work"* in *Retail Merchandiser (Vol. 51, July-August 2011, No. 4, pp. 43)*
Description: Profile of Anthony DiPaolo and his purchase of the Work 'N Gear retail store in 2002. The brick and mortar shop sells work wear and healthcare apparel and DiPaolo believes customer respect is essential to his success. Availability: Online.

3041 ■ *McQueen of Scots*
Released: 2014. Description: Profile of the life of fashion designer Alexander McQueen, and how his heritage impacted his work. Availability: Streaming.

3042 ■ *"Military Brides Can Get Free Wedding Gowns"* in *Virginian-Pilot (November 10, 2010)*
Pub: The Virginian-Pilot
Contact: Kevin Goyette, Director
E-mail: kgoyette@dailypress.com
Ed: Jamesetta M. Walker. Description: Seventy-five designer wedding gowns will be given to military brides on a first-come, first-served basis at Maya Couture through the Brides Across America's wedding gown giveaway program. Gowns are valued between $500 to $3,000 and are donated by designers Maggie Sottero, Pronovias and Essense of Australia. Availability: Online.

3043 ■ *"New Beat for Marley's Daughter: Offspring of Reggae Royalty Opens Vintage Clothing Shop with Pal"* in *Los Angeles Business Journal (Vol. 34, March 12, 2012, No. 11, pp. 3)*
Pub: CBJ L.P.
Contact: Laura Garrett, Vice President Publisher
E-mail: garrett@ocbj.com
Ed: Bethany Firnhaber. Description: Karen Marley, daughter of famous reggae musician Bob Marley, explains her passion for vintage clothing. Karen and her fried Monique Aquino have partnered to open a resale consignment store in Los Angeles selling designer and vintage clothing. Availability: Online.

3044 ■ *"Options Abound in Winter Wares"* in *Pet Product News (Vol. 64, November 2010, No. 11, pp. 1)*
Ed: Maggie M. Shein. Description: Pet supply manufacturers emphasize creating top-notch construction and functional design in creating winter clothing for pets. Meanwhile, retailers and pet owners seek human-inspired style, quality, and versatility for pets' winter clothing. How retailers generate successful sales of pets' winter clothing outside of traditional brand marketing is also examined. Availability: Online.

3045 ■ *Overdressed: The Shockingly High Cost of Cheap Fashion*
Ed: Elizabeth L. Cline. Released: August 27, 2013. Price: $12.82, Paperback; 12.99, E-Book. Description: Explores the impact cheap fashion has on our planet and society. With stores producing these clothes to keep up with the newest trends, people find it easier to discard clothes and pay for new, than to fix up what they already have. What is this costing our wallets and out environment?. Availability: E-book; Print.

3046 ■ *"Panera Breadwinner Tries on Tattu Designer Jeans"* in *Houston Business Journal (Vol. 40, December 18, 2009, No. 32, pp. 1)*
Pub: Houston Business Journal
Contact: Bob Charlet, President
E-mail: bcharlet@bizjournals.com
Ed: Allison Wollam. Description: Chuck Cain, the franchisee who introduced Panera Bread to Houston, Texas has partnered with tax accountant Jim Jacobsen to introduce custom-make Tattu Jeans. As more Tattu Jeans outlets are being planned, Cain is using entrepreneurial lessons learned from Panera Bread in the new venture. Both Panera Bread and Tattu Jeans were opened by Cain during economic downturns. Availability: Print; Online.

3047 ■ *"Portland Wooing Under Armour to West Coast Facility"* in *Baltimore Business Journal (Vol. 27, January 29, 2010, No. 39, pp. 1)*
Pub: Baltimore Business Journal
Contact: Rhonda Pringle, President
E-mail: rpringle@bizjournals.com
Ed: Andy Giegerich. Description: Baltimore, Maryland sports apparel maker, Under Armour, is planning a west coast expansion with Portland, Oregon among the sites considered to house its apparel and footwear design center. Portland officials counting on the concentration of nearly 10,000 activewear workers in the city will help lure the company to the city. Availability: Print; Online.

3048 ■ *"Rule of the Masses: Reinventing Fashion Via Crowdsourcing"* in *WWD (Vol. 200, July 26, 2010, No. 17, pp. 1)*
Pub: Conde Nast Publications
Contact: Agnes Chu, President

Ed: Cate T. Corcoran. **Description:** Large apparel brands and retailers are crowdsourcing as a way to increase customer loyalty and to build their businesses. **Availability:** PDF; Download; Online.

3049 ■ *"Three Ways Columbia's Stock Can Keep Rising" in Business Journal Portland (Vol. 30, February 21, 2014, No. 51, pp. 8)*
Pub: American City Business Journals, Inc.
Contact: Mike Olivieri, Executive Vice President

Released: Weekly. **Price:** $4, Introductory 4-week offer(Digital & Print). **Description:** The shares of Columbia Sportswear Company reached a record high of $88.25 in February 2014. The company's cold-weather gear, its TurboDown technology and its new joint venture with China are expected to contribute significantly in keeping stock prices high. **Availability:** Print; Online.

3050 ■ *"Trousseaus of Memories Trail Behind Wedding Gowns" in Oregonian (September 4, 2010)*
Pub: The Oregonian
Contact: John Maher, President

Ed: Anne Saker. **Description:** Readers are asked to share stories about their wedding gowns and what that garment meant to them at the time and now. **Availability:** Online.

3051 ■ *"Under Armour's Founder On Learning to Leverage Celebrity Endorsements" in Harvard Business Review (Vol. 90, May 2012, No. 5, pp. 45)*
Pub: Harvard Business Review Press
Contact: Moderna V. Pfizer, Contact

Ed: Kevin Plank. **Description:** Using his athletic apparel company Under Armour as an illustration, the author identifies two key points in effective utilization of endorsement advertising: balancing freebies with fair-price contracts, and offering stock opportunities so that celebrities can be personally engaged with growth.

3052 ■ *"Vision Statement: How This First Lady Moves Markets" in Harvard Business Review (Vol. 88, November 2010, No. 11, pp. 38)*
Pub: Harvard Business Publishing
Contact: Diane Belcher, Managing Director

Ed: David Yermack. **Price:** $6, PDF. **Description:** A chart is presented demonstrating how First Lady Michelle Obama's choice of fashion designer has impacted the clothing industry. **Availability:** Online; PDF.

3053 ■ *Wardrobe Crisis: How We Went from Sunday Best to Fast Fashion*
Ed: Clare Press. **Released:** February 20, 2018. **Price:** $10.95, Paperback; $12.99, E-Book. **Description:** Throughout history, everyone knew where their clothes came from — they made it themselves or a local person was hired. In our modern times, our clothes are made around the world, with an emphasis on discarding our clothes soon after we buy them. Explores famous fashion icons and the entire fashion industry. **Availability:** E-book; Print.

3054 ■ *"Well-Heeled Startup Plots Course for a Run at Garmin" in Business Journal Portland (Vol. 27, November 12, 2010, No. 37, pp. 1)*
Pub: Portland Business Journal
Contact: Andy Giegerich, Managing Editor
E-mail: agiegerich@bizjournals.com

Description: Oh! Shoes LLC expects to receive about $1.5 million in funding from angel investors, while marketing a new line of high heel shoes that are comfortable, healthy, and attractive. The new line of shoes will use the technology of athletic footwear while having the look of an Italian designer. Oh! Shoes hopes to generate $35 million in sales by 2014. **Availability:** Print; Online.

3055 ■ *"Why the Future of Streetwear is Female" in The Wall Street Journal (August 21, 2019)*
URL(s): www.wsj.com/articles/why-the-future-of-streetwear-is-female-11566390771

Ed: Jessica Iredale. **Released:** August 21, 2019. **Description:** Traditionally, streetwear has been dominated by male designers and the men who wear this clothing, but female designers are introducing new concepts into this fashion genre. **Availability:** Online.

3056 ■ *"Why the Gap is Stalking Lululemon" in Canadian Business (Vol. 85, August 22, 2012, No. 14, pp. 7)*
Ed: Jim Sutherland. **Description:** Lululemon Athletica is facing competition against Gap Inc.'s Athleta as the retail giant plans to have about 50 new shops across Canada by the end of 2012. Athleta is also carrying lines of yoga- and activewear similar to that of Lululemon's and are even located near their stores. **Availability:** Online.

3057 ■ *"Zara Eludes the Pain in Spain: Clothing Giant Inditex Sees Its First-Quarter Profits Rise By 30 Percent" in Canadian Business (Vol. 85, September 17, 2012, No. 14, pp. 67)*
Ed: Bryan Borzykowski. **Released:** September 17, 2012. **Description:** Clothing retailer Inditex reported a 30 percent increase in profit in the first quarter of 2012 and 15 percent increase in sales year over year. The company's unique business model was attributed to its growth, which also appeals to income investors.

SOURCES OF SUPPLY

3058 ■ *American Apparel Producers' Network--Directory for Sourcing Apparel*
Americas Apparel Producers' Network
Contact: Carlos Arias, Chief Executive Officer
URL(s): www.aapnetwork.net/search-members

Released: Annual **Description:** Covers over 300 member contractors, manufacturers, and suppliers in the apparel industry. **Entries include:** Firm name, address, phone, names and titles of key personnel, apparel and services provided. **Arrangement:** Alphabetical. **Indexes:** Company name, type of apparel. **Availability:** Print; Online.

STATISTICAL SOURCES

3059 ■ *Men's Clothing Stores Industry in the US - Market Research Report*
URL(s): www.ibisworld.com/united-states/market-research-reports/mens-clothing-stores-industry/
Price: $925. **Description:** Downloadable report analyzing the current and future trends in the men's clothing store industry. **Availability:** Online.

3060 ■ *Women's Clothing Stores Industry in the US - Market Research Report*
URL(s): www.ibisworld.com/united-states/market-research-reports/womens-clothing-stores-industry/
Price: $925. **Description:** Downloadable report analyzing the current and future trends in the women's clothing store industry. **Availability:** Online.

TRADE PERIODICALS

3061 ■ *Visionaire*
Pub: Visionaire Publishing L.L.C.
Contact: Cecilia Dean, Contact
URL(s): visionaireworld.com/pages/about
Facebook: www.facebook.com/Visionaireworld
Description: Limited edition multi-format journal of art and fashion. **Availability:** Print.

VIDEO/AUDIO MEDIA

3062 ■ *The How of Business: From Idea to Fashion Product with Zack Hurley*
URL(s): www.thehowofbusiness.com/episode-344-zack-hurley

Ed: Henry Lopez. **Released:** December 14, 2020. **Description:** Podcast explains how to launch a fashion business.

3063 ■ *How I Built My Small Business: Eric Henry - Crafting an Eco-Friendly Clothing Empire with TS Designs and the Fight Against Fashion's Waste Crisis*
URL(s): www.annemcginty.com/transcripts/erichenry
Ed: Anne McGinty. **Released:** August 20, 2024. **Description:** Podcast features a clothing designer with environmentally friendly supply chain practices.

3064 ■ *How I Built This: M.M. LaFleur: Sarah LaFleur*
URL(s): www.npr.org/2020/01/03/1069928106/m-m-lafleur-sarah-lafleur-2020
Ed: Guy Raz. **Released:** January 10, 2022. **Description:** Podcast offers a discussion with the founder of a clothing line for working women.

3065 ■ *How I Built This: Suitsupply: Fokke de Jone*
URL(s): wondery.com/shows/how-i-built-this/episode/10386-suitsupply-fokke-de-jong
Ed: Guy Raz. **Released:** May 01, 2023. **Description:** Podcast explains how a college student sold suits of his dorm room and now has 150 locations worldwide.

3066 ■ *How I Built This: Vuori: Joe Kudla*
URL(s): wondery.com/shows/how-i-built-this/episode/10386-vuori-joe-kudla
Ed: Guy Raz. **Released:** October 02, 2023. **Description:** Podcast explains how Vuori pivoted from selling in small stores to DTC (direct-to-consumer).

TRADE SHOWS AND CONVENTIONS

3067 ■ *Semi-Annual Costume Convention*
National Costumers Association (NCA)
PO Box 13347
Chicago, IL 60613
Ph: (708)646-2799
Co. E-mail: office@costumers.org
URL: http://www.costumers.org
Contact: Ed Avis, Executive Director
E-mail: executivedirector@costumers.org
URL(s): www.costumers.org/about-the-national-costumers-association

Frequency: Semiannual. **Description:** Offer exemplary teaching and training programs. **Audience:** Costume industry professionals. **Principal Exhibits:** Offer exemplary teaching and training programs.

LIBRARIES

3068 ■ *Academy of Art University Library*
180 New Montgomery St., 6th Fl.
San Francisco, CA 94105
Ph: (415)618-3842
Co. E-mail: library@academyart.edu
URL: http://library.academyart.edu
Contact: Debra Sampson, Director
E-mail: dsampson@academyart.edu
Facebook: www.facebook.com/academyartlibrary
Instagram: www.instagram.com/aaulibrary
Scope: Art; design. **Services:** Only for Students, Faculty and research people; Interlibrary Loan; Printing; Copying; and Scanning. **Founded:** 1929.

3069 ■ *American Intercontinental University Library*
2200 E Germann Rd., Ste. 100
Chandler, AZ 85286-1585
URL: http://www.aiuniv.edu/campus-locations/atlanta/student-life
Scope: Education. **Founded:** 1982. **Holdings:** Figures not available.

3070 ■ *Brooklyn Museum*
200 E Pky.
Brooklyn, NY 11238-6052
Ph: (718)638-5000
Co. E-mail: information@brooklynmuseum.org

URL: http://www.brooklynmuseum.org
Contact: Deborah Wythe, Manager, Collections Archivist
Facebook: www.facebook.com/brooklynmuseum
X (Twitter): x.com/brooklynmuseum
Instagram: www.instagram.com/brooklynmuseum
Description: Publishes works on the visual arts. **Scope:** Museum's collections; history. **Services:** Library open to the public by appointment; Copying. **Founded:** 1897. **Holdings:** 3,200 linear feet of records; books; letters; photographs; bills; layouts; documents; audiovisual.

3071 ■ **Conde Nast Publications Library and Information Services**
1 World Trade Ctr.
  New York, NY 10007
Co. E-mail: communications@condenast.com
URL: http://www.condenast.com
Contact: Roger Lynch, Chief Executive Officer
Linkedin: www.linkedin.com/company/conde-nast
X (Twitter): x.com/condenast
Instagram: www.instagram.com/condenast
Description: Produces in-depth research for the world's most celebrated media brands. **Scope:** Fashion; houses; gardens; home furnishings; interior design; health; personalities; photographs. **Services:** Library not open to public. **Founded:** 1935. **Holdings:** 7,000 volumes.

3072 ■ **Fashion Institute of Design and Merchandising (FIDM) - Library**
919 S Grand Ave.
  Los Angeles, CA 90015
Ph: (213)624-1200
Free: 800-624-1200
URL: http://fidm.edu
Contact: Tonian Hohberg, President
Facebook: www.facebook.com/FIDMCollege
Linkedin: www.linkedin.com/school/fidm
X (Twitter): x.com/FIDM
YouTube: www.youtube.com/fidm
Pinterest: www.pinterest.com/fidm
Scope: Textile design and research; fashion; business and marketing; interior design; retailing and costumes. **Services:** Copying; interlibrary loan. **Founded:** 1969. **Subscriptions:** 200 magazines Books; periodicals; publications; newspapers; DVDs; CDs.

3073 ■ **Fashion Institute of Design & Merchandising (FIDM) - Orange County Library**
17590 Gillette Ave.
  Irvine, CA 92614
URL: http://fidm.edu/en/majors/merchandise+marketing/experience/bios/molly+stolen
Scope: Textile design; textile design; marketing; interior design; retailing; costumes. **Services:** Copying; library open to the public by appointment. **Founded:** 1980. **Holdings:** 3,000 books; 130 bound periodical volumes; 40 pamphlet headings; 475 videotapes; 135 slide sets; 300 retail catalogs; 100 annual reports; 50 CD-ROMs. **Subscriptions:** 80 journals and other serials; 8 newspapers.

3074 ■ **George Brown College Archives**
500 Macpherson Ave., Rm. F-103
  Toronto, ON, Canada M5R 1M1
Ph: (416)415-5000
Fax: (416)415-4772
URL: http://www.georgebrown.ca/about/archives
Contact: Clay Thibodeau, Archivist
E-mail: cthibodeau@georgebrown.ca

Facebook: www.facebook.com/georgebrowncollege
Linkedin: www.linkedin.com/school/george-brown-college
X (Twitter): x.com/GBCollege
Instagram: www.instagram.com/gbcollege
YouTube: www.youtube.com/user/georgebrowncollege
Scope: Education materials. **Services:** Copying; archives open to the public with restrictions and by appointment only. **Founded:** 1975. **Holdings:** 3,700 linear meters publications.

3075 ■ **Metropolitan Museum of Art - Irene Lewisohn Costume Reference Library**
1000 5th Ave.
  New York, NY 10028
Co. E-mail: costumeinstitute.library@metmuseum.org
URL: http://www.metmuseum.org/art/libraries-and-research-centers/the-irene-lewisohn-costume-reference-library
Scope: History of costume; fashion. **Services:** Copying; library open to professional designers and research scholars by appointment. **Holdings:** Art books; exhibition history documentation; designer archives; fashion plates; photography collections, scrapbooks; ephemera.

3076 ■ **Otis College of Art and Design - Millard Sheets Library**
9045 Lincoln Blvd.
  Los Angeles, CA 90045
Ph: (310)665-6930
Co. E-mail: library@otis.edu
URL: http://otis.libguides.com/LibraryHome
Contact: Sue Maberry, Director
E-mail: maberry@otis.edu
Scope: Art and design. **Services:** Interlibrary loan; library open to the public. **Founded:** 1917. **Holdings:** 40,000 books, 130,000 e-books; online databases with millions of articles; special collections that include 3,000 artists books.

3077 ■ **Parsons School of Design - Adam & Sophie Gimbel Design Library**
66 5th Ave.
  New York, NY 10011
URL: http://www.newschool.edu
Contact: David E. van Zandt, President
Scope: Education materials. **Services:** Interlibrary loan. **Founded:** 1896. **Holdings:** Figures not available.

3078 ■ **Southern New Hampshire University - Shapiro Library**
2500 N River Rd.
  Manchester, NH 03106
Ph: (603)645-9605
Co. E-mail: library@snhu.libanswers.com
URL: http://www.snhu.edu/student-experience/campus-experience/shapiro-library
Contact: Jennifer Harris, Executive Director
Description: Library delivers information and instruction necessary for academic success and lifelong learning. **Scope:** Education. **Services:** Interlibrary loan; copying; library open to the public. **Holdings:** 500,000 eBooks; Magazines; Reports; Newspapers; Journals.

3079 ■ **State University of New York - Fashion Institute of Technology - Gladys Marcus Library**
227 W 27th St.
  New York, NY 10001-5992

Ph: (212)217-7999
URL: http://www.fitnyc.edu/library/index.php
Description: Library supports the academic and research needs of the institute. **Scope:** Fashion, fashion history, textiles, fashion trend forecasting. **Services:** Interlibrary loan; library open by appointment. **Founded:** 1944. **Holdings:** 300,000 print, non-print, and electronic materials, including sketch collections, clipping files, and fashion show DVDs.

3080 ■ **Thomas Jefferson University - Paul J. Gutman Library**
4201 Henry Ave.
  Philadelphia, PA 19144
Ph: (215)951-2848
Co. E-mail: askgutman@jefferson.edu
URL: http://library.jefferson.edu/gutman.cfm
Contact: DaVonne Armstrong, Director, Operations
E-mail: davonne.rooney@jefferson.edu
Scope: Textiles; fashion; architecture; design; business; engineering; health; science; social science. **Services:** Interlibrary loan; Library not open to public with restrictions. **Founded:** 1992. **Holdings:** Books; videos; journal; articles.

3081 ■ **University of British Columbia Music, Art and Architecture Library**
1961 E Mall
  Vancouver, BC, Canada V6T 1Z1
Ph: (604)822-3943
Co. E-mail: maa.library@ubc.ca
URL: http://maa.library.ubc.ca
Contact: Paula Farrar, Head
E-mail: paula.farrar@ubc.ca
Scope: Music; art history; visual art and theory; architecture; landscape; regional planning. **Founded:** 1967. **Holdings:** Figures not available.

3082 ■ **University of Cincinnati (UC) - Robert A. Deshon and Karl J. Schlachter Library for Design, Architecture, Art, and Planning [DAAP Library]**
5480 Aronoff Center for Design & Art, 2600 Clifton Ave.
  Cincinnati, OH 45221-0016
Ph: (513)556-1335
URL: http://www.libraries.uc.edu/daap.html
Contact: Cade Stevens, Manager, Operations Supervisor
E-mail: stevencd@uc.edu
Description: Fosters excellence in art and design scholarship by providing its users with on-site access to nearly 100,000 monographs and bound journals, hundreds of the most important art and design periodicals in print, and a growing special collection that comprises new, important, rare, aged, and handcrafted books and objects. **Scope:** Fashion design; industrial design; graphic design; architecture; interior design; landscape design; horticulture; art history; art education and fine art. **Services:** Interlibrary loan; copying; library open to the public; pay fine. **Founded:** 1929. **Holdings:** Books; articles; journals.

3083 ■ **Woodbury University Library**
7500 N Glenoaks Blvd.
  Burbank, CA 91510
Ph: (818)252-5200
Co. E-mail: reference@woodbury.edu
URL: http://library.woodbury.edu
Contact: Eric Garcia, Librarian, Reference
E-mail: eric.garcia@woodbury.edu
Facebook: www.facebook.com/wulibrary
X (Twitter): x.com/woodburylib
Instagram: www.instagram.com/woodburyuniversitylibrary
Scope: Education. **Services:** Interlibrary loan (limited). **Founded:** 1884. **Holdings:** Books; journals.

Clothing Store

START-UP INFORMATION

3084 ■ *"Mount Laurel Woman Launches Venture Into Children's Used Clothing"* in *Philadelphia Inquirer (September 17, 2010)*
Pub: The Philadelphia Inquirer
Contact: Elizabeth H. Hughes, Chief Executive Officer

Ed: Maria Panaritis. **Description:** Profile of Jennifer Frisch, stay-at-home mom turned entrepreneur. Frisch started a used-clothing store Once Upon a Child after opening her franchised Plato's Closet, selling unwanted and used baby clothing and accessories at her new shop, while offering used merchandise to teens at Plato's Closet.

3085 ■ *Start Your Own Fashion Accessories Business*
Pub: Entrepreneur Media Inc.
Contact: Dan Bova, Director
E-mail: dbova@entrepreneur.com

Ed: Eileen Figure Sandlin. **Released:** Second edition. **Description:** Entrepreneurs wishing to start a fashion accessories business will find important information for setting up a home workshop and office, exploring the market, managing finances, publicizing and advertising the business and more.

3086 ■ *"Upscale Consignment Shop Opens In Brandon"* in *Tampa Tribune (January 25, 2012)*

Ed: Yvette C. Hammett. **Description:** Agape Chic Consignment Boutique opened February 4, 2012. The owners, Dena Ham and Stacy Ulrey Regan became friends working on their children's school PTA. Their business partnership hopes that people walking into their new shop will feel as if they are walking into an upscale boutique. The store offers designer labels in sizes 2-20. **Availability:** Print; Online.

ASSOCIATIONS AND OTHER ORGANIZATIONS

3087 ■ **International Formalwear Association (IFA)**
1810 University Blvd.
Tuscaloosa, AL 35401
Ph: (303)887-2519
Co. E-mail: info@formalwear.org
URL: http://www.formalwear.org
Contact: Kellie G. Burch, Executive Director
E-mail: kellie@selectformalwear.com
Facebook: www.facebook.com/makeitformal
YouTube: www.youtube.com/channel/UCEXN6eMFNBbwtkThJRegLog

Description: Specialists working to promote the formal wear industry. Conducts educational programs through seminars and exhibitions. **Founded:** 1973. **Publications:** *Formaltimes* (Biweekly); *International Formalwear Association--Member Directory*. **Geographic Preference:** National.

3088 ■ **National Retail Federation (NRF) - Retail Library**
1101 New York Ave. NW, Ste. 1200
Washington, DC 20005
Ph: (202)783-7971
Free: 800-673-4692
Fax: (202)737-2849
Co. E-mail: contact@nrf.com
URL: http://www.nrf.com
Contact: Matthew R. Shay, President
Facebook: www.facebook.com/NationalRetailFederation
Linkedin: www.linkedin.com/company/national-retail-federation
X (Twitter): x.com/NRFnews
Instagram: www.instagram.com/nrf
YouTube: www.youtube.com/user/NRFInternet

Description: Represents state retail associations, several dozen national retail associations, as well as large and small corporate members representing the breadth and diversity of the retail industry's establishment and employees. Conducts informational and educational conferences related to all phases of retailing including financial planning and cash management, taxation, economic forecasting, expense planning. **Scope:** Careers; economy; loss prevention; mobile; retail trends; store operations; chain restaurants; global; marketing; online; small business; supply chain; consumer trends; human resources; merchandising; public policy; social responsibility; technology. **Founded:** 1911. **Holdings:** Figures Not Available. **Publications:** *Stores*; *NRF Foundation Focus* (Quarterly); *NRF Update* (Monthly); *STORES: The Magazine of NRF* (9/year); *Washington Retail Report* (Weekly); *STORES--Top 100 Retailers Issue* (Annual); *Software SourceBook*. **Educational Activities:** Human Resources Executives Summit; NRF Retail's Big Show (Annual); NRF PROTECT – Retail's Loss Prevention & Cyber Risk Event (Annual); National Retail Federation Annual Convention & Expo (Annual). **Awards:** NRF Gold Medal Award (Annual); NRF International Retailer of the Year (Annual); J. Thomas Weyant Award (Annual); NRF Gold Medal in Retailing (Annual). **Geographic Preference:** National.

REFERENCE WORKS

3089 ■ *"American Apparel: When Dov Cries"* in *Canadian Business (Vol. 83, June 15, 2010, No. 10, pp. 71)*
Pub: Rogers Media Inc.
Contact: Neil Spivak, Chief Executive Officer

Ed: Joe Castaldo. **Description:** American Apparel disclosed that they will have problems meeting one of its debt covenants which could trigger a chain reaction that could lead to bankruptcy. The prospects look bleak, but eccentric company founder Dov Charney, has always defied expectations. **Availability:** Online.

3090 ■ *"Best Days and Weekends to Shop for Clothing"* in *U.S. News and World Report (April 23, 2018)*

Ed: Kristin McGrath. **Released:** April 23, 2018. **Description:** General tips for clothes shopping throughout the year and when to hit the stores and online for the best deals to stretch your budget. **Availability:** Online.

3091 ■ *"Betsey Johnson Falls Out of Fashion"* in *Canadian Business (Vol. 85, June 11, 2012, No. 10, pp. 14)*

Ed: Sarah Barmak. **Description:** Fashion label Betsey Johnson LLC filed for Chapter 11 bankruptcy protection in April 2012 that would result in 350 layoffs and closure of most of its 63 stores. The company cited severe liquidity constraints and $4.1 million in outstanding unsecured obligations to creditors in its filing. **Availability:** Print; Online.

3092 ■ *"Better Than New Runs on Tried-and-True Model"* in *Bellingham Business Journal (Vol. February 2010, pp. 16)*
Pub: Sound Publishing Inc.
Contact: Josh O'Connor, President

Ed: Ashley Mitchell. **Description:** Profile of family owned Better Than New clothing store that sells overstock items from department stores and clothing manufacturers. The stores location makes it easy to miss and its only advertising is a large sign posted outside. This is the sixth store owned by the couple, Keijeo and Sirba Halmekanqas.

3093 ■ *"Bringing Charities More Bang for Their Buck"* in *Crain's Chicago Business (Vol. 34, May 23, 2011, No. 21, pp. 31)*
Pub: Crain Communications Inc.
Contact: Barry Asin, President

Ed: Lisa Bertagnoli. **Description:** Marcy-Newberry Association connects charities with manufacturers in order to use excess items such as clothing, janitorial and office supplies. **Availability:** Online.

3094 ■ *"Buy the Pants, Save the Planet?"* in *Globe & Mail (February 5, 2007, pp. B1)*

Description: The marketing campaign of the clothing company Diesel S.p.A. is discussed. The company has based its latest collection of T-shirt designs on the problem of global warming. **Availability:** Online.

3095 ■ *Canadian Apparel Directory*
Pub: Canadian Apparel Federation
Contact: Flora Kodl, Contact
URL(s): www.apparel.ca/directories.html

Description: Publication includes lists of Canadian industry suppliers, and manufacturers of apparel. **Entries include:** Company name, address, phone, fax, names and titles of key personnel, name and title of contact, product/service, description of company business activities. **Arrangement:** Alphabetical. **Indexes:** Trade name, product/service, geographical. **Availability:** Print; Online.

3096 ■ *"Celebrate Innovation, No Matter Where It Occurs"* in *Harvard Business Review (Vol. 90, April 2012, No. 4, pp. 36)*
Pub: Harvard Business Review Press
Contact: Moderna V. Pfizer, Contact

Ed: Nitin Nohria. **Price:** $6, hardcover. **Description:** Yoga is used to illustrate the global success of a given concept not originally construed as a product or service. Although yoga emerged in ancient India, it is now practiced worldwide and is at the center of many businesses and disciplines, from the health care industry to clothing and accessories. **Availability:** PDF; Online.

3097 ■ *"The CEO of TJX On How To Train First-Class Buyers"* **in Harvard Business Review (Vol. 92, May 2014, No. 5, pp. 45)**
Pub: Harvard Business Press
Contact: Gabriela Allmi, Regional Manager
E-mail: gabriela.allmi@hbsp.harvard.edu
Released: 2014. **Price:** $8.95. **Description:** The CEO of clothing retailer TJX Companies Inc. emphasizes the importance of buyer training to ensure that store merchandise inventory optimizes consumer response. Buyers must be curious, knowledgeable about customers, and willing to take risks. **Availability:** Print; Online; PDF.

3098 ■ *"A Change Would Do You Good"* **in Canadian Business (Vol. 80, November 19, 2007, No. 23, pp. 15)**
Description: Western Glove Works will be manufacturing clothing offshore, including Sheryl Crow's jeans collection, in countries such as China and the Philippines. The company decided to operate offshore after 86 years of existence due to the high price of manufacturing jeans in Canada. Western Glove's focus on producing celebrity-endorsed goods is discussed. **Availability:** Print; Online.

3099 ■ *"Consignment Shop Offers Children's Clothes, Products"* **in Frederick News-Post (August 19, 2010)**
Pub: Federick News-Post
Contact: Connie Hastings, Director
E-mail: chastings@newspost.com
Ed: Ed Waters, Jr. **Description:** Sweet Pea Consignments for Children offers used items for newborns to pre-teens. The shop carries name brand clothing as well as toys, books and baby products. **Availability:** Print; Online.

3100 ■ *"Consignment Shop Opens in Spring Township To Serve Hard-To-Find Sizes"* **in Reading Eagle (June 16, 2012)**
Ed: Shannon Simcox. **Description:** BeautiFull Figure is a plus-size consignment store located in Spring Township, Pennsylvania. The owner, Elizabeth Reach, is also a full-time student. Many consignment shops will not accept clothing over size 16 and Reach saw an opportunity to serve plus-size women. She offers 50-50 split of profits on consigned items. **Availability:** Print; Online.

3101 ■ *"Consignment Shops Form Friendly Alliance in Eagle Plaza"* **in Mail Tribune (August 7, 2012)**
Ed: Greg Stiles. **Description:** Loren Clear was concerned about opening his men's only consignment shop in a plaza already housing three other consignment stores. However, all four retailers have found it to be an asset, each having their own specialty. Along with Clear's men's clothing consignment, there is a children's store, a plus-size shop, and a women's clothing and accessory business. Clear said there are few men's consignment stores and it is an answer for the businessman to purchase better quality clothing and suits at better prices., Loren Clear thought opening his men's only consignment shop in the same plaza shared with three other consignment stores might be a bad idea. However, all three retailers have found it to be an asset. Along with Clear's men's only shop called Men's Hangups, there is a plus-size shop, a women's store, and a children's store. **Availability:** Online.

3102 ■ *"ConsignPro Elevates Nature of Consignment Business, Encourages Designer Resale"* **in Internet Wire (May 15, 2012)**
Description: Forbes magazine recently highlighted an article on an upscale thrift store located in New York called Designer Resale. The shop features fashion-forward retail merchandies sold on consignment. These new boutique-type resale shops are growing in popularity across the country. **Availability:** Print; Online.

3103 ■ *"Crowdsourcing their Way into One Big Mess"* **in Brandweek (Vol. 51, October 25, 2010, No. 38, pp. 26)**
Description: The Gap, was counting on crowdsourcing to provide feedback for its new logo, but it did not prove positive for the retailer. However, a massive outcry of negative opinion, via crowdsourcing, may not always equal valid, constructive criticism. **Availability:** Online.

3104 ■ *"Design '07 (Fashion): Haute Flyers"* **in Canadian Business (Vol. 80, November 19, 2007, No. 23, pp. 68)**
Pub: Rogers Media Inc.
Contact: Neil Spivak, Chief Executive Officer
Ed: Rachel Pulfer. **Description:** Duckie Brown has been nominated by the Council of Fashion Designers of America as best menswear designer in the U.S. for 2007, along with leaders Calvin Klein and Ralph Lauren. The New York-based company was formed the day after September 11, 2001, but the timing did not hamper its growth. The works and plans of owners Steven Cox and Daniel Silver are described. **Availability:** Online.

3105 ■ *"Designing Women? Apparel Apparatchic at Kmart"* **in Barron's (Vol. 88, March 17, 2008, No. 11, pp. 16)**
Pub: Dow Jones & Company Inc.
Contact: Almar Latour, Chief Executive Officer
Ed: Robin Goldwyn Blumenthal. **Description:** Kmart began a nationwide search for women to represent the company in a national advertising campaign. Contestants need to upload their photos to Kmart's website and winners will be chosen by a panel of celebrity judges. The contest aims to reverse preconceived negative notions about the store's quality and service. **Availability:** Online.

3106 ■ **Directory of Apparel Specialty Stores**
Pub: Chain Store Guide
Contact: Kaitlyn Toner, Account Manager
URL(s): www.chainstoreguide.com/c-75-apparel-specialty-store-leads.aspx
Released: Annual **Price:** $1,850, for plus one year subscription. **Description:** Covers 5,040 apparel and sporting goods specialty retailers in the United States and Canada, operating more than 70,700 stores. Apparel retailers must have annual retail sales of at least $500,000; sporting goods specialty retailers must also have $500,000 in annual sales, with the condition that at least 20% of product sales are from sporting goods equipment. **Entries include:** Company name, phone, and fax numbers; physical and mailing addresses; company e-mail and web addresses; Internet order processing indicator; percentage of Internet sales; type of business; listing type; product lines; total, industry, and product group sales; total selling square footage; store prototype sizes; total stores; trading areas; projected openings and remodeling; units by trade name; distribution center locations; resident buyer's name and location; mail order indicator; percentage of mail order sales; catalog names; private label indicator; private label credit card indicator; apparel price lines; average number of checkouts; year founded; public company indicator; parent company name and location; and key personnel with titles; 7,200 personnel email addresses. **Arrangement:** Geographical. **Indexes:** Alphabetical, product lines, exclusions. **Availability:** Online.

3107 ■ *"Don't Tweak Your Supply Chain - Rethink It End to End"* **in Harvard Business Review (Vol. 88, October 2010, No. 10, pp. 62)**
Pub: Harvard Business Publishing
Contact: Diane Belcher, Managing Director
Ed: Hau L. Lee. **Price:** $8.95, PDF. **Description:** Hong Kong apparel firm Esquel Apparel Ltd. is used to illustrate supply chain reorganization to improve a firm's sustainability. Discussion focuses on taking a broad approach rather than addressing individual steps or processes. **Availability:** Online; PDF.

3108 ■ *"Dress Professionally Cool for Summer"* **in Women In Business (Vol. 62, June 2010, No. 2, pp. 38)**
Description: Summer clothing for business and career women is discussed with regard to traditional and relaxed work places. Fabric considerations, tips on choosing blazers and a list of clothes and other items that are not appropriate for the workplace are presented. **Availability:** Print; Online.

3109 ■ *"Dressbarn Announces First Round of Closings for June and July. Is Yours on the List?"* **in USA Today (June 21, 2019)**
URL(s): www.usatoday.com/story/money/2019/06/21/dressbarn-store-closings-first-locations-shutter-june-and-july/1527716001/
Ed: Kelly Tyko. **Released:** June 21, 2019. **Description:** All 650 Dressbarn locations are scheduled to close, but the closings will happen in waves. June and July are expected to be shuttered, with more listed at a later date. **Availability:** Online.

3110 ■ *"Fall Fever"* **in Canadian Business (Vol. 81, October 13, 2008, No. 17, pp. S12)**
Description: Buyer's guide of men's suits and jackets for fall are presented, including a suit by Boss Hugo Boss recommended for fun in the city after finishing work. Designers Ermenegildo, Michael Kors, and Arnold Brant are also highlighted. **Availability:** Print; Online.

3111 ■ *"Fashionistas Weigh in on the Super-Thin"* **in Charlotte Observer (February 7, 2007)**
Description: Council of Fashion Designers of America held a panel discussion regarding the weight and ages of models used to highlight clothing. **Availability:** Online.

3112 ■ *"Five Reasons Why the Gap Fell Out of Fashion"* **in Globe & Mail (January 27, 2007, pp. B4)**
Description: The five major market trends that have caused the decline of fashion clothing retailer Gap Inc.'s sales are discussed. The shift in brand, workplace fashion culture, competition, demographics, and consumer preferences have lead to the Gap's brand identity. **Availability:** Online.

3113 ■ *"Fledgling Brands May Take the Fall With Steve & Barry's"* **in Advertising Age (Vol. 79, July 7, 2008, No. 26, pp. 6)**
Pub: Crain Communications, Inc.
Contact: Jessica Botos, Manager, Marketing
E-mail: jessica.botos@crainsnewyork.com
Ed: Natalie Zmuda. **Description:** Steve & Barry's, a retailer that holds licensing deals with a number of designers and celebrities, may have to declare bankruptcy; this leaves the fate of the retailer's hundreds of licensing deals and exclusive celebrity lines in question. **Availability:** Online.

3114 ■ *"Forget Your Pants, Calvin Klein Wants Into Your Bedroom"* **in Globe & Mail (March 31, 2007, pp. B4)**
Ed: Barrie McKenna. **Description:** The plans of Phillips-Van Heusen Corp. to open more Calvin Klein stores for selling the new ranges of clothing, personal care products, luggage and mattresses are discussed. **Availability:** Online.

3115 ■ *"From New York to Park Avenue: Red Carpet Fashion at a Discount"* **in Orlando Business Journal (Vol. 30, February 14, 2014, No. 34, pp. 3)**
Pub: American City Business Journals, Inc.
Contact: Mike Olivieri, Executive Vice President
Released: Weekly. **Price:** $8, introductory 4-week offer(Digital & Print). **Description:** Red Carpet Couture & Gems is known for selling high-end discount business attire and accessories. Owner, Caralyce Buford decided to buy from sample sales in

New York before opening the store in October 2013. Her retail store caters to women of all sizes. **Availability:** Print; Online.

3116 ■ *"Girls Will Gossip: Psst! Buzz About Target"* in *Barron's (Vol. 89, July 27, 2009, No. 30, pp. 15)*
Pub: Dow Jones & Company Inc.
Contact: Almar Latour, Chief Executive Officer
Ed: Katherine Cheng. **Description:** Target rebutted the rumor that they will disassociate themselves from a line of clothing inspired by the television show 'Gossip Girl'. Target's spokesman says that the retailer intends to remain closely identified with the show. Target's sales should benefit from the hotly anticipated clothing line. **Availability:** Online.

3117 ■ *"Goodwill, the Original Thrift Store, Goes Digital"* in *The Business of Fashion (June 11, 2019)*
URL(s): www.businessoffashion.com/articles/news-bites/goodwill-the-original-thrift-store-goes-digital
Released: June 11, 2019. **Description:** Goodwill, America's staple thrift store chain, has teamed up with OfferUp to sell it's goods online. **Availability:** Online.

3118 ■ *"Gowns Ready to Go"* in *Houston Chronicle (June 3, 2010)*
Pub: Houston Chronicle
Ed: Molly Glentzer. **Description:** Wedding gowns with slender silhouettes travel well for destination weddings. Amsale, Oscar del la Renta and Monique Lhuillier dresses are highlighted. **Availability:** Online.

3119 ■ *"Green It Like You Mean It"* in *Special Events Magazine (Vol. 28, February 1, 2009, No. 2)*
Description: Eco-friendly party planners offer advice for planning and hosting green parties or events. Tips include information for using recycled paper products, organic food and drinks. The Eco Nouveau Fashion Show held by Serene Star Productions reused old garments to create new fashions as well as art pieces from discarded doors and window frames for the show; eco-friendly treats and gift bags were highlighted at the event.

3120 ■ *"H&M Offers a Dress for Less"* in *Canadian Business (Vol. 83, September 14, 2010, No. 15, pp. 20)*
Pub: Rogers Media Inc.
Contact: Neil Spivak, Chief Executive Officer
Ed: Laura Cameron. **Description:** Swedish clothing company H&M has implemented loss leader strategy by pricing some dresses at extremely low prices. The economy has forced retailers to keep prices down despite the increasing cost of manufacturing, partly due to Chinese labor becoming more expensive. How the trend will affect apparel companies is discussed. **Availability:** Print; Online.

3121 ■ *"Hedge Funds Prevail In Merger"* in *Baltimore Business Journal (Vol. 31, March 21, 2014, No. 47, pp. 8)*
Pub: American City Business Journals, Inc.
Contact: Mike Olivieri, Executive Vice President
Released: Weekly. **Price:** $4, introductory 4-week offer(Digital & Print). **Description:** Contrary to expectations of the retail experts, after five months of internal strife, Jos. A Bank accepted Men's Wearhouse's offer and closed this hot deal. Men's Wearhouse purchased the Jos. A. Bank Clothiers Inc. for $1.8 billion and is planning to continue both brands. However, this will result in the Greater Baltimore area losing one more corporate headquarters. As the two companies combine operations, Jos. A. Banks stores will close, thus cutting more jobs. **Availability:** Print; Online.

3122 ■ *"Hoop Culture Opens Showroom, Expands Reach Globally"* in *Orlando Business Journal (Vol. 30, February 28, 2014, No. 36, pp. 3)*
Pub: American City Business Journals, Inc.
Contact: Mike Olivieri, Executive Vice President
Released: Weekly. **Description:** Hoop Culture Inc. president, Mike Brown, shares how the online basketball apparel retailer/wholesaler online store has expanded globally. He mentions that Orlando, Florida is one of their biggest markets. **Availability:** Print; Online.

3123 ■ *"How I Did It: Timberland's CEO On Standing Up to 65,000 Angry Activists"* in *Harvard Business Review (Vol. 88, September 2010, No. 9, pp. 39)*
Pub: Harvard Business Publishing
Contact: Diane Belcher, Managing Director
Ed: Jeff Swartz. **Price:** $8.95, PDF. **Description:** Timberland Company avoided a potential boycott by taking a two-way approach. It addressed a supplier issue that posed a threat to the environment, and launched an email campaign to keep Greenpeace activists informed of the development of a new supplier agreement. **Availability:** Online; PDF.

3124 ■ *"Image Consultants"* in *Entrepreneur (June 2014)*
Pub: Entrepreneur Media Inc.
Contact: Dan Bova, Director
E-mail: dbova@entrepreneur.com
Description: The ASAP54 mobile application, created by a company of the same name, uses visual recognition technology to help users determine the name of the designer or retailer of a clothing item using photographs. The company has compiled a database consisting of more than 1 million products from its retail partners. It claims an average of 5 percent commission on purchases completed through the application. Other useful wearable gadgets include Nymi, which authenticates identities based on cardiac rhythms, and Netatmo, a bracelet that measures daily sun exposure. **Availability:** Online.

3125 ■ *"It's So You! Consignment Shop Owner Thrilled to See Vision Come to Fruition"* in *News-Herald (August 27, 2010)*
Pub: The News Herald
Contact: Tricia Ambrose, Executive Editor
E-mail: tambrose@news-herald.com
Ed: Brandon C. Baker. **Description:** Profile of Laurel Howes and her It's So You! Boutique. The consignment shop is located in Willoughby's Pine Ride Plaza in Ohio. The shop targets all women, but particularly those who are not that comfortable with shopping consignment. **Availability:** Online.

3126 ■ *"Izod, Loft Outlets Coming To Tanger"* in *New Hampshire Business Review (Vol. 33, March 25, 2011, No. 6, pp. 30)*
Description: Izod and Lots stores will open at the Tanger Outlet Center in Tilton, New Hampshire. Both stores will feature fashions and accessories. **Availability:** Online.

3127 ■ *"Jordan Still Soaring"* in *Business Journal Portland (Vol. 30, January 17, 2014, No. 46, pp. 7)*
Pub: American City Business Journals, Inc.
Contact: Mike Olivieri, Executive Vice President
Released: Weekly. **Price:** $4, introductory 4-week offer(Digital only). **Description:** Nike Inc. is planning to open retail stores that will exclusively sell Jordan Brand merchandise. The company is seeking to grow its direct-to-consumer sales to $8 billion by 2017. Nike's capital spending is also expected to increase by 3 to 4 percent. **Availability:** Print; Online.

3128 ■ *"Juicy Couture (1997-2014) Couldn't Evolve When Its Cachet Dried Up"* in *Canadian Business (Vol. 87, July 2014, No. 7, pp. 16)*
Description: Fashion brand Juicy Couture was started by Pamela Skaist-Ley and Gela Nash-Taylor in Los Angeles, California in 1997 and was acquired by Fifth & Pacific Companies in 2003. Fifth & Pacific put Juicy Couture up for sale in fall 2013, with Authentic Brands Group owning the rights to the brand name for $195 million. The last of the Canadian outlets will close June 30, 2014. **Availability:** Online.

3129 ■ *"Longtime Peoria Heights Second-Hand Clothing Shop Closing"* in *Journal Star (December 18, 2010)*
Pub: Journal Star
Ed: Scott Hilyard. **Description:** The Happy Hangar, a consignment clothing store located in Peoria Heights, Illinois is closing after 31 years of selling second-hand clothing. **Availability:** Print; Online.

3130 ■ *"Luxury Still Sells Well"* in *Puget Sound Business Journal (Vol. 29, September 5, 2008, No. 20, pp. 1)*
Description: High fashion retailers are planning to open stores in the Puget Sound area despite the economic slowdown, citing high incomes in the area despite the weak U.S. dollar.

3131 ■ *"Making It Work"* in *Retail Merchandiser (Vol. 51, July-August 2011, No. 4, pp. 43)*
Description: Profile of Anthony DiPaolo and his purchase of the Work 'N Gear retail store in 2002. The brick and mortar shop sells work wear and healthcare apparel and DiPaolo believes customer respect is essential to his success. **Availability:** Online.

3132 ■ *"Military Brides Can Get Free Wedding Gowns"* in *Virginian-Pilot (November 10, 2010)*
Pub: The Virginian-Pilot
Contact: Kevin Goyette, Director
E-mail: kgoyette@dailypress.com
Ed: Jamesetta M. Walker. **Description:** Seventy-five designer wedding gowns will be given to military brides on a first-come, first-served basis at Maya Couture through the Brides Across America's wedding gown giveaway program. Gowns are valued between $500 to $3,000 and are donated by designers Maggie Sottero, Pronovias and Essense of Australia. **Availability:** Online.

3133 ■ *"New Beat for Marley's Daughter: Offspring of Reggae Royalty Opens Vintage Clothing Shop with Pal"* in *Los Angeles Business Journal (Vol. 34, March 12, 2012, No. 11, pp. 3)*
Pub: CBJ L.P.
Contact: Laura Garrett, Vice President Publisher
E-mail: garrett@ocbj.com
Ed: Bethany Firnhaber. **Description:** Karen Marley, daughter of famous reggae musician Bob Marley, explains her passion for vintage clothing. Karen and her fried Monique Aquino have partnered to open a resale consignment store in Los Angeles selling designer and vintage clothing. **Availability:** Online.

3134 ■ *"The Ode: S. M. Whitney Co. (1868 – 2010)"* in *Canadian Business (Vol. 83, October 12, 2010, No. 17, pp. 27)*
Pub: Rogers Media Inc.
Contact: Neil Spivak, Chief Executive Officer
Ed: Angelina Chapin. **Released:** October 12, 2010. **Description:** A history of S.M. Whitney Company is presented. The cotton company was opened in 1868. The cotton is sold to textile manufacturers after crops have been picked, ginned and baled. The company closed down in 2010 after chief executive officer Barry Whitney decided to sell his last bale of cotton. **Availability:** Print; Online.

3135 ■ *"Owners Consider Remodeling Westlake Center"* in *Puget Sound Business Journal (Vol. 33, September 28, 2012, No. 23, pp. 1)*
Pub: Baltimore Business Journal
Contact: Rhonda Pringle, President
E-mail: rpringle@bizjournals.com
Ed: Jeanne Lang Jones. **Description:** General Growth Properties Inc. is considering a major remodel of the Westlake Center shopping mall in Seattle, Washington and international fashion chain Zara is negotiating for space at Westlake. Such activities benefit the city's retailers and landlords along with providing a broader civic benefit to the town square. **Availability:** Print; Online.

3136 ■ "Panera Breadwinner Tries on Tattu Designer Jeans" in Houston Business Journal (Vol. 40, December 18, 2009, No. 32, pp. 1)
Pub: Houston Business Journal
Contact: Bob Charlet, President
E-mail: bcharlet@bizjournals.com

Ed: Allison Wollam. Description: Chuck Cain, the franchisee who introduced Panera Bread to Houston, Texas has partnered with tax accountant Jim Jacobsen to introduce custom-make Tattu Jeans. As more Tattu Jeans outlets are being planned, Cain is using entrepreneurial lessons learned from Panera Bread in the new venture. Both Panera Bread and Tattu Jeans were opened by Cain during economic downturns. Availability: Print; Online.

3137 ■ "Pending Shutdown of Coldwater Creek Will Affect Eight Stores In Massachusetts" in Boston Business Journal (Vol. 34, April 11, 2014, No. 10)
Pub: American City Business Journals, Inc.
Contact: Mike Olivieri, Executive Vice President

Released: Weekly. Description: Coldwater Creek's pending closure of its stores will adversely affect Massachusetts malls. The women's clothing retailer filed for Chapter 11 bankruptcy to help smooth the pending closures after being unable to find a potential buyer. The company's revenue dropped to $743 million in 2012, down dramatically from the $1.1 billion reported in 2006. Availability: Print; Online.

3138 ■ "Pink Label: Victoria's Sales Secret" in Advertising Age (Vol. 79, July 7, 2008, No. 26, pp. 4)
Pub: Crain Communications, Inc.
Contact: Jessica Botos, Manager, Marketing
E-mail: jessica.botos@crainsnewyork.com

Ed: Natalie Zmuda. Description: Victoria Secret's Pink label accounted for roughly 17 percent of the retailer's total sales last year. The company is launching a Collegiate Collection which will be promoted by a campus tour program. Availability: Print; Online.

3139 ■ "Portland Wooing Under Armour to West Coast Facility" in Baltimore Business Journal (Vol. 27, January 29, 2010, No. 39, pp. 1)
Pub: Baltimore Business Journal
Contact: Rhonda Pringle, President
E-mail: rpringle@bizjournals.com

Ed: Andy Giegerich. Description: Baltimore, Maryland sports apparel maker, Under Armour, is planning a west coast expansion with Portland, Oregon among the sites considered to house its apparel and footwear design center. Portland officials counting on the concentration of nearly 10,000 activewear workers in the city will help lure the company to the city. Availability: Print; Online.

3140 ■ "Revive To Sell Women's Apparel in Downtown Space" in Memphis Business Journal (Vol. 33, February 3, 2012, No. 43, pp. 1)
Pub: Baltimore Business Journal
Contact: Rhonda Pringle, President
E-mail: rpringle@bizjournals.com

Ed: Andy Ashby. Description: Revive has signed a rental agreement with Memphis Commerce Square Partners LLC for the vacant space at One Commerce Square in Memphis, Tennessee. Revive plans to sell women's clothing, shoes and accessories in the downtown space. Availability: Print; Online.

3141 ■ "Rule of the Masses: Reinventing Fashion Via Crowdsourcing" in WWD (Vol. 200, July 26, 2010, No. 17, pp. 1)
Pub: Conde Nast Publications
Contact: Agnes Chu, President

Ed: Cate T. Corcoran. Description: Large apparel brands and retailers are crowdsourcing as a way to increase customer loyalty and to build their businesses. Availability: PDF; Download; Online.

3142 ■ "The Smell of Fear: Is a Bottom Near?" in Barron's (Vol. 88, March 17, 2008, No. 11, pp. M3)
Pub: Dow Jones & Company Inc.
Contact: Almar Latour, Chief Executive Officer

Ed: Kopin Tan. Description: Liquidity problems at Bear Stearns frightened investors in markets around the world due to the fear of the prospects of a big bank's failure. Shares of health maintenance organizations got battered led by WellPoint, and Humana but longer-term investors who could weather short-term volatility may find value here. The value of J. Crew shares is also discussed. Availability: Online.

3143 ■ "Suited for Success" in Retail Merchandiser (Vol. 51, July-August 2011, No. 4, pp. 6)
Description: MyBestFit is a size-matching body scanner that helps consumers find the perfect size clothing for themselves, giving brick and mortar retailers an edge on ecommerce competitors. Availability: Online.

3144 ■ "ThredUp Is Helping Big Stores Sell Recyled Clothes" in Quartzy (August 21, 2019)
URL(s): qz.com/quartzy/1692050/thredup-is-giving-retailers-a-plug-and-play-platform-to-sell-used-clothes/

Ed: Marc Bain. Released: August 21, 2019. Description: ThredUp has announced its new program, Resale-As-A-Servie (RAAS), which will allow big box clothes retailers to sell directly from its used clothing inventory. Availability: Online.

3145 ■ Too Good to be Threw: The Complete Operations Manual for Resale & Consignment Shops
Pub: Katydid Press

Ed: Kate Holmes. Price: $76.95. Description: Revised edition covers all the information needed to start and run a buy-outright or consignment shop, covering anything from clothing to furniture resale.

3146 ■ "The Transparent Supply Chain" in Harvard Business Review (Vol. 88, October 2010, No. 10, pp. 76)
Pub: Harvard Business Publishing
Contact: Diane Belcher, Managing Director

Ed: Steve New. Price: $8.95, PDF. Description: Examination of the use of new technologies to create a transparent supply chain, such as next-generation 2D bar codes in clothing labels that can provide data on a garment's provenance. Availability: Online; PDF.

3147 ■ "Trousseaus of Memories Trail Behind Wedding Gowns" in Oregonian (September 4, 2010)
Pub: The Oregonian
Contact: John Maher, President

Ed: Anne Saker. Description: Readers are asked to share stories about their wedding gowns and what that garment meant to them at the time and now. Availability: Online.

3148 ■ "Under Armour Wants to Equip Athletes, Too" in Boston Business Journal (Vol. 29, July 8, 2011, No. 9, pp. 1)
Pub: Boston Business Journal
Contact: Carolyn M. Jones, President
E-mail: cmjones@bizjournals.com

Ed: Ryan Sharrow. Description: Baltimore sportswear maker Under Armour advances plans to enter into the equipment field, aiming to strengthen its hold on football, basketball and lacrosse markets where it already has a strong market share. The company is now cooking up licensing deals to bolster the firm's presence among athletes. Availability: Print; Online.

3149 ■ "Under Armour's Founder On Learning to Leverage Celebrity Endorsements" in Harvard Business Review (Vol. 90, May 2012, No. 5, pp. 45)
Pub: Harvard Business Review Press
Contact: Moderna V. Pfizer, Contact

Ed: Kevin Plank. Description: Using his athletic apparel company Under Armour as an illustration, the author identifies two key points in effective utilization of endorsement advertising: balancing freebies with fair-price contracts, and offering stock opportunities so that celebrities can be personally engaged with growth.

3150 ■ "Uptick in Clicks: Nordstrom's Online Sales Surging" in Puget Sound Business Journal (Vol. 29, August 22, 2008, No. 18, pp. 1)
Description: Nordstrom Inc.'s online division grew its sales by 15 percent in the second quarter of 2008, compared to 2007's 4.3 percent in overall decline. The company expects their online net sales to reach $700 million in 2008 capturing eight percent of overall sales. Availability: Print; Online.

3151 ■ "Vision Statement: How This First Lady Moves Markets" in Harvard Business Review (Vol. 88, November 2010, No. 11, pp. 38)
Pub: Harvard Business Publishing
Contact: Diane Belcher, Managing Director

Ed: David Yermack. Price: $6, PDF. Description: A chart is presented demonstrating how First Lady Michelle Obama's choice of fashion designer has impacted the clothing industry. Availability: Online; PDF.

3152 ■ "Wave of Resale, Consignment Shops Pop Up In Springs" in Gazette (March 19, 2012)
Ed: Bill Radford. Description: The depressed economy has spurred the growth of consignment shops across the nation. Colorado Springs, Colorado area urges people to shop at these resale locations because they promote green initiatives by recycling goods. WeeCycle, Knit Wits, Once Upon a Child and Re-Generation, Moutain Equipment Recyclers, and Gearonimo, are among the established consignment stores in the area. Availability: Print.

3153 ■ "What's More Important: Talent or Engagement? A Study With Retailer ANN INC. Seeks To Find the Essential Ingredients To High-Performing Managers and Employees" in Gallup Business Journal (April 22, 2014)
Pub: Gallup, Inc.
Contact: Jon Clifton, Chief Executive Officer

Description: ANN INC. is a leading women's clothing retailer that is exploring the necessary steps to achieving both high-performing managers and employees. The firm found that hiring people with the right talent and engaging them will maximize performance. Availability: Online.

3154 ■ "Why the Gap is Stalking Lululemon" in Canadian Business (Vol. 85, August 22, 2012, No. 14, pp. 7)
Ed: Jim Sutherland. Description: Lululemon Athletica is facing competition against Gap Inc.'s Athleta as the retail giant plans to have about 50 new shops across Canada by the end of 2012. Athleta is also carrying lines of yoga- and activewear similar to that of Lululemon's and are even located near their stores. Availability: Online.

3155 ■ "Zacks Industry Outlook Highlights: Starbucks, Nike, Big Lots, Deckers Outdoor and Family Dollar Stores" in PR Newswire (August 8, 2012)
Pub: PR Newswire Association LLC.

Description: Zacks takes a look at the retail industry and covers the outlook for this highly competitive sector. Retailers discussed include: Starbucks Corporation, Nike Inc., Big Lots Inc., Deckers Outdoor Corporation, and Family Dollar Stores Inc. Availability: Online.

3156 ■ "Zara Eludes the Pain in Spain: Clothing Giant Inditex Sees Its First-Quarter Profits Rise By 30 Percent" in Canadian Business (Vol. 85, September 17, 2012, No. 14, pp. 67)
Ed: Bryan Borzykowski. Released: September 17, 2012. Description: Clothing retailer Inditex reported a 30 percent increase in profit in the first quarter of

2012 and 15 percent increase in sales year over year. The company's unique business model was attributed to its growth, which also appeals to income investors.

STATISTICAL SOURCES

3157 ■ *Men's Clothing Stores Industry in the US - Market Research Report*
URL(s): www.ibisworld.com/united-states/market-research-reports/mens-clothing-stores-industry/
Price: $925. **Description:** Downloadable report analyzing the current and future trends in the men's clothing store industry. **Availability:** Online.

3158 ■ *RMA Annual Statement Studies*
Pub: Risk Management Association
Contact: Nancy Foster, President
Released: Annual. **Description:** Contains composite balance sheets and income statements for more than 360 industries, including the accounting, auditing, and bookkeeping industries. Also contains five years of comparative historical data for discerning trends. Includes 16 commonly used ratios, computed for most of the size groupings for nearly every industry.

3159 ■ *Standard & Poor's Industry Surveys*
Pub: Standard And Poor's Financial Services LLC.
Contact: Douglas L. Peterson, President
Description: Two-volume book that examines the prospects for specific industries, including trucking. Also provides analyses of trends and problems, statistical tables and charts, and comparative company analyses.

3160 ■ *Women's Clothing Stores Industry in the US - Market Research Report*
URL(s): www.ibisworld.com/united-states/market-research-reports/womens-clothing-stores-industry/
Price: $925. **Description:** Downloadable report analyzing the current and future trends in the women's clothing store industry. **Availability:** Online.

VIDEO/AUDIO MEDIA

3161 ■ *The How of Business: Adam Siegel - Fashion Resale Business*
Released: January 01, 2024. **Description:** Podcast discusses the details of starting a tech-enabled resale business.

3162 ■ *Main Street Business Insights: Danny Reynolds, Stephenson's Clothing*
URL(s): mainstreet.org/resources/knowledge-hub/podcast/danny-reynolds-stephensons-clothing
Ed: Matt Wagner. **Released:** October 04, 2023. **Description:** Podcast discusses the legacy of a longtime fashion retailer.

3163 ■ *Marketplace: The Second-Hand Clothing Reseller Who's Bundling Up Style*
URL(s): www.marketplace.org/2023/08/17/secondhand-clothing-resale-bella-mcminn
Ed: Livi Burdette. **Released:** August 17, 2023. **Description:** Podcast explains how a business student turned her side hustle to see old clothing into a possible career.

TRADE SHOWS AND CONVENTIONS

3164 ■ Independent Retailers Buying Group Spring Trade Show
URL(s): n2b.goexposoftware.com/events/wbg22sp/goExpo/public/login.php
Frequency: Annual. **Description:** Retailer tradeshow with a focus on shooting sports, sporting goods, and fall/winter apparel and footwear. **Principal Exhibits:** Retailer tradeshow with a focus on shooting sports, sporting goods, and fall/winter apparel and footwear.

3165 ■ New England Apparel Club
New England Apparel Club (NEAC)
69 Milk St., Ste. 96
Westborough, MA 01581
Ph: (781)326-9223
Fax: (781)326-6892
URL: http://neacshow.com
Contact: David Murphy, President
URL(s): neacshow.com/show/manchester-signature-show-mar-2025
Frequency: Irregular. **Description:** Clothing and related equipment, supplies, and services. **Audience:** Wholesale sales representatives and qualified retailers. **Principal Exhibits:** Clothing and related equipment, supplies, and services.

3166 ■ Trendz Show
Florida Fashion Focus, Inc.
URL(s): www.trendzshow.com/show-dates
Frequency: Irregular. **Description:** Ladies ready-to-wear clothing, handbags, jewelry, and accessories. Order-writing for future delivery. **Audience:** Industry professionals. **Principal Exhibits:** Ladies ready-to-wear clothing, handbags, jewelry, and accessories. Order-writing for future delivery. Dates and Locations: Palm Beach County Convention Center, Palm Beach, FL.

FRANCHISES AND BUSINESS OPPORTUNITIES

3167 ■ Children's Orchard (CO)
13625 Grove Dr.
Maple Grove, MN 55311
Ph: (952)232-5603
Co. E-mail: maplegrove@childrensorchard.com
URL: http://www.childrensorchard.com
Facebook: www.facebook.com/ChildOrchard
Instagram: www.instagram.com/childrensorchard
Description: Children's upscale/resale retail store. **No. of Franchise Units:** 93. **No. of Company-Owned Units:** 1. **Founded:** 1980. **Franchised:** 1985. **Equity Capital Needed:** $115,600-$197,000. **Franchise Fee:** $25,000. **Royalty Fee:** 5%. **Training:** Provides 12 days training at headquarters, 3 days onsite and ongoing support.

3168 ■ Compuchild
Compuchild Services of America
3736 Fallon Rd., Ste. 125
Dublin, CA 94568
Ph: (317)817-9817
Free: 800-619-5437
Fax: (317)818-8184
Contact: Shubhra Kant, President
Facebook: www.facebook.com/CompuChild
Linkedin: www.linkedin.com/company/compuchild/about
X (Twitter): x.com/CompuChild
Instagram: www.instagram.com/compuchild_franchise
YouTube: www.youtube.com/channel/UCEHzHydnaCoZKj_Ut5piemg
Pinterest: www.pinterest.com/compuchild
Description: Computer education to children. **No. of Franchise Units:** 69. **No. of Company-Owned Units:** 1. **Founded:** 1994. **Franchised:** 1995. **Equity Capital Needed:** $15,000. **Franchise Fee:** $12,500 or $17,500. **Financial Assistance:** Yes **Training:** Yes.

3169 ■ Fully Promoted (FP)
2121 Vista Pky.
West Palm Beach, FL 33411
Free: 800-727-6720
URL: http://fullypromoted.com
Contact: Michael Brugger, President
Facebook: www.facebook.com/fullypromoted.corporate
Linkedin: www.linkedin.com/company/fully-promoted
X (Twitter): x.com/fullypromoted
Instagram: www.instagram.com/fullypromoted
YouTube: www.youtube.com/channel/UCBAgIKlUgbV3JEYN8IejFoQ
Pinterest: pinterest.com/FullyPromoted
Description: Custom apparel and merchandise specializing in embroidered pieces. **Founded:** 2000. **Training:** 4 weeks of training, marketing, merchandising and support (2 weeks in FL, 2 weeks onsite) and ongoing support.

LIBRARIES

3170 ■ Conde Nast Publications Library and Information Services
1 World Trade Ctr.
New York, NY 10007
Co. E-mail: communications@condenast.com
URL: http://www.condenast.com
Contact: Roger Lynch, Chief Executive Officer
Linkedin: www.linkedin.com/company/conde-nast
X (Twitter): x.com/condenast
Instagram: www.instagram.com/condenast
Description: Produces in-depth research for the world's most celebrated media brands. **Scope:** Fashion; houses; gardens; home furnishings; interior design; health; personalities; photographs. **Services:** Library not open to public. **Founded:** 1935. **Holdings:** 7,000 volumes.

3171 ■ Fashion Institute of Design and Merchandising (FIDM) - Library
919 S Grand Ave.
Los Angeles, CA 90015
Ph: (213)624-1200
Free: 800-624-1200
URL: http://fidm.edu
Contact: Tonian Hohberg, President
Facebook: www.facebook.com/FIDMCollege
Linkedin: www.linkedin.com/school/fidm
X (Twitter): x.com/FIDM
YouTube: www.youtube.com/fidm
Pinterest: www.pinterest.com/fidm
Scope: Textile design and research; fashion; business and marketing; interior design; retailing and costumes. **Services:** Copying; interlibrary loan. **Founded:** 1969. **Subscriptions:** 200 magazines Books; periodicals; publications; newspapers; DVDs; CDs.

3172 ■ State University of New York - Fashion Institute of Technology - Gladys Marcus Library
227 W 27th St.
New York, NY 10001-5992
Ph: (212)217-7999
URL: http://www.fitnyc.edu/library/index.php
Description: Library supports the academic and research needs of the institute. **Scope:** Fashion, fashion history, textiles, fashion trend forecasting. **Services:** Interlibrary loan; library open by appointment. **Founded:** 1944. **Holdings:** 300,000 print, non-print, and electronic materials, including sketch collections, clipping files, and fashion show DVDs.

Coffee Service

ASSOCIATIONS AND OTHER ORGANIZATIONS

3173 ■ National Coffee Association of U.S.A. Inc. (NCA)
45 Broadway, Ste. 1140
New York, NY 10006
Ph: (212)766-4007
Fax: (212)766-5815
Co. E-mail: info@ncausa.org
URL: http://www.ncausa.org
Contact: William Murray, President
E-mail: wmmurray@ncausa.org
Facebook: www.facebook.com/nationalcoffeeassociation
X (Twitter): x.com/nationalcoffee
Description: Green coffee importers, jobbers, brokers, and agents; instant coffee and liquid extract processors; roasters and allied coffee industries; exporters; retailers. Promotes sound business relations and mutual understanding among members of the trade. Collects and publishes consumer, market and technical information on the coffee industry. **Founded:** 1911. **Publications:** *Coffee Reporter Weekly* (Weekly); *CoffeeTrax* (Quarterly); *National Coffee Data Trends (NCDT)* (Semiannual); *US Coffee Industry Review 2005*; *The Coffee Reporter* (Weekly). **Educational Activities:** National Coffee Association of U.S.A. Annual Convention (Annual). **Geographic Preference:** National.

3174 ■ Specialty Coffee Association (SCA)
117 W 4th St., Ste. 300
Santa Ana, CA 92701
Ph: (562)624-4100
Co. E-mail: membership@sca.coffee
URL: http://sca.coffee
Contact: Colleen Anunu, President
Facebook: www.facebook.com/SpecialtyCoffeeAssociation
Linkedin: www.linkedin.com/company/3481060
X (Twitter): x.com/SpecialtyCoffee
Instagram: www.instagram.com/specialtycoffeeassociation
YouTube: www.youtube.com/SpecialtyCoffeeAssociation/featured
Description: Coffee roasters, green coffee brokers, retailers, distributors, and others involved in the gourmet coffee industry. Provides business, professional, promotional, and educational assistance in the areas of cultivation, processing, preparation, and marketing of specialty coffee; increase consumer awareness, understanding, and consumption of specialty coffee. **Founded:** 2017. **Publications:** *Specialty Coffee Association of America--Member Directory*. **Educational Activities:** SCAA Planning Meeting; Re:co Symposium (Annual); SCAA Leadership Summit. **Awards:** SCAA Achievement Awards (Annual); SCAA Sustainability Award (Annual); SCAA Best New Product (Annual); Mose Drachman Sales and Service Award (Annual). **Geographic Preference:** National.

REFERENCE WORKS

3175 ■ *5 Impactful Ways to Grow Your Coffee Business This Year*
Ed: Bruce Hakutizwi. **Description:** There are a number of ways that boutique and independent coffee shops can become financially sustainable and deliver a satisfactory return on investment, with the right tools in place. This article discusses the top five ways to grow your coffee business. **Availability:** Online.

3176 ■ *"10 Startup Tips From Affordable Franchise Coffee News" in Small Business Trends (September 12, 2017)*
Ed: Gabrielle Pickard-Whitehead. **Released:** September 12, 2017. **Description:** Provides ten important business tips for coffee service startups from a small business owner who has grown to reach international success. **Availability:** Online.

3177 ■ *Coffee Business Technology*
Ed: John Lister. **Description:** Technology is a key part of running a coffee shop from coffee machines and self-service to contactless payment and customer data. This article details technology you should consider and how it will benefit your business. **Availability:** Online.

3178 ■ *"Coffee Shop Startup Costs" in Cardconnect.com*
Description: This article provides in-depth information on opening your own coffee shop from business planning, equipment, and hiring to inventory, vendors, and marketing. **Availability:** Online.

3179 ■ *"Coinstar, Inc. and Seattle's Best Coffee Sign Exclusive Agreement to Roll Out Thousands of the New Rubi Kiosks in Grocery, Drug and Mass Channels" in Marketing Weekly News (June 23 2012, pp. 77)*
Pub: PR Newswire Association LLC.
Description: Seattles' Best Coffee, a firm of Starbucks Corporation, has partnered with Coinstar Inc. to install coffee kiosks in grocery, drug and mass merchant retailers featuring Seattle's Best coffee drinks. Rubi kiosk is the third automated kiosk owned by Coinstar. Details of the deal are included.

3180 ■ *"Colombia's Green Coffee Company Earns RA Certification for All It's Farms" in Daily Coffee News (November 26, 2021)*
Ed: Nick Brown. **Released:** November 26, 2021. **Description:** Discusses Green Coffee Company attaining the Rainforest Alliance certification for all of its farms and how the company is looking to further enhance its sustainable practices.

3181 ■ *"Grounds for Success" in Canadian Business (Vol. 87, July 2014, No. 7, pp. 73)*
Description: ECS Coffee Inc. has continued to evolve its business of selling single-serve brewing systems and market changes and growing competitors. The company has seen growth of 1,026 percent from 2008 to 2013, earning it the top 69 spot in the 2014 Profit ranking of fastest growing companies in Canada. **Availability:** Online.

3182 ■ *"How Coffee Producers Can Adapt to Climate Change" in Perfect Daily Grind (November 7, 2019)*
URL(s): www.perfectdailygrind.com/2019/11/how-coffee-producers-can-adapt-to-climate-change/
Ed: Sarah Charles. **Released:** November 07, 2019. **Description:** Examines how climate change can and will affect coffee producers since most growers are smaller farms and the crop needs a specific temperature and rainfall pattern. Pest and diseases are also detrimental to coffee crops and climate change has released these outbreaks as well. Included are suggestions to help offset damage from climate change. **Availability:** Online.

3183 ■ *"How to Run Your Own Coffee Shop" in Investopedia (December 2, 2019)*
Ed: Jesse Neugarten. **Released:** December 02, 2019. **Description:** If you dream of owning a coffee shop, however, with hard work, solid experience, analytical skills, and a well-designed business plan, you can succeed. Understanding the economics of owning a coffee shop is a vital step. This article provides details about startup costs, fixed costs, variable costs, and ergonomics. **Availability:** Online.

3184 ■ *How to Start a Coffee Shop in a Small Town*
Ed: Frankie Wallace. **Released:** January 11, 2020. **Description:** Every small town needs a cozy hangout spot for coffee, baked goods, and conversation. This article details things you need to know to start a coffee shop in a small town from legal issues to marketing. **Availability:** Online.

3185 ■ *"How to Start a Successful Coffee Shop" in The Balance Small Business (December 5, 2019)*
Ed: Susan Ward. **Released:** December 05, 2019. **Description:** Serving quality coffees and snacks in a trendy, relaxing atmosphere is a hugely successful business model. If you are looking for a business opportunity in the coffee industry, this article provides a guide to startup and success. **Availability:** Online.

3186 ■ *How to Start a Thriving Drive-Thru Coffee Shop*
Ed: Larry Alton. **Description:** While owning a drive-thru coffee shop can be profitable, there are some lesser-known secrets to creating a thriving coffee business. This article discusses 5 tips to consider to increase profitability. **Availability:** Online.

3187 ■ *"Nespresso Professional Introduces Momento Line for Office Service" in Vending Times (October 8, 2019)*
URL(s): www.vendingtimes.com/articles/nespresso-professional-introduces-momento-line-for-12994
Ed: Tim Sanford. **Released:** October 08, 2019. **Description:** Nespresso Professional has launched its intuitive coffee system, Nespresso Momento. This

one-touch system features fully-recyclable single-serve aluminum capsules to serve up coffee and Americanos. Designed from feedback obtained from offices, this machine should meet the needs of the office. **Availability:** Online.

3188 ■ *"One Thing You Can Do: Brew a Greener Cup of Coffee" in The New York Times (March 27, 2019)*
URL(s): www.nytimes.com/2019/03/27/climate/nyt-climate-newsletter-coffee.html
Ed: Tik Root, Somini Sengupta. **Released:** March 27, 2019. **Description:** Practical tips on making coffee that lowers the environmental impact. There are beans that can be bought and used that are sourced with care, and ditching those single-serve pods. Cutting back on electricity and using a press is also a good idea. **Availability:** Online.

3189 ■ *"Pumpkin Spice is Coming Early to Dunkin' and Starbucks" in The New York Times (August 13, 2019)*
URL(s): www.nytimes.com/2019/08/13/business/pumpkin-spice-starbucks-dunkin.html
Ed: Emily S. Rueb. **Released:** August 13, 2019. **Description:** Is it too soon to start serving pumpkin lattes? Dunkin' and Starbucks don't think so and are rolling out the popular spiced drinks a week earlier than usual this August. This is due to customer feedback and an attempt to capitalize on the popularity of the famous fall beverage. **Availability:** Online.

3190 ■ *"Starbucks and Alibaba Launch Voice Ordering and Delivery" in Vending Times (October 4, 2019)*
URL(s): www.vendingtimes.com/articles/starbucks-and-alibaba-launch-voice-ordering-and-de-12983
Ed: Emily Jed. **Released:** October 04, 2019. **Description:** Starbucks is expanding its hold on coffee delivery by teaming up with Alibaba and launching voice ordering with the smart speaker, Tmall Genie. This service is currently only available in China. **Availability:** Online.

3191 ■ *Starting a Coffee Service Business*
Description: Starting a coffee service business is your ticket to owning a good, stable business but it's important to plan out the business in detail before you start. This article provides nuts-and-bolts information to improve your startup process. **Availability:** Online.

3192 ■ *"What Does It Costs to Open a Coffee Shop?" in The New York Times (October 17, 2019)*
URL(s): www.nytimes.com/2019/10/17/business/cost-to-open-coffee-shop.html
Ed: Julia Rothman, Shaina Feinberg. **Released:** October 17, 2019. **Description:** This illustrated article outlines the true costs of opening a coffee shop, the high cost of rent, the price of drinks, and how others in the business stay afloat. **Availability:** Online.

3193 ■ *Why Start a Mobile Coffee Business?*
Description: A mobile coffee business is a great way to enter into the retail coffee industry while reducing the inherent risk and financial burden of starting a brick-and-mortar coffee business. This article discusses different types of mobile coffee businesses as well as how to grow and develop your mobile coffee business. **Availability:** Online.

3194 ■ *"Zacks Industry Outlook Highlights: Starbucks, Nike, Big Lots, Deckers Outdoor and Family Dollar Stores" in PR Newswire (August 8, 2012)*
Pub: PR Newswire Association LLC.
Description: Zacks takes a look at the retail industry and covers the outlook for this highly competitive sector. Retailers discussed include: Starbucks Corporation, Nike Inc., Big Lots Inc., Deckers Outdoor Corporation, and Family Dollar Stores Inc. **Availability:** Online.

SOURCES OF SUPPLY

3195 ■ *Automatic Merchandiser--Blue Book Buyer's Guide Issue*
Contact: Michael Martin, President
URL(s): www.vendingmarketwatch.com/directorywww.vendingmarketwatch.com
Ed: Elliot Maras. **Released:** Annual **Description:** Publication includes suppliers of products, services, and equipment to the merchandise vending, contract foodservice, and office coffee service industries. **Entries include:** Company name, address, phone, names of executives, trade and brand names, and products or services offered. **Arrangement:** Classified by type of business. **Indexes:** Alphabetical, product. **Availability:** Print; Online.

STATISTICAL SOURCES

3196 ■ *Coffee & Snack Shops Industry in the US - Market Research Report*
URL(s): www.ibisworld.com/united-states/market-research-reports/coffee-snack-shops-industry/
Price: $925. **Description:** Downloadable report analyzing the coffee and snack shop industry and projecting growth through the year 2026. Delivers key concepts and industry outlooks. **Availability:** Download.

3197 ■ *The Retail Market for Coffee Industry in the US - Market Research Report*
URL(s): www.ibisworld.com/united-states/market-research-reports/the-retail-market-for-coffee-industry/
Price: $925. **Description:** Downloadable report analyzing current and future trends in the retail coffee industry. **Availability:** Online.

3198 ■ *Standard & Poor's Industry Surveys*
Pub: Standard And Poor's Financial Services LLC.
Contact: Douglas L. Peterson, President
Description: Two-volume book that examines the prospects for specific industries, including trucking. Also provides analyses of trends and problems, statistical tables and charts, and comparative company analyses.

TRADE PERIODICALS

3199 ■ *Automatic Merchandiser: The Monthly Management Magazine for Vending and OCS Professionals*
Contact: Denise Singsime, Manager, Sales
E-mail: denise.singsime@vendingmarketwatch.com
Released: Monthly **Price:** Free. **Description:** Vending and office coffee service industry trade magazine. **Availability:** Print; Online.

VIDEO/AUDIO MEDIA

3200 ■ *How I Built My Small Business: Danielle Connor - A Successful Local Coffee Shop Can Make How Much? Retrograde Coffee Roasters Reveals Secrets*
URL(s): www.annemcginty.com/transcripts/danielleconnor
Ed: Anne McGinty. **Released:** July 22, 2024. **Description:** Podcast features the founder of a green coffee roasting brand.

3201 ■ *How I Built This: Dutch Bros. Coffee: Travis Boersma*
URL(s): wondery.com/shows/how-i-built-this/episode/10386-dutch-bros-coffee-travis-boersma
Ed: Guy Raz. **Released:** June 26, 2023. **Description:** Podcast explains how a pushcart coffee business turned into multimillion IPO.

TRADE SHOWS AND CONVENTIONS

3202 ■ *Atlantic Coast Exposition*
Virginia Automatic Merchandising Association (VAMA)
PO Box 4407
Cary, NC 27519
Ph: (919)387-1221
Fax: (919)249-1394
Co. E-mail: info@virginiavend.org
URL: http://vama.wildapricot.org
Contact: Karen Harlow, President
URL(s): atlanticcoastexpo.com/About-Us
Frequency: Annual. **Description:** Vending machines, office coffee service equipment, food stuffs, and related goods and services. **Audience:** Food service industry professionals. **Principal Exhibits:** Vending machines, office coffee service equipment, food stuffs, and related goods and services. Dates and Locations: Embassy Suites/Kingston Plantation, Myrtle Beach, SC; 2025 Oct 09-11 Embassy Suites/Kingston Plantation, Myrtle Beach; 2025 Oct 09-11 Embassy Suites/Kingston Plantation, Myrtle Beach, SC; 2026 Oct 08-10 Embassy Suites/Kingston Plantation, Myrtle Beach, SC. **Telecommunication Services:** info@atlanticcoastexpo.com.

3203 ■ *The Event - Specialty Coffee Association of America*
URL(s): coffeeexpo.org
Frequency: Annual. **Description:** In-depth tradeshow featuring everything needed in the coffee world. **Principal Exhibits:** In-depth tradeshow featuring everything needed in the coffee world.

3204 ■ *National Coffee Association of U.S.A. Annual Convention*
National Coffee Association of U.S.A. Inc. (NCA)
45 Broadway, Ste. 1140
New York, NY 10006
Ph: (212)766-4007
Fax: (212)766-5815
Co. E-mail: info@ncausa.org
URL: http://www.ncausa.org
Contact: William Murray, President
E-mail: wmmurray@ncausa.org
URL(s): www.ncausa.org/Industry-Resources/NCA-Annual-Convention
Frequency: Annual. **Description:** Exhibits relating to coffee and the industry. **Audience:** Industry professionals. **Principal Exhibits:** Exhibits relating to coffee and the industry. Dates and Locations: 2025 Mar 06-08 The Marriott Marquis Houston, Houston, TX. **Telecommunication Services:** tana@stellatosolutions.com.

FRANCHISES AND BUSINESS OPPORTUNITIES

3205 ■ *Blenz Coffee*
220-21320 Gordon Way
Richmond, BC, Canada V6W 1J8
Ph: (604)682-2995
Co. E-mail: concerns@blenz.com
URL: http://blenz.com
Facebook: www.facebook.com/BlenzCoffee
X (Twitter): x.com/BlenzCoffee
Instagram: www.instagram.com/BlenzCoffee
Description: Chain of coffee shop. **Founded:** 1992. **Training:** Yes.

3206 ■ *Cafe Ala Carte*
19512 S Coquina Way
Weston, FL 33332
Ph: (954)349-1030
Fax: (954)349-3100
URL: http://www.cafealacarte.com
Contact: Bonnie Fimiano, Contact
E-mail: dominick@cafealacarte.com
Facebook: www.facebook.com/cafealacarteofsouthflorida
X (Twitter): x.com/CafeAlaCarte
Instagram: www.instagram.com/cafealacartesouthflorida
Description: Provider of gourmet coffee catering service. **Founded:** 1994. **Financial Assistance:** Yes **Training:** Provides 1 week at headquarters, 1 week in Fort Lauderdale, FL with ongoing support.

3207 ■ *The Coffee Beanery Ltd. (CB)*
3429 Pierson Pl.
Flushing, MI 48433
Ph: (810)733-1020

Free: 800-441-2255
Co. E-mail: marketplace@coffeebeanery.com
URL: http://www.coffeebeanery.com
Contact: Joanne Shaw, President
Facebook: www.facebook.com/CoffeeBeaneryHeadquarters
Linkedin: www.linkedin.com/company/coffee-beanery
X (Twitter): x.com/coffeebeaneryHQ
Instagram: www.instagram.com/coffeebeanery1976
YouTube: www.youtube.com/channel/UCpwD_5_ag1P5Ntb4mT1Zz2Q
Pinterest: www.pinterest.com/coffeebeanery

Description: Producer and retailer of whole bean coffees, tea and beverages such as flavored coffee, half caff coffee, green tea, herbal tea. Also provides gifts, brewers and accessories. **Founded:** 1976. **Training:** 4 weeks training at corporate headquarters plus 1 week orientation including customer service, merchandising, marketing & daily operations. Additional on-site training, site selection assistance, lease negotiation, layout & construction supervision and on.

3208 ■ Joe To Go Coffee [Groundwork Coffee Co]
1501 N Cahuenga Blvd.
Hollywood, CA 90028
Ph: (818)762-9189
Co. E-mail: customerservice@groundworkcoffee.com
Facebook: www.facebook.com/joetogocoffee

Description: Producer and distributor of coffee roaster. **Founded:** 1995. **Franchised:** 2001. **Financial Assistance:** Yes **Training:** Provides 1 week at headquarters, 1 week at franchisee's location, 1 week at a corporate store and ongoing support.

3209 ■ Williams Fresh Cafe Inc.
615 West St.
Brantford, ON, Canada N3R 7C5
Free: 888-741-7417
URL: http://williamsfreshcafe.com
Contact: Peter Druxerman, Vice President, Marketing
Facebook: www.facebook.com/williamsfreshcafe
X (Twitter): twitter.com/williams_fresh
Instagram: www.instagram.com/williamsfreshcafe

Description: Chain of fast food restaurants. **Founded:** 1993. **Franchised:** 2004. **Equity Capital Needed:** $350,000-$650,000. **Franchise Fee:** $35,000 for 10 year agreement. **Royalty Fee:** 0.06. **Training:** Offers 8-12 weeks of training.

Coin/Stamp Dealer

ASSOCIATIONS AND OTHER ORGANIZATIONS

3210 ■ American Hatpin Society (AHS)
845 Sonoma Dr.
 Lake Arrowhead, CA 92352
Co. E-mail: americanhatpinsociety@aol.com
URL: http://www.americanhatpinsociety.com
Contact: Carla Walters, Editor
Description: Collectors of hatpins. Promotes collection, preservation, and restoration of hatpins and related fashion accessories. Serves as a clearinghouse on hatpins and their history; facilitates exchange of information among members; conducts educational programs. **Founded:** 1989. **Publications:** *American Hatpin Society Newsletter* (Quarterly). **Geographic Preference:** Multinational.

3211 ■ American Numismatic Association (ANA) - Dwight N. Manley Numismatic Library
818 N Cascade Ave.
 Colorado Springs, CO 80903
Ph: (719)632-2646
Free: 800-367-9723
Fax: (719)634-4085
Co. E-mail: ana@money.org
URL: http://www.money.org
Contact: Kim Kiick, Executive Director
E-mail: kiick@money.org
Facebook: www.facebook.com/numismatics
X (Twitter): x.com/anacoins
Instagram: www.instagram.com/AmericanNumismatic
YouTube: www.youtube.com/user/ AmericanNumismatic
Description: Collectors of coins, medals, tokens, and paper money. Promotes the study, research, and publication of articles on coins, coinage, and history of money. Sponsors correspondence courses; conducts research. Maintains museum, archive, authentication service for coins, and hall of fame. Sponsors National Coin Week; operates speakers' bureau. **Scope:** Coins; paper money; tokens; medals; military orders and decorations; stocks and bonds. **Services:** Open to the public; interlibrary loan to the members; copying. **Founded:** 1891. **Holdings:** 128,000 books; auction catalogs; periodicals; videos; DVDs. **Publications:** *ANA Journal Advanced Studies in Numismatics* (Quarterly); *The Numismatist* (Monthly). **Educational Activities:** World's Fair of Money (Annual). **Awards:** ANA Medal of Merit (Annual); Paper Money, Kagin Family Award (Annual); Numismatic Art Award for Excellence in Medallic Sculpture (Annual); Farran Zerbe Memorial Award (Annual); Glenn Smedley Memorial Award (Annual); ANA Lifetime Achievement Award (Annual); ANA Exemplary Service Award (Annual); ANA Outstanding local Club Publication (Annual); ANA Outstanding Young Numismatist of the Year (Annual); Lawrence J. Gentile, Sr. Memorial Award for Outstanding Adult Advisor (Annual); Lelan G. Rogers Memorial Exhibit Award (Annual); Sidney W. Smith/William Donlon Memorial Exhibit Award (Annual); Burton Saxton/George Bauer Memorial Exhibit Award (Annual); B. P. Wright Memorial Exhibit Award (Annual); Dr. Charles W. Crowe Memorial Exhibit Award (Annual); John S. Davenport Memorial Exhibit Award (Annual); Gaston DiBello/Melvin and Leona Kohl Memorial Exhibit Award (Annual); Henry Christensen/John Jay Pittman Sr. Memorial Exhibit Award (Annual); William C. Henderson/Fred Cihon Memorial Exhibit Award (Annual); Numismatic Error Collectors Exhibit Award (Annual); Love Token Society Exhibit Award (Annual); Menachem Chaim and Simcha Tova Mizel Memorial Exhibit Award (Annual); Edgerton-Lenker Memorial Youth Exhibit Award (Annual); James L. Betton Memorial Award (Annual); Charles "Cheech" Litman Memorial Youth Exhibit Award (Annual). **Geographic Preference:** National.

3212 ■ American Numismatic Society (ANS) - Harry W. Bass Jr. Library
75 Varick St., 11th Fl.
 New York, NY 10013
Ph: (212)571-4470
Co. E-mail: membership@numismatics.org
URL: http://numismatics.org
Contact: Dr. Ute Wartenberg, President
Facebook: www.facebook.com/AmericanNumismaticSociety
X (Twitter): x.com/anscoins
Instagram: www.instagram.com/americannumismaticsociety
YouTube: www.youtube.com/user/ANSCoins
Pinterest: www.pinterest.com/anscoins
Description: Collectors and others interested in coins, medals, and related materials. Advances numismatic knowledge as it relates to history, art, archaeology, and economics by collecting coins, medals, tokens, decorations, and paper money. Maintains only museum devoted entirely to numismatics. Presents annual Graduate Fellowship in Numismatics. Sponsors Graduate Seminar in Numismatics, a nine-week individual study program for ten students. **Scope:** Numismatics. Supports study and research through grants-in-aid and fellowships including the Frances M. Schwartz Fellowship. **Services:** Library access free to members and students; Non-members $20 per day; scanning; copying. **Founded:** 1858. **Holdings:** 100000 items; books; periodicals; manuscripts; photographs; pamphlets; auction catalogs; microforms. **Publications:** *ANS Magazine* (Quarterly); *Coinage of the Americas Conference Proceedings (COAC)*; *Index to American Journal of Numismatics* (Annual); *Numismatic Literature* (Quarterly); *Numismatic Notes and Monographs*; *Numismatic Studies*; *American Numismatic Society Magazine* (Quarterly); *ANS Annual Report* (Annual); *Journal of Early American Numismatics* (Semiannual); *American Journal of Numismatics* (Annual). **Educational Activities:** ANS Coinage of the Americas Conference (COAC); Eric P. Newman Graduate Seminar in Numismatics (Annual). **Awards:** Archer M. Huntington Medal Award (Annual); Huntington Award Medal (Annual); Saltus Medal Award (Periodic); Frances M. Schwartz Fellowship (Annual); J. Sanford Saltus Medal Award (Periodic); Donald Groves Fund Awards; Donald Groves Fund. **Geographic Preference:** National.

3213 ■ American Philatelic Congress (APC)
c/o Charles Wooster
3991 Gulf Shore Blvd. N, Apt. 301
 Naples, FL 34103
Co. E-mail: info@americanphilateliccongress.org
URL: http://americanphilateliccongress.org
Contact: Nancy B. Clark, President
Description: Promotes philatelic writing and research. **Founded:** 1935. **Publications:** *Congress Comments* (Periodic). **Geographic Preference:** National.

3214 ■ American Philatelic Society (APS) - American Philatelic Research Library
100 Match Factory Pl.
 Bellefonte, PA 16823
Ph: (814)933-3803
Fax: (814)933-6128
Co. E-mail: info@stamps.org
URL: http://stamps.org
Contact: Robert A. Zeigler, President
Facebook: www.facebook.com/american.philatelic.society
X (Twitter): x.com/APS_stamps
Description: Collectors of postage and revenue stamps, first day covers, postal history, and related philatelic items. **Scope:** Stamp collecting; postal history; U.S. postal records; stamp production. **Services:** Interlibrary loan; copying; scanning; library open to the public for reference use only. **Founded:** 1886. **Subscriptions:** 5700 journals and other serials Catalogs; government documents; auction catalogs and price lists; stamp show programs and palmares; exhibits; bibliographies and indexes; 23,000 book titles and ebooks; CDs; DVDs. **Publications:** *Philatelic Literature Review* (Quarterly); *The American Philatelist* (Monthly); *Philatelic Observer--Junior Philatelists of America Directory Issue*; *American Philatelic Society CAC Newsletter*. **Educational Activities:** APS Stampshow (Annual); AmeriStamp Expo (Annual). **Awards:** Luff Award (Annual); APS Champion of Champions (Annual); APS Hall of Fame (Annual). **Geographic Preference:** National.

3215 ■ American Stamp Dealers Association (ASDA)
PO Box 513
 Centre Hall, PA 16828
Free: 800-369-8207
Co. E-mail: asda@americanstampdealer.com
URL: http://www.americanstampdealer.com
Contact: Dana Guyer, Executive Director
E-mail: dana@americanstampdealer.com
Facebook: www.facebook.com/americanstampdealersassociationinc
Description: Dealers and wholesalers of stamps, albums and other philatelic materials. Sponsors National Stamp Collecting Week in November. **Founded:** 1914. **Publications:** *American Stamp Dealers Association--Membership Directory* (Annual); *The American Stamp Dealer & Collector* (11/year); *Members Only Newsletter* (Monthly).

3216 ■ L'Association Canadienne Marchands Numismatiques
PO Box 10272
　Winona Post Office
　Stoney Creek, ON, Canada L8E 5R1
Ph: (905)643-4988
URL: http://www.cand.org
Description: Dealers in numismatic materials. Seeks to advance the numismatic collectibles industry. Facilitates communication and cooperation among members; represents members' interests. **Founded:** 1975. **Geographic Preference:** National.

3217 ■ Association Royale de Numismatique du Canada (ARNC) [Royal Canadian Numismatic Association (RCNA)]
5694 Highway No. 7 E, Ste. 432
　Markham, ON, Canada L3P 1B4
Ph: (647)401-4014
Fax: (905)472-9645
Co. E-mail: info@rcna.ca
URL: http://www.rcna.ca
Contact: Stephen Woodland, President
Facebook: www.facebook.com/TheRCNA
Description: Promotes collection of numismatic materials. Serves as a clearinghouse on numismatic materials and their collection and preservation; provides assistance to members. **Founded:** 1950. **Publications:** *The CN Journal* (Annual). **Educational Activities:** RCNA Annual Convention (Annual). **Awards:** Fellow of the RaCNA Award (Annual); Guy Potter Literary Award (Annual); J. Douglas Ferguson Award (Annual); Jean Bullen Award (Annual); Jerome H. Remick III Literary Award (Annual); Louise Graham Memorial Club of the Year Award (Annual). **Geographic Preference:** National.

3218 ■ Bicycle Stamps Club (BSC)
Seattle, WA 98121
URL: http://www.bicyclestampsclub.org
Contact: Jari Majander, President
Description: Philatelists interested in collecting stamps depicting bicycles and cycling themes. **Founded:** 1980. **Publications:** *Bicycle Stamps* (Quarterly). **Geographic Preference:** National.

3219 ■ Canadian Aerophilatelic Society (CAS) - Library
c/o Chris Hargreaves, Editor
　4060 Bath Rd.
　Kingston, ON, Canada K7M 4Y4
Co. E-mail: hargreavescp@sympatico.ca
URL: http://www.aerophilately.ca
Contact: Steve Johnson, President
E-mail: steverman@rogers.com
Description: Individuals interested in the history of Canadian and Newfoundland air mail service and aerophilately. Promotes study of Canadian postal history and collection of aerophilatelic materials. Conducts research and educational programs; sponsors competitions. **Scope:** Aero philately. **Services:** Open to public for reference use. **Founded:** 1986. **Holdings:** Figures not available. **Publications:** *Canadian Aerophilatelist* (Quarterly). **Educational Activities:** CAS Annual General Meeting (Annual). **Geographic Preference:** National.

3220 ■ *Canadian Aerophilatelist*
c/o Chris Hargreaves, Editor
　4060 Bath Rd.
　Kingston, ON, Canada K7M 4Y4
Co. E-mail: hargreavescp@sympatico.ca
URL: http://www.aerophilately.ca
Contact: Steve Johnson, President
E-mail: steverman@rogers.com
Released: Quarterly **Description:** Features aerophilatelic data. **Availability:** PDF.

3221 ■ Canadian Numismatic Research Society (CNRS)
c/o Lorne Barnes
　PO Box 35020
　London, ON, Canada N5W 5M0
Co. E-mail: 1wdin5@gmail.com
URL: http://www.nunet.ca/cnrs.htm
Contact: David Bergeron, President
Description: Numismatists and other individuals with an interest in coins, tokens, paper money, and medals; membership by invitation only. Seeks to advance numismatic study in Canada. Sponsors research and educational programs. **Founded:** 1963. **Publications:** *Numismatica Canada* (Annual). **Geographic Preference:** National.

3222 ■ *The Canadian Philatelist*
PO Box 69080
　St Clair Post Office
　Toronto, ON, Canada M4T 3A1
Ph: (416)921-2077
Free: 888-285-4143
Fax: (416)921-1282
Co. E-mail: info@rpsc.org
URL: http://www.rpsc.org
Contact: Sam Chiu, President
E-mail: chiusam@hotmail.com
URL(s): www.rpsc.org/tcp/index.php
Ed: Tony Shaman. **Released:** Bimonthly **Price:** $30, Members for per year; $30, Nonmembers for per year. **Description:** Journal containing news and information for stamp collectors. **Availability:** Print; Online; Download; PDF.

3223 ■ *The CN Journal*
5694 Highway No. 7 E, Ste. 432
　Markham, ON, Canada L3P 1B4
Ph: (647)401-4014
Fax: (905)472-9645
Co. E-mail: info@rcna.ca
URL: http://www.rcna.ca
Contact: Stephen Woodland, President
URL(s): www.rcna.ca/journal.php
Ed: Henry Nienhuis. **Released:** Annual **Description:** Contains articles dealing with Canadian numismatics, upcoming coin show information, updates and reports, and news about the Royal Canadian Mint's products and people. **Availability:** Print; PDF; Online.

3224 ■ Cracker Jack Collectors Association (CJCA)
c/o Fred Joyce, 415 Soft Shadow Ln.
　Debary, FL 32713-2343
Co. E-mail: brazeaufamily@charter.net
URL: http://www.crackerjackcollectors.com
Contact: Fred Joyce, Contact
Description: Collectors of Cracker Jack prizes and related items. Promotes collection and preservation of Cracker Jack memorabilia. Gathers and disseminates information on Cracker Jack collectibles and their availability; facilitates exchange of information and promotes good fellowship among members. **Founded:** 1994. **Geographic Preference:** National.

3225 ■ The Fostoria Glass Society of America, Inc. (FGSA)
511 Tomlinson Ave.
　Moundsville, WV 26041
Ph: (304)845-9188
Co. E-mail: museum@fostoriaglass.org
URL: http://www.fostoriaglass.org
Contact: Jim Davis, President
Description: Represents Fostoria Glass collectors. Promotes interest in glass collecting. Offers referrals. **Founded:** 1988. **Educational Activities:** Annual F.G.S.A. Convention and Elegant Glass Show (Annual). **Geographic Preference:** National.

3226 ■ Glass Paperweight Foundation
410 S Michigan Ave., Ste. 206
　Chicago, IL 60616
Ph: (312)419-0403
Co. E-mail: glasspaperweightfoundation@gmail.com
URL: http://www.glasspaperweightfoundation.com
Contact: Wes Clark, Contact
Description: Promotes paperweight collecting. Conducts educational programs. Runs a speakers' bureau. **Founded:** 1995. **Geographic Preference:** National.

3227 ■ International Harvester Collectors (IHC)
c/o Gary Spina, Secretary
　6205 Highview Dr. SE
　Cedar Rapids, IA 52403
Ph: (319)366-3019
Co. E-mail: spinaih106@gmail.com
URL: http://nationalihcollectors.com
Contact: Robert Buxton, President
E-mail: rbuxton1943@gmail.com
Description: Owners and admirers of farm machinery produced by International Harvester. Promotes preservation and restoration of International Harvester equipment. Facilitates communication among members; serves as a clearinghouse on International Harvester tractors and other farm equipment. **Founded:** 1990. **Educational Activities:** Red Power Round-up (Annual). **Geographic Preference:** National.

3228 ■ La Societe Royale de Philatelie du Canada (RPSC) [Royal Philatelic Society of Canada (RPSC)]
PO Box 69080
　St Clair Post Office
　Toronto, ON, Canada M4T 3A1
Ph: (416)921-2077
Free: 888-285-4143
Fax: (416)921-1282
Co. E-mail: info@rpsc.org
URL: http://www.rpsc.org
Contact: Sam Chiu, President
E-mail: chiusam@hotmail.com
Facebook: www.facebook.com/Royal.Philatelic.Society.Canada
Description: Promotes interest in stamps and postal history. Conducts educational and social programs; facilitates exchange of information among members. Sponsors competitions. **Founded:** 1887. **Publications:** *The Canadian Philatelist* (Bimonthly). **Awards:** Fellow of the Royal Philatelic Society of Canada (Periodic); Geldert medal (Annual). **Geographic Preference:** National.

3229 ■ National Coin & Bullion Association (NCBA)
PO Box 237
　Dacula, GA 30019
Ph: (678)430-3252
Co. E-mail: ncba@ncbassoc.org
URL: http://www.ncbassoc.org
Contact: David Crenshaw, Executive Director
E-mail: david.crenshaw@ncbassoc.org
Facebook: www.facebook.com/IndustryCouncilTangibleAssets
Linkedin: www.linkedin.com/company/industry-council-for-tangible
X (Twitter): x.com/wearencba
Instagram: www.instagram.com/wearencba
Description: Individuals and firms engaged in the fabrication, manufacture, importation, wholesale distribution, or retail sale of any tangible asset (precious or other metals, coins, antiques, stamps, or art objects). Cooperates in maintaining an appropriate and favorable regulatory climate in the U.S.; serves as liaison with governmental and other agencies. **Founded:** 1983. **Publications:** *ICTA Washington Wire* (Quarterly). **Geographic Preference:** National.

3230 ■ Numismatics International (NI) - Library
PO Box 570842
　Dallas, TX 75357-0842
Co. E-mail: secretary@numis.org
URL: http://numis.org
Contact: F. Howard, President
Description: Works to: encourage and promote the science of numismatics; cultivate fraternal relations among collectors and numismatic students. **Scope:** Coins. **Founded:** 1964. **Holdings:** 2,800 titles; books; periodicals. **Publications:** *NI Bulletin* (6/year). **Geographic Preference:** Multinational.

3231 ■ *PHSC Journal*
10 Summerhill Ave.
　Toronto, ON, Canada M4T 1A8
Co. E-mail: phscdb@postalhistorycanada.net
URL: http://www.postalhistorycanada.net/php/index.php
Contact: Stephane Cloutier, Contact
URL(s): www.postalhistorycanada.net/php/Library/journal.php

Description: Contains many articles on all aspects of postal history from early to modern. **Availability:** Print; Online.

3232 ■ Postal History Society of Canada (PHSC)
10 Summerhill Ave.
Toronto, ON, Canada M4T 1A8
Co. E-mail: phscdb@postalhistorycanada.net
URL: http://www.postalhistorycanada.net/php/index.php
Contact: Stephane Cloutier, Contact

Description: Postal historians and philatelists. Disseminates information on Canadian postal history. Conducts postal history mail auction. Maintains specialized study groups. **Founded:** 1972. **Publications:** PHSC Journal. **Awards:** PHSC Certificate of Merit (Annual); PHSC Citation of Merit (Annual); Frank W. Campbell Award (Annual); Stan Shantz Award (Annual). **Geographic Preference:** National.

3233 ■ Professional Currency Dealers Association (PCDA)
c/o James A. Simek
PO Box 7157
Westchester, IL 60154
URL: http://perakiscurrency.com/pcda-dealers

Description: Dealers of rare paper money and other printed media of exchange including stocks, bonds, fiscal documents, and related ephemera. Promotes the study of and interest in collectible paper media of exchange; maintains standards in commercial aspects of syngraphics. Sponsors research project to identify U.S. national banks whose large size note issues are undiscovered. **Founded:** 1985. **Educational Activities:** Professional Currency Dealers Association Conference; Professional Currency Dealers Association Meeting. **Awards:** John Hickman National Bank Note Exhibit Award (Annual). **Geographic Preference:** National.

3234 ■ Professional Numismatists Guild (PNG)
27890 Clinton Keith Rd., Ste. D141
Murrieta, CA 92562
Ph: (951)587-8300
Co. E-mail: info@pngdealers.org
URL: http://www.pngdealers.org
Contact: James Sego, President
Facebook: www.facebook.com/ProfessionalNumismatistsGuild
Linkedin: www.linkedin.com/company/professional-numismatists-guild-png
X (Twitter): x.com/profnumguild
Instagram: www.instagram.com/pngdealers
YouTube: www.youtube.com/channel/UCb5co6ZLKPitRAw-6pDxeCw

Description: Represents coin dealers who have been involved full-time in the profession for at least five years. Establishes, promotes, and defends ethics in the hobby of numismatics. **Founded:** 1955. **Publications:** The Pleasure of Coin Collecting; What You Should Know Before You Invest in Coins. **Awards:** Robert Friedberg Award (Annual); Sol Kaplan Award (Annual); Abe Kosoff Founders Award (Annual); Harvey G. Stack Lifetime Achievement Award (Annual). **Geographic Preference:** National.

REFERENCE WORKS

3235 ■ "Counterfeits Plague Many Collectibles" in Coin World (September 16, 2019)
URL(s): www.coinworld.com/news/us-coins/monday-morning-brief-for-sept-16-2019-counterfeits-plague-many-collectibles

Ed: William T. Gibbs. **Released:** September 16, 2019. **Description:** Counterfeit stamps are sold on eBay and other internet sites, in order to get quick cash. Most of the time the postal service will kick out these stamps if they are placed on envelopes and return to sender. Others make it through. Coins and other collectibles are also taking a hit, as counterfeits are manufactured overseas in China. **Availability:** Online.

3236 ■ "Do Coin Shops Have a Future?" in Numismatic News (June 1, 2015)
URL(s): www.numismaticnews.net/article/do-coin-shops-have-a-future

Ed: Pat Heller. **Released:** June 01, 2015. **Description:** Explores the reality of brick-and-mortar coin shops losing out from the advancement of the internet and online sales. However, all is not lost because these stores could potentially extend their markets and products in order to increase their foot traffic. **Availability:** Online.

3237 ■ "Stamped Out" in The New York Times (September 29, 2017)
URL(s): www.nytimes.com/2017/09/29/opinion/stamp-collecting-philately.html

Ed: Eugene L. Meyer. **Released:** September 29, 2017. **Description:** With the decline in stamps being produced and used, the stamp collecting as a hobby is dying out. Whole collections that used to be worth a fair amount are now not worth much, due to the collectors passing away and the younger generation not having an interest in the hobby. **Availability:** Online.

TRADE PERIODICALS

3238 ■ Canada Numismatica
Pub: Canadian Association of Token Collectors
Contact: Scott E. Douglas, President
E-mail: sdouglas333@gmail.com

Released: Quarterly **Description:** Includes detailed information on various aspects of token collecting. **Availability:** Print.

3239 ■ Canadian Coin News
Pub: Trajan Publishing Corp.
Contact: Bret Evans, Managing Editor Associate Publisher
E-mail: bret@trajan.ca
URL(s): canadiancoinnews.com
Facebook: www.facebook.com/CanadianCoinNews
X (Twitter): x.com/trajanpublisher

Ed: Bret Evans. **Released:** 26/year. **Price:** C$6.50, Single issue for digital 1 issue; C$112.99, for 2 years/52 issues print US or international; C$164.99, for 3 years/78 issues print US or international; C$41.99, for digital 1 year US or international; C$164.99, for 2 year print + privacy wrap; C$242.99, for 3 year print + privacy wrap; C$85.99, for 1 year print + privacy wrap; C$69.99, for print + digital one year; C$132.99, for 2 year print + digital; 194.99, for 3 year print + digital; C$59.99, for 1 year/26 issues print. **Description:** Newspaper consumer magazine for coin collectors. **Availability:** Print; Online.

3240 ■ Canadian Stamp News
Pub: Trajan Publishing Corp.
Contact: Bret Evans, Managing Editor Associate Publisher
E-mail: bret@trajan.ca
URL(s): canadianstampnews.com
Facebook: www.facebook.com/canadianstampnews
X (Twitter): x.com/trajanpublisher

Released: 26/yr. **Price:** $289.99, Other countries for 1 year print (26 issues); C$164.99, Canada for 3 year print (78 issues); C$112.99, Canada for 2 year print (52 issues); C$59.99, Canada for 1 year print (26 issues); C$194.99, Canada for 3 year print + digital; C$69.99, Canada for 1 year print + digital; C$41.99, Canada for 1 year digital only; $75.99, U.S. for 1 year print (26 issues); $85.99, U.S. for 1 year print + digital; $41.99, U.S. for 1 year digital only; $6.50, Single issue for digital; $299.99, for 1 year print + digital international; $41.99, for 1 year digital only international; C$132.99, for 2 year print + digital. **Description:** Hobby newspaper presenting philatelic news. **Availability:** Print; Online.

3241 ■ Coin World: World's 1 Publication for Coin Collectors
Contact: William T. Gibbs, Managing Editor
E-mail: bgibbs@amospress.com
URL(s): www.coinworldonline.comwww.coinworld.com
Facebook: www.facebook.com/CoinWorld
X (Twitter): twitter.com/coinworld

Ed: Steve Roach. **Released:** Weekly **Price:** $69.99, U.S. /week print; $29.99, U.S. /week online; $24.99, U.S. /month print; $19.99, U.S. /month online. **Description:** Newspaper for coin collectors. **Availability:** Print; PDF; Online.

3242 ■ Coins Magazine
Contact: Robert R. Van Ryzin, Editor
URL(s): numismaster.com/ta/inside_numis.jsp?page=CoinsMagazine

Ed: Robert R. Van Ryzin. **Released:** Monthly **Price:** $22.98, U.S. for U.S Print; $47.98, for International Print; $19.98, for U.S,Canada and International online; $37.98, for Canada Print. **Description:** Magazine on coin collecting. **Availability:** Print; Online.

3243 ■ The Collectors Club Philatelist (CCP)
Pub: The Collectors Club
Contact: Lawrence Haber, President
E-mail: president@collectorsclub.org
URL(s): www.collectorsclub.org/ccp/about-the-ccp

Ed: Wayne L. Youngblood. **Released:** Bimonthly; January, March, May, July, September, November. **Description:** Magazine publishing articles devoted to philatelic study and research. **Availability:** Print; Online; PDF.

3244 ■ David Hall's Inside View
Pub: David Hall Rare Coins
Contact: Van Simmons, Contact
URL(s): davidhall.com/pages/about-us

Released: Monthly **Description:** Provides advisory information on collecting and investing in rare coins. **Availability:** Print.

3245 ■ Linn's Stamp News: World's Largest Weekly Stamp Newspaper
Pub: Linn's Stamp News
Contact: David Pistello, Director, Sales
E-mail: dpistello@amosmedia.com
URL(s): www.linns.com
Facebook: www.facebook.com/LinnsStampNews
X (Twitter): x.com/linnsstampnews
Instagram: www.instagram.com/linns_stamp_news
YouTube: www.youtube.com/user/LinnsStampNews

Ed: Michael Baadke. **Released:** Weekly **Price:** $39.99, for print & digital; $59.99, for print & digital premium; $44.99, for digital; $79.99, for print; $99.99, for print & digital premium; $24.99, for digital edition. **Description:** Magazine (tabloid) for stamp collectors. **Availability:** Print; Online.

3246 ■ Numismatic News
Contact: David C. Harper, Editor
URL(s): www.numismaticnews.net
Facebook: www.facebook.com/kpnumismatics
X (Twitter): twitter.com/kpnumismatics

Ed: David C. Harper. **Released:** twice a week on tuesdays and fridays. **Description:** U.S. coin collecting magazine. **Availability:** Online.

3247 ■ The Numismatist
Pub: American Numismatic Association
Contact: Kim Kiick, Executive Director
E-mail: kiick@money.org
URL(s): www.money.org/numismatist

Released: Monthly **Price:** $35, for per year; $55, Members for platinum; $35, Members for gold. **Description:** Magazine for collectors of coins, medals, tokens, and paper money. **Availability:** Print; Online.

3248 ■ Philatelic Literature Review
Pub: American Philatelic Society
Contact: Robert A. Zeigler, President
URL(s): classic.stamps.org/Quarterly-Journal

Ed: Barbara Boal. **Released:** Quarterly; January, April, July, October. **Description:** Journal featuring bibliographies, indexes, and commentary on philatelic literature. **Availability:** Print; Online.

3249 ■ The Posthorn: Journal of the Scandinavian Collectors Club
Pub: Scandinavian Collectors Club
Contact: Dahle Christopher, Vice President

URL(s): www.scc-online.org/posthorn
Ed: Paul Albright. **Released:** Latest Volume 76. **Description:** Journal covering philately, specifically Scandinavian stamps and postal history. **Availability:** Print; PDF; Download.

3250 ■ *World Coin News*
Contact: Maggie Pahl, Director, Editorial
E-mail: maggie.judkins@fwmedia.com
URL(s): numismaster.com/ta/inside_numis.jsp?page=WorldCoinNewssubscriptions.worldcoinnews.net/World-Coin-News/Magazine
Released: Monthly **Price:** $25.99, U.S. for annual subscription; $40.99, Canada for annual subscription; $55.99, for annual subscription in International. **Description:** World coin collectors' magazine. **Availability:** Print; Online.

TRADE SHOWS AND CONVENTIONS

3251 ■ AmeriStamp Expo (ASE)
American Philatelic Society (APS)
100 Match Factory Pl.
Bellefonte, PA 16823
Ph: (814)933-3803
Fax: (814)933-6128
Co. E-mail: info@stamps.org
URL: http://stamps.org
Contact: Robert A. Zeigler, President
URL(s): stamps.org/about/history/past-winter-meetings
Frequency: Annual. **Description:** Exhibits relating to postage stamps. **Audience:** Professionals and collectors. **Principal Exhibits:** Exhibits relating to postage stamps.

3252 ■ National Topical Stamp Show (NTSS)
American Topical Association (ATA)
100 N Division St., Fl. 2
Carterville, IL 62918
Ph: (618)985-5100
Fax: (618)985-5100
Co. E-mail: americantopical@msn.com
URL: http://www.americantopicalassn.org
Contact: Jack André Denys, President
E-mail: jdenys@verizon.net
URL(s): americantopicalassn.org/ntssgeneral.shtml
Frequency: Annual. **Description:** Stamp bourse with 35 dealers, convention meetings, tours, receptions, banquet, exhibition. **Audience:** Stamp collectors and dealers. **Principal Exhibits:** Stamp bourse with 35 dealers, convention meetings, tours, receptions, banquet, exhibition.

3253 ■ RCNA Annual Convention
Association Royale de Numismatique du Canada (ARNC)
5694 Highway No. 7 E, Ste. 432
Markham, ON, Canada L3P 1B4
Ph: (647)401-4014
Fax: (905)472-9645
Co. E-mail: info@rcna.ca
URL: http://www.rcna.ca
Contact: Stephen Woodland, President
URL(s): www.rcna.ca/2024
Frequency: Annual. **Description:** Coins, currency, medals, and tokens. **Audience:** Industry professionals. **Principal Exhibits:** Coins, currency, medals, and tokens. **Telecommunication Services:** taylormaj22@gmail.com.

LIBRARIES

3254 ■ American Numismatic Society (ANS) - Harry W. Bass Jr. Library
75 Varick St., 11th Fl.
New York, NY 10013
Ph: (212)571-4470
Co. E-mail: membership@numismatics.org
URL: http://numismatics.org
Contact: Dr. Ute Wartenberg, President
Facebook: www.facebook.com/AmericanNumismaticSociety
X (Twitter): x.com/anscoins
Instagram: www.instagram.com/americannumismaticsociety
YouTube: www.youtube.com/user/ANSCoins
Pinterest: www.pinterest.com/anscoins
Description: Collectors and others interested in coins, medals, and related materials. Advances numismatic knowledge as it relates to history, art, archaeology, and economics by collecting coins, medals, tokens, decorations, and paper money. Maintains only museum devoted entirely to numismatics. Presents annual Graduate Fellowship in Numismatics. Sponsors Graduate Seminar in Numismatics, a nine-week individual study program for ten students. **Scope:** Numismatics. Supports study and research through grants-in-aid and fellowships including the Frances M. Schwartz Fellowship. **Services:** Library access free to members and students; Non-members $20 per day; scanning; copying. **Founded:** 1858. **Holdings:** 100000 items; books; periodicals; manuscripts; photographs; pamphlets; auction catalogs; microforms. **Publications:** *ANS Magazine* (Quarterly); *Coinage of the Americas Conference Proceedings (COAC)*; *Index to American Journal of Numismatics* (Annual); *Numismatic Literature* (Quarterly); *Numismatic Notes and Monographs*; *Numismatic Studies*; *American Numismatic Society Magazine* (Quarterly); *ANS Annual Report* (Annual); *Journal of Early American Numismatics* (Semiannual); *American Journal of Numismatics* (Annual). **Educational Activities:** ANS Coinage of the Americas Conference (COAC) (Annual); Eric P. Newman Graduate Seminar in Numismatics (Annual). **Awards:** Archer M. Huntington Medal Award (Annual); Huntington Award Medal (Annual); Saltus Medal Award (Periodic); Frances M. Schwartz Fellowship (Annual); J. Sanford Saltus Medal Award (Periodic); Donald Groves Fund Awards; Donald Groves Fund. **Geographic Preference:** National.

3255 ■ American Philatelic Society (APS) - American Philatelic Research Library
100 Match Factory Pl.
Bellefonte, PA 16823
Ph: (814)933-3803
Fax: (814)933-6128
Co. E-mail: info@stamps.org
URL: http://stamps.org
Contact: Robert A. Zeigler, President
Facebook: www.facebook.com/american.philatelic.society
X (Twitter): x.com/APS_stamps
Description: Collectors of postage and revenue stamps, first day covers, postal history, and related philatelic items. **Scope:** Stamp collecting; postal history; U.S. postal records; stamp production. **Services:** Interlibrary loan; copying; scanning; library open to the public for reference use only. **Founded:** 1886. **Subscriptions:** 5700 journals and other serials Catalogs; government documents; auction catalogs and price lists; stamp show programs and palmares; exhibits; bibliographies and indexes; 23,000 book titles and ebooks; CDs; DVDs. **Publications:** *Philatelic Literature Review* (Quarterly); *The American Philatelist* (Monthly); *Philatelic Observer--Junior Philatelists of America Directory Issue*; *American Philatelic Society CAC Newsletter*. **Educational Activities:** APS Stampshow (Annual); AmeriStamp Expo (ASE) (Annual). **Awards:** Luff Award (Annual); APS Champion of Champions (Annual); APS Hall of Fame (Annual). **Geographic Preference:** National.

3256 ■ The Collectors Club (CC) - Library
22 E 35th St.
New York, NY 10016-3806
Ph: (212)683-0559
Co. E-mail: info@collectorsclub.org
URL: http://www.collectorsclub.org
Contact: Lawrence Haber, President
E-mail: president@collectorsclub.org
Description: Stamp collectors united to promote interest and knowledge of philately among members and the public. Encourages the exchange of information with other philatelic organizations and to enlarge and develop the cultural and historical aspects of philately. Sponsors philatelic research and lectures. Maintains library. Holds public and private exhibitions. **Scope:** Philatelic. **Services:** Library open to the public; interlibrary loan. **Founded:** 1896. **Subscriptions:** periodicals (includes journals) 150,000 volumes; books; pamphlets. **Publications:** *The Collectors Club Philatelist (CCP)* (Bimonthly). **Awards:** Alfred F. Lichtenstein Memorial Award (Annual). **Geographic Preference:** National.

3257 ■ Collectors Club of Chicago (CCC) - Library
1029 N Dearborn St.
Chicago, IL 60610-2803
Ph: (312)642-7981
Co. E-mail: email@collectorsclubchicago.org
URL: http://www.collectorsclubchicago.org
Contact: William O. Maddocks, President
Facebook: www.facebook.com/CollectorsClubofChicago
Instagram: www.instagram.com/ccc_stamps
Description: Publishes specialized books for the philatelists. Reaches market through direct mail and advertisements. Accepts unsolicited manuscripts. **Scope:** Philatelic literature. **Services:** Library open to the public. **Founded:** 1928. **Subscriptions:** periodicals (includes journals) 35,000 items; 1,000 books, pamphlets. **Geographic Preference:** National.

3258 ■ Friends of the Western Philatelic Library (FWPL)
3004 Spring St.
Redwood City, CA 94063
Ph: (650)306-9150
Co. E-mail: info@fwpl.org
URL: http://www.fwpl.org
Contact: Nestor Nunez, Treasurer
E-mail: nnunez@fwpl.org
Description: Aims to enhance the preservation and dissemination of philatelic knowledge by acquiring, organizing, interpreting and distributing information resources in a globally networked community. **Scope:** Philatelic. **Services:** Open to the public; Scanning; Copying. **Founded:** 1969. **Holdings:** 15,700 book and monographs; 5,200 journals; 13,300 sheets; stamps; pamphlets.

3259 ■ Numismatics International (NI) - Library
PO Box 570842
Dallas, TX 75357-0842
Co. E-mail: secretary@numis.org
URL: http://numis.org
Contact: F. Howard, President
Description: Works to: encourage and promote the science of numismatics; cultivate fraternal relations among collectors and numismatic students. **Scope:** Coins. **Founded:** 1964. **Holdings:** 2,800 titles; books; periodicals. **Publications:** *NI Bulletin* (6/year). **Geographic Preference:** Multinational.

3260 ■ Philatelic Foundation Archives and Library (PF)
353 Lexington Ave., Ste. 804
New York, NY 10016
Ph: (212)221-6555
Fax: (212)221-6208
Co. E-mail: philatelicfoundation@verizon.net
URL: http://www.philatelicfoundation.org/expertizing-process/the-process
Contact: Larry Lyons, Executive Director
Scope: Philately. **Founded:** 1945. **Holdings:** 5,000 volumes catalogs.

3261 ■ Royal Canadian Numismatic Association Library
c/o Daniel Gosling, Librarian
52131 Range Rd., No. 210
Sherwood Park, AB, Canada T8G 1A2
Ph: (780)922-5743
Co. E-mail: dan@gosling.ca
URL: http://www.rcna.ca/library.php
Contact: Daniel Gosling, Librarian
E-mail: dan@gosling.ca
Scope: History of Canadian coins. **Services:** Interlibrary loan (members). **Founded:** 1950. **Holdings:** Books; slides; films; videos.

RESEARCH CENTERS

3262 ■ American Numismatic Society (ANS) - Harry W. Bass Jr. Library
75 Varick St., 11th Fl.
New York, NY 10013
Ph: (212)571-4470
Co. E-mail: membership@numismatics.org
URL: http://numismatics.org
Contact: Dr. Ute Wartenberg, President
Facebook: www.facebook.com/AmericanNumismaticSociety
X (Twitter): x.com/anscoins
Instagram: www.instagram.com/americannumismaticsociety
YouTube: www.youtube.com/user/ANSCoins
Pinterest: www.pinterest.com/anscoins

Description: Collectors and others interested in coins, medals, and related materials. Advances numismatic knowledge as it relates to history, art, archaeology, and economics by collecting coins, medals, tokens, decorations, and paper money. Maintains only museum devoted entirely to numismatics. Presents annual Graduate Fellowship in Numismatics. Sponsors Graduate Seminar in Numismatics, a nine-week individual study program for ten students. **Scope:** Numismatics. Supports study and research through grants-in-aid and fellowships including the Frances M. Schwartz Fellowship. **Services:** Library access free to members and students; Non-members $20 per day; scanning; copying. **Founded:** 1858. **Holdings:** 100000 items; books; periodicals; manuscripts; photographs; pamphlets; auction catalogs; microforms. **Publications:** *ANS Magazine* (Quarterly); *Coinage of the Americas Conference Proceedings (COAC)*; *Index to American Journal of Numismatics* (Annual); *Numismatic Literature* (Quarterly); *Numismatic Notes and Monographs*; *Numismatic Studies*; *American Numismatic Society Magazine* (Quarterly); *ANS Annual Report* (Annual); *Journal of Early American Numismatics* (Semiannual); *American Journal of Numismatics* (Annual). **Educational Activities:** ANS Coinage of the Americas Conference (COAC) (Annual); Eric P. Newman Graduate Seminar in Numismatics (Annual). **Awards:** Archer M. Huntington Medal Award (Annual); Huntington Award Medal (Annual); Saltus Medal Award (Periodic); Frances M. Schwartz Fellowship (Annual); J. Sanford Saltus Medal Award (Periodic); Donald Groves Fund Awards; Donald Groves Fund. **Geographic Preference:** National.

Comic Book/Collectibles Store

ASSOCIATIONS AND OTHER ORGANIZATIONS

3263 ■ Canadian Association of Token Collectors (CATC)
c/o Ian Spears, Secretary-Treasurer
3280 Bloor St., W Ste. 1140
Toronto, ON, Canada M8X 2X3
Co. E-mail: ian.speers@utoronto.ca
URL: http://www.nunetcan.net/catc.htm
Contact: Scott E. Douglas, President
E-mail: sdouglas333@gmail.com

Description: Collectors of Canadian tokens. Promotes collection of tokens and other memorabilia as a recreational pastime. Facilitates exchange of information among members; serves as a clearinghouse on the preservation, availability, and value of tokens. **Founded:** 1972. **Publications:** Canada Numismatica (Quarterly). **Geographic Preference:** National.

3264 ■ Cartoonists Northwest (CNW)
4350 8th Ave., NE
Seattle, WA 98105
Ph: (206)545-0091
URL: http://www.cartoonistsnorthwest.com
Contact: Bill Morse, President

Description: Promotes cartooning as an art form. Provides networking opportunities and referral services. Conducts educational programs. **Founded:** 1981. **Awards:** CNW Toonie Awards (Annual). **Geographic Preference:** National.

3265 ■ Haviland Collectors International Foundation (HCIF)
PO Box 5163
Buffalo Grove, IL 60089
Co. E-mail: hcifmembership@gmail.com
URL: http://havilandcollectors.com
Facebook: www.facebook.com/groups/Havilan dCollectorsInternational

Description: Owners and admirers of Haviland China objects. Promotes "the study of porcelain and pottery produced by the Haviland family in France and America!!br0ken!! Facilitates communication and cooperation among members; serves as a clearinghouse on Haviland China; promotes China exhibits. **Founded:** 1990. **Publications:** Haviland Annual (Annual). **Geographic Preference:** National.

REFERENCE WORKS

3266 ■ "As Comic Book Industry Grows, Smaller Publishers Learn to Adapt" in The New York Times (May 8, 2019)
URL(s): www.nytimes.com/2019/05/08/business/lion -forge-oni-merger.html

Released: May 08, 2019. **Description:** With DC Comics and Marvel dominating the comic scene, smaller independent publishers are getting creative in order to compete. Some are merging, while others are doing direct-to-consumer sales. **Availability:** Online.

3267 ■ Bookman's Price Index: A Guide to the Values of Rare and Other Out of Print Books
Contact: Anne F. McGrath, Editor
URL(s): www.cengage.com/search/productOverview .do?N=197+4294904574+4294917619&Ntk=P_EPI &Ntt=2077532438577406048358410 2251450 516386&Ntx=mode%2Bmatchallpartial

Ed: Anne F. McGrath. **Released:** 3 to 4 volumes per year. **Price:** $775, Individuals. **Description:** Covers rare and collectible books offered for sale by 150 bookdealers in the United States, Canada, and the United Kingdom. **Entries include:** Book title, author's name, date and place of publication, description of book's condition, name of dealer, catalog and item number, year of catalog in which listing appeared, price; dealer's address is given in a separate list. **Arrangement:** Alphabetical by author name; separate sections for association copies, books with special bindings, and books with fore-edge paintings. **Availability:** Print.

3268 ■ Comic Shop: The Retail Mavericks Who Gave Us a New Geek Culture
Ed: Tom Spurgeon. **Released:** October 13, 2017. **Price:** $26.95, Hardcover; $10.20, E-Book. **Description:** Traces the history of the modern comic book shop from it's origins in the 1970s to today with digital platforms and the evolving retail landscape. **Availability:** E-book; Print.

3269 ■ "Comics Retailers Hope to Rebound in 2018" in Publishers Weekly (February 9, 2018)
URL(s): www.publishersweekly.com/pw/by-topic/in dustry-news/comics/article/76031-comics-retailers -hope-to-rebound-in-2018.html

Released: February 09, 2018. **Description:** An in-depth look at the state of the comic book store in America. Comic book sales have been trending downward and store owners discuss what's driving this trend and how they, and others, can combat it to grow the industry again. **Availability:** Online.

3270 ■ Fandom Directory (Science fiction, fantasy, comics)
Pub: Fandata Publications
URL(s): www.fandata.com/backishf.htm

Price: $9.95, for 2000-2001 edition. **Description:** Covers over 20,000 fans, fan clubs, fan magazine publishers, and fan events in the field of science fiction, fantasy, television and movies, old radio programs, computer games, comic books; location of large or rare manuscript collections; over 9,000 stores that serve fans and collectors. **Entries include:** Club, individual, or firm name, address, phone, special interest(s). **Arrangement:** Geographical. **Indexes:** Alphabetical, interest, geographical. **Availability:** Online.

3271 ■ "Fifty Comic Stores That Have Closed Since January 2017" in Bleeding Cool (January 19, 2018)
URL(s): www.bleedingcool.com/2018/01/19/fifty -comic-stores-closed-since-january-2017/

Ed: Rich Johnston. **Released:** January 19, 2018. **Description:** While some comic book stores are just launching, the trend seems to be downwards. Contained is a list of all fifty stores. **Availability:** Online.

TRADE PERIODICALS

3272 ■ Antique Bottle & Glass Collector
Pub: Antique Bottle and Glass Collector
Contact: Jim Hagenbuch, Founder
URL(s): www.fohbc.org/bottles-extras

Released: Bimonthly **Price:** $145, for first class mail 3 years w/1 associate; $125, for standard mail 3 years w/1 Associate; $60, for first class mail w/1 associate; $45, for Standard Mail w/1 Associate; $125, for first class mail 3 years; $110, for standard mail 3 years; $55, U.S. for first class mail; $60, Canada for first Class Mail; $80, Other countries for first Class Mail; $40, for standard mail; $7, for sample issue. **Description:** Trade magazine for antique bottle and glass collectors. **Availability:** Print; PDF; Online.

3273 ■ Beer Cans and Brewery Collectibles Magazine
Pub: Brewery Collectibles Club of America
Contact: David J. Ohlendorf, Contact
URL(s): bcca.com/page/publications

Ed: Marcia Butterbaugh. **Released:** Bimonthly **Description:** Contains information on collecting beer cans and brewery paraphernalia. **Availability:** Print; Online.

3274 ■ Canada Numismatica
Pub: Canadian Association of Token Collectors
Contact: Scott E. Douglas, President
E-mail: sdouglas333@gmail.com

Released: Quarterly **Description:** Includes detailed information on various aspects of token collecting. **Availability:** Print.

FRANCHISES AND BUSINESS OPPORTUNITIES

3275 ■ All Nations Flag Co., Inc.
Patriot Enterprises LLC
114 W 5th St.
Kansas City, MO 64105
Ph: (816)842-8798
Free: 800-533-3524
Contact: Greg Wald, Owner
Facebook: www.facebook.com/kcflag
X (Twitter): x.com/AllNationsFlags
YouTube: www.youtube.com/channel/UCSM _t3dKioFGyLwncg0YEUg

Description: Custom flags and banners. **No. of Company-Owned Units:** 1. **Founded:** 1924. **Franchised:** 1996. **Equity Capital Needed:** $125,000 minimum. **Franchise Fee:** $15,000. **Training:** Yes.

LIBRARIES

3276 ■ Michigan State University - Special Collections Division - Russel B. Nye Popular Culture Collection
366 W Cir., Dr.
 East Lansing, MI 48824
URL: http://libguides.lib.msu.edu/c.php?g=96015
Scope: Popular culture; information; instruction; research. **Services:** Interlibrary loan; copying; collections open to the public for reference use only with required identification. **Holdings:** Figures not available.

3277 ■ Museum of Western Colorado - Loyd Files Research Library
462 Ute Ave.
 Grand Junction, CO 81501
URL: http://www.museumofwesternco.com/museum-of-the-west-virtual-tour
Scope: Local history; archaeology. **Services:** Copying; photographic reproduction (including scanning); center open to the public. **Founded:** 1965. **Holdings:** 3,000 books and monographs; 18,000 historical and aerial photographs; 2,200 audiocassettes; maps and vertical files; institutional archives; reels of microfilm; National Park Service publications on historic preservation; site inventories; internal databases; Internet.

3278 ■ Ohio State University - Billy Ireland Cartoon Library and Museum
Sullivant Hall
 1813 N High St.
 Columbus, OH 43210
Ph: (614)292-0538
Fax: (614)292-9101
Co. E-mail: cartoons@osu.edu
URL: http://cartoons.osu.edu
Contact: Jenny Robb, Curator Head
E-mail: robb.41@osu.edu
Facebook: www.facebook.com/TheBillyIrelandCartoonLibraryAndMuseum
X (Twitter): x.com/CartoonLibrary
Description: Contains reference materials, journals, books, online materials, and video and audio materials on cartoons. **Scope:** Cartoons and comics. **Services:** Copying; digital reproduction services; library open to the public upon registration. **Founded:** 1977. **Holdings:** 36,000 books on cartoon art; more than 450,000 original cartoons; 3,000 linear feet of manuscript materials; 2.5 million comic strip clippings; representative holdings of original art from editorial cartoonists, comic book artists, and comic strip artists. **Subscriptions:** 51,000 journals and other serials.

3279 ■ University of Minnesota - Children's Literature Research Collections (CLRC)
113 Elmer L. Andersen Library
 222 21st Ave. S
 Minneapolis, MN 55455
Ph: (612)624-4576
Co. E-mail: asc-clrc@umn.edu
URL: http://www.lib.umn.edu/collections/special/clrc
Contact: Lisa von Drasek, Curator Librarian
E-mail: lvondras@umn.edu
Scope: Historical and modern children's literature. **Services:** Copying; scanning; collection open for research only. **Founded:** 1949. **Holdings:** Books; manuscripts; illustrations; comic books; story papers; children's literature. **Awards:** Ezra Jack Keats/Kerlan Memorial Fellowship (Annual); The Kerlan Essay Award (Annual).

Commercial/Graphic Art Business

START-UP INFORMATION

3280 ■ *"Savvy Solutions" in Black Enterprise (Vol. 41, December 2010, No. 5, pp. 42)*
Pub: Earl G. Graves Ltd.
Contact: Earl Graves, Jr., President
Ed: Tennille M. Robinson. **Description:** Individual asks for advice in launching a graphic design business, particularly grants available in a slow economy.

ASSOCIATIONS AND OTHER ORGANIZATIONS

3281 ■ **Advertising Production Club of New York (APC-NY)**
60 E 42nd St., Ste. 721
New York, NY 10165
Co. E-mail: hello@apc-nyc.org
URL: http://apc-nyc.org
Contact: Natalie Alcide, Officer
E-mail: nataliealcide@gmail.com
Facebook: www.facebook.com/apcnyc
X (Twitter): x.comcom/apcnyc
Instagram: www.instagram.com/apcny
Description: A community of production professionals in traditional, digital, and emerging media. Aims to educate the members with the latest technology and trends in the industry. **Awards:** Tuition Assistance Award (Annual); APC High School Scholarship (Annual). **Geographic Preference:** National.

3282 ■ **American Institute of Graphic Arts (AIGA)**
228 Pk. Ave. S, Ste. 58603
New York, NY 10003
Ph: (212)807-1990
Co. E-mail: general@aiga.org
URL: http://www.aiga.org
Contact: Ashleigh Axios, President
Facebook: www.facebook.com/AIGAdesign
Linkedin: www.linkedin.com/company/aiga
X (Twitter): x.com/AIGAdesign
Instagram: www.instagram.com/AIGAdesign
YouTube: www.youtube.com/user/AIGAdesign
Pinterest: www.pinterest.com/aigadesign
Description: Publishes books. A national nonprofit membership organization with chapters in forty-two cities. It conducts an interrelated program of competitions, exhibitions, publications and educational activities to promote excellence in graphic design. Reaches market through direct mail. Does not accept unsolicited manuscripts. **Scope:** History of American communication design. **Services:** Library not open to the public. **Founded:** 1914. **Holdings:** Rare book; manuscript. **Publications:** *Trace: AIGA Journal of Design* (Triennial); *Gain: AIGA Journal of Business and Design* (Semiannual); *Voice: Journal of Design* (Quarterly); *365: AIGA Year in Design* (Annual). **Educational Activities:** AIGA Design Conference (Annual). **Awards:** AIGA Corporate Leadership Award (Periodic); AIGA Medal (Annual); AIGA 50 Books/50 Covers Competition (Annual). **Geographic Preference:** National.

3283 ■ **Associated Designers of Canada (ADC) [Association des Designers Canadiens]**
401 Richmond St. W, Ste. 350
Toronto, ON, Canada M5V 3A8
Ph: (416)907-5829
Co. E-mail: adc@designers.ca
URL: http://www.designers.ca
Contact: Ken MacKenzie, President
E-mail: president@designers.ca
Facebook: www.facebook.com/AssociatedDesignersOfCanada
X (Twitter): x.com/assocdesigncda
Instagram: www.instagram.com/associateddesignersofcanada
Description: Theatre designers, including set, costume, lighting, and sound. Promotes the professional advancement of members. Facilitates communication and cooperation among members. Conducts continuing professional development programs. **Founded:** 1965. **Geographic Preference:** National.

3284 ■ **Au Bas de l'Echelle [Rank and File (RF)]**
500 boul Gouin E ste., 207
Montreal, QC, Canada H3L 3R9
Ph: (514)270-7878
Co. E-mail: abe@aubasdelechelle.ca
URL: http://www.aubasdelechelle.ca
Contact: Colin Lefebvre-Bouchard, President
Description: Promotes increased recognition of the working rights of nonsyndicated workers. Represents members' interests; gathers and disseminates information to increase public awareness of conditions faced by nonsyndicated workers. **Founded:** 1975. **Publications:** *Aub bas de l'echelle...pas pour toujours* (Quarterly). **Geographic Preference:** National.

3285 ■ *Aub bas de l'echelle...pas pour toujours*
500 boul Gouin E ste., 207
Montreal, QC, Canada H3L 3R9
Ph: (514)270-7878
Co. E-mail: abe@aubasdelechelle.ca
URL: http://www.aubasdelechelle.ca
Contact: Colin Lefebvre-Bouchard, President
URL(s): www.aubasdelechelle.ca/publications-interventions/bulletins
Released: Quarterly **Availability:** Print.

3286 ■ **California Society of Printmakers (CSP) - Library**
PO Box 194202
San Francisco, CA 94119-4202
Co. E-mail: info@caprintmakers.org
URL: http://www.caprintmakers.org
Contact: Karen Gallagher Iverson, Vice President
Facebook: www.facebook.com/caprintmakers
Instagram: www.instagram.com/californiasocietyofprintmakers
Description: Fosters the appreciation of prints and printmaking; sponsors education programs, including exhibitions. **Scope:** Printmaker. **Founded:** 1912. **Holdings:** Figures not available. **Publications:** *California Printmaker* (Annual). **Educational Activities:** Annual Membership Exhibition (Annual). **Geographic Preference:** National.

3287 ■ **Canadian Association of Professional Image Creators (CAPIC) [L'Association Canadienne des Createurs Professionnels de L'Image]**
RPO Galleria
Toronto, ON, Canada M6H 4H7
Ph: (416)462-3677
Free: 888-252-2742
Co. E-mail: info@capic.org
URL: http://www.capic.org
Contact: Hai Au Bui, President
E-mail: natlpresident@capic.org
Facebook: www.facebook.com/CAPICnational
X (Twitter): x.com/CapicNational
Instagram: www.instagram.com/capicnational
Description: Photographers and illustrators employed in communications. Promotes professional and artistic advancement of members. Represents members' interests before industrial organizations; formulates standards of ethics and practice for members. **Founded:** 1978. **Geographic Preference:** National.

3288 ■ **Design Professionals of Canada (GDC) [Societe des designers graphiques du Canada]**
Arts Court, 2 Daly Ave.
Ottawa, ON, Canada K1N 6E2
Free: 877-496-4453
URL: http://descan.ca
Contact: Marga Lopez, President
E-mail: president@descan.ca
Description: Certification body for graphic arts and design in Canada. Members include graphic designers, administrators, educators, students, and organizations promoting graphic design. Promotes professional development. **Founded:** 1956. **Publications:** *Graphic Design* (Periodic); *Regional Newsletter* (Periodic); *The National*. **Awards:** Ray Hrynkow Scholarship (Annual); The Cheryl Lynn Rutledge Northern Indigenous Student Award (Annual); Society of Graphic Designers of Canada Adobe Scholarships (Annual); Society of Graphic Designers of Canada Applied Arts Scholarships (Annual); Society of Graphic Designers of Canada Veer Scholarships (Annual). **Geographic Preference:** National.

3289 ■ **National Oil and Acrylic Painters' Society (NOAPS)**
PO Box 1485
Montgomery, TX 77356
Co. E-mail: membership@noaps.org
URL: http://www.noaps.org
Contact: Patricia Tribastone, President

Facebook: www.facebook.com/NOAPSociety
Instagram: www.instagram.com/natoilan dacrylicsociety
YouTube: www.youtube.com/channel/UCWZib0mlg 3J8L1fluYsb_nA
Pinterest: www.pinterest.com/noaps
Description: Represents artists and others interested in exhibition and sales of original oil and acrylic paintings. **Founded:** 1991. **Publications:** *NOAPS Newsletter* (Semiannual). **Geographic Preference:** National.

3290 ■ Organization of Black Designers (OBD)
300 M St. SW, Ste. N110
  Washington, DC 20024
Ph: (937)837-6319
Co. E-mail: orgblackdesigners@gmail.com
URL: http://obd.org
Contact: Michael Chabbi, President
Facebook: www.facebook.com/groups/OrganizationBlackDesigners
Description: Black designers involved in graphic design, animation, Web design, film/video, illustration, user interface design, or mobile app design. Strives to support black designers through program development, business opportunities, scholarly pursuit, and continuing education. **Founded:** 1968. **Publications:** *DesigNation* (Biennial); *OBData* (Weekly). **Educational Activities:** DesigNation. **Geographic Preference:** National; Multinational.

3291 ■ Society for Experiential Graphic Design (SEGD)
1900 L St. NW, Ste. 710
  Washington, DC 20036
Ph: (202)638-5555
Co. E-mail: segd@segd.org
URL: http://segd.org
Contact: Anna Crider, President
Facebook: www.facebook.com/SEGDcommunity
X (Twitter): x.com/segd
Pinterest: www.pinterest.com/segdpin
Description: Designers and manufacturers of sign systems and environmental graphics. Establishes educational guidelines for professional development and governmental guidelines for environmental graphics programs; provides a forum for interaction and communication among members who are from a variety of design disciplines; compiles and disseminates technical data. **Scope:** Design. **Services:** Library not open to the public. **Founded:** 1974. **Holdings:** Educational materials; slide collection. **Publications:** *Industry Directory* (Annual); *Society for Environmental Graphic Design--Industry Directory* (Annual); *SEGD Membership Directory* (Annual); *eg Magazine* (Annual); *Professional Firm Directory* (Annual); *SEGD Compensation & Billing Survey*; *SEGD Green Paper: Best Practices, Strategies, and Scenarios for Sustainability in Environmental Graphic Design*; *What is Exhibition Design*; *You Are Here: Graphics That Direct, Explain & Entertain*. **Educational Activities:** SEGD Conference Experience (Annual). **Awards:** SEGD Distinguished Member Award (Annual); SEGD Gold Arrow Award (Irregular). **Geographic Preference:** National.

REFERENCE WORKS

3292 ■ *"3M Teams Up with Graphic Design Company Wrapmate"* in *Twin Cities Business* (September 25, 2019)
URL(s): tcbmag.com/news/articles/2019/september/3m-teams-up-with-graphic-design-company-wrapmate
Ed: Amanda Ostuni. **Released:** September 25, 2019. **Description:** A new partnership between 3M and a California-based design company named Wrapmate is providing businesses a new way to create vehicle graphics. **Availability:** Online.

3293 ■ *"6 Tips to Find Graphic Designers for Your Small Businesses"* in *DesignHill* (December 20, 2017)
Ed: Alice Jackson. **Released:** December 20, 2017. **Description:** Discusses the importance of utilizing graphic design services for your startup or small business. This article discusses six tips to find graphic designers who can design what you need to help your small business. **Availability:** Online.

3294 ■ *"8 Reasons Why Small Businesses Need to Make Graphic Design a Priority"* in *penjji.co* (December 12, 2018)
Ed: Jie Kuang. **Released:** December 12, 2018. **Description:** Discusses the importance of utilizing good graphic design from the start of your business to ensure that you are capturing and maintaining the audience you want and closing on the sales you need. This article details eight reasons to make graphic design a priority. **Availability:** Online.

3295 ■ *"10 Powerful Marketing Strategies for Designers"* in *JUST Creative Blog* (March 9, 2020)
Ed: Lidia Staron. **Released:** March 09, 2020. **Description:** Creating a successful marketing strategy for your design business does not have to be complicated. This article discusses simple ways to make an effective marketing strategy to help you grown your brand. **Availability:** Online.

3296 ■ *"12 Ways to Promote Your Freelance Graphic Design Business"* in *millo.com* (April 2, 2020)
Ed: Chris Walker. **Released:** April 02, 2020. **Description:** Provides thirteen easy, actionable, and powerful strategies that graphic designers can use to win new clients. **Availability:** Online.

3297 ■ *26 Best Small Business Ideas for Graphic Designers in 2020*
Description: Graphic designers create logos, posters, newsletters, brochures, signs, and other forms of visual communication, and the industry includes many activities, including corporate identity/branding, advertising, print production, and web design. This article offers a variety of small business ideas for graphic designers to earn income. **Availability:** Online.

3298 ■ *"Agfa To Debut New: M-Press Leopard"* in *American Printer* (Vol. 128, June 1, 2011, No. 6)
Description: M-Press Leopard is a new version of the machine that offers advanced ink jet technology at a lower price point. Agfa Graphics introduced the new version that allows for new applications that require more manual handling. **Availability:** Print; Online.

3299 ■ *"Avanti Hosts 19th Annual User's Conference in Washington, DC"* in *American Printer* (Vol. 128, July 1, 2011, No. 7)
Description: Avanti Computer Systems Ltd. hosted its 19th annual users conference in Washington DC. In-plant and commercial printers were in attendance. **Availability:** Online.

3300 ■ *"Avoid a Tablet Generation Gap"* in *American Printer* (Vol. 128, July 1, 2011, No. 7)
Description: Individuals between the ages of 18-34 are the only generation that is more likely to own a laptop computer or netbook insead of a desktop computer. Statistical data included. **Availability:** Online.

3301 ■ *"Ben Hulse"* in *Canadian Business* (Vol. 85, August 13, 2012, No. 13, pp. 55)
Ed: Graham F. Scott. **Description:** Graphic designer Ben Hulse explains the reason for rebranding Canada's Olympic team and how it differs from rebranding a private corporate logo. Hulse discusses his background in music and how he shifted to design. **Availability:** Print; Online.

3302 ■ *"Challenges Await Quad in Going Public"* in *Milwaukee Business Journal* (Vol. 27, January 29, 2010, No. 18, pp. A1)
Pub: The Business Journal
Contact: Heather Ladage, President
E-mail: hladage@bizjournals.com
Ed: Rich Rovito. **Description:** Sussex, Wisconsin-based Quad/Graphics Inc.'s impending acquisition of rival Canadian World Color Press Inc. will transform it into a publicly held entity for the first time. Quad has operated as a private company for nearly 40 years and will need to adjust to changes, such as the way management shares information with Quad/Graphics' employees. Details of the merger are included. **Availability:** Print; Online.

3303 ■ *"ContiTech Celebrates 100 Years"* in *American Printer* (Vol. 128, July 1, 2011, No. 7)
Description: ContiTech celebrated 100 years in business. The firm started in 1911 after developing the first elastic printing blanket. Other milestones for the firm include its manufacturing process for compressible printing blankets, the Conti-Air brand and climate-neutral printing blankets. **Availability:** Print; Online.

3304 ■ *"Crouser Releases Offline UV Coating Price Report"* in *American Printer* (Vol. 128, June 1, 2011, No. 6)
Description: Crouser and Associates will offer the 'Pricing Off-Line UV Coating' report that provides background information on all three types of protective printing coatings and price guidance. The report will also offer comparisons of four popular types of offline equipment.

3305 ■ *"Design Center Shows Quality of Digital Paper"* in *American Printer* (Vol. 128, June 1, 2011, No. 6)
Description: Digital Design Centers allows printers to customize marketing tools in order to promote their own digital printing capabilities. **Availability:** Online.

3306 ■ *"Digital Printing Walks the Plank"* in *American Printer* (Vol. 128, August 1, 2011, No. 8)
Description: Digital print manufacturing is discussed. **Availability:** Online.

3307 ■ *"Feeding the Elephants While Searching for Greener Pastures"* in *American Printer* (Vol. 128, July 1, 2011, No. 7)
Ed: Bob Rosen. **Description:** Three steps to help printers to build a new business while facing the challenges to the existing business are outlined. **Availability:** Print.

3308 ■ *"Flint Group Raises Prices of Offset Inks in EMEA"* in *American Printer* (Vol. 128, August 1, 2011, No. 8)
Description: Due to the rising cost for raw materials, Flint Group is raising their prices for inks and coatings in North American. **Availability:** Online.

3309 ■ *"Formula One Makes Room(s) for Aspiring Entrepreneur in Austin"* in *Austin Business Journal* (Vol. 31, July 1, 2011, No. 17, pp. 1)
Pub: Austin Business Journal
Contact: Rachel McGrath, Director
E-mail: rmcgrath@bizjournals.com
Ed: Vicky Garza. **Description:** Formula One fan and graphic designer Danielle Crespo cashes in on the June 17, 2012 racing event in Austin, Texas via hosting a Website that allows users to book hotel rooms. She invested less than $100 and long hours on this enterprise which now has 74,000-plus visitors. **Availability:** Print; Online.

3310 ■ *"Four Exhibition Considerations"* in *American Printer* (Vol. 128, August 1, 2011, No. 8)
Description: Four questions to ask at the Graph Expo will help printers improve their own business. **Availability:** Print; Download; PDF.

3311 ■ *"Fujifilm Invites Printers to Take the 'Onset Challenge"* in *American Printer* (Vol. 128, August 1, 2011, No. 8)
Description: Fujifilm North American Corporation's Graphic Systems Division offers a new five-step product selection and return-on-investment calculator for the Onset family of wide-format printers. **Availability:** Online.

3312 ■ *"Graphic Design for Small Businesses: Fake It 'Til You Make It"* in *WSI* (February 26, 2020)
Ed: Cecilia Decima. **Released:** February 26, 2020. **Description:** Discusses the impact that graphic design can make on the presentation of your business. Affording a good graphic design company is not always feasible for startups or small businesses. This article discusses another option -- a web app called Canva -- that all small businesses should keep in their arsenal for times when a using a professional isn't feasible. **Availability:** Online.

3313 ■ *Graphic Monthly--Estimators' & Buyers' Guide Issue (Canada)*
Pub: Masthead Publishing Ltd.
Contact: Sandy Donald, Publisher
E-mail: s.donald@northisland.ca
URL(s): www.ebguide.ca
Ed: Filomena Tamburri. **Released:** Latest edition:- 2019. **Price:** $12, for per copy (Western Edition); $25, for per copy (Ontario Edition. **Description:** Publication includes list of about 800 suppliers of graphic arts products and services, such as trade printers, art studios, film houses, binding equipment manufacturers, and printing equipment manufacturers. **Entries include:** Company name, address, phone, product or service. **Arrangement:** Classified by product/service. **Indexes:** Product/service. **Availability:** Print; Online.

3314 ■ *"Graphic Tech Acquires First U.S. :M-Press Tiger with Inline Screen Printing"* in *American Printer* (Vol. 128, June 1, 2011, No. 6)
Description: Graphic Tech located in California bought M-Press Tiger, the first in North America with an inline screen printing unit. **Availability:** Online.

3315 ■ *How to Market Your Graphic Designs*
Ed: Miranda Brookins. **Description:** Graphic designers create everything from logos and marketing collateral to wedding invitations and book cover designs. This article discusses how freelancers can market their designs and promote their services to attract new clients.

3316 ■ *How to Outsource Graphic Design (and Grow Your Business)*
Ed: Lindsay Kramer. **Description:** Outsourcing makes it possible for companies to serve their clients efficiently by delegating tasks to others who can do them better. This article discusses the economics of outsourcing graphic design and whether it's right for your small business. **Availability:** Online.

3317 ■ *"How to Start Your Own Graphic Design Business: Step-by-Step"* in *JUST Creative Blog* (December 17, 2018)
Released: December 17, 2018. **Description:** Provides a 13-step guide to start your own graphic design business. **Availability:** Online.

3318 ■ *"Interchangeable or Irreplaceable?"* in *American Printer* (Vol. 128, August 1, 2011, No. 8)
Description: Creating and maintaining customers is important for all graphic design and printing companies. Tips are shared to help maintain good customer satisfaction and repeat business. **Availability:** Online.

3319 ■ *"KBA, Graphic Art System Partner on Cold Foil"* in *American Printer* (Vol. 128, June 1, 2011, No. 6)
Description: KBA North America has partnered with Graphic Art System to retrofit and equip presses with cold foil machines. **Availability:** Online.

3320 ■ *"Kodak Offers Cloud-Based Operating Option"* in *American Printer* (Vol. 128, June 1, 2011, No. 6)
Description: Kodak partnered with VMware to offer its first Virtual Operating Environment option for Kodak Unified Workflow Solutions. The new feature enables cost savings, increased efficiency and failover protection. **Availability:** Online.

3321 ■ *"New Approach to Mechanical Binding"* in *American Printer* (Vol. 128, July 1, 2011, No. 7)
Description: EcoBinder coil binding system from Kugler-Womako eliminates traditional plastic combs or wire spiral with the use of 22-mm wide printable paper rings. **Availability:** Online.

3322 ■ *"One World"* in *American Printer* (Vol. 128, August 1, 2011, No. 8)
Description: Graph Expo will highlight entrepreneurs focused on the connection between content, technology and business models. **Availability:** Print; Online.

3323 ■ *"Paper Replaces PVC for Gift Cards"* in *American Printer* (Vol. 128, June 1, 2011, No. 6)
Description: Monadnock Envi Card Stock replaces paper for gift cards, loyalty cards, membership cards, hotel keys and durable signage. This renewable wood fiber alternative to PVC card materials comes from Monadock Paper Mills. **Availability:** Online.

3324 ■ *"Partnering for Success"* in *Art Business News* (Vol. 36, October 2009, No. 10, pp. 4)
Description: In such a volatile economy many savvy artists and gallery owners are turning to out-of-the-box partnerships for continued success; these partnerships are also pervading the Internet, especially with such social media networks as Facebook and Twitter where artists and businesses can develop a loyal following. **Availability:** PDF; Online.

3325 ■ *"PrintCity Shares Guide for Carbon Footprinting"* in *American Printer* (Vol. 128, June 1, 2011, No. 6)
Description: PrintCity Alliance published its new report, 'Carbon Footprint & Energy Reduction for Graphic Industry Value Chain.' The report aims to help improve the environmental performance of printers, converters, publishers, brand owners and their suppliers. **Availability:** Online.

3326 ■ *"Printers to the Trade"* in *American Printer* (Vol. 128, July 1, 2011, No. 7)
Description: Wholesale printing is discussed. Two wholesale printers share insight into their success, from business philosophies in general to practices that build strong relationships. **Availability:** Online.

3327 ■ *"The Rage Offstage at Marvel"* in *Barron's* (Vol. 88, June 30, 2008, No. 26, pp. 19)
Pub: Dow Jones & Company Inc.
Contact: Almar Latour, Chief Executive Officer
Ed: Bill Alpert. **Description:** Lawsuits against Marvel Entertainment and Stan Lee are pushing the claims from Peter F. Paul that Stan Lee Media was undone by the actions of the accused. Paul's associates argue that Stan Lee Media owns rights to Marvel characters and that they want half the profits that Marvel is making. **Availability:** Online.

3328 ■ *"Reducing the Book's Carbon Footprint"* in *American Printer* (Vol. 128, July 1, 2011, No. 7)
Description: Green Press Initiative's Book Industry Environmental Council is working to achieve a 20 percent reduction in the book industry's carbon footprint by 2020. The Council is made up of publishers, printers, paper suppliers, and non-governmental organizations. **Availability:** Online.

3329 ■ *"Sappi Announces North American 'Printers of the Year' Gold Winners"* in *American Printer* (Vol. 128, July 1, 2011, No. 7)
Description: Sappi Fine Paper North America honored ten gold winners of its 14th North American Printers of the Year awards. Each gold winning printer will receive $20,000 to support marketing and brand initiatives. **Availability:** Print; Online.

3330 ■ *"Seeing the Light"* in *American Printer* (Vol. 128, July 1, 2011, No. 7)
Description: Four printing demos on sheetfed, digital, label and pad printing equipment were highlighted at the Fifth UV Days held in Stuttgart, Germany in May 2011. **Availability:** Online.

3331 ■ *"Seen & Noted: A Home's Identity in Black and White"* in *Crain's Chicago Business* (Vol. 31, April 21, 2008, No. 16, pp. 35)
Pub: Crain Communications Inc.
Contact: Barry Asin, President
Ed: Lisa Bertagnoli. **Description:** Real estate agents are finding that showing customers a written floor plan is a trend that is growing since many buyers feel that Online virtual tours distort a room. Although floor plans cost up to $500 to have drawn up, they clearly show potential buyers the exact dimensions of rooms and how they connect. **Availability:** Online.

3332 ■ *Seven Days in the Art World*
Pub: W.W. Norton & Company Ltd.
Contact: Stanley Kubrick, Director
Ed: Sarah Thornton. **Price:** $17.95, paperback. **Description:** A sociologist renders the interplay among buyers, critics, curators and makers of contemporary art. **Availability:** Print.

3333 ■ *"Seven Tips for Continuous Improvement"* in *American Printer* (Vol. 128, July 1, 2011, No. 7)
Description: Seven tips are given to help any graphic arts or printing company improve by integrating lean manufacturing into operations. **Availability:** Online.

3334 ■ *"Successful First Year for Twin Rivers"* in *American Printer* (Vol. 128, June 1, 2011, No. 6)
Description: Profile of Twin Rivers located in Maine. The firm manufactured 380,000 tons of free sheet and hybrid-groundwood papers in its first year. **Availability:** Online.

3335 ■ *"Tic-Tac-Show: Line Up the Opportunities at Graph Expo"* in *American Printer* (Vol. 128, August 1, 2011, No. 8)
Description: Graph Expo has become the US print industry's main event. There will be as many as 500 exhibitors at this year's event and the Graphic Arts Show Company lists over 30 co-located events as well as 53 new sessions in the seminar program's 28 education categories. **Availability:** PDF; Online.

3336 ■ *"Transcontinental to Exchange Assets with Quad/Graphics"* in *American Printer* (Vol. 128, August 1, 2011, No. 8)
Description: Transcontinental Inc. and Quad/Graphics Inc. entered into an agreement where Transcontinental will indirectly acquire all shares of Quad Graphics Canada Inc. **Availability:** Print; Online.

3337 ■ *"Try a Little Social Media"* in *American Printer* (Vol. 128, June 1, 2011, No. 6)
Description: Social media helps keep Ussery Printing on customers radar. Jim David, VP of marketing for the firm, states that 350 people following them on Facebook are from the local area. **Availability:** Print; Mailing list; Online.

3338 ■ *"Web to Print"* in *American Printer* (Vol. 128, August 1, 2011, No. 8)
Description: Jerry Kennelly, CEO and founder of Tweak.com believes that Web-to-Design is middleware with no content. His firm offers an easy to use interface that flows right into the printer's workflow with no additional costs. **Availability:** Online.

3339 ■ *Why Good Graphic Design Will Make Your Small Business Better*
Ed: Jennifer Kamerman. **Description:** Looks at why good graphic design will help your small business and why you should consider hiring a professional for your various graphic design needs.

STATISTICAL SOURCES

3340 ■ *RMA Annual Statement Studies*
Pub: Risk Management Association
Contact: Nancy Foster, President
Released: Annual. **Description:** Contains composite balance sheets and income statements for more than 360 industries, including the accounting, auditing, and bookkeeping industries. Also contains five years of comparative historical data for discerning trends. Includes 16 commonly used ratios, computed for most of the size groupings for nearly every industry.

TRADE PERIODICALS

3341 ■ *Applied Arts Magazine*
Pub: Applied Arts Inc.
Facebook: www.facebook.com/AppliedArtsMag
LinkedIn: www.linkedin.com/company/applied-arts-magazine
X (Twitter): x.com/appliedarts
Instagram: www.instagram.com/appliedartsmag
Pinterest: www.pinterest.ca/Appliedartsawards
Ed: Will Novosedlik. **Released:** Semiannual; Summer and Winter. **Price:** $60, for 1 year print & digital US; $75, for 1 year print & digital international; C$40, for print & digital only Canada 1 years; C$19.99, for 1 year digital only USA & international; $19.99, for 1 year digital only Canada; $30, for cover price per annual; C$9.99, for single issue online. **Description:** Visual communication arts magazine for designers, art directors, photographers, illustrators and other professionals in related fields. **Availability:** Print; Online.

3342 ■ *Before & After: How to Design Cool Stuff*
Pub: Before and After
URL(s): www.bamagazine.com
Facebook: www.facebook.com/beforeandaftermagazine
X (Twitter): twitter.com/bamagazine
Released: Bimonthly **Price:** $219, for one year price; $9, for one copy print price. **Description:** Trade magazine covering graphic design. **Availability:** Print; DVD; PDF; Online.

3343 ■ *Graphic Communicator*
Pub: International Brotherhood of Teamsters - Graphic Communications Conference
Contact: Kurt Freeman, President
E-mail: kfreeman@gciu.org
URL(s): teamster.org/graphic-communicator-archive
Ed: George Tedeschi. **Released:** Quarterly; January-February-March, April-May-June, July August-September, October November-December. **Price:** $12, U.S. and Canada; $15, Other countries. **Description:** Trade newspaper of the Graphic Communications International Union. **Availability:** Print; PDF.

3344 ■ *The Graphic Monthly*
Pub: North Island Publishing
Contact: Sandy Donald, President
E-mail: s.donald@northisland.ca
URL(s): www.graphicmonthly.ca
Ed: Filomena Tamburri. **Released:** Bimonthly **Description:** Printing and graphic design magazine. **Availability:** Print; Online.

TRADE SHOWS AND CONVENTIONS

3345 ■ Graphics of the Americas
Florida Graphics Alliance (FGA)
10524 Moss Pk. Rd., Ste. 204
Orlando, FL 32822
Ph: (407)240-8009
Co. E-mail: gabe@floridagraphics.org
URL: http://www.floridagraphics.org
Contact: Art Abbott, Contact
E-mail: art@abbottcg.com
URL(s): www.floridagraphics.org/member-news
X (Twitter): twitter.com/goaexpo
Description: Graphic arts and specialty printing equipment, supplies, and services. **Audience:** Commercial printers, digital printers, label printers, wide format printers, graphic designers, screen printers, packaging printers, specialty printers, sign printers, book printers, publishers, binders, converting professionals, print and media buyers. **Principal Exhibits:** Graphic arts and specialty printing equipment, supplies, and services.

3346 ■ Graphics Canada
Graphics Canada
180 Duncan Mill Rd., 4th Fl.
Toronto, ON, Canada M3B 1Z6
Ph: (416)385-2030
Co. E-mail: info@graphicscanada.com
URL: http://graphicscanada.com
Contact: Dan Mustata, Show Manager
E-mail: danmustata@graphicscanada.com
URL(s): graphicscanada.com
LinkedIn: www.linkedin.com/in/graphics-canada-expo-65073139
X (Twitter): twitter.com/graphicscanada
Frequency: Biennial. **Audience:** Professionals, printers, and other interested in graphics. Dates and Locations: 2025 Apr 09-11 Toronto International Centre, Mississauga, ON. **Telecommunication Services:** danmustata@graphicscanada.com.

CONSULTANTS

3347 ■ Concord Associates Co.
20 W Pk. St., Ste. 1
Lebanon, NH 03766
Ph: (603)448-1100
Co. E-mail: balagurassociates@gmail.com
URL: http://www.balagurassociates.com
Contact: Richard Balagur, Owner
Description: Offers business counsel and market and marketing consulting assistance in key areas of both the consumer and professional digital imaging fields. Primary emphasis is in digital cameras, ink jet and dye sublimation printers, digital mini labs and related or ancillary products such as flash memory cards for digital cameras. **Scope:** Offers business counsel and market and marketing consulting assistance in key areas of both the consumer and professional digital imaging fields. Primary emphasis is in digital cameras, ink jet and dye sublimation printers, digital mini labs and related or ancillary products such as flash memory cards for digital cameras. **Founded:** 1982.

3348 ■ Gate Group USA Inc.
137 Varick St., Rm. 400
New York, NY 10013-1105
Contact: Isaac Savitt, Chief Executive Officer
Description: Provider of foreign trade and international marketing consulting services and specializes in the graphic arts and printing-related industries. **Scope:** Provider of foreign trade and international marketing consulting services and specializes in the graphic arts and printing-related industries.

3349 ■ KiBiz Inc.
432 Knollwood Dr.
Thousand Oaks, CA 91320
Ph: (805)499-4912
Free: 800-946-2854
Co. E-mail: info@kibizsystems.com
URL: http://www.kibizsystems.com
Contact: Allen Imbarrato, President
Facebook: www.facebook.com/kibizsystems
LinkedIn: www.linkedin.com/company/kibiz-systems
Description: Training company specializing in learning technologies creates customized programs to develop an organization, do extensive needs analysis on the current level of organizational functioning and assesses leadership skills and develops individualized leadership development programs to improve leadership skills. **Scope:** Training company specializing in learning technologies creates customized programs to develop an organization, do extensive needs analysis on the current level of organizational functioning and assesses leadership skills and develops individualized leadership development programs to improve leadership skills. **Founded:** 1985. **Training:** Winning at Work and at Life; Developing a High Performance Organization; Maximizing Productivity with Fundamental Macintosh Tools; Creating Presentations with a Computer; Break through Technology. **Special Services:** KiBizSystem 4.5; KiShop; KiPoint; KiBizSystem 5.0.; KiBiz Accounting; KiBiz Production Management; Ki Sales Automation via EDI or XML.

3350 ■ LandaJob Advertising Staffing Specialists
8700 State Line Rd.
Leawood, KS 66206
LinkedIn: www.linkedin.com/company/landajob-advertising-&-marketing-talent
Description: Firm provides marketing, creative staffing, and career development services. **Scope:** Firm provides marketing, creative staffing, and career development services. **Founded:** 1985.

3351 ■ Landor Associates
WPP plc
44 Montgomery St., Fl. 17
San Francisco, CA 94104
Ph: 44 20 7282 4600
Fax: 44 20 7493 6819
URL: http://www.wpp.com
Description: Firm offers branding consultancy and strategic design services. **Scope:** A global brand consulting and strategic design firm. **Founded:** 1941. **Publications:** "Brand simple" Palgrave Macmillan, 2006.

3352 ■ Phillips & Associates L.L.C.
15825 Shady Grove Rd., Ste. 40
Rockville, MD 20850
Ph: (301)519-3280
Fax: (301)519-2790
Co. E-mail: contact@pallcfirm.com
URL: http://pallcfirm.com
Contact: Andrew W. Phillips, Contact
E-mail: aphillips@pallcfirm.com
Description: Business and financial planning consultants providing services in mergers and acquisitions, strategic planning and tax planning. Serves insurance agencies and the graphic arts industry. **Scope:** Business and financial planning consultants providing services in mergers and acquisitions, strategic planning and tax planning. Serves insurance agencies and the graphic arts industry. **Founded:** 1982.

3353 ■ Teague
110 Union St., Ste. 400
Seattle, WA 98101
Ph: (206)838-4200
Co. E-mail: hello@teague.com
URL: http://teague.com
LinkedIn: www.linkedin.com/company/teague
X (Twitter): x.com/teague1926
Instagram: www.instagram.com/teague1926
Description: Firm offers designing and consulting services. **Founded:** 1926.

3354 ■ VMS Inc.
02400 37 1/2 St.
Gobles, MI 49055
Ph: (269)377-0234
Co. E-mail: vms.texts@gmail.com
URL: http://vms-online.com
Contact: Michael S. Walsh, Contact
Description: Wholesaler. Specializes in textbooks, videos, and computer software for vocational education. Reaches market through direct mail, telephone sales, and trade shows. Stocks 3,000 text titles, publishes 60.Offers co-op display service, mailing service. **Scope:** Provider of marketing services to clients producing training materials for vocational schools, colleges, and industry. Assists in identifying and preparing training materials, training staff to prepare training materials, packaging, and developing marketing plans. Works with traditional publishers and clients wishing to convert internal training materials for external sale. Industries served: Automotive, building and machine trades, software, graphic arts and government in the U.S. and Canada. **Founded:** 1986. **Training:** Product Marketing; Direct Mail; Trade

Show Boothmanship; Product Evaluation. **Special Services:** Corel WordPerfect X4: Academic Version; WordPerfect Office X3 Essential Training; CorelDRAW Graphics Suite X4: Academic Version; AutoCAD LT 2010 for Windows; AutoCAD LT 2010 Student Version: 61 month License; TurboCAD Pro 16 Platinum Ed: Academic; TurboCAD PRO 16 Architectural: Academic; TurboCAD Mac PRO: Academic; TurboCAD Mac Deluxe 2D/3D: Academic; TurboFLOORPLAN 3D Home and Landscape PRO.

FRANCHISES AND BUSINESS OPPORTUNITIES

3355 ■ Greenbaum Marketing Communications
263 Calle Palacio
  Henderson, NV 89012
URL: http://greenbaummarketing.com
Contact: Martin Greenbaum, Chief Executive Officer
E-mail: mg@greenbaummarketing.com
Description: Firm provides lead generation, website development, online marketing and much more services. **Founded:** 2004.

3356 ■ Kwik Kopy Business Centers, Inc.
12715 Telge Rd.
  Cypress, TX 77429
Contact: Jay Groot, President
Description: Provider of printing and copying services. **Founded:** 2001. **Financial Assistance:** Yes **Managerial Assistance:** Provide business support, advertising, and marketing materials. **Training:** Owners attend classroom and field training, as well as ongoing training through workshops and conferences.

3357 ■ Sign Biz Inc. (SB)
24681 La Plz., Ste. 270
  Dana Point, CA 92629
Free: 800-633-5580
Fax: (949)234-0426
Co. E-mail: sosa@signbiz.com
URL: http://www.signbiz.com
Contact: Teresa M. Young, President
Facebook: www.facebook.com/SIGNBIZ
X (Twitter): x.com/SIGNBIZ
Instagram: www.instagram.com/signbiznetwork
YouTube: www.youtube.com/signbiznetwork
Description: Visual communication stores developing digital sign making. **Founded:** 1989. **Training:** 2 weeks initial training at corporate office and 1-2 week home study program.

COMPUTERIZED DATABASES

3358 ■ *Art Index*™
EBSCO Information Services
  10 Estes St.
  Ipswich, MA 01938
Ph: (978)356-6500
Free: 800-653-2726
Co. E-mail: information@ebsco.com
URL: http://www.ebsco.com
Contact: Tim Collins, Chief Executive Officer
URL(s): www.ebsco.com/products/research-databases/art-index
Description: Indexing for over 680 periodicals and 14,000 art dissertations. **Availability:** Online. **Type:** Bibliographic.

3359 ■ *Art on Screen Database*™
Program for Art on Film Inc.
  c/o Pratt SILS, 200 Willoughby Ave.
  Brooklyn, NY 11205
Ph: (718)399-4506
Fax: (718)399-4507
Co. E-mail: info@artfilm.org
URL: http://www.artfilm.org
Contact: J. Paul Getty Trust, Founder
URL(s): www.artfilm.org/aosdb.htm
Availability: CD-ROM; Online. **Type:** Directory.

3360 ■ *Impressionism and Its Sources*
TDC Interactive - Technology Dynamics Corp.
  1601 N Sepulveda Blvd., No. 374
  Manhattan Beach, CA 90267
Ph: (310)406-1803
Fax: (310)406-0833
Co. E-mail: contact@tdcinteractive.com
URL: http://www.tdcinteractive.net
URL(s): www.tdcinteractive.net/Impres.htm
Price: $49.95, Single issue. **Availability:** CD-ROM; Online. **Type:** Full-text; Image.

LIBRARIES

3361 ■ Art Center College of Design - James Lemont Fogg Memorial Library
1700 Lida St.
  Pasadena, CA 91103
Co. E-mail: library@artcenter.edu
URL: http://www.artcenter.edu/about/campus/hillside-campus/facilities/james-lemont-fogg-memorial-library.html
Contact: Mario Ascencio, Librarian
Scope: Educational material. **Services:** Copying. **Holdings:** 100,000 volumes of books and periodicals; 13,000 DVDs; 90,000 visual file. **Subscriptions:** 400 magazines.

3362 ■ Art Institute of Boston at Lesley University Library [AIB Library]
Lesley University 29 Everett St.
  Cambridge, MA 02138
Ph: (617)868-9600
URL: http://lesley.edu
Contact: Abby Mancini, Librarian
E-mail: amancini@lesley.edu
Description: Collects and preserves manuscripts, publications, administrative records, photographs, audiovisual materials, school memorabilia, and related ephemera that document the history of Lesley since its founding in 1909 to the present. **Scope:** Education materials. **Services:** Copying; scanning; Library open to the public for reference use only; borrowing materials; course reserves; interlibrary loan; research help; library liaison program; library instruction; off-campus services; alumni services; museum passes; study spaces and lockers; printers, copiers and scanners. **Founded:** 1969. **Holdings:** 140,000 books; 45,000 slides; 12,000 art books; 13,000 children's literature titles. **Subscriptions:** journals and other serials journals.

3363 ■ Baltimore Museum of Art (BMA) - The E. Kirkbride Miller Art Research Library
10 Art Museum Dr.
  Baltimore, MD 21218-3898
Ph: (443)573-1700
Fax: (443)573-1582
Co. E-mail: info@artbma.org
URL: http://www.artbma.org
Contact: Christine Dietze, Chief Operating Officer
Facebook: www.facebook.com/artbma
X (Twitter): x.com/artbma
YouTube: www.youtube.com/user/artBMA
Description: Publishes uncatalogued of exhibitions and collections. Does not accept unsolicited manuscripts. **Scope:** Architectural plans. **Services:** Open to the public by appointment. **Founded:** 1914. **Holdings:** 71,000 items; monographs; reference books; periodicals; vertical files; photographs; films; audio recordings.

3364 ■ California College of the Arts Libraries - Meyer Library
Meyer Library, 5212 Broadway
  Oakland, CA 94618
URL: http://libraries.cca.edu/about-us/about-us/policies/collection-development-policy
Description: Collections begin from that time and focus on the fine arts and visual and critical studies. Special Collections include artists' books, the Hamaguchi Study Print Collection, Faculty Development Collection, Games Collection, CCA / C College Archives and the Capp Street Project archive. **Scope:** Fine arts; architecture; design; visual and critical studies; writing and literature. **Services:** Open to the public. **Founded:** 1907. **Subscriptions:** magazines newspapers periodicals (includes journals) Books; records.

3365 ■ Cleveland Institute of Art (CIA) - Jessica R. Gund Memorial Library
11610 Euclid Ave.
  Cleveland, OH 44106
Ph: (216)421-7418
Co. E-mail: marketing@cia.edu
URL: http://www.cia.edu/library
Contact: Kathryn Heidemann, President
Facebook: www.facebook.com/cleinstituteart
Linkedin: www.linkedin.com/edu/school
X (Twitter): x.com/cleinstituteart
Instagram: www.instagram.com/cleinstituteart
YouTube: www.youtube.com/user/cleinstituteart
Scope: Visual art; design; and craft. **Services:** Interlibrary loan; copying; library open to the public. **Founded:** 1882. **Holdings:** 47,000 books, exhibition catalogs, and CD-ROMs; 10,000 bound periodical volumes; 125,000 slides; 9,000 pictures; 37 volumes and boxes of archival materials; 4,000 reels of microfilm; 15,000 microfiche; 600 videotapes, DVDs and films; 1,600 sound recordings.

3366 ■ Des Moines Art Center Library
4700 Grand Ave.
  Des Moines, IA 50312
Ph: (515)277-4405
Co. E-mail: marketing@desmoinesartcenter.org
URL: http://www.desmoinesartcenter.org
Contact: Jeff Fleming, Museum Director
E-mail: jfleming@desmoinesartcenter.org
Facebook: www.facebook.com/DesMoinesArtCenter
X (Twitter): x.com/dmartcenter
Instagram: www.instagram.com/desmoinesartcenter
YouTube: www.youtube.com/user/DesMoinesArtCenter
Pinterest: www.pinterest.com/dmartcenter
Description: The not-for-profit Des Moines Art Center engages diverse local and international audiences with the art of today through its museum and school, adding to the cultural record through collections and programs. **Scope:** Arts. **Services:** Library open to the public. **Founded:** 1948. **Holdings:** 5,000 works of art; 4,000 works on paper.

3367 ■ Free Library of Philadelphia - Art Department
1901 Vine St., Fl. 2nd
  Philadelphia, PA 19103
Ph: (215)686-5403
Co. E-mail: erefart@freelibrary.org
Facebook: www.facebook.com/people/Art-Department-Free-Library-of-Philadelphia/100064316034731
Scope: Art history; African and African-American art; architecture; painting; sculpture; costume history; drawing; decorative arts; ceramics; cartoons; crafts; design; commercial art; photography; graphic arts; numismatics. **Services:** Interlibrary loan; copying. **Founded:** 1891. **Holdings:** 60,000 volumes; 35,000 pamphlets and clippings; 735 periodical titles; card index of 15,700 artists; 1,500 original graphics (1491 to present); 800,000 photographs and art reproductions in loan collection; postcards; greeting cards; posters. **Subscriptions:** 220 journals and other serials.

3368 ■ Hallmark Cards, Inc.
Hallmark Cards, Inc.
  2501 McGee St.
  Kansas City, MO 64108
Ph: (816)274-5111
Free: 800-425-5627
URL: http://corporate.hallmark.com
Contact: Mike Perry, President
URL(s): www.hallmark.com
Facebook: www.facebook.com/Hallmark
X (Twitter): twitter.com/Hallmark
Instagram: www.instagram.com/hallmark
YouTube: www.youtube.com/user/hallmarkcards
Pinterest: www.pinterest.com/hallmark

Description: Manufacturer of greeting cards, stationery, and related products. **Founded:** 1910. **Educational Activities:** FMI Midwinter Executive Conference (Annual).

3369 ■ Milwaukee Area Technical College - Rasche Memorial Library
Downtown Milwaukee Campus, 700 W State St.
Milwaukee, WI 53233-1443
Ph: (414)297-6282
Co. E-mail: info@matc.edu
URL: http://www.matc.edu/library/index.cfm
Contact: Dr. Vicki J. Martin, President
Facebook: www.facebook.com/matcmilwaukee
X (Twitter): twitter.com/matcmilwaukee
Instagram: www.instagram.com/matcmilwaukee
YouTube: www.youtube.com/user/InsideMATC
Description: It consists of books, journals, references, videos, and posters. **Scope:** Applied science and technology; graphic arts; liberal arts; health sciences. **Services:** Interlibrary loan; copying; Library open to the public. **Founded:** 1937. **Holdings:** 70,000 volumes.

3370 ■ Milwaukee Art Museum - George Peckham Miller Art Research Library
700 N Art Museum Dr.
Milwaukee, WI 53202
Co. E-mail: library@mam.org
URL: http://mam.org/collection/research-center
Contact: Heather Winter, Archivist Librarian
Scope: History of art and design. **Services:** interlibrary loan ; Library open to Art Museum patrons. **Founded:** 1916. **Holdings:** 20,000 volumes. **Subscriptions:** 70 journals and other serials.

3371 ■ Milwaukee Institute of Art & Design Library (MIAD Library)
273 E Erie St.
Milwaukee, WI 53202
Ph: (414)847-3342
Co. E-mail: library@miad.edu
URL: http://sites.google.com/miad.edu/miadlibrary
Contact: Nancy Siker, Director, Library Services
E-mail: nancysiker@miad.edu
Scope: Art history; design. **Services:** Copying; library open to the public with restrictions. **Founded:** 1977. **Holdings:** 18,800 books, videos and DVD's;82 current periodicals.

3372 ■ Minneapolis College of Art and Design Library (MCAD)
2501 Stevens Ave.
Minneapolis, MN 55404
URL: http://www.mcad.edu/campus-info/library
Scope: Literary; artistic resource. **Services:** open to the public for reference use only. **Founded:** 1886. **Holdings:** 50000 volumes; 145,000 slides; college archives.

3373 ■ Modern Art Museum of Fort Worth Library
3200 Darnell St.
Fort Worth, TX 76107
URL: http://www.themodern.org/about-modern
Description: Modern art museum and library. **Scope:** Art. **Founded:** 1892. **Holdings:** Figures not available.

3374 ■ Paier College of Art Inc. Library
20 Gorham Ave.
Hamden, CT 06514
Ph: (203)287-3031
Fax: (203)287-3021
URL: http://www.paier.edu
Contact: Robert E. Zappalorti, Director
Description: The library consists of newspapers, general education and art books, periodicals, slides and pictures, a digital slide collection, and audiovisual materials. **Scope:** Fine arts, graphic design, interior design, photography, illustration, general academics. **Services:** Library open to the public for research only. **Founded:** 1985. **Holdings:** 13,000 books; 71 periodical titles; 30,000 pictures; 16,000 slides.

3375 ■ Parsons School of Design - Adam & Sophie Gimbel Design Library
66 5th Ave.
New York, NY 10011
URL: http://www.newschool.edu
Contact: David E. van Zandt, President
Scope: Education materials. **Services:** Interlibrary loan. **Founded:** 1896. **Holdings:** Figures not available.

3376 ■ Printing Brokerage/Buyers Association International (PB/BA) - Library
1530 Locust St., Mezzanine 124
Philadelphia, PA 19102
Ph: (215)821-6581
URL: http://pbba.org
Description: Promotes understanding, cooperation, and interaction among members while obtaining the highest standard of professionalism in the graphic arts industry. **Scope:** Printing and publishing marketing and corporate development specialists, whose services include start ups, joint ventures, acquisitions, mergers, contract negotiation, international trade, seminars, workshops, facilities planning, and cost reduction programs. Serves private industries as well as government agencies. **Founded:** 1985. **Holdings:** Figures not available. **Publications:** "Hot Markets for 2007-2008," Jan, 2005. **Training:** How to Sell Printing Effectively; Sales Compensation and Management; How to Buy Printing Effectively; Hot Markets; International Priority Commerce. **Awards:** PBBA Printing Broker Reseller of the Year (Annual). **Geographic Preference:** Multinational. **Special Services:** Findprint®; Salesort®.

3377 ■ Printing United Alliance Center for Technology and Research - Library [Printing Industries of America's Center for Technology and Research]
2000 Corporate Dr., Ste. 205
Wexford, PA 15090
Ph: (412)259-1710
Co. E-mail: info@printing.org
URL: http://www.printing.org/programs/technology-research
Facebook: www.facebook.com/printingunited
Linkedin: www.linkedin.com/company/printingunited
Instagram: www.instagram.com/printingind
Description: Serves the international graphic communications industries. Conducts research in graphic processes and their commercial applications, along with seminars and forums on graphic arts and environmental subjects. Conducts educational programs, including the publishing of graphic arts textbooks and learning modules, in addition to training and certification program in sheet-fed offset press operating, Web offset press operating, image assembly, and desktop publishing. Produces test images and quality control devices for the industry. Performs technical services for the graphic arts industry, including problem-solving, material evaluation, and plant audits. **Scope:** Human resources; economics; technologies; business growth. **Founded:** 1924. **Holdings:** Figures not available. **Publications:** "Re-Energize Your Printing Business," Partnership Publishing L.L.C.; "Handbook for Digital Printing and Variable-Data Printing"; "Flexography Primer"; "Process Controls Primer"; "The PDF Print Production Guide". **Training:** Creating Print Ready Files that Work Every Time; What Designers Need to Know about Sustainability; What Every Designer Must Know About Color and Press Oks; New Frontiers for the 21st Century Graphic Designer; Color Management for Printing and Packaging; Web to Print Primer; Designing for Prepress Success; Profit Opportunity Expanding into New Markets with Ancillary Services; Winning Ways to Market Web to Print Work flow to Customers; PDF Preflight and Repair for Newbies; Cross Media Methods n Magic URLS, Microsites and More; Good Jobs Gone Bad 2009 Edition; Fine Tune Your Color Management; Automating for Survival; Best Practice Primer Winning Digital Printing Workflows; Maximize Press time with Pit Stop Maintenance; A How to Tactical Plan for Sustainability Success; Optimizing Your Digital Press Where it Works and Where its Broken; Offset Press Optimization How to Troubleshoot, Control and Accelerate; Performance Dashboard Stalking Waste in the Printers Processes; Technology Forecast What's Hot and What's Not; Lean n Green Tactics and Techniques for Removing Waste; Controlling the Print Process How to Avoid Customer Rejects; Process Control for Color Management Prepress through Press. **Educational Activities:** President's Conference (Annual). **Awards:** Naomi Berber Memorial Award (Annual); Printing Industries of America Education Award of Excellence (Annual); InterTech Technology Awards (Annual); Robert F. Reed Technology Medal (Annual); William D. Schaeffer Environmental Award (Annual); Frederick D. Kagy Education Award of Excellence (Annual). **Geographic Preference:** National.

3378 ■ Ringling College of Art and Design - Kimbrough Memorial Library
2700 N Tamiami Trl.
Sarasota, FL 34234
Ph: (941)351-5100
Co. E-mail: admissions@ringling.edu
URL: http://www.ringling.edu/news/dr-thompson-in-srq-daily
Contact: Dr. Larry Thompson, President
Description: Contains reference materials, journals, books, online materials, and video and audio materials on arts. **Scope:** Art history; interior design; graphic design; computer animation; photography; architecture; fine arts; decorative arts; illustration. **Services:** Interlibrary loan; copying; library open to artists and researchers. **Founded:** 1932. **Holdings:** 49,000 books; 110,000 art slides; 34 16mm films; 3,000 videocassettes and DVDs. **Subscriptions:** 320 journals and other serials.

3379 ■ Rochester Institute of Technology - Melbert B. Cary, Jr. Graphic Arts Collection
90 Lomb Memorial Dr.
Rochester, NY 14623
URL: http://archivesspace.rit.edu/repositories/2/resources/235
Scope: Graphic art. **Holdings:** 45,000 volumes.

3380 ■ School of Visual Arts Library (SVA)
380 2nd Ave., 2nd Fl.
New York, NY 10010
Ph: (212)592-2660
Co. E-mail: admissions@sva.edu
URL: http://sva.edu/life-at-sva/academic-life/library
Contact: Caitlin Kilgallen, Director
E-mail: ckilgallen@sva.edu
Facebook: www.facebook.com/SVALibrary
Instagram: www.instagram.com/svalibrary
Scope: Art and design study. **Services:** Copying; library open to students, faculty, staff, and alumni (METRO passes honored). **Founded:** 1978. **Holdings:** Figures not available.

3381 ■ Smithsonian Institution - Smithsonian American Art Museum - National Portrait Gallery Library
Victor Bldg., Ste. 2100, 750 9th St. NW
Washington, DC 20001
Ph: (202)633-8230
Fax: (202)633-8232
Co. E-mail: aapglibrary@si.edu
URL: http://library.si.edu/libraries/american-art-and-portrait-gallery
Contact: Anne Evenhaugen, Librarian Head
Description: Supports the research of the Smithsonian American Art Museum, the National Portrait Gallery and the Archives of American Art, the AA/PG Library collection of 180,000 books, exhibition catalogs, catalogues raisonnes, serials and dissertations is concentrated in the area of American art, history, and biography with supportive materials on European art. **Scope:** American art, history; European art. **Founded:** 1937. **Holdings:** 23,000 works.

3382 ■ Smithsonian Institution - Smithsonian American Art Museum Photograph Archives
8th and G Sts., NW
Washington, DC 20004
URL: http://americanart.si.edu/art/highlights/photography

Scope: American art; Painting; Sculpture; Graphics. **Services:** Copying;Open to researchers by appointment. **Founded:** 1983.

3383 ■ Springfield Art Museum Library (SAM)
1111 E Brookside Dr.
Springfield, MO 65807
Ph: (417)837-5700
Co. E-mail: artmuseum@springfieldmo.gov
URL: http://www.sgfmuseum.org
Contact: Nick Nelson, Director
E-mail: nnelson@springfieldmo.gov
Facebook: www.facebook.com/sgfmuseum
X (Twitter): x.com/sgfmuseum
Instagram: www.instagram.com/sgfmuseum
Scope: Cultural; art. **Services:** Library open to the research by appointment only. **Founded:** 1926. **Holdings:** 10,000 art; 6,000 volumes. **Awards:** Springfield Art Museum Watercolor U.S.A. (Annual). **Geographic Preference:** National.

3384 ■ Universidad de Puerto Rico Recinto de Río Piedras Sistema de Bibliotecas Colección de las Artes [University of Puerto Rico - Library System - Arts Collection]
PO Box 23302
San Juan, PR 00931
Ph: (787)764-0000
URL: http://www.upr.edu/biblioteca-rrp/biblioteca-y-colecciones
Scope: Arts; historical and education materials. **Services:** Copying; library open to the public with restrictions. **Founded:** 1953. **Holdings:** 27,900 books; 205 slides; manuscripts; photographs; artist books; rare books; CDs.

3385 ■ University of Guam - Robert F. Kennedy Memorial Library Instructional Media Division
UOG Sta.
Mangilao, GU 96913
URL: http://www.uog.edu/student-services/rfk-library
Description: University library. **Scope:** Educational material. **Services:** Interlibrary loan; library open to the public. **Founded:** 1952. **Holdings:** 119,000 print titles and 213,916 print holdings; over 5,000 microfilm/microfiche units; 55 print serial titles; 7,718 audiovisual items and software; over 200, 000 eBooks.

3386 ■ University of Minnesota - Eric Sevareid Journalism Library
499 Wilson Library 309 19th Ave. S
Minneapolis, MN 55455
Ph: (612)624-3321
URL: http://www.lib.umn.edu/spaces/journalism/hours
Description: University of Minnesota Libraries. **Scope:** Journalism. **Services:** Interlibrary loan. **Founded:** 1941. **Subscriptions:** journals Books.

3387 ■ Walker Art Center - Library & Archives
725 Vineland Pl.
Minneapolis, MN 55403
Ph: (612)375-7680
Co. E-mail: library.archives@walkerart.org
URL: http://walkerart.org/library-research
Contact: Jill Vuchetich, Archivist Head
Description: Library consists of Walker's artist's book collections. **Scope:** Art; history. **Services:** Copying; reference services; open to the public by appointment. **Founded:** 1950. **Subscriptions:** 150 journals 35,000 books; 1,800 art books; 5,200 artist files; 4,000 linear feet records; 6,000 audio, video, and film titles; 640,000 still images.

3388 ■ Williams College - Chapin Library of Rare Books
26 Hopkins Hall Dr.
Williamstown, MA 01267
URL: http://specialcollections.williams.edu/collection-guides
Contact: Anne Peale, Librarian
E-mail: aep3@williams.edu
Description: Publishes catalogs and monographs describing library exhibitions and collections. Offers postcards from library collections. Does not accept unsolicited manuscripts. Reaches market through direct mail, reviews, listings, and distributors. **Scope:** Literature; history of science; art; architecture. **Services:** Library Open to the public; copying. **Founded:** 1923. **Holdings:** 3,000 books; 60,000 volumes; 100,000 manuscripts, prints, drawings, paintings, maps, photographs, bookplates, ephemera, memorabilia.

RESEARCH CENTERS

3389 ■ University of California, Los Angeles - Grunwald Center for the Graphic Arts
10899 Wilshire Blvd.
Los Angeles, CA 90024
Ph: (310)443-7078
Co. E-mail: info@hammer.ucla.edu
URL: http://hammer.ucla.edu/collections/grunwald-center-collection
Description: Integral unit of University of California, Los Angeles. Offers Friends of the Graphic Arts support group. **Scope:** Graphic arts, including 15th through 21st century prints and drawings, contemporary American photography, and artist illustrated books. **Founded:** 1956. **Publications:** *Exhibition catalogues* (Occasionally).

Commercial Mail Receiving Agency

ASSOCIATIONS AND OTHER ORGANIZATIONS

3390 ■ **Association of Alternate Postal Systems (AAPS)**
1965 E Avis Dr.
 Madison Heights, MI 48071
Ph: (248)268-8090
URL: http://www.aapsinc.org
Contact: Keith Somers, President
E-mail: ksomers@acimediagroup.com
Description: Companies in the business of delivering private postal advertising material to residences. Seeks to improve industry credibility and increase the public's awareness of the private postal industry. **Founded:** 1973. **Publications:** *Association of Alternate Postal Systems--Membership Directory* (Annual); *Association of Alternate Postal Systems--Member Directory; Association of Alternate Postal Systems--Update*. **Awards:** AAPS Lifetime Achievement Award (Annual). **Geographic Preference:** National.

REFERENCE WORKS

3391 ■ *"Ecovative Moves Beyond Packaging" in Business Review Albany (Vol. 41, August 1, 2014, No. 19, pp. 12)*
Description: Ecovative Design of Green Island, NY has started making new packaging materials to add to its biodegradable product line, including the Myco Board, a material similar to particleboard. Clients range from computer manufacturers to furniture retailers. **Availability:** Print; Online.

TRADE PERIODICALS

3392 ■ *Mailing Systems Technology (MAST)*
Pub: RB Publishing Co.
URL(s): mailingsystemstechnology.com/flex-1-Home
 .html
Linkedin: www.linkedin.com/grp/home?gid=2076240
X (Twitter): twitter.com/MailSystemsTech
YouTube: www.youtube.com/channel/UCqW8H40P
 _daZu1VRWaUUoYA
Ed: Amanda Armendariz. **Released:** 6/year **Description:** Trade magazine covering mailing and office practices. **Availability:** Print; Online.

3393 ■ *Postal Bulletin*
Pub: United States Postal Service
URL(s): about.usps.com/resources/postal-bulletin
 .htm
Released: Biweekly **Description:** Bulletin reporting U.S. Postal Service news. **Availability:** Download; PDF; Online.

TRADE SHOWS AND CONVENTIONS

3394 ■ **National Association of Postmasters of the United States Convention**
National Association of Postmasters of the United States (NAPUS)
8 Herbert St.
 Alexandria, VA 22305
Ph: (703)683-9027
Fax: (703)683-0923
Co. E-mail: membership@napus.org
URL: http://www.napus.org
URL(s): www.unitedpma.org/events/events/events-de
 tails/2020/08/01/default-calendar/4th-upma-national
 -convention
Frequency: Annual. **Description:** Office supplies and materials for the postal service. **Audience:** Postmasters and retirees. **Principal Exhibits:** Office supplies and materials for the postal service.

FRANCHISES AND BUSINESS OPPORTUNITIES

3395 ■ **Annex Brands, Inc.**
Annex Brands, Inc.
 7580 Metropolitan Dr., Ste. 200
 San Diego, CA 92108-4417
Ph: (619)563-4800
Free: 800-456-1525
Fax: (619)563-9850
URL: http://www.annexbrands.com
Contact: Patrick F. Edd, President
Description: Provider of postal, communication and business services in the convenience of a store setting. **Founded:** 1985. **Financial Assistance:** Yes **Training:** 2 week training at home office, plus 1 week at location. Ongoing training and support provided.

3396 ■ **Mail Boxes Etc. - MBEC Communications, Inc.**
1115 N Service Rd., Unit 1
 Oakville, ON, Canada L6M 2V9
Ph: (905)338-9754
URL: http://www.theupsstore.ca
Contact: David Druker, President
Facebook: www.facebook.com/TheUPSStoreCA
Linkedin: www.linkedin.com/company/the-ups-store
 -canada
X (Twitter): x.com/theupsstore_can
Instagram: www.instagram.com/theupsstoreca
YouTube: www.youtube.com/user/TheUPSS
 toreCanada
Description: With over 4,000 locations worldwide and over 260 centers operating in Canada, MBE is one of the largest and fastest growing business and communications service franchise. Services include expert packing services, shipping, worldwide courier services, black and white and color photocopies, electronic document services, digital color printing, fax sending and receiving, computer rental, word processing, Internet/email access and mail receiving services. **No. of Franchise Units:** 351. **Founded:** 1990. **Franchised:** 1991. **Equity Capital Needed:** $146,150-$179,550 plus working capital. **Franchise Fee:** $35,900. **Royalty Fee:** 6% of gross. **Training:** Complete pre-opening support provided, including site selection, lease negotiation, design and construction, training, marketing, as well as ongoing operational and marketing field support.

3397 ■ **Navis Pack & Ship Centers**
3005 Pennsylvania Ave.
 Colorado Springs, CO 80907
Ph: (719)633-2988
Co. E-mail: co1013@gonavis.com
URL: http://www.gonavis.com
Contact: Ethan Clark, Contact
Description: Packaging and shipping industry. **No. of Franchise Units:** 46. **Founded:** 1984. **Franchised:** 2001. **Equity Capital Needed:** $500,000 liquid capital; $200,000 net worth; actual $96,950-$172,650. **Franchise Fee:** $29,500. **Financial Assistance:** Yes **Training:** Offers 3 weeks training and certification course.

3398 ■ **Navis Pack and Ship Centers**
910 Rowntree Dairy Rd., Ste. 10
 Woodbridge, ON, Canada L4L 5W5
Ph: (416)201-4441
Co. E-mail: cn1005@gonavis.com
URL: http://www.gonavis.com
Contact: Ray Friedman, Contact
Description: Provider of packing, palletizing, crating, boxing and shipping services. **Founded:** 1990. **Training:** Yes.

3399 ■ **Packaging and Shipping Specialists (PASS)**
5211 85th St., Ste. 104
 Lubbock, TX 79424
Ph: (806)438-4477
Free: 800-877-8884
Co. E-mail: info@packship.com
URL: http://www.packship.com
Contact: Mike Gallagher, Founder
E-mail: mike@packship.com
Description: Firm provides packaging and shipping management services. **Founded:** 1981. **Training:** In classroom and on-the-job training.

3400 ■ **Pak Mail**
2443 S University Blvd.
 Denver, CO 80210
Ph: (303)744-6245
Fax: (303)744-6246
Co. E-mail: us013@pakmail.com
URL: http://www.pakmail.com
Facebook: www.facebook.com/OfficialPakMail
Description: One-stop shop offers the customer a convenient location to send packages, make copies, send or receive a fax or rent a private mailbox. **No. of Operating Units:** 400. **Founded:** 1984. **Equity Capital Needed:** $50,000 cash or liquid assets ; $150,000 net worth. **Franchise Fee:** $29,550. **Financial Assistance:** Yes **Training:** Provides training, education & ongoing support to build your business.

3401 ■ **Pak Mail Centres Ltd.**
501 Passmore Ave., Ste. 30
 Toronto, ON, Canada M1V 5G4
Free: 800-387-8335
Fax: (416)335-9080
Co. E-mail: info@pakmailcanada.com

URL: http://www.pakmailcanada.com
Contact: Cheryl Kostopoulos, President
Description: Provider of crating and shipping services including freight, logistics, mailbox rental, retail moving and packaging supplies services. **Founded:** 1983. **Equity Capital Needed:** $15,000-$25,000. **Franchise Fee:** 29500. **Royalty Fee:** 0.06. **Training:** Offers 4 weeks initial and ongoing support.

3402 ■ Postal Connections of America (PCA)
6136 Frisco Sq., Blvd., Ste. 400
 Frisco, TX 75034
Free: 800-767-8257
Co. E-mail: info@postalconnections.com
URL: http://www.postalconnections.com
Contact: Fred Morache, Managing Director Owner
Facebook: www.facebook.com/PostalConnectionsInc
Linkedin: www.linkedin.com/company/postal-connec tions
X (Twitter): x.com/PCA_CORP
YouTube: www.youtube.com/channel/UCPO 3Pi7Wgc9BZwbZ2zO1Ftw
Description: Firm provides packaging supplies, notary services, mail box rentals, printing, copying, fax services, shipping, office and shipping supplies and computer services. **Founded:** 1985. **Financial Assistance:** Yes **Training:** Extensive training prior to & after opening. Franchisee's receive 5 days live action training in a regional training store, Unique Act video training program & 4 days onsite.

3403 ■ PostNet
143 Union Blvd., Ste. 600
 Lakewood, CO 80228
Ph: (303)771-7100
Free: 800-841-7171
URL: http://www.postnet.com
Contact: Ryan Farris, President
Facebook: www.facebook.com/PostNet
Linkedin: www.linkedin.com/company/postnet
X (Twitter): x.com/postnet
Instagram: www.instagram.com/postnetnorthamerica
Description: Offers site location assistance based on proven criteria, high tech design layout, development services, state of-the-art equipment, startup inventory, full color promotional materials, plus 800 line, fax, internet and regional support. **No. of Franchise Units:** 700.0. **Founded:** 1993. **Equity Capital Needed:** $169,767 to $212,275 ; $60,000. **Franchise Fee:** $35,000. **Royalty Fee:** 5%. **Financial Assistance:** Yes **Training:** In-depth 3-step training process includes classroom, onsite and follow-up. Continuous ongoing support provided.

3404 ■ Sunshine Pack & Ship
7580 Metropolitan Dr., Ste. No.200
 San Diego, CA 92108
Ph: (619)563-4800
Free: 800-456-1525
Fax: (619)563-9850
URL: http://www.sunshinepackandship.com
Contact: Jack Lentz, Chief Executive Officer
Description: Provider of packing and shipping, custom crating and boxing for art, antiques and furniture for residential, business and commercial customers. **Founded:** 1993. **Franchised:** 2000. **Financial Assistance:** Yes **Training:** Offers 40 hours at headquarters, 40 hours at franchisees location and additional training as needed.

3405 ■ The UPS Store Canada
1115 N Service Rd. W, Unit 1
 Oakville, ON, Canada L6M 2V9
Free: 800-661-6232
Co. E-mail: custsvccaen@ups.com
URL: http://www.theupsstore.ca
Contact: David Druker, President
Facebook: www.facebook.com/TheUPSStoreCA
Linkedin: www.linkedin.com/company/the-ups-store -canada
X (Twitter): x.com/theupsstore_can
Instagram: www.instagram.com/theupsstoreca
YouTube: www.youtube.com/user/TheUPSS toreCanada
Description: Provider of small business solutions, digital printing, mailbox services, packaging and shipping and postal services. **No. of Franchise Units:** 360. **Founded:** 1988. **Equity Capital Needed:** $80,000-$100,000. **Educational Activities:** ACUHO-I Conference & Expo (Annual).

3406 ■ The UPS Store Inc.
United Parcel Service, Inc. (UPS)
 6060 Cornerstone Ct. W
 San Diego, CA 92121-3795
Ph: (404)828-4147
Free: 800-742-5877
Co. E-mail: custsvcgben@ups.com
URL: http://www.ups.com
Contact: Sarah Casalan Bittle, President
URL(s): www.ups.com
Facebook: www.facebook.com/theupsstore
Linkedin: www.linkedin.com/company/201257
X (Twitter): x.com/theupsstore
Instagram: www.instagram.com/theupsstore
YouTube: www.youtube.com/user/theupsstore
Description: Firm provides trucking and transportation services. **Founded:** 1980.

3407 ■ Worldwide Express
WWEX Group
 2323 Victory Ave., Ste. 1600
 Dallas, TX 75219
Free: 800-758-7447
URL: http://wwexgroup.com
Contact: Rob Rose, President
Facebook: www.facebook.com/WorldwideExpress
Linkedin: www.linkedin.com/company/worldwide -express
X (Twitter): x.com/CorporateWWE
Instagram: www.instagram.com/worldwideexpress
Description: Discounted air express services. **No. of Franchise Units:** 208. **Founded:** 1992. **Franchised:** 1994. **Franchise Fee:** $28,125-$315,000. **Training:** Training available at headquarters and onsite.

RESEARCH CENTERS

3408 ■ University of Colorado at Boulder - Center for Advanced Manufacturing and Packaging of Microwave, Optical and Digital Electronics (CAMPMODE)
1111 Engineering Dr., 422 UCB
 Boulder, CO 80309-0427
URL: http://www.colorado.edu/faculty/lee-yc/about
Description: National Science Foundation Industry/University Cooperative Research Center at the University of Colorado at Boulder, operated through the Department of Mechanical Engineering. **Scope:** Development of computer-aided designs, packaging and manufacturing technologies for high-quality, low-cost production of electronic systems. **Founded:** 1995.

Compact Disc/Record Store

ASSOCIATIONS AND OTHER ORGANIZATIONS

3409 ■ **Coalition of Independent Music Stores (CIMS)**
3738 4th Ter. N
Birmingham, AL 35222
Ph: (205)595-1932
Fax: (205)595-1938
URL: http://www.cimsmusic.com
Contact: Andrea Paschal, Executive Director
E-mail: andrea@cimsmusic.com
Description: Coalition of record stores promoting and supporting the music store industry. **Founded:** 1995.

3410 ■ **Music Business Association (MBA)**
PO Box 746
Marlton, NJ 08053
Co. E-mail: info@musicbiz.org
URL: http://musicbiz.org
Contact: Portia Sabin, President
E-mail: portia@musicbiz.org
Facebook: www.facebook.com/MusicBizAssoc
X (Twitter): x.com/musicbizassoc
Instagram: www.instagram.com/musicbizassoc
Description: Serves the music and other prerecorded entertainment software industry as a forum for insight and dialogue; members include retailers, wholesalers, distributors, entertainment software suppliers, and suppliers of related products and services. **Founded:** 1958. **Publications:** *Music Biz Membership Directory*; *NARM Convention Official Guide* (Annual); *NARM News Bits* (Monthly); *NARM Research Briefs* (Monthly). **Educational Activities:** Insights and Sounds. **Awards:** Harry Chapin Memorial Humanitarian Award (Periodic); Music Business Association Presidential Award for Sustained Executive Achievement (Periodic). **Geographic Preference:** National.

REFERENCE WORKS

3411 ■ *"The Pain of Losing a Local Record Store"* in The New York Times (August 17 2019)
URL(s): www.nytimes.com/2019/08/17/opinion/sunday/local-record-store.html
Ed: David Sax. **Released:** August 17, 2019. **Description:** The impact closing a beloved record store can have on the people who once shopped there. June Records in Toronto was one such store that was special to the community and holds a sense of nostalgia as more and more people watch old brick-and-mortar stores close up shop for good. **Availability:** Online.

3412 ■ *"Record Store Day Black Friday Promises 177 Titles, Including Paul McCartney, Cardi B, Lizzo"* in Variety (October 8, 2019)
Ed: Chris Willman. **Released:** October 08, 2019. **Description:** Some big holiday releases are coming to local record stores as musicians release new albums to the public.

3413 ■ *The Rhythm of Success: How an Immigrant Produced His Own American Dream*
Pub: Penguin Publishing Group
Ed: Emilio Estefan. **Description:** Emilio Estefan, husband to singer Gloria Estefan and founder of the Latin pop legend Miami Sound Machine, is the classic example of the American dream. He shares his guiding principles that entrepreneurs need to start and grow a business. **Availability:** E-book; Print.

TRADE PERIODICALS

3414 ■ *Music Inc.*
Pub: Maher Publications
URL(s): www.musicincmag.com
Facebook: www.facebook.com/MusicIncMagazine
Linkedin: www.linkedin.com/company/music-inc-magazine
X (Twitter): x.com/musicincmag
Instagram: www.instagram.com/musicincmagazine
Released: Monthly; except May. **Description:** Magazine serving retailers of music and sound products. **Availability:** Print; PDF; Online.

FRANCHISES AND BUSINESS OPPORTUNITIES

3415 ■ **CD Tradepost Inc.**
2318 SW 10th
Topeka, KS 66604
Ph: (785)233-0675
URL: http://tradepostentertainment.com/programs
Contact: Travis Youngblood, Chief Executive Officer
Facebook: www.facebook.com/TradepostEntertainmentCDTradepost
X (Twitter): x.com/tradepost
Instagram: www.instagram.com/tradepostentertainment
Description: Retailer of used CDs, videos and video games. **Founded:** 1998. **Training:** Provides 2 weeks at headquarters with ongoing support including grand opening support.

LIBRARIES

3416 ■ **Chicago Public Library - Visual & Performing Arts Division - Music Information Center**
400 S State St.
Chicago, IL 60605
URL: http://www.chipublib.org/archival_subject/theater
Contact: Deanie Adams, Director
E-mail: dadams@chipublib.org
Scope: History and theory of music, biographies of musicians and composers, music education, opera, musical comedy, sacred music, popular music, discography, music business, musical instruments, vocal and instrumental pedagogy, music therapy, folk music, composition and orchestration, arranging. **Services:** Interlibrary loan; copying; listening/viewing center; practice rooms; music chamber; center open to the public. **Founded:** 1915. **Holdings:** 49,800 books; 8,025 bound periodical volumes; 67,000 bound volumes of music; 30,000 pieces of music; 15 VF drawers of pamphlets and clippings; 6,102 microfiche of music; 2,220 reels of microfilm of periodicals; 169,000 phonograph records, compact discs, audiocassettes; 3,900 music videos; 334 laserdiscs; 4,250 photographs; 51,957 uncatalogued scores.

Computer Consulting

START-UP INFORMATION

3417 ■ *"SBA Program Helped New Company Survive As It Built Company Base"* in *Philadelphia Business Journal (Vol. 33, May 9, 2014, No. 13, pp. 4)*
Pub: American City Business Journals, Inc.
Contact: Mike Olivieri, Executive Vice President
Released: Weekly. **Description:** The Small Business Administration (SBA) Indiana District Business Office helped Netwise Resources set up its information technology (IT) consulting business with a six-month SBA-backed loan and the 8(a) Business Development Program for small disadvantaged businesses. Owner, Mark Gibson, attributes Netwise Resources' success to its focus on branding, recruiting skilled staff, and establishing relationships with clients within the target market. **Availability:** Print; Online.

ASSOCIATIONS AND OTHER ORGANIZATIONS

3418 ■ **Association Canadienne de Traitement d'Images et de Reconnaissance des Formes**
c/o Prof. Michael Jenkin, President
4700 Keele St.
Toronto, ON, Canada M3J 1P3
Ph: (416)736-2100
Co. E-mail: president@gmail.com
URL: http://www.cipprs.org
Contact: Michael Jenkin, President
E-mail: president@gmail.com
Description: Strives to advance the theory and practice of signal and image processing for pattern analysis and classification, scene or speech understanding and recognition. **Founded:** 1978. **Publications:** *Computer and Robot Vision (CRV)* (Annual). **Educational Activities:** Conference on Computer and Robot Vision (Annual). **Awards:** CIPPRS John Barron Doctoral Dissertation Award (Annual). **Geographic Preference:** National.

3419 ■ **Association of Professional Canadian Consultants (APCC)**
157 Adelaide St W, Ste., 703
Toronto, ON, Canada M5H 4E7
Co. E-mail: information@apcconline.com
URL: http://www.apcconline.com
Contact: Frank McCrea, President
Facebook: www.facebook.com/APCCOnline
Linkedin: www.linkedin.com/company/apcc---associa tion-of-professional-computer-consultants
X (Twitter): x.com/APCC_Canada
Description: Promotes the interests of independent contractors in Canada. Serves as industry advocate before government bodies. **Founded:** 1985. **Publications:** *Gateway* (Monthly). **Geographic Preference:** National.

3420 ■ **BC Tech Association**
210 - 1401 W 8th Ave.
Vancouver, BC, Canada V6H 1C9
Ph: (604)683-6159
Co. E-mail: hello@wearebctech.com
URL: http://wearebctech.com
Contact: Jill Tipping, President
E-mail: jtipping@wearebctech.com
Facebook: www.facebook.com/wearebctech
X (Twitter): x.com/wearebctech
Instagram: www.instagram.com/wearebctech
Description: Fosters the growth and development of the Province's technology industries and member companies. Provides programs, services and activities designed to meet the needs and interests of members in the areas of networking, education, public awareness, and government relations. Offers a forum for members to review industry issues, acquire new business knowledge from leading industry professionals, to supply input on existing and proposed legislation and generally work together to advance the industry's interests. **Publications:** *Impact* (Annual). **Geographic Preference:** Local.

3421 ■ *Computer and Robot Vision (CRV)*
c/o Prof. Michael Jenkin, President
4700 Keele St.
Toronto, ON, Canada M3J 1P3
Ph: (416)736-2100
Co. E-mail: president@gmail.com
URL: http://www.cipprs.org
Contact: Michael Jenkin, President
E-mail: president@gmail.com
URL(s): www.cipprs.org
Released: Annual **Availability:** Print.

3422 ■ **International Association for Computer Information Systems (IACIS) - Library**
Abingdon OX14 4RN, United Kingdom
URL: http://www.iacis.org
Contact: Joanna Paliszkiewicz, President
E-mail: joanna.paliszkiewicz@iacis.org
Description: Seeks to promote the knowledge, use, and teaching of computers, and technology; dedicated to the improvement of information systems and computer professionals. **Scope:** Information systems; technology. **Holdings:** Figures not available. **Publications:** *IACIS Newsletter* (Semiannual); *Journal of Computer Information Systems (JCIS)* (6/year). **Educational Activities:** Annual IACIS Conference (Annual). **Awards:** Computer Educator of the Year Award (Annual); Ben Bauman Award for Excellence (Annual). **Geographic Preference:** Multinational.

3423 ■ **TechServe Alliance**
1420 King St., Ste. 610
Alexandria, VA 22314
Ph: (703)838-2050
Fax: (703)838-3610
Co. E-mail: staff@techservealliance.org
URL: http://www.techservealliance.org
Contact: Mark B. Roberts, Chief Executive Officer
E-mail: roberts@techservealliance.org
Facebook: www.facebook.com/techservealliance
Linkedin: www.linkedin.com/company/2015634
X (Twitter): x.com/TechServe_Assoc
Description: Businesses that provide the services of highly technical professionals, such as computer programmers, systems analysts, engineers, to clients in need of temporary technical support. Promotes legal and economic environment favorable to the technical services industry, including protection of a firm's freedom to choose either employees or independent contractors when supplying services to clients. Encourages professional standards in the industry; serves as a support mechanism for members. Provides industry-specific educational information and insurance discounts. **Founded:** 1987. **Publications:** *Directory of Members Firms* (Periodic); *TechServe Alliance Monitor* (Quarterly); *NACCB Newsletter* (Quarterly). **Geographic Preference:** National; National.

REFERENCE WORKS

3424 ■ *"Auctions and Bidding: A Guide for Computer Scientists"* in *ACM Computing Surveys (Vol. 43, Summer 2011, No. 2, pp. 10)*
Pub: Association for Computing Machinery
Contact: Yannis Ioannidis, President
Ed: Simon Parsons, Juan A. Rodriguez-Aguilar, Mark Klein. **Released:** Volume 43 Issue 2. **Price:** $10, Members; $15, Nonmembers; $5, Students. **Description:** There are various actions: single dimensional, multi-dimensional, single-sided, double-sided, first-price, second-price, English, Dutch, Japanese, sealed-bid, and these have been extensively discussed and analyzed in economics literature. This literature is surveyed from a computer science perspective, primarily from the viewpoint of computer scientists who are interested in learning about auction theory, and to provide pointers into the economics literature for those who want a deeper technical understanding. In addition, since auctions are an increasingly important topic in computer science, the article also looks at work on auctions from the computer science literature. The aim is to identify what both bodies of work tell us about creating electronic auctions. **Availability:** Download; PDF.

3425 ■ *"Consumer Trust in E-Commerce Web Sites: a Meta-Study"* in *ACM Computing Surveys (Vol. 43, Fall 2011, No. 3, pp. 14)*
Pub: Association for Computing Machinery
Contact: Yannis Ioannidis, President
Ed: Patricia Beatty, Ian Reay, Scott Dick, James Miller. **Released:** Volume 43 Issue 3. **Price:** $10, Members; $15, Nonmembers; $5, Students. **Description:** Trust is at once an elusive, imprecise concept, and a critical attribute that must be engineered into e-commerce systems. Engineering trust is examined. **Availability:** Download; PDF.

3426 ■ *"Discrete Wavelet Transform-Based Time Series Analysis and Mining"* in *ACM Computing Surveys (Vol. 43, Summer 2011, No. 2, pp. 6)*
Pub: Association for Computing Machinery
Contact: Yannis Ioannidis, President

Ed: Pimwadee Chaovalit, Aryya Gangopadhyay, George Karabatis, Zhiyuan Chen. **Released:** Volume 43 Issue 2. **Price:** $10, Members; $15, Nonmembers; $5, Students. **Description:** Time series are recorded values of an interesting phenomenon such as stock prices, household items, or patient heart rates over a period of time. Time series data mining focuses on discovering interesting patterns in such data. An introduction to a wavelet-based times series data analysis is provided with a systematic survey of various analysis techniques that use discrete wavelet transformation (DWT) in time series data mining, and outlines the benefits of this approach demonstrated by previous studies performed on diverse application domains, including image classification, multimedia retrieval, and computer network anomaly detection. **Availability:** Download; PDF.

3427 ■ *"The Failure Detector Abstraction" in ACM Computing Surveys (Vol. 43, Summer 2011, No. 2, pp. 9)*
Pub: Association for Computing Machinery
Contact: Yannis Ioannidis, President

Ed: Felix C. Freiling, Rachid Guerraoui, Petr Kuznetsov. **Released:** Volume 43 Issue 2. **Price:** $10, Members; $15, Nonmembers; $5, Students. **Description:** A failure detector is a fundamental abstraction in distributed computing. This article surveys this abstraction through two dimensions. First it studies failure detectors as building blocks to simplify the design of reliable distributed algorithms, particularly how failure detectors can factor out timing assumptions to detect failures in distributed agreement algorithms. Second, failure detectors as computability benchmarks are studied. Some limitations of the failure detector abstraction along each of the dimensions are also highlighted. **Availability:** Download; PDF.

3428 ■ *"Free Speech Vs. Privacy in Data Mining" in Information Today (Vol. 28, September 2011, No. 8, pp. 22)*
Pub: Information Today Inc.
Contact: Thomas H. Hogan, President

Ed: George H. Pike. **Description:** The U.S. Constitution does not explicitly guarantee the right of privacy. Organizations and businesses that require obtaining and disseminating information can be caught in the middle of privacy rights. The long-term impact on data mining, Internet marketing, and Internet privacy issues are examined.

3429 ■ *"Human Activity Analysis: a Review" in ACM Computing Surveys (Vol. 43, Fall 2011, No. 3, pp. 16)*
Pub: Association for Computing Machinery
Contact: Yannis Ioannidis, President

Ed: J. K. Aggarwal, M. S. Ryoo. **Description:** Human activity recognition is an important area of computer vision research and is studied in this report. **Availability:** Download; PDF; Online.

3430 ■ *"Implementing Statically Typed Object-Oriented Programming Languages" in ACM Computing Surveys (Vol. 43, Fall 2011, No. 3, pp. 18)*
Pub: Association for Computing Machinery
Contact: Yannis Ioannidis, President

Ed: Roland Ducournau. **Released:** Volume 43 Issue 3. **Price:** $10, Members; $15, Nonmembers; $5, Students. **Description:** Object-oriented programming represents an original implementation issue due to its philosophy of making the program behavior depend on the dynamic type of objects. A review of the various implementation techniques available in static typing and in the three cases of single inheritance, multiple inheritance, and multiple subtyping are reviewed. **Availability:** Download; PDF.

3431 ■ *"Lighter Than Air" in Game Developer (Vol. 18, November 1, 2011, No. 10, pp. 38)*
Pub: Think Services

Description: Floating point performance tips and tricks are outlined. Floating point allows freedom of representation when implementing algorithms and is both intuitive to set up and simple to work with; hardware is also improved so that it is faster to use floating point math as opposed to integer in many environments. **Availability:** Print; Online.

3432 ■ *"Machine Transliteration Survey" in ACM Computing Surveys (Vol. 43, Fall 2011, No. 3, pp. 17)*
Pub: Association for Computing Machinery
Contact: Yannis Ioannidis, President

Ed: Sarvnaz Karimi, Falk Scholer, Andrew Turpin. **Released:** Volume 43 Issue 3. **Price:** $10, Members; $15, Nonmembers; $5, Students. **Description:** Machine transliteration is the process of automatically transforming the script of a word from a source language to a target language, while preserving pronunciation. The development of algorithms specifically for machine transliteration began over a decade ago based on the phonetics of source and target languages, followed by approaches using statistical and language-specific methods. In this survey, the key methodologies introduced in transliteration literature are reviewed. The approaches are categorized based on the resources and algorithms used, and the effectiveness is compared. **Availability:** Download; PDF.

3433 ■ *"Software Developers" in Business Review Albany (Vol. 41, July 18, 2014, No. 17, pp. 9)*

Description: The top software development companies in Albany, New York are ranked by local software revenue in 2013. CMA Consulting Services is listed in the top spot, with GCOM Software following in second place. **Availability:** Online.

3434 ■ *"Strict Intersection Types for the Lambda Calculus" in ACM Computing Surveys (Vol. 43, Fall 2011, No. 3, pp. 20)*
Pub: Association for Computing Machinery
Contact: Yannis Ioannidis, President

Ed: Steffen Van Bakel. **Description:** The usefulness and elegance of strict intersection types for the Lambda Calculus, that are strict in the sense that they are the representatives of equivalence classes of types in the BCD-system is shown. Focus in directed on the essential intersection type assignment; this system is almost syntax directed, and the article will show that all major properties hold that are known to hold for other intersection systems, like the approximation theorem, the characterization of (head/strong) normalization, completeness of type assignment using filter semantics, strong normalization for cut-elimination and the principal pair property. In part, the proofs for these properties are new. A brief comparison of the essential system with other existing systems is given. **Availability:** PDF; Online.

3435 ■ *"A Survey of Combinatorial Testing" in ACM Computing Surveys (Vol. 43, Summer 2011, No. 2, pp. 11)*
Pub: Association for Computing Machinery
Contact: Yannis Ioannidis, President

Ed: Changhai Nie, Hareton Leung. **Description:** Combinatorial Testing (CT) can detect failures triggered by interactions of parameters in the Software Under Test (SUT) with a covering array test suite generated by some sampling mechanisms. Basic concepts and notations of CT are covered. **Availability:** Download; PDF; Online.

3436 ■ *"A Survey of Comparison-Based System-Level Diagnosis" in ACM Computing Surveys (Vol. 43, Fall 2011, No. 3, pp. 22)*
Pub: Association for Computing Machinery
Contact: Yannis Ioannidis, President

Ed: Elias P. Duarte, Jr., Roverli P. Ziwich, Luiz C. P. Albini. **Released:** Volume 43 Issue 3. **Price:** $10, Members; $15, Nonmembers; $5, Students. **Description:** The growing complexity and dependability requirements of hardware, software, and networks demand efficient techniques for discovering disruptive behavior in those systems. Comparison-based diagnosis is a realistic approach to detect faulty units based on the outputs of tasks executed by system units. This survey integrates the vast amount of research efforts that have been produced in this field. **Availability:** Download; PDF.

3437 ■ *"A Survey of DHT Security Techniques" in ACM Computing Surveys (Vol. 43, Summer 2011, No. 2, pp. 8)*
Pub: Association for Computing Machinery
Contact: Yannis Ioannidis, President

Ed: Guido Urdaneta, Guillaume Pierre, Maarten Van Steen. **Released:** Volume 43 Issue 2. **Price:** $10, Members; $15, Nonmembers; $5, Students. **Description:** Peer-to-peer networks based on distributed hash tables (DHTs) have received considerable attention since their introduction in 2001. Unfortunately, DHT-based systems have been shown to be difficult to protect against security attacks. An overview of techniques reported in literature for making DHT-based systems resistant to the three most important attacks that can be launched by malicious nodes participating in the DHT is given: the Sybil attack, the Eclipse attack, and routing and storage attacks. **Availability:** Download; PDF.

3438 ■ *"What is the Future of Disk Drives, Death or Rebirth?" in ACM Computing Surveys (Vol. 43, Fall 2011, No. 3, pp. 23)*
Pub: Association for Computing Machinery
Contact: Yannis Ioannidis, President

Ed: Yuhui Deng. **Released:** Volume 43 Issue 3. **Price:** $10, Members; $15, Nonmembers; $5, Students. **Description:** Disk drives have experienced dramatic development to meet performance requirements since the IBM 1301 disk drive was announced in 1961. However, the performance gap between memory and disk drives has widened to 6 orders of magnitude and continues to widen by about 50 percent per year. Challenges and opportunities facing these storage devices are explored. **Availability:** Download; PDF.

TRADE PERIODICALS

3439 ■ *DCL News*
Pub: Data Conversion Laboratory
Contact: Mark Gross, President
URL(s): www.dataconversionlaboratory.com/newsletter

Released: Monthly **Description:** E-journal providing you insider information on XML and SGML, along with the latest technology and e-publishing news. **Availability:** Online.

3440 ■ *Microprocessor Report*
Pub: MicroDesign Resources
URL(s): www.linleygroup.com/mpr/index.php?j=MPR

Price: $500, Other countries print, /year; $700, Individuals print, 2 years; $300, U.S. and Canada print, /year; $400, U.S. and Canada print, 2 years. **Description:** The leading technical publication for the microprocessor industry. Dedicated to providing unbiased, in-depth, critical analysis of new high-performance microprocessor developments. This newsletter is exclusively subscriber-supported. **Availability:** Print; Online.

3441 ■ *Online Searcher*
Pub: Information Today Inc.
Contact: Thomas H. Hogan, President
URL(s): www.infotoday.com/OnlineSearcher

Released: Bimonthly; January/February, March/April, May/June, July/August, September/October, and November/December. **Description:** Edited for librarians, Webmasters, site designers, content managers, and others concerned with knowledge/information management. Includes critical reviews of Web sites, software, search engines, and information services. (Formerly published by Online, Inc.). **Availability:** Print; Online.

3442 ■ *Productivity Software*
Pub: Worldwide Videotex
URL(s): wvpubs.com/publications

Released: Annual **Price:** $200, Individuals for hard copy; $185, Individuals for hard copy; $165, Other countries for e-file (PDF or DOC). **Description:** Provides information on computer software. **Availability:** Print; Online; PDF.

TRADE SHOWS AND CONVENTIONS

3443 ■ AIIP Annual Conference
ProQuest
Montreal, QC, Canada H4S 1V9
Ph: (514)333-9040
Fax: (514)336-8217
URL: http://www.proquest.com
URL(s): www.aiip.org/conference
Frequency: Annual. **Description:** Independent information professionals involved in computer and manual organization, retrieval, and dissemination of information. **Audience:** Industry professionals. **Principal Exhibits:** Independent information professionals involved in computer and manual organization, retrieval, and dissemination of information. **Telecommunication Services:** conference@aiip.org.

CONSULTANTS

3444 ■ Allstream Business Inc.
Zayo Group L.L.C.
5160 Orbitor Dr.
Mississauga, ON, Canada L4W 5H2
Free: 866-364-6033
Co. E-mail: sales@zayo.com
URL: http://www.zayo.com
Contact: Michael Strople, President
Facebook: www.facebook.com/allstream
Linkedin: www.linkedin.com/company/allstream
X (Twitter): twitter.com/Allstream
Instagram: www.instagram.com/allstream
Description: Firm provides communication solutions provider which offers effective and reliable connectivity, IT services and network infrastructure management. **Scope:** A communication solutions provider offering connectivity, IT services and network infrastructure management. **Founded:** 1846. **Publications:** "Le site Yelp: un engouement justifie?" Oct, 2010; "Tenir un blogue d entreprise ca vaut le coup?" Oct, 2010; "Construction et renovation pour un bureau vert et securitaire, attention aux materiaux toxiques" Oct, 2010; "Faire bonne impression en invitant le client a faire la fete!" Oct, 2010; "Les cinq meilleurs conseils aux gens des petites entreprises pour reduire leur stress" Oct, 2010; "10 etapes pour une rentabilite assuree dans le temps des Fetes" Oct, 2010; "Conseils fiscaux pour travailleurs autonomes" Jun, 2010; "Faites sourire votre personnel" Jun, 2010; "Les tribulations de Google Buzz" Jun, 2010; "Pour profiter des fonds du gouvernement federal" Jun, 2010; "Les affaires sont prosperes I ete a Montreal" Jun, 2010; "8 Les regles d or de la redaction" Apr, 2010; "Dix conseils pour dynamiser votre strategie de vente" Apr, 2010; "Reduction des couts indirects: Produits gratuits pour faciliter les deplacements d affaires" Apr, 2010; "Wavelength Solutions"; "Unified Communications Managed Services"; "Drive the productivity of your Human Infrastructure and make your organization more effective". **Training:** UC Meets Cloud, Toronto on Mar, 2012.

3445 ■ Applied Business Technologies Corp.
3182 Portsmouth Ave.
Cincinnati, OH 45208
Contact: Michael D. Rice, Contact
Description: Services: Computer consulting in strategic planning, project management and software development. **Scope:** Services: Computer consulting in strategic planning, project management and software development.

3446 ■ Business Automation Associates Inc.
11811 N Tatum Blvd., Ste. 3031-113
Phoenix, AZ 85028-1632
Ph: (602)264-9263
URL: http://www.bizauto.com
Contact: Brooks Hilliard, President
E-mail: brooks@bizauto.com
Description: Firm provides consultancy services on independent management and information systems. **Scope:** Firm provides consultancy services on independent management and information systems. **Founded:** 1980. **Publications:** "Buying a Computer For Your Growing Business: An Insider's Guide," Dow-Jones. **Training:** Seven Corporate Keys to Succeeding on the Internet; Using the Internet to Accelerate Your Selling Cycle; Spiral Marketing-How to build Internet traffic and customer commitment; Web Site Synergy Can Energize Your Business; Staying Ahead of the Curve in an Internet-Enabled World; The Five Most Common Internet Mistakes and How to Beat Them; Leveraging Your 'Bricks and Mortar' to Defeat Your Web-based Competitors; Essential Computer, Internet and Telephone Technology for the Small Office; From 'Zero to Sixty' in 90 Minutes.

3447 ■ Business Breakthroughs Inc.
1 Lone Hollow
Sandy, UT 84092
Contact: Robert S. Osborne, Contact
Description: Firm provides advanced methods education and mentoring programs. Presents instructor-led courses, seminars and related consulting services on software engineering techniques, client-server and object-oriented analysis and design, business process re-engineering, project management and related areas. Sessions and programs are offered at management, practitioner and non-technical user levels. **Scope:** Firm provides advanced methods education and mentoring programs. Presents instructor-led courses, seminars and related consulting services on software engineering techniques, client-server and object-oriented analysis and design, business process re-engineering, project management and related areas. Sessions and programs are offered at management, practitioner and non-technical user levels. **Publications:** "Unpaid Consulting: the "New Breed" of Service that Every Purchasing Department Needs". **Training:** Practical Lean for Real Results, Salt Lake City, Mar, 2007; Profit and Performance: Effective Cost-Reduction Strategies and Tools; Executive Overview of Lean Manufacturing Techniques and Tools; Value Stream Mapping and Analysis; Rapid Changeover. **Special Services:** BVSMethod™; BVSMFramework™; Business Value SystemMethod™; Business Value System Method Framework™; Integrated Business Value System Model™.

3448 ■ Business & Decision USA
10 E 40th St. 31st Fl.
New York, NY 10005
Ph: (212)251-2072
Co. E-mail: contact.us@bndna.com
URL: http://www.businessdecision.us
Contact: Dean Allen, President
Facebook: www.facebook.com/Business.and.Decision
Linkedin: www.linkedin.com/company/business-&-decision
X (Twitter): twitter.com/bd_group
YouTube: www.youtube.com/user/BandD75
Description: Firm provides consulting and systems integration services to help clients build and improve their internet operations and offers strategy and site design, assistance in e-commerce B2C and B2B, operations management, and supply chain services.

3449 ■ Business Systems Consultants Inc. (BSCI)
333 N Michigan Ave., Ste. 912
Chicago, IL 60601
Ph: (312)553-1253
Fax: (312)553-1256
Co. E-mail: bsci@bscichicago.com
URL: http://www.bscichicago.com
Contact: Jon R. Guenther, President
E-mail: jrguenther@bscichicago.com
Facebook: www.facebook.com/businesssystemsandconsultants
YouTube: www.youtube.com/channel/UCMjz_kEpbwz3y3IDKg_oXvg
Description: Provider of software solutions for member-based organizations, associations, solutions, and service offerings include business process and systems analysis, association e-business expertise, association management software implementation and development, database and IT managed services, professional development services, and customer support. **Scope:** Provider of software solutions for member-based organizations, associations, solutions, and service offerings include business process and systems analysis, association e-business expertise, association management software implementation and development, database and IT managed services, professional development services, and customer support. **Founded:** 1987. **Training:** BSCI iMIS Workshops; BSCI Crystal Report Workshops. **Special Services:** iMIS15.

3450 ■ Business Technology Associates
Decision Resources Inc.
3883 Turtle Creek Blvd.
Dallas, TX 75219
Ph: (412)562-9660
Co. E-mail: info@decision.com
URL: http://www.decision.com
Description: Development of business management software and implementation services for mid-sized manufacturers, distributors, and services businesses.

3451 ■ Business Technology Consultants, Inc.
725 Oak Branch Dr.
Oak Park, CA 91377
Contact: David Alan Borys, Contact
Description: Firm provides technology consulting services including computer installation and support, network design and installation, disaster planning and recovery, virus prevention and eradication, technology planning and budgeting, communications and broadband integration, network security and training. **Scope:** Firm provides technology consulting services including computer installation and support, network design and installation, disaster planning and recovery, virus prevention and eradication, technology planning and budgeting, communications and broadband integration, network security and training. **Training:** Computer Installation & Support; Network Design & Installation; Disaster Planning & Recovery; Virus Prevention & Eradication; Technology Planning & Budgeting; Communications & Broadband Integration; Network Security.

3452 ■ Business Technology Partners L.L.P.
1751 W Lake Cook Rd., Ste. 400
Deerfield, IL 60015
Co. E-mail: info@btpartners.com
URL: http://www.btpartners.com
Contact: Todd Perlman, President
E-mail: tperlman@btpartners.com
Linkedin: www.linkedin.com/company/business-technology-partners-llp
X (Twitter): x.com/btpartners
Description: Firm provides information technology solutions. **Scope:** Firm provides information technology solutions. **Special Services:** AutoMate™; CITRIX™; CLEO®; Versalex®; BarTender®; ddxSuite™; Jet Stream mfg™.

3453 ■ Business Works of Ohio L.L.C.
PO Box 242
Blacklick, OH 43004
URL: http://businessworks-llc.com
Contact: Charles D. Amata, Jr., President
Description: Provider of management consulting and technology services to small and mid-sized businesses. **Scope:** Provider of management consulting and technology services to small and mid-sized businesses. **Founded:** 2009.

3454 ■ COTC Technologies Inc.
PO Box 17413
Denver, CO 80217
Contact: Thomas I. Renz, Contact
Description: Firm provides software consulting services to organizations that require assistance with their HP3000 computer system. Firm provides systems analysis, programming, operations support and system management. Also provides PC software and hardware support and consulting. Additionally provides various training for the HP3000 computer system. **Scope:** Firm provides software consulting services to organizations that require assistance with their HP3000 computer system. Firm provides

systems analysis, programming, operations support and system management. Also provides PC software and hardware support and consulting. Additionally provides various training for the HP3000 computer system.

3455 ■ Encore Business Solutions Inc.
No. 1 467 Provencher Blvd.
 Winnipeg, MB, Canada R2J 0B8
Ph: (204)989-4330
Free: 888-898-4330
Co. E-mail: encore@encorebusiness.com
URL: http://www.encorebusiness.com
Contact: Ken Chartrand, Chief Executive Officer
Facebook: www.facebook.com/Encorebusinesssolutions
Linkedin: www.linkedin.com/company/encore-business-solutions
X (Twitter): x.com/encorebusiness
YouTube: www.youtube.com/encorebusiness
Description: Business technology consulting services includes training, process improvement, project management, IT services and business intelligence. **Scope:** Business technology consulting services includes training, process improvement, project management, IT services and business intelligence. **Founded:** 1990.

3456 ■ Executive Analytics & Design Inc.
108 West 13th St.
 Wilmington, DE 19801
Description: A technology consultant engaged in business process improvement services. The company specializes in providing regulatory compliant automated accounting and financial systems solutions. **Founded:** 1996. **Training:** Technology and Networking for Better Business Performance.

3457 ■ Hardy Stevenson and Associates Ltd.
364 Davenport Rd., Ste. 1
 Toronto, ON, Canada M5R 2Y4
Ph: (416)944-8444
Free: 877-267-7794
Co. E-mail: info@hardystevenson.com
URL: http://www.hardystevenson.com
Contact: Dave Hardy, Contact
Facebook: www.facebook.com/HardyStevensonandAssociatesLimited
Linkedin: www.linkedin.com/company/hardy-stevenson-and-associates-limited
X (Twitter): x.com/HardyStevenson
Description: Offers environmental planning, assessment, facilitation, conflict resolution community relations, strategic planning and project management consulting. **Scope:** Offers environmental planning, assessment, facilitation, conflict resolution community relations, strategic planning and project management consulting. **Founded:** 1990.

3458 ■ IBM Global Services - Business Continuity and Resiliency Services
1 New Orchard Rd.
 Armonk, NY 10504-1722
URL: http://www.ibm.com
Contact: Arvind Krishna, Chief Executive Officer
Description: Provider of services such as business process and operations, business resiliency, business strategy and design, and application services, and much more. **Scope:** Provider of services such as business process and operations, business resiliency, business strategy and design, and application services, and much more. **Training:** Plan development workshop, Tampa, Jun, 2007.

3459 ■ InSite Business Solutions Inc.
1012 Market St., Ste. 202
 Fort Mill, SC 29708
Co. E-mail: info@insitebiz.com
URL: http://www.insitebiz.com
Contact: John Blomberg, Contact
Description: Internet business consulting firm specializes in internet strategy, application development, design and marketing offers application and marketing strategy, custom software development, database design and integration, software architecture and development, business process automation, user experience and integrated branding campaigns. **Founded:** 1998.

3460 ■ Interactive Business Systems Inc.
Planet Group Inc.
 4400 Easton Commons Way Ste. 125
 Columbus, OH 43219
Description: Firm provides information technology consulting services.

3461 ■ Interactive Business Systems Inc.
Planet Group Inc.
 165 S Union Blvd., Ste. 605
 Lakewood, CO 80228
Founded: 1981.

3462 ■ IT Business Management Solutions Inc. (ITBMS)
1967 Rte. 27, Ste. 27
 Edison, NJ 08817
Ph: (732)287-4343
Fax: (732)909-2624
Co. E-mail: enquiry@itbmsinc.com
URL: http://www.itbmsglobal.com
Facebook: www.facebook.com/ItbmsRecruitment
Linkedin: www.linkedin.com/company/itbms-inc
X (Twitter): x.com/Itbms_Inc
Instagram: www.instagram.com/itbms
Pinterest: www.pinterest.com/itbmsinc
Description: Firm provides IT solutions in business software, resource management, enterprise system implementation and remote support services. **Scope:** Firm provides IT solutions in business software, resource management, enterprise system implementation and remote support services. **Founded:** 2005.

3463 ■ National Cybersecurity Society (NCSS)
1215 31st St. NW, Ste. 3921
 Washington, DC 20027
Ph: (703)340-7757
Co. E-mail: me@nationalcybersecurity.org
URL: http://nationalcybersecuritysociety.org
Contact: Mary Ellen Seale, Chief Executive Officer
Facebook: www.facebook.com/thencss.org
X (Twitter): x.com/thencss
Description: Information technology security companies and professionals. Provides cybersecurity education, awareness, and advocacy for small businesses. Seeks to empower and enable small business owners to obtain cybersecurity services, assist them in understanding their cyber risk, and educating them on the type of protection they need.

3464 ■ Richard I. Anderson
San Francisco, CA
URL: http://www.blogger.com
Contact: Richard I. Anderson, Contact
X (Twitter): twitter.com/Riander
Description: Provider of design practice, management, and organizational strategy consulting services. **Scope:** Provider of design practice, management, and organizational strategy consulting services. **Training:** User-Centered Design/Usability Engineering, May, 2000; Addressing Organizational Obstacles to and Achieving Greater Business Benefits; User-Centered Design; Ethnographic Research; Multidisciplinary Collaboration; Managing User Experience Groups; Meeting the Needs of a Multidisciplinary Profession; User Experience Managers and Executives Speak; Changing the Role User Experience Plays in Your Business.

3465 ■ SPARK Business Works
161 E Michigan Ave., Ste. 400N
 Kalamazoo, MI 49007
Free: 866-277-2752
Co. E-mail: info@sparkbusinessworks.com
URL: http://www.sparkbusinessworks.com
Linkedin: www.linkedin.com/company/spark-business-works
Description: Builds custom websites, mobile apps, and dashboards to make clients' businesses better. Services include software strategy, custom software, digital marketing, and website services. **Scope:** Builds custom websites, mobile apps, and dashboards to make clients' businesses better. Services include software strategy, custom software, digital marketing, and website services. **Founded:** 2017.

FRANCHISES AND BUSINESS OPPORTUNITIES

3466 ■ Rescuecom
2560 Burnet Ave.
 Syracuse, NY 13206
Ph: (315)431-4147
Free: 800-737-2837
Co. E-mail: sales@rescuecom.com
URL: http://www.rescuecom.com
Contact: David A. Milman, Chief Executive Officer
E-mail: david@rescuecom.com
X (Twitter): x.com/rescuecom
Instagram: www.instagram.com/rescuecom
Description: Provides constantly developing new techniques to make getting high-quality computer support. **Founded:** 1985. **Franchise Fee:** $1,495-$18,800. **Financial Assistance:** Yes **Training:** Yes.

PUBLICATIONS

3467 ■ "How Small Businesses Can Fund Their Ransomware Protection" in BizTech (October 7, 2021)
Ed: Nick Suda. **Released:** October 07, 2021. **Description:** Discusses the logistics of small companies preparing for ransomware attacks. **Availability:** Online.

LIBRARIES

3468 ■ Colorado Technical University, Inc. (CTU) - Library
Perdoceo Education Corporation
 1575 Garden of the Gods Rd., Ste. 100
 Colorado Springs, CO 80907
Ph: (847)781-3600
Co. E-mail: inquiries@perdoceoed.com
URL: http://www.perdoceoed.com
Contact: Elise Baskel, President
Facebook: www.facebook.com/coloradotech
Linkedin: www.linkedin.com/company/colorado-technical-university
X (Twitter): x.com/ctuniversity
YouTube: www.youtube.com/user/ctuniversity
Description: Technical college offers associate degree, certificate, and diploma programs. **Scope:** Education. **Founded:** 1965. **Holdings:** Figures not available.

3469 ■ DeVry University Library
2149 W Dunlap Ave.
 Phoenix, AZ 85021
Ph: (602)749-4500
URL: http://www.devry.edu
Contact: Lenore Goldberg, Officer
URL(s): library.devry.edu
X (Twitter): x.com/DeVryUniv
Instagram: www.instagram.com/devryuniversity
YouTube: www.youtube.com/user/TheDevryUniversity
Scope: Electronics; bio/med technology; game programming; computer languages; business operations; computers; accounting; electronic engineering; telecommunications; internet. **Services:** Copying; virtual reference service; library open to the public for reference use only. **Founded:** 1925. **Holdings:** 25,000 books; 25 CD audio books.

3470 ■ Goldey Beacom College - J. Wilbur Hirons Library
4701 Limestone Rd.
 Wilmington, DE 19808
Ph: (302)225-6227
Co. E-mail: gethelp@libanswers.com
URL: http://gbc.libguides.com/homepage
Contact: Russell Michalak, Director
Scope: Educational material. **Services:** Interlibrary loan; copying; library open to the public for reference use only. **Holdings:** 300,000 books and journals;

19,500 bound periodical volumes; transparencies; maps; 786 AV programs; 1,234 reels of microfilm; 44,637 microfiche; 700 corporation annual reports.

3471 ■ Intel Corporation Library
1900 Prairie City Rd.
 Folsom, CA 95630
URL: http://www.intel.com/content/www/us/en/
 developer/tools/documentation.html

Scope: Telecommunications. **Services:** Library not open to the public. **Founded:** 1985. **Holdings:** Figures not available. **Subscriptions:** 100 journals and other serials.

3472 ■ Walt Disney World Global Business Technology Strategy Library
PO Box 10000
 Lake Buena Vista, FL 32830

URL: http://disneyworld.disney.go.com
Scope: Computer science, human resources, general business. **Services:** Center not open to the public. **Founded:** 1986. **Holdings:** 4,000 books, videos, DVDs, and CD-ROMs; 100 AV equipment. **Subscriptions:** 200 journals and other serials; 3 newspapers.

Computer Data Storage Company

START-UP INFORMATION

3473 ■ *"3 Question for Stephen Purpura, CEO of the Big-Data Startup Context Relevant"* in *Puget Sound Business Journal* (Vol. 35, May 23, 2014, No. 5, pp. 10)
Pub: American City Business Journals, Inc.
Contact: Mike Olivieri, Executive Vice President
Description: Stephne Purpura, CEO of Seattle, Washington-based big data startup, Context Relevant, shares his vision for the company in the financial industry data market. He explains why they decided to seek strategic investment in the company.
Availability: Online.

ASSOCIATIONS AND OTHER ORGANIZATIONS

3474 ■ **Information Storage Industry Consortium (INSIC)**
PO Box 638
Monroe, VA 24574-0638
Ph: (619)392-0895
Co. E-mail: insic@insic.org
URL: http://insic.org
Description: Brings together companies and universities involved in computer data storage research, united to accomplish mutual goals. Creates and manages joint precompetitive research programs among its members. Performs studies to develop long-term roadmaps for various data storage technologies. **Founded:** 1991. **Geographic Preference:** National.

3475 ■ **Material Handling Industry of America - Order Fulfillment Solutions (MHI)**
8720 Red Oak Blvd., Ste. 201
Charlotte, NC 28217
URL: http://www.mhi.org/OFC
Contact: Anupam Berry Bose, Executive
E-mail: abose@mhi.org
Description: Trade associations comprising storage industries. Compiles statistics; sponsors research and educational programs. **Founded:** 1986. **Awards:** MHEFI scholarship (Annual). **Geographic Preference:** National.

INCUBATORS/RESEARCH AND TECHNOLOGY PARKS

3476 ■ **Plug and Play - Internet of Things (-IoT)**
440 N Wolfe Rd.
Sunnyvale, CA 94085
URL: http://www.plugandplaytechcenter.com/insights/government-and-innovation-to-catalyze-change-post
Description: An accelerator for startups in the internet of things industry. Provides support with venture and angel partners, mentorship, a data center, office space, and networking opportunities. The featured program focuses on Industrial IoT, A.I and Big Data, smart infrastructure, workflow optimization, robotics and animation, building analysis, VR, energy/efficiency, machine learning, edge computing, machine-to-machine communication.

REFERENCE WORKS

3477 ■ *"2nd Watch Rides AWS Market Maturity to 400% Growth"* in *Computer Business Week* (August 28, 2014, pp. 21)
Description: 2nd Watch reports record earnings for the second quarter of 2014. The firm helps companies develop and implement IT strategies that are based on Amazon Web Services (AWS). Details of the companies business strategies are outlined. **Availability:** Print; Online.

3478 ■ *"3Par: Storing Up Value"* in *Barron's* (Vol. 90, August 30, 2010, No. 35, pp. 30)
Pub: Barron's Editorial & Corporate Headquarters
Ed: Mark Veverka. **Description:** Dell and Hewlett Packard are both bidding for data storage company 3Par. The acquisition would help Dell and Hewlett Packard provide customers with a one-stop shop as customers move to a private cloud in the Internet. **Availability:** Online.

3479 ■ *"11 Ways to Avert a Data-Storage Disaster"* in *Nature* (2019)
URL(s): www.nature.com/articles/d41586-019-01040-w
Ed: Jeffrey M. Perkel. **Released:** 2019. **Description:** Expert tips on how to safeguard your data with various storage media, and what advantages and disadvantages the consumer can expect. **Availability:** Online.

3480 ■ *"Actian, Data Transformed and Yellowfin BI Mashup Helps Kollaras Group Reap Big Data Rewards"* in *Computer Business Week* (August 28, 2014, pp. 22)
Pub: NewsRX LLC.
Contact: Kalani Rosell, Contact
Description: Actian announced that Australian liquor, hospitality and property investment company, Kollaras Group can now access real-time analytics; fast, simple and accurate data warehousing; and Yellowfin's Business Intelligence (BI) platform is examined. The BI provides better insights and decision-making across diverse business units. **Availability:** Online.

3481 ■ *"Austin Realtors Cozy Up To Trulia"* in *Austin Business Journal* (Vol. 34, May 9, 2014, No. 12, pp. 6)
Pub: American City Business Journals, Inc.
Contact: Mike Olivieri, Executive Vice President
Released: Weekly. **Price:** $4, Introductory 4-week offer(Digital & Print). **Description:** Austin Board of Realtors (ABOR) MLS Advisory Committee chairman Lisa Messana explains the organization's decision to share data exclusively with Trulia.com. She describes member response to the announcement to end ABOR's data license agreement with ListHub. **Availability:** Print; Online.

3482 ■ *"Back-Tested ETFs Draw Assets, Flub Returns"* in *Barron's* (Vol. 92, July 23, 2012, No. 30, pp. 26)
Pub: Dow Jones & Company Inc.
Contact: Almar Latour, Chief Executive Officer
Ed: Janet Paskin. **Description:** New exchange-traded funds are attracting investors by using 'back-tested' data offered by the indexes they track. Investors are substituting real performance for these hypothetical returns, which measure past performance of indexes had they been in existence. **Availability:** Online.

3483 ■ *"Baltimore Developer Caves Valley Partners Bids for $750M Social Security Project - County Tract Pitched for Data Center"* in *Baltimore Business Journal* (Vol. 28, July 23, 2010, No. 11, pp. 1)
Pub: Baltimore Business Journal
Contact: Rhonda Pringle, President
E-mail: rpringle@bizjournals.com
Ed: Scott Dance. **Description:** One hundred acres of land in Woodlawn, Maryland is set to be sold for use in the construction of a data center for the U.S. Social Security Administration. Baltimore County has submitted a bid for the $750M construction project. **Availability:** Print.

3484 ■ *"Big Data at Work: Dispelling the Myths, Uncovering the Opportunities"*
Pub: Harvard Business Review Press
Contact: Moderna V. Pfizer, Contact
Released: February 25, 2014. **Price:** $35, Hardcover/Hardcopy. **Description:** What big data means from a technical, consumer, and management perspective; what big data opportunities cost; where it can have business impact; and what aspect of big data have been oversold. Insight is provided to help small businesses us big data to work to strengthen customer relationships. **Availability:** E-book; Print.

3485 ■ *The Big Switch: Rewiring the World, from Edison to Google*
Pub: W.W. Norton & Company Ltd.
Contact: Stanley Kubrick, Director
Ed: Nicholas Carr. **Released:** June 10, 2013. **Price:** $16.95, paperback; $26.95, hardcover. **Description:** Companies such as Google, Microsoft, and Amazon.com are building huge centers in order to create massive data centers. Together these centers form a giant computing grid that will deliver the digital universe to scientific labs, companies and homes in the future. This trend could bring about a new, darker phase for the Internet, one where these networks could operate as a fearsome entity that will dominate the lives of individuals worldwide. **Availability:** Print.

3486 ■ *"Bitcoin 'Killer App' Or the Currency of the Future?"* in *Providence Business News* (Vol. 28, January 6, 2014, No. 40, pp. 1)
Pub: American City Business Journals, Inc.
Contact: Mike Olivieri, Executive Vice President
URL(s): pbn.com/bitcoin-killer-app-or-the-currency-of-the-future94158

Description: The Providence Bitcoin Meetup has gathered several technology experts to discuss Bitcoin, the popular digital currency. However, software developers, engineers and entrepreneurs see Bitcoin as the next killer app for the Internet and is changing how information and data is stored, shared and verified. The Bitcoin's impact in Rhode Island is examined. **Availability:** Online. **Telecommunication Services:** Anderson@pbn.com.

3487 ■ *"BlackBerry 10 Unlikely to Save RIM. RIM Has Few Options. Staying the Course Isn't One of Them"* in *Canadian Business* (Vol. 85, July 16, 2012, No. 11-12, pp. 12)

Ed: Joe Castaldo. **Description:** Research in Motion (RIM) plans to launch a new line of Blackberry 10 Smartphones in 2012 as part of a strategy to stay in business despite expected operating loss in the first quarter and strong competition. Other options for RIM include a sale, opening its network to offer added security and data compression services, or reinventing itself as a niche handset provider. **Availability:** Print; Online.

3488 ■ *"Buyout Rumors Have Rackspace Back in the News"* in *San Antonio Business Journal* (Vol. 28, September 12, 2014, No. 31, pp. 6)

Pub: American City Business Journals, Inc.
Contact: Mike Olivieri, Executive Vice President
Description: Louisiana-based CenturyLink Inc. has offered to buyout San Antonio, Texas-based Rackspace Hosting in order to boost its Internet and cloud services. The latest stock market valuation of Rackspace was at $5.33 billion. The potential impact of the CenturyLink and Rackspace merger deal on the managed hosting services market is also analyzed. **Availability:** Online.

3489 ■ *"Cloud City: An Industry - and a Region - On the Rise"* in *Puget Sound Business Journal* (Vol. 34, February 28, 2014, No. 46, pp. 4)

Pub: American City Business Journals, Inc.
Contact: Mike Olivieri, Executive Vice President
Description: Seattle, Washington is experiencing an influx of the world's most innovative cloud companies. Businesses are shifting their applications from in-house servers or private data center into public cloud infrastructure, which is less expensive than buying the servers and managing the data systems. Seattle software companies are taking advantage of this trend and developing products. **Availability:** Online.

3490 ■ *Cloud Storage Made Easy: Securely Backup and Share Your Files*

Ed: James Bernstein. **Released:** November 08, 2018. **Price:** $14.99, Paperback; $0, E-Book. **Description:** A guide to help the consumer understand what cloud storage is and how to utilize it. Useful for home and small business use. **Availability:** E-book; Print.

3491 ■ *"Clouds in the Forecast"* in *Information Today* (Vol. 28, September 2011, No. 8, pp. 10)

Pub: Information Today Inc.
Contact: Thomas H. Hogan, President
Ed: Paula J. Hane. **Description:** Cloud computing is software, applications, and data stored remotely and accessed via the Internet with output displayed on a client device. Recent developments in cloud computing are explored.

3492 ■ *"Cloudy Future for VMware?"* in *Barron's* (Vol. 90, September 13, 2010, No. 37, pp. 21)

Pub: Barron's Editorial & Corporate Headquarters
Ed: Jonathan R. Laing. **Description:** VMWare dominated the virtualization market for years, but it may be ending as it faces more competition from rivals that offer cloud computing services. The company's stocks are also expensive and are vulnerable to the smallest mishap. **Availability:** Online.

3493 ■ *"Customer Data Represents Huge Opportunities and Challenges: My, What Big Data You Have"* in *Canadian Business* (Vol. 85, August 13, 2012, No. 13, pp. 14)

Ed: Dominic Barton. **Description:** Mining gigabytes of data provides an opportunity for companies to better understand customer behavior at a lesser cost and with unimaginable precision. Human intuition and experience remain significant factors in maximizing the potential of understanding huge amounts of customer data. **Availability:** Print; Online.

3494 ■ *"A Cyber Breach: More Likely Than a Fire"* in *Philadelphia Business Journal* (Vol. 33, June 13, 2014, No. 18, pp. 6)

Pub: American City Business Journals, Inc.
Contact: Mike Olivieri, Executive Vice President
Released: June 13, 2014. **Price:** $4, introductory 4-week offer(Digital only). **Description:** Robert D'Ovidio, an IT, crime and criminal justice system researcher, and Norman Balchunas, director of strategic studies of Drexel Cybersecurity Institute, give their views on cyber security. According to them, the profile of a cyber thief has undergone a change and with it the role of security professionals in corporations globally. They state that a good information security plan that also addresses privacy would be good in security company data. **Availability:** Print; Mailing list; Online.

3495 ■ *"Cynergy Data May Pick Memphis for HQ Move"* in *Memphis Business Journal* (Vol. 33, February 10, 2012, No. 44, pp. 1)

Pub: Baltimore Business Journal
Contact: Rhonda Pringle, President
E-mail: rpringle@bizjournals.com
Ed: Christopher Sheffield. **Description:** Cynergy Data LLC is planning to relocate its corporate headquarters to Memphis, Tennessee. The company will move 200 jobs to the new facility. **Availability:** Print; Online.

3496 ■ *"Data Center Operators are Finding San Antonio has the Right Stuff"* in *San Antonio Business Journal* (Vol. 28, February 28, 2014, No. 3, pp. 4)

Pub: American City Business Journals, Inc.
Contact: Mike Olivieri, Executive Vice President
Released: Weekly. **Price:** $4, Introductory 4-week offer(Digital only). **Description:** A number of data center operators have been opening facilities in San Antonio, Texas. CyrusOne Inc. will build 50,000 square feet of space in the city. Such data centers have also been generating new jobs. **Availability:** Print; Online.

3497 ■ *"Data Security is No. 1 Compliance Concern"* in *HRMagazine* (Vol. 53, October 2008, No. 10, pp. 32)

Description: Electronic data protection and data privacy are the leading ethics and compliance issues faced by companies today. **Availability:** Print; Online.

3498 ■ *"Digital Realty Routes $50 Million for Data Center Improvements"* in *St.Louis Business Journal* (Vol. 33, September 14, 2012, No. 3, pp. 1)

Pub: Baltimore Business Journal
Contact: Rhonda Pringle, President
E-mail: rpringle@bizjournals.com
Description: Digital Realty Trust is planning to invest up to $50 millionto renovate its data center in Saint Louis, Missouri. The facility is expected to become one of the largest data centers in the region. **Availability:** Print; Online.

3499 ■ *"Discrete Wavelet Transform-Based Time Series Analysis and Mining"* in *ACM Computing Surveys* (Vol. 43, Summer 2011, No. 2, pp. 6)

Pub: Association for Computing Machinery
Contact: Yannis Ioannidis, President
Ed: Pimwadee Chaovalit, Aryya Gangopadhyay, George Karabatis, Zhiyuan Chen. **Released:** Volume 43 Issue 2. **Price:** $10, Members; $15, Nonmembers; $5, Students. **Description:** Time series are recorded values of an interesting phenomenon such as stock prices, household items, or patient heart rates over a period of time. Time series data mining focuses on discovering interesting patterns in such data. An introduction to a wavelet-based times series data analysis is provided with a systematic survey of various analysis techniques that use discrete wavelet transformation (DWT) in time series data mining, and outlines the benefits of this approach demonstrated by previous studies performed on diverse application domains, including image classification, multimedia retrieval, and computer network anomaly detection. **Availability:** Download; PDF.

3500 ■ *"Distributed Data Management Using mapReduce"* in *ACM Computing Surveys* (Vol. 46, Fall 2014, No. 3, pp. 31)

Pub: Association for Computing Machinery - University of Wyoming
Contact: Ed Seidel, President
E-mail: uwpres@uwyo.edu
Description: MapReduce is a framework for processing and managing large-scale datasets in a distributed cluster, which has been used for applications such as generating search indexes, document clustering, access log analysis, and various other forms of data analytics. A comprehensive review of a wide range of proposals and systems that focus on the support of distributed data management and processing using MapReduce framework is examined. **Availability:** Online.

3501 ■ *"E-Medical Records Save Money, Time in Ann Arbor"* in *Crain's Detroit Business* (Vol. 24, January 21, 2008, No. 3, pp. 6)

Pub: Crain Communications Inc.
Contact: Barry Asin, President
Ed: Jay Greene. **Description:** Ann Arbor Area Health Information Exchange is improving patient outcomes by sharing clinical and administrative data in electronic medical record systems. **Availability:** Online.

3502 ■ *"The Failure Detector Abstraction"* in *ACM Computing Surveys* (Vol. 43, Summer 2011, No. 2, pp. 9)

Pub: Association for Computing Machinery
Contact: Yannis Ioannidis, President
Ed: Felix C. Freiling, Rachid Guerraoui, Petr Kuznetsov. **Released:** Volume 43 Issue 2. **Price:** $10, Members; $15, Nonmembers; $5, Students. **Description:** A failure detector is a fundamental abstraction in distributed computing. This article surveys this abstraction through two dimensions. First it studies failure detectors as building blocks to simplify the design of reliable distributed algorithms, particularly how failure detectors can factor out timing assumptions to detect failures in distributed agreement algorithms. Second, failure detectors as computability benchmarks are studied. Some limitations of the failure detector abstraction along each of the dimensions are also highlighted. **Availability:** Download; PDF.

3503 ■ *"Free Speech Vs. Privacy in Data Mining"* in *Information Today* (Vol. 28, September 2011, No. 8, pp. 22)

Pub: Information Today Inc.
Contact: Thomas H. Hogan, President
Ed: George H. Pike. **Description:** The U.S. Constitution does not explicitly guarantee the right of privacy. Organizations and businesses that require obtaining and disseminating information can be caught in the middle of privacy rights. The long-term impact on data mining, Internet marketing, and Internet privacy issues are examined.

3504 ■ *"Google 'Drive' May Run Over Some Local Cloud Competitors"* in *Silicon Valley/San Jose Business Journal* (Vol. 29, February 17, 2012, No. 47, pp. 1)

Pub: Baltimore Business Journal
Contact: Rhonda Pringle, President
E-mail: rpringle@bizjournals.com

Description: Google Inc. has been preparing to roll out a cloud storage service called "Drive" that will allow people to store large files online. However, the move would put Google in competition with companies offering similar services and it could affect other companies looking to enter the space. Insights on reactions of the other companies are also provided. **Availability:** Print; Online.

3505 ■ "Growth at E Solutions Part of 'Opportunistic' Data Center Market" in Tampa Bay Business Journal (Vol. 30, January 29, 2010, No. 6, pp. 1)
Pub: Tampa Bay Business Journal
Contact: Ian Anderson, President
E-mail: ianderson@bizjournals.com

Ed: Michael Hinman. **Description:** E Solutions Corporation is experiencing growth amid the economic downturn, with its Park Tower data center occupancy in Tampa Florida expanding from 14,000 square feet to 20,000 square feet. Details on the increased operations fueled by demand for information storage and management services offered by the company are discussed. **Availability:** Print; Online.

3506 ■ "Health IT Regulations Generate Static Among Providers" in Philadelphia Business Journal (Vol. 28, January 29, 2010, No. 50, pp. 1)
Pub: Philadelphia Business Journal
Contact: Sierra Quinn, Director
E-mail: squinn@bizjournals.com

Ed: John George. **Description:** US Centers for Medicaid and Medicare Services and the Office of the National Coordinator for Health Information Technology have proposed rules regarding the meaningful use of electronic health records. The rules must be complied with by hospitals and physicians to qualify for federal stimulus funds. **Availability:** Online.

3507 ■ "Help Wanted: 100 Hospital IT Workers" in Business Courier (Vol. 27, October 8, 2010, No. 23, pp. 1)
Pub: Business Courier

Ed: James Ritchie. **Description:** Hospitals in the Greater Cincinnati area are expected to hire more than 100 information technology (IT) workers to help digitize medical records. Financial incentives from the health care reform bill encouraged investments in electronic medical record systems, increasing the demand for IT workers that would help make information exchange across the healthcare system easier. **Availability:** Print; Online.

3508 ■ "High Touch Expands, Purchases Dallas Firms" in Wichita Business Journal (Vol. 27, February 3, 2012, No. 5, pp. 1)
Pub: Baltimore Business Journal
Contact: Rhonda Pringle, President
E-mail: rpringle@bizjournals.com

Description: Wichita, Kansas-based High Touch Inc. has finalized the acquisitions of the Dallas, Texas-based UniCom Data and Dallas Data Center, after a similar purchase of Newbase LLC at the start of the year. High Touch believes the acquisitions helped the company further expand its regional presence and services. **Availability:** Print; Online.

3509 ■ "How to Play the Tech Mergers" in Barron's (Vol. 90, August 30, 2010, No. 35, pp. 18)
Pub: Barron's Editorial & Corporate Headquarters

Ed: Tiernan Ray. **Description:** The intense bidding by Hewlett-Packard and Dell for 3Par was foreseen in a previous Barron's cover story and 3Par's stock has nearly tripled since reported. Other possible acquisition targets in the tech industry include Brocade Communication Systems, NetApp, Xyratex, and Isilon Systems. **Availability:** Online.

3510 ■ "Image Consultants" in Entrepreneur (June 2014)
Pub: Entrepreneur Media Inc.
Contact: Dan Bova, Director
E-mail: dbova@entrepreneur.com

Description: The ASAP54 mobile application, created by a company of the same name, uses visual recognition technology to help users determine the name of the designer or retailer of a clothing item using photographs. The company has compiled a database consisting of more than 1 million products from its retail partners. It claims an average of 5 percent commission on purchases completed through the application. Other useful wearable gadgets include Nymi, which authenticates identities based on cardiac rhythms, and Netatmo, a bracelet that measures daily sun exposure. **Availability:** Online.

3511 ■ Information Technology for the Small Business: How to Make IT Work For Your Company
Description: Basics of information technology to help small companies maximize benefits are covered. Topics include pitfalls to avoid, email and Internet use, data backup, recovery and overall IT organization.

3512 ■ "Inside Waterloo's Quiet Tech Titan" in Canadian Business (Vol. 87, July 2014, No. 7, pp. 39)
Description: OpenText chief executive officer Mark Barrenechea feels confident about the financial health of the Waterloo, Ontario-based software company. He adds that the company is exploring opportunities by the big data phenomenon. **Availability:** Online.

3513 ■ "Investing in an HR Team Can Ease the Burden of Mass Hiring" in Crain's Detroit Business (Vol. 36, September 8, 2014, No. 36, pp. 15)
Pub: American City Business Journals, Inc.
Contact: Mike Olivieri, Executive Vice President

Description: Computing Source is a computer networking firm that helps small businesses recover computer files from backup tapes, particularly for law firms. Profile of the company and information about its CEO, Mark St. Peter is included. **Availability:** Print; Online.

3514 ■ "Lawyers Object to New Online Court Fees" in Sacramento Business Journal (Vol. 31, August 8, 2014, No. 24, pp. 3)
Pub: American City Business Journals, Inc.
Contact: Mike Olivieri, Executive Vice President

Description: Lawyers and consumer advocates have complained that the Sacramento County Superior Court's new fee system for online access to online court records hinders access to justice. However, court administrators argue that the charging of fees will only help offset the online record system's maintenance costs. **Availability:** Print; Online.

3515 ■ "MMRGlobal Home Health and Senior Care Programs to Be Showcased at Visiting Nurse Associations of America's Annual Meeting" in Marketwired (April 12, 2012)
Pub: Comtex News Network Inc.
Contact: Kan Devnani, President

Description: MMR Global Inc. will highlight its storage and solutions and electronic document management and imaging systems for healthcare professionals at the Visiting Nurse Associations of America (VNAA) 30th Annual Meeting in Phoenix, Arizona. Personal Health Records (PHRs), MyEsafeDepositBox and other programs are profiled. **Availability:** Print; Online.

3516 ■ "N.C. Data-Center Plan Bearing Fruit From Apple, Spec Center" in Charlotte Business Journal (Vol. 25, October 15, 2010, No. 30, pp. 1)
Pub: Charlotte Business Journal
Contact: Robert Morris, Editor
E-mail: rmorris@bizjournals.com

Ed: Ken Elkins. **Description:** Apple Inc. is planning to expand its server farm at the North Carolina Data Center Corridor in Catawba County. T5 Partners, on the other hand, will build a shell building to house a server on the site. Infocrossing Inc. will also build an open data center in the area. **Availability:** Print; Online.

3517 ■ "New Wave of Business Security Products Ushers in the Kaspersky Anti-Malware Protection System" in Internet Wire (October 26, 2010)
Description: Kaspersky Anti-Malware System provides anti-malware protection that requires minimal in-house resources for small businesses. The system offers a full range of tightly integrated end-to-end protection solutions, ensuring unified protection across an entire network, from endpoint and mobile device protection to file server, mail server, network storage and gateway protection. It provides flexible centralized management, immediate threat visibility and a level of responsiveness not seen in other anti-malware approaches. **Availability:** Print; Online.

3518 ■ "Number-Cruncher Gets 'Pushback'" in Philadelphia Business Journal (Vol. 33, August 22, 2014, No. 28, pp. 10)
Pub: American City Business Journals, Inc.
Contact: Mike Olivieri, Executive Vice President

Released: Weekly. **Price:** $4, introductory 4-week offer(Digital only). **Description:** Bryan Wellen, senior director of clinical informatics for Continuum Health Alliance (CHA), asserts that while some physicians are receptive to patient information, others respond with an element of 'pushback' and criticism of the data. CHA and Horizon Blue Cross Blue Shield of New Jersey are using data analysis to create strategies that improve health care and reduce costs. **Availability:** Print; Online.

3519 ■ "Scanning Dell's Shopping List" in Barron's (Vol. 89, July 13, 2009, No. 28, pp. 24)
Pub: Dow Jones & Company Inc.
Contact: Almar Latour, Chief Executive Officer

Ed: Mark Veverka. **Description:** It is believed that Dell will be looking for companies to acquire since they poached an experienced mergers-and-acquisitions executive. In addition Dell's CEO is reportedly telling people he plans to go shopping. Dell executives have also stated an interest in data storage. **Availability:** Online.

3520 ■ "Search Engines: Image Conscious" in Canadian Business (Vol. 81, February 26, 2008, No. 4, pp. 36)
Pub: Rogers Media Inc.
Contact: Neil Spivak, Chief Executive Officer

Ed: Andrew Wahl. **Description:** Idee Inc. is testing an Internet search engine for images that does not rely on tags but compares its visual data to a database of other images. The company was founded and managed by Leila Boujnane as an off-shoot of their risk-management software firm. Their software has already been used by image companies to track copyrighted images and to find images within their own archives. **Availability:** Online.

3521 ■ "Shellshocked: Dealing With Cyber Insecurity" in Philadelphia Business Journal (Vol. 33, June 13, 2014, No. 18, pp. 4)
Pub: American City Business Journals, Inc.
Contact: Mike Olivieri, Executive Vice President

Description: The threat of cyber theft or data breach is increasing globally as technology becomes advanced and more companies start storing their important data electronically. Therefore, the importance of cyber security has increased. Although big businesses suffer more from data breaches, small companies can also take a beating if data breach happens. A survey found that small businesses were wary of spending money on security issues; good investment in IT and creating a privacy policy will help companies fight cyber threats. **Availability:** Online.

3522 ■ "The Signal and the Noise: Why So Many Predictions Fail - but Some Don't"
Released: February 03, 2015. **Price:** $18, paperback; $27.95, hardcover; $14.99, e-book; $17.50, audiobook. **Description:** Statistician, writer, and founder of The New York Times political blog, FiveThirtyEight.com, describes the science of forecasting and shows what happens when Big Data meets baseball,

weather forecasting, earthquake prediction, economics and polling and shows that predictions can go wrong because they are based on biases, vested interests, and overconfidence. **Availability:** E-book; Print.

3523 ■ "Spinout Success: New Leadership Steps In At UW's C4C" in *Puget Sound Business Journal (Vol. 35, June 27, 2014, No. 10, pp. 11)*
Pub: American City Business Journals, Inc.
Contact: Mike Olivieri, Executive Vice President
Description: University of Washington's Center for Commercialization vice provost, Vikram Jandhyala, talks about his new position with the school. Jandhyala says he plans to build more synergy between the medical school and engineering and between social sciences and computer science. He also says the medical and software industry need to grow to accommodate the volume of data crossing and stored within the Internet. **Availability:** Online.

3524 ■ "The Story of a Complex Project, Seen From a Bridge" in *Business Review Albany (Vol. 41, June 27, 2014, No. 14, pp. 7)*
Pub: American City Business Journals, Inc.
Contact: Mike Olivieri, Executive Vice President
Released: Weekly. **Price:** $4, introductory 4-week offer(Digital only). **Description:** The bridge connecting the manufacturing and technology development buildings at GlobalFoundries in Malta, NY allows employees to transport computer chip-containing wafers without the risk of contamination. The connector is a cleanroom and has its own air conditioning system and foundation vibration control. **Availability:** Print; Online.

3525 ■ "A Survey of DHT Security Techniques" in *ACM Computing Surveys (Vol. 43, Summer 2011, No. 2, pp. 8)*
Pub: Association for Computing Machinery
Contact: Yannis Ioannidis, President
Ed: Guido Urdaneta, Guillaume Pierre, Maarten Van Steen. **Released:** Volume 43 Issue 2. **Price:** $10, Members; $15, Nonmembers; $5, Students. **Description:** Peer-to-peer networks based on distributed hash tables (DHTs) have received considerable attention since their introduction in 2001. Unfortunately, DHT-based systems have been shown to be difficult to protect against security attacks. An overview of techniques reported in literature for making DHT-based systems resistant to the three most important attacks that can be launched by malicious nodes participating in the DHT is given: the Sybil attack, the Eclipse attack, and routing and storage attacks. **Availability:** Download; PDF.

3526 ■ "Sutter Court Win is Part of Trend" in *Sacramento Business Journal (Vol. 31, July 25, 2014, No. 22, pp. 3)*
Pub: American City Business Journals, Inc.
Contact: Mike Olivieri, Executive Vice President
Released: July 25, 2014. **Description:** The Third District Court of Appeals dismissed 13 coordinated data-breach lawsuits filed against Sutter Health of Sacramento, California. The plaintiffs claim $4 billion in damages over theft of patient data from a local Sutter Health office in October 2011.

3527 ■ "Tax Preparation Made Easier With Carbonite Online Backup" in *Investment Weekly News (March 10, 2012, pp. 783)*
Pub: PR Newswire Association LLC.
Description: Carbonite, Inc. provides a secure backup protection service, making tax preparation easier for consumers and small- to medium-sized businesses. Details on Carbonite.com and its services are included. **Availability:** Online.

3528 ■ "Tech Data Launches Unified Communications and Network Security Specialized Business Units" in *Wireless News (October 22,2009)*
Description: Responding to the growing demand for unified communications and network security, Tech Data announced the formation of two new Specialized Business Units. **Availability:** Online.

3529 ■ "URI Centre Seen as Bridge From Campus to Employment" in *Providence Business News (Vol. 29, June 30, 2014, No. 13, pp. 4)*
Pub: American City Business Journals, Inc.
Contact: Mike Olivieri, Executive Vice President
URL(s): pbn.com/uri-center-seen-as-bridge-from-campus-to-employment98182
Description: Kimberly S. Washor is the first director of University of Rhode Island's (URIs) new Centre for Career and Experiential Education that combines the missions of Experiential Learning and Community Engagement along with Career Services and Employer Relations. By joining the two offices, URI is implementing a new database that will meet the needs of both career and internship advising, where adviser will be able to track industry human resource partners. **Telecommunication Services:** Daddona@pbn.com.

3530 ■ "Watson May Study New Field" in *Business Review Albany (Vol. 41, July 18, 2014, No. 17, pp. 10)*
Description: IBM Corporation has extended its Watson computer system's cognitive capacities to the Cloud. Rensselaer Polytechnic Institute has been training Watson to be a data advisor. It is also using the system to study human thought and cognition. **Availability:** Print; Online.

3531 ■ "Wegmans Uses Database for Recall" in *Supermarket News (Vol. 56, September 22, 2008, No. 38)*
Pub: Informa USA, Inc.
Contact: Stephen A. Carter, Chief Executive Officer
Ed: Carol Angrisani. **Description:** Wegmans used data obtained through its loyalty card that, in turn, sent automated telephone calls to every customer who had purchased tainted pet food when Mars Petcare recalled dog food products.

3532 ■ "What is the Future of Disk Drives, Death or Rebirth?" in *ACM Computing Surveys (Vol. 43, Fall 2011, No. 3, pp. 23)*
Pub: Association for Computing Machinery
Contact: Yannis Ioannidis, President
Ed: Yuhui Deng. **Released:** Volume 43 Issue 3. **Price:** $10, Members; $15, Nonmembers; $5, Students. **Description:** Disk drives have experienced dramatic development to meet performance requirements since the IBM 1301 disk drive was announced in 1961. However, the performance gap between memory and disk drives has widened to 6 orders of magnitude and continues to widen by about 50 percent per year. Challenges and opportunities facing these storage devices are explored. **Availability:** Download; PDF.

3533 ■ "Why Life Science Needs Its Own Silicon Valley: Human Genomics Won't Reach Its Full Potential Until It Has a Sizable Industry Cluster" in *Harvard Business Review (Vol. 90, July-August 2012, No. 7-8, pp. 25)*
Pub: Harvard Business Review Press
Contact: Moderna V. Pfizer, Contact
Ed: Fariborz Ghadar, John Sviokla, Dietrich A. Stephan. **Price:** $6, PDF and hardcover black and white. **Description:** The creation of an industry cluster will be key to advancing human genomics research. High degrees of specialization via multiple contributors will be needed to generate significant innovations; an accessible, coherent data source will also be necessary. **Availability:** Print; PDF; Online.

TRADE PERIODICALS

3534 ■ *Journal of Database Management (JDM)*
Pub: IGI Global
Contact: Jan Travers, Director
URL(s): www.igi-global.com/journal/journal-database-management/1072

Released: Continuous **Price:** $500, Individuals for print; $500, Institutions for print. **Description:** Journal covering the research of database administrators and managers. **Availability:** Print; Download; PDF; Online.

3535 ■ *Online Searcher*
Pub: Information Today Inc.
Contact: Thomas H. Hogan, President
URL(s): www.infotoday.com/OnlineSearcher
Released: Bimonthly; January/February, March/April, May/June, July/August, September/October, and November/December. **Description:** Edited for librarians, Webmasters, site designers, content managers, and others concerned with knowledge/information management. Includes critical reviews of Web sites, software, search engines, and information services. (Formerly published by Online, Inc.). **Availability:** Print; Online.

3536 ■ *SIGIR Forum*
Pub: Association for Computing Machinery - Special Interest Group on Array Programming Languages
URL(s): sigir.org
Released: Semiannual; June and December. **Price:** Included in membership. **Description:** Concerned with how machines may be used in the storage, retrieval, and dissemination of information, including news and information relating to retrieval theory, programming, file preparation, searching strategy, output schemes, systems evaluation, and development of equipment best suited for these tasks. Also contains proceedings of annual international SIGIR conferences. **Availability:** Print; PDF; Online.

COMPUTERIZED DATABASES

3537 ■ *Business Wire*
Business Wire, Inc.
101 California St., 20th Fl.
San Francisco, CA 94111
Co. E-mail: info@businesswire.com
URL: http://www.businesswire.com
Contact: Geff Scott, Chief Executive Officer
Description: Contains more than 1.4 million records that make up the complete text of press releases from public and private companies and other organizations, such as hospitals and universities. **Availability:** Online. **Type:** Full-text.

3538 ■ *Computer Database*
URL(s): www.cengage.com/search/productOverview.do?Ntt=37823093771748009945578022605349357&N=197+4294922389&Ntk=P_EPIwww.proquest.com/customer-care/title-lists/ProQuest-Dialog-Prosheets.html
Description: Provides one year of full-text online for 150 leading computer-related publications. Also includes 70,000 product specifications and brief profiles of 13,000 computer product vendors and manufacturers. Inquire as to prices and availability. **Availability:** Online. **Type:** Bibliographic; Full-text.

3539 ■ *Computerworld*
International Data Group, Inc.
140 Kendrick St., Bldg. B
Needham, MA 02494
Ph: (508)872-8200
Co. E-mail: leads@idc.com
URL: http://www.idc.com
Contact: Crawford del Prete, President
URL(s): www.idginc.com/about
Availability: Online. **Type:** Full-text.

LIBRARIES

3540 ■ University of Minnesota - Charles Babbage Institute for Computing, Information, and Culture - Erwin Tomash Library
University of Minnesota, Charles Babbage Institute
211 Andersen Library
222 21st Ave. S
Minneapolis, MN 55455
Co. E-mail: cbi@umn.edu
URL: http://cse.umn.edu/cbi

Contact: Dr. Jeffrey R. Yost, Professor
E-mail: yostx003@umn.edu
Facebook: www.facebook.com/babbageinstitute
X (Twitter): x.com/BabbageInst

Description: Facilitates, fosters, and conducts research to advance the understanding of computing, information, and culture. Studies the development of information processing, including technical and socioeconomic aspects, and works to promote increased awareness of the impact of that development on society. Provides counsel and research assistance to other scholars in the field. Maintains archives, including 320 oral histories of computing pioneers. **Scope:** History of information science and technology, including development of computer technology, applications of information processing techniques ranging from banking to science research, automation techniques in archival development and historical database generation, history and social impacts of the information processing field, and entrepreneurial activity of the information industry. Identifies and makes accessible important letters, diaries, manuscripts, unpublished reports, industry records, financial information, interviews, and photographs that document and interpret the information revolution. Acts as a clearinghouse on the location of historical material. **Services:** Copying; collection open to researchers. **Founded:** 1979. **Holdings:** Corporate records; manuscript materials; records of professional associations; oral history interviews; trade publications; periodicals; photographs; films; videos; and reference materials.; 550 photos; 40 videos; 100,000 photographs depicts books; journals.; . **Subscriptions:** ; books. **Publications:** *Iterations: Interdisciplinary Journal of Software History*; *Charles Babbage Institute Newsletter* (Semiannual). **Educational Activities:** CBI Lecture series. **Awards:** Arthur L. Norberg Travel Fund (Annual); Arthur L. Norberg Travel Fund (Annual); The Adelle and Erwin Tomash Fellowship in the History of Information Technology (Annual). **Geographic Preference:** National.

3541 ■ University of Minnesota Libraries Business Information
499 Wilson Library
  309 19th Ave., S
  Minneapolis, MN 55455
Ph: (612)624-3321
Co. E-mail: busref@umn.edu
URL: http://libguides.umn.edu/c.php?g=1056521
Contact: Caroline Lilyard, Contact
E-mail: lily@umn.edu
Facebook: www.facebook.com/umnlib
X (Twitter): x.com/umnlib
Instagram: www.instagram.com/umnlib
YouTube: www.youtube.com/user/umnLibraries
Pinterest: www.pinterest.com/umnlibraries

Scope: Accounting; business and economics statistics; business legal forms; career and employment research; case studies; consumer resources and agencies; economic census; entrepreneurship; finance; financial ratios; human resource development; industrial relations; industry resources; information systems; information technology industry; insurance; international business and global markets; international trade statistics; management; Minnesota business; operations and management science; taxation. **Holdings:** Books; reports; statistics; newspapers; publications; journals; articles.

RESEARCH CENTERS

3542 ■ Boston University Department of Electrical & Computer Engineering - Multimedia Communications Laboratory (MCL)
8 St. Mary " s St.
  Boston, MA 02215
URL: http://sites.bu.edu/mcl

Description: Integral unit of Department of Electrical and Computer Engineering, Boston University. **Scope:** Time-dependent data and their support by storage and communication as typified by on demand interactive multimedia applications. Topics include physical data organizations for audio and video storage, protocols for scalable video services, scheduling in real-time communications, data distribution and management in distributed multimedia systems, temporal data modeling, and content-based retrieval of multimedia. **Founded:** 1991. **Publications:** *MCL Technical reports*. **Educational Activities:** MCL Research seminars.

3543 ■ University of Florida - Database Systems Research Center (DSR)
Gainesville, FL
URL: http://dsr.cise.ufl.edu
Contact: Daisy Zhe Wang, Director
E-mail: daisyw@cise.ufl.edu

Description: Interdisciplinary unit in the College of Engineering, University of Florida. Offers editorial service to technical journals. **Scope:** The Center focuses on solving complex problems requiring the use and integration of technologies such as database management, distributed objects, information retrieval, artificial intelligence, knowledge management, data transformations and warehousing, database triggering and alerting systems, mobile computing, web services, and distributed and parallel computing. **Founded:** 1977. **Publications:** *Database Systems Research Center Conference proceedings*; *Database Systems Research Center Journal* (5/year). **Educational Activities:** Research workshops, Offered to industrial companies, government organizations, and academic institutions.; Technical seminars (Periodic).

Computer Learning/Training Center

ASSOCIATIONS AND OTHER ORGANIZATIONS

3544 ■ Association for Talent Development (ATD) - Library
1640 King St.
  Alexandria, VA 22313-1443
Ph: (703)683-8100
Free: 800-628-2783
Fax: (703)683-1523
Co. E-mail: customercare@td.org
URL: http://www.td.org
Contact: Tony Bingham, President
Facebook: www.facebook.com/ATD
Linkedin: www.linkedin.com/company/15989
X (Twitter): x.com/ATD
Instagram: www.instagram.com/atdnational
Pinterest: www.pinterest.com/ATDofficial
Description: Supports the talent development profession by providing trusted content in the form of research, books, webcasts, events, and education programs. **Scope:** Management; leadership. **Services:** Library open to members only. **Founded:** 1943. **Holdings:** 170 monographs; 100 books; 100 newspapers. **Publications:** *American Society Training and Development Buyer's Guide and Consultant Directory* (Annual); *Technical Training Basics*; *ASTD Buyer's Guide & Consultant Directory* (Annual); *TD at Work* (Monthly); *Learning Circuits* (Monthly); *TD Magazine* (Monthly); *Member Information Exchange (MIX)*; *TRAINET*; *ATD Buyer's Guide*; *ATD Buyer's Guide*; *American Society for Training and Development--Training Video Directory*; *Who's Who in Training and Development* (Annual). **Educational Activities:** ATD International Conference and Exposition (Annual); ATD TechKnowledge Conference (Annual); TechKnowledge Conference and Exposition (Annual). **Awards:** ATD BEST Award (Annual); Awards in the Advancing Workplace Learning and Performance; ATD Excellence in Practice Awards (Annual); Gordon M. Bliss Memorial Award (Annual); ATD Dissertation Award (Annual); ASTD Talent Development Thought Leader Award (Annual); ATD Torch Award (Annual). **Geographic Preference:** Multinational.

3545 ■ Computer Assisted Language Instruction Consortium (CALICO) - Library
Texas State University
  214 Centennial Hall
  San Marcos, TX 78666
Ph: (512)245-1417
Fax: (512)245-9089
Co. E-mail: info@calico.org
URL: http://calico.org
Contact: Randall Sadler, President
E-mail: rsadler@illinois.edu
Description: Seeks to apply primarily computer-related technology to the teaching, learning, and processing of first and second languages. **Scope:** Research; technology development. **Founded:** 1999. **Holdings:** Figures not available. **Publications:** *CALICO Resource Guide*; *CALICO* (3/year). **Educational Activities:** CALICO (Annual). **Awards:** Outstanding CALICO Journal Article Award (Annual); CALICO Outstanding Graduate Student Award (Annual). **Geographic Preference:** Multinational.

3546 ■ International Association for Computer Information Systems (IACIS) - Library
Abingdon OX14 4RN, United Kingdom
URL: http://www.iacis.org
Contact: Joanna Paliszkiewicz, President
E-mail: joanna.paliszkiewicz@iacis.org
Description: Seeks to promote the knowledge, use, and teaching of computers, and technology; dedicated to the improvement of information systems and computer professionals. **Scope:** Information systems; technology. **Holdings:** Figures not available. **Publications:** *IACIS Newsletter* (Semiannual); *Journal of Computer Information Systems (JCIS)* (6/year). **Educational Activities:** Annual IACIS Conference (Annual). **Awards:** Computer Educator of the Year Award (Annual); Ben Bauman Award for Excellence (Annual). **Geographic Preference:** Multinational.

3547 ■ Jobs for the Future (JFF)
505 14th St., Ste. 340
  Oakland, CA 94612
Ph: (617)728-4446
Co. E-mail: info@jff.org
URL: http://www.jff.org
Contact: Maria Flynn, President
Facebook: www.facebook.com/jobsforthefuture
YouTube: www.youtube.com/user/JobsForTheFuture
Description: Seeks to integrate quality education and work opportunities. Offers technical assistance and training to educators, executives, and policy makers. Conducts research and disseminates results on trends in learning among students and employees. **Founded:** 1983. **Publications:** *Newswire* (Bimonthly). **Geographic Preference:** National.

3548 ■ Learning Resources Network (LERN)
c/o Tammy Peterson, Director, Customer Service,
  Information Specialist
  PO Box 9
  River Falls, WI 54022
Free: 800-678-5376
Fax: (888)234-8633
Co. E-mail: info@lern.org
URL: http://lern.com/lern
Contact: William A. Draves, President
E-mail: draves@lern.org
Facebook: www.facebook.com/
  LearningResourcesNetwork
X (Twitter): x.com/LernUpdates
YouTube: www.youtube.com/user/lerninternational
Pinterest: www.pinterest.com/lernupdates
Description: Objectives are: to help people and communities start adult learning programs; to provide technical assistance to existing adult learning organizations; to promote alternative education and social change at the national level. Serves as a national technical assistance network in adult learning and noncredit programming. Provides speakers and technical assistance to members and nonmembers. Sponsors seminars; compiles statistics. **Scope:** Provides programming, management support and marketing techniques for adult education providers, including online classes and in-house seminars. **Founded:** 1974. **Publications:** Learning association involves in "Course Trends"; "Marketing Recreation Classes"; "LERN"; "Creating and Sustaining Partnerships"; "Continuing Education: The Essentials"; "Teaching Online"; "Generational Learning Styles"; "Nine Shift"; "Marketing Manual"; "Contract Training Manual"; "How To Teach Adults"; "Developing Successful New Programs.". **Training:** Negotiation: Strategies to Get More and Give More; Designing Brochures for Results; Developing Your One-Year Marketing Plan; Building an Information-Age Organization. **Educational Activities:** LERN Conferences (Annual); LERN Annual Virtual Conferences (Annual). **Geographic Preference:** National.

REFERENCE WORKS

3549 ■ "Computer Science for All: Can Schools Pull It Off?" in Education Week (February 19, 2018)
URL(s): www.edweek.org/ew/articles/2018/02/20/
  computer-science-for-all-can-schools-pull.html
Ed: Benjamin Herold. **Released:** February 18, 2018. **Description:** The White House has backed a vision to get more computer-science courses and technology into the classrooms, in order to get more kids interested in the subject. However, there is debate on whether the new initiative should focus on preparing students for jobs or to teach them new ways to think. Also, there is the practical challenge of getting the tech into the classroom and keeping it updated. **Availability:** Online.

3550 ■ "A New Approach to Learning Centers" in Scholastic
URL(s): www.scholastic.com/teachers/articles/
  teaching-content/new-approach-learning-centers/
Description: A discussion of setting up learning centers within a classroom, which often include technology and the Internet. **Availability:** Online.

3551 ■ "Technology in the Classroom: What the Research Tells Us" in Inside Higher Ed (December 12, 2018)
URL(s): www.insidehighered.com/digital-learning/
  views/2018/12/12/what-research-tells-us-abou
  t-using-technology-classroom-opinion
Ed: Aaron S. Richmond, Jordan D. Troisi. **Released:** December 12, 2018. **Description:** Takes a look at how technology introduced into the classroom is being used and whether or not it is helping or harming education. **Availability:** Online.

3552 ■ "Using Technology as a Learning Tool, Not Just the Cool New Thing" in Educause
URL(s): www.educause.edu/research-and-publica
  tions/books/educating-net-generation/using
  -technology-learning-tool-not-just-cool-new-thing

Description: Discusses the goals of this generation in the classroom in regards to technology, with the emphasis on college-level courses. **Availability:** Online.

3553 ■ "What 126 Studies Say About Education Technology" in MIT News (February 26, 2019)
URL(s): news.mit.edu/2019/mit-jpal-what-126-studies-tell-us-about-education-technology-impact-0226
Released: February 26, 2019. **Description:** Within the education sphere, technology used in classrooms has boomed. However, there are times when technology can actually harm student learning due to inequality in the classroom. Also, just having the equipment doesn't necessarily mean that grades improve, it just means that the student learns how to use that particular piece of technology. **Availability:** Online.

TRADE PERIODICALS

3554 ■ *Computer Science Education*
Pub: Taylor And Francis Group
Contact: Annie Callanan, Chief Executive Officer
URL(s): www.tandfonline.com/journals/ncse20
Ed: Brian Dorn, Jan Vahrenhold, Sally Fincher, Laurie Murphy. **Released:** Quarterly; latest edition: volume 34, issue 2 2024. **Price:** $1,690, Institutions for print & online only; $1,607, Institutions for online only; $524, Individuals for print only. **Description:** Computer journal. **Availability:** Print; Download; PDF; Online.

3555 ■ *DCL News*
Pub: Data Conversion Laboratory
Contact: Mark Gross, President
URL(s): www.dataconversionlaboratory.com/newsletter
Released: Monthly **Description:** E-journal providing you insider information on XML and SGML, along with the latest technology and e-publishing news. **Availability:** Online.

3556 ■ *Educational Technology Magazine: Magazine for Managers of Change in Education*
Contact: Lawrence Lipsitz, Senior Editor
URL(s): booksforead.com/etp
Released: 6/yr. **Price:** $289, U.S. /year; $329, /year (Foreign). **Description:** Magazine covering the entire field of educational technology. **Availability:** Print; Online; PDF.

3557 ■ *Online Searcher*
Pub: Information Today Inc.
Contact: Thomas H. Hogan, President
URL(s): www.infotoday.com/OnlineSearcher
Released: Bimonthly; January/February, March/April, May/June, July/August, September/October, and November/December. **Description:** Edited for librarians, Webmasters, site designers, content managers, and others concerned with knowledge/information management. Includes critical reviews of Web sites, software, search engines, and information services. (Formerly published by Online, Inc.). **Availability:** Print; Online.

3558 ■ *TechTrends*
Pub: Springer US
Contact: Derk Haank, Chief Executive Officer
URL(s): link.springer.com/journal/11528
Released: 6/year **Description:** Professional journal for educators and trainers in the educational communication and technology field. **Availability:** Print; PDF; Download; Online.

TRADE SHOWS AND CONVENTIONS

3559 ■ Computers in Libraries
Information Today Inc. (ITI)
  143 Old Marlton Pke.
  Medford, NJ 08055-8750
Ph: (609)654-6266
Free: 800-300-9868
Fax: (609)654-4309
Co. E-mail: custserv@infotoday.com
URL: http://www.infotoday.com
Contact: Thomas H. Hogan, President
URL(s): computersinlibraries.infotoday.com/2024/default.aspx
Facebook: www.facebook.com/ComputersInLibraries
Frequency: Annual. **Description:** Products in all aspects of library technology, including web-based products and services, integrated library and information systems, search engine software, library furniture, document delivery services, digital management services, Internet software tools, content suppliers, and networking services. **Audience:** Academic, public, corporate, government, special, and school librarians, library directors and executives, information managers, information architects and specialists, researchers, system professionals, content managers, technical managers, information professionals. **Principal Exhibits:** Products in all aspects of library technology, including web-based products and services, integrated library and information systems, search engine software, library furniture, document delivery services, digital management services, Internet software tools, content suppliers, and networking services. Dates and Locations: 2025 Mar 25-27. **Telecommunication Services:** jane@dysartjones.com.

3560 ■ Michigan Association for Computer Users in Learning Conference
Michigan Association for Computer Users in Learning (MACUL)
  520 S Creyts Rd.
  Lansing, MI 48917
Ph: (517)882-1403
Fax: (517)882-2362
Co. E-mail: macul@macul.org
URL: http://macul.org
Contact: Mark Smith, Executive Director
E-mail: msmith@macul.org
URL(s): maculconference.org
Frequency: Annual; held in March. **Audience:** Educators and students. Dates and Locations: 2025 Mar 19-21 Detroit, MI; 2026 Mar 18-20 Grand Rapids, MI; 2027 Mar 17-19 Detroit, MI. **Telecommunication Services:** msmith@macul.org.

FRANCHISES AND BUSINESS OPPORTUNITIES

3561 ■ CMIT Solutions Inc.
925 S Mo Pac Expy. St. b225
Austin, TX 78746
Ph: (512)879-4555
Co. E-mail: cmit@cmitsolutions.com
URL: http://cmitsolutions.com
Contact: Mario Zambrano, President
Facebook: www.facebook.com/CMITdtaustin
Linkedin: www.linkedin.com/company-beta/3743915
X (Twitter): x.com/cmitatx
YouTube: www.youtube.com/user/cmitsolutions
Description: Firm provides it services and computer support to small businesses. **Founded:** 1996. **Training:** Offers 3 weeks training at headquarters, 1 week onsite with ongoing support.

3562 ■ Compuchild
Compuchild Services of America
  3736 Fallon Rd., Ste. 125
  Dublin, CA 94568
Ph: (317)817-9817
Free: 800-619-5437
Fax: (317)818-8184
Contact: Shubhra Kant, President
Facebook: www.facebook.com/CompuChild
Linkedin: www.linkedin.com/company/compuchild/about
X (Twitter): x.com/CompuChild
Instagram: www.instagram.com/compuchild_franchise
YouTube: www.youtube.com/channel/UCEHzHydnaCoZKj_Ut5piemg
Pinterest: www.pinterest.com/compuchild
Description: Computer education to children. **No. of Franchise Units:** 69. **No. of Company-Owned Units:** 1. **Founded:** 1994. **Franchised:** 1995. **Equity Capital Needed:** $15,000. **Franchise Fee:** $12,500 or $17,500. **Financial Assistance:** Yes **Training:** Yes.

3563 ■ New Horizons Computer Learning Centers Inc.
New Horizons Worldwide, Inc.
  2502 N ROCKY POINT Dr., Ste. 500
  Tampa, FL 33607
Ph: (714)221-3100
Co. E-mail: info@nhsocal.com
URL: http://www.newhorizons.com/home
Description: Provider of training, certification and job placement. **Scope:** Specializes in PC and Macintosh computer training. Offers expertise in Novell, Microsoft and Lotus. **Publications:** "How to reward your best employees," Mar, 2009; "Mentored Learning Goes Digital," Talent Management, Jun, 2009; **Training:** Microsoft Seminar, New Horizons, Sep, 2009; PMP Seminar, Jul, 2009; Career Watch, Jun, 2009; SQL Server Seminar, Jun, 2009; WS 2008 Seminar, Jun, 2009; Microsoft Office Test Drive, Jun, 2009. **Special Services:** Online LIVE?; Mentored Learning?.

COMPUTERIZED DATABASES

3564 ■ *Business Wire*
Business Wire, Inc.
  101 California St., 20th Fl.
  San Francisco, CA 94111
Co. E-mail: info@businesswire.com
URL: http://www.businesswire.com
Contact: Geff Scott, Chief Executive Officer
Description: Contains more than 1.4 million records that make up the complete text of press releases from public and private companies and other organizations, such as hospitals and universities. **Availability:** Online. **Type:** Full-text.

3565 ■ *Computer Database*
URL(s): www.cengage.com/search/productOverview.do?Ntt=37823093717480099455780226053493 57&N=197+4294922389&Ntk=P_EPIwww.proquest.com/customer-care/title-lists/ProQuest-Dialog-Prosheets.html
Description: Provides one year of full-text online for 150 leading computer-related publications. Also includes 70,000 product specifications and brief profiles of 13,000 computer product vendors and manufacturers. Inquire as to prices and availability. **Availability:** Online. **Type:** Bibliographic; Full-text.

3566 ■ *Computerworld*
International Data Group, Inc.
  140 Kendrick St., Bldg. B
  Needham, MA 02494
Ph: (508)872-8200
Co. E-mail: leads@idc.com
URL: http://www.idc.com
Contact: Crawford del Prete, President
URL(s): www.idginc.com/about
Availability: Online. **Type:** Full-text.

RESEARCH CENTERS

3567 ■ Massachusetts Institute of Technology - Center for Collective Intelligence (CCI)
245 First St., E94
  Cambridge, MA 02142
URL: http://cci.mit.edu
Contact: Kathleen Kennedy, Executive Director
Description: Integral unit of Massachusetts Institute of Technology. **Scope:** Research focuses on how new communications technologies, especially the Internet, allow large numbers of people all over the world to work together in new ways. **Founded:** 1989. **Publications:** CCI Working papers. **Educational Activities:** ACM Collective Intelligence Conference Series.

3568 ■ Michigan State University - Software Engineering and Network Systems Laboratory (SENS)
3312 Engineering Bldg.
East Lansing, MI 48824
URL: http://engineering.msu.edu/about/departments/cse/research
Contact: Dr. Betty H. C. Cheng, Contact
E-mail: chengb@msu.edu

Description: Integral unit of Michigan State University. **Scope:** Methods for software systems development. **Educational Activities:** IEEE International Conference On Requirements Engineering (Annual); IEEE International Conference On Software Engineering (Annual); SENS Workshop on Industrial Strength Formal Specification Techniques.

3569 ■ Rice University - Ken Kennedy Institute for Information Technology (K2I)
6100 Main St.
Houston, TX 77005-1827
Ph: (713)348-5823
Co. E-mail: kenkennedy@rice.edu
URL: http://kenkennedy.rice.edu/about-ken-kennedy
Contact: Angela Wilkins, Executive Director
E-mail: angela.d.wilkins@rice.edu

Description: Interdisciplinary research group at Rice University; comprised of faculty from the departments of computer science, electrical and computer engineering, statistics, computational and applied mathematics, chemical engineering, mechanical and civil engineering, physics astronomy, biochemistry and cell biology, geology and geophysics chemistry, and psychology. Offers electronic software distribution system for access to public domain and licensable software; short courses and research symposia. **Scope:** Parallel computation, performance of parallel and distributed architectures, advanced programming systems, distributed software systems, supercomputer compiler systems, computational mathematics, computational science, robotics, machine vision and image processing, motion planning and control, digital signal processing and communications, and cognitive science. Develops methods for the generation, transmission, storage, and processing of information. Activities emphasize parallel computation, including parallel computational architectures, software support for parallel programs, and parallel algorithms. Also studies the use of technologies for teaching and learning. **Founded:** 1987. **Publications:** *CITI Technical reports*. **Educational Activities:** Artificial Intelligence Symposium; Compaq/Rice High Performance Software Symposium; Graduate and undergraduate student training; U.S. Army Conference on Applied Statistics, On applied statistics.

3570 ■ U.S. Department of Energy - Los Alamos National Laboratory - Computer, Computational, and Statistical Sciences Division (CCS)
PO Box 1663
Los Alamos, NM 87545
URL: http://www.lanl.gov/org/ddste/aldsc/computer-computational-statistical-sciences/index.php

Description: Integral unit of Los Alamos National Laboratory. Named as Department of Energy High Performance Computing Research Center. Offers technology transfer agreements with universities, industry, vendors, and funding agencies. **Scope:** Research center focuses on computational science and technology, computer science, systems simulation, and mathematical analysis, focusing on parallel computers with teraflop computational rates, local and national networks operating at gigabit speeds, high-performance graphics workstations capable of 3-D color imaging, high-performance computing, distributed computing, and visualization. **Publications:** *Journal of the Advanced Computer Laboratory*.

Computer Maintenance and Repair Service

START-UP INFORMATION

3571 ■ *"Three Common Computer Repair Franchise Funding Sources Revealed by SP Home Run Inc."* in *Investment Weekly News* **(May 12, 2012)**
Description: SP Home Run discusses three popular sources for initial funding capital when starting a computer repair franchise: family, friends, and fools. It is advised that if money could become a problem within any relationship it is best to avoid that type of funding source. **Availability:** Online.

ASSOCIATIONS AND OTHER ORGANIZATIONS

3572 ■ **International Society of Certified Electronics Technicians (ISCET) - Library**
PO Box 378
  Hillsboro, TX 76645
Ph: (817)921-9101
Free: 800-946-0201
Fax: (817)921-3741
Co. E-mail: info@iscet.org
URL: http://www.iscet.org
Contact: Steve Gelman, President
E-mail: steve@nationalservicealliance.com
Description: Seeks to provide a fraternal bond among certified electronics technicians, raise their public image and improve the effectiveness of industry education programs for technicians. Offers training programs in new electronics information. **Scope:** Electronics; technicians. **Founded:** 1965. **Holdings:** Figures not available. **Publications:** *ISCET Update* (Quarterly); *ProService Directory and Yearbook* (Annual). **Educational Activities:** National Professional Service Convention (NPSC) (Annual). **Awards:** Technician of the Year (Annual). **Geographic Preference:** National.

3573 ■ **National Electronics Service Dealers Association (NESDA)**
PO Box 378
  Hillsboro, TX 76645
Ph: (817)921-9061
Free: 800-797-9197
Co. E-mail: info@nesda.com
URL: http://nesda.wildapricot.org
Contact: Paul Burgio, President
Facebook: www.facebook.com/TVRepairPros
Description: Local and state electronic service associations and companies. Supplies technical service information on business management training to electronic service dealers. Offers certification and training programs through International Society of Certified Electronics Technicians. Conducts technical service and business management seminars. **Founded:** 1963. **Publications:** *ProService Magazine* (Monthly); *Find a TV Repair Pro*; *ProService Directory and Yearbook* (Annual); *Proservice Directory*. **Educational Activities:** National Professional Service Convention (NPSC) (Annual). **Awards:** NESDA Associate Leadership Excellence Award (Annual); Fay S. Wood EHF Membership Award (Annual); Gerry M. McCann CET/CSM, EHF Memorial Award (Annual); M.L. Finneburgh, Sr., Award of Excellence (Annual); National Friend of Service Award (Annual); NESDA Outstanding Associate President Award (Annual); NESDA Outstanding Committee Chairperson Award (Annual); NSDA Person of the Year (Annual); Richard Mildenberger Outstanding NESDA Officer (Annual). **Geographic Preference:** National.

EDUCATIONAL PROGRAMS

3574 ■ **Penn Foster Career School**
925 Oak St.
  Scranton, PA 18515
Ph: (570)961-4033
Free: 800-275-4410
Fax: (570)702-8380
Co. E-mail: infoims@pennfoster.com
URL: http://www.pennfoster.edu
URL(s): penn-foster.com
Description: Home-study school offering a small business management program. **Founded:** 1958.

REFERENCE WORKS

3575 ■ *"Houston (Texas) Computer Repair Adds U-Haul Rentals"* in *Benzinga.com* **(March 29, 2012)**
Pub: PR Newswire Association LLC.
Description: Houston Computer Repair has added U-Haul truck and trailer rentals in order to diversify the company. The firm also offers moving equipment and supplies for household furnishings, which includes moving vans, open trailers, closed trailers, furniture pads, appliance dollies, furniture dollies, tow dollies and auto transports. The company also continues to provide computer repair service along with shipping and packaging services. **Availability:** Online.

3576 ■ *"How to Service Your Own Computer: 7 Easy Things Computer Repair Places Do"* in *How-To Geek* **(November 12, 2018)**
URL(s): www.howtogeek.com/132470/how-to-service-your-own-computer-7-easy-things-computer-repair-places-do/
Ed: Chris Hoffman. **Released:** November 12, 2018. **Description:** A practical guide to doing basic computer repairs on your home, before heading out to the local computer repair store. Most issues can be fixed by the average user and it may be worth it to give these tips a chance before dropping off your computer with an expert. **Availability:** Online.

3577 ■ *"Keeping Data Secure When Your Laptop Is in the Shop"* in *The New York Times* **(December 6, 2017)**
URL(s): www.nytimes.com/2017/12/06/technology/personaltech/laptop-data-repairs.html
Ed: J.D. Biersdorfer. **Released:** December 06, 2017. **Description:** Dropping off your computer to a repair shop can be stressful because how does one protect their personal data from being seen by the repair person? Encrypting your files and doing some basic deleting are your best option. **Availability:** Online.

3578 ■ *"Ringgold Computer Repair Owner Accused of Swindling Customers"* in *Chattanooga Times/Free Press* **(February 15, 2012)**
Availability: Online.

STATISTICAL SOURCES

3579 ■ *Electronic & Computer Repair Services Industry in the US - Market Research Report*
URL(s): www.ibisworld.com/united-states/market-research-reports/electronic-computer-repair-services-industry/
Price: $925. **Description:** Downloadable report analyzing current and future trends in the electronic and computer repair industry. **Availability:** Download.

TRADE PERIODICALS

3580 ■ *The High-Tech News*
Pub: Electronics Technicians Association
  International
Contact: Bryan Allen, President
URL(s): www.etai.org/high_tech_news.html
Released: Bimonthly **Price:** $25, Nonmembers for print. **Description:** Serves member technicians with news of the Association and the electronics industry, including items on service, education, employment, management, and events. Contains information on membership, management, telecommunications, and business and technical training programs. Recurring features include editorials, news of research, letters to the editor, book reviews, and a calendar of events. **Availability:** Print; PDF; Online.

3581 ■ *Microprocessor Report*
Pub: MicroDesign Resources
URL(s): www.linleygroup.com/mpr/index.php?j=MPR
Price: $500, Other countries print, /year; $700, Individuals print, 2 years; $300, U.S. and Canada print, /year; $400, U.S. and Canada print, 2 years. **Description:** The leading technical publication for the microprocessor industry. Dedicated to providing unbiased, in-depth, critical analysis of new high-performance microprocessor developments. This newsletter is exclusively subscriber-supported. **Availability:** Print; Online.

FRANCHISES AND BUSINESS OPPORTUNITIES

3582 ■ **Cm It Solutions**
925 S MoPac Expy., Ste. B225
Austin, TX 78746

Ph: (512)879-4555
Free: 800-399-2648
Co. E-mail: techhelpone@cmitsolutions.com
URL: http://cmitsolutions.com
Contact: Mario Zambrano, President
Facebook: www.facebook.com/CMITdtaustin
X (Twitter): x.com/cmitatx
YouTube: www.youtube.com/user/cmitsolutions

Description: Provider of Computer support services system maintenance, problem resolution, upgrades, network design and training needs to business owners and professionals. **Founded:** 1996. **Training:** Training includes 2 weeks at corporate office, business coaching, support website and telephone line, email exchange, newsgroups, meetings and conferences.

3583 ■ Computer Troubleshooters Midtown East, NY
149 Madison Ave.
New York, NY 10016
Ph: (212)686-1234
URL: http://www.technology-solved.com/midtown-east-ny

Description: Onsite computer service franchise, with over 340 locations in 18 countries. Provide IT services to small businesses and residential users in their area. **Scope:** Firm provides solutions, consultation and upgrading services for computer problems and specializes in hardware and software troubleshooting, internet and email support, upgrade and installation, data recovery and networking, they also provide custom software and website development. **No. of Franchise Units:** 460. **No. of Company-Owned Units:** 1. **Founded:** 1997. **Franchised:** 1997. **Equity Capital Needed:** $29,000 estimated start-up costs. **Franchise Fee:** $14,500. **Training:** Yes.

3584 ■ Data Doctors
2045 S Vineyard -, Ste. 124
Mesa, AZ 85210
Free: 800-486-0048
Co. E-mail: info@datadoctors.com
URL: http://www.datadoctors.com
Contact: Ken Colburn, President
Linkedin: www.linkedin.com/company/data-doctors
X (Twitter): x.com/DataDoctors

Description: Provider of data recovery and computer repair services. **Founded:** 1988. **Financial Assistance:** Yes **Training:** Initial 11 day training at headquarters, 1 week onsite prior to opening and 1 week following opening and ongoing support.

3585 ■ Debugit Computer Services
Marlton, NJ
URL: http://pcmedicsofnj.com
Contact: Eric Ducorsky, Owner

Description: Computer maintenance services. **Training:** 5 days at headquarters, 3 days at franchisee's location and ongoing.

3586 ■ Expetec Technology Services
Expetec Corp.
20 3rd Ave. SE
Aberdeen, SD 57401
Ph: (605)725-6992
URL: http://www.expetecofaberdeen.com
Facebook: www.facebook.com/people/Expetec-of-Aberdeen/100066688493623

Description: Offering more personalized services than any other Managed Services Provider (MSP). Expetec provides the specialized IT support that can help you achieve your business goals. **Founded:** 1992. **Financial Assistance:** Yes **Training:** Provides training on franchise management, customer service, marketing & advertising.

3587 ■ Fast-teks On-site Computer Services
17425 Bridge Hill Ct., Ste. 200
Tampa, FL 33647
Ph: (908)824-9222
Free: 800-262-1671
Co. E-mail: corporate@fastteks.com
URL: http://www.fastteks.com

Description: Onsite computer repair services. **Founded:** 2003. **Franchised:** 2004. **Financial Assistance:** Yes **Training:** Offers 2 days training at headquarters and 2 days onsite with ongoing support provided.

3588 ■ Friendly Computers
3616 N Rancho Dr.
Las Vegas, NV 89130
Ph: (702)272-2780
Co. E-mail: info@friendlycomputers.com
URL: http://www.friendlycomputers.com
Contact: Byron K. Jones, President
Facebook: www.facebook.com/FriendlyComputersCorporate
X (Twitter): x.com/whycallageek
Pinterest: www.pinterest.com/friendlycomp100

Description: Onsite service and sales of computers to homes and businesses within a given territory. **No. of Franchise Units:** 80.0. **Founded:** 1992. **Franchised:** 2000. **Equity Capital Needed:** Full Service Center $111,110 - $144,980 ; Home Based Service $56,500 - $81,480. **Franchise Fee:** $25,000. **Royalty Fee:** Weekly Royalty – 8% ; Weekly Royalty – 8%. **Financial Assistance:** No **Training:** 1 Week training at Corporate Store and an additional week of training at franchisees location.

3589 ■ Geeks On The Way
Calgary, AB, Canada
Ph: (403)283-3316
Free: 800-875-5017
Co. E-mail: info@geeksontheway.com
URL: http://www.geeksontheway.com
Facebook: www.facebook.com/GeeksOnTheWay
X (Twitter): x.com/GEEKSONTHEWAY

Description: Mobile computer repair services such as removing viruses, removing viruses and computer network support services. **Founded:** 2002. **Training:** Provides 2 weeks then weekly consultations for one year.

3590 ■ Nerd Force
97 New Dorp Plz., 2nd Fl.
Staten Island, NY 10306
Contact: Ilir Sela, Chief Executive Officer

Description: firm provides on-site technical support services. **Founded:** 2003. **Training:** Provides 1 week at headquarters, 1 week at franchisee's location and ongoing support.

3591 ■ TeamLogic IT
Franchise Services Inc. (FSI)
27525 Puerta Real, Ste. 318
Anaheim, CA 92804
Free: 800-854-3321
Co. E-mail: success@franserv.com
URL: http://franserv.com
Contact: Don F. Lowe, Chief Executive Officer
Facebook: www.facebook.com/teamlogicitonline
X (Twitter): x.com/TeamLogicIT
YouTube: www.youtube.com/user/TeamLogicit

Description: Firm offers computer consultation, maintenance and repair service to small and mid-sized businesses. **Founded:** 2004. **Financial Assistance:** Yes **Training:** Yes.

LIBRARIES

3592 ■ DeVry University, Chicago Campus Library
1900 W Lawrence Ave., Ste. 100
Chicago, IL 60640
Ph: (773)929-8500
Free: 866-388-7934
URL: http://www.devry.edu/about/campus-locations/illinois/chicago.html
Facebook: www.facebook.com/DEVRYUNIVERSITY
Linkedin: www.linkedin.com/school/devry-university
X (Twitter): x.com/DeVryUniv
Instagram: www.instagram.com/devryuniversity
YouTube: www.youtube.com/user/TheDevryUniversity

Scope: Business; electronics; computer science; telecommunications. **Services:** Interlibrary loan; copying; center open to the public for reference use only. **Founded:** 1931. **Holdings:** Figures not available.

3593 ■ DeVry University, Columbus Campus Library
2 Easton Oval, Ste. 210
Columbus, OH 43219
Ph: (614)253-7291
URL: http://www.devry.edu/about/campus-locations/ohio/columbus.html

Scope: Electronics technology; computer science; business operations; accounting. **Services:** Library open to the students. **Founded:** 1970. **Holdings:** 23,000 volumes.

3594 ■ DeVry University - James E. Lovan Library
1310 E 104th St., Ste. 120
Kansas City, MO 64131
Ph: (816)943-7300
URL: http://www.kc.devry.edu/Library.html
Facebook: www.facebook.com/DEVRYUNIVERSITY
Linkedin: www.linkedin.com/school/devry-university
X (Twitter): twitter.com/DeVryUniv
Instagram: www.instagram.com/devryuniversity

Scope: Electronics; computer information systems; business; accounting; telecommunications. **Services:** Copying; Center open to the public for reference use only. **Founded:** 1931. **Holdings:** Figures not available.

3595 ■ DeVry University Library Services
4800 Regent Blvd., Ste. 200
Irving, TX 75063
Ph: (972)929-6777
Free: 866-338-7934
URL: http://www.devry.edu/about/campus-locations/texas/irving.html
Contact: Thomas L. Monahan, III, President
Facebook: www.facebook.com/DEVRYUNIVERSITY
Linkedin: www.linkedin.com/school/devry-university
X (Twitter): x.com/DeVryUniv
Instagram: www.instagram.com/devryuniversity
YouTube: www.youtube.com/user/TheDevryUniversity

Description: The library contains 350,000 books, eBooks, databases, and eJournals. **Scope:** Educational materials. **Services:** Information services for disabled persons; center open to the public for reference use only. **Founded:** 1969. **Holdings:** Books; articles.

3596 ■ Walt Disney World Global Business Technology Strategy Library
PO Box 10000
Lake Buena Vista, FL 32830
URL: http://disneyworld.disney.go.com

Scope: Computer science, human resources, general business. **Services:** Center not open to the public. **Founded:** 1986. **Holdings:** 4,000 books, videos, DVDs, and CD-ROMs; 100 AV equipment. **Subscriptions:** 200 journals and other serials; 3 newspapers.

Computer Programming and Data Processing Service

START-UP INFORMATION

3597 ■ *"3 Question for Stephen Purpura, CEO of the Big-Data Startup Context Relevant" in Puget Sound Business Journal (Vol. 35, May 23, 2014, No. 5, pp. 10)*
Pub: American City Business Journals, Inc.
Contact: Mike Olivieri, Executive Vice President
Description: Stephne Purpura, CEO of Seattle, Washington-based big data startup, Context Relevant, shares his vision for the company in the financial industry data market. He explains why they decided to seek strategic investment in the company.
Availability: Online.

3598 ■ *"Probability Processing Chip: Lyric Semiconductor" in Inc. (Volume 32, December 2010, No. 10, pp. 52)*
Pub: Inc. Magazine
Ed: Christine Lagorio. **Description:** Lyric Semiconductor, a start up located in Cambridge, Massachusetts, has developed a computer chip that also uses values that fall between zero and one, resulting in a chip that can process information using probabilities, considering many possible answers that find the best fit. **Availability:** Online.

ASSOCIATIONS AND OTHER ORGANIZATIONS

3599 ■ **Association Canadienne de Traitement d'Images et de Reconnaissance des Formes**
c/o Prof. Michael Jenkin, President
4700 Keele St.
Toronto, ON, Canada M3J 1P3
Ph: (416)736-2100
Co. E-mail: president@gmail.com
URL: http://www.cipprs.org
Contact: Michael Jenkin, President
E-mail: president@gmail.com
Description: Strives to advance the theory and practice of signal and image processing for pattern analysis and classification, scene or speech understanding and recognition. **Founded:** 1978. **Publications:** *Computer and Robot Vision (CRV)* (Annual). **Educational Activities:** Conference on Computer and Robot Vision (Annual). **Awards:** CIPPRS John Barron Doctoral Dissertation Award (Annual). **Geographic Preference:** National.

3600 ■ **Association for Women in Computing (AWC)**
PO Box 2768
Oakland, CA 94602
Co. E-mail: info@awc-hq.org
URL: http://www.awc-hq.org/home.html
Contact: Jill Sweeney, President
Description: Individuals interested in promoting the education, professional development, and advancement of women in computing. **Founded:** 1978.
Awards: Ada Lovelace Awards (Annual). **Geographic Preference:** National.

3601 ■ **BC Tech Association**
210 - 1401 W 8th Ave.
Vancouver, BC, Canada V6H 1C9
Ph: (604)683-6159
Co. E-mail: hello@wearebctech.com
URL: http://wearebctech.com
Contact: Jill Tipping, President
E-mail: jtipping@wearebctech.com
Facebook: www.facebook.com/wearebctech
X (Twitter): x.com/wearebctech
Instagram: www.instagram.com/wearebctech
Description: Fosters the growth and development of the Province's technology industries and member companies. Provides programs, services and activities designed to meet the needs and interests of members in the areas of networking, education, public awareness, and government relations. Offers a forum for members to review industry issues, acquire new business knowledge from leading industry professionals, to supply input on existing and proposed legislation and generally work together to advance the industry's interests. **Publications:** *Impact* (Annual). **Geographic Preference:** Local.

3602 ■ **Black Data Processing Associates (BDPA)**
9500 Arena Dr., Ste. 106
Largo, MD 20774
Ph: (531)781-9758
Co. E-mail: info@bdpa.org
URL: http://bdpa.org
Contact: Terry Morris, President
E-mail: terry.morris@bdpa.org
Facebook: www.facebook.com/NBDPAConference
Linkedin: www.linkedin.com/company/national-bdpa
X (Twitter): x.com/BDPA
Instagram: www.instagram.com/nationalbdpa
Description: Represents persons employed in the information processing industry, including electronic data processing, electronic word processing and data communications; others interested in information processing. Seeks to accumulate and share information processing knowledge and business expertise to increase the career and business potential of minorities in the information processing field. Conducts professional seminars, workshops, tutoring services and community introductions to data processing. Makes annual donation to the United Negro College Fund. **Founded:** 1975. **Educational Activities:** Black Data Processing Associates Annual Conference (Annual). **Awards:** Dr. Jesse L. Bemley Scholarship Award (Annual). **Geographic Preference:** National; Local.

3603 ■ **Blissymbolics Communication International (BCI)**
c/o Margareta Jennische
Uppsala University Department of Public Health and Caring Sciences
P.O PO Box 564
SE-751 22 Uppsala, Sweden
Co. E-mail: bci@blissymbolics.org
URL: http://www.blissymbolics.org
Contact: Katherine Seybold, Secretary
Description: Promotes appropriate use of Blissymbol applications in software, publications, and educational materials. Conducts research and educational programs. **Founded:** 1975. **Geographic Preference:** Multinational.

3604 ■ *Computer and Robot Vision (CRV)*
c/o Prof. Michael Jenkin, President
4700 Keele St.
Toronto, ON, Canada M3J 1P3
Ph: (416)736-2100
Co. E-mail: president@gmail.com
URL: http://www.cipprs.org
Contact: Michael Jenkin, President
E-mail: president@gmail.com
URL(s): www.cipprs.org
Released: Annual **Availability:** Print.

3605 ■ **I.T. Financial Management Association (ITFMA)**
PO Box 30188
Santa Barbara, CA 93130
Ph: (805)687-7390
URL: http://www.itfma.com
Description: Individuals and corporations interested in the financial management of information technology (IT) organizations. Works for the education and improvement of members and the industry. Offers certification in IT financial management. Conducts peer studies, in-house seminars, and chargeback system reviews. Operates educational programs. **Founded:** 1988. **Publications:** *Journal of IS Financial Management* (Triennial); *Journal of IT Financial Management* (3/year). **Awards:** ITFMA Education Certification Program (Annual). **Geographic Preference:** National.

3606 ■ **TechServe Alliance**
1420 King St., Ste. 610
Alexandria, VA 22314
Ph: (703)838-2050
Fax: (703)838-3610
Co. E-mail: staff@techservealliance.org
URL: http://www.techservealliance.org
Contact: Mark B. Roberts, Chief Executive Officer
E-mail: roberts@techservealliance.org
Facebook: www.facebook.com/techservealliance
Linkedin: www.linkedin.com/company/2015634
X (Twitter): x.com/TechServe_Assoc
Description: Businesses that provide the services of highly technical professionals, such as computer programmers, systems analysts, engineers, to clients in need of temporary technical support. Promotes legal and economic environment favorable to the technical services industry, including protection of a firm's freedom to choose either employees or independent contractors when supplying services to clients. Encourages professional standards in the industry; serves as a support mechanism for members. Provides industry-specific educational information and insurance discounts. **Founded:** 1987.
Publications: *Directory of Members Firms* (Periodic);

TechServe Alliance Monitor (Quarterly); *NACCB Newsletter* (Quarterly). **Geographic Preference:** National; National.

REFERENCE WORKS

3607 ■ *"2nd Watch Rides AWS Market Maturity to 400% Growth"* in *Computer Business Week* (August 28, 2014, pp. 21)
Description: 2nd Watch reports record earnings for the second quarter of 2014. The firm helps companies develop and implement IT strategies that are based on Amazon Web Services (AWS). Details of the companies business strategies are outlined. **Availability:** Print; Online.

3608 ■ *"Auctions and Bidding: A Guide for Computer Scientists"* in *ACM Computing Surveys* (Vol. 43, Summer 2011, No. 2, pp. 10)
Pub: Association for Computing Machinery
Contact: Yannis Ioannidis, President
Ed: Simon Parsons, Juan A. Rodriguez-Aguilar, Mark Klein. **Released:** Volume 43 Issue 2. **Price:** $10, Members; $15, Nonmembers; $5, Students. **Description:** There are various actions: single dimensional, multi-dimensional, single-sided, double-sided, first-price, second-price, English, Dutch, Japanese, sealed-bid, and these have been extensively discussed and analyzed in economics literature. This literature is surveyed from a computer science perspective, primarily from the viewpoint of computer scientists who are interested in learning about auction theory, and to provide pointers into the economics literature for those who want a deeper technical understanding. In addition, since auctions are an increasingly important topic in computer science, the article also looks at work on auctions from the computer science literature. The aim is to identify what both bodies of work tell us about creating electronic auctions. **Availability:** Download; PDF.

3609 ■ *"Best Free PowerShell Training Resources"* in *Business News Daily* (March 16, 2023)
URL(s): www.businessnewsdaily.com/10760-best-free-powershell-training-resources.html
Ed: Kim Lindros. **Released:** March 16, 2023. **Description:** Provides resources for IT professionals looking to advance their PowerShell knowledge to help further their career. **Availability:** Online.

3610 ■ *"Big Data at Work: Dispelling the Myths, Uncovering the Opportunities"*
Pub: Harvard Business Review Press
Contact: Moderna V. Pfizer, Contact
Released: February 25, 2014. **Price:** $35, Hardcover/Hardcopy. **Description:** What big data means from a technical, consumer, and management perspective; what big data opportunities cost; where it can have business impact; and what aspect of big data have been oversold. Insight is provided to help small businesses us big data to work to strengthen customer relationships. **Availability:** E-book; Print.

3611 ■ *"Bitcoin 'Killer App' Or the Currency of the Future?"* in *Providence Business News* (Vol. 28, January 6, 2014, No. 40, pp. 1)
Pub: American City Business Journals, Inc.
Contact: Mike Olivieri, Executive Vice President
URL(s): pbn.com/bitcoin-killer-app-or-the-currency-of-the-future94158
Description: The Providence Bitcoin Meetup has gathered several technology experts to discuss Bitcoin, the popular digital currency. However, software developers, engineers and entrepreneurs see Bitcoin as the next killer app for the Internet and is changing how information and data is stored, shared and verified. The Bitcoin's impact in Rhode Island is examined. **Availability:** Online. **Telecommunication Services:** Anderson@pbn.com.

3612 ■ *"BlackBerry 10 Unlikely to Save RIM. RIM Has Few Options. Staying the Course Isn't One of Them"* in *Canadian Business* (Vol. 85, July 16, 2012, No. 11-12, pp. 12)
Ed: Joe Castaldo. **Description:** Research in Motion (RIM) plans to launch a new line of Blackberry 10 Smartphones in 2012 as part of a strategy to stay in business despite expected operating loss in the first quarter and strong competition. Other options for RIM include a sale, opening its network to offer added security and data compression services, or reinventing itself as a niche handset provider. **Availability:** Print; Online.

3613 ■ *"Cloud City: An Industry - and a Region - On the Rise"* in *Puget Sound Business Journal* (Vol. 34, February 28, 2014, No. 46, pp. 4)
Pub: American City Business Journals, Inc.
Contact: Mike Olivieri, Executive Vice President
Description: Seattle, Washington is experiencing an influx of the world's most innovative cloud companies. Businesses are shifting their applications from in-house servers or private data center into public cloud infrastructure, which is less expensive than buying the servers and managing the data systems. Seattle software companies are taking advantage of this trend and developing products. **Availability:** Online.

3614 ■ *"Cloudy Future for VMware?"* in *Barron's* (Vol. 90, September 13, 2010, No. 37, pp. 21)
Pub: Barron's Editorial & Corporate Headquarters
Ed: Jonathan R. Laing. **Description:** VMWare dominated the virtualization market for years, but it may be ending as it faces more competition from rivals that offer cloud computing services. The company's stocks are also expensive and are vulnerable to the smallest mishap. **Availability:** Online.

3615 ■ *"Consumer Trust in E-Commerce Web Sites: a Meta-Study"* in *ACM Computing Surveys* (Vol. 43, Fall 2011, No. 3, pp. 14)
Pub: Association for Computing Machinery
Contact: Yannis Ioannidis, President
Ed: Patricia Beatty, Ian Reay, Scott Dick, James Miller. **Released:** Volume 43 Issue 3. **Price:** $10, Members; $15, Nonmembers; $5, Students. **Description:** Trust is at once an elusive, imprecise concept, and a critical attribute that must be engineered into e-commerce systems. Engineering trust is examined. **Availability:** Download; PDF.

3616 ■ *"Customer Data Represents Huge Opportunities and Challenges: My, What Big Data You Have"* in *Canadian Business* (Vol. 85, August 13, 2012, No. 13, pp. 14)
Ed: Dominic Barton. **Description:** Mining gigabytes of data provides an opportunity for companies to better understand customer behavior at a lesser cost and with unimaginable precision. Human intuition and experience remain significant factors in maximizing the potential of understanding huge amounts of customer data. **Availability:** Print; Online.

3617 ■ *"Data Center Operators are Finding San Antonio has the Right Stuff"* in *San Antonio Business Journal* (Vol. 28, February 28, 2014, No. 3, pp. 4)
Pub: American City Business Journals, Inc.
Contact: Mike Olivieri, Executive Vice President
Released: Weekly. **Price:** $4, Introductory 4-week offer(Digital only). **Description:** A number of data center operators have been opening facilities in San Antonio, Texas. CyrusOne Inc. will build 50,000 square feet of space in the city. Such data centers have also been generating new jobs. **Availability:** Print; Online.

3618 ■ *"Discrete Wavelet Transform-Based Time Series Analysis and Mining"* in *ACM Computing Surveys* (Vol. 43, Summer 2011, No. 2, pp. 6)
Pub: Association for Computing Machinery
Contact: Yannis Ioannidis, President
Ed: Pimwadee Chaovalit, Aryya Gangopadhyay, George Karabatis, Zhiyuan Chen. **Released:** Volume 43 Issue 2. **Price:** $10, Members; $15, Nonmembers; $5, Students. **Description:** Time series are recorded values of an interesting phenomenon such as stock prices, household items, or patient heart rates over a period of time. Time series data mining focuses on discovering interesting patterns in such data. An introduction to a wavelet-based times series data analysis is provided with a systematic survey of various analysis techniques that use discrete wavelet transformation (DWT) in time series data mining, and outlines the benefits of this approach demonstrated by previous studies performed on diverse application domains, including image classification, multimedia retrieval, and computer network anomaly detection. **Availability:** Download; PDF.

3619 ■ *"Distributed Data Management Using mapReduce"* in *ACM Computing Surveys* (Vol. 46, Fall 2014, No. 3, pp. 31)
Pub: Association for Computing Machinery - University of Wyoming
Contact: Ed Seidel, President
E-mail: uwpres@uwyo.edu
Description: MapReduce is a framework for processing and managing large-scale datasets in a distributed cluster, which has been used for applications such as generating search indexes, document clustering, access log analysis, and various other forms of data analytics. A comprehensive review of a wide range of proposals and systems that focus on the support of distributed data management and processing using MapReduce framework is examined. **Availability:** Online.

3620 ■ *"DMW Gets MBE Certification"* in *Wireless News* (July 29, 2012)
Description: Towson, Maryland's Daft McCune Walker (DMW) received the Minority Business Enterprise (MBE) Certification from the State of Maryland for Engineering, Surveying, Environmental and CAD services. The firm is a multidisciplinary consulting organization and is woman-owned. **Availability:** Print; Online.

3621 ■ *"The Failure Detector Abstraction"* in *ACM Computing Surveys* (Vol. 43, Summer 2011, No. 2, pp. 9)
Pub: Association for Computing Machinery
Contact: Yannis Ioannidis, President
Ed: Felix C. Freiling, Rachid Guerraoui, Petr Kuznetsov. **Released:** Volume 43 Issue 2. **Price:** $10, Members; $15, Nonmembers; $5, Students. **Description:** A failure detector is a fundamental abstraction in distributed computing. This article surveys this abstraction through two dimensions. First it studies failure detectors as building blocks to simplify the design of reliable distributed algorithms, particularly how failure detectors can factor out timing assumptions to detect failures in distributed agreement algorithms. Second, failure detectors as computability benchmarks are studied. Some limitations of the failure detector abstraction along each of the dimensions are also highlighted. **Availability:** Download; PDF.

3622 ■ *"Growth at E Solutions Part of 'Opportunistic' Data Center Market"* in *Tampa Bay Business Journal* (Vol. 30, January 29, 2010, No. 6, pp. 1)
Pub: Tampa Bay Business Journal
Contact: Ian Anderson, President
E-mail: ianderson@bizjournals.com
Ed: Michael Hinman. **Description:** E Solutions Corporation is experiencing growth amid the economic downturn, with its Park Tower data center occupancy in Tampa Florida expanding from 14,000 square feet to 20,000 square feet. Details on the increased operations fueled by demand for information storage and management services offered by the company are discussed. **Availability:** Print; Online.

3623 ■ *"Health IT Regulations Generate Static Among Providers"* in *Philadelphia Business Journal* (Vol. 28, January 29, 2010, No. 50, pp. 1)
Pub: Philadelphia Business Journal
Contact: Sierra Quinn, Director
E-mail: squinn@bizjournals.com
Ed: John George. **Description:** US Centers for Medicaid and Medicare Services and the Office of the National Coordinator for Health Information Technology have proposed rules regarding the

meaningful use of electronic health records. The rules must be complied with by hospitals and physicians to qualify for federal stimulus funds. **Availability:** Online.

3624 ■ *"Help Wanted: 100 Hospital IT Workers"* in *Business Courier (Vol. 27, October 8, 2010, No. 23, pp. 1)*
Pub: Business Courier
Ed: James Ritchie. **Description:** Hospitals in the Greater Cincinnati area are expected to hire more than 100 information technology (IT) workers to help digitize medical records. Financial incentives from the health care reform bill encouraged investments in electronic medical record systems, increasing the demand for IT workers that would help make information exchange across the healthcare system easier. **Availability:** Print; Online.

3625 ■ *"Human Activity Analysis: a Review"* in *ACM Computing Surveys (Vol. 43, Fall 2011, No. 3, pp. 16)*
Pub: Association for Computing Machinery
Contact: Yannis Ioannidis, President
Ed: J. K. Aggarwal, M. S. Ryoo. **Description:** Human activity recognition is an important area of computer vision research and is studied in this report. **Availability:** Download; PDF; Online.

3626 ■ *"Implementing Statically Typed Object-Oriented Programming Languages"* in *ACM Computing Surveys (Vol. 43, Fall 2011, No. 3, pp. 18)*
Pub: Association for Computing Machinery
Contact: Yannis Ioannidis, President
Ed: Roland Ducournau. **Released:** Volume 43 Issue 3. **Price:** $10, Members; $15, Nonmembers; $5, Students. **Description:** Object-oriented programming represents an original implementation issue due to its philosophy of making the program behavior depend on the dynamic type of objects. A review of the various implementation techniques available in static typing and in the three cases of single inheritance, multiple inheritance, and multiple subtyping are reviewed. **Availability:** Download; PDF.

3627 ■ *"Investing in an HR Team Can Ease the Burden of Mass Hiring"* in *Crain's Detroit Business (Vol. 36, September 8, 2014, No. 36, pp. 15)*
Pub: American City Business Journals, Inc.
Contact: Mike Olivieri, Executive Vice President
Description: Computing Source is a computer networking firm that helps small businesses recover computer files from backup tapes, particularly for law firms. Profile of the company and information about its CEO, Mark St. Peter is included. **Availability:** Print; Online.

3628 ■ *"Lighter Than Air"* in *Game Developer (Vol. 18, November 1, 2011, No. 10, pp. 38)*
Pub: Think Services
Description: Floating point performance tips and tricks are outlined. Floating point allows freedom of representation when implementing algorithms and is both intuitive to set up and simple to work with; hardware is also improved so that it is faster to use floating point math as opposed to integer in many environments. **Availability:** Print; Online.

3629 ■ *"The Lines of Code That Changed Everything"* in *Slate (October 14, 2019)*
URL(s): slate.com/technology/2019/10/consequential-computer-code-software-history.html
Released: October 14, 2019. **Description:** Highlights the major pieces of coding that have shaped our modern times and had a huge influence in our lives. Discussed are the very first codes, video game code, the origins of email, worms, and many others. **Availability:** Online.

3630 ■ *"Longwood's FamiLab More Than Just a Hackerspace: It's a Free Form Research and Development Lab"* in *Orlando Business Journal (Vol. 30, January 17, 2014, No. 30, pp. 4)*
Pub: American City Business Journals, Inc.
Contact: Mike Olivieri, Executive Vice President
Description: FamiLab is a nonprofit hackerspace in Longwood, Florida that has turned into a free-form research and development outfit. The group has at least 70 members who share the same passion for technology and push the limits and boundaries of computer hardware and software, and sometimes start their own business. **Availability:** Print; Online.

3631 ■ *"Machine Transliteration Survey"* in *ACM Computing Surveys (Vol. 43, Fall 2011, No. 3, pp. 17)*
Pub: Association for Computing Machinery
Contact: Yannis Ioannidis, President
Ed: Sarvnaz Karimi, Falk Scholer, Andrew Turpin. **Released:** Volume 43 Issue 3. **Price:** $10, Members; $15, Nonmembers; $5, Students. **Description:** Machine transliteration is the process of automatically transforming the script of a word from a source language to a target language, while preserving pronunciation. The development of algorithms specifically for machine transliteration began over a decade ago based on the phonetics of source and target languages, followed by approaches using statistical and language-specific methods. In this survey, the key methodologies introduced in transliteration literature are reviewed. The approaches are categorized based on the resources and algorithms used, and the effectiveness is compared. **Availability:** Download; PDF.

3632 ■ *"N.C. Data-Center Plan Bearing Fruit From Apple, Spec Center"* in *Charlotte Business Journal (Vol. 25, October 15, 2010, No. 30, pp. 1)*
Pub: Charlotte Business Journal
Contact: Robert Morris, Editor
E-mail: rmorris@bizjournals.com
Ed: Ken Elkins. **Description:** Apple Inc. is planning to expand its server farm at the North Carolina Data Center Corridor in Catawba County. T5 Partners, on the other hand, will build a shell building to house a server on the site. Infocrossing Inc. will also build an open data center in the area. **Availability:** Print; Online.

3633 ■ *"Network Detection and Response Explained"* in *Small Business Trends (March 23, 2023)*
Pub: Small Business Trends, LLC
Contact: Anita Campbell, Chief Executive Officer
URL(s): smallbiztrends.com/2023/03/network-detection-and-response.html
Ed: Gabrielle Pickard-Whitehead. **Released:** March 23, 2023. **Description:** Explains network detection and response in terms of cybersecurity for your small business. **Availability:** Online.

3634 ■ *"Number-Cruncher Gets 'Pushback'"* in *Philadelphia Business Journal (Vol. 33, August 22, 2014, No. 28, pp. 10)*
Pub: American City Business Journals, Inc.
Contact: Mike Olivieri, Executive Vice President
Released: Weekly. **Price:** $4, introductory 4-week offer(Digital only). **Description:** Bryan Wellen, senior director of clinical informatics for Continuum Health Alliance (CHA), asserts that while some physicians are receptive to patient information, others respond with an element of 'pushback' and criticism of the data. CHA and Horizon Blue Cross Blue Shield of New Jersey are using data analysis to create strategies that improve health care and reduce costs. **Availability:** Print; Online.

3635 ■ *Python and Algorithmic Thinking for the Complete Beginner: Learn to Think Like a Programmer*
Ed: Aristides S. Bouras. **Released:** June 19, 2019. **Price:** $42.74, Paperback; $9.99, E-Book. **Description:** A complete guide on how to learn Python programming. This book is designed for anyone who does not know anything about programming, but who wishes to learn at their own pace. **Availability:** E-book; Print.

3636 ■ *"Questioning Authority"* in *Entrepreneur (June 2014)*
Pub: Society for the Study of Myth and Tradition
Contact: Tracy Cochran, Director
Description: Smarterer is a platform that facilitates the evaluation of prospective hires through crowd-sourced assessment tests quantifying their professional skills and strengths. The platform has more than 900 multiple-choice tests covering a variety of professions. It uses an adaptive machine-learning algorithm that ensures the uniqueness of every test. Users can choose to make their test results public and can perform do-overs on some tests. The platform was launched in 2010 as a way of identifying potential talent and identifying skill inventories among existing employees. **Availability:** Print; Online.

3637 ■ *"Search Engines: Image Conscious"* in *Canadian Business (Vol. 81, February 26, 2008, No. 4, pp. 36)*
Pub: Rogers Media Inc.
Contact: Neil Spivak, Chief Executive Officer
Ed: Andrew Wahl. **Description:** Idee Inc. is testing an Internet search engine for images that does not rely on tags but compares its visual data to a database of other images. The company was founded and managed by Leila Boujnane as an off-shoot of their risk-management software firm. Their software has already been used by image companies to track copyrighted images and to find images within their own archives. **Availability:** Online.

3638 ■ *"The Secret Behind Building Your Own Apps? It's Not As Hard As You Think"* in *Mashable (October 20, 2019)*
URL(s): mashable.com/shopping/oct-20-the-complete-javascript-course-pcmag/
Ed: Haley Henschel. **Released:** October 20, 2019. **Description:** The most popular programming language, JaveScript, is being offered as an online class with a steep discount. On-demand video training and articles are included, and the user will receive real-world experience by completed three apps. **Availability:** Online.

3639 ■ *"Shellshocked: Dealing With Cyber Insecurity"* in *Philadelphia Business Journal (Vol. 33, June 13, 2014, No. 18, pp. 4)*
Pub: American City Business Journals, Inc.
Contact: Mike Olivieri, Executive Vice President
Description: The threat of cyber theft or data breach is increasing globally as technology becomes advanced and more companies start storing their important data electronically. Therefore, the importance of cyber security has increased. Although big businesses suffer more from data breaches, small companies can also take a beating if data breach happens. A survey found that small businesses were wary of spending money on security issues; good investment in IT and creating a privacy policy will help companies fight cyber threats. **Availability:** Online.

3640 ■ *"The Signal and the Noise: Why So Many Predictions Fail - but Some Don't"*
Released: February 03, 2015. **Price:** $18, paperback; $27.95, hardcover; $14.99, e-book; $17.50, audiobook. **Description:** Statistician, writer, and founder of The New York Times political blog, FiveThirtyEight.com, describes the science of forecasting and shows what happens when Big Data meets baseball, weather forecasting, earthquake prediction, economics and polling and shows that predictions can go wrong because they are based on biases, vested interests, and overconfidence. **Availability:** E-book; Print.

3641 ■ *"Spinout Success: New Leadership Steps In At UW's C4C"* in *Puget Sound Business Journal (Vol. 35, June 27, 2014, No. 10, pp. 11)*
Pub: American City Business Journals, Inc.
Contact: Mike Olivieri, Executive Vice President

Description: University of Washington's Center for Commercialization vice provost, Vikram Jandhyala, talks about his new position with the school. Jandhyala says he plans to build more synergy between the medical school and engineering and between social sciences and computer science. He also says the medical and software industry need to grow to accommodate the volume of data crossing and stored within the Internet. **Availability:** Online.

3642 ■ *"Strict Intersection Types for the Lambda Calculus" in ACM Computing Surveys (Vol. 43, Fall 2011, No. 3, pp. 20)*
Pub: Association for Computing Machinery
Contact: Yannis Ioannidis, President
Ed: Steffen Van Bakel. **Description:** The usefulness and elegance of strict intersection types for the Lambda Calculus, that are strict in the sense that they are the representatives of equivalence classes of types in the BCD-system is shown. Focus in directed on the essential intersection type assignment; this system is almost syntax directed, and the article will show that all major properties hold that are known to hold for other intersection systems, like the approximation theorem, the characterization of (head/strong) normalization, completeness of type assignment using filter semantics, strong normalization for cut-elimination and the principal pair property. In part, the proofs for these properties are new. A brief comparison of the essential system with other existing systems is given. **Availability:** PDF; Online.

3643 ■ *"Stuff that Works for You: In the Mobikey of Life" in Canadian Business (Vol. 81, June 11, 2008, No. 11, pp. 42)*
Pub: Rogers Media Inc.
Contact: Neil Spivak, Chief Executive Officer
Ed: John Gray. **Description:** Toronto-based Route1 has created a data security software system that allows employees to access files and programs stored in the head office without permanently transferring data to the actual computer being used. Mobikey technology is useful in protecting laptops of chief executive officers, which contain confidential financial and customer data. **Availability:** Online.

3644 ■ *"A Survey of Combinatorial Testing" in ACM Computing Surveys (Vol. 43, Summer 2011, No. 2, pp. 11)*
Pub: Association for Computing Machinery
Contact: Yannis Ioannidis, President
Ed: Changhai Nie, Hareton Leung. **Description:** Combinatorial Testing (CT) can detect failures triggered by interactions of parameters in the Software Under Test (SUT) with a covering array test suite generated by some sampling mechanisms. Basic concepts and notations of CT are covered. **Availability:** Download; PDF; Online.

3645 ■ *"A Survey of Comparison-Based System-Level Diagnosis" in ACM Computing Surveys (Vol. 43, Fall 2011, No. 3, pp. 22)*
Pub: Association for Computing Machinery
Contact: Yannis Ioannidis, President
Ed: Elias P. Duarte, Jr., Roverli P. Ziwich, Luiz C. P. Albini. **Released:** Volume 43 Issue 3. **Price:** $10, Members; $15, Nonmembers; $5, Students. **Description:** The growing complexity and dependability requirements of hardware, software, and networks demand efficient techniques for discovering disruptive behavior in those systems. Comparison-based diagnosis is a realistic approach to detect faulty units based on the outputs of tasks executed by system units. This survey integrates the vast amount of research efforts that have been produced in this field. **Availability:** Download; PDF.

3646 ■ *"A Survey of DHT Security Techniques" in ACM Computing Surveys (Vol. 43, Summer 2011, No. 2, pp. 8)*
Pub: Association for Computing Machinery
Contact: Yannis Ioannidis, President
Ed: Guido Urdaneta, Guillaume Pierre, Maarten Van Steen. **Released:** Volume 43 Issue 2. **Price:** $10, Members; $15, Nonmembers; $5, Students. **Description:** Peer-to-peer networks based on distributed hash tables (DHTs) have received considerable attention since their introduction in 2001. Unfortunately, DHT-based systems have been shown to be difficult to protect against security attacks. An overview of techniques reported in literature for making DHT-based systems resistant to the three most important attacks that can be launched by malicious nodes participating in the DHT is given: the Sybil attack, the Eclipse attack, and routing and storage attacks. **Availability:** Download; PDF.

3647 ■ *"Tufts Wins Grant for K-2 Coding Education" in TuftsNow (October 21, 2019)*
URL(s): now.tufts.edu/articles/tufts-wins-grant-k-2-coding-education
Ed: Angela Nelson. **Released:** October 21, 2019. **Description:** A four-year, $4 million grant was awarded to Tufts professor Marina Umaschi Bers to collaborate with the Norfolk Public Schools in order to train 450 early childhood teachers in technology and bring the ScratchJr app to the students.The researchers involved are looking at ways to best teach computer science and coding as another language in order to develop a free, publicly available K-2 computer science curriculum. **Availability:** Online.

3648 ■ *"What is the Future of Disk Drives, Death or Rebirth?" in ACM Computing Surveys (Vol. 43, Fall 2011, No. 3, pp. 23)*
Pub: Association for Computing Machinery
Contact: Yannis Ioannidis, President
Ed: Yuhui Deng. **Released:** Volume 43 Issue 3. **Price:** $10, Members; $15, Nonmembers; $5, Students. **Description:** Disk drives have experienced dramatic development to meet performance requirements since the IBM 1301 disk drive was announced in 1961. However, the performance gap between memory and disk drives has widened to 6 orders of magnitude and continues to widen by about 50 percent per year. Challenges and opportunities facing these storage devices are explored. **Availability:** Download; PDF.

3649 ■ *"Why Life Science Needs Its Own Silicon Valley: Human Genomics Won't Reach Its Full Potential Until It Has a Sizable Industry Cluster" in Harvard Business Review (Vol. 90, July-August 2012, No. 7-8, pp. 25)*
Pub: Harvard Business Review Press
Contact: Moderna V. Pfizer, Contact
Ed: Fariborz Ghadar, John Sviokla, Dietrich A. Stephan. **Price:** $6, PDF and hardcover black and white. **Description:** The creation of an industry cluster will be key to advancing human genomics research. High degrees of specialization via multiple contributors will be needed to generate significant innovations; an accessible, coherent data source will also be necessary. **Availability:** Print; PDF; Online.

3650 ■ *"Xtium Has Its Head in the Clouds" in Philadelphia Business Journal (Vol. 30, September 23, 2011, No. 32, pp. 1)*
Pub: Philadelphia Business Journal
Contact: Sierra Quinn, Director
E-mail: squinn@bizjournals.com
Ed: Peter Key. **Description:** Philadelphia-based cloud computing firm Xtium LLC received an $11.5 million first-round investment from Boston-Massachusetts-based OpenView Venture Partners. Catering to midsize businesses and unit of bigger firms, Xtium offers disaster-recovery, hosting, and managed-information-technology-infrastructure services. **Availability:** Online.

STATISTICAL SOURCES

3651 ■ *RMA Annual Statement Studies*
Pub: Risk Management Association
Contact: Nancy Foster, President
Released: Annual. **Description:** Contains composite balance sheets and income statements for more than 360 industries, including the accounting, auditing, and bookkeeping industries. Also contains five years of comparative historical data for discerning trends. Includes 16 commonly used ratios, computed for most of the size groupings for nearly every industry.

3652 ■ *Standard & Poor's Industry Surveys*
Pub: Standard And Poor's Financial Services LLC.
Contact: Douglas L. Peterson, President
Description: Two-volume book that examines the prospects for specific industries, including trucking. Also provides analyses of trends and problems, statistical tables and charts, and comparative company analyses.

TRADE PERIODICALS

3653 ■ *Computing Reviews (CR)*
Pub: Association for Computing Machinery
Contact: Yannis Ioannidis, President
URL(s): libraries.acm.org/digital-library/acm-computing-reviewscomputingreviews.com/index_dynamic.cfm
Released: Monthly **Description:** Journal presenting reviews of literature on computer science and computer applications. **Availability:** PDF; Online.

3654 ■ *International Journal of Intelligent Systems*
Pub: Wiley Periodicals Inc.
Contact: Brian Napack, Chief Executive Officer
URL(s): onlinelibrary.wiley.com/journal/ijiswww.wiley.com/en-in/International+Journal+of+Intelligent+Systems-p-9780471541431
Ed: Jin Li. **Released:** Latest Volume 2024, Issue 1. **Description:** International, peer-reviewed journal devoted to the systematic development of the theory necessary for the construction of intelligent systems. Includes research papers, tutorial reviews, and short communications on theoretical as well as developmental issues. **Availability:** Print; PDF; Download; Online.

3655 ■ *Journal of Database Management (JDM)*
Pub: IGI Global
Contact: Jan Travers, Director
URL(s): www.igi-global.com/journal/journal-database-management/1072
Released: Continuous **Price:** $500, Individuals for print; $500, Institutions for print. **Description:** Journal covering the research of database administrators and managers. **Availability:** Print; Download; PDF; Online.

3656 ■ *Online Searcher*
Pub: Information Today Inc.
Contact: Thomas H. Hogan, President
URL(s): www.infotoday.com/OnlineSearcher
Released: Bimonthly; January/February, March/April, May/June, July/August, September/October, and November/December. **Description:** Edited for librarians, Webmasters, site designers, content managers, and others concerned with knowledge/information management. Includes critical reviews of Web sites, software, search engines, and information services. (Formerly published by Online, Inc.). **Availability:** Print; Online.

3657 ■ *SIGSOFT Software Engineering Notes*
Pub: Association for Computing Machinery
Contact: Yannis Ioannidis, President
URL(s): www.sigsoft.org/SENwww.acm.org/special-interest-groups/sigs/sigsoft
Released: Quarterly **Description:** Tracks developments in programming and software maintenance processes, as well as the use of computers to provide and maintain timely, higher quality, cost-effective, and durable software. Contains proceedings of software engineering workshops and symposia. **Availability:** Print; PDF; Online.

CONSULTANTS

3658 ■ *AiAdertising, Inc.*
1114 S St. Mary's, Ste. 120
San Antonio, TX 78210
Ph: (210)920-9380
Free: 800-573-0927
URL: http://www.aiadvertising.com
Contact: Jerry Hug, Chief Executive Officer
Facebook: www.facebook.com/GoAiAd/

Linkedin: www.linkedin.com/company/go-aiad/
X (Twitter): twitter.com/Go_AiAd
Instagram: www.instagram.com/go_aiad/
YouTube: www.youtube.com/channel/UCWKx6P_Nmj0ysIB3jRu_WKQ
Description: Firm provides mobile and e-commerce solutions for mid-size online sellers in the retail and business to business industries. **Founded:** 1998.

3659 ■ Broadsword Solutions Corp. (BSC)
3795 Dorothy Ln.
Waterford, MI 48329
Co. E-mail: info@broadswordsolutions.com
Contact: Jeffrey R. Dalton, President
Description: Firm provides consulting, appraisals, workshops and training services. **Training:** CMMI Accelerator Boxed Set v2.1. **Special Services:** AgileCMMI.

3660 ■ Cloud 9
Amazon Web Services, Inc. (AWS)
222 Bloomingdale Rd.
White Plains, NY 10605
Description: Provider of It consulting, internet, web hosting, voice over IP and much more. **Founded:** 1993.

3661 ■ Cloud[8]Sixteen, Inc.
13359 N Hwy. 183, Ste. 406
Austin, TX 78750
Free: 800-267-1704
Fax: (512)532-6667
URL: http://www.cloud8sixteen.com
Contact: Dolly Ames, Chief Financial Officer
Facebook: www.facebook.com/Cloud8Sixteen
Linkedin: www.linkedin.com/company/cloud-8-sixteen-inc
X (Twitter): x.com/cloud8sixteen
Description: Provider of search engine optimization, live chat and PPC management services. **Founded:** 2008.

3662 ■ CloudSmartz
145 Culver Rd.
Rochester, NY 14620
Co. E-mail: info@cloudsmartz.com
URL: http://cloudsmartz.com
Contact: Dan Wagner, Chief Executive Officer
Facebook: www.facebook.com/cloudsmartz
Linkedin: www.linkedin.com/company/cloudsmartz
X (Twitter): x.com/cloudsmartz
YouTube: www.youtube.com/channel/UCurPiwNqIlb9PfA7PRL-VAQ
Description: IT Services company providing a full spectrum of IT services for mid-enterprise customers and strategic partners in the communication industry. **Founded:** 2012.

3663 ■ Girl Develop It (gdi)
113 Ave., A Apt. No. 4A
New York, NY 10009
Co. E-mail: info@girldevelopit.com
URL: http://girldevelopit.com
Contact: Katie Franco, Executive Director
E-mail: katie@girldevelopit.com
Facebook: www.facebook.com/girldevelopit
Linkedin: www.linkedin.com/company/girl-develop-it
X (Twitter): x.com/girldevelopit
Instagram: www.instagram.com/girldevelopit
YouTube: www.youtube.com/channel/UCJ1eFK1yld6ovBHakju7kSA
Description: Seeks to create supportive opportunities for women to learn software development skills. Provides Web and software development training. **Founded:** 2010.

3664 ■ Ingram Micro ITAD
Ingram Micro Inc.
Atlanta, GA
Ph: (714)566-1000
URL: http://www.ingrammicro.com
Description: Firm provides information technology asset disposition, onsite data destruction, and e-waste recycling services.

3665 ■ Innovative Business Systems Inc. (IBS)
4714 Highview Ct.
Milton, WI 53563
Ph: (516)829-3913
Co. E-mail: info@ibs-ny.com
URL: http://www.ibs-ny.com
Description: IT advisor and solution provider offers programming and software packages for retail, wholesale, manufacturing and engineering companies. **Scope:** IT advisor and solution provider offers programming and software packages for retail, wholesale, manufacturing and engineering companies. **Founded:** 1980.

3666 ■ Paragon Micro
2 Corporate Dr., Ste. 105
Lake Zurich, IL 60047
Free: 866-380-8663
Fax: (847)637-8172
Co. E-mail: custserv@paragonmicro.com
URL: http://www.paragonmicro.com
Contact: Jeff Reimer, President
X (Twitter): x.com/paragonmicro
Description: Firm that provides information technology and services. **Founded:** 2008.

3667 ■ SGA Business Systems, Inc.
Hillsborough Township, NJ
Ph: (908)359-4626
URL: http://sga.com
Contact: Wayne Scarano, Contact
E-mail: wscarano@sga.com
Description: Provider of cloud strategy, architecture, research, development, security, PoC, and training. **Scope:** Provider of cloud strategy, architecture, research, development, security, PoC, and training. **Publications:** "A Clever Way to Manage Your Notes Servers," Lotus Notes Advisor, Apr, 1997. **Special Services:** Team Iterative Approach™.

3668 ■ Sterling-Hoffman (SH)
610 Chartwell Rd., Ste. 101
Oakville, ON, Canada L6J 4A5
URL: http://sterlinghoffman.com
Description: Firm provides executive-search, leadership evaluation and corporate development and their services include finance, education, research, accounting, architecture, engineering, media and software. **Scope:** Firm provides executive-search, leadership evaluation and corporate development and their services include finance, education, research, accounting, architecture, engineering, media and software. **Publications:** "Missed the Number? Send Your CEO a Japanese Death Poem"; "Want to Win? Forget YOU Exist"; "Secrets from the Farm: On Fear, Honor, and Building Companies"; "Bruce Lee says your new VP Sales will Fail"; "Tragic Flaws: Why Software Companies Really Fail". **Training:** What CEOs want HR to know, Toronto.

3669 ■ Switch
117 Hudson St.
New York, NY 10013
Co. E-mail: info@women2.com
URL: http://www.women2.com
Contact: Kate Brodock, Chief Executive Officer
E-mail: kate@women2.com
Facebook: www.facebook.com/women2
X (Twitter): twitter.com/women2
Instagram: www.instagram.com/women2dot0
Description: Media and technology company that provides resources and support for women business owners in the tech sector. Offers workshops and consulting services. **Founded:** 2006.

PUBLICATIONS

3670 ■ *Application Development Trends Magazine (ADT)*
URL(s): adtmag.com
X (Twitter): twitter.com/adtmag
Description: Publishes information on the latest enterprise application news and information. **Availability:** Online.

3671 ■ *BizTech*
URL(s): biztechmagazine.com
X (Twitter): twitter.com/BizTechMagazine
Released: Quarterly **Description:** Provides insightful articles on various technology and business topics. **Availability:** Print; Online.

3672 ■ *International Journal of Digital Strategy, Governance, and Business Transformation (IJDSGBT)*
701 E Chocolate Ave.
Hershey, PA 17033
Ph: (717)533-8845
Free: 866-342-6657
Fax: (717)533-8661
Co. E-mail: cust@igi-global.com
URL: http://www.igi-global.com
Contact: Jan Travers, Director
URL(s): www.igi-global.com/journal/international-journal-digital-strategy-governance/224364
Ed: Steven De Haes. **Released:** Continuous **Description:** Peer-reviewed journal focusing on the information technology business management and governance. **Availability:** Print; PDF; Download; Online.

3673 ■ *Plunkett's Engineering and Research Industry Almanac: The Only Complete Guide to the Business of Research, Development, and Engineering*
PO Box 541737
Houston, TX 77254-1737
Ph: (713)932-0000
Fax: (713)932-7080
Co. E-mail: customersupport@plunkettresearch.com
URL: http://www.plunkettresearch.com
Contact: Jack W. Plunkett, Chief Executive Officer
URL(s): www.plunkettresearch.com/industries/engineering-rd-technology-market-research
Released: last edition May 2023. **Price:** $399.99, for print; $399.99, for e-book; $2,495, for single user; $6,995, for 5 users; $1,995, for eBook, enterprise-wide use (instant download). **Description:** Covers 500 of the largest companies involved in research, engineering and development in the biotech, electronics, aerospace and infotech industries. **Entries include:** Name, address, phone, fax, names and titles of key personnel, subsidiary and branch names and locations, financial data, salaries and benefits, description of products/services, overview of company culture/activities. **Indexes:** Industry, location, sales rank, profit rank. **Availability:** Print; Online.

3674 ■ *"What Small Businesses Should Know About Application Modernization"* in *BizTech (June 17, 2021)*
Ed: Jason Palkovics, Larry Burt. **Released:** June 17, 2021. **Description:** Discusses the concept of updating the platforms that existing apps use in order to align with newer technology. **Availability:** Online.

COMPUTERIZED DATABASES

3675 ■ *Computer Database*
URL(s): www.cengage.com/search/productOverview.do?Ntt=378230937717480099455780226053493 57&N=197+4294922389&Ntk=P_EPIwww.proquest.com/customer-care/title-lists/ProQuest-Dialog-Prosheets.html
Description: Provides one year of full-text online for 150 leading computer-related publications. Also includes 70,000 product specifications and brief profiles of 13,000 computer product vendors and manufacturers. Inquire as to prices and availability. **Availability:** Online. **Type:** Bibliographic; Full-text.

LIBRARIES

3676 ■ Ernst & Young LLP Center for Business Knowledge - Library
8484 Westpark Dr.
McLean, VA 22102
URL: http://www.ey.com
Scope: Business. **Founded:** 1990. **Holdings:** Figures not available.

3677 ■ IBM Corporation - IBM Knowledge Center
11400 Burnet Rd.
 Austin, TX 78758
URL: http://www.ibm.com/support/pages/what-ibm-knowledge-center
Description: Access to information for planning, installing, and maintaining IBM Mainframes. **Scope:** Management. **Founded:** 2014. **Subscriptions:** journals Logical files, Physical files.

3678 ■ International Data Group, Inc. (IDC) - Library
140 Kendrick St., Bldg. B
 Needham, MA 02494
Ph: (508)872-8200
Co. E-mail: leads@idc.com
URL: http://www.idc.com
Contact: Crawford del Prete, President
Linkedin: www.linkedin.com/company/idc
X (Twitter): x.com/IDC
Description: Provides market intelligence, advisory services, and events for the information technology, telecommunications, and consumer technology markets. **Scope:** Information technology; telecommunications; advisory services. **Founded:** 1964. **Holdings:** Figures not available. **Publications:** *Computerworld*; *The Standard*; *Macworld*; *IDG.net*; *WebSolutionsWorld Newsletter Online*; *E-Commerce Newsletter Online*; *Security-Informer Newsletter Online*; *TechInformer Newsletter Online*; *dummies.com*; *cliffsnotes.com*; *Arthur Frommer's Budget Travel Online*; *Network World, Inc.*; *CIO Online*; *Computerworld Online*; *Darwin Magazine Online*; *JavaWorld Online*; *LinuxWorld.com*; *InfoWorld.com*; *NetworkWorld.com*; *SunWorld Magazine Online*; *GamePro.com*; *MacWorld Online* (Monthly); *Publish.com*; *Financial News Channel*; *International News Channel*; *E-Commerce News Channel*; *Enterprise News Channel*; *Personal Computing News Channel*; *How-To & Advice News Channel*; *Multimedia & Leisure News Channel*; *Telecom & Connectivity News Channel*; *Security News Channel*; *Networking & Systems News Channel*; *Technical Development News Channel*; *IDC Research*; *ExecuTrain Corporation*; *China Network World* (Weekly); *Network World*; *IT Forecaster* (Biweekly).

3679 ■ Kansas State University, Salina - Libraries
2310 Centennial Rd., Academic Success Ctr.,
 Technology Ctr 111
 Salina, KS 67401
Ph: (785)260-6809
Co. E-mail: sallib@k-state.edu
URL: http://www.salina.k-state.edu/academics/library
Contact: Ruth Mirtz, Director
E-mail: mirtz@ksu.edu
Scope: Modern computing; telecommunications technology; technical and scientific information. **Services:** Interlibrary loan; copying; library open to the public. **Founded:** 1965. **Holdings:** Books.

3680 ■ Lockheed Martin Manassas Library
9500 Godwin Dr.
 Manassas, VA 20110
Ph: (703)367-2121
URL: http://www.lockheedmartin.com
Contact: James D. Taiclet, President
Scope: Computer systems and technology; signal processing; electronics; sonar. **Services:** Interlibrary loan. **Holdings:** 10,000 books; 2,000 bound periodical volumes; 100 reports.

3681 ■ Manufacturing Advocacy & Growth Network (MAGNET) - Library
1768 E 25th St.
 Cleveland, OH 44114
Ph: (216)391-7002
Co. E-mail: info@magnetwork.org
URL: http://www.manufacturingsuccess.org
Contact: Dr. Ethan Karp, President
E-mail: ekarp@manufacturingsuccess.org
Linkedin: www.linkedin.com/company/manufacturingsuccess
X (Twitter): x.com/magnetohio
Instagram: www.instagram.com/magnetohio
YouTube: www.youtube.com/user/TheMAGNETVideo
Description: Business incubation program provides a comprehensive package of business assistance services to support the growth of technology-oriented companies. **Scope:** Manufacturer of modernization projects, business management practices, information technology, human resource and work force development, and much more. **Founded:** 1984. **Holdings:** Figures not available. **Publications:** "NE Ohio manufacturers learn of options to diversify customer bases," Jun, 2009; "The manufacturing workforce of today and tomorrow needs the rights kills, training and certifications," Jul, 2009; "Invest in employees now," Jul, 2009; "Product design and engineering are manufacturing careers with a bright future," Jun, 2009. **Training:** Dream It. Do It, Ohio, Jan, 2007; Cuyahoga County New Product Development and Entrepreneurship Loan Fund; Manufacturer's Resource Link; Manufacturing Extension Program (MEP); Advanced manufacturing jobs in northeast Ohio require readily available high-tech training; Get Ready for the Rebound: Featuring Phillip Van Hooser.

3682 ■ Mayo Clinic - Richard A. Robb Biomedical Imaging Lab Library
200 1st St. SW
 Rochester, MN 55905
Ph: (507)284-2511
URL: http://www.mayo.edu/research/core-resources/biomedical-imaging-resource-core/about
Contact: Richard A. Robb, Director
Scope: Biomedical imaging; visualization science; software systems; workstations; networks; computer graphics; virtual reality. **Services:** Interlibrary loan; library open to the public. **Founded:** 1970. **Holdings:** 100 books; 200 bound periodical volumes; 100 reports; 35 patents.

3683 ■ Walt Disney World Global Business Technology Strategy Library
PO Box 10000
 Lake Buena Vista, FL 32830
URL: http://disneyworld.disney.go.com
Scope: Computer science, human resources, general business. **Services:** Center not open to the public. **Founded:** 1986. **Holdings:** 4,000 books, videos, DVDs, and CD-ROMs; 100 AV equipment. **Subscriptions:** 200 journals and other serials; 3 newspapers.

3684 ■ Xerox Corporation - Wilsonville Library
8200 SW Wilsonville Rd.
 Wilsonville, OR 97070
Ph: (503)682-2744
Co. E-mail: info@wplf.org
URL: http://wplf.org/tag/wilsonville-library
Contact: Caroline Berry, President
Scope: Color computer printers; programming; electronics; business and management. **Services:** Interlibrary loan; SDI. **Founded:** 1998. **Holdings:** 4,000 books.

RESEARCH CENTERS

3685 ■ Ohio State University - Advanced Computing Center for the Arts and Design (ACCAD)
1813 N High St.
 Columbus, OH 43210
Ph: (614)292-3416
Fax: (614)292-7776
Co. E-mail: accad-info@osu.edu
URL: http://accad.osu.edu
Contact: Maria Palazzi, Director
E-mail: palazzi.1@osu.edu
Facebook: www.facebook.com/ACCADatOSU
YouTube: www.youtube.com/user/accadosu
Description: Integral unit of Ohio State University. **Scope:** Computer arts and design, and scientific visualization. Research and development, outreach, and collaboration are essential components of ACCAD's mission. Partnerships within academia, industry, public and social services enable OSU students and faculty to have impact beyond the Center. ACCAD has supported the development of hundreds of industry and research experts from both the sciences and the arts in the field of computer graphics and animation for over 30 years. **Founded:** 1987. **Publications:** *Newsletter On-line* (Periodic). **Educational Activities:** ACCAD Digital Animation: A Technology Mentoring Program for Young Women, Free summer program, to learn computer animation.; ACCAD Open House (Annual), Offers a unique opportunity to showcase an ever changing landscape of new projects in a lively and engaging event.

3686 ■ University at Albany, State University of New York - Institute for Informatics, Logics, and Security Studies (ILS)
1400 Washington Ave.
 Albany, NY 12222
URL: http://www.albany.edu/cehc/research
Description: Integral unit of Department of Computer Science, University at Albany, State University of New York, and affiliated with a group at Rensselaer Polytechnic Institute. **Scope:** Formal methods and associated logic for hardware and software systems, as well as in algebraic and geometric reasoning methods in solid modeling and computer vision. **Founded:** 1991. **Publications:** *ILS Technical reports*.

3687 ■ University of Georgia Department of Geography - Center for Geospatial Research (CGR)
210 Field St., Rm. 204
 Athens, GA 30602
URL: http://geography.uga.edu/research/lab/center-geospatial-research
Contact: Marguerite Madden, Director
E-mail: mmaden@uga.edu
Description: Integral unit of Department of Geography, University of Georgia. **Scope:** Image and geographic information system data processing technologies for applications in the physical, biological, and mapping sciences. **Founded:** 1984.

3688 ■ University of Southern California School of Engineering - Information Sciences Institute (ISI)
4676 Admiralty Way, Ste. 1001
 Marina del Rey, CA 90292
Ph: (310)822-1511
Fax: (310)823-6714
Co. E-mail: info@isi.edu
URL: http://www.isi.edu
Contact: Craig Knoblock, Executive Director
E-mail: knoblock@isi.edu
Facebook: www.facebook.com/USCISI
Linkedin: www.linkedin.com/company/information-sciences-institute
X (Twitter): x.com/USC_ISI
Instagram: www.instagram.com/usc_isi_edu
YouTube: www.youtube.com/user/USCISI
Description: Integral unit of University of Southern California. **Scope:** Computer science research. **Founded:** 1972.

Computer Store

ASSOCIATIONS AND OTHER ORGANIZATIONS

3689 ■ Information Technology Industry Council (ITI)
700 K St. NW, Ste. 600
Washington, DC 20001
Ph: (202)737-8888
Fax: (202)638-4922
Co. E-mail: info@itic.org
URL: http://www.itic.org
Contact: Jason Oxman, President
Facebook: www.facebook.com/ITI.dc
Linkedin: www.linkedin.com/company/information-technology-industry-council
X (Twitter): x.com/iti_techtweets
YouTube: www.youtube.com/channel/UCo4j-sW0ti0RiiXupgo2L_A
Description: Represents manufacturers of information technology products. Serves as secretariat and technology for ANSI-accredited standards committee X3 information technology group. Conducts public policy programs; compiles industry statistics. **Founded:** 1916. **Publications:** *Washington Letter* (Biweekly). **Geographic Preference:** National.

3690 ■ Transaction Processing Performance Council (TPC)
781 Beach St., Ste. 302
San Francisco, CA 94109-1245
Ph: (415)561-6272
Fax: (415)561-6120
Co. E-mail: info@tpc.org
URL: http://www.tpc.org
Contact: Tom Sawyer, Co-Founder
Facebook: www.facebook.com/TPCbenchmarks
Linkedin: www.linkedin.com/company/tpcbenchmarks
X (Twitter): x.com/TPCBenchmarks
Description: Disseminates objective, verifiable performance data to the industry. Conducts activities such as Benchmark development and maintenance, publication and dissemination of results. **Founded:** 1988. **Publications:** *Benchmark Status Report* (Bimonthly). **Educational Activities:** Transaction Processing Performance Council Meeting (5/year). **Geographic Preference:** Multinational.

REFERENCE WORKS

3691 ■ *"3Par: Storing Up Value"* in *Barron's* (Vol. 90, August 30, 2010, No. 35, pp. 30)
Pub: Barron's Editorial & Corporate Headquarters
Ed: Mark Veverka. **Description:** Dell and Hewlett Packard are both bidding for data storage company 3Par. The acquisition would help Dell and Hewlett Packard provide customers with a one-stop shop as customers move to a private cloud in the Internet. **Availability:** Online.

3692 ■ *"Acacia Subsidiary Acquires Patents Related to Shared Memory for Multimedia Processing from a Major Corporation"* in *Economics & Business Week* (April 26, 2014, pp. 5)
Pub: NewsRX LLC.
Contact: Kalani Rosell, Contact
Description: Acacia Research Corporation that a subsidiary has acquired U.S. patents and foreign counterparts related to the use of shared memory in multimedia processing systems such as mobile phones, tablets and other consumer electronic devices. **Availability:** Online.

3693 ■ *"Agricharts Launches New Mobile App for Ag Market"* in *Farm Industry News* (December 1, 2011)
Pub: Informa Business Media, Inc.
Contact: Charlie McCurdy, President
Description: AgriCharts provides market data, agribusiness Website hosting and technology solutions for the agricultural industry. AgriCharts is a division of Barchart.com Inc. and announced the release of a new mobile applications that offers real-time or delayed platform for viewing quotes, charts and analysis of grains, livestock and other commodity markets. **Availability:** Print; Online.

3694 ■ *"App Brings Real-Time Personal Security, Company Says"* in *Philadelphia Business Journal* (Vol. 33, July 4, 2014, No. 21, pp. 11)
Pub: American City Business Journals, Inc.
Contact: Mike Olivieri, Executive Vice President
Released: Weekly. **Price:** $4, Introductory 4-week offer(Digital & Print). **Description:** EmergenSee, which is a mobile technology that transforms smartphones or tablets into personal security systems by downloading the app. It has the ability to stream live video and audio. **Availability:** Print; Online.

3695 ■ *"As Windows 8 Looms, Tech Investors Hold Their Breath"* in *Barron's* (Vol. 92, July 23, 2012, No. 30, pp. 22)
Pub: Dow Jones & Company Inc.
Contact: Almar Latour, Chief Executive Officer
Ed: Tiernan Ray. **Description:** Launch of the Microsoft Windows 8 operating system could affect the stock prices of Microsoft and Intel. The effects of the software's introduction on the market share of personal computers remains uncertain. **Availability:** Online.

3696 ■ *"Avanti Hosts 19th Annual User's Conference in Washington, DC"* in *American Printer* (Vol. 128, July 1, 2011, No. 7)
Description: Avanti Computer Systems Ltd. hosted its 19th annual users conference in Washington DC. In-plant and commercial printers were in attendance. **Availability:** Online.

3697 ■ *"Better than Advertised: Chip Plant Beats Expectations"* in *Business Review Albany* (Vol. 41, June 27, 2014, No. 14, pp. 4)
Pub: American City Business Journals, Inc.
Contact: Mike Olivieri, Executive Vice President
Released: Weekly. **Price:** $4, introductory 4-week offer(Digital only). **Description:** The $8.5 billion computer chip manufacturing plant and research center of GlobalFoundries in Malta, New York has strengthened the local economy in Saratoga County and helped the local manufacturing and construction industries recover from the recession. The Malta Plant construction project created more than 2,000 direct new construction jobs and over 10,000 indirect positions. **Availability:** Print; Online.

3698 ■ *"Cirrus Logic: Too Much Apple?"* in *Austin Business Journal* (Vol. 32, April 6, 2012, No. 5, pp. A1)
Pub: American City Business Journals, Inc.
Contact: Mike Olivieri, Executive Vice President
Ed: Christopher Calnan. **Description:** Austin, Texas-based Cirrus Logic has been moving to reduce its growing dependence on supplying components for Apple Inc. products. Cirrus Logic has disclosed that it deveoped a controller designed to enable light dimmer switches for incandescent lights to work with light emitting diodes. Insights on Cirrus Logic's sale to Apple are also given. **Availability:** Online.

3699 ■ *"Clouds in the Forecast"* in *Information Today* (Vol. 28, September 2011, No. 8, pp. 10)
Pub: Information Today Inc.
Contact: Thomas H. Hogan, President
Ed: Paula J. Hane. **Description:** Cloud computing is software, applications, and data stored remotely and accessed via the Internet with output displayed on a client device. Recent developments in cloud computing are explored.

3700 ■ Computing Technology Industry Association--Membership Directory
Pub: CompTIA
Contact: Todd Thibodeaux, President
Description: Covers 7,500 member computer hardware and software manufacturers, distributors, associate members, and resellers. **Entries include:** For manufacturers and distributors--Company name, address, phone, fax, name and title of contact, products. For resellers--Personal name, company name, address, phone, fax, vertical markets served and CPU brands sold. **Arrangement:** Alphabetical. **Indexes:** Company name, geographical, vertical market, CPU, contact name. **Availability:** PDF.

3701 ■ *"The Day That Apple Called"* in *Business Journal Portland* (Vol. 31, March 28, 2014, No. 4, pp. 9)
Pub: American City Business Journals, Inc.
Contact: Mike Olivieri, Executive Vice President
Description: Cathy Filgas recalls the time when she became part of Dilithium Press, a textbook publisher based in Beaverton, Oregon that developed a how-to book for Apple in 1984 to help launch the Macintosh computer. Filgas says Dilithium grew too fast and closed a few years after working with Apple. **Availability:** Print; Online.

3702 ■ *"Death of the PC"* in *Canadian Business* (Vol. 83, October 12, 2010, No. 17, pp. 44)
Description: The future of the personal computer (PC) is looking bleak as consumers are relying more on new mobile devices instead of their PC. A 'Wall

Street Journal' article published in September 2010 reported that the iPad had cannibalized sales of laptops by as much as 50 percent. The emergence of tablet computers running alternative operating systems is also explained. **Availability:** Print; Online.

3703 ■ *"Delphi Latest In Fight Over Offshore Tax Shelters"* in *Crain's Detroit Business (Vol. 30, July 7, 2014, No. 27, pp. 1)*
Pub: Crain Communications Inc.
Contact: Barry Asin, President
Description: Internal Revenue Service is investigating Delphi Automotive and other American companies over the use of offshore tax shelters. The latest in Delphi's dispute with the federal government over tax practices is expected to cost the supplier millions. Delphi manufactures electronics and technologies for vehicles. Apple Inc. and Google Inc. have also been targeted by the IRS for incorporating portions of the businesses offshore allowing them to avoid U.S. taxes as well as other foreign taxes. **Availability:** Online.

3704 ■ *"Etextbook Space Heats Up"* in *Information Today (Vol. 28, November 2011, No. 10, pp. 10)*
Pub: Information Today Inc.
Contact: Thomas H. Hogan, President
Ed: Paula J. Hane. **Description:** The use of etextbooks is expected to grow with the use of mobile devices and tablets. A new group of activists is asking students, faculty members and others to sign a petition urging higher education leaders to prioritize affordable textbooks or free ebooks over the traditional, expensive new books required for classes.

3705 ■ *"Facebook Purchased Push Pop Press"* in *Information Today (Vol. 28, October 2011, No. 9, pp. 12)*
Description: Facebook purchased Push Pop Press, a digital publishing company that developed a multi-touch interface for ebook publishing on the iPad.

3706 ■ *"For Apple, It's Showtime Again"* in *Barron's (Vol. 90, August 30, 2010, No. 35, pp. 29)*
Pub: Barron's Editorial & Corporate Headquarters
Ed: Eric J. Savitz. **Description:** Speculations on what Apple Inc. will unveil at its product launch event are presented. These products include a possible new iPhone Nano, a new update to its Apple TV, and possibly a deal with the Beatles to distribute their songs over iTunes. **Availability:** Online.

3707 ■ *"For Tech Companies, Holding Onto Prized Patents Can Be Expensive"* in *Puget Sound Business Journal (Vol. 33, May 18, 2012, No. 4, pp. 1)*
Pub: Baltimore Business Journal
Contact: Rhonda Pringle, President
E-mail: rpringle@bizjournals.com
Description: Patent lawsuits have been rising steadily over the past 20 years and the damage rewards are also growing. Microsoft is currently engaged in more than 60 patent infringement lawsuits worldwide and the largest is a 2 year fight over a series of patents that Motorola holds and Microsoft uses. **Availability:** Print; Online.

3708 ■ *"Getting Emotional Over Microsoft's Minecraft"* in *Puget Sound Business Journal (Vol. 35, September 19, 2014, No. 22, pp. 7)*
Pub: American City Business Journals, Inc.
Contact: Mike Olivieri, Executive Vice President
Description: Microsoft's acquisition of Minecraft maker Mojan AB is helps to promote STEM education. Microsoft will purchase the company for $2.5 billion. Minecraft game creator, Markus Persson, will not be joining the new Microsoft team. **Availability:** Online.

3709 ■ *"Heartbleed Headache Will Pound For Years"* in *Puget Sound Business Journal (Vol. 34, April 18, 2014, No. 53, pp. 7)*
Pub: American City Business Journals, Inc.
Contact: Mike Olivieri, Executive Vice President

Description: Seattle, Washington-based technology experts expressed concerns about the cybersecurity implications of the Heartbleed bug for years to come. The bug affected most virtual private network (VPN) software, which is the way most encrypted communications travel. The impact of the Heartbleed bug on critical infrastructure is examined. **Availability:** Online.

3710 ■ *"Helping Apple Go Wearable"* in *Austin Business Journal (Vol. 34, July 4, 2014, No. 20, pp. 13)*
Pub: American City Business Journals, Inc.
Contact: Mike Olivieri, Executive Vice President
Released: July 04, 2014. **Price:** $4, introductory 4-week offer(Digital only). **Description:** Andrew Hamra, CEO and designer at Red Street Ventures will launch the Runnur Hands Free iPad Clip and Carry Case across the U.S. in July 2014 following the success of his flagship product the Hands Free Carry-All. Hamra builds and designs the products and controls startup costs by outsourcing most of the production to China's Xiamen Uptex Industrial Company Ltd. **Availability:** Print; Online.

3711 ■ *"Holiday Sales Look Uncertain for Microsoft and PC Sellers"* in *Puget Sound Business Journal (Vol. 29, November 28, 2008, No. 32)*
Ed: Todd Bishop. **Description:** Personal computer makers face uncertain holiday sales for 2008 as a result of the weak U.S. economy and a shift toward low-cost computers. Personal computer shipments for the fourth quarter 2008 are forecast to drop 1 percent compared to the same quarter 2007. **Availability:** Online.

3712 ■ *How to Get Rich*
Ed: Felix Dennis. **Released:** 2013. **Price:** $8.16, paperback. **Description:** The author, publisher of Maxim, The Week, and Stuff magazines, discusses the mistakes he made running his companies. He didn't understand that people who buy computer gaming magazines wanted a free game with each copy, as one of his rivals was offering. And he laments not diversifying into television and exploiting the Internet. **Availability:** E-book; Print.

3713 ■ *"How to Play the Tech Mergers"* in *Barron's (Vol. 90, August 30, 2010, No. 35, pp. 18)*
Pub: Barron's Editorial & Corporate Headquarters
Ed: Tiernan Ray. **Description:** The intense bidding by Hewlett-Packard and Dell for 3Par was foreseen in a previous Barron's cover story and 3Par's stock has nearly tripled since reported. Other possible acquisition targets in the tech industry include Brocade Communication Systems, NetApp, Xyratex, and Isilon Systems. **Availability:** Online.

3714 ■ *"How to Reuse Or Recycle Your Old Tech: eWaste Is on the Rise but You Can Help Combat It By Using Old PCs and Electronics in Different Ways"* in *PC Magazine (Vol. 31, February 2012, No. 2, pp. 108)*
Description: US recycling businesses employ 30,000 workers to recycle 3.5 million tons of electronic waste, that does not include the number of devices that go to landfills. Simple and cheap ways to recycle or put old electronics to work are examined. **Availability:** Online.

3715 ■ *Information Technology for the Small Business: How to Make IT Work For Your Company*
Description: Basics of information technology to help small companies maximize benefits are covered. Topics include pitfalls to avoid, email and Internet use, data backup, recovery and overall IT organization.

3716 ■ *The Innovators: How a Group of Hackers, Geniuses, and Geeks Created the Digital Revolution*
Pub: Simon & Schuster, Inc.
Contact: Jonathan Karp, President

Released: October 2014. **Price:** $17.99, paperback; $29.99, abridged compact disk; $13.99, e-book; $29.99, unabridged audio download; $49.99, abridged audio download; $29.99, unabridged compact disk, plus shipping charges; 13.99, trade paperback. **Description:** Profiles of the individuals who created the computer and the Internet are provided describing the talents of certain inventors and entrepreneurs who are able to turn their business visions and goals into realities, while others have failed. The author begins with Ada Lovelace, Lord Byron's daughter, who pioneered computer programming back in the 1840s and continues by exploring the minds of Vannevar Bush, Alan Turing, John von Neumann, J.C.R. Licklider, Doug Englebart, Robert Noyce, Bill Gates, Steve Wozniak, Steve Jobs, Tim Berners-Lee and Larry Page. **Availability:** CD-ROM; E-book; Print; Audio.

3717 ■ *"The Intel Trinity: How Robert Noyce, Gordon Moore, and Andy Grove Built the World's Most Important Company"*
Pub: Harper Business
Contact: Hollis Heimbouch, Senior Vice President Publisher
Released: July 15, 2014. **Price:** $34.99, hardcover; $11.74, e-book; $4.34, kindle; $19.42, hardcover; $4.30, hardcover(69 used from $4.30); $15.17, hardcover(56 new from $15.17); $19.99, hardcover(1 collectible from $19.99); $31.74, paperback; $22.95, paperback(10 used from $22.95); $19.13, paperback(4 new from $19.13). **Description:** A complete history of Intel Corporation, the essential company of the digital age, is presented. After over four decades Intel remains the most important company in the world, a defining company of the global digital economy. The inventors of the microprocessor that powers nearly every intelligent electronic device worldwide are profiled. These entrepreneurs made the personal computer, Internet, telecommunications, and personal electronics all possible. The challenges and successes of the company and its ability to maintain its dominance, its culture and its legacy are examined. **Availability:** E-book; Print; Online.

3718 ■ *"The Internet Of You"* in *Canadian Business (Vol. 87, July 2014, No. 7, pp. 43)*
Description: Wearable computers like smart watches, fitness trackers, and bracelets like Nymi are starting to break down the barrier between human beings and the digital world. The Nymi is a wrist-worn device developed by Bionym that allows the wearer to be instantly recognizable to any wireless device. **Availability:** Online.

3719 ■ *"It Was a Very Good Year..To Be Ted Rogers"* in *Canadian Business (Vol. 80, Winter 2007, No. 24, pp. 121)*
Description: Ted Rogers had a banner year in 2007 as Rogers Communications Inc. (RCI) took in huge profits from its phone and wireless business and his personal wealth grew sixty-seven percent to $7.6 billion. Rogers has record of betting on technologies that get the best returns relative to the investment in the marketplace such as its use of the GSM network and its cable hybrid fiber coaxial network.

3720 ■ *"MBlox, Which Sends Coupons to Phones and Tables, Raises $43.5M"* in *Atlanta Business Chronicle (July 11, 2014, pp. 12A)*
Pub: American City Business Journals, Inc.
Contact: Mike Olivieri, Executive Vice President
Released: Weekly. **Price:** $4, introductory 4-week offer(Digital only). **Description:** mBlox, the mobile technology firm that sends coupons to hphones and tablets has managed to successfully raise $43.5 million to undertake global expansion. **Availability:** Print; Online.

3721 ■ *"Microsoft Releases Office Security Updates"* in *Mac World (Vol. 27, November 2010, No. 11, pp. 66)*
Description: Office for Mac and Mac Business Unit are Microsoft's pair of security- and stability-enhancing updates for Office 2008 and Office 2004. The software will improve the stability and compat-

ibility and fixes vulnerabilities that would allow attackers to overwrite Mac's memory with malicious code. **Availability:** Online.

3722 ■ *Mobile Office: The Essential Small Business Guide to Office Technology*
Released: September 1, 2009. **Price:** $6.95. **Description:** Essential pocket guide for startup businesses and entrepreneurs which provides information to create a mobile office in order to maximize business potential while using current technologies.

3723 ■ *"Motors and Motion Control" in Canadian Electronics (Vol. 23, February 2008, No. 1, pp. 23)*
Description: A new version of MicroMo Electronics Inc.'s Smoovy Series 0303.B has been added to MicroMo's DC motor product line. United Electronic Industries, on the other hand, has introduced the new UEIPAC series of programmable automation controllers that can offer solutions to various applications such as unmanned vehicle controllers. Features and functions of other new motors and motion control devices are given.

3724 ■ *"My Favorite Tool for Organizing Data" in Inc. (Vol. 33, November 2011, No. 9, pp. 46)*
Pub: Inc. Magazine
Ed: Abram Brown. **Description:** Intelligence software firm uses Roambi, a Web-based service that turns spreadsheet data into interactive files for iPhones and iPads. **Availability:** Online.

3725 ■ *"MyWireless.org Commends Arizona Congressman Trent Franks for Committing to Wireless Tax Relief for American Consumers and Businesses" in PR Newswire (September 21, 2012)*
Pub: PR Newswire Association LLC.
Description: MyWireless.org presented Congressman Trent Franks from Arizona with the 2012 Wireless Consumer Hero Award for his work on wireless tax relief for American consumers and businesses. Franks' 'Wireless Tax Fairness Act' (HR 1002) promotes access to wireless networks as a key ingredient of millions of Americans' livelihoods, whether phone, broadband Internet necessary to run a small business. **Availability:** Print; Online.

3726 ■ *"Not Your Father's Whiteboard" in Inc. (Vol. 33, November 2011, No. 9, pp. 50)*
Pub: Inc. Magazine
Ed: Adam Baer. **Description:** Sharp's new interactive whiteboard is really a 70-inch touch screen monitor with software for importing presentations from any Windows 7 computer. **Availability:** Online.

3727 ■ *"One Laptop Per Child Weighs Going For-Profit" in Boston Business Journal (Vol. 31, May 20, 2011, No. 17, pp. 1)*
Pub: Boston Business Journal
Contact: Carolyn M. Jones, President
E-mail: cmjones@bizjournals.com
Ed: Mary Moore. **Released:** Weekly. **Price:** $4, Print. **Description:** Nonprofit organization One Laptop Per Child is thinking of shifting into a for-profit structure in order to raise as much as $10 million in capital to achieve its goal of distributing more XO laptops to poor children worldwide. The organization has distributed 2 million computers since 2008 with Uruguay, Peru and Rwanda as its biggest markets. **Availability:** Print; Online.

3728 ■ *"PC Connection Acquires Cloud Software Provider" in New Hampshire Business Review (Vol. 33, March 25, 2011, No. 6, pp. 8)*
Description: Merrimack-based PC Connection Inc. acquired ValCom Technology, a provider of cloud-based IT service management software. Details of the deal are included. **Availability:** Print; Online.

3729 ■ *"PC Running Slowly? How to Rev Up Your Machine" in Inc. (Vol. 33, November 2011, No. 9, pp. 46)*
Pub: Mansueto Ventures L.L.C.
Contact: Stephanie Mehta, Chief Executive Officer

Ed: John Brandon. **Released:** November 01, 2011. **Description:** Software that keeps PCs tuned up and running smoothing are profiled: AUSLO6ICS BOOSTSPEED 5, $50; Tuneup Utilities 2011, $40; Slimware Slimcleaner 1.9, free; and IOBIT Advanced Systemcare Pro 4, $20 a year. **Availability:** Print; Online.

3730 ■ *"Port of Call" in Entrepreneur (Vol. 35, November 2007, No. 11, pp. 66)*
Ed: Amanda C. Kooser. **Released:** July 01, 2016. **Description:** List of the latest USB (universal serial bus) devices for upgrading technology for a small business is presented. **Availability:** Online.

3731 ■ *"The Pre-Tail Revolution" in Canadian Business (Vol. 87, October 2014, No. 10, pp. 10)*
Description: A number of products that succeeded in security support from crowdfunding platforms, Kickstarter and Indiegogo, and those that failed are presented. Included are the do-it-yourself computer kit Kano, Bluetooth speakers Edge.sound, three-dimensional printer The Micro, Coolest Cooler the insect control device BugASalt, hexacopter Hexo+, and the Ubuntu Edge. **Availability:** Print; Online.

3732 ■ *"Press Release: Trimble Introduces CFX-750 Display" in Farm Industry News (January 4, 2011)*
Description: Trimble is offering a touch screen display called the CFX-750. The new 8-inch full-color display allows farmers to choose the specific guidance, steering and precision agriculture capabilities that best fit their farm's particular needs. The display can be upgraded as business needs change, including the addition of GLONASS capabilities, or the addition of section and rate control for crop inputs such as seed, chemicals and fertilizer. **Availability:** Print; Online.

3733 ■ *Resource Directory*
Pub: Closing the Gap Inc.
Contact: Megan Turek, Contact
URL(s): www.closingthegap.com/resource-directory
Released: Annual **Description:** Covers about 300 suppliers of computer hardware and software designed for use by persons with disabilities. **Entries include:** Company or organization name, address, phone, description of products. **Arrangement:** Alphabetical. **Indexes:** Product/service, subject, supplier name. **Availability:** Download; Online.

3734 ■ *"Samsung's Metamorphosis in Austin" in Austin Business Journal (Vol. 31, May 20, 2011, No. 11, pp. 1)*
Pub: Austin Business Journal
Contact: Rachel McGrath, Director
E-mail: rmcgrath@bizjournals.com
Ed: Christopher Calnan. **Description:** Samsung Austin Semiconductor LP, a developer of semiconductors for smartphones and tablet computers, plans to diversify its offerings to include niche products: flash memory devices and microprocessing devices. In light of this strategy, Samsung Austin will be hiring 300 engineers as part of a $3.6 billion expansion of its plant. **Availability:** Print; Online.

3735 ■ *"The Solution Became the Problem" in Barron's (Vol. 92, August 25, 2012, No. 35, pp. 45)*
Pub: Dow Jones & Company Inc.
Contact: Almar Latour, Chief Executive Officer
Ed: John Steele Gordon. **Description:** Computers were seen as a solution to technology glitches affecting Wall Street during the 1960s. Telephones and paper proved inadequate in handling rising stock market volumes during the period. **Availability:** Online.

3736 ■ *"A Souped-Up Digital Pen" in Inc. (Vol. 33, November 2011, No. 9, pp. 50)*
Pub: Inc. Magazine
Ed: Adam Baer. **Description:** Wacom's Inkling is a digital pen designed to record drawings and can save layers of sketches and add or remove them at a later date. Animation of these drawings can also be played. Files can be saved on the receiver which has a 2GB memory and they can then be transferred to a computer. **Availability:** Online.

3737 ■ *"The Story of a Complex Project, Seen From a Bridge" in Business Review Albany (Vol. 41, June 27, 2014, No. 14, pp. 7)*
Pub: American City Business Journals, Inc.
Contact: Mike Olivieri, Executive Vice President
Released: Weekly. **Price:** $4, introductory 4-week offer(Digital only). **Description:** The bridge connecting the manufacturing and technology development buildings at GlobalFoundries in Malta, NY allows employees to transport computer chip-containing wafers without the risk of contamination. The connector is a cleanroom and has its own air conditioning system and foundation vibration control. **Availability:** Print; Online.

3738 ■ *"TomTom GO910: On the Road Again" in Black Enterprise (Vol. 37, January 2007, No. 6, pp. 52)*
Pub: Earl G. Graves Ltd.
Contact: Earl Graves, Jr., President
Ed: Stephanie Young. **Description:** TomTom GO 910 is a GPS navigator that offers detailed maps of the U.S., Canada, and Europe. Consumers view their routes by a customizable LCD screen showing everything from the quickest to the shortest routes available or how to avoid toll roads. Business travelers may find this product invaluable as it also functions as a cell phone and connects to a variety of other multi-media devices. **Availability:** Online.

3739 ■ *"Total Defense Launches Mobile Security for Business" in Benzinga.com (August 1, 2012)*
Pub: Benzinga.com
Contact: Jason Raznick, Founder
Ed: Aaron Wise. **Description:** Total Defense Inc. launched its Total Defense Mobile Secuirty Suite, a cloud-based solution for business that secures and manages mobile devices. Total Defense is a leading provider of malware protection against cybercrime. **Availability:** Online.

3740 ■ *"Two Local Firms Make Inc. List: Minority Business" in Indianapolis Business Journal (Vol. 31, August 30, 2010, No. 26, pp. 13A)*
Description: Smart IT staffing agency and Entap Inc., an IT outsourcing firm were among the top ten fastest growing black-owned businesses in the U.S. by Inc. magazine. **Availability:** Print; Online.

3741 ■ *"What is the Future of Disk Drives, Death or Rebirth?" in ACM Computing Surveys (Vol. 43, Fall 2011, No. 3, pp. 23)*
Pub: Association for Computing Machinery
Contact: Yannis Ioannidis, President
Ed: Yuhui Deng. **Released:** Volume 43 Issue 3. **Price:** $10, Members; $15, Nonmembers; $5, Students. **Description:** Disk drives have experienced dramatic development to meet performance requirements since the IBM 1301 disk drive was announced in 1961. However, the performance gap between memory and disk drives has widened to 6 orders of magnitude and continues to widen by about 50 percent per year. Challenges and opportunities facing these storage devices are explored. **Availability:** Download; PDF.

3742 ■ *"Will mCommerce Make Black Friday Green?" in Retail Merchandiser (Vol. 51, September-October 2011, No. 5, pp. 8)*
Description: Retailers speculate the possibilities of mobile commerce and are implementing strategies at their stores. Consumers using mobile devices accounted for only 0.1 percent of visits to retail Websites on Black Friday 2009 and rose to 5.6 percent in 2010; numbers are expected to rise for 2011. **Availability:** Print; Online.

3743 ■ *"Work for Play: Careers in Video Game Development" in Occupational Outlook Quarterly (Vol. 55, Fall 2011, No. 3, pp. 2)*
Pub: U.S. Department of Labor Bureau of Labor Statistics
Contact: Amrit Kohli, Director

E-mail: kohli.amrit@bls.gov
Ed: Drew Liming, Dennis Vilorio. **Description:** Game developers make a living creating the games the public enjoys playing. The video gaming industry reported sales over $10 billion in 2009 and employed 32,000 people in 34 states. Career options in video game development are featured. **Availability:** PDF; Online.

3744 ■ *"Xbox 360 Excels As a Media Hub" in Hispanic Business (October 2009, pp. 40)*
Ed: Jeremy Nisen. **Description:** Xbox 360 video game console from Microsoft offers games, amazing graphics and state-of-the-art accessories. The trend towards purchase of the Xbox includes more than teenagers.

3745 ■ *"Xtium Has Its Head in the Clouds" in Philadelphia Business Journal (Vol. 30, September 23, 2011, No. 32, pp. 1)*
Pub: Philadelphia Business Journal
Contact: Sierra Quinn, Director
E-mail: squinn@bizjournals.com
Ed: Peter Key. **Description:** Philadelphia-based cloud computing firm Xtium LLC received an $11.5 million first-round investment from Boston-Massachusetts-based OpenView Venture Partners. Catering to midsize businesses and unit of bigger firms, Xtium offers disaster-recovery, hosting, and managed-information-technology-infrastructure services. **Availability:** Online.

STATISTICAL SOURCES

3746 ■ *Computer Stores Industry in the US - Market Research Report*
URL(s): www.ibisworld.com/united-states/market-research-reports/computer-stores-industry/
Price: $925. **Description:** Downloadable report analyzing the current and future trends in the computer store industry. **Availability:** Download.

3747 ■ *RMA Annual Statement Studies*
Pub: Risk Management Association
Contact: Nancy Foster, President
Released: Annual. **Description:** Contains composite balance sheets and income statements for more than 360 industries, including the accounting, auditing, and bookkeeping industries. Also contains five years of comparative historical data for discerning trends. Includes 16 commonly used ratios, computed for most of the size groupings for nearly every industry.

3748 ■ *Standard & Poor's Industry Surveys*
Pub: Standard And Poor's Financial Services LLC.
Contact: Douglas L. Peterson, President
Description: Two-volume book that examines the prospects for specific industries, including trucking. Also provides analyses of trends and problems, statistical tables and charts, and comparative company analyses.

TRADE PERIODICALS

3749 ■ *DCL News*
Pub: Data Conversion Laboratory
Contact: Mark Gross, President
URL(s): www.dataconversionlaboratory.com/newsletter

Released: Monthly **Description:** E-journal providing you insider information on XML and SGML, along with the latest technology and e-publishing news. **Availability:** Online.

3750 ■ *Microprocessor Report*
Pub: MicroDesign Resources
URL(s): www.linleygroup.com/mpr/index.php?j=MPR
Price: $500, Other countries print, /year; $700, Individuals print, 2 years; $300, U.S. and Canada print, /year; $400, U.S. and Canada print, 2 years.
Description: The leading technical publication for the microprocessor industry. Dedicated to providing unbiased, in-depth, critical analysis of new high-performance microprocessor developments. This newsletter is exclusively subscriber-supported. **Availability:** Print; Online.

3751 ■ *Online Searcher*
Pub: Information Today Inc.
Contact: Thomas H. Hogan, President
URL(s): www.infotoday.com/OnlineSearcher
Released: Bimonthly; January/February, March/April, May/June, July/August, September/October, and November/December. **Description:** Edited for librarians, Webmasters, site designers, content managers, and others concerned with knowledge/information management. Includes critical reviews of Web sites, software, search engines, and information services. (Formerly published by Online, Inc.). **Availability:** Print; Online.

TRADE SHOWS AND CONVENTIONS

3752 ■ **Game Developers' Conference (GDC)**
UBM L.L.C.
2 Penn Plz.
New York, NY 10121
Ph: (212)600-3000
URL: http://www.ubm.com
Contact: Tim Cobbold, Chief Executive Officer
URL(s): www.gdconf.com/about
Price: $1,599, Pre-registered all-access pass; $2,099, Onsite all-access pass. **Frequency:** Annual. **Description:** Equipment, supplies, and services for developers and producers of computer games. **Audience:** Programmers, artists, producers, game designers, audio professionals, and business leaders. **Principal Exhibits:** Equipment, supplies, and services for developers and producers of computer games.

FRANCHISES AND BUSINESS OPPORTUNITIES

3753 ■ **Computer Renaissance**
595 New Loudon Rd., Newton Plz. II
Latham, NY 12110
Ph: (518)220-4445
Free: 888-266-7736
URL: http://compren.com/stores/latham/index
X (Twitter): x.com/comprencorp
Description: Firm engages in buying, selling and trading new and used computer equipment. **Franchised:** 1993. **Financial Assistance:** Yes **Training:** Includes 2 weeks training at headquarters, 1 week at franchisee's location and ongoing support.

3754 ■ **Data Doctors**
2045 S Vineyard -, Ste. 124
Mesa, AZ 85210
Free: 800-486-0048
Co. E-mail: info@datadoctors.com
URL: http://www.datadoctors.com
Contact: Ken Colburn, President
Linkedin: www.linkedin.com/company/data-doctors
X (Twitter): x.com/DataDoctors
Description: Provider of data recovery and computer repair services. **Founded:** 1988. **Financial Assistance:** Yes **Training:** Initial 11 day training at headquarters, 1 week onsite prior to opening and 1 week following opening and ongoing support.

3755 ■ **Palm Tree Tech Center**
19 E Broadway St.
Oviedo, FL 32765
Ph: (407)796-5100
Fax: (407)796-5115
Co. E-mail: oviedo@palmtreetechcenter.com
URL: http://palmtreetechcenter.com
Contact: Frank Hernandez, Manager
Facebook: www.facebook.com/PalmTreeTechCenter
X (Twitter): x.com/PTCSofAmerica
YouTube: www.youtube.com/user/PalmTreeComputers
Description: Firm provides computer repair services. **Founded:** 1996. **Training:** Yes.

COMPUTERIZED DATABASES

3756 ■ *Computer Database*
URL(s): www.cengage.com/search/productOverview.do?Ntt=37823093717480099455780226053493 57&N=197+4294922389&Ntk=P_EPIwww.proquest.com/customer-care/title-lists/ProQuest-Dialog-Prosheets.html
Description: Provides one year of full-text online for 150 leading computer-related publications. Also includes 70,000 product specifications and brief profiles of 13,000 computer product vendors and manufacturers. Inquire as to prices and availability. **Availability:** Online. **Type:** Bibliographic; Full-text.

LIBRARIES

3757 ■ **Fujitsu Semiconductor America Inc. (FMI) - FMI Library**
1250 E Arques Ave., M/S 333
Sunnyvale, CA 94085-5401
Ph: (408)737-5600
Fax: (408)737-5999
URL: http://www.fujitsu.com/us
Contact: Takahito Tokita, Chief Executive Officer
X (Twitter): x.com/Fujitsu_Global
Description: Manufacturer of semiconductors and electronic devices. **Scope:** Semiconductor industry and products; computer industry and products; telecommunications; electronics industry. **Services:** Interlibrary loan; SDI; library not open to the public. **Founded:** 1979. **Holdings:** 500 books and conference proceedings; 250 market research reports and newsletters; CDs.

3758 ■ **Walt Disney World Global Business Technology Strategy Library**
PO Box 10000
Lake Buena Vista, FL 32830
URL: http://disneyworld.disney.go.com
Scope: Computer science, human resources, general business. **Services:** Center not open to the public. **Founded:** 1986. **Holdings:** 4,000 books, videos, DVDs, and CD-ROMs; 100 AV equipment. **Subscriptions:** 200 journals and other serials; 3 newspapers.

Computer System Integrators

START-UP INFORMATION

3759 ■ *"Probability Processing Chip: Lyric Semiconductor"* in *Inc.* (Volume 32, December 2010, No. 10, pp. 52)
Pub: Inc. Magazine
Ed: Christine Lagorio. **Description:** Lyric Semiconductor, a start up located in Cambridge, Massachusetts, has developed a computer chip that also uses values that fall between zero and one, resulting in a chip that can process information using probabilities, considering many possible answers that find the best fit. **Availability:** Online.

ASSOCIATIONS AND OTHER ORGANIZATIONS

3760 ■ **Agile Alliance (AA)**
1914 Skillman St., Ste. 110-399
Dallas, TX 75206
Co. E-mail: info@agilealliance.org
URL: http://www.agilealliance.org
Contact: Paul Hammond, Chairman
Facebook: www.facebook.com/agileallianceofficial
Linkedin: www.linkedin.com/company/agilealliance
X (Twitter): x.com/AgileAlliance
Instagram: www.instagram.com/agilealliance
Pinterest: www.pinterest.com/agilealliance
Description: Promotes the concepts of Agile software development, and supports and serve the Agile software community around the world. **Founded:** 2001.

3761 ■ **Association of Computer Engineers and Technicians (ACET)**
Association House, St. David's Bridge, Kent
Cranbrook TN17 3HL, United Kingdom
Ph: 44 1 207-117-2431
Fax: 44 8 44-870-7062
Co. E-mail: info@ace-acet.org
URL: http://www.ace-acet.org
Contact: Christopher Charles Jones, Director
Description: Promotes professional standards within the IT industry,. **Founded:** 2004.

3762 ■ **Association for Computing Machinery (ACM) - Library**
1601 Broadway
10th Fl.
New York, NY 10019-7434
Ph: (212)869-7440
Free: 800-342-6626
Fax: (212)944-1318
Co. E-mail: acmhelp@acm.org
URL: http://www.acm.org
Contact: Yannis Ioannidis, President
Facebook: www.facebook.com/AssociationForComputingMachinery
Linkedin: www.linkedin.com/company/association-for-computing-machinery
X (Twitter): x.com/theofficialacm
Instagram: www.instagram.com/theofficialacm
YouTube: www.youtube.com/user/TheOfficialACM
Description: Biological, medical, behavioral, and computer scientists; hospital administrators; programmers and others interested in application of computer methods to biological, behavioral, and medical problems. Works to advance the art, science, engineering, and application of information technology. Fosters the open interchange of information and by promoting the highest professional and ethical standards. **Scope:** Technology innovations. **Founded:** 1947. **Subscriptions:** journals magazines Proceedings; newsletters. **Publications:** *Interactions* (Bimonthly); *ACM Queue* (Bimonthly); *XRDS* (Quarterly); *TECHNews* (3/week); *Ubiquity* (Monthly); *Transactions on Software Engineering and Methodology (TOSEM)* (8/year); *ACM Transactions on Asian and Low-Resource Language Information Processing (ACM TALIP)* (Monthly); *Communications of the ACM* (Monthly); *Computing Reviews (CR)* (Monthly); *netWorker* (Quarterly); *The Collected Algorithms* (Quarterly); *Interactions* (Bimonthly); *Journal of Experimental Algorithmics (JEA)*; *StandardView* (Quarterly); *Transactions on Computer-Human Interaction*; *Transactions on Design Automation of Electronic Systems (TODAES)* (6/year); *Transactions on Modeling and Computer Simulation (TOMACS)* (Quarterly); *ACM Transactions on Networking* (Bimonthly); *ACM Digital Library*; *SIGACT News*; *SIGSOFT Software Engineering Notes* (Quarterly); *SIGSAC Review: Security Audit and Control Review* (Quarterly); *Computer Graphics*; *ACM Transactions on Computational Logic* (Quarterly); *ELearn Magazine* (Monthly); *ACM Transactions on Programming Languages and Systems (TOPLAS)* (Quarterly); *Transactions on Information Systems (TOIS)* (Quarterly); *Journal of the ACM (JACM)* (Bimonthly); *ACM Electronic Guide to Computing Literature: Bibliographic Listing, Author Index, Keyword Index, Category Index, Proper Noun Subject Index, Reviewer Index, Source Index* (Quarterly); *ACM Computing Surveys: The Survey and Tutorial Journal of the ACM*; *Graduate Assistantship Directory in Computing*; *ACM/SIGGRAPH Computer Graphics Education Directory*; *The Data Base for Advances in Information Systems* (Quarterly); *Computers in Entertainment (CIE)*; *ACM Transactions on Computing Education (TOCE)*; *ACM Transactions on Algorithms* (Quarterly); *ACM Transactions on Applied Perception (TAP)* (Quarterly); *ACM Transactions on Architecture and Code Optimization (TACO)* (Quarterly); *ACM Transactions on Embedded Computing Systems (TECS)* (6/year); *ACM Transactions on Design Automation of Electronic Systems (TODAES)* (Quarterly); *ACM Transactions on Internet Technology (ACM TOIT)* (Quarterly); *ACM Transactions on Multimedia Computing, Communications and Applications (TOMM)* (7/year); *IEEE/ACM Transactions on Computational Biology and Bioinformatics (TCBB)* (Bimonthly); *ACM Transactions on Sensor Networks (TOSN)* (Quarterly); *IEEE/ACM Transactions on Speech and Language Processing* (Quarterly); *ACM Transactions on Storage (TOS)* (Quarterly); *Computing Reviews*; *ACM Portal to Computing Literature*; *ACM Transactions on Privacy and Security (TOPS)*; *Journal on Emerging Technologies in Computing (JETC)* (Quarterly); *Computing Surveys (CSUR)* (Bimonthly); *ACM Transactions on Computer Systems (TOCS)* (Quarterly); *Transactions on Database Systems (TODS)* (Quarterly); *ACM Transactions on Graphics (TOG)* (6/year); *ACM Transactions on Mathematical Software (TOMS)* (Quarterly). **Educational Activities:** ACM Multimedia (ACMMM) (Annual); Design Automation Conference (Annual); Supercomputing - The International Conference for High Performance Computing and Communications (Annual). **Awards:** A. M. Turing Award (Annual); ACM Fellow (Annual); Karl V. Karlstrom Outstanding Educator Award (Annual); Grace Murray Hopper Award (Annual); ACM Outstanding Contribution to ACM Award (Annual); ACM Software System Award (Annual); ACM/AAAI Allen Newell Award (Annual); ACM Paris Kanellakis Theory and Practice Award (Annual); ACM Distinguished Service Award (Annual); SIAM/ACM Prize in Computational Science and Engineering (Biennial); Gordon Bell Prize (Annual); ACM Doctoral Dissertation Award (Annual); Eugene L. Lawler Award for Humanitarian Contributions within Computer Science and Informatics (Biennial). **Geographic Preference:** Multinational.

3763 ■ **Association of Independent Information Professionals (AIIP)**
8550 United Plz. Blvd., Ste. 1001
Baton Rouge, LA 70809
Co. E-mail: office@aiip.org
URL: http://www.aiip.org
Contact: Denise Carter, President
Facebook: www.facebook.com/officialaiip
X (Twitter): x.com/aiip
Description: Independent information professionals involved in computer and manual organization, retrieval, and dissemination of information. **Founded:** 1987. **Publications:** *AIIP Business Directory*. **Educational Activities:** AIIP Annual Conference (Annual). **Awards:** AIIP Technology Award (Annual); Myra T. Grenier Award; Marilyn Levine AIIP President's Award (Annual); Sue Rugge Memorial Award (Annual). **Geographic Preference:** Multinational.

3764 ■ **Association of Software Professionals (ASP)**
PO Box 1522
Martinsville, IN 46151
URL: http://asp-software.org
Contact: Jeff Gibson, President
Facebook: www.facebook.com/AssocSoftwareProfessionals
Linkedin: www.linkedin.com/company/association-of-software-professionals
Description: Contains information for computer software developers and distributors, providing resources, aid, and assistance in improving their products and their business operations. **Founded:** 1987. **Awards:** ASP Hall of Fame (Annual). **Geographic Preference:** National.

3765 ■ **BC Tech Association**
210 - 1401 W 8th Ave.
Vancouver, BC, Canada V6H 1C9
Ph: (604)683-6159
Co. E-mail: hello@wearebctech.com

URL: http://wearebctech.com
Contact: Jill Tipping, President
E-mail: jtipping@wearebctech.com
Facebook: www.facebook.com/wearebctech
X (Twitter): x.com/wearebctech
Instagram: www.instagram.com/wearebctech

Description: Fosters the growth and development of the Province's technology industries and member companies. Provides programs, services and activities designed to meet the needs and interests of members in the areas of networking, education, public awareness, and government relations. Offers a forum for members to review industry issues, acquire new business knowledge from leading industry professionals, to supply input on existing and proposed legislation and generally work together to advance the industry's interests. **Publications:** *Impact* (Annual). **Geographic Preference:** Local.

3766 ■ CompTIA [Computing Technology Industry Association]
3500 Lacey Rd., Ste. 100
  Downers Grove, IL 60515
Ph: (630)678-8300
Free: 866-835-8020
Fax: (630)678-8384
Co. E-mail: membership@comptia.org
URL: http://www.comptia.org
Contact: Todd Thibodeaux, President
Facebook: www.facebook.com/CompTIA
Linkedin: www.linkedin.com/company/comptia
X (Twitter): x.com/comptia
Instagram: www.instagram.com/comptiaphotos
YouTube: www.youtube.com/comptiatv

Description: Serves as information clearinghouse and resource for the industry; sponsors educational programs. **Founded:** 1982. **Publications:** *Information Executive (IE)* (6/year); *Information Executive* (Bimonthly); *Information Executive: A Monthly Publication for DPMA and the Information Systems Profession* (Irregular); *Computing Technology Industry Association--Membership Directory*. **Educational Activities:** Infotec (Annual). **Geographic Preference:** National.

3767 ■ Computer and Communications Industry Association (CCIA)
25 Massachusetts Ave., Ste. 300C
  Washington, DC 20001
Ph: (202)783-0070
Co. E-mail: info@ccianet.org
URL: http://www.ccianet.org
Contact: Matthew Schruers, President
Facebook: www.facebook.com/ccianet
Linkedin: www.linkedin.com/company/computer
  -&-communications-industry-association
X (Twitter): x.com/ccianet

Description: An international non-profit advocacy organization which represents computer, internet, information technology, and telecommunications industries. It serves as the eyes, ears, and voice of the world's leading providers of technology products and services in Washington and Brussels promoting open markets, open systems, open networks, and full, fair, and open competition. **Founded:** 1972. **Publications:** *CyberInsecurity: The Cost of Monopoly*. **Educational Activities:** Washington Caucus. **Geographic Preference:** National.

REFERENCE WORKS

3768 ■ "7 Trends Affecting the Security Technology Business" in *IP SecurityWatch.com* (March 2012)
Ed: Geoff Kohl. **Description:** Scott Harkins, president of Honeywell Security Products for the Americas, outlines the seven trends affecting the security technology business. He covers smart phones and tablets, home automation, intercrive services, integration beyond security systems, cloud services, standards, and apps. **Availability:** Online.

3769 ■ "Acacia Subsidiary Acquires Patents Related to Shared Memory for Multimedia Processing from a Major Corporation" in *Economics & Business Week* (April 26, 2014, pp. 5)
Pub: NewsRX LLC.
Contact: Kalani Rosell, Contact
Description: Acacia Research Corporation that a subsidiary has acquired U.S. patents and foreign counterparts related to the use of shared memory in multimedia processing systems such as mobile phones, tablets and other consumer electronic devices. **Availability:** Online.

3770 ■ "MyWireless.org Commends Arizona Congressman Trent Franks for Committing to Wireless Tax Relief for American Consumers and Businesses" in *PR Newswire* (September 21, 2012)
Pub: PR Newswire Association LLC.
Description: MyWireless.org presented Congressman Trent Franks from Arizona with the 2012 Wireless Consumer Hero Award for his work on wireless tax relief for American consumers and businesses. Franks' 'Wireless Tax Fairness Act' (HR 1002) promotes access to wireless networks as a key ingredient of millions of Americans' livelihoods, whether phone, broadband Internet necessary to run a small business. **Availability:** Print; Online.

3771 ■ "On Technology: The Web Gets Real" in *Canadian Business* (Vol. 79, July 17, 2006, No. 14-15, pp. 19)
Pub: Rogers Media Inc.
Contact: Neil Spivak, Chief Executive Officer
Ed: Andrew Wahl. **Description:** Ron Lake's efforts of bringing the virtual and physical worlds more closely together by using Geographic Markup Language (GML) are presented. **Availability:** Print; PDF; Online.

3772 ■ "Tech Data Launches Unified Communications and Network Security Specialized Business Units" in *Wireless News* (October 22,2009)
Description: Responding to the growing demand for unified communications and network security, Tech Data announced the formation of two new Specialized Business Units. **Availability:** Online.

3773 ■ "VASCO DIGIPASS GO3 in Combination With IDENTIKEY Enhances the Security of Business Intelligence Solution Developed by CDS for General Motors Brazil" in *News Bites US* (March 29, 2012)
Description: VASCO Data Security International Inc. will provide Condominio de Corporativas, a vendor and business solutions integrator, its DIGIPASS GO 3 authentication solution along with IDENTIKEY Authentacation Server to provide security to the BI Retail Program developed for General Motors Brazil. VASCO is a leading software security firm specializing in authentication products. **Availability:** Print; Online.

3774 ■ "Xtium Has Its Head in the Clouds" in *Philadelphia Business Journal* (Vol. 30, September 23, 2011, No. 32, pp. 1)
Pub: Philadelphia Business Journal
Contact: Sierra Quinn, Director
E-mail: squinn@bizjournals.com
Ed: Peter Key. **Description:** Philadelphia-based cloud computing firm Xtium LLC received an $11.5 million first-round investment from Boston-Massachusetts-based OpenView Venture Partners. Catering to midsize businesses and unit of bigger firms, Xtium offers disaster-recovery, hosting, and managed-information-technology-infrastructure services. **Availability:** Online.

TRADE PERIODICALS

3775 ■ *International Journal of Intelligent Systems*
Pub: Wiley Periodicals Inc.
Contact: Brian Napack, Chief Executive Officer
URL(s): onlinelibrary.wiley.com/journal/ijiswww.wiley
 .com/en-in/International+Journal+of+Intelligent+Sys
 tems-p-9780471541431
Ed: Jin Li. **Released:** Latest Volume 2024, Issue 1. **Description:** International, peer-reviewed journal devoted to the systematic development of the theory necessary for the construction of intelligent systems. Includes research papers, tutorial reviews, and short communications on theoretical as well as developmental issues. **Availability:** Print; PDF; Download; Online.

3776 ■ *Microprocessor Report*
Pub: MicroDesign Resources
URL(s): www.linleygroup.com/mpr/index.php?j=MPR
Price: $500, Other countries print, /year; $700, Individuals print, 2 years; $300, U.S. and Canada print, /year; $400, U.S. and Canada print, 2 years.
Description: The leading technical publication for the microprocessor industry. Dedicated to providing unbiased, in-depth, critical analysis of new high-performance microprocessor developments. This newsletter is exclusively subscriber-supported. **Availability:** Print; Online.

3777 ■ *Online Searcher*
Pub: Information Today Inc.
Contact: Thomas H. Hogan, President
URL(s): www.infotoday.com/OnlineSearcher
Released: Bimonthly; January/February, March/April, May/June, July/August, September/October, and November/December. **Description:** Edited for librarians, Webmasters, site designers, content managers, and others concerned with knowledge/information management. Includes critical reviews of Web sites, software, search engines, and information services. (Formerly published by Online, Inc.). **Availability:** Print; Online.

TRADE SHOWS AND CONVENTIONS

3778 ■ Data Center World
URL(s): www.datacenterworld.com
Facebook: www.facebook.com/DataCenterWorld
Linkedin: www.linkedin.com/groups/41479
X (Twitter): twitter.com/DataCenterWorld
YouTube: www.youtube.com/channel/UCFANU4hY
 2_8LJerzuDq5xiA
Description: Presents key topic sessions in the world of IT Infrastructure, data center design, data security, and AI. Also hosts professional development opportunities. **Principal Exhibits:** Presents key topic sessions in the world of IT Infrastructure, data center design, data security, and AI. Also hosts professional development opportunities.

CONSULTANTS

3779 ■ Alpha Business Communications (ABC)
12523 Limonite Ave.
  Mira Loma, CA 91752
Ph: (951)456-2071
Co. E-mail: support@abcld.net
URL: http://www.abcld.net
Facebook: www.facebook.com/
 AlphaBusinessCommunications

Description: Firm provides networking, website hosting and design services. **Scope:** Telecommunication agency offering discounted phone services and networking services to southern California communities. Offers network consulting services, project management services, network management and security vulnerability assessment. **Founded:** 1992.

3780 ■ Beyer Business Solutions Inc.
1250 Stratford Rd.
  Deerfield, IL 60015
URL: http://beyerbusinesssolutions.com
Description: Firm offers in ERP, supply chain, CRM and web development business solutions. Specializes in the implementation, management and enhancement of new and existing software systems. **Scope:** Firm offers in ERP, supply chain, CRM and

web development business solutions. Specializes in the implementation, management and enhancement of new and existing software systems.

3781 ■ Business Information Group Inc. (BIG)
156 N George St., Ste. 100
  York, PA 17401
Ph: (717)854-9983
Free: 877-508-9983
Co. E-mail: hello@businessinformationgroup.com
URL: http://businessinformationgroup.com
Contact: Scott Dolmetsch, Chief Executive Officer
Facebook: www.facebook.com/BusinessInforma
  tionGroup
Linkedin: www.linkedin.com/company/business
  -information-group_3
X (Twitter): x.com/BIGTechTalks

Description: A wireless integration, security, and IT consulting firm. Designs, builds and manages large, high-speed wireless, data and VoIP broadband networks. Provides computer sales and service; IT consulting; and network security consulting, custom reporting, database services and application development services. **Founded:** 1992. **Publications:** *Building* (6/year); *Hardware Merchandising: Solutions for home improvement retailers* (Monthly); *Canadian Packaging* (10/year); *Canadian Underwriter* (Monthly); *Food in Canada: The Voice of the Canadian Food & Beverage Industry* (10/year); *Canadian Industrial Equipment News*.

3782 ■ Business Tech, Ltd. (BTA)
5910 Courtyard Dr., Ste. 200
  Austin, TX 78731
Contact: Steven Baker, Contact

Description: Firm provides business management software and implementation services for mid-sized manufacturers, distributors, and service businesses. **Scope:** Firm provides business management software and implementation services for mid-sized manufacturers, distributors, and service businesses. **Founded:** 1987.

3783 ■ The Centech Group, Inc.
4437 Brookfield Corporate Dr., Ste. 207
  Chantilly, VA 20151
Ph: (703)525-4444
URL: http://www.centechgroup.com
Contact: Fernando V. Galaviz, President

Description: Program management service contractor offers service solutions and systems for federal government agencies including business operations support, systems engineering, computer data center operations, training transfer and logistics support systems, cyber security, network and infrastructure, acquisition management support, software development and maintenance, test and evaluation, web solutions and services. **Founded:** 1988.

3784 ■ COTC Technologies Inc.
PO Box 17413
  Denver, CO 80217
Contact: Thomas I. Renz, Contact

Description: Firm provides software consulting services to organizations that require assistance with their HP3000 computer system. Firm provides systems analysis, programming, operations support and system management. Also provides PC software and hardware support and consulting. Additionally provides various training for the HP3000 computer system. **Scope:** Firm provides software consulting services to organizations that require assistance with their HP3000 computer system. Firm provides systems analysis, programming, operations support and system management. Also provides PC software and hardware support and consulting. Additionally provides various training for the HP3000 computer system.

3785 ■ Global Business Solutions L.L.C.
817 Cary Dr.
  Auburn, AL 36830
Co. E-mail: info@gbscpa.net
URL: http://www.gbscpa.net
Contact: Stacy Bruce Stallworth, Contact

Description: Firm provides consulting services in the selection and implementation of business and manufacturing systems. Provides technical training for Unix, Progress, and MFG/PRO. Offers MFG/PRO installations and upgrades. Develops data conversion plans and programs from old business systems to MFG/PRO. Performs installation and integration of third party packages into MFG/PRO. Unix system administrative services include backup/restore, disaster recovery planning, printer setup, user setup, scripting, and process scheduling through CRON. Provides technical guidance in the selection, design, and implementation of business and manufacturing systems. Designs, develops and implements custom Progress applications. Designs and develops application interfaces between business systems and third party packages. Designs, develops, and implements custom "C" and "C++" algorithms and interfaces. **Scope:** Firm provides consulting services in the selection and implementation of business and manufacturing systems. Provides technical training for Unix, Progress, and MFG/PRO. Offers MFG/PRO installations and upgrades. Develops data conversion plans and programs from old business systems to MFG/PRO. Performs installation and integration of third party packages into MFG/PRO. Unix system administrative services include backup/restore, disaster recovery planning, printer setup, user setup, scripting, and process scheduling through CRON. Provides technical guidance in the selection, design, and implementation of business and manufacturing systems. Designs, develops and implements custom Progress applications. Designs and develops application interfaces between business systems and third party packages. Designs, develops, and implements custom "C" and "C++" algorithms and interfaces. **Founded:** 1999.

3786 ■ Pathways Unlimited, Inc.
1331 S Knoxville
  Tulsa, OK 74112
Contact: Dorothy Stice, Contact

Description: Engaged in database publishing. Serving as a Microsoft fox pro development partner, data publishing systems have been developed to input and process directory information seamlessly from databases and lotus into publishing systems. Serves the publishing industry. **Scope:** Engaged in database publishing. Serving as a Microsoft fox pro development partner, data publishing systems have been developed to input and process directory information seamlessly from databases and lotus into publishing systems. Serves the publishing industry.

3787 ■ Saffire Systems & Development Inc.
1650 Upper Ironhorse Loop H-5
  Park City, UT 84060
Contact: Stacy Dymalski, Officer

Description: Diverse consulting firm that provides system integration, including software and utility development, training and technical writing. Serves private industries as well as government agencies. Woman owned firm. **Scope:** Diverse consulting firm that provides system integration, including software and utility development, training and technical writing. Serves private industries as well as government agencies. Woman owned firm. **Publications:** "Interleaf Tips & Tricks," Onward Press, Santa Fe, NM; "The Interleaf Exercise Book," Onward Press, Santa Fe, NM. **Training:** Desktop publishing. **Special Services:** HAGNET.

3788 ■ STN Inc.
4200 Forbes Blvd., Ste. 206
  Lanham, MD 20706
Ph: (410)721-4004
URL: http://www.stn.com

Description: Provider of browser-based database development, internet and network security, RFID planning and implementation, and much more. **Founded:** 1981. **Publications:** "File Pro Developers Reference Manual". **Training:** Browser-Based filePro On Your Local Area Network, 2009; Advanced filePro Input and Output Techniques, Sep, 2008; filePro for Database Managers and Programmers New To filePro, Jul, 2008. **Special Services:** filePro®; WorkLine™; MoveTrac™; LeadTrac™; MoveBill™.

3789 ■ TIC Business Consultants Ltd.
360 N Main St.
  Andover, MA 01810
Ph: (617)884-1086
Co. E-mail: support@ticbiz.com
URL: http://www.ticbiz.com
Contact: Susan J. Bishop, President
Facebook: www.facebook.com/TICBusinessconsul
  tants

Description: Firm provides services such as network monitoring, technical support, project management, and cloud migration. **Scope:** Firm provides services such as network monitoring, technical support, project management, and cloud migration. **Founded:** 1989. **Training:** Cash flow Management; Cost Cutting Strategies for Small Business.

3790 ■ Verizon Business Group
1318 F St. NW
  Washington, DC 20004
Free: 877-297-7816
URL: http://www.verizon.com/business
Contact: Hans Vestberg, Chief Executive Officer
YouTube: www.youtube.com/channel/UCL9bd7Pw6c
  _HXXusLswHGYw

Description: Firm provides technical solutions for construction, healthcare, insurance, manufacturing, and much more industries. **Scope:** Firm provides technical solutions for construction, healthcare, insurance, manufacturing, and much more industries. **Founded:** 1968. **Publications:** "Analyst Research: 6 Myths About Continuity and Disaster Recovery".

FRANCHISES AND BUSINESS OPPORTUNITIES

3791 ■ IntelliShift (VTS)
152 Veterans Memorial Hwy.
  Commack, NY 11725
Free: 800-887-0198
Co. E-mail: info@intellishift.com
URL: http://intellishift.com
Contact: John M. Cunningham, Jr., Chief Executive Officer
Facebook: www.facebook.com/IntelliShift
Linkedin: www.linkedin.com/company/-intellishift
X (Twitter): x.com/IntelliShift
Instagram: www.instagram.com/intellishift_

Description: Firm provides asset tracking, vehicle tracking, GPS tracking, fleet management, telematics and fleet tracking services. **Founded:** 2002. **Financial Assistance:** Yes **Training:** 1 week training program provided at headquarters followed by 2 days on-site.

PUBLICATIONS

3792 ■ *"The Cybersecurity Shortage Is Real, and Women May Be the Solution" in BizTech (August 4, 2021)*

Released: August 04, 2021. **Description:** Discusses the opportunities businesses have to bring women on board for technical positions, especially in the cybersecurity field, to help fill these open positions. **Availability:** Online.

3793 ■ *Mass Customization Information Systems in Business*
701 E Chocolate Ave.
  Hershey, PA 17033
Ph: (717)533-8845
Free: 866-342-6657
Fax: (717)533-8661
Co. E-mail: cust@igi-global.com
URL: http://www.igi-global.com
Contact: Jan Travers, Director
URL(s): www.igi-global.com/book/mass-customiza
  tion-information-systems-business/743

Price: $195, for hard cover e-book; $37.50, for demand (individual chapters); $165, for hard cover; $165, for e-book. **Description:** Describes original, innovative works on IT systems for mass customization, and provides a multitude of solutions, tools, concepts and successful realizations of IT systems for mass customization. **Availability:** E-book; Print; PDF; Download.

COMPUTERIZED DATABASES

3794 ■ *Business Wire*
Business Wire, Inc.
 101 California St., 20th Fl.
 San Francisco, CA 94111
Co. E-mail: info@businesswire.com
URL: http://www.businesswire.com
Contact: Geff Scott, Chief Executive Officer
Description: Contains more than 1.4 million records that make up the complete text of press releases from public and private companies and other organizations, such as hospitals and universities. **Availability:** Online. **Type:** Full-text.

3795 ■ *Computer Database*
URL(s): www.cengage.com/search/productOverview
 .do?Ntt=37823093771748009945578022605349
 357&N=197+4294922389&Ntk=P_EPIwww
 .proquest.com/customer-care/title-lists/ProQues
 t-Dialog-Prosheets.html
Description: Provides one year of full-text online for 150 leading computer-related publications. Also includes 70,000 product specifications and brief profiles of 13,000 computer product vendors and manufacturers. Inquire as to prices and availability. **Availability:** Online. **Type:** Bibliographic; Full-text.

3796 ■ *Computerworld*
International Data Group, Inc.
 140 Kendrick St., Bldg. B
 Needham, MA 02494
Ph: (508)872-8200
Co. E-mail: leads@idc.com
URL: http://www.idc.com
Contact: Crawford del Prete, President
URL(s): www.idginc.com/about
Availability: Online. **Type:** Full-text.

LIBRARIES

3797 ■ *Agilent Technologies, Inc.*
Agilent Technologies, Inc.
 5301 Stevens Creek Blvd.
 Santa Clara, CA 95051
Ph: (408)345-8886
Free: 877-424-4536
Fax: (408)345-8474
Co. E-mail: contact_us@agilent.com
URL: http://www.agilent.com
Contact: Mike McMullen, President
Facebook: www.facebook.com/Agilent.Tech
Linkedin: www.linkedin.com/company/agilen
 t-technologies
X (Twitter): twitter.com/Agilent
YouTube: www.youtube.com/user/agilent
Description: Engaged in providing application-focused solutions including reagents, instruments, software, services, and consumables used in life sciences, diagnostics and applied chemical laboratory identification, interrogation, quantification and analysis applications. The company also conducts centralized order fulfillment and supply chain operations. **Founded:** 1999. **Publications:** "Using a design to test capability for LTE MIMO," Oct, 2009; "Test solutions soup up for 4G," Apr, 2009; "Why Use One Radio When Four Will Do," Oct, 2008; "3GPP LTE Introducing Single Carrier FDMA," Jan, 2008; "Examining the Design and Test Challenges of 3GPP LTE," Nov, 2007; "First Pass Accuracy with Momentum GX for WiMAX Design," Nov, 2007; "Addressing the new challenges of MIMO wireless LAN manufacturing test," Oct, 2006. **Educational Activities:** EMBL International PhD Symposium; American Chemical Society Southeastern Regional Meeting and Conference (SERMACS) (Annual). **Preferred Investment Size:** $500,000 to $10,000,000. **Industry Preferences:** Communications and media, semiconductors and other electronics, biotechnology, medical and health, and industrial and energy.

RESEARCH CENTERS

3798 ■ **HEC Montreal - Groupe de Recherche en Systemes d'Information (GReSI) [HEC Montreal - Information Systems Research Group]**
3000, Chemin de La Cote-St. e-Catherine
 Montreal, QC, Canada H3T 2A7
Ph: (514)340-6274
Co. E-mail: gresi@hec.ca
URL: http://gresi.hec.ca/en
Description: Separately incorporated research group, associated with HEC Montreal. **Scope:** Information technology management, group decision support systems, organizational impact of information technology, and information systems development. **Founded:** 1986. **Publications:** *Cahiers du GReSI* (Annual). **Educational Activities:** Information Systems Research Group Conferences.

3799 ■ **Stanford University Department of Electrical Engineering - Information Systems Laboratory (ISL)**
350 Serra Mall
 Stanford, CA 94305-9510
Fax: (650)723-8473
URL: http://isl.stanford.edu
Contact: Stephen P. Boyd, Director
E-mail: boyd@stanford.edu
Description: Integral unit of Department of Electrical Engineering, Stanford University. **Scope:** Signal processing, information and communication theory, error control coding, array processing and adaptive filtering, broadcast and multiple access communication systems, analog to digital conversion, data compression, speech coding and recognition, multivariable systems, identification and digital control, and algorithms and architecture for very-large-scale integrated circuits. Adaptive signal processing, pattern recognition, machine learning, diagnostic medical imaging systems, fourier and statistical optics, optical data processing and computing. **Founded:** 1960.

3800 ■ **University of Illinois at Urbana, Champaign Coordinated Science Laboratory (CRHPC) - Reliable and High Performance Computing Research Group**
306 N Wright St MC 702
 Urbana, IL 61801
URL: http://ece.illinois.edu/research/centers-an
 d-groups
Contact: Timothy L. Killeen, President
E-mail: tkilleen@illinois.edu
Description: Integral unit of Coordinated Science Laboratory, University of Illinois at Urbana-Champaign. **Scope:** Reliable and fault-tolerant computing, testing and design for testability, high performance very-large-scale integrated (VLSI) architectures, high performance knowledge and data engineering, and computer-aided design tools for VLSI. Performs experimental studies of computer systems. **Founded:** 1988.

3801 ■ **University of Maryland at College Park - A. James Clark School of Engineering - Institute for Systems Research (ISR)**
8223 Paint Branch Dr. University of Maryland
 College Park, MD 20742
Ph: (301)405-6615
URL: http://isr.umd.edu
Contact: Adam Porter, Director
E-mail: aporter@umd.edu
X (Twitter): x.com/ISR_UMD
YouTube: www.youtube.com/user/ISRUMD
Description: Integral unit of School of Engineering, University of Maryland at College Park. Hosts Research Review Day: annual free showcase event of research held in the spring. **Scope:** Complex, heterogeneous, and dynamic problems of engineering technology and systems. Research includes: global communication systems, next generation manufacturing operations research, societal infrastructures, systems engineering education, and sensor and actuator networks. **Founded:** 1985. **Publications:** *Institute for Systems Research Technical Reports*; *ISR's System Solutions* (Annual). **Educational Activities:** ISR Seminars (Irregular); ISR Workshops; Industrial Review Meeting; Systems Symposium. **Awards:** ISR Fellowships (Annual); ISR Graduate Research Assistantships (GRA) (Annual).

3802 ■ **University of Maryland at College Park - Institute for Advanced Computer Studies (UMIACS)**
8125 Paint Branch Dr.
 College Park, MD 20742
Ph: (301)405-6722
URL: http://www.umiacs.umd.edu
Contact: Emily Hartz, Executive Director
E-mail: ehartz@umiacs.umd.edu
URL(s): cmns.umd.edu/research/research-centers-an
 d-institutes/institute-advanced-computer-studies
Linkedin: www.linkedin.com/company/university-of
 -maryland-institute-for-advanced-computer-studies
X (Twitter): x.com/umiacs
YouTube: www.youtube.com/channel/UC2rl1ZIIOx
 3qScsXGtDA1XA
Description: Integral unit of University of Maryland at College Park. **Scope:** High performance computing, computer vision, artificial intelligence, software engineering, internet computing, databases, multimedia, natural language processing, computational science, and theory of computing. **Founded:** 1985. **Publications:** *Technical report series*.

Computerized Billing Service

REFERENCE WORKS

3803 ■ *"Audit: Bad Billing System Costs Glens Falls Hospital $38 Million in Revenue"* in *The Post Star* (March 7, 2019)
URL(s): poststar.com/news/local/audit-bad-billing-sys
tem-costs-glens-falls-hospital-million-in/article_4b
430f4f-859f-59ba-bac0-5e886c8b9d85.html
Ed: Kathleen Moore. **Released:** March 07, 2019.
Description: Glens Falls Hospital instituted a new billing system, which malfunctioned in 2017 and ended up costing the hospital $38 million. The mistake costs many employees their jobs in order to help make up the difference. **Availability:** Online.

3804 ■ *"Death by 1,000 Clicks: Where Electronic Health Records Went Wrong"* in *Kaiser Health News* (March 18, 2019)
URL(s): khn.org/news/death-by-a-thousand-clicks/
Ed: Fred Schulte, Erika Fry. **Released:** March 18, 2019. **Description:** Troubling evidence of health practices that use electronic coding and billing, which has caused issues to patient safety and it's also used to overcharge insurance companies and patients.
Availability: Online.

3805 ■ *"The Keeper of Records"* in *Black Enterprise* (Vol. 41, December 2010, No. 5, pp. 54)
Pub: Earl G. Graves Ltd.
Contact: Earl Graves, Jr., President
Ed: Denise A. Campbell. **Description:** Medical billing and coding, submission of claims to health insurance companies and Medicare or Medicaid for payment is one of the fastest growing disciplines in healthcare.
Availability: Online.

CONSULTANTS

3806 ■ **Creative Business Consultants Inc.**
42 MeadowRue Ct.
Mount Laurel, NJ 08054
URL: http://www.cbc-group.net
Description: Firm specializes in providing billing services and management systems for medical practices. **Scope:** Firm specializes in providing billing services and management systems for medical practices. **Founded:** 1989. **Special Services:** CPT®.

3807 ■ **Health Management Systems Inc.**
28 Liberty St.
New York, NY 10005
Contact: Mark Knickrehm, Chief Executive Officer
Description: Provider of information management and data processing services for the healthcare industry, developer of healthcare software. **Scope:** Provides cost containment solutions for government-funded, commercial and private entities. Services to make the healthcare system better by improving access, impacting outcomes, containing costs, recovering dollars and creating efficiencies. Services include the following areas: Coordination of Benefits, Program Integrity, Eligibility and Enrollment, Customer Service Operations and Pharmacy Services. **Publications:** "Credit Balance Recovery"; "Preparing for a Historic 2009"; "Introducing the New HMS".

3808 ■ **Kluger and Associates Inc.**
70 Mitchell Blvd., Ste. 106
San Rafael, CA 94903
Contact: Homeyra Docarmo, Contact
Description: Provider of professional practice management specialization in accounting and billing services and serves health care. **Scope:** Provider of professional practice management specialization in accounting and billing services and serves health care.

LIBRARIES

3809 ■ **International Data Group, Inc. (IDC) - Library**
140 Kendrick St., Bldg. B
Needham, MA 02494
Ph: (508)872-8200
Co. E-mail: leads@idc.com
URL: http://www.idc.com
Contact: Crawford del Prete, President
Linkedin: www.linkedin.com/company/idc
X (Twitter): x.com/IDC
Description: Provides market intelligence, advisory services, and events for the information technology, telecommunications, and consumer technology markets. **Scope:** Information technology; telecommunications; advisory services. **Founded:** 1964.
Holdings: Figures not available. **Publications:** *Computerworld*; *The Standard*; *Macworld*; *IDG.net*; *WebSolutionsWorld Newsletter Online*; *E-Commerce Newsletter Online*; *Security-Informer Newsletter Online*; *TechInformer Newsletter Online*; *dummies.com*; *cliffsnotes.com*; *Arthur Frommer's Budget Travel Online*; *Network World, Inc.*; *CIO Online*; *Computerworld Online*; *Darwin Magazine Online*; *JavaWorld Online*; *LinuxWorld.com*; *InfoWorld.com*; *NetworkWorld.com*; *SunWorld Magazine Online*; *GamePro.com*; *MacWorld Online* (Monthly); *Publish.com*; *Financial News Channel*; *International News Channel*; *E-Commerce News Channel*; *Enterprise News Channel*; *Personal Computing News Channel*; *How-To & Advice News Channel*; *Multimedia & Leisure News Channel*; *Telecom & Connectivity News Channel*; *Security News Channel*; *Networking & Systems News Channel*; *Technical Development News Channel*; *IDC Research*; *ExecuTrain Corporation*; *China Network World* (Weekly); *Network World*; *IT Forecaster* (Biweekly).

RESEARCH CENTERS

3810 ■ **University of Tennessee at Chattanooga College of Engineering and Computer Science - SimCenter-Center of Excellence in Applied Computational Science and Engineering (CEACSE)**
615 McCallie Ave., Dept 5305
Chattanooga, TN 37403-2598
Ph: (423)425-5497
Fax: (423)425-5517
Co. E-mail: simcenter@utc.edu
URL: http://www.utc.edu/research/simcenter/simcen
ter-center-of-excellence-applied-computational
-science-and-engineering-ceacse
Contact: Dr. Anthony Skjellum, Director
E-mail: tony-skjellum@utc.edu
Description: Integral unit of College of Engineering and Computer Science, University of Tennessee at Chattanooga. **Scope:** New computer applications, especially in the fields of industry and education. Activities include studies of artificial intelligence, knowledge engineering, expert systems, productivity enhancement, office/factory automation systems, the development of voice-activated hardware for disabled persons, multimedia and hypermedia systems, and visualization technology. **Founded:** 2002.

3811 ■ **University of Texas at Arlington - Center for Information Technologies Management (CITM)**
c/o Sumit Sircar, Director
Rm. 535A, Business Bldg.
Arlington, TX 76019-0437
Ph: (817)272-3569
URL: http://grad.pci.uta.edu/about/catalog/archive/
www.uta.edu/gradcatalog/2002/facilities.html#info
tech
Contact: Sumit Sircar, Director
Description: Integral unit of Department of Information Systems and Management Sciences, College of Business Administration, University of Texas at Arlington. Offers consulting for industry in information systems, management science, production and operations management, and statistics. Coordinates research activities to complement the needs of local industry. **Scope:** Provides research and development facilities to outside organizations. Involves in information resource management, business systems planning, disaster recovery planning, business process reengineering. **Founded:** 1984. **Educational Activities:** Disaster Recovery Institute seminars.

Computerized Matching Service

REFERENCE WORKS

3812 ■ *"Facebook Launches Online Dating Service in US"* in *Financial Times (September 5, 2019)*
URL(s): www.ft.com/content/fd63af00-cb38-11e9-a1f4-3669401ba76f
Ed: Camilla Hodgson. **Released:** September 05, 2019. **Description:** Facebook Dating is launching in order to help users have meaningful relationships. However, concerns about how this social media platform is going to use personal data are being raised. **Availability:** Online.

3813 ■ *"FTC Sues Owner of Online Dating Service Match.com For Using Fake Love Interest Ads to Trick Consumers into Paying for a Match.com Subscription"* in *Federal Trade Commission (September 25, 2019)*
URL(s): www.ftc.gov/news-events/press-releases/2019/09/ftc-sues-owner-online-dating-service-matchcom-using-fake-love
Released: September 25, 2019. **Description:** The FTC has sued Match.com over unfair business practices, resulting in consumers being tricked into buying paid subscriptions to Match.com. Users need a paid subscription to Match.com in order to respond to messages they may receive from potential suitors, and those with free accounts were sent ads by the company in an effort to get them to sign up and pay for a paid account. **Availability:** Online.

3814 ■ *"Grey Power: On Target"* in *Canadian Business (Vol. 81, July 22, 2008, No. 12-13, pp. 45)*
Pub: Rogers Media Inc.
Contact: Neil Spivak, Chief Executive Officer
Ed: Calvin Leung. **Description:** Companies such as LavalifePRIME, a dating website devoted to singles 45 and older, discuss the value of marketing and services aimed at Canada's older consumers. One-third of Canada's 33 million people are 50-plus, controlling 77 percent of the countries wealth. **Availability:** Print; Online.

3815 ■ *"In the 2019 Dating World, Nobody Meets in Person Anymore"* in *The Philadelphia Inquirer (February 13, 2019)*
URL(s): www.inquirer.com/news/online-dating-tinder-bumble-okcupid-match-meet-cute-20190213.html
Ed: Anna Orso. **Released:** February 13, 2019. **Description:** Technology has changed how people date, where users can look up profiles on their phones and try to find their ideal match. Old-fashioned face-to-face meetings are becoming rare as people prefer the ease of using apps where most of the guesswork is eliminated, which eases fears and decreases anxiety of having to walk up and introduce oneself. **Availability:** Online.

3816 ■ *"Over-50 Singles Might Have the Best Luck Online"* in *USA Today (August 31, 2019)*
URL(s): www.usatoday.com/story/life/2019/08/31/online-dating-over-50/2129198001/
Ed: Valerie Finholm. **Released:** August 31, 2019. **Description:** Dating past 50 can be nerve-wracking, but online dating seems to be helping to ease those jitters. There are sites such as OurTime.com and Stitch that are designed specifically for people in their 50s, and even eHarmony.com and Match.com are being used by people in this demographic. **Availability:** Online.

3817 ■ *"Should We Be Worried About Computerized Facial Recognition?"* in *The New Yorker (December 10, 2018)*
URL(s): www.newyorker.com/magazine/2018/12/17/should-we-be-worried-about-computerized-facial-recognition
Ed: David Owen. **Released:** December 10, 2018. **Description:** Examines the rise of facial recognition systems and their usage in real-life situations and across multiple industries. **Availability:** Online.

VIDEO/AUDIO MEDIA

3818 ■ *How I Built This: Hinge: Justin McLeod*
URL(s): wondery.com/shows/how-i-built-this/episode/10386-hinge-justin-mcleod-2021
Ed: Guy Raz. **Released:** May 08, 2023. **Description:** Podcast explains how personal circumstances led to Hinge's design change and success.

Concession Stand Business

START-UP INFORMATION

3819 ■ *"Culinary School Puts a Food Truck on the Road" in St. Louis Post-Dispatch (March 21, 2012)*
Ed: Joe Bonwich. **Description:** Le Food Truck is a teach tool to help students learn about the fast-growing food truck market. Tony Hedger, instructor at L'Ecole Culinaire, a career college located in Laude, Missouri, coordinated the new program. The school also operates the Presentation Room, a restaurant used as part of the classroom. **Availability:** Print; Online.

3820 ■ *"Dining Notes: The Salty Fig is Jacksonville's Newest Food Truck" in Florida Times-Union (July 13, 2012)*
Ed: Gary T. Mills. **Description:** Jeff and John Stanford has selected locations throughout the city of Jacksonville, Florida to operate the food truck operation called, The Salty Fig. The brothers serve New American Southern style food along with a bar drink menu. The Salty Fig is named after the trees the boys enjoyed at their grandparent's home. **Availability:** Online.

3821 ■ *"Faces: Q&A with Kevin Huyck, Chef/Owner of R.A. MacSammy's Food Truck Specializing in Mac and Cheese" in Saint Paul Pioneer Press (March 28, 2012)*
Ed: Kathie Jenkins. **Description:** Profile of 48 year old Kevin Huyck, chef and owner of his R.A. MacSammy food truck. Huyck specializes in serving a variety of macaroni and cheese dishes. He wanted to own his own restaurant but did not have the capital for such an investment at the time and hopes to expand with either another food truck or possibly a restaurant that features mac and cheese dishes. **Availability:** Online.

3822 ■ *"Faces: Q&A With Katie Johnson, Co-Owner of Bloomy's Roast Beef Food Truck" in Saint Paul Pioneer Press (June 13, 2012)*
Ed: Kathie Jenkins. **Description:** Profile of Katie Johnson, 29 year old co-owner of Bloomy's Roast Beef food truck. Johnson discusses how her and her friend Ryan planned and started their food truck business and why they chose roast beef for their menu. **Availability:** Print; Online.

3823 ■ *Food Truck Business: Complete Guide for Beginners. How to Start, Manage & Grow YOUR OWN Food Truck Business*
Ed: Tony Smith. **Description:** As more and more people are enjoying the options available in food trucks, the opportunity to grow your own food truck business is growing. This guide discusses how to start, using social media, food safety, profits, plus more. **Availability:** Print.

3824 ■ *"The Food Truck Handbook: Start, Grow, and Succeed in the Mobile Food Business"*
Pub: John Wiley & Sons, Inc.
Contact: Christina Van Tassell, Executive Vice President Chief Financial Officer
Released: March 2012. **Price:** $19.95, paperback; $12.99, e-book. **Description:** Food truck businesses have grown so much in popularity, there are actually food truck competitions and was once a television show featuring them. A practical, step-by-step handbook is offered to help an entrepreneur start a mobile food delivery service. Information includes tips on choosing vending locations, opening and closing checklists; creation of a business plan with budget and finding vendor services, daily operation issues; common operating mistakes; and insight into delivery high quality food. **Availability:** E-book; Print.

3825 ■ *"Mercyhurst Rolls Out Culinary Cab Food Truck" in Erie Times-News (June 19, 2012)*
Ed: Erica Erwin. **Description:** Mercyhurst University's food service company launched a Culinary Cab, or food truck, offering a variety of food choices to the campus community. Details of Parkhurst Dining Services plan for the mobile restaurant are outlined.

3826 ■ *Mobile Vending: How to Run a Traveling Food or Merchandise Concession*
Ed: Jarvis Hooten. **Description:** Discusses strategies for starting and maintaining food trucks and festival food concession stands. **Availability:** Print.

3827 ■ *"Pot Watch: Magic Butter Delivers THC-infused Food Truck" in Puget Sound Business Journal (Vol. 35, May 30, 2014, No. 6, pp. 10)*
Pub: American City Business Journals, Inc.
Contact: Mike Olivieri, Executive Vice President
Description: Magical Butter is a startup in Seattle, Washington that sells a botanical extractor for infusing herbs into food ingredients like the active ingredient in marijuana known as THC into butter or oil. Career chef, Jeremy Cooper, has perfected the peanut butter and jelly sandwich with THC and sells them from the company's food truck business in Denver, Colorado. **Availability:** Online.

3828 ■ *"Radio Producer Launches Food Truck, New Show" in Dickinson Press (April 18, 2012)*
Description: Jason Spiess left his radio job to open The Rolling Stove mobile food truck in Dickinson, North Dakota. He will broadcast a new radio show from the food truck called, 'Talkin' Bakken' while serving breakfast and barbecue. He's using a 1973 Indian Winnebago that he bought from Craigslist.com and converted it into a barbecue smoker. **Availability:** Online.

3829 ■ *"So You Want To Be a Food Truck Vendor?" in Philadelphia Business Journal (Vol. 33, August 15, 2014, No. 27, pp. 7)*
Pub: American City Business Journals, Inc.
Contact: Mike Olivieri, Executive Vice President
Released: Weekly. **Price:** $4, introductory 4-week offer(Digital only). **Description:** Food truck vendors assert that the most challenging part of starting a food truck business is acquiring a license as well as the price and number of licenses and permits required. Other costs include additional fees to vend in prime locations, maintenance, and inventory. **Availability:** Print; Online.

3830 ■ *"Street Bistro Brings Food Truck Treats to Bangor" in Bangor Daily News (June 26, 2012)*
Ed: Emily Burnham. **Description:** Chef Kim Smith launched her food truck, Street Bistro in Bangor, Maine. Smith took a year off after closing her two restaurants called Unbridled Bistro and Bennett's Market. Smith and her husband purchased a Snap-On truck and redesigned it into a kitchen. Menu items range from French to Tex-Mex to Thai to American. **Availability:** Video; Online.

ASSOCIATIONS AND OTHER ORGANIZATIONS

3831 ■ **National Association of Concessionaires (NAC)**
180 N Michigan Ave., Ste. 2215
Chicago, IL 60601
Ph: (312)236-3858
Fax: (312)236-7809
Co. E-mail: info@naconline.org
URL: http://www.naconline.org
Contact: Adam Gottlieb, President
X (Twitter): x.com/nacconcessions
Description: Represents popcorn processors, manufacturers, and merchandisers; operators of food and beverage concessions in theaters, amusement parks, sports arenas, and other recreational facilities; equipment manufacturers and suppliers. Works to professionalize the concession industry. Provides information services and audiovisual training programs for concession managers and employees. Maintains certification program for concession industry. **Founded:** 1944. **Publications:** *Concession Profession* (Annual); *Concessionworks* (Semiannual). **Educational Activities:** The Concession & Hospitality Expo (Annual); ShoWest Convention and Trade Fair.

3832 ■ **National Restaurant Association (NRA)**
2055 L St. NW, Ste. 700
Washington, DC 20036
Ph: (202)331-5900
Free: 800-424-5156
Co. E-mail: askus@restaurant.org
URL: http://www.restaurant.org
Contact: Michelle Korsmo, President
Facebook: www.facebook.com/WeRRestaurants
Linkedin: www.linkedin.com/company/22205
X (Twitter): x.com/WeRRestaurants
Instagram: www.instagram.com/werrestaurants
YouTube: www.youtube.com/user/restaurantdotorg

Description: Restaurants, cafeterias, contract foodservice management, drive-ins, caterers, institutional food services and other members of the foodservice industry; represents establishments belonging to non-affiliated state and local restaurant associations in governmental affairs. Supports foodservice education and research in several educational institutions. Affiliated with the Educational Foundation of the National Restaurant Association to provide training and education for operators, food and equipment manufacturers, distributors and educators. **Founded:** 1919. **Publications:** *Restaurants USA: The Monthly Magazine of the National Restaurant Assn* (Monthly); *Who's Who in the Foodservice Industry*; *Restaurant Information Abstracts* (Biweekly); *Foodservice/Hospitality College Directory* (Irregular); *National Restaurant Association--Washington Report* (Semimonthly); *Restaurant Operations Report*. **Educational Activities:** National Restaurant Association Restaurant and Hotel-Motel Show (Annual). **Awards:** John L. Hennessy Award (Annual); NRA Restaurant Neighbor Award (Annual). **Geographic Preference:** National.

3833 ■ **Outdoor Amusement Business Association (OABA)**
1305 Memorial Ave.
 West Springfield, MA 01089-3578
Ph: (407)848-4958
Co. E-mail: oaba@oaba.org
URL: http://oaba.org
Contact: Greg Chiecko, President
E-mail: gregc@oaba.org
Facebook: www.facebook.com/OutdoorAmusementBusinessAssn
X (Twitter): x.com/oabainfo
Instagram: www.instagram.com/outdooramusementbusinessassn
YouTube: www.youtube.com/user/OABAinfo
Description: Represents executives and employees of carnivals and fairs; ride owners; independent food and games concessionaires; manufacturers and suppliers of equipment. Promotes and lobbies on behalf of the interests of the outdoor amusement industry; provides a center for dissemination of information. **Founded:** 1965. **Publications:** *Midway Marquee* (Annual). **Geographic Preference:** National.

3834 ■ **Restaurants Canada - Library**
1155 Queen St. W
 Toronto, ON, Canada M6J 1J4
Ph: (416)923-8416
Free: 800-387-5649
Fax: (416)923-1450
Co. E-mail: info@restaurantscanada.org
URL: http://www.restaurantscanada.org
Contact: Christian Buhagiar, Co-Chief Executive Officer Co-President
Facebook: www.facebook.com/RestaurantsCanada
Linkedin: www.linkedin.com/company/restaurants-canada
X (Twitter): x.com/RestaurantsCA
Instagram: www.instagram.com/RestaurantsCanada
YouTube: www.youtube.com/channel/UCxVckfCBIISII9LOuflNX8w
Description: Restaurant and food service corporations, hotels, caterers, and food service suppliers and educators, seeks to create a favorable business environment for members. **Scope:** Food service; quantity cooking; legislation; administration; management; statistics; training; customer attitude surveys. **Services:** Copying; open to the public on fee basis. **Founded:** 1944. **Publications:** *CRFA National Hospitality News*; *Canadian Foodservice Industry Operations Report* (Biennial); *Foodservice Facts* (Annual); *Legislation Guide* (Quarterly). **Educational Activities:** Restaurants Canada Show (Annual); ApEx. **Geographic Preference:** National.

3835 ■ **Western Fairs Association (WFA) - Library**
1776 Tribute Rd., Ste. 210
 Sacramento, CA 95815
Ph: (916)927-3100
Fax: (916)927-6397
Co. E-mail: info@fairsnet.org
URL: http://www.westernfairs.org
Contact: Sarah Cummings, President
Facebook: www.facebook.com/westernfairs
X (Twitter): x.com/westernfairs
Description: State and county fairs, carnival operators, food concessionaires, entertainment agents, and commercial exhibitors. Seeks to improve conditions in the fair industry by maintaining good relations with governmental agencies. Maintains hall of fame. Compiles statistics. **Scope:** Fair industry. **Founded:** 1922. **Holdings:** Figures not available. **Publications:** *WFA Newsletter* (Monthly); *Western Fairs Association Date List and Membership Directory* (Annual); *Fair Dealer* (Quarterly). **Educational Activities:** WFA Remix Convention & Trade Show (Annual). **Geographic Preference:** National.

REFERENCE WORKS

3836 ■ *"Baltimore Vendors Brave Heat, Red Tape to Eke Out a Living: Working the Streets"* **in Baltimore Business Journal (Vol. 28, July 30, 2010, No. 12, pp. 1)**
Pub: Baltimore Business Journal
Contact: Rhonda Pringle, President
E-mail: rpringle@bizjournals.com
Ed: Amanda Pino. **Description:** Reports show that street vendors are popping up on new corners in Baltimore, Maryland, with city-inspected stainless steel food carts in tow. Applications for street vending licenses shot up at the end of 2009 and into this summer. It is believed that pinning down the exact number of vendors operating at any one point is difficult. **Availability:** Print.

3837 ■ *"Bonnaroo 2012: Food Truck Oasis Returns With 9 Delicious Trucks"* **in International Business Times (June 4, 2012)**
Pub: International Business Times
Contact: Michael Learmonth, Editor
Ed: Amanda Remling. **Description:** Manchester, Tennessee is the location for the Bonnaroo 2012 food truck event. The nine food trucks will be features offering their fares include: Eatbox, Gastropod, Good You, Gypsy Queen, Petro's Chili & Chips, Pot Kettle Black, Roti Rolls, Savory And Sweet, Tex's Tacos. **Availability:** Print.

3838 ■ *"Co-Working Space by Day, Cocktail Lounge by Night"* **in OakPark.com (July 16, 2019)**
URL(s): www.oakpark.com/News/Articles/7-16-2019/Co_working-space-by-day,-cocktail-lounge-by-night/
Released: July 16, 2019. **Description:** Flourish Lounge, which operates as a bar in the evening, also functions as a co-working space during the day hours. Typical office space, conference rooms, and breakout rooms are available and later the area turns into a self-pour lounge. **Availability:** Online.

3839 ■ **Concession Profession**
Pub: National Association of Concessionaires
Contact: Adam Gottlieb, President
URL(s): naconline.org/programs-services/publications
Released: Annual **Description:** Covers about 900 member equipment manufacturers, suppliers, jobber/distributors, popcorn processors, theaters, amusement parks, stadiums, rinks, and other concession operators in the United States and Canada. **Entries include:** For operators--Company name, address, phone, name of contact. For manufacturers and suppliers--Company name, address, phone, names and titles of up to four executives, brief description of service or products. **Arrangement:** Classified by type of concession or business activity. **Indexes:** Name, geographical. **Availability:** Print.

3840 ■ *"Eastern Market's New Bite?"* **in Washington Business Journal (Vol. 33, August 8, 2014, No. 16, pp. 6)**
Pub: American City Business Journals, Inc.
Contact: Mike Olivieri, Executive Vice President
Price: $4, Introductory 4-Week Offer(Digital & Print). **Description:** Eastern Market continues to operate despite allegations of financial mismanagement on the part of Washington DC auditors. Many of the market's vendors have been operating their stands with expired leases for more than five years. However, the Department of General Services has vowed to draw a new standard contract for renting and renegotiate new leases. **Availability:** Print; Online.

3841 ■ *"First Food Truck Festival Features Enticing Fare, Frustrating Waits"* **in Saint Paul Pioneer Press (August 6, 2012)**
Pub: McClatchy-Tribune Regional News
Ed: Megan Boldt. **Description:** The first Minnesota Food Truck Fest was held in downtown Minneapolis, Minnesota. Despite best intentions, attendees were left waiting in long lines and two vendors ran out of food in two hours. Fourteen food vendors and 25 craft beer trucks were representing this trend in food service. **Availability:** Print; Online.

3842 ■ *"Food Truck Group Backs Proposed Regulations"* **in Buffalo News (January 18, 2012)**
Ed: Aaron Besecker. **Description:** Food truck operators in the city of Buffalo, New York have accepted the newly created rules governing their operations in the city, despite the higher-than-expected $1,000 permit fee. An attorney for the Western New York Food Truck Association stated that the proposed rules would be acceptable to the membership. **Availability:** Print; Online.

3843 ■ *"Food Truck Weddings Gain Popularity, Buck Tradition"* **in Tampa Tribune (June 24, 2012)**
Ed: Jeff Houck. **Description:** A new trend crossing the nation is the use of a food truck for feeding guests as wedding receptions. Food trucks allow the bride and groom to provide a more casual atmosphere for their wedding party and is less expensive than a formal dinner. **Availability:** Print; Online.

3844 ■ *"Food Trucks Savor Rebirth in City"* **in Providence Business News (Vol. 27, April 16, 2012, No. 2, pp. 1)**
Description: Providence, Rhode Island has been experiencing the growth of the food truck business as the trucks and their devoted followers become regular fixtures in the city. Food trucks have a strong presence in the West Coast and have proliferated across the U.S. in recent years. Insights into Providence's food truck community are also given. **Availability:** Online.

3845 ■ *"Fuel Costs Curb Food Truck Trend"* **in Tampa Tribune (March 26, 2012)**
Ed: Jeff Houck. **Description:** Owner of Maggie on the Move food truck, Margaret Loflin, has had to raise the cost of drinks served in order to cover the increased cost of gasoline to run her business. She also added smaller, less costly items to her menu. Her husband has gone back to a part-time job in he hopes of keeping their food truck running. **Availability:** Print; Online.

3846 ■ *"How I... Operate a Food Truck on the Streets of Honolulu"* **in Pacific Business News (Vol. 21, July 18, 2014, No. 21, pp. 19)**
Pub: American City Business Journals, Inc.
Contact: Mike Olivieri, Executive Vice President
Released: Weekly. **Price:** $4, Introductory 4-week offer(Digital only). **Description:** Jennifer Hino, co-owner of The Girls Who Bake Next Door, believes that social media is important as it helps create and reach a wider customer base for her business, which she runs out of a food truck in Honolulu. She also posts photos on the site, which helps reinforce her brand. **Availability:** Print; Online.

3847 ■ *"In Atlanta, Concessions Prices Go Down and Revenue Goes Up"* **in The New York Times (January 25, 2018)**
URL(s): www.nytimes.com/2018/01/25/sports/football/nfl-concessions.html
Ed: Ken Belson. **Released:** January 25, 2018. **Description:** Within the new Mercedes-Benz Stadium in Atlanta, the expected high-end food and drink concessions were established but included is a value stand, where affordable options are given. With the

high cost of tickets and attending the games, it's a welcome relief to be able to enjoy snacks without shelling out a whole lot more money. This actually increased fan spending, as the value menu has become a huge hit. **Availability:** Online.

3848 ■ *"Longmont's Comida Food Truck Now a Brick-and-Mortar Restaurant, Too" in Las Cruces Sun-News (February 17, 2012)*
Pub: Tribune News Service
Contact: Jack Barry, Vice President, Operations
E-mail: jbarry@tribpub.com

Ed: Tony Kindelspire. **Description:** Rayme Rosello discusses her plans to open her new Mexican-style restaurant, Comida Cantina, which grew from her pink food truck. Rosello started her food truck in 2010 and has frequented neighborhood parties as well as office parks to build her business. Details of the new restaurant are provided. **Availability:** Print; Online.

3849 ■ *"Meals on Wheels; Chicago Puts the Brakes on Upwardly Mobile Food Truck Operators" in Wall Street Journal (August 7, 2012, pp. A12)*
Pub: Dow Jones & Company Inc.
Contact: Almar Latour, Chief Executive Officer

Description: Details on the City of Chicago's move to regulate mobile food truck operators is presented. **Availability:** Online.

3850 ■ *"Minnesota State Fair Vendors Accept Big Risks for Big Rewards" in Business Journal (Vol. 32, August 22, 2014, No. 13, pp. 10)*
Pub: American City Business Journals, Inc.
Contact: Mike Olivieri, Executive Vice President

Released: Weekly. **Price:** $4, introductory 4-week offer(Digital & Print). **Description:** Food and beverage concessionaires compete for booths at the Minnesota State Fair and there are many vendors that wait for years to get one, especially a large booth with room for tables and a beer garden. The State Fair has been a good business opportunity and a family bonding experience for most of the vendors. **Availability:** Video; Print; Online.

3851 ■ *"One of the First Food Trucks in Montreal" in America's Intelligence Wire (May 31, 2012)*

Description: Food Trucks in Montreal launched its grand opening June 1, 2012. La Mangeoire offers five types of sandwiches and will serve food at festivals and locations permitted by the city during the summer. **Availability:** Online.

3852 ■ *"PayDragon Brings Mobile Payment App to Food-Truck Vendors" in PaymentsSource (April 16, 2012)*
Pub: SourceMedia LLC
Contact: Gemma Postlethwaite, Chief Executive Officer

Ed: David Heun. **Description:** PayDragon is a new App for food truck vendors to collect payments. It is also used by other small merchants. Paperlinks, developed this unit to provide a fast technology that enables consumers to securely order and pay for food with credit and debit cards using email, which elimiantes these steps for the vendors. **Availability:** Print; Online.

3853 ■ *"Rice & Roll Onigiri Food Truck to Tour Los Angeles Area" in Entertainment Close-Up (July 30, 2012)*

Description: Rice & Roll Onigiri food truck service is entering the US market, offering Japanese stuffed rice balls in a variety of flavors and fillings. Asian cuisine is popular in restaurants and markets. The ten locations to visit Rice & Roll in California are listed.

3854 ■ *"Riverview Food Truck Event Draws Huge Crowds" in Tampa Tribune (January 25, 2012)*

Ed: Lois Kindle. **Description:** Brandon, Florida's first food truck rally offered sampling dishes to attendees. Over 6,000 people tasted food from 14 trucks serving gourmet and specialty foods. **Availability:** Print; Online.

3855 ■ *"Sabra Food Truck Gives Canadians a New Reason to Take a Dip This Summer" in America's Intelligence Wire (August 1, 2012)*

Description: Sabra Canada Inc. is taking its food truck on tour of Canada's largest cities, offering people an opportunity to sample their hummus and dips. A schedule of the various stops is provided. **Availability:** Online.

3856 ■ *"State Reverses Food Truck Order" in Cape Cod Times (May 15, 2012)*

Ed: Patrick Cassidy. **Description:** Massachusetts Department of Transportation is developing a plan that will allow food truck owners to operate under a new pilot program. Owners must obtain a license to operate through the Transportation Department's legal division. License requirements will be modeled on present license applications and some modifications may be necessary. Insurance issues must be addressed. **Availability:** Online.

3857 ■ *"Want to Start Your Own Food Truck? Read This First" in Eater (November 21, 2019)*
URL(s): www.eater.com/young-guns-rising-stars/20 19/11/21/20970846/how-to-run-food-truck-business

Ed: Annie Burdick. **Released:** November 21, 2019. **Description:** More and more chefs are taking the plunge of opening up food trucks instead of a brick and mortar restaurant thinking it will be easier. Three food truck owners discuss their own experiences and successes in this industry. **Availability:** Online.

TRADE PERIODICALS

3858 ■ *Tourist Attractions and Parks*
Pub: Kane Communications Inc.
Contact: Scott Borowsky, President
Facebook: www.facebook.com/people/Tourist-Attractions-Parks-Magazine/100063983651750
X (Twitter): x.com/tapmagazine1

Ed: Scott C. Borowsky. **Released:** Last Issue 2019. **Description:** Magazine on the management of amusement parks, carnivals, arcades, museums, zoos, campgrounds, fun centers, arenas, miniature golf, and water sports. **Availability:** Online.

TRADE SHOWS AND CONVENTIONS

3859 ■ **IAFE Trade Show**
International Association of Fairs and Expositions (IAFE)
3043 E Cairo St.
Springfield, MO 65802
Ph: (417)862-5771
Free: 800-516-0313
Co. E-mail: iafe@fairsandexpos.com
URL: http://www.fairsandexpos.com
Contact: Marla Calico, President
URL(s): www.iafeconvention.com

Frequency: Annual. **Description:** Talent agencies, concessionaires, novelties, amusement devices, insurance, ribbons, plaques, attractions, and equipment. Products and services for the fair industry. **Audience:** IAFE members, special event producers, entertainment buyers, carnival executives, concessionaires, facility managers, Fair industry professionals. **Principal Exhibits:** Talent agencies, concessionaires, novelties, amusement devices, insurance, ribbons, plaques, attractions, and equipment. Products and services for the fair industry. **Telecommunication Services:** registration@fairsandexpos.com.

FRANCHISES AND BUSINESS OPPORTUNITIES

3860 ■ **Camille's Sidewalk Cafe**
9548 S 96TH E Ave.
Tulsa, OK 74133
Co. E-mail: riverside@camillescafe.com
Contact: David Rutkauskas, Contact

Description: Chain of fast food restaurants. **Founded:** 1996. **Financial Assistance:** Yes **Training:** Yes.

3861 ■ **Carvel Franchisor SPV LLC**
GOTO Foods
5620 Glenridge Dr. NE
Atlanta, GA 30342
Ph: (404)255-3250
Free: 800-227-8353
URL: http://www.gotofoods.com
Contact: Sarah E. Powell, Contact
Facebook: www.facebook.com/CarvelIceCream
X (Twitter): x.com/CarvelIceCream
Instagram: www.instagram.com/carvelicecream

Description: Firm offers custom ice cream desserts and novelties. **Founded:** 1934. **Training:** 2 week ice cream training school; access to the Carvel Development Network (real estate brokers, architects, lenders, contractors, etc.); Design & construction support & assistance; Grand opening support and toll-free hotline available.

3862 ■ **Different Twist Pretzel Co.**
6052 William Flynn Hwy.
Bakerstown, PA 15007

Description: Retailer of food products such as pretzels pizza, pretzel cheese wraps, pretzel pups. **Franchised:** 1992. **Training:** Yes.

3863 ■ **Pretzelmaker Inc.**
Global Franchise Group L.L.C. (GFG)
2841 Greenbriar Pkwy
Atlanta, GA 30311
Ph: (770)514-4500
Free: 800-524-6444
Fax: (770)514-4903
Co. E-mail: franchiseinfo@gfgmanagement.com
URL: http://www.globalfranchise.com
Facebook: www.facebook.com/pretzelmaker
X (Twitter): x.com/Pretzelmaker
Instagram: www.instagram.com/pretzelmaker

Description: Operator of pretzels franchise store. **Founded:** 1991. **Training:** Yes.

3864 ■ **Willy Dogs**
800 Proctor Ave.
Ogdensburg, NY 13669
Free: 800-915-4683
Co. E-mail: willydog.sales@gmail.com
URL: http://willydogs.com
Contact: Will Hodgskiss, Owner
X (Twitter): x.com/Willydog_topdog
YouTube: www.youtube.com/channel/UC4Vf4aWHR6xhldK3zl94trQ

Description: Hot dog cart resembling giant hot dog. **Founded:** 1989. **Training:** Yes.

LIBRARIES

3865 ■ **American Beverage Association (ABA)**
1275 Pennsylvania Ave. NW, Ste. 1100
Washington, DC 20004
Ph: (202)463-6774
Fax: (202)463-8277
Co. E-mail: media@americanbeverage.org
URL: http://www.americanbeverage.org/about-us/aba-team
Contact: Katherine Lugar, President

Description: Conducts government affairs activities on the national and state levels, discussion of industry problems, and general improvement of operating procedures. Conducts research on beverage laws. **Founded:** 1919. **Publications:** *Promoting Recycling to the Public*; *Directory of Members & Buyers Guide*. **Geographic Preference:** National.

3866 ■ **Food Institute (FI)**
330 Changebridge Rd., Ste. 101
Pine Brook, NJ 07058
Ph: (201)791-5570
Free: 855-791-5570
Co. E-mail: questions@foodinstitute.com
URL: http://www.foodinstitute.com
Contact: Anika Wilson, Contact

E-mail: anika.wilson@foodinstitute.com
Facebook: www.facebook.com/foodinstitutenj
Linkedin: www.linkedin.com/company/the-food-institute
X (Twitter): x.com/FoodInstitute
Instagram: www.instagram.com/foodinstitute
YouTube: www.youtube.com/channel/UCYAPI0TXNtJa04aQre4h4pA

Description: Strives to provide food industry-related information to its members. **Scope:** The food industry. **Services:** Center open to the public on fee basis. **Founded:** 1928. **Holdings:** Figures not available. **Publications:** *Today in Food*; *Get It Out, Get It Right, Get It Over! Avoiding Food Product Recalls*; *The Food Institute* (Weekly); *Almanac of the Canning, Freezing, Preserving Industries* (Annual); *Food Business Mergers and Acquisitions*; *OSHA Inspection Manual*; *Regulatory Directory* (Periodic); *Food Business Mergers & Acquisitions*. **Geographic Preference:** Multinational.

RESEARCH CENTERS

3867 ■ The National Food Lab (NFL)
13755 First Ave. North Ste. 500
Plymouth, MN 55441
URL: http://www.thenfl.com
Contact: Alan Roberts, President
E-mail: alanroberts@eurofinsus.com
Linkedin: www.linkedin.com/company/the-national-food-laboratory

Description: Consulting firm for the food, beverage and consumer products industries. Expertise in new food product strategy, commercialization, food safety, consumer insights, sensory evaluation, chemistry and microbiology. Offers new food product introductions to clients and provides support throughout the product lifecycle. Key services include descriptive analysis, consensus panel, descriptive panel training, quality audit panels, terminology training, discrimination testing and joint multivariate analysis. **Scope:** Consulting firm for the food, beverage and consumer products industries. Expertise in new food product strategy, commercialization, food safety, consumer insights, sensory evaluation, chemistry and microbiology. Offers new food product introductions to clients and provides support throughout the product lifecycle. Key services include descriptive analysis, consensus panel, descriptive panel training, quality audit panels, terminology training, discrimination testing and joint multivariate analysis. **Founded:** 1976. **Publications:** "Gaining Deeper Reformulation Information from Product Guidance Tests"; "Assessing Your Package-to-Product Fit to improve brand alignment". **Training:** Latin American Pesticide Residue Workshop.

Concierge/Virtual Assistant Service

ASSOCIATIONS AND OTHER ORGANIZATIONS

3868 ■ National Concierge Association (NCA)
2920 Idaho Ave. N
Minneapolis, MN 55427
Ph: (612)834-7295
Co. E-mail: info@ncakey.org
URL: http://www.ncakey.org
Contact: Pat Brengman, President
E-mail: patb@mplsclub.org
Facebook: www.facebook.com/NationalConciergeAssociation
Linkedin: www.linkedin.com/company/ncanational
X (Twitter): x.com/NCANational
Instagram: www.instagram.com/nationalconciergeassoc
YouTube: www.youtube.com/user/NationalConcierge
Description: Represents concierges of all types and affiliated hospitality related businesses whose exceptional products and services are of benefit to concierge clientele. **Founded:** 1998. **Publications:** NCA Keynotes; National Concierge Association Brochure. **Educational Activities:** NCA Education Conference (Annual). **Awards:** NCA Concierge Outstanding Service (Annual); NCA Chapter of the Year (Annual); NCA International Partner of the Year (Annual). **Geographic Preference:** Multinational.

REFERENCE WORKS

3869 ■ "Baby Boomers Look to Senior Concierge Services to Raise Income" in The New York Times (May 19, 2017)
URL(s): www.nytimes.com/2017/05/19/business/retirement/boomers-retiring-concierge.html

Ed: Liz Moyer. **Released:** May 19, 2017. **Description:** Elder concierge is a growing industry of mostly part-time workers who assist older clients with living independently. They help out around the house, drive clients to appointments, run small errands, and are often an extra set of eyes and ears. Organizations are looking for workers and it's often ideal for stay-at-home parents looking for some extra income, or a retired person. **Availability:** Online.

3870 ■ "The Downfall of the Virtual Assistant (So Far)" in ComputerWorld (June 20, 2019)
URL(s): www.computerworld.com/article/3403332/downfall-virtual-assistant.html

Ed: JR Raphael. **Released:** June 20, 2019. **Description:** Virtual assistants such as Alexa, Siri, and Google Assistant are all features that people are starting to rely on more and more. However, the success rate isn't as high as expected when it comes to completing tasks. More simple tasks, such as pulling up the weather, are easily accomplished by these virtual assistants, but consumers are becoming frustrated when complex tasks can't be completed by the AI. **Availability:** Online.

3871 ■ "Everything You Ever Wondered About Hiring a Virtual Assistant (and More)" in HubSpot
URL(s): blog.hubspot.com/sales/virtual-assistant
Ed: Meg Prater. **Description:** Have you ever wanted an assistant to help with day to day tasks? Virtual assistants are available on a contract basis to help with your needs — from data entry to setting up your office to helping with your taxes. **Availability:** Online.

3872 ■ "The Great Concierge Debate: Digital or Personal?" in The New York Times (October 20, 2017)
URL(s): www.nytimes.com/2017/10/20/travel/digital-vs-personal-concierges.html
Ed: Mike Seely. **Released:** October 20, 2017. **Description:** When in Roam, a new concierge app, was launched by Krista Krauss Miller and is competing with other well-known concierge apps. Miller's app is able to reach people staying in an Airbnb or a hotel without a concierge service. **Availability:** Online.

3873 ■ "How Concierge Roles Are Changing in an Internet Age" in Hotel News Now (July 9, 2018)
URL(s): www.hotelnewsnow.com/Articles/287216/How-concierge-roles-are-changing-in-an-internet-age
Ed: Laura Koss-Feder. **Released:** July 09, 2018. **Description:** With so many people plugged into their phones, they have everything they need to enjoy a trip. Online reviews of restaurants, shows, and attractions are at their fingertips. How do traditional concierges compete? . **Availability:** Online.

3874 ■ "Offering Service With a :)" in Puget Sound Business Journal (Vol. 35, July 11, 2014, No. 12, pp. 12)
Pub: American City Business Journals, Inc.
Contact: Mike Olivieri, Executive Vice President
Description: Sorrento Hotel's Sorrento Ambassadors of Memories is an entry level job that allows young people to perform menial tasks for hotel guests. Randall Obrecht, Sorrento's general manager, states that the young workers actually serve as personalized butlers or concierges. The program helps hotel staff deal with high occupancy rates. **Availability:** Online.

3875 ■ "Opportunity Knocks" in Small Business Opportunities (September 2008)
Description: Profile of YourOffice USA, a franchise that provides home-based and small businesses cost-effective and efficient support through "virtual" offices that are available as much or as little as the client needs it; they also supply necessary tools such as a professional business address, private mailbox service, personalized telephone answering and more that supports clients who want to look, act and operate with an advanced business image. **Availability:** Online.

3876 ■ "Professional Help: Cross That Off Your To-Do List" in Inc. (November 2007, pp. 89-90, 92)
Ed: Alison Stein Wellner. **Description:** Small business owners are finding that it pays to hire someone to takeover the personal tasks of daily living, including hiring a personal assistant, chauffeur, chef, stylist, pet caregiver, or concierge service. **Availability:** Online.

3877 ■ "Siri Creator SRI International Hopes Lola Cashes In, Too" in Silicon Valley/San Jose Business Journal (Vol. 30, July 6, 2012, No. 15, pp. 1)
Pub: Baltimore Business Journal
Contact: Rhonda Pringle, President
E-mail: rpringle@bizjournals.com
Description: Software developer and SRI and BBVA have partnered to create virtual personal assistant Lola. The program assists customers with their banking needs. Program features and dimensions are also included. **Availability:** Print; Online.

STATISTICAL SOURCES

3878 ■ Virtual Assistants
URL(s): www.marketresearch.com/Global-Industry-Analysts-v1039/Virtual-Assistants-32480211/
Price: $4,950. **Description:** Report covering the virtual assistant industry. Includes a market overview, global market perspective, and select competitors. **Availability:** PDF.

Consignment Shop

START-UP INFORMATION

3879 ■ *eBay Business the Smart Way*
Released: 3rd edition. **Description:** eBay commands ninety percent of all online auction business. Computer and software expert and online entrepreneur shares information to help online sellers get started and move merchandise on eBay. Tips include the best ways to build credibility, find products to sell, manage inventory, create a storefront Website, and more. **Availability:** Print; PDF.

3880 ■ *The eBay Business Start-Up Kit: With 100s of Live Links to All the Information & Tools You Need*
Pub: Nolo
Contact: Chris Braun, President
Ed: Richard Stim. **Description:** Interactive kit that provides in-depth information and practical advice in launching an eBay business. **Availability:** Print.

3881 ■ *"Mount Laurel Woman Launches Venture Into Children's Used Clothing"* in *Philadelphia Inquirer* (September 17, 2010)
Pub: The Philadelphia Inquirer
Contact: Elizabeth H. Hughes, Chief Executive Officer
Ed: Maria Panaritis. **Description:** Profile of Jennifer Frisch, stay-at-home mom turned entrepreneur. Frisch started a used-clothing store Once Upon a Child after opening her franchised Plato's Closet, selling unwanted and used baby clothing and accessories at her new shop, while offering used merchandise to teens at Plato's Closet.

3882 ■ *"Upscale Consignment Shop Opens In Brandon"* in *Tampa Tribune* (January 25, 2012)
Ed: Yvette C. Hammett. **Description:** Agape Chic Consignment Boutique opened February 4, 2012. The owners, Dena Ham and Stacy Ulrey Regan became friends working on their children's school PTA. Their business partnership hopes that people walking into their new shop will feel as if they are walking into an upscale boutique. The store offers designer labels in sizes 2-20. **Availability:** Print; Online.

ASSOCIATIONS AND OTHER ORGANIZATIONS

3883 ■ NARTS - The Association of Resale Professionals
PO Box 190
 Saint Clair Shores, MI 48080
Ph: (586)294-6700
Free: 800-544-0751
Fax: (586)588-7018
Co. E-mail: info@narts.org
URL: http://www.narts.org/i4a/pages/index.cfm ?pageid=1
Contact: Adele R. Meyer, Executive Director
E-mail: adele@narts.org
Facebook: www.facebook.com/TheAssocia tionofResaleProfessionals
X (Twitter): x.com/NARTS_Conf
Description: Works for the exchange of ideas and information among members, develops public recognition and knowledge of the field, and promotes professionalism in the industry. **Founded:** 1984. **Publications:** *Your NARTS Network* (Monthly). **Awards:** NARTS Educational Service Award (Annual); Renee River Award. **Geographic Preference:** National.

REFERENCE WORKS

3884 ■ *"6 Top Online Consignment Shops for Selling Your Clothes"* in *U.S. News & World Report* (February 21, 2019)
URL(s): money.usnews.com/money/personal-finance/ saving-and-budgeting/articles/6-top-online -consignment-shops-for-selling-your-clothes
Ed: Maryalene LaPonsie. **Released:** February 21, 2019. **Description:** Online consignment shops and apps are trending upwards, making it easier for consumers to upload photos of their items and reaching more potential buyers. Some online shops focus solely on high-end brands, while some will take everyday clothes. A discussion of six popular online consignment shops with pros and cons listed, along with their fees is given. **Availability:** Online.

3885 ■ *"Auction Company Grows with Much Smaller Sites"* in *Automotive News* (Vol. 86, October 31, 2011, No. 6488, pp. 23)
Pub: Crain Communications Inc.
Contact: Barry Asin, President
Ed: Arlena Sawyers. **Description:** Auction Broadcasting Company has launched auction sites and is expanding into new areas. The family-owned business will provide auctions half the size traditionally used. The firm reports that 40 percent of the General Motors factory-owned vehicles sold on consignment were purchased by online buyers, up 30 percent over 2010. **Availability:** Online.

3886 ■ *"Consignment Shop Blends Business With a Giving Spirit"* in *Gazette* (January 17, 2012)
Ed: Bill Radford. **Description:** Mountain Equipment Recyclers, located in Colorado Springs, Colorado, sells outdoor gear. Mike Mazzola, owner, has expanded his consignment shop to include a nonprofit entity to raise money for our veterans and their families. So far, he has exceeded his goal by giving five percent of sales of consigned gear and 50 percent of donated gear to three nonprofit organizations: AspenPoint, which helps veterans and their families; The Home Front Cares, supporting families of deployed soliders; and LifeQuest Transitions, which helps soldiers and veterans relearn life skills through cognitive exercises and adventure sports. The funds are split equally to the three agencies. **Availability:** Online.

3887 ■ *"Consignment Shop Offers Children's Clothes, Products"* in *Frederick News-Post* (August 19, 2010)
Pub: Federick News-Post
Contact: Connie Hastings, Director
E-mail: chastings@newspost.com
Ed: Ed Waters, Jr. **Description:** Sweet Pea Consignments for Children offers used items for newborns to pre-teens. The shop carries name brand clothing as well as toys, books and baby products. **Availability:** Print; Online.

3888 ■ *"Consignment Shop Opens In Spring Township To Serve Hard-To-Find Sizes"* in *Reading Eagle* (June 16, 2012)
Ed: Shannon Simcox. **Description:** BeautiFull Figure is a plus-size consignment store located in Spring Township, Pennsylvania. The owner, Elizabeth Reach, is also a full-time student. Many consignment shops will not accept clothing over size 16 and Reach saw an opportunity to serve plus-size women. She offers 50-50 split of profits on consigned items. **Availability:** Print; Online.

3889 ■ *"Consignment Shops Form Friendly Alliance in Eagle Plaza"* in *Mail Tribune* (August 7, 2012)
Ed: Greg Stiles. **Description:** Loren Clear was concerned about opening his men's only consignment shop in a plaza already housing three other consignment stores. However, all four retailers have found it to be an asset, each having their own specialty. Along with Clear's men's clothing consignment, there is a children's store, a plus-size shop, and a women's clothing and accessory business. Clear said there are few men's consignment stores and it is an answer for the businessman to purchase better quality clothing and suits at better prices., Loren Clear thought opening his men's only consignment shop in the same plaza shared with three other consignment stores might be a bad idea. However, all three retailers have found it to be an asset. Along with Clear's men's only shop called Men's Hangups, there is a plus-size shop, a women's store, and a children's store. **Availability:** Online.

3890 ■ *"Consignment Shops Use Web To Help Sell Used Clothing"* in *Chattanooga Times/Free Press* (March 17, 2012)
Ed: Carey O'Neil. **Description:** Chattanooga, Tennessee boasts a strong market for consignment shops. Children's clothing and toys are among best sellers. Tips are given to help increase sales for consignment/resale shops. **Availability:** Print; Online.

3891 ■ *"ConsignPro Elevates Nature of Consignment Business, Encourages Designer Resale"* in *Internet Wire* (May 15, 2012)
Description: Forbes magazine recently highlighted an article on an upscale thrift store located in New York called Designer Resale. The shop features

fashion-forward retail merchandies sold on consignment. These new boutique-type resale shops are growing in popularity across the country. **Availability:** Print; Online.

3892 ■ *"Greene Street Consignment May Be the Most Happening Area Company You've Never Heard Of" in Philadelphia Inquirer (April 20, 2012)*
Ed: Kathy Boccella. **Description:** Greene Street Consignment has grown to seven locations featuring fashionable resale items. Lynne Mastrilli, owner of the boutiques does not use social media to market her business. Her sister, Donna, runs a nonprofit offshoot of the business called Greene Street Animal Rescue. Details of the two businesses are included.

3893 ■ *"How to Sell, Donate, or Recycle Your Stuff" in The New York Times (January 11, 2019)*
URL(s): www.nytimes.com/2019/01/11/realestate/how-to-sell-donate-or-recycle-your-stuff.html
Ed: Ronda Kaysen. **Released:** January 11, 2019. **Description:** If you are taking the time to clean out your home, resist the urge to throw away the old items and instead sell, donate, or recycle. You may be able to make some quick cash too. Various tips for getting rid of your unwanted items, including selling at consignment shops, are given. **Availability:** Online.

3894 ■ *"I Brake for Yard Sales: And Flea Markets, Thrift Shops, Auctions, and the Occasional Dumpster"*
Released: April 01, 2012. **Price:** $24.95, Paperback. **Description:** Lara Spencer, self-confessed frugalista and new correspondent, shares her passion for shopping at yard sales, consignment shops, and estate sales for decorating her home as well as her friend's homes. She shares her bargain hunting secrets and tells where to shop, what to look for, how to pay for sales, how to restore items, and how to decorate. **Availability:** E-book; Print.

3895 ■ *"It's So You! Consignment Shop Owner Thrilled to See Vision Come to Fruition" in News-Herald (August 27, 2010)*
Pub: The News Herald
Contact: Tricia Ambrose, Executive Editor
E-mail: tambrose@news-herald.com
Ed: Brandon C. Baker. **Description:** Profile of Laurel Howes and her It's So You! Boutique. The consignment shop is located in Willoughby's Pine Ride Plaza in Ohio. The shop targets all women, but particularly those who are not that comfortable with shopping consignment. **Availability:** Online.

3896 ■ *"Local Resale Shops Give Tips for Buying, Selling Used Items" in News Tribune (July 21, 2019)*
URL(s): www.newstribune.com/news/features/story/2019/jul/21/secondhand-sales-growing-trend-takes-hold-in-mid-missourilocal-resale-shops-give-tips-for-buying-selling-used-items/787438/
Ed: Madeleine Leroux. **Released:** July 21, 2019. **Description:** The growing resale trend is getting stronger as the younger generations are looking to save money buy buying secondhand. Local resale shop owner Sherry King walks us through the steps of selling your items in a consignment shop and how to be successful at it. **Availability:** Online.

3897 ■ *"Longtime Peoria Heights Second-Hand Clothing Shop Closing" in Journal Star (December 18, 2010)*
Pub: Journal Star
Ed: Scott Hilyard. **Description:** The Happy Hangar, a consignment clothing store located in Peoria Heights, Illinois is closing after 31 years of selling second-hand clothing. **Availability:** Print; Online.

3898 ■ *"New Beat for Marley's Daughter: Offspring of Reggae Royalty Opens Vintage Clothing Shop with Pal" in Los Angeles Business Journal (Vol. 34, March 12, 2012, No. 11, pp. 3)*
Pub: CBJ L.P.
Contact: Laura Garrett, Vice President Publisher
E-mail: garrett@ocbj.com
Ed: Bethany Firnhaber. **Description:** Karen Marley, daughter of famous reggae musician Bob Marley, explains her passion for vintage clothing. Karen and her fried Monique Aquino have partnered to open a resale consignment store in Los Angeles selling designer and vintage clothing. **Availability:** Online.

3899 ■ *"Online Consignment Is Big Business and a Bargain Hunter's Heaven" in CBS News (April 13, 2017)*
URL(s): www.cbsnews.com/news/clothing-consignment-fashion-bargain-online/
Released: April 03, 2017. **Description:** There is a big boom in online consignment shops, with it now being an $18 billion industry. ThredUp is one of the main online sites dealing with used clothing, while The RealReal is another site dealing with mostly high-end designer items. Both sites cash in because so many people out there are looking for good bargains on quality clothing. **Availability:** Online.

3900 ■ *"Parkland Approves First "Luxury" Consignment Shop" in Sun Sentinel (May 7, 2012)*
Ed: Lisa J. Huriash. **Description:** SincerelyYours is a very upscale consignment shop located in the upscale area of Parkland, Florida. This trend toward high-end luxury consignment boutiques is being seen across the country because consumers of luxury goods can be rid of their items, while those wishing high quality things can purchase at a substantial savings. **Availability:** Print; Online.

3901 ■ *"SPOILED! Children's Consignment Boutique Now Collecting Donations To Support Baby2Baby & Help Children In Need" in Benzinga.com (July 30, 2012)*
Pub: Benzinga.com
Contact: Jason Raznick, Founder
Ed: Aaron Wise. **Description:** CeCe Hendriks opened her high-end children's consignment store in response to wanting to provide quality clothing for her son. Because children outgrow their clothing so fast, she decided a consignment shop is what all mom's needed. Hendriks offers a 50 percent consignment to donors and if the item isn't sold in 90 days, the consignee can choos to have the item returned or donate it to Baby2Baby. Hendriks also gives 10 percent of proceeds from sales to Baby2Baby, a nonprofit that works with homeles and domestic violence shelters. **Availability:** Online.

3902 ■ *"Therealreal's Online Luxury Consignment Shop" in The New Yorker (October 14, 2019)*
URL(s): www.newyorker.com/magazine/2019/10/21/therealreals-online-luxury-consignment-shop
Ed: Susan Orlean. **Released:** October 14, 2019. **Description:** TheRealReal's online consignment site specializes in high-end designer clothes, jewelry, and handbags. With the online presence to go along with their brick-and-mortar store, items can be seen by more people around the world, especially since the used-clothes market is trending upward. **Availability:** Online.

3903 ■ *"ThredUP Launches Online Concierge Service to Compete With Children's Consignment" in Benzinga.com (January 25, 2012)*
Description: Concierge is a new service offered by thredUP, the top online site for used children's clothing. Concierge simplifies the process of recycling children's clothing. Users sign up at the Website and request a prepaid, ready to ship recycling bag. After filling the bag, it is placed on the doorstep, and thredUp takes it from there. After consignors inspect the items, senders are given rewards up to $5 per piece, based on quality and quantity of items shipped. The received items are then sold on thredUP's online shop.

3904 ■ *Too Good to be Threw: The Complete Operations Manual for Resale & Consignment Shops*
Pub: Katydid Press
Ed: Kate Holmes. **Price:** $76.95. **Description:** Revised edition covers all the information needed to start and run a buy-outright or consignment shop, covering anything from clothing to furniture resale.

3905 ■ *"Wave of Resale, Consignment Shops Pop Up In Springs" in Gazette (March 19, 2012)*
Ed: Bill Radford. **Description:** The depressed economy has spurred the growth of consignment shops across the nation. Colorado Springs, Colorado area urges people to shop at these resale locations because they promote green initiatives by recycling goods. WeeCycle, Knit Wits, Once Upon a Child and Re-Generation, Moutain Equipment Recyclers, and Gearonimo, are among the established consignment stores in the area. **Availability:** Print.

3906 ■ *"What's That Business? Part of Savers Thrift Store Proceeds Go To Charity" in Duluth News-Tribune (February 27, 2012)*
Ed: Candace Renalls. **Description:** Savers Inc., a thrift store that sells housewares, furniture, clothing and collectibles allows customers to pick the charity it would like part of the store's proceeds to be given. The Duluth Savers Store has partnered with the Disabled American Veterans of Minnesota. Details of the stores, their customers and practices are highlighted. **Availability:** Online.

TRADE PERIODICALS

3907 ■ *Swap Meet Magazine*
Pub: Forum Publishing Co.
URL(s): www.swapmeetmag.com
Released: Monthly **Price:** $10, for printed sample; $125, for foreign; $75, for year. **Description:** Covers over 5,000 manufacturers and importers of jewelry, electronics, clothing, cosmetics, watches, novelties, and other items that are sold to merchandise retailers and flee market vendors at wholesale prices. **Entries include:** Company name, address, phone, products or services. **Availability:** Print; Download; Online.

VIDEO/AUDIO MEDIA

3908 ■ *The How of Business: Adam Siegel - Fashion Resale Business*
Released: January 01, 2024. **Description:** Podcast discusses the details of starting a tech-enabled resale business.

FRANCHISES AND BUSINESS OPPORTUNITIES

3909 ■ **Once Upon a Child**
605 Hwy. 169 N, Ste. 400
Minneapolis, MN 55441
Ph: (763)520-8500
Co. E-mail: ouac-corporate-operations@ouac.com
URL: http://www.onceuponachild.com
Contact: Tamara L. Harmon, Contact
Facebook: www.facebook.com/onceuponachild
X (Twitter): x.com/OnceUponAChild
Instagram: www.instagram.com/onceuponachild
YouTube: www.youtube.com/user/OnceUponAchildTV

Description: Franchises consignment shops featuring children products including toys, books, furniture and apparel. **Founded:** 1985. **Equity Capital Needed:** $250,000 ; $75,000 – Cash or liquid assets. **Training:** Yes.

3910 ■ **Plato's Closet**
12951 Ridgedale Dr., Ste. 365
Minnetonka, MN 55305
Ph: (952)512-3647
Co. E-mail: pc-corporate-operations@platoscloset.com
URL: http://www.platoscloset.com/home
Facebook: www.facebook.com/people/Platos-Closet-Minnetonka-MN/61557584116791

Instagram: www.instagram.com/platosclosetminnetonka1

Description: Retailer of apparel and accessories. **Founded:** 1998. **Franchised:** 1999. **Training:** Training program includes product acquisition, fashion trends, inventory management, and proprietary point-of-sale computer system. Annual franchise conferences, owner only website, and onsite business consultations.

3911 ■ Play it Again Sports (PIAS)
Winmark Corporation
  605 Hwy. 169 N, Ste. 400
  Minneapolis, MN 55441
Ph: (763)520-8500
Fax: (763)520-8410
Co. E-mail: winmark.information@winmarkcorporation.com
URL: http://www.winmarkcorporation.com
Contact: Tamara L. Harmon, Contact

Facebook: www.facebook.com/playitagainsports
Instagram: www.instagram.com/playitagainsports

Description: Retailer of new and used sports equipment and clothing's. **Founded:** 1983. **Training:** Training includes product acquisition, inventory management, staff hiring and training, customer service, advertising and marketing, and merchandising. Ongoing regional meetings and national training conferences held annually.

Construction Company

ASSOCIATIONS AND OTHER ORGANIZATIONS

3912 ■ Accessibility Professionals Association (APA)
5114 Balcones Woods Dr., Ste. 307-103
Austin, TX 78759
Ph: (512)222-3676
URL: http://accessibilityprofessionals.org
Contact: D. Clark Teel, Member
Facebook: www.facebook.com/Accessibility-Professionals-Association-160450904016330
Linkedin: www.linkedin.com/company/accessibility-professionals-association

Description: Professionals focusing on accessibility in the built environment. Offers continuing education in accessibility standards and regulations, as well as training on the federal ADA standards and other accessibility codes and standards. Promotes the services of members within in the industry, and participates in the development, interpretation, and adoption of accessibility regulations. **Founded:** 1999.

3913 ■ American Concrete Institute (ACI)
38800 Country Club Dr.
Farmington Hills, MI 48331-3439
Ph: (248)848-3800
Fax: (248)848-3701
Co. E-mail: social@concrete.org
URL: http://www.concrete.org
Contact: Antonio Nanni, President
Facebook: www.facebook.com/AmericanConcreteInstitute
X (Twitter): x.com/concreteaci
Instagram: www.instagram.com/concreteaci
YouTube: www.youtube.com/c/aci

Description: Develops and distributes consensus-based standards, technical resources, educational and training programs, certification programs, and proven expertise for individuals and organizations involved in concrete design, construction, and materials. Also publishes books and periodicals on concrete products and concrete structures. Provides technical information. **Scope:** Characteristics of concrete as a material and its structural application, including studies on design, construction, and maintenance of concrete structures, manufacture and use of concrete products, and establishment of building code requirements for concrete. **Founded:** 1904. **Publications:** *Textile-Reinforced Concrete (TRC)*; *Slag Cement Concrete*; *Concrete Abstracts*; *ACI Collection*; *Fiber-Reinforced Concrete in Practice*; *Concrete: The Sustainable Material Choice*; *Frontiers in the Use of Polymers in Concrete*; *ACI Structural Journal: Journal of the American Concrete Institute* (Bimonthly); *Concrete Abstracts*; *Concrete Repair Manual*; *Green House: The Energy Efficient Home*; *Design and Applications of Textile-Reinforced Concrete*; *Seismic Strengthening of Concrete Buildings Using FRP Composites*; *Fabrication Technologies for Thin Cementitious Products*; *Thomas T.C. Hsu Symposium on Shear and Torsion in Concrete Structures*; *Modeling As a Solution to Concrete Problems*; *Fiber-Reinforced Self-Consolidating Concrete: Research and Applications*; *Fiber-Reinforced Polymer Reinforcement for Concrete Structures: 10th International Symposium*; *ACI Collection of Concrete Codes, Specifications, and Practices (MCP)*; *Concrete International* (Monthly); *ACI Materials Journal* (Bimonthly); *Health Monitoring Systems and Sensors for Assessing Concrete*; *Designing Concrete Structures for Fire Safety*; *Nanotechnology of Concrete: The Next Big Thing is Small*; *Advances in the Material Science of Concrete*; *Structural Concrete in Performance-Based Seismic Design of Bridges*; *Recent Advances in Maintenance and Repair of Concrete Bridges*; *Innovations in Fire Design of Concrete Structures*; *Advances in FRC Durability and Field Applications*; *Behavior of Concrete Structures Subjected to Blast and Impact Loadings*; *Understanding Adhesive Anchors: Behavior, Materials, Installation, Design*; *Andy Scanlon Symposium on Serviceability and Safety of Concrete Structures*; *Concrete Construction and Structural Evaluation: A Symposium Honoring Dov Kaminetzky*; *A Fracture Approach for FRP-Concrete Structures*. **Educational Activities:** ACI Conventions (Semiannual); World of Concrete (WOC) (Annual). **Awards:** ACI Construction Award (Annual); ACI Fellow (Annual); ACI Design Award (Annual); Kumar Mehta Scholarship (Annual); Arthur R. Anderson Medal (Irregular); Delmar L. Bloem Distinguished Service Award (Annual); ACI Chapter Activities Award (Annual); Roger H. Corbetta Concrete Constructor Award (Irregular); ACI Commemorative Lecture Series (Annual); ACI Honorary Members (Annual); Clyde E. Kesler Education Award (Irregular); Henry L. Kennedy Award (Irregular); Mete A. Sozen Award for Excellence in Structural Research (Annual); Henry C. Turner Medal (Irregular); Wason Medal for Materials Research (Irregular); Wason Medal for Most Meritorious Paper (Annual); Charles S. Whitney Medal (Annual); Cedric Willson Lightweight Aggregate Concrete Award (Annual); Arthur J. Boase Award (Annual); Walter P. Moore Jr. Faculty Achievement Award (Annual); ACI Young Member Award for Professional Achievement (Annual); ACI BASF Construction Chemicals Student Fellowship (Annual); ACI Cagley Student Fellowship (Annual); ACI President's Fellowships (Annual); ACI Foundation Scholarships (Annual); ACI Baker Student Fellowships (Annual); ACI Elmer Baker Student Fellowship (Annual); ACI W.R. Grace Scholarships (Annual); Katharine & Bryant Mather Scholarship (Annual); ACI Charles Pankow Student Fellowship (Annual); Bertold E. Weinberg Scholarship (Annual); ACI Richard N. White Student Fellowship (Annual). **Geographic Preference:** Multinational.

3914 ■ American Council for Construction Education (ACCE)
300 Decker Dr., Ste. 330
Irving, TX 75062
Ph: (972)600-8800
Co. E-mail: acce@acce-hq.org
URL: http://www.acce-hq.org
Contact: Charlie Roesset, Chairperson
Facebook: www.facebook.com/accehq.org
Linkedin: www.linkedin.com/company/american-council-for-construction-education
X (Twitter): x.com/acce_hq
Instagram: www.instagram.com/acceinsta

Description: Promotes and improves construction education at the postsecondary level. Engages in accrediting construction education programs offered by colleges and universities nationwide. **Founded:** 1974. **Geographic Preference:** National.

3915 ■ American Fence Association (AFA)
4100 International Pky., Ste. 2400
Carrollton, TX 75007
Free: 800-822-4342
Fax: (314)480-7118
Co. E-mail: memberservices@americanfenceassociation.com
URL: http://www.americanfenceassociation.com
Contact: Randy Ward, President
E-mail: randy@wmshomes.us
Facebook: www.facebook.com/americanfenceassociation
Linkedin: www.linkedin.com/company/afafence
X (Twitter): x.com/AFAFence

Description: Fence contractors, manufacturers and wholesalers; associate members are general contractors, architects and insurance companies. Promotes the fence industry in 17 countries. Sponsors field training school and certification program. **Founded:** 1962. **Publications:** *Robinwood Directory*; *Who's Who in Fencing--Membership Directory*; *Who's Who In AFA* (Biennial); *Davison Fence Blue Book* (Annual); *Fencepost* (Bimonthly). **Awards:** AFA Ambassador Award (Annual); AFA Distinguished Service Award (Annual); AFA Fence Project of the Year Award (Annual); AFA Hall of Fame Award (Annual). **Geographic Preference:** National.

3916 ■ American Institute of Constructors (AIC)
19 Mantua Rd.
Mount Royal, NJ 08061
Ph: (703)683-4999
Co. E-mail: info@professionalconstructor.org
URL: http://aic-builds.org
Contact: Geno Hogan, President
Facebook: www.facebook.com/aicccc

Description: Professionals engaged in construction practice, education, and research. Serves as the certifying body for the professional constructor. Promotes the study and advances the practice of construction. Facilitates the exchange of information and ideas relating to construction. **Founded:** 1971. **Publications:** *Professional Constructor Journal* (Semiannual); *Constructor Certification Exam Study Guide Level II*; *Membership Roster* (Annual). **Educational Activities:** American Institute of Constructors Annual Forum (Annual). **Awards:** AIC Award (Annual); Jack Kinnaman AIC Leadership Award (Annual); Victor C. Smith Professional Constructor Award (Occasionally); Walter A. Nashert, Sr. Constructor Award (Annual). **Geographic Preference:** National.

3917 ■ American Society of Professional Estimators (ASPE)
2525 Perimeter Pl. Dr., Ste. 103
Nashville, TN 37214
Ph: (615)316-9200
Fax: (615)316-9800
URL: http://www.aspenational.org
Contact: Chris Morton, President
E-mail: cmortonfcpe@outlook.com
Facebook: www.facebook.com/ASPE.estimators
Linkedin: www.linkedin.com/company/american-society-of-professional-estimators
YouTube: www.youtube.com/channel/UC6qS7pHNAvqJuJF6Go9B8kA

Description: Construction cost estimators. Develops professional and ethical standards in construction estimating. Offers continuing education to established professionals; provides certification for estimators. **Founded:** 1956. **Publications:** American Society of Professional Estimators--Membership Directory and Buyers' Guide (Annual). **Awards:** ASPE Estimator of the Year (Annual). **Geographic Preference:** National.

3918 ■ American Sports Builders Association (ASBA)
2331 Rock Spring Rd.
Forest Hill, MD 21050
Ph: (443)640-1042
Free: 866-501-2722
Co. E-mail: info@sportsbuilders.org
URL: http://sportsbuilders.org
Contact: Fred Stringfellow, Executive Director
Facebook: www.facebook.com/sportsbuilders
Linkedin: www.linkedin.com/company/sportsbuilders
X (Twitter): x.com/sportsbuilders

Description: Contractors who install running tracks, synthetic turf fields, tennis courts and indoor sports surfaces; manufacturers who supply basic materials for construction; accessory suppliers, designers, architects, and consultants of facilities. Provides guidelines for tennis court construction, running track construction, fencing, synthetic turf field construction and lighting. Offers certification and awards programs. **Founded:** 1965. **Publications:** American Sports Builders Association--Membership Directory (Annual); Buyers Guide for Tennis Court Construction; Running Tracks: A Construction & Maintenance Manual; Tennis and Track Construction Guidelines (Periodic); U.S. Tennis Court and Track Builders Association Membership Directory (Annual). **Educational Activities:** ASBA Technical Meeting (Annual); ASBA Winter Meeting (Annual). **Geographic Preference:** National.

3919 ■ American Welding Society (AWS)
8669 NW 36 St., No. 130
Miami, FL 33166-6672
Ph: (305)443-9353
Free: 800-443-9353
Co. E-mail: mediasales@aws.org
URL: http://www.aws.org/home
Contact: W. Richard Polanin, President
E-mail: rpolanin@mtco.com
Linkedin: www.linkedin.com/company/americanweldingsociety
YouTube: www.youtube.com/user/videoaws

Description: One of several sponsors of the Welding Research Council and the Materials Properties Council. Professional engineering society in the field of welding. Sponsors seminars. Maintains over 130 technical and handbook committees, 171 sections, educational committees, and task forces. **Founded:** 1919. **Publications:** Welding Handbook; Retired Executives Volunteer Directory; American Welding Society--Consultants Directory (Annual); Filler Metal Comparison Charts and Filler Metal Data Manager; Welding Journal (Monthly). **Educational Activities:** FABTECH; North American Conference on Molecular Beam Epitaxy (NAMBE) (Annual); American Welding Society International Welding & Fabricating Exposition & Convention (Annual). **Awards:** AWS Past President Scholarship (Annual); McKay-Helm Award (Annual); Comfort A. Adams Lecture Award (Annual); Adams Memorial Membership Award (Annual); Howard E. Adkins Memorial Instructor Membership Award (Annual); A. F. Davis Silver Medal Award (Annual); Dalton E. Hamilton Memorial National CWI of the Year Award (Annual); W. H. Hobart Memorial Medal Award (Annual); AWS Honorary Membership Award (Annual); William Irrgang Memorial Award (Annual); Charles H. Jennings Memorial Award (Annual); James F. Lincoln Gold Medal Award (Irregular); Samuel Wylie Miller Memorial Medal Award (Annual); AWS National Meritorious Award (Annual); Plummer Memorial Education Lecture Award (Annual); Warren F. Savage Memorial Award (Annual); William Spraragen Memorial Award (Annual); Airgas - Terry Jarvis Memorial Scholarship (Annual); John C. Lincoln Memorial Scholarship (Annual); Miller Electric International WorldSkills Competition Scholarship (Biennial); Robert L. Peaslee Brazing Scholarship (Annual); Ronald C. and Joyce Pierce - Mobile Section Named Scholarships (Annual); Praxair International Scholarship (Annual); Resistance Welding Manufacturers Alliance Scholarship (Annual); James A. Turner, Jr. Memorial Scholarship (Annual); Amos and Marilyn Winsand - Detroit Section Named Scholarship (Annual); R. D. Thomas Memorial Award (Annual); Robert J. Conkling Memorial Award (Annual); Robert L. Peaslee Memorial Brazing Award (Annual); Professor Koichi Masubuchi Award (Annual); George E. Willis Award (Annual); Kenneth L. Brown Memorial Safety and Health Award (Annual); Historical Welded Structure Award (Annual); Howard E. and Wilma J. Adkins Memorial Scholarship (Annual); American Welding Society District Scholarships (Annual); AWS International Scholarships (Annual); American Welding Society National Scholarships (Annual); American Welding Society Past Presidents Scholarships (Annual); American Welding Society Graduate Research Fellowships (Annual); Arsham Amirikian Engineering Scholarship (Annual); Airgas - Jerry Baker Scholarship (Annual); Jack R. Barckhoff Welding Management Scholarship (Annual); Edward J. Brady Memorial Scholarship (Annual); William A. and Ann M. Brothers Scholarship (Annual); Donald F. Hastings Scholarship (Annual); Donald and Shirley Hastings Scholarship (Annual); William B. Howell Memorial Scholarship (Annual); Hypertherm International HyTech Leadership Scholarships (Annual); ITW Welding Companies Scholarships. **Geographic Preference:** Multinational.

3920 ■ Architectural Glass and Metal Contractors Association (AGMCA)
619 Liverpool Rd.
Pickering, ON, Canada L1W 1R1
Ph: (905)420-7272
Fax: (905)420-7288
Co. E-mail: info@agmca.ca
URL: http://www.agmca.ca
Contact: Noel Marsella, Executive Director
E-mail: noel@agmca.ca
X (Twitter): x.com/TheAGMCA
Instagram: www.instagram.com/theagmca

Description: Architectural glass and metal contractors. Promotes advancement of the building industries; seeks to insure adherence to high standards of ethics and practice among members. Represents members' interests before industrial organizations, government agencies, and the public. Facilitates communication and cooperation among members; serves as a clearinghouse on the architectural glass and metal industries. **Founded:** 1979. **Geographic Preference:** National.

3921 ■ Associated Builders and Contractors, Inc. (ABC)
440 1st St. NW, Ste. 200
Washington, DC 20001
Ph: (202)595-1505
Co. E-mail: gotquestions@abc.org
URL: http://www.abc.org
Contact: Michael D. Bellaman, President
Facebook: www.facebook.com/ABCNational
Linkedin: www.linkedin.com/company/associated-builders-and-contractors
X (Twitter): x.com/ABCNational
Instagram: www.instagram.com/abc_national
YouTube: www.youtube.com/user/theabcnational

Description: Construction contractors, subcontractors, suppliers and associates. Aims to foster and perpetuate the principles of rewarding construction workers and management on the basis of merit. Sponsors management education programs and craft training; also sponsors apprenticeship and skill training programs. Disseminates technological and labor relations information. **Founded:** 1950. **Publications:** Construction Executive: The Magazine for the Business of Construction (CE) (9/year); ABC Today--Associated Builders and Contractors National Membership Directory Issue (Annual). **Awards:** ABC Excellence in Construction Awards (Annual); ABC Contractor of the Year (Annual); CURT Construction Industry Safety Excellence Awards (CURT-CISE) (Annual); ABC National Safety Excellence Awards (Annual); ABC STEP Diamond, Platinum, and Gold (Annual). **Geographic Preference:** National; Local.

3922 ■ Associated General Contractors of America (AGC)
2300 Wilson Blvd., Ste. 300
Arlington, VA 22201
Ph: (703)548-3118
Free: 800-242-1767
Fax: (703)548-3119
Co. E-mail: info@agc.org
URL: http://www.agc.org
Contact: Thomas L. Brown, President
Facebook: www.facebook.com/AGCofA
Linkedin: www.linkedin.com/company/agcofa
X (Twitter): x.com/AGCofA
YouTube: www.youtube.com/user/agcofamerica

Description: General construction contractors; subcontractors; industry suppliers; service firms. Provides market services through its divisions. Conducts special conferences and seminars designed specifically for construction firms. Compiles statistics on job accidents reported by member firms. Maintains 65 committees, including joint cooperative committees with other associations and liaison committees with federal agencies. **Founded:** 1918. **Publications:** Constructor: The Construction Management Magazine (Bimonthly); AGC Membership Directory and Buyers' Guide (Annual); AGC AI News & Views eNewsletter. **Educational Activities:** CON-EXPO-CON/AGG (Triennial); CONEXPO-CON/AGG (Triennial). **Awards:** AGC Education and Research Foundation Scholarships (Annual); AGC Build America Awards (Annual); AGC Construction Safety Excellence Awards (CSEA) (Annual); AGC Foundation Outstanding Educator Award (Annual). **Geographic Preference:** National.

3923 ■ Associated Schools of Construction (ASC)
PO Box 21367
Cheyenne, WY 82003
Ph: (970)818-1041
Co. E-mail: info@ascweb.org
URL: http://www.ascweb.org
Contact: David Gunderson, President
X (Twitter): x.com/asc_national

Description: Aims to establish objectives for the development of construction education and to assist institutions of higher education in establishing construction education and management programs. Compiles statistics. **Founded:** 1965. **Publications:** International Journal of Construction Education and Research (Quarterly); Proceedings of the Annual Meeting (Annual). **Educational Activities:** ASC International Conference (Annual). **Awards:** ASC Lifetime Achievement Award (Annual); ASC National Excellence Teaching Award (Annual); ASC Outstanding Educator Award (Annual); ASC National Outstanding Researcher Award (Annual); ASC Regional Excellence Teaching Award (Annual). **Geographic Preference:** Multinational.

3924 ■ Association For Bridge Construction And Design (ABCD)
c/o Mark Olstad, Treasurer
AECOM 40 British American Blvd.
Latham, NY 12110
Ph: (518)951-2323
Co. E-mail: contactus@abcdeny.org
URL: http://www.abcdeny.org
Contact: Michael Belsky, Secretary

Description: Represents persons and firms having a direct or indirect interest in the design and construction of bridges. **Founded:** 1976. **Geographic Preference:** National.

3925 ■ The Association of Union Constructors (TAUC)
1501 Langston Blvd., Ste. 202
Arlington, VA 22209-1109
Ph: (703)524-3336
Fax: (703)524-3364
URL: http://tauc.org
Contact: David Acord, Director, Communications
E-mail: dacord@tauc.org
Facebook: www.facebook.com/taucbuilt
Linkedin: www.linkedin.com/company/tauc
X (Twitter): x.com/TAUCbuilt

Description: Active members are union construction companies. Associate members are engaged in the manufacture of products and equipment or providing services generally used in the construction industry. Objectives include developing industry standards, communicating governmental regulations to members, promoting safe work practices, and expanding opportunities for job training and increasing job skills. **Founded:** 1969. **Publications:** THE CONSTRUCTION USER 2.0 (Weekly); NEA Notes Newsletter (Monthly). **Educational Activities:** NEA - The Association of Union Constructors Meeting (Annual). **Geographic Preference:** National.

3926 ■ Canadian Construction Association (CCA) [Association Canadienne de la Construction]
250 Albert St., Ste. 300
Ottawa, ON, Canada K1P 6M1
Ph: (613)236-9455
Fax: (613)236-9526
Co. E-mail: cca@cca-acc.com
URL: http://www.cca-acc.com
Contact: Mary van Buren, President
E-mail: mvanburen@cca-acc.com
Linkedin: www.linkedin.com/company/canadian-construction-association---association-canadienne-de-la-construction
X (Twitter): x.com/ConstructionCAN
YouTube: www.youtube.com/user/ConstructionCAN

Description: Promotes the growth and development of the building industries in Canada. Represents contractors, suppliers, and related business working within the non-residential construction industry. **Founded:** 1919. **Awards:** CCA Environmental Achievement Award (Annual); CCA Excellence in Innovation Award (Annual); CCA Excellence in Innovation Award (Annual); CCA Person of the Year Award (Annual). **Geographic Preference:** National.

3927 ■ Canadian Home Builders Association (CHBA)
141 Laurier Ave. W
Ottawa, ON, Canada K1P 5J4
Ph: (613)230-3060
Co. E-mail: chba@chba.ca
URL: http://www.chba.ca
Contact: Larry Clay, President
Facebook: www.facebook.com/chbanational
Linkedin: www.linkedin.com/company/canadian-home-builders%27-association---national
X (Twitter): x.com/CHBANational
Instagram: www.instagram.com/chbanational
YouTube: www.youtube.com/channel/UC-XTMoxLDcDf53B0cAa7Rrg
Pinterest: www.pinterest.ca/CHBANational

Description: Home builders and contractors. Promotes growth and development of the residential building industries. Represents members' interests. **Founded:** 1943. **Publications:** The National (Quarterly). **Geographic Preference:** National.

3928 ■ Canadian Institute of Steel Construction (CISC) [Institut canadien de la construction en acier]
445 Apple Creek Blvd, Ste. 102.
Markham, ON, Canada L3R 9X7
Ph: (905)604-3231
Co. E-mail: info@cisc-icca.ca
URL: http://www.cisc-icca.ca
Contact: Ed Whalen, President
E-mail: ewhalen@cisc-icca.ca
Facebook: www.facebook.com/CISCWeAreSteel
X (Twitter): x.com/cisc_icca
Instagram: www.instagram.com/cisc_icca
YouTube: www.youtube.com/channel/UCvmfPlIJ8psVfkeswe3Hnig

Description: Represents the structural steel, open-web steel joist and steel platework fabricating industries; operates as a technical, marketing and government relations organization. **Founded:** 1930. **Publications:** Advantage Steel. **Geographic Preference:** National.

3929 ■ Ceilings and Interior Systems Construction Association (CISCA)
1010 Jorie Blvd., Ste. 30
Oak Brook, IL 60523
Ph: (630)584-1919
Fax: (866)560-8537
Co. E-mail: cisca@cisca.org
URL: http://www.cisca.org/i4a/pages/index.cfm
Contact: Shirley Wodynski, Executive Director
E-mail: shirley.wodynski@cisca.org
Facebook: www.facebook.com/ciscaassociation
X (Twitter): x.com/ciscassociation

Description: International trade association for the advancement of the interior commercial construction industry. Provides quality education, resources and a forum for communication among its members. **Founded:** 1949. **Publications:** Ceilings & Interior Systems Construction Association--Industry Resource Guide (Annual); Acoustical Interior Construction (Quarterly); Ceiling Systems. **Educational Activities:** CISCA Convention (Annual). **Awards:** CISCA Construction Excellence Award. **Geographic Preference:** Multinational.

3930 ■ Concrete Foundations Association (CFA)
402 1st Ave. SE
Mount Vernon, IA 52314
Ph: (319)895-6940
Fax: (320)213-5556
Co. E-mail: info@cfawalls.org
URL: http://www.cfaconcretepros.org
Contact: Jason Ells, President

Description: Contractors, suppliers, and manufacturers engaged in poured concrete wall construction. Prepares and distributes technical information on products and methods related to special needs; informs members of new trends, specifications, codes, rules, and regulations regarding the industry. Reviews EPA, OSHA, and other governmental agency practices and regulations as they affect the industry and represents the industry before governmental agencies. **Founded:** 1975. **Educational Activities:** World of Concrete (WOC) (Annual). **Awards:** Robert D. Sawyer Award (Occasionally); CFA Contractor of the Year Award (Annual); CFA Project of the Year (Annual). **Geographic Preference:** National.

3931 ■ *Construction Canada*
15 Wertheim Ct., Ste. 710
Richmond Hill, ON, Canada L4B 3H7
Ph: (905)771-7333
Free: 800-409-8688
Fax: (905)771-7336
Co. E-mail: sales@kenilworth.com
URL: http://www.kenilworth.com
Contact: Erik Tolles, Chief Executive Officer
URL(s): www.constructioncanada.net
X (Twitter): x.com/constructCanMag
Instagram: www.instagram.com/constructcanmag

Released: 9/year **Price:** $120, for 1 year foreign; $88, U.S. for 1 year; $56, Canada. **Description:** Magazine covers architecture and engineering construction. **Availability:** Print; Online.

3932 ■ Construction Financial Management Association (CFMA)
100 Village Blvd., Ste. 200
Princeton, NJ 08540
Ph: (609)452-8000
Free: 888-421-9996
Fax: (609)452-0474
Co. E-mail: info@cfma.org
URL: http://cfma.org
Contact: Stuart Binstock, President
E-mail: sbinstock@cfma.org
Facebook: www.facebook.com/ConstructionFinancialManagementAssociation
Linkedin: www.linkedin.com/company/cfma
X (Twitter): x.com/CFMA
YouTube: www.youtube.com/user/CFMAPrinceton

Description: Contractors, subcontractors, architects, real estate developers and engineers; associate members are equipment and material suppliers, accountants, lawyers, bankers and others involved with the financial management of the construction industry. Provides a forum for the exchange of ideas; coordinates educational programs dedicated to improving the professional standards of financial management in the construction industry. Offers expanded national programs, technical assistance and industry representation. Conducts research programs. **Founded:** 1981. **Publications:** CFMA Building Profits (6/year); Construction Industry Annual Financial Survey (Annual); CFMA's Information Technology Survey for the Construction Industry (Biennial); The Source. **Educational Activities:** Construction Financial Management Association Annual Conference and Exhibition (Annual). **Awards:** Danny B. Parrish Outstanding Leadership Award (Irregular); Debra Hahn Memorial Award (Annual); Joe Quigley Memorial Award (Annual). **Geographic Preference:** National.

3933 ■ Construction Management Association of America (CMAA)
200 Lawyers Rd., NW, No. 1968
Vienna, VA 22183
Ph: (703)356-2622
Co. E-mail: communications@cmaanet.org
URL: http://www.cmaanet.org
Contact: Andrea S. Rutledge, President
E-mail: president@cmaanet.org
Facebook: www.facebook.com/CMAAHQ
Linkedin: www.linkedin.com/company/cmaa
X (Twitter): x.com/CMAA_HQ
YouTube: www.youtube.com/user/jjmckeon

Description: Promotes the growth and development of construction management as a professional service; encourages high professional standards. Conducts conferences and forums on construction management topics. Sponsors a professional certification program. **Founded:** 1982. **Publications:** CM Advisor; Construction Management Association of America (CMAA)--Directory of Construction Managers; CMAA Documents: Standard CM Services and Practice (Annual). **Awards:** CMAA Person of the Year Award (Annual); CMAA Project Achievement Awards (Annual). **Geographic Preference:** National.

3934 ■ Construction Owners Association of America (COAA)
5000 Austell Powder Springs Rd., Ste. 151
Austell, GA 30106
Free: 800-994-2622
Co. E-mail: coaa@coaa.org
URL: http://www.coaa.org
Contact: John V. Zahor, President
Facebook: www.facebook.com/COAAHQ
Linkedin: www.linkedin.com/company/construction-owners-association-of-america
X (Twitter): x.com/coaahq

Description: Represents public and private owners and developers of construction projects all across America. Aims to make a significant and lasting impact on the construction industry by educating its membership and by providing a collective voice for owners and developers of construction projects. **Founded:** 1994. **Publications:** Owners Perspective (Semiannual). **Educational Activities:** Conference Owners Spring Leadership Conference (Annual). **Awards:** COAA Project Leadership Award (Annual). **Geographic Preference:** National.

3935 ■ Construction Specifications Canada (CSC)
120 Carlton St., Ste. 312
Toronto, ON, Canada 652452
Ph: (416)777-2198

Fax: (416)777-2197
Co. E-mail: info@csc-dcc.ca
URL: http://www.csc-dcc.ca
Contact: Kimberly Tompkins, President
E-mail: kim@tecagencies.com
Facebook: www.facebook.com/CSCDCC
Linkedin: www.linkedin.com/company/construction-specifications-canada
X (Twitter): x.com/csc_dcc
Instagram: www.instagram.com/csc_dcc

Description: Seeks to insure adherence to high standards of practice in the building industries. **Founded:** 1954. **Publications:** *Construction Canada* (9/year); *National Master Specification (NMS)*; *Construction Specifications Canada--Directory of Members* (Annual); *Chapter Specifiers* (10/year); *CSC News in Brief* (Bimonthly). **Awards:** CSC Chapter Award of Merit (Annual); Lloyd Boddy Chapter of the Year Award (Annual); CSC-DCC President's Award (Periodic). **Geographic Preference:** National.

3936 ■ Construction Specifications Institute (CSI)
123 N Pitt St., Ste. 450
Alexandria, VA 22314
Free: 800-689-2900
Co. E-mail: csi@csinet.org
URL: http://www.csiresources.org/home
Contact: Mark Dorsey, Chief Executive Officer
E-mail: ceo@csinet.org
Facebook: www.facebook.com/CSIConstruction
X (Twitter): x.com/csiconstruction
YouTube: www.youtube.com/user/CSIConstruction

Description: Certifies construction specifiers and others involved in construction and allied industries. Maintains 20 committees including Certification, Credentials, Specifications Competition, and Technical Documents. Sponsors competitions; maintains speaker's bureau; offers seminars. **Founded:** 1948. **Publications:** *The Construction Specifier* (Monthly); *SPEC-DATA Program/SPEC-DATA Index* (Annual); *Construction Specifier: For Commercial and Industrial Construction* (Monthly); *Construction Specifications Institute Member Directory*; *The SPEC-DATA Program* (Annual); *CSI Weekly* (Weekly); *NewsBrief* (Weekly). **Awards:** CSI Fellowship (Annual); Robert P. Brosseau Award for the Advancement of CSI (Annual); CSI Distinguished Service Award (Annual); Distinguished & Honorary Membership (Irregular); CSI Organizational Certificate of Appreciation (Irregular); CSI President's Plaques (Annual); Ben John Small Technical Writing Award (Annual); J. Norman Hunter Award for Innovative Allied Organization Cooperation (Periodic). **Geographic Preference:** National.

3937 ■ Energy and Environmental Building Alliance (EEBA)
PO Box 47204
Plymouth, MN 55447
Ph: (612)325-5719
Fax: (952)881-3048
Co. E-mail: inquiry@eeba.org
URL: http://www.eeba.org
Contact: Nancy Bakeman, Executive Vice President
E-mail: nancy@eeba.org
Facebook: www.facebook.com/goeeba
Linkedin: www.linkedin.com/company/1535574
X (Twitter): x.com/GoEEBA
Instagram: www.instagram.com/goeeba
YouTube: www.youtube.com/channel/UC_2YrGXzEST_PTDUrx5Mb4g

Description: Professional association of builders, architects, consultants, designers, researchers, educators, government agencies, suppliers, and manufactures. Promotes the awareness, education, and development of energy-efficient and environmentally responsible buildings and communities. **Founded:** 1982. **Publications:** *EEBA News* (Quarterly). **Educational Activities:** Excellence in Building Conference (Annual). **Geographic Preference:** National.

3938 ■ Engineering Contractors Association (ECA)
1000 Apollo Way, Ste. 100
Santa Rosa, CA 95407
Ph: (704)546-5500
URL: http://nceca.org
Contact: Walt Turner, President
Facebook: www.facebook.com/Northern-California-Engineering-Contractors-Association-308292491136
YouTube: www.youtube.com/channel/UCqp6bBvs_uBLBO95jK2Up8g

Description: Engineering construction contractors and suppliers. Represents members in labor and legislation matters and negotiates disputes within the industry. **Scope:** Serves the general engineering construction industry in matters of labor relations, government relations, legislative direction and public relations. Seeks to create a networking forum through association membership meetings, conventions, seminars, committee activities and educational resources. Industries served: heavy construction contractors specializing in water, sewer and storm drain pipeline construction, road building, paving and grading. **Founded:** 1972. **Publications:** "Injury and Illness Prevention Program". **Training:** Trench Safety Class; Safety in Construction. **Geographic Preference:** National; Regional.

3939 ■ Finishing Contractors Association International (FCA)
1 Parkview Plz., Ste. 610
Oakbrook Terrace, IL 60181
Ph: (630)537-1042
Free: 866-322-3477
Co. E-mail: fca@finishingcontractors.org
URL: http://finishingcontractors.org
Contact: Anthony Darkangelo, Chief Executive Officer
E-mail: ceo@finishingcontractors.org
Facebook: www.facebook.com/FCAInternational
Linkedin: www.linkedin.com/company/fca
YouTube: www.youtube.com/user/FCAVideos

Description: Union finishing contractors in the following market sectors: drywall finishing, glass/glazing flooring, painting/decorating, signs/display and other related industries. Engages in governmental affairs and labor-management relations activities designed to provide a competitive advantage for its members over the non-union contractor. **Founded:** 1997. **Geographic Preference:** Multinational.

3940 ■ International Masonry Institute (IMI)
17101 Science Dr.
Bowie, MD 20715
Free: 800-464-0988
Co. E-mail: masonryquestions@imiweb.org
URL: http://www.imiweb.org
Contact: Caryn Halifax, President
E-mail: chalifax@imiweb.org
Facebook: www.facebook.com/InternationalMasonryInstitute
X (Twitter): x.com/imiweb
YouTube: www.youtube.com/channel/UCRP7teSaUSNtO5agB06QQzg/featured

Description: Joint labor/management trust fund of the International Union of Bricklayers and Allied Craftworkers and union masonry contractors. Advances quality masonry construction through national and regional training, advertising and labor management relations programs in the U.S. and Canada. Provides support and materials for local/regional masonry promotion groups in the U.S. and Canada, and cooperates with national groups and organizations promoting the industry. Sponsors craft training and research programs. Maintains museum. **Founded:** 1970. **Publications:** *IMI Today* (Bimonthly). **Educational Activities:** Masonry Day Educational Conference and Tradeshow. **Geographic Preference:** National.

3941 ■ Just the Fax
280 Albert St., Ste.701
Ottawa, ON, Canada K1P 5G8
Ph: (613)232-0492
Fax: (613)235-2793
Co. E-mail: mcac@mcac.ca
URL: http://www.mcac.ca
Contact: Derek Erman, President
URL(s): mcabc.org/membership/mechanical-contractors-association-of-canada-2

Description: Includes news concerning Mechanical Contractors Association of Canada. **Availability:** Print.

3942 ■ Mechanical Contractors Association of Canada (MCAC)
280 Albert St., Ste.701
Ottawa, ON, Canada K1P 5G8
Ph: (613)232-0492
Fax: (613)235-2793
Co. E-mail: mcac@mcac.ca
URL: http://www.mcac.ca
Contact: Derek Erman, President
Facebook: www.facebook.com/MechanicalContractorsAssociationofCanada
Linkedin: www.linkedin.com/groups/4893930/profile
X (Twitter): x.com/MecConCA

Description: Promotes growth and development of members' businesses; works to ensure high standards of ethics and practice in the mechanical contracting industry. **Founded:** 1895. **Publications:** *Just the Fax*; *National Bulletin* (Semiannual). **Awards:** MCAC Life Member Award (Annual). **Geographic Preference:** National.

3943 ■ Metal Building Contractors and Erectors Association (MBCEA)
PO Box 3429
Bethlehem, PA 18017
Ph: (484)239-3337
URL: http://www.mbcea.org
Contact: Jennifer Heimburger, President
Facebook: www.facebook.com/MBCEANational
Linkedin: www.linkedin.com/company/metal-building-contractors-and-erectors-association
X (Twitter): x.com/MBCEA_News
YouTube: www.youtube.com/mbcea

Description: Firms engaged in marketing metal buildings; suppliers and manufacturers. Promotes increased use of metal buildings and better relations among members and owners, public bodies, architects, engineers, and associated manufacturers. Provides information on business practices, new markets, and sales techniques. **Founded:** 1968. **Publications:** *Metal Building Jobsite Safety Reference Guide*; *MBCEAtoday* (Monthly). **Educational Activities:** Annual MBCEA Conference (Annual). **Awards:** MBCEA Building of the Year Awards (Annual). **Geographic Preference:** National.

3944 ■ Metal Building Manufacturers Association (MBMA)
1300 Sumner Ave.
Cleveland, OH 44115-2851
Ph: (216)241-7333
Fax: (216)241-0105
URL: http://www.mbma.com
Contact: Lee W. Shoemaker, Director, Research Director, Engineering
X (Twitter): x.com/learnaboutmbma
YouTube: www.youtube.com/channel/UC-cZRHvML4-cgJg95uS7LcA

Description: Manufacturers of metal building and roofing systems. Conducts research programs and compiles statistics. **Founded:** 1956. **Publications:** *AISC-MB Certified Excellence Brochure*; *Bay Industries High Profile Case Study*; *Institutional Solutions*. **Awards:** MBMA Manufacturer Safety Awards (Annual). **Geographic Preference:** National.

3945 ■ Metal Construction Association (MCA)
8735 W Higgins Rd., Ste. 300
Chicago, IL 60631
Ph: (847)375-4718
Fax: (847)375-6488
Co. E-mail: info@metalconstruction.org
URL: http://www.metalconstruction.org
Contact: Dick Bus, President
Facebook: www.facebook.com/MetalConstructionAssociation
Linkedin: www.linkedin.com/company/metal-construction-association

X (Twitter): x.com/MetalAssoc
Instagram: www.instagram.com/metalassoc
YouTube: www.youtube.com/user/MetalConstructAssoc
Description: Promotes the metal construction industry in order to expand the use of all metals used in construction, including structure erection, estimating, and bookkeeping. Compiles statistics. **Founded:** 1983. **Publications:** *Member Directory*; *Metal Construction Association--Newsletter* (Monthly). **Educational Activities:** Metalcon (Annual). **Awards:** Larry A. Swaney Award (Irregular); President's Awards; President's Awards. **Geographic Preference:** National.

3946 ■ Metal Framing Manufacturers Association (MFMA)
330 N Wabash Ave.
Chicago, IL 60611
Ph: (312)644-6610
Co. E-mail: mfmastats@smithbucklin.com
URL: http://www.metalframingmfg.org
Contact: Mark Thorsby, Executive Director
Description: Manufacturers of ferrous and nonferrous metal framing systems. Promotes the use of metal framing (continuous slot metal channel) systems; develops industry standards; collects industry statistics. **Founded:** 1981. **Geographic Preference:** National.

3947 ■ Michigan Mason Contractors Association (MMCA)
1619 Montgomery Dr.
Hartland, MI 48353
URL: http://www.michiganmasoncontractorsassoc.com
Contact: Jon Davenport, Chairman
Description: Seeks to educate, promote, and enhance the masonry industry throughout the state of Michigan. **Founded:** 1968.

3948 ■ Modular Building Institute (MBI)
285 Hydraulic Ridge Rd., Ste. 6
Charlottesville, VA 22901
Ph: (434)296-3288
Free: 888-811-3288
Fax: (434)296-3361
Co. E-mail: info@modular.org
URL: http://www.modular.org
Contact: Michael Wilmot, President
Facebook: www.facebook.com/ModularConstruction
Linkedin: www.linkedin.com/company/modular-building-institute
X (Twitter): x.com/rethinkmodular
Description: Manufacturers and dealers of mobile and modular commercial units. Serves as a national structure for dealing with regulations. Enhances the future growth and capabilities of the industry by encouraging innovation and quality among its members. Conducts surveys of the industry. Compiles statistics from industry and government surveys. Operates educational programs. **Founded:** 1983. **Publications:** *State of the Industry Report* (Annual). **Awards:** MBI Outstanding Achievement Award (Annual); MBI Award of Distinction (Annual); MBI Hall of Fame (Annual). **Geographic Preference:** Multinational.

3949 ■ NAHB Leading Suppliers Council (NAHB)
1201 15th St. NW
Washington, DC 20005
URL: http://www.nahb.org/nahb-community/councils/leading-suppliers-council
Contact: Tucker Bernard, Contact
E-mail: tbernard@nahb.org
Description: Manufacturers of goods and services for the American housing industry. Provides support for the effort of the industry to fill the housing needs of American families. **Founded:** 1964. **Geographic Preference:** National.

3950 ■ National Association of Black Women in Construction, Inc. (NABWIC)
c/o Ann McNeill, Founder
6600 NW 27th Ave. No. 208
Haverhill, FL 33417
URL: http://nabwic.org
Description: Promotes the advancement of black women in the construction industry. Supports aspiring construction executives. Provides advocacy, mentorship and professional development for its members. **Founded:** 1991. **Geographic Preference:** National.

3951 ■ National Association of Home Builders (NAHB)
1201 15th St. NW
Washington, DC 20005
Free: 800-368-5242
Co. E-mail: info@nahb.org
URL: http://www.nahb.org
Contact: James W. Tobin, III, President
Facebook: www.facebook.com/NAHBhome
Linkedin: www.linkedin.com/company/national-association-of-home-builders
X (Twitter): twitter.com/nahbhome
YouTube: www.youtube.com/NAHBTV
Description: Individuals and companies in the home building industry. **Founded:** 1942. **Publications:** *55+ Housing Magazine* (Quarterly); *Commercial Builder* (Quarterly); *Building Women* (Semiannual); *Seniors' Housing News* (Quarterly); *Sales & Marketing Ideas (SMI)* (Annual); *Land Development*. **Educational Activities:** NAHB International Builders' Show (NAHB IBS) (Annual). **Awards:** Best in American Living™ Awards (Annual); NAHB Associates Committee Chairman's Award (Annual).

3952 ■ National Association of Home Builders of the U.S.
503 N Main St., Ste. 710/711
Pueblo, CO 81006-9483
Ph: (719)545-9484
Fax: (719)545-9489
Co. E-mail: pueblohba@gmail.com
URL: http://www.nahb.org/nahb-community/nahb-directories/local-associations-directory
Contact: Betty Jean Tripp, Executive Officer
URL(s): www.pueblohba.org
Description: Represents single and multifamily home builders, commercial builders, and others associated with the building industry. **Founded:** 1950. **Geographic Preference:** Local.

3953 ■ National Association of Professional Women in Construction (PWC)
1411 Broadway, 16th Fl.
New York, NY 10018
Ph: (215)486-4712
Co. E-mail: pwc@pwcusa.org
URL: http://www.pwcusa.org
Contact: Melinda Johnson, President
URL(s): pwc-ny.org/index.php
Facebook: www.facebook.com/pwcusa
Linkedin: www.linkedin.com/company/professional-women-in-construction
Instagram: www.instagram.com/pwctalk
Description: Represents women engaged in the construction business at managerial levels. **Founded:** 1980. **Publications:** *e-PWC* (Quarterly). **Educational Activities:** Transportation Forum - Aviation (Annual). **Awards:** PWC Salute to Women of Achievement (Annual). **Geographic Preference:** National.

3954 ■ National Association of Reinforcing Steel Contractors (NARSC)
PO Box 280
Fairfax, VA 22038
Ph: (703)591-1870
Fax: (703)591-1895
Co. E-mail: info@narsc.com
URL: http://www.narsc.com
Description: Companies engaged primarily in the placing of reinforcing steel and post-tensioning systems; associate members are suppliers of services and materials. Serves as a unified voice for reinforcing steel contractors. Disseminates information on topics such as trade practices, construction techniques, efficient operation, safety standards, and welfare. Advises members on congressional legislation, wage settlements throughout the country, and other matters. Conducts studies on apprenticeship and training, equal employment, and labor relations. **Founded:** 1969. **Geographic Preference:** National.

3955 ■ National Association of the Remodeling Industry (NARI)
700 Astor Ln.
Wheeling, IL 60090
Ph: (847)298-9200
Fax: (847)298-9225
Co. E-mail: info@nari.org
URL: http://www.nari.org
Contact: Chris Egner, President
X (Twitter): x.com/NARI_National
YouTube: www.youtube.com/user/RemodelWithNARI
Pinterest: www.pinterest.com/NARI_National
Description: Represents remodeling contractors, manufacturers of remodeling/building products, lending institutions and wholesalers and distributors. Promotes the common business interests of those engaged in the home improvement and remodeling industries. Encourages ethical conduct, good business practices and professionalism in the remodeling industry. Conducts seminars, workshops and promotional programs and has developed an extensive certification program. Local chapters monitor legislations and regulations affecting the industry. **Founded:** 1982. **Educational Activities:** Atlanta Home Show (Annual). **Awards:** Henry Fenderbosch Leadership Award (Annual); Harold Hammerman Spirit of Education Award (Annual); NARI Government Affairs Award (Annual); NARI Distributor of the Year Award (Annual); NARI Chapter Excellence Award (Annual); Mary Busey Harris, CAE, Professionalism Award (Annual); Peter H. Johnson Image Award (Annual); NARI Remodeler of the Year (Annual); Spirit of Education Award (Annual). **Geographic Preference:** National.

3956 ■ National Association of Women in Construction (NAWIC)
327 S Adams St.
Fort Worth, TX 76104
Ph: (817)877-5551
Free: 800-552-3506
Fax: (817)877-0324
Co. E-mail: nawic@nawic.org
URL: http://nawic.org
Contact: Crissy Ingram, Executive Director
E-mail: crissyi@nawic.org
Facebook: www.facebook.com/nawicnational
Linkedin: www.linkedin.com/company/national-association-of-women-in-construction
X (Twitter): x.com/nawicnational
Instagram: www.instagram.com/nawicnational
Description: Seeks to enhance the success of women in the construction industry. **Founded:** 1955. **Publications:** *The NAWIC Image* (Bimonthly); *Women's Business Enterprise Directory*. **Awards:** NAWIC Crystal Vision Awards (Annual); NAWIC Construction Trades Scholarship (Annual); NAWIC Founders Undergraduate Scholarship (Annual). **Geographic Preference:** Multinational.

3957 ■ National Demolition Association (NDA)
2001 K St. NW, 3rd Fl. N
Washington, DC 20006
Ph: (202)367-1152
Co. E-mail: info@demolitionassociation.com
URL: http://www.demolitionassociation.com
Contact: Jeff Lambert, Executive Director
Facebook: www.facebook.com/pg/DemolitionAssoc
Linkedin: www.linkedin.com/company/national-demolition-association
X (Twitter): x.com/NDAmakingway
YouTube: www.youtube.com/channel/UCpZQtRpi9658P5Sx71ZFzlw
Description: Demolition contractors and equipment manufacturers. Seeks to foster goodwill and to encourage the exchange of ideas among the public and members. **Founded:** 1972. **Publications:** *Demolition Age* (Monthly); *Demolition Safety Manual*. **Educational Activities:** NDA Annual Convention & Expo (Annual). **Awards:** NDA Lifetime Achievement Award (Irregular). **Geographic Preference:** National.

3958 ■ National Frame Building Association (NFBA)
7250 Poe Ave., Ste. 410
Dayton, OH 45414
Free: 800-557-6957
Co. E-mail: info@nfba.org
URL: http://www.nfba.org/aws/NFBA/pt/sp/home_page
Contact: Robyn Ommen, President
Facebook: www.facebook.com/NtlFrameBuildingAssn
Linkedin: www.linkedin.com/company/national-frame-building-association
X (Twitter): x.com/NFBAframebuild
YouTube: www.youtube.com/channel/UCRqAbOd3uzPqdz3nW12oNNQ

Description: Construction contractors specializing in post frame structures for agricultural, residential, industrial and commercial uses. Seeks to enhance the image of the industry and improve management and construction techniques. Conducts educational programs on safety and other vital matters. **Founded:** 1974. **Publications:** Frame Building News (5/year); Frame Building News (5/year). **Educational Activities:** NFBA Frame Building Expo (Annual). **Awards:** Bernon G. Perkins Award (Annual); NFBA Building of the Year (Annual); NFBA Crew Foreman of the Month Award (Monthly); Gail Miller Safety Award (Annual). **Geographic Preference:** National.

3959 ■ National Housing Endowment (NHE)
1201 15th St. NW
Washington, DC 20005
Free: 800-368-5242
URL: http://www.nationalhousingendowment.org
Contact: Mark Pursell, President
E-mail: mpursell@nahb.org
Facebook: www.facebook.com/NationalHousingEndowment
X (Twitter): x.com/NHendowment
Instagram: www.instagram.com/nationalhousingendowment

Description: Works to 'build a foundation' to help make the American dream of homeownership a reality for present and future generations. Provides a permanent source of funds to address long-term industry concerns at the national level. Helps the industry to develop more effective approaches to home building. Enhances the ways to educate and train future generations of leaders in residential construction and increase the body of knowledge on housing issues. Supports innovative and effective programs that further Education, Training, and Research. **Founded:** 1987. **Publications:** Blueprint (3/year). **Awards:** International Builders Show Scholarship Program (Annual); Lee S. Evans/National Housing Endowment Scholarship (Annual); Herman J. Smith Scholarship (Annual). **Geographic Preference:** National.

3960 ■ National Insulation Association (NIA)
516 Herndon Pky., Ste. D
Herndon, VA 20170
Ph: (703)464-6422
Fax: (703)464-5896
URL: http://www.insulation.org
Contact: Dan Bofinger, Co-President
Facebook: www.facebook.com/NIAinfo
Linkedin: www.linkedin.com/company/niainfo
YouTube: www.youtube.com/niainfo

Description: Insulation contractors, distributors, and manufacturers. **Founded:** 1953. **Publications:** NIA News (Quarterly); Insulation Outlook (Monthly); National Commercial & Industrial Insulation Standards Manual; Safety Handbook for Insulation Distributors & Fabricators; Insulation Outlook: Business Solutions for Expanding or Relocating Companies (Monthly); Asbestos Abatement Industry Directory; National Insulation Association--Membership Directory and Resource Guide. **Educational Activities:** NIA Annual Convention (Annual); National Insulation Association Annual Convention (Annual). **Geographic Preference:** National.

3961 ■ National Wood Flooring Association (NWFA)
111 Chesterfield Industrial Blvd.
Chesterfield, MO 63005
Free: 800-422-4556
Co. E-mail: info@nwfa.org
URL: http://nwfa.org
Contact: Michael Martin, President
E-mail: michael.martin@nwfa.org
Facebook: www.facebook.com/nwfahardwoodfloorsmag
Linkedin: www.linkedin.com/company/nwfa-national-wood-flooring-association
X (Twitter): x.com/nwfa_woodfloors
Instagram: www.instagram.com/nwfa_hardwoodfloorsmag
YouTube: www.youtube.com/channel/UC9oDz6XiFGWFEHn-GiKMvLg
Pinterest: www.pinterest.com/nwfa_hfm

Description: Manufacturers of wood flooring. Promotes standardization; conducts grade labeling and inspection service; maintains research program in grading, handling, and installation; compiles statistics. **Founded:** 1985. **Publications:** Religious Colleges and Universities in America: A Selected Bibliography. **Educational Activities:** National Wood Flooring Association Annual Convention; Certified Wood Flooring Inspector Schools; Hardwood Flooring Installation School. **Awards:** NWFA Craftsman Degree; NWFA Vanguard Degree; NWFA Master Craftsman Degree (Annual). **Geographic Preference:** National.

3962 ■ North American Building Material Distribution Association (NBMDA)
330 N Wabash Ave., Ste. 2000
Chicago, IL 60611
Ph: (312)321-6845
Free: 888-747-7862
Fax: (312)644-0310
Co. E-mail: info@nbmda.org
URL: http://www.nbmda.org
Contact: Scott Narug, Manager, Sales
Facebook: www.facebook.com/NBMDA
Linkedin: www.linkedin.com/company/north-american-building-material-distribution-association-nbmda-
YouTube: www.youtube.com/user/NBMDAheadquarters

Description: Building material distributors and manufacturers operating in more than 1500 locations. Represents the industry when appropriate. Distributes member and industry information; provides networking opportunities to distributors and manufacturers in the building material industry. Maintains education foundation; provides charitable programs. **Founded:** 1952. **Publications:** NBMDA Membership and Product Directory (Annual); North American Building Material Distribution Association--Membership Directory. **Educational Activities:** University of Innovative Distribution (Annual); North American Building Material Distribution Association Convention (Annual). **Geographic Preference:** National.

3963 ■ Professional Construction Estimators Association of America, Inc. (PCEA)
PO Box 680336
Charlotte, NC 28216
Ph: (704)421-4601
Free: 877-521-7232
Co. E-mail: pcea@pcea.org
URL: http://www.pcea.org
Contact: Adam Blalock, President
E-mail: ablalock@brockcontract.com
Facebook: www.facebook.com/pceanational
Linkedin: www.linkedin.com/in/pcea
X (Twitter): x.com/pcea6

Description: Professional construction estimators. Objectives are to further recognition of construction estimating as a professional field of endeavor; to collect and disseminate information; to research and solve problems related to the construction industry; to establish educational programs for youth and promote construction estimating as a career; to maintain ethical standards. **Founded:** 1956. **Publications:** PCEA National Membership & Resource Directory (Annual). **Educational Activities:** Annual PCEA National Convention (Annual). **Awards:** Ted G. Wilson Memorial Scholarships (Annual); Rudolph John Barnes Award (Annual); Bill Helms Chapter of the Year (Annual); Ted G. Wilson Memorial Scholarship (Annual). **Geographic Preference:** National.

3964 ■ Structural Building Components Association (SBCA)
6300 Enterprise Ln.
Madison, WI 53719
Ph: (608)274-4849
Fax: (608)274-3329
URL: http://www.sbcindustry.com
Contact: Michael Ruede, President
Facebook: www.facebook.com/SBCIndustry
Linkedin: www.linkedin.com/company/structural-building-components-association
YouTube: www.youtube.com/channel/UCp4TMjsuPH1PTgQLVzk3HMA

Description: Manufacturers and suppliers of structural wood components. Promotes the interests of members, manufacturers, and suppliers of related products. Encourages the use of structural wood components; supports research and development; provides educational services. **Founded:** 1983. **Publications:** Metal Plate Connected Wood Trusses; Structural Building Components (Monthly); Wage and Benefit and Financial Performance Survey (Biennial). **Educational Activities:** Building Component Manufacturers Conference (Annual). **Awards:** Dick Bowman Industry Enthusiast Award (Annual); SBCA Hall of Fame (Annual). **Geographic Preference:** Multinational; Local.

3965 ■ Stucco Manufacturers Association (SMA)
5753 E Santa Ana Cyn Rd., No. G-156
Anaheim, CA 92807
URL: http://stuccomfgassoc.com
Contact: Michael Griffin, President

Description: Manufacturers of stucco products in North America and their related suppliers. Promotes the products manufactured by the members, while holding high standards. Maintains the highest levels of product quality, business ethics and professionalism among the membership and the building industry. **Founded:** 1957. **Geographic Preference:** National.

3966 ■ Women Construction Owners and Executives U.S.A. (WCOE USA)
1032 15th St. NW, Ste. 300
Washington, DC 20005
Ph: (202)276-0646
Co. E-mail: info@wcoeusa.org
URL: http://www.womenbuildamerica.com
Contact: Lorraine D'Angelo, President
Facebook: www.facebook.com/wcoeusa
X (Twitter): x.com/wcoe
Instagram: www.instagram.com/wcoeusa

Description: Promotes the interests of women construction owners and executives. Provides legislation, business, educational, and networking opportunities. **Founded:** 1984. **Educational Activities:** Women Construction Owners and Executives, U.S.A Annual Meeting (Annual). **Geographic Preference:** National.

INCUBATORS/RESEARCH AND TECHNOLOGY PARKS

3967 ■ Plug and Play - Real Estate and Construction
440 N Wolfe Rd.
Sunnyvale, CA 94085
URL: http://www.plugandplaytechcenter.com/real-estate-tech

Description: An accelerator for startups in the real estate and construction tech industry. Provides support with venture and angel partners, mentorship, a data center, office space, and networking opportunities. This program focuses on planning and design, project management, land use, construction, workforce optimization, safety and building analysis, asset and property management, financing and appraisal, smart cities, connected IoT and sensors, and energy and sustainability.

EDUCATIONAL PROGRAMS

3968 ■ Construction Contracting
Seminar Information Service Inc. (SIS)
250 El Camino Real., Ste. 112
Tustin, CA 92780
Ph: (714)508-0340
Free: 877-736-4636
Fax: (714)734-8027
Co. E-mail: info@seminarinformation.com
URL: http://www.seminarinformation.com
Contact: Catherine Bellizzi, President
URL(s): www.seminarinformation.com/qqbssf/construction-contracting
Description: Gain an understanding of the entire contracting process to deal effectively with all parties involved. **Audience:** Contractors, owners, and government agency reps. **Principal Exhibits:** Gain an understanding of the entire contracting process to deal effectively with all parties involved.

REFERENCE WORKS

3969 ■ "Three Ways Proposed New $300M-$400M Megamall, Hotel May Change I-Drive" in Orlando Business Journal (Vol. 30, May 9, 2014, No. 46, pp. 9)
Pub: American City Business Journals, Inc.
Contact: Mike Olivieri, Executive Vice President
Released: Weekly. **Price:** $8, introductory 4-week offer(Digital only). **Description:** A number of ways in which the new 31-story megamall with hotel may transform the North I-Drive corridor in Orlando, Florida are presented. iSquare Mall & Hotel Development LLC applied for approval to construct the upscale, multistory retail mall with 1,253 hotel rooms in two towers. **Availability:** Print; Online.

3970 ■ "$1.2 Billion Master-Planned Community in Celina Back on Track" in Dallas Business Journal (Vol. 35, June 8, 2012, No. 39, pp. 1)
Pub: Baltimore Business Journal
Contact: Rhonda Pringle, President
E-mail: rpringle@bizjournals.com
Ed: Candace Carlisle. **Description:** Developer, Republic Property Group, has started at its $1.2 billion residential development project in Celina, Texas and aims to deliver 400 home lots in its initial phase to contruction home builders by April 2012. The Light Farms master-planned community will feature a $5 million amenity and welcome center as well as a $13 million greenbelt. **Availability:** Print; Online.

3971 ■ "$100 Million Plan for Jefferson Arms" in Saint Louis Business Journal (Vol. 32, October 14, 2011, No. 7, pp. 1)
Pub: Saint Louis Business Journal
Contact: Robert Bobroff, President
E-mail: rbobroff@bizjournals.com
Ed: Evan Binns. **Description:** Teach for America is planning a $100 million renovation project of the former Jefferson Arms hotel in St. Louis, Missouri. The organization has signed a letter of intent to occupy the space. Financing of the project will be mainly through tax credits. **Availability:** Print; Online.

3972 ■ "$100M Complex To Be Built on Purple People Bridge" in Business Courier (Vol. 27, November 12, 2010, No. 28, pp. 1)
Pub: Business Courier
Ed: Lucy May. **Description:** A development firm closed a deal with the Newport Southbank Bridge Company for a $100M entertainment complex that will be built on top of the Purple People Bridge. The proposed project will cover 150,000 square feet with attractions such as restaurants, a boutique hotel, and pubs. **Availability:** Print; Online.

3973 ■ "$161.9M 'Pit Stop' Fix-Up Will Create About 1,600 Jobs" in Orlando Business Journal (Vol. 26, January 22, 2010, No. 34, pp. 1)
Pub: Orlando Business Journal
Contact: Julie Swyers, Director
E-mail: jswyers@bizjournals.com
Ed: Anjali Fluker. **Description:** State of Florida will be providing $161.9 million to renovate eight service plazas starting November 2010. The project is expected to create 1,600 jobs across the state and is expected to be completed by 2012. Details on bid advertisements and facilities slated for improvement are discussed. **Availability:** Print; Online.

3974 ■ "2010: Important Year Ahead for Waterfront" in Bellingham Business Journal (Vol. March 2010, pp. 2)
Description: A tentative timeline has been established for the environmental impact statement (EIS) slated for completion in May 2010. The plan for the Waterfront District includes detailed economic and architectural analysis of the feasibility of reusing remaining structures and retaining some industrial icons. **Availability:** Print; Online.

3975 ■ "2015 Marketing Calendar for Real Estate Pros: Own It"
Pub: CreateSpace
Released: October 14, 2014. **Price:** $9.56, paperback. **Description:** Real estate agents, mortgage loan agents, and new home builders and site and listing agents are shown how to use low-cost, high yield, proven marketing techniques to create digital real estate listings, find more customers, and sell more homes. Advice for building a brand and public relations; attracting renters and buyers; developing a good Website; and a digital marketing plan are explained. **Availability:** Print.

3976 ■ "Adventures at Hydronicahh" in Contractor (Vol. 56, September 2009, No. 9, pp. 52)
Ed: Mark Eatherton. **Released:** Part 6. **Description:** Installations of the heating system of a lakeview room are described. The room's radiant windows are powered by electricity from a solar PV array and a propane-powered hydrogen fuel cell. The system will be programmed to use the most energy available. **Availability:** Print; Online.

3977 ■ "Agricultural Community Implements Green Technologies, Building Team" in Contractor (Vol. 56, September 2009, No. 9, pp. 5)
Ed: Candace Roulo. **Description:** John DeWald and Associates has initiated a residential development project which uses green technologies in Illinois. The community features a community center, organic farm and recreational trails. Comments from executives are also provided. **Availability:** Print; Online.

3978 ■ "Aircraft Maker May Land in Austin" in Austin Business Journal (Vol. 31, April 15, 2011, No. 6, pp. 1)
Pub: Austin Business Journal
Contact: Rachel McGrath, Director
E-mail: rmcgrath@bizjournals.com
Ed: Jacob Dirr. **Description:** Icon Aircraft Inc. is planning to build a manufacturing facility in Austin, Texas. The company needs 100,000 square feet of space in a new or renovated plant. Executive comments are included. **Availability:** Print; Online.

3979 ■ "All About The Benjamins" in Canadian Business (Vol. 81, September 29, 2008, No. 16, pp. 92)
Description: Discusses real estate developer Royal Indian Raj International Corp., a company that planned to build a $3 billion "smart city" near the Bangalore airport; to this day nothing has ever been built. The company was incorporated in 1999 by Manoj C. Benjamin one investor, Bill Zack, has been sued by the developer for libel due to his website that calls the company a scam. Benjamin has had a previous case of fraud issued against him as well as a string of liabilities and lawsuits. **Availability:** Online.

3980 ■ "Ambitious Horse Center Is In the Works for Southeastern Idaho" in Idaho Business Review (August 25, 2014)
Pub: BridgeTower Media
Contact: Adam Reinebach, President
Price: $99, Digital & Mobile Only(1 Year); $11.99, Print, Digital & Mobile(1 Month); $149, Print, Digital & Mobile(1 Year); $99, Digital & Mobile Only(For 1 Year); $11.99, Print, Digital & Mobile (For 1 Month Intro Rate); $149, Print, Digital & Mobile (For 1 Year). **Description:** Ernest Bleinberger is planning to develop a 167-acre mixed-use project called Horse Station and will be located in Cache Valley, Idaho. Horse Station will include stables for about 250 horses and an arena, along with medical facilities, a hotel, retail shopping center, and a farmers market. **Availability:** Print; Online.

3981 ■ "Analysts: Intel Site May Be Last Major U.S.-Built Fab" in Business Journal-Serving Phoenix and the Valley of the Sun (October 18, 2007)
Pub: Phoenix Business Journal
Contact: Alex McAlister, Director
E-mail: amcalister@bizjournals.com
Ed: Ty Young. **Description:** Intel's million-square-foot manufacturing facility, called Fab 32, is expected to open in 2007. The plant will mass-produce the 45-nanometer microchip. Industry analysts believe Fab 32 may be the last of its kind to be built in the U.S., as construction costs are higher in America than in other countries. Intel's future in Chandler is examined. **Availability:** Print; Online.

3982 ■ "Anderson Pitches Liberty Towne Place" in Business Courier (Vol. 27, June 18, 2010, No. 7, pp. 1)
Pub: Business Courier
Ed: Dan Monk. **Description:** Jeffrey R. Anderson Real Estate Inc.'s plan for a retail center in Butler County, Ohio could have three department stores in the 1.1 million-square-foot property. An outdoor sports retailer is also part of the plans. **Availability:** Print; Online.

3983 ■ "Apartment Action: A Renewal in Rentals" in Barron's (Vol. 88, March 17, 2008, No. 11, pp. 17)
Pub: Dow Jones & Company Inc.
Contact: Almar Latour, Chief Executive Officer
Ed: Robin Goldwyn Blumenthal. **Description:** Discusses the projected entry of the estimated 82 million echo-boomers into the rentals market and the influx of immigrants and displaced homeowners which could turn apartments into lucrative investments again. While apartment-building completions rose slowly since 2003, demand is expected to increase steeply until 2015. **Availability:** Print; Online.

3984 ■ "Apartments Head to Schilling Farms: $48 Million Investment Includes Office, Retail Space" in Memphis Business Journal (Vol. 34, August 17, 2012, No. 18, pp. 1)
Pub: Baltimore Business Journal
Contact: Rhonda Pringle, President
E-mail: rpringle@bizjournals.com
Description: Boyle Investment Company is planning to launch three new projects at its Schiling Farms development in Memphis, Tennessee. The construction plans include multifamily units and rental space. **Availability:** Print; Online.

3985 ■ "Architects On Track for Ambitious Depot Renovation" in Sacramento Business Journal (Vol. 29, September 21, 2012, No. 30, pp. 1)
Pub: Baltimore Business Journal
Contact: Rhonda Pringle, President
E-mail: rpringle@bizjournals.com
Ed: Sanford Nax. **Description:** Page & Turnbull has set a plan to begin a major renovation of Sacramento Valley Station, a historic railroad depot in California and one of Amtrak's busiest stations. The city council has selected the Portland, Oregon-based Zimmer Gunsul Frasca Architects to lead the remodel and expects the construction to begin in fall 2013. **Availability:** Print; Online.

3986 ■ "Architecture Panel Pushes Bozzuto" in Baltimore Business Journal (Vol. 31, March 21, 2014, No. 47, pp. 4)
Pub: American City Business Journals, Inc.
Contact: Mike Olivieri, Executive Vice President

Released: Weekly. Price: $4, introductory 4-week offer(Digital & Print). Description: The Bozzuto Group along with the Solstice Partners LLC, is developing its most ambitious $80 million Locust Point apartment project in Baltimore. Notorious for getting pretty tough with architects, the members of the city's Urban Design and Architecture Panel are highly focused on getting the building right. Designed in a unique S-shape, this building was approved by the UDARP panelists and they are planning to refine the details with the concerned architect within a week's time. Availability: Print; Online.

3987 ■ "Areva Diversifies Further Into Wind" in Wall Street Journal Eastern Edition (November 29, 2011, pp. B7)
Pub: Dow Jones & Company Inc.
Contact: Almar Latour, Chief Executive Officer
Ed: Max Colchester, Noemie Bisserbe. Description: French engineering company Areva SA is diversifying and moving away from nuclear energy projects. One sign of that is its recent discussion to construct 120 wind turbines to be located at two German wind farms. Such a deal, if signed, would be worth about US$1.59 billion. Availability: Online.

3988 ■ "Army Surplus Store Rebuilding Again" in Spokesman-Review (November 17, 2010)
Pub: Spokesman Review
Contact: Kristi Burns, Director
E-mail: kristib@spokesman.com
Ed: Chelsea Bannach. Description: Retail business owner, David Arnold Sr., is rebuilding his Army Surplus store in Spokane, Washington after a truck crashed into the building. Availability: Print; Online.

3989 ■ "Austin Ponders Annexing Formula One Racetrack" in Austin Business Journal (Vol. 31, July 8, 2011, No. 18, pp. 1)
Pub: Austin Business Journal
Contact: Rachel McGrath, Director
E-mail: rmcgrath@bizjournals.com
Ed: Vicky Garza. Description: City planners in Austin, Texas are studying the feasibility of annexing the land under and around the Circuit of the Americas Formula One Racetrack being constructed east of the city. The annexation could generate at least $13 million in financial gain over 25 years from property taxes alone. Availability: Print; Online.

3990 ■ "BABs in Bond Land" in Barron's (Vol. 89, July 6, 2009, No. 27, pp. 14)
Pub: Dow Jones & Company Inc.
Contact: Almar Latour, Chief Executive Officer
Ed: Jim McTague. Description: American Recovery and Reinvestment Act has created taxable Build America Bonds (BAB) to finance new construction projects. The issuance of the two varieties of taxable BABs is expected to benefit the municipal bond market. Availability: Online.

3991 ■ "Baltimore-Area Hospital Tower Projects Could Add Hundreds of New Jobs" in Baltimore Business Journal (Vol. 28, June 25, 2010, No. 7, pp. 1)
Pub: Baltimore Business Journal
Contact: Rhonda Pringle, President
E-mail: rpringle@bizjournals.com
Ed: Scott Graham. Description: Greater Baltimore, Maryland has four hospitals that are in the middle of transforming their campuses with new facilities for treating various patients. Construction at Mercy Medical Center, Johns Hopkins Hospital, Franklin Square Hospital and Anne Rundle Hospital has helped bring the construction industry back to life. Insights into the hiring plans of these hospitals are also included.

3992 ■ "Baltimore Developer Caves Valley Partners Bids for $750M Social Security Project - County Tract Pitched for Data Center" in Baltimore Business Journal (Vol. 28, July 23, 2010, No. 11, pp. 1)
Pub: Baltimore Business Journal
Contact: Rhonda Pringle, President
E-mail: rpringle@bizjournals.com

Ed: Scott Dance. Description: One hundred acres of land in Woodlawn, Maryland is set to be sold for use in the construction of a data center for the U.S. Social Security Administration. Baltimore County has submitted a bid for the $750M construction project. Availability: Print.

3993 ■ "Baltimore Eyeing Tax Breaks for New Arena" in Boston Business Journal (Vol. 29, June 3, 2011, No. 4, pp. 1)
Pub: Boston Business Journal
Contact: Carolyn M. Jones, President
E-mail: cmjones@bizjournals.com
Ed: Daniel J. Sernovitz. Description: Baltimore City is opting to give millions of dollars in tax breaks and construction loans to a group of private investors led by William Hackerman who is proposing to build a new arena and hotel at the Baltimore Convention Center. The project will cost $500 million with the state putting up another $400 million for the center's expansion.

3994 ■ "Baltimore Rejects Plans for Waxter Site" in Baltimore Business Journal (Vol. 30, May 25, 2012, No. 3, pp. 1)
Pub: American City Business Journals, Inc.
Contact: Mike Olivieri, Executive Vice President
Ed: James Briggs. Description: The City of Baltimore, Maryland has turned down a proposal for a mixed-use development project at the Waxter Center in Mount Vernon. The project is estimated to cost up to $70 million. Availability: Print; Online.

3995 ■ "Bankruptcies" in Crain's Detroit Business (Vol. 24, March 24, 2008, No. 12, pp. 6)
Pub: Crain Communications Inc.
Contact: Barry Asin, President
Description: Current list of business that filed for Chapter 7 or 11 protection in U.S. Bankruptcy Court in Detroit include a construction company, a medical care company, a physical therapy firm and a communications firm. Availability: Online.

3996 ■ "Be Wary of Dual-Flush Conversion Kits" in Contractor (Vol. 56, September 2009, No. 9, pp. 66)
Ed: John Koeller, Bill Gauley. Description: Recommendation of untested dual-flush conversion devices for tank-type toilets in the United States has been questioned. The products are being advertised as having the ability to convert single-flush to a dual-flush toilet. No evidence of water conservation from using such devices has been recorded. Availability: Print; Online.

3997 ■ "Better than Advertised: Chip Plant Beats Expectations" in Business Review Albany (Vol. 41, June 27, 2014, No. 14, pp. 4)
Pub: American City Business Journals, Inc.
Contact: Mike Olivieri, Executive Vice President
Released: Weekly. Price: $4, introductory 4-week offer(Digital only). Description: The $8.5 billion computer chip manufacturing plant and research center of GlobalFoundries in Malta, New York has strengthened the local economy in Saratoga County and helped the local manufacturing and construction industries recover from the recession. The Malta Plant construction project created more than 2,000 direct new construction jobs and over 10,000 indirect positions. Availability: Print; Online.

3998 ■ "'Better Together:' OCO LPA Executives Discuss Recent Merger" in San Antonio Business Journal (Vol. 28, July 4, 2014, No. 21, pp. 8)
Pub: American City Business Journals, Inc.
Contact: Mike Olivieri, Executive Vice President
Released: Weekly. Price: $4, introductory 4-week offer(Digital & Print). Description: Texas-based OCO Architects agreed to merge with LPA Inc. of Irvine, California effective July 1, 2014 and the local firm will initially operate as OCO LPA before it officially becomes LPA in January 2015. The merger is expected to keep OCO LPA relevant in the residential and commercial real estate sectors. Availability: Print; Online.

3999 ■ "Bidding On Airport Terminal is Big Job In Itself" in Wichita Business Journal (Vol. 27, February 10, 2012, No. 6, pp. 1)
Pub: Baltimore Business Journal
Contact: Rhonda Pringle, President
E-mail: rpringle@bizjournals.com
Description: The city of Wichita, Kansas has started calling for construction bids to build the new terminal at Wichita Mid-Continent Airport, a project considered a big job in construction industry norms. Efforts that have been done by construction firms in making bids are discussed, along with the economic impact of this project. Availability: Print; Online.

4000 ■ "Bill Feinberg on Building the Model of Success - 'Strive for 100 Percent Satisfaction'" in South Florida Business Journal (Vol. 34, June 27, 2014, No. 49, pp. 13)
Pub: American City Business Journals, Inc.
Contact: Mike Olivieri, Executive Vice President
Released: Weekly. Price: $8, introductory 4-week offer(Digital only). Description: Allied Kitchen & Bath president and CEO, Bill Feinberg, is profiled. The entrepreneur discusses his advocacy for helping to find a cure for leukemia and lymphoma. He enjoys cooking and traveling with family. Availability: Print; Online.

4001 ■ "BIM and You: Know Its Benefits and Risks" in Contractor (Vol. 57, January 2010, No. 1, pp. 46)
Ed: Susan Linden McGreevy. Description: Building Information Modeling is intended to be "collaborative" and this could raise legal issues if a contractor sends an electronic bid and it is filtered out. Other legal issues that mechanical contractors need to consider before using this technology are discussed. Availability: Print; Online.

4002 ■ "Blach Builds on Teamwork" in Silicon Valley/San Jose Business Journal (Vol. 30, August 24, 2012, No. 22, pp. 1)
Pub: Baltimore Business Journal
Contact: Rhonda Pringle, President
E-mail: rpringle@bizjournals.com
Description: Blach Construction chief executive, Mike Blach, has grown the firm into a top contractor in San Jose, California. The construction company's earnings have increased to $98 million in 2011. Availability: Print; Online.

4003 ■ "Bond Hill Cinema Site To See New Life" in Business Courier (Vol. 27, October 29, 2010, No. 26, pp. 1)
Pub: Business Courier
Ed: Dan Monk. Description: Avondale, Ohio's Corinthian Baptist Church will redevelop the 30-acre former Showcase Cinema property to a mixed-use site that could feature a college, senior home, and retail. Corinthian Baptist, which is one of the largest African-American churches in the region, is also planning to relocate the church. Availability: Print; Online.

4004 ■ "Bowman Funeral Directors Building New, Larger Facility in Garden City" in Idaho Business Review (March 13, 2014)
Pub: BridgeTower Media
Contact: Adam Reinebach, President
Description: Bowman Funeral Directors has started construction of a 6,500 square foot building in Garden City, Idaho. Owner, Gary Bowman, is a licensed mortician and reports that the new funeral home will have a great room for services with audio and visual component services available, preparations and storage rooms, crematorium, offices, and a kitchen.

4005 ■ "Braves' Parking Pitch Fails to Connect With Property Owners" in Atlanta Business Chronicle (June 27, 2014, pp. 1)
Pub: American City Business Journals, Inc.
Contact: Mike Olivieri, Executive Vice President
Released: June 27, 2014. Price: $4, introductory 4-week offer(Digital only). Description: A new $672 million ballpark plan of the Atlanta Braves was given

the green light by Cobb County Commissioners recently. However, the Braves are facing a new hurdle for securing parking spaces in the office complexes around the proposed ballpark site. The stadium itself will have more than 6,000 parking spots, but the Braves also want an additional 4,000 to 5,000 spaces, and although the Braves are said to be offering building owners around the stadium up to $100 per space, the owners have not been swayed to give access to their parking. **Availability:** Print; Mailing list; Online.

4006 ■ *"Bridging the Bay"* **in Business Journal Serving Greater Tampa Bay (Vol. 30, November 5, 2010, No. 46, pp. 1)**
Pub: Tampa Bay Business Journal
Contact: Ian Anderson, President
E-mail: ianderson@bizjournals.com

Ed: Mark Holan. **Description:** The Florida Department of Transportation has launched a study to design the proposed addition to the Howard Frankland Bridge. The bridge would be designed to accommodate more than personal vehicles. **Availability:** Print; Online.

4007 ■ *"Brought To You By the Letter 'W'"* **in Washington Business Journal (Vol. 33, August 29, 2014, No. 19, pp. 6)**
Pub: American City Business Journals, Inc.
Contact: Mike Olivieri, Executive Vice President
Released: Weekly. **Price:** $4, introductory 4-week offer(Digital & Print). **Description:** W Hotel, Washington DC's food and beverage spaces are undergoing renovations. Hotel guests will see a new roof and a more stylish, upscale restaurant. W Hotel's plan to offer a luxury experience is discussed. **Availability:** Print; Online.

4008 ■ *"Brown's Goal: 1,300 New Apartments and Condos"* **in Business First of Buffalo (Vol. 30, February 28, 2014, No. 24, pp. 6)**
Pub: American City Business Journals, Inc.
Contact: Mike Olivieri, Executive Vice President
Released: February 28, 2014. **Price:** $140, Digital & Print; $115, Digital only. **Description:** Buffalo, New York Mayor Bryan Brown is planning for at least 1,300 new, market-rate residential units in the city's central business district over the next four years. The additional residential units are incorporated in Brown's larger strategy for creating a 24/7 downtown Buffalo. The impact of the residential development plan on the area's periphery is examined. **Availability:** Print; Online.

4009 ■ *"Builder Confidence Boost Highest in Nearly 10 Years"* **in Small Business Trends(February 17, 2023)**
URL(s): smallbiztrends.com/2023/02/nahb-wells-fargo-housing-market-index-february-2023.html

Ed: Lisa Price. **Released:** February 17, 2023. **Description:** The National Association of Home Builders/Wells Fargo Housing Market Index was released, showing gains for builder confidence. **Availability:** Online.

4010 ■ *"Builder Confidence Continues Cautious Increase"* **in Small Business Trends (March 16, 2023).**
URL(s): smallbiztrends.com/2023/03/builder-confidence-continues-cautious-increase.html
Released: March 16, 2023. **Description:** The National Association of Home Builders (NAHB) announced builders confidence is up to 44%, which is a slight raise. Contains an explanation of how the number is calculated. **Availability:** Online.

4011 ■ *"Builders Aim to Cut Costs: Pushing Changes to Regain Share of Residential Market; Seek Council's Help"* **in Crain's New York Business**
Pub: Crain Communications, Inc.
Contact: Jessica Botos, Manager, Marketing
E-mail: jessica.botos@crainsnewyork.com

Ed: Erik Engquist. **Description:** Union contractors and workers are worried about a decline in their market share for housing so they intend to ask the City Council to impose new safety and benefit standards on all contractors to avoid being undercut by nonunion competitors. **Availability:** Print; Online.

4012 ■ *"Builder's Bankruptcy Fans Fears"* **in Crain's Cleveland Business (Vol. 28, October 22, 2007, No. 42, pp. 1)**
Pub: Crain Communications Inc.
Contact: K. C. Crain, President

Ed: Stan Bullard. **Description:** Whitlatch & Co., Northeast Ohio's largest builder by unit volume in the early 1990s, has filed for Chapter 11 bankruptcy. This is causing builders and others in the real estate industry to wonder how long and severe the housing slump will be and which companies will survive. **Availability:** Online.

4013 ■ *"Builder's Comeback Highlights Uptick in Demand for New Homes"* **in Boston Business Journal (Vol. 29, June 3, 2011, No. 4, pp. 1)**
Pub: Boston Business Journal
Contact: Carolyn M. Jones, President
E-mail: cmjones@bizjournals.com

Ed: Gary Haber. **Description:** The return of builder Michael Canock after a series of credit crisis and the funding for his new projects are discussed in light of the recent upsurge in the home-building industry in the Baltimore area. New single-family homes numbered 318 in first quarter 2011 which is a 20 percent increase from first quarter 2010.

4014 ■ *"Builders: Land Prices Up, Bank Lending Down"* **in Orlando Business Journal (Vol. 30, January 31, 2014, No. 32, pp. 5)**
Pub: American City Business Journals, Inc.
Contact: Mike Olivieri, Executive Vice President
Released: Weekly. **Price:** $8, introductory 4-week offer(Digital & Print). **Description:** A look at the views of residential real estate executives on the rising land prices and financing of construction is presented. The limited supply of lots in great locations has resulted in landowners raising asking prices. The real estate downturn has also resulted in the reluctance of many banks to lend money to home builders to finance construction in Central Florida. **Availability:** Print; Online.

4015 ■ *"Building Fast-Growing Companies"* **in South Florida Business Journal (Vol. 35, September 19, 2014, No. 8, pp. 16)**
Pub: American City Business Journals, Inc.
Contact: Mike Olivieri, Executive Vice President
Description: Members of Florida's construction industry have registered continuous growth in 2014. Recovery from the economic crisis is driving the construction growth. Economic resilience and proper debt management have also contributed to the sector's growth. **Availability:** Online.

4016 ■ *"Building Targeted for Marriott in Violation"* **in Business Journal-Milwaukee (Vol. 28, December 24, 2010, No. 12, pp. A1)**
Pub: The Business Journal
Contact: Heather Ladage, President
E-mail: hladage@bizjournals.com

Ed: Sean Ryan. **Description:** Milwaukee, Wisconsin's Department of Neighborhood Services has ordered structural improvements and safeguards for the Pioneer Building after three violations from structural failures were found. Pioneer was among the five buildings wanted by Jackson Street Management LLC to demolish for the new Marriott Hotel. **Availability:** Print; Online.

4017 ■ *"Buildings to Flank Broken Spoke: Legendary Country Dance Hall To Be Surrounded But Won't Be Touched"* **in Austin Business Journal (Vol. 32, April 13, 2012, No. 6, pp. 1)**
Pub: American City Business Journals, Inc.
Contact: Mike Olivieri, Executive Vice President

Ed: Vicky Garza. **Description:** A $60 million mixed use development tentatively called 704 at the Spoke is being planned along South Lamar Boulevard in Austin, Texas. The plan includes 378 apartments and 20,000 square feet of restaurant and retail space. The project will have the historic Broken Spoke Dance Hall as its hub. **Availability:** Online.

4018 ■ *"A Burning Issue: Lives Are at Stake Every Day"* **in Contractor (Vol. 56, October 2009, No. 10, pp. 29)**
Description: American Society of Plumbing Engineers has been accused of being biased for supporting rules that require residential fire sprinklers although the society's members will not receive any benefit from their installation. The organization trains and certifies plumbing engineers who design life-saving fire protection systems. **Availability:** Online.

4019 ■ *"C. Fla. Notches $5B in Real Estate Property Sales in Last 12 Months"* **in Orlando Business Journal (Vol. 31, July 4, 2014, No. 1, pp. 4)**
Pub: American City Business Journals, Inc.
Contact: Mike Olivieri, Executive Vice President
Released: Weekly. **Price:** $8, Introductory 4-week offer(Digital & Print). **Description:** Real estate company Real Capital Analytics reports sales volumes totaling $5 billion in Central Florida's commercial real estate market between June 2013 and May 2014. Real estate deals in the region reflect investor interest in the Orlando market, as private equity and development firms renovate existing properties or build new construction projects, thus increasing property values, creating jobs and boosting the local economy. **Availability:** Print; Online.

4020 ■ *"Cabi to Develop Major Retail Project"* **in South Florida Business Journal (Vol. 32, July 6, 2012, No. 50, pp. 1)**
Pub: Baltimore Business Journal
Contact: Rhonda Pringle, President
E-mail: rpringle@bizjournals.com

Description: Aventura, Florida-based Cabi Developers has received a bankruptcy court approval to begin construction of a major retail project called Capital Brickell Place in the Brickell neighborhood. Mexican real estate developer GICSA will finance the project and Cabi has been talking with retailers like Costco, Targt and Trader Joe's as potential tenants. **Availability:** Print; Online.

4021 ■ *"Cadillac Tower Largest to Start in a Decade"* **in Globe & Mail (March 28, 2006, pp. B5)**
Ed: Elizabeth Church. **Description:** The plans of Cadillac Fairview Corporation Ltd. to build office towers, in downtown Canada, are presented. **Availability:** Print; Online.

4022 ■ *"Canada's Largest Bakery Officially Opened Today"* **in Ecology,Environment & Conservation Business (October 15, 2011, pp. 7)**
Description: Maple Leaf Foods opened Canada's largest commercial bakery in Hamilton, Ontario. The firm's 385,000 square foot Trillium bakery benefits from efficient design flow and best-in-class technologies. **Availability:** Print; Online.

4023 ■ *"Capital Metro May Soon Seek Contractor"* **in Austin Business Journal (Vol. 31, June 10, 2011, No. 14, pp. 1)**
Pub: Austin Business Journal
Contact: Rachel McGrath, Director
E-mail: rmcgrath@bizjournals.com

Ed: Vicky Garza. **Description:** Capital Metropolitan Transportation Authority may be forced to contract out its bus services provided by StarTran Inc. as early as September 2012 following legislation approved by the Texas legislature. The bill originates in a report by the Sunset Advisory Commission. Details are included. **Availability:** Print; Online.

4024 ■ *"Capital One Expanding Campus in Plano"* **in Dallas Business Journal (Vol. 35, April 20, 2012, No. 2, pp. 1)**
Pub: Baltimore Business Journal
Contact: Rhonda Pringle, President
E-mail: rpringle@bizjournals.com

Ed: Candace Carlisle. **Description:** The financial services division of Capital One Financial Corporation in Plano, Texas will hire an additional 300 employees and start construction of two office buildings and 2,600-space parking garage in summer 2012. Cost of the 400,000-square-foot office space is estimated at $76 million and $19.5 million for the garage. **Availability:** Print; Online.

4025 ■ *"Chicago Public Schools District Builds Green"* in Contractor (Vol. 56, October 2009, No. 10, pp. 5)
Ed: Candace Roulo. **Description:** Chicago Public Schools district has already built six U.S. Green Building Council LEED certified schools and one addition in five years and will continue to build new green buildings. The district has an Environmental Action Plan that strives to reduce energy usage, improve indoor air quality, and reduce contribution to climate change. **Availability:** Print; Online.

4026 ■ *"Children's Hospital to Grow"* in Austin Business Journal (Vol. 31, July 22, 2011, No. 20, pp. A1)
Pub: Austin Business Journal
Contact: Rachel McGrath, Director
E-mail: rmcgrath@bizjournals.com
Ed: Sandra Zaragoza. **Description:** Austin, Texas-based Dell Children's Medical Center is set to embark on a tower expansion. The plan will accommodate more patients and make room for the hospital's growing specialty program. **Availability:** Print; Online.

4027 ■ *"Cincinnati Museum Center to Exhibit New Look"* in Business Courier (Vol. 24, February 21, 2008, No. 46, pp. 1)
Pub: American City Business Journals, Inc.
Contact: Mike Olivieri, Executive Vice President
Ed: Dan Monk. **Description:** Discusses a $120 million renovation is being planned for the Cincinnati Museum Center complex at Union Terminal. The project aims to build a 14-acre park and office spaces in the area. Details of the Museum Center's renovation plans are given. **Availability:** Online.

4028 ■ *"Citrus Bowl Construction Bids Going Out This Year"* in Orlando Business Journal (Vol. 29, June 29, 2012, No. 2, pp. 1)
Pub: Baltimore Business Journal
Contact: Rhonda Pringle, President
E-mail: rpringle@bizjournals.com
Description: The city of Orlando, Florida is expected to seek construction bids for the Florida Citrus Bowl's renovation in 2012. The project is estimated to cost $175 million. **Availability:** Print; Online.

4029 ■ *"City-Owned Buildings Get an Injection of Solar Power"* in America's Intelligence Wire (September 11, 2012)
Description: City of Toronto, Ontario, Canada and Toronto Hydro-Electric System Ltd. have launched the first phase of a program that will outfit city-owned buildings with over 8,800 solar photovoltaic (PV) panels. Construction begins at MimicoArena, York Mills Arena, and Goulding Park Community Centre/Arena. Details of the project are included. **Availability:** Online.

4030 ■ *"City Seeks More Minorities"* in Austin Business Journal Inc. (Vol. 28, November 7, 2008, No. 34, pp. A1)
Pub: Austin Business Journal
Contact: Rachel McGrath, Director
E-mail: rmcgrath@bizjournals.com
Ed: Jean Kwon. **Description:** Austin, Texas is planning to increase the participation of minority- and women-owned businesses in government contracts. Contractors are required to show 'good faith' to comply with the specified goals. The city is planning to effect the changes in the construction and professional services sector. **Availability:** Print; Online.

4031 ■ *"Collateral Damage"* in Business Courier (Vol. 26, October 16, 2009, No. 25, pp. 1)
Pub: American City Business Journals, Inc.
Contact: Mike Olivieri, Executive Vice President

Ed: Jon Newberry. **Description:** Non-union construction firms representing Ohio Valley Associated Builders and Contractors Inc. have filed cases against unionized shops claiming violations of wage law in Ohio. Defendants say the violations are minor, however, they believe they are caught in the middle of the group's campaign to change the state's wage law. **Availability:** Print; Online.

4032 ■ *"Combo Dorm-Field House Built to Attain LEED Gold"* in Contractor (Vol. 56, September 2009, No. 9, pp. 1)
Ed: Candace Roulo, Robert P. Mader. **Description:** North Central College in Illinois has built a new dormitory that is expected to attain Leadership in Energy and Environmental Design Gold certification from the United States Green Building Council. The structure features a geo-exchange heat pump system and radiant floor heat. A description of the facility is also provided. **Availability:** Print; Online.

4033 ■ *"Commercial Builders Take It on the Chin"* in Crain's Chicago Business (Vol. 31, April 28, 2008, No. 17, pp. 16)
Pub: Crain Communications Inc.
Contact: Barry Asin, President
Ed: Alby Gallun. **Description:** Although the health care development sector has seen growth, the rest of Chicago's local commercial building industry has seen steep declines in the first quarter of this year. According to McGraw-Hill Construction, Chicago-area non-residential construction starts totaled $731 million in the quarter, a 60 percent drop from the year-earlier period. Volume in the retail, office and hotel markets fell by nearly 70 percent. **Availability:** Online.

4034 ■ *"Commercial Real Estate Developers"* in Business Review Albany (Vol. 41, August 8, 2014, No. 20, pp. 8)
Description: A listing of the top 22 commercial real estate developers in Albany, New York are ranked by square feet of property owned is presented. The Galesi Group is ranked number one, with Nigro Companies following in second place. **Availability:** Print; Online.

4035 ■ *"Commercial Real Estate May Be Cooling, While Residential Clamors to Meet Demand"* in Houston Business Journal (Vol. 44, January 3, 2014, No. 35, pp. 6)
Pub: American City Business Journals, Inc.
Contact: Mike Olivieri, Executive Vice President
Released: January 03, 2014. **Description:** Greater Houston Partnership has predicted that the real estate industry will remain active for the years ahead in Houston, Texas. However, commercial real estate might cool down while residential sales are expected to remain hot with demand outpacing supply. Houston's construction boom in each sector is also discussed. **Availability:** Print; Online.

4036 ■ *"Con Roundup: Novi Eyed for $11 Million, 100-Bed Medilodge"* in Crain's Detroit Business (Vol. 25, June 1, 2009, No. 22, pp. M032)
Pub: Crain Communications Inc.
Contact: Barry Asin, President
Description: Novi, Michigan is one of the cities being considered for construction of a new 110-bed skilled nursing facility. Details of the project are included. **Availability:** Online.

4037 ■ *"Concrete Company Makes Lasting Impression in Valley"* in Silicon Valley/San Jose Business Journal (Vol. 30, August 10, 2012, No. 20, pp. 1)
Pub: Baltimore Business Journal
Contact: Rhonda Pringle, President
E-mail: rpringle@bizjournals.com
Ed: Gloria Wang Shawber. **Description:** Joseph J. Albanese Inc. has made a lasting impression on projects throughout Silicon Valley for nearly 60 years. President and CEO, John Albanese, started his family owned concrete company as concrete contractors and it was often selected as the subcontractor for various general contractors in the valley. **Availability:** Print; Online.

4038 ■ *"Construction"* in Inc. (Vol. 36, September 2014, No. 7, pp. 166)
Pub: Mansueto Ventures L.L.C.
Contact: Stephanie Mehta, Chief Executive Officer
Description: Listing of the fastest growing construction companies across the United States is presented. **Availability:** Online.

4039 ■ *"Contractors Debate Maximizing Green Opportunities, Education"* in Contractor (Vol. 56, November 2009, No. 11, pp. 3)
Ed: Robert P. Mader. **Description:** Attendees at the Mechanical Service Contractors Association convention were urged to get involved with their local U.S. Green Building Council chapter by one presenter. Another presenter says that one green opportunity for contractors is the commissioning of new buildings. **Availability:** Print; Online.

4040 ■ *"Contractors Must be Lead Certified"* in Contractor (Vol. 57, February 2010, No. 2, pp. 3)
Description: Contractors should be trained and certified to comply with the U.S. Environmental Protection Agency's Lead Renovation, Repair, and Painting regulation if they work on housing built before 1978 by April 2010. Contractors with previous lead abatement training must be trained and certified under this new program. **Availability:** Print; Online.

4041 ■ *"Convenience Store Expanding"* in Clovis News Journal (November 9, 2010)
Description: Allsup's convenience store on North Prince Street in Clovis, New Mexico will expand its facilities. The current building is being demolished to make way for the new construction.

4042 ■ *"Convention Ctr. Rehab To Impact Hotels, Eateries"* in Silicon Valley/San Jose Business Journal (Vol. 30, May 18, 2012, No. 8, pp. 1)
Pub: Baltimore Business Journal
Contact: Rhonda Pringle, President
E-mail: rpringle@bizjournals.com
Description: The renovation of the San Jose McEnery Convention Center is seen to adversely impact businesses in the area. Contractors have already demolished the former Martin Luther King Jr. Main Library. Business sales in the area are expected to decline owing to the renovation.

4043 ■ *"Corporate Park Retrofits for Water Savings"* in Contractor (Vol. 56, October 2009, No. 10, pp. 5)
Description: Merrit Corporate Park in Norwalk, Connecticut has been interested in improving building efficiency and one of their buildings has been retrofitted with water-efficient plumbing systems which will allow them to save as much as two million gallons of water. ADP Service Corp. helped the park upgrade their plumbing system. **Availability:** Online.

4044 ■ *"Corrales Site of New Senior Living/Care Complex"* in America's Intelligence Wire (August 13, 2012)
Description: David Dronet, developer of Corrales Senior Living LLC, has chosen Corrales, New Mexico as its newest site to construct a continuum of care for senior citizens. The project entails a $60 million complex of private homes and health care units with amenities like a restaurant, fitness areas, and gardens. **Availability:** Print; Online.

4045 ■ *"Corus Eases Off Ailing Condo Market"* in Crain's Chicago Business (April 28, 2008)
Pub: Crain Communications Inc.
Contact: Barry Asin, President
Ed: H. Lee Murphy. **Description:** Corus Bankshares Inc., a specialist in lending for the condominium high-rise construction market, is diversifying its portfolio by making loans to office developers and expects to be investing in hotels through the rest of the year. Corus' $7.57 billion loan portfolio is also discussed in detail as well as the company's earnings and share price. Statistical data included. **Availability:** Online.

4046 ■ "Could Bond OK Bring Back the Charlotte Housing Battle?" in Charlotte Business Journal (Vol. 25, November 5, 2010, No. 33, pp. 1)
Pub: Charlotte Business Journal
Contact: Robert Morris, Editor
E-mail: rmorris@bizjournals.com

Ed: Susan Stabley. Description: The approval of the $15 million housing bond in Charlotte, North Carolina could bring back the debates on housing in the region. Protesters have opposed affordable housing developments that were proposed in the area since 2008. Other information on the recently approved housing bond and on other real estate issues in North Carolina is presented. Availability: Print; Online.

4047 ■ "Councilman Addresses Union Harassment Accusations" in Philadelphia Business Journal (Vol. 33, March 28, 2014, No. 7, pp. 7)
Pub: American City Business Journals, Inc.
Contact: Mike Olivieri, Executive Vice President

Released: Weekly. Price: $4, introductory 4-week offer(Digital & Print). Description: City Councilman Bobby Heron shares his perspective on the alleged violence and intimidation from building and trade unions in Philadelphia, Pennsylvania. Heron believes that the indictment of the leadership of the Ironworkers Local 401 for harassment was an isolated incident and should not reflect on the good and hardworking building and trades construction workers they represent. Availability: Print; Online.

4048 ■ "Craning for Workers: Seattle Is Full of Cranes, but Not Enough Operators" in Puget Sound Business Journal (Vol. 35, August 15, 2014, No. 17, pp. 4)
Pub: American City Business Journals, Inc.
Contact: Mike Olivieri, Executive Vice President

Released: August 15, 2014. Description: The U.S. Department of Labor statistics show that Washington State has 15, 510 laborers in 2013. However, construction companies are having difficulty hiring skilled workers, particularly as apprentices. The Associated General Contractors of Washington's expansion of training slots for crane and other heave equipment operators is discussed. Availability: Print; Online.

4049 ■ "Crystal Hotel Resumes Construction" in Business Journal Portland (Vol. 27, December 31, 2010, No. 44, pp. 1)
Pub: Portland Business Journal
Contact: Andy Giegerich, Managing Editor
E-mail: agiegerich@bizjournals.com

Ed: Wendy Culverwell. Description: McMenamins Pubs and Breweries has resumed construction of its Crystal Hotel project. The company has been working to convert a former bath house into a 51-room hotel. The hotel is expected to open in 2011. Availability: Print; Online.

4050 ■ "Decorated Marine Sues Contractor" in Wall Street Journal Eastern Edition (November 29, 2011, pp. A4)
Pub: Dow Jones & Company Inc.
Contact: Almar Latour, Chief Executive Officer

Ed: Julian E. Barnes. Description: Marine Devon Maylie, who was awarded the Congressional Medal of Honor for bravery, has filed a lawsuit against defense contractor BAE Systems PLC claiming that the company prevented his hiring by another firm by saying he has a mental condition and a drinking problem. Maylie says that this was in retaliation for his objections to the company's plan to sell the Pakistani military high-tech sniper scopes. Availability: Online.

4051 ■ "Denver Airport Picks New Contractors As It Struggles to Conclude Previous Relationship" in ConstructionDive (October 14, 2019)
URL(s): www.constructiondive.com/news/denver-airport-picks-new-contractors-as-it-struggles-to-conclude-previous-r/564859/

Ed: Kim Slowey. Released: October 14, 2019. Description: Denver International Airport has chosen construction manager and general contractor Hensel Phelps for Phase 1, replacing Great Hall Partners. Stantec is the preferred lead designer for the entire project. Plans are in place to settle the terms to end the old construction relationship. Availability: Online.

4052 ■ "Design '07 (Housing): Prince of the City" in Canadian Business (Vol. 80, November 19, 2007, No. 23, pp. 62)
Pub: Rogers Media Inc.
Contact: Neil Spivak, Chief Executive Officer

Ed: Rachel Pulfer. Description: Robert Fung and the Salilent Group aim to revive the poverty-stricken communities in Vancouver by transforming the city's old buildings into designer condominiums using city incentives. Fung and his partners have increased property values in the most unlikely neighborhoods by creating luxury real estate. Fung's recommendations on Vancouver's real estate development are given. Availability: Online.

4053 ■ "Detroit Residential Market Slows; Bright Spots Emerge" in Crain's Detroit Business (Vol. 24, October 6, 2008, No. 40, pp. 11)
Pub: Crain Communications Inc.
Contact: Barry Asin, President

Ed: Daniel Duggan. Description: Discusses the state of the residential real estate market in Detroit; although condominium projects receive the most attention, deals for single-family homes are taking place in greater numbers due to financing issues. Buyers can purchase a single family home with a 3.5 percent down payment compared to 20 percent for some condo deals because of the number of first-time homebuyer programs under the Federal Housing Administration.

4054 ■ "Developer To Use New Owasso Senior Care Center as Template for More Services, Expansion" in Journal Record (May 23, 2012)
Description: A new $7.5 million senior care and rehabilitation center will be built in Owasso, Oklahoma. The builder, Steve Cox, is using his Senior Suites of Owasso as his model. JRJ Construction of Weatherford, Texas will complete the 105-bed private-suite facility by spring 2013. Availability: Print; Online.

4055 ■ "Developer Tries to Bring Homes to Buda" in Austin Business JournalInc. (Vol. 28, December 26, 2008, No. 41, pp. 1)
Description: Real estate developer Jeremiah Venture LP is planning a residential, single-family development on about 600 acres near Buda, Texas. The company also plans to construct a membrane waste treatment plant, and has applied to do land application. However, several groups have come forward to ask for more information on the application due to concerns about soil density. Availability: Print; Online.

4056 ■ "Developers Accommodate Need for Rooms" in Puget Sound Business Journal (Vol. 35, September 19, 2014, No. 22, pp. 8)
Pub: American City Business Journals, Inc.
Contact: Mike Olivieri, Executive Vice President

Description: The number of hotel rooms in Bellevue, Washington has been steadily increasing. Access to capital by investors is seen to contribute to the development. Seven new hotel construction projects are underway in Seattle, Washington. Availability: Online.

4057 ■ "Developers Give Big to Stephanie Rawlings-Blake Bid for Mayor" in Baltimore Business Journal (Vol. 29, August 26, 2011, No. 16, pp. 1)
Pub: Boston Business Journal
Contact: Carolyn M. Jones, President
E-mail: cmjones@bizjournals.com

Ed: Scott Dance. Description: Mayor Stephanie Rawlings-Blake received thousands of dollars in her political campaign from companies of real estate developers who are vying to build key development projects in Baltimore, Maryland. Rawlings-Blake created a major fundraising advantage over other mayoral candidates with the help of those contributions. Availability: Online.

4058 ■ "Developers Give City Dwellings a Modern Spin" in Crain's Cleveland Business (Vol. 28, November 5, 2007, No. 44, pp. 18)
Pub: Crain Communications Inc.
Contact: K. C. Crain, President

Ed: Stan Bullard. Description: Cleveland is increasingly becoming a canvas for fresh, cutting-edge design due to several recent projects, some at prominent sites. Availability: Online.

4059 ■ "Developers Move Forward Along Seattle's Waterfront" in Puget Sound Business Journal (Vol. 35, July 25, 2014, No. 14, pp. 4)
Pub: American City Business Journals, Inc.
Contact: Mike Olivieri, Executive Vice President

Released: Weekly. Description: Seattle, Washington's waterfront development continues to flourish with plans for two more projects on the horizon. Brick Road Holdings is planning construction of a seven-story Natasha market-rate project with 160 apartments. Six other new projects by the following companies are profiled: Schuster Group, Gerding Edlen, Mack Urban, Daniels Real Estate, Goodman Real Estate, and Martin Selig Real Estate. Availability: Print; Online.

4060 ■ "Developers Poised to Pull Trigers" in Boston Business Journal (Vol. 30, November 12, 2010, No. 42, pp. 1)
Description: Large residential projects are expected to break ground in Boston, Massachusetts in 2011, as real estate developers expect growth for the industry. Real estate experts expect more than 2,000 rental units to be available by 2011. Information on key real estate projects in Boston is presented. Availability: Print; Online.

4061 ■ "Developers Tout Benefits of Federal Tax Breaks" in Business First of Buffalo (Vol. 30, March 14, 2014, No. 26, pp. 4)
Pub: American City Business Journals, Inc.
Contact: Mike Olivieri, Executive Vice President

Released: Weekly. Price: $140, Digital & Print; $115, Digital only. Description: President Obama has included a Federal tax credit program in the 2015 Federal budget that provides some relief to the local development community. Congressman Mark Higgins promised to support the program that offers tax breaks to urban developers who rehabilitate older buildings with new investments. The tax credit's economic benefits are also discussed. Availability: Print; Online.

4062 ■ "DIA Contract Sets a Record for Denver Minority, Woman-Owned Business" in Denver Business Journal (Vol. 65, February 21, 2014, No. 41)
Pub: American City Business Journals, Inc.
Contact: Mike Olivieri, Executive Vice President

Released: Weekly. Description: The City of Denver, Colorado has awarded a $39.6 million contract to Burgess Services Inc. to construct a transit and hotel project near the Denver International Airport. Burgess Services is owned by Denise Burgess. This is the largest public contract awarded to a woman0 or minority-owned business in the city's history. Availability: Print; Online.

4063 ■ "Digging Dallas-Fort Worth: How Top 10 Major Construction Projects Will Change North Texas" in Dallas Business Journal (Vol. 37, May 23, 2014, No. 37, pp. 4)
Pub: American City Business Journals, Inc.
Contact: Mike Olivieri, Executive Vice President

Price: $4, print. Description: A list of the top ten largest construction projects in North Dallas in 2013 and their impact on local economies is presented. Included are the $303 million State Farm Insurance campus in Plano, $138.74 million termination renovation at Dallas-Fort Worth International Airport, and the $133.82 million Nebraska Furniture Mart in the Colony. **Availability:** Print; Online.

4064 ■ *"Disunion in the House: the Steep Price We Pay" in Philadelphia Business Journal (Vol. 33, March 28, 2014, No. 7, pp. 4)*
Pub: American City Business Journals, Inc.
Contact: Mike Olivieri, Executive Vice President
Released: Weekly. **Price:** $4, introductory 4-week offer(Digital & Print). **Description:** Some members of the Ironworkers Local 401 Union in Philadelphia, Pennsylvania face federal indictment on charges of participating in an alleged conspiracy to commit extortion, arson, assault and destruction of property. The alleged motive of their actions was to force construction contractors to hire union ironworkers. **Availability:** Print; Online.

4065 ■ *"Docs Might Hold Cure for Baltimore-Area Real Estate, Banks" in Baltimore Business Journal (Vol. 28, November 5, 2010, No. 26, pp. 1)*
Pub: Baltimore Business Journal
Contact: Rhonda Pringle, President
E-mail: rpringle@bizjournals.com
Ed: Gary Haber. **Description:** Health care providers, including physicians are purchasing their office space instead of renting it as banks lower interest rates to 6 percent on mortgages for medical offices. The rise in demand offers relief to the commercial real estate market. It has also resulted in a boom in building new medical offices. **Availability:** Print; Online.

4066 ■ *"Downtown Light Rail Plans Up in the Air" in Business Journal Serving Greater Tampa Bay (Vol. 30, October 22, 2010, No. 44, pp. 1)*
Pub: Tampa Bay Business Journal
Contact: Ian Anderson, President
E-mail: ianderson@bizjournals.com
Ed: Mark Holan. **Description:** Construction of Tampa's $2 billion light rail transit is suspended pending the result of the November 2, 2010 referendum. The routes, usage, and financing of the light rail project will be decided on the referendum. Whether the light rail will be elevated is also discussed. **Availability:** Print; Online.

4067 ■ *"East Coast Solar" in Contractor (Vol. 57, February 2010, No. 2, pp. 17)*
Ed: Dave Yates. **Description:** U.S. Department of Energy's Solar Decathlon lets 20 college student-led teams from around the world compete to design and build a solar-powered home. A mechanical contractor discusses his work as an advisor during the competition. **Availability:** Print; Online.

4068 ■ *"Eco Smart Home Will Showcase Green Technology" in Contractor (Vol. 56, September 2009, No. 9, pp. 3)*
Ed: Steve Spaulding. **Description:** Eco Smart World Wide is building the Eco Smart Demonstration House to promote the latest in sustainable, renewable and high-efficiency practices and products. The company will use insulated concrete forms in the construction of the building. Features and dimensions of the structure are also presented. **Availability:** Print; Online.

4069 ■ *"Electrolux Feeding Economy: Contracts for Local Firms at $64 Million; Supplier Bids Up Next" in Memphis Business Journal (Vol. 34, June 22, 2012, No. 10, pp. 1)*
Pub: Baltimore Business Journal
Contact: Rhonda Pringle, President
E-mail: rpringle@bizjournals.com
Ed: Michael Sheffield. **Description:** Electrolux Home Products Inc. has awarded almost $64 million of its construction contracts to local companies in Memphis, Tennessee while planning the search for suppliers for its 700,000 square foot manufacturing facility. The company aims to complete the facility by the end of 2012. **Availability:** Print; Online.

4070 ■ *"Empty Lots Could Be Full of Promise" in San Francisco Business Times (Vol. 28, March 14, 2014, No. 34, pp. 4)*
Pub: American City Business Journals, Inc.
Contact: Mike Olivieri, Executive Vice President
Price: $4, Introductory 4-Week Offer(Digital Only). **Description:** San Francisco, California officials are looking at the city's own landholdings in order to start constructing new homes. However, the use of city-owned land does not ensure that the home permit process will be trouble-free. **Availability:** Print; Online.

4071 ■ *"EPA Finalizes WaterSense for Homes" in Contractor (Vol. 57, January 2010, No. 1, pp. 70)*
Ed: Robert P. Mader. **Description:** U.S. Environmental Protection Agency released its "final" version of the WaterSense for Homes standard. The standard's provisions that affect plumbing contractors include the specification that everything has to be leak tested and final service pressure cannot exceed 60 psi. **Availability:** Print; Online.

4072 ■ *"EPA to Tighten Energy Star Standards for 2011" in Contractor (Vol. 56, September 2009, No. 9, pp. 6)*
Description: United States Environmental Protection Agency will tighten standards for its Energy Star for Homes program in 2011. The green trend in the construction industry has been cited as reason for the plan. The agency is adding requirements for energy-efficient equipment and building techniques. **Availability:** Print; Online.

4073 ■ *"Everett Hospice Planned" in Puget Sound Business Journal (Vol. 29, September 26, 2008, No. 23, pp. 1)*
Description: Providence Senior and Community Services is pursuing a purchase-and-sales agreement for land in Everett to build a $9.7 million 20-bed hospice facility. The organization plans to break ground on the new facility in 2009. **Availability:** Print; Online.

4074 ■ *"Extreme Amenities" in Puget Sound Business Journal (Vol. 35, May 9, 2014, No. 3, pp. 4)*
Released: Weekly. **Price:** $4, introductory 4-week offer(Digital & Print). **Description:** Reports show that some developers are designing apartment buildings with themes. Alison Jeffries of Red Propeller believes that these buildings will rent faster if they have their own stories. This construction trend of such buildings is expected to appeal to the Millennial generation. **Availability:** Print; Online.

4075 ■ *"Falcons' Blank Kicking Off 'Westside Works' Job Training Program" in Atlanta Business Chronicle (May 30, 2014, pp. 6A)*
Pub: American City Business Journals, Inc.
Contact: Mike Olivieri, Executive Vice President
Description: Arthur Blank, owner of the Atlanta Falcons, is kicking off 'Westside Works', an initiative to build a world-class football/soccer stadium in Atlanta and transform the adjacent communities. Westside Works, a partnership between The Arthur M. Blank Family Foundation, the Construction Education Foundation of Georgia, and Integrity CDC will provide construction jobs for at least 100 men and women from the Westside neighborhoods in the next 12 months. The program will also provide job training, skills assessment, adult education programs, interview preparedness, and job placement. **Availability:** Print; Online.

4076 ■ *"Fast-Growing Companies Stepped Up Pace in 2011" in Sacramento Business Journal (Vol. 29, July 6, 2012, No. 19, pp. 1)*
Pub: Baltimore Business Journal
Contact: Rhonda Pringle, President
E-mail: rpringle@bizjournals.com
Description: The growth of Sacramento, California-based businesses is seen as a sign of strong economic recovery, as reflected in this publication's annual list has revealed. Stuart James Construction Inc. got the top spot. Businesses registered two-year growth rates ranging from 29 to 632 percent. **Availability:** Print; Online.

4077 ■ *"Faux Down Below" in Entrepreneur (May 2014)*
Pub: Entrepreneur Media Inc.
Contact: Dan Bova, Director
E-mail: dbova@entrepreneur.com
Description: Walter Marine of Orange Beach, Alabama has installed over 35,000 artificial reefs in waters in the U.S. and other countries to help prevent erosion and boost the tourism business. David Walter started his business in 1986 by sinking junk cars and items such as helicopters and kitchen sinks. Walter Marine is now focusing on custom-designed artificial reefs that are made of limestone and concrete. The company is hoping to increase its business by means of privately commissioned reefs. **Availability:** Print.

4078 ■ *"Federal Buildings to Achieve Zero-Net Energy by 2030" in Contractor (Vol. 56, December 2009, No. 12, pp. 5)*
Ed: Candace Roulo. **Description:** United States president Barack Obama has issued sustainable goals for federal buildings. Federal agencies are also required to increase energy efficiency, conserve water and support sustainable communities. Obama has also announced a $3.4 billion investment in a smart energy creed. **Availability:** Print; Online.

4079 ■ *"Finally, New Life For Old IBM Offices" in Austin Business Journal (Vol. 34, June 6, 2014, No. 16, pp. A4)*
Pub: American City Business Journals, Inc.
Contact: Mike Olivieri, Executive Vice President
Released: Weekly. **Price:** $4, introductory 4-week offer(Digital only). **Description:** Two nondescript, 1970s-style industrial buildings, occupied in the 1970s by IBM Corporation, were purchased by an Austin-based contracting and construction management company. Burt-Watts Industries, from Powell Austin Properties Ltd., a local family. The company spent $3 million to renovate all the spaces into attractive, contemporary offices. Tommy Burt, co-founder of Burt-Watts was helped in this endeavor by Clay Little, partner in NoackLittle Architecture & Interiors. **Availability:** Print; Online.

4080 ■ *"Firms Sue Doracon to Recoup More Than $1M in Unpaid Bills" in Baltimore Business Journal (Vol. 28, July 9, 2010, No. 9, pp. 1)*
Pub: Baltimore Business Journal
Contact: Rhonda Pringle, President
E-mail: rpringle@bizjournals.com
Ed: Scott Dance. **Description:** Concrete supplier Paul J. Rach Inc., Selective Insurance Company, and equipment leasing firm Colonial Pacific Leasing Corporation intend to sue Baltimore, Maryland-based Doracon Contracting Inc. for $1 million in unpaid bills. Doracon owed Colonial Pacific $794,000 and the equipment is still in Doracon's possession. Selective Insurance and Paul J. Rach respectively seek $132,000 and $88,000. **Availability:** Print.

4081 ■ *"First Look at Downtown's JW Marriott" in Houston Business Journal (Vol. 45, June 27, 2014, No. 7, pp. 10A)*
Pub: American City Business Journals, Inc.
Contact: Mike Olivieri, Executive Vice President
Released: Weekly. **Price:** $4, Introductory 4-week offer(Digital & Print). **Description:** The JW Marriott is one of several new hotels being developed for downtown Houston and construction scheduled to be completed in time for the 2017 Super Bowl to be held in the city. The hotel includes two ballrooms, the Picasso and the Monet, a spa with eight treatment rooms, a yoga studio, and an executive lounge for platinum and gold members. **Availability:** Print; Online.

4082 ■ *"First Woman To Lead Builders Group" in Philadelphia Business Journal (Vol. 32, January 31, 2014, No. 51, pp. 8)*
Pub: American City Business Journals, Inc.
Contact: Mike Olivieri, Executive Vice President

Released: Weekly. Price: $4, introductory 4-week offer(Digital & Print). Description: Anne Faldoun, president of the Building Industry Association of Philadelphia (BIA), reveals that she has always been interested in architecture. She shares that she worked at the Dorado Neighborhood Improvement Company after she attended graduate school. Her views about the BIA's policy on tax abatement are also discussed. Availability: Print; Online.

4083 ■ "A Flood of New Construction: Will You Tap into the $400B Seawall Pipeline?" in ConstructionDive (October 16, 2019)
URL(s): www.constructiondive.com/news/a-flood-of-new-construction-will-you-tap-into-the-400b-seawall-pipeline/565083/
Ed: Jean Goodman. Released: October 16, 2019. Description: With rising sea levels, many U.S. communities are bidding out new seawall projects, which is projected to produce a construction boom. It's being advised for construction firms to start planning now to get into these projects and to start bidding on the work. Availability: Online.

4084 ■ "Florida Fast 100: D&D Construction Services" in South Florida Business Journal (Vol. 35, September 19, 2014, No. 8, pp. 16)
Pub: American City Business Journals, Inc.
Contact: Mike Olivieri, Executive Vice President
Description: Profile of D and D Construction, who reports increased earnings in 2013 totaling $26.5 million. The increase has been attributed to the commercial real estate market's recovery from the economic recession. The company is focusing on offering hospitality (restaurant, hotel) projects. Availability: Online.

4085 ■ "Florida Hospital Planning $104.1M in Expansions" in Orlando Business Journal (Vol. 29, June 8, 2012, No. 53, pp. 1)
Pub: Baltimore Business Journal
Contact: Rhonda Pringle, President
E-mail: rpringle@bizjournals.com
Description: Florida Hospital is planning $104.1 million in expansion projects that will create about 140 new permanent health care jobs and 576 temporary contruction jobs. The projects include an emergency department and medical office space in Winter Garden, an expanded emergency department at Florida Hospital East Orlando and additional floors in Ginsburg Tower at Florida Hospital Orlando. Availability: Print; Online.

4086 ■ "Flurry of Activity from Restaurant Groups as Industry Strengthens" in Wichita Business Journal (Vol. 27, February 17, 2012, No. 7, pp. 1)
Pub: Baltimore Business Journal
Contact: Rhonda Pringle, President
E-mail: rpringle@bizjournals.com
Description: Atlanta, Georgia-based Chick-fil-A chain is set to open two restaurants in Wichita, Kansas and those additions were highly anticipated. However, there were other local management groups and franchisees that are investing on new buildings and refurbishing stores. Insights on the increasing restaurant constructions are also given. Availability: Print; Online.

4087 ■ "Footage Shows Workers Concerned About Hard Rock New Orleans Before Deadly Collapse" in ConstructionDive (October 18, 2019)
URL(s): www.constructiondive.com/news/footage-shows-workers-concerned-about-hard-rock-new-orleans-before-deadly-c/565338/
Ed: Kim Slowey. Released: October 18, 2019. Description: On October 12, three people died and 30 others were injured when a portion of the Hard Rock Hotel in New Orleans fell. Video has surfaced showing workers concerned about the shoring holding up a concrete slab on the upper floors. An expert points out some general observations about the incident. Availability: Online.

4088 ■ "For One Homebuilder, It's Pretty Easy Being Green, Even in Houston" in Houston Business Journal (Vol. 44, April 11, 2014, No. 49, pp. 7)
Pub: American City Business Journals, Inc.
Contact: Mike Olivieri, Executive Vice President
Released: Weekly. Price: $4, introductory 4-week offer(Digital only). Description: Frankel Building Group vice president, Scott Frankel, says new housing projects in Houston, Texas have been getting bigger. He also said that industry members are facing the problem of lack of residential lots in the region. Frankel added that the company builds its homes to LEED-certified standards. Availability: Print; Online.

4089 ■ "Former Tech Execs Want to Tap Building Trend in Austin" in Austin Business Journal (Vol. 31, May 13, 2011, No. 10, pp. A1)
Pub: Austin Business Journal
Contact: Rachel McGrath, Director
E-mail: rmcgrath@bizjournals.com
Ed: Cody Lyon. Description: Falcon Containers moved to a 51-acre site in Far East Austin, Texas and started construction of a 2,500-square-foot headquarters made from eight 40-foot shipping containers. Falcon's CEO Stephen Shang plans to use his headquarters building as a showroom to attract upscale, urban hipsters. Insights on the construction's environmental and social impact are shared. Availability: Print; Online.

4090 ■ "Fred Weber CEO Tom Dunne: Sales Talks Confidential" in Saint Louis Business Journal (Vol. 32, September 23, 2011, No. 4, pp. 1)
Pub: Saint Louis Business Journal
Contact: Robert Bobroff, President
E-mail: rbobroff@bizjournals.com
Ed: Evan Binns. Description: Fred Weber Inc. CEO Tom Dunne Sr. signed a letter of confidentiality as part of an inquiry made by interested party to the construction company. However, Dunne denied the company is in a fire sale and has been continuing to bid for work and has not stopped securing projects. Availability: Print; Online.

4091 ■ "From Malls to Steel Plants" in Crain's Chicago Business (Vol. 31, April 28, 2008, No. 17, pp. 30)
Pub: Crain Communications Inc.
Contact: Barry Asin, President
Ed: Samantha Stainburn. Description: Profile of the company Graycor Inc. which started out as a sand-blasting and concrete-breaking firm but has grown into four businesses due to innovation and acquisitions. Graycor's businesses include: Graycor Industrial Constructors Inc., which builds and renovates power plants and steel mills; Graycor Construction Co., which erects stores, medical centers and office buildings; Graycor Blasting Co., which uses explosives and blasts tunnels for industrial cleaning, and Graycor International Inc., which provides construction services in Mexico. Availability: Online.

4092 ■ "Funding Drought Stalls Biotech Incubators" in Saint Louis Business Journal (Vol. 31, July 29, 2011, No. 49, pp. 1)
Pub: Saint Louis Business Journal
Contact: Robert Bobroff, President
E-mail: rbobroff@bizjournals.com
Ed: Angela Mueller. Description: Economic slowdown took its toll on cash-strapped startups that fill incubators such as the Bio-Research and Development Growth (BRDG) Park in Creve Coeur, Missouri and the Center for Emerging Technologies in Midtown St. Louis. BRDG put a hold on construction of of its two buildings. Availability: Print; Online.

4093 ■ "Galveston Invests In Future as Major Cruise Destination" in Houston Business Journal (Vol. 44, February 28, 2014, No. 43, pp. 4)
Pub: American City Business Journals, Inc.
Contact: Mike Olivieri, Executive Vice President

Released: Weekly. Price: $4, introductory 4-week offer(Digital only). Description: The Port of Galveston in Texas is planning to build a third cruise terminal to capitalize on the growing cruise industry as it faces new competition with the Bayport Cruise terminal of the Port of Houston Authority. Architecture firm McTigue of Los Angeles, California was commissioned to design the new terminal. Availability: Print; Online.

4094 ■ "Generation Gap: TV Sports Audience Growing Older" in San Francisco Business Times (Vol. 28, January 10, 2014, No. 25, pp. 4)
Pub: American City Business Journals, Inc.
Contact: Mike Olivieri, Executive Vice President
Description: Reports show that the demand for retirement housing in the U.S. continues to increase. The results of a study indicate that the population of people older than 65 in the country could exceed 81 million in 2050. However, some nonprofit housing developers experience construction problems due to the lack of funds. Availability: Online.

4095 ■ "Generation Y Driving Portland Multifamily" in Daily Journal of Commerce, Portland (October 29, 2010)
Ed: Nick Bjork. Description: Generation Y, young adults between the ages of 18-30, are interested in multifamily residents in the Portland, Oregon area. Developers in the area, particularly North Portland, have recognized this trend and are looking into multifamily investments.

4096 ■ "Germans Win Solar Decathlon Again" in Contractor (Vol. 56, November 2009, No. 11, pp. 1)
Ed: Robert P. Mader. Description: Students from Technische Universtat Darmstadt won the U.S. Department of Energy's Solar Decathlon by designing and building the most attractive and efficient solar-powered home. The winner's design produced a surplus of power even during three days of rain and photovoltaic panels covered nearly every exterior surface. Availability: Print; Online.

4097 ■ "Get Online Quick in the Office Or in the Field" in Contractor (Vol. 56, October 2009, No. 10, pp. 47)
Ed: William Feldman, Patti Feldman. Description: Contractors can set up a web site in minutes using the www.1and1.com website. Verizon's Novatel MIFI 2372 HSPA personal hotspot device lets contractors go online in the field. The StarTech scalable business management system helps contractors manage daily operations. Availability: Print; Online.

4098 ■ "Giant Garages Could Rise Up in Downtown Cincinnati" in Business Courier (Vol. 27, October 22, 2010, No. 25, pp. 1)
Pub: Business Courier
Ed: Dan Monk. Description: More than 2,500 new parking spaces could rise up to the eastern edge of downtown Cincinnati, Ohio as public and private investors collect resources for new garage projects. These projects are expected to accommodate almost 1,500 monthly parkers who will lose access at Broadway Commons due to the construction of Harrah's casino. Availability: Print; Mailing list; Online.

4099 ■ "Glenmede at Liberty To Show Off Space" in Philadelphia Business Journal (Vol. 32, January 24, 2014, No. 50, pp. 8)
Pub: American City Business Journals, Inc.
Contact: Mike Olivieri, Executive Vice President
Released: Weekly. Price: $4, introductory 4-week offer(Digital & Print). Description: Glenmede Trust Company decided to undertake a full office renovation after renewing its lease at One Liberty Place. The investment company decided to replace drywall with glass and more informal meeting places were constructed. The firm, which focuses on employee engagement, aims to improve the work environment. Availability: Print; Online.

4100 ■ *"GM's Decision to Boot Dealer Prompts Sale"* in *Baltimore Business Journal (Vol. 27, November 6, 2009, No. 26, pp. 1)*
Pub: Baltimore Business Journal
Contact: Rhonda Pringle, President
E-mail: rpringle@bizjournals.com
Ed: Daniel J. Sernovitz. **Description:** General Motors Corporation's (GM) decision to strip Baltimore's Anderson Automotive Group Inc. of its GM franchise has prompted the owner, Bruce Mortimer, to close the automotive dealership and sell the land to a developer. The new project could make way for new homes, a shopping center and supermarket. **Availability:** Print; Online.

4101 ■ *"Got to be Smarter than the Average Bear"* in *Contractor (Vol. 56, September 2009, No. 9, pp. 82)*
Ed: Robert P. Mader. **Description:** International Association of Plumbing and Mechanical Officials Green Technical Committee has debated the need for contractors to have certifications in installing green plumbing. Some have argued that qualifications would discourage homeowners from improving their properties. Comments from executives are also included. **Availability:** Print; Online.

4102 ■ *"Grainger Show Highlights Building Green, Economic Recovery"* in *Contractor (Vol. 57, February 2010, No. 2, pp. 3)*
Ed: Candace Roulo. **Description:** Chief U.S. economist told attendees of the Grainger's 2010 Total MRO Solutions National Customer Show that the economic recovery would be subdued. Mechanical contractors who attended the event also learned about building sustainable, green products, and technologies, and economic and business challenges. **Availability:** Print; Online.

4103 ■ *"Green Collar: Green Buildings Support Job Creation, Workforce Transformation and Economic Recovery"* in *Environmental Design and Construction (Vol. 15, July 2012, No. 7, pp. 31)*
Pub: BNP Media
Contact: Harper Henderson, Owner Co-Chief Executive Officer
Ed: Maggie Comstock. **Description:** Despite construction being at an all-time low, green building construction has maintained its hold on nonresidential buildings. It has even shown growth in some sectors and accounts for over one-third of all nonresidential design and construction jobs and is expected to show further growth through 2014. Statistical details included.

4104 ■ *"GreenTech Gears Up for Production"* in *Memphis Business Journal (Vol. 33, April 6, 2012, No. 52, pp. 1)*
Pub: Baltimore Business Journal
Contact: Rhonda Pringle, President
E-mail: rpringle@bizjournals.com
Description: GreenTech Automotive has broken ground for construction of a new production facility in Tunica, Tennessee. The company will focus its manufacturing operations in the new facility. **Availability:** Print; Online.

4105 ■ *"Ground Readied for Construction of $4.5 Million Senior Care Center in Crown Point"* in *Times (August 9, 2012)*
Description: Bickford Senior Living will begin construction on a $4.5 million senior care center in Munster, Indiana. The facility will include assisted living apartments for seniors with various needs. Sixteen of the units will care for individuals with memory loss. Nurses and caregivers will be on staff 24 hours a day. **Availability:** Print; Online.

4106 ■ *"Grounded Condo Development Poised for Construction Takeoff"* in *Memphis Business Journal (Vol. 35, February 7, 2014, No. 44, pp. 4)*
Pub: American City Business Journals, Inc.
Contact: Mike Olivieri, Executive Vice President
Released: Weekly. **Price:** $4, introductory 4-week offer(Digital only). **Description:** Developers in Memphis, Tennessee are hoping that the economic recovery will help revive the condominium market. However, industry experts believe that inventory will have to all and prices will have to rise before the market recovers. The impact of loose lending practices on condominium developers is also discussed. **Availability:** Print; Online.

4107 ■ *"'Groundhog Day' B&B Likely Will Be Converted Into One In Real Life"* in *Chicago Tribune (October 21, 2008)*
Pub: Tribune News Service
Contact: Jack Barry, Vice President, Operations
E-mail: jbarry@tribpub.com
Ed: Carolyn Starks. **Description:** Everton Martin and Karla Stewart Martin have purchased the Victorian house that was featured as a bed-and-breakfast in the 1993 hit move "Groundhog Day"; the couple was initially unaware of the structure's celebrity status when they purchased it with the hope of fulfilling their dream of owning a bed-and-breakfast. **Availability:** Print; Online.

4108 ■ *"A Guide to Starting a Driveway Paving Business"* in *Home Business (September 27, 2022)*
URL(s): homebusinessmag.com/business-start-up/how-to-guides/guide-starting-driveway-paving-business/
Released: September 27, 2022. **Description:** Describes what you need to consider before starting a driveway paving business. Includes tips on marketing, registering your business, and creating a business plan. **Availability:** Online.

4109 ■ *"Habitat, Home Depot Expand Building Program"* in *Contractor (Vol. 56, September 2009, No. 9, pp. 16)*
Description: Habitat for Humanity International and The Home Depot Foundation are planning to expand their Partners in Sustainable Building program. The program will provide funds to help Habitat affiliates build 5,000 homes. Comments from executives are also included. **Availability:** Print; Online.

4110 ■ *"Hanson's to Widen Marketing Window; Company Plans Mall Kiosks, to Attend Events"* in *Crain's Detroit Business (Vol. 28, May 28, 2012, No. 22, pp. 3)*
Pub: Crain Communications Inc.
Contact: Barry Asin, President
Ed: Sherri Welch. **Description:** Hanson's Window and Construction Company is expanding its presence through the use of kiosks installed at malls as well as attending local events in order to increase awareness of their firm. Las year Hanson spent nearly $9.2 million on marketing their vinyl replacement windows, siding and roofing for homes. **Availability:** Print; Online.

4111 ■ *"Hard Times Are 'In the Rearview Mirror' for Local Construction Industry"* in *San Antonio Business Journal (Vol. 28, March 14, 2014, No. 5, pp. 10)*
Pub: American City Business Journals, Inc.
Contact: Mike Olivieri, Executive Vice President
Released: March 14, 2014. **Price:** $4, Introductory 4-Week Offer(Digital & Print). **Description:** Analysts believe that San Antonio, Texas' construction industry is back on a growth track. Reports show that the sector had its second-best year in 2013, when it generated $1.14 billion worth of work. The public sector is widely seen as a prime market for the city's contractors. **Availability:** Print; Online.

4112 ■ *"Health-Care Highway"* in *Saint Louis Business Journal (Vol. 32, October 14, 2011, No. 7, pp. 1)*
Pub: Saint Louis Business Journal
Contact: Robert Bobroff, President
E-mail: rbobroff@bizjournals.com
Ed: Angela Mueller. **Description:** Around $2.6 billion will be invested in health care facilities along the Highway 64/40 corridor in St. Louis, Missouri. Mercy Hospital is planning to invest $19 million in a virtual care center. St. Elizabeth's Hospital on the other hand, will purchase 105 acres in the corridor. **Availability:** Print; Online.

4113 ■ *"Health Centers Plan Expansion: $3M from D.C. Expected; Uninsured a Target"* in *Crain's Detroit Business (Vol. 25, June 15, 2009, No. 24, pp. 3)*
Pub: Crain Communications Inc.
Contact: Barry Asin, President
Ed: Jay Greene. **Description:** Detroit has five federally qualified health centers that plan to receive over $3 million in federal stimulus money that will be used to expand projects that will care for uninsured patients. **Availability:** Print; Online.

4114 ■ *"Healthcare Facilities Increasingly Embracing Dynamic Glass to Benefit Patients"* in *Ecology, Environment & Conservation Business (May 24, 2014)*
Pub: NewsRX LLC.
Contact: Kalani Rosell, Contact
Description: According to research, optimizing natural daylight and outdoor views in healthcare facilities helps to improve outcomes and shorter recovery times for patients. Therefore, a growing number of healthcare facilities are incorporating SageGlass(R) dynamic glass, a product of Saint-Gobain, into their new construction and remodeling/renovation designs. **Availability:** Online.

4115 ■ *Heart: Building a Great Brand in the Digital Age*
Pub: CreateSpace
Released: September 29, 2014. **Price:** $3.70, paperback. **Description:** Business leader and consultant who works with designers, contractors and service providers in the green industry helps business owners develop and implement company systems and increase revenue. His is a third-generation horticulturist and small business owner and share the challenges of being an entrepreneur. **Availability:** Print.

4116 ■ *"Hennelly Aims to Increase Building Work in Great Lakes Region for Ryan Cos."* in *Crain's Chicago Business (Vol. 34, May 23, 2011, No. 21, pp. 6)*
Pub: Crain Communications Inc.
Contact: Barry Asin, President
Ed: Eddie Baeb. **Description:** Profile of Tim Hennelly, who is working to make Ryan Company known as a pure builder rather than a developer-builder. **Availability:** Print; Online.

4117 ■ *"Highland Row Joins Fray of Development Around U of M"* in *Memphis Business Journal (No. 35, February 14, 2014, No. 45, pp. 7)*
Released: February 14, 2014. **Description:** Real estate developer Milhaus is planning a 354-unit apartment complex and retail development project at the site of the Highland Church of Christ near the University of Memphis in Tennessee. other developers are also planning their own projects near the site including Shepherd Construction Company and Rael Development Corporation.

4118 ■ *"Historic Is Hot, But Challenging, in Bham"* in *Birmingham Business Journal (Vol. 31, August 1, 2014, No. 31, pp. 10)*
Pub: American City Business Journals, Inc.
Contact: Mike Olivieri, Executive Vice President
Description: Birmingham, Alabama is witnessing a growing trend of restoring old and historic buildings for modern office spaces, driven by the new state credit for the projects. However, developers state that renovation projects present numerous challenges, including complying with current building codes and the use of energy-efficient innovation. **Availability:** Print; Online.

4119 ■ *"Hollander 95 Business Park Project Getting Bigger"* in *Baltimore Business Journal (Vol. 29, September 23, 2011, No. 20, pp. 1)*
Pub: Boston Business Journal
Contact: Carolyn M. Jones, President

E-mail: cmjones@bizjournals.com
Ed: Gary Haber. Description: Hollander 95 Business Park is in for a huge change as its new owners plan a $50 million expansion which calls for building as many as eight more buildings or a total of more than 500,000 square feed. FRP Development bought the site for $4.35 million at a foreclosure sale in July 2010 and is now seeking city approval for an Industrial Planned Unit Development designation. Availability: Online.

4120 ■ *"Home Developers Buy 9 Acres in Lakewood"* in *Dallas Business Journal (Vol. 35, August 10, 2012, No. 48, pp. 1)*
Pub: Baltimore Business Journal
Contact: Rhonda Pringle, President
E-mail: rpringle@bizjournals.com
Ed: Candace Carlisle. Description: Megatel Homes, together with Centurion American Development Group, has purchased a 9.4 acre land in Lakewood, Dallas for $35 million. Centurion plans to begin real estate development of 59 single-family home lots in the next three months, while Megatel plans construction to build Tudor style homes. The infill land is considered a prime investment for its desireable location.

4121 ■ *"Home Improvement Service Chain Had to Fix Its Own House"* in *Crain's Detroit Business (Vol. 30, October 13, 2014, No. 41, pp. 15)*
Pub: Crain Communications Inc.
Contact: Barry Asin, President
Description: Mr. Handyman International LLC is the franchising arm for the Mr. Handyman home improvement service chain. The franchises provide smaller home repair and improvement projects, mostly residential with only 15 percent of the jobs being commercial. Statistical data included. Availability: Online.

4122 ■ *"Home Price Trends from a Financial Perspective"* in *Real Estate Review (Vol. 41, Spring 2012, No. 1, pp. 5)*
Description: Factors responsible for home price volatility are examined. Home prices have increased by four percent annually in the past quarter century. The availability of credit and underwriting standards are seen to account for home price variations. Meanwhile, home builders and mortgage lenders are also seen to contribute to home price volatility. Availability: Print; Online.

4123 ■ *"Home Prices Sag"* in *Crain's Chicago Business (Vol. 31, April 28, 2008, No. 17, pp. 3)*
Pub: Crain Communications Inc.
Contact: Barry Asin, President
Ed: Alby Gallun. Description: Since the slump in the housing market is continuing with no sign of recovery, Chicago-area home prices are poised for an even steeper drop this year. In 2007, the region's home prices fell nearly 5 percent and according to a forecast by Fiserv Inc., they will decline 8.1 percent this year and another 2.2 percent in 2009. Statistical data included. Availability: Online.

4124 ■ *"Home, Sweet Shipping Container"* in *Washington Business Journal (Vol. 33, July 18, 2014, No. 13, pp. 4)*
Pub: American City Business Journals, Inc.
Contact: Mike Olivieri, Executive Vice President
Description: Brookland Equity Group LLC is converting a single-family hom ein Brookland into a three-story, four-unit shipping container apartment building in Washington DC. According to the Department of Consumer Regulatory Affairs, the application was reviewed for lighting, ventilation, insulation, and other construction standards. Discussion on the new micro small living spaces trend is presented. Availability: Print; Online.

4125 ■ *"Homebuilder Confidence Buried Under Snow"* in *Birmingham Business Journal (Vol. 31, February 21, 2014, No. 8, pp. 7)*
Pub: American City Business Journals, Inc.
Contact: Mike Olivieri, Executive Vice President
Released: Weekly. Description: The National Association of Home Builders/Wells Fargo Housing Market Index has fallen by 10 points from the score of 56 in January to 46 in February as a result of 2014's harsh winter. The index is based on the survey of home builders' perceptions on the current and near-term housing market. Availability: Print; Online.

4126 ■ *"Homebuilders Continue to be Our Nemesis"* in *Contractor (Vol. 56, July 2009, No. 7, pp. 50)*
Ed: Robert P. Mader. Description: Homebuilders rank high on the greed scale along with Wall Street brokers. There is this one instance when a builder gave copies of another contractor's quotes that have just been blackened out and another instance when one builder let other bidders visit a site while the current mechanical contractor is working. Availability: Print; Online.

4127 ■ *"Homebuilding Numbers Going Up"* in *Memphis Business Journal (Vol. 33, January 27, 2012, No. 42, pp. 1)*
Pub: Baltimore Business Journal
Contact: Rhonda Pringle, President
E-mail: rpringle@bizjournals.com
Ed: Cole Epley. Description: Homebuilding construction activity in Memphis, Tennessee has increased in 2011. Home buyers are also seen to show sign of return to normalcy. Availability: Print; Online.

4128 ■ *"Homebuilding Thrives on Lot Prices"* in *Memphis Business Journal (Vol. 33, February 24, 2012, No. 46, pp. 1)*
Pub: Baltimore Business Journal
Contact: Rhonda Pringle, President
E-mail: rpringle@bizjournals.com
Ed: Christopher Sheffield. Description: Homebuilders in Memphis, Tennessee have survived the economic crises owing to the decrease in prices of lots. However, the increasein the purchase of lots is seen to adversely impact the sector in the long run. Availability: Print; Online.

4129 ■ *"Hotel Expected to Jump Start Downtown Revitalization"* in *Houston Business Journal (Vol. 44, March 28, 2014, No. 47, pp. 10)*
Pub: American City Business Journals, Inc.
Contact: Mike Olivieri, Executive Vice President
Released: Weekly. Price: $4, introductory 4-week offer(Digital only). Description: Hotel Alessandra has the potential to become the key to revitalize downtown Houston, Texas. Gensler's design principal, Kap Malik, believes the hotel would become a landmark building and together with other projects will bring a lot of excitement and activity to the area. Other hotels that are under construction or planned for downtown are presented. Availability: Print; Online.

4130 ■ *"Hotel Pitched by Mortenson Would Be Among First Of Its Kind in U.S."* in *Business Journal (Vol. 31, February 14, 2014, No. 38, pp. 10)*
Pub: American City Business Journals, Inc.
Contact: Mike Olivieri, Executive Vice President
Released: February 14, 2014. Price: $4, Introductory 4-week offer(Digital & Print). Description: A $63 million, 300-room hotel is proposed by Mortenson Development near the new Minnesota Vikings stadium. The proposed hotel will be co-branded under two Marriott International Inc. brands, AC Hotels and SpringHill Suites. Availability: Print; Online.

4131 ■ *"Hotel Woes Reflect Area Struggle"* in *Business Journal Serving Greater Tampa Bay (Vol. 30, December 3, 2010, No. 50, pp. 1)*
Pub: Tampa Bay Business Journal
Contact: Ian Anderson, President
E-mail: ianderson@bizjournals.com
Ed: Mark Holan. Description: Quality Inn and Suites in East Tampa, Florida has struggled against the sluggish economy but remained open to guests despite facing a foreclosure. The hotel project is the center of East Tampa's redevelopment plans and public officials defend the $650,000 investment in public amenities near the building. Availability: Print; Online.

4132 ■ *"Housing Slide Picks Up Speed"* in *Crain's Chicago Business (Vol. 31, April 19, 2008, No. 16, pp. 2)*
Pub: Crain Communications Inc.
Contact: Barry Asin, President
Ed: Eddie Baeb. Description: According to Tracy Cross & Associates Inc., a real estate consultancy, sales of new homes in the Chicago area dropped 61 percent from the year-earlier period which is more bad news for homebuilders, contractors and real estate agents who are eager for an indication that market conditions are improving. Availability: Online.

4133 ■ *"Houston Firm To Build World's Largest Plant of Its Kind"* in *Houston Business Journal (Vol. 44, April 25, 2014, No. 51, pp. 4A)*
Pub: American City Business Journals, Inc.
Contact: Mike Olivieri, Executive Vice President
Released: April 25, 2014. Price: $4, introductory 4-week offer(Digital only). Description: Enterprise Products Partners LP is constructing its largest refrigerate ethane export plant in Houston, Texas and the facility is expected to be operational by the third quarter of 2016. According to CEO, Michael Creel, the facility is designed to process up to 240,000 barrels a day. Availability: Print; Online.

4134 ■ *"How Contractors Can Survive a Downturn"* in *ConstructionDive (October 21, 2019)*
URL(s): www.constructiondive.com/news/how-contractors-can-survive-a-downturn/565058/
Ed: Kim Slowey. Released: October 21, 2019. Description: Even though there is a huge construction boom happening, recessions are bound to happen and the construction industry always slows down as a result. Managing cash flow is one of several tips to get contractors and small construction companies from folding. Availability: Online.

4135 ■ *"How I Did It: Mel Zuckerman, Chairman, Canyon Ranch"* in *Inc. (December 2007, pp. 140-142)*
Ed: Daniel McGinn. Description: Profile of Mel Zuckerman, who tells how transformed his life as a middle-aged, overweight homebuilder to a healthy addition to the fitness and spa industry with his posh Canyon Ranch retreats. Availability: Online.

4136 ■ *"Huge Fight Over Tiny Apartments"* in *Puget Sound Business Journal (Vol. 35, September 12, 2014, No. 21, pp. 8)*
Pub: American City Business Journals, Inc.
Contact: Mike Olivieri, Executive Vice President
Description: Smart Growth Seattle director, Roger Valdez and Seattle City Council member, Mike O'Brien, share their views about the proposed new rules and regulations governing micro-apartment buildings. Valdes says O'Brien's proposal would eliminate a choice for many people and force them to pay more or live elsewhere. O'Brien says the bill aims to apply existing construction rules to micro-housing in a fair way. Availability: Online.

4137 ■ *"'Human Error' Cited for Deadly Google Seattle Crane Collapse, 3 Firms Fined $107K"* in *ConstructionDive (October 21, 2019)*
URL(s): www.constructiondive.com/news/human-error-cited-for-deadly-google-seattle-crane-collapse-3-firms-fined/565416/
Ed: Kim Slowey. Released: October 21, 2019. Description: Three contractors were fined a total of $107,200 over the deadly tower crane collapse at the Google office project in Seattle. Four people were killed. It was determined that the contractors and their workers ignored the proper instructions for dismantling the crane, causing it to weaken and fall. Availability: Online.

4138 ■ "Hunt Valley Towne Center Gears Up for Growth; Ray Lewis Project Scrapped" in Baltimore Business Journal (Vol. 30, May 11, 2012, No. 1, pp. 1)
Pub: American City Business Journals, Inc.
Contact: Mike Olivieri, Executive Vice President
Ed: James Briggs. Description: Greenberg Gibbons Commercial Corporation has plans for a 400-unit apartment complex and retail space at Hunt Valley Towne Centre in Baltimore, Maryland. The developer is also considering big-box stores to rent the vacant space that was supposed to be occupied by the failed bowling and entertainment venture MVP Lanes. Availability: Print; Online.

4139 ■ "Hunter Capital's Malone Relishes Role of Renovator" in Puget Sound Business Journal (Vol. 35, June 13, 2014, No. 8, pp. 9)
Pub: American City Business Journals, Inc.
Contact: Mike Olivieri, Executive Vice President
Description: Hunter Capital's founder, Michael Malone, says Seattle, Washington's real estate development needs to be balanced. He also stated that his company is set to renovate the old Dunn Automotive Building. He added that his firm will continue with its construction restoration projects. Availability: Online.

4140 ■ "IAPMO GTC Votes to Limit Showers to 2.0-GPM" in Contractor (Vol. 56, September 2009, No. 9, pp. 1)
Description: Green Technical Committee of the International Association of Plumbing and Mechanical Officials has voted to limit showers to 2.0 GPM. It is also developing a Green Plumbing and Mechanical Supplement. Comments from executives are also supplied. Availability: Print; Online.

4141 ■ "ICC Works on Prescriptive Green Construction Code" in Contractor (Vol. 56, October 2009, No. 10, pp. 1)
Ed: Robert P. Mader. Description: International Code Council launched an initiative to create a green construction code that focuses on existing commercial buildings. The initiative's timeline will include public meetings leading up to a final draft that will be available in 2010. Availability: Print; Online.

4142 ■ "If They Build It, Will Customers Come?" in Business Journal Portland (Vol. 30, February 7, 2014, No. 49, pp. 7)
Pub: American City Business Journals, Inc.
Contact: Mike Olivieri, Executive Vice President
Price: $4, Introductory 4-week offer(Digital & Print). Description: The Portland Trail Blazers partnered with Levy Restaurants to open a 10,000-square-foot restaurant at Moda Center in Oregon in spring 2014. GBD Architects and Lorentz Brunn Construction were enlisted for the project. Availability: Print; Online.

4143 ■ "If We Build Them, Will They Rent Them?" in Birmingham Business Journal (Vol. 31, August 1, 2014, No. 31, pp. 4)
Pub: American City Business Journals, Inc.
Contact: Mike Olivieri, Executive Vice President
Released: August 1, 2014. Description: Developers and experts opine that the current demand for multi-family homes in Birmingham, Alabama will continue to grow, despite doubts by Housing and Urban Development over the city center's ability to sustain such growth. The key factors in the city's multi-family market as well as the risks and challenges facing developers are examined.

4144 ■ "Incapital Set to Add Jobs, Expand Space" in South Florida Business Journal (Vol. 33, August 3, 2012, No. 1, pp. 1)
Pub: Baltimore Business Journal
Contact: Rhonda Pringle, President
E-mail: rpringle@bizjournals.com
Description: Chicago, Illinois-based Incapital has announced plans to hire 25 to 30 more financial professionals over the next 12 months. Incapital is also planning to expand its Boca Raton, Florida construction totalling 5,000 additional square feet to accommodate future growth. Availability: Print; Online.

4145 ■ "Independence Station Utilizes Sustainable Technologies" in Contractor (Vol. 56, September 2009, No. 9, pp. 3)
Ed: Candace Roulo. Description: Independence Station building in Oregon is seen to receive the most LEED points ever awarded by the United States Green Building Council. The building will use an ice-based cooling storage system, biofuel cogeneration system and phovoltaic system. Other building features and dimensions are also supplied. Availability: Print; Online.

4146 ■ "Infrastructure: Things Fall Apart" in Canadian Business (Vol. 80, October 8, 2007, No. 20, pp. 187)
Pub: Rogers Media Inc.
Contact: Neil Spivak, Chief Executive Officer
Ed: Jeff Sanford. Description: Infrastructure crisis in Canada and in other countries in North America is examined. Incidents that demonstrate this crisis, such as the collapse of a bridge in Minneapolis and the collapse of an overpass in Quebec, Canada are presented. It is estimated that the reconstruction in the country will cost between C$44 billion and C$200 billion. Availability: Print; Online.

4147 ■ "Iogen in Talks to Build Ethanol Plant in Canada" in Globe & Mail (March 21, 2007, pp. B7)
Ed: Shawn McCarthy. Description: Ottawa based Iogen Corp. is planning to construct a cellulosic ethanol plant in Saskatchewan region. The company will be investing an estimated $500 million for this purpose. Availability: Print; Online.

4148 ■ "Is Fannie Mae the Next Government Bailout?" in Barron's (Vol. 88, March 10, 2008, No. 10, pp. 21)
Pub: Dow Jones & Company Inc.
Contact: Almar Latour, Chief Executive Officer
Ed: Jonathan R. Laing. Description: Fannie Mae may need a government bailout as it faces huge hits brought about by the effects of the housing crisis. The shares of the government-sponsored enterprise have dropped 65 percent since the housing crisis began. Availability: Online.

4149 ■ "It's What You Know. It's Who You Know. It's China" in Inc. (Vol. 33, October 2011, No. 8, pp. 80)
Description: Michael Lee will be the first American entrepreneur to build big in China. The company is piloting two large commercial real estate developments, one in New York City the other in Nanjing, China. Availability: Print; Online.

4150 ■ "J.C. Evans Files for Ch. 11 Protection" in Austin Business Journal (Vol. 31, August 12, 2011, No. 23, pp. A1)
Pub: Austin Business Journal
Contact: Rachel McGrath, Director
E-mail: rmcgrath@bizjournals.com
Ed: Vicky Garza. Description: J.C. Evans Construction Holdings Inc., as well as its affiliated companies, has filed for Chapter 11 bankruptcy following its continued financial breakdown which it blames on the tough economy. Details are included. Availability: Print; Online.

4151 ■ "KC Incentives Debate Rages on Unabated" in The Business Journal-Serving Metropolitan Kansas City (Vol. 26, September 5, 2008, No. 52)
Pub: American City Business Journals, Inc.
Contact: Mike Olivieri, Executive Vice President
Ed: Rob Roberts. Description: Debate on the new economic development and incentives policy adopted by the Kansas City Council is still on. The city's Planned Industrial Expansion Authority has rejected a standard property tax abatement proposal. The real estate development community has opposed the rejection of proposed the tax incentives policy. Availability: Online.

4152 ■ "KXAN Seeks Larger Studio, Office Space in Austin" in Austin Business Journal (Vol. 31, May 27, 2011, No. 12, pp. A1)
Pub: Austin Business Journal
Contact: Rachel McGrath, Director
E-mail: rmcgrath@bizjournals.com
Ed: Cody Lyon. Description: Austin NBC affiliate KXAN Television is opting to sell its property north of downtown and relocate to another site. The station is now inspecting possible sites to house its broadcasting facility and employees totaling as many as 200 people. Estimated cost of the construction of the studios and offices is $13 million plus another million in moving the equipment. Availability: Print; Online.

4153 ■ "La Cantera Resort Expects to Benefit from Big Transformation" in San Antonio Business Journal (Vol. 28, July 18, 2014, No. 23, pp. 8)
Pub: American City Business Journals, Inc.
Contact: Mike Olivieri, Executive Vice President
Released: Weekly. Price: $4, Introductory 4-week offer(Digital & Print). Description: La Cantera Hill County Resort in San Antonio, Texas is planning a multimillion dollar major renovation of the property and the addition of a spa. The resort announced the suspension of overnight accommodations and restaurant operations during the major phase of the construction from November 3, 2014 until early April 2015. Availability: Print; Online.

4154 ■ "LA Passes HET Ordinance, California Greens Code" in Contractor (Vol. 56, September 2009, No. 9, pp. 1)
Ed: Candace Roulo. Description: Los Angeles City Council has passed a Water Efficiency Requirements ordinance. The law mandates lower low-flow plumbing requirements for plumbing fixtures installed in new buildings and retrofits. Under the ordinance, a toilet's maximum flush volume may not exceed 1.28-gpf. Availability: Print; Online.

4155 ■ "Labor Shortage Creates Growing Pains" in Orlando Business Journal (Vol. 30, January 31, 2014, NO. 32, pp. 5)
Pub: American City Business Journals, Inc.
Contact: Mike Olivieri, Executive Vice President
Released: January 31, 2014. Description: The reactions of residential real estate industry executives on the labor shortage created by the growing demand for new homes is presented. There were plenty of tradesmen and laborers on hand when the housing market recovery began, however, construction management faces labor competition from other builders and this trend slows the industry. Availability: Print; Online.

4156 ■ "Land Squeeze Stalls Portland Homebuilders" in Business Journal Portland (Vol. 31, March 21, 2014, No. 3, pp. 4)
Pub: American City Business Journals, Inc.
Contact: Mike Olivieri, Executive Vice President
Released: March 21, 2014. Price: $4, Introductory 4-Week Offer(Digital & Print). Description: Homebuilders in Portland, Oregon are building fewer homes that before the recession due to the impact of the 2008 economic collapse and the lack of available land on which to build. Prices in the residential real estate market are expected to increase as new single family home construction fails to keep pace with growing demand. Availability: Print; Online.

4157 ■ "Land Swap Key to Ending Royal Oak Project Impasse" in Crain's Detroit Business (Vol. 25, June 8, 2009, No. 23, pp. 20)
Pub: Crain Communications Inc.
Contact: Barry Asin, President
Ed: Chad Halcom. Description: Details of the new construction of the LA Fitness health club near Woodward and Washington Avenues in Royal Oak, Michigan are discussed. Availability: Online.

4158 ■ "Large Homes can be Energy Efficient Too" in Contractor (Vol. 56, October 2009, No. 10, pp. 5)
Ed: Candace Roulo. Description: Eco Estate at Briggs Chaney subdivision in Silver Spring, Maryland has model houses that use sustainable technologies

and products and the homes that will be built on the subdivision will feature some of the technologies featured on the model home. The energy efficient HVAC system of the model homes are discussed. **Availability:** Print; Online.

4159 ■ *"The Latest on E-Verify"* in *Contractor (Vol. 56, September 2009, No. 9, pp. 58)*
Ed: Susan McGreevy. **Description:** United States government has required federal contractors to use its E-Verify program to verify the eligibility of incoming and existent employees. The use of the program is seen to eliminate Social Security mismatches. **Availability:** Print; Online.

4160 ■ *"Legal Barriers Keep 16-Story Horizon at Ground Level"* in *Memphis Business Journal (Vol. 34, August 24, 2012, No. 19, pp. 1)*
Pub: Baltimore Business Journal
Contact: Rhonda Pringle, President
E-mail: rpringle@bizjournals.com
Description: Construction on the Horizon building at 717 Riverside Drive remains unfinished as legal battles ensue among banks and construction firms involved in the project. The root of the legal proceedings is the Bryan Company's defaulting from a $58.6 million loan from four banks and the foreclosureof the property. **Availability:** Print; Online.

4161 ■ *"Legoland Florida Theme Park Construction to Start in May"* in *Orlando Business Journal (Vol. 26, January 29, 2010, No. 35, pp. 1)*
Pub: Orlando Business Journal
Contact: Julie Swyers, Director
E-mail: jswyers@bizjournals.com
Ed: Richard Bilbao. **Description:** Merlin Entertainments Group purchased the closed Cypress Garden theme park in Winter Haven, Florida for $22.3 million and plans to spend a reported $100 million or more to begin transforming it into the world's largest Legoland. Winter Haven businesses are expecting a windfall from the theme park's constructions workers. **Availability:** Print; Online.

4162 ■ *"Lending Door Slams"* in *Puget Sound Business Journal (Vol. 29, October 24, 2008, No. 27, pp. 1)*
Description: KeyBank's closure of its Puget Sound unit that services single-family homebuilders is part of a nationwide shutdown that includes similar closures in other cities. Bank of America is adopting more conservative terms for homebuilding loans while Union Bank of California is still offering credit for market rate housing. **Availability:** Print; Online.

4163 ■ *"Long Live Rock"* in *Inc. (November 2007, pp. 130)*
Ed: Nitasha Tiku. **Description:** Profile of a family business using chemistry to recycle concrete products. **Availability:** Print; Online.

4164 ■ *"A Look Ahead at How Rail Could Change Ala Moana"* in *Pacific Business News (Vol. 52, August 22, 2014, No. 26, pp. 7)*
Pub: American City Business Journals, Inc.
Contact: Mike Olivieri, Executive Vice President
Released: August 22, 2014. **Price:** $4, Introductory 4-Week Offer(Digital & Print). **Description:** The City and County of Honolulu has hired Nate Cherry, vice president of California-based architectural firm RTKL, to create a new plan for Ala Moana in anticipation of the completed $5.16 billion Honolulu rail project. Cherry's plans for the neighborhood under the Transit Oriented Development project include better streets with wider sidewalks, wider tree canopies, bicycle trails and parks. **Availability:** Print; Online.

4165 ■ *"Looming Labor Crunch Already Pushing Up Construction Prices"* in *Business Journal (Vol. 32, August 8, 2014, No. 11, pp. 10)*
Pub: American City Business Journals, Inc.
Contact: Mike Olivieri, Executive Vice President
Released: Weekly. **Price:** $4, introductory 4-week offer(Digital & Print). **Description:** Minneapolis, Minnesota's construction sector is expected to suffer from a worker shortage. An increase in the demand for construction labor will result in higher wages. Meanwhile, higher wages are expected to drive up construction costs. **Availability:** Print; Online.

4166 ■ *"Magellan Companies Establishes Century 21 Beachhead in Boise"* in *Idaho Business Review (September 15, 2014)*
Pub: BridgeTower Media
Contact: Adam Reinebach, President
Description: New Jersey-based Century 21, the largest real estate franchise worldwide, has entered the Idaho market under the name Century 21 Magellan Realty with five agents. Wesley Flacker, builder, home renovator, broker, and property manager purchased the franchise and expects to have 60 agents by 2015.

4167 ■ *"Major Advances in Heat Pump Technology"* in *Contractor (Vol. 57, January 2010, No. 1, pp. 42)*
Ed: Mark Eatherton. **Description:** Tax credits make ground-source heat pump technology more economically feasible. Suggestions on how to choose the right ground-source heat pump technology to install in a house are discussed. **Availability:** Print; Online.

4168 ■ *"The Making of a Building Boom"* in *Philadelphia Business Journal (Vol. 32, January 31, 2014, No. 51, pp. 4)*
Pub: American City Business Journals, Inc.
Contact: Mike Olivieri, Executive Vice President
Released: Weekly. **Price:** $4, introductory 4-week offer(Digital & Print). **Description:** Reports show that construction activity in Philadelphia, Pennsylvania is on the rise. However, the results of a recent study indicate that near-term shortages or skilled workers could be problematic. Projections on the cost of construction in 2014 are also discussed. **Availability:** Print; Online.

4169 ■ *"Mall On a Mission: KOP to Get $150 Million Makeover"* in *Philadelphia Business Journal (Vol. 33, March 14, 2014, No. 5, pp. 6)*
Pub: American City Business Journals, Inc.
Contact: Mike Olivieri, Executive Vice President
Released: Weekly. **Price:** $4, introductory 4-week offer(Digital & Print). **Description:** Philadelphia, Pennsylvania-based King of Prussia Mall is set to undergo a $150 million renovation. The plan involves construction of about 250,000 square feet of space for retailers. Mall owner, Simon Property Group, has contracted IMC Construction to handle the project. **Availability:** Print; Online.

4170 ■ *"Managing the Federal HOME Program: Past and Future"* in *Real Estate Review (Vol. 41, Spring 2012, No. 1, pp. 29)*
Released: Spring 2012. **Description:** The US Department of Housing and Urban Development's Home Investment Partnerships Program (HOME) is discussed. The program is allocated to eligible state and local governments, with the goal of increasing affordable housing. HOME has been criticized for idling home construction projects.

4171 ■ *"Mayor Rawlings Pushes for South Dallas Development to Take Root"* in *Dallas Business Journal (Vol. 35, March 16, 2012, No. 27, pp. 1)*
Pub: Baltimore Business Journal
Contact: Rhonda Pringle, President
E-mail: rpringle@bizjournals.com
Ed: Candace Carlisle. **Description:** Mayor Mike Rawlings has initiated efforts to create affordable housing options in southern Dallas, Texas. Rawligs has been exploring land opportunities and assessing how to leverage those land opportunities appropriately for home construction.

4172 ■ *"Mechanic Theatre's Brutalist Style at Battle's Center"* in *Baltimore Business Journal (Vol. 30, May 11, 2012, No. 1, pp. 1)*
Pub: American City Business Journals, Inc.
Contact: Mike Olivieri, Executive Vice President
Ed: James Briggs. **Description:** David S. Brown Enterprises Ltd. plans to demolish the Morris A. Mechanic Theatre in Baltimore, Maryland and replace it with two 30-story towers that include 600 apartment units, retail, and parking spaces. The local chapter of the American Institute of Architects opposes the proposal and calls for the preservation of the former theatre's brutalist achitecture. **Availability:** Print; Online.

4173 ■ *"Meet the Next Big Name in Residential Construction"* in *Houston Business Journal (Vol. 44, February 21, 2014, No. 42, pp. 8)*
Pub: American City Business Journals, Inc.
Contact: Mike Olivieri, Executive Vice President
Released: Weekly. **Price:** $4, introductory 4-week offer(Digital only). **Description:** Hillwood Communities of Dallas, Texas will break ground on the Pomona master-planned community in Manvel, 20 miles south of downtown Houston. The development will include 2,100 single-family homes ranging from $250,000 to $400,000, a new elementary school and a new junior high school. **Availability:** Print; Online.

4174 ■ *"Methodist Plans Richardson Hospital"* in *Dallas Business Journal (Vol. 35, June 29, 2012, No. 42, pp. 1)*
Pub: Baltimore Business Journal
Contact: Rhonda Pringle, President
E-mail: rpringle@bizjournals.com
Ed: Bill Hethcock. **Description:** Methodist Health System is planning to build a hospital in Richardson, Texas. The hospital will have a capacity of 125 beds and employ around 900 people. Comments from executives are included. **Availability:** Print; Online.

4175 ■ *"Minnesota ABC Event Looks at Government Contracting"* in *Finance and Commerce Daily Newspaper (November 23, 2010)*
Ed: Brian Johnson. **Description:** Minnesota Associated Builders and Contractors hosted an event focusing on doing business with government agencies. Topics included bidding work, awarding jobs, paperwork, guidelines, certifications and upcoming projects. **Availability:** Online.

4176 ■ *"Minor-League Baseball's Sliders Plan Stock Offering"* in *Crain's Detroit Business (Vol. 25, June 15, 2009, No. 24, pp. 3)*
Pub: Crain Communications Inc.
Contact: Barry Asin, President
Ed: Bill Shea. **Description:** New minor-league baseball team is raising funds to build a new stadium in Waterford Township, Michigan because banks are unwilling to provide loans for the project. Owners of the Midwest Sliders in Ypsilanti, Michigan are waiting for the federal Securities and Exchange Commission to approve a Regulation A public offering. **Availability:** Print; Online.

4177 ■ *"A Model Development"* in *Crain's Cleveland Business (Vol. 28, October 1, 2007, No. 39, pp. 12)*
Pub: Crain Communications Inc.
Contact: K. C. Crain, President
Ed: Scott Suttell. **Description:** Profile a Forest City Enterprises Inc., a firm that is developing a project in New Mexico called Mesa del Sol. The Albuquerque development is being seen as the vanguard of master-planned communities with its high-tech economic development center which is expected to become the site of 60,000 jobs, 38,000 homes and a town center. **Availability:** PDF.

4178 ■ *"More Gains in the Pipeline"* in *Barron's (Vol. 89, August 3, 2009, No. 31, pp. M5)*
Description: Shares of El Paso Corp. could recover as the company concludes a deal with a private-equity group to fund pipeline construction. The company's shares are trading at $10.06 and could move up to $12 as bad news has already been priced into the stock. **Availability:** Online.

4179 ■ *"N.C. Data-Center Plan Bearing Fruit From Apple, Spec Center"* in *Charlotte Business Journal (Vol. 25, October 15, 2010, No. 30, pp. 1)*
Pub: Charlotte Business Journal
Contact: Robert Morris, Editor
E-mail: rmorris@bizjournals.com
Ed: Ken Elkins. **Description:** Apple Inc. is planning to expand its server farm at the North Carolina Data Center Corridor in Catawba County. T5 Partners, on the other hand, will build a shell building to house a server on the site. Infocrossing Inc. will also build an open data center in the area. **Availability:** Print; Online.

4180 ■ *"A Necessary Balancing Act: Bookkeeping"* in *Contractor (Vol. 56, November 2009, No. 11, pp. 22)*
Ed: Al Schwartz. **Description:** Pros and cons of getting a bookkeeper or a certified public accountant for the subcontractor are discussed. A bookkeeper can help a subcontractor get new accounting software up and running while an accountant will more than likely keep after the books at regular intervals throughout the year. **Availability:** Print; Online.

4181 ■ *"New Apartments To Rise Downtown"* in *Memphis Business Journal (Vol. 33, January 27, 2012, No. 42, pp. 1)*
Pub: Baltimore Business Journal
Contact: Rhonda Pringle, President
E-mail: rpringle@bizjournals.com
Ed: Andy Ashby. **Description:** TOV Virginia LP is planning to build an apartment complex in Memphis, Tennessee. The construction project is estimated to cost around $10.5 million. The development wll be focused on affordable housing and will use local and federal incentives. **Availability:** Print; Online.

4182 ■ *"New APS AZ Sun Launches"* in *Manufacturing Close-Up (September 19, 2012)*
Description: Permit process has begun to construct the Hyder II Solar Power Plant located in Hyder, Arizona. The project is a partnership between Arizona Public Service and McCarthy Building Companies. The Arizona Sun Program is adding 200 MW of solar photovoltaic power plants across Arizona by 2015. **Availability:** Print; Online.

4183 ■ *"New Argentine Investment Taps Real Estate"* in *South Florida Business Journal (Vol. 32, June 22, 2012, No. 48, pp. 1)*
Pub: Baltimore Business Journal
Contact: Rhonda Pringle, President
E-mail: rpringle@bizjournals.com
Description: Industry experts believe that Miami, Florida is becoming the go-to-investment destination of Argentines looking for real estate development opportunities. For example, Consultatio paid $220 million for 5.5 acres in Bal Harbour where it plans to construct condominiums. It appears Argentines are selecting sites in Miami as investments. **Availability:** Print; Online.

4184 ■ *"New 'Build California' Program Hopes to Grow Workforce"* in *Electrical Contractor (October, 2019)*
URL(s): www.ecmag.com/section/your-business/new-build-california-program-hopes-grow-workforce
Ed: Katie Kuehner-Hebert. **Released:** October 2019. **Description:** Build California, a new workforce development initiative, is recruiting in order to help fill up empty construction spots. A one-year high school pilot program is underway to promote trade organizations.

4185 ■ *"New Holiday Inns Set for Airport Area, Graceland"* in *Memphis Business Journal (Vol. 34, August 17, 2012, No. 18, pp. 1)*
Pub: Baltimore Business Journal
Contact: Rhonda Pringle, President
E-mail: rpringle@bizjournals.com
Description: Two new Holiday Inn hotels are to be constructed in Memphis, Tennessee in the next two years. The plan is in line with the company's celebration of its 60th anniversary. **Availability:** Print; Online.

4186 ■ *"New Hydronic Heating Technologies Work"* in *Contractor (Vol. 57, January 2010, No. 1, pp. 58)*
Ed: Carol Fey. **Released:** January 01, 2010. **Description:** Technology behind hydronic heating systems is reviewed. These technologies include radiant and geothermal hydronic heating. System requirements for installing these greener forms of heating are discussed.

4187 ■ *"New PHH Building Still Going Up In Amherst Despite Job Cuts"* in *Business First of Buffalo (Vol. 30, February 28, 2014, No. 24, pp. 5)*
Pub: American City Business Journals, Inc.
Contact: Mike Olivieri, Executive Vice President
Released: Weekly. **Price:** $140, Digital & Print; $115, Digital only. **Description:** New Jersey-based PHH Mortgage Company has maintained the construction of its $34 million back-office complex in Amherst, New York despite eliminating 135 employees. PHH confirms that lower industry-wide demand in the mortgage business has caused the job cuts. The Erie County Industrial Development Agency's adoption of a recapture policy is also examined. **Availability:** Print; Online.

4188 ■ *"New State Rules Require Cranes and Operators to be Certified"* in *Bellingham Business Journal (Vol. February 2010, pp. 11)*
Pub: Sound Publishing Inc.
Contact: Josh O'Connor, President
Ed: Isaac Bonnell. **Description:** All construction cranes in Washington state must be inspected annually to be certified for use. The move is part of a larger L&I crane safety program that also requires crane operators to pass a written exam and a skill test.

4189 ■ *"Next Stage of Green Building will be Water Efficiency"* in *Contractor (Vol. 56, July 2009, No. 7, pp. 41)*
Description: One market report says that water efficiency and conservation will become critical factors in green design, construction, and product selection in the next five years from 2009. The report outlines how critical it will be for the construction industry to address responsible water practices in the future. **Availability:** Print; Online.

4190 ■ *"Northwest Washington Fair Building New Horse Arena"* in *Bellingham Business Journal (Vol. March 2010, pp. 6)*
Pub: Sound Publishing Inc.
Contact: Josh O'Connor, President
Ed: Isaac Bonnell. **Description:** Northwest Washington Fair is building a new equestrian arena that will provide larger show space for the horse community. The existing arena will function as a warm-up arena when hosting large shows.

4191 ■ *"Oahu Contractors Worry About Worker Shortage"* in *Pacific Business News (Vol. 52, March 14, 2014, No. 3, pp. 3)*
Pub: American City Business Journals, Inc.
Contact: Mike Olivieri, Executive Vice President
Released: Weekly. **Price:** $4, introductory 4-week offer(Digital only). **Description:** Members of Oahu's construction sector have expressed concerned over the short supply of workers. The industry is expected to add about 5,000 new jobs by 2014. **Availability:** Print; Online.

4192 ■ *"On the House: Housing Developers Try to Read Generation Y"* in *Philadelphia Inquirer (December 2, 2010)*
Pub: The Philadelphia Inquirer
Contact: Elizabeth H. Hughes, Chief Executive Officer
Ed: Al Heavens. **Description:** Results of a survey conducted with Generation Y individuals are examined, focusing on housing developments and whether this particular generation prefers suburban or rural lifestyles. Generation Y encompasses people ages 18 to 32 years old. Statistical data included. **Availability:** Online.

4193 ■ *"Orlando City Lions May Score MLS Dream With Stadium"* in *Orlando Business Journal (Vol. 29, August 31, 2012, No. 11, pp. 1)*
Pub: Baltimore Business Journal
Contact: Rhonda Pringle, President
E-mail: rpringle@bizjournals.com
Description: The Orlando City Lions soccer team may play Major League Soccer as early as 2014 or 2015 if it gets its own stadium. Although the MLS did not assign a stadium as a requirement for joining the league, it did ask the team if it could build a 22,000-seater stadium. The team has plans to find land and create a design for the facility, with construction costs estimated at around $200 million. **Availability:** Print; Online.

4194 ■ *"Orlando Health to Build $24M Proton Therapy Facility"* in *Orlando Business Journal (Vol. 26, January 22, 2010, No. 34, pp. 1)*
Pub: Orlando Business Journal
Contact: Julie Swyers, Director
E-mail: jswyers@bizjournals.com
Ed: Melanie Stawicki Azam. **Description:** Orlando Health is planning to construct a $24 million proton therapy facility at its MD Anderson Cancer Center Orlando in Florida. The facility, which aims for a 2011 opening, will be using radiation for more accurate targeting of tumors and avoiding the damage to surrounding tissues and organs. **Availability:** Print; Online.

4195 ■ *"Outlook 2008 (9 Sectors to Watch): Construction"* in *Canadian Business (Vol. 81, December 19, 2007, No. 1, pp. 48)*
Pub: Rogers Media Inc.
Contact: Neil Spivak, Chief Executive Officer
Ed: Jeff Sanford. **Description:** Infrastructure deficit of C$123 billion, and still growing, was recently reported by the Federation of Canadian Municipalities. Details on plans for infrastructure projects and forecasts on the construction sector for 2008 are discussed. **Availability:** Print; Online.

4196 ■ *"Overseas Marketing Key to Success of Chicago Spire"* in *Commercial Property News (March 17, 2008)*
Description: New construction of the Chicago Spire, a condominium project located on Lake Michigan's shore, is being marketed to would-be clients in Asia where Chicago is viewed as an emerging world city. **Availability:** Online.

4197 ■ *"Pathology Firm Building New HQ: Poplar Healthcare Facility Will Be Near FedEx Corp."* in *Memphis Business Journal (Vol. 34, June 29, 2012, No. 11, pp. 1)*
Pub: Baltimore Business Journal
Contact: Rhonda Pringle, President
E-mail: rpringle@bizjournals.com
Ed: Andy Ashby. **Description:** Poplar Healthcare Management LLC is building a new 113,000 square foot coporate headquarters in Southeast Memphis, Tennessee. The laboratory services company purchased the 18.6 acre property for $1.2 million and filed an $11.5 million construction permit for the office building. **Availability:** Print; Online.

4198 ■ *"Pentagon Awards $17.6B Contract for EB-Built Subs Through 2018"* in *Providence Business News (Vol. 29, April 28, 2014, No. 4)*
Pub: American City Business Journals, Inc.
Contact: Mike Olivieri, Executive Vice President
URL(s): pbn.com/pentagon-awards-176b-contract-for-eb-built-subs-through-20189678
Description: The U.S. Navy has signed a $17.6 billion contract with Newport News Shipbuilding and General Dynamics Corporation for construction of 10 new naval submarines. The deal will help employment at General Dynamics' Quonset Business Park

Electric Boat production site. The submarines are scheduled to be built between 2014-2018. Electric Boat expects to hire 650 additional workers.

4199 ■ *"Physicians Development Groupn Kicks Off $13M Skilled Nursing Facility in NE Wichita"* in **Wichita Business Journal** *(Vol. 27, January 20, 2012, No. 3, pp. 1)*
Pub: Baltimore Business Journal
Contact: Rhonda Pringle, President
E-mail: rpringle@bizjournals.com
Description: Physicians Development Group has started construction of a skilled nursing facility in Wichita, Kansas. The 80-bed nursing facility is estimated to cost around $13 million. **Availability:** Print; Online.

4200 ■ *"Pipeline Dreams"* in **Canadian Business** *(Vol. 80, October 22, 2007, No. 21, pp. 19)*
Description: Northwest Mackenzie Valley Pipeline has been under review by the National Energy Board since 2004. Hearings on the construction of the gas pipeline will wrap up in 2008. Pius Rolheiser, the spokesman of Imperial Oil Company Inc. believes the change of government in the area will not affect the negotiations on the pipeline construction. **Availability:** Print; Online.

4201 ■ *"Plan Would Give Face-Lift to Section of Italian Market"* in **Philadelphia Business Journal** *(Vol. 28, June 29, 2012, No. 20, pp. 1)*
Pub: Baltimore Business Journal
Contact: Rhonda Pringle, President
E-mail: rpringle@bizjournals.com
Description: Midwood Investment & Development is planning construction on a 32,000 square foot shopping center dubbed the Italian Marketplace in South Philadelphia, Pennsylvania. Under the Lower Italian Market Revitalization Plan, the retail space will have improved storefronts, landscaping and bike lanes. It is slated to open in the first half of 2014. **Availability:** Print; Online.

4202 ■ *"Plans for $160M Condo Resort in Wisconsin Dells Moves Forward"* in **Commercial Property News** *(March 18, 2008)*
Description: Plans for the Grand Cambrian Resort in the Wisconsin Dells is discussed. The luxury condominium resort will include condos, townhomes, and condo-hotel style residences, two water parts, meeting space and indoor entertainment space, as well as a spa, four restaurants and retail offerings. **Availability:** Online.

4203 ■ *"Power Partnerships"* in **Business Courier** *(Vol. 27, October 22, 2010, No. 25, pp. 1)*
Description: The $400 million Harrah's casino and the $47 million redevelopment and expansion of Washington Park are project aimed at boosting the economy in downtown Cincinnati, Ohio. These projects will be done in cooperation with the National Association for the Advancement of Colored People. Insights into the role of minority-owned businesses in regional economic development are explored. **Availability:** Print; Online.

4204 ■ *"Preleasing Drives Wedgewood Start"* in **Memphis Business Journal** *(Vol. 33, February 17, 2012, No. 45, pp. 1)*
Pub: Baltimore Business Journal
Contact: Rhonda Pringle, President
E-mail: rpringle@bizjournals.com
Ed: Andy Ashby. **Description:** Austin-Texas-based StoneCrest Investments LLC has started construction on the second phase of its $32 million Wedgewood Commons Shopping Center in Olive Branch at Memphis, Tennessee. The commercial real estate development company has managed to complete enough preleasing to begin construction in the retail center. **Availability:** Print; Online.

4205 ■ *"Public Bathroom Pressure Woes Resolved"* in **Contractor** *(Vol. 56, September 2009, No. 9, pp. 44)*
Ed: Dave Yates. **Description:** Design and construction of a public bathroom's plumbing system in the United States are discussed. Installed plumbing fixtures with flush valves would not function properly. The installation of Grundfos SQE variable-speed pumps has resolved problems with the bathroom's water pressure. **Availability:** Print; Online.

4206 ■ *"ReachLocal Plans to Double DFW Space, is Hunting for 150K Square Feet"* in **Dallas Business Journal** *(Vol. 35, March 23, 2012, No. 28, pp. 1)*
Pub: Baltimore Business Journal
Contact: Rhonda Pringle, President
E-mail: rpringle@bizjournals.com
Description: Online marketing firm ReachLocal Inc. is planning to double its presence in North Texas. The company is considering building up to 150,000-square-feet of space in the area. Construction plans are included. **Availability:** Print; Online.

4207 ■ *"Reagan HQ In Limbo"* in **Austin Business Journal** *(Vol. 32, April 6, 2012, No. 5, pp. A1)*
Pub: American City Business Journals, Inc.
Contact: Mike Olivieri, Executive Vice President
Ed: Vicky Garza. **Description:** Reagan National Advertising has been awaiting the Austin City Council decision on whether it would be allowed to build a new headquarters that was on the drawing board for more than five years. However, approval of Reagan's plan would cut down several trees and that would violate the Heritage tree ordinance. **Availability:** Online.

4208 ■ *"Real Estate Dealmakers of the Year: Where Are They Now?"* in **San Francisco Business Times** *(Vol. 28, March 28, 2014, No. 36)*
Pub: American City Business Journals, Inc.
Contact: Mike Olivieri, Executive Vice President
Released: Weekly. **Description:** Maria Ayerdi-Kaplan has been named the Business Times Dealmaker of the Year for 2013. Ayerdi-Kaplan is the Transbay Joint Powers Authority Executive Director and is in charge of oversight for the planned Transbay Transit Center. The center is part of a $4.5 billion construction project in San Francisco, California. **Availability:** Print; Online.

4209 ■ *"Recovery on Tap for 2010?"* in **Orlando Business Journal** *(Vol. 26, January 1, 2010, No. 31, pp. 1)*
Pub: Orlando Business Journal
Contact: Julie Swyers, Director
E-mail: jswyers@bizjournals.com
Ed: Melanie Stawicki Azam, Richard Bilbao, Christopher Boyd, Anjali Fluker. **Description:** Economic forecasts for Central Florida's leading business sectors in 2010 are presented. These sectors include housing, film and TV, sports business, law, restaurants, aviation, tourism and hospitality, banking and finance, commercial real estate, retail, health care, insurance, higher education, and manufacturing. According to some local executives, Central Florida's economy will slowly recover in 2010. **Availability:** Online.

4210 ■ *"Remington Developer Says Project May Not Include Second Big Box"* in **Baltimore Business Journal** *(Vol. 30, June 8, 2012, No. 5, pp. 1)*
Pub: American City Business Journals, Inc.
Contact: Mike Olivieri, Executive Vice President
Ed: James Briggs. **Price:** $4, introductory 4-week offer(Digital only). **Description:** WV Urban Developments will proceed with the 25th Street Station retail and housing project in Baltimore, Maryland with Wal-Mart Stores Inc. as the remaining retail anchor occupying 229,383 feet of space. Lowe's Cos. has backed out of the lease due to petitions filed by Wal-Mart components calling to overturn the plan. **Availability:** Print; Online.

4211 ■ *"Remote Work in Construction: 3 Tips for Success"* in **Home Business Magazine** *(Jan. 27, 2022)*
URL(s): homebusinessmag.com/businesses/success-tips/remote-work-construction-3-tips-success/
Ed: Alex Minett. **Released:** January 27, 2022. **Description:** Discusses how remote work during the pandemic has changed aspects of the construction business. Provides tips for construction business owners to set up a remote team for success. **Availability:** Online.

4212 ■ *"Research, Treatment to Expand"* in **Philadelphia Business Journal** *(Vol. 28, June 22, 2012, No. 19, pp. 1)*
Pub: Baltimore Business Journal
Contact: Rhonda Pringle, President
E-mail: rpringle@bizjournals.com
Description: Fox Chase Cancer Center and Temple University Health System have been planning several projects once their merger is completed. Their plans include the construction of a unit for cancer patients on the third floor of the Founder's Building at Jeanes Hospital and a granting mechanism to fund research collaborations. **Availability:** Print; Online.

4213 ■ *"ReVenture Plan Appears Close to Landing Key N.C. Legislative Deal"* in **Charlotte Business Journal** *(Vol. 25, July 9, 2010, No. 16, pp. 1)*
Pub: Charlotte Business Journal
Contact: Robert Morris, Editor
E-mail: rmorris@bizjournals.com
Ed: John Downey. **Description:** North Carolina lawmakers acted on special legislation that would boost development of Forsite Development 667-acre ReVenture Energy Park. The legislation could also improve chances that Duke Energy Carolinas will contract to purchase the power from the planned 50-megawatt biomass power plant located at the park. How utilities would benefit from the legislation is also discussed. **Availability:** Print; Online.

4214 ■ *"A Rise in Rental Units"* in **Philadelphia Business Journal** *(Vol. 30, October 7, 2011, No. 34, pp. 1)*
Pub: Philadelphia Business Journal
Contact: Sierra Quinn, Director
E-mail: squinn@bizjournals.com
Ed: Natalie Kostelni. **Description:** Housing developers have been stepping up the construction of new apartment complexes throughout the suburbs of Pennsylvania in order to capture growing demand for rental properties. BPG Properties Ltd. has nearly 1,000 new apartments under construction. **Availability:** Online.

4215 ■ *"Ritz Kapalua Sells 93 Suites for $176M to Fund Renovation"* in **Commercial Property News** *(March 17, 2008)*
Description: Ritz-Carlton, Kapalua in Lahaina, Hawaii sold ninety-three of its units in order to fund renovations of 463 rooms and suites along with construction of a new spa and fitness center, new and expanded restaurants and pools and an environmental education center for children. **Availability:** Online.

4216 ■ *"Riverfront Revival in Pawtucket?"* in **Providence Business News** *(Vol. 28, March 17, 2014, No. 50, pp. 1)*
Pub: American City Business Journals, Inc.
Contact: Mike Olivieri, Executive Vice President
URL(s): pbn.com/Riverfront-revival-in-Pawtucket,95766
Description: Pawtucket, Rhode Island is focusing on riverfront redevelopment projects due to an improving economy. City planning director, Barney Heath, reveals that Tai-O Group, Peregrine Group and Apex Development Company have already responded to a request for qualifications to begin construction projects. **Availability:** Online. **Telecommunication Services:** Anderson@pbn.com.

4217 ■ *"Roger Hickel Contracting: Smoothing the Road for Owners"* in **Alaska Business Monthly** *(Vol. 27, October 2011, No. 10, pp. 114)*
Pub: Alaska Business Publishing Company Inc.
Contact: Charles Bell, Vice President, Sales and Marketing
E-mail: cbell@akbizmag.com

Ed: Gail West. Description: Profile of Roger Hickel and his contracting company that reports nearly $60 million annually in gross revenue. The firm focuses on customer service. Availability: Print; Online.

4218 ■ "RT Seeking Ways to Finance Expansion" in Sacramento Business Journal (Vol. 28, July 29, 2011, No. 22, pp. 1)
Pub: Sacramento Business Journal
Contact: Stephanie Fretwell, Director
E-mail: sfretwell@bizjournals.com
Ed: Melanie Turner. Description: Sacramento Regional Transit District is considering ways to finance all its capital projects outlined in a 30-year transit master plan which would cost more than $7 billion to complete. Current funding sources include developer fees and state and federal assistance and fares. Part of the master plan is a light-rail line to Sacramento International Airport. Availability: Print.

4219 ■ "Rudy's Tortillas Wraps Up Expansion Plan in Carrollton" in Dallas Business Journal (Vol. 35, August 31, 2012, No. 51, pp. 1)
Pub: Baltimore Business Journal
Contact: Rhonda Pringle, President
E-mail: rpringle@bizjournals.com
Ed: Candace Carlisle. Released: Weekly. Description: Rudy's Tortillas Corporation, a 67-year old family business based in Dallas, Texas, is moving into a new plant on Belt Line Road, Carrollton. The expansion will also involve the hiring of 150 new workers and enable the company to expand its operations. Rudy's will spend $14 million dollars on construction and equipment on the new tortilla plant. Availability: Print; Online.

4220 ■ "Salvation Army Prepares to Break Ground on South Mountain Community Center" in The Business Journal - Serving Phoenix and the Valley of the Sun (Vol. 28, September 12, 2008, No. 53, pp. 1)
Pub: Phoenix Business Journal
Contact: Alex McAlister, Director
E-mail: amcalister@bizjournals.com
Ed: Jan Buchholz. Description: Construction will begin in early 2009 on an $80 million Ray and Joan Kroc Community Center in Phoenix, Arizona. It will be located adjacent to the Salvation Army, which received a $1.9 billion contribution from Joan Kroc after her death in 2003. This fund will be divided to construct 30 community centers across the country. Availability: Print; Online.

4221 ■ "San Antonio Office Market: What a Difference a Year Makes" in San Antonio Business Journal (Vol. 28, August 8, 2014, No. 26, pp. 8)
Pub: American City Business Journals, Inc.
Contact: Mike Olivieri, Executive Vice President
Released: August 08, 2014. Price: $4, Introductory 4-Week Offer(Digital & Print). Description: The San Antonio, Texas office market has grown in 2014. The market has absorbed over 610,000-square-feet of space during the first six months of the year. Meanwhile, a number of new office building construction projects are underway. Availability: Print; Online.

4222 ■ "Science Museum, Theater Seeking State Loans" in Sacramento Business Journal (Vol. 31, May 30, 2014, No. 14, pp. 4)
Pub: American City Business Journals, Inc.
Contact: Mike Olivieri, Executive Vice President
Released: Weekly. Price: $4, Introductory 4-week offer(Digital & Print). Description: The Powerhouse Science Center and B Street Theatre in Sacramento, California are hoping to secure loans from the California Infrastructure and Economic Development Bank. Both nonprofit organizations are planning to start their own construction projects as soon as loans are received. Availability: Print; Online.

4223 ■ "SCO Expanding to Meet Optometry Growth" in Memphis Business Journal (Vol. 33, March 2, 2012, No. 47, pp. 1)
Pub: Baltimore Business Journal
Contact: Rhonda Pringle, President
E-mail: rpringle@bizjournals.com
Ed: Christopher Sheffield. Description: Southern College of Optometry (SCO) has begun construction of a $9.4 million expansion that will provide new classrooms, a flexible state-of-the-art lecture hall, and a glass atrium and grand hall. The project was designed to secure SCO's position among the top US optometry school as demand for its graduates grow. Availability: Print; Online.

4224 ■ "A Second Chance at Road Dollars" in Orlando Business Journal (Vol. 26, February 5, 2010, No. 36, pp. 1)
Pub: Orlando Business Journal
Contact: Julie Swyers, Director
E-mail: jswyers@bizjournals.com
Description: Nearly $10 million worth of construction projects in Central Florida would give construction companies that missed the initial round of federal stimulus-funded local road building projects another opportunity. Cost savings in the initial round of road projects enabled Orange, Osceola, and Seminole Counties to secure additional projects. Availability: Print; Online.

4225 ■ "Self-Employment in the United States" in Montly Labor Review (Vol. 133, September 2010, No. 9, pp. 17)
Pub: U.S. Department of Labor Bureau of Labor Statistics
Contact: Amrit Kohli, Director
E-mail: kohli.amrit@bls.gov
Description: Self employment in 2009 in the U.S. continued to be more common among men, Whites, Asians, and older workers and in the agriculture, construction, and services industries. Availability: PDF; Online.

4226 ■ "Sellers Face Excess Land Dilemma" in Crain's Cleveland Business (Vol. 28, November 16, 2007, No. 45, pp. 1)
Pub: Crain Communications Inc.
Contact: K. C. Crain, President
Ed: Stan Bullard. Description: Overview on the way in which the housing slump is effecting builders, land developers and lot prices. Statistical data included. Availability: Online.

4227 ■ Shedworking: The Alternative Workplace Revolution
Pub: Frances Lincoln Ltd.
Contact: Philip Cooper, Publisher
E-mail: philip.cooper@quarto.com
Ed: Alex Johnson. Description: Shedworking is an alternative office space for those working at home. The book features shedworkers and shedbuilders from around the world who are leading this alternative workplace revolution and why this trend is working. Availability: Print.

4228 ■ "Six Arkansas Construction Projects Get LEED Certification" in Arkansas Business (Vol. 29, July 23, 2012, No. 30, pp. 19)
Pub: Arkansas Business Publishing Group
Contact: Mitch Bettis, President
Ed: Lance Turner. Description: State of Arkansas has bestowed its Leadership in Energy and Environmental Design certification on 55 projects throughout the state. Six projects are identified and described. A list of all projects is included. Availability: Online.

4229 ■ "Sneak Preview: Alamo Revamp" in Austin Business JournalInc. (Vol. 28, December 12, 2008, No. 39, pp. 1)
Description: Austin, Texas-based Alamo Drafthouse Cinemas is planning to build a new Circle C Ranch. The new theater will showcase digital projectors and the latest sound systems to show 3-D movies. The company is in lease negotiations with developer Stratus Properties Inc. Availability: Print; Online.

4230 ■ "South Loop Site Lands a Buyer" in Crain's Chicago Business (Vol. 31, March 24, 2008, No. 12, pp. 1)
Pub: Crain Communications Inc.
Contact: Barry Asin, President
Ed: Alby Gallun. Description: Russland Capital Group, a little-known condominium developer from Skokie, recently purchased a 6.5-acre riverside property in the site known as Franklin Point for $40 million. Availability: Online.

4231 ■ "Spec Homes are Back as Builders Gain Confidence" in Sacramento Business Journal (Vol. 29, August 31, 2012, No. 27, pp. 1)
Pub: Baltimore Business Journal
Contact: Rhonda Pringle, President
E-mail: rpringle@bizjournals.com
Ed: Sanford Nax. Description: Home builders in California are looking to obtain more permits in anticipation of increased residential construction activity. Builders are also looking to rebuild housing supply and are more confident that these homes will sell quickly.

4232 ■ "State Center Lease Deal High for Md." in Baltimore Business Journal (Vol. 28, August 6, 2010, No. 13, pp. 1)
Pub: Baltimore Business Journal
Contact: Rhonda Pringle, President
E-mail: rpringle@bizjournals.com
Ed: Daniel J. Sernovitz. Description: The proposed $1.5 billion State Center development project in Midtown Baltimore might cause the State of Maryland to pay the most expensive rental rates in the city. The state will have to pay an effective rental rate of $34 per square foot, including expenses, on the leasing. Other details of the redevelopment project are discussed. Availability: Print; Online.

4233 ■ "Stay In Your Home" in Consumer Reports Money (Vol. 9, May 20, 2012, No. 5, pp. 1)
Pub: Consumer Reports Books
Contact: Marta L. Tellado, President
Description: Renovations to help the elderly remain in their homes are covered. Availability: Online.

4234 ■ "Still No Arena Financing Plan" in Sacramento Business Journal (Vol. 28, May 27, 2011, No. 13, pp. 1)
Pub: Sacramento Business Journal
Contact: Stephanie Fretwell, Director
E-mail: sfretwell@bizjournals.com
Ed: Kelly Johnson. Description: The government of Sacramento, California has yet to devise a plan to finance the construction of a proposed stadium. The arena is estimated to cost $387 million. A brief description of the facility is also included. Availability: Online.

4235 ■ "Stung by Recession, Hemmer Regroups with New Strategy" in Business Courier (Vol. 27, June 4, 2010, No. 5, pp. 1)
Pub: Business Courier
Ed: Lucy May. Description: Paul Hemmer Companies reduced its work force and outsourced operations such as marketing and architecture, in order for the commercial and construction firm to survive the recession. Hammer's total core revenue in 2009 dropped to less than $30 million forcing the closure of its Chicago office. Availability: PDF; Online.

4236 ■ "SunEdison Sells 30MW Spectrum Solar Project To Southern Company and Turner Renewable Energy" in Benzinga.com (September 28, 2012)
Pub: Benzinga.com
Contact: Jason Raznick, Founder
Ed: Paul Quintaro. Description: SunEdison sold its Spectrum Solar Project, a 30 MW solar photovoltaic power plant, to Southern Company and Turner Renewable Energy. Construction of the project is planned to begin in October 2012 in Clark County, Nevada. Details are included. Availability: Print; Online.

4237 ■ "SunRail Route Apartments Coming in 2013" in Orlando Business Journal (Vol. 29, September 14, 2012, No. 13, pp. 1)
Pub: Baltimore Business Journal
Contact: Rhonda Pringle, President

E-mail: rpringle@bizjournals.com

Ed: Anjali Fluker. **Description:** Real estate developers are planning to start construction of four apartment projects at SunRail stations in Florida. The projects are estimated to be worth $121 million. They are also seen to drive commercialization of the area. **Availability:** Print; Online.

4238 ■ *"Survey: Don't Expect Big Results From Stimulus"* in *Crain's Detroit Business (Vol. 25, June 1, 2009, No. 22)*
Pub: Crain Communications Inc.
Contact: Barry Asin, President

Ed: Nancy Kaffer, Chad Halcom. **Description:** In a recent survey, Michigan business owners, operators or managers showed that 48 percent of respondents oppose the President's stimulus package and believe it will have little or no effect on the economy. **Availability:** Print.

4239 ■ *"Sustainability Is Top Priority for GreenTown Chicago"* in *Contractor (Vol. 56, November 2009, No. 11, pp. 1)*
Pub: American City Business Journals, Inc.

Ed: Candace Roulo. **Description:** GreenTown Chicago 2009 conference tackled energy-efficient practices and technologies, green design and building, and sustainable policies. Water conservation was also a topic at the conference and one mayor who made a presentation said that reducing the water loss in the system is a priority in the city's endeavor. **Availability:** Print; Online.

4240 ■ *"Swope: Breakup Won't Delay East Village"* in *The Business Journal-Serving Metropolitan Kansas City (Vol. 26, August 22, 2008, No. 50, pp. 1)*
Pub: American City Business Journals, Inc.
Contact: Mike Olivieri, Executive Vice President

Ed: Rob Roberts. **Description:** Swope Community Builders said that the Kansas City Redevelopment Project will not be delayed by the breakup of their partnership with Sherman Associates Inc. Swopes will be the sole master developer of the project. **Availability:** Online.

4241 ■ *"Taylor Tests Land Grant Program"* in *Austin Business Journal (Vol. 31, June 3, 2011, No. 13, pp. 1)*
Pub: Austin Business Journal
Contact: Rachel McGrath, Director
E-mail: rmcgrath@bizjournals.com

Ed: Vicky Garza. **Description:** Taylor Economic Development Corporation implemented a land grant program called Build On Our Lot to lure businesses to Taylor City, Austin, Texas. They are targeting small businesses, especially those in the renewable energy, advanced manufacturing, technical services and food products. Program details are included. **Availability:** Print; Online.

4242 ■ *"That Empty Feeling"* in *Crain's Cleveland Business (Vol. 28, October 15, 2007, No. 41, pp. 1)*
Pub: Crain Communications Inc.
Contact: K. C. Crain, President

Ed: Stan Bullard. **Description:** Townhouses, cluster homes and condominiums lured both buyers and builders for most of this decade but now that market is suffering to an even greater degree than the single-family home market. Statistical data included. **Availability:** Online.

4243 ■ *"These Are the Women Who Really Mean Business"* in *Canadian Business (Vol. 87, October 2014, No. 10, pp. 67)*

Description: A list of the top 100 women entrepreneurs in Canada are ranked, based on sales, three-year revenue growth rate, and profitability of their businesses is presented. Included in the list are Janet Stimpson of White House Design Company, Inc.; builder, Allison Grafton of Rockwood Custom Homes Inc.; and Janet Jing Di Zhang of Vancouver, BC of New Immigrants Information Services Inc. **Availability:** Online.

4244 ■ *"'Those Days In New York Are Over"* in *Philadelphia Business Journal (Vol. 33, March 28, 2014, No. 7, pp. 6)*
Pub: American City Business Journals, Inc.
Contact: Mike Olivieri, Executive Vice President
Released: Weekly. **Price:** $4, introductory 4-week offer(Digital & Print). **Description:** Building Trades Employers' Association of New York president and CEO, Louis J. Coletti, comments on the alleged intimidating union activity in Philadelphia, Pennsylvania to hire union members outlined in a federal indictment against Ironworkers Local 401. Coletti believes the limited open-shop market era will remain in the New York construction industry. **Availability:** Print; Online.

4245 ■ *"Threat of New Office Space Records Rent Hikes"* in *Globe & Mail (March 21, 2007, pp. B4)*
Description: The increasing commercial rent prices in the Toronto region amid the high office building construction market are discussed. **Availability:** Online.

4246 ■ *"Toll Talker: CEO Takes Stock of His Company, the Housing Market"* in *Philadelphia Business Journal (Vol. 33, May 9, 2014, No. 13, pp. 4)*
Pub: American City Business Journals, Inc.
Contact: Mike Olivieri, Executive Vice President
Released: Weekly. **Price:** $4, introductory 4-week offer(Digital only). **Description:** Douglas C. Yearley, Jr., CEO of Toll Brothers Inc. discusses how his company capitalized on the economic recession in the housing market by acquiring large tracts of land between 2008 and 2010, including Shapell Homes in California for $1.2 billion. Yearley believes that while the housing downturn trend led to a rise in apartment living, the concept of home ownership remains relatively strong in the U.S., thus spurring construction. **Availability:** Print; Online.

4247 ■ *"Top Architecture Firms"* in *South Florida Business Journal (Vol. 34, June 13, 2014, No. 47, pp. 13)*
Pub: American City Business Journals, Inc.
Contact: Mike Olivieri, Executive Vice President
Description: The top architectural firms in South Florida, as of June 13, 2014, ranked by gross billings are listed. AECOM Technology Corporation got the top spot, ADD Inc. ranked third. **Availability:** Print; Online.

4248 ■ *"Top Stadium Builders Likely To Vie For Vikings Project"* in *Business Journal (Vol. 29, May 18, 2012, No. 51, pp. 1)*
Ed: John Vomhof Jr. **Description:** The $975 million Minnesota Vikings stadium project has been approved and is expected to attract big construction firms to bid for the project. A new Minnesota Sports Facility Authority will need to be appointed first, however, before actual selection of design-build team. Architecture firm Populous and contractor Mortenson Construction are among the frontrunners for the project. **Availability:** Print; Online.

4249 ■ *"Two New Apartment Complexes on Tap for West Orange County"* in *Orlando Business Journal (Vol. 29, September 7, 2012, No. 12, pp. 1)*
Pub: Baltimore Business Journal
Contact: Rhonda Pringle, President
E-mail: rpringle@bizjournals.com

Ed: Anjali Fluker. **Description:** Unicorp National Development Inc. and Altamonte Springs, Florida-based LeCesse Development Inc. are seeking the City of Ocoee's approval for the construction of 458 apartment units on vacant land on Maguire Road. The two real estate developers are scheduled to meet with city planners to discuss the project and submit building plans.

4250 ■ *"University Place Building Gets an Anchor Tenant: Groundbreaking 2.0"* in *Philadelphia Business Journal (Vol. 30, September 23, 2011, No. 32, pp. 1)*
Pub: Philadelphia Business Journal
Contact: Sierra Quinn, Director

E-mail: squinn@bizjournals.com

Ed: Natalie Kostelni. **Description:** University Place Associates, the developer of 2.0 University Place in West Philadelphia, Pennsylvania, will break ground on a five-story, 97,000-square-foot office building in December 2011. The decision follows the Citizenship and Immigration Services signing of a 15-year lease as anchor tenant. **Availability:** Online.

4251 ■ *"USF Plans $30M Sports Complex"* in *Tampa Bay Business Journal (Vol. 29, October 23, 2009, No. 44, pp. 1)*
Pub: Tampa Bay Business Journal
Contact: Ian Anderson, President
E-mail: ianderson@bizjournals.com

Ed: Jane Meinhardt. **Description:** University of South Florida (USF) is going to build a new sports complex with the aid of a $30 million loan from BB&T. The project, which is also comprised of new and renovated athletic facilities on USF's Tampa campus, is projected to create more than $37 million in revenue in its first year. Revenues from the said facilities are expected to achieve an annual growth of at least four percent. **Availability:** Print; Online.

4252 ■ *"VA Seeking Bidders for Fort Howard"* in *Baltimore Business Journal (Vol. 28, June 25, 2010, No. 7, pp. 1)*
Pub: Baltimore Business Journal
Contact: Rhonda Pringle, President
E-mail: rpringle@bizjournals.com

Ed: Daniel J. Servnoitz. **Description:** The Veterans Affairs Maryland Health Care Systems has requested proposals from developers to build a retirement community at Fort Howard in Baltimore County. The historic site, which has about 36 mostly vacant buildings, could become the home to hundreds of war veterans. Details of the proposed development are discussed. **Availability:** Print; Online.

4253 ■ *"Vision for Camden in Better Focus"* in *Philadelphia Business Journal (Vol. 30, September 30, 2011, No. 33, pp. 1)*
Pub: Philadelphia Business Journal
Contact: Sierra Quinn, Director
E-mail: squinn@bizjournals.com

Ed: Natalie Kostelni. **Description:** More than $500 million worth of projects aimed at redeveloping the downtown and waterfront areas of Camden, New Jersey are being planned. These include the construction of residential, commercial, and education buildings. **Availability:** Online.

4254 ■ *"Wal-Mart Proposed for Timmerman Plaza"* in *Business Journal-Milwaukee (Vol. 28, December 31, 2010, No. 14, pp. A1)*
Pub: The Business Journal
Contact: Heather Ladage, President
E-mail: hladage@bizjournals.com

Ed: Sean Ryan. **Description:** Dickson, Tennessee-based Gatlin Development Company Inc. owner Franklin C. Gatlin III revealed plans for a new Wal-Mart store in Timmerman Plaza in Milwaukee, Wisconsin. Wal-Mart plans to open up approximately 18 new stores in southeast Wisconsin in 2012 and the Timmerman project is the first of four that Gatlin will submit for city approval. **Availability:** Print; Online.

4255 ■ *"Walnut Hill Sheds Its Past, Name"* in *Philadelphia Business Journal (Vol. 33, April 4, 2014, No. 8, pp. 8)*
Pub: American City Business Journals, Inc.
Contact: Mike Olivieri, Executive Vice President

Released: Weekly. **Price:** $4, introductory 4-week offer(Digital & Print). **Description:** Walnut Hill Plaza was bought by a fund comprised of Miller Investment Management and Hayden Real Estate at an auction in 2012 for $11 million and they spent $2 million in construction renovations. The property was also re-branded as 150 Walnut Warner and the once forlorn building is up to 100% leased space. The tenants renting space in the building are also highlighted. **Availability:** Print; Online.

4256 ■ *"Water Conservation Helps GC's Building Attain LEED Gold Status"* in *Contractor* (Vol. 56, September 2009, No. 9, pp. 5)
Description: Green contractor Marshall Erdman has built a new office building using green design. The facility is seen to become a prime Leadership in Energy and Environmental Design (LEED) building model. Details of the building's design and features are also provided. **Availability:** Print; Online.

4257 ■ *"Wayne, Oakland Counties Create Own 'Medical Corridor"* in *Crain's Detroit Business* (Vol. 24, October 6, 2008, No. 40, pp. 8)
Pub: Crain Communications Inc.
Contact: Barry Asin, President
Ed: Jay Greene. **Description:** Woodward Medical Corridor that runs along Woodward Avenue and currently encompasses twelve hospitals and is rapidly growing with additional physician offices, advanced oncology centers and new hospitals. Beaumont Hospital is building a $160 million proton-beam therapy cancer center on its Royal Oak campus in a joint venture with Procure Treatment Centers of Bloomington Ind. That is expected to open in 2010 and will employ approximately 145 new workers. **Availability:** Online.

4258 ■ *"What Happens in Vegas Could Happen in Baltimore, Too"* in *Boston Business Journal* (Vol. 29, June 17, 2011, No. 6, pp. 1)
Pub: Boston Business Journal
Contact: Carolyn M. Jones, President
E-mail: cmjones@bizjournals.com
Ed: Daniel J. Sernovitz. **Description:** At least 36 companies expressed their interest in developing a casino in South Baltimore following the state commission's announcement for bids. Developers have until July 28, 2011 to submit their proposals. Baltimore's strong economy is the major factor for the interest, yet the fact that blackjack and poker are outlawed in Maryland could be a drawback. **Availability:** Print; Online.

4259 ■ *"What's Good Faith Got to Do With Contracts?"* in *Contractor* (Vol. 56, November 2009, No. 11, pp. 41)
Ed: Susan Linden McGreevy. **Description:** Uniform Commercial Code makes the obligation to act in good faith a term of every commercial transaction. The code generally applies to the sale of goods and not to construction contracts but parties to a construction contract have the right to expect people to act in good faith and forego actions not related to the contract itself. **Availability:** Online.

4260 ■ *"Where Are All the Builders?"* in *U.S. News & World Report* (June 15, 2018)
URL(s): www.usnews.com/news/the-report/articles/20 18-06-15/the-us-construction-industry-is-booming -but-where-are-the-builders
Ed: Andrew Soergel. **Released:** June 15, 2018. **Description:** With the booming economy in the US, lots of construction projects are popping up. However, projects have been delayed and even redesigned due to a major shortage of construction workers. In the first quarter of 2018, employers were looking to fill 225,000 construction jobs per month, making it difficult to find skilled workers among the whole industry. **Availability:** Online.

4261 ■ *"Will Home Buyers Pay for Green Features?"* in *Contractor* (Vol. 56, October 2009, No. 10, pp. 70)
Ed: Robert P. Mader. **Description:** National Association of Home Builders commissioned a survey which shows that homeowners are interested in green as long as they do not have to pay much for it. The association did not allow a board member to read the survey which raises questions about how the questions were phrased and how the sample was selected. **Availability:** Print; Online.

4262 ■ *"With Building Plans in Flux, County Could Sell Key Site"* in *Crain's Cleveland Business* (Vol. 28, October 8, 2007, No. 40, pp. 1)
Pub: Crain Communications Inc.
Contact: K. C. Crain, President
Ed: Jay Miller. **Description:** Due to such issues as financial and administrative problems, Cuyahoga County commissioners have pushed back the construction timeline for a planned county administration center and are saying that they are considering selling the site in downtown Cleveland to developers who would erect a new office building that another large tenant could occupy. **Availability:** Online.

4263 ■ *"The Witte Museum to Undergo Major Makeover This Fall"* in *San Antonio Business Journal* (Vol. 28, July 25, 2014, No. 24, pp. 7)
Pub: American City Business Journals, Inc.
Contact: Mike Olivieri, Executive Vice President
Released: Weekly. **Price:** $4, introductory 4-week offer(Digital & Print). **Description:** The Witte Museum along Broadway in San Antonio, Texas is working on a $60 million expansion and renovation that will provide the 90-year-old institution with additional exhibition and activity space. Such construction improvements are expected to better connect the museum with the San Antonio River and the Broadway corridor. **Availability:** Print; Online.

4264 ■ *"Wood Increasingly Used in School Construction"* in *Arkansas Business* (Vol. 29, July 23, 2012, No. 30, pp. 11)
Pub: Arkansas Business Publishing Group
Contact: Mitch Bettis, President
Ed: Jan Cottingham. **Description:** Arkansas state guidelines have increased the use of wood in school building construction. Wood is believed to provide strength and durability along with cost effectiveness and environmental benefits. **Availability:** Online.

4265 ■ *"Yates Helps Turn Log Home Green"* in *Contractor* (Vol. 56, November 2009, No. 11, pp. 1)
Description: Dave Yates of F.W. Behler Inc. helped homeowners from James Creek, Pennsylvania achieve energy efficiency on the heating system of their log cabin. The mechanical system installed on the cabin had high-temp "THW" water-to-water geothermal system by ClimateMaster, two twin-coil indirect water heaters, and several pre-assembled, pre-engineered Hydronex panels by Watts Radiant. **Availability:** Print; Online.

4266 ■ *"Yudelson Challenges San Antonio Groups"* in *Contractor* (Vol. 56, October 2009, No. 10, pp. 6)
Description: Green building consultant and author Jerry Yudelson made a presentation for the Central Texas Green Building Council and Leadership San Antonio where he discussed the European approach to sustainability and how it can be used for designing green buildings. Yudelson also discussed how to use sustainable practices for planning 25 years into the future. **Availability:** Print; Online.

STATISTICAL SOURCES

4267 ■ **Means Labor Rates for the Construction Industry**
Pub: R. S. Means Company Inc.
Contact: Mark Schiff, Contact
Price: $910. **Availability:** Print.

4268 ■ **RMA Annual Statement Studies**
Pub: Risk Management Association
Contact: Nancy Foster, President
Released: Annual. **Description:** Contains composite balance sheets and income statements for more than 360 industries, including the accounting, auditing, and bookkeeping industries. Also contains five years of comparative historical data for discerning trends. Includes 16 commonly used ratios, computed for most of the size groupings for nearly every industry.

4269 ■ **Standard & Poor's Industry Surveys**
Pub: Standard And Poor's Financial Services LLC.
Contact: Douglas L. Peterson, President
Description: Two-volume book that examines the prospects for specific industries, including trucking. Also provides analyses of trends and problems, statistical tables and charts, and comparative company analyses.

TRADE PERIODICALS

4270 ■ *Acoustical Interior Construction*
Pub: Ceilings and Interior Systems Construction Association
Contact: Shirley Wodynski, Executive Director
E-mail: shirley.wodynski@cisca.org
URL(s): www.cisca.org/i4a/pages/index.cfm?pagei d=3618
Released: Quarterly; Spring, Summer, Fall and Winter. **Price:** $45, Members; $80, Nonmembers. **Description:** Magazine covering interior system construction. **Availability:** Print.

4271 ■ *Builder: The Magazine of the National Association of Home Builders*
Pub: Zonda Home
Contact: Jeff Meyers, Chief Executive Officer
E-mail: jmeyers@zondahome.com
URL(s): www.builderonline.com
Facebook: www.facebook.com/buildermagazine
Linkedin: www.linkedin.com/company/builder -magazine
X (Twitter): x.com/builderonline
Pinterest: www.pinterest.com/builderonline
Released: Monthly **Description:** Magazine covering housing and construction industry. **Availability:** Print; Online.

4272 ■ *The BuildingGreen Report*
Pub: Building Green Inc.
Contact: Jerelyn Wilson, Chief Executive Officer
URL(s): www.buildinggreen.com/downloads
Released: Monthly **Description:** Covers the building trade with an environmental slant. Covers nontoxic materials, better landscaping and water use, and resources for energy conservation in a technical manner. **Availability:** PDF; Download; Online.

4273 ■ *California Builder & Engineer*
Pub: Associated Construction Publications
Contact: John White, President
Description: Magazine on California, Hawaii, Western Nevada, and Western Arizona building and engineering. **Availability:** Print.

4274 ■ *CFMA Building Profits*
Pub: Construction Financial Management Association
Contact: Stuart Binstock, President
E-mail: sbinstock@cfma.org
URL(s): cfma.org/bpmagazine
Released: 6/year **Description:** Trade magazine covering the financial side of the construction industry. Features employment opportunities for financial professionals in the construction industry. **Availability:** Print; Online.

4275 ■ *Civil + Structural Engineer*
Contact: Bob Drake, Editor
E-mail: bdrake@zweiggroup.com
URL(s): www.cenews.com
Facebook: www.facebook.com/ csENGINEERmagazine
X (Twitter): twitter.com/csENGINEERmag
Ed: Bob Drake. **Released:** Monthly **Description:** Trade magazine serving civil engineers and land surveyors engaged in land development, highways, bridges, structural, environmental, geotechnical, water resources, and industrial engineering projects including surveying. **Availability:** Print; PDF; Online.

4276 ■ *Construction Briefings*
Pub: Thomson West
URL(s): store.legal.thomsonreuters.com/law-produc ts/Forms/Construction-Briefings/p/100029521

Released: Monthly Price: $9,648, Individuals for annual subscription; $381, Individuals for member. Description: Covers issues in construction contracting. Availability: Online.

4277 ■ Construction Contracts Law Report
Pub: Thomson Reuters Corporation
Contact: Jim Smith, President
URL(s): store.legal.thomsonreuters.com/law-products/Forms/Construction-Contracts-Law-Report/p/100029519
Released: Biweekly; Updated every other week. Price: $11,076, Individuals for Annual subscription; $202, Individuals for 2024. Description: Contains news, insight, and analysis of construction industry developments and cases. Availability: Print.

4278 ■ Construction Executive: The Magazine for the Business of Construction (CE)
Pub: Associated Builders and Contractors, Inc.
Contact: Michael D. Bellaman, President
URL(s): www.constructionexec.com
Facebook: www.facebook.com/ConstructionMag
Linkedin: www.linkedin.com/company/construction-executive
X (Twitter): x.com/ConstructionMag
Ed: Christopher Durso. Released: 9/year Price: $15, Members for per year; $65, Nonmembers for per year. Description: Magazine for contractors and subcontractors. Includes articles on national and regional construction news, construction management, project case histories, new products, building design, and legislative and regulatory updates. Availability: Print; PDF; Download; Online.

4279 ■ Construction Litigation Reporter
Pub: Thomson Reuters Corporation
Contact: Jim Smith, President
URL(s): store.legal.thomsonreuters.com/law-products/Newsletter/Construction-Litigation-Reporter/p/106154454
Released: Monthly Price: $9,084, Individuals for annual subscription. Description: Consists of articles, case digests, and commentary covering recent litigation in the construction field. Recurring features include lists of expert witnesses. Availability: Print.

4280 ■ The Construction Specifier
Pub: Construction Specifications Institute
Contact: Mark Dorsey, Chief Executive Officer
E-mail: ceo@csinet.org
URL(s): www.constructionspecifier.com
X (Twitter): x.com/specifiermagcsi
Released: Monthly Description: Provides architects, engineers, specifiers, contractors, and others with technical information on construction materials, methods, and products. Availability: Print; Online.

4281 ■ Constructor: The Construction Management Magazine
Pub: Associated General Contractors of America
Contact: Thomas L. Brown, President
URL(s): www.constructormagazine.com
Released: Bimonthly Description: Management magazine for the construction industry. Availability: Print; PDF; Download; Online.

4282 ■ Construire
Pub: Association de la construction du Quebec
URL(s): www.acq.org/documentation/publications/magazine-construire
Released: Latest edition MAY 2024. Description: French language trade magazine for the commercial industrial, institutional, and residential construction companies within the province of Quebec. Availability: PDF; Online.

4283 ■ Design Cost Data: Cost Estimating Magazine for Design and Construction
Contact: Barbara Castelli, Publisher
E-mail: barb@dcd.com
URL(s): www.dcd.com/about-dcd
Facebook: www.facebook.com/dcdmagazine
X (Twitter): twitter.com/DCDMagazine

Released: Bimonthly Price: $159, For one year.; $239, For two year.; $174.80, Canada and Mexico For one year.; $274.80, Canada and Mexico For two year. Description: Publication providing real cost data case studies of various types completed around the country for design and building professionals. Availability: Print; Online.

4284 ■ Heavy Equipment Guide
Pub: Baum Publications Ltd.
Contact: Engelbert Baum, Co-President
URL(s): www.heavyequipmentguide.ca
Facebook: www.facebook.com/HeavyEquipmentGuide
X (Twitter): x.com/HeavyEquipGuide
YouTube: www.youtube.com/channel/UCK4eU7B8jVlMa-8ZR1u-Zzw
Released: 8/year; January/February, March, April, May/June, July/August, September, October, and November/December. Price: C$91, for price; $149, for price outside Canada. Description: Trade publication for the construction, mining, truck, and municipal industries. Availability: Print; Online.

4285 ■ Panel World
Pub: Hatton-Brown Publishers Inc.
Contact: Cindy Segrest, Director
URL(s): www.panelworldmag.com
Facebook: www.facebook.com/panelworld
Linkedin: www.linkedin.com/showcase/panel-world
X (Twitter): x.com/panelworldmag
YouTube: www.youtube.com/channel/UClWVW3xAd7T9kjxAv-nnj1g
Released: 6/year Description: Business magazine serving the worldwide veneer, plywood, and panel board industry. Availability: Print; Online.

4286 ■ Pavement: The International Journal of the Asphalt Aftermarket
Contact: Barb Levin, Sales Representative
E-mail: barb.levin@cygnuspub.com
URL(s): www.forconstructionpros.com/pavement-maintenance
Ed: Allan Heydorn. Released: 8/year Price: Free. Description: Trade magazine serving contractors who work in the paving, sealcoating, pavement marking and sweeping industry. Availability: Print; Online.

4287 ■ Practice Periodical on Structural Design and Construction
Pub: American Society of Civil Engineers
Contact: Marsia Geldert-Murphey, President
URL(s): ascelibrary.org/journal/ppscfx
Released: Quarterly Price: $511, Institutions for online only domestic and international; $782, Institutions for print domestic; $804, Institutions for print international; $1,037, Institutions for print and online domestic; $1,059, Institutions for print and online international; $128, Members for online domestic and international; $195, Members for print domestic; $217, Members for print international; $259, Members for print and online domestic; $281, Members for print and online international. Description: Peer-reviewed journal publishing articles on practical solutions to structural design problems and construction challenges. Availability: Print; PDF; Download; Online.

4288 ■ Professional Builder: The Magazine of the Housing and Light Construction Industry
Pub: Scranton Gillette Communications Inc.
Contact: Ed Gillette, President
URL(s): www.probuilder.com
Facebook: www.facebook.com/ProBuilder
Linkedin: www.linkedin.com/company/professional-builder-magazine
X (Twitter): x.com/ProBuildermag
YouTube: www.youtube.com/channel/UCx8lAYP672YeU34oMb8hluQ
Released: 6/year; Jan, Mar, May, July, Sept, Nov. Price: $200, Canada and Mexico for per year; $15, U.S. for single copies; $121, U.S. for per year; $30, for single copies international; $300, for all other international. Description: The integrated engineering magazine of the building construction industry. Availability: Print; PDF; Download; Online.

4289 ■ Roofing Contractor
Pub: BNP Media
Contact: Harper Henderson, Owner Co-Chief Executive Officer
URL(s): www.roofingcontractor.comeblast.bnpmedia.com/RC/eMag/0623/RC0623-eMag.html
Facebook: www.facebook.com/RoofingContractor
Linkedin: www.linkedin.com/company/roofing-contractor-magazine
X (Twitter): twitter.com/RoofContr
Instagram: www.instagram.com/roofingcontractormedia
YouTube: www.youtube.com/user/RoofingContractorMag
Ed: Art Aisner. Released: Monthly Price: Free. Description: Trade magazine on roofing and insulation. Availability: Print; Online.

4290 ■ Solar Today
Pub: American Solar Energy Society
Contact: Carly Rixham, Executive Director
E-mail: crixham@ases.org
URL(s): ases.org/solartoday
Released: Quarterly Description: Journal covering the business, policy and technology of renewable energy, from wind systems and energy-efficient devices to green building. Availability: Print; PDF; Online.

4291 ■ Timber Framing: Journal of the Timber Framers Guild
Pub: Timber Framers Guild
Contact: Chris Koehn, President
E-mail: president@tfguild.org
URL(s): www.tfguild.org/store/timber-framing-journal
Ed: Ken Rower. Released: Quarterly; March, June, September, and December. Price: $115, for international; $75, U.S.; $85, Canada. Description: Trade magazine covering timber frame design home construction, history, restoration, and preservation. Availability: Print; Online.

4292 ■ Wood Design & Building
Pub: Conseil Canadien du Bois
Contact: Rick Jeffery, President
URL(s): www.wooddesignandbuilding.com
X (Twitter): x.com/wooddesignmag
Instagram: www.instagram.com/wooddesignmag
Ed: Theresa Rogers. Released: 3/year Description: Magazine publishing articles for construction professionals in the U.S. Availability: Print; Online.

TRADE SHOWS AND CONVENTIONS

4293 ■ Associated Builders and Contractors Convention
Frequency: Annual. Description: Convention for those in the building trades. Principal Exhibits: Convention for those in the building trades.

4294 ■ Chicago Build
Frequency: Annual. Description: Provides networking, an exhibit hall, and key topic sessions about real estate, architecture, construction, and health and safety. Audience: Industry leaders in the building and construction trade. Principal Exhibits: Provides networking, an exhibit hall, and key topic sessions about real estate, architecture, construction, and health and safety.

4295 ■ CONEXPO-CON/AGG
National Stone, Sand and Gravel Association (NSSGA)
66 Canal Center Plz., Ste. 300
Alexandria, VA 22314
Ph: (703)525-8788
URL: http://www.nssga.org
Contact: Michael Johnson, President
URL(s): www.conexpoconagg.com
Facebook: www.facebook.com/conexpoconagg
X (Twitter): twitter.com/conexpoconagg
Frequency: Triennial. Description: Construction and construction materials industry equipment, supplies, and services, including asphalt, aggregates, concrete, earthmoving, lifting, mining, and utilities. Audience:

industry professionals. **Principal Exhibits:** Construction and construction materials industry equipment, supplies, and services, including asphalt, aggregates, concrete, earthmoving, lifting, mining, and utilities. Dates and Locations: 2026 Mar 03-7 Las Vegas Convention Center, Las Vegas, NV. **Telecommunication Services:** exhibitors@aem.org.

4296 ■ Indiana's Midwest Builders Convention
Indiana Builders Association (IBA)
101 W Ohio St., Ste. 710
Indianapolis, IN 46204
Ph: (317)917-1100
Co. E-mail: info@buildindiana.org
URL: http://buildindiana.org
Contact: Rick Wajda, Chief Executive Officer
E-mail: rick@buildindiana.org
URL(s): www.buildindiana.org

Description: Building supplies, including windows, doors, and insulation; title insurance information. **Audience:** Builders, remodelers, subcontractors and professionals. **Principal Exhibits:** Building supplies, including windows, doors, and insulation; title insurance information.

4297 ■ INTEX Expo
URL(s): www.intexconstructionexpo.com

Frequency: Annual. **Description:** Trade show featuring products and services from the wall and ceiling industry. **Principal Exhibits:** Trade show featuring products and services from the wall and ceiling industry.

4298 ■ Michigan Construction Design Tradeshow
Eastern Orthopaedic Association (EOA)
110 W Rd., Ste. 227
Towson, MD 21204
Free: 866-362-1409
Fax: (410)494-0515
Co. E-mail: info@eoa-assn.org
URL: http://www.eoa-assn.org
Contact: Amar S. Ranawat, President
URL(s): www.buildwithcam.com/tradeshow

Frequency: Annual. **Description:** Construction industry equipment, supplies, and services. **Audience:** Construction owners, contractors, suppliers, architects, and engineers. **Principal Exhibits:** Construction industry equipment, supplies, and services. **Telecommunication Services:** riegel@buildwithcam.com.

4299 ■ National Ready Mixed Concrete Association Annual Convention
URL(s): www.nrmca.org/conferences-events/nrmca-annual-convention

Frequency: Annual. **Description:** Provides education and talks about working with ready made concrete. **Principal Exhibits:** Provides education and talks about working with ready made concrete.

4300 ■ NDA Annual Convention & Expo
National Demolition Association (NDA)
2001 K St. NW, 3rd Fl. N
Washington, DC 20006
Ph: (202)367-1152
Co. E-mail: info@demolitionassociation.com
URL: http://www.demolitionassociation.com
Contact: Jeff Lambert, Executive Director
URL(s): www.demolitionassociation.com/Education-Events/Demolition-San-Antonio

Price: $675, Members; $795, Non-members; $295, Members Spouse/Guest; $415, Non-members Spouse/Guest; $125, Child age 4 to 17. **Frequency:** Annual. **Description:** Exhibits related to demolition equipment, supplies, and services. **Audience:** Demolition contractors and equipment manufacturers. **Principal Exhibits:** Exhibits related to demolition equipment, supplies, and services. Dates and Locations: 2025 Mar 05-08 New Orleans, LA; 2026 Feb 04-07 Phoenix, AZ. **Telecommunication Services:** ahaigh@demolitionassociation.com.

4301 ■ PCBC
California Building Industry Association (CBIA)
1215 K St., Ste. 1200
Sacramento, CA 95814
Ph: (916)443-7933
Fax: (916)443-1960
Co. E-mail: info@cbia.org
URL: http://cbia.org
Contact: Dan Dunmoyer, II, President
URL(s): www.pcbc.com/pcbc2024/public/enter.aspx

Frequency: Annual. **Description:** Exhibits relating to the building industry. **Audience:** Builders, developers, architects, remodelers, designers, contractors, dealers/distributors and suppliers/manufacturers. **Principal Exhibits:** Exhibits relating to the building industry. Dates and Locations: 2025 Jun 11-12 Anaheim Convention Center, Anaheim, CA. **Telecommunication Services:** showinfo@pcbc.com.

4302 ■ Pipeline Pigging and Integrity Management Conference
URL(s): www.ppimhouston.com

Frequency: Annual. **Description:** Training courses, conference, and an exhibition featuring pipeline operators and decision makers from the industry. **Principal Exhibits:** Training courses, conference, and an exhibition featuring pipeline operators and decision makers from the industry.

4303 ■ World of Asphalt Show & Conference
Wilfrid Laurier University
75 University Ave. W
Waterloo, ON, Canada N2L 3C5
Ph: (519)884-1970
Co. E-mail: chooselaurier@wlu.ca
URL: http://www.wlu.ca
Contact: Deborah MacLatchy, President
E-mail: president@wlu.ca
URL(s): www.worldofasphalt.com

Frequency: Annual. **Description:** Includes education sessions and various exhibits. **Audience:** Professionals such as highway contractors, pavement maintenance contractors, traffic safety professionals, road crews, plant operators, and public officials. **Principal Exhibits:** Includes education sessions and various exhibits. Dates and Locations: 2025 Mar 25-27 America's Center Convention Complex, St. Louis, MO. **Telecommunication Services:** exhibitors@aem.org.

CONSULTANTS

4304 ■ A/R/C Associates Inc.
601 N Fern Creek Ave., Ste. 100
Orlando, FL 32803-4899
Ph: (407)896-7875
Fax: (407)898-6043
Co. E-mail: info@arc-arc.com
URL: http://www.arc-arc.com
Contact: Joseph J. Williams, President

Description: Firm provides building survey, priority maintenance program. **Scope:** Firm provides building survey, priority maintenance program. **Founded:** 1982.

4305 ■ Advanced Business Concepts
118 Fairlane Dr.
Industry, PA 15052
Contact: John J. Nornek, Owner

Description: Firm offers consultation in construction materials and equipment. **Scope:** Firm offers consultation in construction materials and equipment.

4306 ■ Breen & Associates Inc.
161 Great Frontier Dr.
Georgetown, TX 78633-4595
Contact: James E. Breen, President

Description: Firm provides structural, foundation and drainage evaluation services.

4307 ■ Capital Project Management Inc. (CPMI)
1777 Sentry Pky. W, VEVA Bldg. 11, Ste. 300
Blue Bell, PA 19422
Ph: (267)464-0500
Fax: (267)464-0400

URL: http://cpmiteam.com
Contact: Michael F. d'Onofrio, President
E-mail: mdonofrio@cpmiteam.com

Description: Engineering consultant specializes in analysis, resolutions, and prevention of complex construction disputes. **Scope:** Engineering consultant specializes in analysis, resolutions, and prevention of complex construction disputes. **Founded:** 1996. **Publications:** "Dealing with Mid-Course Adjustments in Project Planning and Scheduling, and Resultant Claims"; "The ABCs of DRBs"; "Identifying Concurrent Delay"; "When the Best-Laid Plans Go Astray"; "Techniques and Methods for Assessing Delays". **Training:** Demystifying Scheduling, New York, Mar, 2007; Handling Construction Risks2006, Allocate Now or Litigate Later, New York, Apr, 2006; 2005 CPM Case Law - Year in Review and One Slice In Time: Two Competing Perspectives for Analyzing Project Delay, Orlando, Apr, 2006.

4308 ■ Commercial Cost Control Inc. (CCC)
301 College Ave.
Fort Worth, TX 76104
Contact: Calvin Boydstun, Chief Executive Officer

Description: A construction audit firm dedicated to providing value to clients by reducing or recovering capital and expense cost items while maintaining sensitivity to the partnership between clients and their vendors. Services include construction audit services, lease audit services, subtenant portfolio audits, utility audit and consultation, bill verification, rate audits, deregulation opportunity assessments and accounts payable audit services. **Scope:** A construction audit firm dedicated to providing value to clients by reducing or recovering capital and expense cost items while maintaining sensitivity to the partnership between clients and their vendors. Services include construction audit services, lease audit services, subtenant portfolio audits, utility audit and consultation, bill verification, rate audits, deregulation opportunity assessments and accounts payable audit services. **Founded:** 1996.

4309 ■ Construction Experts Inc. (CEI)
PO Box 231832
Encinitas, CA 92023
Ph: (760)634-2474
URL: http://constructionclasses.com/online
Contact: Lisa Thibodeaux, President
E-mail: lisa@constructionclasses.com
Facebook: www.facebook.com/constructionclasses

Description: Provider of consultation, assistance, and guidance to educational institutions and non-profit industry organizations. **Scope:** Provider of consultation, assistance, and guidance to educational institutions and non-profit industry organizations. **Founded:** 1994. **Publications:** "Scheduling for Estimators"; "The Cost of Training Construction People"; "Eichleay Formula Calculations". **Training:** Training Programs for Construction; Introduction to Construction Estimating; Construction Blueprint Reading; Eichleay Formula Calculations; How to Estimate the Cost of Training.

4310 ■ Construction Interface Services Inc.
3803 Wrightsville Ave., Unit 12
Wilmington, NC 28403
Ph: (910)762-4165
Free: 888-899-6312
Co. E-mail: info@constructioninterface.com
URL: http://constructioninterface.com
Contact: Ethan Crouch, Consultant
Linkedin: www.linkedin.com/company/construction-interface-services-inc-

Description: Provider of project management consulting services and seminars to contractors, attorneys, sureties, lending institutions, owners and design professionals. **Scope:** Provider of project management consulting services and seminars to contractors, attorneys, sureties, lending institutions, owners and design professionals. **Founded:** 1991. **Training:** Training and seminars on scheduling, productivity, cost control, documentation, negotiation, change order preparation and claims management.

4311 ■ Construction Testing Inc. (CTI)
925 N Jerome St., Lehigh
Allentown, PA 18109
Contact: Dolores Demyan, President
Description: Firm specializes in testing and inspection of concrete, soil structural steel, aggregates, concrete masonry units and mortar, structural clay bricks, bituminous concrete and high strength non-shrink grout. **Scope:** Firm specializes in testing and inspection of concrete, soil structural steel, aggregates, concrete masonry units and mortar, structural clay bricks, bituminous concrete and high strength non-shrink grout.

4312 ■ Draper & Associates
5665 New Northside Dr., Ste. 100
Atlanta, GA 30328
Ph: (404)256-3601
Fax: (404)256-3922
URL: http://draperandassociates.com
Contact: Gary W. Draper, President
E-mail: gary@draperandassociates.com
Description: Provider of construction project management services. Has managed projects ranging from single facility renovations to billion-dollar multi-project environments. **Scope:** Provider of construction project management services. Has managed projects ranging from single facility renovations to billion-dollar multi-project environments. **Founded:** 1960. **Publications:** "Our Economy Stinks. Your Projects Don't Have To," Sep, 2009; "The Demolition of Bowen Homes," Jul, 2009; "The Art of Listening," Jul, 2009; "Another Meeting," May, 2009; "Giving Hope to All Atlantans," May, 2009; "Do You Need an Upgrade," May, 2009. **Training:** Champagne Services of a Beer Budget, Sep, 2009.

4313 ■ Empire Building Diagnostics Inc. (EBD)
400 Ingham Ave.
Lackawanna, NY 14218
Ph: (716)685-4588
Co. E-mail: busdev@ebdinc.com
URL: http://www.ebdinc.com
Facebook: www.facebook.com/Empire-Building
 -Diagnostics-491511191008889/timeline
Linkedin: www.linkedin.com/company/empire-building
 -diagnostics
Description: Consulting firm that provides a full range of pre-renovation contracting services. Specializes in asbestos abatement, asbestos inspections/consulting, asbestos emergency response, lead testing and abatement, third party representation, project management/specification, concrete/CMU saw cutting/removal, radon testing/consulting, site and structure demolition, industrial services and contracting, commercial cleaning, indoor air quality and tank removal and soil remediation. **Scope:** Consulting firm that provides a full range of pre-renovation contracting services. Specializes in asbestos abatement, asbestos inspections/consulting, asbestos emergency response, lead testing and abatement, third party representation, project management/specification, concrete/CMU saw cutting/removal, radon testing/consulting, site and structure demolition, industrial services and contracting, commercial cleaning, indoor air quality and tank removal and soil remediation. **Founded:** 1988.

4314 ■ Engineering and Technical Consultants Inc. (ETC)
46040 Center Oak Plz., Ste. 100
Sterling, VA 20166
Ph: (703)450-6220
Fax: (703)444-2285
Co. E-mail: mindy@etc-web.com
URL: http://www.etc-web.com
Contact: Joseph D. Shuffleton, President
Facebook: www.facebook.com/engineeringan
 dtechncialconsultants
Linkedin: www.linkedin.com/company/engineering-an
 d-technical-consultants-inc
Instagram: www.instagram.com/engineeringandtech
YouTube: www.youtube.com/channel/UC
 3IARhXGqbKBtSxZvEv_tnA

Description: Provider of evaluations, intrusive evaluation, design and specifications, solicitation and review of bids, construction monitoring, administration, forensic investigation, testing, document review, research and negotiations services. **Scope:** Provider of evaluations, intrusive evaluation, design and specifications, solicitation and review of bids, construction monitoring, administration, forensic investigation, testing, document review, research and negotiations services. **Founded:** 1982.

4315 ■ Environmental & Engineering Services Inc. (EESI)
428 NW 5th St.
Corvallis, OR 97330
Ph: (541)754-1062
Co. E-mail: esinet5@peak.org
URL: http://www.eesinet.com
Contact: Peter Sanford, Manager
Linkedin: www.linkedin.com/company/environmental
 -and-engineering-services-inc-
Description: Firm provides design consulting services focused in the mechanical, plumbing and electrical disciplines and offers a wide range of HVAC, electrical and controls engineering services including feasibility assessments, master planning, budgeting, cost analysis, design, computer-aided drafting, and much more. **Founded:** 1979.

4316 ■ Fanning, Fanning & Associates Inc.
2555 74th St.
Lubbock, TX 79423
Ph: (806)745-2533
Fax: (806)745-3596
Co. E-mail: nfanning@fanningfanning.com
URL: http://www.fanningfanning.com
Contact: Scott Fanning, President
Facebook: www.facebook.com/FFAconsul
 tingengineers
Description: Specializes in engineering services including mechanical, electrical, plumbing design and plant layout, HVAC, energy conservation and management, utilities, fire protection and alarms, central heating and cooling plants and communications for institutional, commercial and industrial buildings. Offers design services for drawings, specifications and bid documents, master planning, engineering reports, estimates, analysis, feasibility studies and construction phase services. **Scope:** Specializes in engineering services including mechanical, electrical, plumbing design and plant layout, HVAC, energy conservation and management, utilities, fire protection and alarms, central heating and cooling plants and communications for institutional, commercial and industrial buildings. Offers design services for drawings, specifications and bid documents, master planning, engineering reports, estimates, analysis, feasibility studies and construction phase services.

4317 ■ Fard Engineers Inc.
200 Gregory Ln., Bldg. A
Pleasant Hill, CA 94523
Ph: (925)932-5505
Fax: (925)932-0555
URL: http://www.fard.com
Contact: Max E. Saiidnia, President
E-mail: max@fard.com
Description: Firm designs mechanical and electrical systems for all types of buildings and serves the construction industry in California, Oregon, Arizona, Washington and Nevada and specializing in apartment buildings, senior housing complexes, and school renovation. **Scope:** Firm designs mechanical and electrical systems for all types of buildings and serves the construction industry in California, Oregon, Arizona, Washington and Nevada and specializing in apartment buildings, senior housing complexes, and school renovation. **Founded:** 1993. **Special Services:** Autocad and Paradox.

4318 ■ GHT Ltd.
1110 N Glebe Rd., Ste. 300
Arlington, VA 22201
Ph: (703)243-1200
Fax: (703)276-1376
Co. E-mail: info@ghtltd.com
URL: http://www.ghtltd.com

Contact: Patrick Kunze, President
Facebook: www.facebook.com/GHTLimited
Linkedin: www.linkedin.com/company/ght-limited
Description: Firm provides consulting on engineering design services such as telecommunications and security engineering service, life safety engineering service, utilities planning service and much more. **Scope:** Firm provides consulting on engineering design services such as telecommunications and security engineering service, life safety engineering service, utilities planning service and much more. **Founded:** 1965. **Publications:** "Critical spaces keep the pace of business humming," May, 2004; "To avoid staticlater, hire right telecom consultant," Oct, 2007. **Special Services:** LEED®.

4319 ■ Hatch Properierty Ltd.
Sheridan Science & Technology Pk., 2800 Speakman Dr.
Mississauga, ON, Canada L5K 2R7
Ph: (905)855-7600
URL: http://www.hatch.com
Contact: John Bianchini, Chief Executive Officer
Linkedin: www.linkedin.com/company/hatch
YouTube: www.youtube.com/user/HatchLtdVideos
Description: Provides process and business consulting, information technology, engineering and project and construction management services to the mining, metallurgical, manufacturing, energy and infrastructure industries. **Scope:** Provides process and business consulting, information technology, engineering and project and construction management services to the mining, metallurgical, manufacturing, energy and infrastructure industries. **Founded:** 1955.

4320 ■ Historic Exterior Paint Colors Consulting
3661 Waldenwood Dr.
Ann Arbor, MI 48105
Ph: (734)668-0298
Co. E-mail: robs@umich.edu
URL: http://historichousecolors.com
Contact: Robert Schweitzer, Contact
Description: Provider of exterior paint color consulting services for historic, contemporary, and much more. **Scope:** Provider of exterior paint color consulting services for historic, contemporary, and much more. **Publications:** "Proof that Paint Color Lends Detail," Arts and Crafts Homes, 2006; "Bungalow Colors- Exteriors," Gibbs-Smith Publishers, 2002; "Color Scheming," Design NJ, 2002; "Colonial Revival Homes," Victorian Homes, Feb, 2003; "America's Favorite Homes"; "Color a New World," '60s Ranch Color Makeover, Romantic Homes, Aug, 2001; "How Shall I Paint my House," American Bungalow, 1999; "Color Concepts and Bungalow Basics," Cottages & Bungalows.

4321 ■ Home Builders Network (HBN)
6200 Georgetown Blvd., Ste. F
Eldersburg, MD 21784
Free: 800-823-4344
Fax: (301)829-8907
URL: http://www.hbnnet.com
Contact: Al Trellis, Consultant
YouTube: www.youtube.com/user/HomeBuildersNe
 twork
Description: Services: Information and consultancy for home builders. **Scope:** Services: Information and consultancy for home builders. **Founded:** 1991. **Publications:** "Documents Contracts and Worksheets for Home Builders," Jun, 1998. **Training:** The Value-Driven Builder; Price it Right; Sales Are About; Spec for Success; The Builders Guide to Marketing Success; The Design Advantage; The New and Improved Builder Money Making Machine; Strategies and Tactics for a Competitive Market; The Art of War; Negotiation for Profit Creating the Customer; Beating the Competition Marketing Success; Creating the Brand Image; Lots of Opportunity-Land and Spec Houses; The Rd to Success; The Sequence of Success; Its About Time; Making a Difference in the Marketplace.

4322 ■ The Home Star Group
550 N St. Clair St. Clair St., Apt. 1001
Chicago, IL 60611

Description: A full service construction consulting firm specializing in analyzing and reorganizing construction projects that not progressing as planned. Provides project analysis, financial analysis, project recovery services and litigation support. **Scope:** A full service construction consulting firm specializing in analyzing and reorganizing construction projects that not progressing as planned. Provides project analysis, financial analysis, project recovery services and litigation support.

4323 ■ Irvine Team
1980 Post Oak Blvd., Ste. 2020A
Houston, TX 77056
Ph: (713)840-1880
Co. E-mail: info@irvineteam.com
URL: http://www.irvineteam.com
Contact: Dennis Irvine, President
Description: Developer of real estate properties. **Founded:** 2002.

4324 ■ IRZ Consulting L.L.C.
Lindsay Corporation
500 N First St.
Hermiston, OR 97838
Ph: (402)829-6800
Free: 800-829-5300
Fax: (402)829-6834
URL: http://www.lindsay.com
Contact: Fred Ziari, Contact
E-mail: fred.ziari@irz.com
Description: Firm is engaged in the water resource engineering with technologically advanced irrigation, resource management and conservation services and it also provides web-based information system solutions to clients. **Founded:** 1984. **Training:** Umatilla Sub-Basin Replacement Water (SB 1069) Workshop, Oct, 2008.

4325 ■ JDE Construction Management Ltd.
14321-112 Ave.
Edmonton, AB, Canada T5M 2V3
URL: http://www.jdemarine.com/aboutus.htm
Contact: John Dawson-Edwards, Contact
Description: Provider of solutions that encourage the prevention, mitigation and equitable settlement of construction disputes. **Scope:** Provider of solutions that encourage the prevention, mitigation and equitable settlement of construction disputes. **Founded:** 1991.

4326 ■ Joe Turner
3135 Adams St.
Denver, CO 80205
Contact: Joel Turner, Contact
Description: Provider of customer service consulting, materials, software and training for the new home industry. Specializes in construction defect litigation. Specific problem solving, including recruiting, validating employment information, meeting with homeowners and strategic assessment are available. Produces homeowner manuals for builders and developers. **Scope:** Provider of customer service consulting, materials, software and training for the new home industry. Specializes in construction defect litigation. Specific problem solving, including recruiting, validating employment information, meeting with homeowners and strategic assessment are available. Produces homeowner manuals for builders and developers. **Founded:** 1982. **Training:** TeamTraks.

4327 ■ Kalin Associates Inc. (KA)
21 Eliot St.
Natick, MA 01760
Ph: (617)964-5477
URL: http://www.kalinassociates.com
Contact: Mark Kalin, Founder
E-mail: mark@kalinassociates.com
Facebook: www.facebook.com/kalinassociates
Linkedin: www.linkedin.com/company/kalin-associates-inc-
Description: Independent specifications firm specializing in preparation of technical specifications and bidding documents for construction projects, and preparation of guide specifications for building product manufacturers. Related service include development of master specifications for agencies and design firms; computer automation of technical documents; specification coordination for large projects. **Scope:** Independent specifications firm specializing in preparation of technical specifications and bidding documents for construction projects, and preparation of guide specifications for building product manufacturers. Related service include development of master specifications for agencies and design firms; computer automation of technical documents; specification coordination for large projects. **Founded:** 1984. **Publications:** "Specifying Green Building Products," Rs Means, 2002. **Training:** Integrating BIM and Specifications at Ecobuild, Washington, DC.

4328 ■ Kohn Engineering
4220 Mountain Rd.
Macungie, PA 18062
Ph: (610)967-4766
Co. E-mail: kohnengineering@ptd.net
URL: http://www.kohnengineering.com
Contact: Don Kohn, Contact
Description: Provider of fire protection engineering services. **Scope:** Provider of fire protection engineering services. **Founded:** 1995. **Training:** Fire Protection in Nuclear Power Plants.

4329 ■ Kora Management Ltd.
8-70 Yorkville Ave.
Toronto, ON, Canada M5R 1B9
Ph: (807)675-2251
Free: 866-435-3748
Co. E-mail: mrspeigel@koramgt.com
URL: http://www.koramgt.com
Facebook: www.facebook.com/areversemortgage
Linkedin: www.linkedin.com/company/kora-management-ltd
X (Twitter): twitter.com/mrspeigel
YouTube: www.youtube.com/embed/be_mq9hWxlQ
Description: Firm provides construction, real estate development, management advice and dispute resolution services. **Scope:** Firm provides construction, real estate development, management advice and dispute resolution services. **Founded:** 1995.

4330 ■ Lawrence Siegel-Consultant (LSC)
5292 Eliots Oak Rd.
Columbia, MD 21044
Ph: (410)997-9210
Co. E-mail: consult@lscourt.com
URL: http://www.lscourt.com
Contact: Lawrence Siegel, Consultant
E-mail: consult@lscourt.com
Description: Firm specializes in facility planning, security consulting, and technical support services for court, correctional, police, and other government facilities, and architectural companies. **Founded:** 1975. **Publications:** "The Image Of Justice"; "Space Management and the Courts"; "Some Issues inCourt Security," The Court Manager, 1997.

4331 ■ McKay/Moore Consultants L.L.C. (MM)
7323 11th Ave. NW
Seattle, WA 98117-4142
Ph: (206)781-0676
Fax: (888)680-4987
Co. E-mail: mckaymoore@strabo.com
URL: http://www.mckaymoore.com
Description: Provider of cost estimating/consulting services for all disciplines of a construction project - architectural, structural, mechanical, electrical, and civil. Services include: value engineering cost support, expert witness, and cost estimate review/quality; control and administrative support services. **Scope:** Provider of cost estimating/consulting services for all disciplines of a construction project - architectural, structural, mechanical, electrical, and civil. Services include: value engineering cost support, expert witness, and cost estimate review/quality; control and administrative support services. **Founded:** 1996. **Publications:** "Estimating Mechanical Systems". **Training:** Port of Seattle Engineering Department Estimating; Plywood Manufacturing.

4332 ■ MDA Engineering Inc.
1415 Holland Rd., Ste.B
Maumee, OH 43537
Ph: (419)893-3141
Co. E-mail: mda@mdaengr.com
URL: http://www.mdaengr.com
Contact: Kevin P. Lafferty, President
Linkedin: www.linkedin.com/company-beta/882446
Description: Firm provides mechanical, electrical and telecommunication engineering services, the company engineers systems for new building construction, building renovations and industrial process support and offers a spectrum of mechanical engineering and consulting services. **Founded:** 1976.

4333 ■ Mueser Rutledge Consulting Engineers (MRCE)
14 Penn Plz., 225 W 34th St.
New York, NY 10122
Ph: (917)339-9300
Co. E-mail: mhuguet@mrce.com
URL: http://www.mrce.com
Contact: Jan Cermak, Principal
E-mail: jcermak@mrce.com
Facebook: www.facebook.com/Mueser-Rutledge-Consulting-Engineers-239556726057375
Linkedin: www.linkedin.com/company/mueser-rutledge-consulting-engineers
X (Twitter): x.com/mueserrutledge
Instagram: www.instagram.com/mueser_rutledge
Description: Geotechnical and structural foundation engineering services provides foundation design such as building foundations, transportation, special and temporary structures, excavation and claim support, underpinning, geotechnical services investigations, analysis and recommendations, field observation and testing, groundwater control and waste containment, ground improvement. **Scope:** Geotechnical and structural foundation engineering services provides foundation design such as building foundations, transportation, special and temporary structures, excavation and claim support, underpinning, geotechnical services investigations, analysis and recommendations, field observation and testing, groundwater control and waste containment, ground improvement. **Founded:** 1910. **Publications:** "Deep Foundations in Washington, DC," 2006; "Urban Sites present firms with foundation challenges," 2006; "Woodrow Wilson Bridge Cofferdams," 2005; "Slurry Trench Design and Construction in Difficult Conditions," 2005; "Lessons Learned from Installation of ACIP Piles in Various Geologic Settings of the NYC Region," 2004; "Auger Cast Piles Founded in Compressible Bearing Stratum," 2004; "Design and Construction of the Watauga Raw Water Facility in Karstic Limestone near the City of Johnson City, TN"; "Construction Dewatering and Groundwater Control"; "90 Years of Foundation Engineering The Last 15 Years"; "A Tale of Two Towers," Civil Engineering Magazine, Jun, 2004; "Cantilever Frozen Ground Structure to Support 18M Deep Excavation"; "North American Tunneling," Apr, 2004; "Marine Foundations of Bridges in the Northeastern USA"; "Superjet Grouting A New Technology for In situ Soil Improvement," 2000. **Training:** Proceedings of the Deep Foundation Institutes Marine Foundations; Underground Construction In Urban Environments; DFI Specialty; Marine Foundations: Proceedings of the Deep Foundation Institutes Marine Foundations Committee Specialty.

4334 ■ PJ Materials Consultants Ltd.
11 Wagoners Trl.
Guelph, ON, Canada N1G 3M9
Ph: (519)767-0702
URL: http://www.pjmc.net
Contact: Paul Jeffs, Founder
E-mail: pjeffs@pjmc.net
Linkedin: www.linkedin.com/company/pj-materials-consultants-ltd
Description: Provider of a wide range of specialist concrete and masonry consulting services for concrete and masonry structures, their services include provision of materials technology expertise and technical training, offers technical consulting services for the design, specification, construction, restoration,

and protection of concrete and masonry structures. **Scope:** Provider of a wide range of specialist concrete and masonry consulting services for concrete and masonry structures, their services include provision of materials technology expertise and technical training, offers technical consulting services for the design, specification, construction, restoration, and protection of concrete and masonry structures. **Founded:** 1989. **Training:** Restoration and Conservation of Masonry Structures; Concrete in the Arabian Peninsular Today; Concrete Slabs on Grade; Modern Concrete Materials and Practices; Modern Concrete Materials and Practices.

4335 ■ R. L. Townsend & Associates Inc.
5056 Tennyson Pky., Ste. 100
Plano, TX 75024
Ph: (972)403-1829
URL: http://www.rltownsend.com
Contact: Debbie Townsend, President
E-mail: datownsend@rltownsend.com
Description: Provider of construction contract cost control advisory and audit services to owner organizations. Its clients include design and construction management firms and construction contractors. **Scope:** Provider of construction contract cost control advisory and audit services to owner organizations. Its clients include design and construction management firms and construction contractors. **Founded:** 1984. **Publications:** "Contracting for Construction Projects," Rich Townsend, Jun, 1993. **Training:** Auditing Construction Activity, Austin, 2009; Controlling Construction Costs, Madison, 2009; Controlling Construction Costs, Madison, 2007; Managing Construction Projects, Madison, 2007; Effective Auditing of Construction Activity, Orlando, 2007.

4336 ■ Revay and Associates Ltd.
4333 St. Catherine St. W, Ste. 500
Montreal, QC, Canada H3Z 1P9
Ph: (514)932-2188
Fax: (514)939-0776
Co. E-mail: montreal@revay.com
URL: http://www.revay.com
Contact: Zey Emir, President
E-mail: zemir@revay.com
Linkedin: www.linkedin.com/company/revay-an
  d-associates-limited
Description: Firm provides project management, risk management, dispute resolution service to construction, engineering and energy sectors. **Scope:** Firm provides project management, risk management, dispute resolution service to construction, engineering and energy sectors. **Founded:** 1970.

4337 ■ Richmond Sterling Inc.
969 Moores Mill Rd.
Atlanta, GA 30327
Ph: (404)525-9606
Co. E-mail: contact@richmondsterling.com
URL: http://www.richmondsterling.com
Contact: Paul N. Marston, Chief Executive Officer
Description: Provider of construction consulting services. It offers project and cost management, budgeting, and scheduling solutions. **Scope:** Provider of construction consulting services. It offers project and cost management, budgeting, and scheduling solutions. **Founded:** 1995.

4338 ■ Saunders Construction, Inc.
86 Inverness Pl. N
Englewood, CO 80112
Ph: (303)699-9000
URL: http://www.saundersinc.com
Contact: Greg Schmidt, Chief Executive Officer
E-mail: g.schmidt@saundersinc.com
Facebook: www.facebook.com/pages/Saunders
  -Construction-Inc/193597420690293
Linkedin: www.linkedin.com/company/saunders-cons
  truction
X (Twitter): x.com/saundersinc
Instagram: www.instagram.com/saundersconstruc
  tioninc
Description: Provider of healthcare, commercial, concrete, express and tenant improvement and retail services. **Scope:** Provider of healthcare, commercial, concrete, express and tenant improvement and retail services. **Founded:** 1972. **Training:** Pilot Leadership Training, Jan, 2008.

4339 ■ Steinmann Facility Development Consultants (SFDC)
9702 N Lake Blvd.
Kings Beach, CA 96143
Ph: (530)546-4429
Co. E-mail: sfdc@jimsteinmann.com
URL: http://www.jimsteinmann.com
Contact: Jim Steinmann, Contact
Description: Provider of facility programming and planning consulting services for government and private sectors and specializing in needs assessment, facility programming, pre-architectural, strategic and justice system planning, and much more. **Scope:** Provider of facility programming and planning consulting services for government and private sectors and specializing in needs assessment, facility programming, pre-architectural, strategic and justice system planning, and much more. **Founded:** 1972.

4340 ■ Swanson Associates
6705 Hwy. 290 W, Ste. 502-126
Austin, TX 78735
Ph: (512)288-9097
Fax: (512)288-9096
URL: http://geoswan.com
Contact: George Swanson, Contact
E-mail: georgeswanson245@yahoo.com
Description: Environmentally-conscience construction firm services include non-toxic, breathing construction consulting; natural low impact energy and site utility development consulting; CADD custom and stock natural building design plans; site supervision, construction management and general contracting. **Scope:** Environmentally-conscience construction firm services include non-toxic, breathing construction consulting; natural low impact energy and site utility development consulting; CADD custom and stock natural building design plans; site supervision, construction management and general contracting. **Publications:** "Dome Scrapbook," 1981. **Training:** Sustainable Development and Concrete Technology; Traditional Straw/Clay Slip form Construction; Natural design and construction; Benefits of natural building design.

4341 ■ TechniScan, LLC
10367 W Centennial Rd.
Littleton, CO 80127
Ph: (303)329-0535
Co. E-mail: inquiries@techniscan.com
URL: http://techniscan.com
Description: Architectural consultancy is engaged in providing roofing and building envelope solutions, the company provides detailed facilities assessment analysis, construction documentation, and quality assurance services for building facades, roofing systems, curtain walls, windows and parking structures and serves building owners, developers, facilitators, property managers, architects, contractors, and roofers. **Founded:** 1986. **Training:** Roofing asset portfolio. **Special Services:** TechniScan®.

4342 ■ US Aquatics Inc.
10343 County Rd. 16 SE
Delano, MN 55328
Ph: (763)972-5897
Co. E-mail: info@usaquaticsinc.com
URL: http://www.usaquaticsinc.com
Contact: Thomas R. Schaffer, President
Facebook: www.facebook.com/USAquatics-Inc-50
  1180310231966
Linkedin: www.linkedin.com/company/usaquatics-inc
Description: Firm provides aquatics consulting, design and engineering such as industry expertise, design and consultation, feasibility analysis, 3D modeling, and CPO training. **Scope:** Firm provides aquatics consulting, design and engineering such as industry expertise, design and consultation, feasibility analysis, 3D modeling, and CPO training. **Founded:** 1991.

FRANCHISES AND BUSINESS OPPORTUNITIES

4343 ■ A-1 Concrete Leveling Inc.
388 S Main St., Ste. 402b
Akron, OH 44311
Free: 888-675-3835
URL: http://www.a1concrete.com
Contact: James W. Creed, President
YouTube: www.youtube.com/user/A1Concre
  teCorporate
Description: Provider of commercial and residential concrete leveling and foundation repair services. **No. of Franchise Units:** 50.0. **Founded:** 1992. **Financial Assistance:** Yes **Training:** Provides 1 week at headquarters, 2 weeks of onsite and ongoing support including newsletter, meetings toll-free phone line, Internet, security/safety procedures, and field operations/evaluations.

4344 ■ ABC Inc.
3001 Fiechtner Dr.
Fargo, ND 58103
Ph: (701)293-5952
Free: 800-732-6577
Co. E-mail: theduck@abcseamless.com
URL: http://abcseamless.com
Contact: Chris Lalonde, Manager, Production
Facebook: www.facebook.com/ABCSeamless
X (Twitter): x.com/abcseamless
Instagram: www.instagram.com/abc.seamless
YouTube: www.youtube.com/user/abcseamless
Pinterest: www.pinterest.com/seamlessabc
Description: Manufactures steel siding, steel gutters, steel roofing, energy-efficient windows, soffit and facia, log siding, and sunrooms. **Founded:** 1978. **Financial Assistance:** Yes **Training:** Yes.

4345 ■ ANDY OnCall (AOC)
6701 Shallowford Rd.
Chattanooga, TN 37421
Ph: (423)624-9800
Co. E-mail: aocchattanooga@andyoncall.com
URL: http://andyoncall.com
Contact: Tamara Harris, Contact
Facebook: www.facebook.com/andyoncall
Linkedin: www.linkedin.com/in/andyoncallcorp
X (Twitter): x.com/Andy_OnCall
Description: Managed independent contractors to fulfill homeowners' small job needs, management and organizational skills, no construction experience needed, strong and growing demand for service in marketplace. **Founded:** 1993. **Financial Assistance:** Yes **Training:** Training at corporate office, onsite, and ongoing support in all areas of business.

4346 ■ The BrickKicker
849 N Ellsworth St.
Naperville, IL 60563
Free: 800-821-1820
Fax: (630)420-2270
Co. E-mail: request@brickkicker.com
URL: http://www.brickkicker.com
Contact: Ron Ewald, Co-Founder
Facebook: www.facebook.com/The.BrickKicker
X (Twitter): x.com/BrickKickerHQ
Description: Building inspection service. **No. of Franchise Units:** 152. **Founded:** 1989. **Franchised:** 1995. **Equity Capital Needed:** $15,000-$40,000. **Franchise Fee:** $9,000-$40,000. **Financial Assistance:** Yes **Training:** Yes.

4347 ■ Case Handyman and Remodeling Services LLC
3601 W Hundred Rd., Ste. 10
Chester, VA 23831
Ph: (804)748-8500
Fax: (804)748-2808
Co. E-mail: casechester@gmail.com
URL: http://www.casechester.com
Contact: Fred Case, Chief Executive Officer
Facebook: www.facebook.com/casehan
  dymanservices
Pinterest: www.pinterest.com/casechester

Description: Handyman services. **No. of Franchise Units:** 57. **No. of Company-Owned Units:** 4. **Founded:** 1992. **Franchised:** 1997. **Equity Capital Needed:** $105,000-$150,000. **Franchise Fee:** $25,000. **Royalty Fee:** 4-6%. **Training:** Includes 3 weeks training at headquarters, 2 days at franchisee's location and ongoing support.

4348 ■ Epcon Communities
500 Stonehenge Pky.
Dublin, OH 43017
Free: 888-893-0590
Fax: (614)761-1155
URL: http://www.epconcommunities.com
Contact: Joel Rhoades, Chief Executive Officer
Facebook: www.facebook.com/EpconCommunitiesInc
Linkedin: www.linkedin.com/company/epcon-communities-franchising

Description: Provider of construction services for homes. **Founded:** 1986. **Training:** Available at headquarters, onsite and with ongoing support. Provides additional training at sales conference and construction conference.

4349 ■ Handyman Connection
Mamar Inc.
11115 Kenwood Rd.
Blue Ash, OH 45242
Facebook: www.facebook.com/HandymanConnectionCorporate
Linkedin: www.linkedin.com/company/handyman-connection
X (Twitter): x.com/handymancorp
Instagram: www.instagram.com/handymanconnection_homeoffice
YouTube: www.youtube.com/user/handymancorporate

Description: Small to medium home repairs and remodeling. **No. of Franchise Units:** 160. **No. of Company-Owned Units:** 1. **Founded:** 1990. **Franchised:** 1993. **Equity Capital Needed:** $90,000-$125,000. **Franchise Fee:** $25,000-$40,000. **Training:** 2 weeks at corporate training center and 1 week grand opening onsite.

4350 ■ Hickory Dickory Decks (HDD)
115 Dundas St. W, Hwy. No. 5, Clappison Cor.
Dundas, ON, Canada L9H 7L6
Ph: (905)689-4774
Free: 800-263-4774
Fax: (905)689-9753
Co. E-mail: office@decks.ca
URL: http://decks.ca
Contact: Tom Jacques, President
Facebook: www.facebook.com/decks.ca
YouTube: www.youtube.com/user/HickoryDickoryDeck/videos

Description: Custom builders of decks and gazebos. **No. of Franchise Units:** 32. **No. of Company-Owned Units:** 15. **Founded:** 1987. **Franchised:** 1999. **Equity Capital Needed:** $50,000-$100,000. **Franchise Fee:** $25,000. **Training:** Provides 3 weeks training.

4351 ■ Maintenance Made Simple
630 Peter Jefferson Pky., Ste. 200
Charlottesville, VA 22911
URL: http://m2simpleweston.wordpress.com

Description: Handyman and home improvement services. **No. of Franchise Units:** 32. **Founded:** 2003. **Franchised:** 2003. **Equity Capital Needed:** $69,900-$114,900. **Franchise Fee:** $30,000. **Royalty Fee:** 7%. **Training:** Yes.

4352 ■ Perma-Jack Co.
4173 Hoffmeister Ave.
Saint Louis, MO 63125
Ph: (314)544-1957
Free: 800-843-1888
URL: http://www.permajack.com
Contact: John F. Langenbach, Contact

Description: Firm provides frictionless steel pier system services to stabilize foundation and slab setting structures. **Founded:** 1974. **Training:** Yes.

4353 ■ Sealmaster
2520 S Campbell St.
Sandusky, OH 44870
Ph: (419)626-4375
Free: 800-395-7325
URL: http://sealmaster.net
Facebook: www.facebook.com/SealMasterNet
X (Twitter): x.com/SealMasterNet
Instagram: www.instagram.com/sealmasterpros
YouTube: www.youtube.com/user/SealMasterNet

Description: Manufacturer of pavement sealers and supply a complete line of pavement maintenance products and equipment including crack fillers, traffic paints, sport surfaces and tools. **Founded:** 1969. **Franchised:** 1993. **Equity Capital Needed:** Individual franchise $650,000 To $950,000 ; Conversion franchise $64,000 to $600,000. **Franchise Fee:** Individual franchise $35,000 ; Conversion franchise $25,000. **Royalty Fee:** 5% of gross sales. **Financial Assistance:** Yes **Training:** Technical and administrative training, operations manual. Scheduled consulting visits by operations experts. **Educational Activities:** World of Asphalt Show and Conference (Annual).

4354 ■ Tile Outlet Always in Stock
1356 S Carson City
Carson City, NV 89701
Ph: (775)434-1839
Co. E-mail: carsoncity@tileoutlet.net
URL: http://www.tileoutlet.net
Facebook: www.facebook.com/CarsonCityTileOutlet
X (Twitter): x.com/TileOutletNVCA

Description: Discount retail tile store selling granite counters, tile, slate, travertine, marble and related products. Our customers include the general public, contractors and builders. The corporate office directly imports products and sells to our franchisees to allow them to focus on selling. Great overhead, high profit margin business with no previous experience required. **No. of Franchise Units:** 44. **No. of Company-Owned Units:** 6. **Founded:** 2000. **Franchised:** 2002. **Equity Capital Needed:** $59,850-$104,600, franchise fee for additional units $15,000. **Franchise Fee:** $20,000 for 1st. **Training:** Provides 3 days of complete training at our corporate facility, 5 days of onsite training at your location and unlimited ongoing support through phone, fax, email, web page and in person visits.

4355 ■ UBuildIt
UBuildIt Holdings, LLC.
Edmond, OK
X (Twitter): x.com/UBuildItBrand
Pinterest: www.pinterest.com/ubuildit/the-builder-in-you

Description: Building or remodeling general contractors. **No. of Franchise Units:** 31. **Founded:** 1988. **Franchised:** 1998. **Equity Capital Needed:** $100,000-$225,000. **Franchise Fee:** $37,500. **Training:** Pretraining business start-up assistance, 2 week training and ongoing support.

PUBLICATIONS

4356 ■ BNi Publications Inc.
990 Pk. Ctr. Dr., Ste. E
Vista, CA 92081
Free: 888-264-2665
URL: http://www.bnibooks.com
Contact: Linda Dawson, Contact

Description: Publishes construction and engineering books. **Founded:** 1946.

4357 ■ *Construction Business Owner (CBO)*
1900 28th Ave. S, Ste.200
Birmingham, AL 35209
Ph: (205)212-9402
URL: http://www.cahabamedia.com
Contact: Matthew G. Conroy, Contact
URL(s): www.constructionbusinessowner.com
Facebook: www.facebook.com/constructionbusinessowner
Linkedin: www.linkedin.com/company/construction-business-owner-magazine
X (Twitter): x.com/CBOMagazine
Instagram: www.instagram.com/cbomagazine
Released: Monthly **Price:** $125, Other countries; $15, Other countries; $5, Single issue; $48, for annual. **Description:** Magazine that provides information for construction management and industry business information. **Availability:** Print; PDF; Online.

4358 ■ *Tunnel Business Magazine: Covering the North American Tunneling Market*
10050 Brecksville Rd.
Brecksville, OH 44141
Ph: (330)467-7588
Co. E-mail: info@benjaminmedia.com
URL: http://benjaminmedia.com
Contact: Rob Krzys, President
URL(s): tunnelingonline.combenjaminmedia.com/tbm-tunnel-business-magazine
Facebook: www.facebook.com/TunnelBusinessMag
Linkedin: www.linkedin.com/showcase/tbm-tunnel-business-magazine
X (Twitter): x.com/TBMag
Released: 6/year **Description:** Magazine featuring tunnel construction and engineering in North America. **Availability:** Print; Online.

PUBLISHERS

4359 ■ *"IDI Plans Spec Industrial Space" in Memphis Business Journal (Vol. 33, February 10, 2012, No. 44, pp. 1)*
Baltimore Business Journal
36 S Charles St., Ste. 2500
Baltimore, MD 21201
Ph: (410)576-1161
Fax: (410)752-3112
Co. E-mail: baltimore@bizjournals.com
URL: http://www.bizjournals.com/baltimore
Contact: Rhonda Pringle, President
E-mail: rpringle@bizjournals.com

Ed: Andy Ashby. **Description:** Industrial real estate company IDI is planning to start construction of two buildings in Memphis, Tennessee. The project is the company's first speculative new construction in four years. **Availability:** Print; Online.

LIBRARIES

4360 ■ Boston Architectural Center - Alfred Shaw and Edward Durell Stone Library
320 Newbury St.
Boston, MA 02115
URL: http://the-bac.edu/info-for/campus-and-community/shaw-and-stone-library
Contact: Robert Adams, Director

Scope: Educational material. **Services:** Interlibrary Loan. **Founded:** 1966. **Subscriptions:** 120 journals 600,000 titles; 52,000 physical items; 120 print periodical titles; theses; films; maps; eBooks; books.

4361 ■ California Real Estate Services Division Library
707 3rd St., Fl. 4
West Sacramento, CA 95605
URL: http://www.dgs.ca.gov/resd

Scope: Construction industry standards, architecture, electrical and mechanical engineering, building products, interior design. **Services:** Interlibrary loan; copying; library open to other state agencies. **Founded:** 1958. **Holdings:** 400 books; 30 bound periodical volumes; 1500 catalogs; titles 1-26 of the California Code of Regulations.

4362 ■ Canada National Research Council - CISTI Institute for Research in Construction Branch - National Science Library
1200 Montreal Rd., Bldg. M-55
Ottawa, ON, Canada K1A 0R6
Ph: (613)993-9101
Free: 877-672-2672
Fax: (613)991-9096
Co. E-mail: info@nrc-cnrc.gc.ca
URL: http://nrc.canada.ca/en
X (Twitter): x.com/nrc_cnrc
Instagram: www.instagram.com/nrc_cnrc

Scope: Publications in science; technology; engineering and health. Services: Interlibrary loan; copying; branch open to the public. Founded: 1948. Holdings: Figures not available.

4363 ■ Foundation of the Wall and Ceiling Industry (FWCI) - John H. Hampshire Memorial Library
513 W Broad St., Ste. 210
 Falls Church, VA 22046
Ph: (703)538-1600
Co. E-mail: selvitelli@awci.org
URL: http://www.awci.org/foundation
Contact: Adm. (Ret.) Johnny Barnes, President
Facebook: www.facebook.com/AWCIwall
Linkedin: www.linkedin.com/company/association-of-the-wall-and-ceiling-industry
X (Twitter): x.com/awci_info
Instagram: www.instagram.com/awci_fwci
YouTube: www.youtube.com/user/AWCImedia
Description: National and local contractors, manufacturers of construction products, architects, specifiers, and distributors/suppliers of wall and ceiling products. Supports the wall and ceiling industry's educational and research activities. Operates information clearinghouse. Scope: Industry specifications; historical reference materials. Services: Open to members for research only. Founded: 1918. Holdings: 10,000 valuable and historical reference materials. Publications: Standard Practice for the Testing and Inspections of Field Applied Sprayed Fire-Resistive Materials: An Annotated Guide. Geographic Preference: National.

4364 ■ Hill International, Inc.
Global Infrastructure Solutions Inc. (GISI)
 18000 Horizon Way, Ste. 200
 Mount Laurel Township, NJ 08054
Ph: (213)640-8159
URL: http://www.gisi.com
Contact: Raouf S. Ghali, Chief Executive Officer
Facebook: www.facebook.com/Hillintl
Linkedin: www.linkedin.com/company/hill-international
X (Twitter): x.com/hillintl
Instagram: www.instagram.com/hill_international
YouTube: www.youtube.com/user/HillInternational
Description: Global construction management company serving sectors including buildings, transportation, power, industrial and process, oil and gas, manufacturing, telecom and technology, and environmental. Provides fee-based construction management services to clients, as well as expertise in program and project management, oversight, troubled project turnaround, staff augmentation, commissioning, estimating and cost management, labor compliance management, and facilities management services. Founded: 1976. Training: Claims Recognition, Analysis and Resolution; CPM Scheduling for Owners, Architects and Engineers; CPM Scheduling for Attorneys; Right to Payment and Variations; Extension of Time, Delay Analysis, LDs; Delay, Disruption, Acceleration Claims; The Make or Break Power of Project Labor Agreements.

4365 ■ Missouri History Museum Architecture Collection
225 S Skinker
 Saint Louis, MO 63101
Ph: (314)588-1746
Co. E-mail: archives@mohistory.org
URL: http://www.stlarchivists.org/missouri-history-museum-architectural-collection
Contact: Sabrina Gorse, Co-Chairman of the Board
E-mail: sabrina.gorse@gmail.com
Scope: Architecture; construction. Services: Interlibrary loan; collection open to the public. Founded: 1993. Subscriptions: 150 newspapers 90,000 books; 2,000 journals; 3,300 trade catalogs; periodicals; maps; microfilms; records; directories; letters.

4366 ■ North Carolina State University Libraries - D.H. Hill Library Special Collections Research Center (SCRC)
2 Broughton Dr.
 Raleigh, NC 27695-7111
Ph: (919)515-2273

URL: http://www.lib.ncsu.edu/scrc
Contact: Brian Dietz, Librarian, Special Collections
E-mail: bjdietz@ncsu.edu
X (Twitter): x.com/NCSU_SCRC
Scope: Architecture and design; engineering and technology; history of science; textiles; ncsu history; plant and forestry; veterinary medicine; entomology; animal welfare; zoological health. Services: Copying; Digitization; Library open to the public. Founded: 1995. Holdings: 22,000 lin.ft. of documenting materials.

4367 ■ PG&E Corporation (PG&E)
PG&E Corporation (PG&E)
 300 Lakeside Dr.
 San Francisco, CA 94177
Ph: (415)973-7000
Free: 800-743-5000
Fax: (415)973-8719
URL: http://www.pgecorp.com
Contact: Patricia K. Pope, Chief Executive Officer
Facebook: www.facebook.com/pacificgasandelectric
Linkedin: www.linkedin.com/company/pacific-gas-and-electric-company
X (Twitter): twitter.com/pge4me
Instagram: www.instagram.com/pacificgasandelectric/
YouTube: www.youtube.com/user/pgevideo
Description: Provides electricity through geothermal, hydroelectric, fossil fuel, biomass, solar and nuclear power plants. Generates, procures, distributes, and stores power sources like natural gas and nuclear energy, and provides natural gas transportation services. Founded: 1905. Educational Activities: ACEEE Summer Study on Energy Efficiency in Buildings (Biennial); ACEEE Summer Study on Energy Efficiency in Industry (Biennial).

4368 ■ Portland Cement Association (PCA) - Library
200 Massachusetts Ave. NW, Ste. 200
 Washington, DC 20001
Ph: (202)408-9494
Co. E-mail: info@cement.org
URL: http://www.cement.org
Contact: Michael Ireland, President
E-mail: mireland@cement.org
Facebook: www.facebook.com/PCACement
Linkedin: www.linkedin.com/company/portland-cement-association
X (Twitter): x.com/pca_daily
Description: Companies in the U.S. and Canada. Seeks to improve and extend the uses of Portland cement and concrete through market promotion, research and development, educational programs, and representation with governmental entities. Conducts research on concrete technology and durability; concrete pavement design; load-bearing capacities, field performance, and fire resistance of concrete; transportation, building, and structural uses of concrete. Operates Construction Technology Laboratories, which conducts research and technical services in construction materials, products, and applications. Sponsors a public affairs program in Washington, DC. Scope: Cement and concrete. Services: Interlibrary loan; open to the public by appointment. Founded: 1916. Holdings: Books; journals; periodicals; proceedings. Educational Activities: World of Concrete (WOC) (Annual). Geographic Preference: National.

4369 ■ Societe d'Habitation du Quebec - Centre de Documentation
500, boul. Rene-Levesque West Ste. 18
 Montreal, QC, Canada H2Z 1W7
Ph: (514)844-6170
Free: 888-528-7741
URL: http://www.habitation.gouv.qc.ca
Scope: Housing; residential construction; architecture; urban planning. Services: Interlibrary loan; copying; library open to the public by appointment. Founded: 1987. Holdings: 15,000 books and reports; 150 audio/visual materials.

4370 ■ U.S. Department of Housing and Urban Development Library (HUD)
451 7th St. SW Rm. 8141
 Washington, DC 20410
Co. E-mail: library@hud.gov
URL: http://www.hud.gov/program_offices/administration/library
Scope: Housing. Founded: 1934. Holdings: Figures not available.

4371 ■ U.S. National Park Service - Blue Ridge Parkway Archives
199 Hemphill Knob Rd.
 Asheville, NC 28803-8686
Ph: (828)298-0398
Co. E-mail: blri_public_affairs@nps.gov
URL: http://www.nps.gov/blri/index.htm
Contact: Moses Cone, Contact
Facebook: www.facebook.com/BlueRidgeNPS
X (Twitter): x.com/BlueRidgeNPS
Instagram: www.instagram.com/BlueRidgeNPS
YouTube: www.youtube.com/user/BlueRidgeParkwayNPS
Scope: Blue ridge parkway – history. Services: Archives open to researchers by appointment only. Founded: 1990. Holdings: 350,000 archives.

4372 ■ University of Nevada, Las Vegas Architecture Studies Library
4505 S Maryland Pky.
 Las Vegas, NV 89154-4049
Ph: (702)895-1959
Co. E-mail: libasl@unlv.edu
URL: http://www.library.unlv.edu/arch
Contact: Richard Saladino, Librarian
E-mail: richard.saladino@unlv.edu
Scope: Architecture. Services: Interlibrary loan; Copying. Founded: 1997. Holdings: Books; journals.

4373 ■ Virginia Tech University Art & Architecture Library
100 Cowgill Hall
 Blacksburg, VA 24060
Ph: (540)231-9271
Co. E-mail: artarchlibrary-g@vt.edu
URL: http://lib.vt.edu/about-us/libraries/artarch-library.html
Scope: Visual arts; art history; architecture; decorative arts and design. Subscriptions: 200 journals and other serials 200 journals; 85,000 print volumes.

4374 ■ Zachry Construction Corporation (ZCC) - Library
14410 Wurzbach Pky., Ste. 120
 San Antonio, TX 78216
Ph: (210)871-2700
Free: 877-884-9247
URL: http://www.zachryconstructioncorp.com
Contact: David S. Zachry, President
Facebook: www.facebook.com/zachryconstructioncorp
Linkedin: www.linkedin.com/company/zachry-corporation
X (Twitter): x.com/ZachryCorp
Instagram: www.instagram.com/zachryconstruction
Description: Construction company that provides design, build, project development, program management, infrastructure operations and maintenance services. Scope: Construction - design, build, project development, program management, and infrastructure operations and maintenance. Founded: 1924. Holdings: Figures not available.

RESEARCH CENTERS

4375 ■ Concordia University - Department of Building, Civil and Environmental Engineering (BCEE)
1455 De Maisonneuve Blvd. W EV 6. 139
 Montreal, QC, Canada H3G 1M8
Ph: (514)848-2424
URL: http://www.concordia.ca/ginacody/building-civil-environmental-eng.html
Contact: Dr. Ashutosh Bagchi, Professor
E-mail: ashutosh.bagchi@concordia.ca

Description: Integral unit of Concordia University. Offers research development and information transfer services; master's and doctoral degrees. **Scope:** Research center carries out research in the following areas; Building environment, building science, building structures, and construction management, including energy efficiency, air quality, air infiltration and rain penetration of enclosure systems, building envelope performance. **Publications:** *CBS Annual Report* (Annual); *CBS Research papers*.

4376 ■ National Institute of Building Sciences (NIBS)
1090 Vermont Ave., NW Ste. 700
Washington, DC 20005
Ph: (202)289-7800
Co. E-mail: nibs@nibs.org
URL: http://www.nibs.org
Contact: Roger J. Grant, Vice President
Facebook: www.facebook.com/bldgsciences
Linkedin: www.linkedin.com/company/national-institute-of-bldg-sciences
X (Twitter): x.com/bldgsciences

Description: Individuals and organizations, including architects, engineers, builders, contractors, realtors, universities, and all levels of government interested in the building industry. **Scope:** Improvement of the building and the construction regulation process in the U. S. and to encourage the use of safe, innovative building technology. **Founded:** 1974. **Publications:** *Directory of Online Databases for Building and Construction*; *National Institute of Building Sciences--Directory of Building Community Organizations*; *Guidance Manual, Asbestos Operations & Maintenance Work Practices* (Periodic); *Construction Criteria Base (CCB)*; *Building Sciences Newsletter* (Monthly); *CCB Bulletin* (Quarterly). **Educational Activities:** BETEC Symposia, A collection of leading experts who will share the latest information available on a variety of fenestration technology and performance topics. **Awards:** NIBS Honor Award (Annual); NIBS Member Award (Irregular); NIBS President's Award. **Geographic Preference:** National.

4377 ■ University of Hartford - Construction Institute
1137 Main St., Ste. 206
East Hartford, CT 06108
Ph: (860)929-3001
Co. E-mail: admin@construction.org
URL: http://www.construction.org
Contact: Nancy Greenwald, Executive Director
E-mail: ngreenwald@construction.org
YouTube: www.youtube.com/channel/UCCrJXp0Hfl1SxJp0HTSi4WQ

Description: Integral unit of University of Hartford and a statewide, nonprofit, nonpartisan professional association of building and construction industry personnel concerned with the challenges of the built environment. Provides information: to industry and public officials. **Scope:** Construction industry and concerns, especially in Connecticut, including the infrastructure system in Connecticut, labor relations, affordable insurance, and the size, scope, and impact of the Connecticut construction industry. Serves as a neutral forum in which construction industry professionals from all disciplines examine issues and resolve major problems. **Founded:** 1976. **Publications:** *Construction Institute Newsletter*. **Educational Activities:** Construction Institute Forums (Annual); Construction Institute Conferences (Annual), For constuction industry research and development.

4378 ■ University of Illinois at Urbana-Champaign College of Fine and Applied Arts - Illinois School of Architecture - Building Research Council (BRC)
117 Temple Hoyne Buell Hall
611 Lorado Taft Dr.
Champaign, IL 61820
URL: http://arch.illinois.edu/about/statements

Scope: Methods and materials for building construction, particularly light frame construction including thermographic analysis, environmental effects on building materials, mitigation of natural disasters, and roofing and waterproofing materials. Investigates and develops planning standards for space design in housing construction. **Educational Activities:** High performance building analyses; Weatherization training and building energy assessments. **Geographic Preference:** National.

4379 ■ University of Texas at Arlington - Construction Research Center (CRC)
701 S Nedderman Dr.
Arlington, TX 76019
URL: http://www.uta.edu/academics/schools-colleges/engineering/academics/departments/civil/research

Description: Integral unit of University of Texas at Arlington. **Scope:** Addresses the needs of the construction industry through construction research and educational programs. **Founded:** 1972. **Educational Activities:** CRC Seminars, To address the practical needs of the various construction and building industry members.

Consumer Electronics Store

ASSOCIATIONS AND OTHER ORGANIZATIONS

4380 ■ **Electronics Representatives Association (ERA)**
1325 S Arlington Heights Rd., Ste. 204
Elk Grove Village, IL 60007
Ph: (312)419-1432
Fax: (312)419-1660
Co. E-mail: info@era.org
URL: http://www.era.org
Contact: Walter Tobin, Chief Executive Officer
E-mail: wtobin@era.org
Facebook: www.facebook.com/ElectronicsRepresentativesAssociation
Linkedin: www.linkedin.com/groups/2806290/profile
X (Twitter): x.com/era_org
Instagram: www.instagram.com/electronics_reps_association
Description: Professional field sales organizations selling components and materials; computer, instrumentation and data communications products; audiovisual, security, land/mobile communications and commercial sound components and consumer products to the electronics industry. Sponsors insurance programs and educational conference for members. **Founded:** 1935. **Publications:** *Lines Available Bulletin*; *Representor* (Quarterly); *Locator of Professional Field Sales Organizations* (Annual); *Electronics Industry Showcase* (Annual); *ERA Rep Locator*. **Educational Activities:** Northcon Electronics Show and Convention; Electronic Distribution Show (Annual). **Geographic Preference:** National.

4381 ■ **National Electronics Service Dealers Association (NESDA)**
PO Box 378
Hillsboro, TX 76645
Ph: (817)921-9061
Free: 800-797-9197
Co. E-mail: info@nesda.com
URL: http://nesda.wildapricot.org
Contact: Paul Burgio, President
Facebook: www.facebook.com/TVRepairPros
Description: Local and state electronic service associations and companies. Supplies technical service information on business management training to electronic service dealers. Offers certification and training programs through International Society of Certified Electronics Technicians. Conducts technical service and business management seminars. **Founded:** 1963. **Publications:** *ProService Magazine* (Monthly); *Find a TV Repair Pro*; *ProService Directory and Yearbook* (Annual); *Proservice Directory*. **Educational Activities:** National Professional Service Convention (NPSC) (Annual). **Awards:** NESDA Associate Leadership Excellence Award (Annual); Fay S. Wood EHF Membership Award (Annual); Gerry M. McCann CET/CSM, EHF Memorial Award (Annual); M.L. Finneburgh, Sr., Award of Excellence (Annual); National Friend of Service Award (Annual); NESDA Outstanding Associate President Award (Annual); NESDA Outstanding Committee Chairperson Award (Annual); NSDA Person of the Year (Annual); Richard Mildenberger Outstanding NESDA Officer (Annual). **Geographic Preference:** National.

REFERENCE WORKS

4382 ■ *"2019 Top 100 Retailers Power Players: Consumer Electronics/Telecoms"* in Stores.org (July 1, 2019)
URL(s): stores.org/2019/07/01/2019-top-100-retailers-power-players-consumer-electronics-telecoms/
Released: July 01, 2019. **Description:** Profile of one of the top 100 consumer electronics stores, Best Buy. The new leader of the company, Corie Barry, has made changes to the business model which has made it competitive again with online stores. **Availability:** Online.

4383 ■ *"Abt Electronics and Appliances Announces the Second Annual Earth Day Recycle Drive"* in Ecology, Environment & Conservation Business (May 3, 2014, pp. 3)
Pub: NewsRX LLC.
Contact: Kalani Rosell, Contact
Description: Abt Electronics and Appliances is the largest independent, single-store appliance and electronics retailer in the U.S. In honor of Earth Day, Abt has partnered with the City of Chicago to help local residents recycle e-waste, such as electronics and appliances, in an environmentally friendly way for the second year in a row. **Availability:** Online.

4384 ■ *"Acacia Subsidiary Acquires Patents Related to Shared Memory for Multimedia Processing from a Major Corporation"* in Economics & Business Week (April 26, 2014, pp. 5)
Pub: NewsRX LLC.
Contact: Kalani Rosell, Contact
Description: Acacia Research Corporation that a subsidiary has acquired U.S. patents and foreign counterparts related to the use of shared memory in multimedia processing systems such as mobile phones, tablets and other consumer electronic devices. **Availability:** Online.

4385 ■ *"Amazon Beats Best Buy As Top Electronics Retailer"* in RetailDive (April 17, 2018)
URL(s): www.retaildive.com/news/amazon-beats-best-buy-as-top-electronics-retailer/521505/
Ed: Daphne Howland. **Released:** April 17, 2018. **Description:** Dealerscope released it's Top 101 Consumer Electronics Retailers list, and Amazon has taken over the lead from Best Buy. Amazon grew its electronics sales by more than 18.5%. **Availability:** Online.

4386 ■ *"Best Online Stores for Personal Electronics"* in Money Crashers
URL(s): www.moneycrashers.com/best-online-stores-consumer-electronics/
Ed: Chris Bibey. **Description:** If you are looking for a deal and larger selection on electronics, check out the online stores that specialize in these gadgets. Six of the best online sites are listed with a description of their merchandise and deals. **Availability:** Online.

4387 ■ *"Bose Seeking Expansion Options in Framingham"* in Boston Business Journal (Vol. 34, June 13, 2014, No. 19, pp. 15)
Pub: American City Business Journals, Inc.
Contact: Mike Olivieri, Executive Vice President
Released: Weekly. **Description:** Bose Corporation, the Framingham-based high-end audio products manufacturer, is in talks to buy a 10-acre property near its headquarters. Bose is negotiating with the owner of three buildings on Pennsylvania Avenue near the Bose headquarters. Bose already owns five buildings in Framingham, but is looking at real estate for growth and expansion. **Availability:** Print; Online.

4388 ■ *"Clusters Last Stand?"* in Canadian Electronics (Vol. 23, February 2008, No. 1, pp. 6)
Description: Survival of technology clusters was the focus of Strategic Microelectronics Council's conference entitled, "The Power of Community: Building Technology Clusters in Canada". Clusters can help foster growth in the microelectronics sector, and it was recognized that government intervention is needed to maintain these clusters. **Availability:** Download; PDF; Online.

4389 ■ *"Consumers Turned Off? Not at Best Buy"* in Barron's (Vol. 88, March 24, 2008, No. 12, pp. 29)
Pub: Dow Jones & Company Inc.
Contact: Almar Latour, Chief Executive Officer
Ed: Sandra Ward. **Description:** Shares of Best Buy, trading at $42.41 each, are expected to rise to an average of $52 a share due to the company's solid fundamentals. The company's shares have fallen 20 percent from their 52-week high and are attractive given the company's bright prospects in the video game sector and high-definition video. **Availability:** Online.

4390 ■ *"Defense Mobile Joins Forces with RadioShack to launch New Military Focuses Mobile Service this Fall"* in Defense & Aerospace Business (September 10, 2014, pp. 7)
Pub: NewsRX LLC.
Contact: Kalani Rosell, Contact
Description: RadioShack and Defense Mobile Corporation have partnered for RadioShack to be the exclusive national retailer for Defense Mobile's new nationwide 4G LTE mobile services. Defense Mobile was launched by veterans and supported by a 100 percent veteran-staffed Member Service organization and its mobile services are designed to benefit, honor and reward active U.S. military and veterans for their commitment and service. **Availability:** Online.

4391 ■ *"The Devolution of Home-Electronics Stores"* in *Philadelphia Business Journal (Vol. 28, June 8, 2012, No. 17, pp. 1)*
Pub: Baltimore Business Journal
Contact: Rhonda Pringle, President
E-mail: rpringle@bizjournals.com
Description: Philadelphia, Pennsylvania-area consumer electronics stores have mirrored the national trend in which big-box retailers are taking a bigger share of the home-electronics market. However, smaller, locally-based chains are competing in terms of pricing transparency and custom electronics. Availability: Print; Online.

4392 ■ *"Digital Power Management and the PMBus"* in *Canadian Electronics (Vol. 23, June-July 2008, No. 4, pp. 8)*
Pub: Annex Buisness Media
Contact: Mike Fredericks, President
Ed: Torbjorn Holmberg. Description: PMBus is an interface that can be applied to a variety of devices including power management devices. Information on digital power management products using this interface are also provided. Availability: Print; Online.

4393 ■ *"Electronics Recyclers Poised to Grow"* in *Austin Business Journal (Vol. 31, July 22, 2011, No. 20, pp. A1)*
Pub: Austin Business Journal
Contact: Rachel McGrath, Director
E-mail: rmcgrath@bizjournals.com
Ed: Cody Lyon. Description: Electronic Recycling and Trading Inc. has leased 138,000 square feet of space in North Austin, Texas. The company requires more space for bigger equipment. Availability: Print; Online.

4394 ■ *"German Firm Ifm Electronic to Open Second Local Unit"* in *Philadelphia Business Journal (Vol. 28, July 20, 2012, No. 23, pp. 1)*
Pub: Baltimore Business Journal
Contact: Rhonda Pringle, President
E-mail: rpringle@bizjournals.com
Description: German electronic control and sensor manufacturer, ifm electronic gmbh, has established ifm prover USA in January 2012, its second subsidiary in Exton, Pennsylvania after ifm efector Inc. Ifm prover will relocate in July 2012 to a new 36,000 square foot building that features a product development area and multiple laboraties for testing and quality control. Availability: Print; Online.

4395 ■ *"How I Did It: Best Buy's CEO On Learning to Love Social Media"* in *Harvard Business Review (Vol. 88, December 2010, No. 12, pp. 43)*
Pub: Harvard Business Publishing
Contact: Diane Belcher, Managing Director
Ed: Brian J. Dunn. Price: $8.95, PDF. Description: Effective utilization of online social networks to enhance brand identity, connect with consumers, and address bad publicity scenarios is examined. Availability: Online; PDF.

4396 ■ *"The Intel Trinity: How Robert Noyce, Gordon Moore, and Andy Grove Built the World's Most Important Company"*
Pub: Harper Business
Contact: Hollis Heimbouch, Senior Vice President Publisher
Released: July 15, 2014. Price: $34.99, hardcover; $11.74, e-book; $4.34, kindle; $19.42, hardcover; $4.30, hardcover(69 used from $4.30); $15.17, hardcover(56 new from $15.17); $19.99, hardcover(1 collectible from $19.99); $31.74, paperback; $22.95, paperback(10 used from $22.95); $19.13, paperback(4 new from $19.13). Description: A complete history of Intel Corporation, the essential company of the digital age, is presented. After over four decades Intel remains the most important company in the world, a defining company of the global digital economy. The inventors of the microprocessor that powers nearly every intelligent electronic device worldwide are profiled. These entrepreneurs made the personal computer, Internet, telecommunications, and personal electronics all possible. The challenges and successes of the company and its ability to maintain its dominance, its culture and its legacy are examined. Availability: E-book; Print; Online.

4397 ■ *"Manufacturing Behind the Great Wall: What Works, What Doesn't"* in *Canadian Electronics (Vol. 23, February 2008, No. 1, pp. 6)*
Description: Electronic component producers are increasingly transitioning their manufacturing operations to China in order to take advantage of the growing Chinese manufacturing industry. It is believed that manufacturers have to carefully consider whether their run sizes are appropriate for Chinese manufacturing before moving their operations. Availability: PDF.

4398 ■ *"Miller's Crossroad"* in *Canadian Business (Vol. 83, September 14, 2010, No. 15, pp. 58)*
Ed: Joe Castaldo. Released: September 14, 2010. Description: Future Electronics founder and billionaire Robert Miller shares the secret of Future's unique operating model, which is based on inventory and market research. Miller attributes much of the company's success to its privately held status that enables quick movement against competitors. Availability: Print; Online.

4399 ■ *"Mosaid Grants First Wireless Patent License To Matsushita"* in *Canadian Electronics (Vol. 23, June-July 2008, No. 5, pp. 1)*
Pub: Annex Buisness Media
Contact: Mike Fredericks, President
Description: Matsushita Electric Industrial Co. Ltd. has been granted a six-and-a-half-year license by Mosaid Technologies Inc. to manufacture the latter's products. The patent portfolio license agreement covers Mosaid's Wi-Fi, Wi-Max, CDMA-enabled notebook computers and other products.

4400 ■ *"Motors and Motion Control"* in *Canadian Electronics (Vol. 23, February 2008, No. 1, pp. 23)*
Description: A new version of MicroMo Electronics Inc.'s Smoovy Series 0303.B has been added to MicroMo's DC motor product line. United Electronic Industries, on the other hand, has introduced the new UEIPAC series of programmable automation controllers that can offer solutions to various applications such as unmanned vehicle controllers. Features and functions of other new motors and motion control devices are given.

4401 ■ *"Nvidia Shares Clobbered After Gloomy Warning"* in *Barron's (Vol. 88, July 7, 2008, No. 27, pp. 25)*
Pub: Dow Jones & Company Inc.
Contact: Almar Latour, Chief Executive Officer
Ed: Eric J. Savitz. Description: Shares of graphics chip manufacturer Nvidia suffered a 30 percent drop in its share price after the company warned that revenue and gross margin forecasts for the quarter ending July 27, 2008 will be below expectations. Stan Glasgow, chief operating officer of Sony Electronics, believes the US economic slowdown will not affect demand for the company's products. Statistical data included. Availability: Online.

4402 ■ *"The Pre-Tail Revolution"* in *Canadian Business (Vol. 87, October 2014, No. 10, pp. 10)*
Description: A number of products that succeeded in security support from crowdfunding platforms, Kickstarter and Indiegogo, and those that failed are presented. Included are the do-it-yourself computer kit Kano, Bluetooth speakers Edge.sound, three-dimensional printer The Micro, Coolest Cooler the insect control device BugASalt, hexacopter Hexo+, and the Ubuntu Edge. Availability: Print; Online.

4403 ■ *"Provinces Tackle E-Waste Problem"* in *Canadian Electronics (Vol. 23, June-July 2008, No. 4, pp. 1)*
Pub: Action Communication Inc.
Ed: Ken Manchen. Description: Canadian provinces are implementing measures concerning the safe and environmentally friendly disposal of electronic waste. Alberta, British Columbia, Nova Scotia, and Saskatchewan impose an e-waste recycling fee on electronic equipment purchases. Availability: Online.

4404 ■ *"Remember Crazy Eddie? His Prices Were Insane!"* in *Small Business Trends (August 29, 2022)*
URL(s): smallbiztrends.com/2022/08/the-insane-real-life-story-of-crazy-eddie.html
Released: August 29, 2022. Description: Interview with author Gary Weiss who wrote a book about the real-life Crazy Eddie, who owned an electronics store in New York and made over 7,500 catchy commercials. Availability: Online.

4405 ■ *"Soda Says, a Curated Consumer Electronics Retail Platform, Launches in the US"* in *TechCrunch (May 29, 2019)*
URL(s): techcrunch.com/2019/05/29/soda-says-a-curated-consumer-electronics-retail-platform-launches-in-the-u-s/
Ed: Jordan Crook. Released: May 29, 2019. Description: Soda Says, a new e-commerce marketplace launched in the US. This platform focuses on lifestyle gadgets that are useful and pleasing to the eye. They are also offering pop-up stores within traditional department stores. Availability: Online.

4406 ■ *"Sources"* in *Canadian Electronics (Vol. 23, August 2008, No. 5, pp. 12)*
Description: Directory of electronic manufacturers, distributors and representatives in Canada is provided. The list presents distributors and representatives under each manufacturer.

4407 ■ *"STMicroelectronics"* in *Canadian Electronics (Vol. 23, February 2008, No. 1, pp. 1)*
Description: STMicroelectronics, a semiconductor maker, revealed that it plans to acquire Genesis Microchip Inc. Genesis develops image and video processing systems. It was reported that the acquisition has been approved by Genesis' Board of Directors. It is expected that Genesis will enhance STMicroelectronics' technological capabilities. Availability: Online.

4408 ■ *"TomTom GO910: On the Road Again"* in *Black Enterprise (Vol. 37, January 2007, No. 6, pp. 52)*
Pub: Earl G. Graves Ltd.
Contact: Earl Graves, Jr., President
Ed: Stephanie Young. Description: TomTom GO 910 is a GPS navigator that offers detailed maps of the U.S., Canada, and Europe. Consumers view their routes by a customizable LCD screen showing everything from the quickest to the shortest routes available or how to avoid toll roads. Business travelers may find this product invaluable as it also functions as a cell phone and connects to a variety of other multi-media devices. Availability: Online.

4409 ■ *"Veteran-Owned Business 3E Services Gains Recognition in 2011 and Welcomes 2012 With New Offerings"* in *Marketwired (January 10, 2012)*
Pub: Comtex News Network Inc.
Contact: Kan Devnani, President
Description: 3E Services Inc. specializes in the selling, repairing, and remanufacturing of electrical components. It is a veteran-owned busiens located in Tucker, Georgia near Atlanta.The Washington Post recognized 3E as an exemplary veteran-owned business. David Loftin, president and founder, learned his skills as a US Navy nuclear electrician and attributes that training to his firm's growth and success. Availability: Print; Online.

4410 ■ *"What Marketers Misunderstand about Online Reviews: Managers Must Analyze What's Really Driving Buying Decisions - and Adjust Their Strategies Accordingly"* in *Harvard Business Review (Vol. 92, January-February 2014, No. 1-2, pp. 23)*
Pub: Harvard Business Press
Contact: Gabriela Allmi, Regional Manager

E-mail: gabriela.allmi@hbsp.harvard.edu
Price: $6, hardcopy black and white. **Description:** Companies may overestimate the influence of online reviews, as consumers do not turn to reviews for certain products and services (for example, habitual low-involvement purchases such as groceries). Others' opinions matter more for purchases such as independent restaurants and electronics. **Availability:** Print; PDF; Online.

4411 ■ "Winning With Women" in Marketing to Women (Vol. 22, August 2009, No. 8, pp. 6)
Description: Women shoppers are buying more utilitarian categories despite the overall fall in consumer electronics sales. Among the top five purchases women will defer in the next three months are personal consumer electronics, such as MP3 players and digital cameras, as well as home entertainment items. **Availability:** Online.

STATISTICAL SOURCES

4412 ■ Consumer Electronics & Appliances Rental Industry in the US - Market Research Report
URL(s): www.ibisworld.com/united-states/market-research-reports/consumer-electronics-appliances-rental-industry/
Price: $925. **Description:** Downloadable report analyzing the current and future trends in the consumer electronics and appliance rental industries. **Availability:** Download.

4413 ■ RMA Annual Statement Studies
Pub: Risk Management Association
Contact: Nancy Foster, President
Released: Annual. **Description:** Contains composite balance sheets and income statements for more than 360 industries, including the accounting, auditing, and bookkeeping industries. Also contains five years of comparative historical data for discerning trends. Includes 16 commonly used ratios, computed for most of the size groupings for nearly every industry.

TRADE SHOWS AND CONVENTIONS

4414 ■ Electronic Distribution Show
Electronic Distribution Show Corp.
2214 Rock Hill Rd., Ste. 170
Herndon, VA 20170
Ph: (312)648-1140
Fax: (312)648-4282
Co. E-mail: eds@edsconnects.com
URL: http://www.edsconnects.com
Contact: Craig Anderson, President
URL(s): edssummit.com
Frequency: Annual. **Description:** Electronic products. **Audience:** Electronics professionals. **Principal Exhibits:** Electronic products. Dates and Locations: 2025 May 19-23 RESORTS WORLD, Las Vegas, NV. **Telecommunication Services:** info@edssummit.com.

4415 ■ National Professional Service Convention (NPSC)
National Electronics Service Dealers Association (NESDA)
PO Box 378
Hillsboro, TX 76645
Ph: (817)921-9061
Free: 800-797-9197
Co. E-mail: info@nesda.com
URL: http://nesda.wildapricot.org
Contact: Paul Burgio, President
URL(s): nesda.wildapricot.org/event-4950665
Frequency: Annual. **Description:** Electronics, receivers, recorders, and supplies; software; telecommunications equipment; computers; videocassette recorders; parts and accessories, business forms, warranty companies, and magazines/associations. **Audience:** Technicians, officers, managers, instructors, writers, editors, and publishers. **Principal Exhibits:** Electronics, receivers, recorders, and supplies; software; telecommunications equipment; computers; videocassette recorders; parts and accessories, business forms, warranty companies, and magazines/associations.

FRANCHISES AND BUSINESS OPPORTUNITIES

4416 ■ Handypro
995 S Main St.
Plymouth, MI 48170
Ph: (734)335-1010
URL: http://www.handypro.com
Contact: Keith A. Paul, Co-Founder
Description: Provides residential and business home renovation services. **Founded:** 1996.

4417 ■ K and N Mobile Distribution Systems
Fort Worth, TX
URL: http://kandnmobile.com
Contact: Jerry Nelson, Founder
Description: Distributor of electrical products and fasteners from a mobile warehouse. **Founded:** 1972. **Training:** Initial 10-day training course is conducted at corporate headquarters. Trainer accompanies franchisee during the first 3-10 days in the field. During the first year, a trainer rides with the franchisee at least 2 days per quarter. After the franchisee has been in business for 1 year, a corporate representative will spend 4 or more days with the franchisee each year.

4418 ■ Rapid Refill Fargo and Total Imaging LLC
Rapid Refill Ink Intl., Corp.
3051 25th St., South, Ste. H
Fargo, ND 58103
Ph: (952)238-1000
Free: 877-880-4465
Fax: (952)238-1009
Facebook: www.facebook.com/RapidRefillFargo
Linkedin: www.linkedin.com/in/william-bill-erickson-3b4b0410a
Description: Remanufacturing of inkjet & laser toner cartridges. **No. of Franchise Units:** 92. **No. of Company-Owned Units:** 1. **Founded:** 2002. **Franchised:** 2004. **Equity Capital Needed:** $23,200-$142,400. **Franchise Fee:** $15,000-$30,000. **Royalty Fee:** 6%. **Financial Assistance:** Yes **Training:** Provides 2 weeks training at headquarters, including 3 days business training.

LIBRARIES

4419 ■ Agilent Technologies, Inc.
Agilent Technologies, Inc.
5301 Stevens Creek Blvd.
Santa Clara, CA 95051
Ph: (408)345-8886
Free: 877-424-4536
Fax: (408)345-8474
Co. E-mail: contact_us@agilent.com
URL: http://www.agilent.com
Contact: Mike McMullen, President
Facebook: www.facebook.com/Agilent.Tech
Linkedin: www.linkedin.com/company/agilent-technologies
X (Twitter): twitter.com/Agilent
YouTube: www.youtube.com/user/agilent
Description: Engaged in providing application-focused solutions including reagents, instruments, software, services, and consumables used in life sciences, diagnostics and applied chemical laboratory identification, interrogation, quantification and analysis applications. The company also conducts centralized order fulfillment and supply chain operations. **Founded:** 1999. **Publications:** "Using a design to test capability for LTE MIMO," Oct, 2009; "Test solutions soup up for 4G," Apr, 2009; "Why Use One Radio When Four Will Do," Oct, 2008; "3GPP LTE Introducing Single Carrier FDMA," Jan, 2008; "Examining the Design and Test Challenges of 3GPP LTE," Nov, 2007; "First Pass Accuracy with Momentum GX for WiMAX Design," Nov, 2007; "Addressing the new challenges of MIMO wireless LAN manufacturing test," Oct, 2006. **Educational Activities:** EMBL International PhD Symposium; American Chemical Society Southeastern Regional Meeting and Conference (SERMACS) (Annual). **Preferred Investment Size:** $500,000 to $10,000,000. **Industry Preferences:** Communications and media, semiconductors and other electronics, biotechnology, medical and health, and industrial and energy.

4420 ■ Fujitsu Semiconductor America Inc. (FMI) - FMI Library
1250 E Arques Ave., M/S 333
Sunnyvale, CA 94085-5401
Ph: (408)737-5600
Fax: (408)737-5999
URL: http://www.fujitsu.com/us
Contact: Takahito Tokita, Chief Executive Officer
X (Twitter): x.com/Fujitsu_Global
Description: Manufacturer of semiconductors and electronic devices. **Scope:** Semiconductor industry and products; computer industry and products; telecommunications; electronics industry. **Services:** Interlibrary loan; SDI; library not open to the public. **Founded:** 1979. **Holdings:** 500 books and conference proceedings; 250 market research reports and newsletters; CDs.

Convenience Store

START-UP INFORMATION

4421 ■ *Convenience Stores Industry in the US - Market Research Report*
URL(s): www.ibisworld.com/united-states/market-research-reports/convenience-stores-industry/
Price: $925. **Description:** Downloadable report analyzing the current and future trends in the convenience stores industry. **Availability:** Download.

ASSOCIATIONS AND OTHER ORGANIZATIONS

4422 ■ **Food Marketing Institute (FMI)**
2345 Crystal Dr., Ste. 800
Arlington, VA 22202
Ph: (202)452-8444
Fax: (202)429-4519
URL: http://www.fmi.org
Contact: Leslie G. Sarasin, President
Linkedin: www.linkedin.com/company/fmithefoodindustryassociation
X (Twitter): x.com/FMI_ORG
Instagram: www.instagram.com/fmi_org
YouTube: www.youtube.com/user/FMIorg
Description: Grocery retailers and wholesalers. Maintains liaison with government and consumers. Conducts 30 educational conferences and seminars per year. Conducts research programs; compiles statistics. **Scope:** Retail and wholesale grocery operations, food industry research, and consumer behavior and attitudes regarding grocery shopping. **Founded:** 1977. **Publications:** *FMI Newsletter*; *FMI News: Aisle by Aisle* (Monthly); *Advantage* (Monthly); *Information Systems Directory* (Biennial); *Facts About Supermarket Development* (Annual); *Food Marketing Industry Speaks* (Annual); *Food Retailing Industry Speaks* (Annual); *Operating Results of Independent Supermarkets*. **Educational Activities:** FMI Midwinter Executive Conference (Annual). **Awards:** William H. Albers Industry Relations Award (Annual); Esther Peterson Consumer Service Award (Periodic); Sidney R. Rabb Award for Statesmanship (Annual). **Geographic Preference:** National.

4423 ■ **NACS: The Association for Convenience and Fuel Retailing - Library**
1600 Duke St., 7th Fl.
Alexandria, VA 22314
Ph: (703)684-3600
Free: 800-966-6227
Fax: (703)836-4564
URL: http://www.convenience.org
Contact: Brian Kimmel, Executive Vice President Chief Financial Officer Chief Operating Officer
Description: Represents retail stores that sell gasoline, fast foods, soft drinks, dairy products, beer, cigarettes, publications, grocery items, snacks and nonfood items and are usually open seven days per week for longer hours than conventional supermarkets. Serves the convenience and fuel retailing industry by providing industry knowledge, connections and advocacy to ensure the competitive viability of its members' businesses. Conducts educational and legislative activities and sponsors management seminars. **Scope:** Global trade. **Founded:** 1961. **Holdings:** Figures not available. **Publications:** *National Association of Convenience Stores-- Membership Directory*; *NACS*; *Compensation Survey* (Annual); *NACS Magazine* (Monthly); *State of the Industry Report/Factbook* (Annual). **Educational Activities:** NACS Show (Annual). **Awards:** NACS Scholarship (Annual). **Geographic Preference:** Multinational.

4424 ■ **National Grocers Association (NGA)**
601 Pennsylvania Ave. NW, Ste. 375N
Washington, DC 20004
Ph: (202)938-2570
Fax: (202)938-2574
Co. E-mail: communications@nationalgrocers.org
URL: http://www.nationalgrocers.org
Contact: Greg Ferrara, President
Facebook: www.facebook.com/NationalGrocersAssn
Linkedin: www.linkedin.com/company/national-grocers-association
X (Twitter): x.com/NationalGrocers
Instagram: www.instagram.com/nationalgrocers
YouTube: www.youtube.com/NationalGrocers
Description: Independent food retailers; wholesale food distributors servicing 29,000 food stores. Promotes industry interests and works to advance understanding, trade and cooperation among all sectors of the food industry. Represents member's interests before the government. Aids in the development of programs designed to improve the productivity and efficiency of the food distribution industry. **Founded:** 1980. **Publications:** *Congressional or Regulatory Update* (Periodic). **Educational Activities:** NGA Show (Annual); The NGA Show; America's Supermarket Showcase (Annual). **Awards:** Clarence G. Adamy Great American Award (Annual); NGA Spirit of America Award (Annual). **Geographic Preference:** National.

REFERENCE WORKS

4425 ■ *"7-Eleven Considers Private Label Ice Cream" in Ice Cream Reporter (Vol. 22, December 20, 2008, No. 1, pp. 1)*
Description: 7-Eleven is considering the introduction of a private label of snack foods, including ice cream desserts. **Availability:** Print; Online.

4426 ■ *"Amcon Distributing Expands Into Northwest Arkansas" in Arkansas Business (Vol. 26, November 9, 2009, No. 45, pp. 13)*
Pub: Arkansas Business Publishing Group
Contact: Mitch Bettis, President
Description: Amcon Distributing Co., a consumer products company, has bought the convenience store distribution assets of Discount Distributors from its parent, Harps Food Stores Inc., significantly increasing its wholesale distribution presence in the northwest Arkansas market. The acquisition will be funded through Amcon's existing credit facilities. **Availability:** Online.

4427 ■ *"Ampm Focus Has BP Working Overtime" in Crain's Chicago Business (April 28, 2008)*
Pub: Crain Communications Inc.
Contact: Barry Asin, President
Ed: John T. Slania. **Description:** Britian's oil giant BP PLC is opening its ampm convenience stores in the Chicago market and has already begun converting most of its 78 Chicago-area gas stations to ampms. The company has also started to franchise the stores to independent operators. BP is promoting the brand with both traditional and unconventional marketing techniques such s real or simulated 3D snacks embedded in bus shelter ads and an in-store Guitar Hero contest featuring finalists from a recent contest at the House of Blues. **Availability:** Online.

4428 ■ *"Consumer Tastes Are Redefining Convenience Retail" in Food Business News (July 2, 2019)*
URL(s): www.foodbusinessnews.net/articles/14055-consumer-tastes-are-redefining-convenience-retail
Ed: Monica Watrous. **Released:** July 02, 2019. **Description:** Moving away from traditional unhealthy snacks and other offerings, convenience stores are now starting to sell fresh and healthy food and premium coffee. This is actually taking away market share from other health food stores. **Availability:** Online.

4429 ■ *"Convenience Store Deal for Cardtronics" in American Banker (Vol. 174, July 28, 2009, No. 143, pp. 12)*
Pub: SourceMedia LLC
Contact: Gemma Postlethwaite, Chief Executive Officer
Description: Royal Buying Group, Inc., a convenience store marketing company, has agreed to recommend automated teller machine services from Cardtronics Inc., to its clients.

4430 ■ *"Convenience Store Expanding" in Clovis News Journal (November 9, 2010)*
Description: Allsup's convenience store on North Prince Street in Clovis, New Mexico will expand its facilities. The current building is being demolished to make way for the new construction.

4431 ■ *"Convenience Store Owners Will Request New Zoning Once More" in Daily Republic (November 1, 2010)*
Pub: McClatchy Tribune Information Services
Contact: Patrick J. Talamantes, President
Ed: Tom Lawrence. **Description:** Zoning change has been requested for a proposed convenience store in Mitchell, South Dakota. Details are included. **Availability:** Online.

4432 ■ *"A Dollar, a Dream, and a Cup of Joe"* in *Business Review Albany* (Vol. 41, July 25, 2014, No. 18, pp. 6)
Description: Stewart Shops has boosted its revenues from selling lottery tickets. The company has reported $175.7 million in New York lottery sales in 2013. Steward also gets free publicity when there is a big winner. **Availability:** Print; Online.

4433 ■ *"Forget the Pretzels and Soda, Shoppers Are Scooping Up Flowers and Salads at Convenience Stores"* in *CNBC.com* (April 6, 2019)
URL(s): www.cnbc.com/2019/04/05/convenience-s tores-see-record-sales-as-shoppers-buy-more-fresh -food.html
Ed: Maggie Fitzgerald. **Released:** April 06, 2019.
Description: Convenience stores keep experiencing record sales and a lot of it has to do with the expanded selection of items they are selling. Instead of just chips and pop, these stores have started to sell fruits, vegetables, and healthier options for pre-made food. **Availability:** Online.

4434 ■ *"The Formula for Growth: Through a Mixture of Vision and Partnerships, Leon Richardson has ChemicoMays in Expansion Mode"* in *Black Enterprise* (Vol. 44, June 2014, No. 10, pp. 66)
Pub: Earl G. Graves Ltd.
Contact: Earl Graves, Jr., President
Description: Profile of Leon Richardson, who has his family-owned business poised for growth. At the age of 13, Leon helped his family in their convenience store located in West Haven, Connecticut. He has gone from managing storefronts to overseeing a chemical management business during his entrepreneurial career.

4435 ■ *"'Frozen' Assets: Refrigeration Goes High Tech as Hussmann Invests $7 Million in Global Hub"* in *St. Louis Business Journal* (Vol. 33, September 21, 2012, No. 4, pp. 1)
Pub: Baltimore Business Journal
Contact: Rhonda Pringle, President
E-mail: rpringle@bizjournals.com
Description: Hussmann Corporation is spending $7 million to create a high-tech innovation and clients collaboration center that will be called Global Hub, a venue for grocery food retailers, industry trend setters and through leaders. The company is also focusing on tapping the potential of convenience marts and dollar-store retailers. **Availability:** Print.

4436 ■ *"The Future of Foodservice Equipment"* in *ConvenienceStoreNews* (November 24, 2021)
Ed: Renee Covino. **Released:** November 24, 2021.
Description: Advancements are being made in foodservice equipment that will restructure the convenience store kitchen. Items such as touchless payments, self-checkout, and even robotic chefs are being developed. **Availability:** Online.

4437 ■ *"Green and Clean"* in *Retail Merchandiser* (Vol. 51, July-August 2011, No. 4, pp. 56)
Description: Green Valley Grocery partnered with Paragon Solutions consulting firm to make their stores environmentally green. **Availability:** Print; Online.

4438 ■ *"HBSDealer Stock Watch: In the FAST Lane"* in *Chain Store Age* (Vol. 85, November 2009, No. 11, pp. 44)
Ed: Samantha Murphy. **Description:** Quick Chek, which operates some 120 convenience stores in New Jersey and southern New York, is testing a new self-checkout system in order to examine how speed affects its in-store experience. **Availability:** Online.

4439 ■ *"Javo Beverage to Feature On-Demand Coffee System and Introduce New Specialty Dispensed Beverages at the National Convenience Store Show"* in *GlobeNewswire* (October 20, 2009)
Pub: Comtex News Network Inc.
Contact: Kan Devnani, President
Description: During the National Association of Convenience Store Show (NACS) at the Las Vegas Convention Center, Javo Beverage Company, Inc., a leading provider of premium dispensable coffee and tea-based beverages to the foodservice industry, will introduce its on-demand hot coffee system as well as a new line of products for the convenience store industry. **Availability:** Online.

4440 ■ *"Kwik Shop Finishing New South Seneca Store"* in *Wichita Business Journal* (Vol. 27, January 13, 2012, No. 2, pp. 1)
Pub: Baltimore Business Journal
Contact: Rhonda Pringle, President
E-mail: rpringle@bizjournals.com
Ed: Josh Heck. **Description:** Kwik Shop is set to complete a new convenience store in Wichita, Kansas. The company has investedmore than $1 million on the new facility. **Availability:** Print; Online.

4441 ■ *"Liquor-Sales Issue in Kansas Creates Strange Bedfellows"* in *Wichita Business Journal* (Vol. 27, February 10, 2012, No. 6, pp. 1)
Pub: Baltimore Business Journal
Contact: Rhonda Pringle, President
E-mail: rpringle@bizjournals.com
Description: How the business community in Kansas has reacted to House Bill 2532, a legislation that would alter the way liquor is sold in the state, is presented. Under the legislation, groceries and convenience stores would be allowed to get licenses to sell liquor, wine and full-strength beer. On the other hand, liquor stores would be permitted to sell other products on the premises. **Availability:** Print; Online.

4442 ■ *"Meet the New Convenience Store"* in *Supermarket News* (August 3, 2018)
URL(s): www.supermarketnews.com/retail-financial/ meet-new-convenience-store
Ed: Gloria Dawson. **Released:** August 03, 2018.
Description: Convenience stores have grown from a place to grab some candy, pop, and other snacks to offering more and better options for healthier pre-packed food. Consumers are craving more high-end products, and these new stores are delivering and growing the trend. **Availability:** Online.

4443 ■ *"MillerCoors Needs the Quickie Mart"* in *Crain's Chicago Business* (Vol. 32, November 16, 2009, No. 46, pp. 2)
Pub: Crain Communications Inc.
Contact: Barry Asin, President
Ed: David Sterrett. **Description:** Power Marts convenience store owner Sam Odeh says that Chicago-based MillerCoors LLC has done a poor job at promoting its brand, keeping its signs up to date and stocking the shelves at his stores. He complains that the company's service has been awful and the marketing pathetic. Convenience stores accounted for more than $14 billion in beer sales in the past year. **Availability:** Online.

4444 ■ *Progressive Grocer's Marketing Guidebook: The Comprehensive Source for Grocery, Drug and Mass Merchant Insights*
URL(s): retailbuyers.net/custom-retail-database-solu tions/marketing-guidebook
Released: Annual; latest edition 2015. **Price:** $1,085, Individuals ADVANTAGE (Includes more than 10,500 personal e-Mail addresses); $685, Individuals (Personal e-Mail addresses not included). **Description:** Covers over 2,800 U.S. and Canadian supermarket chains, large independents and wholesalers; also includes 350 specialty distributors include smaller food wholesalers, food brokers, non-food distributors, and candy/tobacco/media distributors and over 24,800 key executives and buyers. **Entries include:** For retailers and wholesalers--Company name, address, phone, email and websites, number of stores operated or served, areas of operation, major grocery supplier, three-year financial summary, buying policies, private label information, lists of executives, buyers, and merchandisers. For specialty distributors--Name, address, phone, list of key personnel including buyers' categories, list of items handled, URL. **Arrangement:** Alphabetical by hierarchy, geographical by eight regions and 50 market areas. **Indexes:** Grocery related organizations, chain and wholesalers, state index, store operating name/parent company reference. **Availability:** CD-ROM; Print.

4445 ■ *"TMC Development Closes $1.1 Million Real Estate Purchase for Mansa, LLC Using SBA 504 Real Estate Financing"* in *Marketwired* (September 17, 2009)
Pub: Comtex News Network Inc.
Contact: Kan Devnani, President
Description: TMC Development announced the closing of a $1.1 million real estate purchase for Mansa, LLC dba Kwikee Mart, a Napa-based convenience store; TMC helped the company secure a Small Business Administration 504 loan in order to purchase the acquisition of a 3,464 square foot building. SBA created the 504 loan program to provide financing for growing small and medium-sized businesses. **Availability:** Online.

STATISTICAL SOURCES

4446 ■ *RMA Annual Statement Studies*
Pub: Risk Management Association
Contact: Nancy Foster, President
Released: Annual. **Description:** Contains composite balance sheets and income statements for more than 360 industries, including the accounting, auditing, and bookkeeping industries. Also contains five years of comparative historical data for discerning trends. Includes 16 commonly used ratios, computed for most of the size groupings for nearly every industry.

4447 ■ *Standard & Poor's Industry Surveys*
Pub: Standard And Poor's Financial Services LLC.
Contact: Douglas L. Peterson, President
Description: Two-volume book that examines the prospects for specific industries, including trucking. Also provides analyses of trends and problems, statistical tables and charts, and comparative company analyses.

4448 ■ *US Convenience Stores Market Report 2020*
URL(s): store.mintel.com/report/us-convenience-s tores-market-report
Price: $4,366.35. **Description:** Downloadable report analyzing data about the US convenience store industry and the challenges facing it. Report includes an executive summary, interactive databook, PowerPoint presentation, infographic overview, report PDF, and previous years data. **Availability:** PDF.

TRADE SHOWS AND CONVENTIONS

4449 ■ **Convenience Distribution Marketplace**
Convenience Distribution Association (CDA)
11250 Roger Bacon Dr. 8
Reston, VA 20190
Ph: (703)208-3358
Free: 800-482-2962
Fax: (703)573-5738
Co. E-mail: info@cdaweb.net
URL: http://www.cdaweb.net
Contact: Kimberly Bolin, President
E-mail: kimberlyb@cdaweb.net
URL(s): www.cdaweb.net/events/marketplace
Frequency: Annual. **Description:** Candy, snacks, fast food, beverages, general merchandise, tobacco, health care products and distribution software, hardware, equipment, business services, and food services. **Audience:** Convenience products distributors and wholesale buyers. **Principal Exhibits:** Candy, snacks, fast food, beverages, general merchandise, tobacco, health care products and distribution software, hardware, equipment, business services, and food services. Dates and Locations: 2025 Feb 17-19 The Woodlands Waterway Marriott Hotel & Convention Center, Woodlands, TX; 2026 Feb 16-18; 2027 Feb 22-24. **Telecommunication Services:** jennf@cdaweb.net.

4450 ■ Great Lakes Ice Cream and Fast Food Trade Show
URL(s): www.glicffa.com/convention-trade-show
Frequency: Annual. **Description:** Ice cream, frozen desserts, and fast food products for those who have purchasing power for their companies and markets. **Audience:** Qualified buyers for the frozen dessert and fast food industry. **Principal Exhibits:** Ice cream, frozen desserts, and fast food products for those who have purchasing power for their companies and markets.

FRANCHISES AND BUSINESS OPPORTUNITIES

4451 ■ 7-Eleven, Inc.
7-Eleven, Inc.
 3200 Hackberry Rd.
 Irving, TX 75063
Ph: (972)828-7011
Free: 800-255-0711
URL: http://www.7-eleven.com
Contact: Stanley Reynolds, President
Facebook: www.facebook.com/7eleven
X (Twitter): twitter.com/7Eleven
Instagram: www.instagram.com/7eleven
YouTube: www.youtube.com/user/7ElevenInc
Description: Chain of convenience stores. **Founded:** 1927. **Training:** Provides 6 weeks training and ongoing support.

4452 ■ Circle K Arizona
PO Box 52085
 Phoenix, AZ 85072
Ph: (602)728-8000
URL: http://www.circlek.com
Facebook: www.facebook.com/CircleKStores
Instagram: www.instagram.com/circlekstores
Description: Chain of food convenience stores. **Founded:** 1951. **Equity Capital Needed:** $100,000 in liquid assets - $500,000 in net worth. **Franchise Fee:** $25,000. **Royalty Fee:** 4.5%. **Financial Assistance:** Yes **Training:** 2 weeks training at headquarters, 2 weeks at franchisee's location and ongoing support.

4453 ■ Just-A-Buck (JAB)
563 Temple Hill Rd.
 New Windsor, NY 12553
Ph: (845)561-7411
Fax: (845)561-7433
Co. E-mail: info@justabuck.com
URL: http://www.justabuck.com
Contact: Robert Capone, Co-Founder
Facebook: www.facebook.com/justabuckcorp
Instagram: www.instagram.com/justabuckcorp
Description: Operator of the dollar store. **Founded:** 1988. **Franchised:** 1992. **Equity Capital Needed:** Minimum initial liquid capital required $50,000. **Financial Assistance:** Yes **Training:** Provides corporate and onsite training.

4454 ■ Street Corner Inc.
2945 SW Wanamaker Dr.
 Topeka, KS 66614
Ph: (785)272-8529
URL: http://www.streetcorner.com
Contact: Peter La Colla, President
E-mail: peter@streetcorner.com
Facebook: www.facebook.com/StreetCornerFranchise
X (Twitter): x.com/Street_Corner
YouTube: www.youtube.com/user/streetcornervideo
Description: Operator of the convenience store and newsstand. **Founded:** 1988. **Franchised:** 1995. **Equity Capital Needed:** $23,000 to $1,500,000. **Franchise Fee:** $19,900 - $24,900. **Royalty Fee:** 4.95% of the Gross Revenue. **Financial Assistance:** No **Training:** Training available at headquarters upon request, 1 week at franchisee's location and ongoing support.

LIBRARIES

4455 ■ NACS: The Association for Convenience and Fuel Retailing - Library
1600 Duke St., 7th Fl.
 Alexandria, VA 22314
Ph: (703)684-3600
Free: 800-966-6227
Fax: (703)836-4564
URL: http://www.convenience.org
Contact: Brian Kimmel, Executive Vice President
 Chief Financial Officer Chief Operating Officer

Description: Represents retail stores that sell gasoline, fast foods, soft drinks, dairy products, beer, cigarettes, publications, grocery items, snacks and nonfood items and are usually open seven days per week for longer hours than conventional supermarkets. Serves the convenience and fuel retailing industry by providing industry knowledge, connections and advocacy to ensure the competitive viability of its members' businesses. Conducts educational and legislative activities and sponsors management seminars. **Scope:** Global trade. **Founded:** 1961. **Holdings:** Figures not available. **Publications:** *National Association of Convenience Stores--Membership Directory*; *NACS*; *Compensation Survey* (Annual); *NACS Magazine* (Monthly); *State of the Industry Report/Factbook* (Annual). **Educational Activities:** NACS Show (Annual). **Awards:** NACS Scholarship (Annual). **Geographic Preference:** Multinational.

Cooking School

ASSOCIATIONS AND OTHER ORGANIZATIONS

4456 ■ American Culinary Federation (ACF)
6816 Southpoint Pky., Ste. 400
Jacksonville, FL 32216
Ph: (904)824-4468
Fax: (904)940-0741
Co. E-mail: helpdesk@acfchefs.org
URL: http://www.acfchefs.org
Contact: Kimberly Brock Brown, President
E-mail: chefkbb@acfchefs.org
Facebook: www.facebook.com/ACFChefs
Linkedin: www.linkedin.com/company/american-culinary-federation
X (Twitter): x.com/acfchefs
Instagram: www.instagram.com/ACF_CHEFS
Description: Aims to promote the culinary profession and provide on-going educational training and networking for members. Provides opportunities for competition, professional recognition, and access to educational forums with other culinary experts at local, regional, national, and international events. Operates the National Apprenticeship Program for Cooks and pastry cooks. Offers programs that address certification of the individual chef's skills, accreditation of culinary programs, apprenticeship of cooks and pastry cooks, professional development, and the fight against childhood hunger. **Founded:** 1929. **Publications:** *Sizzle: The American Culinary Federation Quarterly for Students of Cooking* (Quarterly); *The Culinary Insider* (Biweekly); *The National Culinary Review (NCR)* (6/year). **Educational Activities:** ACF National Convention (Annual); American Culinary Federation Convention (Annual); ACF Central Regional Conference (Annual); ACF Northeast Regional Conference (Annual); ACF Southeast Regional Conference. **Awards:** Spice Box Grants (Annual); Balestreri/Cutino Scholarship (Annual); Chaîne des Rôtisseurs Scholarships (Annual); Linda Cullen Memorial Scholarship (Annual); Andrew Macrina Scholarship (Annual); Ray and Gertrude Marshall Scholarship (Annual); Hermann G. Rusch Scholarship (Annual); ACF Chef Educator of the Year Award (Annual); ACF USA's Chef of the Year Award (Annual); Dr. L.J. Minor Chef Professionalism Award (Annual); ACF Hermann G. Rusch Chef's Achievement Award (Annual); ACF Pastry Chef of the Year Award (Annual); ACF Student Chef of the Year Award (Annual); ACF American Culinary Classic. **Geographic Preference:** National.

4457 ■ American Personal and Private Chef Association (APPCA)
4572 Delaware St.
San Diego, CA 92116
Ph: (619)294-2436
Free: 800-644-8389
Co. E-mail: info@personalchef.com
URL: http://www.personalchef.com
Contact: Mike Baskette, Director, Operations
Facebook: www.facebook.com/personalchefassociation
X (Twitter): x.com/AmerPersChef
Description: Promotes the advancement of personal and private chefs. Facilitates communication, networking with colleagues, continuing education, online mentoring, support and exchange of ideas among members. **Publications:** *Ala Minute* (Bimonthly). **Geographic Preference:** National.

4458 ■ International Association of Culinary Professionals (IACP)
3097 E Shadowlawn Ave., NE
Atlanta, GA 30305
Co. E-mail: rsvp@iacp.com
URL: http://www.iacp.com
Contact: Nancy Hopkins, Executive Director
E-mail: nancy@iacp.com
Facebook: www.facebook.com/iacpculinary
X (Twitter): x.com/IACPculinary
Description: Encourages the exchange of information and education. Promotes professional standards and accreditation procedures. Maintains a Foundation to award culinary scholarships and grants. **Founded:** 1978. **Publications:** *Frontburner* (Quarterly); *International Association of Culinary Professionals Food Forum Quarterly* (Quarterly). **Educational Activities:** IACP Conference (Annual). **Awards:** IACP Awards - Milestone; IACP Awards - Lifetime Achievement (Annual); IACP Awards - Volunteer of the Year; IACP Awards - Local Community Service; IACP Awards - Culinary Educator of the Year; IACP Awards - Culinary Professional of the Year; IACP Awards - Culinary School Award of Excellence; Culinary Travel Writing (Annual); IACP Awards - Humanitarian (Annual); IACP Cookbook Awards (Annual); Cookbook Awards - Chefs & Restaurants (Annual). **Geographic Preference:** Multinational.

4459 ■ International Council on Hotel, Restaurant, and Institutional Education (ICHRIE)
3900 Westerre Pky, Ste. 300
Richmond, VA 23233
Ph: (804)346-4800
Fax: (804)346-5009
Co. E-mail: membership@chrie.org
URL: http://www.chrie.org
Contact: Chrystel Masdupuy, President
E-mail: chrystel.masdupuy@institutpaulbocuse.com
Facebook: www.facebook.com/ichrie
Linkedin: www.linkedin.com/company/internationalchrie
Description: Provides programs and services to continually improve the quality of global education, research, service and business operations in the hospitality and tourism industry. **Founded:** 1946. **Publications:** *Journal of Hospitality & Tourism Research: The Professional Journal of the International Council on Hotel, Restaurant, and Institutional Education (JHTR)* (8/year); *Council on Hotel, Restaurant and Institutional Education--Member Directory and Resource Guide* (Biennial); *A Guide to College Programs in Hospitality, Tourism, & Culinary Arts*; *Guide to Hospitality Education* (Semiannual); *Hosteur Magazine* (Biennial); *Journal of Hospitality and Tourism Education (JHTE)* (Quarterly); *Membership Directory and Research Guide* (Annual). **Awards:** Chef Herman Breithaupt Award (Annual); Stevenson W. Fletcher Achievement Award (Annual); ICHRIE Industry Recognition Award; W. Bradford Wiley Memorial Best Research Paper of the Year Award (Annual); Howard B. Meek Award (Annual); ICHRIE Lifetime Research Achievement Award (Annual). **Geographic Preference:** National.

4460 ■ National Restaurant Association Educational Foundation (NRAEF)
2055 L St. NW
Washington, DC 20036
Free: 800-424-5156
Co. E-mail: comms@nraef.org
URL: http://chooserestaurants.org
Contact: Michelle Korsmo, Chief Executive Officer
Facebook: www.facebook.com/nraefoundation
Linkedin: www.linkedin.com/company/nraef
X (Twitter): x.com/nraef
Instagram: www.instagram.com/nraefoundation
YouTube: www.youtube.com/c/NRAEF
Description: Serves as an educational foundation supported by the National Restaurant Association and all segments of the foodservice industry including restaurateurs, foodservice companies, food and equipment manufacturers, distributors and trade associations. Advances the professional standards of the industry through education and research. Offers video training programs, management courses and careers information. Conducts research and maintains hall of fame. **Founded:** 1987. **Publications:** *Directory of Computer Hardware and Software for the Food Service Industry*; *Foodservice/Hospitality College Directory* (Irregular). **Educational Activities:** NSPA Conference. **Awards:** NRAEF Scholarships (Annual); Thad and Alice Eure Ambassador of Hospitality Award (Annual); Al Schuman/Ecolab Undergraduate Entrepreneurial Scholarship (Annual). **Geographic Preference:** National.

REFERENCE WORKS

4461 ■ "18 Online Cooking Classes for the Busy Budding Chef" in SheKnows (March 27, 2019)
URL(s): www.sheknows.com/food-and-recipes/articles/1079046/best-online-cooking-classes/
Ed: Heather Barnett. **Released:** March 27, 2019.
Description: Cooking classes don't have to taken at a traditional school. Instead, if you are short on time there are online courses you can enroll in. Included is a list of 18 options so you can find the best fit for you and your wallet. **Availability:** Online.

4462 ■ "American Farmland Trust, The Culinary Institute of America, Fabulous Beekman Boys Hold Special Event to Raise Awareness in Culinary Students" in Ecology, Environment & Conservation Business (April 19, 2014, pp. 3)
Pub: NewsRX LLC.
Contact: Kalani Rosell, Contact

Description: American Farmland Trust and The Culinary Institute of American were joined by the Fabulous Beekman Boys, Brent Ridge and Josh Kilmer-Purcell of Beekman 1802, to host a screening of The First Season, a documentary film about dairy farming in New York. The event was held to raise awareness in culinary arts students about the issues faced by farmers today. **Availability:** Online.

4463 ■ *"Beyond Grits: The Many Varieties of Southern Cuisine" in Women In Business (Vol. 62, June 2010, No. 2, pp. 14)*
Pub: American Business Women's Association
Contact: Rene Street, Executive Director

Ed: Debbie Gold. **Released:** June 01, 2010. **Description:** Southern cuisine is believed to be associated with grits, but the cuisine is not always with grits and offers varieties from Europe, Native American and African cooking. Southern cuisine varieties include soul food, Creole food, Cajun food and Low Country food. Examples are provided. **Availability:** Online.

4464 ■ *"A Failed Promise: A Dream Job Gone..or Just Delayed?" in Restaurant Business (Vol. 107, September 2008, No. 9, pp. 34)*

Description: Profile of Jeremy Lycan, executive chef who taught at the California Culinary Academy. Lycan tells of accepting a position as executive chef from his mentor, and later started his own restaurant. **Availability:** Online.

4465 ■ *"Hottest Culinary School Vacations" in TravelChannel.com*
URL(s): www.travelchannel.com/interests/food-and-drink/articles/hottest-culinary-school-vacations

Ed: Meghann Foye. **Description:** Culinary tourism is on the rise and is something that everyone can participate in because it's not a huge time commitment and it can be a fun adventure when on vacation. These classes are held throughout the world, so where ever you are on vacation, you can find a class or two to help increase your skill knowledge and help you take in the local culture. **Availability:** Online.

4466 ■ *"Intrepid Souls: Meet a Few Who've Made the Big Leap" in Crain's Chicago Business (Vol. 31, November 10, 2008, No. 45, pp. 26)*

Description: Advice is given from entrepreneurs who have launched businesses in the last year despite the economic crisis. Among the types of businesses featured are a cooking school, a child day-care center, a children's clothing store and an Internet-based company. **Availability:** Online.

4467 ■ *"Is Culinary School Still Worth It? Four Chefs Weigh In" in Food&Wine (November 14, 2017)*
URL(s): www.foodandwine.com/lifestyle/culinary-school-worth-it-four-chefs-weigh-in

Ed: Gowri Chandra. **Released:** November 14, 2017. **Description:** Culinary school is often expensive and it begs the question: Is it worth attending? That depends on what your individual goals are because these schools can and do open doors into the industry. Other options are explored, such as receiving training in a kitchen and apply those skills to the job. **Availability:** Online.

4468 ■ *"A Master Chef's Recipe for Business Success" in Business Strategy Review (Vol. 23, Spring 2012, No. 1, pp. 65)*

Description: Often called the world's greatest chef, Ferran Adria, longtime owner of El Built, Spain's three-star Michelin rated revolutionary restaurant, is now embarking on a new venture: the El Built Foundation, a place where chefs can create, interact, and discuss their ideas with researchers from other disciplines. He recently spoke at London Business School as part of his tour of a number of select universities to invite students to enter a competition to design an innovative business model for the new Foundation. **Availability:** Print; Online.

4469 ■ *"Nurturing Talent for Tomorrow" in Restaurants and Institutions (Vol. 118, September 15, 2008, No. 14, pp. 90)*
Description: Hormel Foods Corporation and The Culinary Institute of America (CIA) have teamed to develop The Culinary Enrichment and Innovation Program that supports future culinary leaders by providing creative and competitive staff development. Sixteen students attend four three-day sessions at the CIA's campus in Hyde Park, New York; sessions include classroom teaching, one-on-one interaction with leading culinarians, and hands-on kitchen time.

4470 ■ *"The Rise in Virtual Cooking Classes" in Integris Health (April 9, 2021)*
URL(s): integrisok.com/resources/on-your-health/2021/april/the-rise-in-virtual-cooking-classes
Released: April 09, 2021. **Description:** With the onset of the COVID-19 pandemic, closures in restaurants, and people wanting to stay home, online cooking classes have taken off. Virtual cooking classes often have a variety of topics to choose from, plus many are pre-recorded which gives the user the benefit of learning at their own pace. **Availability:** Online.

4471 ■ *"Truffles & Trifles' Marci Arthur Plans YouTube Channel, Cookbook" in Orlando Business Journal (Vol. 30, May 2, 2014, No. 45, pp. 3)*
Pub: American City Business Journals, Inc.
Contact: Mike Olivieri, Executive Vice President
Released: Weekly. **Price:** $8, introductory 4-week offer(Digital & Print). **Description:** Marci Arthur, founder of Truffles & Trifles Cooking School, plans to create a YouTube channel and publish a cookbook. Arthur believes that the survival of her business can be attributed to the devotion and integrity of her employees. Reports show that the school has been receiving donations from sponsors such as Wolf Appliances and Sub-Zero. **Availability:** Print; Online.

STATISTICAL SOURCES

4472 ■ *Cooking Classes Industry in the US - Market Research Report*
URL(s): www.ibisworld.com/united-states/market-research-reports/cooking-classes-industry/
Price: $925. **Description:** Downloadable report analyzing the current and future trends in the cooking class industry. **Availability:** Download.

TRADE PERIODICALS

4473 ■ *Bon Appetit: America's Food and Entertaining Magazine*
Pub: Conde Nast Publications
Contact: Agnes Chu, President
URL(s): www.bonappetit.com
Facebook: www.facebook.com/bonappetitmag
Instagram: www.instagram.com/bonappetitmag
YouTube: www.youtube.com/channel/UCbpMy0Fg74eXXkvxJrtEn3w
Pinterest: www.pinterest.com/bonappetitmag
Released: Monthly; except the combined June/July and Dec/Jan issues. **Price:** $79.99, for regular. **Description:** Lifestyle magazine covering food, travel, and entertaining. **Availability:** Print; Online.

4474 ■ *Cooking for Profit*
Released: Monthly **Description:** Food service trade publication for owners/operators of food service businesses. Profiles successful operations, offers management tips, recipes with photos and step-by-step instructions, new and improved uses and maintenance of gas equipment. **Availability:** Print; Online.

LIBRARIES

4475 ■ **Atlantic Cape Community College - William Spangler Library**
5100 Black Horse Pke.
Mays Landing, NJ 08330-2699
Ph: (609)343-4951
Co. E-mail: library@atlanticcape.edu
URL: http://www.atlanticcape.edu/about/leadership/board/board-resource-collection.php
Scope: Educational material. **Services:** Interlibrary loan; copying; library open to the public. **Founded:** 1966. **Holdings:** Books.

4476 ■ **City College of San Francisco (CCSF) - Culinary Arts and Hospitality Studies - Alice Statler Library**
50 Frida Kahlo Way
Statler Wing, Rm. 10
San Francisco, CA 94112
Ph: (415)239-3460
URL: http://library.ccsf.edu/locations/statler
Scope: Culinary arts and hospitality study; historical menus; notable titles; local chefs, restaurateurs, hoteliers and entrepreneurs in the industry. **Services:** Copying; Wi-Fi; library open to the public for reference use only. **Founded:** 1964. **Holdings:** Books; menus; archives; monographs; periodicals; DVDs.

4477 ■ **Culinary Institute of America - Conrad N. Hilton Library**
1946 Campus Dr.
Hyde Park, NY 12538-1430
Ph: (845)451-1747
Co. E-mail: library@culinary.edu
URL: http://library.culinary.edu/index
Contact: Jon Grennan, Director
E-mail: j_grenna@culinary.edu
Scope: Arts materials. **Services:** Interlibrary loan; copying; library open to the public by appointment. **Founded:** 1946. **Holdings:** 86,000 volumes; 30,000 menus; 4,500 DVDs and videos. **Subscriptions:** 280 journals and other serials.

4478 ■ **Johnson & Wales University-Harborside Culinary Library (JWU)**
321 Harborside Blvd.
Providence, RI 02905
Ph: (401)598-1466
Co. E-mail: ask@jwu-ri.libanswers.com
URL: http://pvd.library.jwu.edu/lticulinary
Contact: Lisa Spicola, Librarian
E-mail: lisa.helwigpayne@jwu.edu
X (Twitter): x.com/jwulibrary
YouTube: www.youtube.com/user/JWULibraryPVD
Scope: Food service; menu planning; nutrition; professional management; catering and banquets; household manuals; canning; preserving and freezing; hotel and motel management. **Services:** Copying; Library open to the public. **Founded:** 1979.

4479 ■ **Lamar University - Mary and John Gray Library - Justice Cookery Collection**
211 Red Bird Ln.
Beaumont, TX 77710
URL: http://www.lamar.edu/library/services/university-archive/the-dishmanjustice-cookbook-collection.html
Contact: Penny Clark, Associate Professor
Scope: Educational material. **Services:** Interlibrary loan. **Founded:** 1923. **Holdings:** Books.

4480 ■ **Le Cordon Bleu College of Culinary Arts Library**
350 Rhode Island St.
San Francisco, CA 94103
URL: http://www.careered.com/closedschool/locations
Scope: Culinary arts; nutrition; restaurant and hospitality industry. **Services:** Library open to the public by special appointment only. **Founded:** 1989. **Holdings:** 3,500 books.

4481 ■ **Paul Smith's College of Arts & Sciences - Joan Weill Adirondack Library**
7777 NY-30
Paul Smiths, NY 12970
Free: 800-421-2605
Co. E-mail: info@paulsmiths.edu
URL: http://www.paulsmiths.edu
Contact: Matthew Purcell, President
Facebook: www.facebook.com/paulsmithscollege
X (Twitter): x.com/paulsmiths
Instagram: www.instagram.com/paulsmiths

YouTube: www.youtube.com/user/PaulSmithsCollege518

Description: Educational institute providing higher education. **Scope:** Hotel and restaurant management; chef training; culinary arts; forestry; urban tree management; environmental science; forest recreation; surveying; ecotourism; natural resources management; fisheries management; business management. **Services:** Interlibrary loan; copying; library open to the public with restrictions. **Founded:** 1946. **Holdings:** 54,000 books; pamphlets.

4482 ■ Prince Edward Island Food Technology Centre - Information Services
101 Belvedere Ave.
 Charlottetown, PE, Canada C1A 7N8
Ph: (902)368-5548
Free: 877-368-5548
Fax: (902)368-5549
Co. E-mail: biofoodtech@biofoodtech.ca
URL: http://www.biofoodtechpei.ca
Contact: Jillian Sproul, Executive Director
Facebook: www.facebook.com/concept.pilot.market
X (Twitter): twitter.com/BioFoodTech

Scope: Agriculture; food; technology; food research. **Services:** Interlibrary loan; library open to the public by permission only. **Founded:** 1987. **Holdings:** 200 books; 9 bound periodical volumes.

4483 ■ Restaurants Canada - Library
1155 Queen St. W
 Toronto, ON, Canada M6J 1J4
Ph: (416)923-8416
Free: 800-387-5649
Fax: (416)923-1450
Co. E-mail: info@restaurantscanada.org
URL: http://www.restaurantscanada.org
Contact: Christian Buhagiar, Co-Chief Executive Officer Co-President
Facebook: www.facebook.com/RestaurantsCanada
Linkedin: www.linkedin.com/company/restaurants-canada
X (Twitter): x.com/RestaurantsCA
Instagram: www.instagram.com/RestaurantsCanada
YouTube: www.youtube.com/channel/UCxVckfCBIISII9LOuflNX8w

Description: Restaurant and food service corporations, hotels, caterers, and food service suppliers and educators, seeks to create a favorable business environment for members. **Scope:** Food service; quantity cooking; legislation; administration; management; statistics; training; customer attitude surveys. **Services:** Copying; open to the public on fee basis. **Founded:** 1944. **Publications:** *CRFA National Hospitality News*; *Canadian Foodservice Industry Operations Report* (Biennial); *Foodservice Facts* (Annual); *Legislation Guide* (Quarterly). **Educational Activities:** Restaurants Canada Show (Annual); ApEx. **Geographic Preference:** National.

4484 ■ Societe Culinaire Philanthropique (SCP)
305 E 47th St., No 11B
 New York, NY 10017
Ph: (212)308-0628
Co. E-mail: info@societeculinaire.com
URL: http://www.societeculinaire.com
Contact: Pascal Guillotin, President

Description: Mutual benefit insurance society for cooks, pastry cooks, butchers, and bakers. Sponsors exhibition and Culinarians' Home Foundation, a home for aged culinarians and their spouses. **Founded:** 1865. **Educational Activities:** Salon of Culinary Arts (Annual). **Geographic Preference:** National.

4485 ■ University of Denver - Penrose Library Special Collections and Archives
2150 E Evans Ave.
 Denver, CO 80208
Co. E-mail: library-avstaff@du.edu
URL: http://library.du.edu/collections-library-materials/special-collections-archives/mission-statement-and-collection-development-policy
Contact: Kate Crowe, Curator
E-mail: katherine.crowe@du.edu

Scope: University of Denver archives. **Founded:** 1864. **Holdings:** Archives.

Copy Shop

ASSOCIATIONS AND OTHER ORGANIZATIONS

4486 ■ Association of Printing and Data Solutions Professionals (APDSP)
c/o Ed Avis Associates
PO Box 2249
Oak Park, IL 60303
Ph: (708)218-7755
Co. E-mail: ed.avis@irga.com
URL: http://www.apdsp.org
Contact: Ed Avis, Managing Director
Linkedin: www.linkedin.com/groups/International-Reprographic-Association-1911647
Description: Commercial blue print and photocopy firms, engineering supply stores, and materials and equipment suppliers. Conducts annual photo-tech, marketing, management, and business planning seminars. **Founded:** 1927. **Publications:** *Reprographers & Design Imaging--Directory Issue* (Irregular); *Repro Report: The magazine for methods and technology for design reproduction*; *IRgA News Digest* (Monthly); *Repro Report* (Bimonthly). **Educational Activities:** International Reprographic Association Trade Show (Annual). **Awards:** George K. Bukovsky Award (Annual). **Geographic Preference:** National.

4487 ■ Copyright Clearance Center Inc. (CCC) - Library
Copyright Clearance Center Inc. (CCC)
222 Rosewood Dr.
Danvers, MA 01923
Ph: (978)750-8400
Co. E-mail: info@copyright.com
URL: http://www.copyright.com
Contact: Tracey Armstrong, President
Facebook: www.facebook.com/CopyrightClear
Linkedin: www.linkedin.com/company/copyright-clearance-center
X (Twitter): x.com/copyrightclear
YouTube: www.youtube.com/user/copyrightclear
Description: Facilitates compliance with U.S. copyright law. Provides licensing systems for the reproduction and distribution of copyrighted materials in print and electronic formats throughout the world. Manages rights relating to over 1.75 million works and represents more than 9600 publishers and hundreds of thousands of authors and other creators, directly or through their representatives. **Scope:** An international licensing organization, representing authors, publishers and creators from around the world, licenses the rights to books, journals, newspapers, websites, eBooks, images, blogs and more. Works with thought leaders, government agencies and policy makers to streamline copyright licensing across the globe. **Founded:** 1978. **Holdings:** Videos; white papers; case studies. **Publications:** *Document Delivery*. **Training:** 110th Semi-annual Cancer Seminar of the California Tumor Tissue Registry, 2006. **Geographic Preference:** National. **Special Services:** Makes the Titles and Fees Catalog available on magnetic tape.

REFERENCE WORKS

4488 ■ "Time For a Change at Canon?" in Barron's (Vol. 92, July 23, 2012, No. 30, pp. 17)
Pub: Dow Jones & Company Inc.
Contact: Almar Latour, Chief Executive Officer
Ed: Neil A. Martin. **Description:** Stocks of Japanese imaging equipment maker Canon could lose value unless the company undergoes changes in operations and governance. Prices of the company's American Depositary Receipts could fall 20 percent from $37.22 per share within 12 months. **Availability:** Online.

4489 ■ "Xerox Diverts Waste from Landfills" in Canadian Electronics (Vol. 23, February 2008, No. 1, pp. 1)
Description: Xerox Corporation revealed that it was able to divert more than two billion pounds of electronic waste from landfills through waste-free initiatives. The company's program, which was launched in 1991, covers waste avoidance in imaging supplies and parts reuse. Environmental priorities are also integrated into manufacturing operations. **Availability:** Print; Online; PDF.

STATISTICAL SOURCES

4490 ■ *RMA Annual Statement Studies*
Pub: Risk Management Association
Contact: Nancy Foster, President
Released: Annual. **Description:** Contains composite balance sheets and income statements for more than 360 industries, including the accounting, auditing, and bookkeeping industries. Also contains five years of comparative historical data for discerning trends. Includes 16 commonly used ratios, computed for most of the size groupings for nearly every industry.

TRADE PERIODICALS

4491 ■ *Quick Printing: The Information Source for Commercial Copyshops & Printshops*
Contact: Kelly Holmes, Publisher
E-mail: kelly@quickprinting.com
Ed: Karen Lowery Hall. **Released:** Monthly **Price:** Free. **Description:** For Quick and Small Commercial Printers. **Availability:** Print; Online.

TRADE SHOWS AND CONVENTIONS

4492 ■ International Reprographic Association Trade Show
Association of Printing and Data Solutions Professionals (APDSP)
c/o Ed Avis Associates
PO Box 2249
Oak Park, IL 60303
Ph: (708)218-7755
Co. E-mail: ed.avis@irga.com
URL: http://www.apdsp.org
Contact: Ed Avis, Managing Director
URL(s): www.apdsp.org/2014-ERA-IRGA-Convention-Vendor-Page
Frequency: Annual. **Description:** Reprographic equipment, supplies, and services for color graphics, reprographic and digital imaging service supplies. **Audience:** Reprographic professionals. **Principal Exhibits:** Reprographic equipment, supplies, and services for color graphics, reprographic and digital imaging service supplies. **Telecommunication Services:** info@irga.com.

CONSULTANTS

4493 ■ Concord Associates Co.
20 W Pk. St., Ste. 1
Lebanon, NH 03766
Ph: (603)448-1100
Co. E-mail: balagurassociates@gmail.com
URL: http://www.balagurassociates.com
Contact: Richard Balagur, Owner
Description: Offers business counsel and market and marketing consulting assistance in key areas of both the consumer and professional digital imaging fields. Primary emphasis is in digital cameras, ink jet and dye sublimation printers, digital mini labs and related or ancillary products such as flash memory cards for digital cameras. **Scope:** Offers business counsel and market and marketing consulting assistance in key areas of both the consumer and professional digital imaging fields. Primary emphasis is in digital cameras, ink jet and dye sublimation printers, digital mini labs and related or ancillary products such as flash memory cards for digital cameras. **Founded:** 1982.

FRANCHISES AND BUSINESS OPPORTUNITIES

4494 ■ Kwik Kopy Business Centers, Inc.
12715 Telge Rd.
Cypress, TX 77429
Contact: Jay Groot, President
Description: Provider of printing and copying services. **Founded:** 2001. **Financial Assistance:** Yes **Managerial Assistance:** Provide business support, advertising, and marketing materials. **Training:** Owners attend classroom and field training, as well as ongoing training through workshops and conferences.

4495 ■ PIP, Inc.
26722 Plz.
Mission Viejo, CA 92691
Co. E-mail: marketing@pip.com
URL: http://www.pip.com
Contact: Richard Lowe, President
Facebook: www.facebook.com/PIPCorporate
Linkedin: www.linkedin.com/company/pip-inc
X (Twitter): x.com/pipcorp

YouTube: www.youtube.com/user/pipcorp
Description: Firm provides printing, marketing and signage services. **Founded:** 1963. **Financial Assistance:** Yes **Training:** 2 1/2 weeks of training at PIP University and field visit within the first six months of operation.

4496 ■ Postal Connections of America (PCA)
6136 Frisco Sq., Blvd., Ste. 400
Frisco, TX 75034
Free: 800-767-8257
Co. E-mail: info@postalconnections.com
URL: http://www.postalconnections.com
Contact: Fred Morache, Managing Director Owner
Facebook: www.facebook.com/PostalConnectionsInc
Linkedin: www.linkedin.com/company/postal-connections
X (Twitter): x.com/PCA_CORP
YouTube: www.youtube.com/channel/UCPO3Pi7Wgc9BZwbZ2zO1Ftw
Description: Firm provides packaging supplies, notary services, mail box rentals, printing, copying, fax services, shipping, office and shipping supplies and computer services. **Founded:** 1985. **Financial Assistance:** Yes **Training:** Extensive training prior to & after opening. Franchisee's receive 5 days live action training in a regional training store, Unique Act video training program & 4 days onsite.

4497 ■ Sir Speedy Inc. [Sir Speedy Print Signs Marketing]
26722 Plz.
Mission Viejo, CA 92691
Free: 800-854-3321
Co. E-mail: marketing@sirspeedy.com
URL: http://www.sirspeedy.com
Contact: Richard Lowe, President
Facebook: www.facebook.com/SirSpeedyCorporate
Linkedin: www.linkedin.com/company/sir-speedy
X (Twitter): x.com/sirspeedycorp
YouTube: www.youtube.com/user/sirspeedycorp
Description: Provider of printing, signage and marketing services. **Founded:** 1968. **Training:** Available at headquarters 2 weeks, 2 weeks at franchisee's location, at regional meeings 1-3 days, and ongoing support.

4498 ■ Sure Print & Copy Centers
Ste. 101-12465 82nd Ave.
Courtenay, BC, Canada V3W 3E8
Ph: (250)334-2836
Co. E-mail: info@surecopy.com
URL: http://surecopy.com
Linkedin: www.linkedin.com/company/sure-copy-centres
Description: Firm provides printing services such as post cards, rack cards, business cards and much more. **Founded:** 1984. **Training:** Full training and guidance provided prior to start-up and on an ongoing basis as required.

Cosmetics Business

ASSOCIATIONS AND OTHER ORGANIZATIONS

4499 ■ Coalition of Handcrafted Entrepreneurs (COHE)
URL: http://www.coalitionofhandcraftedentrepreneurs.com
X (Twitter): x.com/YourCOHE

Description: Seeks to support small businesses in the craft soap and cosmetic industry, whose products are typically made in small batches and sold at farmers markets, home parties, community fundraisers, and craft shows. Advocates for a "small producer rule" that provides exemptions to Food and Drug Administration (FDA) requirements regarding manufacturing facilities, products, and ingredients.

4500 ■ Cosmetic Executive Women (CEW)
250 W 57th St., Ste. 918
New York, NY 10107
Ph: (646)929-8000
Fax: (212)685-3334
Co. E-mail: info@cew.org
URL: http://cew.org
Contact: Carlotta Jacobson, President
E-mail: cjacobson@cew.org
Facebook: www.facebook.com/CosmeticExecutiveWomen
Linkedin: www.linkedin.com/company/cew
X (Twitter): x.com/CEWinsider
Instagram: www.instagram.com/cewinsider

Description: Women in the cosmetic and allied industries. Unites women executives in the cosmetic field for industry awareness and business advancement. Promotes products, people, professional development and philanthropy. **Founded:** 1954. **Publications:** *Membership Roster.* **Awards:** CEW Beauty Awards (Annual); Cosmetic Executive Women Achiever Award (Irregular). **Geographic Preference:** National.

4501 ■ Cosmetic Industry Buyers and Suppliers (CIBS)
740 Blue Point Rd.
Holtsville, NY 11742
Ph: (631)758-4200
URL: http://www.cibsonline.com
Contact: Veronica Cruz, President
Facebook: www.facebook.com/CIBSOnlineOfficial
Linkedin: www.linkedin.com/company/cosmetic-industry-buyers-&-suppliers
X (Twitter): x.com/cibs_online
Instagram: www.instagram.com/cibs_online

Description: Buyers and suppliers of essential oils, chemicals, packaging, and finished goods relative to the cosmetic industry. Enhances growth, stability, prosperity, and protection of the American cosmetic industry through close personal contact and the exchange of ideas and experiences. **Founded:** 1948. **Geographic Preference:** National.

4502 ■ Cosmetic Ingredient Review (CIR)
1620 L St. NW, Ste. 1200
Washington, DC 20036-4702
Ph: (202)331-0651
Fax: (202)331-0088
Co. E-mail: cirinfo@cir-safety.org
URL: http://www.cir-safety.org
Contact: Dr. Bart Heldreth, Executive Director

Description: A cosmetic industry self-regulatory organization sponsored by the Cosmetic, Toiletry, and Fragrance Association. Seeks to assure the safety of ingredients used in cosmetics. Reviews scientific data on the safety of ingredients used in cosmetics; documents validity of tests used to study ingredients. **Founded:** 1976. **Publications:** *CIR Annual Report* (Annual); *Ingredient Report.* **Educational Activities:** CIR Expert Panel Meeting (Quarterly). **Geographic Preference:** National.

4503 ■ Cosmetics Alliance Canada (CAC)
420 Britannia Rd. E, Ste. 102
Mississauga, ON, Canada L4Z 3L5
Ph: (905)890-5161
Fax: (905)890-2607
Co. E-mail: ca@cosmeticsalliance.ca
URL: http://www.cosmeticsalliance.ca
Contact: Darren Praznik, President
Facebook: www.facebook.com/CosmeticsAlliance
X (Twitter): x.com/cosm_alliance
YouTube: www.youtube.com/user/CCTFA

Description: Manufacturers of personal care products, cosmetics, and perfumes. Seeks to advance the cosmetics and toiletries industries. Represents members before labor and industrial organizations, government agencies, and the public. Sponsors cosmetic safety research. **Founded:** 1928. **Publications:** *International Regulatory Resource Manual; CCA News Newsletter.* **Geographic Preference:** National.

4504 ■ International Spa Association (ISPA)
2365 Harrodsburg Rd., Ste. A325
Lexington, KY 40504
Contact: Lynne Walker McNees, President

Description: Raises awareness of the spa industry and educates the public and industry professionals about the benefits of the spa experience. **Publications:** *Pulse* (8/year); *LiveSpa.* **Educational Activities:** ISPA Conference & Expo (Annual). **Awards:** ISPA Foundation Mary Tabacchi Scholarship (Annual). **Geographic Preference:** Multinational.

4505 ■ National Beauty Culturists' League, Inc. (NBCL)
25 Logan Cir., NW
Washington, DC 20005-3725
Ph: (202)332-2695
Fax: (202)332-0940
URL: http://www.nbcl.info
Contact: Dr. Katie B. Catalon, President

Description: Encourages standardized, scientific, and approved methods of hair, scalp, and skin treatments. Offers scholarships and plans to establish a research center. **Founded:** 1919. **Educational Activities:** National Beauty Culturists' League Annual Trade Show (Annual). **Geographic Preference:** National.

4506 ■ National-Interstate Council of State Boards of Cosmetology (NIC)
7622 Briarwood Cir.
Little Rock, AR 72205
Ph: (501)227-8262
URL: http://nictesting.org
Contact: Anwar Saleem, President

Description: Persons commissioned by 50 state governments as administrators of cosmetology laws and examiners of applicants for licenses to practice cosmetology. **Founded:** 1956. **Educational Activities:** National - Interstate Council of State Boards of Cosmetology Seminar. **Geographic Preference:** National.

4507 ■ Personal Care Product Council
1620 L St. NW, Ste. 1200
Washington, DC 20036
Ph: (202)331-1770
Fax: (202)331-1969
Co. E-mail: membership@personalcarecouncil.org
URL: http://www.personalcarecouncil.org
Contact: Lezlee Westine, President
Facebook: www.facebook.com/Personal-Care-Products-Council-1443878795835012
Linkedin: www.linkedin.com/company/464630
X (Twitter): x.com/PCPC_News
YouTube: www.youtube.com/user/PersonalCareCouncil

Description: Manufacturers and distributors of finished cosmetics, fragrances, and personal care products; suppliers of raw materials and services. Provides scientific, legal, regulatory, and legislative services. Coordinates public service, educational, and public affairs activities. **Founded:** 1894. **Publications:** *Member Directory; Executive Update; International Cosmetic Legal & Regulatory Database (IRDB)* (Annual); *On-Line INFOBASE; CTFA News* (Bi-weekly); *International Color Handbook; International Resource Manual.* **Geographic Preference:** National.

REFERENCE WORKS

4508 ■ "The 25 Best Places to Shop for Beauty Products" in StyleCaster
URL(s): stylecaster.com/beauty/best-beauty-stores/

Description: The best places to shop for cosmetics, which may help you get out of your makeup rut and try something and someplace new. Includes a slideshow of all the best places. **Availability:** Online.

4509 ■ *Business as Usual*

Description: Founder of The Body Shop shares her story and gives her opinion on everything from cynical cosmetic companies to destructive consultants.

4510 ■ *"Cosmetics Are a Case Study for Embracing Diversity in Marketing"* in Forbes (October 17, 2019)
URL(s): www.forbes.com/sites/kylewong/2019/10/17/cosmetics-are-a-case-study-for-embracing-diversity-in-marketing/#5437c6c2144d
Ed: Kyle Wong. **Released:** October 17, 2019. **Availability:** Online.

4511 ■ *"Eco-Preneuring"* in Small Business Opportunities (Feb. 6, 2012)
Pub: Harris Publishing, Inc.
Contact: Janet Chase, Contact
Description: Iceland Naturally is a joint marketing effort among tourism and business interests hoping to increase demand for Icelandic products including frozen seafood, bottled water, agriculture, and tourism in North America.

4512 ■ *"Fair and Lovely: Building an Integrated Model to Examine How Peer Influence Mediates the Effects of Skin-Lightening Advertisements On College Women In Singapore"* in International Journal of Advertising (Vol. 31, February 2012, No. 1, pp. 189)
Ed: Stella C. Chia, Yuen Ting Chay, Poh Kwan Cheong. **Released:** January 02, 2012. **Description:** Research uses an integrated model with which suggested that perceptions of peers and interpersonal communication with peers each mediate the influence of skin-lightening advertisements on college women in the South Asian country, Singapore. The model is build based on the influence-of-presumed-influence model. The study found that college women in Singapore tended to infer their peers' advertising exposure and the corresponding advertising influence on peers based on the own advertising exposure. Their exposure to the skin-lightening advertisements also induced their discussions about fair-skinned appearance with peers, resulting in favorable attitudes towards fair-skinned appearance. **Availability:** Online.

4513 ■ *"The Growth Opportunity That Lies Next Door: How Will the Logic of Globalization Change for Corporations from Countries such as India, China, Indonesia, Brazil, and Turkey if the Growth Opportunities..."* in (Vol. 90, July-August 2012, No. 7-8, pp. 141)
Pub: Harvard Business Review Press
Contact: Moderna V. Pfizer, Contact
Ed: Geoffrey G. Jones. **Description:** Brazilian company Natura Cosmeticos found that focusing on expanding into the emerging markets represented by neighboring countries, rather than on well-established markets in developed nations, offered more opportunities and greater rewards.

4514 ■ *"How I Did It: Bobbi Brown, Founder and CEO, Bobbi Brown Cosmetics"* in Inc. (November 2007, pp. 110-112)
Ed: Athena Schindelheim. **Description:** Profile of Bobbi Brown, CEO and founder of Bobbi Brown Cosmetics, designed to highlight a woman's natural look. Brown opened her first freestanding retail store recently that houses a makeup artistry school in the back. **Availability:** Online.

4515 ■ *"Longtime Advocacy for Green Skin Care Is Paying Off"* in Providence Business News (Vol. 29, June 2, 2014, No. 9, pp. 24)
Pub: American City Business Journals, Inc.
Contact: Mike Olivieri, Executive Vice President
Released: February 01, 2014. **Description:** Brenda Brock, entrepreneur and founder of Farmaesthetics, achieved success with her line of green, sustainable skin care products. She is now expanding her business to start new outlets. **Availability:** Print; Online.

4516 ■ *"Master of His Domain"* in Canadian Business (Vol. 81, December 8, 2008, No. 21, pp. S17)
Description: L'Oreal Canada chief executive Javier San Juan believes in being close to consumers and travels to one of his company's fifteen locations in Canada about once a month. San Juan's job is to build the L'Oreal brand in Canada. **Availability:** Online.

4517 ■ *Member Directory (Cosmetics industry)*
Pub: Personal Care Product Council
Contact: Lezlee Westine, President
URL(s): www.personalcarecouncil.org/about-us/member-companies
Description: Covers more than 1,000 member companies. **Entries include:** Company name, address, phone, telex/TWX number, Internet site, names and titles of key personnel, parent company name, affiliates and subsidiaries, products and services, designation as manufacturer, distributor, supplier, or private-label manufacturer. **Arrangement:** Alphabetical within membership categories. **Indexes:** Company name. **Availability:** Online.

4518 ■ *"Mother and Daughter Create Tool to Unbraid 8 Braids at One Time"* in Black Enterprise (February 25, 2023)
URL(s): www.blackenterprise.com/mother-and-daughter-create-tool-to-unbraid-8-braids-at-one-time/
Released: February 25, 2023. **Description:** A mother and daughter duo launched a company to develop and create The Original Unbraider, which is being used in salons and sold at hair shows. **Availability:** Online.

4519 ■ *"Owner of Skin Care Business Offers Westfield State Scholarships If Ex-President Drops Lawsuit"* in Boston Business Journal (Vol. 34, April 25, 2014, No. 12, pp. 5)
Pub: American City Business Journals, Inc.
Contact: Mike Olivieri, Executive Vice President
Description: John Walsh, CEO of Elizabeth Grady Company, has offered $100,000 in scholarships if Westfield State University President, Evan Dobelle, drops his lawsuits against the university. Dobelle decided to sue the school after he was placed on paid leave by three trustees. **Availability:** Print; Online.

4520 ■ *"Polish Family-Owned Cosmetics Company Bases U.S. Flagship in W.VA."* in West Virginia Public Broadcasting (October 21, 2019)
URL(s): www.wvpublic.org/post/polish-family-owned-cosmetics-company-bases-us-flagship-wva#stream/0
Ed: Liz McCormick. **Released:** October 21, 2019. **Description:** Polish cosmetics company BANDI Cosmetics is setting up their new US flagship store in West Virginia. This will be the first time the line will be available in the US. **Availability:** Online.

4521 ■ *"The State & Future of CBD in Beauty"* in Global Cosmetic Industry (October 12, 2019)
URL(s): www.gcimagazine.com/business/rd/ingredients/The-State--Future-of-CBD-in-Beauty--562936001.html
Released: October 12, 2019. **Description:** Examines the popularity of CBD, cannabidiol, extract. With this new product still untested in many areas, including the beauty industry, there is a sense to proceed with caution when it comes to this ingredient. **Availability:** Online.

4522 ■ *"Suburban Retailers Go Urban"* in Philadelphia Business Journal (Vol. 28, August 17, 2012, No. 27, pp. 1)
Pub: Baltimore Business Journal
Contact: Rhonda Pringle, President
E-mail: rpringle@bizjournals.com
Description: Traditional suburban retailers in the retail corridor of Philadelphia, Pennsylvania such as cosmetics retailer Ulta Beauty have been seeking population density and are relocating to urban settings, which represent untapped markets. How Vesper Property Group signed with Ulta Beauty a long-term lease on three levels totaling 13,600 square feet is also discussed. **Availability:** Print; Online.

4523 ■ *"Top 10 Most Popular Online Makeup Stores in the U.S."* in US Unlocked
URL(s): www.usunlocked.com/top-10-us-makeup-stores/
Ed: Linda Hemerik. **Description:** Online beauty stores are more popular than ever thanks to beauty vloggers and influencers. Included are some of the best places to buy cosmetics online. **Availability:** Online.

4524 ■ *"What's Behind the Rise of G-Beauty"* in The New York Times (April 10, 2019)
URL(s): www.nytimes.com/2019/04/10/style/german-beauty.html
Ed: Bee Shapiro. **Released:** April 10, 2019. **Description:** The rise in popularity of German beauty products is investigated. With it's minimalist packaging and lack of toxins, these products are gaining control of the market share. **Availability:** Online.

STATISTICAL SOURCES

4525 ■ *Online Beauty Retailing - US - 2021*
URL(s): store.mintel.com/report/online-beauty-retailing-us-2021
Price: $4,366.35. **Description:** A downloadable report with insights on how the Covid-19 pandemic affected consumers and the way they shop. However, people still bought beauty products and this report gives the reasons, methods, considerations, and attitudes towards these purchases. The full report includes an executive summary, interactive databook, PowerPoint presentation, infographic overview, report PDF, and previous years data. **Availability:** PDF.

4526 ■ *US Cannabeauty: CBD and Hemp in BPC Market Report 2021*
URL(s): store.mintel.com/report/us-cannabeauty-cbd-and-hemp-in-bpc-market-report
Price: $4,366.35. **Description:** Downloadable report detailing how consumers are receiving hemp and CBD in their beauty products, especially as a source of self-care. Report includes executive summary, interactive databook, PowerPoint presentation, Infographic overview, report PDF, and previous years data. **Availability:** PDF.

4527 ■ *US Gen Z Beauty Consumer Market Report 2021*
URL(s): store.mintel.com/report/us-gen-z-beauty-consumer-market-report
Price: $4,366.35. **Description:** Downloadable report detailing the shopping habits of Generation Z as they purchase beauty products. Report includes executive summary, interactive databook, PowerPoint presentation, infographic overview, report pdf, and previous years data. **Availability:** PDF.

4528 ■ *US Teen and Tween Beauty and Personal Care Market Report 2020*
URL(s): store.mintel.com/report/us-teen-and-tween-beauty-and-personal-care-consumer-market-report
Price: $4,366.35. **Description:** Downloadable report giving data and analysis on the habits of tween and teen consumers in relation to the beauty and personal care industry. Report includes an executive summary, interactive databook, PowerPoint presentation, infographic overview, report PDF, and previous years data. **Availability:** PDF.

TRADE PERIODICALS

4529 ■ *Cosmetics & Toiletries: The International Magazine of Cosmetic Technology*
Pub: Allured Business Media
Contact: Janet Ludwig, President
E-mail: jludwig@allured.com
URL(s): www.cosmeticsandtoiletries.com
Facebook: www.facebook.com/CandTmagazine
Linkedin: www.linkedin.com/company/cosmeticsandtoiletries
Instagram: www.instagram.com/cosmeticsandtoiletries

Small Business Profiles

Released: 10/year; Jan., Feb., March, April, May, June, July/Aug., Sept., Oct. and Nov./Dec. **Price:** $199, for print. **Description:** Trade magazine on cosmetic and toiletries manufacturing with an emphasis on product research and development issues. **Availability:** Print; PDF; Online.

4530 ■ *FDAnews Drug Daily Bulletin*
URL(s): www.fdanews.com/newsletters/6-fdanews
-drug-daily-bulletin

Description: Seeks to provide a detailed analysis of federal regulatory activity relating to food, drugs, and cosmetics. Interprets policy and regulatory changes, focusing on the impact of specific actions on industry in both the long and short term. **Availability:** Print; Online.

4531 ■ *Skin Inc.: Professional Skin Care*
Contact: Katie Anderson, Managing Editor
E-mail: kanderson@allured.com
URL(s): www.skininc.com
Facebook: www.facebook.com/SkinInc
X (Twitter): twitter.com/SkinIncMagazine

Released: Monthly **Description:** The complete business guide for face and body care. **Availability:** Print; PDF; Online.

VIDEO/AUDIO MEDIA

4532 ■ *How I Built This: Burt's Bees: Roxanne Quimby*
URL(s): www.npr.org/2021/08/19/1029305404/burts
-bees-roxanne-quimby-2019

Ed: Guy Raz. **Released:** August 23, 2021. **Description:** Podcast explains how Roxanne Quimby's meeting with a reclusive beekeeper led to selling honey at local markets, which in turn led to Burt's Bees lip balm and skin care products. .

4533 ■ *How I Built This: Harry's Razors: Andy Katz-Mayfield and Jeff Raider*
URL(s): wondery.com/shows/how-i-built-this/episode/
10386-harrys-razors-andy-katz-mayfield-and-jeff-rai
der

Ed: Guy Raz. **Released:** June 12, 2023. **Description:** Podcast discusses how Harry's Razors founder took on the Goliath of the shaving industry with its direct-to-consumer razor company.

4534 ■ *How I Built This: Mielle Organics: Monique Rodriguez*
URL(s): wondery.com/shows/how-i-built-this/episode/
10386-mielle-organics-monique-rodriguez

Ed: Guy Raz. **Released:** May 15, 2023. **Description:** Podcast explains how homegrown haircare experiments posted on Instagram evolved into a global haircare and beauty brand.

4535 ■ *How I Built This: Tarte Cosmetics: Maureen Kelly*
URL(s): wondery.com/shows/how-i-built-this/episode/
10386-tarte-cosmetics-maureen-kelly

Ed: Guy Raz. **Released:** January 23, 2023. **Description:** Podcast explains how a PhD candidate in psychology launched a cosmetics company with no significant start-up money, no experience, and no connections.

4536 ■ *How I Built This: The Lip Bar (TLB): Melissa Butler*
URL(s): wondery.com/shows/how-i-built-this/episode/
10386-the-lip-bar-tlb-melissa-butler-2020

Released: July 03, 2023. **Description:** Podcast explains how a hobby evolved into the largest Black-owned makeup brand sold in Target stores.

TRADE SHOWS AND CONVENTIONS

4537 ■ AACS Annual Convention & Expo
American Association of Cosmetology Schools (AACS)
20 F St., NW, Ste. 700
Washington, DC 20001
Ph: (202)963-5730
Co. E-mail: info@beautyschools.org

URL: http://myaacs.org
Contact: Cecil Kidd, Executive Director
E-mail: cecil@myaacs.org
URL(s): myaacs.org/annual-conference

Frequency: Annual. **Description:** Exhibits related to beauty supplies and products, and cosmetology services. **Audience:** Industry professionals. **Principal Exhibits:** Exhibits related to beauty supplies and products, and cosmetology services. **Telecommunication Services:** kimber@myaacs.org.

4538 ■ Handcrafted Soap & Cosmetic Guild Conference
URL(s): www.soapguild.org/conference

Frequency: Annual. **Description:** Provides education and key topic sessions on the handcrafted soap and cosmetics industry. **Principal Exhibits:** Provides education and key topic sessions on the handcrafted soap and cosmetics industry.

FRANCHISES AND BUSINESS OPPORTUNITIES

4539 ■ Caryl Baker Visage (CBV)
31 Wingold Ave.
Toronto, ON, Canada M6B 1P8
Ph: (416)789-7191
Co. E-mail: info@carylbakervisage.com
URL: http://carylbakervisage.com
Facebook: www.facebook.com/CarylBakerVisage
Instagram: www.instagram.com/cbvisage

Description: Manufacturer, distributor, and retailer of cosmetics and skincare products and also provides skincare, cosmetics, beauty treatment, and spa services. **Founded:** 1969. **Equity Capital Needed:** 200000. **Franchise Fee:** $20,000. **Financial Assistance:** Yes **Training:** Canada's go-to destination for beauty products and services, such as Brow Waxing, Facials, Ear Piercing, Eye Lash Extensions, Teeth Whitening, and more.

4540 ■ Faces Cosmetics
Sequoia Capital
520 Garyray Dr.
Toronto, ON, Canada M9L 1R1
Ph: 91 80 412 458 80
Co. E-mail: analystapplication.india@sequoiacap
.com
URL: http://www.sequoiacap.com
Facebook: www.facebook.com/facesfcgi
Instagram: www.instagram.com/facesfcgi

Description: Retailer of makeup, skincare products and personal care accessories. **Founded:** 1974. **Royalty Fee:** 6%. **Training:** Initial training and ongoing support.

4541 ■ Ideal Image Development Corporation
1 N Dale Mabry Hwy., Ste. 100 A
Tampa, FL 33609
Ph: (813)347-9152
Free: 800-234-3325
URL: http://www.idealimage.com
Contact: David Prokupek, Chief Executive Officer
Facebook: www.facebook.com/IdealImage
X (Twitter): x.com/idealimage
Instagram: www.instagram.com/idealimage
YouTube: www.youtube.com/laserexperts

Description: Personal care and spa company that specializes in skin treatments, hair removal, and nonsurgical weight loss procedures. **Founded:** 2001. **Franchised:** 2004. **Training:** Offers 2-4 weeks at headquarters, onsite as needed, and i-Learn online training ongoing.

4542 ■ Merle Norman Cosmetics Inc. (MNC)
9130 Bellanca Ave.
Los Angeles, CA 90045
Free: 800-788-1191
Co. E-mail: customercare@merlenorman.com
URL: http://www.merlenorman.com
Contact: Jack B. Nethercutt, II, Chief Executive Officer
Facebook: www.facebook.com/MerleNormanInc
X (Twitter): x.com/MerleNormanInc
Instagram: www.instagram.com/merlenormaninc
YouTube: www.youtube.com/user/MerleNormanInc

Pinterest: www.pinterest.com/merlenormaninc

Description: Offers a complete line of Merle Norman cosmetics along with professional cosmetic advice from trained consultants. Locations feature unique interior designs and are situated in major shopping centers and strip malls. **Founded:** 1931. **Financial Assistance:** Yes **Training:** Offers 2 week home office training and ongoing field support.

4543 ■ Top of the Line Fragrances
515 Bath Ave.
Long Branch, NJ 07740
Ph: (226)214-3047
URL: http://thefranchisemall.com
Contact: Steve Ozonian, Chief Executive Officer
Facebook: www.facebook.com/FranchiseMall
X (Twitter): x.com/FranchiseMall
Instagram: www.instagram.com/thefranchisemall
Pinterest: www.pinterest.ca/franchisemall

Description: Manufacturer and distributor of cosmetics and fragrances products. **Founded:** 1983. **Franchised:** 1987. **Training:** Offered at franchisee's location for 7-10 days with ongoing support.

4544 ■ Women's Health Boutique (WHB)
605 N 6th St.
Longview, TX 75601
Ph: (903)758-9904
Free: 800-525-2420
Fax: (903)236-9786
Co. E-mail: info@whblongview.com
URL: http://www.mywhb.com
Contact: Vicki Jones, President
Facebook: www.facebook.com/womenshealthbou
tique
X (Twitter): x.com/WHBgirls
Pinterest: www.pinterest.com/whbladies

Description: Products and services related to pre and postnatal care, post-mastectomy, compression therapy, hair loss, incontinence, and skin care. **No. of Franchise Units:** 13. **Founded:** 1991. **Franchised:** 1994. **Equity Capital Needed:** $49,000 minimum start-up cash. **Training:** Yes.

PUBLICATIONS

4545 ■ *Global Cosmetic Industry: The Business Magazine for the Global Beauty Industry (GCI)*
336 Gundersen Dr., Ste. D
Carol Stream, IL 60188-2403
Ph: (630)653-2155
Fax: (630)653-2192
Co. E-mail: customerservice@allured.com
URL: http://www.allured.com
Contact: Janet Ludwig, President
E-mail: jludwig@allured.com
URL(s): www.gcimagazine.com
Facebook: www.facebook.com/GlobalCosmeticIn
dustry
X (Twitter): x.com/GCI_Magazine
Instagram: www.instagram.com/globalcosmeticin
dustry

Released: 11/year; Jan., Feb., March, April, May, June, July/Aug., Sept., Oct., Nov. and Dec. **Price:** $199, for print. **Description:** Trade publication covering the cosmetics industry worldwide. **Availability:** Print; Online.

INTERNET DATABASES

4546 ■ *Business of Beauty: A Resource Guide*
URL(s): guides.loc.gov/business-of-beauty

Description: This online resource contains links to further resources on the history of the beauty business. Also contains links to current practices; retail, wholesale, and manufacturing; trade data, and print and electronic sources. **Availability:** Online.

LIBRARIES

4547 ■ Colgate-Palmolive Company - Library
Colgate-Palmolive Company
  300 Park Ave.
  New York, NY 10022
Ph: (212)310-2000
Free: 800-468-6502
Fax: (212)310-3745
Co. E-mail: ethics@colpal.com
URL: http://www.colgatepalmolive.com
Contact: Noel Wallace, President
Linkedin: www.linkedin.com/company/colgate-palmolive
X (Twitter): twitter.com/cp_news
YouTube: www.youtube.com/user/colgatepalmolive
Description: Global manufacturer and distributor of consumer oral care, personal care, home care, pet nutrition products, and pharmaceutical products for dentists and other oral health professionals. **Scope:** Health; hygiene. **Founded:** 1806. **Holdings:** Figures not available. **Educational Activities:** Business Today International Conference (Annual). **Awards:** ACS Award in Colloid Chemistry (Annual); Make the U (Annual).

4548 ■ Mary Kay Inc. Information Resources
16251 N Dallas Pky.
  Addison, TX 75001
URL: http://www.marykay.com
Scope: Cosmetics; dermatology; toxicology; chemistry; business; marketing. **Services:** Interlibrary loan. **Holdings:** 2000 books; 500 bound periodical volumes.

4549 ■ Unilever HPC NA Research Library
40 Merritt Blvd.
  Trumbull, CT 06611
URL: http://www.unilever.com/brands/innovation/our-r-and-d-locations/trumbull-north-america
Scope: Cosmetic science; dermatology. **Founded:** 1959. **Holdings:** 5,000 books; 2,000 bound periodical volumes.

4550 ■ U.S. Food & Drug Administration Biosciences Library (FDA) - Center for Food Safety and Applied Nutrition Branch Library (CFSAN) [FDA]
5001 Campus Dr., HFS-009
  College Park, MD 20740-3835
Free: 888-723-3366
URL: http://www.fda.gov/about-fda/fda-organization/center-food-safety-and-applied-nutrition-cfsan
Contact: Dr. Susan T. Mayne, Director
Scope: Food technology; nutrition; cosmetics. **Services:** Interlibrary loan; Library open to the public. **Founded:** 1961. **Holdings:** Printed material; Videos. **Subscriptions:** 100 journals and other serials.

Costume Shop

ASSOCIATIONS AND OTHER ORGANIZATIONS

4551 ■ Costume Society of America (CSA)
c/o Kristen Miller Zohn, Executive Director
PO Box 852
Columbus, GA 31902-0852
Free: 800-272-9447
Co. E-mail: national.office@costumesocietyamerica.com
URL: http://www.costumesocietyamerica.com
Contact: Kristen Miller Zohn, Executive Director
E-mail: kmzohn@costumesocietyamerica.com
Facebook: www.facebook.com/costumesocie tyofamerica
X (Twitter): x.com/costumesociety
Instagram: www.instagram.com/costumesocie tyamerica
YouTube: www.youtube.com/channel/UC0Me-A0gzYoy32TRV7jtP2g

Description: Museum and historical society personnel; college/university faculty of costume history, retailing, material culture, apparel design, social-psychological aspects, economics; theatre/film fashion designers; conservators; costume and textile collectors/dealers; and re-enactors. Focuses on the scholarly study of all aspects of dress and appearance. Promotes the study of dress through education, research, preservation, and design. Supports scholarship and its dissemination through research papers and publications; collects and disseminates information on the preservation, interpretation, and exhibition of costumes; provides referrals for the identification and conservation of costumes, sponsors international study tours. **Founded:** 1973. **Publications:** *CSA E-News* (Monthly); *DRESS: The Journal of The Costume Society of America* (Semiannual); *Southeastern Regional Newsletter* (Semiannual); *Costume Society of America Membership Directory* (Annual). **Educational Activities:** Costume Society of America Annual Meeting and Symposium (Annual). **Awards:** CSA College and University Collection Care Grant (Annual); CSA Costume Design Award (Annual); CSA Costume Society of America Fellow Award (Annual); CSA Scholars' Roundtable Honor (Annual); Adele Filene Student Presenter Grant (Annual); CSA Travel Research Grants (Annual); Small Museums Collection Care Grants (Annual); Millia Davenport Publication Award (Annual); Richard Martin Exhibition Award (Annual); Stella Blum Student Research Grant (Annual). **Geographic Preference:** National.

4552 ■ National Costumers Association (NCA)
PO Box 13347
Chicago, IL 60613
Ph: (708)646-2799
Co. E-mail: office@costumers.org
URL: http://www.costumers.org
Contact: Ed Avis, Executive Director
E-mail: executivedirector@costumers.org
Facebook: www.facebook.com/NATLCostumers

Description: Designers, producers, and renters of costumes for all occasions. Works to establish and maintain professional and ethical standards of business in the costume industry. Encourages and promotes a greater and more diversified use of costumes in all fields of human activity. Offers Play Plot, Book services; conducts educational programs during conventions; buyer's group discounts, website listing, book service, and debt recovery source. **Founded:** 1923. **Publications:** *National Costumers Magazine* (Quarterly). **Educational Activities:** Semi-Annual Costume Convention (Semiannual); Halloween Dance Apparel and Costume Show (Annual). **Awards:** Memorial Fund Scholarship (Annual). **Geographic Preference:** National.

REFERENCE WORKS

4553 ■ "Halloween Pop-Up Stores, Explained" in Vox (October 29, 2018)
URL(s): www.vox.com/the-goods/2018/10/25/18023130/spirit-halloween-party-city-pop-up-stores
Released: October 29, 2018. **Description:** Pop-up Halloween stores are a big part of the autumn scene. Taking over vacant big box stores, they are jam packed with costumes and lawn decorations. With the decline in retail, these costume shops have been doing extremely well with their temporary leases and short time frame they are open. **Availability:** Online.

4554 ■ "In Somerville, a Powerhouse of Custom Costume-making for Boston and Beyond" in Boston Globe (July 4, 2019)
URL(s): www.bostonglobe.com/arts/theater/dance/2019/07/04/somerville-powerhouse-custom-costume-making-for-boston-and-beyond/mi35voWYzOmF8uW1FlcdrM/story.html
Ed: Marella Gayla. **Released:** July 04, 2019. **Description:** A profile of Costume Works, a popular costume shop specializing in bespoke works for theater, opera, dance, and even elaborate Halloween costumes. **Availability:** Online.

4555 ■ "On With the Show: A.T. Jones & Sons, the Oldest Costume Shop in America, Turns 150" in Baltimore Magazine
URL(s): www.baltimoremagazine.com/2018/3/12/on-with-the-show-a-t-jones-sons-costume-shop-turns-150
Ed: Lauren LaRocca. **Description:** Profile of A.T. Jones & Sons, which is the oldest continually running costume shop in the country. Theatrical costumes for plays and operas were and still are being created and sewn on-site, and is the spot to rent costumes for most holidays. Discusses how the business has grown over time and adapted its business model. **Availability:** Online.

STATISTICAL SOURCES

4556 ■ Formal Wear & Costume Rental Industry in the US - Market Research Report
URL(s): www.ibisworld.com/united-states/market-research-reports/formal-wear-costume-rental-industry/
Price: $925. **Description:** Downloadable report analyzing the current and future trends in the formal wear and costume rental industries. **Availability:** Download.

TRADE SHOWS AND CONVENTIONS

4557 ■ Semi-Annual Costume Convention
National Costumers Association (NCA)
PO Box 13347
Chicago, IL 60613
Ph: (708)646-2799
Co. E-mail: office@costumers.org
URL: http://www.costumers.org
Contact: Ed Avis, Executive Director
E-mail: executivedirector@costumers.org
URL(s): www.costumers.org/about-the-national-costumers-association

Frequency: Semiannual. **Description:** Offer exemplary teaching and training programs. **Audience:** Costume industry professionals. **Principal Exhibits:** Offer exemplary teaching and training programs.

FRANCHISES AND BUSINESS OPPORTUNITIES

4558 ■ Halloween Express
c/o Halloween Express 7505 Sussex Dr.
Florence, KY 41042
Ph: (859)282-5550
Co. E-mail: brad.butler@halloweenexpress.com
URL: http://www.halloweenexpress.com
Contact: Brad Butler, Contact
E-mail: brad.butler@halloweenexpress.com
Facebook: www.facebook.com/HalloweenExpress
X (Twitter): twitter.com/HalloweenXperts
Instagram: www.instagram.com/halloweenexpressdotcom
YouTube: www.youtube.com/c/HalloweenExpress
Pinterest: www.pinterest.com/halloweenxpress

Description: Distributor of costume accessories, props, patriotic costumes and accessories for party and holidays. **Founded:** 1992. **Training:** Train and assist you in setting up your business, including site selection and guidance throughout the lease process.

LIBRARIES

4559 ■ Carnegie Library of Pittsburgh - Music Department
4400 Forbes Ave.
Pittsburgh, PA 15213
Ph: (412)622-3114
Co. E-mail: musicdept@carnegielibrary.org
URL: http://www.carnegielibrary.org/services/music-resources

Scope: History; music. **Services:** Reference and reader's assistance; department open to the public. **Founded:** 1938. **Holdings:** 85,000 music books and scores; 28,000 sound recordings; 54,000 slides; 1,700 videos and DVDs; 400 periodical, newsletter and serial titles; mounted pictures.

4560 ■ Eugene O'Neill Theater Center - Liebling-Wood Library - Monte Cristo Cottage Collection
325 Pequot Ave.
  New London, CT 06320
Co. E-mail: theaterlives@theoneill.org
URL: http://www.theoneill.org/mcc
Contact: Louis Sheaffer, Contact
Scope: Drama; dramatic literature; costume design; theatre memorabilia. **Services:** Copying; collection open to the public. **Founded:** 1840. **Holdings:** 5,000 books; playbills; theater scrapbooks; photographic stills; manuscripts; letters; set and costume designs; television manuscripts; clipping files; periodicals.

4561 ■ Fashion Institute of Design & Merchandising (FIDM) - Orange County Library
17590 Gillette Ave.
  Irvine, CA 92614
URL: http://fidm.edu/en/majors/merchandise+marketing/experience/bios/molly+stolen
Scope: Textile design; textile design; marketing; interior design; retailing; costumes. **Services:** Copying; library open to the public by appointment. **Founded:** 1980. **Holdings:** 3,000 books; 130 bound periodical volumes; 40 pamphlet headings; 475 videotapes; 135 slide sets; 300 retail catalogs; 100 annual reports; 50 CD-ROMs. **Subscriptions:** 80 journals and other serials; 8 newspapers.

4562 ■ Guthrie Theater Foundation - Staff Reference Library
818 S 2nd St.
  Minneapolis, MN 55415
Ph: (612)377-2224
Free: 877-447-8243
Co. E-mail: store@guthrietheater.org
URL: http://www.guthrietheater.org
Contact: James L. Chosy, Chairman
Facebook: www.facebook.com/guthrietheater
X (Twitter): x.com/GuthrieTheater
Instagram: www.instagram.com/guthrietheater
YouTube: www.youtube.com/channel/UCwysb4Tjiwn8bKJe0zNuSnA
Scope: Costume design and history; decorative arts; architecture; history of theater; actors and acting; stage lighting and design; technical production; dramatic literature and critical works; poetry; music; general history and geography. **Services:** Library not open to the public. **Holdings:** 4,500 books; 3,900 plays; 8 VF drawers of slides; 12 VF drawers of photographs of past productions; 10 VF drawers of scripts from past productions.

4563 ■ Kansas State University - Hale Library - Research, Education, and Engagement Division - Richard L.D. and Marjorie J. Morse Department of Special Collections
1117 Mid-Campus Dr. N
  Manhattan, KS 66506
Ph: (785)532-3014
Co. E-mail: libsc@k-state.edu
URL: http://lib.k-state.edu/research-find/special-collections-and-archives
Scope: Consumer movement; cookery; Kansas culture and K-State history. **Services:** Interlibrary loan. **Founded:** 1966. **Holdings:** 38,000 cookery; records; manuscripts; books; photographs; ephemera.

4564 ■ Los Angeles County Museum of Art (LACMA) - Balch Art Research Library
5905 Wilshire Blvd.
  Los Angeles, CA 90036
Ph: (323)857-6010
Co. E-mail: publicinfo@lacma.org
URL: http://www.lacma.org
Contact: Wallis Annenberg, Director
Facebook: www.facebook.com/LACMA
X (Twitter): x.com/lacma
Instagram: www.instagram.com/lacma
YouTube: www.youtube.com/channel/UCBrtMtJE5tqHLpCCqoPw-lg
Pinterest: www.pinterest.com/lacma
Description: A museum principally engaged in the collection, preservation, exhibition and intellectual interpretation of a broad range of cultural works, including art, music and film collections, through public programs, research facilities, educational outreach and digital initiatives. **Scope:** Art. **Services:** Interlibrary loan; copying; library open to the public by appointment only. **Founded:** 1910. **Holdings:** 175,000 books; 450 current periodical; 24,107 microfiche; 74 reels of microfilm; current auction catalogs; 150 VF drawers of artist ephemera.; Original textile designs; sketches from fashion, film and theatre designers; period fashion plates; drawings; engravings; manuscripts; books; journals and magazines; photographs; slides; research files; archives. **Publications:** *Bibliografia Mesoamericana*; *John Montgomery Dictionary of Maya Hieroglyphs*.

4565 ■ Metropolitan Museum of Art - Irene Lewisohn Costume Reference Library
1000 5th Ave.
  New York, NY 10028
Co. E-mail: costumeinstitute.library@metmuseum.org
URL: http://www.metmuseum.org/art/libraries-and-research-centers/the-irene-lewisohn-costume-reference-library
Scope: History of costume; fashion. **Services:** Copying; library open to professional designers and research scholars by appointment. **Holdings:** Art books; exhibition history documentation; designer archives; fashion plates; photography collections, scrapbooks; ephemera.

4566 ■ Minneapolis College of Art and Design Library (MCAD)
2501 Stevens Ave.
  Minneapolis, MN 55404
URL: http://www.mcad.edu/campus-info/library
Scope: Literary; artistic resource. **Services:** open to the public for reference use only. **Founded:** 1886. **Holdings:** 50000 volumes; 145,000 slides; college archives.

4567 ■ Museum of the City of New York - Department of Collections Access
1220 5th Ave., 103rd St.
  New York, NY 10029
URL: http://www.mcny.org/collections-policies
Description: Museum in the city of New York. **Scope:** Prints and Photographs; Paintings and Sculpture; Theater Collection; Costume and Textiles. **Services:** Scanning; collection open to qualified scholars and researchers by appointment. **Founded:** 1926. **Holdings:** 400,000 prints and negatives; 22,000 prints; books; pamphlets; manuscripts; drawing; 1500 paintings; 200,000 accessioned objects.

4568 ■ Newark Public Library Reference Center
Main Library, 2nd Fl.
  5 Washington St.
  Newark, NJ 07102
Ph: (973)733-7820
Fax: (973)733-5648
Co. E-mail: reference@npl.org
URL: http://www.npl.org/collections-services/reference-center
Contact: Charles F. Cummings, Contact

Scope: African American culture and history; art; business; literature; music and more. **Services:** Center open to the public. **Founded:** 1888. **Holdings:** Figures not available. **Preferred Investment Size:** Newark Public Library - Arts & Humanities Division and Newark Public Library - Business, Science & Technology Division.

4569 ■ State University of New York - Fashion Institute of Technology - Gladys Marcus Library
227 W 27th St.
  New York, NY 10001-5992
Ph: (212)217-7999
URL: http://www.fitnyc.edu/library/index.php
Description: Library supports the academic and research needs of the institute. **Scope:** Fashion, fashion history, textiles, fashion trend forecasting. **Services:** Interlibrary loan; library open by appointment. **Founded:** 1944. **Holdings:** 300,000 print, non-print, and electronic materials, including sketch collections, clipping files, and fashion show DVDs.

4570 ■ University of Wisconsin--Madison - Ruth Ketterer Harris Library - Helen Louise Allen Textile Collection
School of Human Ecology, Nancy Nicholas Hall,
  1300 Linden Dr.
  Madison, WI 53706
Ph: (608)262-1162
Co. E-mail: hlatc@sohe.wisc.edu
URL: http://cdmc.wisc.edu/textiles/helen-louise-allen-textile-collection
URL(s): humanecology.wisc.edu/about/collections-and-galleries
Scope: Textiles (history). **Services:** library open to the public with restrictions. **Founded:** 1993. **Holdings:** Figures not available.

4571 ■ Western Costume Company - Research Library
11041 Vanowen St.
  North Hollywood, CA 91605
Ph: (818)760-0900
Co. E-mail: wccmail@westerncostume.com
URL: http://www.westerncostume.com
Contact: Edward Marks, President
Facebook: www.facebook.com/westerncostumecompany
Instagram: www.instagram.com/westerncostumecompany
Description: Western wardeobe shop. **Scope:** Costume materials. **Founded:** 1912. **Holdings:** 20,000 books; Catalogs; Periodicals; Clipping files; Dress.

4572 ■ Yale University Drama Collection
PO Box 208240
  New Haven, CT 06520-8240
Ph: (203)432-1775
URL: http://library.yale.edu/collection-development/statements/haas-arts-library-drama-collection
Contact: Stephen F. Gates, Librarian
Description: It includes thousands of play scripts, books on the history of theater, theater architecture, dramaturgy, journals, dramatic criticism, costume, and stage design, stage lighting and production, theater management, biographies, related reference books and journals, and performance recordings on various media. **Scope:** Plays by American, British, and foreign playwrights; history of the theater; theater architecture; drama criticism; costume and set design; stage lighting; acting; direction; production; theater administration. **Services:** Interlibrary loan; copying; audio and video cassette players; library open to the public for reference use only (circulation limited to Yale University card holders). **Founded:** 1925. **Holdings:** Playscripts; books; journals; images; DVDs; CDs; e-books; datasets.

Craft Artisan

START-UP INFORMATION

4573 ■ *"Etsy: Etsy Business for Beginners! Master Etsy and Build a Profitable Business In No Time"*
Released: December 23, 2014. **Price:** $6.99, regular price is $13.99. **Description:** Craft artisans take note: information is offered to start an online business through Etsy. Whether handmade home accessories, clothing, or knick-knacks, Etsy is the perfect option for artists and crafters to start a home-based, online retail operation. **Availability:** Print; Download.

4574 ■ *How to Start a Faux Painting or Mural Business*
Pub: Allworth Press
Contact: Tad Crawford, Founder
Ed: Rebecca Pittman. **Released:** Second edition. **Price:** $24.95, paperback. **Description:** Updated and expanded to cover better ways to advertise, innovative supplies (such as Venetian plasters and stained cements), unique bidding and studio setups required for new plasters and varnishes. **Availability:** E-book; Print.

4575 ■ *How to Start a Home-based Craft Business*
Ed: Kenn Oberrecht, Patrice Lewis. **Released:** Sixth edition. **Price:** $18.99, e-book; Paperback. **Description:** Step-by-step guide for starting and growing a home-based craft business. **Availability:** Print.

4576 ■ *Scrapbooking for Profit: Cashing in on Retail, Home-Based and Internet Opportunities*
Pub: Allworth Press
Contact: Tad Crawford, Founder
Ed: Rebecca Pittman. **Released:** June 01, 2005. **Price:** $16.95, paperback; $19.99, Ebook; $19.95, Paperback. **Description:** Eleven strategies for starting a scrapbooking business, including brick-and-mortar stores, home-based businesses, and online retail and wholesale outlets. **Availability:** E-book; Print.

4577 ■ *Setting Up Your Ceramic Studio: Ideas and Plans from Working Artists*
Released: First edition. **Description:** Floor plans and advice for setting up a creative ceramics studio are provided, focusing on equipment, workflow, and safety issues. **Availability:** Print.

ASSOCIATIONS AND OTHER ORGANIZATIONS

4578 ■ Aid to Artisans (ATA)
4445 Willard Ave., Ste. 400
Chevy Chase, MD 20815
Ph: (202)772-0505
Co. E-mail: info@creativelearning.org
URL: http://ata.creativelearning.org
Contact: William Kruvant, President
Facebook: www.facebook.com/aidtoartisans
X (Twitter): x.com/AidtoArtisans
Description: Fosters artistic traditions and cultural vitality to improve livelihood and keep communities healthy, strong and growing. **Founded:** 1976. **Geographic Preference:** Multinational.

4579 ■ American Craft Council (ACC) - Library
1224 Marshall St. NE, Ste. 200
Minneapolis, MN 55413
Ph: (612)206-3100
Fax: (612)355-2330
Co. E-mail: council@craftcouncil.org
URL: http://craftcouncil.org
Contact: Gary J. Smith, Chairman
Facebook: www.facebook.com/CraftCouncil
X (Twitter): x.com/craftcouncil
Instagram: www.instagram.com/craftcouncil
YouTube: www.youtube.com/user/AmericanCraftCouncil
Pinterest: www.pinterest.com/craftcouncil
Description: Promotes understanding and appreciation of contemporary American craft. **Scope:** American craft. **Services:** Open to public for on-site visits by appointment only. **Founded:** 1943. **Holdings:** 20,000 books; 3,000 photographs; 700 periodicals; 150 current subscriptions; newsletters; slides; correspondence; other ephemera. **Publications:** *American Craft* (Quarterly); *American Craft--News Section* (Bimonthly); *American Craft Council--Crafts Fair Directory*; *American Craft--American Craft Guide to Craft Galleries & Shops USA Issue*. **Educational Activities:** ACC Craft Show Baltimore (Annual); ACC Craft Show San Francisco (Annual). **Awards:** ACC College of Fellows (Irregular); ACC Gold Medal for Consummate Craftsmanship (Biennial); Aileen Osborn Webb Award for Philanthropy (Irregular). **Geographic Preference:** National.

4580 ■ Guild of American Papercutters (GAP)
214 S Harrison Ave.
Somerset, PA 15501
Ph: (814)443-2433
Co. E-mail: gapguild@gmail.com
URL: http://papercutters.org
Contact: Randall Williams, President
E-mail: president@papercutters.org
Facebook: www.facebook.com/guildofamericanpapercutters
Instagram: www.instagram.com/guildofamericanpapercutters
Description: Unites fellow papercutters to share ideas, display artwork, and increase public appreciation and awareness of this art form. Offers demonstrations and exhibits. **Founded:** 1988. **Educational Activities:** Guild of American Papercutters Collection (Biennial). **Geographic Preference:** National.

4581 ■ Handweavers Guild of America, Inc. (HGA)
1201 Peachtree St., NE, Ste. 200
Atlanta, GA 30361
Ph: (678)730-0010
Fax: (678)730-0836
Co. E-mail: hga@weavespindye.org
URL: http://www.weavespindye.org
Contact: Suzi Ballenger, President
E-mail: suzi@weavespindye.org
Facebook: www.facebook.com/HandweaversGuildofAmerica
X (Twitter): x.com/weavespindye
Instagram: www.instagram.com/instahga
YouTube: www.youtube.com/user/hgaweavespindye
Pinterest: www.pinterest.com/weavespindye
Description: Individuals, weaving arts guilds, educational institutions, teachers, suppliers, and libraries. Seeks to promote participation and interest in handcrafted textiles; encourage the development of places to work, sell, exhibit, and teach; bring about cooperation among agencies and individuals interested in the textile arts, fiber arts and related fields. **Founded:** 1969. **Publications:** *Shuttle Spindle and Dyepot* (Quarterly); *Handweavers Guild of America--Suppliers Directory*; *Education Directory*; *Speakers Bureau Directory*. **Educational Activities:** HGA Biennial Convergence (Biennial). **Awards:** Certificate of Excellence (Annual); Convergence Assistantship Grants; Mearl K. Gable II Memorial Grant (Annual); The Dendel Scholarship (Annual); Silvio and Eugenia Petrini Grants (Annual); HGA Award (Annual). **Geographic Preference:** National.

4582 ■ Knifemakers' Guild (KG)
c/o Charlie B. Mathews, 121 Mt. Pisgah Church Rd.
Statesboro, GA 30458
Ph: (912)865-9098
Co. E-mail: theknifemakersguild@gmail.com
URL: http://knifemakersguild.com
Contact: Charlie B. Mathews, Contact
Facebook: www.facebook.com/knifemakers.guild
Description: Knifemakers and interested others. Promotes knives and knifemakers; provides technical assistance to knifemakers; encourages ethical and professional business conduct. **Founded:** 1970. **Geographic Preference:** National.

4583 ■ The Knitting Guild Association (TKGA)
1100-H Brandywine Blvd.
Zanesville, OH 43701-7303
Co. E-mail: info@tkga.org
URL: http://tkga.org
Contact: Arenda Holladay, President
E-mail: ahollady@tkga.org
Facebook: www.facebook.com/TKGA.CastOn
X (Twitter): x.com/TKGAGuild
Instagram: www.instagram.com/TheKnittingGuildAssociation
YouTube: www.youtube.com/c/theknittingguildassociation
Description: Represents shop owners and individuals interested in knitting. Provides education and a means of communication to those wishing to improve the quality of workmanship and creativity of their knitting projects. **Founded:** 1984. **Publications:** *Convention Brochure* (Annual); *Seminar Brochure* (Quarterly); *International Journal of Cloud Applications and*

Computing (IJCAC) (Continuous); *Cast On* (Quarterly). **Awards:** TKGA Memorial Scholarship Award (Annual). **Geographic Preference:** Multinational.

4584 ■ Smocking Arts Guild of America (SAGA)
3712 Ringgold Rd. No. 309
Chattanooga, TN 37412
Ph: (817)350-4883
URL: http://www.smocking.org
Contact: Beth Westlake, President
E-mail: president@smocking.org
Facebook: www.facebook.com/smockingartsguildofamerica
Instagram: www.instagram.com/smockingartsguildamerica
YouTube: www.youtube.com/channel/UCCNZQa0XCNSdme8zVNZqPNQ
Pinterest: www.pinterest.com/smockingartsguildamerica

Description: Works to preserve and foster the art of smocking and related needlework through education communication and quality workmanship. Conducts artisan program in four areas of study including smocking, embroidery and heirloom stitching. Offers correspondence courses. **Founded:** 1979. **Geographic Preference:** Multinational.

REFERENCE WORKS

4585 ■ *"11 Minutes That Rocked the Sneaker World"* in *Business Journal Portland (Vol. 30, February 14, 2014, No. 50, pp. 8)*
Pub: American City Business Journals, Inc.
Contact: Mike Olivieri, Executive Vice President

Released: Weekly. **Price:** $4, Introductory 4-week offer(Digital & Print). **Description:** The sale of the Nike Air Yeezy 2, the latest shoes from a partnership with artist Kanye West, sparked a social media debate on the importance of limited edition shoes for the Nike brand. The shoes sold out in 11 minutes and made their way to eBay for as much as $10,000. **Availability:** Print; Online.

4586 ■ *"Artscape Looks for Last Big Donations"* in *Baltimore Business Journal (Vol. 32, July 11, 2014, No. 10, pp. 4)*
Pub: American City Business Journals, Inc.
Contact: Mike Olivieri, Executive Vice President

Released: Weekly. **Price:** $4, introductory 4-week offer(Digital only). **Description:** Kathy Hornig, festivals director for Baltimore's Office of Promotion and the Arts, discusses last-minute efforts to raise the final $100,000 in donations for Artscape from mobile marketers and festival goers. The event, to be held July 18-23, 2014 in Baltimore, will focus on dance and movement. **Availability:** Print; Online.

4587 ■ *"Carving Passion, Talent Help Couple Craft Business on Wood-Rich Land"* in *Crain's Cleveland Business (October 8, 2007)*
Pub: Crain Communications Inc.
Contact: K. C. Crain, President

Ed: Sharon Schnall. **Description:** Profile of Wood-carved Art Gallery & Studio, a family-owned business which includes several ventures of the husband-and-wife team, Jim Stadtlander and Diane Harto. **Availability:** Online.

4588 ■ *"Craft Businesses That Make (the MOST) Money"* in *Made Urban (April 12, 2018)*
URL(s): www.madeurban.com/blog/craft-businesses-that-make-money/

Released: April 12, 2018. **Description:** If you are a crafter and engage in selling your crafts, are you considering all of your costs? It may surprise you how little profit, if any, you are making. Some crafts have a larger demand than others, so there is a bigger chance of making more money by selling those crafts. Included is a list of these types of crafts and a discussion about each one. **Availability:** Online.

4589 ■ *Crafted*
Released: 2015. **Description:** Documentary about five artisans who share a passion to create. **Availability:** Streaming.

4590 ■ *"A Decent Proposal"* in *Hawaii Business (Vol. 53, March 2008, No. 9, pp. 52)*
Pub: PacificBasin Communications
Contact: Chuck Tindle, Director
E-mail: chuckt@pacificbasin.net

Ed: Jacy L. Youn. **Description:** Bonnie Cooper and Brian Joy own Big Rock Manufacturing Inc., a stone manufacturing company, which sells carved rocks and bowls, lava benches, waterfalls, and Buddhas. Details about the company's growth are discussed. **Availability:** Print; Online.

4591 ■ *"Etsy Alternatives for Crafty Entrepreneurs"* in *Business News Daily (February 21, 2023)*
URL(s): www.businessnewsdaily.com/5287-etsy-alternatives-handmade-sites.html

Ed: Max Freedman. **Released:** February 21, 2023. **Description:** Sometimes the craft website Etsy is not the best option to sell your handmade crafts. Listed are various other sites to help you launch or expand your online business. **Availability:** Online.

4592 ■ *"From Craft Biz To Wholesale Giant"* in *Women Entrepreneur (January 19, 2009)*
Description: Advice is given on how to turn a small craft business into a full-time venture; tips to help one transition from a part-time designer to a full-time wholesaler and brand are also included.

4593 ■ *"Greg Lueck: Glass Blowing"* in *Inc. (Volume 32, December 2010, No. 10, pp. 36)*
Pub: Mansueto Ventures L.L.C.
Contact: Stephanie Mehta, Chief Executive Officer

Ed: April Joyner. **Description:** Profile of Greg Lueck, partner and COO of Centerstance, a tech consulting firm in Portland, Oregon. Lueck opened Firehouse Glass, a studio that provides workspace and equipment for glass blowers. He says glass blowing serves as a welcome counterbalance to the cerebral work he does at the office. **Availability:** Online.

4594 ■ *Handmade Business--Show List*
Pub: Handmade Business
Contact: Diana Jones, Publisher
URL(s): handmade-business.com/craft-show-listings

Ed: Bernadette Finnerty. **Description:** Publication includes list of forthcoming arts and crafts shows, articles for craft industry. Includes articles for craft industry. **Entries include:** Show name, name and address of contact, sizes, fees, attendance. **Arrangement:** Chronological. **Availability:** Print.

4595 ■ *"Innovation Can Be Imperative for Those in Hands-On Trades"* in *Crain's Cleveland Business (Vol. 28, November 12, 2007, No. 45)*
Pub: Crain Communications Inc.
Contact: K. C. Crain, President

Ed: Harriet Tramer. **Description:** Discusses the importance of networking and innovative marketing concerning those in art and restoration trades. **Availability:** Online.

4596 ■ *"Jo-Ann Fabric and Craft Stores Joins ArtFire.com to Offer Free Online Craft Marketplace"* in *Marketwired (January 26, 2010)*
Pub: Comtex News Network Inc.
Contact: Kan Devnani, President

Description: Jo-Ann Fabric and Craft Stores has entered into a partnership with ArtFire.com which will provide sewers and crafters all the tools they need in order to make and sell their products from an online venue. **Availability:** Print; Online.

4597 ■ *"Laws for Selling Handmade Soap & Cosmetics"* in *Made Urban (July 6, 2015)*
URL(s): www.madeurban.com/blog/selling_handmade_soap_these_are_the_cosmetic_label/

Released: July 06, 2015. **Description:** For crafters who make cosmetics, soaps, and other like products, this is a guide to the laws that must be followed when creating labels. US and Canadian law is discussed. **Availability:** Online.

4598 ■ *"Let the Light Shine"* in *Retail Merchandiser (Vol. 51, July-August 2011, No. 4, pp. 74)*
Description: For over 25 years, The Thomas Kinkade Company has been producing art that is collected by both old and young, and is the only company that publishes Thomas Kinkade art. **Availability:** Print; Online.

4599 ■ *"Millennials Are Ready for Crafting, but Is the $36B Crafting Industry Ready for Them?"* in *Forbes*
URL(s): www.forbes.com/sites/pamdanziger/2018/07/08/millennials-are-ready-for-crafting-but-is-the-36b-crafting-industry-ready-for-them/#5a660ad73a2c

Ed: Pamela N. Danziger. **Released:** July 08, 2018. **Description:** Crafting is trending upwards, especially with millennials who are looking for ways to personalize items and to be creative, however, craft stores haven't adapted that well to this new generation. Some, like Joann Fabric and Craft Stores, have been slowly adapting and they recently launched a new concept store. **Availability:** Online.

4600 ■ *"Off the Wall: Keith Collins' Larger-Than-Life Designs"* in *Black Enterprise (Vol. 37, February 2007, No. 7, pp. 138)*
Pub: Earl G. Graves Ltd.
Contact: Earl Graves, Jr., President

Ed: Sonia Alleyne. **Description:** Profile of Keith Collins, an entrepreneur who makes carpets for the likes of Jay Leno, Nicolas Cage, Arnold Schwarzenegger, Janet Jackson, and Will Smith. Collins is passionate about this ancient art form and saw a future in it despite the negative feedback from those around him. **Availability:** Online.

4601 ■ *"Partnering for Success"* in *Art Business News (Vol. 36, October 2009, No. 10, pp. 4)*
Description: In such a volatile economy many savvy artists and gallery owners are turning to out-of-the-box partnerships for continued success; these partnerships are also pervading the Internet, especially with such social media networks as Facebook and Twitter where artists and businesses can develop a loyal following. **Availability:** PDF; Online.

4602 ■ *"Pick A Name, Not Just Any Name"* in *Women Entrepreneur (December 17, 2008)*
Description: Craft business owners must choose a name that sounds personal since customers who buy hand-made products want to feel that they are buying from an individual rather than an institution. Tips for choosing a name are provided.

4603 ■ *Seven Days in the Art World*
Pub: W.W. Norton & Company Ltd.
Contact: Stanley Kubrick, Director

Ed: Sarah Thornton. **Price:** $17.95, paperback. **Description:** A sociologist renders the interplay among buyers, critics, curators and makers of contemporary art. **Availability:** Print.

4604 ■ *"Side Income: Is It a Hobby or a Business?"* in *Money Under 30 (March 12, 2019)*
URL(s): www.moneyunder30.com/side-income-hobby-or-a-business

Ed: Amber Gilstrap. **Released:** March 12, 2019. **Description:** A practical discussion of how to determine if your hobby that you love is actually a business. The IRS has some guidelines and questions, and if you meet certain criteria, you can then deduct expenses and report it to the IRS. **Availability:** Online.

4605 ■ *Supermaker: Crafting Business on Your Own Terms*
Released: September 08, 2020. **Description:** A guide for entrepreneurs who are interested in starting a small business, especially crafting or maker-centered. Sections on branding, product development, social media marketing, scaling, PR, and customer engagement are included. **Availability:** E-book.

4606 ■ *Tasty's Made By Hand*
Released: 2018. **Description:** A showcase of artisans who demonstrate how to make America's favorite foods from scratch. **Availability:** Streaming.

4607 ■ *"Tattooed Bellwethers of Economic Development" in Austin Business Journal (Vol. 34, May 2, 2014, No. 11, pp. A4)*
Pub: American City Business Journals, Inc.
Contact: Mike Olivieri, Executive Vice President
Released: Weekly. **Price:** $4, Introductory 4-week offer(Digital & Print). **Description:** The creative community's art-centered business have helped Austin, Texas' growth by moving into transitional areas with low rents. Their kind of pioneering spirit primes the area for later commercial and residential development. The city's assistance programs for creative enterprises are also presented. **Availability:** Print; Online.

4608 ■ *"This Is Your Brain on Crafting" in CNN.com (January 5, 2015)*
URL(s): www.cnn.com/2014/03/25/health/brain-crafting-benefits/index.html
Ed: Jacque Wilson. **Released:** January 05, 2015. **Description:** A report on how participating in crafting can ease anxiety, depression, and even chronic pain. **Availability:** Online.

4609 ■ *"You Call It Craft, I Call It Art" in The New York Times (August 23, 2019)*
URL(s): www.nytimes.com/2019/08/23/arts/design/folk-art-market-santa-fe.html
Ed: Guy Trebay. **Released:** August 23, 2019. **Description:** Explores the creative process of craftspeople and discusses the shifting perceptions of art, folk art, and crafting within the context of social media. With the rise of social media, more people are exposed to new ideas and various artistic work. **Availability:** Online.

STATISTICAL SOURCES

4610 ■ *U.S. The Arts and Crafts Consumer Market Report 2021*
URL(s): store.mintel.com/report/us-the-arts-and-crafts-consumer-market-report
Price: $4,366.35. **Description:** Downloadable report discussing data about the arts and crafts industry and how US consumers are participating in that market. Report includes an executive summary, interactive databook, PowerPoint presentation, infographic overview, report PDF, and previous years data. **Availability:** PDF.

TRADE PERIODICALS

4611 ■ *American Ceramic Society Bulletin*
Pub: American Ceramic Society
Contact: Mark Mecklenborg, Executive Director
E-mail: mmecklenborg@ceramics.org
URL(s): ceramics.org/publications-resources/the-bulletin-of-the-american-ceramic-society
Ed: Eileen De Guire. **Released:** Monthly; except for February, July, and November. **Price:** $150, Nonmembers for international; $3, U.S. and Canada for per item; $8, for per item; $6, Other countries for per item; $135, Nonmembers for 1 year; $100, for online; $100, Single issue; $6, Members for January–December; $15, Nonmembers for nonmember. **Description:** Contains items of interest to the ceramics community, and provides current information on RandD, technology, manufacturing, engineered ceramics, fuel cells, nanotechnology, glass, refractories, environmental concerns, whitewares, etc. Bulletin publishes "the Glass Researcher" as a quarterly feature section. The December issue of Bulletin includes ceramic Source, an annual buyer's guide. **Availability:** Print; Download; Online; PDF.

4612 ■ *Ceramics Monthly*
Pub: American Ceramic Society
Contact: Mark Mecklenborg, Executive Director
E-mail: mmecklenborg@ceramics.org
URL(s): ceramicartsnetwork.org/ceramics-monthly
Facebook: www.facebook.com/CeramicsMonthlyMagazine
X (Twitter): twitter.com/ceramicsmonthly
Instagram: www.instagram.com/ceramics_monthly
Pinterest: www.pinterest.com/CeramicsMonthly
Ed: Holly Goring. **Released:** 10/year; Published monthly except for the June/July/August summer issue. **Price:** $41.99, U.S. for print only; $65, Canada for print only; $76, for print only rest of world; $56, U.S. for annual; $80, Canada for annual; $89, for annual rest of world. **Description:** Consumer magazine containing ceramic art and craft. Features articles on ceramic artists, exhibitions, production processes, critical commentary, book and video reviews, clay and glaze recipes, and kiln designs. **Availability:** Print; PDF; Online.

4613 ■ *The China Painter*
Pub: World Organization of China Painters
Contact: Nancy Crites, Contact
URL(s): www.wocporg.com/magazine.html
Ed: Pat Dickerson. **Released:** Quarterly **Price:** $50, Single issue for per year; $67, for out side of US. **Description:** Magazine about china painting for students, teachers, and artists. **Availability:** Print; Online.

4614 ■ *Chip Chats*
Pub: National Wood Carvers Association
Contact: Tim Crawford, President
URL(s): chipchats.org/About
Released: Bimonthly **Description:** Journal for amateur and professional wood carvers. **Availability:** Print; Online.

4615 ■ *Craftideas*
Pub: Amos Media Co.
Contact: John M. Garmhausen, Contact
URL(s): www.amosmedia.com/market-place.html
Description: Craft magazine. **Availability:** Print; Online.

4616 ■ *The Home Shop Machinist*
Pub: The Home Shop Machinist
Contact: Gretchen Christensen, Manager, Advertising
E-mail: gretchen@villagepress.com
URL(s): homeshopmachinist.net/magazine/about
Ed: George Bulliss. **Released:** Bimonthly **Price:** $61.95, U.S. for 2 years 12 issue print and online; $86.95, U.S. for 3 years 18 issue print and online; $32.95, U.S. for 1 year 6 issue print and online; $52.95, Canada for print and online first class; $113.95, Canada for print and online 3 year; $50.95, U.S. for print and online 1st class; $42.95, Canada for print and online 1 year; $80.95, Canada for print and online 2 year; $80.95, for print and online 1st class foreign; $123.95, for print and online 3 year foreign; $47.95, for print and online 1 year foreign; $89.95, for print and online 2 year foreign. **Description:** Magazine for the amateur small shop machinist. **Availability:** Print; Online.

4617 ■ *Loomsong*
Pub: Atlantic Spinners and Handweavers
Contact: Scott Manor, Contact
URL(s): www.ashguild.ca/loomsong
Released: 8/year; 2 special sample issues. **Description:** Discusses weaving and spinning. Recurring features include a calendar of events, reports of meetings, news of educational opportunities, book reviews. **Availability:** Print.

4618 ■ *Machinist's Workshop*
Pub: VP Demand Creation Services
Contact: Dave Moore, President
URL(s): machinistsworkshop.net
Ed: Kelly Wagner, George Bulliss. **Released:** Bimonthly **Price:** $78.95, for three year; $55.95, for two year; $29.95, for per year; $5, for back issue; $8.50, for print. **Description:** Magazine describing metal working techniques and projects for hobby machinists. **Availability:** Print; Online; Download.

4619 ■ *Painting*
Contact: Irene Mueller, Editor
E-mail: imueller@amoscraft.com
URL(s): paintingmagazine.net
Ed: Irene Mueller. **Released:** Bimonthly **Price:** $24.95, Individuals online only; $26.95, Individuals print and online; $34.45, Canada print and online; $41.95, Other countries print and online. **Description:** Magazine for tole and decorative painters, featuring columns, and how-to and educational articles. **Availability:** Print; Online.

4620 ■ *Soft Dolls & Animals*
URL(s): www.scottpublications.com/catalog/product_info.php/products_id/211
Price: $2, online. **Description:** Magazine covering fabric dolls, teddy bears, and other fabric figures for hobbyists and crafters.

4621 ■ *Woodshop News: The News Magazine for Professional Woodworkers*
Pub: Cruz Bay Publishing Inc.
Contact: Andrew W. Clurman, President
E-mail: aclurman@aimmedia.com
URL(s): www.woodshopnews.com
Linkedin: www.linkedin.com/company/woodshop-news
X (Twitter): x.com/woodshopnews
Ed: Tod Riggio. **Released:** Monthly **Price:** $10, for 1 year (12 issues); $18, Two years for (24 issues). **Description:** Newspaper (tabloid) focusing on people and businesses involved in woodworking. **Availability:** Print; PDF; Online.

4622 ■ *Woodsmith*
Pub: Active Interest Media
Contact: Andrew W. Clurman, President
E-mail: aclurman@aimmedia.com
URL(s): www.woodsmith.comwww.aimmedia.com/woodsmith
Facebook: www.facebook.com/woodsmithmagazine
X (Twitter): x.com/WoodsmithMag
Instagram: www.instagram.com/WoodsmithMagazine
YouTube: www.youtube.com/channel/UCPBZdSldE4xJub4tagay4Jw
Pinterest: www.pinterest.com/woodsmithmedia
Ed: Terry J. Strohman. **Released:** Bimonthly; issue 274. **Price:** $10, for one year, 6 issues International; $31, for 2 years (12 issues); $29, for per year; $7.95, for national; $7.99, Single issue. **Description:** Magazine for woodworking hobbyists. **Availability:** Print; Online.

4623 ■ *Wool Gathering*
Pub: Schoolhouse Press
Contact: Alex Swansen, Contact
URL(s): www.schoolhousepress.com/patterns/wool-gathering-subscription-issues.html
Price: $25, U.S.; $30, for international. **Description:** Provides hand-knitters with original designs by Elizabeth Zimmermann and Meg Swansen. Includes reviews of knitting trends, information on wools, book reviews, and video news. **Availability:** Online.

VIDEO/AUDIO MEDIA

4624 ■ *Bookkeeping for Creatives with Alisha Thomas*
URL(s): www.makinggoodpodcast.com/episodes/244
Ed: Lauren Tilden. **Released:** June 25, 2024. **Description:** Explains how creative small business owners can manage and understand their finances.

4625 ■ *The Business of Craft with Abby Glassenberg*
URL(s): www.makinggoodpodcast.com/episodes/257
Ed: Lauren Tilden. **Released:** September 03, 2024. **Description:** Podcast explains what successful small craft businesses have in common, how to stay in it long term, and the role of mindset.

4626 ■ *Elevated Entrepreneurship: Art as a Business with Jessica Abel*
URL(s): mikemichalowicz.com/podcast/episode-244-with-jessica-abel
Ed: Mike Michalowiicz. **Released:** June 17, 2019. **Description:** Podcast explains how artist-owners need to embrace financials to continue to create art.

4627 ■ *The How of Business: Dyan Jahraus - Etsy Business*
URL(s): www.thehowofbusiness.com/529-dylan-jahraus-etsy-business
Ed: Henry Lopez. **Released:** July 15, 2024. **Description:** Podcast discusses starting an Etsy business.

4628 ■ *The How of Business: William Warren - The Conquering Creative*
URL(s): www.thehowofbusiness.com/472-william-warren-conquering-creative
Ed: Henry Lopez. **Released:** August 15, 2023. **Description:** Podcast discusses leveraging creativity in a small business.

4629 ■ *Trends and Opportunities for Makers and Retail Businesses with Carla Pellicano of Faire*
URL(s): beingboss.club/podcast/trends-and-opportunities-for-makers-and-retail-businesses
Ed: Emily Thompson. **Released:** November 08, 2022. **Description:** Podcast discusses the unique struggles for small business retailers and makers.

TRADE SHOWS AND CONVENTIONS

4630 ■ CHA Create and Connect Conference and Trade Show
Association For Creative Industries (AFCI)
330 N Wabash Ave., Ste. 2000
Chicago, IL 60611
Ph: (312)321-6811
Co. E-mail: info@creativeindustries.org
URL: http://creativeindustries.org
Contact: Peter Finn, Executive Director
E-mail: pfinn@creativeindustries.org
URL(s): www.craftandhobby.org/eweb/DynamicPage.aspx?WebKey=E94EE351-A89C-492E-888F-A45138487AA6
Frequency: Annual. **Description:** Crafts, ceramics, floral accessories, dollhouse miniatures, aromatics, art materials and frames, jewelry findings, fabrics, needlework and quilting supplies, home decor, rubber stamps, stencils and scrapbooking supplies. **Audience:** Owners, corporate officers and buyers from craft, general merchandise stores, wholesalers, professional crafters and CHA professionals. **Principal Exhibits:** Crafts, ceramics, floral accessories, dollhouse miniatures, aromatics, art materials and frames, jewelry findings, fabrics, needlework and quilting supplies, home decor, rubber stamps, stencils and scrapbooking supplies.

4631 ■ TNNA Winter Trade Show
Offinger Management Co.
1100-H Brandywine Blvd.
Zanesville, OH 43701-7303
Ph: (740)452-4541
Fax: (740)452-2552
URL: http://www.offinger.com
URL(s): www.tnna.org/?page=Winter
Description: Upscale needle art products such as needlepoint, knitting, counted thread, embroidery, and crochet supplies as well as related products such as buttons, beads, trims, frames, fibers, books, etc. **Audience:** Needlearts professionals and the public. **Principal Exhibits:** Upscale needle art products such as needlepoint, knitting, counted thread, embroidery, and crochet supplies as well as related products such as buttons, beads, trims, frames, fibers, books, etc. **Telecommunication Services:** info@tnna.org.

FRANCHISES AND BUSINESS OPPORTUNITIES

4632 ■ Crock A Doodle
299 Wayne Gretzky Pky.
Brantford, ON, Canada N3R 8A5
Ph: (519)752-8080
Co. E-mail: headoffice@crockadoo.com
URL: http://crockadoodle.com
Contact: Annette Brennan, Founder
X (Twitter): x.com/crockadoodle
Instagram: www.instagram.com/crockadoodlepyop
YouTube: www.youtube.com/user/CrockADoodlePottery
Pinterest: www.pinterest.ca/crockadoodle
Description: Provider of pottery painting services for kids birthday parties, ladies nights, teambuilding and corporate events. **Founded:** 2002. **Equity Capital Needed:** $75,000-$120,000. **Franchise Fee:** $20,000. **Training:** Provides 2 weeks plus ongoing support.

4633 ■ The Painted Penguin L.L.C.
6115 Monroe Ct.
Morton Grove, IL 60053
Ph: (847)764-0891
Co. E-mail: franchise@thepaintedpenguin.com
URL: http://www.paintedpenguin.net
Contact: Helene Safford, Vice President
Facebook: www.facebook.com/ThePaintedPenguinLLC
Description: Offers the opportunity to get in on the ground floor of the booming craft industry with a well respected, growth oriented franchise that combines business ownership with a fun environment. **Founded:** 2000. **Franchised:** 2003. **Training:** Comprehensive training, marketing guidance, site selection assistance and other on-going support.

PUBLICATIONS

4634 ■ *Handmade Business*
N7528 Aanstad Rd.
Iola, WI 54945
Ph: (715)445-5000
Free: 800-331-0038
Fax: (715)445-4053
Co. E-mail: customercare@jonespublishing.us
URL: http://handmade-business.com
Contact: Diana Jones, Publisher
URL(s): handmade-business.com/archive
Facebook: www.facebook.com/HandmadeBusinessMag
X (Twitter): x.com/handmadebizmag
Instagram: www.instagram.com/explore/tags/handmadebusinessmagazine
Ed: Stephanie Hintz. **Released:** Monthly **Price:** $10, Single issue. **Description:** Business Magazine for Professional Craft Community. **Availability:** Print; Online.

COMPUTERIZED DATABASES

4635 ■ *Art on Screen Database™*
Program for Art on Film Inc.
c/o Pratt SILS, 200 Willoughby Ave.
Brooklyn, NY 11205
Ph: (718)399-4506
Fax: (718)399-4507
Co. E-mail: info@artfilm.org
URL: http://www.artfilm.org
Contact: J. Paul Getty Trust, Founder
URL(s): www.artfilm.org/aosdb.htm
Availability: CD-ROM; Online. **Type:** Directory.

4636 ■ *Consumer InSite*
Type: Full-text.

4637 ■ *Humanities Full Text™*
EBSCO Information Services
10 Estes St.
Ipswich, MA 01938
Ph: (978)356-6500
Free: 800-653-2726
Co. E-mail: information@ebsco.com
URL: http://www.ebsco.com
Contact: Tim Collins, Chief Executive Officer
URL(s): www.ebsco.com/products/research-databases/humanities-full-text
Availability: Online. **Type:** Full-text; Bibliographic.

LIBRARIES

4638 ■ American Craft Council (ACC) - Library
1224 Marshall St. NE, Ste. 200
Minneapolis, MN 55413
Ph: (612)206-3100
Fax: (612)355-2330
Co. E-mail: council@craftcouncil.org
URL: http://craftcouncil.org
Contact: Gary J. Smith, Chairman
Facebook: www.facebook.com/CraftCouncil
X (Twitter): x.com/craftcouncil
Instagram: www.instagram.com/craftcouncil
YouTube: www.youtube.com/user/AmericanCraftCouncil
Pinterest: www.pinterest.com/craftcouncil
Description: Promotes understanding and appreciation of contemporary American craft. **Scope:** American craft. **Services:** Open to public for on-site visits by appointment only. **Founded:** 1943. **Holdings:** 20,000 books; 3,000 photographs; 700 periodicals; 150 current subscriptions; newsletters; slides; correspondence; other ephemera. **Publications:** *American Craft* (Quarterly); *American Craft--News Section* (Bimonthly); *American Craft Council--Crafts Fair Directory*; *American Craft--American Craft Guide to Craft Galleries & Shops USA Issue*. **Educational Activities:** ACC Craft Show Baltimore (Annual); ACC Craft Show San Francisco (Annual). **Awards:** ACC College of Fellows (Irregular); ACC Gold Medal for Consummate Craftsmanship (Biennial); Aileen Osborn Webb Award for Philanthropy (Irregular). **Geographic Preference:** National.

4639 ■ California College of the Arts Libraries - Meyer Library
Meyer Library, 5212 Broadway
Oakland, CA 94618
URL: http://libraries.cca.edu/about-us/about-us/policies/collection-development-policy
Description: Collections begin from that time and focus on the fine arts and visual and critical studies. Special Collections include artists' books, the Hamaguchi Study Print Collection, Faculty Development Collection, Games Collection, CCA / C College Archives and the Capp Street Project archive. **Scope:** Fine arts; architecture; design; visual and critical studies; writing and literature. **Services:** Open to the public. **Founded:** 1907. **Subscriptions:** magazines newspapers periodicals (includes journals) Books; records.

4640 ■ Cleveland Institute of Art (CIA) - Jessica R. Gund Memorial Library
11610 Euclid Ave.
Cleveland, OH 44106
Ph: (216)421-7418
Co. E-mail: marketing@cia.edu
URL: http://www.cia.edu/library
Contact: Kathryn Heidemann, President
Facebook: www.facebook.com/cleinstituteart
Linkedin: www.linkedin.com/edu/school
X (Twitter): x.com/cleinstituteart
Instagram: www.instagram.com/cleinstituteart
YouTube: www.youtube.com/user/cleinstituteart
Scope: Visual art; design; and craft. **Services:** Interlibrary loan; copying; library open to the public. **Founded:** 1882. **Holdings:** 47,000 books, exhibition catalogs, and CD-ROMs; 10,000 bound periodical volumes; 125,000 slides; 9,000 pictures; 37 volumes and boxes of archival materials; 4,000 reels of microfilm; 15,000 microfiche; 600 videotapes, DVDs and films; 1,600 sound recordings.

4641 ■ Haystack Mountain School of Crafts Library
PO Box 518
Deer Isle, ME 04627
Ph: (207)348-2306
Co. E-mail: haystack@haystack-mtn.org
URL: http://www.haystack-mtn.org
Contact: Ayumi Horie, President
Facebook: www.facebook.com/Haystack-Mountain-School-of-Crafts-90810472119
Instagram: www.instagram.com/haystack_school

YouTube: www.youtube.com/channel/UC25-NaGw3xPfkcTejEYqzzg
Scope: Fine arts; weaving; design and architecture. **Founded:** 1950. **Holdings:** 1,000 Books; Craft; Art; Design and Architecture.

4642 ■ Manitoba Crafts Museum & Library (MCML) - Gladys Chown Memorial Library
Ste. 1-329 Cumberland Ave.
Winnipeg, MB, Canada R3B 1T2
URL: http://c2centreforcraft.ca/about-mcml
Scope: Historical. **Services:** Copying; library open to the public. **Founded:** 1930. **Holdings:** 3,500 volumes. **Subscriptions:** 1,500 journals and other serials.

4643 ■ Museum of Contemporary Craft Library
724 NW Davis St.
Portland, OR 97209
Ph: (503)223-2654
Fax: (503)223-0190
Co. E-mail: info@museumofcontemporarycraft.org
URL: http://www.museumofcontemporarycraft.org
Contact: Kathy Abraham, President
Scope: Modern and contemporary craft heritage. **Services:** Library open during Museum hours. **Founded:** 1937. **Holdings:** 1,300 objects of modern and contemporary craft ; photographs; slides; ephemera.

4644 ■ Parsons School of Design - Adam & Sophie Gimbel Design Library
66 5th Ave.
New York, NY 10011
URL: http://www.newschool.edu
Contact: David E. van Zandt, President
Scope: Education materials. **Services:** Interlibrary loan. **Founded:** 1896. **Holdings:** Figures not available.

4645 ■ University of Hartford - William H. Mortensen Library - Anne Bunce Cheney Art Collection
200 Bloomfield Ave.
West Hartford, CT 06117
URL: http://www.hartford.edu/academics/library/about-us/libraries-and-collections.aspx
Description: Mortensen Library houses the Anne Bunce Cheney Art Collection. It consists of: - Art books and journals, exhibition catalogs, guidebooks, and mounted reproductions. - Books and journals are filed in the appropriate areas of the Mortensen Library general collection. - Wadsworth Atheneum catalogs are in the Reserves area on the main level. - Reproductions are in the Art Plates Room on the upper level. - Periodicals and reference books, as well as selected materials held on Reserve at Circulation, are for library use only. **Scope:** History of the university of Hartford and its predecessor schools. **Services:** Interlibrary loan. **Founded:** 1963.

Craft/Hobby Business

START-UP INFORMATION

4646 ■ *Careers for Self-Starters and Other Entrepreneurial Types*
Released: Second Edition. **Description:** Advice to entrepreneurs wishing to start their own small company. Tips for turning hobbies into job skills are included. **Availability:** Print.

4647 ■ *How to Start a Home-based Craft Business*
Ed: Kenn Oberrecht, Patrice Lewis. **Released:** Sixth edition. **Price:** $18.99, e-book; Paperback. **Description:** Step-by-step guide for starting and growing a home-based craft business. **Availability:** Print.

4648 ■ *Scrapbooking for Profit: Cashing in on Retail, Home-Based and Internet Opportunities*
Pub: Allworth Press
Contact: Tad Crawford, Founder
Ed: Rebecca Pittman. **Released:** June 01, 2005. **Price:** $16.95, paperback; $19.99, Ebook; $19.95, Paperback. **Description:** Eleven strategies for starting a scrapbooking business, including brick-and-mortar stores, home-based businesses, and online retail and wholesale outlets. **Availability:** E-book; Print.

4649 ■ *Setting Up Your Ceramic Studio: Ideas and Plans from Working Artists*
Released: First edition. **Description:** Floor plans and advice for setting up a creative ceramics studio are provided, focusing on equipment, workflow, and safety issues. **Availability:** Print.

4650 ■ *Soul Proprietor: 101 Lessons from a Lifestyle Entrepreneur*
Price: $9.95. **Description:** More than 100 tips and stores to inspire and guide any would-be entrepreneur to earn a living from a favorite hobby or passion. **Availability:** E-book; Online.

4651 ■ *Start Your Crafting Business*
Ed: Mary Meinking. **Description:** A guide to setting up your own craft business. **Availability:** E-book.

ASSOCIATIONS AND OTHER ORGANIZATIONS

4652 ■ **American Craft Council (ACC) - Library**
1224 Marshall St. NE, Ste. 200
Minneapolis, MN 55413
Ph: (612)206-3100
Fax: (612)355-2330
Co. E-mail: council@craftcouncil.org
URL: http://craftcouncil.org
Contact: Gary J. Smith, Chairman
Facebook: www.facebook.com/CraftCouncil
X (Twitter): x.com/craftcouncil
Instagram: www.instagram.com/craftcouncil
YouTube: www.youtube.com/user/AmericanCraftCouncil
Pinterest: www.pinterest.com/craftcouncil
Description: Promotes understanding and appreciation of contemporary American craft. **Scope:** American craft. **Services:** Open to public for on-site visits by appointment only. **Founded:** 1943. **Holdings:** 20,000 books; 3,000 photographs; 700 periodicals; 150 current subscriptions; newsletters; slides; correspondence; other ephemera. **Publications:** *American Craft* (Quarterly); *American Craft--News Section* (Bimonthly); *American Craft Council--Crafts Fair Directory*; *American Craft--American Craft Guide to Craft Galleries & Shops USA Issue*. **Educational Activities:** ACC Craft Show Baltimore (Annual); ACC Craft Show San Francisco (Annual). **Awards:** ACC College of Fellows (Irregular); ACC Gold Medal for Consummate Craftsmanship (Biennial); Aileen Osborn Webb Award for Philanthropy (Irregular). **Geographic Preference:** National.

4653 ■ **American Sewing Guild (ASG)**
9660 Hillcroft, Ste. 510
Houston, TX 77096
Ph: (713)729-3000
Fax: (713)721-9230
Co. E-mail: info@asg.org
URL: http://www.asg.org
Contact: Margo Martin, Executive Director
Facebook: www.facebook.com/sewingguild
Instagram: www.instagram.com/asguildhq
YouTube: www.youtube.com/channel/UCaNyoekwXVAJMn18tS4mUsg
Pinterest: www.pinterest.com/asghq
Description: Home sewers and people interested in sewing. Provides current sewing information and advice through lectures, demonstrations, classes, seminars, and fashion shows. Seeks to improve communication between home sewers and sewing industry. Encourages the development of neighborhood workshop groups. **Founded:** 1978. **Geographic Preference:** National.

4654 ■ **Coalition of Handcrafted Entrepreneurs (COHE)**
URL: http://www.coalitionofhandcraftedentrepreneurs.com
X (Twitter): x.com/YourCOHE
Description: Seeks to support small businesses in the craft soap and cosmetic industry, whose products are typically made in small batches and sold at farmers markets, home parties, community fundraisers, and craft shows. Advocates for a "small producer rule" that provides exemptions to Food and Drug Administration (FDA) requirements regarding manufacturing facilities, products, and ingredients.

4655 ■ **Embroiderers' Guild of America (EGA) - The Dorothy Babcock Memorial Library**
1205 E Washington St., Ste. 104
Louisville, KY 40206
Ph: (502)589-6956
Fax: (502)584-7900
URL: http://egausa.org
Contact: Janet Noble, President
Facebook: www.facebook.com/EGAUSA
X (Twitter): x.com/egausa
Instagram: www.instagram.com/ega_usa
YouTube: www.youtube.com/user/EGAUSA
Pinterest: www.pinterest.com/ega_usa
Description: People interested in the art of needlework. Aims to set and maintain high standards of design, color, and workmanship in all kinds of embroidery. **Scope:** Embroidery. **Founded:** 1958. **Holdings:** 2,000 needlework books, historic materials. **Publications:** *Needle Arts* (Quarterly); *Inside EGA* (Quarterly); *EGA Needle Arts Magazine* (Quarterly). **Awards:** EGA Gold Thread Award (Annual); EGA Research Fellowship (Annual). **Geographic Preference:** National.

REFERENCE WORKS

4656 ■ *"Craft Businesses That Make (the MOST) Money" in Made Urban (April 12, 2018)*
URL(s): www.madeurban.com/blog/craft-businesses-that-make-money/
Released: April 12, 2018. **Description:** If you are a crafter and engage in selling your crafts, are you considering all of your costs? It may surprise you how little profit, if any, you are making. Some crafts have a larger demand than others, so there is a bigger chance of making more money by selling those crafts. Included is a list of these types of crafts and a discussion about each one. **Availability:** Online.

4657 ■ *"Greg Lueck: Glass Blowing" in Inc. (Volume 32, December 2010, No. 10, pp. 36)*
Pub: Mansueto Ventures L.L.C
Contact: Stephanie Mehta, Chief Executive Officer
Ed: April Joyner. **Description:** Profile of Greg Lueck, partner and COO of Centerstance, a tech consulting firm in Portland, Oregon. Lueck opened Firehouse Glass, a studio that provides workspace and equipment for glass blowers. He says glass blowing serves as a welcome counterbalance to the cerebral work he does at the office. **Availability:** Online.

4658 ■ *Handmade Business--Show List*
Pub: Handmade Business
Contact: Diana Jones, Publisher
URL(s): handmade-business.com/craft-show-listings
Ed: Bernadette Finnerty. **Description:** Publication includes list of forthcoming arts and crafts shows, articles for craft industry. Includes articles for craft industry. **Entries include:** Show name, name and address of contact, sizes, fees, attendance. **Arrangement:** Chronological. **Availability:** Print.

4659 ■ *Hobby Merchandiser Annual Trade Directory*
Pub: Hobby Publications Inc.
URL(s): www.hobbymerchandiser.com/about.htm
Released: Annual **Price:** $30, Individuals. **Description:** Covers manufacturers, wholesalers, industry suppliers, and publishers of books and periodicals in the hobby trade industry. **Entries include:** For manufacturers--Company name, address, phone,

name and title of contact. For wholesalers--Company name, address, phone, specialty, geographical area covered. For publishers--Company name, address, phone, name and title of contact; types of books, periodicals, or other media published or produced. For industry suppliers--Company name, address, phone, name and title of contact, product. **Arrangement:** Manufacturers, publishers, and suppliers are alphabetical; wholesalers are geographical. **Indexes:** Product. **Availability:** PDF.

4660 ■ *"Jo-Ann Fabric and Craft Stores Joins ArtFire.com to Offer Free Online Craft Marketplace" in Marketwired (January 26, 2010)*
Pub: Comtex News Network Inc.
Contact: Kan Devnani, President
Description: Jo-Ann Fabric and Craft Stores has entered into a partnership with ArtFire.com which will provide sewers and crafters all the tools they need in order to make and sell their products from an online venue. **Availability:** Print; Online.

4661 ■ *"Jo-Ann Launches Quilt Your Colors Contest to Celebrate National Sewing Month" in Marketwired (September 10, 2010)*
Pub: Comtex News Network Inc.
Contact: Kan Devnani, President
Description: Jo-Ann Fabric and Craft Stores featured a contest to create a quilt in order to promote National Sewing Month.

4662 ■ *"Laws for Selling Handmade Soap & Cosmetics" in Made Urban (July 6, 2015)*
URL(s): www.madeurban.com/blog/selling_handmade_soap_these_are_the_cosmetic_label/
Released: July 06, 2015. **Description:** For crafters who make cosmetics, soaps, and other like products, this is a guide to the laws that must be followed when creating labels. US and Canadian law is discussed. **Availability:** Online.

4663 ■ *"Sewing Is a Life Skill; Teaching To Sew Is An Art" in Virginia-Pilot (August 31, 2010)*
Pub: The Virginian-Pilot
Contact: Kevin Goyette, Director
E-mail: kgoyette@dailypress.com
Ed: Jamesetta M. Walker. **Description:** In conjunction with National Sewing Month, the American Sewing Guild is sponsoring a two-day workshop featuring Stephanie Kimura. **Availability:** Print; Online.

4664 ■ *"Side Income: Is It a Hobby or a Business?" in Money Under 30 (March 12, 2019)*
URL(s): www.moneyunder30.com/side-income-hobby-or-a-business
Ed: Amber Gilstrap. **Released:** March 12, 2019. **Description:** A practical discussion of how to determine if your hobby that you love is actually a business. The IRS has some guidelines and questions, and if you meet certain criteria, you can then deduct expenses and report it to the IRS. **Availability:** Online.

4665 ■ *Supermaker: Crafting Business on Your Own Terms*
Released: September 08, 2020. **Description:** A guide for entrepreneurs who are interested in starting a small business, especially crafting or maker-centered. Sections on branding, product development, social media marketing, scaling, PR, and customer engagement are included. **Availability:** E-book.

STATISTICAL SOURCES

4666 ■ *RMA Annual Statement Studies*
Pub: Risk Management Association
Contact: Nancy Foster, President
Released: Annual. **Description:** Contains composite balance sheets and income statements for more than 360 industries, including the accounting, auditing, and bookkeeping industries. Also contains five years of comparative historical data for discerning trends. Includes 16 commonly used ratios, computed for most of the size groupings for nearly every industry.

4667 ■ *U.S. The Arts and Crafts Consumer Market Report 2021*
URL(s): store.mintel.com/report/us-the-arts-and-crafts-consumer-market-report
Price: $4,366.35. **Description:** Downloadable report discussing data about the arts and crafts industry and how US consumers are participating in that market. Report includes an executive summary, interactive databook, PowerPoint presentation, infographic overview, report PDF, and previous years data. **Availability:** PDF.

TRADE PERIODICALS

4668 ■ *American Craft*
Pub: American Craft Council
Contact: Gary J. Smith, Chairman
URL(s): www.craftcouncil.org/magazine/american-craft
Released: Quarterly **Price:** $12, Single issue. **Description:** Journal covering contemporary crafts. **Availability:** Print; Online.

4669 ■ *Antique Bottle & Glass Collector*
Pub: Antique Bottle and Glass Collector
Contact: Jim Hagenbuch, Founder
URL(s): www.fohbc.org/bottles-extras
Released: Bimonthly **Price:** $145, for first class mail 3 years w/1 associate; $125, for standard mail 3 years w/1 Associate; $60, for first class mail w/1 associate; $45, for Standard Mail w/1 Associate; $125, for first class mail 3 years; $110, for standard mail 3 years; $55, U.S. for first class mail; $60, Canada for first Class Mail; $80, Other countries for first Class Mail; $40, for standard mail; $7, for sample issue. **Description:** Trade magazine for antique bottle and glass collectors. **Availability:** Print; PDF; Online.

4670 ■ *Ceramics Monthly*
Pub: American Ceramic Society
Contact: Mark Mecklenborg, Executive Director
E-mail: mmecklenborg@ceramics.org
URL(s): ceramicartsnetwork.org/ceramics-monthly
Facebook: www.facebook.com/CeramicsMonthlyMagazine
X (Twitter): twitter.com/ceramicsmonthly
Instagram: www.instagram.com/ceramics_monthly
Pinterest: www.pinterest.com/CeramicsMonthly
Ed: Holly Goring. **Released:** 10/year; Published monthly except for the June/July/August summer issue. **Price:** $41.99, U.S. for print only; $65, Canada for print only; $76, for print only rest of world; $56, U.S. for annual; $80, Canada for annual; $89, for annual rest of world. **Description:** Consumer magazine containing ceramic art and craft. Features articles on ceramic artists, exhibitions, production processes, critical commentary, book and video reviews, clay and glaze recipes, and kiln designs. **Availability:** Print; PDF; Online.

4671 ■ *Craftideas*
Pub: Amos Media Co.
Contact: John M. Garmhausen, Contact
URL(s): www.amosmedia.com/market-place.html
Description: Craft magazine. **Availability:** Print; Online.

4672 ■ *Dungeons & Dragon Magazine (D&D)*
Pub: Wizards Of The Coast LLC
Contact: Deborah Thomas, Governor
URL(s): dnd.wizards.com
Facebook: www.facebook.com/dungeonsanddragons
X (Twitter): twitter.com/Wizards_DnD
Instagram: www.instagram.com/dndwizards
YouTube: www.youtube.com/user/DNDWizards
Description: Magazine featuring Dungeons & Dragons and other role-playing games. **Availability:** Print; Online.

4673 ■ *Garden Railways*
Pub: Kalmbach Media
Contact: Dan Hickey, Chief Executive Officer
URL(s): www.trains.com/grw
Ed: Marc Horovitz. **Released:** Latest Edition 2020. **Price:** $7.99, Single issue. **Description:** Magazine highlighting outdoor railroading, including layouts, projects with instructions, product reviews, and planting tips. **Availability:** Print; Online.

4674 ■ *Glass Patterns Quarterly (GPQ)*
Pub: Glass Patterns Quarterly Inc.
Contact: Maureen James, Publisher
URL(s): www.glasspatterns.com/magazines/about-gpq.html
Released: Quarterly; spring, summer, fall, winter. **Price:** $9, for back issue; $13, for print and online; $22, for outside us print and online; $36, for 1 year print and online; $36, for online. **Description:** Consumer magazine covering instructional stained glass making for a general and professional audience. Leading international glass magazine featuring patterns and instruction on glass etching, fusing, leading, copper foil, beveling, tiffany-style lamp construction, slumping, painting, beadmaking. Over 100 how-to photographs, steb-by-step instructions. **Availability:** Print; Online.

4675 ■ *Hobby Merchandiser*
Pub: Hobby Merchandiser
Contact: Robert Gherman, President
E-mail: robgherman77@gmail.com
URL(s): www.hobbymerchandiser.com
Released: Monthly **Price:** $29, U.S. for one year; $85, for one year (Foreign-Surface); $120, for one year (Foreign-Air Mail). **Description:** Trade magazine for the model and hobby industry. **Availability:** Print; PDF; Online.

4676 ■ *Model Airplane News: The World's Premier R/C Modeling Magazine*
Pub: Air Age Publishing Inc.
Contact: Louis DeFrancesco, Jr., President
URL(s): simplecirc.com/subscribe/model-airplane-news/I0BB06
Facebook: www.facebook.com/ModelAirplaneNews
Released: Annual **Price:** $69.95, for one year print and online (international); $129.95, for 2 year print and online (international); $99.95, Canada for two years print and online; $69.95, U.S. for 2 years print and online; $39.95, U.S. for one year online + print; $54.95, Canada for 1 year print and online. **Description:** Magazine on radio-controlled model airplanes and helicopters. **Availability:** Print; Online.

4677 ■ *Model Railroader*
Pub: Kalmbach Media
Contact: Dan Hickey, Chief Executive Officer
URL(s): www.trains.com/mrr
Released: Monthly **Price:** $49.95, for print and digital subscription; $39.95, for digital subscription. **Description:** Model railroad hobby magazine. **Availability:** Print; Online.

4678 ■ *Needlework Retailer*
Pub: Yarn Tree Design Inc.
URL(s): needleworkretailer.com
Facebook: www.facebook.com/NeedleworkRetailer
X (Twitter): x.com/NeedleworkRtlr
Instagram: www.instagram.com/needleworkretailer
YouTube: www.youtube.com/channel/UCv5g5swU2GJVz5arwkz7X9w
Pinterest: www.pinterest.com/NeedleworkRetailer
Ed: Megan Chriswisser. **Released:** Bimonthly **Price:** $14, for 6 issues US; $20, for 6 issues Canada; $43, for 6 issues other Countries; $28, Canada for 1 year; $17, U.S. for 1 year; $65, for overseas and Mexico. **Description:** Trade magazine for the needlework industry, especially small, independent needlework retailers. **Availability:** Print; Online.

4679 ■ *Out Your Backdoor (OYB)*
Pub: Out Your Backdoor
Contact: Jeff Potter, Contact
E-mail: jeff@outyourbackdoor.com
URL(s): www.outyourbackdoor.com/about
Facebook: www.facebook.com/outyourbackdoor
YouTube: www.youtube.com/channel/UCTCegrAm3X-THTkSNEJ0k0A

Description: Magazine focusing on bicycling, adventure, culture, the outdoors, hobbies, and sports. **Availability:** Print.

4680 ■ *Railroad Model Craftsman*
Pub: White River Productions
Contact: Kevin Eudaly, President
URL(s): rrmodelcraftsman.com
Facebook: www.facebook.com/modelcraftsman
Ed: Stephen M. Priest. **Released:** Monthly **Price:** $56, U.S. for print edition; $245, Canada for print (first class mail); $98, U.S. for print (first class mail); $76, Canada for print; $10.99, Single issue; $370, for print, international (FIRST CLASS MAIL); $91, for print international. **Description:** Model railroading (building, operating, and collecting) magazine. **Availability:** Print; Online.

4681 ■ *Scrap & Stamp Arts*
Description: Consumer magazine covering rubber stamping for hobbyists. **Availability:** Print.

4682 ■ *Soft Dolls & Animals*
URL(s): www.scottpublications.com/catalog/produc t_info.php/products_id/211
Price: $2, online. **Description:** Magazine covering fabric dolls, teddy bears, and other fabric figures for hobbyists and crafters.

4683 ■ *Uncoverings*
Pub: American Quilt Study Group
Contact: Jayne Steffens, President
URL(s): www.americanquiltstudygroup.org/conten t.aspx?page_id=22&club_id=267008&module_i d=484671
Ed: Lynne Bassett. **Released:** Annual **Price:** $25, for vol 44. **Description:** Scholarly journal covering quilts, textiles and quilt makers. **Availability:** Print.

TRADE SHOWS AND CONVENTIONS

4684 ■ ACC Craft Show Baltimore
American Craft Council (ACC)
1224 Marshall St. NE, Ste. 200
Minneapolis, MN 55413
Ph: (612)206-3100
Fax: (612)355-2330
Co. E-mail: council@craftcouncil.org
URL: http://craftcouncil.org
Contact: Gary J. Smith, Chairman
URL(s): www.craftcouncil.org/american-craft-made -baltimore-overview?overridden_route_name=entity .node.canonical&base_route_name=entity.node .canonical&page_manager_page=node_view&page _manager_page_variant=node_defaults&page _manager_page_variant_weight=-10
Frequency: Annual. **Description:** Handmade items in the areas of glass, leather, jewelry, wood, clay, metal, and fiber. **Audience:** Craft artists, collectors, craft enthusiasts, and public. **Principal Exhibits:** Handmade items in the areas of glass, leather, jewelry, wood, clay, metal, and fiber. Dates and Locations: Baltimore Convention Center, Baltimore, MD; 2025 Feb 21-23. **Telecommunication Services:** shows@craftcouncil.org.

4685 ■ CHA Create and Connect Conference and Trade Show
Association For Creative Industries (AFCI)
330 N Wabash Ave., Ste. 2000
Chicago, IL 60611
Ph: (312)321-6811
Co. E-mail: info@creativeindustries.org
URL: http://creativeindustries.org
Contact: Peter Finn, Executive Director
E-mail: pfinn@creativeindustries.org
URL(s): www.craftandhobby.org/eweb/DynamicPage .aspx?WebKey=E94EE351-A89C-492E-888F-A 45138487AA6
Frequency: Annual. **Description:** Crafts, ceramics, floral accessories, dollhouse miniatures, aromatics, art materials and frames, jewelry findings, fabrics, needlework and quilting supplies, home decor, rubber stamps, stencils and scrapbooking supplies. **Audience:** Owners, corporate officers and buyers from craft, general merchandise stores, wholesalers, professional crafters and CHA professionals. **Principal Exhibits:** Crafts, ceramics, floral accessories, dollhouse miniatures, aromatics, art materials and frames, jewelry findings, fabrics, needlework and quilting supplies, home decor, rubber stamps, stencils and scrapbooking supplies.

FRANCHISES AND BUSINESS OPPORTUNITIES

4686 ■ Hobbytown USA (H)
1133 Libra Dr.
Lincoln, NE 68512
Ph: (530)894-5041
Free: 844-714-3445
Co. E-mail: customerservice@hobbytown.com
URL: http://www.hobbytown.com
Contact: Mary Hayes, Co-Founder
Facebook: www.facebook.com/hobbytown
X (Twitter): x.com/hobbytown
Instagram: www.instagram.com/hobbytown
YouTube: www.youtube.com/hobbytowntv
Pinterest: www.pinterest.com/hobbytown
Description: Retailer of toys such as radio controlled vehicles, games, collectible cards, die cast, toys, gifts, accessories. **No. of Operating Units:** 150. **Founded:** 1985. **Franchised:** 1986. **Equity Capital Needed:** (1,200 SQ. FT. – 1,999 SQ. FT.) - $147,000 – $175,000; (2,000 SQ. FT. – 4,000 SQ. FT.) - $185,000 – $317,500. **Franchise Fee:** $20,000 ($10,000 For Veterans). **Royalty Fee:** 3% of gross sales. **Financial Assistance:** Yes **Training:** 3 week comprehensive training program, including home office and onsite field training.

4687 ■ Pinch a Penny Inc.
PO Box 6025
Clearwater, FL 33758
Ph: (727)531-8913
URL: http://pinchapenny.com
Contact: James Eisch, Jr., President
Facebook: www.facebook.com/PinchAPennyPool
Instagram: www.instagram.com/pinchapennypool
Pinterest: www.pinterest.com/pinchapennypool
Description: Swimming pool supplies & spa supplies. **Founded:** 1975. **Training:** Offers 4 weeks training in Clearwater, FL.

4688 ■ Remote Control Hobbies (RCH)
5435 Boatworks Dr., Unit 1
Littleton, CO 80120
Ph: (303)804-0470
Co. E-mail: rch@rc-hobbies.com
URL: http://rc-hobbies.com
Facebook: www.facebook.com/RemoteCon trolHobbiesLittleton
Description: Distributor and retailer of remote control hobby vehicles, parts and accessories. **Founded:** 2003. **Franchised:** 2004. **Training:** Provides 7 weeks training at headquarters, 6 weeks onsite with ongoing support.

LIBRARIES

4689 ■ American Craft Council (ACC) - Library
1224 Marshall St. NE, Ste. 200
Minneapolis, MN 55413
Ph: (612)206-3100
Fax: (612)355-2330
Co. E-mail: council@craftcouncil.org
URL: http://craftcouncil.org
Contact: Gary J. Smith, Chairman
Facebook: www.facebook.com/CraftCouncil
X (Twitter): x.com/craftcouncil
Instagram: www.instagram.com/craftcouncil
YouTube: www.youtube.com/user/AmericanCraf tCouncil
Pinterest: www.pinterest.com/craftcouncil
Description: Promotes understanding and appreciation of contemporary American craft. **Scope:** American craft. **Services:** Open to public for on-site visits by appointment only. **Founded:** 1943. **Holdings:** 20,000 books; 3,000 photographs; 700 periodicals; 150 current subscriptions; newsletters; slides; correspondence; other ephemera. **Publications:** *American Craft* (Quarterly); *American Craft--News Section* (Bimonthly); *American Craft Council--Crafts Fair Directory*; *American Craft--American Craft Guide to Craft Galleries & Shops USA Issue.* **Educational Activities:** ACC Craft Show Baltimore (Annual); ACC Craft Show San Francisco (Annual). **Awards:** ACC College of Fellows (Irregular); ACC Gold Medal for Consummate Craftsmanship (Biennial); Aileen Osborn Webb Award for Philanthropy (Irregular). **Geographic Preference:** National.

4690 ■ American Museum of Magic - Lund Memorial Library
107 E Michigan Ave.
Marshall, MI 49068
URL: http://americanmuseumofmagic.com
Description: Academy where magic is being conducted. **Scope:** Craftsman style building designed. **Services:** Library open to the public with restrictions. **Founded:** 1978. **Holdings:** 15,000 books; 30,000 magazines; 150,000 letters; 3,000 posters; newspaper clippings; programs; photographs; films; manuscripts. **Subscriptions:** 25 journals and other serials books photographs archival material.

4691 ■ California College of the Arts Libraries - Meyer Library
Meyer Library, 5212 Broadway
Oakland, CA 94618
URL: http://libraries.cca.edu/about-us/about-us/ policies/collection-development-policy
Description: Collections begin from that time and focus on the fine arts and visual and critical studies. Special Collections include artists' books, the Hamaguchi Study Print Collection, Faculty Development Collection, Games Collection, CCA / C College Archives and the Capp Street Project archive. **Scope:** Fine arts; architecture; design; visual and critical studies; writing and literature. **Services:** Open to the public. **Founded:** 1907. **Subscriptions:** magazines newspapers periodicals (includes journals) Books; records.

4692 ■ Craft Council of Newfoundland and Labrador (CCNL)
155 Water St.
Saint John's, NL, Canada A1C 1B3
Ph: (709)753-2749
Co. E-mail: info@craftcouncil.nl.ca
URL: http://www.craftcouncilnl.ca
Contact: Rowena House, Executive Director
E-mail: rhouse@craftcouncil.nl.ca
Facebook: www.facebook.com/CraftCouncilNL
Linkedin: www.linkedin.com/in/craft-council-of-nl-6b 370518
X (Twitter): x.com/craftcouncilnl
Instagram: www.instagram.com/craftcouncilnl
Description: Publishes guides and workbooks on craft training and businesses. Does not accept unsolicited manuscripts. Reaches market through direct mail. **Founded:** 1972. **Publications:** *Craft Council of Newfoundland & Labrador News* (Bimonthly).

4693 ■ Ferrum College - Blue Ridge Heritage Archive
20 Museum Dr.
Ferrum, VA 24088
URL: http://blueridgeinstitute.org/about/blue-ridge -heritage-archives
Scope: Folk culture; music. **Services:** Copying; archive open to the public by appointment. **Holdings:** 4,000 musical performances; 500 photographic images; photographs; video recordings; audio recordings; books and documents.

4694 ■ Haystack Mountain School of Crafts Library
PO Box 518
Deer Isle, ME 04627
Ph: (207)348-2306
Co. E-mail: haystack@haystack-mtn.org
URL: http://www.haystack-mtn.org
Contact: Ayumi Horie, President

Facebook: www.facebook.com/Haystack-Mountain
-School-of-Crafts-90810472119
Instagram: www.instagram.com/haystack_school
YouTube: www.youtube.com/channel/UC25-NaGw
3xPfkcTejEYqzzg
Scope: Fine arts; weaving; design and architecture. **Founded:** 1950. **Holdings:** 1,000 Books; Craft; Art; Design and Architecture.

4695 ■ John Michael Kohler Arts Center Resource Center
608 New York Ave.
Sheboygan, WI 53081
Ph: (920)458-6144
Fax: (920)458-4473
Co. E-mail: info@jmkac.org
URL: http://www.jmkac.org
Contact: Anthony Rammer, President
Facebook: www.facebook.com/jmkac
X (Twitter): x.com/JMKAC
Instagram: www.instagram.com/jmkac
YouTube: www.youtube.com/jmkac2011
Pinterest: www.pinterest.com/jmkac
Scope: Arts. **Founded:** 1967. **Holdings:** Books; Slides; Periodicals and articles.

4696 ■ Manitoba Crafts Museum & Library (MCML) - Gladys Chown Memorial Library
Ste. 1-329 Cumberland Ave.
Winnipeg, MB, Canada R3B 1T2
URL: http://c2centreforcraft.ca/about-mcml
Scope: Historical. **Services:** Copying; library open to the public. **Founded:** 1930. **Holdings:** 3,500 volumes. **Subscriptions:** 1,500 journals and other serials.

4697 ■ Museum of Contemporary Craft Library
724 NW Davis St.
Portland, OR 97209
Ph: (503)223-2654
Fax: (503)223-0190
Co. E-mail: info@museumofcontemporarycraft.org
URL: http://www.museumofcontemporarycraft.org
Contact: Kathy Abraham, President
Scope: Modern and contemporary craft heritage. **Services:** Library open during Museum hours. **Founded:** 1937. **Holdings:** 1,300 objects of modern and contemporary craft ; photographs; slides; ephemera.

4698 ■ Oregon College of Art and Craft Library (OCAC)
8245 SW Barnes Rd.
Portland, OR 97225
Ph: (503)297-5544
Free: 800-390-0632
Fax: (503)297-9651
Co. E-mail: library@ocac.edu
URL: http://library.ocac.edu
Facebook: www.facebook.com/ocac.edu
X (Twitter): twitter.com/OCAC_edu
Instagram: www.instagram.com/ocac_edu
Scope: Textiles; ceramics; woodworking; drawing and design; metals; book arts; photography; calligraphy; painting; sculpture; art history; art criticism. **Services:** Interlibrary loan; library open to the public. **Founded:** 1907. **Holdings:** 9,000 books; 28,000 slides. **Subscriptions:** 90 journals and other serials.

4699 ■ San Francisco Public Library - Bernard Osher Foundation Art, Music & Recreation Center
100 Larkin St.
San Francisco, CA 94102
Ph: (415)557-4525
Co. E-mail: artmusicrec@sfpl.org
URL: http://sfpl.org/locations/main-library/art-music
Scope: Visual arts; performing arts; music; sports and recreation. **Services:** Center open to the public. **Holdings:** Books; serials; scores; CD-ROMs; DVDs.

4700 ■ University of Hartford - William H. Mortensen Library - Anne Bunce Cheney Art Collection
200 Bloomfield Ave.
West Hartford, CT 06117
URL: http://www.hartford.edu/academics/library/about-us/libraries-and-collections.aspx
Description: Mortensen Library houses the Anne Bunce Cheney Art Collection. It consists of: - Art books and journals, exhibition catalogs, guidebooks, and mounted reproductions. - Books and journals are filed in the appropriate areas of the Mortensen Library general collection. - Wadsworth Atheneum catalogs are in the Reserves area on the main level. - Reproductions are in the Art Plates Room on the upper level. - Periodicals and reference books, as well as selected materials held on Reserve at Circulation, are for library use only. **Scope:** History of the university of Hartford and its predecessor schools. **Services:** Interlibrary loan. **Founded:** 1963.

RESEARCH CENTERS

4701 ■ Canadian Crafts Federation (CCF) [Fédération canadienne des métiers d'art (FCMA)]
Arts Court Building 2 Daly Avenue, Suite 280
Ottawa, ON, Canada K1N 6E2
Ph: (506)462-9560
Co. E-mail: info@canadiancraftsfederation.ca
URL: http://canadiancraftsfederation.ca
Contact: David Freeman, President
E-mail: timelessgtrs@sasktel.net
Facebook: www.facebook.com/craftsmetiersdart
X (Twitter): x.com/CCFFCMA
Instagram: www.instagram.com/CCFFCMA
Description: Acts through advocacy, policy initiatives, and programs. Completes Canada's comprehensive crafts infrastructure, which extends from local to international levels. **Scope:** Market development strategies for Canadian crafts in Canada and internationally. **Founded:** 1900. **Geographic Preference:** National.

4702 ■ Museum of International Folk Art (MOIFA) - The Bartlett Library
706 Camino Lejo, on Museum Hill
Santa Fe, NM 87505
Ph: (505)476-1210
Co. E-mail: bartlett.library@state.nm.us
URL: http://www.internationalfolkart.org/learn/library-and-archives.html
Description: Research and educational division of the New Mexico Department of Cultural Affairs. **Scope:** International folk arts and crafts, anthropology, and folklore. Research is conducted by staff and independent and associate researchers and relates to the Museum's ongoing exhibition and curatorial programs. **Services:** Interlibrary loan; copying; library open to the public for reference use only. **Founded:** 1953. **Holdings:** books; slides; tapes; phonograph records; archival materials; postcards; papers; recordings. **Publications:** Exhibition Catalogs; Reports Curriculum for K-12. **Educational Activities:** MOIFA Docent-led tours, Educational talks and tours.; MOIFA Exhibitions (Annual); MOIFA Gallery Talks; MOIFA Lecture/Film Series, In relation to exhibits, family and school programs.; MOIFA Public school outreach programs; MOIFA Staff development programs; MOIFA Teacher Training Institute for Elementary Teachers; MOIFA Workshops, demonstrations.

Create-Your-Own... Store

START-UP INFORMATION

4703 ■ *Setting Up Your Ceramic Studio: Ideas and Plans from Working Artists*
Released: First edition. **Description:** Floor plans and advice for setting up a creative ceramics studio are provided, focusing on equipment, workflow, and safety issues. **Availability:** Print.

REFERENCE WORKS

4704 ■ *"How to (Realistically) Start an Online Ecommerce Busines That Actually Grows in 2019" in Big Commerce*
URL(s): www.bigcommerce.com/blog/how-to-create-online-store/#learn-how-to-create-your-own-online-store
Ed: Tracey Wallace. **Description:** A 9-chapter guide on everything you need to know to start an online business. Topics include how to find niche products to sell; how to evaluate the market; online market research; conducting a competitive analysis; business laws; how to analyze your target market; how to source and manufacture products; and how to create, setup, and launch an online store. **Availability:** PDF; Online.

TRADE SHOWS AND CONVENTIONS

4705 ■ **AQSG Seminar**
American Quilt Study Group (AQSG)
1610 L St.
Lincoln, NE 68508-2509
Ph: (402)477-1181
Fax: (402)477-1181
Co. E-mail: aqsg2@americanquiltstudygroup.org
URL: http://www.americanquiltstudygroup.org
Contact: Jayne Steffens, President
URL(s): www.americanquiltstudygroup.org/content.aspx?page_id=22&club_id=267008&module_id=491050
Frequency: Annual. **Description:** Includes presentation of research papers. **Audience:** Enthusiasts and scholars. **Principal Exhibits:** Includes presentation of research papers. Dates and Locations: 2025 Oct 15-19 Holiday Inn By the Bay, Portland, ME.

FRANCHISES AND BUSINESS OPPORTUNITIES

4706 ■ **Color Me Mine Franchising Inc.**
3722 San Fernando Rd.
Glendale, CA 91204
Co. E-mail: franchising@colormemine.com
URL: http://colorminefranchising.com
Facebook: www.facebook.com/colormemine
X (Twitter): x.com/colormemine
No. of Operating Units: 140. **Founded:** 1991. **Equity Capital Needed:** $141,300-$184,800. **Franchise Fee:** $30,000. **Royalty Fee:** 5% of sales. **Financial Assistance:** Yes **Training:** Yes.

4707 ■ **Dream Dinners Inc.**
502 1st St.
Snohomish, WA 98290-3060
Ph: (360)804-2020
Co. E-mail: customerservice@dreamdinners.com
URL: http://dreamdinners.com
Contact: Cristen Ellis, Governor
Instagram: www.instagram.com/dreamdinners
Pinterest: www.pinterest.com/dreamdinners
Description: Provides prepared meals through stores in the United States. **Founded:** 2002. **Franchised:** 2003. **Equity Capital Needed:** $260,700 to $ 448,000. **Franchise Fee:** $5,000 to $35,000. **Financial Assistance:** Yes **Training:** Provides 1 week at headquarters, 2 days at franchisees location with ongoing support. **Educational Activities:** Crescenta Valley Chamber of Commerce Banquet (Annual).

4708 ■ **Super Suppers**
4317 Miraloma Dr.
Fort Worth, TX 76126
Contact: David D. Rapp, Director
Description: Firm offers food assembly catering services. **Founded:** 1986. **Training:** Offers 1 week at headquarters, 3 days at franchisees location, regional seminars and ongoing support.

Credit Card Issuing Service

REFERENCE WORKS

4709 ■ *"4 Things You Need To Know About Credit Scores: What Millennials Don't Know Can Hurt Their Finances"* in *Black Enterprise* (Vol. 45, July-August 2014, No. 1, pp. 64)
Pub: Earl G. Graves Ltd.
Contact: Earl Graves, Jr., President
Released: December 12, 2018. **Description:** The Consumer Federation of America and VantageScore Solutions LLC report their fourth annual survey on consumers' understanding of credit scores. Six types of businesses using credit scores, include electric company, cell phone company, home insurer, landlord, mortgage lender, and credit card issuer. Age, payment history, debt, years of having credit, last credit application date, and type of credit all factor into scores.

4710 ■ *"Best Credit Card Processing Companies of 2023"* in *Business News Daily* (February 24,2023)
URL(s): www.businessnewsdaily.com/8061-best-credit-card-processing.html
Ed: Mike Berner. **Released:** February 24, 2023. **Description:** Credit processing companies are reviewed and a comparison guide is given. **Availability:** Online.

4711 ■ *"Citadel EFT (CDFT) Contracts With New Search Engine Optimization (SEO) and Banner Ad Web Marketing Companies"* in *Internet Wire* (August 8, 2012)
Pub: Comtex News Network Inc.
Contact: Kan Devnani, President
Description: Citafel EFT Inc. provides credit card terminals, online, mail order and retail credit card processing services. The firm has contracted with two Web marketing companies to increase its awareness on the Internet. **Availability:** Print; Online.

4712 ■ *"Cost of Md.'s Business Banking May Soon Go Up"* in *Baltimore Business Journal* (Vol. 28, October 29, 2010, No. 25, pp. 1)
Pub: Baltimore Business Journal
Contact: Rhonda Pringle, President
E-mail: rpringle@bizjournals.com
Ed: Gary Haber. **Released:** Weekly. **Description:** Experts in the financial industry expect banks to charge credit card transactions, especially to small business owners and consumers to recover about $11 million in lost revenue annually. Banks are expected to charge old fees and new ones, including $5 to $10 a month for a checking account. **Availability:** Print; Online.

4713 ■ *"Credit Card Issuers vs. Networks — What's the Difference?"* in *Credit Card Insider* (October 21, 2019)
URL(s): www.creditcardinsider.com/learn/issuers-networks/

Ed: Brendan Harkness. **Released:** October 21, 2019. **Description:** A quick and easy guide to learn the difference between credit card issuers and networks. **Availability:** Online.

4714 ■ *"Credit Conditions Improve for Small Businesses"* in *Small Business Economic Trends* (February 2008, pp. 12)
Pub: National Federation of Independent Business
Contact: Brad Close, President
Ed: William C. Dunkelberg, Holly Wade. **Description:** Graphs and tables that present the credit conditions of small businesses in the U.S. are provided. The tables include figures on availability of loans, interest rates, and expected credit conditions. **Availability:** Print; PDF; Online.

4715 ■ *"Curbing the Debt Collector"* in *Business Journal-Portland* (Vol. 24, October 5, 2007, No. 32, pp. 1)
Pub: Portland Business Journal
Contact: Andy Giegerich, Managing Editor
E-mail: agiegerich@bizjournals.com
Ed: Andy Giergerich. **Description:** Republican representative Sal Esquivel, who had a bad personal experience with a Houston collector, is developing legislation that would give the state attorney general's office enforcement powers over debt collecting agencies. The existing Oregon legislation concerning the debt collection industry is also discussed. **Availability:** Print; Online.

4716 ■ *"Doria Camaraza on the Best Advice She's Ever Received 'Leave Your Ego at the Door'"* in *South Florida Business Journal* (Vol. 34, June 20, 2014, No. 43, pp. 13)
Pub: American City Business Journals, Inc.
Contact: Mike Olivieri, Executive Vice President
Description: Doria Camaraza, senior vice president and general manager of American Express Service Centers in Fort Lauderdale, Mexico and Argentina, share advice for successfully running service centers for the credit card company. She describes ways in which she inspires creativity and drive, while promoting employee team building with her workers. **Availability:** Print; Online.

4717 ■ *"Economic Trends for Small Business"* in *Small Business Economic Trends* (April 2008, pp. 1)
Description: Summary of economic trends for small businesses in the U.S. is presented. Economic indicators such as capital spending, inventories and sales, inflation, and profits are given. Analysis of credit markets is also provided. **Availability:** Online.

4718 ■ *"End of the Beginning"* in *Canadian Business* (Vol. 81, November 10, 2008, No. 19, pp. 17)
Ed: David Wolf. **Released:** September 30, 2016. **Description:** The freeze in the money markets and historic decline in equity markets around the world finally forced governments into aggressive coordinated action. The asset price inflation brought on by cheap credit will now work in reverse and the tightening of credit will be difficult economically. Canada is exposed to the fallout everywhere, given that the U.S, the U.K. and Japan buy 30 percent of Canada's output. **Availability:** Print; Online.

4719 ■ *"Everything You Need to Know About Credit Card Issuers"* in *Experian.com* (March 27, 2018)
URL(s): www.experian.com/blogs/ask-experian/everything-you-need-to-know-about-credit-card-issuers/
Ed: Jason Steele. **Released:** March 27, 2018. **Description:** Discusses how card issuers work and what their responsibilities are between the cardholder and their accounts. **Availability:** Online.

4720 ■ *"Higher Payouts Should Be In the Cards"* in *Barron's* (Vol. 92, July 23, 2012, No. 30, pp. 14)
Pub: Dow Jones & Company Inc.
Contact: Almar Latour, Chief Executive Officer
Ed: Michael Santoli. **Description:** Credit card companies Visa and MasterCard should be more generous to shareholders and pay higher dividends. Both have low dividend yields, with Visa paying $0.88/share a year and MasterCard paying $1.20/share annually. **Availability:** Online.

4721 ■ *"List of Credit Card Companies, Card Networks & Major Cards"* in *WalletHub* (August 11, 2019)
URL(s): wallethub.com/edu/cc/credit-card-companies/20409/
Ed: John S. Kiernan. **Released:** August 11, 2019. **Description:** A very easy guide to understanding credit cards. Includes lists of the major companies and the number of cards they have issued, and a discussion of each of the major issuers with their contact information. **Availability:** Online.

4722 ■ *"Littleton Firm Chips In On Security Solution"* in *Denver Business Journal* (Vol. 65, May 9, 2014, No. 52, pp. A6)
Pub: American City Business Journals, Inc.
Contact: Mike Olivieri, Executive Vice President
Released: Weekly. **Price:** $4, introductory 4-week offer(Digital & Print). **Description:** CPI Card Group of Littleton, Colorado has been preparing for the nationwide transition to computer chip cards to secure credit and debit cards in the U.S. Banks and merchants in the country need to make the switch by October 2015 or risk being financially liable for fraud if not using the chipped cards in their retail establishments. **Availability:** Print; Online.

4723 ■ *"NetSpend and Family Dollar Announce New Prepaid Card Agreement"* in *GlobeNewswire* (May 10, 2012)
Pub: Comtex News Network Inc.
Contact: Kan Devnani, President
Description: Partnership between Family Dollar and NetSpend will offer customers a NetSpend Visa(R) Prepaid Debit Card to be used at Family Dollar's 7,200 locations. NetSpend is a leading provider of

general-purpose reloadable (GPR) prepaid debit cards and other related financial services. **Availability:** Print; Online.

4724 ■ *"New Rule Rankles In Jersey" in Philadelphia Business Journal (Vol. 30, September 16, 2011, No. 31, pp. 1)*
Pub: Philadelphia Business Journal
Contact: Sierra Quinn, Director
E-mail: squinn@bizjournals.com
Ed: Jeff Blumenthal. **Description:** A new rule in New Jersey which taxes out-of-state companies that conduct business in the state earned the ire of several banks, mortgage lenders and credit card companies and prompted opponents to threaten to file lawsuits. The new rule is an amendment to New Jersey Division of Taxation's corporate business tax regulation and is retroactive to 2002. Details are given. **Availability:** Online.

4725 ■ *"Summary. Economic Trends for Small Business" in Small Business Economic Trends (February 2008, pp. 1)*
Pub: National Federation of Independent Business
Contact: Brad Close, President
Ed: William C. Dunkelberg, Holly Wade. **Description:** Summary of economic trends for small businesses in the U.S. is provided. Economic indicators such as capital spending, inventories and sales, inflation, and profits are given. Analysis of credit markets is also provided.

4726 ■ *"Travel Rewards Take Off" in Inc. (Vol. 33, October 2011, No. 8, pp. 46)*
Description: Credit card companies are offering travel reward cards with special perks, including sign-up bonuses; three such cards are described. **Availability:** Online.

4727 ■ *"What Is a Credit Card Issuer?" in The Balance (July 30, 2018)*
URL(s): www.thebalance.com/credit-card-issuer-9 59984
Ed: Latoya Irby. **Released:** July 30, 2018. **Description:** Provides a clear explanation of what a credit card issuer is, their responsibilites to merchants, how they isse credit cards. **Availability:** Online.

4728 ■ *"Your Guide to Credit Counseling Services" in Forbes Advisor (August 3, 2021)*
Ed: Rebecca Lake, Daphne Foreman. **Released:** August 03, 2021. **Description:** Discusses the role consumer credit counseling plays in helping people get their personal debt under control.

Credit Repair Service

START-UP INFORMATION

4729 ■ *Credit Repair Services Business Book: Secrets to Start-up, Finance, market, How to Fix Credit & Make Massive Money Right Now!*
Ed: Brian Mahoney. **Released:** October 19, 2016. **Description:** A how-to book on setting up a credit repair business. Includes information on applying for grants, wholesale resources, and a business plan. **Availability:** Print.

4730 ■ *How to Start a Bankruptcy Forms Processing Service*
Released: First edition. **Description:** Due to the increase in bankruptcy filings, attorneys are outsourcing related jobs in order to reduce overhead.

4731 ■ *The Ultimate Guide to Starting a Credit Repair Business*
Ed: Daniel Rosen. **Released:** April 15, 2016. **Description:** Launching a credit repair business out of the home is a great career choice for those who are looking for their own business opportunities. There are several methods of setting up this business and the author relates the steps to get the best possible results. Tips on credit repair basics, how to work with clients, how to remove difficult items from credit report, and many more. **Availability:** Print.

ASSOCIATIONS AND OTHER ORGANIZATIONS

4732 ■ **American Financial Services Association (AFSA)**
919 18th St. NW, Ste. 300
Washington, DC 20006
Ph: (202)296-5544
Co. E-mail: info@afsamail.org
URL: http://afsaonline.org
Contact: Tom Hudgins, President
Facebook: www.facebook.com/afsaonline
Linkedin: www.linkedin.com/company/american-financial-services-association
X (Twitter): x.com/afsa_dc
Instagram: www.instagram.com/afsa_dc
YouTube: www.youtube.com/user/afsaonline
Description: Represents companies whose business is primarily direct credit lending to consumers and/or the purchase of sales finance paper on consumer goods. Has members that have insurance and retail subsidiaries; some are themselves subsidiaries of highly diversified parent corporations. Encourages the business of financing individuals and families for necessary and useful purposes at reasonable charges, including interest; promotes consumer understanding of basic money management principles as well as constructive uses of consumer credit. Includes educational services such as films, textbooks and study units for the classroom and budgeting guides for individuals and families. **Founded:** 1916. **Publications:** *Credit*; *Credit* (Monthly); *Independent Operations* (Quarterly). **Awards:** AFSA Distinguished Service Award. **Geographic Preference:** National.

4733 ■ **Credit Professionals International (CPI)**
PO Box 866
Corrales, NM 87048
URL: http://www.creditprofessionals.org
Contact: Barbara Hall, Executive Director
E-mail: bahall2145@gmail.com
Description: Represents individuals employed in credit or collection departments of business firms or professional offices. Conducts educational program in credit work. Sponsors Career Club composed of members who have been involved in credit work for at least 25 years. **Founded:** 1937. **Publications:** *The Credit Professional* (Semiannual). **Awards:** CPI Credit Professional of the Year (Annual). **Geographic Preference:** National.

4734 ■ **Credit Research Foundation (CRF) - Library**
1812 Baltimore Blvd., Ste. H
Westminster, MD 21157
Ph: (443)821-3000
Fax: (443)821-3627
URL: http://www.crfonline.org
Contact: Bill Balduino, President
Linkedin: www.linkedin.com/company/credit-research-foundation
YouTube: www.youtube.com/channel/UCl3ulPzpwNOPvHq2nOMDtsg
Description: Represents credit, financial, and working capital executives of manufacturing and banking concerns. Aims to create a better understanding of the impact of credit on the economy. Plans, supervises, and administers research and educational programs. Conducts surveys on economic conditions, trends, policies, practices, theory, systems, and methodology. Sponsors formal educational programs in credit and financial management. Maintains library on credit, collections, and management. **Scope:** Financial management, including management theory, electronic data processing, human resources management, business practices and techniques, economic impact of business credit, credit and receivables management, working capital management, international credit and finance, and related subjects. **Services:** Library open to the public; copying. **Founded:** 1949. **Holdings:** 500 articles; books; Cds. **Publications:** *Credit Professional's Handbook*; *Perspective by CRF* (Quarterly); *National Summary of Domestic Trade Receivables* (Quarterly); *Annual Collection Productivity Report*; *Credit Executives Handbook*; *Net Bad-Debt Writeoffs and Allowance for Uncollectibles* (Annual); *Credit and Financial Management Review* (Quarterly). **Educational Activities:** CRF Credit and Accounts Receivable Open Forums (Irregular). **Geographic Preference:** National.

4735 ■ **National Association of Credit Management (NACM)**
8840 Columbia 100 Pky.
Columbia, MD 21045
Ph: (410)740-5560
Fax: (410)740-5574
Co. E-mail: nacm_national@nacm.org
URL: http://nacm.org
Contact: Robin Schauseil, President
Linkedin: www.linkedin.com/company/national-association-of-credit-management
X (Twitter): x.com/nacm_national
Pinterest: www.pinterest.com/nacmnational
Description: Credit and financial executives representing manufacturers, wholesalers, financial institutions, insurance companies, utilities, and other businesses interested in business credit. Promotes sound credit practices and legislation. Conducts Graduate School of Credit and Financial Management at Dartmouth College, Hanover, NH. **Founded:** 1896. **Publications:** *Credit Executives Handbook*; *Manual of Credit and Commercial Laws*; *Business Credit: The Publication for Credit and Finance Professionals* (9/year). **Educational Activities:** NACM Credit Congress and Exposition (Annual); Credit Congress & Exposition (Annual). **Awards:** O.D. Glaus Credit Executive of Distinction Award (Annual); Alice M.H. McGregor Award of Exceptional Achievement (Periodic); CCE Designation of Excellence Award (Annual); NACM Mentor of the Year (Annual). **Geographic Preference:** National.

4736 ■ **National Foundation for Credit Counseling (NFCC)**
2000 K St., NW, Ste. 425
Washington, DC 20006
Free: 800-388-2227
Co. E-mail: info@nfcc.org
URL: http://www.nfcc.org
Contact: Gary Volmer, President
Facebook: www.facebook.com/NFCCDebtAdvice
Linkedin: www.linkedin.com/company/national-foundation-for-credit-counseling
X (Twitter): x.com/nfcc
YouTube: www.youtube.com/user/NFCC09
Description: Promotes the wise use of credit through education, counseling and debt repayment programs. **Founded:** 1951. **Publications:** *NFCC Directory of Members*; *Notables* (Semiannual). **Geographic Preference:** National.

REFERENCE WORKS

4737 ■ *"4 Credit Repair Company Lies — and How to Fix Your Score Without Help" in MoneyTalksNews (June 18, 2019)*
URL(s): www.moneytalksnews.com/5-lies-credit-repair-companies-tell-and-how-to-fix-your-score-on-your-own/
Ed: Maryalene LaPonsie. **Released:** June 18, 2019. **Description:** Advises consumers on four common untruths that disreputable credit repair companies tell in order to gain your trust and your money. **Availability:** Online.

4738 ■ *"4 Things You Need To Know About Credit Scores: What Millennials Don't Know Can Hurt Their Finances"* **in Black Enterprise (Vol. 45, July-August 2014, No. 1, pp. 64)**
Pub: Earl G. Graves Ltd.
Contact: Earl Graves, Jr., President
Released: December 12, 2018. **Description:** The Consumer Federation of America and VantageScore Solutions LLC report their fourth annual survey on consumers' understanding of credit scores. Six types of businesses using credit scores, include electric company, cell phone company, home insurer, landlord, mortgage lender, and credit card issuer. Age, payment history, debt, years of having credit, last credit application date, and type of credit all factor into scores.

4739 ■ *"The Best Option for All"* **in American Executive (Vol. 7, September 2009, No. 5, pp. 170)**
Ed: Ashley McGown. **Description:** Plaza Associates, a collections agency that conducts business primarily in the accounts receivable management sector, is the first in the industry to purchase 100 percent of the company from the founders through the formation of a leveraged Employee Stock Ownership Plan (ESOP).

4740 ■ *"Beware of Credit 'Repair' Companies, Consumer Watchdogs Say"* **in The New York Times (May 10 2019)**
URL(s): www.nytimes.com/2019/05/10/your-money/credit-repair-companies-complaints.html
Ed: Ann Carrns. **Released:** May 10, 2019. **Description:** A warning about credit repair companies that may be targeting people struggling with loans and bad credit. These companies are illegally charging for upfront credit reapir, which is against the law. Deceptive practices are also occurring and misleading consumers as well. **Availability:** Online.

4741 ■ *"Collection Agency Issues Whitepaper on Legal and Ethical Methods of Collecting on Overdue Accounts"* **in Marketwired (July 20, 2009)**
Pub: Comtex News Network Inc.
Contact: Kan Devnani, President
Description: American Profit Recovery, a collection agency based in Massachusetts and Michigan, has updated and reissued a whitepaper on what businesses can and cannot do regarding conversing with their customers in an attempt to collect on overdue accounts and payments. A detailed summary on the federal laws associated with collecting on overdue accounts is outlined in such a way that any business owner, manager, or responsible party can easily understand. **Availability:** Print; Online.

4742 ■ *"Credit Conditions Improve for Small Businesses"* **in Small Business Economic Trends (February 2008, pp. 12)**
Pub: National Federation of Independent Business
Contact: Brad Close, President
Ed: William C. Dunkelberg, Holly Wade. **Description:** Graphs and tables that present the credit conditions of small businesses in the U.S. are provided. The tables include figures on availability of loans, interest rates, and expected credit conditions. **Availability:** Print; PDF; Online.

4743 ■ *Credit Repair Business: 2 Manuscripts How to Fix Your Credit from Poor to Excellent and Raising Your Credit Score to 720+*
Ed: Ruben Hanson. **Released:** February 02, 2020. **Description:** A guide to boosting your credit score on your own. Discusses eradicating low credit scores in order to improve interest rates on loans and securing mortgages. **Availability:** Print.

4744 ■ *"Curbing the Debt Collector"* **in Business Journal-Portland (Vol. 24, October 5, 2007, No. 32, pp. 1)**
Pub: Portland Business Journal
Contact: Andy Giegerich, Managing Editor
E-mail: agiegerich@bizjournals.com
Ed: Andy Giegerich. **Description:** Republican representative Sal Esquivel, who had a bad personal experience with a Houston collector, is developing legislation that would give the state attorney general's office enforcement powers over debt collecting agencies. The existing Oregon legislation concerning the debt collection industry is also discussed. **Availability:** Print; Online.

4745 ■ *"Economic Trends for Small Business"* **in Small Business Economic Trends (April 2008, pp. 1)**
Description: Summary of economic trends for small businesses in the U.S. is presented. Economic indicators such as capital spending, inventories and sales, inflation, and profits are given. Analysis of credit markets is also provided. **Availability:** Online.

4746 ■ *"End of the Beginning"* **in Canadian Business (Vol. 81, November 10, 2008, No. 19, pp. 17)**
Ed: David Wolf. **Released:** September 30, 2016. **Description:** The freeze in the money markets and historic decline in equity markets around the world finally forced governments into aggressive coordinated action. The asset price inflation brought on by cheap credit will now work in reverse and the tightening of credit will be difficult economically. Canada is exposed to the fallout everywhere, given that the U.S, the U.K. and Japan buy 30 percent of Canada's output. **Availability:** Print; Online.

4747 ■ *"How To Find Reputable Credit Repair Services"* **in U.S. News & World Report (October 24,2019)**
URL(s): creditcards.usnews.com/articles/how-to-find-reputable-credit-repair-services
Ed: Michele Lerner, Lance Cothern. **Released:** October 24, 2019. **Description:** A guide to navigating the credit repair services industry. Gives a definition and list of behaviors that disreputable companies engage in, thus acting as a warning to avoid those companies that exhibit these behaviors. Also gives a list of things to look for that trustworthy companies provide. **Availability:** Online.

4748 ■ *"Identity Theft Can Have Long-Lasting Impact"* **in Providence Business News (Vol. 28, February 10, 2014, No. 45, pp. 7)**
Pub: American City Business Journals, Inc.
Contact: Mike Olivieri, Executive Vice President
URL(s): pbn.com/identity-theft-can-have-long-lasting-impact94959
Description: According to mortgage credit experts, recently reported massive data breaches at Nieman Marcus, Target, and other merchants could have negative impacts on several real estate deals scheduled for the upcoming months. Although victims are not liable for the unlawful debts, their credit reports and scores can be damaged for months, thus endangering loan applications for mortgages on home sale transactions. **Availability:** Online.

4749 ■ *"Portfolio Recovery Associates Expands Its Hampton Call Center"* **in Marketwired (January 20, 2010)**
Pub: Comtex News Network Inc.
Contact: Kan Devnani, President
Description: Entering into a lease amendment in order to expand its Hampton, Virginia call center and extend its lease agreement, Portfolio Recovery Associates, Inc., a company that collects, purchases and manages defaulted consumer debt, plans to upgrade the existing space enabling them to draw on local talent. **Availability:** Print; Online.

4750 ■ *"Summary. Economic Trends for Small Business"* **in Small Business Economic Trends (February 2008, pp. 1)**
Pub: National Federation of Independent Business
Contact: Brad Close, President
Ed: William C. Dunkelberg, Holly Wade. **Description:** Summary of economic trends for small businesses in the U.S. is provided. Economic indicators such as capital spending, inventories and sales, inflation, and profits are given. Analysis of credit markets is also provided.

4751 ■ *"The Survey Says"* **in Collections and Credit Risk (Vol. 14, September 1, 2009, No. 8, pp. 16)**
Description: Revenue for the top accounts receivable management firms rose nearly 20 percent in 2008 despite lower liquidation rates, a poor economy and riskier, albeit cheaper debt portfolios; the trend may continue this year as collection agencies expect revenue, on average, to increase 5.8 percent. Debt buyers, however, found that their revenue fell nearly 7 percent in 2008 and expect it to fall another 12 percent this year. **Availability:** Print; Online.

4752 ■ *"Your Guide to Credit Counseling Services"* **in Forbes Advisor (August 3, 2021)**
Ed: Rebecca Lake, Daphne Foreman. **Released:** August 03, 2021. **Description:** Discusses the role consumer credit counseling plays in helping people get their personal debt under control.

STATISTICAL SOURCES

4753 ■ *Credit Counselors, Surveyors & Appraisers Industry in the US - Market Research Report*
URL(s): ibisworld.com/united-states/market-research-reports/credit-counselors-surveyors-appraisers-industry/
Price: $925. **Description:** Downloadable report analyzing the current and future trends in various industries that include credit counselors, surveyors, and appraisers. **Availability:** Download.

LIBRARIES

4754 ■ **National Foundation for Credit Counseling (NFCC)**
2000 K St., NW, Ste. 425
Washington, DC 20006
Free: 800-388-2227
Co. E-mail: info@nfcc.org
URL: http://www.nfcc.org
Contact: Gary Volmer, President
Facebook: www.facebook.com/NFCCDebtAdvice
Linkedin: www.linkedin.com/company/national-foundation-for-credit-counseling
X (Twitter): x.com/nfcc
YouTube: www.youtube.com/user/NFCC09
Description: Promotes the wise use of credit through education, counseling and debt repayment programs. **Founded:** 1951. **Publications:** *NFCC Directory of Members*; *Notables* (Semiannual). **Geographic Preference:** National.

Credit Reporting and Collection Service

START-UP INFORMATION

4755 ■ *How to Start a Bankruptcy Forms Processing Service*
Released: First edition. **Description:** Due to the increase in bankruptcy filings, attorneys are outsourcing related jobs in order to reduce overhead.

ASSOCIATIONS AND OTHER ORGANIZATIONS

4756 ■ **ACA International (ACA) [Association of Credit and Collections Professionals]**
3200 Courthouse Ln.
  Eagan, MN 55121-1585
Ph: (952)926-6547
Free: 800-269-1607
Co. E-mail: comm@acainternational.org
URL: http://www.acainternational.org
Contact: Alhaji David Williams, President
Facebook: www.facebook.com/acaintl
Linkedin: www.linkedin.com/company/aca-international
X (Twitter): x.com/acaintl
Description: Collection services handling overdue accounts for retail, professional, and commercial credit grantors. Maintains specialized programs in the areas of healthcare, checks, and government which provide services for members who work with credit grantors in these areas. Conducts research. Offers specialized education; compiles statistics. **Founded:** 1939. **Publications:** *Collector* (Bimonthly); *ACA International - Member Directory*; *Collector: The Official Publication of the ACA International* (Bimonthly). **Educational Activities:** ACA International Annual Convention & Expo (Annual). **Awards:** ACA Honorary Membership (Annual); ACA Unit Certificate of Excellence (Annual); ACA International Member of the Year Award (Annual); James K. Erickson Continuous Service Award (Annual); ACA International Fellowship of Certified Collection Executives (IFCCE) (Annual); Charles F. Lindemann Certified Instructor of the Year (Irregular); ACA Enterprises Award of Merit (Annual); Fred Kirschner Instructor Achievement Award (Annual); ACA International Foundation Fellow Award (Annual); ACA Unit Leader of the Year (Annual). **Geographic Preference:** Multinational.

4757 ■ **Consumer Data Industry Association (CDIA)**
1090 Vermont Ave. NW, Ste. 200
  Washington, DC 20005
Ph: (202)371-0910
Co. E-mail: cdia_media@cdiaonline.org
URL: http://www.cdiaonline.org
Contact: Francis Creighton, President
Linkedin: www.linkedin.com/company/consumer-data-industry-association
X (Twitter): x.com/cdiaonline
Description: Serves as international association of credit reporting and collection service offices. Maintains hall of fame and biographical archives; conducts specialized educational programs. Offers computerized services and compiles statistics. **Founded:** 1906. **Geographic Preference:** Multinational.

4758 ■ **Credit Professionals International (CPI)**
PO Box 866
  Corrales, NM 87048
URL: http://www.creditprofessionals.org
Contact: Barbara Hall, Executive Director
E-mail: bahall2145@gmail.com
Description: Represents individuals employed in credit or collection departments of business firms or professional offices. Conducts educational program in credit work. Sponsors Career Club composed of members who have been involved in credit work for at least 25 years. **Founded:** 1937. **Publications:** *The Credit Professional* (Semiannual). **Awards:** CPI Credit Professional of the Year (Annual). **Geographic Preference:** National.

4759 ■ **International Association of Commercial Collectors (IACC)**
3200 Courthouse Ln.
  Eagan, MN 55121-1585
Ph: (952)925-0760
Free: 800-859-9526
Fax: (952)926-1624
Co. E-mail: iacc@commercialcollector.com
URL: http://www.commercialcollector.com
Contact: Brad Lohner, President
E-mail: brad.lohner@pcmcorp.com
Description: Increasing awareness in the commercial credit industry of the benefits of using an IACC member to collect commercial accounts. **Founded:** 1970. **Publications:** *Scope* (Monthly); *Commercial Collection Guidelines for Credit Grantors*. **Educational Activities:** IACC Conference (Annual). **Geographic Preference:** Multinational.

4760 ■ **International Association of Financial Crimes Investigators (IAFCI)**
1020 Suncast Ln., Ste. 102
  El Dorado Hills, CA 95762
Ph: (916)939-5000
Co. E-mail: support@iafci.org
URL: http://www.iafci.org
Facebook: www.facebook.com/IAFCI
X (Twitter): x.com/iafci
YouTube: www.youtube.com/channel/UCe5Op8DWRYh2pa16IUZIzXw/featured
Description: Special agents, investigators who investigate criminal violations of credit card laws and prosecute offenders; law enforcement officers, prosecutors, or related officials who investigate, apprehend, and prosecute credit card offenders; employees of card issuing institutions who are responsible for credit card security and investigations; management personnel of companies performing services for the credit card industry. Aids in the establishment of effective credit card security programs; suppresses fraudulent use of credit cards; and detects and proceeds with the apprehension of credit card thieves. **Founded:** 1968. **Publications:** *IAFCI News* (Quarterly); *International Association of Financial Crimes Investigators: Membership Directory* (Annual); *International Association of Financial Crimes Investigators--Membership Directory*. **Educational Activities:** IAFCI Annual Training Conference (Annual). **Geographic Preference:** National.

4761 ■ **National Association of Credit Management (NACM)**
8840 Columbia 100 Pky.
  Columbia, MD 21045
Ph: (410)740-5560
Fax: (410)740-5574
Co. E-mail: nacm_national@nacm.org
URL: http://nacm.org
Contact: Robin Schauseil, President
Linkedin: www.linkedin.com/company/national-association-of-credit-management
X (Twitter): x.com/nacm_national
Pinterest: www.pinterest.com/nacmnational
Description: Credit and financial executives representing manufacturers, wholesalers, financial institutions, insurance companies, utilities, and other businesses interested in business credit. Promotes sound credit practices and legislation. Conducts Graduate School of Credit and Financial Management at Dartmouth College, Hanover, NH. **Founded:** 1896. **Publications:** *Credit Executives Handbook*; *Manual of Credit and Commercial Laws*; *Business Credit: The Publication for Credit and Finance Professionals* (9/year). **Educational Activities:** NACM Credit Congress and Exposition (Annual); Credit Congress & Exposition (Annual). **Awards:** O.D. Glaus Credit Executive of Distinction Award (Annual); Alice M.H. McGregor Award of Exceptional Achievement (Periodic); CCE Designation of Excellence Award (Annual); NACM Mentor of the Year (Annual). **Geographic Preference:** National.

REFERENCE WORKS

4762 ■ *"4 Things You Need To Know About Credit Scores: What Millennials Don't Know Can Hurt Their Finances"* in *Black Enterprise* (Vol. 45, July-August 2014, No. 1, pp. 64)
Pub: Earl G. Graves Ltd.
Contact: Earl Graves, Jr., President
Released: December 12, 2018. **Description:** The Consumer Federation of America and VantageScore Solutions LLC report their fourth annual survey on consumers' understanding of credit scores. Six types of businesses using credit scores, include electric company, cell phone company, home insurer, landlord, mortgage lender, and credit card issuer. Age, payment history, debt, years of having credit, last credit application date, and type of credit all factor into scores.

4763 ■ *"11th Circuit: Don't Break the Law to Comply with It"* in *Miami Daily Business Review* (October 21, 2009)
Pub: Incisive Media Inc.
Contact: Jonathon Whiteley, Chief Executive Officer

Ed: Janet L. Conley. **Description:** Niagara Credit Solutions argued with a three-judge panel that the company broke the rule saying debt collectors must identify themselves so that they could comply with a rule barring debt collectors from communicating about a debt with third parties. **Availability:** Print; Online.

4764 ■ ACA International - Member Directory
Pub: ACA International
Contact: Alhaji David Williams, President
URL(s): me.acainternational.org/Membership/Membership-Directory

Ed: Tim Dressen. **Description:** Publication includes list of about 3,600 debt collection agencies, 1,000 credit grantors and 700 collection attorneys, and services in 55 countries. **Entries include:** Firm name, address, phone, fax, URL, e-mail, names and names and titles of key personnel. **Arrangement:** Geographical. **Availability:** Print.

4765 ■ "All-Star Advice 2010" in Black Enterprise (Vol. 41, October 2010, No. 3, pp. 97)
Pub: Earl G. Graves Ltd.
Contact: Earl Graves, Jr., President

Ed: Renita Burns, Sheiresa Ngo, Marcia Wade Talbert. **Description:** Financial experts share tips on real estate, investing, taxes, insurance and debt management. **Availability:** Online.

4766 ■ "American Apparel: When Dov Cries" in Canadian Business (Vol. 83, June 15, 2010, No. 10, pp. 71)
Pub: Rogers Media Inc.
Contact: Neil Spivak, Chief Executive Officer

Ed: Joe Castaldo. **Description:** American Apparel disclosed that they will have problems meeting one of its debt covenants which could trigger a chain reaction that could lead to bankruptcy. The prospects look bleak, but eccentric company founder Dov Charney, has always defied expectations. **Availability:** Online.

4767 ■ "App Helps Consumers Spot Suspicious Charges" in Black Enterprise (Vol. 44, June 2014, No. 10, pp. 34)
Pub: Earl G. Graves Ltd.
Contact: Earl Graves, Jr., President

Description: BiliGuard is a mobile app used to track activity on credit and debit card accounts. The app allows users to notify a merchant as soon as they see an unfamiliar charge. BiliGuard can also alert users to fees. **Availability:** Online.

4768 ■ "Arkansas Attorney General Sues Collection Agency" in PaymentsSource (July 18, 2012)

Description: National Credit Adjusters is being sued by Arkansas Attorney General Dustin McDaniel's office. The lawsuit alleges that the collection agency violated the Arkansas Deceptive Trade Practices Act while attempting to collect debts from payday and high-interest installment loan debts. **Availability:** Print; Online.

4769 ■ "Banks, Retailers Squabble Over Fees" in Baltimore Business Journal (Vol. 28, June 18, 2010, No. 6, pp. 1)
Pub: Baltimore Business Journal
Contact: Rhonda Pringle, President
E-mail: rpringle@bizjournals.com

Ed: Gary Haber. **Description:** How an amendment to the financial regulatory reform bill would affect the bankers' and retailers' conflict over interchange fees is discussed. Interchange fees are paid for by retailers every time consumers make purchases through debit cards. Industry estimates indicate that approximately $50 million in such fees are paid by retailers. **Availability:** Print; Online.

4770 ■ "The Best Option for All" in American Executive (Vol. 7, September 2009, No. 5, pp. 170)

Ed: Ashley McGown. **Description:** Plaza Associates, a collections agency that conducts business primarily in the accounts receivable management sector, is the first in the industry to purchase 100 percent of the company from the founders through the formation of a leveraged Employee Stock Ownership Plan (ESOP).

4771 ■ "Canada Seeks Collection Agency To Pursue $129M In Fines" in PaymentsSource (August 21, 2012)

Description: Canada's federal government has posted a letter of interest seeking a collection agency to recover about $129 million in unpaid fines. Details of the program are covered. **Availability:** Print; Online.

4772 ■ "Cincinnati Hospitals Feel Pain from Slow Economy" in Business Courier (Vol. 27, September 3, 2010, No. 18, pp. 1)
Pub: Business Courier

Ed: James Ritchie. **Description:** Hospitals in Cincinnati, Ohio have suffered from decreased revenues owing to the economic crises. Declining patient volumes and bad debt have also adversely impacted hospitals. **Availability:** Print; Online.

4773 ■ "Clock Ticks On Columbia Sussex Debt" in Business Courier (Vol. 27, July 30, 2010, No. 13, pp. 1)
Pub: Business Courier

Ed: Dan Monk. **Description:** Cincinnati, Ohio-based Columbia Sussex Corporation has made plans to restructure a $1 billion loan bundle that was scheduled to mature in October 2010. The privately held hotel has strived in a weak hotel market to keep pace with its $3 billion debt load. **Availability:** Print; Online.

4774 ■ "Collection Agency Issues Whitepaper on Legal and Ethical Methods of Collecting on Overdue Accounts" in Marketwired (July 20, 2009)
Pub: Comtex News Network Inc.
Contact: Kan Devnani, President

Description: American Profit Recovery, a collection agency based in Massachusetts and Michigan, has updated and reissued a whitepaper on what businesses can and cannot do regarding conversing with their customers in an attempt to collect on overdue accounts and payments. A detailed summary on the federal laws associated with collecting on overdue accounts is outlined in such a way that any business owner, manager, or responsible party can easily understand. **Availability:** Print; Online.

4775 ■ The Complete Idiot's Guide to Starting an eBay® Business
Pub: Penguin Publishing Group
Released: April 03, 2012. **Price:** $19.95, paperback; $12.99, e-book. **Description:** Guide for starting an eBay business includes information on products to sell, how to price merchandise, and details for working with services like PayPal, and how to organize fulfillment services. **Availability:** E-book; Print.

4776 ■ "Cost of Md.'s Business Banking May Soon Go Up" in Baltimore Business Journal (Vol. 28, October 29, 2010, No. 25, pp. 1)
Pub: Baltimore Business Journal
Contact: Rhonda Pringle, President
E-mail: rpringle@bizjournals.com

Ed: Gary Haber. **Released:** Weekly. **Description:** Experts in the financial industry expect banks to charge credit card transactions, especially to small business owners and consumers to recover about $11 million in lost revenue annually. Banks are expected to charge old fees and new ones, including $5 to $10 a month for a checking account. **Availability:** Print; Online.

4777 ■ "Credit Conditions Improve for Small Businesses" in Small Business Economic Trends (February 2008, pp. 12)
Pub: National Federation of Independent Business
Contact: Brad Close, President

Ed: William C. Dunkelberg, Holly Wade. **Description:** Graphs and tables that present the credit conditions of small businesses in the U.S. are provided. The tables include figures on availability of loans, interest rates, and expected credit conditions. **Availability:** Print; PDF; Online.

4778 ■ "Credit Reporting Agencies Face Pressure from Skeptical U.S. Congress" in Reuters (February 26, 2019)
URL(s): www.reuters.com/article/us-usa-house-credi treporting/credit-reporting-agencies-face-pressure -from-skeptical-u-s-congress-idUSKCN1QF2KM

Ed: Pete Schroeder. **Released:** February 26, 2019. **Description:** After the massive data breach in 2017 from Equifax, Congress has been looking into overhauling the nation's entire credit industry. Executives from the top three major credit reporting agencies reported to Washington to defend their business models. **Availability:** Online.

4779 ■ "Curbing the Debt Collector" in Business Journal-Portland (Vol. 24, October 5, 2007, No. 32, pp. 1)
Pub: Portland Business Journal
Contact: Andy Giegerich, Managing Editor
E-mail: agiegerich@bizjournals.com

Ed: Andy Giergerich. **Description:** Republican representative Sal Esquivel, who had a bad personal experience with a Houston collector, is developing legislation that would give the state attorney general's office enforcement powers over debt collecting agencies. The existing Oregon legislation concerning the debt collection industry is also discussed. **Availability:** Print; Online.

4780 ■ "Death Spiral" in Business Journal Serving Greater Tampa Bay (Vol. 30, October 29, 2010, No. 45, pp. 1)
Pub: Tampa Bay Business Journal
Contact: Ian Anderson, President
E-mail: ianderson@bizjournals.com

Description: Bay Cities Bank has started working on the loan portfolio of its acquisition, Progress Bank of Florida. Regulators closed Progress Bank in October 2010 after capital collapsed due to charge-offs and increases in the provision for future loan losses. **Availability:** Print; Online.

4781 ■ "Debt-Collection Agency to Lay Off 368 in Hampton Center" in Virginian-Pilot (December 4, 2010)
Pub: The Virginian-Pilot
Contact: Kevin Goyette, Director
E-mail: kgoyette@dailypress.com

Ed: Tom Shean. **Description:** NCO Financial Systems Inc., provider of debt-collection and outsourcing services will permanently lay off 368 workers at its Hampton call center in 2011. **Availability:** Print; Online.

4782 ■ "Direct Recovery Associates Debt Collection Agency Beats Industry Record" in Internet Wire (June 24, 2010)

Description: Direct Recovery Associates Inc. was named as one of the highest collection records in the industry, which has consistently improved over 18 years. The firm is an international attorney-based debt collection agency. **Availability:** Print; Online.

4783 ■ "Directors May Revise HCA Collection Agency Regulations" in Standard-Speaker (May 20, 2012)
Pub: McClatchy Tribune Information Services
Contact: Patrick J. Talamantes, President

Ed: Sam Galski. **Description:** Hazelton, Pennsylvania authorities are thinking about changing ts 42-year-old regulations, thus having a collection agency pursue payment of outstanding water and trash fees. Details of the plan are included. **Availability:** Online.

4784 ■ "Dog Days and Stimulus Fatigue" in Barron's (Vol. 92, August 25, 2012, No. 38, pp. M10)
Pub: Dow Jones & Company Inc.
Contact: Almar Latour, Chief Executive Officer

Ed: Michael Aneiro. **Description:** Credit market movements in August 2012 have been influenced by small news and speculation. US Federal Reserve

Chairman Ben Bernanke has been more transparent, yet this transparency can also confound investors. **Availability:** Online.

4785 ■ *EBay Income: How ANYONE of Any Age, Location, and/or Background Can Build a Highly Profitable Online Business with eBay*
Pub: Atlantic Publishing Co.
Contact: Dr. Heather L. Johnson, Contact
Description: A complete overview of eBay is given and guides any small company through the entire process of creating the auction and auction strategies, photography, writing copy, text and formatting, multiple sales, programming tricks, PayPal, accounting, creating marketing, merchandising, managing email lists, advertising plans, taxes and sales tax, best time to list items and for how long, sniping programs, international customers, opening a storefront, electronic commerce, buy-it now pricing, keywords, Google marketing and eBay secrets.

4786 ■ *"Economic Trends for Small Business"* in *Small Business Economic Trends (April 2008, pp. 1)*
Description: Summary of economic trends for small businesses in the U.S. is presented. Economic indicators such as capital spending, inventories and sales, inflation, and profits are given. Analysis of credit markets is also provided. **Availability:** Online.

4787 ■ *"End of the Beginning"* in *Canadian Business (Vol. 81, November 10, 2008, No. 19, pp. 17)*
Ed: David Wolf. **Released:** September 30, 2016.
Description: The freeze in the money markets and historic decline in equity markets around the world finally forced governments into aggressive coordinated action. The asset price inflation brought on by cheap credit will now work in reverse and the tightening of credit will be difficult economically. Canada is exposed to the fallout everywhere, given that the U.S, the U.K. and Japan buy 30 percent of Canada's output. **Availability:** Print; Online.

4788 ■ *"Fight Ensues Over Irreplaceable Princess Diana Gowns"* in *Tampa Bay Business Journal (Vol. 30, January 15, 2010, No. 4, pp. 1)*
Pub: Tampa Bay Business Journal
Contact: Ian Anderson, President
E-mail: ianderson@bizjournals.com
Ed: Janet Leiser. **Description:** People's Princess Charitable Foundation Inc. founder Maureen Rorech Dunkel has sought Chapter 11 bankruptcy protection before a state court decides on the fate of the five of 13 Princess Diana Gowns. Dunkel and the nonprofit were sued by Patricia Sullivan of HRH Venture LLC who claimed they defaulted on $1.5 million in loans. **Availability:** Print; Online.

4789 ■ *"Firms Sue Doracon to Recoup More Than $1M in Unpaid Bills"* in *Baltimore Business Journal (Vol. 28, July 9, 2010, No. 9, pp. 1)*
Pub: Baltimore Business Journal
Contact: Rhonda Pringle, President
E-mail: rpringle@bizjournals.com
Ed: Scott Dance. **Description:** Concrete supplier Paul J. Rach Inc., Selective Insurance Company, and equipment leasing firm Colonial Pacific Leasing Corporation intend to sue Baltimore, Maryland-based Doracon Contracting Inc. for $1 million in unpaid bills. Doracon owed Colonial Pacific $794,000 and the equipment is still in Doracon's possession. Selective Insurance and Paul J. Rach respectively seek $132,000 and $88,000. **Availability:** Print.

4790 ■ *"Former Collection Agency CFO Sentenced"* in *PaymentsSource (April 24, 2012)*
Description: Leslie Jean McIntosh, CFO of FITEC LLC, a collection agency located in Kalispell, Montana was sentenced to 21 months in federal prison for tax evasion. McIntosh was ordered to pay $159,000 in restitution. McIntosh deposited $131,000 in client money into her personal account. **Availability:** Print; Online.

4791 ■ *"Identity Theft Can Have Long-Lasting Impact"* in *Providence Business News (Vol. 28, February 10, 2014, No. 45, pp. 7)*
Pub: American City Business Journals, Inc.
Contact: Mike Olivieri, Executive Vice President
URL(s): pbn.com/identity-theft-can-have-long-lasting-impact94959
Description: According to mortgage credit experts, recently reported massive data breaches at Nieman Marcus, Target, and other merchants could have negative impacts on several real estate deals scheduled for the upcoming months. Although victims are not liable for the unlawful debts, their credit reports and scores can be damaged for months, thus endangering loan applications for mortgages on home sale transactions. **Availability:** Online.

4792 ■ *"Illinois Regulators Revoke Collection Agency's License"* in *Collections & Credit Risk (Vol. 15, August 1, 2010, No. 7, pp. 13)*
Pub: SourceMedia LLC
Contact: Gemma Postlethwaite, Chief Executive Officer
Description: Creditors Service Bureau of Springfield, Illinois had its license revoked by a state regulatory agency and was fined $55,000 because the owner and president, Craig W. Lewis, did not turn over portions of collected funds to clients. **Availability:** Print; Online.

4793 ■ *"Indiana Collection Agency Announces Expansion Plans"* in *PaymentsSource (March 23, 2012)*
Description: DECA Financial Services plans to buy a vacant building in Fishers, Indiana and renovate the property. The agency specializes in collection consumer and tax debts for both companies and government agencies. The company plans to hire 140 new employees over the next 3 years. **Availability:** Print; Mailing list.

4794 ■ *"Indiana Town Reports Success With Collection Agency"* in *PaymentsSource (August 20, 2012)*
Description: Capital Recovery Systems has collected nearly $80,000 in unpaid parking fines in Bloomington, Indiana. The city's agreement with the collection agency allows them to pursue an unlimited amount of unpaid parking tickets at least 30 days late. **Availability:** Print; Online.

4795 ■ *"Industry Associations Seek Clarity of CFPB's Large Collection Agency Definition"* in *PaymentsSource (May 24, 2012)*
Description: ACA International and DBA International are questioning the Consumer Financial Protection Bureau's definition of a large collection agency. The ACA has filed comments arguing that the threshold needs to be raised to $250 million, rather than the $10 million or more in annual receipts or money recovered as its definition. Details are provided. **Availability:** Print; Online.

4796 ■ *"Lawsuit Seeks To Shut Down Illinois Collection Agency"* in *PaymentsSource (January 12, 2012)*
Pub: SourceMedia LLC
Contact: Gemma Postlethwaite, Chief Executive Officer
Description: PN Financial is facing charges by the Illinois State Attorney General's Office, alleging that the company used abusive and threatening actions against consumers. Details of the lawsuit are covered. **Availability:** Online.

4797 ■ *"Littleton Firm Chips In On Security Solution"* in *Denver Business Journal (Vol. 65, May 9, 2014, No. 52, pp. A6)*
Pub: American City Business Journals, Inc.
Contact: Mike Olivieri, Executive Vice President
Released: Weekly. **Price:** $4, introductory 4-week offer(Digital & Print). **Description:** CPI Card Group of Littleton, Colorado has been preparing for the nationwide transition to computer chip cards to secure credit and debit cards in the U.S. Banks and merchants in the country need to make the switch by October 2015 or risk being financially liable for fraud if not using the chipped cards in their retail establishments. **Availability:** Print; Online.

4798 ■ *"Making Automated Royalty Payments Work for Your Franchise"* in *Franchising World (Vol. 42, October 2010, No. 10, pp. 30)*
Pub: International Franchise Association
Contact: Matthew Haller, President
E-mail: mhaller@franchise.org
Ed: J.P. O'Brien. **Released:** October 10, 2010.
Description: In the past, royalty payments were sent by franchisees through regular postal mail and accompanied by a single slip of paper with handwritten notes indicating the month's revenue numbers and royalty amounts. **Availability:** PDF; Online.

4799 ■ *"Markets: The Great Deleveraging"* in *Canadian Business (Vol. 81, October 13, 2008, No. 17, pp. 45)*
Pub: Rogers Media Inc.
Contact: Neil Spivak, Chief Executive Officer
Ed: Jeff Sanford. **Description:** 'Hell Week' of financial crisis on Wall Street is believed to have started with the downgrade of AIG Inc.'s credit rating. AIG is a major player in the credit derivatives market, and its bankruptcy would have affected firms on Wall Street. **Availability:** Online.

4800 ■ *"Md.'s Boring Bonds Gain Pizzazz as Investors Flock to Debt Issues"* in *Baltimore Business Journal (Vol. 28, June 11, 2010, No. 5, pp. 1)*
Pub: Baltimore Business Journal
Contact: Rhonda Pringle, President
E-mail: rpringle@bizjournals.com
Ed: Gary Haber. **Description:** Companies and nonprofit organizations have increased the pace of bond offerings in order to take advantage of the bonds' appeal among willing investors. Companies mostly issued corporate bonds to replace existing debt at lower interest rates and save them money from interest payments.

4801 ■ *"Medical Collection Agency Refutes Allegations In AG's Report"* in *PaymentsSource (May 1, 2012)*
Description: Accretive Health Inc. denies allegations by the Minnesota State Attorney General's Office that the firm used heavy-handed tactics pressuring patients to pay for services before receiving treatment. The medical collection agency's report states 'inaccuracies, innuendo and unfounded speculation' in the charges. **Availability:** Print; Online.

4802 ■ *"The Mortgage Red Flags that Bankers See"* in *Providence Business News (Vol. 29, August 4, 2014, No. 18, pp. 9)*
Pub: American City Business Journals, Inc.
Contact: Mike Olivieri, Executive Vice President
URL(s): pbn.com/the-mortgage-red-flags-that-bankers-see98980
Description: A survey of credit-score company FICO reveals that an excessive debt-to-income (DTI) ratio is the biggest reason why credit-risk managers reject potential new home buyers when applying for mortgages. Other factors that affect mortgage applications include new buyers credit scores and numerous recent credit applications.

4803 ■ *"North Carolina Town Hires Collection Agency"* in *PaymentsSource (April 24, 2012)*
Description: Selma, North Carolina hired TekCollect to collect about $500,000 in unpaid utility bills. The collection agency will be paid $13,000 up frnt for guaranteed collections on 500 of the 1,200 acccounts. **Availability:** Online.

4804 ■ *"Ohio Regulator Sues Collection Agency"* in PaymentsSource (September 21, 2012)
Pub: SourceMedia LLC
Contact: Gemma Postlethwaite, Chief Executive Officer
Description: Mike DeWine, Ohio Attorney General, is suing Royal Oak Financial Services, a collection agency doing business as Collection and Recovery Bureau. The suit alleges that the firm used collection tactics banned by federal law and also attempting to collect unverified debts.

4805 ■ *"Portfolio Recovery Associates Expands Its Hampton Call Center"* in Marketwired (January 20, 2010)
Pub: Comtex News Network Inc.
Contact: Kan Devnani, President
Description: Entering into a lease amendment in order to expand its Hampton, Virginia call center and extend its lease agreement, Portfolio Recovery Associates, Inc., a company that collects, purchases and manages defaulted consumer debt, plans to upgrade the existing space enabling them to draw on local talent. **Availability:** Print; Online.

4806 ■ *Practical Debt Collecting for Small Companies and Traders*
Description: Credit and collection guide for small companies. **Availability:** Online.

4807 ■ *"Scoring Boost Should be Coming for Renters' Credit"* in Providence Business News (Vol. 29, July 14, 2014, No. 15, pp. 7)
Pub: American City Business Journals, Inc.
Contact: Mike Olivieri, Executive Vice President
Released: July 12, 2014. **Description:** National credit bureaus, Experian and TransUnion, are working with online rental payment service RentTrack to include verified rental payment data into credit files so that it may be included in calculating consumer scores during mortgage applications. In addition, a study by TransUnion finds that consumer scores increase when their rental data is included in bureau records and when they move from renter status to homeowner. **Availability:** Print; Online.

4808 ■ *"Senator Grills Collection Agency, Health System Executives"* in Collections & Credit Risk (May 31, 2012)
Pub: SourceMedia LLC
Contact: Gemma Postlethwaite, Chief Executive Officer
Description: Accretive Health Inc. and Fairview Health Services executives were questioned by Senator Al Franken about its debt collection practices. The suit was initiated after unencrypted private information on 23,500 patients was stolen from an Acrretive employee's vehicle. Details of the lawsuit are outlined.

4809 ■ *"Summary. Economic Trends for Small Business"* in Small Business Economic Trends (February 2008, pp. 1)
Pub: National Federation of Independent Business
Contact: Brad Close, President
Ed: William C. Dunkelberg, Holly Wade. **Description:** Summary of economic trends for small businesses in the U.S. is provided. Economic indicators such as capital spending, inventories and sales, inflation, and profits are given. Analysis of credit markets is also provided.

4810 ■ *"The Survey Says"* in Collections and Credit Risk (Vol. 14, September 1, 2009, No. 8, pp. 16)
Description: Revenue for the top accounts receivable management firms rose nearly 20 percent in 2008 despite lower liquidation rates, a poor economy and riskier, albeit cheaper debt portfolios; the trend may continue this year as collection agencies expect revenue, on average, to increase 5.8 percent. Debt buyers, however, found that their revenue fell nearly 7 percent in 2008 and expect it to fall another 12 percent this year. **Availability:** Print; Online.

4811 ■ *"Travel Rewards Take Off"* in Inc. (Vol. 33, October 2011, No. 8, pp. 46)
Description: Credit card companies are offering travel reward cards with special perks, including sign-up bonuses; three such cards are described. **Availability:** Online.

4812 ■ *"Two Major Credit Reporting Agencies Have Been Lying to Consumers"* in The Atlantic (January 4, 2017)
URL(s): www.theatlantic.com/business/archive/2017/01/credit-scores-cfpb/512162/
Ed: Gillian B. White. **Released:** January 04, 2017.
Description: The Consumer Financial Protection Bureau found that Equifax and Tansunion have been deceiving consumers and must pay $23 million in fines and restitution. **Availability:** Online.

4813 ■ *"Unfair Distraction of Employees"* in Business Owner (Vol. 35, March-April 2011, No. 2, pp. 8)
Description: Fair Credit Collection Practices Act makes it illegal for collectors to contact a debtor at his or her place of employment if the collector is made aware that it is against personnel policy of the employer for the worker to take such a call. **Availability:** Print; Online.

4814 ■ *"Unlicensed Utah Collection Agency Settles with State Finance Department"* in Idaho Business Review, Boise (July 15, 2010)
Pub: Idaho Business Review
Contact: Autumn Kersey, Sales Executive
E-mail: akersey@idahobusinessreview.com
Description: Federal Recovery Acceptance Inc., doing business as Paramount Acceptance in Utah, agreed to pay penalties and expenses after the firm was investigated by the state for improprieties. The firm was charged with conducting unlicensed collection activity. **Availability:** Print; Online.

4815 ■ *"Utah Collection Agency Settles File-Sharing Charges"* inPaymentsSource (June 11, 2012)
Pub: SourceMedia LLC
Contact: Gemma Postlethwaite, Chief Executive Officer
Ed: Darren Waggoner. **Description:** EPN Inc., doing business as Checknet Inc., settled charges filed by the Federal Trade Commission that it exposed sensitive information on its computers and networks creating a potential security risk to the consumer information it stored. Details of the suit are provided.

4816 ■ *"What the Future Holds for Consumers"* in Black Enterprise (Vol. 41, August 2010, No. 1, pp. 47)
Pub: Earl G. Graves Ltd.
Contact: Earl Graves, Jr., President
Ed: Sheiresa Ngo. **Description:** The way people purchase goods and service has changed with technology. With an increased focus on security (as well as privacy and fairness) the U.S. Congress began regulating the credit card industry with the Fair Credit Reporting Act of 1970 and the Credit Card Accountability, Responsibility, and Disclosure (CARD) Act of 2009. **Availability:** Online.

4817 ■ *"What Is a Credit Card Issuer?"* in The Balance (July 30, 2018)
URL(s): www.thebalance.com/credit-card-issuer-9 59984
Ed: Latoya Irby. **Released:** July 30, 2018. **Description:** Provides a clear explanation of what a credit card issuer is, their responsibilites to merchants, how they issue credit cards. **Availability:** Online.

4818 ■ *"A Word With Connie Runia of Collection Bureau"* in Idaho Business Review (September 8, 2014)
Pub: BridgeTower Media
Contact: Adam Reinebach, President
Description: Connie Runia, attorney and general counsel for Collection Bureau, located in Nampa, Idaho, joined the firm four years ago. These collection bureaus are licensed by the Department of Finance and regulated by the Federal Trade Commission. The Consumer Financial Protection Bureau is developing new rules for collection agencies. Statistical data included. **Availability:** Online.

4819 ■ *"Your Guide to Credit Counseling Services"* in Forbes Advisor (August 3, 2021)
Ed: Rebecca Lake, Daphne Foreman. **Released:** August 03, 2021. **Description:** Discusses the role consumer credit counseling plays in helping people get their personal debt under control.

TRADE PERIODICALS

4820 ■ *Collector: The Official Publication of the ACA International*
Pub: ACA International
Contact: Alhaji David Williams, President
URL(s): www.acainternational.org/news/publications
Released: Bimonthly; we also print one special edition a year: the July/August issue. **Description:** Magazine on consumer credit and debt collection services. **Availability:** Print; PDF; Online.

FRANCHISES AND BUSINESS OPPORTUNITIES

4821 ■ **National Tenant Network Inc. (NTN)**
PO Box 1664
Lake Oswego, OR 97035
Free: 800-228-0989
Fax: (800)340-1116
Co. E-mail: info@ntnonline.com
URL: http://ntnonline.com
Description: Resident screening company. **Founded:** 1980. **Financial Assistance:** Yes **Training:** Yes.

COMPUTER SYSTEMS/SOFTWARE

4822 ■ *Collection-Master*
URL(s): www.collectionsoftware.com
Description: Available for IBM computers and compatibles. System provides collection agencies with data management and word processing. **Availability:** Online.

4823 ■ *ComtronicSystems Debtmaster: Debt Collection Software*
Comtronic Systems LLC.
110 E 2nd St.
Cle Elum, WA 98922
Ph: (509)573-4300
Free: 800-414-2814
Co. E-mail: sales@comtronic.com
URL: http://www.comtronicsystems.com
Contact: Jeffrey A. Dantzler, Governor
URL(s): debtmaster.com/debtmaster
Description: Debt collector software with varied capabilities such as collector work schedules, account assignments, and general ledger accounting. **Availability:** Online.

LIBRARIES

4824 ■ **RMA Information Center (RMA)**
2005 Market St., 1 Commerce Sq.
Philadelphia, PA 19103
Free: 800-677-7621
Fax: (215)446-4100
Co. E-mail: customers@rmahq.org
URL: http://www.rmahq.org/?gmssopc=1
Contact: Jodi Richard, Chairman of the Board
Description: A member-driven professional association whose sole purpose is to advance sound risk management principles in the financial services industry. **Scope:** Banking and finance; lending/credit; industry/analysis. **Services:** Library not open to the public. **Subscriptions:** periodicals (includes journals) 1,500 books.

Damage Restoration Service

ASSOCIATIONS AND OTHER ORGANIZATIONS

4825 ■ National Association of Flood and Stormwater Management Agencies (NAFSMA)
PO Box 56764
Washington, DC 20040
Ph: (202)289-8625
Co. E-mail: info@nafsma.org
URL: http://www.nafsma.org
Contact: Steve Parrish, President

Description: State, county, and local governments; special districts concerned with management of water resources. Objectives are to reduce or eliminate flooding and provide for improved storm water management and conservation of watersheds. **Founded:** 1978. **Publications:** *NAFSMA Bulletin*; *NAFSMA Newsletter* (Monthly); *Survey of Local Storm Water Utilities*. **Geographic Preference:** National.

4826 ■ University of Colorado at Boulder - Natural Hazards Center - Library
1440 15th St.
Boulder, CO 80309
Ph: (303)735-5844
Fax: (303)492-2151
Co. E-mail: hazctr@colorado.edu
URL: http://hazards.colorado.edu
Contact: Lori Peek, Director
E-mail: lori.peek@colorado.edu
URL(s): www.colorado.edu/geologicalsciences/research/natural-hazards
Facebook: www.facebook.com/hazcenter
X (Twitter): x.com/HazCenter

Description: Advances and communicates knowledge on hazards mitigation and disaster preparedness, response, and recovery. Fosters information sharing and integration of activities among researchers, practitioners, and policy makers from around the world; supports and conducts research; and provides educational opportunities for the next generation of hazards scholars and professionals. **Scope:** National clearinghouse of research information concerned with economic loss, human suffering, and social disruption caused by earthquakes, floods, hurricanes, and other natural disasters. Emphasizes strengthening communications among research workers, individuals, organizations, and agencies concerned with public action relating to natural hazards. Supports University research in the area of natural hazards. Provides a quick response program to send researchers to the site of disasters soon after their occurrence. **Services:** Interlibrary loan (limited); open to the public; copying (limited). **Founded:** 1976. **Holdings:** Figures not available. **Publications:** *Natural Hazards Informer* (Periodic); *Natural Hazards Research Working Papers*; *Disaster Research (DR)*; *Natural Hazards Observer* (Bimonthly); *Quick Response Research Reports Series* (Periodic); *Special Publications Series* (Periodic); *Topical Bibliographies Series*. **Educational Activities:** Invitational Workshop on Natural Hazards (Annual), Exhibit relating to hazard research.; Hazards Research and Applications Workshop (Annual). **Awards:** Mary Fran Myers Scholarship (Annual). **Geographic Preference:** National.

REFERENCE WORKS

4827 ■ "Web Exclusive: What happens after disaster strikes?" in Hotel Business (October 21, 2021)
URL(s): www.hotelbusiness.com/web-exclusive-what-happens-after-disaster-strikes

Ed: Abby Elyssa. **Description:** When a disaster strikes a community, hotels are often the first place affected people turn to, but what happens when the hotel is hit by disaster? Tips on choosing restoration partners and what to expect out of the process are explained. **Availability:** Online.

TRADE PERIODICALS

4828 ■ *Cleaning & Restoration*
Pub: Restoration Industry Association
Contact: Ben Looper, President
URL(s): www.candrmagazine.com
Facebook: www.facebook.com/CandRMagazine
Linkedin: www.linkedin.com/company/c-r-magazine
Instagram: www.instagram.com/candrmagazine
YouTube: www.youtube.com/channel/UCTcMptOovWyW7re6tvfYm6g

Released: Quarterly **Description:** Journal covering drapery, rug, upholstery, and carpet cleaning; fire and water damage; and disaster restoration and mechanical systems cleaning and inspection. **Availability:** Print; Online.

TRADE SHOWS AND CONVENTIONS

4829 ■ Can Clean
ISSA Canada
910 Dundas St. W
Whitby, ON, Canada L1P 1P7
Ph: (905)665-8001
Free: 866-684-8273
Co. E-mail: info@issa-canada.com
URL: http://www.issa-canada.com/en
Contact: Mike Nosko, Executive Director
E-mail: mike@issa-canada.com
URL(s): cssa.com/2015n/en/events/trade-shows/can-clean-2015-m

Frequency: Annual. **Description:** Sanitary maintenance products. **Audience:** Cleaning and maintenance professionals. **Principal Exhibits:** Sanitary maintenance products.

4830 ■ Restoration Industry Association International Restoration Convention & Industry Expo
Restoration Industry Association (RIA)
1120 Rte. 73, Ste. 200
Mount Laurel, NJ 08054
Ph: (856)439-9222
Co. E-mail: info@restorationindustry.org
URL: http://www.restorationindustry.org
Contact: Ben Looper, President
URL(s): convention.restorationindustry.org

Frequency: Annual. **Description:** Carpet, upholstery, and draperies cleaning and restoration equipment, duct cleaning supplies and services. **Audience:** Restoration and reconstruction professionals, and vendors. **Principal Exhibits:** Carpet, upholstery, and draperies cleaning and restoration equipment, duct cleaning supplies and services. Dates and Locations: 2025 Apr 28-30 West Palm Beach, FL. **Telecommunication Services:** meetings@restorationindustry.org.

FRANCHISES AND BUSINESS OPPORTUNITIES

4831 ■ Deck Renewal Systems USA L.L.C.
505 E Pearl St.
Miamisburg, OH 45342
Ph: (937)434-3256
Co. E-mail: cincinnati@deckrenewalsystems.com
URL: http://deckrenewalsystems.com
Facebook: www.facebook.com/DeckFencerenewalsystems
YouTube: www.youtube.com/channel/UC9siJiHTMxnKIRcfL26pg4A

Description: Firm provides wood restoration services such as deck cleaning, sealing and repairing services. **Founded:** 1993. **Training:** 1 week training at headquarters, 1 week at franchisee's location and ongoing support.

4832 ■ Disaster Kleenup International (DKI)
DKI Ventures, LLC
25 NW Point Blvd., Ste. 1000
Elk Grove Village, IL 60007
Ph: (630)350-3000
Free: 877-307-1621
Fax: (630)350-9354
URL: http://www.dkiservices.com
Facebook: www.facebook.com/DKIservices
Linkedin: www.linkedin.com/company/dki-services-corp
X (Twitter): x.com/DisasterKleenup
YouTube: www.youtube.com/user/DisasterKleen

Description: Provider of property restoration services to residential, commercial and insurance customers. **Founded:** 1974. **Franchised:** 1994. **Financial Assistance:** No **Training:** Offers 1 day and ongoing training, including 2-5 days national & regional conferences & meetings.

4833 ■ Servpro Industries, Inc.
801 Industrial Blvd.
Gallatin, TN 37066
Ph: (615)451-0200
Fax: (615)675-2312
Co. E-mail: franchisesales@servpronet.com
URL: http://www.servpro.com
Contact: Rick Forster, President
Facebook: www.facebook.com/SERVPRO
Linkedin: www.linkedin.com/company/servpro-industries
X (Twitter): x.com/servpro
YouTube: www.youtube.com/user/SERVPROCorporate

Description: Provider of cleaning and restoration services. **Founded:** 1967. **Educational Activities:** PLRB Claims Conference & Insurance Services Expo (Annual).

Dance School

ASSOCIATIONS AND OTHER ORGANIZATIONS

4834 ■ American Dance Guild (ADG)
c/o Gloria McLean, President
320 W 83rd St., Apt. 7D
New York, NY 10024
Co. E-mail: adgfest@gmail.com
URL: http://www.americandanceguild.org
Contact: Gloria McLean, President
E-mail: gloria.mclean@earthlink.net
Facebook: www.facebook.com/AmericanDanceGuild
X (Twitter): x.com/ADGfestival
Instagram: www.instagram.com/adgfestival
Description: Serves the dance professional by providing: a networking system between dance artists and dance educators; an informed voice on behalf of the dance field to governmental, educational and corporate institutions and the general public; international dance festivals, conferences and dance film festivals; educational publications and videos; the ADG Fannie Weiss Scholarship; the ADG Harkness Resource for Dance Study. **Founded:** 1956. **Publications:** *ADG Newsletter* (Semiannual); *Souvenir Journal* (Annual). **Awards:** American Dance Guild Annual Award (Annual); Jacob's Pillow Scholarship (Annual). **Geographic Preference:** National.

4835 ■ American Dance Therapy Association (ADTA)
10632 Little Patuxent Pky., Ste. 108
Columbia, MD 21044
Ph: (410)997-4040
Fax: (410)997-4048
URL: http://www.adta.org
Contact: Ambria Cunningham, Secretary
E-mail: secretary@adta.org
Facebook: www.facebook.com/AmericanDanceTherapyAssociation
Description: Individuals professionally practicing dance therapy, students interested in becoming dance therapists, university departments with dance therapy programs, and individuals in related therapeutic fields. Establishes and maintains high standards of professional education and competence in dance therapy. **Founded:** 1966. **Publications:** *American Dance Therapy Association--Membership Directory*; *Conference Proceedings* (Annual); *Dance Therapy Bibliography*; *American Journal of Dance Therapy* (Semiannual). **Geographic Preference:** National.

4836 ■ American Society for the Alexander Technique (AMSAT)
22640 Hazel Ln.
Rapid City, SD 57702
Ph: (937)586-3732
Free: 800-473-0620
Co. E-mail: info@amsatonline.org
URL: http://alexandertechniqueusa.org
Contact: Lisa DeAngelis, Chairman of the Board
Facebook: www.facebook.com/AmSATonline
Linkedin: www.linkedin.com/company/american-society-for-the-alexander-technique

X (Twitter): x.com/amsatonline
Description: Promotes communication and the interchange of skills and information between the society and other teachers in the Alexander Technique (a method for improving posture). Works to achieve reciprocal memberships between such organizations. **Founded:** 1987. **Publications:** *AMSAT News* (Quarterly); *List of Certified Training Courses* (Annual); *Teaching Members List* (Annual). **Educational Activities:** Annual Conference and General Meeting (ACGM) (Annual). **Geographic Preference:** National.

4837 ■ Cecchetti Council of America (CCA)
23393 Meadows Ave.
Flat Rock, MI 48134
Ph: (734)379-6710
Fax: (734)379-3886
Co. E-mail: ccainfo@aol.com
URL: http://www.cecchetti.org
Contact: Laura McCarthy, President
E-mail: laura.mccarthy@comcast.net
Facebook: www.facebook.com/cecchettiamerica
Description: Aims to raise the quality of ballet teaching and to promote the Cecchetti method of ballet training. (Named for Cavalier Enrico Cecchetti, 1850-1928, Italian ballet dancer and teacher.) Uses the teachings and writings of Cecchetti in a sequence of grades measured to the degree of difficulty and physical development; provides a system of accredited examinations to test the student's proficiency within those grades. **Founded:** 1951. **Publications:** *National CCA Newsletter* (Semiannual). **Geographic Preference:** National.

4838 ■ Country Dance and Song Society (CDSS)
116 Pleasant St., Ste. 345
Easthampton, MA 01027-2759
Ph: (413)203-5467
Fax: (413)203-5471
Co. E-mail: address@cdss.org
URL: http://www.cdss.org
Contact: Gaye Fifer, President
Facebook: www.facebook.com/cdss.org
Instagram: www.instagram.com/CDSSorg
YouTube: www.youtube.com/user/CDSSorg
Description: Amateur and professional musicians; dance historians and recreational dancers. Promotes modern use of English and Anglo-American folk dances, songs, and music. Holds 11 week-long adult camps per year and 3 week-long family camps. **Founded:** 1915. **Publications:** *Country Dance and Song Society--Group Directory*; *Country Dance and Song Society--Newsletter* (Quarterly). **Geographic Preference:** National.

4839 ■ Cross-Cultural Dance Resources, Inc. (CCDR) - Library
611 E Orange St., Rm. 120
Tempe, AZ 85281
Ph: (602)790-0363
Co. E-mail: ccdr@ccdr.org
URL: http://www.ccdr.org

Contact: Pegge Vissicaro, President
Description: Promotes dance performances; preserves and researches dance materials. **Scope:** Performing arts, focusing on dance cultures. **Founded:** 1981. **Holdings:** 15,000 monographs, journals, photographs, slides, films, video, audio recordings, dolls, textiles, cultural artifacts, musical instruments, masks, costumes, puppets. **Publications:** *CCDR Newsletter* (Periodic); *Tibet Week in Flagstaff*. **Educational Activities:** CCDR Symposium. **Geographic Preference:** Multinational.

4840 ■ Dance Educators of America (DEA)
PO Box 740387
Boynton Beach, FL 33474
Ph: (914)636-3200
Co. E-mail: info@dancedea.com
URL: http://www.dancedea.com
Contact: Kelli Dickens, President
E-mail: president@dancedea.com
Facebook: www.facebook.com/DanceEducatorsofAmerica
Instagram: www.instagram.com/dancedea
YouTube: www.youtube.com/channel/UCQ7jBt342tNiyVsZcbssp8A
Description: Qualified dance teachers who pass an examination and subscribe to a code of ethics and advertising rules and regulations. Promotes teachers education in the performing arts and stage arts and of dance in all its forms. Conducts training schools at New York and Las Vegas. **Founded:** 1932. **Educational Activities:** Dance Educators of America Seminar. **Geographic Preference:** Multinational.

4841 ■ Dance Notation Bureau (DNB) - Library
178 E 109th St. No. 5
New York, NY 10029
Ph: (212)571-7011
Co. E-mail: dnbinfo@dancenotation.org
URL: http://www.dancenotation.org
Contact: Lynne Weber, Executive Director
E-mail: lynnjweber@aol.com
Facebook: www.facebook.com/DanceNotationBureau
Description: Documents dance works through the use of graphic notation. Conducts research into movement-related analysis techniques and programs. Maintains extension at Ohio State University, Columbus. Maintains placement service; assists choreographers in copyrighting, licensing, and restaging of their dance works. Offers service for dance reconstructors and circulating library materials to members. Maintains archive of original Labanotated dance scores in the world. **Scope:** Dance; lab notated dance scores. **Services:** Copying; open to the public by appointment. **Founded:** 1940. **Holdings:** Audiotapes; videotapes. **Educational Activities:** Dance Notation Bureau Professional Advisory Committee. **Geographic Preference:** Multinational.

4842 ■ International Association for Creative Dance (IACD)
c/o Ethridge, 325 W 45 St., No. 303A
New York, NY 10036

Co. E-mail: iacdwebsite@gmail.com
URL: http://www.dancecreative.org
Contact: Yael Schweitzer, President
Facebook: www.facebook.com/iacdance
Description: Represents individuals with an interest in Mettler-based creative dance. Works to advance the field of creative dance and sponsors opportunities for the study and teaching of creative dance. **Founded:** 1996. **Educational Activities:** Creative Dance Congress (Annual). **Geographic Preference:** Multinational.

4843 ■ **International Dance Entrepreneurs Association (IDEA)**
PO Box 2150
Norton, MA 02766
Ph: (508)285-6650
Co. E-mail: customerservice@ideadance.org
URL: http://ideadance.org
Contact: Greg Bettencourt, Executive Director
Facebook: www.facebook.com/IDEAMembership
Linkedin: www.linkedin.com/in/i-d-e-a-association-550606125
X (Twitter): x.com/ideaassociation
Instagram: www.instagram.com/ideaassociation
Description: Strives to assist owners of dance schools to growth their businesses and create a culture that fosters successful dance students in a professional and supportive environment. **Founded:** 2016.

4844 ■ **International Tap Association (ITA)**
7325 Gaines Mill Ln.
Austin, TX 78745
URL: http://www.tapdancingresources.com/organizations/by-name/international-tap-association.html
Description: Promotes understanding, preservation, and development of tap dance as an art form. Encourages the creation of new tap performance venues and touring circuits. Preserves the history of tap through archival documentation and research. Establishes support mechanisms and communication networks for tap. **Founded:** 1987. **Publications:** On Tap (5/year). **Geographic Preference:** Multinational.

4845 ■ **National Association of Schools of Dance (NASD)**
11250 Roger Bacon Dr., Ste. 21
Reston, VA 20190-5248
Ph: (703)437-0700
Fax: (703)437-6312
Co. E-mail: info@arts-accredit.org
URL: http://nasd.arts-accredit.org
Contact: Karen P. Moynahan, Executive Director
E-mail: kmoynahan@arts-accredit.org
Description: Serves as accrediting agency for educational programs in dance. Provides prospective students with current, accurate information about schools offering instruction in dance. Seeks to establish standards in the field regarding budget, class time requirements, faculty qualifications, faculty-student ratios, and library and physical facilities. **Founded:** 1981. **Publications:** NASD Handbook. **Geographic Preference:** National.

4846 ■ **National Ballroom & Entertainment Association (NBEA)**
c/o Larry Bowers, President
200 Chestnut St.
Mankato, MN 56001
Ph: (507)304-0421
Co. E-mail: nbea@hickorytech.net
URL: http://www.nbea.com
Contact: Larry Bowers, President
E-mail: nbea@hickorytech.net
Facebook: www.facebook.com/thenbea
Description: Represents owners and operators of ballrooms; entertainment members are band leaders and others in positions related to live music dancing. **Founded:** 1947. **Geographic Preference:** National.

4847 ■ **NextMove Dance (NMD)**
1412 Chestnut St.
Philadelphia, PA 19102
URL: http://princetheater.org/next-move
Contact: Randy Swartz, Director
Description: Selects the U.S. team for participation in the annual International Ballet Competition (the "Olympics of Dance"). Works to establish the U.S. as a major force in ballet; to stimulate interest in international competitions and festivals; to encourage young American dancers to strive for world-class excellence; and to build an ongoing program to finance and support further international competitions. Raises funds from private and corporate sources; secures federal grants and sells promotional items. **Founded:** 1979. **Geographic Preference:** National.

4848 ■ **Royal Academy of Dance (RAD)**
2625 S Greeley St., No. 360
Milwaukee, WI 53207
Ph: (414)747-9060
Co. E-mail: info@radusa.org
URL: http://us.royalacademyofdance.org
Contact: Dame Darcey Bussell, President
Facebook: www.facebook.com/RoyalAcademyofDanceUSA
Linkedin: www.linkedin.com/company/royal-academy-of-dance
Instagram: www.instagram.com/royalacademyofdance
Description: International examining body working to maintain a high standard of classical ballet training. Provides teachers with an examination syllabus. Conducts teachers' courses and summer schools for children and teachers. **Founded:** 1920. **Educational Activities:** Royal Academy of Dance Teachers' Workshop. **Geographic Preference:** Multinational.

REFERENCE WORKS

4849 ■ **"21 Dance Studio Industry Stats for 2021" in Studio Director (January 28, 2021)**
Released: January 28, 2021. **Description:** Discusses revenue stats, demographics, and an overview of the dance studio industry for 2021.

4850 ■ **"67 Creative and Effective Ways to Get Students to Register for Dance Class" in DanceStudioOwner**
URL(s): www.dancestudioowner.com/public/67_Ways_Register_for_Class.cfm
Description: A list of ideas for small dance studio owners to use to get students to sign up for dance classes. **Availability:** Online.

4851 ■ **"Artscape Looks for Last Big Donations" in Baltimore Business Journal (Vol. 32, July 11, 2014, No. 10, pp. 4)**
Pub: American City Business Journals, Inc.
Contact: Mike Olivieri, Executive Vice President
Released: Weekly. **Price:** $4, introductory 4-week offer(Digital only). **Description:** Kathy Hornig, festivals director for Baltimore's Office of Promotion and the Arts, discusses last-minute efforts to raise the final $100,000 in donations for Artscape from mobile marketers and festival goers. The event, to be held July 18-23, 2014 in Baltimore, will focus on dance and movement. **Availability:** Print; Online.

4852 ■ **Dance Magazine College Guide**
Pub: Dance Magazine Inc.
Contact: Joanna Harp, President
E-mail: jharp@dancemedia.com
URL(s): collegeguide.dancemagazine.com
Ed: Karen Hildebrand. **Description:** Covers approximately 600 college-level dance programs. **Entries include:** College name, address, phone, and name of contact for dance department; degrees offered; degree requirements; facilities; special programs; admission requirements; tuition and fees; financial aid available. Also includes articles on issues in dance education. **Arrangement:** Alphabetical, geographical. **Indexes:** College or University name. **Availability:** Print.

4853 ■ **"Inside the High-Drama World of Youth Competition Dance" in The New York Times (December 21, 2017)**
URL(s): www.nytimes.com/2017/12/21/magazine/inside-the-high-drama-world-of-youth-competition-dance.html
Ed: Lizzie Feidelson. **Released:** December 21, 2017. **Description:** A look inside the world of children's dance competitions and the amount of time, effort, and money that goes into entering these competitions. **Availability:** Online.

4854 ■ **National Guild for Community Arts Education--Membership Directory**
Pub: National Guild for Community Arts Education
Contact: Quanice G. Floyd, Executive Director
URL(s): nationalguild.org/member/member-directory
Description: Covers over 320 member schools, including community schools, social service centers, and collegiate divisions with programs in music, dance, drama, visual arts, and creative writing; about 150 individual members, business affiliate members, trustees, and board members; coverage includes Canada. **Entries include:** For schools--School name, address, phone, fax, e-mail addresses, website addresses, name and title of director, year established, year and status of NGCSA membership, number of branches (affiliate programs), areas of instruction, organizational affiliations, profile of school guild membership, special programs and classes, number of students. For individuals--Name, title, affiliation, address. For business affilates--Name, address, phone, fax, e-mail, website, name and title of main contacts, description of products and services. **Arrangement:** Institutions are geographical; individuals and business affiliates are alphabetical. **Indexes:** Regional chapter; school director; geographical. **Availability:** Online.

4855 ■ **"So You Think You Want to Own a Dance Studio?" in DanceTeacher (September 12, 2017)**
URL(s): www.dance-teacher.com/so-you-think-you-want-to-own-a-dance-studio-2392417191.html
Ed: Rachel Rizzuto. **Released:** September 12, 2017. **Description:** Tips on the best way to start your own dance studio businesses. Becoming an apprentice, making a name for yourself, and practicing good business techniques can help make a successful dance studio. **Availability:** Online.

4856 ■ **"Summer Camp Uses Dance to Teach Students Life Skills" in U.S. News & World Report (July 22, 2019)**
URL(s): www.usnews.com/news/best-states/georgia/articles/2019-07-22/summer-aileycamp-provides-dance-training-life-skills
Ed: Andrea Smith. **Released:** July 22, 2019. **Description:** Profile of AileyCamp, a free six-week program for young children facing a variety of difficulties, which has a focus on dance, arts, and writing. **Availability:** Online.

STATISTICAL SOURCES

4857 ■ **Ballet Schools Industry in the US - Market Research Report**
URL(s): www.ibisworld.com/united-states/market-research-reports/ballet-schools-industry/
Price: $925. **Description:** Downloadable report analyzing the current and future trends in the ballet school industry. **Availability:** Download.

TRADE PERIODICALS

4858 ■ **Country Dance and Song Society--Newsletter**
Pub: Country Dance and Song Society
Contact: Gaye Fifer, President

URL(s): cdss.org/publications/read/online-library/
sannella-annotated-bibliography
Released: Quarterly **Description:** Promotes the study and enjoyment of traditional Anglo-American and English folk dances, songs, and music. Carries Society news, reports from dance centers across the country, book reviews, and recordings. **Availability:** Print.

4859 ■ Dance International
Pub: Vancouver Ballet Society
Contact: Maureen Allen, President
URL(s): www.vancouverballetsociety.com/about
Facebook: www.facebook.com/DanceInternationalMagazine
X (Twitter): x.com/DIMagazine
Instagram: www.instagram.com/danceinternationalmagazine
Released: Quarterly **Description:** Magazine covering dance in Canada and worldwide. **Availability:** Print.

4860 ■ Dance Magazine
Pub: Dance Magazine Inc.
Contact: Joanna Harp, President
E-mail: jharp@dancemedia.com
Facebook: www.facebook.com/DanceMagazine
Linkedin: www.linkedin.com/showcase/dance-magazine
X (Twitter): x.com/dance_magazine
Instagram: www.instagram.com/dancemagazine
YouTube: www.youtube.com/c/dancemagazine
Pinterest: www.pinterest.com/dancemagazine
Ed: Wendy Perron. **Released:** Monthly **Price:** $29.95, for print 24 issues - two years; $19.95, for print 12 issues - one year; $8.99, Single issue. **Description:** Performing arts magazine featuring all forms of dance with profiles, news, photos, reviews of performances, and information on books, videos, films, schools, health, and technique. **Availability:** Print; Online.

TRADE SHOWS AND CONVENTIONS

4861 ■ California Association for Health, Physical Education, Recreation, and Dance State Conference
California Association for Health, Physical Education, Recreation, and Dance (CAHPERD)
1501 El Camino Ave., Ste. 3
Sacramento, CA 95815
Ph: (916)922-3596
Co. E-mail: reception@cahperd.org
URL: http://www.cahperd.org
Contact: Joanie Verderber, Treasurer
URL(s): www.cahperd.org/Public/Public/Conferences.aspx
Frequency: Annual. **Description:** Event includes reception and awards. **Audience:** Member and nonmember professionals, presenters, guests, and vendors. **Principal Exhibits:** Event includes reception and awards. Dates and Locations: 2025 Jan 22-25 Pasadena Convention Center, Pasadena, CA. **Telecommunication Services:** reception@cahperd.org.

FRANCHISES AND BUSINESS OPPORTUNITIES

4862 ■ Fred Astaire Dance Studios Inc. (FADS)
10 Bliss Rd.
Longmeadow, MA 01106
Ph: (413)567-3200
Fax: (413)565-2298
Co. E-mail: gilbert@fredastaire.com
URL: http://www.fredastaire.com
Contact: Sue Clark, Director

E-mail: sclark@fredastaire.com
Facebook: www.facebook.com/FredAstaireDanceStudios
X (Twitter): x.com/FredAstaireCorp
Instagram: www.instagram.com/fred_astaire_dance_studios
YouTube: www.youtube.com/user/fredastairedance
Description: Adult ballroom dance instruction. **Founded:** 1947. **Training:** Yes.

4863 ■ Webby Dance Co.
1369 E 28th St.
Signal Hill, CA 90755
Ph: (562)438-4466
Free: 888-243-2623
Co. E-mail: info@webbydancecompany.com
URL: http://webbydancecompany.com
Contact: Becky Weber, Owner
E-mail: bweber@webbydancecompany.com
Facebook: www.facebook.com/WEBBYDanceCompany
Description: Mobile dance business. **No. of Franchise Units:** 4. **No. of Company-Owned Units:** 2. **Founded:** 1975. **Franchised:** 1999. **Equity Capital Needed:** $22,700-$31,000. **Franchise Fee:** $15,000. **Training:** Yes.

LIBRARIES

4864 ■ Dance Films Association (DFA) - Library
75 Broad St., Ste. 304
New York, NY 10004
Ph: (347)505-8649
Co. E-mail: info@dancefilms.org
URL: http://www.dancefilms.org
Contact: Ron Honsa, President
Facebook: www.facebook.com/dancefilms
X (Twitter): x.com/DanceFilms
Instagram: www.instagram.com/dancefilms
Description: Strives to further the art of dance film. Connects artists and organizations. Fosters new works for new audiences and shares essential resources. Seeks to be a catalyst for innovation in and preservation of dance on camera. Conducts Dance On Camera Festival, annual event since 1971. Acts as a fiscal sponsor for dance filmmakers. **Scope:** Dance; film. **Founded:** 1956. **Holdings:** Figures not available. **Publications:** Dance on Camera Journal (Semimonthly). **Educational Activities:** Annual Dance on Camera Festival (Annual). **Awards:** DFA Production Grant (Annual). **Geographic Preference:** Multinational.

4865 ■ Los Angeles Public Library Arts, Music and Recreation Department
630 W 5th St.
Los Angeles, CA 90071
Ph: (213)228-7225
Fax: (213)228-7239
URL: http://www.lapl.org/branches/central-library/departments/art-music-recreation
Contact: Ani Boyadjian, Manager
Description: The Los Angeles Public Library provides free and easy access to information, ideas, books and technology that enrich, educate and empower every individual in our city's diverse communities. **Scope:** Art; architecture; music; sports and recreation; film; gardening. **Services:** department open to the public. **Founded:** 1872. **Holdings:** 300,000 volumes; 2,000 orchestral scores;.

4866 ■ New York Public Library - Jerome Robbins Dance Division
40 Lincoln Center Plz., 3rd Fl.
New York, NY 10023
Ph: (212)870-1657
Co. E-mail: dance@nypl.org
URL: http://www.nypl.org/about/divisions/jerome-robbins-dance-division

Facebook: www.facebook.com/JeromeRobbinsDanceDivision
X (Twitter): x.com/nypldance
Description: The George Arents Collection comprises two distinct groupings of materials under a single umbrella. The first portion of the collection, the Arents Tobacco Collection, constitutes the largest and most comprehensive library in the world devoted to the history, literature, and lore of tobacco. **Scope:** History of dance. **Services:** Copying; collection open to the public. **Founded:** 1944. **Subscriptions:** periodicals (includes journals) 44,000 books; papers; manuscript collections; moving image; 40,000 audio recordings, clippings; program files; original prints and designs; commercial DVDs; 25,000 titles of moving image materials on a variety of film, video.

4867 ■ St. Norbert Arts Centre Archives (SNAC)
100 rue des Ruines du Monastere
Winnipeg, MB, Canada R3V 1L6
Ph: (204)269-0564
Co. E-mail: snac@snac.mb.ca
URL: http://www.snac.mb.ca
Contact: Naomi Gerrard, Chairman of the Board
Facebook: www.facebook.com/StNorbertArtsCentre
YouTube: www.youtube.com/channel/UC2yIUhtsPQPin4LkfA86pqQ
Founded: 1991. **Holdings:** Figures not available.

4868 ■ Toronto Reference Library - Arts Centre
789 Yonge St.
Toronto, ON, Canada M4W 2G8
URL: http://www.torontopubliclibrary.ca/books-video-music/specialized-collections/performing-arts-centre.jsp
Scope: Music; dance; film; theatre; television. **Services:** Library open to the public; photocopy. **Founded:** 1915. **Holdings:** Books; periodicals; music scores; sound recordings; archival materials.

4869 ■ University of Cincinnati College Conservatory of Music - Albino Gorno Memorial Music Library
600 Blegen Library, 2602 University Cir.
Cincinnati, OH 45221
URL: http://libraries.uc.edu/libraries/ccm.html
Description: Serves the research and instructional needs of the students and faculty of the UC College-Conservatory of Music (CCM). **Scope:** Music; musical theatre; dance; theatre and drama. **Services:** Interlibrary loan; copying; library open to the public for reference use only. **Founded:** 1949. **Holdings:** 4,650,472 Volumes; 1895,398, e-books; 2,682,693 Articles.

4870 ■ University of North Carolina at Greensboro - Special Collections & Rare Books, Jackson Library - Dance Collection
320 College Ave.
Greensboro, NC 27412-0001
URL: http://library.uncg.edu/info/depts/scua/collections/rare_books/items.aspx#other
Scope: Dance studies.

4871 ■ University of North Carolina School of the Arts - Semans Library
1533 S Main St.
Winston Salem, NC 27127-2738
Ph: (336)770-3399
URL: http://www.uncsa.edu/faculty-staff-hub/around-campus/facilities-maintenance/design-and-construction-projects/semans-renovation.aspx
Description: Library collects, organizes, describes and preserves access to records of permanent administrative, legal, fiscal and historical value. **Scope:** Art and design. **Services:** Interlibrary loan; library open to the public; copying; printing; scanning. **Founded:** 1965. **Holdings:** Books; periodicals; music and media.

RESEARCH CENTERS

4872 ■ Laban/Bartenieff Institute of Movement Studies (LIMS) - Library
138 South Oxford St Ste. 2D
Brooklyn, NY 11217
Ph: (212)643-8888
Co. E-mail: connect@labaninstitute.org
URL: http://labaninstitute.org
Contact: Karen Bradley, President
E-mail: karenbradley@labaninstitute.org
Facebook: www.facebook.com/LabanInstitute
Instagram: www.instagram.com/labaninstitute

Description: Professional movement educators, dancers, choreographers, dance therapists, behavioral researchers, teachers, fitness and athletic trainers, health practitioners, and students. Devoted to the study of human movement. Studies the role of movement in human behavior through training, research, and practical application. Offers certificate program in Laban movement studies, workshops, and seminars. Supports research and development projects of practicing movement analysts. **Scope:** Perception, description, and analysis of human movement for applications in dance and theater, physical therapy, psychotherapy, nonverbal communication, management consulting, anthropology, and fitness and sports training. The Institute's mission is to further the studies of the principles of movement formulated by Rudolf Laban (1879-1958), an Austro-Hungarian dancer, choreographer, and philosopher, and Irmgard Bartenieff (1900-1981), who applied her Laban training to physical therapy, dance therapy, anthropology, and dance. **Founded:** 1978. **Holdings:** Figures not available. **Publications:** *Movement Studies* (Annual); *Journal of Laban Movement Studies* (Semiannual); *Movement News* (Annual). **Geographic Preference:** Multinational.

Delicatessen/Sandwich Shop

START-UP INFORMATION

4873 ■ *Culinary Careers: How to Get Your Dream Job in Food with Advice from Top Culinary Professionals*
Pub: Clarkson Potter
Ed: Rick Smilow, Anne E. McBride. **Released:** May 04, 2010. **Price:** $23.99, paperback. **Description:** Top culinary experts offer advice for working in or owning a food service firm. **Availability:** E-book; Print.

4874 ■ *"Franchises with an Eye on Chicago" in Crain's Chicago Business (Vol. 34, March 14, 2011, No. 11, pp. 20)*
Pub: Crain Communications Inc.
Contact: Barry Asin, President
Ed: Kevin McKeough. **Description:** Profiles of franchise companies seeking franchisees for the Chicago area include: Extreme Pita, a sandwich shop; Hand and Stone, offering massage, facial and waxing services; Molly Maid, home-cleaning service; Primrose Schools, private accredited schools for children 6 months to 6 hears and after-school programs; Protect Painters, residential and light-commercial painting contractor; and Wingstop, a restaurant offering chicken wings in nine flavors, fries and side dishes. **Availability:** Online.

4875 ■ *Start and Run a Delicatessen: Small Business Starters Series*
Description: Information for starting and running a successful delicatessen is provided. Insight is offered into selecting a location, researching the market, writing a business plan and more.

4876 ■ *Start Small, Finish Big*
Released: December 15, 2012. **Description:** Fred DeLuca is profiled; after founding the multi-billion dollar chain of Subway sandwich restaurants, DeLuca is committed to helping microentrepreneurs, people who start successful small businesses with less than $1,000. **Availability:** Print; Online.

ASSOCIATIONS AND OTHER ORGANIZATIONS

4877 ■ **International Dairy-Deli-Bakery Association (IDDBA)**
8317 Elderberry Rd.
Madison, WI 53717-2603
Ph: (608)310-5000
Fax: (608)238-6330
Co. E-mail: iddba@iddba.org
URL: http://www.iddba.org
Contact: Mike Eardley, President
Facebook: www.facebook.com/myiddba
Linkedin: www.linkedin.com/company/iddba
X (Twitter): x.com/myiddba
Description: Companies and organizations engaged in the production, processing, packaging, marketing, promotion, and/or selling of cheese and cheese products, bakery, or delicatessen and delicatessen-related items. Aims to further the relationship between manufacturing, production, marketing and distribution channels utilized in the delivery of deli, dairy, and bakery foods to the marketplace. Develops and disseminates information concerning deli, dairy, and bakery foods. **Founded:** 1964. **Publications:** *IDBA Membership Directory (Public)*; *WrapUp* (Quarterly); *IDDBA Legis-Letter*; *Dairy-Deli-Bake Digest* (Monthly); *IDDBA and You* (Monthly); *Trainer's Tool Kit*. **Educational Activities:** IDDBA Show (Annual). **Awards:** Scholarship for Growing the Future (Annual). **Geographic Preference:** Multinational.

4878 ■ **National Restaurant Association (NRA)**
2055 L St. NW, Ste. 700
Washington, DC 20036
Ph: (202)331-5900
Free: 800-424-5156
Co. E-mail: askus@restaurant.org
URL: http://www.restaurant.org
Contact: Michelle Korsmo, President
Facebook: www.facebook.com/WeRRestaurants
Linkedin: www.linkedin.com/company/22205
X (Twitter): x.com/WeRRestaurants
Instagram: www.instagram.com/werrestaurants
YouTube: www.youtube.com/user/restaurantdotorg
Description: Restaurants, cafeterias, contract foodservice management, drive-ins, caterers, institutional food services and other members of the foodservice industry; represents establishments belonging to non-affiliated state and local restaurant associations in governmental affairs. Supports foodservice education and research in several educational institutions. Affiliated with the Educational Foundation of the National Restaurant Association to provide training and education for operators, food and equipment manufacturers, distributors and educators. **Founded:** 1919. **Publications:** *Restaurants USA: The Monthly Magazine of the National Restaurant Association* (Monthly); *Who's Who in the Foodservice Industry*; *Restaurant Information Abstracts* (Biweekly); *Foodservice/Hospitality College Directory* (Irregular); *National Restaurant Association--Washington Report* (Semimonthly); *Restaurant Operations Report*. **Educational Activities:** National Restaurant Association Restaurant and Hotel-Motel Show (Annual). **Awards:** John L. Hennessy Award (Annual); NRA Restaurant Neighbor Award (Annual). **Geographic Preference:** National.

4879 ■ **Restaurants Canada - Library**
1155 Queen St. W
Toronto, ON, Canada M6J 1J4
Ph: (416)923-8416
Free: 800-387-5649
Fax: (416)923-1450
Co. E-mail: info@restaurantscanada.org
URL: http://www.restaurantscanada.org
Contact: Christian Buhagiar, Co-Chief Executive Officer Co-President
Facebook: www.facebook.com/RestaurantsCanada
Linkedin: www.linkedin.com/company/restaurants-canada
X (Twitter): x.com/RestaurantsCA
Instagram: www.instagram.com/RestaurantsCanada
YouTube: www.youtube.com/channel/UCxVckfCBIISII9LOuflNX8w
Description: Restaurant and food service corporations, hotels, caterers, and food service suppliers and educators, seeks to create a favorable business environment for members. **Scope:** Food service; quantity cooking; legislation; administration; management; statistics; training; customer attitude surveys. **Services:** Copying; open to the public on fee basis. **Founded:** 1944. **Publications:** *CRFA National Hospitality News*; *Canadian Foodservice Industry Operations Report* (Biennial); *Foodservice Facts* (Annual); *Legislation Guide* (Quarterly). **Educational Activities:** Restaurants Canada Show (Annual); ApEx. **Geographic Preference:** National.

REFERENCE WORKS

4880 ■ *"Baltimore's Burger Market Sizzling with Newcomers" in Boston Business Journal (Vol. 29, June 10, 2011, No. 5, pp. 1)*
Pub: Boston Business Journal
Contact: Carolyn M. Jones, President
E-mail: cmjones@bizjournals.com
Ed: Ryan Sharrow. **Description:** The burger trend in Maryland is on the rise with burger joints either opening up or expanding into several branches. Startup costs for this kind of business range between $250,000 to $400,000. With a growth rate of roughly 17 percent in 2009, this so-called better burger segment of the burger categories is expected to dominate the market for quite some time. **Availability:** Print; Online.

4881 ■ *"Detroit Deli Named Among Best Sandwidh Shops in America" in Click On Detroit (July 23, 2019)*
URL(s): www.clickondetroit.com/all-about-michigan/michigan-eats/detroit-deli-named-among-best-sandwich-shops-in-america
Ed: Ken Haddad. **Released:** July 23, 2019. **Description:** Mudgie's, located in the Corktown-area in Detroit, was named one of the nations's best sandiwch shops by Thrillist for 2019. **Availability:** Online.

4882 ■ *"New Food Concepts Flood Market" in Business Journal (Vol. 30, June 8, 2012, No. 2, pp. 1)*
Pub: American City Business Journals, Inc.
Contact: Mike Olivieri, Executive Vice President
Ed: John Vomhof, Jr. **Released:** Weekly. **Price:** $4, introductory 4-week offer(Digital only). **Description:** Twin Cities Metropolitan Area has seen the boom of the frozen yogurt segment over the past few years and the rise of fast casual sandwich shops, which are helping fuel activity in Minnesota's real estate market. However, there are skeptics who doubt whether all of the new concepts can survive. **Availability:** Print; Online.

4883 ■ Delicatessen/Sandwich Shop

4883 ■ "Potbelly Sandwich Shop Inks Multi-Unit Development Deal to Open Restaurants in Macy's Stores" in Franchising.com (October 9, 2019)
URL(s): www.franchising.com/news/20191009_po tbelly_sandwich_shop_inks_multiunit_developmen t_.html

Released: October 09, 2019. **Description:** The Potbelly Sandwich Shop has announced that it has signed a multi-unit franchise agreement to open up shops in Macy's department stores. Four units are planned, with three of them being located in California and the other one in New York. **Availability:** Online.

4884 ■ "The Rise and Fall and Rise of the Old New Jewish Deli" in Haaretz (January 16, 2018)
URL(s): www.haaretz.com/us-news/.premium.MAGA-ZINE-new-deli-the-rise-and-fall-and-rise-of-the-old-n -y-jewish-deli-1.5730860

Ed: Tzach Yoked. **Released:** January 16, 2018. **Description:** Explores the topic of the disappearing Jewish deli in New York City. Once home to over a thousand delis, there are now only 20 left. Not only was the traditional Jewish deli a place to order kosher food, it was also a place for Jewish people to gather and form a community, something that was especially important for Jewish immigrants earlier in the last century. **Availability:** Online.

4885 ■ :Subway Closings Accerlerate as Cold-Cuts Fail to Draw in Diners" in Bloomberg (March 28, 2019)
URL(s): www.bloomberg.com/news/articles/2019-0 3-28/subway-closings-accelerate-as-cold-cut-subs -don-t-draw-in-diners

Ed: Leslie Patton. **Released:** March 28, 2019. **Description:** Subway Restaurants are closing stores at a faster pace than years past, due to slumping sales. Americans are not buying Subway as much as they used to, which resulted in 1,100 shops closing in 2018 and 800 in 2017. **Availability:** Online.

4886 ■ "Subway Launches Expanded Cafes, Drive-Thru Window Locations" in South Florida Business Journal (Vol. 33, August 10, 2012, No. 2, pp. 1)
Pub: Baltimore Business Journal
Contact: Rhonda Pringle, President
E-mail: rpringle@bizjournals.com

Description: Subway launched its larger cafe concept at Florida Atlantic University and plans to open more drive-thru restaurants in South Florida. This could change preferred leasing locations to Subway franchisees, which are also moving into nontraditional locations. Site selection issues are covered. **Availability:** Print; Online.

4887 ■ "What the Popeyes Chicken Sandwich Feeding Frenzy Means for Rivals" in Barron's (September 10, 2019)
URL(s): www.barrons.com/articles/popeyes-chicken -sandwich-frenzy-spells-bad-news-for-rivals-51568 109600

Ed: Connor Smith. **Released:** September 10, 2019. **Description:** The summer of 2019 produced one of the biggest debuts in the fast food business: the Popeyes chicken sandwich. Due to a Twitter war between Chick-Fil-A and Wendy's, Popeye's emerged with their own sandwich resulting in long lines and shortages at their restaurants. The company needed to step in and remove the item from its menu in order to regroup. However, the popular sandwich will be back. **Availability:** Online.

TRADE SHOWS AND CONVENTIONS

4888 ■ IDDBA Show
International Dairy-Deli-Bakery Association (IDDBA)
8317 Elderberry Rd.
Madison, WI 53717-2603
Ph: (608)310-5000
Fax: (608)238-6330
Co. E-mail: iddba@iddba.org
URL: http://www.iddba.org
Contact: Mike Eardley, President
URL(s): www.iddba.org/iddba-show/about/iddba-2025

Frequency: Annual. **Description:** Topics include those related to the food industry. Event contains speakers, exhibitions, workshops, and entertainment. **Audience:** Buyers, bakers, merchandisers, and executives who have a shared passion for food and the industry. **Principal Exhibits:** Topics include those related to the food industry. Event contains speakers, exhibitions, workshops, and entertainment. Dates and Locations: 2025 Jun 01-3 Ernest N. Morial Convention Center, New Orleans, LA. **Telecommunication Services:** wisl@iddba.org.

CONSULTANTS

4889 ■ Riedel Marketing Group (RMG)
5327 E Pinchot Ave.
Phoenix, AZ 85018
Contact: Ann Riedel, Member
E-mail: ajr@4rmg.com

Description: The house wares and food service industry strategic marketing planning experts. Help manufacturers of house wares and food products solve marketing problems and identify and exploit marketing opportunities. Provides a full-range of strategic marketing planning services including development of marketing strategy, development of fact-based sales presentations, category management, definition of market opportunities and new product development exclusively to the house wares and food service industries. **Scope:** The house wares and food service industry strategic marketing planning experts. Help manufacturers of house wares and food products solve marketing problems and identify and exploit marketing opportunities. Provides a full-range of strategic marketing planning services including development of marketing strategy, development of fact-based sales presentations, category management, definition of market opportunities and new product development exclusively to the house wares and food service industries. **Founded:** 1991. **Publications:** "Your Key Consumer: Her Take on the International Home & Housewares Show," Mar, 2008; "What's Hot, What's Not: The Consumer Speaks," Mar, 2006; "HIPsters SPEAK: What We Love to Buy and Why," Apr, 2005; "Influentials: Who They Are and Why You Should Care," Jun, 2004; "The Seven Secrets to Selling More Housewares," Jan, 2003. **Training:** Consumers Speak: What We Love to Buy and Why, What Do Those Consumers Think; The Seven Secrets to Selling More House wares. **Special Services:** Home Trend Influentials Panel.

FRANCHISES AND BUSINESS OPPORTUNITIES

4890 ■ Atlantic City Sub Shops Inc.
6825 Tilton Rd.
Egg Harbor Township, NJ 08234
Ph: (609)646-7799
Co. E-mail: acsubshops@gmail.com
URL: http://www.acsubshop.com
Facebook: www.facebook.com/ACSubShops
Instagram: www.instagram.com/acsubshops

Description: Producer of cold subs, pizolas, soups, salads. **Founded:** 1986. **Training:** Yes.

4891 ■ Big Town Hero (BTH)
1921 14th St. SE, D-405
Albany, OR 97321
Ph: (541)926-1880
Co. E-mail: franchise@bigtownhero.com
URL: http://bigtownhero.com
Contact: Christy Schaeffer, Owner
Facebook: www.facebook.com/BigTownHero
Linkedin: www.linkedin.com/company/big-town-hero -franchise
X (Twitter): x.com/bigtownhero
YouTube: www.youtube.com/channel/ UCeZmUH9nIjKghC9AlUHREqA

Description: Sandwiches, salads, soups, fresh bread and baked goods from scratch. Fast and friendly. **No. of Franchise Units:** 34. **Founded:** 1982. **Franchised:** 1989. **Equity Capital Needed:** $75,000-$175,000. **Franchise Fee:** $20,000. **Training:** Yes.

4892 ■ Camille's Sidewalk Cafe
9548 S 96TH E Ave.
Tulsa, OK 74133
Co. E-mail: riverside@camillescafe.com
Contact: David Rutkauskas, Contact

Description: Chain of fast food restaurants. **Founded:** 1996. **Financial Assistance:** Yes **Training:** Yes.

4893 ■ Capt. Submarine
245 Robie St.
Truro, NS, Canada B2N 5N6
Co. E-mail: customerservice@captsub.com
URL: http://captsub.com
Facebook: www.facebook.com/captainsub
Instagram: www.instagram.com/capt.submarine

Description: Operator of restaurant. **Training:** Offers management and staff on start-up.

4894 ■ Cheba Hut Toasted Subs
Boulder, CO
Ph: (970)482-7267
Co. E-mail: orders@chebahut.com
URL: http://chebahut.com
Contact: Scott Jennings, Founder
Facebook: www.facebook.com/chebahut
Instagram: www.instagram.com/chebahut

Description: Chain of restaurant. **Founded:** 1998. **Financial Assistance:** Yes **Training:** Available 14 days at headquarters, 7 days onsite and ongoing support.

4895 ■ Chedd's Gourmet Grilled Cheese
1906 Pearl St.
Denver, CO 80203
Contact: Dirk Bruley, Contact

Description: Gourmet grilled cheese sandwiches. **Training:** Provides 2-3 weeks training at headquarters, 1 week at franchisee's location and ongoing support.

4896 ■ Coffee Time Donuts Inc.
2195 Midland Ave.
Scarborough, ON, Canada M1P 3E7
Ph: (647)351-8463
URL: http://coffeetime.com

Description: Chain of coffee shops. **Founded:** 1982. **Training:** Yes.

4897 ■ Cousins Subs
N83 W13400 Leon Rd.
Menomonee Falls, WI 53051
Ph: (262)253-7700
URL: http://www.cousinssubs.com
Facebook: www.facebook.com/cousinssubs
X (Twitter): x.com/cousinssubs
Instagram: www.instagram.com/cousinssubs

Description: Submarine sandwich operation, with over 20 years of expertise. Volume-oriented, fast-service concept in an upscale, in-line, strip or free-standing location, some with drive-up windows. Franchising opportunities available for single, multi-unit and area developer franchisees, seminars and training classes. A corporate area representative meets with each franchise location management 3 times per month to maintain communications and assist in problem solving. **No. of Franchise Units:** 141. **No. of Company-Owned Units:** 16. **Founded:** 1972. **Franchised:** 1985. **Equity Capital Needed:** $80,000 cash, $106,700-$288,300 total investment. **Franchise Fee:** $25,000. **Training:** Includes a store building seminar for site selection, lease negotiation and construction 30 days of hands-on training, plus 10 days of opening assistance and training. National and local store marketing support.

4898 ■ Doc Green's Gourmet Salad and Sandwich Bar
3220 Cobb Pky. SE
Atlanta, GA 30339
Ph: (770)953-3627

Co. E-mail: docgreensllc@gmail.com
URL: http://docgreens.com
Facebook: www.facebook.com/docgreensatl
Instagram: www.instagram.com/docgreensinc
Description: Producer and retailer of wraps, sandwiches and salads. **No. of Franchise Units:** 12. **No. of Company-Owned Units:** 1. **Founded:** 2003. **Franchised:** 2004. **Equity Capital Needed:** $367,000-$655,000. **Franchise Fee:** $25,000. **Royalty Fee:** 5%. **Training:** Offers 2 1/2 weeks training at headquarters, 1 week at franchisee's location and ongoing support.

4899 ■ Earl of Sandwich L.L.C.
4700 Millenia Blvd., Ste. 400
Orlando, FL 32839
Ph: (407)903-5500
Free: 877-426-3275
Fax: (407)992-2987
Co. E-mail: info@earlofsandwichusa.com
URL: http://www.earlofsandwichusa.com
Contact: Thomas Avallone, President
Facebook: www.facebook.com/earlofsandwich
X (Twitter): x.com/earlofsandwich
Instagram: www.instagram.com/earlofsandwich
Description: Sandwiches, wraps, salads, and desserts. **Founded:** 2003. **Equity Capital Needed:** $200,000 of liquid non-borrowed assets. **Royalty Fee:** 6%. **Financial Assistance:** Yes

4900 ■ East Coast Subs
RCLC Enterprises, Inc.
6056 S State St.
Murray, UT 84107
Ph: (801)352-1400
Fax: (801)619-4038
Description: Sandwiches and Philly subs. **No. of Franchise Units:** 2. **No. of Company-Owned Units:** 2. **Founded:** 1991. **Franchised:** 2005. **Equity Capital Needed:** $90,500-$113,500. **Franchise Fee:** $12,500. **Training:** Yes.

4901 ■ Erbert & Gerbert's Sandwich Shops
2308 E Clairemont Ave.
Eau Claire, WI 54701
Ph: (715)552-4449
URL: http://www.erbertandgerberts.com
Facebook: www.facebook.com/erbertandgerberts
X (Twitter): x.com/erbertgerberts
Instagram: www.instagram.com/erbertandgerberts
YouTube: www.youtube.com/user/ErbertAndGerberts
Description: Offers top-quality, gourmet submarine and club sandwiches on bread baked fresh onsite. A delivery service complements eat-in and carry-out services. **No. of Franchise Units:** 52. **No. of Company-Owned Units:** 1. **Founded:** 1988. **Franchised:** 1992. **Equity Capital Needed:** Net worth of $300,000, $75,000 liquid. **Franchise Fee:** $26,500. **Training:** 3 week training with control and quality standards covered in the first weekly section. The second week involves administrative and management training required for cost control, payroll, financial management, etc. This is followed by 1 week of training at the time of start-up in the franchisees store.

4902 ■ Groucho's Deli
611 Harden St.
Columbia, SC 29205
Ph: (803)710-7600
Co. E-mail: brand@grouchos.com
URL: http://www.grouchos.com
Facebook: www.facebook.com/GROUCHOSDELI
X (Twitter): x.com/GrouchosDeli
Instagram: www.instagram.com/grouchos_deli
Description: Operator of restaurant. **Founded:** 1941. **Franchised:** 2000. **Equity Capital Needed:** minimum net worth of $200,000; minimum of $40,000 in liquid assets. **Franchise Fee:** $20,000. **Royalty Fee:** 5.25%. **Training:** Available at headquarters: 134-166 hours. Available at franchisee's location and ongoing support.

4903 ■ Jersey Mike's Franchise Systems Inc.
2251 Landmark Pl.
Manasquan, NJ 08736
Free: 800-321-7676
Co. E-mail: marketing@jerseymikes.com
URL: http://www.jerseymikes.com
Contact: Peter Cancro, Chief Executive Officer
Facebook: www.facebook.com/jerseymikes
X (Twitter): x.com/jerseymikes
YouTube: www.youtube.com/user/jerseymikestv
Description: Chain of restaurants that serve sandwiches and related items.. **No. of Franchise Units:** 195. **Founded:** 1956. **Franchised:** 1987. **Equity Capital Needed:** $201,357 - $471,164.50. **Franchise Fee:** $18,500. **Financial Assistance:** No **Training:** Offers 9 week training program with ongoing support.

4904 ■ Jimmy John's Franchisor SPV, LLC (JJ)
Inspire Brands, Inc.
2212 Fox Dr.
Champaign, IL 61820
Ph: (678)514-4100
Co. E-mail: franchising@inspirebrands.com
URL: http://inspirebrands.com
Contact: James North, President
Facebook: www.facebook.com/jimmyjohns
X (Twitter): x.com/jimmyjohns
Instagram: www.instagram.com/jimmyjohns
YouTube: www.youtube.com/user/jimmyjohns
Description: Operator of restaurants offers sandwiches and beverages, also provides catering services. **Founded:** 1983.

4905 ■ Larry's Giant Subs
4479 Deerwood Lake Pky.
Jacksonville, FL 32216
Ph: (904)425-4060
Fax: (904)425-4064
Co. E-mail: bigone@larryssubs.com
URL: http://larryssubs.com
Contact: Larry Raikes, Chief Executive Officer
Facebook: www.facebook.com/LarrysGiantSubs
Instagram: www.instagram.com/larrysgiantsubs
YouTube: www.youtube.com/user/larryssubs
Founded: 1982. **Franchised:** 1986. **Equity Capital Needed:** $175,000-$254,000. **Franchise Fee:** $20,000. **Royalty Fee:** 6%. **Financial Assistance:** Yes **Training:** Provides 3 weeks at corporate headquarters, 1-2 weeks on-site with ongoing support.

4906 ■ Little King Inc.
14005 Q St.
Omaha, NE 68137
Ph: (402)896-6347
Co. E-mail: mark@littlekingsubs.com
URL: http://littlekingsubs.com
Contact: Sid Wertheim, Founder
Facebook: www.facebook.com/LittleKingDeliAndSubs
X (Twitter): x.com/LittleKingSubs
Description: Operator of restaurants and also provides catering services. **Founded:** 1969. **Franchised:** 1978. **Financial Assistance:** Yes **Training:** Offers 15 days in Omaha and 7-10 days when opening.

4907 ■ Maid-Rite Sandwich Shoppe
125 N Broadway
Greenville, OH 45331
Ph: (937)548-9340
Co. E-mail: maidritegreenville@gmail.com
URL: http://maidrite-greenville.com
Contact: M. W. Koontz, Contact
Description: Retailer of sandwiches and shakes. **Founded:** 1934. **Franchised:** 1926. **Training:** Yes.

4908 ■ McAlister's Deli
GOTO Foods
5620 Glenridge Dr. NE
Atlanta, GA 30342
Ph: (404)255-3250
Free: 800-227-8353
URL: http://www.gotofoods.com
Contact: Michael Freeman, President
Facebook: www.facebook.com/mcalistersdeli
X (Twitter): x.com/McAlistersDeli
Instagram: www.instagram.com/mcalistersdeli
Description: Chain restaurant. **Founded:** 1989. **Training:** Yes.

4909 ■ Miami Subs Grill
7781 Pines Blvd.
Pembroke Pines, FL 33024
Ph: (754)816-3146
URL: http://mymiamigrill.com
Facebook: www.facebook.com/mymiamigrill
X (Twitter): x.com/MiamiGrill
Instagram: www.instagram.com/miamigrill
Description: Chain of a restaurant. **Founded:** 1988. **Training:** Yes.

4910 ■ Mikes Restaurants Inc.
Montreal, QC, Canada
Co. E-mail: contactmarketing@mikesrestaurants.com
URL: http://toujoursmikes.ca
Facebook: www.facebook.com/LesRestaurantsToujoursMikes
Linkedin: www.linkedin.com/company/toujoursmikes
X (Twitter): x.com/ToujoursMikes
Instagram: www.instagram.com/toujoursmikes
YouTube: www.youtube.com/channel/UCckCU3kCfyx-SB9tDmSkJhQ
Description: Chain of fast-food restaurants. **Founded:** 1967. **Training:** Provides 10 weeks training.

4911 ■ Mr. Goodcents Franchise Systems Inc.
8997 Commerce Dr.
De Soto, KS 66018
Free: 800-648-2368
Co. E-mail: info@goocentssubs.com
URL: http://goodcentssubs.com
Contact: Mike O'Toole, President
X (Twitter): x.com/eatgoodcents
Description: Quick service submarine sandwiches and pasta. **No. of Franchise Units:** 80.0. **Founded:** 1989. **Franchised:** 1990. **Equity Capital Needed:** $155,150 - $292,401. **Franchise Fee:** $20,000. **Financial Assistance:** No **Training:** Offers 5 days training at headquarters, 20 days at franchisee's location and ongoing support.

4912 ■ Mr. Goodcents Subs & Pastas
8997 Commerce Dr.
De Soto, KS 66018
URL: http://goodcentssubs.com
Contact: Joseph Bisogno, Founder
Description: Chain of fast food restaurants. **Founded:** 1989. **Franchised:** 1990. **Training:** 30 days of comprehensive in-house training.

4913 ■ Mr. Pickle's Sandwich Shop
445 Grass Valley Hwy., (Hwy. 49)
Auburn, CA 95603
Ph: (530)823-3359
Free: 855-677-4255
Co. E-mail: corp@mrpickles.com
URL: http://www.mrpickles.com
Facebook: www.facebook.com/Mr.PicklesSandwichShops
X (Twitter): x.com/MrPicklesShops
Instagram: www.instagram.com/mrpicklessandwichshops
Description: Owner and operator of sandwich shop franchise. It offers menus such as sandwiches, salads, deli meats and cheeses. **Founded:** 1995. **Training:** 2 weeks training included at franchisee's location and ongoing support.

4914 ■ Mr. Pita
22661 Gratiot
Eastpointe, MI 48021
Ph: (586)771-0008
URL: http://mrpita.com
Description: Chain of restaurants. **Financial Assistance:** Yes **Training:** Yes.

4915 ■ Must Be Heaven Franchise Corp.
107 W Alamo St.
Brenham, TX 77833
Ph: (979)830-8536
URL: http://www.mustbeheaven.com
Contact: Shirley Syptak, President
Facebook: www.facebook.com/BrenhamMBH
Description: Chain of the fast-food restaurant. **Founded:** 1987. **Franchised:** 1999. **Training:** Yes.

4916 ■ Mustard Cafe & Grill
41 Auto Center Dr., Ste. 103
Foothill Ranch, CA 92610
Ph: (949)716-1000
Co. E-mail: info@mustardcafeandgrill.com
URL: http://www.mustardcafeandgrill.com
Facebook: www.facebook.com/people/Mustard-Cafe-Grill/100090502055326
Instagram: www.instagram.com/mustardcafeandgrill
Description: Producer and retailer of sandwiches, Panini's, wraps, salads, soups and delectable desserts. **Training:** Offers 2 weeks training at headquarters, 4 weeks at franchisee's location and ongoing support.

4917 ■ Penn Station Inc.
1226 US Hwy. 50
Milford, OH 45150
Co. E-mail: info@penn-station.com
URL: http://www.penn-station.com
Facebook: www.facebook.com/pennstation
Description: Retail sale of various cheesecake and submarine sandwiches, fresh-cut fries and fresh-squeezed lemonade. **Founded:** 1985. **Financial Assistance:** No **Training:** Yes.

4918 ■ Perfecto's Caffe
79 N Main St.
Andover, MA 01810
Ph: (978)749-7022
URL: http://www.perfectoscaffe.com
Contact: Max Gabriello, Contact
Description: Operator of coffee restaurant. **Founded:** 1993. **Training:** Yes.

4919 ■ Port of Subs, Inc.
5365 Mae Anne Ave., Ste. A-29
Reno, NV 89523
Free: 800-245-0245
Co. E-mail: feedback@portofsubs.com
URL: http://www.portofsubs.com
Contact: John Larsen, Contact
Description: Submarine sandwich franchise, featuring unique front-line method of preparing specialty sandwiches, soups, salads and party platters. Bread is baked fresh daily on premises. **No. of Operating Units:** 140.0. **Founded:** 1972. **Franchised:** 1985. **Equity Capital Needed:** $197,100 - $358,000. **Franchise Fee:** $18,500. **Royalty Fee:** 5.5%. **Financial Assistance:** No **Managerial Assistance:** operations assistance. **Training:** Offers 2 weeks of training, plus 2 weeks in the franchisee's unit during initial opening.

4920 ■ The Quizno's Master L.L.C.
PO Box 6340
Denver, CO 80206
Description: Chain of restaurants that provides toasted sandwiches, soups, and salads for lunch or dinner. **Founded:** 1981. **Training:** Twenty two day training program includes classroom and in-store training. Grand opening and initial onsite assistance.

4921 ■ Schlotzsky's
GOTO Foods
200 W 4th St.
Austin, TX 78701
Ph: (404)255-3250
Free: 800-227-8353
URL: http://www.gotofoods.com
Contact: John C. Wooley, Contact
Description: Bread & Other Bakery Products. **Founded:** 1971.

4922 ■ Subway IP LLC
Roark Capital Group
325 Sub Way
Milford, CT 06461
Ph: (404)591-5200
Fax: (404)591-5201
Co. E-mail: contact@roarkcapital.com
URL: http://www.roarkcapital.com
Contact: John Chidsey, Chief Executive Officer
Facebook: www.facebook.com/subway
X (Twitter): twitter.com/subway
Instagram: www.instagram.com/subway
YouTube: www.youtube.com/user/subway
Description: Operates chain of fast food restaurants. **Founded:** 1965. **Training:** Provides training and assistance to franchisees in all areas of business operation.

4923 ■ Sweet Peppers Deli (SPD)
Jackson Sq., 2017 Hwy. 45 N
Columbus, MS 39701
Ph: (662)327-6982
Fax: (662)328-6889
URL: http://sweetpeppersdeli.com
Contact: John Bean, President
Description: Producer of sandwiches, salads, wraps and much more. **Founded:** 1984. **Franchised:** 2002. **Franchise Fee:** $30,000. **Royalty Fee:** 5%. **Training:** Yes.

4924 ■ Togo's Eateries, LLC
18 N San Pedro St.
San Jose, CA 95110
URL: http://www.togos.com
Contact: Glenn Lunde, President
Facebook: www.facebook.com/togossandwiches
X (Twitter): x.com/togossandwiches
Description: Operator of fast food restaurant offers sandwiches, meals, soups, drinks and other food products. **Founded:** 1971. **Training:** Offers 2 weeks of onsite training, with periodic follow-up.

4925 ■ Tubby's Sub Shops Inc.
Tubby's Sub Shops Inc.
30551 Edison Dr.
Roseville, MI 48066
Ph: (586)293-5088
Co. E-mail: info@tubbys.com
URL: http://www.tubbys.com
Contact: Robert Paganes, Chief Executive Officer
Facebook: www.facebook.com/TubbysGrilledSubmarines
X (Twitter): x.com/TubbysSubShops
Description: Operates as a restaurant. **Founded:** 1968. **Franchised:** 1978. **Training:** Classroom sessions where very facet of your business is covered. Additional on-site assistance is given just prior to opening and during your first few weeks of operation.

4926 ■ W.G. Grinders
2820 Fishinger Rd.
Columbus, OH 43221
Ph: (614)766-2313
Fax: (614)766-4030
URL: http://www.wggrinders.com/2016
Contact: Michael J. Bellisari, Contact
Description: Upscale quick service gourmet deli. **No. of Franchise Units:** 13. **No. of Company-Owned Units:** 8. **Founded:** 1989. **Franchised:** 1995. **Equity Capital Needed:** $239,000-$314,000 estimated initial investment required. **Franchise Fee:** $15,000 thru 2011. **Financial Assistance:** Yes **Training:** Yes.

4927 ■ Which Wich Superior Sandwiches
1412 Main St., Ste. 2000
Dallas, TX 75202
Ph: (214)747-9424
Free: 866-944-2494
Co. E-mail: franchise@whichwich.com
URL: http://www.whichwich.com
Contact: Jeff Sinelli, Founder Officer
Facebook: www.facebook.com/whichwich
X (Twitter): x.com/whichwich
Instagram: www.instagram.com/whichwich
YouTube: www.youtube.com/user/whichwich
Description: Chain of sandwiches restaurants. **No. of Operating Units:** 500.0. **Founded:** 2003. **Franchised:** 2005. **Equity Capital Needed:** net worth of $500,000 ; $250,000 in liquid assets. **Franchise Fee:** $25,000 - $30,000. **Royalty Fee:** 6% of Gross Sales. **Financial Assistance:** No **Training:** Provides 3 weeks training at headquarters, 1-2 weeks at franchisee's location and ongoing support.

4928 ■ Zero's Subs
5760 Northampton Blvd., Ste. 100
Virginia Beach, VA 23455
Ph: (757)460-3203
URL: http://www.zerossub.com
Contact: David Miele, Director
Description: A Fast-food, sit-down and to-go restaurant, serving Italian submarine sandwiches and pizzas. **Founded:** 1967. **Training:** Yes.

LIBRARIES

4929 ■ Food Institute (FI)
330 Changebridge Rd., Ste. 101
Pine Brook, NJ 07058
Ph: (201)791-5570
Free: 855-791-5570
Co. E-mail: questions@foodinstitute.com
URL: http://www.foodinstitute.com
Contact: Anika Wilson, Contact
E-mail: anika.wilson@foodinstitute.com
Facebook: www.facebook.com/foodinstitutenj
Linkedin: www.linkedin.com/company/the-food-institute
X (Twitter): x.com/FoodInstitute
Instagram: www.instagram.com/foodinstitute
YouTube: www.youtube.com/channel/UCYAPI0TXNtJa04aQre4h4pA
Description: Strives to provide food industry-related information to its members. **Scope:** The food industry. **Services:** Center open to the public on fee basis. **Founded:** 1928. **Holdings:** Figures not available. **Publications:** Today in Food; Get It Out, Get It Right, Get It Over! Avoiding Food Product Recalls; The Food Institute (Weekly); Almanac of the Canning, Freezing, Preserving Industries (Annual); Food Business Mergers and Acquisitions; OSHA Inspection Manual; Regulatory Directory (Periodic); Food Business Mergers & Acquisitions. **Geographic Preference:** Multinational.

Desktop Publishing Company

START-UP INFORMATION

4930 ■ *"9 Strategies to BUILD and GROW Your Author Platform: A Step-by-Step Book Marketing Plan to Get More Exposure and Sales"*
Released: May 04, 2016. **Description:** A nine-step formula for marketing self-published books is presented. The author has sold over 103,000 books using this method since 2008 and continues to grow her customer base through email and followers. **Availability:** Print.

ASSOCIATIONS AND OTHER ORGANIZATIONS

4931 ■ **Association of Proposal Management Professionals (APMP)**
20130 Lakeview Ctr. Plz., Ste. 400
Ashburn, VA 20147
Free: 866-466-2767
Co. E-mail: membership@apmp.org
URL: http://www.apmp.org
Contact: Rick Harris, Chief Executive Officer
E-mail: rick.harris@apmp.org
Facebook: www.facebook.com/APMP.org
Linkedin: www.linkedin.com/company/apmp
X (Twitter): x.com/apmp_connect
YouTube: www.youtube.com/channel/UCAX6bGyVUHu89aBBq92rxQQ

Description: Proposal managers, proposal planners, proposal writers, consultants, desktop publishers and marketing managers. Encourages unity and cooperation among industry professionals. Seeks to broaden member knowledge and skills through developmental, educational and social activities. **Founded:** 1989. **Publications:** *Journal of the Association of Proposal Management Professionals* (Semiannual). **Awards:** APMP Fellows Award (Annual). **Geographic Preference:** National.

4932 ■ **Association of Publishers for Special Sales (APSS)**
c/o Kaye Krasner
PO Box 9725
Colorado Springs, CO 80932-0725
Ph: (719)924-5534
Fax: (719)213-2602
URL: http://community.bookapss.org
Contact: Brian Jud, Executive Director
E-mail: brianjud@bookapss.org
Facebook: www.facebook.com/bookapss
X (Twitter): x.com/APSSBrianJud

Description: For self-publishers, authors and small presses. Works to advance the image and profits of independent publishers through education and marketing. Offers continuing education, co-op buying power and sales and networking opportunities, plus discounts on many products and services. Publishes monthly newsletter. **Founded:** 1996. **Geographic Preference:** National.

EDUCATIONAL PROGRAMS

4933 ■ **EEI Communications Becoming a Publications Manager**
URL(s): www.eeicom.com
Description: Covers defining responsibilities, managing workflow, organizational and recruitment skills, providing feedback, and utilizing technology. **Audience:** Writers, designers, project and publications managers. **Principal Exhibits:** Covers defining responsibilities, managing workflow, organizational and recruitment skills, providing feedback, and utilizing technology. **Telecommunication Services:** train@eeicom.com.

4934 ■ **EEI Communications Design for Print**
URL(s): www.eeicom.com
Price: $745.00. **Description:** Covers basic design principles, utilizing color and typography, composition, and preparing files for the printing process. **Audience:** Designers, programmers, and production specialists. **Principal Exhibits:** Covers basic design principles, utilizing color and typography, composition, and preparing files for the printing process. **Telecommunication Services:** train@eeicom.com.

4935 ■ **EEI Communications Visual Thinking II: Color Theory**
URL(s): www.eeicom.com
Description: Covers the design elements of color, including the color wheel, the seven color contrasts, and the psychological aspects of color. **Audience:** Industry professionals. **Principal Exhibits:** Covers the design elements of color, including the color wheel, the seven color contrasts, and the psychological aspects of color. **Telecommunication Services:** train@eeicom.com.

REFERENCE WORKS

4936 ■ *"Best Desktop Publishing Software of 2019" in Top Ten Reviews (January 8, 2019)*
URL(s): www.toptenreviews.com/best-desktop-publishing-software
Ed: Rebecca Spear. **Released:** January 08, 2019. **Description:** An in-depth look at the best desktop publishing software packages. Prices and detailed descriptions, with a review of the pros and cons are given for each of the ten picks. **Availability:** Online.

4937 ■ *"Freelance Writer Creates LI Bridal Blog" in Long Island Business News (September 10, 2010)*
Pub: BridgeTower Media
Contact: Adam Reinebach, President
Ed: Gregory Zeller. **Description:** Profile of Claudia Copquin, freelance journalist who created a blog for brides on the Internet. **Availability:** Online; Audio.

4938 ■ *"Interactive Stores a Big Part of Borders' Turnaround Plan" in Crain's Detroit Business (Vol. 24, February 18, 2008, No. 7, pp. 4)*
Pub: Crain Communications Inc.
Contact: Barry Asin, President
Ed: Nathan Skid. **Description:** Borders Group Inc. is using digital technology and interactive media as a part of the firm's turnaround plan. The digital store will allow shoppers to create CDs, download audio books, publish their own works, print photos and search family genealogy. **Availability:** Online.

4939 ■ *Literary Market Place: The Directory of the American Book Publishing Industry*
Pub: Information Today Inc.
Contact: Thomas H. Hogan, President
URL(s): store.infotoday.com/product/literary-market-place
Released: Latest edition 84th Edition 2024. **Price:** $539.50, for outside North America; $529.50, for Canada or Mexico; $507.50, Individuals. **Description:** Covers over 12,500 firms or organizations offering services related to the publishing industry, including book publishers in the United States and Canada who issued three or more books during the preceding year, plus a small press section of publishers who publish less than three titles per year or those who are self-published. Also included: book printers and binders; book clubs; book trade and literary associations; selected syndicates, newspapers, periodicals, and radio and TV programs that use book reviews or book publishing news; translators and literary agents. **Entries include:** For publishers--Company name, address, phone, address for orders, principal executives, editorial directors, and managers, date founded, number of titles in previous year, number of backlist titles in print, types of books published, ISBN prefixes, representatives, imprints, and affiliations. For suppliers, etc.--Listings usually show firm name, address, phone, executives, services, etc. **Arrangement:** Classified by line of business. **Indexes:** Principal index is 35,000-item combined index of publishers, publications, and personnel; several sections have geographical and/or subject indexes; translators are indexed by source and target language. **Availability:** Print; Online.

4940 ■ *"Publishing: Art or Science? Reflections from an Editorial Perspective" in Accounting and Finance (Vol. 52, June 2012, No. 2, pp. 359)*
Released: February 01, 2012. **Description:** Insights into the 'journal process' is shared by an experienced editor. Three basics messages emerge from the discussion. First, if a study is to be successful, it must address an interesting and important topic to investigate; secondly, the study must be communicated in a transparent and accessible way so the work can be critically evaluated; finally, authors are advised to subject their work to external scrutiny before submitting for peer review. **Availability:** Print; PDF; Online.

4941 ■ *"Savvy Solutions" in Black Enterprise (Vol. 41, November 2010, No. 4, pp. 42)*
Description: Society of Children's Book Writers and Illustrators offers members many benefits, including directories of agencies looking for new writers of books. **Availability:** Online.

4942 ■ "What Is Desktop Publishing?" in Lifewire (May 22, 2019)
URL(s): www.lifewire.com/what-is-desktop-publishing-1073862
Ed: Jacci Howard Bear. **Released:** May 22, 2019. **Description:** A brief guide on exactly what desktop publishing is and what the average consumer can make from the software. **Availability:** Online.

4943 ■ "Why You Don't Get Published: An Editor's View" in Accounting and Finance (Vol. 52, June 2012, No. 2, pp. 343)
Ed: Michael E. Bradbury. **Released:** March 12, 2012. **Description:** This paper uses content analysis to examine 66 reviews on 33 manuscripts submitted to 'Accounting and Finance'. Selected extracts from reviews are provided to illustrate the issues considered important to reviewers. The main message is that papers need to be work-shopped and more care taken over editorial matters. A checklist for prospective authors is provided. **Availability:** Print; Online.

STATISTICAL SOURCES

4944 ■ Document Preparation Services Industry in the US - Market Research Report
URL(s): www.ibisworld.com/united-states/market-research-reports/document-preparation-services-industry/
Price: $925. **Description:** Downloadable report analyzing data about the document preparation industry and the competition it faces from other similar industries. **Availability:** Download.

TRADE PERIODICALS

4945 ■ KMWorld: Creating and Managing the Knowledge-Based Enterprise
Pub: Information Today Inc.
Contact: Thomas H. Hogan, President
URL(s): www.kmworld.com
Facebook: www.facebook.com/KMWorldMagazine
Ed: Sandra Haimila. **Released:** Bimonthly **Price:** $121, Canada and Mexico for 1 year; $153, for surface 1 year; $289, for airmail 1 year; $99.95, U.S. **Description:** Journal focusing on the applications of knowledge management solutions as they apply to business and corporations. **Availability:** Print; Online.

4946 ■ Oregon Publisher
Pub: Oregon Newspaper Publishers Association
Contact: Laurie Hieb, Executive Director
E-mail: laurie@orenews.com
URL(s): www.orenews.com/onpa-publications
Released: Quarterly **Description:** Covers journalism and publishing topics. **Availability:** PDF; Online.

CONSULTANTS

4947 ■ Editorial Code and Data Inc. (ECDI)
814 Wolverine Dr., Ste. 2
  Wolverine Lake, MI 48390
Ph: (248)245-4500
Co. E-mail: monique.magee@gmail.com
URL: http://www.marketsize.com
Contact: Arsen J. Darnay, Editor
Facebook: www.facebook.com/EditorialCodeAndData
Description: Developer of statistical publishing and software development services. **Scope:** Developer of statistical publishing and software development services. **Founded:** 1990. **Holdings:** ECDI has wide holdings of U.S. government data in print and electronic format. **Publications:** "Market Share Reporter"; "Encyclopedia of Products & Industries"; "Economic Indicators Handbook"; "American Salaries and Wages Survey"; "Dun and Bradstreet & Gale: Industrial Handbook"; "Reference American Cost of Living Survey".

4948 ■ Intercollegiate Broadcasting System Inc. (IBS)
PO Box 870
  La Grange, IL 60525
Ph: (312)725-3072
Co. E-mail: ibs@ibsradio.org
URL: http://www.ibsradio.org
Contact: Chris Thomas, President
Description: Radio stations at schools, colleges, and universities. Offers educational, informational, and consulting services. Compiles statistics; conducts research and seminars. **Scope:** Communications media specialists with focus on Macintosh computing, desktop publishing, graphic production layout, database, spreadsheet, and training. Possesses particular expertise on AV systems and setups. Serves private industries as well as government agencies. **Founded:** 1940. **Publications:** *Radio Newsletter* (Monthly); *The Journal of College Radio* (Quarterly). **Educational Activities:** Intercollegiate Broadcasting System Conference (Annual). **Geographic Preference:** National.

4949 ■ The Live Oak Press L.L.C.
PO Box 60036
  Palo Alto, CA 94306
URL: http://liveoakpress.com
Contact: David M. Hamilton, Publisher
Description: Manages design and implementation of publishing programs. Also offers complete book and magazine preparation and publishing consulting, including web resources, advertising, concept development, manuscript, design, development and production through finished product. Specializes in high-technology clients and electronic publishing. **Scope:** Manages design and implementation of publishing programs. Also offers complete book and magazine preparation and publishing consulting, including web resources, advertising, concept development, manuscript, design, development and production through finished product. Specializes in high-technology clients and electronic publishing. **Founded:** 1970. **Publications:** "The Tools of My Trade"; "To the Yukon with Jack London"; "Earthquakes and Young Volcanoes"; "The Lost Cement Mine"; "Inner Voyage"; "Studies in the Development of Consciousness"; "Dialectical Realism: Studies on a Philosophy of Growth"; "Mammoth Lakes Sierra"; "Deepest Valley"; "Mammoth Gold"; "Old Mammoth". **Training:** Internet publishing Seminar.

4950 ■ Lovelady Consulting
14480 Santa Fe Dr.
  Olive Branch, MS 38654
Ph: (662)470-6151
URL: http://www.loveladyconsulting.com
Contact: Carol Lovelady, Consultant Owner
E-mail: carol@loveladyconsulting.com
Description: Firm is engaged in electronic publishing and office automation applications, offers consultation, design and training, specializes in graphics and related applications and develops customized corporate training programs and serves private industries as well as government agencies. **Scope:** Firm is engaged in electronic publishing and office automation applications, offers consultation, design and training, specializes in graphics and related applications and develops customized corporate training programs and serves private industries as well as government agencies. **Founded:** 1986. **Publications:** "Adobe Acrobat 9 Quick start Guide"; "Adobe Acrobat 9 How-To's"; "How to Do Everything with Acrobat 9"; "Corel Ventura 10"; "CorelDraw X4 Upgrade"; "CorelDraw X4 Full Version"; "Adobe Acrobat 9 Professional Upgrade"; "Adobe Acrobat 9 Standard Upgrade"; "CorelDraw Graphics Suite X3"; "Adobe Acrobat 8 Quick Start Guide"; "How To Do Everything with Acrobat 7"; "Acrobat 8 Upgrade from Standard to Professional". **Training:** Corel Ventura 10 Introduction, 2007; Adobe Acrobat Advanced; Corel Ventura 10 Transition; CorelDRAW X3 Introduction, 2007; CorelDRAW X3 Advanced; Adobe Acrobat Advanced; Corel Database Publisher 8/10; Ventura Tips and Tricks, 2005; Adobe In Design Introduction, 2005; Corel Database Publisher 8/10; CorelDRAW 11/12 Introduction; Ventura Tips & Tricks; Corel PhotoPAINT Introduction. **Special Services:** CorelDraw X4 or X3; Adobe Acrobat 8 or 9; Corel Ventura 10; CorelDRAW 11/12; Corel Ventura 10.

4951 ■ LPD Enterprises
925 Salamanca NW
  Los Ranchos, NM 87107-5647
Ph: (505)344-9382
Co. E-mail: lpdpress@q.com
URL: http://www.nmsantos.com
Contact: Paul Rhetts, Co-Founder
Description: Specializing in providing comprehensive information about Southwestern United Statesxe2x80 Native American and Hispanic art, culture, and history through the publishing of magazines and books. **Founded:** 1984. **Publications:** "Shoes for Santo Nino"; "Genizaro & the Artist"; "Old West Trivia"; "Tale of Prong horned Cantaloupe"; "Saints of the Pueblos"; "A Century of Masters"; "Visions Underground"; "Avenging Victorio". **Training:** Balloon Safety.

4952 ■ Nostradamus Advertising
884 W End Ave., No. 2
  New York, NY 10025
Ph: (212)581-1362
Co. E-mail: nos@nostradamus.net
URL: http://www.nostradamus.net
Contact: Barry Nostradamus Sher, Founder Creative Director
E-mail: nos@nostradamus.net
Description: Firm provides graphic design, advertising, and marketing services to small businesses and not-for-profit organizations, the company offers design services for websites, direct mail advertising, books, and Jewish organizations and also provides political consulting, logo and identity, and brochure, button, and newsletter design services.

4953 ■ PubCom/i-Imagery Design
7417 Holly Ave.
  Takoma Park, MD 20912
Ph: (301)585-8805
URL: http://www.pubcom.com
Contact: Bevi Chagnon, Partner
Description: Firm specializes in training, consulting, and design offers a complete suite of tools and services such as design development, desktop and publishing consulting, blogs, and much more. **Founded:** 1985. **Training:** Advertising 101 for Small Businesses, 2006; Marketing on a Small Budget, 2006; Strategies for Promoting your Exhibit Booth, 2006; Beginner and advanced hands-on training in desktop publishing; Cross-Media Publishing with Adobe In Design: Publishing for Press and Web; 508 Compliance with Adobe In Design; Management of Multi-Tiered Enterprise Websites and Intranets; New Directions in Publishing Technology.

4954 ■ SketchPad Graphic Design
812 Mountain View St.
  Fillmore, CA 93015
Ph: (805)990-1189
URL: http://www.sketchpadgraphicdesign.com
Contact: Norma Holt, Owner
Facebook: www.facebook.com/sketchpadgraphicdesign
Description: Firm provides website designing and development services. **Founded:** 1986. **Publications:** "Please Let Me Fly"; "ATRA Magazine"; "Fillmore Directory". **Training:** Desktop publishing; Ventura Publisher and PageMaker.

4955 ■ Systems Service Enterprises Inc. (SSE)
1835 Lackland Hill Pky.
  Saint Louis, MO 63146
Ph: (314)439-4700
Fax: (314)439-4799
Co. E-mail: info@sseinc.com
URL: http://www.sseinc.com
Contact: Elizabeth Elliott Niedringhaus, President
Facebook: www.facebook.com/SSEnetwork
Linkedin: www.linkedin.com/company/sse
X (Twitter): twitter.com/_SSEinc
YouTube: www.youtube.com/channel/UCs5LUnTLvnjdEdOg4AX1SKg
Description: Provider of computer systems consulting and training. **Scope:** Provides services like advisory services, custom solutions, custom elearning and mobile learning. Provides solutions that

transform workforce effectiveness and foster organizational change that is measurable. Enables to implement strategic initiatives across organizations with custom learning solutions that simply work. **Founded:** 1966. **Publications:** "IT Budget Got your Stomach in Knots"; "We Have a Guy Who Does That"; "Tight Economy Forced a Hold on IT Spending? Now What?"; "Considering Telecommute Questions to Answer". **Special Services:** Pretecht™; SSEwinEngine™; SSElearn Portal™; SSEanalytics™.

LIBRARIES

4956 ■ Printing United Alliance Center for Technology and Research - Library [Printing Industries of America's Center for Technology and Research]
2000 Corporate Dr., Ste. 205
Wexford, PA 15090
Ph: (412)259-1710
Co. E-mail: info@printing.org
URL: http://www.printing.org/programs/technology-research
Facebook: www.facebook.com/printingunited
Linkedin: www.linkedin.com/company/printingunited
Instagram: www.instagram.com/printingind

Description: Serves the international graphic communications industries. Conducts research in graphic processes and their commercial applications, along with seminars and forums on graphic arts and environmental subjects. Conducts educational programs, including the publishing of graphic arts textbooks and learning modules, in addition to training and certification program in sheet-fed offset press operating, Web offset press operating, image assembly, and desktop publishing. Produces test images and quality control devices for the industry. Performs technical services for the graphic arts industry, including problem-solving, material evaluation, and plant audits. **Scope:** Human resources; economics; technologies; business growth. **Founded:** 1924. **Holdings:** Figures not available. **Publications:** "Re-Energize Your Printing Business," Partnership Publishing L.L.C.; "Handbook for Digital Printing and Variable-Data Printing"; "Flexography Primer"; "Process Controls Primer"; "The PDF Print Production Guide". **Training:** Creating Print Ready Files that Work Every Time; What Designers Need to Know about Sustainability; What Every Designer Must Know About Color and Press Oks; New Frontiers for the 21st Century Graphic Designer; Color Management for Printing and Packaging; Web to Print Primer; Designing for Prepress Success; Profit Opportunity Expanding into New Markets with Ancillary Services; Winning Ways to Market Web to Print Work flow to Customers; PDF Preflight and Repair for Newbies; Cross Media Methods n Magic URLS, Microsites and More; Good Jobs Gone Bad 2009 Edition; Fine Tune Your Color Management; Automating for Survival; Best Practice Primer Winning Digital Printing Workflows; Maximize Press time with Pit Stop Maintenance; A How to Tactical Plan for Sustainability Success; Optimizing Your Digital Press Where it Works and Where its Broken; Offset Press Optimization How to Troubleshoot, Control and Accelerate; Performance Dashboard Stalking Waste in the Printers Processes; Technology Forecast What's Hot and What's Not; Lean n Green Tactics and Techniques for Removing Waste; Controlling the Print Process How to Avoid Customer Rejects; Process Control for Color Management Prepress through Press. **Educational Activities:** President's Conference (Annual). **Awards:** Naomi Berber Memorial Award (Annual); Printing Industries of America Education Award of Excellence (Annual); InterTech Technology Awards (Annual); Robert F. Reed Technology Medal (Annual); William D. Schaeffer Environmental Award (Annual); Frederick D. Kagy Education Award of Excellence (Annual). **Geographic Preference:** National.

Dial-It Services

TRADE PERIODICALS

4957 ■ *Telephone IP News*
Pub: Worldwide Videotex
URL(s): wvpubs.com/publications
Released: Annual **Price:** $200, for north America hard copy; $165, for outside north America; $185, U.S. for hard copy. **Description:** Provides information provider (IP) industry news for various telephone services, such as 900, 970, and 976 numbers. Covers new products, public service commission rulings, and marketing strategies. **Availability:** Print; PDF; Online.

LIBRARIES

4958 ■ U.S. Federal Communications Commission (FCC)
45 L St. NE
Washington, DC 20554
Free: 888-225-5322
Fax: (866)418-0232
URL: http://www.fcc.gov
Contact: Jessica Rosenworcel, Chairperson
E-mail: jessica.rosenworcel@fcc.gov
Facebook: www.facebook.com/FCC
X (Twitter): x.com/fcc
Instagram: www.instagram.com/fcc
YouTube: www.youtube.com/fcc
Description: An independent government agency engaged in the regulation of interstate and international communications by radio, television, wire, satellite and cable. The commission serves as the primary authority for communications law, regulation and technology innovation in the United States. **Founded:** 1934. **Publications:** *AM Radio Database Query (AMQ)*; *FCC Amateur License Data Search*; *FM Radio Database Query (FMQ)*; *FCC Universal Licensing System (ULS)*; *FCC Antenna Structure Registration (ASR)*; *AM/FM Broadcast Financial Data/TV Broadcast Financial Data*; *TV Database Query (TVQ)*; *Universal Licensing System License Search*; *Universal Licensing System Aircraft License Search*; *Universal Licensing System Commercial/Restricted Permits License Search*; *Universal Licensing System General Mobile Radio License Search (GMRS)*; *Universal Licensing System Ship License Search*; *Universal Licensing System Geographic Search*; *Universal Licensing System Market Based License Search*; *Filed Comments Search*; *Equipment Authorization System Generic Search*; *Electronic Document Management System Search (EDOCS)*; *Part 68 Registration Search*; *Station Search*; *Application Search*; *EEO Filing Search - Broadcast*; *Ownership Report Search* (Continuous); *Antenna Search*.

Disc Jockey Service

ASSOCIATIONS AND OTHER ORGANIZATIONS

4959 ■ American Disc Jockey Association (ADJA)
20118 N 67th Ave., Ste. 300-605
  Glendale, AZ 85308
Free: 888-723-5776
Fax: (866)310-4676
Co. E-mail: info@adja.org
URL: http://adja.org
Contact: Brian Graham, Contact
E-mail: secretary@dev.adja.org
Facebook: www.facebook.com/4ADJA
X (Twitter): x.com/4ADJA
YouTube: www.youtube.com/4ADJA

Description: Mobile and night club disc jockeys. Seeks to promote the disc jockey as a professional form of entertainment; improves the industry by establishing standards, procedures, and benefits. Assists and trains members; provides forums for professional disc jockeys; conducts educational, charitable, and research programs. **Founded:** 1992. **Publications:** *Mobile Beat* (Monthly). **Awards:** ADJA Chapter of the Year (Annual); Michael Butler Humanitarian Award (Annual); Peter Merry Leadership Award (Annual). **Geographic Preference:** National.

4960 ■ Canadian Disc Jockey Association (CDJA)
Abbey Market
  Oakville, ON, Canada L6M 3H5
Free: 844-235-2357
Co. E-mail: info@cdja.ca
URL: http://cdja.ca
Contact: Luka Miller, President
E-mail: president@cdja.ca
Facebook: www.facebook.com/cdja.ca
Instagram: www.instagram.com/canadian
  discjockeyassociation
YouTube: www.youtube.com/channel/UCCh
  -ZlzkvlEnvESz79x5_dg

Description: Represents the Canadian disc jockey industry. Promotes excellence in service through education, information, networking, and support. **Founded:** 1976. **Publications:** *CUED-UP Street*; *DJ Pulse* (Quarterly). **Awards:** CDJA National President's Award (Annual). **Geographic Preference:** National.

4961 ■ United States Disc Jockey Association (USDJA)
Baltimore, MD
Ph: (443)903-2013
Co. E-mail: info@usdja.com
URL: http://www.usdja.org
Contact: Jason Walsh, President
E-mail: jason@usdja.com
Facebook: www.facebook.com/usdja
X (Twitter): x.com/USDJA
Founded: 2006.

REFERENCE WORKS

4962 ■ "All the Things Your Wedding DJ Can Do (Besides Play Music)" in WeddingWire (July 20, 2018)
URL(s): www.weddingwire.com/wedding-ideas/things
  -wedding-dj-can-do

Ed: Kim Forrest. **Released:** July 20, 2018. **Description:** Hiring a DJ service for your wedding can be a smart move if you need help delegating certain tasks to help make the day run smoothly. The DJ can do more than just play music during the reception — setting the tone for the evening is a big part of their jobs. Covering any hiccups during the reception to help things stay on track, serving as emcee, and even supplying special lighting can be negotiated into a DJ contract. **Availability:** Online.

4963 ■ "Wedding DJ Cost Guide" in WeddingWire
URL(s): www.weddingwire.com/cost/wedding-dj

Description: A guide to how much money a wedding DJ costs. Includes a discussion on what services are included and what to expect from the DJ on your big day. **Availability:** Online.

TRADE PERIODICALS

4964 ■ DJ Times: The International Magazine for the Professional Mobile and Club DJ
Pub: Testa Communications
URL(s): www.djtimes.com

Ed: Jim Tremayne. **Released:** Monthly; except for January, March, May, September and November. **Price:** $19.40, for US; $59.99, for other countries; $39.99, for Canada. **Description:** DJ Times offers the most comprehensive coverage of what the professional DJ wants and needs. **Availability:** Print; Online.

Dispensary (Cannabis)

ASSOCIATIONS AND OTHER ORGANIZATIONS

4965 ■ American Trade Association for Cannabis & Hemp (ATACH)
712 H St. NE Unit No.518
Washington, DC 20002
Co. E-mail: info@atach.org
URL: http://atach.org
Contact: Andy Brassington, President
Description: Promotes the expansion, protection, and preservation of businesses engaged in the legal trade of industrial, medical, and recreational cannabis and hemp-based products. Strives to advance the industry and end prohibition of these products.

4966 ■ Americans for Safe Access (ASA)
1624 U St. NW, Ste. 200
Washington, DC 20009
Ph: (202)857-4272
Co. E-mail: info@safeaccessnow.org
URL: http://www.safeaccessnow.org
Contact: Steph Sherer, President
E-mail: steph@safeaccessnow.org
Facebook: www.facebook.com/safeaccessnow
X (Twitter): x.com/safeaccess
Instagram: www.instagram.com/americansforsafeaccess
YouTube: www.youtube.com/SafeAccess
Description: Seeks to advance legal medical marijuana therapeutics and research. Promotes safe and legal access to cannabis for therapeutic use and research. Works to overcome political and legal barriers by creating policies that improve access to medical cannabis for patients and researchers. Provides legislation, education, litigation, grassroots actions, advocacy, and services for patients and caregivers. **Founded:** 2002. **Publications:** *Activist Newsletter* (Monthly); *ASA Activist* (Monthly). **Geographic Preference:** National.

4967 ■ Arizona Dispensaries Association (ADA)
1846 E Innovation Pk. Dr., Ste. 100
Oro Valley, AZ 85755
Ph: (602)741-0866
Co. E-mail: info@azdispensaries.org
URL: http://azdispensaries.org
Contact: Lilach Mazor Mazor Power, President
Linkedin: www.linkedin.com/company/arizona-dispensaries
Description: Advocates for a safe cannabis industry in Arizona. **Founded:** 2013.

4968 ■ Cannabis Business Association
600 17th St., Ste. 2800 S
Denver, CO 80202-5428
Contact: Chloe Villano, Contact
Facebook: www.facebook.com/CannaBizAssoc
X (Twitter): x.com/CannaBizAssoc
Instagram: www.instagram.com/cannabisbusinessassociation
Description: Advocates for the legalization of cannabis, and provides best practices and business standards to professionals in an effort of create a stable, regulated cannabis industry. **Founded:** 2007.

4969 ■ Cannabis Business Solutions, Inc. (CBS)
GL Brands, Inc.
2202 N Westshore Blvd., Ste. 200
Tampa, FL 33607
Ph: (720)717-3646
Free: 888-811-4367
Co. E-mail: info@glbrands.com
URL: http://glbrands.com
Contact: Catherine M. Zito, Chief Executive Officer
Facebook: www.facebook.com/pages/category/Medical-Cannabis-Dispensary/Cannabis-Business-Solutions-Inc-102222854455470
X (Twitter): x.com/CatherineMZito
Description: Provides various services for the cannabis industry, including investment opportunities for cannabis businesses, special events and webinars, in addition to banking and payment solutions.

4970 ■ Cannabis Marketing Association (CMA)
Denver, CO
Co. E-mail: info@marketingcannabis.org
URL: http://thecannabismarketingassociation.com
Contact: Lisa Buffo, Chief Executive Officer
Facebook: www.facebook.com/CannaMarketingAssociation
Linkedin: www.linkedin.com/company/cannabis-marketing-association
X (Twitter): x.com/cannamarketing
Instagram: www.instagram.com/cannamarketing
Description: Promotes effective and responsible marketing and public relations for cannabis entrepreneurs. **Founded:** 2016.

4971 ■ Colorado Leads
1312 17th St., No. 1302
Denver, CO 80202
URL: http://coleads.org
Contact: Chuck Smith, President
X (Twitter): x.com/coloradoleads
Description: Co-business alliance educates the public about the benefits of cannabis.

4972 ■ Commonwealth Dispensary Association (CDA)
1 State St., 15Th Fl.
Boston, MA 02109
Contact: Brandon Pollock, President
Description: Advocates for the cannabis industry, particularly at the State House and at the Cannabis Control Commission in Massachusetts. Helps licensed operators navigate the complex industry. **Founded:** 2015.

4973 ■ Connecticut Pharmacists Association (CPA) - Academy of Medical Marijuana Dispensaries
35 Cold Spring Rd., Ste. 121
Rocky Hill, CT 06067
URL: http://ctpharmacists.org/academy-of-medical-marijuana-dispensaries
Contact: Marissa Salvo, President
Description: Offers communication, expertise, information, experiences, and suggestions to advance medical marijuana dispensaries in Connecticut. **Founded:** 2014.

4974 ■ Minority Cannabis Business Association (MCBA)
805 SW Broadway, Ste. 2400
Portland, OR 97205
Ph: (202)681-2889
Co. E-mail: info@minoritycannabis.org
URL: http://minoritycannabis.org
Contact: Kaliko Castille, President
Facebook: www.facebook.com/MCBA.org
X (Twitter): x.com/MinCannBusAssoc
Instagram: www.instagram.com/minoritycannabis
Description: Seeks to serve the specific needs of minority cannabis entrepreneurs, workers, and patients/consumers across the United States. Advocates for the creation and fair enforcement of sensible policies. Aims to act as an economic accelerator and creator of opportunity, and to improve critical social and health measures of all communities. **Founded:** 2015.

4975 ■ Mobile Cuisine, LLC
30450 Orchard Lake Rd., Ste. 59
Farmington Hills, MI 48334
Ph: (248)254-3912
URL: http://mobile-cuisine.com
Facebook: www.facebook.com/MobileCuisine
Linkedin: www.linkedin.com/company/mobile-cuisine-magazine
Description: Provides online information and resources for the mobile food industry. **Publications:** *Mobile Cuisine Magazine*; *Mobile Cuisine*.

4976 ■ National Association of Cannabis Businesses (NACB)
17145 W Bluemound Rd., Ste. J-281
Brookfield, WI 53005
Ph: (720)926-6881
Co. E-mail: info@nacb.com
URL: http://www.nacb.com
Contact: Gina Kranwinkel, President
Facebook: www.facebook.com/TheNACB
Linkedin: www.linkedin.com/nationalassociationofcannabisbusinesses
X (Twitter): x.com/thenacb
Instagram: www.instagram.com/thenacb
Description: Provides services to shape the future of cannabis into a safe, ethical, and responsible industry. **Founded:** 2017.

4977 ■ National Cannabis Chamber of Commerce (NCCC)
86 W Mango Rd.
Lake Worth, FL 33467
Free: 800-305-4133
Co. E-mail: contact@nationalcannabischamber.com

URL: http://nationalcannabischamberofcommerce.com
Contact: Michael Miller, President
Facebook: www.facebook.com/National-Cannabis-Chamber-of-Commerce-174535209396257
X (Twitter): x.com/nationalCCC
Instagram: www.instagram.com/nationalcannabischamber
Description: Seeks to create professional standards and to provide advocacy, education, visibility, and networking opportunities to business owners involved in every aspect of the cannabis industry.

4978 ■ National Cannabis Industry Association (NCIA)
128 C St. NW
Washington, DC 20001
Free: 888-683-5650
Co. E-mail: info@thecannabisindustry.org
URL: http://thecannabisindustry.org
Contact: Aaron Smith, Chief Executive Officer
Facebook: www.facebook.com/TheNCIA
Linkedin: www.linkedin.com/company/national-cannabis-industry-association
X (Twitter): x.com/NCIAorg
Instagram: www.instagram.com/nationalcannabisindustry
Description: Represents businesses and organizations in America's emerging cannabis industry. Works to advance the interests of cannabis-related businesses on the national level. Promotes the growth of a responsible and legitimate cannabis industry and works for a favorable social, economic and legal environment for the industry in the U.S. **Founded:** 2010. **Publications:** National Cannabis Industry Association Member Directory. **Geographic Preference:** National.

4979 ■ National Hemp Association (NHA)
1629 K St. NW, Ste. 300
Washington, DC 20006
Ph: (202)706-3911
Co. E-mail: info@nationalhempassociation.org
URL: http://nationalhempassociation.org
Contact: Erica Stark, Executive Director
E-mail: execdir@nationalhempassociation.org
Facebook: www.facebook.com/HempAssociation
X (Twitter): x.com/NatHempAssoc
Description: Supports all aspects of the U.S. industrial hemp industry, including growers, processors, manufacturers, researchers, educators, and investors. **Founded:** 2014.

4980 ■ National Organization for the Reform of Marijuana Laws (NORML)
1420 K St., NW, Ste. 350
Washington, DC 20005
Ph: (202)483-5500
Co. E-mail: norml@norml.org
URL: http://norml.org
Contact: Erik Altieri, Executive Director
Facebook: www.facebook.com/norml
Linkedin: www.linkedin.com/company/norml/about
X (Twitter): x.com/norml
Instagram: www.instagram.com/natlnorml
YouTube: www.youtube.com/user/NatlNORML
Description: Works for change in U.S. policy regarding marijuana. Seeks a more reasonable treatment of marijuana consumers in federal, state, and local laws and policies. **Founded:** 1970. **Geographic Preference:** National.

4981 ■ United Cannabis Business Association (UCBA)
Los Angeles, CA
URL: http://ucba.com
Contact: Jerred Kiloh, President
Facebook: www.facebook.com/UCBANetwork
Linkedin: www.linkedin.com/company/ucba
X (Twitter): x.com/UCBA_Network
Instagram: www.instagram.com/ucbanetwork
Description: Represents cannabis retailers in California. Introduces legislation, addresses taxation issues, and works on social equity programs. **Founded:** 2015.

4982 ■ Vote Hemp (VH)
712 H St. NE
Washington, DC 20002
Ph: (202)318-8999
Co. E-mail: hempinfo@votehemp.com
URL: http://www.votehemp.com
Contact: Eric Steenstra, President
Facebook: www.facebook.com/votehemp
X (Twitter): x.com/votehemp
Instagram: www.instagram.com/vote_hemp
YouTube: www.youtube.com/votehemp
Pinterest: www.pinterest.com/votehemp
Description: Advocates for the acceptance of and free market for industrial hemp, low-THC oilseed and fiber varieties of Cannabis. Works to defend against any new laws, regulations or policies that would prohibit or restrict hemp commerce or imports. **Founded:** 2000. **Geographic Preference:** National.

REFERENCE WORKS

4983 ■ *5 Things You Need to Know Before Opening a Dispensary*
Description: Opening a dispensary is a dream for some and a profitable opportunity for others. With more and more states legalizing marijuana use, the market is strong for dispensaries. This article discusses things to know before starting your own business, including capital, funding, a solid business plan, risks and obstacles, and legalities. **Availability:** Online.

4984 ■ *"20 Small Business Ideas in the Growing Cannabis Industry" in Small Business Trends (October 9, 2016)*
Ed: Annie Pilon. **Released:** October 09, 2016. **Description:** Interview with CFO for the Honest Marijuana Company that discusses twenty potential business ideas for entrepreneurs in the cannabis industry. **Availability:** Online.

4985 ■ *"40 Creative Marijuana & Cannabis Business Ideas for 2020" in Everything But The Plant (March 9, 2020)*
Ed: Laura Newcomer. **Released:** March 09, 2020. **Description:** Details 40 innovative ways to enter the cannabis industry. **Availability:** Online.

4986 ■ *"2020 Could Be a Defining Year For the Cannabis Industry" in CNN Business (January 10, 2020)*
Ed: Alicia Wallace. **Released:** January 10, 2020. **Description:** Discusses the fast pace of the growing cannabis industry including information on legalization in U.S. states, federal legalization, regulations, and business successes and failures. **Availability:** Online.

4987 ■ *"Art & Design in Cannabis Packaging" in Cannabis Business Executive (August 6, 2020)*
Ed: Phillip Mandel. **Released:** August 06, 2020. **Description:** As the recreational and medical cannabis industries continue to expand, new opportunities have arisen as it relates to product packaging. This article discusses the importance of product design, not only for safety and utility considerations, but for attracting consumers. **Availability:** Online.

4988 ■ *Best Cannabis Marketing Guide*
Description: A detailed cannabis marketing guide that shows how to successfully market your cannabis business online and offline.

4989 ■ *"Best Practices for Labeling Infused Products" in Cannabis Business Executive (May 1, 2020)*
Ed: Austin Stevenson. **Released:** May 01, 2020. **Description:** Discusses how to legally and effectively label products for your cannabis business. **Availability:** Online.

4990 ■ *"Black Pot Entrepreneurs Fight for Piece of Washington's Very White Marijuana Industry" in Crosscut (February 13, 2020)*
Ed: Melissa Santos. **Released:** February 13, 2020. **Description:** Details unique challenges that African-American cannabis entrepreneurs are facing as they try to work within the growing cannabis industry. **Availability:** Online.

4991 ■ *"Boom Times for Cannabis Businesses as Californians, in a Pandemic Fog, Isolate Indoors" in Los Angeles Times (April 18, 2020)*
Ed: Susanne Rust, Carolyn Cole. **Released:** April 18, 2020. **Description:** Local business owner, Ryan Moran, operations manager for the Flower Co, discusses the state of cannabis business during shelter-in-place orders during the Coronavirus Pandemic. **Availability:** Online.

4992 ■ *"Cannabis Company Basics: Compliance Is Key" in Cannabis Business Executive (October 29, 2020)*
Released: October 29, 2020. **Description:** Failure to get in the mindset of compliance for your cannabis business can lead to devastating consequences. Compliance means more than just not engaging in criminal or openly unlawful conduct. This article discusses the importance of having a good compliance program. **Availability:** Online.

4993 ■ *"Cannabis Financing: Cannabis Equipment Financing Options in 2020" in Nav (October 21, 2020)*
Ed: Ashley Sweren. **Released:** October 21, 2020. **Description:** Explores cannabis equipment financing options to help you find the best fit when it comes to buying the things you need to take your cannabis business to the next level. **Availability:** Online.

4994 ■ *"Cannabis Industry Growth Potential for 2021" in Business News Daily (September 16, 2020)*
Ed: Adam Uzialko. **Released:** September 16, 2020. **Description:** Details growth potential in the cannabis industry. Includes information on the value of the U.S. cannabis industry, legalization, how to start a business in the cannabis industry, and common challenges for cannabis businesses. **Availability:** Online.

4995 ■ *"Cannabis Industry Job Growth Up 50 Percent" in Green Market Report (October 20, 2020)*
Ed: Kaitlin Domangue. **Released:** October 20, 2020. **Description:** Provides details on huge job growth in the cannabis industry as well as information on job recruitment and career fairs. **Availability:** Online.

4996 ■ *"Cannabis Industry Recruiting Best Practices" in Cannabis Business Executive (November 3, 2020)*
Ed: Liesl Bernard. **Released:** November 03, 2020. **Description:** Discusses the importance of recruiting executive and non-executive employees for your cannabis business and how to find the employees you need. **Availability:** Online.

4997 ■ *"Consumers Are Buying and Using CBD Products Incorrectly" in CBD Today (October 26, 2020)*
Ed: Zora DeGrandpre. **Released:** October 26, 2020. **Description:** Author, Dr. Zora DeGrandpre, practices naturopathic medicine. In this article, she discusses how consumers may be buying and using CBD products incorrectly for their respective health conditions. **Availability:** Online.

4998 ■ *"Eight Cannabis Leaders Discuss Emerging Trends in the Industry Going Forward: 2020" in Forbes (May 6, 2020)*
Ed: Warren Bobrow. **Released:** May 06, 2020. **Description:** Discusses emerging trends in the cannabis industry with leading industry experts. **Availability:** Online.

4999 ■ "Emergency Cannabis Small Business Health and Safety Act - A Legislative Update" in Cannabis Industry Journal (May 4, 2020)
Ed: Steve Levine, Megan Herr, Meghan Brennan. **Released:** May 04, 2020. **Description:** Discusses the Emergency Cannabis Small Business Health and Safety Act, a bill sent to the House of Representatives. This act would allow state-legal medical and recreational cannabis businesses to take advantage of the multi-trillion dollar stimulus packages to help small businesses harmed by COVID-19. **Availability:** Online.

5000 ■ "The Evolution of Cannabis Advertising" in Cannabis Business Executive (June 15, 2020)
Ed: Scott Berman. **Released:** June 15, 2020. **Description:** Discusses the evolution of advertising in the ever-changing cannabis industry from what things were like pre-2014 when the "adult-use market opened in Colorado to today's landscape and major trends. **Availability:** Online.

5001 ■ Ganjapreneur
Description: Provides essential daily news and insights to cannabis entrepreneurs, investors, and industry participants. Also hosts a podcast, conducts interviews with cannabis experts, distributes press releases for cannabis companies, and offers a variety of ways for cannabis-focused brands to reach a wider audience. **Availability:** Online.

5002 ■ "Green Peak Innovations to Open First of Planned 30 Marijuana Stores This Week in Bay City" in Crain's Detroit Business(July 8, 2019)
Pub: Crain Communications Inc.
Contact: Barry Asin, President
URL(s): www.crainsdetroit.com/marijuana/green-peak-innovations-open-first-planned-30-marijuana-stores-week-bay-city
Ed: Anisa Jibrell. **Description:** Green Peak Innovations, LLC, a medical cannabis manufacturer based in Michigan, is opening a retail outlet in Bay City, the first of 30 retail centers it aims to open by the end of 2020. **Availability:** Online.

5003 ■ "How to Build a Cannabis Brand That Consumers Trust" in Cannabis Business Executive (June 1, 2020)
Ed: Susan Gunelius. **Released:** June 01, 2020. **Description:** A brand is one of the most important factors in consumers' purchase decisions. Building a cannabis brand that consumers trust should be a top priority for every cannabis business. This article discusses traits that make top brands trustworthy as well as three steps to build cannabis brand trust. **Availability:** Online.

5004 ■ How to Find Cannabis Investors
Description: For those starting cannabis businesses, finding investors is important. With the growth of this industry, many investors are looking for up-and-coming businesses in the cannabis and hemp industries. This article provides tips on how to find investors for your cannabis business. **Availability:** Online.

5005 ■ "How Risk Management Can Make Marijuana Businesses Bulletproof (or at Least Bullet Resistant)" in Green Market Report (May 3, 2019)
Ed: Steve Schain. **Released:** May 03, 2019. **Description:** Many ordinary risk management tools are unavailable to cannabis entrepreneurs because of federal prohibition. This article discusses how, when armed with risk management fundamentals, marijuana related businesses can diminish risk, fortify an enterprise's sustained growth, and make money along the way. **Availability:** Online.

5006 ■ "How Some Cannabis Brands Plan on Breaking Up Vertical Integration" in Marijuana Venture (October 14, 2020)
Ed: Ryan Douglas. **Released:** October 14, 2020. **Description:** Cultivation business expert, Ryan Douglas, offers his take on vertical integration in the cannabis industry. Douglas explains that a vertically integrated company owns every step of a product's value chain and the assumption that quality and consistency can be better controlled in-house. He goes on to discuss why vertical integration may not always be in the best interest of the consumer or the business. **Availability:** Online.

5007 ■ "How to Start a Medical Marijuana Dispensary Business in 2020" in Crowdspring (January 12, 2020)
Ed: Ashlee Brayfield. **Released:** January 12, 2020. **Description:** A 9-step guide for entrepreneurs interested in opening a medical dispensary. **Availability:** Online.

5008 ■ "How Technology Is Shaping and Reshaping CBD Industry" in The Union Journal (October 23, 2020)
Ed: Robert Delong. **Released:** October 27, 2020. **Description:** Details how technology is used to create and leverage new and innovative business growth in the cannabis industry.

5009 ■ "How To Spark Up a Medical Marijuana Firm in Florida - and Not Get Burned in the Process" in Orlando Business Journal (Vol. 30, March 21, 2014, No. 39, pp. 6)
Pub: American City Business Journals, Inc.
Contact: Mike Olivieri, Executive Vice President
Released: Weekly. **Price:** $8, introductory 4-week offer(Digital & Print). **Description:** Colorado business owners and experts offer tips on starting a medical marijuana business in Florida. Andy Williams recalls that he was filled with fear he would wake up in Federal prison and not see his family again when he started Medicine Man. Jerald Bovine of GreenZipp.com advises those interested in entering the medical marijuana field to know the details of regulation of facilities and labs. **Availability:** Print; Online.

5010 ■ "How to Use Dual Process Theory to Promote Your Cannabis Brand" in Cannabis Business Executive (September 8, 2020)
Ed: Susan Gunelius. **Released:** September 08, 2020. **Description:** An essential part of successful marketing in any industry is understanding consumer behavior and how psychology affects purchasing decisions. One theory that can be used to more effectively match marketing tactics to different consumers is dual process theory. This article explains the theory and why you should consider using it as you develop marketing programs for your cannabis brand. **Availability:** Online.

5011 ■ "If Pennsylvania Is Going to Legalize Adult-Use Marijuana, This is How it Should be Done" in Queen Muse (September 15, 2020)
Ed: Queen Muse. **Released:** September 15, 2020. **Description:** Marijuana law experts and advocates weigh in on six things lawmakers keep in mind amid the movement to legalize cannabis. **Availability:** Online.

5012 ■ "Keeping Pace With Creative Compliance in the Fast-Moving Cannabis Space" in Cannabis Business Executive (March 24, 2020)
Ed: Amanda Ostrowitz. **Released:** March 24, 2020. **Description:** For cannabis brands looking to expand, failure to comply with advertising regulations can result in heavy fines and loss of license. This article discusses how to navigate the ever-changing cannabis laws so that you can confidently run creative campaigns. **Availability:** Online.

5013 ■ "Locals Eager for $785M Medical Marijuana Business" in Orlando Business Journal (Vol. 30, March 21, 2014, No. 39, pp. 4)
Pub: American City Business Journals, Inc.
Contact: Mike Olivieri, Executive Vice President
Released: Weekly. **Price:** $8, introductory 4-week offer(Digital & Print). **Description:** A number of local companies in Central Florida are preparing for a ballot initiative to legalize medical marijuana in November 2014. The National Cannabis Association estimates the medical marijuana market in Florida at $785 million, with about 260,000 patients, while Orlando's share is estimated at $89.1 million, with 29,518 potential patients. **Availability:** Print; Online.

5014 ■ Marijuana Business Daily
Description: Daily news source written by professional journalists for the medical marijuana and retail cannabis industry. Provides retailers, professional cultivators, infused product makers, ancillary service providers and finance professionals with the information and networking they need to flourish within the cannabis industry. **Availability:** Online.

5015 ■ Marijuana Business Magazine
Price: Free to qualified US cannabis industry professionals and investors. **Description:** Digital monthly magazine that provides the latest insights into the cannabis industry for executives, investors, and entrepreneurs. **Availability:** Online.

5016 ■ "Medical Pot Backers Say Industry Will Survive" in Sacramento Business Journal (Vol. 28, October 14, 2011, No. 33, pp. 1)
Pub: Sacramento Business Journal
Contact: Stephanie Fretwell, Director
E-mail: sfretwell@bizjournals.com
Ed: Melanie Turner. **Description:** Medical marijuana supporters have expected the industry to decline but will survive the federal restriction on growers and dispensaries across California. California Cannabis Association and National Cannabis Industry Association believe that some of the dispensaries will remain and the shakeout will lead to stronger state regulations. **Availability:** Online.

5017 ■ "Plant These Marketing Seeds to Watch Your Cannabusiness Grow and Thrive" in Cannabis Business Executive (October 22, 2020)
Ed: Tate Behning. **Released:** October 22, 2020. **Description:** Due to the nature of the cannabis industry, many tried-and-true marketing models don't work for cannabis companies. Part of the struggle is tied to the heightened level of regulation the cannabis industry faces. This article discusses the ins-and-outs of successfully and legally marketing your cannabis business. **Availability:** Online.

5018 ■ "Pot Watch: Magic Butter Delivers THC-infused Food Truck" in Puget Sound Business Journal (Vol. 35, May 30, 2014, No. 6, pp. 10)
Pub: American City Business Journals, Inc.
Contact: Mike Olivieri, Executive Vice President
Description: Magical Butter is a startup in Seattle, Washington that sells a botanical extractor for infusing herbs into food ingredients like the active ingredient in marijuana known as THC into butter or oil. Career chef, Jeremy Cooper, has perfected the peanut butter and jelly sandwich with THC and sells them from the company's food truck business in Denver, Colorado. **Availability:** Online.

5019 ■ "Putting Down Roots" in Entrepreneur (August 2014)
Released: October 28, 2016. **Description:** Entrepreneur Justin Hartfield and partner Doug Francis created Weedmaps.com, an online portal for marijuana dispensaries, after California legalized the sale of medical marijuana. Hartfield is looking forward to a billion-dollar business once the federal prohibition of marijuana is ended. Local dispensaries pay a monthly subscription of $420 to appear on the site while doctors pay $295 to be featured on the site. Harfield is seeking partnerships with laboratories that will provide marijuana testing and other services. **Availability:** Online.

5020 ■ "Record Pot Sales Continue with $61M in July; Total for 2020 Eclipses $300M" in Chicago Sun-Times (August 3, 2020)
Ed: Tom Schuba. **Released:** August 03, 2020. **Description:** Details the record-shattering increase in recreational cannabis sales in Illinois in 2020. **Availability:** Online.

5021 ■ *"Small Businesses Face 6 Challenges in the Weed Market" in Green Entrepreneur (April 1, 2019)*
Ed: Scott McGovern. **Released:** April 01, 2019. **Description:** From government regulations to technological advancements, small businesses find themselves facing more competition and growing expenses. This article looks at some of the hurdles facing cannabis entrepreneurs in a growing but fiercely competitive cannabis market. **Availability:** Online.

5022 ■ *"There's a Movement Afoot to Allow Legal States to do Business with Each Other" in Green Entrepreneur (October 20, 2020)*
Released: October 20, 2020. **Description:** Discusses The Alliance for Sensible Markets' commitment to an interstate commerce market for cannabis. **Availability:** Online.

5023 ■ *"Using Quality as a Competitive Differentiator in the Cannabis Industry" in Cannabis Business Executive (February 3, 2020)*
Ed: Susan Gunelius. **Released:** February 03, 2020. **Description:** Because cannabis is illegal at the federal level, there is no set of standards for product testing, manufacturing, growing, packaging, etc. This article discusses the importance of how you can utilize quality to gain a competitive edge in this industry. **Availability:** Online.

5024 ■ *"Waterdog Herb Farm Sees Sunny Times Ahead" in SF Weekly (October 17, 2019)*
URL(s): www.sfweekly.com/news/chemtales/waterdog-herb-farm/
Ed: Zack Ruskin. **Released:** October 17, 2019. **Description:** Profile of Waterdog Herb Farm, specializing in cannabis, and owner Cyril Guthridge. The farm also uses regenerative agriculture, which helps heal the soil for the plants so that in turn, the plants will also have the best soil to grow in. Solar panels provide power to the farm, and rainwater is collected and used, which also helps keep the farm sustainable. **Availability:** Online.

SOURCES OF SUPPLY

5025 ■ *420 Magazine*
420 Magazine
URL(s): www.420magazine.com
Facebook: www.facebook.com/420magazine
X (Twitter): twitter.com/420magazine
Instagram: www.instagram.com/420magazine
YouTube: www.youtube.com/420magazine
Released: Monthly **Description:** Magazine covering the cannabis industry. **Availability:** Online.

5026 ■ *Ganjapreneur*
URL(s): www.ganjapreneur.com
Facebook: www.facebook.com/ganjapreneur
Linkedin: www.linkedin.com/company/ganjapreneur
X (Twitter): twitter.com/ganjapreneur
Instagram: www.instagram.com/ganjapreneur
Description: Online site provides daily coverage of the cannabis industry, along with a company directory and podcast. **Availability:** Online.

5027 ■ *MJBiz Magazine*
Marijuana Business Daily
Contact: Jess Tyler, Chief Revenue Officer
URL(s): mjbizdaily.com/marijuana-business-magazine
Released: 6/year **Description:** Provides information to investors and entrepreneurs about the cannabis industry. **Availability:** PDF; Download; Online.

STATISTICAL SOURCES

5028 ■ *Cannabis Equipment & Accessory Stores Industry in the US - Market Research Report*
URL(s): www.ibisworld.com/united-states/market-research-reports/cannabis-equipment-accessory-stores-industry/
Price: $925. **Description:** Downloadable report analyzing the current and future trends in the cannabis equipment and accessory stores industry. **Availability:** Download.

5029 ■ *Cannabis Industry Journal*
Innovative Publishing Company LLC
Contact: Richard A. Biros, President
URL(s): cannabisindustryjournal.com
Facebook: www.facebook.com/CannaIndustryjournal
X (Twitter): twitter.com/CannabisEditor
Description: Digital publication covering all aspects of the cannabis industry, including news, business trends, technology, and regulations. **Availability:** Print; Online.

5030 ■ *Cannabis in the US*
URL(s): www.marketresearch.com/Euromonitor-International-v746/Cannabis-30770471/
Price: $1,675. **Description:** A comprehensive guide to the size and shape of the cannabis market in the U.S. It provides the latest retail sales data (historic date range), allowing you to identify the key cannabinoid categories driving growth. It outlines the regulatory, cultural and commercial context and offers strategic analysis of key factors influencing the market – legislative developments both current and future, economic/lifestyle influences, illicit consumption, product innovation, distribution and pricing trends. Forecasts to 2026 illustrate how the market is set to expand and change. **Availability:** Download.

5031 ■ *MarijuanaStocks.com*
URL(s): marijuanastocks.com
Released: Daily **Price:** Free. **Description:** Website offers real-time information about all businesses in the cannabis industry, including stock information and trends. **Availability:** Online.

5032 ■ *Medical Marijuana Dispensaries in the US in the US - Industry Market Research Report*
URL(s): www.marketresearch.com/IBISWorld-v2487/Medical-Marijuana-Dispensaries-Research-14688032/
Price: $1,020. **Description:** Report covers the scope, size, disposition and growth of the medical marijuana dispensaries industry including the key sensitivities and success factors. Also included are five-year industry forecasts, growth rates and an analysis of the industry key players and their market shares. **Availability:** Download.

5033 ■ *US Cannabeauty: CBD and Hemp in BPC Market Report 2021*
URL(s): store.mintel.com/report/us-cannabeauty-cbd-and-hemp-in-bpc-market-report
Price: $4,366.35. **Description:** Downloadable report detailing how consumers are receiving hemp and CBD in their beauty products, especially as a source of self-care. Report includes executive summary, interactive databook, PowerPoint presentation, Infographic overview, report PDF, and previous years data. **Availability:** PDF.

5034 ■ *US Cannabidiol (CBD) Market (by Types, Distribution Channels & Products): Insights & Forecast with Potential Impact of COVID-19 (2020-2024)*
URL(s): www.marketresearch.com/Koncept-Analytics-v3494/Cannabidiol-CBD-Types-Distribution-Channels-13727455/
Price: $1,700. **Description:** Report provides a comprehensive analysis of the U.S. cannabidiol market segmented on the basis of type, distribution channel and products. The market dynamics such as growth drivers, market trends and challenges are analyzed in-depth. The competitive landscape of the market, along with the company profiles of leading players (Aphria Inc., Canopy Growth Corporation, Aurora Cannabis Inc., Charlotte's Web Holdings Inc., Medical Marijuana, Inc., and CV Sciences Inc.) are also presented in detail. **Availability:** Download.

TRADE PERIODICALS

5035 ■ *Cannabis Business Times (CBT)*
Pub: GIE Media Inc.
Contact: Chris Foster, President
URL(s): www.cannabisbusinesstimes.com
Facebook: www.facebook.com/canbusinesstimes
Linkedin: www.linkedin.com/company/cannabis-business-times
X (Twitter): x.com/CBTmag
Ed: Noelle Skodzinski. **Released:** Monthly **Description:** Provides business, marketing, and legal information to cultivators of legal cannabis for medical and recreational use. **Availability:** Print.

5036 ■ *Cannabis Culture Magazine*
Pub: Cannabis Culture
URL(s): www.cannabisculture.com
Facebook: www.facebook.com/CCMagazineOnline
X (Twitter): twitter.com/cannabisculture
Instagram: www.instagram.com/cannabisculturemagazine
Released: Bimonthly **Description:** Magazine covering cannabis culture, including grow tips, legal updates, and coverage of Canada's hemp industry. **Availability:** Print; Online.

5037 ■ *Cannabis Now*
Pub: Cannabis Now
URL(s): cannabisnow.com
Facebook: www.facebook.com/cnmagazine
X (Twitter): twitter.com/cannabisnow
Instagram: www.instagram.com/cannabisnow
Released: Bimonthly **Price:** $24, U.S. per year. https://cannabisnow.com/print-digital-magazine/; $7.99, Individuals for newsstand; $24, per year. **Description:** Magazine covering the cannabis industry. **Availability:** Print; Online.

5038 ■ *Cannabis & Tech Today*
Pub: Innovative Properties Worldwide, Inc.
Contact: Charles Warner, Chief Executive Officer
URL(s): cannatechtoday.com
Facebook: www.facebook.com/CannaTechToday
Linkedin: www.linkedin.com/company/cannatechtoday
X (Twitter): x.com/cannatechtoday
Instagram: www.instagram.com/cannatechtoday
YouTube: www.youtube.com/channel/UChKq-U3u6nITIWFquPXe2mA
Released: Quarterly **Price:** $19.95, 1-year subscription; $29.95, Two years https://cannatechtoday.com/ctt-subscribe. **Description:** Covers everything related to the marijuana business, including technology, science, and medicine. **Availability:** Print; Online.

5039 ■ *Dope Magazine*
URL(s): dopemagazine.com
Facebook: www.facebook.com/Dope.Magazine
X (Twitter): twitter.com/DOPE_Magazine
Instagram: www.instagram.com/dopemagazine
Released: Monthly **Price:** $36, 1 year subscription. **Description:** Magazine covering all aspects of the cannabis industry. **Availability:** Print; Online.

5040 ■ *Freedom Leaf*
Pub: GL Brands, Inc.
URL(s): www.freedomleaf.com
Facebook: www.facebook.com/freedomleaf/
X (Twitter): twitter.com/FreedomLeafInc
Released: Quarterly **Description:** Magazine covering the cannabis industry. **Availability:** Print; Online.

5041 ■ *Green Entrepreneur*
Pub: Entrepreneur Media Inc.
Contact: Dan Bova, Director
E-mail: dbova@entrepreneur.com
URL(s): www.entrepreneur.com/green-entrepreneur
Price: $9.99, for print + online 1 year; $10.99, for print and online. **Description:** Cannabis magazine for legal and medical marijuana entrepreneurs. **Availability:** Print; Online.

5042 ■ *Greenhouse Management*
Pub: GIE Media Inc.
Contact: Chris Foster, President
URL(s): www.greenhousemag.com

Facebook: www.facebook.com/
GreenhouseManagementmag
Linkedin: www.linkedin.com/company/greenhouse
-management-magazine
X (Twitter): x.com/Greenhousemag
Instagram: www.instagram.com/
greenhousemanagement
Ed: Karen Varga. **Released:** Monthly **Description:** Commercial greenhouse growers magazine. **Availability:** Print; PDF; Online.

5043 ■ *High Times*
Pub: Hightimes Holding Corp.
Contact: Peter Horvath, Chief Executive Officer
URL(s): hightimes.com
Facebook: www.facebook.com/HighTimesMag
X (Twitter): twitter.com/High_Times_Mag
Instagram: www.instagram.com/hightimesmagazine
YouTube: www.youtube.com/c/hightimes
Ed: Steve Hager. **Released:** Monthly **Price:** $4.99, for online per month; $29.99, for print 1 year. **Description:** Underground magazine which provides expertise on the production of marijuana and the cannabis industry. **Availability:** Print; Online.

5044 ■ *MJBizDaily*
Pub: Marijuana Business Daily
Contact: Jess Tyler, Chief Revenue Officer
URL(s): mjbizdaily.com
Released: Monthly **Description:** Business information resource covering the retail and medical cannabis industry. **Availability:** Print; Online.

5045 ■ *Oregon NORML News*
Pub: Oregon National Organization for the Reform of Marijuana Laws
Description: Contains articles pertaining to all aspects of marijuana-related issues. **Availability:** Print; Online.

5046 ■ *ROOSTER Magazine*
Pub: Premium Source, Inc.
URL(s): therooster.com
Facebook: www.facebook.com/roostermagazine
X (Twitter): x.com/roostermagazine
Released: Monthly **Price:** $36, for 1 year; $60, Two years; $80, for 3 years; $5, Single issue. **Description:** Contains entertaining articles and news on marijuana, music, sex, and Colorado lifestyle. **Availability:** Print.

5047 ■ *Terpenes and Testing Magazine*
Pub: The Cannabis Marketing Lab
URL(s): terpenesandtesting.com
Facebook: www.facebook.com/terpenesandtes
  tingmagazine
Instagram: www.instagram.com/terpenesandtes
  tingmagazine/?hl=en
Released: Bimonthly **Price:** $48, 6 issues; $29, digital subscription, 6 issues. **Description:** Magazine covering cannabis news, laws, and research. **Availability:** Print; Online.

5048 ■ Vermont Cannabis and Hemp Convention
URL(s): necann.com/vermont
Frequency: Annual. **Description:** Workshops, vendor show, and key topic sessions about cannabis in Vermont. **Principal Exhibits:** Workshops, vendor show, and key topic sessions about cannabis in Vermont.

VIDEO/AUDIO MEDIA

5049 ■ *The Culture High*
Contact: Brett Harvey, Director
Released: 2014. **Description:** This documentary looks at the history of the regulation of marijuana in the United States. Considering the moral and legislative issues related to such laws, the filmmakers outline the arguments and motives for both supporters and opposers of current marijuana laws. Related interviews with many interested parties, including rapper Snoop Dogg, parents of ill children, law enforcement, and academics. **Availability:** Streaming; Download; DVD.

5050 ■ *Marijuana Nation*
Price: $19.95. **Description:** National Geographic investigator Lisa Ling explores the murky world of marijuana farming and finds that business is booming. With federal and state laws a complete jumble in light of the question of whether or not medical marijuana is legal, many people are trying to profit off pot by developing better, more potent products, sometimes right in their own living room. Includes interviews with growers, scientists, law enforcement, and everyday users. **Availability:** DVD.

TRADE SHOWS AND CONVENTIONS

5051 ■ Boston Cannabis Convention
URL(s): necann.com/boston-convention
Frequency: Annual. **Description:** Workshops, vendor show, and key topic sessions on cannabis in Massachusetts. **Principal Exhibits:** Workshops, vendor show, and key topic sessions on cannabis in Massachusetts.

5052 ■ Cannabis Industry and Conference Expo
URL(s): 10times.com/cannabis-expo-detroit
Description: Expo and tradeshow for the cannabis industry. **Principal Exhibits:** Expo and tradeshow for the cannabis industry.

5053 ■ CWCBExpo
URL(s): cwcbexpo.com
Frequency: Annual. **Description:** Tradeshow and expo for the cannabis, CBD, and hemp industries. **Principal Exhibits:** Tradeshow and expo for the cannabis, CBD, and hemp industries.

5054 ■ Indo Expo Winter Show
URL(s): www.indoexpo.com/winter-2022
Frequency: Annual. **Description:** Exhibit and tradeshow for the cannabis industry. **Principal Exhibits:** Exhibit and tradeshow for the cannabis industry.

5055 ■ Lucky Leaf Expo
URL(s): luckyleafexpo.com
Frequency: Annual. **Description:** Tradeshow and expo for the cannabis industry. **Principal Exhibits:** Tradeshow and expo for the cannabis industry.

5056 ■ Maine Cannabis Convention
URL(s): necann.com/maine-2
Description: Provides workshops, vendor booths, and key topics sessions on cannabis in Maine. **Principal Exhibits:** Provides workshops, vendor booths, and key topics sessions on cannabis in Maine.

5057 ■ MJBizCon
Marijuana Business Daily
  3900 S Wadsworth Blvd., Ste. 100
  Lakewood, CO 80235
Ph: (720)213-5992
Co. E-mail: customerservice@mjbiz.com
URL: http://mjbiz.com
Contact: Jess Tyler, Chief Revenue Officer
URL(s): mjbizconference.com/mjbizcon-overview
Price: Check mjbizconference.com/vegas/pricing-and-registration for attendance fees. **Frequency:** Annual. **Description:** Cannabis industry B2B event. **Audience:** General public. **Principal Exhibits:** Cannabis industry B2B event. Dates and Locations: Las Vegas Convention Center, Las Vegas, NV. **Telecommunication Services:** mjbiz@maritz.com.

5058 ■ New England Cannabis Convention
URL(s): necann.com/boston-convention
Frequency: Annual. **Description:** Features cannabis products in a large exhibit. **Principal Exhibits:** Features cannabis products in a large exhibit.

5059 ■ New Jersey Cannabis Convention
URL(s): necann.com/new-jersey-convention
Frequency: Annual. **Description:** Workshops, vendor booths, and key topics sessions on cannabis in New Jersey. **Principal Exhibits:** Workshops, vendor booths, and key topics sessions on cannabis in New Jersey.

5060 ■ New York Cannabis Conference
URL(s): necann.com/new-york-convention
Description: Provides workshops, vendor booths, and key topics sessions on cannabis in New York. **Principal Exhibits:** Provides workshops, vendor booths, and key topics sessions on cannabis in New York.

5061 ■ Oklahoma Cannabis Convention
URL(s): necann.com/oklahoma
Frequency: Annual. **Description:** Networking and key topics sessions for the medical marijuana industry in Oklahoma. Features exhibits with new products. **Principal Exhibits:** Networking and key topics sessions for the medical marijuana industry in Oklahoma. Features exhibits with new products.

5062 ■ RAD Expo
MJ Directions L.L.C.
  4000 Airport Way S.
  Seattle, WA 98108
Ph: (425)656-3621
Co. E-mail: sales@marijuanaventure.com
URL: http://www.marijuanaventure.com
Contact: Greg James, Governor
URL(s): www.theradexpo.com
Frequency: Annual. **Description:** National cannabis event featuring various exhibitors, including food, CBD products, and medical products. **Audience:** All retail and dispensary owners, buyers and employees. **Principal Exhibits:** National cannabis event featuring various exhibitors, including food, CBD products, and medical products. **Telecommunication Services:** rad@marijuanaventure.com.

5063 ■ U.S. Cannabis Conference and Expo
URL(s): www.cannabisconference.com
Frequency: Annual. **Description:** Provides education for cannabis business owners, networking, and an exhibit with vendor booths. **Principal Exhibits:** Provides education for cannabis business owners, networking, and an exhibit with vendor booths.

CONSULTANTS

5064 ■ 4 Leaf Consulting
2126 Rheem Dr., Ste. A
  Pleasanton, CA 94588
Ph: (323)607-3079
Co. E-mail: info@4leafconsulting.com
URL: http://4leafconsulting.com
Contact: Toni Forge, Contact
X (Twitter): x.com/4LeafConsulting
Description: Provides regulatory compliance services to new businesses in the cannabis industry. **Scope:** Provides regulatory compliance services to new businesses in the cannabis industry.

5065 ■ American Cannabis Company Inc.
200 Union St., Ste. 200
  Lakewood, CO 80228
Ph: (303)974-4770
URL: http://www.americancannabisconsulting.com
Contact: Ellis Smith, Chairman Founder
Facebook: www.facebook.com/GrowingTheNextFron
  tier
Linkedin: www.linkedin.com/company/american
  -cannabis-company-inc-
X (Twitter): twitter.com/cannabizconsult
Instagram: www.instagram.com/american_cannabis
Description: Provider of advisory and consulting services to the cannabis industry. **Founded:** 2013.

5066 ■ Canna Advisors
2790 Valmont Rd.
  Boulder, CO 80304
Ph: (720)708-3154
Co. E-mail: info@thinkcanna.com
URL: http://thinkcanna.com
Contact: Diane Czarkowski, Co-Founder
Facebook: www.facebook.com/cannaadvisors

Linkedin: www.linkedin.com/company/canna-advisors
X (Twitter): x.com/cannaadvisors
Instagram: www.instagram.com/cannaadvisors
YouTube: www.youtube.com/channel/UC7wYU-r8VM2m11b73-xnGow
Description: Consultants specializing in the cannabis industry.

5067 ■ Green Rush Consulting (GRC)
2700 International Blvd., Ste. 25
 Oakland, CA 94601
Ph: (702)533-4899
Co. E-mail: services@greenrushconsulting.com
URL: http://www.greenrushconsulting.com
Contact: Zeta Ceti, President
Facebook: www.facebook.com/GreenRushConsulting
X (Twitter): x.com/greenrushnews
YouTube: www.youtube.com/channel/UCwb6rSrZ04AHnd9udH1Kr0w
Description: Helps build cannabis businesses than thrive. Services include business plans, license application services, policy and regulation services, business strategy, and investment information.
Scope: Helps build cannabis businesses than thrive. Services include business plans, license application services, policy and regulation services, business strategy, and investment information.

5068 ■ Higher Yields Cannabis Consulting
2590 Walnut St., Ste. 25
 Denver, CO 80205
Free: 844-449-4353
Co. E-mail: info@higheryieldsconsulting.com
URL: http://higheryieldsconsulting.com
Contact: Cory Waggoner, Chief Executive Officer
Facebook: www.facebook.com/higheryieldsconsulting
Linkedin: www.linkedin.com/company/higher-yields-consulting
X (Twitter): x.com/YieldsHigher
Instagram: www.instagram.com/higheryieldscannabisconsulting
YouTube: www.youtube.com/channel/UCfnCVQaOMTJlgUvjixoArTA
Description: Consultants for the cannabis industry, providing startup services, facility design-build, marketing and branding, and growth and scaling services. **Founded:** 2008.

PUBLICATIONS

5069 ■ *Green Rush Daily*
119 W 24th St.
 New York, NY 10011
Ph: (212)387-0500
Fax: (212)475-7684
URL: http://greenrushdaily.com
URL(s): greenrushdaily.com
Facebook: www.facebook.com/greenrushdaily
X (Twitter): twitter.com/greenfushdaily
Instagram: www.instagram.com/greenrushdaily
Pinterest: www.pinterest.com/greenrushdaily/_created
Description: Digital publication focusing on the cannabis industry. **Availability:** Online.

5070 ■ *Hemp Connoisseur*
URL(s): hcmagazine.com
Facebook: www.facebook.com/Hempconnoisseur
X (Twitter): twitter.com/HempConnoisseur
Instagram: www.instagram.com/hempconnoisseur
Description: Magazine seeking to educate on the environmental, economical, and health benefits of the cannabis plant. **Availability:** Online.

INTERNET DATABASES

5071 ■ *Marijuana - MyGreenz Locator*
10866 Wilshire Blvd.
 Los Angeles, CA 90024
URL: http://www.mygreenz.com
URL(s): itunes.apple.com/us/app/marijuana-mygreenz-locator/id443222909?mt=8
Price: Free for ios platform. **Availability:** Download; Online. **Type:** Directory.

Domestic Help/Maid Service

START-UP INFORMATION

5072 ■ *"Franchises with an Eye on Chicago"* **in *Crain's Chicago Business* (Vol. 34, March 14, 2011, No. 11, pp. 20)**
Pub: Crain Communications Inc.
Contact: Barry Asin, President
Ed: Kevin McKeough. **Description:** Profiles of franchise companies seeking franchisees for the Chicago area include: Extreme Pita, a sandwich shop; Hand and Stone, offering massage, facial and waxing services; Molly Maid, home-cleaning service; Primrose Schools, private accredited schools for children 6 months to 6 hears and after-school programs; Protect Painters, residential and light-commercial painting contractor; and Wingstop, a restaurant offering chicken wings in nine flavors, fries and side dishes. **Availability:** Online.

5073 ■ *"Green Clean Machine"* **in *Small Business Opportunities* (Winter 2010)**
Pub: Harris Publishing, Inc.
Contact: Janet Chase, Contact
Description: Eco-friendly maid franchise plans to grow its $62 million sales base. Profile of Maid Brigade, a green-cleaning franchise is planning to expand across the country. **Availability:** Print; Online.

5074 ■ *Housecleaning Business: Organize Your Business - Get Clients and Referrals - Set Rates and Services*
Ed: Laura Jorstad, Melinda Morse. **Price:** Paperback,softback. **Description:** This book shares insight into starting a housecleaning business. It shows how to develop a service manual, screen clients, serve customers, select cleaning products, competition, how to up a home office, using the Internet to grow the business and offering green cleaning options to clients. **Availability:** E-book; Print.

ASSOCIATIONS AND OTHER ORGANIZATIONS

5075 ■ **Canadian Association of Environmental Management (CAEM) [Association Canadienne de Gestion Environnementale]**
Canada
URL: http://www.caenvironmentalmanagement.com
Description: Seeks to advance the environmental profession; promotes adherence to high standards of ethics and practice by members. **Founded:** 1972. **Publications:** *The Quarterly* (Quarterly). **Awards:** CAEM CEH Certification (Annual). **Geographic Preference:** National.

REFERENCE WORKS

5076 ■ *"Does It Make Financial Sense to Hire a Cleaning Service?"* **in *U.S. News & World Report* (March 7 2016)**
URL(s): money.usnews.com/money/personal-finance/articles/2016-03-07/does-it-make-financial-sense-to-hire-a-cleaning-service
Ed: Geoff Williams. **Released:** March 07, 2016. **Description:** Examines the average costs of hiring house cleaners and discusses whether or not it's worth it to hire someone. **Availability:** Online.

5077 ■ *International Sanitary Supply Association--Membership Directory*
Contact: John Garfinkel, Executive Director
URL(s): www.issa.com
Ed: Michael McQueen. **Released:** Annual; spring. **Description:** Covers about 5,500 member associates, manufacturers, manufacturers' representatives, distributors, publishers, and wholesalers of industrial and institutional cleaning and maintenance chemicals, equipment, and supplies; international coverage. Includes list of publishers of trade periodicals. **Entries include:** Company name, address, phone, names of key personnel, line of business; manufacturer listings include product information, email and website. **Arrangement:** Geographical. **Indexes:** Alphabetical, product. **Availability:** Diskette; Print.

5078 ■ *Maid: Hard Work, Low Pay, and a Mother's Will to Survive*
Ed: Stephanie Land. **Released:** January 22, 2019. **Price:** $14.69, Hardcover; $13.99, E-Book. **Description:** A memoir about the author's early life as a maid when she needed to make ends meet in order to provide for her child. She writes about the cycle of poverty and breaking free from it in order to pursue the American Dream. **Availability:** E-book; Print.

CONSULTANTS

5079 ■ **Cleaning Consultant Services Inc. (CCS)**
PO Box 98757
Seattle, WA 98198
URL: http://www.cleaningbusiness.com
Contact: Bill Griffin, Founder
Description: Firm provides engineering and consulting services and deals with claim and dispute resolution, program and material development and cleaning services and also offers business solutions and support services for cleaning professionals, and publishes books on various areas of the cleaning industry. **Scope:** Firm provides engineering and consulting services and deals with claim and dispute resolution, program and material development and cleaning services and also offers business solutions and support services for cleaning professionals, and publishes books on various areas of the cleaning industry. **Founded:** 1973. **Publications:** "Raising the Bar with Science, Training and Upward Mobility," Jan, 2010; "Technology Revolutionizes the Cleaning Process "Cleaning for Health" is the New Mantra," Distribution Sales and Management Magazine, May, 2003; "Bill Griffin's Crystal Balls-Cleaning Trends in the Usa 2001," Floor Care is Hot in 2001," Mar, 2001; "Inclean Magazine (Australia), Feb, 2001; "Maintaining Swimming Pools, Spas, Whirlpool Tubs and Saunas," Executive House keeping, Feb, 2001; "Whats New with Floor Care," 2001. **Training:** Publisher of books and magazines.

FRANCHISES AND BUSINESS OPPORTUNITIES

5080 ■ **BearCom Building Services Inc.**
1042 Fort Union Blvd., No. 1042
Midvale, UT 84047
Ph: (801)569-9500
Fax: (801)569-8400
Co. E-mail: sales@bearcomservices.com
URL: http://www.bearcomservices.com
Facebook: www.facebook.com/UtahCommercialCleaning
Linkedin: www.linkedin.com/company/bearcom-building-services-inc-
X (Twitter): x.com/bearcomcleaning
Description: Firm provides commercial cleaning services. **Founded:** 1971. **Financial Assistance:** Yes **Training:** Offers 24 hours training with ongoing support.

5081 ■ **The Cleaning Authority (TCA)**
Authority Brands
7085 Samuel Morse Dr., Ste. 105
Columbia, MD 21046
Free: 800-496-9019
URL: http://www.authoritybrands.com
Contact: Tim Evankovich, President
Facebook: www.facebook.com/thecleaningauthority
Linkedin: www.linkedin.com/company/the-cleaning-authority
X (Twitter): x.com/livelifeweclean
Instagram: www.instagram.com/the_cleaning_authority
YouTube: www.youtube.com/user/thecleaningauthority
Pinterest: www.pinterest.com/tcauthority
Description: Provider of home cleaning services. **Founded:** 1977. **Training:** 2 week home office training; on-site visits, quarterly newsletter, ongoing training sessions.

5082 ■ **Cleaning Consultant Services Inc. (CCS)**
PO Box 98757
Seattle, WA 98198
URL: http://www.cleaningbusiness.com
Contact: Bill Griffin, Founder
Description: Firm provides engineering and consulting services and deals with claim and dispute resolution, program and material development and cleaning services and also offers business solutions and support services for cleaning professionals, and publishes books on various areas of the cleaning industry. **Scope:** Firm provides engineering and consulting services and deals with claim and dispute

resolution, program and material development and cleaning services and also offers business solutions and support services for cleaning professionals, and publishes books on various areas of the cleaning industry. **Founded:** 1973. **Publications:** "Raising the Bar with Science, Training and Upward Mobility," Jan, 2010; "Technology Revolutionizes the Cleaning Process "Cleaning for Health" is the New Mantra," Distribution Sales and Management Magazine, May, 2003; "Bill Griffin's Crystal Balls-Cleaning Trends in the Usa 2001," Floor Care is Hot in 2001," Mar, 2001; "Inclean Magazine (Australia), Feb, 2001; "Maintaining Swimming Pools, Spas, Whirlpool Tubs and Saunas," Executive House keeping, Feb, 2001; "Whats New with Floor Care," 2001. **Training:** Publisher of books and magazines.

5083 ■ CottageCare Canada (CC)
105-816 Willow Park Dr. SE
 Calgary, AB, Canada T2J-5S1
Ph: (403)278-7845
Co. E-mail: cet@cottagecare.com
URL: http://cottagecare.com
Contact: Tom Schrader, Founder
Description: Provider of housecleaning services such as kitchen cleaning, dusting, carpet vacuuming, bathroom cleaning, furniture cleaning and other cleaning services. **Founded:** 1976. **Training:** Provides 2 weeks training prior to start-up and ongoing support.

5084 ■ CottageCare Inc. (CC)
13035 Holmes Rd., Ste. A
 Kansas City, MO 64145
Ph: (913)469-0220
URL: http://cottagecare.com
Contact: Tom Schrader, Founder
X (Twitter): x.com/cottagecare
YouTube: www.youtube.com/channel/UCCcLW9_EL6vCedi8KyYg1BA
Description: Big business approach to housecleaning. Franchisor markets and signs-up new customers. Franchisee operates business and has a staff that cleans. Jumbo territories with availability of multiple offices in each territory. **Founded:** 1988. **Training:** Provides training at headquarters for 10 days and ongoing support.

5085 ■ Jani-King Canada
190 Victoria Rd., Ste. 203
 Dartmouth, NS, Canada B3A 1W2
Ph: (902)468-5264
Co. E-mail: novascotia@janiking.ca
URL: http://www.janiking.ca
Contact: Ed McNamara, President
E-mail: emcnamara@janiking.ca
X (Twitter): twitter.com/JaniKingCanada
Description: Provider of commercial cleaning program and janitorial services for office buildings, hospitals, hotels, sporting venues, universities, restaurants, manufacturing facilities and more. **Founded:** 1969. **Franchise Fee:** Varies with plan purchased. **Training:** Initial and ongoing support provided.

5086 ■ Maid to Perfection
135-33 231St St.
 Laurelton, NY 11413
Description: Maid to Perfection provides customized cleaning designed to today's sophisticated customer, making service easy to sell. A residential and commercial business. Proven record of offering choices and diversification to franchisees, which leads to higher profits. Unmatched operational format ensures continuous growth. Your business plan adjusts to your market to meet your goals. Success Magazine ranked Maid To Perfection 1 for franchise support & satisfaction 1999. **No. of Franchise Units:** 305. **Founded:** 1980. **Franchised:** 1990. **Equity Capital Needed:** $54,937-$62,635. **Franchise Fee:** $15,000. **Financial Assistance:** Yes **Training:** 6-8 week business start-up planning, 5 day HQ training, includes live in-home estimating, 5 day office setup and field training, training manuals and CD, 11 instructional videos, advertising materials and assistance, computer program available, 800 helpline, national convention, monthly newsletters, ongoing support.

5087 ■ Maid to Sparkle Inc.
2151 Carbon Hill Dr.
 Midlothian, VA 23113-0000
Contact: Jonathan Bergstein, President
Description: Provider of house cleaning services such as cleaning ceiling fans, window sills, base boards, chair rails, dusting furniture, mopping and much more. **Founded:** 1998. **Financial Assistance:** Yes **Training:** Provides 1 week training at headquarters, 1 week onsite and ongoing support.

5088 ■ Maid2Clean
3054 Dundas St., W
 Toronto, ON, Canada M6P 1Z7
Ph: (905)877-0777
Free: 877-265-6243
Co. E-mail: sales@maid2clean.ca
URL: http://www.maid2clean.ca
Contact: George Fluter, Director
E-mail: george.fluter@maid2clean.ca
Description: Provides domestic housekeeping, cleaning & ironing services to thousands of private householders. **Founded:** 1993. **Training:** Provides 2 days training and ongoing support.

5089 ■ MaidPro
90 Canal St. 4th Fl., Rm. 445
 Boston, MA 02114
Ph: (617)742-8080
Co. E-mail: boston@maidpro.com
URL: http://www.maidpro.com
Facebook: www.facebook.com/MaidProFanPage
X (Twitter): x.com/MaidPro
Instagram: www.instagram.com/maidproofficial
YouTube: www.youtube.com/user/MaidProHomeOffice
Description: Firm provides maid services. **Founded:** 1991. **Equity Capital Needed:** $60,000. **Franchise Fee:** $17,000. **Royalty Fee:** 0.065. **Training:** Includes 6-8 weeks in training and ongoing support.

5090 ■ Merry Maids of Canada
117 Lakeshore Rd. E
 Mississauga, ON, Canada L5G 1E5
Ph: (905)891-8735
Free: 877-782-9201
Co. E-mail: info@merrymaidsmississauga.ca
URL: http://merrymaids.ca
Contact: Doug Hart, President
Facebook: www.facebook.com/MerryMaidsofCanada
Instagram: www.instagram.com/merrymaidscanada
Description: Provider of house cleaning services such as floors washed, baseboards washed, furniture moved, pictures dusted and personalized service tailored. **No. of Franchise Units:** 1422. **Founded:** 1979. **Training:** Training includes 10 days at Merry Maids University and ongoing support from Canadian home office included.

5091 ■ Merry Maids L.P.
Roark Capital Group
 1661 N Shelby Oaks Dr., Ste. 108
 Memphis, TN 38134
Ph: (404)591-5200
Fax: (404)591-5201
Co. E-mail: contact@roarkcapital.com
URL: http://www.roarkcapital.com
Contact: Dallen Peterson, Founder
Facebook: www.facebook.com/MerryMaidsMemphis
X (Twitter): x.com/merrymaids
Instagram: www.instagram.com/merrymaidsofficial
YouTube: www.youtube.com/user/merrymaids
Pinterest: www.pinterest.com/merrymaids
Description: Residential cleaning service. Entrepreneur Magazine has ranked Merry Maids first in the industry for 9 consecutive yrs. Black Enterprise magazine ranked Merry Maids one of the Fabulous 15 Low Cost franchises! The company's commitment to training and support is unmatched. Merry Maids provides comprehensive software and equipment and supply package. Products and supplies available online. Member of the ServiceMaster Quality Service Network. **Founded:** 1979. **Financial Assistance:** Yes **Training:** 8 day HQ training; all start-up equipment and supplies for 2 teams Buddy Program, educational programs, 800 number for assistance, national TV ads, free website for each franchise, weekly intranet bulletin board, newsletters, regional meetings, national convention, proprietary intranet website, 17 field regional coordinators.

5092 ■ Mini Maid
3020 Canton Rd., Ste. 224
 Marietta, GA 30066
Ph: (770)656-2726
Co. E-mail: info@minimaid.com
URL: http://minimaid.com
Contact: Leone Hinzman, Founder
Facebook: www.facebook.com/minimaidga
Description: Firm offers cleaning services through maids. **Founded:** 1973. **Training:** Yes.

5093 ■ Molly Maid Inc.
1954 S Industrial Hwy., Ste. C
 Ann Arbor, MI 48104
Ph: (734)890-5285
Free: 800-654-9647
URL: http://www.mollymaid.com
Contact: David McKinnon, Contact
Facebook: www.facebook.com/MollyMaidAnnArbor
X (Twitter): x.com/MollyMaid
Instagram: www.instagram.com/mollymaid
YouTube: www.youtube.com/user/mollymaid
Pinterest: www.pinterest.com/mollymaid
Description: Provides professional residential home cleaning services. **Founded:** 1984.

5094 ■ Mr. Handyman International
40600 Ann Arbor Rd., E Ste.201
 Plymouth, MI 48170
Free: 877-685-1377
URL: http://www.mrhandyman.com
Contact: Mike Tilley, Owner
Facebook: www.facebook.com/MrHandyman
X (Twitter): twitter.com/mrhandyman
Instagram: www.instagram.com/mrhandyman
YouTube: www.youtube.com/user/mrhandyman
Pinterest: www.pinterest.com/mrhandyman
Description: Firm provides handyman and remodeling services for homeowners and the commercial sector. **Founded:** 1996. **Financial Assistance:** Yes **Training:** Yes.

5095 ■ Nature Stone Flooring Inc.
15 N Pk. St.
 Bedford, OH 44146
Ph: (440)786-9100
Free: 855-378-0094
Fax: (440)786-1927
Co. E-mail: contactus@naturestonefloors.com
URL: http://www.naturestone.com
Contact: Russell Masetta, Owner Founder
Facebook: www.facebook.com/NatureStoneFlooring
X (Twitter): x.com/NatureStone
YouTube: www.youtube.com/channel/UCHeiEwaYz6ZfGO5llJemtpg
Pinterest: www.pinterest.com/nsnaturestone
Description: Manufacturer of epoxy resins for stone and epoxy flooring for garage, basement and commercial applications. **Founded:** 1989. **Financial Assistance:** No **Training:** Epoxy stone flooring company.

5096 ■ Royal Maid Service
34921 US 19N, No. 212
 Palm Harbor, FL 34684
Ph: (727)773-0400
Co. E-mail: royalmaidservice007@gmail.com

URL: http://www.royalmaidservice.com
Contact: Joanne Hollindrake, President
URL(s): www.royalmaidservicenorthpinellas.com
Facebook: www.facebook.com/RoyalMaidServiceNorthPinellas
X (Twitter): x.com/RMinPinellas
Description: Firm provides residential and commercial cleaning services. **Founded:** 2001. **Training:** Offers 6-8 week business start up planning, 5 day office set up and on site training including in home estimating and field training and ongoing support.

5097 ■ Servpro Industries, Inc.
801 Industrial Blvd.
Gallatin, TN 37066
Ph: (615)451-0200
Fax: (615)675-2312
Co. E-mail: franchisesales@servpronet.com
URL: http://www.servpro.com
Contact: Rick Forster, President
Facebook: www.facebook.com/SERVPRO
Linkedin: www.linkedin.com/company/servpro-industries
X (Twitter): x.com/servpro
YouTube: www.youtube.com/user/SERVPROCorporate
Description: Provider of cleaning and restoration services. **Founded:** 1967. **Educational Activities:** PLRB Claims Conference & Insurance Services Expo (Annual).

Driving School

ASSOCIATIONS AND OTHER ORGANIZATIONS

5098 ■ American Driver and Traffic Safety Education Association (ADTSEA)
Highway Safety Services
1434 Trim Tree Rd.
Indiana, PA 15701
Ph: (724)801-8246
Fax: (724)349-5042
Co. E-mail: office@adtsea.org
URL: http://www.adtsea.org
Contact: Harold Fleming, President
Facebook: www.facebook.com/adtseaoffice
X (Twitter): x.com/adtsea
Description: Professional organization of teachers and supervisors interested in improving driver and traffic safety education in colleges and secondary and elementary schools. Awards honorary memberships to retired persons distinguished in the field. Provides assistance to state departments of education, colleges and universities, state associations, and local school districts. **Founded:** 1956. **Publications:** *Journal of Traffic Safety Education* (Quarterly); *Washington Wire* (Periodic). **Awards:** NSSP National Community Safety Award (Annual). **Geographic Preference:** National.

5099 ■ Governors Highway Safety Association (GHSA)
660 N Capitol St. NW, Ste. 220
Washington, DC 20001-1642
Ph: (202)789-0942
Co. E-mail: headquarters@ghsa.org
URL: http://www.ghsa.org
Contact: Jonathan Adkins, Executive Director
E-mail: jadkins@ghsa.org
Facebook: www.facebook.com/GHSAhq
Linkedin: www.linkedin.com/company/governors-highway-safety-association
X (Twitter): x.com/ghsahq
Description: Represents the interests of state and territorial officials who administer the Highway Safety Act of 1966. **Founded:** 1966. **Publications:** *Directions in Highway Safety* (Bimonthly). **Educational Activities:** Lifesavers Conference (Annual). **Awards:** James J. Howard Highway Safety Trailblazer Award (Annual); Peter K. O'Rourke Special Achievement Awards (Annual). **Geographic Preference:** National.

REFERENCE WORKS

5100 ■ *The Driving Book: Everything New Drivers Need to Know but Don't Know to Ask*
Ed: Karen Gravelle. **Released:** February 10, 2015. **Price:** $7.39, Paperback; $7.02, E-Book. **Description:** Driver's Ed may be over and the road test taken and passed, but there are still a great many things teens should know about driving. This books guides the reader through multiple scenarios a driver may face and helps navigate each situation. **Availability:** E-book; Print.

5101 ■ *Driving With a Teenage Brain: A State Trooper's Notes on How to Stay Alive*
Ed: Richard Kasper. **Released:** October 25, 2017. **Price:** $14.24, Paperback; $2.99, E-Book. **Description:** A New York State trooper's guide to commonsense driving, geared towards teen drivers. **Availability:** E-book; Print.

5102 ■ *"Helping Teenagers to Be Safer Drivers" in The New York Times (November 26, 2018)*
URL(s): www.nytimes.com/2018/11/26/well/family/helping-teenagers-to-be-safer-drivers.html
Released: November 26, 2018. **Description:** Teen car crashes are on the decline thanks to new nationwide policies of having new drivers pass graduated licensing and phasing in more adult-supervised driving time. Traditional drivers training courses just give the basics but it's up to parents of teens to help make their child a more experienced driver. Getting rid of distractions, such as phones, is also something that helps lower the crash statistics. **Availability:** Online.

5103 ■ *"How to Choose the Best Driving School for Your Teen" in Drivingguide.com (September 24, 2018)*
URL(s): www.drivingguide.com/articles/choose-best-teen-driving-school/
Ed: Jim Thompson. **Released:** September 24, 2018. **Description:** A guide to finding the best driving school that will meet your child's needs. With teen crashes in the forefront of parents' minds, it's important to find a place that will train your teen to drive safely and responsibly. This guide also discusses car insurance and the state graduated driving license programs. **Availability:** Online.

5104 ■ *How to Drive Safely: 49 Expert Tips, Tricks, and Advice for New, Teen Drivers*
Ed: Damian Brindle. **Released:** March 27, 2018. **Price:** $6.99, Paperback. **Description:** A guide to helping first-time drivers learn what they need to know while driving and even before getting in the car. Focuses on how to drive safely and avoid accidents. **Availability:** Print.

5105 ■ *"Street Survival to Offer Teen Driver Training" in Savannah Now (October 15, 2019)*
URL(s): www.savannahnow.com/news/20191015/street-survival-to-offer-teen-driver-training
Ed: Ann Meyer. **Released:** October 15, 2019. **Description:** Tire Rack Street Survival is coming to Savannah to offer classes to teens. This defensive training course will help teens avoid obstacles and avoid accidents while driving on an advanced driving course. **Availability:** Online.

5106 ■ *"What Is Defensive Driving?" in SafeMotorist.com*
URL(s): www.safemotorist.com/Articles/Defensive_Driving.aspx
Description: Explains what defensive driving is and describes the benefits of taking a course in this skill. Also lists defensive driving courses that are available in each state. **Availability:** Online.

TRADE PERIODICALS

5107 ■ *Directions*
Pub: University of North Carolina at Chapel Hill Highway Safety Research Center
Contact: Chris Gomola, Librarian
E-mail: gomola@hsrc.unc.edu
URL(s): www.hsrc.unc.edu/news/directions/directions-archive
Released: Annual **Price:** Free. **Description:** Reports on research being done by the University of North Carolina Highway Safety Research Center, including alcohol and highway safety, motor vehicle inspection, accident investigation and analysis, driver behavior, and education and licensing. Carries news on adult and child passenger safety, including seat belts and child seats, passenger protection laws, and statewide passenger safety efforts. **Availability:** PDF; Download; Online.

5108 ■ *Dual News*
Pub: Driving School Association of the Americas
Contact: Nina Jo Saint, President
E-mail: president@dsaa.org
URL(s): dsaa.org/Partnerships
Released: Quarterly **Description:** Focuses on traffic safety, automobile care (repair and maintenance), teaching methods, and driving, in general. Recurring features include news of research and columns titled Legislation Pertaining to Driving, Teaching Methods, and President's Corner. **Availability:** Print.

TRADE SHOWS AND CONVENTIONS

5109 ■ DSAA Annual Conference
Driving School Association of the Americas (DSAA)
Communications Office
634E. Main St.
Lansdale, PA 19446
Free: 800-270-3722
Fax: (215)699-3015
Co. E-mail: info@dsaa.org
URL: http://dsaa.org
Contact: Nina Jo Saint, President
E-mail: president@dsaa.org
URL(s): dsaa.org/Events
Frequency: Annual; held in October. **Description:** Automobile safety products related to driver training and traffic safety. **Audience:** Driving industry professionals. **Principal Exhibits:** Automobile safety products related to driver training and traffic safety. **Telecommunication Services:** info@thedsaa.org.

FRANCHISES AND BUSINESS OPPORTUNITIES

5110 ■ All Star Franchising L.L.C.
1011 S Main St.
Ann Arbor, MI 48104

5111 ■ Driving School

Contact: Brent Wall, Contact
Description: Distributor of drives education. Founded: 1997. Financial Assistance: Yes Training: Yes.

LIBRARIES

5111 ■ Alabama Department of Transportation (ALDOT)
PO Box 303050
  Montgomery, AL 36130-3050
Ph: (334)353-6554
Co. E-mail: aldotinfo@dot.state.al.us
URL: http://www.dot.state.al.us
Contact: John Cooper, Director
E-mail: cooperjr@dot.state.al.us
Scope: Transportation. Services: Interlibrary loan; library not open to the public. Founded: 1953. Holdings: 1,000 books; 5,000 reports.

5112 ■ American Automobile Association, Inc. (AAA) - Research Library
American Automobile Association, Inc. (AAA)
  1000 AAA Dr.
  Heathrow, FL 32746
Ph: (407)444-4240
Fax: (407)444-4247
URL: http://www.aaa.com/International
URL(s): www.aaasouth.com
Facebook: www.facebook.com/AAAFlorida
Description: Provides emergency roadside service, discounts and travel bookings. Scope: Travel guide books; market studies; highway and traffic safety; driver education; automobiles - history, statistics, insurance. Services: Interlibrary loan; library open to researchers with permission. Founded: 1902. Holdings: 10,000 books; 20 VF drawers of pamphlets; reports. Publications: *Southern California/Las Vegas TourBook*; *Arkansas/Kansas/Missouri/Oklahoma TourBook* (Annual); *New York TourBook* (Annual); *Alabama/Louisiana/Mississippi TourBook* (Annual); *Oregon/Washington TourBook* (Annual); *New Jersey/Pennsylvania TourBook* (Annual); *Arizona/New Mexico TourBook* (Annual); *Atlantic Provinces/Quebec TourBook* (Annual); *Texas TourBook*; *Western Canada/Alaska TourBook* (Annual); *AAA Bridge and Ferry Directory* (Annual); *Great Lakes CampBook* (Annual); *Japan Travel Book* (Annual); *Kenya Travel Book* (Annual); *Malta and Gozo Travel Book* (Annual); *Mexico Travel Book* (Annual); *Morocco Travel Book* (Annual); *New Zealand Travel Book* (Annual); *Portugal Travel Book* (Annual); *Scotland Travel Book* (Annual); *South Africa Travel Book* (Annual); *Switzerland Travel Book* (Annual); *Thailand Travel Book* (Annual); *Tunisia Travel Book* (Annual); *Turkey South Coast Travel Book* (Annual); *Turkey West Coast Travel Book* (Annual); *Europe Travel Book* (Annual).

5113 ■ California State Department of Motor Vehicles - Licensing Operations Division - Research and Development Branch - Traffic Safety Research Library
1120 N St., Rm. 1430
  Sacramento, CA 95814
Ph: (914)654-4601
Co. E-mail: library@dot.ca.gov
URL: http://dot.ca.gov/programs/transportation-library
Scope: Automobile transportation. Services: Copying; library not open to the public. Holdings: 500 books; 10,000 bound periodical volumes; reports; manuscripts. Subscriptions: 20 journals and other serials.

5114 ■ Kansas Department of Transportation (KDOT) - Library
Dwight D. Eisenhower State Office Building 700 SW
  Harrison St.
  Topeka, KS 66603-3745
Ph: (785)296-3566
Fax: (785)368-7415
Co. E-mail: kdot#publicinfo@ks.gov
URL: http://www.ksdot.gov
Contact: Bob Brock, Director
Facebook: www.facebook.com/KSDOTHQ
X (Twitter): x.com/KDOTHQ
YouTube: www.youtube.com/user/kansastransportation
Pinterest: www.pinterest.com/kdothq
Description: Transportation: Local and suburban transit. Scope: Transportation. Founded: 1868. Holdings: Figures not available.

5115 ■ Missouri Department of Transportation-Division of Materials Library
Rm. 200 600 W Main St.
  Jefferson City, MO 65101
URL: http://www.modot.org
Scope: Transportation. Services: Library not open to the public. Holdings: Figures not available.

5116 ■ Montana Department of Transportation (MDT)
2701 Prospect Ave.
  Helena, MT 59601
Ph: (406)444-6200
Co. E-mail: mdtcommteam@mt.gov
Facebook: www.facebook.com/montanadot
Linkedin: www.linkedin.com/company/montana-department-of-transportation
Instagram: www.instagram.com/mtdot
YouTube: www.youtube.com/user/MontanaDOT
Description: Mission is to serve the public by providing a transportation system and services that emphasize quality, safety, cost effectiveness, economic vitality, and sensitivity to the environment. Scope: Transportation. Services: Interlibrary loan; copying. Founded: 1913. Holdings: 20,000 titles.

5117 ■ New Jersey Department of Transportation Research Library (NJDOT)
c/o David J. Goldberg Transportation Complex
  1035 Pky., Ave.
  Trenton, NJ 08625
Ph: (609)963-1982
URL: http://www.nj.gov/transportation/business/research/library
Contact: David J. Goldberg, Contact
Scope: Transportation. Services: Interlibrary loan; copying; library open to the public by appointment. Founded: 1962. Holdings: 300 books; 11,000 reports.

5118 ■ North Dakota Department of Transportation - Materials and Research Division - Library
608 East Blvd. Ave.
  Bismarck, ND 58505-0700
URL: http://www.dot.nd.gov/divisions/materials/materials.htm
Facebook: www.facebook.com/nddot
X (Twitter): x.com/NorthDakotaDOT
YouTube: www.youtube.com/user/NDDOTOnline
Description: Integral unit of North Dakota Department of Transportation. Scope: Transportation. Services: Library not open to the public. Founded: 1970. Holdings: 6,600 reports.

5119 ■ South Carolina Department of Transportation (SCDOT) - Library
955 Pk. St.
  Columbia, SC 29201-3959
Ph: (803)737-1200
Free: 855-467-2368
URL: http://www.scdot.org
Facebook: www.facebook.com/SCDOT
X (Twitter): x.com/SCDOTPress
YouTube: www.youtube.com/user/SCDOTconnectoronline
Scope: Transportation. Founded: 1998. Holdings: Figures not available.

5120 ■ U.S. National Highway Traffic Safety Administration - Technical Information Services (TIS)
1201 New Jersey Ave. SE, E12-100
  Washington, DC 20590
URL: http://www.nhtsa.gov/es/about-nhtsa/electronic-reading-room
Scope: Vehicle and traffic safety information. Services: Copying; TIS open to the public.

5121 ■ University of Kentucky College of Engineering - Kentucky Transportation Center (KTC) - Library
176 Oliver H Raymond Bldg.
  Lexington, KY 40506
Ph: (859)257-4513
URL: http://ktc.uky.edu
URL(s): www.engr.uky.edu/research-faculty/departments/civil-engineering/kentucky-transportation-center
Facebook: www.facebook.com/KYTRANSPORTATION
Linkedin: www.linkedin.com/company/ktc-uky
X (Twitter): x.com/kytransport
YouTube: www.youtube.com/channel/UCCkzZxbfj-2ZzMKYgH6Jn5Q
Description: Integral unit of College of Engineering, University of Kentucky, operating under its own board of control. Offers technology transfer program, including transportation workshops, audiovisual and library materials, mail lists, and technical assistance. Scope: Highways; bridges; the environment; geotechnology; Intelligent Transportation Systems (ITS); pavements; traffic and safety; structures; construction management; transportation policy, planning, and finance. Services: Interlibrary loan; copying; library open to the public. Founded: 1981. Holdings: Books; Reports; Videotapes. Subscriptions: 300 journals and other serials. Publications: *The Link Technology Transfer Newsletter*. Educational Activities: Annual Transportation Forum, Cosponsored with the Advanced Institute for Transportation Systems Science.

RESEARCH CENTERS

5122 ■ Indiana University School of Public Health (IUSPH) - Department of Applied Health Science
1025 E 7th St., Ste. 111
  Bloomington, IN 47405
URL: http://publichealth.indiana.edu/research/departments/applied-health-science/index.html
Description: Research arm of the Department of Applied Health Science of the School of Health, Physical Education and Recreation at Indiana University Bloomington. Offers health and safety consulting to industry and government. Scope: Health behavior, quantitative and qualitative evaluation of instructional materials, and human behavior and attitudes relating to safety and driver education, including studies on industrial safety, health and safety practices in industry and recreational settings, childhood accident prevention and injury control, nutrition, family life, and human development. Founded: 1965.

5123 ■ University of North Carolina at Chapel Hill - Highway Safety Research Center (HSRC)
130 Mason Farm Rd CB No. 3430
  Chapel Hill, NC 27514
Ph: (919)962-2202
Fax: (919)962-8710
Co. E-mail: info@hsrc.unc.edu
URL: http://www.hsrc.unc.edu
Contact: Chris Gomola, Librarian
E-mail: gomola@hsrc.unc.edu
Facebook: www.facebook.com/hsrcinfo
X (Twitter): x.com/hsrcinfo

Description: Integral unit of University of North Carolina at Chapel Hill. **Scope:** Highway traffic safety, including evaluation of state's operational highway safety program, analysis of mass traffic accident data; roadway hazards; seat belt and restraint system incentives; law, policy and usage studies; evaluation of highway safety countermeasure programs; alcohol and highway safety; driver education and licensing; commercial motor vehicle safety; bicycle and pedestrian safety; older and younger driver studies; and driver distraction studies. **Services:** Interlibrary loan; SDI; copying; Library open to the public for reference use only. **Founded:** 1965. **Holdings:** 18,000 books, documents, technical reports; 575 bound periodical volumes; 40,000 research reports on microfiche. **Subscriptions:** 125 journals and other serials.

Publications: *Directions* (Annual). **Educational Activities:** Occupant protection workshops, For health and safety professionals, law enforcement officials, and researchers.; Safe Routes to School Course, For planners.; Transportation Research Board Annual Meetings (Annual).

Drug Store/Pharmacy

ASSOCIATIONS AND OTHER ORGANIZATIONS

5124 ■ Alliance for Pharmacy Compounding (IACP)
100 Daingerfield Rd., Ste. 401
Alexandria, VA 22314
Ph: (281)933-8400
Fax: (281)495-0602
Co. E-mail: info@a4pc.org
URL: http://a4pc.org
Contact: Scott Brunner, Chief Executive Officer
E-mail: scott@a4pc.org
Facebook: www.facebook.com/a4pcrx
Linkedin: www.linkedin.com/company/a4pcrx
X (Twitter): x.com/a4pcrx

Description: Develops and enforces codes of ethics and practice for members; facilitates cooperation and exchange of information among members; sponsors research and educational programs. **Founded:** 1991. **Publications:** *The eLink* (Weekly); *The Pharmacists' Link* (Quarterly). **Educational Activities:** Annual Compounders on Capitol Hill (CCH) (Annual). **Geographic Preference:** Multinational.

5125 ■ American Association of Colleges of Pharmacy (AACP)
1400 Crystal Dr., Ste. 300
Arlington, VA 22202
Ph: (703)739-2330
Fax: (703)836-8982
Co. E-mail: mail@aacp.org
URL: http://www.aacp.org
Facebook: www.facebook.com/AACPharmacy
Linkedin: www.linkedin.com/company/american-association-of-colleges-of-pharmacy
X (Twitter): x.com/AACPharmacy
Instagram: www.instagram.com/AACPharmacy
YouTube: www.youtube.com/user/AACPVideo

Description: The association includes schools of pharmacy and individual members like administrators, faculty and staff, and students. It takes the lead in advancing and enhancing the quality of education and training in its member institutions while respecting the diversity inherent among them. **Founded:** 1900. **Publications:** *American Association of Colleges of Pharmacy--Roster of Teaching Personnel in Colleges and Schools of Pharmacy* (Annual); *Pharmacy School Admission Requirements*; *American Journal of Pharmaceutical Education (AJPE)* (Annual); *Roster of Faculty and Professional Staff in Colleges and Schools of Pharmacy* (Annual); *American Association of Colleges of Pharmacy--Graduate Programs in the Pharmaceutical Sciences* (Annual); *Prescription for a Rewarding Career* (Periodic); *Roster of Faculty and Professional Staff*; *Roster of Teaching Personnel in Colleges of Pharmacy* (Annual). **Awards:** Paul R. Dawson Award (Annual); The Volwiler Research Achievement Award (Annual). **Geographic Preference:** National.

5126 ■ American Association of Pharmacy Technicians (AAPT)
PO Box 391043
Omaha, NE 68139
Ph: (336)252-8761
Co. E-mail: aapt@pharmacytechnician.com
URL: http://www.pharmacytechnician.com
Contact: Melissa Hutchinson, Coordinator
E-mail: office_coordinator@pharmacytechnician.com
Facebook: www.facebook.com/AAPTechs
Linkedin: www.linkedin.com/company/american-association-of-pharmacy-technicians
Instagram: www.instagram.com/americanassociationpt

Description: Pharmacy technicians. Promotes professional advancement of members. Represents members before health care and public organizations; conducts continuing professional development courses; publicizes the role of the pharmacy technician as an "integral part of the patient care team.". **Founded:** 1979. **Awards:** AAPT Founders Award (Annual). **Geographic Preference:** National.

5127 ■ American College of Apothecaries (ACA)
2830 Summer Oaks Dr.
Bartlett, TN 38134
Ph: (901)383-8119
Fax: (901)473-8187
URL: http://acainfo.org
Contact: Steve Pryor, Chairman
E-mail: steve.p@prorx.net

Description: Professional society of pharmacists owning and operating ethical prescription pharmacies, including hospital pharmacists, pharmacy students, and faculty of colleges of pharmacy. Translates and disseminates knowledge, research data, and recent developments in the pharmaceutical industry and public health. Offers continuing education courses and certificate program. Conducts research programs. **Founded:** 1940. **Publications:** *The Voice of Independent Pharmacy* (Quarterly); *ACA/ACVP Education Newsletter* (Monthly); *American College of Apothecaries--Patron's Newsletter* (Monthly); *American College of Apothecaries--Physician's Newsletter* (Monthly); *The Voice of the Pharmacist* (Quarterly). **Geographic Preference:** National.

5128 ■ American Foundation for Pharmaceutical Education (AFPE)
11325 Random Hills Rd., Ste. 360A-105
Fairfax, VA 22030
URL: http://afpepharm.org
Contact: Ellen Woods, President
E-mail: woods@afpepharm.org
Linkedin: www.linkedin.com/in/afpe-foundation-33542683
X (Twitter): x.com/AFPEPharmEd

Description: Association for advancement and support of pharmaceutical sciences education at U.S. schools and colleges of pharmacy by offering fellowships and grants. **Founded:** 1942. **Awards:** AFPE Gateway to Research Award (Annual); AFPE Pre-Doctoral Fellowships in Pharmaceutical Sciences (Annual); AFPE Pre-Doctoral Fellowships in Pharmaceutical Sciences for Underrepresented Minorities (Annual). **Geographic Preference:** National.

5129 ■ American Institute of the History of Pharmacy (AIHP)
777 Highland Ave.
Madison, WI 53705
Ph: (608)262-5378
Co. E-mail: pharmacyinhistory@aihp.org
URL: http://aihp.org
Facebook: www.facebook.com/PharmacyInHistory
X (Twitter): x.com/HistPharm
YouTube: www.youtube.com/channel/UCuS80O24UVthiojfv395YiA

Description: Pharmacists, firms, and organizations interested in historical and social aspects of the pharmaceutical field. Maintains pharmaceutical Americana collection; conducts research programs. **Scope:** Historical aspects of pharmacy as a profession, a science, and an industry, and history of materia medica. Conducts and stimulates research and collects American pharmaceutical manuscript material, for which State Historical Society of Wisconsin serves as depository. Presents recognition awards and grants-in-aid for historical research. Maintains publication and historical markers programs. **Founded:** 1941. **Publications:** *AIHP Pamphlets*; *AIHP Papers*; *History of Pharmacy and Pharmaceuticals* (Semiannual); *Current Newsletter* (Quarterly); *AIHP Notes*. **Educational Activities:** AIHP Annual Business Meetings (Annual); American Institute of the History of Pharmacy Meeting (Annual). **Awards:** Student Recognition Certificate (Annual); Grant-in-Aid Toward Thesis Expenses Related to the History of Pharmacy (Annual); Sonnedecker Grant for Visiting Research in the History of Pharmacy (Biennial). **Geographic Preference:** National.

5130 ■ American Society of Consultant Pharmacists (ASCP)
1240 N Pitt St., Ste. 300
Alexandria, VA 22314
Ph: (703)739-1300
Free: 800-355-2727
Co. E-mail: info@ascp.com
URL: http://www.ascp.com
Contact: Dr. Chad Worz, Chief Executive Officer
Facebook: www.facebook.com/ascpharm
Linkedin: www.linkedin.com/company/ascpharm
X (Twitter): x.com/ASCPharm
Instagram: www.instagram.com/ascpharm

Description: Provides leadership, education, advocacy and resources enabling consultant and senior care pharmacists to enhance quality of care and quality of life for older individuals through the provision of pharmaceutical care and the promotion of healthy aging. Excels in the areas of: knowledge and skills in geriatric pharmacotherapy; expertise in long-term care settings for the frail at-risk elderly and other residents; and patient-centered advocate for seniors at-risk for medication related problems. **Founded:** 1969. **Publications:** *Clinical Consult Newsletter*

(Monthly); *The Consultant Pharmacist* (Monthly); *American Society of Consultant Pharmacists - Update Newsletter* (Monthly); *UPDATE* (Monthly). **Educational Activities:** American Society of Consultant Pharmacists Annual Meeting and Exhibition (Annual); Midwest Regional Conference (Annual); Texas ASCP Spring CE Conference; Senior Care Pharmacy. **Awards:** Armon Neel Senior Care Pharmacist Award (Annual); George F. Archambault Award (Annual); ASCP Leadership in Education Award (Annual); Richard S. Berman Service Award (Annual). **Geographic Preference:** National.

5131 ■ American Society of Health-System Pharmacists (ASHP) - Donald Francke Memorial Library
4500 E-W Hwy., Ste. 900
Bethesda, MD 20814
Ph: (301)664-8700
Free: 866-279-0681
Fax: (301)657-1251
Co. E-mail: custserv@ashp.org
URL: http://www.ashp.org
Contact: Nishaminy Kasbekar, President
Facebook: www.facebook.com/ASHPofficial
Linkedin: www.linkedin.com/company/ashp
X (Twitter): x.com/ashpofficial
Instagram: www.instagram.com/ashpofficial
YouTube: www.youtube.com/user/ASHPOfficial

Description: Professional society of pharmacists employed by hospitals, HMOs, clinics, and other health systems. Provides personnel placement service for members; sponsors professional and personal liability program. Conducts educational and exhibit programs. Maintains 30 practice interest areas, special sections for home care practitioners and clinical specialists, and research and education foundation. **Scope:** Development of the ASHP and pharmacy. **Founded:** 1942. **Holdings:** Books; papers; documents; photographs. **Publications:** *AHFS Drug Information (AHFS-DI)*; *Drug Information Fulltext/IPA*; *International Pharmaceutical Abstracts* (Semimonthly); *Drug Information Fulltext® (DIFT)* (Semiannual); *IPA on TOXLINE Plus*; *AHFS Drug Information on Stat!-Ref*; *MedTeach™/MedTeach™ for Windows*; *Drug Information Fulltext (DIF)*; *International Pharmaceutical Abstracts (IPA)*; *Handbook on Injectable Drugs*; *American Journal of Health System Pharmacy (AJHP)* (Semimonthly); *ASHP Newsletter* (Monthly); *ASHP Handbook on Injectable Drugs*; *ASHP Intersections*. **Educational Activities:** ASHP Midyear Clinical Meeting (Annual). **Awards:** ASHP Distinguished Leadership Award (Annual); ASHP Distinguished Leadership Award (Annual); Board of Director's Award of Honor (Annual); ASHP Board of Directors' Donald E. Francke Medal (Annual); Harvey A.K. Whitney Lecture Award (Annual); ASHP Student Research Awards (Annual); John W. Webb Lecture Award (Annual). **Geographic Preference:** National.

5132 ■ American Society for Pharmacy Law (ASPL)
3309 Robbins Rd., No. 171
Springfield, IL 62704
Ph: (217)529-6948
Co. E-mail: info@aspl.org
URL: http://www.aspl.org
Contact: Erin Albert, President
X (Twitter): x.com/Pharmacy_Law

Description: Pharmacists, lawyers, and students. Aims are to: further legal knowledge; communicate accurate legal information to pharmacists; foster knowledge and education pertaining to the rights and duties of pharmacists; distribute information of interest to members; provide a forum for exchange of information pertaining to pharmacy law. **Founded:** 1974. **Publications:** *Pharma-Law e-News* (Monthly); *Rx Ipsa Loquitur* (Monthly). **Educational Activities:** Developments in Pharmacy Law Seminar (DPL) (Annual); APhA Annual Meeting & Exposition (Annual). **Awards:** Joseph L. Fink III Founders Award (Annual); Larry M. Simonsmeier Writing Award (Periodic). **Geographic Preference:** National.

5133 ■ Association for Accessible Medicines (AAM)
601 New Jersey Ave. NW, Ste. 850
Washington, DC 20001
Ph: (202)249-7100
Fax: (202)249-7105
Co. E-mail: info@accessiblemeds.org
URL: http://accessiblemeds.org
Contact: Dan Leonard, President
E-mail: dan.leonard@accessiblemeds.org
Facebook: www.facebook.com/accessiblemeds
Linkedin: www.linkedin.com/company/accessiblemeds
X (Twitter): x.com/accessiblemeds
Instagram: www.instagram.com/accessiblemeds
YouTube: www.youtube.com/channel/UCX1h-YqFGCGGldb48sWYAtg

Description: Promotes the common interests of the members and the general welfare of the pharmaceutical industry; prepares and disseminates among members and others, accurate and reliable information concerning the industry, products, needs and requirements; participates in international, federal, state and municipal legislative, regulatory and administrative proceedings with respect to law, rules and orders affecting the pharmaceutical industry; participates in scientific research and product development with intent to increase consumer access to generic products; and raises awareness and visibility of the significant benefits and value of generic drugs to the consumers. **Founded:** 2001. **Geographic Preference:** National.

5134 ■ Association Pharmaciens Du Canada (APhC) [Canadian Pharmacists Association (CPhA)]
851 Industrial Ave.
Ottawa, ON, Canada K1G 4L3
Ph: (613)523-7877
Free: 800-917-9489
Fax: (613)523-0445
Co. E-mail: info@pharmacists.ca
URL: http://www.pharmacists.ca
Contact: Shawn Bugden, Chairman
E-mail: executive@pharmacists.ca
Facebook: www.facebook.com/CPhA
Linkedin: www.linkedin.com/company/canadian-pharmacists-association
X (Twitter): x.com/CPhAAPhC
Instagram: www.instagram.com/cpha_aphc
YouTube: www.youtube.com/user/CPhATV

Description: Works to provide leadership for the pharmacy profession. Monitors government health care policies and legislation; lobbies for the interests of pharmacists. **Founded:** 1907. **Publications:** *Canadian Pharmacists Journal (CPJ)* (Bimonthly); *Compendium of Pharmaceuticals and Specialties (CPS)* (Annual); *Sterile Preparations*; *Pharmacy Directory*; *Provincial Drug Benefit Programs* (Semiannual); *Impact* (Quarterly). **Educational Activities:** Canadian Pharmacists Conference (Annual). **Awards:** CPhA New Practitioner Award (Annual); Canadian Pharmacist of the Year (Annual); New Practitioner Award (Annual); CPhA International Leadership Award (Annual); CPhA Patient Care Achievement Award (Annual); CPhA Patient Care Achievement Award for Innovation (Annual); CPhA Patient Care Achievement Award for Specialty Practice (Annual); Dean George A. Burbidge Award (Annual). **Geographic Preference:** National.

5135 ■ Canadian Pharmacists Journal (CPJ)
2455 Teller Rd.
Thousand Oaks, CA 91320
Contact: Tracey Ozmina, President
URL(s): journals.sagepub.com/home/cph

Released: Bimonthly; January / February, March / April, May / June, July / August, September / October, November / December. **Price:** $533, Institutions for combined (print & e-access); $34, Individuals for single print issue; $96, Institutions for single print issue; $156, Individuals for print and online; $453, Institutions for online only; $522, Institutions for print only. **Description:** Peer-reviewed journal publishing research, review papers on a variety of clinical and business topics, pharmacy-related news, and descriptions of innovative practice models across the field of pharmacy practice. Published in association between SAGE and the Canadian Pharmacists Association. **Availability:** Print; PDF; Download; Online.

5136 ■ Chain Drug Marketing Association (CDMA)
43157 W 9 Mile Rd.
Novi, MI 48375
Free: 800-935-2362
Co. E-mail: support@chaindrug.com
URL: http://qualitychoice.com
Contact: Michael Boivin, Chief Executive Officer
Facebook: www.facebook.com/QualityChoiceProducts
Linkedin: www.linkedin.com/company/chain-drug-marketing-association
X (Twitter): x.com/chaindrug
Instagram: www.instagram.com/qcproducts

Description: Drug store chains located throughout the world. Represents members in the market for merchandise; keeps them abreast of trends in relevant fields. **Founded:** 1926. **Geographic Preference:** National.

5137 ■ Foreign Pharmacy Graduate Examination Committee (FPGEC)
c/o National Association of Boards of Pharmacy
1600 Feehanville Dr.
Mount Prospect, IL 60056
Ph: (847)391-4406
Co. E-mail: fp@nabp.pharmacy
URL: http://nabp.pharmacy/programs/foreign-pharmacy

Description: A committee of the National Association of Boards of Pharmacy. Provides information to foreign pharmacy graduates regarding entry into the U.S. pharmacy profession and health care systems. Evaluates qualifications of foreign pharmacy graduates. Gathers and disseminates data on foreign graduates; maintains information on foreign pharmacy schools in order to produce an examination that measures academic competence with regard to U.S. pharmacy school standards. **Founded:** 1982. **Publications:** *National Pharmacy Compliance News*; *State Newsletters* (Quarterly). **Educational Activities:** NABP Annual Meeting (Annual). **Geographic Preference:** National.

5138 ■ Healthcare Distribution Alliance (HDA)
901 N Glebe Rd., Ste. 1000
Arlington, VA 22203
Ph: (703)787-0000
Fax: (703)812-5282
URL: http://www.hda.org
Contact: Ann W. Bittman, Chief Operating Officer Executive Vice President
E-mail: abittman@hda.org
Linkedin: www.linkedin.com/company/hdma
X (Twitter): x.com/HDAConnect

Description: Wholesalers and manufacturers of drug and health care products and industry service providers. Seeks to secure safe and effective distribution of healthcare products, create and exchange industry knowledge affecting the future of distribution management, and influence standards and business processes that produce efficient health care commerce. Compiles statistics; sponsors research and specialized education programs. **Founded:** 1876. **Educational Activities:** Distribution Management Conference and Expo (DMC) (Annual). **Awards:** iBusiness Solutions (Annual); Nexus Award (Annual); DIANA Award (Annual); HDMA Innovation for Success (Annual); Nexus Award for Lifetime Achievement (Annual); HDMA Distribution Management Award (DMA) (Annual); HDMA iBusiness Solution Award (Annual). **Geographic Preference:** National.

5139 ■ International Federation of Pharmaceutical Wholesalers, Inc. (IFPWI)
10569 Crestwood Dr.
Manassas, VA 20109
Ph: (703)331-3714
URL: http://www.ifpw.com
Contact: Mark Parrish, President
E-mail: mark.parrish@ifpw.com
Facebook: www.facebook.com/IFPW1
X (Twitter): x.com/ifpw

Description: Wholesalers and distributors of pharmaceutical products. Promotes efficient delivery of pharmaceuticals to hospitals, physicians, and pharmacists; seeks to increase public awareness of the role played by members in the health care system. Facilitates cooperation and exchange of information among members. **Founded:** 1977. **Geographic Preference:** Multinational.

5140 ■ National Association of Chain Drug Stores (NACDS)
1776 Wilson Blvd., Ste. 200
Arlington, VA 22209
Ph: (703)549-3001
Fax: (703)836-4869
Co. E-mail: contactus@nacds.org
URL: http://www.nacds.org
Contact: Steven C. Anderson, President
Facebook: www.facebook.com/NACDS.org
Linkedin: www.linkedin.com/company/national-association-of-chain-drug-stores-nacds-
X (Twitter): x.com/nacds
YouTube: www.youtube.com/nacdsvid
Description: Represents the concerns of community pharmacies in Washington, in state capitals, and across the country. Members are more than 210 chain community pharmacy companies. Collectively, community pharmacy comprises the largest component of pharmacy practice with over 107,000 FTE pharmacists. **Founded:** 1933. **Publications:** *National Association of Chain Drug Stores--Communications Directory* (Annual). **Educational Activities:** NACDS Total Store Expo (Annual); Marketplace (Annual); Pharmacy Conference and Managed Care Forum. **Awards:** Harold W. Pratt Award (Annual); Robert B. Begley Award (Annual); Sheldon W. Fantle Lifetime Achievement Award (Annual). **Geographic Preference:** National.

5141 ■ National Community Pharmacists Association (NCPA)
100 Daingerfield Rd.
Alexandria, VA 22314
Ph: (703)683-8200
Free: 800-544-7447
Fax: (703)683-3619
Co. E-mail: kathy.doucette@ncpa.org
URL: http://ncpa.org
Contact: Hashim Zaibak, Vice President
Facebook: www.facebook.com/commpharmacy
Linkedin: www.linkedin.com/company/ncpa
X (Twitter): x.com/commpharmacy
Instagram: www.instagram.com/commpharmacy
YouTube: www.youtube.com/user/NCPAvids
Description: Owners and managers of independent drugstores and pharmacists employed in community pharmacies offering pharmacy service. Provides support for undergraduate pharmacy education through National Community Pharmacists Association Foundation. **Scope:** Public policy issues, including but not limited to, taxation, health care, social security and Medicare, pensions and retirement, security, energy and the environment. **Founded:** 1898. **Publications:** *America's Pharmacist: The Voice of the Community Pharmacists* (Monthly); *NCPAA Newsletter* (Quarterly); *Daily Policy Digest* (Daily); *Health Policy Digest* (Weekly); *NCPA Alert* (Bimonthly); *Today at the NCPA* (Daily); *What's New at the NCPA* (Weekly); *NCPA Newsletter* (Semimonthly). **Educational Activities:** Hatton Sumners Distinguished Lecture Series, Offer exemplary teaching programs.; NCPA Public policy forums, Offer exemplary teaching programs.; NCPA Annual Convention (Annual). **Awards:** General NCPA Internships (3/year); J.C. and Rheba Cobb Memorial Scholarships (Annual); NCPA Foundation Presidential Scholarships (Annual); NCPA Summer Internship Program; Neil Pruitt Sr. Memorial Scholarship (Annual); Willard B. Simmons Sr. Memorial Scholarships (Annual). **Geographic Preference:** National.

5142 ■ Pharmaceutical Care Management Association (PCMA)
325 7th St. NW, Ste. 900
Washington, DC 20004
Ph: (202)756-5700
Fax: (202)756-5708
URL: http://www.pcmanet.org
Contact: J. C. Scott, President
Facebook: www.facebook.com/TheOfficialPCMA
Linkedin: www.linkedin.com/company/pharmaceutical-care-management-association-pcma-
X (Twitter): x.com/pcmanet
Description: Represents managed care pharmacy, Pharmaceutical Benefits Management companies (PBMs) and their healthcare partners in pharmaceutical care. Promotes education, legislation, practice standards, and research to foster quality, affordable pharmaceutical care. **Founded:** 1975. **Geographic Preference:** National.

5143 ■ Pharmaceutical Research and Manufacturers of America (PhRMA)
670 Maine Ave., SW, Ste. 1000
Washington, DC 20024
Ph: (202)835-3400
Co. E-mail: info@phrma.org
URL: http://www.phrma.org/en
Contact: Stephen J. Ubl, President
Facebook: www.facebook.com/PhRMA
Linkedin: www.linkedin.com/company/phrma
X (Twitter): x.com/phrma
YouTube: www.youtube.com/phrma
Description: Research based manufacturers of ethical pharmaceutical and biological products that are distributed under their own labels. Encourages high standards for quality control and good manufacturing practices; researches toward the development of new and better medical products; enactment of uniform and reasonable drug legislation for the protection of public health. Disseminates information on governmental regulations and policies, but does not maintain or supply information on specific products, prices, distribution, promotion, or sales policies of its individual members. **Founded:** 1958. **Publications:** *Pharmaceutical Research Manufacturers Association Annual Fact Book*. **Awards:** PhRMA Discoverers' Award (Annual). **Geographic Preference:** National.

REFERENCE WORKS

5144 ■ *"Acquisition to Give Mylan Tax Benefits, Boost Sales"* **in** *Pittsburgh Business Times* **(Vol. 33, July 18, 2014, No. 53, pp. 3)**
Pub: American City Business Journals, Inc.
Contact: Mike Olivieri, Executive Vice President
Released: Weekly. **Price:** $4, introductory 4-week offer(Digital & Print). **Description:** Mylan Inc.'s acquisition of Abbot's foreign specialty and branded generic drug business is a win situation for the company. The acquisition will help Mylan expand and diversify in the largest markets outside the U.S. as well as prove beneficial in growth through enhanced financial flexibility and a more competitive global tax structure. **Availability:** Print; Online.

5145 ■ *"Angiotech to Buy Top Medical Devices Company"* **in** *Globe & Mail* **(February 1, 2006, pp. B1)**
Description: The details on Angiotech Pharmaceuticals Inc.'s acquisition of American Medical Instruments Holdings Inc. are presented. **Availability:** Online.

5146 ■ *"At the Drugstore, the Nurse Will See You Now"* **in** *Globe & Mail* **(April 13, 2007, pp. B1)**
Ed: Marina Strauss. **Description:** The appointment of several health professionals including nurse, podiatrists, etc. by Rexall Co. at its drugstores to face competition from rivals, is discussed. **Availability:** Online.

5147 ■ *"Auxilium Drug's New Use: Putting the Squeeze On Cellulite"* **in** *Philadelphia Business Journal* **(Vol. 30, September 16, 2011, No. 31, pp. 1)**
Pub: Philadelphia Business Journal
Contact: Sierra Quinn, Director
E-mail: squinn@bizjournals.com
Ed: John George. **Description:** Auxilium Pharmaceuticals and BioSpecifics Technologies are getting on with their plans of finding new uses for their drug Xiaflex, a possible treatment for cellulite. The two firms have dismissed their pending litigations and mapped out an amended licensing agreement for their search for the potential uses of the drug. **Availability:** Online.

5148 ■ *"Azaya Therapeutics Taking Big Steps"* **in** *San Antonio Business Journal* **(Vol. 28, March 28, 2014, No. 7, pp. 8)**
Pub: American City Business Journals, Inc.
Contact: Mike Olivieri, Executive Vice President
Released: Weekly. **Price:** $4, Introductory 4-week offer(Digital only). **Description:** Azaya Therapeutics believes that its $5 million funding round will be completed in 2014. The convertible-note bridge funding was initiated in October 2013. The company, which plans to pursue regulatory approval for its cancer medications, is also focusing on expanding the business. **Availability:** Print; Online.

5149 ■ *"Barshop Leading 'Paradigm Shift' In Aging Research"* **in** *San Antonio Business Journal* **(Vol. 28, September 12, 2014, No. 31, pp. 4)**
Pub: American City Business Journals, Inc.
Contact: Mike Olivieri, Executive Vice President
Released: September 12, 2014. **Price:** $4, Introductory 4-week offer(Digital & Print). **Description:** The National Institute of Health has given a $7.5 million five-year grant to University of Texas Health Science at San Antonio's Barshop Insitute for Longevity and Aging Studies. The funding was awarded to help researchers accelerate the discoveries of commercial drugs that slow the aging process. **Availability:** Print; Mailing list; Online.

5150 ■ *"Changing Prescriptions"* **in** *Business North Carolina* **(Vol. 28, March 2008, No. 3, pp. 52)**
Description: Profile of Moose Drug Company, founded by Archibald Walter Moose in 1882. Family owners share how they focus on pharmacoeconomics (cost-benefit analyses of drugs or drug therapy) and customer service. **Availability:** Print; Online.

5151 ■ *"Coinstar, Inc. and Seattle's Best Coffee Sign Exclusive Agreement to Roll Out Thousands of the New Rubi Kiosks in Grocery, Drug and Mass Channels"* **in** *Marketing Weekly News* **(June 23 2012, pp. 77)**
Pub: PR Newswire Association LLC.
Description: Seattles' Best Coffee, a firm of Starbucks Corporation, has partnered with Coinstar Inc. to install coffee kiosks in grocery, drug and mass merchant retailers featuring Seattle's Best coffee drinks. Rubi kiosk is the third automated kiosk owned by Coinstar. Details of the deal are included.

5152 ■ *"Complementary Strengths Fuel Research Duo's Success"* **in** *Providence Business News* **(Vol. 29, June 2, 2014, No. 9, pp. 22)**
Pub: American City Business Journals, Inc.
Contact: Mike Olivieri, Executive Vice President
URL(s): pbn.com/complementary-strengths-fuel-research-duos-success96239
Description: Johnna A. Pezzullo and Lynne A. Haughey achieved success with Omega Medical Research through their complementary strengths. The company has been successful and works with pharmaceutical companies like Pfizer and GlaxoSmithKline. **Telecommunication Services:** Daddona@pbn.com.

5153 ■ *ComputerTalk for the Pharmacist--Buyers Guide*
Pub: ComputerTalk Associates Inc.
Contact: William Lockwood, Jr., President
URL(s): www.computertalk.com/buyers-guide
Released: Semiannual. **Description:** Publication includes list of more than 50 retail pharmacy data processing system suppliers. All listings are paid. Includes table summarizing contents of listings. **Entries include:** Company, name, address, phone; number of installations, entry-level system configuration and price, software available, expandability, additional costs, length and cost of training period, largest system installed, map showing states where

systems are marketed, supplier's statement. **Arrangement:** Alphabetical. **Indexes:** Geographical (code indicates whether location of installation, sales or service office, or distributor), alphabetical (including addresses and phone numbers of headquarters and sales offices or distributors). **Availability:** Print.

5154 ■ *"Cummins Is a Engine of Growth" in Barron's (Vol. 88, July 14, 2008, No. 28, pp. 43)*
Pub: Dow Jones & Company Inc.
Contact: Almar Latour, Chief Executive Officer

Ed: Shirley A. Lazo. **Description:** Engine maker Cummins increased its quarterly common dividend by 40 percent to 17.5 cents per share from 12.5 cents. CVS Caremark's dividend saw a hike of 18.4 percent from 9.5 cents to 11.25 cents per share while its competitor Walgreen is continuing its 75th straight year of dividend distribution and its 33rd straight year of dividend hikes. **Availability:** Online.

5155 ■ *Drug Store and HBC Chains Leads*
Pub: Chain Store Guide
Contact: Kaitlyn Toner, Account Manager
URL(s): www.chainstoreguide.com/c-82-drug-store-and-hbc-chain-leads.aspx

Released: Daily **Price:** $1,850, for one year. **Description:** Covers more than 1,200 drug store chains operation two or more units, including mass merchants and grocers with pharmacies; 215 wholesale drug companies in the United States and Canada. **Entries include:** For retailers--company name; phone and fax numbers; physical and mailing addresses; company e-mail and web addresses; listing type; number of stores; product lines; percentage of sales by product line; total sales; prescription drug sales; percentage of prescriptions filled with generic drugs; number of prescriptions filled daily; percentage of prescriptions filled with private third party, cash, and Medicaid; number of stores by type; mail order pharmacy indicator; managed care division indicator; projected openings and remodeling; store prototype sizes; total selling square footage; trading area; franchise group headquarters' name and location; distribution center and primary wholesaler names and locations; number of specialty departments; packaged liquor indicators; private label indicators; computerized pharmacy indicator; average number of checkouts; year founded; public company indicator; parent company name and location; regional and divisional office locations; headquarters personnel with titles. For wholesalers--company name, address, phone, and fax; e-mail and web addresses; listing type; product lines; percentage of sales by product line; total sales; percentage of sales by customer type; total stores served; number of member and non-member stores served; trading area; group store trading names; wholesaler type; distribution center locations; private label indicator; year founded; public company indicator; headquarters personnel with titles. **Arrangement:** Separate geographical sections for retailers and wholesalers. **Indexes:** Alphabetical, exclusions. **Availability:** Download; Online. **Type:** Directory.

5156 ■ *"Elder Care, Rx Drug Reforms Top Zoeller's Agenda" in Times (December 21, 2010)*
Pub: The Times

Ed: Sarah Tompkins. **Description:** Indiana Attorney General Greg Zoeller is hoping to develop a program in the state that will help regulate care for the elderly; freeze medical licenses for doctors involved in criminal investigations; address illegal drug use; and to establish a program to help individuals dispose of old prescription medications easily at pharmacies. **Availability:** Online.

5157 ■ *"Fast-Growing Envision Joins Billion-Dollar Club" in Sacramento Business Journal (Vol. 29, March 9, 2012, No. 2, pp. 1)*
Pub: Baltimore Business Journal
Contact: Rhonda Pringle, President
E-mail: rpringle@bizjournals.com

Price: $4, Introductory 4-Week Offer(Digital & Print). **Description:** Envision Pharmaceutical Services has generated an annual revenue of $1 billion in 2011. The company helps employers, unions, insurers and governments to control pharmacy costs. It has also increased its market share. **Availability:** Print; Online.

5158 ■ *"For-Profit Medical School Ramping Up for Business" in Sacramento Business Journal (Vol. 30, February 21, 2014, No. 52, pp. 6)*
Pub: American City Business Journals, Inc.
Contact: Mike Olivieri, Executive Vice President

Description: California Northstate University got full accreditation for the College of Pharmacy at Elk Grove in summer 2013 and hopes to start classes in August or September 2014. The university is in talks to acquire a second building in the area worth $15 million. **Availability:** Online.

5159 ■ *"Fred's Launches New Concept" in Memphis Business Journal (Vol. 34, No. 21, September 07, 2012, pp. 1)*
Pub: Baltimore Business Journal
Contact: Rhonda Pringle, President
E-mail: rpringle@bizjournals.com

Description: Memphis, Tennessee-based Fred's Inc. has opened the Getwell Drug & Dollar, a new store concept that could allow the company to open in smaller markets. The store, which opened in Middleton, is focused primarily on its pharmacy located at the front of the store. **Availability:** Print; Online.

5160 ■ *"Frontage Labs Moves, Plans to Hire 100" in Philadelphia Business Journal (Vol. 28, July 13, 2012, No. 22, pp. 1)*
Pub: Baltimore Business Journal
Contact: Rhonda Pringle, President
E-mail: rpringle@bizjournals.com

Ed: Natalie Kostelni, John George. **Description:** Frontage Pharmaceuticals will relocate its headquarters from the Valley Creek Corporate Center in Exton, Pennsylvania after signing a long-term lease on 80,000 square feet of space at the Eagleview Corporate Center. The relocation came as the company intended to consolidate its offices. Frontage Pharmaceuticals will also hire up to 100 new employees. **Availability:** Print; Online.

5161 ■ *"GSK Creating Pathways From Academia to Industry" in Philadelphia Business Journal (Vol. 33, March 7, 2014, No. 4, pp. 8)*
Pub: American City Business Journals, Inc.
Contact: Mike Olivieri, Executive Vice President

Released: Weekly. **Price:** $4, introductory 4-week offer(Digital & Print). **Description:** The Discovery Fast Track Challenge program of GlaxoSmithKline will expand in 2014 to include scientists in North America and Europe. Scientists will be asked to submit information about their innovative drug research proposals and the winner could be offered a deal with the Discovery Partnerships with Academia team. **Availability:** Print; Online.

5162 ■ *"Health Clinic Expansion Fuels Debate Over Care In Massachusetts" in Boston Business Journal (Vol. 34, June 27, 2014, No. 21, pp. 9)*
Pub: American City Business Journals, Inc.
Contact: Mike Olivieri, Executive Vice President

Released: Weekly. **Description:** The announcement of expansion by several retail health clinics has fueled debate over their quality and competiveness. AFC Doctors Express, a fast-growing chain of retail health clinics, announced its plan to open two new locations in Massachusetts in 2014 and CVS's MinuteClinic announced its intention to open nine additional locations. Concerns are being raised about the cost and quality of this type of healthcare, with a medical society expressing concern that this is fragmented care, not comprehensive care. **Availability:** Print; Online.

5163 ■ *"Healthy Dose of New Vitality" in Business Courier (Vol. 24, February 28, 2008, No. 47, pp. 1)*
Pub: American City Business Journals, Inc.
Contact: Mike Olivieri, Executive Vice President

Ed: Dan Monk. **Description:** Healthy Advice plans to become a leading consumer brand and expand to pharmacies and hospitals. The growth opportunities for healthy Advice are discussed. **Availability:** Online.

5164 ■ *"Hope Grows for a Muscular Dystrophy Drug" in Barron's (Vol. 92, August 25, 2012, No. 35, pp. 35)*
Pub: Dow Jones & Company Inc.
Contact: Almar Latour, Chief Executive Officer

Ed: Andrew Bary. **Description:** The stocks of biotechnology firm Sarepta Therapeutics could gain value if trials for eterpirsen, a drug being developed for Duchenne muscular dystrophy, are successful. The company's stock prices could rise from $10/share to as high as $26/share. **Availability:** Online.

5165 ■ *"How Much For a Magic Bullet?" in San Francisco Business Times (Vol. 28, April 25, 2014, No. 40, pp. 4)*
Pub: American City Business Journals, Inc.
Contact: Mike Olivieri, Executive Vice President

Released: April 25, 2014. **Price:** $4, Introductory 4-Week Offer(Digital & Print). **Description:** Novel gene therapies being developed by San Francisco, California--based research companies entail high prices. Gilead Sciences Inc. developed the hepatitis drug called Sovaldt that is being sold for $1,000 per pill. Health insurers may not be able to finance long-term treatments at these high prices. **Availability:** Print; Online.

5166 ■ *"How Quitting Tobacco Reshaped CVS: Q&A with CEO Larry Merlo" in USA Today (September 14, 2019)*
URL(s): www.usatoday.com/story/money/2019/09/03/cvs-pharmacy-tobacco-sales-ceo-larry-merlo/2151148001/

Description: In September 2014, CVS quit selling tobacco products. CEO Larry Merlo discusses the impact that decision has made on its stores and the health of the American people. **Availability:** Online.

5167 ■ *"Kinek Offers Secure Prescription Drop-Off For Online Shoppers" in Pittsburgh Post-Gazette (June 14, 2012)*

Description: Canadian firm, Kinek, founded in 2009 in New Brunswick, provides drop-off point locations for online shoppers. Med-Fast Pharmacy in Western Pennsylvania joined the Kinek network to provide prescription pickup. The service can be used for most online purchases, including those made on Amazon or eBay. Some drop off sites charge a fee, others are free. **Availability:** Print; Online.

5168 ■ *"Kineta Helps Grow Start Group of 5 Biotech Partners" in Puget Sound Business Journal (Vol. 35, June 13, 2014, No. 8, pp. 6)*
Pub: American City Business Journals, Inc.
Contact: Mike Olivieri, Executive Vice President

Description: Kineta Inc is seeking new funding through its KPI Therapeutics. Kineta offers investors a return on their investments after three to five years. KPI Therapeutics is a new collaborative initiative between drug development firms and private investors. KPI's vision is to create a better way to develop early- and mid-stage therapies for patients and will act as an investment group and a strategic research hub. **Availability:** Print; Online.

5169 ■ *"Kroger Family of Pharmacies to Offer Health Assessment Kiosks at Locations Nationwide" in Entertainment Close-Up (August 22, 2012)*
Pub: Close-Up Media Inc.
Contact: Caroline S. Moore, President
E-mail: cms@closeupmedia.com

Description: Kroger HealthCENTER kiosks will be placed in Kroger Company Family of Pharmacies in 1,950 locations across the country. The kiosks are provided by Styhealthy, a wellness solutions firm and will offer self-use health screening to customers. **Availability:** Online.

5170 ■ "Little Guy is Taking On Potent Competition" in Philadelphia Business Journal (Vol 32, January 10, 2014, No. 48, pp. 4)
Pub: American City Business Journals, Inc.
Contact: Mike Olivieri, Executive Vice President
Released: Weekly. **Price:** $4, introductory 4-week offer(Digital & Print). **Description:** Auxilium Pharmaceuticals has introduced the erectile dysfunction drug Stendra, which it licensed from Vivus Inc. in a $300 million deal. Auxilium CEO, Adrian Adams, says Stendra has some advantages over competing products. **Availability:** Print; Online.

5171 ■ "Loss of Tobacco Revenue Is Unlikely To Cost CVS" in Providence Business News (Vol. 28, February 17, 2014, No. 46, pp. 1)
Pub: American City Business Journals, Inc.
Contact: Mike Olivieri, Executive Vice President
URL(s): pbn.com/loss-of-tobacco-revenue-is-unlikely-to-cost-cvs95149
Description: CVS Caremark Corporation will stop selling tobacco products beginning October 1, 2014. CEO, Larry J. Merlo believes the sale of tobacco products is inconsistent with the drug retailer's purpose. The company's role in providing care through its nurse practitioners and pharmacists is also examined. **Availability:** Online. **Telecommunication Services:** Anderson@pbn.com.

5172 ■ "Marketing is Everything, But Timing Helps" in Idaho Business Review (September 9, 2014)
Pub: BridgeTower Media
Contact: Adam Reinebach, President
Description: Profile of Ladd Family Pharmacy, founded by husband and wife Kip and Elaine, who borrowed money from Idaho Banking Company to start their pharmacy. The firm has expanded from three workers in 2008 to 22 to date and reported $6.2 million in revenue for 2013.

5173 ■ "Medicare Fraudsters Turn to Pharmacies" in South Florida Business Journal (Vol. 32, June 15, 2012, No. 47, pp. 1)
Pub: Baltimore Business Journal
Contact: Rhonda Pringle, President
E-mail: rpringle@bizjournals.com
Description: U.S. Department of Health and Human Services, Office of Inspector General reports indicate that 2,637 retail pharmacies, or 4.4 percent of all pharmacies, had dubious Part D practices in 2009. However, the Miami area led the nation with 19.4 percent of its retail pharmacies submitting dubious claims as unethical frauds turn them in. **Availability:** Print; Online.

5174 ■ "Mississippi County Left Without Pharmacy after Chain Closes" in U.S. News & World Report (October 28, 2019)
URL(s): www.usnews.com/news/best-states/mississippi/articles/2019-10-28/mississippi-county-left-without-pharmacy-after-chain-closes
Released: October 28, 2019. **Description:** With the closing of Fred's Pharmacy in DeKalb, Kemper County is left without a pharmacy. Residents will now have to travel to Meridian or Philadelphia to pick up their prescriptions. However, three retailers are in the process of opening up pharmacies in that area. **Availability:** Online.

5175 ■ "MPI Expansion Goes Back to Family Roots" in Crain's Detroit Business (Vol. 25, June 1, 2009, No. 22, pp. M007)
Pub: Crain Communications Inc.
Contact: Barry Asin, President
Ed: Sherri Begin Welch. **Description:** William Parfet, grandson of Upjohn Company founder, is expanding MPI Research's clinical and early clinical research operations into two buildings in Kalamazoo, land which was once part of his grandfather's farm. **Availability:** Print; PDF; Online.

5176 ■ National Drug Code Directory
Pub: U.S. Food & Drug Administration
Contact: Benjamin D. Moncarz, Chief Financial Officer
URL(s): www.fda.gov/drugs/drug-approvals-and-databases/national-drug-code-directory
Released: Daily **Description:** Publication includes list of manufacturers of commercially marketed human prescription drugs. **Entries include:** Drug company name, address, labeler code, product name, description of product, National Drug Code (NDC) number. Principal content of publication is a listing of about 32,000 drug products. **Arrangement:** Alphabetical. **Indexes:** NDC number, drug class, drug name. **Availability:** Database; Online.

5177 ■ "New Jersey Enacts Strict Opioid Prescribing Law" in Pharmacy Times (February 21, 2017)
URL(s): www.pharmacytimes.com/contributor/timothy-o-shea/2017/02/new-jersey-enacts-strict-opioid-prescribing-law
Ed: Timothy O'Shea. **Released:** February 21, 2017. **Description:** Governor Chris Christie of New Jersey signed legislation to help curb the opioid addiction running through the state. With the new legislation, initial opioid prescriptions can only be for a 5-day supply. **Availability:** Online.

5178 ■ "NuPathe: From Tight On Cash to a Big Payday" in Philadelphia Business Journal (Vol. 33, May 16, 2014, No. 14, pp. 6)
Pub: American City Business Journals, Inc.
Contact: Mike Olivieri, Executive Vice President
Released: Weekly. **Price:** $4, introductory 4-week offer(Digital only). **Description:** Armando Anido, former chief executive officer of NuPathe, shares his perspectives about his brief tenure at the Pennsylvania-based company. He discusses the $144 million sale of the company to Teva Pharmaceuticals. **Availability:** Print; Online.

5179 ■ "Pharmacies Vie for Sites, Customers" in Philadelphia Business Journal (Vol. 30, January 6, 2012, No. 47, pp. 1)
Pub: Baltimore Business Journal
Contact: Rhonda Pringle, President
E-mail: rpringle@bizjournals.com
Description: CVS, Rite Aid and Walgreens are set to open new store formats in Philadelphia, Pennsylvania. The stores will offer services such as in-store nurse practitioners. Of the competitors, CVS has the largest market share in the area. **Availability:** Print; Online.

5180 ■ "Professor: More Will Follow CVS Ban on Tobacco" in Philadelphia Business Journal (Vol. 33, February 14, 2014, No. 1, pp. 6)
Pub: American City Business Journals, Inc.
Contact: Mike Olivieri, Executive Vice President
Released: Weekly. **Price:** $4, introductory 4-week offer(Digital & Print). **Description:** Professor Daniel A. Hussar believes that CVS Caremark's decision to discontinue the sale of tobacco products reflects the company's concern for the health of consumers. He thinks that other drugstores will follow suit. The need for CVS Caremark to emphasize the importance of pharmacists' services is also examined. **Availability:** Print; Online.

5181 ■ "Publix Could Be Downtown's Tipping Point" in Birmingham Business Journal (Vol. 31, May 23, 2014, No. 21, pp. 6)
Pub: American City Business Journals, Inc.
Contact: Mike Olivieri, Executive Vice President
Released: Weekly. **Price:** $4, introductory 4-week offer(Digital & Print). **Description:** Publix Super Markets is planning to open a grocery store and pharmacy in downtown Birmingham, Alabama. Customer demand is expected to increase due to the development of hundreds of apartments in the area. The project is also expected to boost the local real estate industry. **Availability:** Print; Online.

5182 ■ "QuaDPharma Tripling Sales" in Business First of Buffalo (Vol. 30, January 31, 2014, No. 20, pp. 3)
Pub: American City Business Journals, Inc.
Contact: Mike Olivieri, Executive Vice President
Released: Weekly. **Price:** $140, One-Year Print & Digital; $115, One-Year Digital. **Description:** New York-based QuaDPharma LLC is predicting growth in 2014. The firm expects sales to increase by 300 percent. QuaDPharma is focusing on the production of pre-commercial and commercial pharmaceutical products. **Availability:** Print; Online.

5183 ■ "Retail in Austin Strong, Will Continue to Be" in Austin Business JournalInc. (Vol. 29, January 22, 2010, No. 46, pp. 1)
Pub: Austin Business Journal
Contact: Rachel McGrath, Director
E-mail: rmcgrath@bizjournals.com
Ed: Jacob Dirr. **Description:** Retail sector in Austin, Texas has outpaced the national average in value, mid-tier, high-end and drugs retail sectors, according to a report by Pitney Bowes. The national consulting firm's report has projected growth in every sector until the end of fiscal 2012. Data regarding other sectors is also included. **Availability:** Print; Online.

5184 ■ "Scepticism Towards DTC Advertising: A Comparative Study of Korean and Caucasian Americans" in International Journal of Advertising (Vol. 31, February 2012, No. 1, pp. 147)
Ed: Jisu Huh, Denise E. DeLorme, Leonard N. Reid. **Description:** Studies of cultural and subcultural differences among consumers are important for advancing knowledge on direct-to-consumer prescription drug advertising (DTCA). This study investigates and compares scepticism towards DTCA between Korean and Caucasian Americans and the relationship of cultural values (collectivism vs individualism) and acculturation to DTCA secpticism. The results of the research is provided.

5185 ■ "Shire Seeking New Digs for Headquarters" in Philadelphia Business Journal (Vol. 30, September 2, 2011, No. 29, pp. 1)
Pub: Philadelphia Business Journal
Contact: Sierra Quinn, Director
E-mail: squinn@bizjournals.com
Ed: Natalie Kostelni. **Description:** Dublin, Ireland-based Shire PLC announced plans to relocate its North American headquarters from Chesterbrook Corporate Center in Wayne, Pennsylvania and currently evaluating their options. The specialty biopharmaceutical firm is also considering a move to New Jersey or Delaware. **Availability:** Online.

5186 ■ "Sinai Doctor's Research May Lead to Rival Plavix Drug" in Baltimore Business Journal (Vol. 28, July 16, 2010, No. 10, pp. 1)
Pub: Baltimore Business Journal
Contact: Rhonda Pringle, President
E-mail: rpringle@bizjournals.com
Ed: Emily Mullin. **Description:** Paul Gurbel, Sinai Hospital Center for Thrombosis Research director, is seeking an FDA approval of Brilinta, a drug which he helped create and test. Gurbel says that the approval could bring the drug to market as early as December 2010. The drug is expected to rival Bristol-Myers' Plavix, which generated almost $6.2 billion in 2009. **Availability:** Print; Online.

5187 ■ "Sleep Apnea Pill Nears Human Tests" in Philadelphia Business Journal (Vol. 33, May 9, 2014, No. 13, pp. 8)
Pub: American City Business Journals, Inc.
Contact: Mike Olivieri, Executive Vice President
Released: Weekly. **Price:** $4, Introductory 4-week offer(Digital & Print). **Description:** Galleon Pharmaceuticals is set to begin human testing of its experimental therapy GAL-160, an oral medicine for sleep apnea, and has already started human testing of GAL-021, an intravenous drug to treat respiratory complications in patients receiving anesthetics and opiate pain medication. Galleon CEO, James C. Man-

nion, hopes that both drugs pass the proof-of-concept stage and move to mid-stage clinical testing in humans by mid-2015. **Availability:** Print; Online.

5188 ■ *"Walgreens Turns to Robots to Fill Prescriptions, as Pharmacists Take on More Responsibilities" in CNBC.com (March 30, 2022)*
URL(s): www.cnbc.com/2022/03/30/walgreens-turns -to-robots-to-fill-prescriptions-as-pharmacists-take -on-more-responsibilities.html
Ed: Melissa Repko. **Description:** Pharmacy jobs are adjusting and pharmacists are taking on different responsibilities. In order to keep serving customers, robot-powered fulfillment centers are being built to keep up with, and even exceed, demand.

5189 ■ *"Want to Work for Amazon? You May Get the Chance Soon" in Pharmacy Times (May 17, 2017)*
URL(s): www.pharmacytimes.com/contributor/timothy -aungst-pharmd/2017/05/want-to-work-for-amazon -you-may-get-the-chance-soon
Ed: Timothy Aungst. **Released:** May 17, 2017. **Description:** Online retail giant, Amazon, is making a play to break into the pharmacy industry. More staff is being hired for Amazon's health care division, which could lead to quick home deliveries for prescriptions. **Availability:** Online.

5190 ■ *"Why CVS May Not Get Burned By Its Tobacco Decision (Part 2); Looking at CVS' Decision To Discontinue Selling Tobacco Products In Purely Dollar Terms Misses the Bigger Picture" in Gallup Business Journal (March 20, 2014)*
Pub: Gallup, Inc.
Contact: Jon Clifton, Chief Executive Officer
Description: Drug retailer, CVS, made a strategic play in organizational identity, mission, and purpose when it decided to quit selling cigarettes at its retail stores. The decision to discontinue sales of tobacco products could, long term, strengthen the company's identity in the U.S. marketplace, thus increasing sales. **Availability:** Print; Online.

5191 ■ *"Wielding a Big Ax" in Barron's (Vol. 89, July 13, 2009, No. 28, pp. 26)*
Pub: Dow Jones & Company Inc.
Contact: Almar Latour, Chief Executive Officer
Ed: Shirley A. Lazo. **Description:** Weyerhaeuser cut their quarterly common payout by 80 percent from 25 cents to a nickel a share which they say will help them preserve their long-term value and improve their performance. Paccar also cut their quarterly dividend by half to nine cents a share. Walgreen however, boosted their quarterly dividend by 22.2 percent to 13.75 cents a share. **Availability:** Online.

SOURCES OF SUPPLY

5192 ■ *Scott's Canadian Pharmacy Directory*
Scott's Directories
URL(s): www.scottsdirectories.com/canadian-busi- ness-database/canadian-pharmacy-directory
Price: $3,299, for prospector unlimited; $1,649, for prospector standard; $1,199, for profiler version. **Description:** Covers approximately 18,000 pharmacists, university pharmacy faculty members, pharmacy suppliers, and drug and poison information centers in Canada, chain drug stores, independent. **Entries include:** Name, address, phone, names and titles of key personnel, biographical data (for pharmacists), geographical area served. **Arrangement:** For pharmacists--Same information available in geographical and alphabetical sections. For others--Classified by line of business, then alphabetical. **Availability:** Online.

STATISTICAL SOURCES

5193 ■ *Evolving eCommerce: Vitamins, Minerals & Supplements: Incl Impact of COVID-19 - US - December 2020*
URL(s): store.mintel.com/report/evolving-ecommerce -vitamins-minerals-supplements-incl-impact-of-covi d-19-us-december-2020

Price: $4,366.35. **Description:** Downloadable report discussing data analysis about the vitamin, mineral, and supplement market and it's growth in online shopping. **Availability:** PDF.

5194 ■ *RMA Annual Statement Studies*
Pub: Risk Management Association
Contact: Nancy Foster, President
Released: Annual. **Description:** Contains composite balance sheets and income statements for more than 360 industries, including the accounting, auditing, and bookkeeping industries. Also contains five years of comparative historical data for discerning trends. Includes 16 commonly used ratios, computed for most of the size groupings for nearly every industry.

5195 ■ *Standard & Poor's Industry Surveys*
Pub: Standard And Poor's Financial Services LLC.
Contact: Douglas L. Peterson, President
Description: Two-volume book that examines the prospects for specific industries, including trucking. Also provides analyses of trends and problems, statistical tables and charts, and comparative company analyses.

5196 ■ *U.S. Drug Stores Market Report 2021*
URL(s): store.mintel.com/report/us-drug-store-retail- ing-market-report
Price: 4,366.35. **Description:** Downloadable report providing data on the U.S. drug store industry. Report includes an executive summary, interactive databook, PowerPoint presentation, infographic overview, report PDF, and previous years data. **Availability:** PDF.

TRADE PERIODICALS

5197 ■ *America's Pharmacist: The Voice of the Community Pharmacists*
Pub: National Community Pharmacists Association
Contact: Hashim Zaibak, Vice President
URL(s): ncpa.org/americas-pharmacist
Ed: Mike Conlan. **Released:** Monthly **Price:** $8.25, Single issue; $50, for 1 year national; $100, for 1 year international. **Description:** Professional magazine. Contains continuing education series, updates, and news from Washington. **Availability:** Print; PDF; Online.

5198 ■ *FDA Week*
Pub: Inside Washington Publishers
Contact: Robert Woolard, Contact
URL(s): insidehealthpolicy.com/fda-week/daily-news
Released: Weekly **Price:** $705, U.S. and Canada for per year; $755, Elsewhere for per year. **Description:** Reports on Food and Drug Administration policy, regulation, and enforcement. **Availability:** Online.

5199 ■ *Journal of the American Pharmacists Association (JAPhA)*
Pub: APhA Academy of Pharmacy Practice and Management
Contact: Mitchel C. Rothholz, Executive Director
E-mail: mrothholz@aphanet.org
URL(s): www.japha.org
X (Twitter): x.com/JAPhAJournal
Released: 6/year; latest Issue 5, September-October, 2024 - in progress. **Price:** $550, Individuals for online international; $450, Individuals for online, US. **Description:** Peer-reviewed journal for pharmacy professionals. **Availability:** Print; Download; PDF; Online.

5200 ■ *Journal of Pharmaceutical Sciences (JPharmSci)*
Pub: American Chemical Society
Contact: Mary K. Carroll, President
URL(s): jpharmsci.org
X (Twitter): x.com/JPharmSciences
Ed: Bradley D. Anderson, Harry G. Brittain. **Released:** Monthly **Price:** $428, Individuals for online only US, Canada, International (12 month). **Description:** Professional journal publishing research articles in the pharmaceutical sciences. **Availability:** Print; Download; PDF; Online.

5201 ■ *Pharmacy Times: Practical Information for Today's Pharmacist*
URL(s): www.pharmacytimes.com
Released: Monthly **Description:** Newsletter providing information on health items (including prescription and over-the-counter drugs and surgical supplies) to independent, chain, and hospital pharmacists. **Availability:** Print; Online.

5202 ■ *Pharmacy Today*
Pub: APhA Academy of Pharmacy Practice and Management
Contact: Mitchel C. Rothholz, Executive Director
E-mail: mrothholz@aphanet.org
URL(s): www.pharmacist.com/Publications/Pharmacy -Today/July-2024
Released: Monthly **Description:** Reports news and opinions of interest to pharmacists. Includes comprehensive coverage of pharmacotherapeutic, legislative, and socioeconomic news of every segment of the pharmacy profession. **Availability:** Print; PDF; Download.

TRADE SHOWS AND CONVENTIONS

5203 ■ **American Society of Consultant Pharmacists Annual Meeting and Exhibition**
American Society of Consultant Pharmacists (ASCP)
1240 N Pitt St., Ste. 300
Alexandria, VA 22314
Ph: (703)739-1300
Free: 800-355-2727
Co. E-mail: info@ascp.com
URL: http://www.ascp.com
Contact: Dr. Chad Worz, Chief Executive Officer
URL(s): annual.ascp.com
Frequency: Annual. **Description:** Pharmaceuticals, drug distribution systems, packaging equipment, computers, durable medical equipment, and medical supplies. **Audience:** Consultants and senior care pharmacists. **Principal Exhibits:** Pharmaceuticals, drug distribution systems, packaging equipment, computers, durable medical equipment, and medical supplies. Dates and Locations: 2025 Oct 23-26 Town and Country, San Diego, CA; 2026 Oct 29-Nov 01 Gaylord National, National Harbor, MD; 2027 Nov 11-14 JW Marriott, San Antonio, TX. **Telecommunication Services:** ascp@discoversb.com.

5204 ■ **Florida Pharmacy Association Annual Meeting and Convention**
Florida Pharmacy Association (FPA)
610 N Adams St.
Tallahassee, FL 32301
Ph: (850)222-2400
Fax: (850)561-6758
Co. E-mail: fpa@pharmview.com
URL: http://www.floridapharmacy.org
Contact: Michael Jackson, Chief Executive Officer
E-mail: jackson@pharmview.com
URL(s): floridapharmacy.org/134th-annual-meeting -convention
Frequency: Annual. **Description:** Pharmaceuticals and other product lines and services provided for and by pharmacists. **Audience:** Pharmacists, and healthcare professionals. **Principal Exhibits:** Pharmaceuticals and other product lines and services provided for and by pharmacists. **Telecommunication Services:** mrivera@pharmview.com.

5205 ■ **NCPA Annual Convention**
National Community Pharmacists Association (NCPA)
100 Daingerfield Rd.
Alexandria, VA 22314
Ph: (703)683-8200
Free: 800-544-7447
Fax: (703)683-3619
Co. E-mail: kathy.doucette@ncpa.org
URL: http://ncpa.org
Contact: Hashim Zaibak, Vice President
URL(s): ncpa.org/annual-convention

5206 ■ Drug Store/Pharmacy

Frequency: Annual. **Description:** To promote the growth of pharmacy business owners. **Audience:** Pharmacist owners, managers, and pharmacists. **Principal Exhibits:** To promote the growth of pharmacy business owners. Dates and Locations: 2025 Oct 18-21 New Orleans, LA; 2026 Oct 03-06 Kansas City, MO. **Telecommunication Services:** questions@american-tradeshow.com.

5206 ■ PDA Annual Meeting
Parenteral Drug Association (PDA)
4350 E W Hhy, Ste. 600
Bethesda, MD 20814
Ph: (301)656-5900
Fax: (301)986-0296
Co. E-mail: info@pda.org
URL: http://www.pda.org
Contact: Richard Johnson, President
E-mail: johnson@pda.org
URL(s): www.pda.org/global-event-calendar/conferences/pda-week-2025

Frequency: Annual. **Description:** Supplies and services related to pharmaceuticals manufacturing the science and technology. **Audience:** Pharmaceutical and biopharmaceutical industry professionals. **Principal Exhibits:** Supplies and services related to pharmaceuticals manufacturing the science and technology. Dates and Locations: 2025 Apr 06-11 Palm Springs Convention Centre, Palm Springs, CA. **Telecommunication Services:** registration@pda.org.

5207 ■ Texas Pharmacy Association Conference and Expo
Texas Pharmacy Association (TPA)
3200 Steck Ave., Ste. 370
Austin, TX 78757-8034
Ph: (512)836-8350
Free: 800-505-5463
Fax: (512)836-0308
URL: http://www.texaspharmacy.org
Contact: Michael Muñiz, President
URL(s): www.texaspharmacy.org/page/confexpo

Frequency: Annual. **Description:** Pharmaceuticals and various services provided to pharmacists. **Audience:** Pharmacists and students. **Principal Exhibits:** Pharmaceuticals and various services provided to pharmacists. **Telecommunication Services:** lgoerlitz@texaspharmacy.org.

FRANCHISES AND BUSINESS OPPORTUNITIES

5208 ■ The Medicine Shoppe Pharmacy
1600-10104 103rd Ave.
Edmonton, AB, Canada T5J 0H8
Free: 800-267-8877
Fax: (780)425-3980
URL: http://www.medicineshoppe.ca
Contact: Deesha Chandan, Coordinator
E-mail: dchandan@medicineshoppe.ca

Description: Retailer of health care products and also provides health advisor services. **Founded:** 1970. **Training:** Yes.

COMPUTERIZED DATABASES

5209 ■ *Clinical Pharmacology*™
Gold Standard Inc.
302 Knights Run Ave., Ste. 800
Tampa, FL 33602
URL: http://www.goldstandard.com
Contact: Youngsuk Chi, Chairman
URL(s): www.elsevier.com/solutions/clinical-pharmacology

Availability: Handheld; Online. **Type:** Full-text; Image.

5210 ■ *International Pharmaceutical Abstracts (IPA)*
Clarivate Analytics
1500 Spring Garden St.
Philadelphia, PA 19130
URL: http://clarivate.com
Contact: Jonathan Gear, Chief Executive Officer

URL(s): clarivate.com/products/dialog-family/dialog-databases
Released: Biweekly **Availability:** PDF; Online. **Type:** Bibliographic.

LIBRARIES

5211 ■ Amgen Inc.
Amgen Inc.
1 Amgen Center Dr.
Thousand Oaks, CA 91320-1799
Ph: (805)447-1000
Free: 888-762-6436
Fax: (805)477-1010
Co. E-mail: medinfo@amgen.com
URL: http://amgen.com
Contact: Robert A. Bradway, Chief Executive Officer
Facebook: www.facebook.com/amgenbiotech
Linkedin: www.linkedin.com/company/amgen
X (Twitter): twitter.com/amgen
Instagram: www.instagram.com/amgenbiotech
YouTube: www.youtube.com/user/amgen

Description: Global independent biotechnology company focused on discovering, developing, manufacturing, and delivering innovative human therapeutics, using tools such as human genetics, pharmaceutical products include treatments for patients with rheumatoid arthritis, plaque psoriasis, active psoriatic arthritis, non-myeloid cancer, anemia caused by chronic kidney disease, and anemia due to chemotherapy. **Founded:** 1980. **Awards:** Amgen Award for Science Teaching Excellence Program (Annual). **Preferred Investment Size:** $1,000,000 to $3,000,000. **Investment Policies:** Early stage. **Industry Preferences:** Biotechnology.

5212 ■ AnMed Health Medical Center - Cancer Learning Center
800 N Fant St. 1st fl.
Anderson, SC 29621
Ph: (864)512-3477
Co. E-mail: foundation@anmedhealth.org
URL: http://anmedhealth.org/give-back/our-foundation

Description: Provides healthcare and medical services. **Scope:** Cancer, oncology, therapy. **Founded:** 1985. **Subscriptions:** journals Booklets; brochures; pamphlets; handbooks; textbooks; cookbooks; treatment guides; survivor stories; video cassette tapes; DVDs.

5213 ■ APhA Academy of Pharmacy Practice and Management (APhA-APPM) - Library
2215 Constitution Ave., NW
Washington, DC 20037
Ph: (202)628-4410
Free: 800-237-2742
Fax: (844)390-3782
Co. E-mail: infocenter@aphanet.org
URL: http://www.pharmacist/apha-appm
Contact: Mitchel C. Rothholz, Executive Director
E-mail: mrothholz@aphanet.org
Facebook: www.facebook.com/APhAPharmacists
Linkedin: www.linkedin.com/company/american-pharmacists-association
X (Twitter): x.com/pharmacists
YouTube: www.youtube.com/channel/UCKAj5RelarlgcZyA8kbiBQA

Description: Pharmacists concerned with rendering professional services directly to the public, without regard for status of employment or environment of practice. Provides a forum whereby pharmacists meet to discuss and implement programs relevant to the practitioner of pharmacy; to recommend courses of action which should be undertaken by the profession; to coordinate academy efforts so as to be an asset to the progress of the profession. Provides continuing education meetings, seminars, and workshops; produces audiovisual materials. **Scope:** Pharmaceuticals. **Founded:** 1965. **Holdings:** Figures not available. **Publications:** *Student Pharmacist* (Bimonthly); *Who's Who in American Pharmacy* (Annual); *Pharmacy Today Newsletter* (Daily); *Pharmacy Today* (Monthly); *Journal of Pharmaceutical Sciences (JPharmSci)* (Monthly); *Pharmaceutical Directory* (Annual); *Journal of the American Pharmacists Association (JAPhA)* (6/year). **Educational Activities:** APhA Annual Meeting & Exposition (Annual). **Awards:** APhA-APPM Distinguished Achievement Award in Administrative Practice (Annual); H. A. B. Dunning Award (Annual); APhA Honorary Membership (Annual); APHA Hubert H. Humphrey Award (Annual); Remington Honor Medal (Annual); Hugo H. Schaefer Award (Irregular); Good Government Pharmacist of the Year Award (Annual); APhA Honorary President (Annual); Gloria Niemeyer Francke Leadership Mentor Award (Annual); APhA-APPM Presentation Merit Awards (Annual); Daniel B. Smith Practice Excellence Award (Annual); Distinguished Achievement Award in Community and Ambulatory Practice (Annual); Distinguished Achievement Award in Clinical/Pharmacotherapeutic Practice; Distinguished Achievement Award in Hospital and Institutional Practice (Annual); APhA-APPM William H. Briner Distinguished Achievement Award in Nuclear Pharmacy Practice (Annual); APhA-APPM Distinguished Achievement Award in Specialized Pharmacy Practice (Annual); APhA-APPM Fellow of the American Pharmacists Association (Annual). **Geographic Preference:** National.

5214 ■ Emmanuel College - Cardinal Cushing Library
400 The Fenway
Boston, MA 02115
Ph: (617)655-7979
URL: http://learningcommons.emmanuel.edu/library
Contact: Diane Zydlewski, Associate Librarian
E-mail: zydlewsd@emmanuel.edu

Scope: Education; research; information literacy. **Services:** Open to Public, Interlibrary loan. **Founded:** 1964. **Holdings:** 250,000 print and e-Books; 3,600 print and electronic journal; 60 online subscription databases; 25,000 online streaming videos.

5215 ■ GlaxoSmithKline - USA (GSK) - Library
GSK plc
2929 Walnut St., Ste. 1700
Philadelphia, PA 19112
Ph: 44 20 8047 5000
Co. E-mail: customer.relations@gsk.com
URL: http://www.gsk.com
Contact: Emma Walmsley, Chief Executive Officer
Facebook: www.facebook.com/GSK
Linkedin: www.linkedin.com/company/glaxosmithkline
X (Twitter): x.com/GSKUS
Instagram: www.instagram.com/gsk

Description: Manufacturer of pharmaceutical products such as prescription and over-the-counter medications and vaccines. **Scope:** Healthcare. **Founded:** 1995. **Holdings:** Figures not available.

5216 ■ Keller and Heckman L.L.P. (KH) - Library
1001 G St. NW Ste. 500 W
Washington, DC 20001
Ph: (202)434-4100
Fax: (202)434-4646
Co. E-mail: info@khlaw.com
URL: http://www.khlaw.com
Contact: Janeanne R. Gorman, Executive Director
E-mail: gorman@khlaw.com
Linkedin: www.linkedin.com/company/keller-and-heckman-llp
X (Twitter): x.com/kellerandheck

Description: Firm provides legal, litigation and business transactions related services for domestic and international clients. **Scope:** Firm has a broad practice in the areas of regulatory law, litigation, and business transactions. Practice areas in advertising and promotion, antitrust, biotechnology, business counseling and transactional, chemical control, employment and labor, environmental, food and drug, government relations, health and safety compliance audit, insurance coverage, intellectual property, international regulatory affairs, litigation, pesticides, privacy and internet, product safety, REACH, telecommunications, trade and professional associations, transportation, and workplace safety and health. **Founded:** 1962. **Holdings:** Figures not available. **Publications:** "Electronic TSCA CDX Reporting

Required Beginning April 7 2012," Apr, 2012; "Whistleblower Alert: OSHA's New Enforcement Memorandum Targets Disciplinary Policies, Incentive Programs," Mar, 2012; "Pole Attachment Make-Ready and Access Issues," Nov, 2009; "Telecom Business Alert," Nov, 2009. **Training:** UTC Joint Use Workshop, Nov, 2009; Issues with Wireless Providers Attaching to Distribution Systems. Oct, 2009; What is a Fair Pole Attachment Rate?, May, 2007.

5217 ■ Lexington Medical Center - LMC Health Library
2720 Sunset Blvd.
West Columbia, SC 29169
Ph: (803)791-2000
URL: http://www.lexmed.com/?aspxerrorpath=/about/community-involvement/health-library
Scope: Medical science; psychology; nutrition; childcare; sports medicine; health care law; general health. **Holdings:** 1,000 books; 500 audiovisual titles.

5218 ■ Maryland Pharmacists Association (MPhA)
9115 Guilford Rd., Ste. 200
Columbia, MD 21046
Ph: (443)583-8000
Fax: (443)583-8006
Co. E-mail: admin@mdpha.com
URL: http://www.marylandpharmacist.org
Contact: W. Chris Charles, President
Facebook: www.facebook.com/MarylandPharmacistsAssociation
X (Twitter): x.com/MDPharmacists
Description: Professional association for pharmacists in Maryland. **Scope:** Pharmacy; allied health sciences. **Services:** Library not open to the public. **Founded:** 1882. **Holdings:** 1,000 volumes. **Publications:** *Maryland Pharmacist Journal* (Quarterly); *MPHA Pharmacy News* (Monthly); *Maryland Pharmacist: The Official Journal of the Maryland Pharmacists Association* (Quarterly). **Educational Activities:** Maryland Pharmacists Association Convention (Annual). **Geographic Preference:** State.

5219 ■ National Association of Boards of Pharmacy (NABP)
1600 Feehanville Dr.
Mount Prospect, IL 60056
Ph: (847)391-4406
Fax: (847)375-1114
Co. E-mail: help@nabp.pharmacy
URL: http://nabp.pharmacy
Contact: Caroline D. Juran, President
Facebook: www.facebook.com/NABP1904
Linkedin: www.linkedin.com/company/national-association-of-boards-of-pharmacy
X (Twitter): x.com/nabp
YouTube: www.youtube.com/channel/UCiRvxhkTgJvoldooGkE7uRg
Description: Pharmacy boards of several states, District of Columbia, Puerto Rico, Virgin Islands, several Canadian provinces, the states of Victoria, Australia, and New South Wales, the Pharmaceutical Society of New Zealand, and the South African Pharmacy Council. Provides for inter-state reciprocity in pharmaceutic licensure based upon a uniform minimum standard of pharmaceutical education and uniform legislation; improves the standards of pharmaceutical education licensure and practice. Provides legislative information; sponsors uniform licensure examination; also provides information on accredited school and college requirements. Maintains pharmacy and drug law statistics. **Founded:** 1904. **Publications:** *Annual Meeting Proceedings* (Annual); *State Newsletters Program* (Quarterly); *Survey of Pharmacy Law* (Annual). **Educational Activities:** Developments in Pharmacy Law Seminar (DPL) (Annual); NABP Annual Meeting (Annual). **Awards:** Fred T. Mahaffey Award (Annual); Henry Cade Memorial Award (Annual); Carmen A. Catizone Honorary President Award (Annual); NABP President's Award (Annual); Lester E. Hosto Distinguished Service Award (Annual). **Geographic Preference:** National.

5220 ■ National Association of Chain Drug Stores Resource Center (NACDS)
1776 Wilson Blvd., Ste. 200
Arlington, VA 22209
Ph: (703)549-3001
Fax: (703)836-4869
Co. E-mail: contactus@nacds.org
URL: http://www.nacds.org
Contact: Steven C. Anderson, President
Facebook: www.facebook.com/NACDS.org
Linkedin: www.linkedin.com/company/national-association-of-chain-drug-stores-nacds-
X (Twitter): x.com/nacds
YouTube: www.youtube.com/nacdsvid
Scope: Industry-related topics; community pharmacy. **Services:** Interlibrary loan; library open to the public at director's discretion. **Founded:** 1933. **Holdings:** 10,000 volumes; 1,000 videocassettes; 500 audiocassettes.

5221 ■ Sanofi-Aventis U.S. LLC
Sanofi S.A.
55 Corporate Dr.
Bridgewater, NJ 08807
Ph: 33 1 537-74000
Co. E-mail: global@sanofi.com
URL: http://www.sanofi.com
Contact: Adam Gluck, Head
Facebook: www.facebook.com/sanofiUS
Linkedin: www.linkedin.com/company/sanofi
X (Twitter): x.com/SanofiUS
Description: Manufacturer of pharmaceuticals includes prescription medication, vaccines and medication for diabetes, cancer, infertility, pain, allergies, hypertension, meningitis, osteoporosis, epilepsy, insomnia and various viral diseases. **Founded:** 2004. **Holdings:** Figures not available.

5222 ■ Southwest Health Center - Medical Library
1400 E Side Rd.
Platteville, WI 53818
Ph: (608)348-2331
Co. E-mail: worekj@southwesthealth.org
URL: http://www.southwesthealth.org
Contact: Doug Rogers, Chairman
Facebook: www.facebook.com/southwesthealth
X (Twitter): x.com/SouthwestHealth
YouTube: www.youtube.com/user/SouthwestHealth
Description: Medical library. **Scope:** Health; medicine; nursing. **Founded:** 1975. **Holdings:** Figures not available.

RESEARCH CENTERS

5223 ■ University of Maryland at Baltimore School of Pharmacy - Center on Drugs and Public Policy (CDPP)
Francis B. Palumbo, PhD, JD, Executive Director
220 Arch St.
Baltimore, MD 21201
Ph: (410)706-0133
Fax: (410)706-5394
Co. E-mail: cdpp@rx.umaryland.edu
URL: http://www.pharmacy.umaryland.edu/centers/cdpp
Contact: Francis B. Palumbo, Executive Director
Description: Integral unit of School of Pharmacy, University of Maryland at Baltimore. Offers consulting services. **Scope:** Dug policy, legal and regulatory; drug utilization review; outpatient drug benefits under the OBRA 90; cost effective drug therapies; pharmaceutical care services; health outcomes related to drug therapy; pharmacoepidemiology, pharmacy manpower; the pharmaceutical industry; impact of changes in the organization and financing of health care services; and patient compliance with prescribed drug regimen. **Founded:** 1987. **Educational Activities:** CDPP Conferences.

Dry Cleaning Service/Coin-Operated Laundry

START-UP INFORMATION

5224 ■ *Coin Laundries - Road to Financial Independence: A Complete Guide to Starting and Operating Profitable Self-Service Laundries*
Released: Revised edition. **Description:** Guide to starting and operating a self-service laundry. **Availability:** Print.

ASSOCIATIONS AND OTHER ORGANIZATIONS

5225 ■ **Coin Laundry Association (CLA)**
17w635 Butterfield Rd., Ste. 145
Oakbrook Terrace, IL 60181
Free: 800-570-5629
Fax: (630)953-7925
Co. E-mail: marketing@coinlaundry.org
URL: http://www.coinlaundry.org
Contact: Brian Wallace, President
Facebook: www.facebook.com/CoinLaundryAssn
Linkedin: www.linkedin.com/company/coin-laundry-association
X (Twitter): x.com/coinlaundryassn
YouTube: www.youtube.com/channel/UCkRLIT4oJRNtx6ctChOdylg
Description: Manufacturers of equipment or supplies used in self-service (coin-operated) laundry or dry cleaning establishments; distributors of equipment services and supplies; owners and operators of self-service laundry and/or dry cleaning stores. Compiles statistics. **Founded:** 1960. **Publications:** *Coin Laundry Association Supplier Directory* (Annual); *The Official Voice of the Coin Laundry Industry* (Monthly); *CLA Management Guidelines* (Quarterly); *PlanetLaundry* (Monthly); *CLA Member Journal*; *Coin Laundry Association Directory: Official Guide to Manufacturers and Distributors of Coin Operated Laundering and Drycleaning Equipment, Services, and Supplies* (Annual). **Educational Activities:** Clean Show (Triennial). **Geographic Preference:** National; Local.

5226 ■ **Drycleaning and Laundry Institute International (DLI) - Library**
14700 Sweitzer Ln.
Laurel, MD 20707
Free: 800-638-2627
Co. E-mail: techline@dlionline.org
URL: http://www.dlionline.org
Contact: Jeffrey Schwegmann, II, President
Linkedin: www.linkedin.com/company/drylauninst
X (Twitter): x.com/drylauninst
Instagram: www.instagram.com/drylauninst
Description: Provides wash ability and dry-clean ability testing for manufacturers of fabrics and related products; offers quality testing and consulting services; conducts research for members. **Scope:** Organizes courses in dry-cleaning, laundering, management, and maintenance. Maintains consulting service, speakers' bureau, research facilities, and library. **Founded:** 1883. **Holdings:** Figures not available. **Publications:** *Fabric Bulletins* (Bimonthly); *Fabricare Resources* (Bimonthly); *Industry Focus* (Bimonthly); *Shirt Laundry Procedures* (Bimonthly); *Technical Bulletins*; *Fabricare* (Quarterly). **Educational Activities:** Clean Show (Triennial). **Geographic Preference:** National.

5227 ■ **Multi-Housing Laundry Association (MLA)**
3739 National Dr., Ste. 202
Raleigh, NC 27612
Ph: (919)861-5579
Fax: (919)787-4916
Co. E-mail: info@mla-online.com
URL: http://www.mla-online.com
Contact: Penney DePas, Executive Director
E-mail: pdepas@firstpointresources.com
Description: Operating and supplier companies. Strives to provide tenants with professionally operated laundry facilities. Sponsors annual convention and trade show. **Founded:** 1959. **Educational Activities:** Multi-Housing Laundry Association Spring Educational Conference (Annual). **Geographic Preference:** Regional; National.

5228 ■ **National Cleaners Association (NCA)**
2218 Broadway, Frnt 2
New York, NY 10024
Ph: (212)967-3002
Co. E-mail: info@nca-i.com
URL: http://www.nca-i.com
Facebook: www.facebook.com/NationalCleanersAssociation
Linkedin: www.linkedin.com/company/national-cleaners-association
X (Twitter): x.com/NcaCleaner
YouTube: www.youtube.com/channel/UC2IQy-9Sx3gRViAk5PZvKCA
Pinterest: www.pinterest.com/ncacleaners
Description: Promotes education, research, and information distribution concerning garment and household fabric care. **Geographic Preference:** Local.

5229 ■ **Pennsylvania and Delaware Cleaners Association (PDCA)**
PO Box 340
Willow Grove, PA 19090
Ph: (215)830-8495
Free: 800-822-7352
Fax: (215)830-8490
Co. E-mail: executivedirector@pdclean.org
URL: http://www.pdclean.org
Contact: Steve Stevenson, President
E-mail: georgestevenson@msn.com
Description: Trade association for professional dry cleaners and launderers; provides information, education, seminars, and trade shows. **Founded:** 1934. **Publications:** *PDCA Press*. **Educational Activities:** Pennsylvania and Delaware Cleaners Association Convention. **Geographic Preference:** Regional.

5230 ■ **Textile Care Allied Trades Association (TCATA)**
5863 Harris Grove Ln.
Charlotte, NC 28212
Ph: (813)348-0075
Co. E-mail: leslie@tcata.org
URL: http://www.tcata.org/i4a/pages/index.cfm?pageid=1
Contact: John Silverman, President
Facebook: www.facebook.com/TCATANJ
X (Twitter): x.com/TextileCare
Description: Represents Manufacturers and distributors of laundry and dry-cleaning machinery, and supplies. **Founded:** 1920. **Publications:** *Roster and Buyers Guide* (Annual). **Educational Activities:** University of Innovative Distribution (Annual); Clean Show (Triennial). **Awards:** TCATA College Scholarship Fund (Annual). **Geographic Preference:** National.

REFERENCE WORKS

5231 ■ *6 Proven Ways to Increase Your Dry Cleaning and Laundry Business Profits*
Ed: Ayesh Goel. **Released:** January 23, 2017. **Description:** This article provides proven practices that can help in increasing your profits and scaling your dry cleaning and laundry business. These techniques are results of 40+ years of expertise in the dry cleaning industry, accurate data provided by different dry cleaners from across the globe, and scientific analysis done as data is meaningless unless not interpreted correctly. **Availability:** Online.

5232 ■ *10 Ideas for Your Laundromat Grand Opening*
Description: Throwing a special grand opening celebration can be a great way to create buzz for your new laundromat, foster customer loyalty, and set the stage for future success. This article provides tips that can help make your laundromat's grand opening a success. **Availability:** Online.

5233 ■ *"Coronavirus Pandemic Upends the Dry Cleaning Industry" in NPR.org (March 31, 2021)*
URL(s): www.npr.org/2021/03/31/982953808/coronavirus-pandemic-upends-the-dry-cleaning-industry
Released: March 21, 2021. **Description:** Discusses the effects the COVID-19 pandemic has had on the dry cleaning business and the Korean American's who own these businesses. **Availability:** Online.

5234 ■ *"Don't Do This!" in Planet Laundry (January 30, 2015)*
Ed: Brian Brunckhorst. **Released:** January 30, 2015. **Description:** Whether you're a seasoned entrepreneur or someone looking to be their own boss for the very first time, the self-service laundry business has many fundamental advantages over other small busi-

nesses. However, there are common mistakes that beginners make in this industry. This article details those mistakes and how to avoid them. **Availability:** Online.

5235 ■ *"Dry Cleaners, Seeking New Ways to Survive, Take Inspiration from Restaurants and Retail" in Chicago Tribune (March 24, 2017)*
URL(s): www.chicagotribune.com/business/ct-dry-cleaning-industry-washing-up-0326-biz-20170324-story.html
Ed: Becky Yerak. **Released:** March 24, 2017. **Description:** Traditional dry cleaners are closing up shop as more people buy easier to wear clothing and fast fashion that is disposed quickly. However, CD One Price Cleaners is taking an innovative approach by marketing other servies, such as cleaning rugs, making pickup and delivery more convenient, and adapting new environmental credentials. **Availability:** Online.

5236 ■ *How Laundromat Owners Can Maximize Profit Margins*
Description: This article provides tips to laundromat owners and investors looking to explore ways to increase revenue and minimize the costs of a laundromat business. **Availability:** Online.

5237 ■ *"How to Market Your Dry Cleaning Business When Business Is Slow" in Kreussler Inc. Blog (April 7, 2020)*
Ed: Peg Fitzpatrick. **Released:** April 07, 2020. **Description:** When your dry cleaning business is slow, turning to marketing via social media may give you the boost you need. This article provides ideas to help bring in business with social media. **Availability:** Online.

5238 ■ *"How to Open a Laundry & Dry Cleaning Business" in Chron (February 12, 2019)*
Ed: Nicky LaMarco. **Released:** February 12, 2019. **Description:** Provides information to think about as you plan to open a laundry or dry cleaning business including business planning, location selection, pricing, licensing, and environmental laws. **Availability:** Online.

5239 ■ *"How Profitable Is a Laundromat Business?" in Laundry Solutions Company (January 23, 2016)*
Released: January 23, 2016. **Description:** Many entrepreneurs are attracted to laundromats because they seem to run on their own. Profitability depends on a variety of features and can vary dramatically from laundromat to laundromat. This article details aspects involved running a profitable laundromat. **Availability:** Online.

5240 ■ *"How to Start a Coin-Operated Laundry" in Entrepreneur (February 15, 2019)*
Released: February 15, 2019. **Description:** With a trend toward coin laundries being more comfortable for the customer, this industry is experiencing a renaissance as they begin to include snack bars, video games, comfortable seating, and the use of swipe cards instead of coins. This article describes the state of the industry, startup costs, how to set yourself apart, and other details on what is involved in starting your own coin-operated laundry. **Availability:** Online.

5241 ■ *"Retail Tech Trend: The Future of Dry Cleaning" in Retail Info Systems (September 8, 2021)*
URL(s): risnews.com/retail-tech-trend-future-dry-cleaning
Ed: Jamie Grill-Goodman. **Released:** September 08, 2021. **Description:** A new concept in the dry cleaning business involves using lockers and creating accounts in order to access mobile apps for dry cleaning. **Availability:** Online.

5242 ■ *"Tips for Running a Successful Laundry Business" in Hydrofinity blog (October 18, 2018)*
Released: October 18, 2018. **Description:** Whether you are running a small neighborhood dry cleaner or a larger commercial laundry operation, this article provides tips to help you find success in the industry. **Availability:** Online.

5243 ■ *"What Equipment Do You Need to Open a Dry Cleaners?" in Careertrend.com (December 27, 2018)*
Ed: Jamie Poteat. **Released:** December 27, 2018. **Description:** This article provides details on the equipment and supplies needed when opening a dry cleaning business. **Availability:** Online.

5244 ■ *"What Really Happens at the Dry Cleaner?" in The Spruce (May 4, 2019)*
URL(s): www.thespruce.com/what-is-dry-cleaning-2145885
Ed: Mary Marlowe Leverette. **Released:** May 04, 2019. **Description:** An explanation of what happens when you drop your clothes off at a typical dry cleaners. Also includes a history of the industry. **Availability:** Online.

STATISTICAL SOURCES

5245 ■ *Dry Cleaners Industry in the US - Market Research Report*
URL(s): www.ibisworld.com/united-states/market-research-reports/dry-cleaners-industry/
Price: $925. **Description:** A downloadable report giving key statistics and analysis of the dry cleaning industry in the US. Includes outlooks for the future. **Availability:** Download.

5246 ■ *RMA Annual Statement Studies*
Pub: Risk Management Association
Contact: Nancy Foster, President
Released: Annual. **Description:** Contains composite balance sheets and income statements for more than 360 industries, including the accounting, auditing, and bookkeeping industries. Also contains five years of comparative historical data for discerning trends. Includes 16 commonly used ratios, computed for most of the size groupings for nearly every industry.

TRADE PERIODICALS

5247 ■ *Fabricare*
Pub: Drycleaning and Laundry Institute International
Contact: Jeffrey Schwegmann, II, President
URL(s): dlionline.org/fabricare
Released: Quarterly **Price:** Included in membership. **Description:** Informs drycleaners and launderers of industry developments and Institute activities. Carries legislative updates, technical data, management ideas, and tips on problem fabrics and garments. **Availability:** Print; PDF; Online.

5248 ■ *Fabricare Canada*
Pub: Fabricare Canada
Contact: Marcia Todd, Publisher
E-mail: marcia@fabricarecanada.com
URL(s): fabricarecanada.com
Facebook: www.facebook.com/FabricareCanada
Ed: Becca Anderson. **Released:** Monthly **Description:** Magazine covering the laundry, dry-cleaning industry. **Availability:** Print; PDF; Online.

5249 ■ *National Clothesline*
Pub: BPS Communications
URL(s): www.nationalclothesline.combpscommunications.com
Facebook: www.facebook.com/nationalclothesline
Ed: Hal Horning. **Released:** Monthly **Price:** $35, U.S.; $40, Canada; $75, Other countries. **Description:** Newspaper (tabloid) for laundry and dry cleaning industry. **Availability:** Print; PDF; Online.

TRADE SHOWS AND CONVENTIONS

5250 ■ Clean Show
Coin Laundry Association (CLA)
17w635 Butterfield Rd., Ste. 145
Oakbrook Terrace, IL 60181
Free: 800-570-5629
Fax: (630)953-7925
Co. E-mail: marketing@coinlaundry.org
URL: http://www.coinlaundry.org
Contact: Brian Wallace, President
URL(s): the-clean-show.us.messefrankfurt.com/us/en.html
Frequency: Triennial. **Description:** Laundry and dry cleaning equipment, supplies, and services. **Audience:** Laundering and dry cleaning personnel, equipment manufacturers, suppliers, and industry professionals. **Principal Exhibits:** Laundry and dry cleaning equipment, supplies, and services. Dates and Locations: 2025 Aug 23-26 Orlando county convention center, Orlando, FL; 2027 Jul Las Vegas Convention Center, Las Vegas, NV. **Telecommunication Services:** cleanshow@usa.messefrankfurt.com.

5251 ■ FABRICARE - Great Western Exhibit
Laundry and Drycleaning Suppliers
7869 S Paramount Blvd.
Pico Rivera, CA 90660
URL(s): fabricareshow.com
Frequency: Annual. **Description:** Laundry and dry cleaning equipment, supplies, and services. **Audience:** Dry cleaning, and laundry plant owners, managers, employees, and investors. **Principal Exhibits:** Laundry and dry cleaning equipment, supplies, and services. **Telecommunication Services:** ccafabricare@gmail.com.

CONSULTANTS

5252 ■ Colburn & Guyette Consulting Partners Inc.
100 Ledgewood Pl., Ste. 104
Rockland, MA 02370
Ph: (781)826-5522
Fax: (800)343-3310
Co. E-mail: general@colburnguyette.com
URL: http://www.colburnguyette.com
Contact: Edward Arons, Managing Director Partner Principal
E-mail: earons@colburnguyette.com
Facebook: www.facebook.com/ColburnGuyette
Linkedin: www.linkedin.com/company/colburn-&-guyette-consulting-partners-inc-
X (Twitter): x.com/ColburnGuyette
Instagram: www.instagram.com/colburnguyette
Description: Provider of consulting and designing services. **Founded:** 1950.

FRANCHISES AND BUSINESS OPPORTUNITIES

5253 ■ Comet Cleaners
8739 Bandera Rd., Ste. 100
San Antonio, TX 78250
Ph: (210)521-6106
Co. E-mail: info@cometsatx.com
URL: http://cometsatx.com
Facebook: www.facebook.com/CometSATX
X (Twitter): x.com/cometsatx
Instagram: www.instagram.com/cometsatx
Description: Dry cleaning and laundry packages. 1-to-2 weeks. **No. of Franchise Units:** 246. **Founded:** 1941. **Franchised:** 1967. **Equity Capital Needed:** Minimum net worth $150,000; typical investment $500,000. **Franchise Fee:** $15,000-$30,000. **Training:** Yes.

5254 ■ Door-To-Door Dry Cleaning
11153 S Parker Rd., Unit B
Parker, CO 80134
Ph: (303)500-5802
Free: 877-769-3667
Fax: (866)731-5471
Co. E-mail: contact@mydoor.biz
URL: http://www.mydoor.biz
Description: Firm provides dry cleaning services. **Training:** Provides 1 week training at headquarters, 1 week onsite and ongoing support.

5255 ■ Dove Cleaners and Cadet Cleaners
1560 Yonge St.
Toronto, ON, Canada M4T 2S9

5256 ■ Dry Cleaning Service/Coin-Operated Laundry

Ph: (416)413-7900
Co. E-mail: fabricare@dovecleaners.com
URL: http://www.dovecleaners.com
Contact: Danny Zarif, President
Facebook: www.facebook.com/DoveClenaers
X (Twitter): x.com/Cleanersdove
Description: Provider of dry cleaning services for bridal, handbags, linens, shirts and more. **Founded:** 1992.

5256 ■ ImageFirst Healthcare Laundry Specialists
900 E 8th Ave., Ste.200
King of Prussia, PA 19406
Free: 800-932-7472
Co. E-mail: info@imagefirst.com
URL: http://www.imagefirst.com
Contact: Jim Cashman, Chief Executive Officer
Facebook: www.facebook.com/ImageFIRST.HLS
Linkedin: www.linkedin.com/company/imagefirst
X (Twitter): x.com/Image1stHCLinen
YouTube: www.youtube.com/user/imagefirstmedical
Description: Provider of laundry services on a rental basis for dentists, physicians and medical clinics. The main services offered are delivering, washing, picking up, monitoring usage and managing inventories. **Founded:** 1967. **Training:** 4 weeks onsite marketing and sales assistance.

5257 ■ Lapels Dry Cleaning
962 Washington St.
Hanover, MA 02339
Ph: (781)829-9935
Free: 866-695-2735
Fax: (781)829-9546
Co. E-mail: customercare@lapelsdrycleaning.com
URL: http://lapelsfranchise.com
Contact: Kevin DuBois, Chief Executive Officer
Facebook: www.facebook.com/LAPELSFRANCHISEOPS
Linkedin: www.linkedin.com/company/lapels-dry-cleaning
X (Twitter): x.com/mylapels
Description: Dry cleaning retail stores. **No. of Franchise Units:** 47. **Founded:** 2000. **Franchised:** 2001. **Equity Capital Needed:** $20,000-$100,000. **Franchise Fee:** $20,000-$30,000. **Financial Assistance:** Yes **Training:** Full training with ongoing support.

5258 ■ Martinizing Dry Cleaning
2060 Coolidge Hwy.
Berkley, MI 48072
Ph: (248)246-7868
Fax: (248)246-7878
Co. E-mail: support@martinizing.com
URL: http://www.martinizing.com
Contact: Jessica McGrath, Vice President General Counsel
Facebook: www.facebook.com/MartinizingCleanersCorp
Linkedin: www.linkedin.com/company/martinizing
X (Twitter): x.com/MartinizingCorp
Description: Provider of dry cleaning services. **Founded:** 1949. **Training:** Comprehensive managerial and technical training in classroom as well as franchisees store; equipment shakedown and ongoing service hotline; grand opening marketing package and ongoing local store and market wide promotional programs; field and operations assistance; ongoing support staff only a toll-free call away.

5259 ■ Nu-Look 1-Hour Cleaners
NLF, Inc.
c/o Karl Dickey, 7777 N Wickham Rd., Ste. 254
Melbourne, FL 32940
Ph: (561)362-4190
Free: 866-533-0146
Fax: (561)362-4229
Contact: Karl Dickey, Contact
Facebook: www.facebook.com/nulookcleaners
X (Twitter): x.com/nulookcleaners
Description: Retail dry cleaner. **No. of Franchise Units:** 13. **Founded:** 1967. **Franchised:** 1969. **Equity Capital Needed:** $195,000. **Franchise Fee:** $20,000. **Royalty Fee:** 2%. **Financial Assistance:** Yes **Training:** Offers 2 weeks at headquarters, 2 weeks at franchisee's location and ongoing support.

5260 ■ Oxxo Care Cleaners
1874 N Young Cir.
Hollywood, FL 33020
Ph: (954)927-7410
Free: 866-462-6996
Fax: (954)927-7357
Co. E-mail: info@oxxousa.com
URL: http://oxxousa.com
Contact: Salomon Mishaan, President
Facebook: www.facebook.com/oxxocarecleaners
Linkedin: www.linkedin.com/company/oxxo-care-cleaners
Instagram: www.instagram.com/oxxocarecleaners
YouTube: www.youtube.com/user/oxxousa
Description: Provider of dry cleaning franchise services. **No. of Franchise Units:** 32. **Founded:** 2001. **Franchised:** 2001. **Equity Capital Needed:** $443,000-$644,500. **Franchise Fee:** 36000. **Royalty Fee:** 4% of the gross revenue. **Financial Assistance:** Yes **Training:** Training is provided in all areas. Technical training in classroom, Training center, as well as franchisee's store. Training in customer service, marketing, quality control, maintenance and ongoing support.

5261 ■ Pressed 4 Time
Eight Clock Tower Pl., Ste. 110
Maynard, MA 01754
URL: http://martinizing.com/pressed-4-time
Description: Firm is engaged in dry cleaning and shoe repair pick-up and delivery services, serving executives and staff at local businesses. **Founded:** 1987. **Training:** Includes 2 days at the corporate offices, including 1 day of hands-on operations, the corporate vehicle and 1 day of intensive classroom training, covering start-up, record keeping, administration, dry cleaning, operations and sales. Also, 2 days of training in the franchisees territory, consisting of marketing training in the field to establish initial accounts.

5262 ■ Zips Dry Cleaners
1571 Maryland Ave., NE
Washington, DC 20002
Ph: (202)808-3341
Co. E-mail: zipscustomercare@321zips.com
URL: http://www.321zips.com
Facebook: www.facebook.com/ZIPSHechingerMallDC
Linkedin: www.linkedin.com/company/zips-dry-cleaners-franchise
X (Twitter): x.com/ZIPSDryCleaners
Instagram: www.instagram.com/zipsdrycleaners
YouTube: www.youtube.com/user/zipsdrycleaners
Description: One price, same day service dry cleaning. **No. of Franchise Units:** 35. **No. of Company-Owned Units:** 1. **Founded:** 2002. **Franchised:** 2006. **Equity Capital Needed:** $616,150-$778,500. **Franchise Fee:** $50,000. **Royalty Fee:** 6%. **Financial Assistance:** Yes **Training:** Yes.

PUBLICATIONS

5263 ■ *PlanetLaundry*
17w635 Butterfield Rd., Ste. 145
Oakbrook Terrace, IL 60181
Free: 800-570-5629
Fax: (630)953-7925
Co. E-mail: marketing@coinlaundry.org
URL: http://www.coinlaundry.org
Contact: Brian Wallace, President
URL(s): planetlaundry.com
Facebook: www.facebook.com/PlanetLaundry
X (Twitter): x.com/planetlaundry
Released: Monthly; Delivers once a month. **Price:** $3, U.S. for single copy one year; $36, U.S. for one year; $40, Canada and Mexico for one year. **Description:** Includes legislative alerts, owner/store profiles and industry forum. **Availability:** Print; PDF; Download; Online.

LIBRARIES

5264 ■ Drycleaning and Laundry Institute International (DLI) - Library
14700 Sweitzer Ln.
Laurel, MD 20707
Free: 800-638-2627
Co. E-mail: techline@dlionline.org
URL: http://www.dlionline.org
Contact: Jeffrey Schwegmann, II, President
Linkedin: www.linkedin.com/company/drylauninst
X (Twitter): x.com/drylauninst
Instagram: www.instagram.com/drylauninst
Description: Provides wash ability and dry-clean ability testing for manufacturers of fabrics and related products; offers quality testing and consulting services; conducts research for members. **Scope:** Organizes courses in dry-cleaning, laundering, management, and maintenance. Maintains consulting service, speakers' bureau, research facilities, and library. **Founded:** 1883. **Holdings:** Figures not available. **Publications:** *Fabric Bulletins* (Bimonthly); *Fabricare Resources* (Bimonthly); *Industry Focus* (Bimonthly); *Shirt Laundry Procedures* (Bimonthly); *Technical Bulletins*; *Fabricare* (Quarterly). **Educational Activities:** Clean Show (Triennial). **Geographic Preference:** National.

RESEARCH CENTERS

5265 ■ Drycleaning and Laundry Institute International (DLI) - Library
14700 Sweitzer Ln.
Laurel, MD 20707
Free: 800-638-2627
Co. E-mail: techline@dlionline.org
URL: http://www.dlionline.org
Contact: Jeffrey Schwegmann, II, President
Linkedin: www.linkedin.com/company/drylauninst
X (Twitter): x.com/drylauninst
Instagram: www.instagram.com/drylauninst
Description: Provides wash ability and dry-clean ability testing for manufacturers of fabrics and related products; offers quality testing and consulting services; conducts research for members. **Scope:** Organizes courses in dry-cleaning, laundering, management, and maintenance. Maintains consulting service, speakers' bureau, research facilities, and library. **Founded:** 1883. **Holdings:** Figures not available. **Publications:** *Fabric Bulletins* (Bimonthly); *Fabricare Resources* (Bimonthly); *Industry Focus* (Bimonthly); *Shirt Laundry Procedures* (Bimonthly); *Technical Bulletins*; *Fabricare* (Quarterly). **Educational Activities:** Clean Show (Triennial). **Geographic Preference:** National.

Editorial/Freelance Writing Business

ASSOCIATIONS AND OTHER ORGANIZATIONS

5266 ■ Active Voice
1507-180 Dundas St. W
Toronto, ON, Canada M5G 1Z8
Ph: (416)975-1379
Co. E-mail: info@editors.ca
URL: http://www.editors.ca
Contact: Natasha Bood, Executive Director
E-mail: executivedirector@editors.ca
URL(s): activevoice.editors.ca
Released: Latest issue Spring/Summer 2019. **Availability:** Print.

5267 ■ American Book Producers Association (ABPA)
23 Waverly Pl., Ste. 6B
New York, NY 10003
Co. E-mail: office@abpaonline.org
URL: http://abpaonline.org
Facebook: www.facebook.com/ABPAbooks
Linkedin: www.linkedin.com/company/abpabooks
X (Twitter): x.com/abpabooks
Instagram: www.instagram.com/abpabooks
Description: Aims to increase the book industry's awareness of members' capabilities and the state of the book producers' art. Facilitates exchange of information for the purpose of improving business and establishing trade standards. **Founded:** 1980. **Publications:** *American Book Producers Association--Newsletter* (Bimonthly). **Geographic Preference:** National.

5268 ■ American Society of Journalists and Authors (ASJA)
355 Lexington Ave. 15th Fl.
New York, NY 10017-6603
Ph: (212)997-0947
Co. E-mail: asjaoffice@asja.org
URL: http://asja.org
Contact: Laura Laing, President
Facebook: www.facebook.com/ASJAinc
X (Twitter): x.com/ASJAhq
Description: Represents freelance writers of nonfiction magazine articles and books. Elevates the professional and economic position of nonfiction writers, provide a forum for discussion of common problems among writers and editors, and promote a code of ethics for writers and editors. Operates writer referral service for individuals, institutions, or companies seeking writers for special projects; sponsors Llewellyn Miller Fund to aid professional writers who no longer able to work due to age, disability, or extraordinary professional crisis. **Founded:** 1948. **Publications:** *American Society of Journalists and Authors--Directory of Writers* (Annual); *ASJA Monthly* (Bimonthly); *American Society of Journalists and Authors--Directory* (Annual); *The ASJA Weekly* (Weekly). **Awards:** Arlene Eisenberg Memorial Fund - Arlene Article Award (Annual); ASJA Outstanding Book Awards (Annual); ASJA Founders Award for Career Achievement (Annual); Donald Robinson Memorial Award for Investigative Journalism (Annual); ASJA Extraordinary Service Award (Annual); June Roth Memorial Awards (Annual); Robert C. Anderson Memorial (Annual); ASJA Outstanding Article Award (Annual); Outstanding Book Award: General Nonfiction (Annual). **Geographic Preference:** National.

5269 ■ Asian American Journalists Association (AAJA)
5 3rd St., Ste. 1108
San Francisco, CA 94103
Ph: (202)729-8383
Co. E-mail: support@aaja.org
URL: http://www.aaja.org
Contact: Michelle Lee, President
Facebook: www.facebook.com/AAJAHQ
Linkedin: www.linkedin.com/company/aaja
X (Twitter): x.com/aaja
Instagram: www.instagram.com/aajaofficial
Description: A professional membership association working toward the visibility and inclusion of Asian Americans and Pacific Islander (AAPI) journalists in newsroom leadership and toward equitable and accurate coverage of AAPIs and AAPI issues. **Founded:** 1981. **Publications:** *Directory of Asian American Journalists*. **Educational Activities:** Journalism Opportunities Conference (Annual). **Awards:** AAJA National Journalism Awards (Annual); AAJA Special Recognition Award (Annual); AAJA Lifetime Achievement Award (Annual); Dr. Suzanne Ahn Award (Irregular). **Geographic Preference:** National.

5270 ■ Asian American Writers Workshop (AAWW)
112 W 27th St., Ste. 600
New York, NY 10001
Ph: (212)494-0061
Co. E-mail: desk@aaww.org
URL: http://aaww.org
Contact: Jafreen Uddin, Executive Director
Facebook: www.facebook.com/AsianAmericanWritersWorkshop
X (Twitter): x.com/aaww
Instagram: www.instagram.com/aaww_nyc
YouTube: www.youtube.com/channel/UCxnl6Pw2L7oJQxEUL-k4ofw
Description: Dedicated to the creation, development, publication, and dissemination of Asian American literature. **Founded:** 1991. **Publications:** *Asian Pacific American Journal (APAJ)*. **Geographic Preference:** National.

5271 ■ Association of Teachers of Technical Writing (ATTW)
Co. E-mail: communcations@attw.org
URL: http://www.attw.org
Contact: Natasha Jones, President
Facebook: www.facebook.com/ATTWorg/info
X (Twitter): x.com/attworg
Description: Teachers and students of technical communication at all levels; technical communicators from government and industry. Serves as a forum of communication among technical writing teachers and acts as a liaison with other professional organizations. Provides current bibliographies of teaching/learning materials and reports of current research in the teaching of technical writing. **Founded:** 1973. **Publications:** *Technical Communication Quarterly: The Official Journal of the Association of Teachers of Technical Writing (TCQ)* (Quarterly). **Geographic Preference:** National.

5272 ■ Association of Writers & Writing Programs (AWP)
5700 Rivertech Ct., Ste. 225
Riverdale Park, MD 20737-1250
Ph: (696)696-7700
Co. E-mail: awp@awpwriter.org
URL: http://www.awpwriter.org
Contact: Cynthia Sherman, Executive Director
Facebook: www.facebook.com/AWPWriter
Linkedin: www.linkedin.com/company/awp-writer
X (Twitter): x.com/awpwriter
Pinterest: www.pinterest.com/awpwriter
Description: Writers; students and teachers in creative writing programs in university departments of English; editors, publishers, and freelance creative and professional writers. Fosters literary talent and achievement; advocates the craft of writing as primary to a liberal and humane education; provides publications and services to the makers and readers of contemporary literature. **Founded:** 1967. **Publications:** *AWP's Guide to Writing Programs*; *The Writer's Chronicle* (Quarterly); *AWP Job List* (7/year). **Educational Activities:** AWP Conference & Bookfair (Annual); AWP Conference & Bookfair (Annual). **Awards:** AWP Award Series (Annual); The Donald Hall Prize for Poetry (Annual); The Grace Paley Prize for Short Fiction (Annual); AWP Prize for Creative Nonfiction (Annual); AWP Prize for the Novel (Annual). **Geographic Preference:** National.

5273 ■ Bay Area Independent Publishers Association (BAIPA)
369-B 3rd St., Ste. 422
San Rafael, CA 94901
Co. E-mail: valpub@yahoo.com
URL: http://baipa.org
Contact: Becky Parker Geist, President
E-mail: becky@proaudiovoices.com
Facebook: www.facebook.com/pg/baipa.org
X (Twitter): x.com/BAIPA
Description: Promotes authors interested in independent publishing as an alternative to the commercial publishing system; printers, artists, typists, and others in allied fields. Aims to become a comprehensive source of self-publishing information and to develop knowledge and expertise to better assist members in promoting, marketing, and publishing their works. Acts as a liaison and clearinghouse of information and provides guidance in all aspects of self-publishing, including copy preparation, book production, and marketing and sales. **Founded:** 1979. **Publications:** *SPEX* (Monthly); *SPEX*. **Geographic Preference:** National.

5274 ■ Boating Writers International (BWI)
108 9th St.
Wilmette, IL 60091
Ph: (847)736-4142
Co. E-mail: newbwiinfo@gmail.com
URL: http://www.bwi.org
Contact: Ben Stein, President
Facebook: www.facebook.com/BWI.org
Linkedin: www.linkedin.com/company/boating-writers-international

Description: Seeks to: cover boating as a competitive as well as recreational sport; promote boating safety; encourage enjoyment of other outdoor water sports. **Founded:** 1970. **Publications:** *BWI Journal* (9/year). **Educational Activities:** BWI meeting (Annual). **Awards:** BWI Writing Contest (Annual). **Geographic Preference:** Multinational.

5275 ■ Broad Universe (BU)
3102 Hoyt Ave., Ste. 12805
Everett, WA 98206
URL: http://broaduniverse.org
Contact: Katherine Villyard, President
E-mail: prez@broaduniverse.org
Facebook: www.facebook.com/BroadUniverse
X (Twitter): x.com/BroadUniverse

Description: Promotes science fiction, fantasy, and horror written by women. **Founded:** 2000. **Geographic Preference:** National.

5276 ■ Canadian Association of Journalists (CAJ) [L'Association Canadienne des Journalistes]
PO Box 117, Station F
Toronto, ON, Canada M4Y 2L4
URL: http://caj.ca
Contact: Brent Jolly, President
E-mail: brent@caj.ca
Facebook: www.facebook.com/CdnAssocJournalists
Linkedin: www.linkedin.com/company/canadian-association-of-journalists
X (Twitter): x.com/caj

Description: Professional organization representing the interests of journalists in Canada. Promotes high professional standards. Disseminates information. **Founded:** 1978. **Publications:** *CAJ Media* (3/year); *Directory of Canadian Journalists* (Annual). **Awards:** CAJ Code of Silence Award (Annual); Awards for Investigative Journalism (Annual); Investigative Journalist Award (Annual). **Geographic Preference:** National.

5277 ■ Canadian Copyright Institute (CCI)
192 Spadina Ave., Ste. 107
Toronto, ON, Canada M5T 2C2
Ph: (416)975-9366
Co. E-mail: info@thecci.ca
URL: http://thecci.ca/default.html
Contact: Anne McClelland, Administrator

Description: Creators, producers, and distributors of copyrighted works. Encourages a more complete understanding of copyright laws among members and the public. Consults with government and judicial bodies regarding reform of copyright laws. Conducts and sponsors research on copyright laws worldwide. Works with organizations pursuing similar goals to improve copyright legislation and enforcement. **Founded:** 1965. **Publications:** *Copyright Reform Legislation Reporting Service* (Periodic). **Geographic Preference:** National.

5278 ■ Communications Workers of America Canada (CWA)
301-2200 Prince of Wales Dr.
Ottawa, ON, Canada K2E 6Z9
Ph: (613)820-9777
Free: 877-486-4292
Fax: (613)820-8188
Co. E-mail: info@cwa-scacanada.ca
URL: http://cwacanada.ca
Contact: Martin O'Hanlon, President
E-mail: mohanlon@cwacanada.ca
Facebook: www.facebook.com/cwacanada
X (Twitter): x.com/cwacanada1

Description: Primarily union of journalists and media workers in Canada, as well as social workers and employees in the manufacturing industry. **Founded:** 1995. **Publications:** *TNG Canada Today* (Monthly). **Awards:** Morton Bahr Scholarship (Annual); David S. Barr Award (Annual); Heywood Broun Awards (Annual); Paul Kidd Courage Prize (Annual); Dick Martin Scholarship Award (Annual); CWA Canada/CAJ Awards for Excellence in Labour Reporting (Annual); Charles B. Dale Guild Service Awards; Joe Beirne Foundation Scholarships (Annual); John Belcarz and Dan Zeidler Memorial Scholarships (Annual); CJFE Tara Singh Hayer Memorial Award (Annual); Kurt Schork Awards in International Journalism - Local Reporter (Annual); Union Plus Scholarship Program (Annual). **Geographic Preference:** National.

5279 ■ Crime Writers of Canada (CWC)
4C-240 Westwood Rd.
Guelph, ON, Canada N1H 7W9
Co. E-mail: info@crimewriterscanada.com
URL: http://www.crimewriterscanada.com
Contact: Alison Bruce, Executive Director
E-mail: ed@crimewriterscanada.com
Facebook: www.facebook.com/Crime.Writers.Canada
X (Twitter): x.com/crimewriterscan
Instagram: www.instagram.com/crimewriterscanada
YouTube: www.youtube.com/channel/UCyyUHLbCFjz_zJiOgktA9JA

Description: Promotes Canadian crime writing and increases awareness of Canadian crime writers from coast to coast. **Founded:** 1982. **Publications:** *Fingerprints* (Quarterly). **Awards:** Arthur Ellis Awards (Annual). **Geographic Preference:** National.

5280 ■ Editorial Freelancers Association (EFA)
266 W 37th St., 20th Fl.
New York, NY 10018
Ph: (212)920-4816
Free: 866-929-5425
Co. E-mail: office@the-efa.org
URL: http://www.the-efa.org
Contact: Joy Drohan, Secretary
E-mail: secretary@the-efa.org
Facebook: www.facebook.com/editorialfreelancersassociation
Linkedin: www.linkedin.com/company/editorial-freelancers
X (Twitter): x.com/EFAFreelancers

Description: Represents persons who work full or part-time as freelance writers or editorial freelancers. Promotes professionalism and facilitates the exchange of information and support. Conducts professional training seminars; and offers job listings. **Founded:** 1970. **Publications:** *The Freelancer* (Quarterly); *Freelance Editorial Association Yellow Pages & Code of Fair Practice* (Annual); *Editorial Freelancers Association--Membership Directory*. **Geographic Preference:** National.

5281 ■ Editors Association of Canada (EAC)
1507-180 Dundas St. W
Toronto, ON, Canada M5G 1Z8
Ph: (416)975-1379
Co. E-mail: info@editors.ca
URL: http://www.editors.ca
Contact: Natasha Bood, Executive Director
E-mail: executivedirector@editors.ca
Facebook: www.facebook.com/EditorsReviseursCanada
X (Twitter): x.com/editorscanada
Instagram: www.instagram.com/editorscanada

Description: Promotes advancement of the profession of editing, and of members' capabilities. **Founded:** 1978. **Publications:** *Active Voice*. **Awards:** Tom Fairley Award for Editorial Excellence (Annual); Claudette Upton Scholarship (Annual); Lee d'Anjou Volunteer of the Year (Annual); EAC President's Award for Volunteer Service (Annual). **Geographic Preference:** National.

5282 ■ Federation of BC Writers (FBCW)
PO Box 3503
Courtenay, BC, Canada V9N 6Z8
Co. E-mail: communications@bcwriters.ca
URL: http://bcwriters.ca
Contact: Bryan Mortensen, Executive Director
Facebook: www.facebook.com/bcwriters
X (Twitter): x.com/bcwriters
Instagram: www.instagram.com/federationbcwriters

Description: Contributes to a supportive environment for writing in the community. **Founded:** 1976. **Geographic Preference:** National.

5283 ■ Horror Writers Association (HWA) [Horror Writers of America]
PO Box 14387
Columbus, OH 43214
Co. E-mail: hwa@horror.org
URL: http://horror.org
Contact: John Edward Lawson, President
E-mail: president@horror.org
X (Twitter): x.com/horrorwriters
Instagram: www.instagram.com/thehorrorwritersassociation
YouTube: www.youtube.com/user/HorrorWriters

Description: Horror writers, including creators of comic strips, screenplays, and role-playing games, who have sold at least one work at professional rates are active members; horror writers who have sold something but not at professional rates are affiliate members. **Founded:** 1980. **Publications:** *Handbook/Directory*. **Awards:** Bram Stoker Awards for Superior Achievement (Annual); Bram Stoker Lifetime Achievement Award (Annual); HWA Specialty Press Award (Annual). **Geographic Preference:** Multinational.

5284 ■ International Bowling Media Association (IBMA)
621 Six Flags Dr.
Arlington, TX 76011
Co. E-mail: ibma@bowlingmedia.org
URL: http://www.bowlingmedia.org
Contact: Juan Campos, President
E-mail: juancampos1289@yahoo.com

Description: Reporters of bowling news. **Founded:** 1937. **Publications:** *IBMA Newsletter* (Semiannual). **Awards:** Luby Hall of Fame Award (Annual); BWAA Meritorious Service (Annual); Kegel Bowler of the Month (Monthly); Bowler of the Year (Annual); Luby Hall of Fame Award (Annual); Alberta E. Crowe Meritorious Service Award (Annual); IBMA Collegiate Bowler of the Year (Annual); IBMA Senior Bowler of the Year (Annual); Chuck Pezzano Scholarship (Annual). **Geographic Preference:** National.

5285 ■ International Food Wine and Travel Writers Association (IFWTWA)
39252 Winchester Rd., Ste. 107, No. 418
Murrieta, CA 92563
Free: 877-439-8929
Fax: (877)439-8929
Co. E-mail: admin@ifwtwa.org
URL: http://www.ifwtwa.org
Contact: Christine Cutler, President
Facebook: www.facebook.com/IFWTWA
X (Twitter): x.com/IFWTWA
Instagram: www.instagram.com/ifwtwa1
Pinterest: www.pinterest.com/ifwtwa

Description: Seeks to bring recognition to those in the food, wine, and travel industry who have met the association's criteria. Offers scholarships in culinary arts and sciences journalism (food-wine-travel). **Founded:** 1956. **Publications:** *Global Writes*; *Membership Benefits* (Annual); *Press Pass*; *International Food, Wine, and Travel Writers Association--Membership Roster* (Annual). **Geographic Preference:** National.

5286 ■ International Foodservice Editorial Council (IFEC)
PO Box 581
Pleasant Valley, NY 12569
Ph: (845)723-4434
Co. E-mail: ifec@ifeconline.com
URL: http://www.ifeconline.com
Contact: Avery Meetre, President
Facebook: www.facebook.com/IFEC56
X (Twitter): x.com/IFECorg

Description: Key communicators within the U.S. foodservice industry, including top editors and marketing and public relations personnel for leading food companies and foodservice educational institutions. Organized to sound the marketing directions of the industry on all levels; seeks to improve communications. **Founded:** 1956. **Publications:** *International Food Service Editorial Council--Directory* (Annual). **Awards:** professional development awards (Annual); International Foodservice Editorial Council Scholarship (Annual). **Geographic Preference:** National.

5287 ■ Investigative Reporters and Editors (IRE) - Resource Center
109 Lee Hills Hall, 221 S Eighth St.
Columbia, MO 65201
Ph: (573)882-2042
Co. E-mail: info@ire.org
URL: http://www.ire.org
Contact: Mark Walker, President
E-mail: mark.walker@nytimes.com
Facebook: www.facebook.com/IRE.NICAR
Linkedin: www.linkedin.com/company/investigative-reporters-and-editors
X (Twitter): x.com/IRE_NICAR
Instagram: www.instagram.com/ire_nicar

Description: Provides educational services, including computer-assisted reporting through its National Institute for Computer-Assisted Reporting. **Scope:** Investigative stories. **Founded:** 1975. **Holdings:** 25,000 stories; 5,000 tipsheets; Audio files; Books; Journal; Newsletter. **Publications:** *Uplink*; *Investigative Reporters and Editors--Membership Directory*; *Beat Book Series*; *IRE Journal* (Quarterly); *IRE Members Directory* (Annual). **Educational Activities:** IRE Conference (Annual); CAR Boot Camps (Continuous). **Awards:** FOI Award (Annual); IRE Awards (Annual); Thomas Renner Award (Annual). **Geographic Preference:** Multinational.

5288 ■ La Fondation des Écrivains Canadiens (FEC) [The Canadian Writers Foundation (CWF)]
PO Box 13281, Kanata Sta.
Ottawa, ON, Canada K2K 1X4
Co. E-mail: info@canadianwritersfoundation.org
URL: http://www.canadianwritersfoundation.org
Contact: Marianne Scott, President

Description: Provides ongoing assistance to notable senior Canadian writers who have made a significant contribution to Canadian writing and are experiencing extreme financial distress. **Founded:** 1931. **Geographic Preference:** National.

5289 ■ Lochmueller Group Inc.
6200 Vogel Rd.
Evansville, IN 47715
Ph: (812)479-6200
Free: 800-423-7411
Co. E-mail: info@lochgroup.com
URL: http://www.lochgroup.com
Contact: Carl Camacho, Chief Operating Officer
Facebook: www.facebook.com/lochgroup
Linkedin: www.linkedin.com/company/lochmueller-group
X (Twitter): x.com/lochgroup
Instagram: www.instagram.com/lochgroup

Description: Professional planning, engineering and environmental firm and services include air quality, civil engineering, economic development, environmental analysis, environmental engineering, land use planning, surveying, traffic engineering, traffic studies, transportation plans, and systems. **Scope:** Professional planning, engineering and environmental firm and services include air quality, civil engineering, economic development, environmental analysis, environmental engineering, land use planning, surveying, traffic engineering, traffic studies, transportation plans, and systems. **Founded:** 1980. **Publications:** *Technical Communication* (Quarterly); *Intercom: The Magazine of the Society for Technical Communication* (8/year); *Technical Communication--Special Issue/Membership Directory* (Annual). **Educational Activities:** STC Technical Communication Summit (Annual). **Awards:** STC Scholarships (Annual); Marian Norby Scholarships.

5290 ■ NASJA Directory
22 Cavalier Way Latham
Latham, NY 12110
URL: http://www.nasja.org
Contact: Jeff Blumenfeld, President
E-mail: jeff@blumenfeldpr.com
URL(s): www.nasja.org/explore-nasja/member-benefits
Availability: Print.

5291 ■ National Association of Black Journalists (NABJ)
1100 Knight Hall, Ste. 3101
College Park, MD 20742
Ph: (301)405-0248
Co. E-mail: contact@nabj.org
URL: http://nabjonline.org
Contact: Dorothy Tucker, President
Facebook: www.facebook.com/NABJOfficial
Linkedin: www.linkedin.com/company/national-association-of-black-journalists-nabj
X (Twitter): x.com/NABJ
Instagram: www.instagram.com/nabjofficial
YouTube: www.youtube.com/user/NABJOfficial

Description: Offers innovative training, career advancement opportunities and advocacy initiatives for Black journalists and media professionals worldwide. **Founded:** 1975. **Publications:** *NABJ Update*. **Awards:** Ida B. Wells Award (Annual); NABJ Hall of Fame (Annual); NABJ Special Honors Awards (Annual); NABJ Salute to Excellence Awards (Annual); NABJ Special Honors Awards (Annual). **Geographic Preference:** National.

5292 ■ National Association of Hispanic Journalists (NAHJ)
1050 Connecticut Ave. NW, Fl. 5TH
Washington, DC 20036
Free: 866-624-5674
Co. E-mail: contact@nahj.org
URL: http://nahj.org
Contact: Yvette Cabrera, President
E-mail: ycabrera@nahj.org
Facebook: www.facebook.com/NAHJFan
Linkedin: www.linkedin.com/company/nahj-national-association-of-hispanic-journalists
X (Twitter): x.com/NAHJ
Instagram: www.instagram.com/officialnahj
YouTube: www.youtube.com/channel/UCIAEbRB48NSgztovHhc0MtA

Description: Promotes fair and accurate media treatment of Hispanics; opposes job discrimination and demeaning stereotypes. Works to increase educational and career opportunities and development for Hispanics in the field. **Founded:** 1984. **Publications:** *NAHJ Newsletter*. **Awards:** NAHJ Hall of Fame (Annual). **Geographic Preference:** National.

5293 ■ National Writers Association (NWA)
10940 S Parker Rd., No. 508
Parker, CO 80134
Co. E-mail: natlwritersassn@hotmail.com
URL: http://www.nationalwriters.com/page/page/1963103.htm
Contact: Sandy Whelchel, Director

Description: Professional full- or part-time freelance writers who specialize in business writing. Aims to serve as a marketplace whereby business editors can easily locate competent writing talent. Establishes communication among editors and writers. **Founded:** 1998. **Publications:** *Professional Freelance Writers Directory* (Annual); *Authorship* (Quarterly). **Awards:** NWA Nonfiction Contest (Annual); NWA Novel Contest (Annual); NWA Poetry Contest (Annual); NWA Short Story Contest (Annual). **Geographic Preference:** National.

5294 ■ Native American Journalists Association (NAJA) [Native American Press Association]
395 W Lindsey St.
Norman, OK 73019
URL: http://najanewsroom.com
Contact: Francine Compton, President
Facebook: www.facebook.com/NativeJournalists
X (Twitter): x.com/najournalists
Instagram: www.instagram.com/najournalists

Description: Journalists of Native American descent. Seeks to serve and empower Native communicators. Conducts educational programs in areas including journalism, Native American culture, politics and history, and free speech and expression. Represents members' professional interests; sponsors lobbying activities. **Founded:** 1984. **Publications:** *NAJA News* (Biweekly). **Awards:** NAJA Scholarship Program (Annual); NAJA National Native Media Awards (Annual). **Geographic Preference:** Multinational.

5295 ■ North American Snowsports Journalists Association (NASJA)
22 Cavalier Way Latham
Latham, NY 12110
URL: http://www.nasja.org
Contact: Jeff Blumenfeld, President
E-mail: jeff@blumenfeldpr.com
Facebook: www.facebook.com/Nasjasnowmedia
X (Twitter): x.com/NASJAsnowscoops

Description: Newspaper, magazine, book, television, radio writers and broadcasters, and photographers who report on skiing and other snow sports. Covers skiing and other snow sports. **Founded:** 1963. **Publications:** *North American Snowsports Journalists Association--Membership Directory* (Annual); *The Inside Edge* (Quinquennial); *NASJA Directory*. **Educational Activities:** North American Snowsports Journalists Association Meeting (Annual). **Awards:** Harold S. Hirsch Award for Excellence in Snowsports Journalism - Blogs (Annual); Harold S. Hirsch Award for Excellence in Snowsports Journalism - Books (Triennial); Harold S. Hirsch Award for Excellence in Snowsports Journalism - Feature Writing (Annual); Carson White Snowsports Achievement Award (Annual); Harold S. Hirsch Award for Excellence in Snowsports Journalism - Columns (Annual); Harold S. Hirsch Award for Excellence in Snowsports Journalism - Video (Annual); Harold S. Hirsch Award for Excellence Image (Annual); Paul Robbins Outstanding Competitor Award (Annual); NASJA Lifetime Achievement Award (Annual). **Geographic Preference:** Multinational.

5296 ■ Novelists Inc. (NINC)
PO Box 331
Covington, KY 41012
Co. E-mail: admin@ninc.com
URL: http://ninc.com
Contact: Caethes Faron, President
Facebook: www.facebook.com/novelists.inc
X (Twitter): x.com/novelists_inc

Description: Works to serve the needs of multi-published writers of popular fiction. **Founded:** 1989. **Geographic Preference:** National.

5297 ■ Outdoor Writers Association of America (OWAA)
2814 Brooks St.
Missoula, MT 59801
Ph: (406)728-7434
Co. E-mail: info@owaa.org
URL: http://owaa.org
Contact: Chez Chesak, Executive Director
Facebook: www.facebook.com/OWAAonline
X (Twitter): x.com/OWAAonline

Description: Professional organization of newspaper, magazine, radio, television and motion picture writers and photographers (both staff and freelance) concerned with outdoor recreation and conservation. Conducts surveys for educational and industrial organizations; compiles market data for writer members and offers liaison aid in writer assignments. **Founded:** 1927. **Publications:** *National Outdoor Writers Directory* (Annual). **Awards:** OWAA Excellence in Craft Award (Annual); J. Hammond Brown Memorial Award (Annual); OWAA's John Madson Fellowship (Annual); Bodie McDowell Scholarship (Annual). **Geographic Preference:** National.

5298 ■ Quebec Writers' Federation (QWF)
1200 Atwater Ave., Ste. 3
Westmount, QC, Canada H3Z 1X4
Ph: (514)933-0878
Co. E-mail: admin@qwf.org
URL: http://qwf.org
Contact: Julie Barlow, President

Facebook: www.facebook.com/quebecwritersfederation
X (Twitter): x.com/OfficialQWF
Instagram: www.instagram.com/OfficialQWF
Description: Works toward ensuring a lasting place for English literature and practitioners on the Quebec cultural scene. **Founded:** 1988. **Awards:** QWF Literary Awards (Annual). **Geographic Preference:** State.

5299 ■ Sisters in Crime (SinC)
574E Ritchie Hwy., No 271
Severna Park, MD 21146
Free: 833-492-7463
Fax: (410)544-4640
URL: http://www.sistersincrime.org
Contact: Jennifer J. Chow, President
Facebook: www.facebook.com/sistersincrime
X (Twitter): x.com/SinCNational
Instagram: www.instagram.com/sincnational
YouTube: www.youtube.com/channel/UCqLdMJuvE_K7ddw87fyVBpg
Description: Promotes the professional development and advancement of women crime writers. **Manufacturing:** Publishes directories for women mystery writers. Seeks to combat discrimination against women in the mystery field, educate publishers and the general public, and promote the professional advancement of women who write mysteries. **Founded:** 1986. **Publications:** Sisters in Crime; InSinC Quarterly (Quarterly). **Geographic Preference:** Multinational; Regional.

5300 ■ United States Harness Writers' Association (USHWA)
PO Box 1314
Mechanicsburg, PA 17055
Co. E-mail: ushwainfo@gmail.com
URL: http://www.usharnesswriters.com
Contact: Barry Lefkowitz, President
Facebook: www.facebook.com/USHarnessWriters
Linkedin: www.linkedin.com/company/ushwa
X (Twitter): x.com/USHWA_
Description: Writers, reporters, editors, broadcasters, columnists, and cartoonists who cover harness racing for the press. Seeks to further the interests of light harness racing. Maintains hall of fame and charitable program. Votes on national awards. **Founded:** 1947. **Educational Activities:** United States Harness Writers' Association Dinner (Annual). **Awards:** Dan Patch Good Guy Award (Annual); Stanley F. Bergstein Proximity Achievement Award (Annual); USHWA Hall of Fame (Annual); USHWAn of the Year (Annual); USHWA Communicator's Hall of Fame (Annual); USHWA Caretaker of the Year (Annual); USHWA Amateur Driver of the Year (Annual); USHWA Driver of the Year (Annual); USHWA Owner of the Year (Annual); USHWA Proximity Award (Annual); USHWA Rising Star Award (Annual). **Geographic Preference:** National.

5301 ■ Women Writing the West (WWW)
PO Box 1886
Durango, CO 81302
Co. E-mail: trego@gmail.com
URL: http://www.womenwritingthewest.org
Contact: Betsy Randolph, President
E-mail: betsy@betsyrandolph.com
Facebook: www.facebook.com/WomenWritingTheWest
X (Twitter): x.com/womenwritewest
Instagram: www.instagram.com/explore/tags/womenwritewest
Pinterest: www.pinterest.com/womenwritingthewest
Description: Serves as a forum for writers and other professionals writing and promoting the Women's West founded by Sybil Downing and Jerrie Hurd. Promotes the legacy of earlier women writers who depicted the life during the hard and dangerous times of the Western American era. **Awards:** WILLA Literary Award (Annual). **Geographic Preference:** National.

EDUCATIONAL PROGRAMS

5302 ■ EEI Communications Copywriting I (Onsite)
URL(s): www.eeicom.com
Description: Topics include understanding your audience, defining your purpose, communication methods, and effective writing structures. **Audience:** Writers and editors. **Principal Exhibits:** Topics include understanding your audience, defining your purpose, communication methods, and effective writing structures.

5303 ■ EEI Communications Copywriting II (Onsite)
URL(s): www.eeicom.com
Description: Covers forming ideas and brainstorming, impact writing, and improving the creative process. **Audience:** Writers and editors. **Principal Exhibits:** Covers forming ideas and brainstorming, impact writing, and improving the creative process. **Telecommunication Services:** info@eeicom.com.

5304 ■ EEI Communications Intensive Review of Grammar (Onsite)
URL(s): www.eeicom.com
Description: Covers the advanced elements of grammar and usage, including adverbs and adjectives, restrictive and nonrestrictive clauses, dependent and independent clauses, tricky punctuation rules, pronoun/antecedent agreement, and subject/verb agreement. **Audience:** Writers, editors, designers, and publication specialists. **Principal Exhibits:** Covers the advanced elements of grammar and usage, including adverbs and adjectives, restrictive and nonrestrictive clauses, dependent and independent clauses, tricky punctuation rules, pronoun/antecedent agreement, and subject/verb agreement. **Telecommunication Services:** train@eeicom.com.

5305 ■ EEI Communications Scientific Editing (Onsite)
URL(s): www.eeicom.com
Description: Covers techniques for editing scientific and technical prose, including convincing writers to revise their manuscript; reducing author reliance on jargon and wordiness; locating and using scientific editing resources; meeting title, abstract, and keyword requirements; editing math and scientific data in graphs, diagrams, and illustrations; handling units, measurements, and numbers; and using scientific and engineering symbols. **Audience:** Writers, editors, designers, and publication specialists. **Principal Exhibits:** Covers techniques for editing scientific and technical prose, including convincing writers to revise their manuscript; reducing author reliance on jargon and wordiness; locating and using scientific editing resources; meeting title, abstract, and keyword requirements; editing math and scientific data in graphs, diagrams, and illustrations; handling units, measurements, and numbers; and using scientific and engineering symbols. **Telecommunication Services:** train@eeicom.com.

5306 ■ EEI Communications The Designing Editor
URL(s): www.eeicom.com
Description: Covers the basics of effective design, including the design process, page layout, design evaluation techniques, and related issues. **Audience:** Editors, graphic/web designers, desktop publishers, writers, content managers, and communications experts. **Principal Exhibits:** Covers the basics of effective design, including the design process, page layout, design evaluation techniques, and related issues. **Telecommunication Services:** train@eeicom.com.

REFERENCE WORKS

5307 ■ "5 Straightforward Ways to Go from Employed to Self-Employed" in Forbes.com(October 26, 2022)
URL(s): www.forbes.com/sites/jodiecook/2022/10/26/5-straightforward-ways-to-go-from-employed-to-self-employed/?sh=9857d4b6304a
Ed: Jodie Cook. **Description:** Transition from your current job working for someone else to being your own boss. Tips are discussed to help ease through this process.

5308 ■ AWP's Guide to Writing Programs
Pub: Association of Writers & Writing Programs
Contact: Cynthia Sherman, Executive Director
URL(s): www.awpwriter.org/guide/guide_writing_programs
Description: Covers about 300 graduate and 400 undergraduate programs in creative writing; approximately 250 writers' conferences, festivals, and centers; coverage includes Canada and the United Kingdom. **Entries include:** Institution name, department name, contact name and address; web site, description of program, including degree or other credit offered; description of faculty, including titles of their publications; tuition fees and dates. **Arrangement:** Alphabetical. **Indexes:** Geographical, degree. **Availability:** Online.

5309 ■ "Bad Reviews Can Boost Sales. Here's Why" in Harvard Business Review (Vol. 90, April 2012, No. 4, pp. 28)
Pub: Harvard Business Review Press
Contact: Moderna V. Pfizer, Contact
Ed: Jonah Berger. **Price:** $6. **Description:** Research on positive and negative book reviews found that sales increased for books with bad reviews, as the review itself made people aware of a work they would not have otherwise known about. **Availability:** Online; PDF.

5310 ■ "Baltimore's Co-Working Spaces Introduces New Kind of Cubicle Culture" in Baltimore Business Journal (Vol. 29, August 19, 2011, No. 15, pp. 1)
Pub: Boston Business Journal
Contact: Carolyn M. Jones, President
E-mail: cmjones@bizjournals.com
Ed: Alexander Jackson. **Description:** Beehive Baltimore offers a co-working space where independent freelancers and entrepreneurs can work. There are two other companies that provide the same service and the value of these services to these professional is that it provides them with an office that is both convenient and affordable aside from letting them network with peers.

5311 ■ Be a Brilliant Business Writer: Write Well, Write Fast, and Whip the Competition
Released: October 05, 2010. **Price:** $14.99, paperback; $5.99. **Description:** Tools for mastering the art of persuasive writing in every document created, from email and client letters to reports and presentations, this book will help any writer convey their message with clarity and power, increase productivity by reducing rewrites, and provide the correct tone for navigating office politics. **Availability:** E-book; Print.

5312 ■ "California vs. Freelance Writers" in National Review (October 22, 2019)
URL(s): www.nationalreview.com/corner/new-california-labor-law-hits-freelance-writers-hard/
Ed: Robert Verbruggen. **Released:** October 22, 2019. **Description:** Freelancers in California are gearing up for major changes to their work when a new law takes effect that will force all companies to treat freelancers as regular employees. **Availability:** Online.

5313 ■ "David Leonhardt on Hiring a Copywriter for Your Small Business" in Small Business Trends(October 18, 2022)
URL(s): smallbiztrends.com/2022/10/how-to-hire-a-copywriter.html
Ed: Holly Chavez. **Released:** October 21, 2022. **Description:** David Leonhardt, President of The Happy Guy (THGM) Writing Services, discusses the benefits of small businesses hiring copywriters in order to communicate clearly to customers. **Availability:** Online.

5314 ■ Editorial Freelancers Association--Membership Directory
Pub: Editorial Freelancers Association
Contact: Joy Drohan, Secretary
E-mail: secretary@the-efa.org
URL(s): www.the-efa.org/membership-directory

Description: Covers 1,100 member editorial freelancers. **Entries include:** Personal name, address, phone, services provided, specialties. **Arrangement:** Alphabetical. **Indexes:** Product/service, special interest, geographical, computer skills. **Availability:** Print.

5315 ■ *"Freelance Writer Creates LI Bridal Blog" in Long Island Business News (September 10, 2010)*
Pub: BridgeTower Media
Contact: Adam Reinebach, President
Ed: Gregory Zeller. **Description:** Profile of Claudia Copquin, freelance journalist who created a blog for brides on the Internet. **Availability:** Online; Audio.

5316 ■ *"From the Editors: Plagiarism Policies and Screening at AMJ" in Academy of Management Journal (Vol. 55, August 2012, No. 4, pp. 749)*
Pub: Academy of Management
Contact: Sharon Alvarez, President
Description: The plagiarism policies and practices of the Academy of Management Journal (AMJ) based on the Committee on Publications Ethics and AOM guidelines are described. The function of the Cross-Check software tool for screening manuscripts for plagiarism is explained. **Availability:** Download; Electronic publishing; PDF; Online.

5317 ■ *"The Gig's Up for Freelancers" in The Wall Street Journal (October 27, 2019)*
URL(s): www.wsj.com/articles/the-gigs-up-for-freelancers-11572208945
Ed: Andy Kessler. **Released:** October 27, 2019. **Description:** Assembly Bill 5 is set to take effect, meaning that most independent contractors will now be considered full-time employees in California. While it could mean that more contract workers receive sick leave and health care but more than likely, contractors will find their livelihoods taken away as employers will stop hiring freelancers from California. **Availability:** Online.

5318 ■ *"I Quit My Day Job 4 Months Ago to Become a Freelance Writer. Here's What My Family of 4 Spends in a Typical Week" in Business Insider (October 14, 2019)*
URL(s): www.businessinsider.com/spending-diary-family-freelance-income-daytona-beach-florida
Ed: Clint Proctor. **Released:** October 14, 2019. **Description:** An honest look at one family's budeting with the breadwinner working a freelance writing job. **Availability:** Online.

5319 ■ *International Literary Market Place: The Directory of the International Book Publishing Industry*
Pub: Information Today Inc.
Contact: Thomas H. Hogan, President
URL(s): store.infotoday.com/product/literary-market-place
Released: Latest edition 84th edition, 2024. **Price:** $539.50, for outside North America; $507.50, Single issue; $529.50, Canada and Mexico. **Description:** Covers over 10,500 publishers in over 180 countries outside the United States and Canada, and about 1,499 trade and professional organizations related to publishing abroad; includes major printers, binders, typesetters, book manufacturers, book dealers, libraries, literary agencies, translators, book clubs, reference books and journals, periodicals, prizes, and international reference section. **Entries include:** For publishers--Name, address, phone, fax, telex, names and titles of key personnel, branches, type of publications, subjects, ISBN prefix. Listings for others include similar information but less detail. **Arrangement:** Classified by business activities, then geographical. **Indexes:** Company name, subject, type of publication. **Availability:** Print; Online.

5320 ■ *Make Money As a Freelance Writer: 7 Simple Steps to Start Your Freelance Writing Business and Earn Your First $1,000*
Ed: Sally Miller, Gina Horkey. **Released:** April 19, 2018. **Price:** $9.99, Paperback. **Description:** A how-to guide for turning your writing hobby into a freelance business. **Availability:** Print.

5321 ■ *Publishers Directory*
Pub: Gale, part of Cengage Group
Contact: Paul Gazzolo, General Manager Senior Vice President
URL(s): www.gale.com/ebooks/9780028670133/publishers-directory
Description: Covers over 20,000 new and established, commercial and nonprofit, private and alternative, corporate and association, government and institution publishing programs and their distributors; includes producers of books, classroom materials, prints, reports, and databases. **Entries include:** Firm name, address, phone, fax, company e-mail address, URL, year founded, ISBN prefix, Standard Address Number, whether firm participates in the Cataloging in Publication program of the Library of Congress, names of principal executives, personal e-mail addresses, number of titles in print, description of firm and its main subject interests, discount and returns policies, affiliated and parent companies, mergers and amalgamations, principal markets, imprints and divisions, alternate formats products are offered; distributors also list firms for which they distribute, special services, terms to publishers and regional offices. **Arrangement:** Alphabetical; distributors listed separately. **Indexes:** Subject, geographical, publisher, imprints, and distributor. **Availability:** Large print; CD-ROM; E-book; Online; DVD; Download. **Type:** Directory.

5322 ■ *"Publishing: Art or Science? Reflections from an Editorial Perspective" in Accounting and Finance (Vol. 52, June 2012, No. 2, pp. 359)*
Released: February 01, 2012. **Description:** Insights into the 'journal process' is shared by an experienced editor. Three basics messages emerge from the discussion. First, if a study is to be successful, it must address an interesting and important topic to investigate; secondly, the study must be communicated in a transparent and accessible way so the work can be critically evaluated; finally, authors are advised to subject their work to external scrutiny before submitting for peer review. **Availability:** Print; PDF; Online.

5323 ■ *"Savvy Solutions" in Black Enterprise (Vol. 41, November 2010, No. 4, pp. 42)*
Description: Society of Children's Book Writers and Illustrators offers members many benefits, including directories of agencies looking for new writers of books. **Availability:** Online.

5324 ■ *Short Story Writers*
Pub: Magill's Choice
URL(s): www.salempress.com/magills_short_story_writers
Ed: Frank N. Magill, Charles E. May. **Released:** last edition October 2007. **Price:** $217, Individuals for print; $217, Individuals for eBook. **Description:** Covers 102 short story writers of the 19th and 20th centuries. **Entries include:** Writer name, principal works of short fiction, other literary forms produced, notable career and technical achievements related to the short story form, brief biography, glossary. **Arrangement:** Alphabetical. **Indexes:** Author surname, title. **Availability:** E-book; Print; PDF.

5325 ■ *Start Your Own Freelance Writing Business: The Complete Guide to Starting and Scaling from Scratch*
Ed: Laura Pennington Briggs. **Released:** July 16, 2019. **Price:** $13.49, Paperback; $9.99, E-Book. **Description:** A helpful guide for those seeking to pursue a freelance writing career. **Availability:** E-book; Print.

5326 ■ *Technical Writing for Dummies*
Pub: John Wiley & Sons, Inc.
Contact: Christina Van Tassell, Executive Vice President Chief Financial Officer
URL(s): www.wiley.com/en-us/Technical+Writing+For+Dummies%2C+2nd+Edition-p-9781394176755
Ed: Sheryl Lindsell-Roberts. **Released:** 2nd edition. **Price:** $29.99, paperback. **Description:** This thorough guide teaches all the aspects related to technical writing in order to start a career in the field or to advance in an established job. **Availability:** Print.

5327 ■ *"The Temp Economy and the Future of Work" in U.S. News & World Report (August 10, 2018)*
URL(s): www.usnews.com/news/the-report/articles/2018-08-10/the-temp-economy-and-the-future-of-work
Ed: Gabrielle Levy. **Description:** Over the years, companies have shifted to using machines and computers and with that came a reduced work staff. Instead of full-time employees, many companies have opted to use independent contractors. Historian Louis Hyman explores the gig economy and if it is sustainable. **Availability:** Online.

5328 ■ *"What You Need to Know about Hiring Independent Contractors" in Legal Zoom (March 22, 2023)*
URL(s): www.legalzoom.com/articles/what-you-need-to-know-about-hiring-independent-contractors
Released: March 23, 2023. **Description:** Independent contractors are an attractive choice for saving some costs, but are they the best choice for your small business? Read about the pros and cons of hiring ICs. **Availability:** Online.

5329 ■ *"Why You Don't Get Published: An Editor's View" in Accounting and Finance (Vol. 52, June 2012, No. 2, pp. 343)*
Ed: Michael E. Bradbury. **Released:** March 12, 2012. **Description:** This paper uses content analysis to examine 66 reviews on 33 manuscripts submitted to 'Accounting and Finance'. Selected extracts from reviews are provided to illustrate the issues considered important to reviewers. The main message is that papers need to be work-shopped and more care taken over editorial matters. A checklist for prospective authors is provided. **Availability:** Print; Online.

5330 ■ *Writing Children's Books for Dummies*
Pub: John Wiley & Sons, Inc.
Contact: Christina Van Tassell, Executive Vice President Chief Financial Officer
URL(s): www.wiley.com/en-us/Writing+Children%27s+Books+For+Dummies%2C+3rd+Edition-p-9781119870036
Ed: Lisa Rojany, Peter Economy. **Released:** 3rd edition. **Price:** $15, e-book; $24.99, paperback. **Description:** Hone your writing skills with this guide and start getting your children's stories published. Includes a section on self-publishing. **Availability:** E-book; Print.

5331 ■ *Writing a Romance Novel for Dummies*
Pub: John Wiley & Sons, Inc.
Contact: Christina Van Tassell, Executive Vice President Chief Financial Officer
URL(s): www.wiley.com/en-us/Writing+a+Romance+Novel+For+Dummies%2C+2nd+Edition-p-9781119989035
Ed: Victorine Lieske, Leslie Wainger. **Released:** 2nd edition. **Price:** $15, e-book; $24.99, paperback. **Description:** Get help with developing and writing your romance novel with this guide. Tips on refining your craft and getting published are included. **Availability:** E-book; Print.

5332 ■ *Writing Sci-Fi, Fantasy, & Horror for Dummies*
Pub: John Wiley & Sons, Ltd.
Contact: Benjamin Noel Wardleworth, Director
URL(s): www.wiley.com/en-us/Writing+Sci-Fi%2C+Fantasy%2C+%26+Horror+For+Dummies-p-9781119839101
Ed: Rick Dakan, Ryan G. Van Cleave. **Released:** February 2022. **Price:** $15, e-book; $24.99, paperback. **Description:** Hone your writing skills with this guide and work towards getting published. **Availability:** E-book; Print.

TRADE PERIODICALS

5333 ■ *The ASJA Weekly*
Pub: American Society of Journalists and Authors
Contact: Laura Laing, President
URL(s): www.multibriefs.com/briefs/asja

Ed: Barbara DeMarco-Barrett. **Released:** Weekly **Description:** Reports on the business meetings of the Society and provides market news as well as news of members, publishers, editors, and association chapters. Recurring features include professional market reports and discussions of magazines, books, and other media. **Availability:** Online.

5334 ■ *Authorship*
Pub: National Writers Association
Contact: Sandy Whelchel, Director
URL(s): www.nationalwriters.com/videos.html

Ed: Sandy Whelchel. **Released:** Quarterly **Price:** $20, Single issue for us. **Description:** Contains information about the freelance writing and publishing fields. Carries market news, lists of editors and publishers against whom many have registered complaints, and updates on publications that have gone out of business or are no longer considering freelance submissions. Recurring features include news of members, editorials, letters to the editor, book reviews, and columns titled Director's Corner and Business Writing News. **Availability:** Print.

5335 ■ *Children's Book Insider*
Pub: Children's Book Insider L.L.C.
Contact: Jon Bard, Co-Founder
URL(s): cbiclubhouse.com
X (Twitter): x.com/write4kids
YouTube: www.youtube.com/cbiclubhouse

Released: Monthly **Price:** $5.49, for per month; $49.95, for full year back issues. **Description:** Discusses writing and selling books and stories for children. Recurring features include interviews, news of educational opportunities, job listings, and columns titled Writing Workshop, Market News, and Trends. **Availability:** Print; Download; Online.

5336 ■ *Freelance Writer's Report (FWR)*
Pub: CNW Publishing, Editing and Promotion Inc.
Contact: Dana K. Cassell, Executive Director
URL(s): www.writers-editors.com/Writers/Membership/Writer_Guidelines/writer_guidelines.htm

Price: Free. **Description:** Offers up-to-date news and information concerning effective marketing/production techniques, writing tips, self-promotion, and other topics of interest "to freelance writers who intend to earn a good income from their work and improve the quality of their work." Recurring features include interviews, book reviews, news of writing seminars, conferences, and market news. **Remarks:** Members of the Florida Freelance Writers Association receive an extra association section (4 pages). **Availability:** Download; PDF.

5337 ■ *The Freelancer*
Pub: Editorial Freelancers Association
Contact: Joy Drohan, Secretary
E-mail: secretary@the-efa.org
URL(s): www.the-efa.org/newsletters

Released: Quarterly; April, July, October, and January. **Description:** Publishes news of the concerns and activities of EFA, whose members "provide freelance editorial services to the publishing and communications industries." Recurring features include letters to the editor, news of members, book reviews, a calendar of events, columns on usage and business, reports on on general meetings, news of member, and columns titled Grammatical Gleanings and Tax Tips. **Availability:** Print.

5338 ■ *International Women's Writing Guild--Network*
Contact: Kristin Conroy, Editor
URL(s): www.iwwg.org/iwwg-documents

Ed: Kristin Conroy. **Released:** Bimonthly **Price:** Included in membership. **Description:** Carries a variety of items for women who write both for personal growth and professionally. Announces opportunities for retreat, publication, and awards. Recurring features include Guild and member news; writing conferences, and workshops; letters; and contests, environmental news, market and publication information. **Availability:** Print; Download; PDF.

5339 ■ *Journal of Technical Writing and Communication (JTWC)*
Pub: SAGE Publications
Contact: Tracey Ozmina, President
URL(s): journals.sagepub.com/home/JTW

Ed: Charles H. Sides. **Released:** Quarterly **Price:** $1,825, Institutions for institutional backfile purchase, e-access; $768, Institutions for subscription, e-access; $243, Institutions for single print issue; $60, Individuals for single print issue; $186, Individuals for print and online; $903, Institutions for print & e-access; $993, Institutions for print and online; $858, Institutions for online only; $885, Institutions for print only. **Description:** International, scholarly, peer-reviewed journal publishing research on communications-related issues, as well as relevant materials on the teaching of technical and professional writing and relevant book reviews. **Availability:** Print; PDF; Online.

5340 ■ *POETALK*
Pub: Bay Area Poets Coalition Inc.
Contact: John Rowe, Officer
URL(s): sites.google.com/site/bayareapoetscoalition/bapc-home/poetalk-poetry-journal
Facebook: www.facebook.com/100063540338646/wall

Released: Annual **Price:** $4, for cover; $2, for back issue; $5, Single issue for current issue, mailed 1st class. **Description:** Publishes quality work by beginner and experienced poets. **Availability:** Print; Online.

5341 ■ *The Writer Magazine: The Pioneer (Oldest) Magazine for Writers*
Pub: Madavor Media LLC.
Contact: Jeffrey C. Wolk, Contact
URL(s): www.writermag.com

Released: Monthly **Price:** C$9.99, Single issue; $8.99, Single issue. **Description:** Magazine for freelance writers. Publishing practical information and advice on how to write publishable material and where to sell it. **Availability:** Download; Online.

VIDEO/AUDIO MEDIA

5342 ■ *Redefining Independence: Changing the Game for Freelancers with Rachel Renock*
URL(s): www.eofire.com/podcast/rachelrenock

Ed: Jon Lee Dumas. **Released:** November 09, 2023. **Description:** Podcast explains how freelancing is reshaping traditional employment, outlines key skills and attitudes necessary to succeed, and suggests how to balance independence with collaboration.

5343 ■ *Small Business, Big Mindset: AI for Writers: Friend or Foe?*
URL(s): podcast.musclecreative.com/924061/episodes/12671949-ai-for-writers-friend-or-foe

Ed: Erin Geiger. **Released:** April 18, 2023. **Description:** Podcast explains how to leverage AI for good.

TRADE SHOWS AND CONVENTIONS

5344 ■ **SABEWNYC Fall Conference**
Society for Advancing Business Editing and Writing (SABEW)
555 N Central Ave., Ste. 302
Phoenix, AZ 85004-1248
Ph: (602)496-7862
Co. E-mail: sabew@sabew.org
URL: http://sabew.org
Contact: Glenn Hall, President
URL(s): sabew.org/event/save-the-date-sabew25-is-heading-to-the-washington-d-c-metro-area-in-2025

Frequency: Annual. **Description:** Exhibits related to active business, economic and financial news writers and editors for newspapers, magazines and other publications, broadcasters of business news, teachers of business or journalism at colleges and universities. **Audience:** Business journalists working in print, online, and broadcast media. **Principal Exhibits:** Exhibits related to active business, economic and financial news writers and editors for newspapers, magazines and other publications, broadcasters of business news, teachers of business or journalism at colleges and universities. **Dates and Locations:** 2025 Apr 03-05 Hyatt Centric Arlington, Washington, DC. **Telecommunication Services:** sklimstra@sabew.org.

CONSULTANTS

5345 ■ **Bob Bly**
31 Cheyenne
Montville, NJ 07045
Ph: (973)263-0562
Co. E-mail: rwbly@bly.com
URL: http://www.bly.com
Contact: Bob Bly, Consultant
Facebook: www.facebook.com/BobBlyCopywriter
Linkedin: www.linkedin.com/in/bobbly
X (Twitter): x.com/Robertbly
Pinterest: www.pinterest.ph/blycopywriter

Description: An independent consultant and copywriter specializing in business-to-business, industrial, hi-tech and direct response advertising, marketing, publicity and promotion. **Scope:** An independent consultant and copywriter specializing in business-to-business, industrial, hi-tech and direct response advertising, marketing, publicity and promotion. **Founded:** 1982. **Publications:** "The Bulletproof Book Proposal "; "Finding A Good Idea For Your Book"; "A Fine Position to Be In"; "What to Do When Your Book Goes Out of Print"; "How To Write a Good Advertisement"; "31 -derfully Simple Ways To Make Your Ads Generate More Inquiries.". **Training:** Active Listening; Become an Instant Guru; Get More Done In Less Time: How To Double Your Personal Productivity; How To Write A Nonfiction Book And Get It Published.

PUBLICATIONS

5346 ■ *"8 Important Things I've Learned in 4 Years of Freelance Writing" in Business 2 Community (October 7, 2021)*
URL(s): ww.business2community.com/small-business/8-important-things-ive-learned-in-4-years-of-freelance-writing-02434952

Ed: Ali Faagba. **Released:** October 7, 2021. **Description:** A freelance writer shares what it was like to set up shop and become a full-time freelancer. Discusses how to pitch for work and learn from mistakes, how to make guest posts, setting rates, marketing, invoicing, and other insights. **Availability:** Online.

5347 ■ *Business and Legal Forms for Authors and Self-Publishers*
307 W 36th St., 11th Fl.
New York, NY 10018
Ph: (212)643-6816
Free: 800-733-3000
Fax: (212)643-6819
URL: http://www.skyhorsepublishing.com/allworth-press
Contact: Tad Crawford, Founder
URL(s): www.skyhorsepublishing.com/allworth-press/9781621534648/business-and-legal-forms-for-authors-and-self-publishers

Ed: Tad Crawford. **Price:** $24.99, Single issue for paperback; $29.95, Single issue for paperback; $18.99, Single issue for eBook. **Description:** Publication includes contact information for volunteer lawyers for the arts. Principal content of publication is instruction and use of business and legal forms for authors and self-publishers. **Availability:** CD-ROM; E-book; Print; Download.

LIBRARIES

5348 ■ **Cleveland Public Library Literature Department**
Main Bldg., 2nd Fl.
325 Superior Ave.
Cleveland, OH 44114
Ph: (216)623-2881
Co. E-mail: literature@cpl.org

URL: http://cpl.org/aboutthelibrary/subjectscollections/literature
Contact: Donald Boozer, Manager
Scope: World Literature and Criticism; Fiction; Poetry; Drama and Theater; Film; Television and Radio and much more. **Services:** Department open to the public; Interlibrary loan. **Founded:** 1869. **Holdings:** 500,000 volumes.

5349 ■ The National Press Club (NPC) - The Eric Freidheim Library
529 14th St. NW, 13th Fl.
Washington, DC 20045
Ph: (202)662-7500
Co. E-mail: members@press.org
URL: http://www.press.org
Contact: Jen Judson, President
Facebook: www.facebook.com/PressClubDC
X (Twitter): x.com/pressclubdc
Instagram: www.instagram.com/pressclubdc
YouTube: www.youtube.com/c/NationalPressClubLive
Description: Reporters, writers and news people employed by newspapers, wire services, magazines, radio and television stations and other forms of news media. Sponsors sports, travel events, rap sessions with news figures and authors and newsmaker breakfasts and luncheons. **Scope:** Journalism. **Services:** Interlibrary loan available upon request. **Founded:** 1908. **Holdings:** Figures not available. **Subscriptions:** newspapers magazines Books. **Publications:** *National Press Club Directory*. **Educational Activities:** National Press Club Seminar. **Awards:** Online Journalism Award (Annual); Washington Regional Reporting Award (Periodic); NPC Consumer Journalism Award (Annual); Edwin M. Hood Award for Diplomatic Correspondence (Annual); NPC Newsletter Journalism Award (Annual); NPC Washington Regional Reporting Award (Annual); Sandy Hume Memorial Award for Excellence in Political Journalism (Annual); Arthur Rowse Award for Press Criticism (Annual); Joseph D. Ryle Award for Excellence in Writing on the Problems of Geriatrics (Annual); Joan M. Friedenberg Online Journalism Award (Annual); Angele Gingras Humor Award (Annual); Ann Cottrell Free Animal Reporting Award (Annual); Michael A. Dornheim Award (Annual). **Geographic Preference:** National.

Electrical Contractor

ASSOCIATIONS AND OTHER ORGANIZATIONS

5350 ■ Association Canadienne des Entrepreneur Electriciens (ACEE) [Canadian Electrical Contractors Association (CECA)]
41 Maple St.
  Toronto, ON, Canada L9P 1C8
Ph: (416)491-2414
Free: 800-387-3226
Fax: (416)765-0009
Co. E-mail: ceca@ceca.org
URL: http://www.ceca.org
Contact: David Mason, President
Facebook: www.facebook.com/cecacanada
X (Twitter): x.com/cecacanada
Description: Federation of provincial and territorial electrical contractor groups in Canada. Represents electrical contractors at the national level. **Founded:** 1955. **Geographic Preference:** National.

5351 ■ Independent Electrical Contractors (IEC)
2900 S Quincy St., Ste. 720
  Arlington, VA 22206
Ph: (703)549-7351
Fax: (703)549-7448
Co. E-mail: info@ieci.org
URL: http://www.ieci.org
Contact: Raeshawn Crosson, Chief Executive Officer
Facebook: www.facebook.com/IEC.National
Linkedin: www.linkedin.com/company/independent-electrical-contractors-iec-
X (Twitter): x.com/IEC_National
Instagram: www.instagram.com/iec_national
YouTube: www.youtube.com/user/DoElectrical
Description: Conducts surveys on volume of sales and purchases and on type of products used. Has formulated National Pattern Standards for Apprentice Training for Electricians. **Founded:** 1957. **Publications:** IEC Insights (6/year); IEC Product Buyer's Guide & Membership Directory (Annual). **Educational Activities:** Independent Electrical Contractors (Annual). **Geographic Preference:** Local; National.

5352 ■ National Association of Electrical Distributors (NAED)
1181 Corporate Lk. Dr.
  Saint Louis, MO 63132
Ph: (314)991-9000
Free: 888-791-2512
Co. E-mail: naedcommunications@naed.org
URL: http://www.naed.org
Contact: Tom Naber, President
E-mail: tnaber@naed.org
Facebook: www.facebook.com/NAEDorg
Linkedin: www.linkedin.com/company/national-association-of-electrical-distributors-naed-
X (Twitter): x.com/NAED_org
Instagram: www.instagram.com/naed_org
YouTube: www.youtube.com/channel/UCHJLWzwi6_hy8pO_zn8ujEA
Description: Serves as wholesale distributors of electrical supplies and apparatus. Aims to serve and protect the electrical distribution channel; maintains several committees. **Founded:** 1908. **Publications:** TED The Electrical Distributor Magazine: Official Publication of the National Association of Electrical Distributors (NAED) (Semimonthly); The Electrical Distributor (Monthly); NAED Newsline (Monthly); Performance Analysis Report (Annual); National Association of Electrical Distributors Industry Directory. **Educational Activities:** National Electrical Leadership Summit. **Awards:** Arthur W. Hooper Achievement Award (Annual); NAED Associate Service Award (Annual); NAED Distributor Distinguished Service Award (Annual); NAED Industry Award of Merit (Annual). **Geographic Preference:** National.

5353 ■ National Electrical Contractors Association (NECA)
1201 Pennsylvania Ave. NW Ste. 1200
  Washington, DC 20004
Ph: (202)991-6300
Fax: (202)217-4171
Co. E-mail: education@necanet.org
URL: http://www.necanet.org
Contact: Kirk Davis, President
Facebook: www.facebook.com/NECANET
Linkedin: www.linkedin.com/company/necanet
X (Twitter): x.com/necanet
YouTube: www.youtube.com/user/NECAadmin
Description: Contractors erecting, installing, repairing, servicing, and maintaining electric wiring, equipment, and appliances. Provides management services and labor relations programs for electrical contractors; conducts seminars for contractor sales and training. Sponsors honorary society, the Academy of Electrical Contracting. **Founded:** 1901. **Publications:** Electrical Contractor--Electrical Product Literature File Issue; A Comparison of Operational Cost of Union vs. Non-Union Contractors; Electrical Contractor (Monthly); Electrical Maintenance Pays Dividends; NECA Manual of Labor Units (MLU); This is NECA. **Educational Activities:** The NECA Show (Annual). **Awards:** Coggeshall Award (Annual); Comstock Award (Annual); NECA Industry Partner Award (Annual); James H. McGraw Award (Annual). **Geographic Preference:** National.

5354 ■ National Electrical Manufacturers Association (NEMA)
1300 N 17th St. N, No. 900
  Arlington, VA 22209
Ph: (703)841-3200
Co. E-mail: communications@nema.org
URL: http://www.nema.org
Contact: Debra Phillips, President
Facebook: www.facebook.com/nemaupdates
Linkedin: www.linkedin.com/company/nema
X (Twitter): x.com/nemaupdates
YouTube: www.youtube.com/nemavue
Description: Represents nearly 350 electrical equipment and medical imaging manufacturers that make safe, reliable, and efficient products and systems. **Founded:** 1926. **Publications:** National Electrical Manufacturers Association--Publications and Materials Catalog (Semiannual); electroindustry (Monthly); Electrical Standards and Product Guide. **Awards:** Bernard H. Falk Award (Annual); NEMA Kite and Key Award (Annual).

5355 ■ National Electrical Manufacturers Representatives Association (NEMRA)
1905 S New Market St., Ste. 257
  Carmel, IN 46032
Ph: (317)975-1999
URL: http://www.nemra.org
Contact: Jim Johnson, President
Facebook: www.facebook.com/NEMRA.org
Linkedin: www.linkedin.com/company/national-electrical-manufacturers-representatives-association
X (Twitter): x.com/nemra_and_nmg
YouTube: www.youtube.com/channel/UCHgySxJ49dHQtCPxtwQeZ2g
Description: North American trade association dedicated to promoting continuing education, professionalism, and the use of independent manufacturers representatives in the electrical industry. Offers professional development programs in business management and sales training, and offers a proprietary computer system for independent electrical representatives. Sponsors educational programs; compiles statistics; and holds an annual networking conference for its representative members and their manufacturers. **Founded:** 1969. **Publications:** NEMRA Locator (Annual); National Electrical Manufacturers Representatives Association--Locator (Annual). **Awards:** Thomas F. Preston Manufacturer of the Year Award (Annual); NEMRA Educational Scholarship Foundation Program (Annual). **Geographic Preference:** National.

EDUCATIONAL PROGRAMS

5356 ■ Arc Flash Electrical Safety NFPA 70E
TPC Trainco Inc.
225 E Robinson St., Ste. 570
  Orlando, FL 32801
Free: 877-978-7246
Co. E-mail: sales@tpctraining.com
URL: http://live.tpctraining.com
URL(s): live.tpctraining.com/public-seminars/electrical-training/fundamentals/arc-flash-electrical-safety-nfpa-70e
Description: A two-day in-house training course designed to save lives, eliminate injuries, and prevent damage to plants, buildings, and equipment. **Audience:** Electricians, maintenance, engineers, supervisors and HVAC technicians. **Principal Exhibits:** A two-day in-house training course designed to save lives, eliminate injuries, and prevent damage to plants, buildings, and equipment.

5357 ■ Electrical Ladder Drawings, Schematics & Diagrams (Onsite)
TPC Trainco Inc.
225 E Robinson St., Ste. 570
  Orlando, FL 32801
Free: 877-978-7246

Co. E-mail: sales@tpctraining.com
URL: http://live.tpctraining.com
URL(s): live.tpctraining.com/public-seminars/electrical-training/electrical-controls/electrical-ladder-drawings-schematics-and-diagrams

Description: Training will include exercises where participants create schematic diagrams based on circuit descriptions, as well as interpreting schematic drawings so that they can provide verbal or written circuit descriptions and an understanding of several types of drawings and diagrams including Block, Pictorial, One-line, Wiring, Terminal, and Schematic. **Audience:** Engineers, electricians, plant and facility managers and mechanics. **Principal Exhibits:** Training will include exercises where participants create schematic diagrams based on circuit descriptions, as well as interpreting schematic drawings so that they can provide verbal or written circuit descriptions and an understanding of several types of drawings and diagrams including Block, Pictorial, One-line, Wiring, Terminal, and Schematic.

5358 ■ Electrical Troubleshooting & Preventive Maintenance (Onsite)
TPC Trainco Inc.
  225 E Robinson St., Ste. 570
  Orlando, FL 32801
Free: 877-978-7246
Co. E-mail: sales@tpctraining.com
URL: http://live.tpctraining.com
URL(s): live.tpctraining.com/public-seminars/electrical-training/fundamentals/electrical-troubleshooting-preventive-maintenance

Description: Two-day seminar designed for anyone who needs to sharpen their electrical troubleshooting skills in order to increase efficiencies and uptime at their industrial plant or building facility. **Audience:** Electricians, Mechanic, HVAC Technicians and students. **Principal Exhibits:** Two-day seminar designed for anyone who needs to sharpen their electrical troubleshooting skills in order to increase efficiencies and uptime at their industrial plant or building facility.

5359 ■ Generators and Emergency Power (Onsite)
TPC Trainco Inc.
  225 E Robinson St., Ste. 570
  Orlando, FL 32801
Free: 877-978-7246
Co. E-mail: sales@tpctraining.com
URL: http://live.tpctraining.com
URL(s): live.tpctraining.com/public-seminars/electrical-training/emergency-power/generators-emergency-power

Frequency: Continuous. **Description:** A two-day seminar specifically designed to help understand the types, applications, operation, maintenance, and testing of onsite power generation systems. **Audience:** Facility managers, engineers, electricians, building owners, and maintenance managers. **Principal Exhibits:** A two-day seminar specifically designed to help understand the types, applications, operation, maintenance, and testing of onsite power generation systems.

5360 ■ Hands-On PLCs: Operation, Installation, Maintenance and Troubleshooting
TPC Trainco Inc.
  225 E Robinson St., Ste. 570
  Orlando, FL 32801
Free: 877-978-7246
Co. E-mail: sales@tpctraining.com
URL: http://live.tpctraining.com
URL(s): www.tpctrainco.com

Description: An intensive, two-day course for those needing "hands-on" work experience with programmable logic controllers. **Audience:** Electricians, technicians, building maintenance personnel, engineers, plant and facility managers. **Principal Exhibits:** An intensive, two-day course for those needing "hands-on" work experience with programmable logic controllers.

5361 ■ Uninterruptable Power Supply Systems for First Responders
TPC Trainco Inc.
  225 E Robinson St., Ste. 570
  Orlando, FL 32801
Free: 877-978-7246
Co. E-mail: sales@tpctraining.com
URL: http://live.tpctraining.com
URL(s): live.tpctraining.com/public-seminars/electrical-training/emergency-power/uninterruptible-power-supply-ups-systems

Description: Understanding the application, installation, operation, and troubleshooting of UPS systems and storage batteries. Held in Oakland, CA; Orange County, CA; Baton Rouge, LA; Boston, MA; Long Island, NY; Columbus, OH; Oklahoma City, OK. **Audience:** Electricians, engineers, and maintenance technicians. **Principal Exhibits:** Understanding the application, installation, operation, and troubleshooting of UPS systems and storage batteries. Held in Oakland, CA; Orange County, CA; Baton Rouge, LA; Boston, MA; Long Island, NY; Columbus, OH; Oklahoma City, OK.

5362 ■ Variable Frequency Drives (Onsite)
TPC Trainco Inc.
  225 E Robinson St., Ste. 570
  Orlando, FL 32801
Free: 877-978-7246
Co. E-mail: sales@tpctraining.com
URL: http://live.tpctraining.com
URL(s): live.tpctraining.com/public-seminars/electrical-training/electrical-controls/variable-frequency-drives

Description: A practical two-day seminar for maintenance technicians. **Audience:** Industry professionals, and maintenance technicians. **Principal Exhibits:** A practical two-day seminar for maintenance technicians.

REFERENCE WORKS

5363 ■ *"Acing the Test" in Contractor (Vol. 57, January 2010, No. 1, pp. 32)*
Pub: Informa USA, Inc.
Contact: Stephen A. Carter, Chief Executive Officer
Ed: Robert P. Mader. **Released:** January 01, 2010. **Description:** A ward winning mechanical system retrofitting of a middle school in Ohio is discussed. The school now operates at 37,800 Btu/sq. ft and reduced a significant amount of pollutants from being emitted into the environment.

5364 ■ *"Are You an Electrical Contractor or a Consultant?" in ecmag.com (February 13, 2018)*
Ed: Wayne D. Moore. **Released:** February 13, 2018. **Description:** Discusses the differences between an electrical contractor and a consultant working in this industry. Contractors often forget that they can consult on sales since customers often trust their contractors and want to know about additional products.

5365 ■ *"BIM and You: Know Its Benefits and Risks" in Contractor (Vol. 57, January 2010, No. 1, pp. 46)*
Ed: Susan Linden McGreevy. **Description:** Building Information Modeling is intended to be "collaborative" and this could raise legal issues if a contractor sends an electronic bid and it is filtered out. Other legal issues that mechanical contractors need to consider before using this technology are discussed. **Availability:** Print; Online.

5366 ■ *"Chicago Public Schools District Builds Green" in Contractor (Vol. 56, October 2009, No. 10, pp. 5)*
Ed: Candace Roulo. **Description:** Chicago Public Schools district has already built six U.S. Green Building Council LEED certified schools and one addition in five years and will continue to build new green buildings. The district has an Environmental Action Plan that strives to reduce energy usage, improve indoor air quality, and reduce contribution to climate change. **Availability:** Print; Online.

5367 ■ *"The Customer Is Always Right Even When He's Wrong" in Contractor (Vol. 57, February 2010, No. 2, pp. 12)*
Ed: Al Schwartz. **Description:** Mechanical contractors should note that customers will make a judgment based upon the impression that they form on their first meeting. Contractors can maintain a professional image by washing their trucks and having the personnel dress uniformly. Contractors have every right to demand that employees clean up and make a better impression on customers. **Availability:** Print; Online.

5368 ■ *"East Coast Solar" in Contractor (Vol. 57, February 2010, No. 2, pp. 17)*
Ed: Dave Yates. **Description:** U.S. Department of Energy's Solar Decathlon lets 20 college student-led teams from around the world compete to design and build a solar-powered home. A mechanical contractor discusses his work as an advisor during the competition. **Availability:** Print; Online.

5369 ■ *"Electrician Tools – Your List for Starting a Business" in Small Business Trends (January 25, 2023)*
URL(s): smallbiztrends.com/2023/01/electrician-tools.html
Ed: Samson Haileyesus. **Released:** January 25, 2023. **Description:** Provides a list of much-needed tools for electricians and why they are needed. **Availability:** Online.

5370 ■ *"EPA to Tighten Energy Star Standards for 2011" in Contractor (Vol. 56, September 2009, No. 9, pp. 6)*
Description: United States Environmental Protection Agency will tighten standards for its Energy Star for Homes program in 2011. The green trend in the construction industry has been cited as reason for the plan. The agency is adding requirements for energy-efficient equipment and building techniques. **Availability:** Print; Online.

5371 ■ *"Federal Buildings to Achieve Zero-Net Energy by 2030" in Contractor (Vol. 56, December 2009, No. 12, pp. 5)*
Ed: Candace Roulo. **Description:** United States president Barack Obama has issued sustainable goals for federal buildings. Federal agencies are also required to increase energy efficiency, conserve water and support sustainable communities. Obama has also announced a $3.4 billion investment in a smart energy creed. **Availability:** Print; Online.

5372 ■ *"FSU's OGZEB Is Test Bed for Sustainable Technology" in Contractor (Vol. 56, October 2009, No. 10, pp. 1)*
Ed: Candace Roulo. **Description:** Florida State University has one of 14 off-grid zero emissions buildings (OGZEB) in the U.S.; it was built to research sustainable and alternative energy systems. The building produces electricity from 30 photovoltaic panels and it also has three AET water heating solar panels on the roof. **Availability:** Print; Online.

5373 ■ *"Get Online Quick in the Office Or in the Field" in Contractor (Vol. 56, October 2009, No. 10, pp. 47)*
Ed: William Feldman, Patti Feldman. **Description:** Contractors can set up a web site in minutes using the www.1and1.com website. Verizon's Novatel MIFI 2372 HSPA personal hotspot device lets contractors go online in the field. The StarTech scalable business management system helps contractors manage daily operations. **Availability:** Print; Online.

5374 ■ *"Grainger Show Highlights Building Green, Economic Recovery" in Contractor (Vol. 57, February 2010, No. 2, pp. 3)*
Ed: Candace Roulo. **Description:** Chief U.S. economist told attendees of the Grainger's 2010 Total MRO Solutions National Customer Show that the economic recovery would be subdued. Mechanical contractors who attended the event also learned about building sustainable, green products, and technologies, and economic and business challenges. **Availability:** Print; Online.

5375 ■ *"Hansen Mechanical Performs Boiler Upgrade at Zoo"* in *Contractor (Vol. 57, February 2010, No. 2, pp. 7)*
Description: Hansen Mechanical installed a donated boiler in the Brookfield Zoo from Weil-McLain. The boilers were installed in the zoo's 'The Swamp' and 'The Living Coast' exhibits. **Availability:** Print; Online.

5376 ■ *"Housing Slide Picks Up Speed"* in *Crain's Chicago Business (Vol. 31, April 19, 2008, No. 16, pp. 2)*
Pub: Crain Communications Inc.
Contact: Barry Asin, President
Ed: Eddie Baeb. **Description:** According to Tracy Cross & Associates Inc., a real estate consultancy, sales of new homes in the Chicago area dropped 61 percent from the year-earlier period which is more bad news for homebuilders, contractors and real estate agents who are eager for an indication that market conditions are improving. **Availability:** Online.

5377 ■ *"How Much Do Electricians Make?"* in *Small Business Trends (March 8, 2023)*
URL(s): smallbiztrends.com/2023/03/how-much-do-electricians-make.html
Ed: Rob Starr. **Released:** March 08, 2023. **Description:** Discusses average pay for those in the electrician industry. Takes into consideration experience, union vs nonunion, and location. **Availability:** Online.

5378 ■ *"How to Start an Electrician Business"* in *Small Business Trends(March 1, 2023)*
URL(s): smallbiztrends.com/2023/03/how-to-start-an-electrician-business.html
Ed: Lisa Price. **Released:** March 01, 2023. **Description:** Discusses and gives tips on starting an Electrician business. **Availability:** Online.

5379 ■ *"The Latest on E-Verify"* in *Contractor (Vol. 56, September 2009, No. 9, pp. 58)*
Ed: Susan McGreevy. **Description:** United States government has required federal contractors to use its E-Verify program to verify the eligibility of incoming and existent employees. The use of the program is seen to eliminate Social Security mismatches. **Availability:** Print; Online.

5380 ■ *"Major Advances in Heat Pump Technology"* in *Contractor (Vol. 57, January 2010, No. 1, pp. 42)*
Ed: Mark Eatherton. **Description:** Tax credits make ground-source heat pump technology more economically feasible. Suggestions on how to choose the right ground-source heat pump technology to install in a house are discussed. **Availability:** Print; Online.

5381 ■ *"Major Advances in Heat Pump Technology - Part Two"* in *Contractor (Vol. 57, February 2010, No. 2, pp. 22)*
Ed: Mark Eatherton. **Description:** Chinese and Japanese companies have come up with refrigerant based heat pump products that are air based which will significantly lower the installed cost of heat pump based systems. Some of these newer models have variable speed, soft start compressors and have the ability to perform high-efficiency heat pump operation on a modulating basis. **Availability:** Print; Online.

5382 ■ *"Most Popular Tools? The Survey Says"* in *Contractor (Vol. 57, February 2010, No. 2, pp. 1)*
Ed: Robert P. Mader. **Description:** According to a survey of individuals in the field, mechanical contractors are purchasing more of their tools at home centers and they are also increasingly working in the service, repair, and retrofit markets. The survey also found that the reciprocating saw is the most used corded power tool. Additional purchasing habits of mechanical contractors are listed. **Availability:** Print; Online.

5383 ■ *"A Necessary Balancing Act: Bookkeeping"* in *Contractor (Vol. 56, November 2009, No. 11, pp. 22)*
Ed: Al Schwartz. **Description:** Pros and cons of getting a bookkeeper or a certified public accountant for the subcontractor are discussed. A bookkeeper can help a subcontractor get new accounting software up and running while an accountant will more than likely keep after the books at regular intervals throughout the year. **Availability:** Print; Online.

5384 ■ *"New 'Build California' Program Hopes to Grow Workforce"* in *Electrical Contractor (October, 2019)*
URL(s): www.ecmag.com/section/your-business/new-build-california-program-hopes-grow-workforce
Ed: Katie Kuehner-Hebert. **Released:** October 2019. **Description:** Build California, a new workforce development initiative, is recruiting in order to help fill up empty construction spots. A one-year high school pilot program is underway to promote trade organizations.

5385 ■ *"New Hydronic Heating Technologies Work"* in *Contractor (Vol. 57, January 2010, No. 1, pp. 58)*
Ed: Carol Fey. **Released:** January 01, 2010. **Description:** Technology behind hydronic heating systems is reviewed. These technologies include radiant and geothermal hydronic heating. System requirements for installing these greener forms of heating are discussed.

5386 ■ *"Selling a Job When There's Buyer's Remorse"* in *Contractor (Vol. 56, December 2009, No. 12, pp. 37)*
Ed: H. Kent Craig. **Description:** Advice on how contractors should manage low-profit jobs in the United States is presented. Efforts should be made to try and find at least one quality field foreman or superintendent. Contractors should also try to respectfully renegotiate the terms of the job. **Availability:** Online.

5387 ■ *"Sustainability Is Top Priority for GreenTown Chicago"* in *Contractor (Vol. 56, November 2009, No. 11, pp. 1)*
Ed: Candace Roulo. **Description:** GreenTown Chicago 2009 conference tackled energy-efficient practices and technologies, green design and building, and sustainable policies. Water conservation was also a topic at the conference and one mayor who made a presentation said that reducing the water loss in the system is a priority in the city's endeavor. **Availability:** Print; Online.

5388 ■ *"Synthetic Drywall Rots Mechanical Product"* in *Contractor (Vol. 56, December 2009, No. 12, pp. 50)*
Ed: Robert P. Mader. **Description:** Chinese-made synthetic drywalls have been found to corrode mechanical and electrical products in homes. Drywalls always contain a certain amount of sulfur. The hydrogen sulfide gas component of synthetic drywalls causes copper and silver sulfide corrosion. **Availability:** Print; Online.

5389 ■ *"Three Productivity Solutions"* in *Contractor (Vol. 57, February 2010, No. 2, pp. 26)*
Ed: William Feldman, Patti Feldman. **Description:** Singletouch is a real-time data capture solution for mechanical and other contractors that work in jobs that require materials and workload tracking. Contractors get information on extreme weather and sudden changes in the cost of materials. The OptimumHVAC optimization software by Optimum Energy is designed to optimize energy savings in commercial buildings. **Availability:** Print; Online.

5390 ■ *"Tracking Your Fleet Can Increase Bottom Line"* in *Contractor (Vol. 56, November 2009, No. 11, pp. 26)*
Ed: Candace Roulo. **Description:** GPS fleet management system can help boost a contractor's profits, employee productivity, and efficiency. These are available as a handheld device or a cell phone that employees carry around or as a piece of hardware installed in a vehicle. These lets managers track assets and communicate with employees about jobs. **Availability:** Online.

5391 ■ *"Trade Craft: Take Pride in Your Trade, Demand Excellence"* in *Contractor (Vol. 56, October 2009, No. 10, pp. 24)*
Ed: Al Schwartz. **Description:** There is a need for teaching, developing, and encouraging trade craft. An apprentice plumber is not only versed in the mechanical aspects of the trade but he also has a working knowledge of algebra, trigonometry, chemistry, and thermal dynamics. Contractors should be demanding on their personnel regarding their trade craft and should only keep and train the very best people they can hire. **Availability:** Print; Online.

5392 ■ *"Veteran-Owned Business 3E Services Gains Recognition in 2011 and Welcomes 2012 With New Offerings"* in *Marketwired (January 10, 2012)*
Pub: Comtex News Network Inc.
Contact: Kan Devnani, President
Description: 3E Services Inc. specializes in the selling, repairing, and remanufacturing of electrical components. It is a veteran-owned busiens located in Tucker, Georgia near Atlanta.The Washington Post recognized 3E as an exemplary veteran-owned business. David Loftin, president and founder, learned his skills as a US Navy nuclear electrician and attributes that training to his firm's growth and success. **Availability:** Print; Online.

5393 ■ *"Yudelson Challenges San Antonio Groups"* in *Contractor (Vol. 56, October 2009, No. 10, pp. 6)*
Description: Green building consultant and author Jerry Yudelson made a presentation for the Central Texas Green Building Council and Leadership San Antonio where he discussed the European approach to sustainability and how it can be used for designing green buildings. Yudelson also discussed how to use sustainable practices for planning 25 years into the future. **Availability:** Print; Online.

STATISTICAL SOURCES

5394 ■ *RMA Annual Statement Studies*
Pub: Risk Management Association
Contact: Nancy Foster, President
Released: Annual. **Description:** Contains composite balance sheets and income statements for more than 360 industries, including the accounting, auditing, and bookkeeping industries. Also contains five years of comparative historical data for discerning trends. Includes 16 commonly used ratios, computed for most of the size groupings for nearly every industry.

TRADE PERIODICALS

5395 ■ *Electrical Contractor*
Pub: National Electrical Contractors Association
Contact: Kirk Davis, President
URL(s): www.ecmag.com
Facebook: www.facebook.com/ElectricalContractorMagazine
Linkedin: www.linkedin.com/company/electricalcontractormagazine
X (Twitter): twitter.com/ECmagdotcom
Instagram: www.instagram.com/ecmagdotcom
YouTube: www.youtube.com/ecmagdotcom
Ed: Julie Mazur, Timothy Johnson. **Released:** Monthly **Description:** Electrical engineering. **Availability:** Print; Online.

5396 ■ *Electrical Wholesaling*
Contact: Bob MacArthur, Publisher
E-mail: bob_macarthur@intertec.com
URL(s): ewweb.com
Facebook: www.facebook.com/pg/elecwholesalingmag/about/?ref=page_internal
Linkedin: www.linkedin.com/groups/2187051/about
X (Twitter): twitter.com/ElecWholesaling
Ed: Doug Chandler. **Description:** Magazine focusing on electrical wholesaling for distributors of electrical supplies. **Availability:** Print; Online.

5397 ■ TED The Electrical Distributor Magazine: Official Publication of the National Association of Electrical Distributors (NAED)
Pub: National Association of Electrical Distributors
Contact: Tom Naber, President
E-mail: tnaber@naed.org
URL(s): tedmag.com

Ed: Misty Byers. **Released:** Semimonthly **Description:** Magazine for electrical distributors. **Availability:** Print; Online.

TRADE SHOWS AND CONVENTIONS

5398 ■ Electrical Safety Workshop
Frequency: Annual. **Description:** Electrical safety educational workshop. Works to advance development work practices. **Principal Exhibits:** Electrical safety educational workshop. Works to advance development work practices.

5399 ■ The NECA Show
National Electrical Contractors Association (NECA)
1201 Pennsylvania Ave. NW Ste. 1200
Washington, DC 20004
Ph: (202)991-6300
Fax: (202)217-4171
Co. E-mail: education@necanet.org
URL: http://www.necanet.org
Contact: Kirk Davis, President
URL(s): www.necaconvention.org/wp-content/uploads/2024/02/NECA2024-SanDiego-Overview24_WEB.pdf

Frequency: Annual. **Description:** Electrical products, publications, computers, software, tools, and equipment. **Audience:** Industry professionals. **Principal Exhibits:** Electrical products, publications, computers, software, tools, and equipment. Dates and Locations: Las Vegas, NV; Indianapolis, IN; 2025 Sep 12-14 Chicago, IL. **Telecommunication Services:** exhibitsales@necanet.org.

CONSULTANTS

5400 ■ Environmental & Engineering Services Inc. (EESI)
428 NW 5th St.
Corvallis, OR 97330
Ph: (541)754-1062
Co. E-mail: esinet5@peak.org
URL: http://www.eesinet.com
Contact: Peter Sanford, Manager
Linkedin: www.linkedin.com/company/environmental-and-engineering-services-inc-

Description: Firm provides design consulting services focused in the mechanical, plumbing and electrical disciplines and offers a wide range of HVAC, electrical and controls engineering services including feasibility assessments, master planning, budgeting, cost analysis, design, computer-aided drafting, and much more. **Founded:** 1979.

5401 ■ GHT Ltd.
1110 N Glebe Rd., Ste. 300
Arlington, VA 22201
Ph: (703)243-1200
Fax: (703)276-1376
Co. E-mail: info@ghtltd.com
URL: http://www.ghtltd.com
Contact: Patrick Kunze, President
Facebook: www.facebook.com/GHTLimited
Linkedin: www.linkedin.com/company/ght-limited

Description: Firm provides consulting on engineering design services such as telecommunications and security engineering service, life safety engineering service, utilities planning service and much more. **Scope:** Firm provides consulting on engineering design services such as telecommunications and security engineering service, life safety engineering service, utilities planning service and much more. **Founded:** 1965. **Publications:** "Critical spaces keep the pace of business humming," May, 2004; "To avoid staticlater, hire right telecom consultant," Oct, 2007. **Special Services:** LEED®.

FRANCHISES AND BUSINESS OPPORTUNITIES

5402 ■ Handyman Connection
Mamar Inc.
11115 Kenwood Rd.
Blue Ash, OH 45242
Facebook: www.facebook.com/HandymanConnectionCorporate
Linkedin: www.linkedin.com/company/handyman-connection
X (Twitter): x.com/handymancorp
Instagram: www.instagram.com/handymanconnection_homeoffice
YouTube: www.youtube.com/user/handymancorporate

Description: Small to medium home repairs and remodeling. **No. of Franchise Units:** 160. **No. of Company-Owned Units:** 1. **Founded:** 1990. **Franchised:** 1993. **Equity Capital Needed:** $90,000-$125,000. **Franchise Fee:** $25,000-$40,000. **Training:** 2 weeks at corporate training center and 1 week grand opening onsite.

5403 ■ Hangtown Electric, Inc. [Mr. Electric]
11423 Sunrise Gold Cir., Ste. 10
Rancho Cordova, CA 95742
Ph: (916)859-0500
URL: http://hangtownelectric.com/index.php
Contact: Terri Lee Smith, Chief Executive Officer
Description: Electrical work. **Founded:** 2004.

5404 ■ Mr. Electric-Canada
Neighborly
Regina, SK, Canada
Free: 800-490-7501
Fax: (877)496-2356
URL: http://www.neighborlybrands.com
Contact: Joel Worthington, President
Description: Provider of electrical services for business and homes. **Founded:** 1994. **Training:** Initial, onsite, intranet and ongoing support.

LIBRARIES

5405 ■ IEEE Information Center
445 Hoes Ln.
Piscataway, NJ 08854-4141
Ph: (732)981-0060
URL: http://www.ieee.org/publications_standards/publications/services/information_center.html

Scope: Electrical and electronic engineering; computer science. **Services:** Center open to IEEE members and staff. **Founded:** 1884. **Holdings:** Figures not available.

5406 ■ James Madison University - Carrier Library Special Collections
Burruss Hall, Rm. 256
MSC 4601 1251 Carrier Dr.
Harrisonburg, VA 22807
Ph: (540)568-6150
Co. E-mail: library-special@jmu.edu
URL: http://www.lib.jmu.edu/special
Facebook: www.facebook.com/JMUSpeColl
X (Twitter): x.com/JMUSpeColl
Instagram: www.instagram.com/jmuspecoll

Scope: Educational material; local history. **Services:** Limited copying; scanning; faxing; manuscript finding aids; library open to the public. **Founded:** 1982. **Holdings:** books; manuscript collections; photographs; Rare Book Collection; Maps; Atlases; Oral Histories.

RESEARCH CENTERS

5407 ■ Tennessee Technological University - College of Engineering - Research and Innovation - Center for Energy Systems Research (CESR)
1020 Stadium Dr., PRSC 231
Cookeville, TN 38505
Ph: (931)372-3615
Fax: (931)372-3875
Co. E-mail: smahajan@tntech.edu
URL: http://www.tntech.edu/engineering/research/cesr/index.php
Contact: Philip Oldham, President

Description: Integral unit of Research and Innovation, College of Engineering, Tennessee Technological University. Third party review of technical issues. **Scope:** Electric power, including electric power industry problems, generation, power systems performance improvement, fossil fuel utilization, advanced technologies, integrated software systems for simulating and analyzing power systems, online techniques for measuring coal and coal ash composition, electromagnetic transients capabilities, environmental issues and energy conservation. **Founded:** 1985. **Publications:** *CESR Annual report* (Annual).

Electrical Lighting Supply Store

ASSOCIATIONS AND OTHER ORGANIZATIONS

5408 ■ American Lighting Association (ALA)
2050 N Stemmons Fwy., Unit 100
Dallas, TX 75207-3206
Ph: (214)698-9898
Free: 800-605-4448
URL: http://alalighting.com
Contact: Richard Alan, Representative
Facebook: www.facebook.com/AmericanLigh
 tingAssociation
Instagram: www.instagram.com/ala.lighting
YouTube: www.youtube.com/user/AmericanLigh
 tingAssn
Description: Manufacturers, manufacturers' representatives, distributors, and retailers of residential lighting fixtures, portable lamps, component parts, accessories, and bulbs. Trains and certifies lighting consultants; conducts showroom sales seminars; disseminates marketing and merchandising information. Compiles statistics. **Founded:** 1945. **Publications:** *Lightrays* (Monthly); *American Lighting Association--Membership Directory and Buyers Guide* (Annual); *Light Up Your Kitchen and Bath*; *Lighting Your Life*. **Educational Activities:** ALA Conference (Annual). **Awards:** Lighting Hall of Fame (Periodic); ALA Pillars of the Industry Awards (Annual). **Geographic Preference:** National.

5409 ■ International Association of Lighting Designers (IALD)
242 N York St., Ste. 514
 Elmhurst, IL 60126
Ph: (312)527-3677
Fax: (312)527-3680
Co. E-mail: iald@iald.org
URL: http://www.iald.org
Contact: Kelly Ashmore, Director
E-mail: kelly@iald.org
Instagram: www.instagram.com/iald
YouTube: www.youtube.com/theiald
Description: Represents professionals, educators, students, and others working in the field of lighting design worldwide. Promotes the benefits of quality lighting design and emphasizes the impact of lighting on architectural design and environmental quality. Furthers professional standards of lighting designers and seeks to increase their function in the interior design industry. **Founded:** 1969. **Publications:** *Reflections* (Monthly); *Why Hire an IALD Lighting Designer*; *International Association of Lighting Designers--Membership Directory*. **Educational Activities:** LIGHTFAIR International (LFI) (Biennial). **Awards:** Thomas M. Lemons Scholarship (Annual); IALD Award (Annual); IALD International Lighting Design Awards (Annual). **Geographic Preference:** National.

5410 ■ National Association of Innovative Lighting Distributors (NAILD)
2885 Country Dr., Ste. 140
 Saint Paul, MN 55117
Ph: (651)336-1601
Co. E-mail: info@naild.org
URL: http://naild.org
Contact: Brian Huff, President
Facebook: www.facebook.com/NAILD.org
Linkedin: www.linkedin.com/company/naild
X (Twitter): x.com/NAILDdotORG
YouTube: www.youtube.com/channel/UCts38
 _wSCNiFn87AFnHENwg
Description: Distributors of specialized lighting products; vendor members are manufacturers and suppliers of lighting goods. Increases effectiveness and profitability through educational programs. Makes available information on the distribution of lighting products develop marketing techniques through an exchange of ideas. Develops methods of exchanging slow-moving inventory among members. Shares solutions to supply and distribution problems. Sponsors educational programs in the areas of accounting, finance, inventory control, general management, personnel training, and product cost analysis. **Founded:** 1977. **Geographic Preference:** National.

5411 ■ National Lighting Bureau (NLB)
1726-C General George Patton Dr.
 Brentwood, TN 37027
Ph: (615)379-7707
Co. E-mail: info@nlb.org
URL: http://nlb.org
Contact: Howard P. Lewis, Director
Facebook: www.facebook.com/National-Lighting-Bu
 reau-153665391335282
X (Twitter): x.com/lightingbureau
Description: Information source sponsored by trade associations, professional societies, manufacturers, utilities, and agencies of the federal government. Focuses on High-Benefit lighting (tm). Does not promote any specific form of lighting or brand name component. **Founded:** 1976. **Awards:** High-Benefit Lighting Awards Program (Annual). **Geographic Preference:** Multinational.

REFERENCE WORKS

5412 ■ "Cirrus Logic: Too Much Apple?" in Austin Business Journal (Vol. 32, April 6, 2012, No. 5, pp. A1)
Pub: American City Business Journals, Inc.
Contact: Mike Olivieri, Executive Vice President
Ed: Christopher Calnan. **Description:** Austin, Texas-based Cirrus Logic has been moving to reduce its growing dependence on supplying components for Apple Inc. products. Cirrus Logic has disclosed that it deveoped a controller designed to enable light dimmer switches for incandescent lights to work with light emitting diodes. Insights on Cirrus Logic's sale to Apple are also given. **Availability:** Online.

5413 ■ "Dominion Electric Supply Inks Lease at Ashburn Crossing Business Park" in Loudoun Times-Mirror (August 1, 2019)
URL(s): www.loudountimes.com/business/dominion
 -electric-supply-inks-lease-at-ashburn-crossing
 -business-park/article_489faf0c-b485-11e9-a37
 1-1f7354fed642.html
Released: August 01, 2019. **Description:** Dominion Electric Supply Company is moving into the Ashburn Crossing business park and bringing five full-time employees along. The company is a distributor of electrical supplies and lighting fixtures for commerical and residential use. **Availability:** Online.

5414 ■ "Goldfarb Lighting & Electric to Close Charleston Showroom" in Charleston Gazette-Mail (July 11, 2019)
URL(s): www.wvgazettemail.com/business/goldfarb
 -lighting-electric-to-close-charleston-showroom/ar
 ticle_90b6327f-1f58-57fc-bc40-df83c6627350.html
Ed: Rebecca Carballo. **Released:** July 11, 2019. **Description:** Goldfard Lighting & Electical is following the nation-wide trend of closing showrooms, but will still be around to offer residential and commercial wiring services and other lighting products. **Availability:** Online.

5415 ■ "'Stalking Horse' Bidder Keeping Plextronics Here" in Pittsburgh Business Times (Vol. 33, March 28, 2014, No. 37, pp. 6)
Pub: American City Business Journals, Inc.
Contact: Mike Olivieri, Executive Vice President
Released: March 28, 2014. **Price:** $4, Introductory 4-week offer(Digital & Print). **Description:** Chemical company Solvay American has acquired solar and lighting company Plextronics Inc. of Pittsburgh, Pennsylvania. Solvay's research and innovation department is seen as a better fit for Plextronics because it is developing a new technology. **Availability:** Print; Online.

5416 ■ "Store Front: Invest in Energy-Efficient Equipment for Your Pet Store" in Pet Product News (Vol. 66, September 2012, No. 9, pp. 43)
Ed: Leila Meyer. **Description:** Developments in energy-efficient lighting, heating, and air conditioning have allowed pet supplies stores to conduct upgrades that result in savings. Pet supplies stores have also been impressing customers by obtaining Energy Start or LEED certification. **Availability:** Print; Online.

TRADE PERIODICALS

5417 ■ LD+A
Pub: Illuminating Engineering Society of North
 America
Contact: Susanne Seitinger, President
URL(s): www.ies.org/lda-magazine
Ed: Paul Tarricone. **Released:** Monthly **Price:** $53, for Domestic, 1 year.; $99, for Domestic, 2 years.; $132, for domestic, 3 years.; $53, Nonmembers for per year; $5, Single issue; $32, Members; $132, for 3 years; $99, for 2 years. **Description:** Magazine presenting current lighting and energy news and applications. **Availability:** Print; PDF; Download; Online.

TRADE SHOWS AND CONVENTIONS

5418 ■ ALA Conference
American Lighting Association (ALA)
2050 N Stemmons Fwy., Unit 100
 Dallas, TX 75207-3206

Ph: (214)698-9898
Free: 800-605-4448
URL: http://alalighting.com
Contact: Richard Alan, Representative
URL(s): web.cvent.com/event/680fb872-d34d-492b-ad8b-3f9162af46ae/register
Frequency: Annual; held in September. **Audience:** Lighting and fan manufacturers, showrooms (retailers), manufacturers representatives, and designers. Dates and Locations: 2025 Sep 07-09 Louisville Marriott Downtown, Louisville, KY; 2026 Sep 27-29 Westin La Paloma, Tucson, AZ; 2027 Sep 12-14 Boston Park Plaza, Boston, MA.

5419 ■ International Association of Lighting Management Companies Conference
International Association of Lighting Management Companies (NALMCO)
1255 SW Prairie Trl., Pky.
Ankeny, IA 50023-7068
Ph: (515)243-2360
Co. E-mail: memberservice@nalmco.org
URL: http://www.nalmco.org
URL(s): nalmco.org/NALMCO/Annual_Convention.aspx
Frequency: Annual. **Description:** Professional lighting management techniques. **Audience:** Lighting management company owners, lighting maintenance service representatives, lighting and energy consultants, electrical contractors, energy service companies, specialty lighting distributors, utilities, other lighting-related associations and manufacturers. **Principal Exhibits:** Professional lighting management techniques.

5420 ■ LIGHTFAIR International (LFI)
AMC Inc.
240 Peachtree St. NW, Ste. 2200
Atlanta, GA 30303
Ph: (404)220-3000
Free: 800-285-6278
Co. E-mail: reghelp@americasmart.com
URL: http://www.americasmart.com
URL(s): lightfair.us.messefrankfurt.com/us/en.html
Facebook: www.facebook.com/Lightfair?ref=ts
Linkedin: www.linkedin.com/company/lightfair-international?trk=tyah
X (Twitter): twitter.com/lightfair
Frequency: Biennial. **Description:** Equipment, supplies, and services related to lighting design and the potential impact of lighting on architectural design and environmental quality. Manufacturers of architectural and commercial lighting and its vertical market product/services. **Audience:** Industry Professionals. **Principal Exhibits:** Equipment, supplies, and services related to lighting design and the potential impact of lighting on architectural design and environmental quality. Manufacturers of architectural and commercial lighting and its vertical market product/services. Dates and Locations: 2025 May 04-08 Las Vegas Convention Center, Las Vegas, NV. **Telecommunication Services:** samantha.nipper@usa.messefrankfurt.com.

FRANCHISES AND BUSINESS OPPORTUNITIES

5421 ■ Living Lighting
294 Walker Dr.
  Brampton, ON, Canada L6T 4Z2
Free: 866-463-4124
URL: http://livinglighting.com
Facebook: www.facebook.com/LivingLightingInc
Instagram: www.instagram.com/living_lighting_inc
Description: Operator of residential lighting store. **Founded:** 1968. **Training:** Yes.

5422 ■ Outdoor Lighting Perspectives Franchise Inc. (OLP)
Empower Brands
  Richmond, VA
Ph: (804)353-6999
URL: http://empowerfranchising.com
Contact: Scott Zide, President
Description: Firm provides outdoor lighting system services. **Founded:** 1995. **Equity Capital Needed:** 40000. **Franchise Fee:** $39,500 . **Training:** 5 days of training at corporate location and 3 days within ninety days of start-up in that city. Product & technical training at manufacturing plant shortly after start-up.

Electronic/Online Publishing

ASSOCIATIONS AND OTHER ORGANIZATIONS

5423 ■ Electronic Literature Organization (ELO)
14204 NE Salmon Creek Ave.
 Vancouver, WA 98686
Ph: (360)546-9101
Co. E-mail: info@eliterature.org
URL: http://eliterature.org
Contact: Caitlin Fisher, President
E-mail: caitlin@eliterature.org
X (Twitter): x.com/eliterature
Description: Strives to facilitate and promote the writing, publishing, and reading of literature in electronic media. **Founded:** 1999. **Publications:** *Acid-Free Bits: Recommendations for Long-Lasting Electronic Literature*; *Born-Again Bits: A Framework for Migrating Electronic Literature*; *Electronic Literature Directory*. **Geographic Preference:** National.

REFERENCE WORKS

5424 ■ "9 Strategies to BUILD and GROW Your Author Platform: A Step-by-Step Book Marketing Plan to Get More Exposure and Sales"
Released: May 04, 2016. **Description:** A nine-step formula for marketing self-published books is presented. The author has sold over 103,000 books using this method since 2008 and continues to grow her customer base through email and followers. **Availability:** Print.

5425 ■ "Boom and Bust in the Book Biz" in Canadian Business (Vol. 83, August 17, 2010, No. 13-14, pp. 16)
Pub: Rogers Media Inc.
Contact: Neil Spivak, Chief Executive Officer
Ed: Jordan Timm. **Description:** Electronic book marketplace is booming with Amazon.com's e-book sales for the Kindle e-reader exceeding the hardcover sales. Kobo Inc. has registered early success with its Kobo e-reader and has partnered with Hong Kong telecom giant on an e-book store. **Availability:** Print; Online.

5426 ■ Kindle Self-Publishing for Beginners: Step by Step Author's Guide to Writing, Publishing and Marketing Your Books on Amazon
Released: May 25, 2018. **Price:** $0, E-Book. **Description:** With the popularity of the Kindle and e-books, the trend to read on a digital device is growing. Included are tips to get your books published on Amazon and to start making money online. **Availability:** E-book.

5427 ■ Touching the Future: My Odyssey from Print to Online Publishing
Released: September 12, 2019. **Price:** $14.95, Paperback; $9.99, E-Book. **Description:** A personal account from the eyes of Roger Fidler about the digital conversion of print and the emergence of online news media. **Availability:** E-book; Print.

FRANCHISES AND BUSINESS OPPORTUNITIES

5428 ■ Jsb Enterprises
3106 Bay St.
 Unionville, MI 48767
Contact: Robert A. Williams, Contact
Description: Telecommunication products and services are offered. **No. of Franchise Units:** 160. **No. of Company-Owned Units:** 3. **Founded:** 1995. **Franchised:** 2001. **Equity Capital Needed:** $75,000 cash minimum. **Franchise Fee:** $30,000. **Training:** 4 weeks in Michigan and 5 days onsite.

Employee Leasing Service

REFERENCE WORKS

5429 ■ *"Employee vs. Independent Contractor: What Employers Need to Know" in Legal Zoom (March 24, 2023)*
URL(s): www.legalzoom.com/articles/employee-vs-independent-contractor-what-employers-need-to-know
Ed: Diane Faulkner. **Released:** March 24, 2023.
Description: Discusses the differences between hiring someone as an employee versus an independent contractor. A list of things to look for from the Department of Labor is given. **Availability:** Online.

STATISTICAL SOURCES

5430 ■ *Employment & Recruiting Agencies Industry in the US - Market Report*
URL(s): www.ibisworld.com/united-states/market-research-reports/employment-recruiting-agencies-industry/
Price: $925. **Description:** Downloadable report analyzing data about the current and future trends of the employment and recruiting industries. **Availability:** Download.

Employment Agency

ASSOCIATIONS AND OTHER ORGANIZATIONS

5431 ■ American Staffing Association (ASA)
277 S Washington St., Ste. 200
Alexandria, VA 22314
Ph: (703)253-2020
Fax: (703)253-2053
URL: http://americanstaffing.net
Contact: Richard Wahlquist, President
Facebook: www.facebook.com/AmericanS
taffingAssociation
Linkedin: www.linkedin.com/company/american-s
taffing-association
X (Twitter): x.com/StaffingTweets
Instagram: www.instagram.com/americans
taffingassociation
YouTube: www.youtube.com/user/ASAStaffingTube
Description: Promotes and represents the staffing industry through legal and legislative advocacy, public relations, education, and the establishment of high standards of ethical conduct. **Founded:** 1966. **Publications:** *Staffing Success* (Bimonthly); *Co-Employment: Employer Liability Issues in Third-Party Staffing Arrangements*; *ASA Member Directory*. **Educational Activities:** ASA Staffing World (Annual). **Awards:** ASA Care Award (Biennial); ASA Staffing VOICE Awards (Annual); ASA Chapter Merit Awards (Annual); ASA Leadership Hall of Fame Award (Annual); ASA National Staffing Employee of the Year (Annual). **Geographic Preference:** National.

5432 ■ Association of Executive Search and Leadership Consultants (AESC)
425 5th Ave., 4th Fl.
New York, NY 10016
Ph: (212)398-9556
Co. E-mail: aesc@aesc.org
URL: http://www.aesc.org
Contact: Karen Greenbaum, President
Facebook: www.facebook.com/AssociationExecu
tiveSearch
Linkedin: www.linkedin.com/company/50934
X (Twitter): x.com/TheAESC
Instagram: www.instagram.com/theaesc
YouTube: www.youtube.com/user/AESCExecu
tiveSearch
Description: Represents executive search consulting firms worldwide, establishes professional and ethical standards for its members, and serves to broaden public understanding of the executive search process. Specialized form of management consulting, conducted through an exclusive engagement with a client organization. **Founded:** 1959. **Publications:** *SearchWire* (Biweekly). **Educational Activities:** AESC European Conference (Annual). **Awards:** AESC Commitment to the Community Award (Annual); AESC Lifetime Achievement Award (Annual). **Geographic Preference:** Multinational.

5433 ■ Career Planning and Adult Development Network (CPADN)
1401 21ST St., Ste. R
Sacramento, CA 95811
Contact: Rich Feller, Chief Executive Officer
Description: Non-profit association of career practitioners who work with youth and adults in job or career transition. **Founded:** 1979. **Publications:** *Career Planning & Adult Development Network Newsletter* (Bimonthly). **Geographic Preference:** National.

5434 ■ International Association of Workforce Professionals (IAWP)
3267 Bee Caves Rd., Ste. 107-104
Austin, TX 78746
Ph: (502)223-4459
Co. E-mail: info@iawponline.org
URL: http://iawponline.org
Contact: Amber Drake, President
Facebook: www.facebook.com/International-Associa
tion-of-Workforce-Professionals-IAWP-782675548
504900
X (Twitter): x.com/iawpcenter
Instagram: www.instagram.com/
workforceprofessionals
Description: An educational association that provides opportunities to those working in the workforce development profession to develop and connect by educating its members on trends within the workforce system, providing information on new laws and rules that impact service delivery, and providing development opportunities to improve and enhance their skills. **Founded:** 1913. **Publications:** *IAPES News* (Bimonthly). **Educational Activities:** IAWP International Educational Conferences (Annual). **Awards:** IAWP Award of Merit - Individual Member (Annual); Freddy L. Jacobs Individual Scholarship. **Geographic Preference:** National.

5435 ■ Michigan Works Association (MWA)
2500 Kerry St., Ste. 210
Lansing, MI 48912
Ph: (517)371-1100
Co. E-mail: mwassociation@michiganworks.org
URL: http://www.michiganworks.org
Contact: Ryan Hundt, Chief Executive Officer
Facebook: www.facebook.com/MichiganWorks
X (Twitter): x.com/MichWorksAssn
YouTube: www.youtube.com/user/
MichiganWorksAssc
Description: Non-profit organization providing workforce development solutions. **Founded:** 1987. **Publications:** *MWA Directory* (Annual).

5436 ■ National Association of Colleges and Employers (NACE) - Library
62 Highland Ave.
Bethlehem, PA 18017
Ph: (610)868-1421
Co. E-mail: customerservice@naceweb.org
URL: http://www.naceweb.org
Contact: Marilyn Mackes, Executive Director
E-mail: mmackes@naceweb.org
Facebook: www.facebook.com/NACEOrg
Linkedin: www.linkedin.com/company/na
tionalassociationofcollegesandemployers
X (Twitter): x.com/naceorg
Instagram: www.instagram.com/NACEOrg
Pinterest: www.pinterest.com/naceorg
Description: Connects more than 5,200 college career services professionals at nearly 2,000 college and universities nationwide, and more than 3,000 HR/staffing professionals focused on college relations and recruiting. Forecasts trends in the job market; tracks legal issues in employment, the job search, and hiring practices; and provides college and employer professionals with benchmarks for their work. **Scope:** College; employment. **Founded:** 1956. **Holdings:** Figures not available. **Publications:** *CPC Career & Job Fair Finder*, *NACE Directory: Who's Who in Career Services and HR/Staffing* (Annual); *Directory: Who's Who in Career Services & HR/Staffing* (Annual); *NACE Journal* (Quarterly); *Job Choices*; *Job Choices for Business & Liberal Arts Students* (Annual); *Job Choices in Business and Liberal Arts Students* (Annual); *NACE--Salary Survey* (Semiannual). **Educational Activities:** NACE National Meeting (Annual). **Awards:** NACE Recruiting Excellence Award (Annual); NACE Diversity and Inclusion Excellence Award (Irregular); NACE Technology Excellence Award (Annual); NACE Innovation Excellence Awards (Annual); Kauffman Award (Annual); NACE Academy of Fellows (Annual); NACE/Chevron Award (Annual); NACE Career Services Excellence Awards (Irregular). **Geographic Preference:** National.

5437 ■ National Association of Personnel Services (NAPS)
800 Dailans Way
Uniontown, PA 15401
Free: 844-NAP-S360
URL: http://www.naps360.org
Contact: Trinette R. Cunningham, President
Facebook: www.facebook.com/NAPS360
Linkedin: www.linkedin.com/company/national
-association-of-personnel-services
X (Twitter): x.com/naps360
Description: Private employment and temporary service firms. Compiles statistics on professional agency growth and development; conducts certification program and educational programs. Association is distinct from former name of National Association of Personnel Consultants. **Founded:** 1961. **Publications:** *National Directory of Personnel Service Firms* (Annual); *Inside NAPS* (Monthly). **Geographic Preference:** National.

5438 ■ National Business and Disability Council (NBDC)
610 Beverly Rancocas Rd.
Willingboro, NJ 08046
URL: http://www.assistivetechnologycenter.org/
resource/national-business-and-disability-council
Description: Acts as a resource for employers seeking to integrate people with disabilities into the workplace and companies seeking to reach them in the consumer market. **Founded:** 1977. **Publications:** *NBDC News* (Quarterly). **Geographic Preference:** National.

Small Business Profiles   Employment Agency ■ 5454

REFERENCE WORKS

5439 ■ *The Career Guide--Dun's Employment Opportunities Directory*
Pub: Dun & Bradstreet Holdings, Inc.
Contact: Anthony Jabbour, Chief Executive Officer
URL(s): txst.locate.ebsco.com/instances/859e455e-ae29-550f-a0fc-31c159ed0a96?option=subject&query=Sales--Vocational%20guidance
Released: Periodic **Description:** Covers more than 10,000 companies on leading employers throughout the U.S. that provide career opportunities in sales, marketing, management, engineering, life and physical sciences, computer science, mathematics, statistics planning, accounting and finance, liberal arts fields, and other technical and professional areas; based on data supplied on questionnaires and through personal interviews. Also covers personnel consultants; includes some public sector employers (governments, schools, etc.) usually not found in similar lists. **Entries include:** Company name, location of headquarters and other offices or plants; entries may also include name, title, address, and phone of employment contact; disciplines or occupational groups hired; brief overview of company, discussion of types of positions that may be available, training and career development programs, benefits offered, internship and work-study programs. **Arrangement:** Employers are alphabetical; geographically by industry, employer branch offices geographically, disciplines hired geographically, employees offering work-study or internship programs and personnel consultants. **Indexes:** Geographical, SIC code. **Availability:** Print.

5440 ■ *"Meet the Golden 100 List's Youngest Firm: Kavaliro" in Orlando Business Journal (Vol. 29, September 21, 2012, No. 14, pp. 1)*
Pub: Baltimore Business Journal
Contact: Rhonda Pringle, President
E-mail: rpringle@bizjournals.com
Description: Technology and information technology staffing firm Kavaliro is the youngest company in the 2012 Golden 100 list of top privately held cmpanies in Central Florida ranked by the 'Orlando Business Journal'. Kavaliro provides 5-10 percent of the local staffing market and has 373 employees, with about 16 working in Central Florida. **Availability:** Print; Online.

5441 ■ *Occupational Outlook Handbook*
Pub: U.S. Department of Labor Bureau of Labor Statistics
Contact: Amrit Kohli, Director
E-mail: kohli.amrit@bls.gov
URL(s): www.bls.gov/ooh/home.htm
Description: Publication includes various occupational organizations that provide career information on hundreds of occupations. **Entries include:** For organizations--Organization name, address. Principal content of publication is profiles of various occupations, which include description of occupation, educational requirements, job outlook, and expected earnings. **Arrangement:** Organizations are classified by occupation. **Availability:** Print.

5442 ■ *"Overseas Overtures" in Business Journal-Portland (Vol. 24, October 26, 2007, No. 35, pp. 1)*
Pub: Portland Business Journal
Contact: Andy Giegerich, Managing Editor
E-mail: agiegerich@bizjournals.com
Ed: Robin J. Mood. **Description:** Oregon has a workforce shortage, specifically for the health care industry. Recruiting agencies, such as the International Recruiting Network Inc., answers the high demand for workforce by recruiting foreign employees. The difficulties recruiting companies experience with regards to foreign labor laws are investigated. **Availability:** Print; Online.

5443 ■ *"Q&A With Devin Ringling: Franchise's Services Go Beyond Elder Care" in Gazette (October 2, 2010)*
Pub: The Gazette
Contact: Vicki Cederholm, Director, Operations
E-mail: vicki.cederholm@gazette.com
Ed: Bill Radford. **Description:** Profile of franchise, Interim HealthCare, in Colorado Springs, Colorado; the company offers home care services that include wound care and specialized feedings to shopping and light housekeeping. It also runs a medical staffing company that provides nurses, therapists and other health care workers to hospitals, prisons, schools and other facilities. **Availability:** Online.

5444 ■ *"The Rise of the Supertemp: The Best Executive and Professional Jobs May No Longer Be Full-Time Gigs" in Harvard Business Review (Vol. 90, May 2012, No. 5, pp. 50)*
Pub: Harvard Business Review Press
Contact: Moderna V. Pfizer, Contact
Ed: Jody Grenstone Miller, Matt Miller. **Price:** $8.95, hardcopy and PDF. **Description:** Supertemps are independent contractors who perform mission-critical work on a project basis. Supertemps enjoy a high degree of flexibility and freedom, and offer companies new opportunities for innovation and growth. **Availability:** Print; Online; PDF.

5445 ■ *"Screening-Oriented Recruitment Messages: Antecedents and Relationships with Applicant Pool Quality" in Human Resource Management (Vol. 51, May- June 2012, No. 3, pp. 343-360)*
Pub: John Wiley & Sons, Inc.
Contact: Christina Van Tassell, Executive Vice President Chief Financial Officer
Ed: Brian R. Dineen, Ian O. Williamson. **Released:** May 25, 2012. **Description:** Factors associated with the use of screening-oriented messages for recruitment are investigated. Results indicate that labor supply perceptions, the reputation of recruiting firms and quality-based compensation incentives are associated with the use of screening-oriented messages, which are associated with the quality of the applicant pool. **Availability:** Print; PDF; Online.

5446 ■ *"Sign of the Times: Temp-To-Perm Attorneys" in HRMagazine (Vol. 54, January 2009, No. 1, pp. 24)*
Description: A growing number of law firms are hiring professional staff on a temp-to-perm basis according to the president of Professional Placement Services in Florida. Firms can save money while testing potential employees on a temporary basis. **Availability:** Print; Online.

5447 ■ *"Skill Seekers" in South Florida Business Journal (Vol. 34, February 7, 2014, No. 29, pp. 15)*
Pub: American City Business Journals, Inc.
Contact: Mike Olivieri, Executive Vice President
Description: Executives talk about the need for schools to help businesses find talent to hire. Robin Sandler of Charter School USA reveals that the organization's 'Leading Edge' program allows teachers to participate in leadership opportunities, while Mason Jackson of WorkForce One Employment Solutions believes that schools need to customize the curriculum in order to support internships. **Availability:** Print; Online.

5448 ■ *"Staffing Firms are Picking Up the Pieces, Seeing Signs of Life" in Milwaukee Business Journal (Vol. 27, February 5, 2010, No. 19)*
Pub: The Business Journal
Contact: Heather Ladage, President
E-mail: hladage@bizjournals.com
Ed: Rich Rovito. **Description:** Milwaukee, Wisconsin-based staffing firms are seeing signs of economic rebound as many businesses turned to temporary employees to fill the demands for goods and services. Economic observers believe the growth in temporary staffing is one of the early indicators of economic recovery. **Availability:** Print; Online.

5449 ■ *"The Temp Economy and the Future of Work" in U.S. News & World Report (August 10, 2018)*
URL(s): www.usnews.com/news/the-report/articles/2018-08-10/the-temp-economy-and-the-future-of-work
Ed: Gabrielle Levy. **Description:** Over the years, companies have shifted to using machines and computers and with that came a reduced work staff. Instead of full-time employees, many companies have opted to use independent contractors. Historian Louis Hyman explores the gig economy and if it is sustainable. **Availability:** Online.

STATISTICAL SOURCES

5450 ■ *RMA Annual Statement Studies*
Pub: Risk Management Association
Contact: Nancy Foster, President
Released: Annual. **Description:** Contains composite balance sheets and income statements for more than 360 industries, including the accounting, auditing, and bookkeeping industries. Also contains five years of comparative historical data for discerning trends. Includes 16 commonly used ratios, computed for most of the size groupings for nearly every industry.

TRADE PERIODICALS

5451 ■ *Journal of Employment Counseling (JEC)*
Pub: American Counseling Association
Contact: Dr. Kent S. Butler, President
URL(s): www.counseling.org/publications/counseling-journals/employment-counseling#onlinelibrary.wiley.com/journal/21611920
Ed: Rebecca Michel. **Released:** Quarterly **Price:** $245, Institutions for online only US, Canada, India; $275, Institutions for print and online US, Canada, India; $256, Institutions for print only US, Canada, India; $275, Institutions for print and online; C$275, Institutions for print and online; $245, Institutions for online only; C$245, Institutions for online only; $256, Institutions for print Only; C$256, Institutions for print Only. **Description:** Peer-reviewed journal focused on theory and practice in employment counseling, including professional experimentation and research, current client vocational problems, and professional concerns of counselors. Official journal of the National Employment Counseling Association (NECA), a division of the American Counseling Association. **Availability:** Print; PDF; Download; Online.

FRANCHISES AND BUSINESS OPPORTUNITIES

5452 ■ *10 Til 2- Part-Time Placement Service*
Aurora, CO 80014
Ph: (303)909-3868
URL: http://tentiltwo.com
Contact: Brian Strandes, President
E-mail: brian@10til2.com
Facebook: www.facebook.com/10til2
Linkedin: www.linkedin.com/company/10-til-2
Description: Part-time employment placement services. **Founded:** 2003. **Franchise Fee:** $35,000. **Training:** Provider of part time placement services.

5453 ■ *AHEAD Human Resources Inc.*
2209 Heather Ln.
Louisville, KY 40218
Free: 888-749-1000
Co. E-mail: ahr@aheadhr.com
URL: http://www.aheadhr.com
Contact: Kristi Hagan-Mullins, President
Facebook: www.facebook.com/AheadHumanResources
Instagram: www.instagram.com/aheadhumanresourceslouky
Description: Provider of human resources and staffing services. **Founded:** 1995. **Financial Assistance:** No **Training:** Yes.

5454 ■ *Careers USA, Inc.*
6501 Congress Ave., Ste. 200
Boca Raton, FL 33487
Ph: (561)995-7000
Free: 888-227-3377
URL: http://www.careersusa.com
Contact: Marilyn J. Ounjian, Founder

Facebook: www.facebook.com/CareersUSA
Linkedin: www.linkedin.com/company/careersusa
X (Twitter): x.com/CareersUSA
Description: Provider of staffing services including temporary, temp-to-hire and direct hire personnel. **Founded:** 1981. **Financial Assistance:** Yes **Training:** Yes.

5455 ■ Express Services, Inc.
Express Services, Inc.
9701 Boardwalk Blvd.
Oklahoma City, OK 73162
Ph: (405)840-5000
URL: http://www.expresspros.com
Facebook: www.facebook.com/ExpressEmploymentInternational
Linkedin: www.linkedin.com/company/expressemploymentinternational
X (Twitter): x.com/expresspros
Instagram: www.instagram.com/expressemploymentinternational
YouTube: www.youtube.com/user/expressep
Description: Firm provides staffing and recruitment services. **Founded:** 1983. **Financial Assistance:** Yes **Training:** 2 week initial training at headquarters, 1 week in certified training office and ongoing field training and support. Followed by additional time in new office with assigned field representative. **Educational Activities:** IFA Annual Convention (Annual).

5456 ■ Interim HomeStyle Services
1551 Sawgrass Corporate Pkwy., Ste. 230
Sunrise, FL 33323
Free: 800-338-7786
Co. E-mail: marketing@interimhealthcare.com
URL: http://www.interimhealthcare.com
Contact: Jennifer Sheets, President
Facebook: www.facebook.com/interimhealthcare
X (Twitter): x.com/interimhealth
Instagram: www.instagram.com/interimhealthcare
YouTube: www.youtube.com/interimhealthcare
Description: Firm provides nursing, therapy, non-medical home care, hospice and healthcare staffing services. **Founded:** 1966. **Training:** Yes.

5457 ■ Labor Finders International Inc. (LFI)
11426 N Jog Rd.
Palm Beach Gardens, FL 33418
Ph: (561)627-6507
Free: 800-864-7749
URL: http://www.laborfinders.com
Contact: Amit Pal Singh, President
Facebook: www.facebook.com/LaborFinders
Linkedin: www.linkedin.com/company/laborfinders
X (Twitter): x.com/LaborFinders
Instagram: www.instagram.com/laborfinders
YouTube: www.youtube.com/user/LaborFindersInt
Description: Firm provides industrial labor staffing services. **Founded:** 1975. **Training:** Sales, operation and owners training program software and help desk.

5458 ■ Management Recruiters International Inc. (MRI)
1735 Market St., Ste. 200
Philadelphia, PA 19103
Contact: Michael S. Castleman, President
Description: Firm provides a complete range of recruitment and human resource services. **Scope:** Offers counsel to management in recruitment of management executives, sales managers and sales and marketing personnel, other administrative personnel, interim executive placement and interim sales managers, sales and marketing personnel and outplacement services. **Publications:** "10 Questions the Boss Should Ask Every Employee"; "10 Tips for Conducting Productive Employee Reviews"; "Behavioral Interviewing"; "Building Motivation Levels"; "Can You Attract Top Talent Without Top Dollars"; "Conducting Effective Meetings"; "Do You Refuse to Hear No"; "Get Your Underperforming Employee to Quit Try Counseling Out"; "How to Get the Most Value from Your Recruiter"; "How to Spot Red Flags on a Resume"; "Intergenerational Miscommunication in the Workplace"; "Managers as Motivators: Understand the Guiding Principles"; "New Employee Retention"; "Terminate 10% of Your Employees Each Year"; "Thinking Well Outside the Box"; "Working the Second Shift in Corporate America. How Managers Can Help Employees Improve Work-Family Balance"; "Will Passive Job Seekers Apply to Your Job"; "Why Conduct Quarterly Employee Reviews"; "Top 4 Strategic Interview Styles"; "Top 10 Recruiting Myths - Busted"; "Top 10 Interview No No's"; "Tips for Successfully On boarding New Employees". **Special Services:** MRINetwork Way™.

5459 ■ PrideStaff
7535 N Palm Ave., Ste. 101
Fresno, CA 93711
Free: 800-774-3316
Fax: (559)432-4371
Co. E-mail: info@pridestaff.com
URL: http://www.pridestaff.com
Contact: Rob Hale, Chief Information Officer
Facebook: www.facebook.com/PrideStaff
Linkedin: www.linkedin.com/company/pridestaff
X (Twitter): x.com/PrideStaff
Instagram: www.instagram.com/pridestaff
YouTube: www.youtube.com/channel/UCjjuj-VBhlwYBDK6gSPU9cQ
Description: Recruiting Agency. **No. of Franchise Units:** 36. **No. of Company-Owned Units:** 3. **Founded:** 1978. **Franchised:** 1995. **Equity Capital Needed:** $162,000-$237,000. **Franchise Fee:** $32,000. **Training:** Yes.

5460 ■ Sanford Rose Associates International Inc. (SRA)
Akron, OH
URL: http://sanfordrose.com
Description: Firm offers executive search solutions, globally, through its franchise network, the company specializes in retained search for experienced executives, management, and individual contributors, it assists clients in filling their mission-critical positions, for candidates, IT firm offers resume and interview preparation, and on-boarding resources. **Founded:** 1959.

5461 ■ Snelling Staffing L.L.C.
HireQuest, Inc.
2360 Campbell Creek Blvd.
Richardson, TX 75082
Ph: (615)254-7444
Free: 800-835-6755
Co. E-mail: info@hirequestllc.com
URL: http://www.hirequest.com
Contact: Joe Quezada, Chief Financial Officer
Facebook: www.facebook.com/SnellingStaffingServices
X (Twitter): twitter.com/SnellingCorp
Description: Provider of workforce solutions. **Founded:** 1951. **Financial Assistance:** Yes

5462 ■ TRC Staffing Services Inc.
5909 Peachtree Dunwoody Rd. Bldg. D, 11th Fl.
Atlanta, GA 30328
Ph: (404)261-0012
URL: http://trctalent.com
Contact: C. Emmanuel, Contact
Linkedin: www.linkedin.com/company/trcstaffingservices
X (Twitter): x.com/TRC_Staffing
Instagram: www.instagram.com/trc_staffing
Pinterest: www.pinterest.com/trcstaffing
Description: Provides office support, clerical, word processing, data processing, marketing and light industrial personnel to businesses. **Scope:** Provider of staffing, contract labor, outsourcing, and other related services. **Founded:** 1980. **Training:** Yes. **Special Services:** TRC®.

5463 ■ White Glove Placement, Inc.
89 Bartlett St.
Brooklyn, NY 11206
Ph: (718)387-8181
Co. E-mail: recruit@whiteglovecare.net
URL: http://www.whiteglovecare.com
Facebook: www.facebook.com/WhiteGlovePlacement
Linkedin: www.linkedin.com/company/white-glove-placement-inc
X (Twitter): x.com/WGPlacement
Instagram: www.instagram.com/whiteglovenursing
Description: Staff hospitals, etc. w/nursing personnel. **No. of Company-Owned Units:** 1. **Founded:** 1995. **Franchised:** 2004. **Equity Capital Needed:** $89,000-$242,900. **Franchise Fee:** $25,000. **Training:** Yes.

COMPUTERIZED DATABASES

5464 ■ Oregon Career Information System
Oregon Career Information System
328 E Broadway
Eugene, OR 97401
Ph: (541)346-3872
Free: 800-495-1266
Fax: (541)346-3823
Co. E-mail: cisservice@uoregon.edu
URL: http://oregoncis.uoregon.edu/Portal.aspx
Contact: Tom Goodhue, Executive Director
E-mail: tgoodhue@obcweb.org
URL(s): oregoncis.uoregon.edu/portal/org/AboutUs.aspx
Price: $19.95, for print three months. **Availability:** Print. **Type:** Directory.

LIBRARIES

5465 ■ Muskegon Community College (MCC) - Hendrik Meijer Library Special Collections
221 S Quarterline Rd.
Muskegon, MI 49442
Co. E-mail: library@muskegoncc.edu
URL: http://www.muskegoncc.edu/library/collections/special-collections
Scope: Educational materials. **Services:** Interlibrary loan; copying; wireless Internet access; library open to the public. **Founded:** 1926. **Holdings:** 54,000 books; 600 bound periodical volumes; 2,000 archives; 20,000 microfiche; 2,000 microfilms.

RESEARCH CENTERS

5466 ■ W.E. Upjohn Institute for Employment Research - Library
300 S Westnedge Ave.
Kalamazoo, MI 49007-4686
Ph: (269)343-5541
Fax: (269)343-3308
Co. E-mail: communications@upjohn.org
URL: http://www.upjohn.org
Contact: Brad J. Hershbein, Director, Research
E-mail: hershbein@upjohn.org
Facebook: www.facebook.com/Upjohn.Institute
Linkedin: www.linkedin.com/company/w.e.-upjohn-institute-for-employment-research
X (Twitter): x.com/UpjohnInstitute
YouTube: www.youtube.com/channel/UCs816XgzMdyFP8O-3Z34ecQ
Description: Focuses its research on the causes and consequences of unemployment. Conducts research on social insurance and income maintenance programs, earnings and benefits, economic development and local labor markets, work arrangements, education and training issues for the workplace, and other methods of alleviating problems related to unemployment. Administers federal and state-funded employment programs and services in a two-county area. Compiles statistics. Maintains job-

training program for the disadvantaged in on-the-job training by contract with Kalamazoo County, MI. Operates publishing program. Research fields include unemployment, unemployment insurance, worker's compensation, labor productivity, profit sharing, the labor market, economic development, earnings, training, and other areas related to employment. **Scope:** Causes and effects of unemployment, including studies on social insurance and income maintenance programs, earnings and benefits, economic development and local labor issues, work arrangements, education and training issues for the workplace, and other methods of alleviating problems related to unemployment. **Founded:** 1945. **Holdings:** Figures not available. **Publications:** *Business Outlook for West Michigan* (Quarterly); *Employment Research Newsletter* (Quarterly). **Educational Activities:** W.E. Upjohn Institute for Employment Research Conference (Annual). **Awards:** Upjohn Institute Dissertation Award (Annual); W.E. Upjohn Institute for Employment Research Grants (Annual); AP-LS Dissertation Award (Annual); Upjohn Institute Early Career Research Awards (ECRA) (Annual). **Geographic Preference:** National.

Engraving/Monogramming Service

REFERENCE WORKS

5467 ■ *"Business Guide and Employment Role"*
Pub: AuthorHouse Inc.
Contact: William Elliott, President
Released: July 10, 2014. **Price:** $4.99, e-book; $15.18, softcover. **Description:** Financial expert discusses the importance of economic and business and their role in employment. The business and finance manager is crucial to any small business. The guide is an essential tool for any entrepreneur, the investor in business enterprise, the individual businessman, the human resources manager, and the business and finance professional to learn the merits to do business and play a role in employment. **Availability:** E-book; Print.

5468 ■ *"The Leadership Equation: 10 Practices That Build Trust, Spark Innovation, and Create High-Performing Organizations"*
Pub: Greenleaf Book Group Press
Contact: Tanya Hall, Chief Executive Officer
Released: September 30, 2014. **Price:** $18.95, U.S., paperback. **Description:** Entrepreneur and business consultant draws upon his work with corporations, government agencies, and nonprofit organizations and their human resource departments to explain the workings of high-performing organizations with his equation: Trust + Spark = Leadership Culture. He describes the ten more important practices for building trust and spark that improves team performance, the business unit, and the entire organization. **Availability:** Print.

5469 ■ *"Monogram Shoppe Found a True Window-Shopping Alternative to Keep Business Going During COVID-19" in Greater Fort Worth Business Weekly (June 30, 2021)*
URL(s): www.fwbusiness.com/fwbusiness/article_ec6c8712-d2d3-57cf-816d-c6fa01e48474.html
Ed: Cindy Larson. **Released:** June 30, 2021. **Description:** The COVID-19 pandemic shut down a lot of small businesses, but some owners were able to use innovative ideas to keep their doors open. The owner of The Monogram Shoppe implemented several new strategies to keep the business running. **Availability:** Online.

5470 ■ *"The Name Game: How Monograms and Personalization Have Become Key Retail Trends" in Shopify (February 1, 2018)*
URL(s): www.shopify.com/retail/the-name-game-how-monogramming-and-personalization-have-become-key-retail-trends
Ed: Karin Eldor. **Released:** February 01, 2018. **Description:** Examines the impact monogram designs can have for retailers who use them. They add some personalization and a sense of gravitas to an item or a brand. **Availability:** Online.

STATISTICAL SOURCES

5471 ■ *Trophy & Engraving Shops Industry in the US - Market Research Report*
URL(s): www.ibisworld.com/united-states/market-research-reports/trophy-engraving-shops-industry/
Price: $925. **Description:** Downloadable report analyzing the current and future trends in the trophy and engraving shop industry. **Availability:** Download.

TRADE PERIODICALS

5472 ■ *Insights*
Pub: Awards and Personalization Association
Contact: Lisa Higginbotham, President
E-mail: lisah@fivestarawards.net
URL(s): personalizationpros.org/InsightsMagazine.aspx
Released: Bimonthly **Description:** Magazine publishing helpful how-to articles, business expertise, technical advice and inspiring success stories. **Availability:** Print; Online.

FRANCHISES AND BUSINESS OPPORTUNITIES

5473 ■ **Crown Trophy Inc.**
9 Skyline Dr.
Hawthorne, NY 10532
URL: http://www.crowntrophy.com
Contact: Charles Weisenfeld, Chief Executive Officer
Description: Offers a complete line of trophies and awards. **Founded:** 1978. **Financial Assistance:** Yes **Training:** Yes.

5474 ■ **Recognition Express**
6290 Harrison Dr., Ste. 7
Las Vegas, NV 89120-4040
Ph: (702)798-0800
Free: 800-457-7030
Fax: (702)798-5054
Co. E-mail: info@recognitionexpress.com
URL: http://www.recognitionexpress.com/realIndex.html?version=13
Contact: Jeff Tino, President
URL(s): www.recognitionexpresslv.com
Facebook: www.facebook.com/RecognitionExpress
X (Twitter): twitter.com/Recognition_Exp
Description: Manufacturer of name badges, lanyards, desk plates, signs, plaques, awards and promotional products for corporations and organizations. **Founded:** 1972. **Training:** Provides 5 days training at headquarters, 2 days at franchisee's location and ongoing support.

Environmental Consultant

START-UP INFORMATION

5475 ■ *How to Start a Home-Based Consulting Business: Define Your Specialty Build a Client Base Make Yourself Indispensable*
Ed: Bert Holtje. **Released:** January 06, 2010. **Price:** Paperback. **Description:** Everything needed for starting and running a successful consulting business from home. **Availability:** Print.

5476 ■ *"Sustainable Advantage" in Inc. (Vol. 36, September 2014, No. 7, pp. 86)*
Pub: Mansueto Ventures L.L.C.
Contact: Stephanie Mehta, Chief Executive Officer
Price: $8.95, hardcopy black and white. **Description:** Four startup companies committed to providing sustainable, eco-friendly products and services while protecting the environment and bettering human health are profiled. Holganix(TM) offers organic lawn care products; Motiv Power Systems electrifies large vehicles; Clean Energy Collective Solar Power builds lareg community solar panel arrays; and Protein Bar offers healthy alternatives to fast food in its chain of restaurants. The company also works with nonprofits focused on wellness and education and has created 167 Learning Gardens nationwide. **Availability:** Print; PDF; Online.

ASSOCIATIONS AND OTHER ORGANIZATIONS

5477 ■ **Canadian Environmental Law Association (CELA) - Resource Library for the Environment and the Law**
55 University Ave., Ste. 1500
Toronto, ON, Canada M5J 2H7
Ph: (416)960-2284
Free: 844-755-1420
Fax: (416)960-9392
Co. E-mail: info@cela.ca
URL: http://cela.ca
Contact: Renee Griffin, President
Facebook: www.facebook.com/CanadianEnvironmentalLawAssociation
Linkedin: www.linkedin.com/company/canadian-environmental-law-association-cela
X (Twitter): x.com/CanEnvLawAssn
Instagram: www.instagram.com/canadianenvironmentallawassoc
YouTube: www.youtube.com/channel/UCrPXm0JvYLLL0fJYsooHyJA
Description: Protects and enhances public health and environmental quality throughout Canada. Advocates for comprehensive laws, standards and policies. Seeks to increase public participation in environmental decision-making. **Scope:** Environmental law and policy. **Services:** Open to the public. **Founded:** 1970. **Holdings:** 7,000 essential publications; comprises books; periodicals; reports. **Publications:** *Intervenor* (Quarterly). **Geographic Preference:** National.

5478 ■ **Canadian Environmental Network [Reseau canadien de l'environment (RCEN)]**
136F Billings Ave.
Ottawa, ON, Canada K1H 5K9
Co. E-mail: info@rcen.ca
URL: http://www.rcen.ca/en/home
Contact: Jade Scognamillo, Executive Director
Facebook: www.facebook.com/CanadianEnvironmentalNetwork
Linkedin: www.linkedin.com/company/canadian-environmental-network-rcen-
X (Twitter): x.com/rcen
Instagram: www.instagram.com/canadianenvironmentalnetwork
Description: Environmental organizations. Seeks to advance the projects and activities of members. Promotes ecologically sustainable development. Serves as a clearinghouse on environmental issues; provides support and assistance to members. **Founded:** 1977. **Publications:** *Canadian Environmental Network News.* **Geographic Preference:** Multinational.

5479 ■ **Canadian Network of Toxicology Centres (CNTC) - Library [Réseau Canadien des Centres de Toxicologie]**
University of Guelph
50 Stone Rd. E
Guelph, ON, Canada N1G 2W1
URL: http://www.uoguelph.ca/toxicology/history_tox_program.html
Description: Seeks to improve human and environmental health through increased understanding of toxic substances and their impact on the environment. **Scope:** Aims to train students in ever-developing fields of toxicology such as risk assessment for health and environmental risk, molecular toxicology, ecotoxicology, nutritional toxicology, biomedical toxicology, analytical toxicology and nanotoxicology. **Founded:** 1982. **Holdings:** Figures not available. **Publications:** *Metals in the Human Environment News*; *MITHE-RN News*; *Toxicology Educators Resource Guide for Secondary School Audiences.* **Geographic Preference:** National.

5480 ■ *Canadian Wilderness*
600-100 Gloucester St.
Ottawa, ON, Canada K2P 0A4
Ph: (613)569-7226
Free: 800-333-9453
Fax: (613)569-7098
Co. E-mail: info@cpaws.org
URL: http://cpaws.org
Contact: Laura Colella, President
URL(s): cpaws.org/media-centre/ourmagazine
Released: Semiannual; (Spring, Fall). **Description:** Magazine delivering wilderness conservation news and views. **Availability:** Print; Online; PDF.

5481 ■ **Earth Day Canada (EDC)**
5818, boulevard Saint-Laurent
Montreal, QC, Canada H2T 1T3
Ph: (514)728-0116
Free: 800-424-8758
Fax: (514)303-0248
Co. E-mail: hello@earthday.ca
URL: http://www.earthday.ca
Contact: Pierre Lussier, President
Facebook: www.facebook.com/EarthDayCanada
Linkedin: www.linkedin.com/company/projets-sain t-laurent-jour-de-la-terre-qu-bec
X (Twitter): x.com/EarthDayCanada
Instagram: www.instagram.com/earthday.ca
Description: Individuals and organizations. Promotes respect for the environment. Seeks to raise public awareness of environmental protection and conservation issues. Conducts educational and charitable programs; makes available children's services. **Founded:** 1970. **Publications:** *Earth Tones* (Quarterly). **Awards:** EDC Youth Hometown Heroes Award (Annual). **Geographic Preference:** National.

5482 ■ **EarthSave Canada - Library**
422 Richards St., Ste. 170
Vancouver, BC, Canada V6B 2Z4
Ph: (604)731-5885
Co. E-mail: office@earthsave.ca
URL: http://www.earthsave.ca
Contact: Dr. David Steele, President
Facebook: www.facebook.com/earthsavecanada
X (Twitter): x.com/earthsavecanada
Instagram: www.instagram.com/earthsavecanada
YouTube: www.youtube.com/user/earthsavecanada
Description: Seeks to increase the awareness of the health, ethical, and environmental impacts of food choices. Promotes transition to a plant-based diet for optimum health, environmental sustainability, and compassion. **Scope:** Charity. **Founded:** 1989. **Holdings:** Figures not available. **Publications:** *Canada EarthSaver* (Quarterly); *Earthsave Canada--Veg Directory.* **Geographic Preference:** National.

5483 ■ **Ecojustice Canada**
Ste. 390, 425 Carrall St.
Vancouver, BC, Canada V6B 6E3
Ph: (604)685-5618
Free: 800-926-7744
Fax: (604)685-7813
Co. E-mail: communications@ecojustice.ca
URL: http://ecojustice.ca
Contact: Lori Williams, President
Facebook: www.facebook.com/ecojustice
Linkedin: www.linkedin.com/company/ecojustice-canada
X (Twitter): x.com/ecojustice_ca
Instagram: www.instagram.com/ecojustice_ca
Description: Represents attorneys and others with an interest in conservation and environmental law. Provides free legal advice and representation to organizations and individuals seeking judgments in cases involving environmental protection. **Founded:** 1990. **Geographic Preference:** National.

5484 ■ **Ecology Action Centre (EAC) - Library [Centre d'Action Écologique]**
2705 Fern Ln.
Halifax, NS, Canada B3K 4L3
Ph: (902)429-2202

Fax: (902)405-3716
Co. E-mail: info@ecologyaction.ca
URL: http://www.ecologyaction.ca
Facebook: www.facebook.com/EcologyActionCentre
Linkedin: www.linkedin.com/company/ecology-action-centre
X (Twitter): x.com/ecologyaction
Description: Works to develop solutions to ecological problems. Fosters communication between members. **Scope:** Environmental issues, including acid rain, deforestation, hazardous wastes, recycling, nuclear power, ecosystem stability, species extinction, global warming, pesticides, and waste management. **Founded:** 1971. **Holdings:** Figures not available. **Publications:** *Between the Issues Newsletter* (3/year). **Geographic Preference:** Multinational.

5485 ■ *Enviro Business Guide*
PO Box 23
Bluffton, AB, Canada T0C 0M0
Ph: (403)843-6563
Co. E-mail: info@recycle.ab.ca
URL: http://recycle.ab.ca
Contact: Don Hughes, President
E-mail: don.hughes@hughesenvironmentalservices.net
URL(s): recycle.ab.ca/enviro-businesses
Availability: Print.

5486 ■ Environmental Business Council of New England (EBCNE)
117 Kendrick St., Ste. 300
Needham, MA 02494
Ph: (617)505-1818
Co. E-mail: ebc@ebcne.org
URL: http://ebcne.org
Contact: Ann Gisinger, President
E-mail: agisinger@ebcne.org
Linkedin: www.linkedin.com/company/environmental-business-council-of-new-england-inc-
X (Twitter): x.com/ebcne
YouTube: www.youtube.com/channel/UCLKLI6DmcaFbOwjJ2aB956g
Description: Fosters the development of an effective and competitive envirotech industry for the purpose of enhancing and maintaining a clean and productive environment. **Founded:** 1990. **Awards:** The Paul G. Keough Environmental-Energy Award for Government Service (Annual). **Geographic Preference:** National.

5487 ■ Environmental Defence
33 Cecil St 1st Fl.
Toronto, ON, Canada M5T 1N1
Ph: (416)323-9521
Free: 877-399-2333
Fax: (416)323-9301
Co. E-mail: info@environmentaldefence.ca
URL: http://environmentaldefence.ca
Contact: Fatima Crerar, President
Facebook: www.facebook.com/EnvironmentalDefenceCanada
Linkedin: www.linkedin.com/company/enviro-defence
X (Twitter): x.com/envirodefence
Instagram: www.instagram.com/envirodefence
YouTube: www.youtube.com/user/environmentaldefence
Description: Provides Canadians with the tools and knowledge needed to protect and improve the environment and health; committed to engaging the public, finding solutions, and protecting the environmental rights of future generations. **Founded:** 1984. **Publications:** *Eco News*. **Geographic Preference:** National.

5488 ■ ENvironnement JEUnesse (ENJEU)
3000, Omer Lavallee St., Ste.122
Montreal, QC, Canada H1Y 3R8
Ph: (514)252-3016
Free: 866-377-3016
Co. E-mail: infoenjeu@enjeu.qc.ca
URL: http://enjeu.qc.ca/en/a-propos
Contact: Erika Salem, President
Facebook: www.facebook.com/environnement.jeunesse
X (Twitter): x.com/ENJEUquebec
Description: Youth and adult leaders. Promotes development in youth of a worldview conducive to sustainable use of natural resources. Conducts educational and social programs to raise awareness among youth of environmental consequences of lifestyle choices. **Founded:** 1979. **Publications:** *L'Enjeu*. **Geographic Preference:** National.

5489 ■ Harmony Foundation [Harmony]
1594 Fairfield Rd., Unit 15
Victoria, BC, Canada V8S 1G1
Ph: (250)380-3001
Fax: (250)380-0887
Co. E-mail: harmony@islandnet.com
URL: http://harmonyfdn.ca
Contact: Jean-Pierre Soublière, President
Facebook: www.facebook.com/HarmonyFoundationCanada
X (Twitter): x.com/HarmonyFDN
YouTube: www.youtube.com/channel/UC2rn8tl3qiiLgyh6zsfn5cw
Description: Seeks to ensure the availability of environmental education resources and skills in schools, workplaces, and the community. Works with educators and community leaders to improve environmental programs. **Founded:** 1985. **Geographic Preference:** Multinational.

5490 ■ *Les Naturalistes*
Jardin botanique de Montreal
4101 Rue Sherbrooke Est, Bureau 262
Montreal, QC, Canada H1X 2B2
Ph: (514)252-3023
Fax: (514)254-8744
Co. E-mail: info@jeunesnaturalistes.org
Contact: Andre St-Arnaud, President
Released: Quarterly **Price:** C$25. **Availability:** Print.

5491 ■ Municipal Waste Association (MWA)
10C Shared Space, 42 Carden St.
Guelph, ON, Canada N1H 3A2
Ph: (519)837-6863
Co. E-mail: mwa@municipalwaste.ca
URL: http://municipalwaste.ca
Contact: David Douglas, Chairman
Description: Promotes more effective and environmentally sustainable removal of solid wastes. Facilitates sharing of municipal waste management, reduction, recycling, and reuse information and facilities. **Founded:** 1987. **Publications:** *For R Information* (Quarterly). **Awards:** MWA Promotion and Education Campaign Award (Annual). **Geographic Preference:** National.

5492 ■ Natural Products Marketing Council (NPMC)
c/o NS Department of Agriculture
Edward F. Lorraine Bldg., 74 Research Dr.
Bible Hill, NS, Canada B6L 2R2
URL: http://novascotia.ca/agri/about-us/agencies-boards-and-commissions/natural-products-marketing
Contact: Danielle Dorn Kouwenberg, Director (Acting)
E-mail: danielle.dornkouwenberg@novascotia.ca
Description: Producers and processors of natural food products and wool. Promotes growth and development of the natural products industries. Supervises natural product marketing boards. **Founded:** 1946. **Geographic Preference:** National.

5493 ■ *On Nature*
214 King St. W, Ste. 612
Toronto, ON, Canada M5H 3S6
Ph: (416)444-8419
Free: 800-440-2366
Co. E-mail: info@ontarionature.org
URL: http://www.ontarionature.org
Contact: Caroline Schultz, Executive Director
URL(s): onnaturemagazine.comontarionature.org/about/on-nature-magazine
Ed: John Hassell. **Released:** Quarterly **Price:** $9.95, Single issue; $50, for annual. **Description:** Features in-depth articles and includes up-to-date news into environmental issues. **Availability:** Print; PDF; Download; Online.

5494 ■ Ontario Nature
214 King St. W, Ste. 612
Toronto, ON, Canada M5H 3S6
Ph: (416)444-8419
Free: 800-440-2366
Co. E-mail: info@ontarionature.org
URL: http://www.ontarionature.org
Contact: Caroline Schultz, Executive Director
Facebook: www.facebook.com/OntarioNature
X (Twitter): x.com/ontarionature
Instagram: www.instagram.com/ontarionature
YouTube: www.youtube.com/user/ONNature
Description: Works to protect Ontario's nature through research, education and conservation action. Champions woodlands, wetlands and wildlife, and preserves essential habitat through a system of nature reserves. **Publications:** *On Nature* (Quarterly); *ON Nature: Ontario's Nature and Environment Magazine* (Quarterly). **Educational Activities:** Ontario Nature Conference. **Awards:** Lee Symmes Municipal Award (Annual); Ontario Nature Achievement Award (Annual); Ontario Nature Corporate Award (Annual); Richards Education Award (Annual); W. E. Saunders Natural History Award (Annual); J. R. Dymond Public Service Award (Annual); W. W. H. Gunn Conservation Award (Annual); Carl Nunn Media and Conservation Award (Annual). **Geographic Preference:** State.

5495 ■ Pembina Institute
No. 802, 322 - 11 Ave., SW
Calgary, AB, Canada T2R 0C5
Ph: (403)269-3344
Fax: (587)606-6423
Co. E-mail: news@pembina.org
URL: http://www.pembina.org
Contact: Chris Severson-Baker, Executive Director
E-mail: executivedirector@pembina.org
Facebook: www.facebook.com/pembina.institute
Linkedin: www.linkedin.com/company/pembina-institute
X (Twitter): x.com/pembina
YouTube: www.youtube.com/user/PembinaInstitute
Description: Promotes increased public awareness of environmental and development issues. **Scope:** Provide research, analysis and recommendations to inform policies and practices related to energy. **Founded:** 1986. **Publications:** *Pembina Institute Annual report* (Annual); *Electronic newsletter* (Monthly). **Geographic Preference:** Multinational.

5496 ■ Pitch-In Canada (PIC)
1-964 Shoppers Row
Campbell River, BC, Canada V9W 2C5
Ph: (250)914-3202
Co. E-mail: pitch-in@pitch-in.ca
Facebook: www.facebook.com/pitchincanada
Description: Promotes reduction of packaging and other refuse discarded in public and wild places. Conducts educational and public relations programs to discourage littering and stimulate community-based clean-up campaigns, including annual Pitch-In Week. Makes available resources and other support and assistance to local antilittering and clean-up projects. **Founded:** 1967. **Awards:** Clean World Award (Annual). **Geographic Preference:** National.

5497 ■ Pollution Probe (PP)
130 Queens Quay E Ste. 902 W Twr.
Toronto, ON, Canada M5A 0P6
Ph: (416)926-1907
Free: 877-926-1907
Co. E-mail: pprobe@pollutionprobe.org
URL: http://www.pollutionprobe.org
Contact: Christopher Hilkene, Chief Executive Officer
E-mail: chilkene@pollutionprobe.org
Facebook: www.facebook.com/PollutionProbe
Linkedin: www.linkedin.com/company/pollution-probe
X (Twitter): x.com/pollutionprobe
Instagram: www.instagram.com/pollutionprobe
YouTube: www.youtube.com/PollutionProbe
Description: Works to define environmental problems through research; seeks to raise public awareness of environmental issues through education; lobbies for environmental protection and remediation before government agencies and industrial associa-

tions. Focuses on smog and climate change, reduction and elimination of mercury in water, child health and the environment, indoor air quality, and water quality. **Scope:** Environmental problems. **Founded:** 1969. **Publications:** *Pollution Probe Reports; Probe-Abilities* (Quarterly); *Probe Post: Canada's Environmental Magazine* (Quarterly); *P2 - Exclusive Donor Newsletter* (Quarterly). **Geographic Preference:** National.

5498 ■ Probe International
225 Brunswick Ave.
Toronto, ON, Canada M5S 2M6
URL: http://journal.probeinternational.org
Contact: Patricia Adams, President
X (Twitter): x.com/ProbeIntl
Description: Seeks to ensure that Canadian foreign aid and trade programs make a positive environmental, social, and economic impact abroad. **Founded:** 1980. **Publications:** *Probe Alert* (Annual). **Geographic Preference:** National.

5499 ■ *RCA Connector*
PO Box 23
Bluffton, AB, Canada T0C 0M0
Ph: (403)843-6563
Co. E-mail: info@recycle.ab.ca
URL: http://recycle.ab.ca
Contact: Don Hughes, President
E-mail: don.hughes@hughesenvironmentalservices.net
URL(s): recycle.ab.ca/newsyear/2024
Released: Monthly **Availability:** Print; Online.

5500 ■ Recycling Council of Alberta (RCA)
PO Box 23
Bluffton, AB, Canada T0C 0M0
Ph: (403)843-6563
Co. E-mail: info@recycle.ab.ca
URL: http://recycle.ab.ca
Contact: Don Hughes, President
E-mail: don.hughes@hughesenvironmentalservices.net
Facebook: www.facebook.com/RecyclingCouncilOfAlberta
Linkedin: www.linkedin.com/company/recycling-council-of-alberta
X (Twitter): x.com/3RsAB
Instagram: www.instagram.com/recyclingcouncilab
Description: Promotes and facilitates waste reduction, recycling and resource conservation in the province of Alberta. **Founded:** 1987. **Publications:** *RCA Connector* (Monthly); *Enviro Business Guide*. **Awards:** R's of Excellence (Annual); Rs of Excellence Awards (Annual). **Geographic Preference:** State.

5501 ■ Saskatchewan Environmental Society (SES)
Offices No. 204 & No. 205a€"220 20th St. W
Saskatoon, SK, Canada S7K 3N9
Ph: (306)665-1915
Co. E-mail: info@environmentalsociety.ca
URL: http://environmentalsociety.ca
Contact: Margret Asmuss, President
Facebook: www.facebook.com/environmentalsociety
Linkedin: www.linkedin.com/company/saskatchewan-environmental-society
X (Twitter): x.com/skenvsociety
Instagram: www.instagram.com/skenvsociety
YouTube: www.youtube.com/user/EnvironmentalSociety
Description: Seeks to support and encourage the creation of a global community in which all needs are met in sustainable ways. **Founded:** 1970. **Publications:** *SES Newsletter* (Quarterly). **Geographic Preference:** National.

5502 ■ Sierra Club Canada Foundation National Office (SCC)
PO Box 2007 STN B
Ottawa, ON, Canada K1P 5W3
Ph: (613)241-4611
Free: 888-810-4204
Co. E-mail: info@sierraclub.ca
URL: http://www.sierraclub.ca
Contact: Ole Hendrickson, President
Facebook: www.facebook.com/sierraclubcanada
X (Twitter): x.com/SierraClubCan
YouTube: www.youtube.com/sierraclubcanada
Description: Individuals and organizations concerned about conservation and environmental protection. Promotes development of public policies mandating environmental responsibility. Seeks to raise public awareness of environmental protection issues. Conducts national campaigns on matters including: increased energy efficiency; clear-cutting of forests; health risks associated with pesticide use; protection of biodiversity. **Founded:** 1963. **Geographic Preference:** National.

5503 ■ Societe pour la nature et les parcs du Canada (CPAWS) [Canadian Parks and Wilderness Society (CPAWS)]
600-100 Gloucester St.
Ottawa, ON, Canada K2P 0A4
Ph: (613)569-7226
Free: 800-333-9453
Fax: (613)569-7098
Co. E-mail: info@cpaws.org
URL: http://cpaws.org
Contact: Laura Colella, President
Facebook: www.facebook.com/cpaws
X (Twitter): twitter.com/cpaws
Instagram: www.instagram.com/cpaws_national
YouTube: www.youtube.com/user/cpawsnational
Description: Individuals and organizations with an interest in the preservation of wilderness areas. Promotes establishment of new protected areas; seeks to improve management of existing parks and wildernesses. Develops proposals for reform of public policies governing wilderness preservation and parks management. Conducts advocacy and educational programs to raise public awareness of wilderness preservation issues. Facilitates formation of partnerships linking environmental groups, aboriginal people's governments and organizations, industries, and government agencies. **Founded:** 1963. **Publications:** *Borealis: The Magazine For Canadian Parks And Wilderness; Canadian Wilderness* (Semiannual). **Awards:** J.B. Harkin Conservation Award (Occasionally); J.B. Harkin Conservation Award (Irregular). **Geographic Preference:** National.

5504 ■ Société Canadienne des Biologistes de l'Environnement (CSEB) [Canadian Society of Environmental Biologists (CSEB)]
PO Box 962, Sta. F
Toronto, ON, Canada M4Y 2N9
URL: http://cseb-scbe.org
Contact: Curt Schroeder, President
E-mail: schroederc@saskpolytech.ca
Facebook: www.facebook.com/canadianenvironmentalbiology
Description: Promotes conservation and wise use of Canada's natural resources. Promulgates and enforces professional standards for environmental biology practice, education, and research. Sponsors public education projects to raise awareness of environmental issues. **Founded:** 1958. **Publications:** *CSEB Newsletter* (Quarterly). **Educational Activities:** CSEB Inland Water Resources. **Geographic Preference:** National.

5505 ■ Société Canadienne de l'énergie du sol (SCES) [Earth Energy Society of Canada (EESC); GeoCanada]
c/o Bill Eggertson, Coordinator
7885 Jock Trl.
Ottawa, ON, Canada K0A 2Z0
Fax: (613)822-4987
URL: http://renewables.ca
Contact: Bill Eggertson, Executive Director
E-mail: eggertson@renewables.ca
Description: Promotes the feasible application of geothermal (earth energy) heat pumps for low-grade thermal energy, both as a standalone technology and as an integral part of the Green Heat Global partnership. **Founded:** 1985. **Geographic Preference:** National.

5506 ■ Society Promoting Environmental Conservation (SPEC) - Library
2305 W 7th Ave.
Vancouver, BC, Canada V6K 1Y4
Ph: (604)736-7732
Co. E-mail: admin@spec.bc.ca
URL: http://www.spec.bc.ca
Contact: Jennifer Henry, Executive Director
Facebook: www.facebook.com/SPEC.bc.ca
X (Twitter): x.com/specbc
Instagram: www.instagram.com/specbc
YouTube: www.youtube.com/user/specbc
Description: Promotes environmental research, advocacy, and education. **Scope:** Urban living. **Founded:** 1969. **Holdings:** Figures not available. **Publications:** *SPECTRUM* (Quarterly). **Geographic Preference:** Multinational.

5507 ■ Trout Unlimited Canada (TUC)
8 -6020 2 Street SE
Calgary, AB, Canada T2H 2L8
Ph: (403)221-8360
Free: 800-909-6040
Co. E-mail: tuc@tucanada.org
URL: http://tucanada.org
Contact: Silvia D'Amelio, Chief Executive Officer
Facebook: www.facebook.com/TroutUnlimitedCanada
X (Twitter): x.com/TUCanada1
YouTube: www.youtube.com/user/TroutUnlimitedCanada
Description: Individuals with interest in trout fishing and conservation of riparian habitats and freshwater ecosystems. Promotes the protection, conservation and restoration of Canada's freshwater ecosystems and their coldwater resources for current and future generations. Conducts educational programs and restoration projects in areas including responsible disposal of household chemicals and other wastes; sustainable fishing practices such as catch and release; sustainable development; purchase and preservation of unique coldwater habitats. Sponsors research and educational programs; maintains speaker's bureau. **Publications:** *Currents* (Quarterly). **Geographic Preference:** National.

5508 ■ University of Calgary - Canadian Institute of Resources Law - Library [University of Calgary Canadian Institute of Resources Law (CIRL)]
Murray Fraser Hall 3353
Calgary, AB, Canada T2N 1N4
Ph: (403)220-3200
Fax: (403)282-6182
Co. E-mail: cirl@ucalgary.ca
URL: http://www.cirl.ca
Contact: Allan Ingelson, Executive Director
E-mail: allan.ingelson@haskayne.ucalgary.ca
Facebook: www.facebook.com/theCIRL
X (Twitter): x.com/resourceslaw
YouTube: www.youtube.com/channel/UCgFvstiakpaW4rxPDiZxrIQ
Description: Promotes research, education, and publication on law relating to Canada's renewable and nonrenewable natural resources. Conducts research and educational programs on topics including the relationship between legal systems, laws, and natural resources, and the development of public policies governing environmental protection and natural resources extraction. Provides advice and assistance to legal and policy-making bodies; gathers and disseminates information on environmental law. **Scope:** Canada's renewable and nonrenewable natural resources. Research and education projects include studies on trade law, water law, mining law, oil and gas law, forestry law, and environmental law. **Services:** Copying; library open to the public with permission. **Founded:** 1979. **Holdings:** Books. **Publications:** *Canada Energy Law Service* (Annual); *Resources* (Quarterly). **Educational Activities:** CIRL Courses, On selected topics of resources law for the legal, professional, and academic community. **Geographic Preference:** National.

5509 ■ Wilderness Committee (WC) [Western Canada Wilderness Committee]
46 E 6th Ave.
Vancouver, BC, Canada V5T 1J4
Ph: (604)683-8220
Free: 800-661-9453
Fax: (604)683-8229
Co. E-mail: organize@wildernesscommittee.org
URL: http://www.wildernesscommittee.org
Contact: Kegan Pepper-Smith, Director
Facebook: www.facebook.com/WildernessCommittee
X (Twitter): x.com/wildernews
Instagram: www.instagram.com/wildernews
YouTube: www.youtube.com/user/wildernesscommittee

Description: Promotes social justice as a prerequisite of environmental protection in developing regions. **Scope:** Preservation of Canadian wilderness and wildlife. **Founded:** 1980. **Publications:** *WCWC Reports*. **Educational Activities:** WCWC Conference (Annual); WCWC Meeting (Monthly); World Temperate Rainforest Conference. **Awards:** Eugene Rogers Award (Annual). **Geographic Preference:** Regional.

5510 ■ Women & Environments International (WEI)
192 Spadina Ave., Ste. 400
Toronto, ON, Canada M5T 2C2
Ph: (416)928-0880
Fax: (416)644-0116
Co. E-mail: office@womenshealthyenvironments.ca
URL: http://www.womenshealthyenvironments.ca
Contact: Kanisha Acharya-Patel, Executive Director
URL(s): www.womenshealthyenvironments.ca/partnerswww.yorku.ca/weimag/index.html

Released: Semiannual **Price:** $7, Single issue for back issues; $11, for back issue double; $5, for photocopies of out-of-print issues. **Availability:** Print; PDF; Online.

5511 ■ Women's Healthy Environments Network (WHEN)
192 Spadina Ave., Ste. 400
Toronto, ON, Canada M5T 2C2
Ph: (416)928-0880
Fax: (416)644-0116
Co. E-mail: office@womenshealthyenvironments.ca
URL: http://www.womenshealthyenvironments.ca
Contact: Kanisha Acharya-Patel, Executive Director
Facebook: www.facebook.com/WHENonlinex
X (Twitter): x.com/WHENonline

Description: Represents women experts in environmental studies and issues. Works to implement community development projects to improve the environment. Advocates environmental protection, anti-discriminatory zoning practices, and the development of affordable housing. **Founded:** 1994. **Publications:** *Women & Environments International (WEI)* (Semiannual). **Geographic Preference:** National.

5512 ■ Yukon Conservation Society (YCS) - Library
302 Hawkins St.
Whitehorse, YT, Canada Y1A 1X6
Ph: (867)668-5678
Co. E-mail: coservices@yukon.ca
URL: http://www.yukonconservation.org
Contact: Kim Melton, Director
Facebook: www.facebook.com/yukonconservationsociety
X (Twitter): x.com/YukonConservati
Instagram: www.instagram.com/yukonconservation

Description: Seeks to protect Canada's natural environment; particularly that of the Yukon region. Encourages the conservation of Yukon wilderness, wildlife and natural resources. **Scope:** Canada's natural environment, particularly that of the Yukon region. **Founded:** 1968. **Holdings:** Figures not available. **Publications:** *Walk Softly*. **Awards:** Ted Parnell Scholarship (Annual). **Geographic Preference:** National.

DIRECTORIES OF EDUCATIONAL PROGRAMS

5513 ■ *The Guide to Graduate Environmental Programs*
Pub: Island Press Center For Resource Economics
Contact: David Miller, President
URL(s): islandpress.org/books/guide-graduate-environmental-programs#desc
Price: $19.99, Single issue; $50.99, for eBook.
Description: Covers graduate study facilities and 160 programs in the environmental sciences in the U.S. **Entries include:** Facility name, address, phone, program name, profile, Number of students and faculty in the program, requirements for master's and doctoral degrees, faculty/advisee ratio, e-mail contact and Web site address, special program features, auxiliary services. **Availability:** E-book; Online.

REFERENCE WORKS

5514 ■ "2010: Important Year Ahead for Waterfront" in *Bellingham Business Journal* (Vol. March 2010, pp. 2)
Description: A tentative timeline has been established for the environmental impact statement (EIS) slated for completion in May 2010. The plan for the Waterfront District includes detailed economic and architectural analysis of the feasibility of reusing remaining structures and retaining some industrial icons. **Availability:** Print; Online.

5515 ■ "2011 FinOvation Awards" in *Farm Industry News* (January 19, 2011)
Pub: Informa Business Media, Inc.
Contact: Charlie McCurdy, President
Ed: Karen McMahon, Jodie Wehrspann. **Description:** The 2011 FinOvation Award winners are announced, covering new products that growers need for corn and soybean crops. Winners range from small turbines and a fuel-efficient pickup to a Class 10 combine and drought-tolerant hybrids. **Availability:** Online.

5516 ■ "2011 a Record Year for New Wind Energy Installations in Canada" in *CNW Group* (September 26, 2011)
Pub: CNW Group Ltd.
Description: Canada reports a record for new wind energy projects in 2011 with about 1,338 MW of newly installed wind energy capacity expected to come on line, compared to 690 MW installed in 2010. Statistical data included. **Availability:** Print; Online.

5517 ■ "Acciona Windpower to Supply 3-Megawatt Turbines to Prince Edward Island Energy" in *Professional Close-Up* (September 11, 2012)
Description: Acciona Windpower and Prince Edward Island Energy Corporation (PEIEC) have partnered to supply turbines for the Hermanville & Clear Springs Wind Project that will provide 10 Acciona Windpower AW3000/116 wind turbine generators with capacity of 3 megawatts and a rotor diameter of 116 meters. Acciona will operate and maintain the turbines for the first 15 years.

5518 ■ "ACE Commits $300,000 to Support Environmental Conservation Initiatives and Green Business Entrepreneurs" in *Insurance Business Weekly* (March 2, 2012, pp. 13)
Pub: NewsRX LLC.
Contact: Kalani Rosell, Contact
Description: ACE Charitable Foundation has commited to a two-year, $300,000 funding of The Conservation Fund for new initiatives that protect key watersheds, expand wildlife migration corridors and investment in local green economies in the United States. **Availability:** Online.

5519 ■ "Acing the Test" in *Contractor* (Vol. 57, January 2010, No. 1, pp. 32)
Pub: Informa USA, Inc.
Contact: Stephen A. Carter, Chief Executive Officer
Ed: Robert P. Mader. **Released:** January 01, 2010. **Description:** A ward winning mechanical system retrofitting of a middle school in Ohio is discussed. The school now operates at 37,800 Btu/sq. ft and reduced a significant amount of pollutants from being emitted into the environment.

5520 ■ "Actiontec and Verizon Team Up for a Smarter Home" in *Ecology,Environment & Conservation Business* (November 5, 2011, pp. 3)
Pub: Comtex News Network Inc.
Contact: Kan Devnani, President
Description: Verizon is implementing Actiontec Electronics' SG200 Service Gateway as a basic component of its Home Monitoring and Control service. This new smart home service allows customers to remotely check their homes, control locks and appliances, view home-energy use and more using a smartphone, PC, or FiOS TV. **Availability:** Online.

5521 ■ "Adventures at Hydronicahh" in *Contractor* (Vol. 56, September 2009, No. 9, pp. 52)
Ed: Mark Eatherton. **Released:** Part 6. **Description:** Installations of the heating system of a lakeview room are described. The room's radiant windows are powered by electricity from a solar PV array and a propane-powered hydrogen fuel cell. The system will be programmed to use the most energy available. **Availability:** Print; Online.

5522 ■ "Agana To Bottle Rain for Whole Foods" in *Austin Business Journal* (Vol. 32, March 30, 2012, No. 4, pp. 1)
Pub: American City Business Journals, Inc.
Contact: Mike Olivieri, Executive Vice President
Ed: Vicky Garza. **Description:** Agana Rainwater has signed a deal to bottle rainwater for Whole Foods Market Inc. Rainwater bottling is seen as a conservation tools as it does not deplete the lake or aquifier. **Availability:** Online.

5523 ■ "Agricultural Community Implements Green Technologies, Building Team" in *Contractor* (Vol. 56, September 2009, No. 9, pp. 5)
Ed: Candace Roulo. **Description:** John DeWald and Associates has initiated a residential development project which uses green technologies in Illinois. The community features a community center, organic farm and recreational trails. Comments from executives are also provided. **Availability:** Print; Online.

5524 ■ "Alberta Carbon Capture Strategy Falters: Alberta's Favoured Emissions-Control Plan is Falling Apart" in *Canadian Business* (Vol. 85, June 11, 2012, No. 10, pp. 13)
Ed: Matthew McClearn. **Description:** The emissions-control plan of Alberta suffered a major setback following cancellations of major carbon capture and storage (CCS) pilot projects. Project Pioneer was cancelled because the saving did not justify the operating costs while discontinuation of Heartland Area Redwater Project was due to the uncertainty surrounding the province's changing CCS rules. **Availability:** Print; Online.

5525 ■ "Albuquerque Entrepreneurs Selected As Top Participants in USHCC Foundation Green Builds Business Program" in *Marketing Weekly News* (April 21, 2012)
Description: Five winners of the 2012 Green Builds Business program was announced by the United States Hispanic Chamber of Commerce Foundation (USHCCF). These winners will receive a combined 24 hours of one-on-one green coaching with Bill Roth, the Green Business Coach for Entrepreneur.com and Founder of Earth 2017. Details are included. **Availability:** Print; Online.

5526 ■ "Allowing Ethanol Tax Incentive to Expire Would Risk Jobs, RFA's Dinneen Says" in *Farm Industry News* (November 3, 2010)
Pub: Informa Business Media, Inc.
Contact: Charlie McCurdy, President

Ed: Lynn Grooms. **Price:** $4, Print and Online; Special Offers only for 4 weeks. **Description:** Jobs would be at risk if the ethanol tax incentive expires. **Availability:** Print; Online.

5527 ■ "Alstom Launches the ECO 122 - 2.7MW Wind Turbine for Low Wind Sites" in CNW Group (September 28, 2011)
Pub: CNW Group Ltd.

Description: Alstom is launching its new ECO 122, a 2.7MW onshore wind turbine that combines high power and high capacity factor (1) to boost energy yield in low wind regions around the world. The ECO 122 will produce about 25 percent increased wind farm yield that current turbines and fewer turbines would be installed in areas. **Availability:** Print; Online.

5528 ■ "Altera Ranks Among Top 25 Greenest Companies in U.S." in Ecology, Environment & Conservation Business (August 9, 2014, pp. 2)
Pub: NewsRX LLC.
Contact: Kalani Rosell, Contact

Description: Altera Corporation was ranked 24 on the Newsweek Magazine 2014 Green Rankings of over 500 companies in the United States. These rankings are one of the world's most recognized assessments of corporate sustainability and environmental impact. Eight specific indicators were used, including conservation and sustainability efforts in the areas of energy, carbon, water, and waste productivity. **Availability:** Online.

5529 ■ "Alternative Energy Calls for Alternative Marketing" in Indoor Comfort Marketing (Vol. 70, June 2011, No. 6, pp. 8)
Pub: Spray Technology & Marketing
Contact: Ava Caridad, Director, Editorial
E-mail: acaridad@spraytm.com

Ed: Richard Rutigliano. **Released:** June 01, 2011. **Description:** Advice for marketing solar energy products and services is given. **Availability:** Print; Online.

5530 ■ "Alternative Energy Is a Major Topic at Agritechnica 2011" in Farm Industry News (November 16, 2011)
Pub: Informa Business Media, Inc.
Contact: Charlie McCurdy, President

Ed: Mark Moore. **Description:** Sustainable agricultural systems were a hot topic at this year's Agritechnia 2011, held in Germany. Germany is a leader in the development of on-farm biogas systems. **Availability:** Online.

5531 ■ "Alternative Fuels Take Center Stage at Houston Auto Show" in Houston Business Journal (Vol. 44, January 31, 2014, No. 39, pp. 8)
Pub: American City Business Journals, Inc.
Contact: Mike Olivieri, Executive Vice President

Released: January 31, 2014. **Price:** $4, Introductory 4-Week Offer(Digital & Print). **Description:** An energy summit was held at the Houston Auto Show in Texas on January 22, 2014, where energy executives discussed new technology and initiatives. They considered the market for electric and natural gas-fueled vehicles as well as other options including hydrogen, fuel cells, and biofuels. **Availability:** Print; Online.

5532 ■ "American Chemistry Council Launches Flagship Blog" in Ecology,Environment & Conservation Business (October 29, 2011, pp. 5)
Pub: PR Newswire Association LLC.

Description: American Chemistry Council (ACC) launched its blog, American Chemistry Matters, where interactive space allows bloggers to respond to news coverage and to discuss policy issues and their impact on innovation, competitiveness, job creation and safety. **Availability:** Online.

5533 ■ "American Indian College Fund to Support Environmental Science and Sustainability Programs, Fellowships, and Internships" in Ecology, Environment & Conservation Business (April 12, 2014, pp. 21)
Pub: NewsRX LLC.
Contact: Kalani Rosell, Contact

Description: Tribal colleges serve communities facing environmental issues, such as water quality, energy development, depletion of natural resources, and agricultural management. The American Indian College Fund has created a new Environmental Science and Sustainability Project of $1.35 million grant money to support tribal colleges and universities in select states that underwrite environmental science and sustainability programs of studies. Details of the project are included. **Availability:** Online.

5534 ■ "Answers About Commercial Wind Farms Could Come from Downstate" in Erie Times-News (September 27, 2011)
Pub: Erie Times News
Contact: Christopher Millette, Managing Editor
E-mail: cmillette@timesnews.com

Ed: Valerie Myers. **Description:** Texas-based Pioneer Green Energy is measuring wind and leasing land in North East Township, Pennsylvania. The firm plans to build a 7,000-acre wind farm along wine-country ridges. About 70 turbines would harness wind in order to generate electricity that would be sold into the eastern power grid. **Availability:** Online.

5535 ■ "Areva Diversifies Further Into Wind" in Wall Street Journal Eastern Edition (November 29, 2011, pp. B7)
Pub: Dow Jones & Company Inc.
Contact: Almar Latour, Chief Executive Officer

Ed: Max Colchester, Noemie Bisserbe. **Description:** French engineering company Areva SA is diversifying and moving away from nuclear energy projects. One sign of that is its recent discussion to construct 120 wind turbines to be located at two German wind farms. Such a deal, if signed, would be worth about US$1.59 billion. **Availability:** Online.

5536 ■ "Art Institute of Chicago Goes Green" in Contractor (Vol. 56, July 2009, No. 7, pp. 1)
Ed: Candace Roulo. **Description:** Art Institute of Chicago's Modern Wing museum addition will receive a certification that makes them one of the most environmentally sound museum expansions in the U.S. A modified variable-air-volume system is being used to meet temperature and humidity requirements in the building and it also has a double curtain wall to capture summer heat. **Availability:** Print; Online.

5537 ■ "Austin to Buy $1.1B of Wind Power from Two" in Austin Business Journal (Vol. 31, August 19, 2011, No. 24, pp. A1)
Pub: Austin Business Journal
Contact: Rachel McGrath, Director
E-mail: rmcgrath@bizjournals.com

Ed: Vicky Garza. **Description:** Austin City Council is set to approve contracts to purchase wind energy from Duke Energy Corporation and MAP Royalty Inc. The city will get 200MW from Duke and 91MW from MAP and the total contract is estimated to be worth $1.1 million. **Availability:** Print; Online.

5538 ■ "Award Win Highlights Slingsby's Green Credentials" in Ecology,Environment & Conservation Business (August 20, 2011, pp. 3)

Description: Slingsby, an industrial and commercial equipment supplier, was joint winner with Hallmark Cards of the Baildon Business in the Community's Yorkshire and Humber Long Term Environmental Improvement Award. The firm cites its commitment to reducing environmental impact. **Availability:** Print; PDF; Online.

5539 ■ "BARS+TONE Achieves Green Business Certification by the City and County of San Francisco" in Benzinga.com (April 26, 2012)
Pub: Benzinga.com
Contact: Jason Raznick, Founder

Ed: Aaron Wise. **Description:** City and County of San Francisco, California presented a Green Business certification to BARS+TONE, a creative video agency. The certification is part of an ongoing effort to reduce environmental impact. **Availability:** Online.

5540 ■ "Be Wary of Dual-Flush Conversion Kits" in Contractor (Vol. 56, September 2009, No. 9, pp. 66)
Ed: John Koeller, Bill Gauley. **Description:** Recommendation of untested dual-flush conversion devices for tank-type toilets in the United States has been questioned. The products are being advertised as having the ability to convert single-flush to a dual-flush toilet. No evidence of water conservation from using such devices has been recorded. **Availability:** Print; Online.

5541 ■ "BETC Backers Plot Future" in Business Journal Portland (Vol. 27, December 10, 2010, No. 41, pp. 1)
Pub: Portland Business Journal
Contact: Andy Giegerich, Managing Editor
E-mail: agiegerich@bizjournals.com

Ed: Erik Siemers. **Description:** A coalition of clean energy groups and industrial manufacturers have spearheaded a campaign aimed at persuading Oregon legislators that the state's Business Energy Tax Credit (BETC) is vital in job creation. Oregon's BETC grants tax credits for 50 percent of an eligible renewable or clean energy project's cost. However, some legislators propose BETC's abolition. **Availability:** Print; Online.

5542 ■ "Beware of E15 Gasoline" in Rental Product News (Vol. 33, October 2011)
Ed: Curt Bennink. **Description:** Environmental Protection Agency (EPA) set a new regulation that grants partial waivers to allow gasoline containing up to 15 percent ethanol (E15) to be introduced into commerce for use in model year 2001 and newer light-duty motor vehicles, subject to certain conditions. **Availability:** Online.

5543 ■ "Beyond Meat (R) Completes Largest Financing Round to Date" in Ecology, Environment & Conservation Business (August 16, 2014, pp. 4)
Pub: NewsRX LLC.
Contact: Kalani Rosell, Contact

Description: Beyond Meat (R) is the first company to recreate meat from plants and is dedicated to improving human health, positively impacting climate change, conserving natural resources and respecting animal welfare. The firm has completed its Series D financing round, which will also help the company promote consumer awareness and increase capacity at its manufacturing facility to meet demand. **Availability:** Online.

5544 ■ "Biodiesel Poised to Regain Growth" in Farm Industry News (January 21, 2011)
Pub: Informa Business Media, Inc.
Contact: Charlie McCurdy, President

Ed: Lynn Grooms. **Description:** According to Gary Haer, vice president of sales and marketing for Renewable Energy Group, the biodiesel industry is positioned to regain growth in 2011 with the reinstatement of the biodiesel blendersa tax credit of $1 per gallon. **Availability:** Print; Online.

5545 ■ "Bioheat - Alternative for Fueling Equipment" in Indoor Comfort Marketing (Vol. 70, May 2011, No. 5, pp. 14)
Description: Profile of Worley and Obetz, supplier of biofuels used as an alternative for fueling industry equipment. **Availability:** Print; Online.

5546 ■ "Bitumen Oilsands: Slick Science" in Canadian Business (Vol. 81, September 15, 2008, No. 14-15, pp. 55)
Pub: Rogers Media Inc.
Contact: Neil Spivak, Chief Executive Officer

Ed: Andrew Nikiforuk. **Description:** N-Solv Corp's John Nenniger has discovered a better alternative to steam-assisted gravity drainage methods for extracting bitumen. Nenniger's technique also relies on gravity but replaces steam with propane, which leaves behind impurities like asphaltenes and heavy metals that are too dirty to burn. **Availability:** Print; Mailing list; Online.

5547 ■ *"Blackwater Is LEED Golden for Port of Portland Building"* in *Contractor (Vol. 56, October 2009, No. 10, pp. 3)*

Ed: Robert P. Mader. **Description:** Worrel Water Technologies' Tidal Wetlands Living Machine recycles blackwater from the toilets and sends it right back to flush the toilets. The Technology is being installed in the new headquarters of the Port of Portland which aims to get awarded a gold certificate from the Leadership in Energy and Environmental Design. **Availability:** Print; Online.

5548 ■ *"Boatyard Expansion 8-Year Odyssey"* in *Providence Business News (Vol. 28, March 31, 2014, No. 52, p. 1)*

Pub: American City Business Journals, Inc.
Contact: Mike Olivieri, Executive Vice President

Released: March 29, 2014. **Description:** Bristol Marine owner, Andy Tyska, has found it challenging to operate and improve the boatyard due to lack of available coastal land and restrictive environmental regulations. Tyska made a large investment in plans for expanding the property he purchased in 1998. Tyska discusses the challenges faced while trying to improve his boatyard. **Availability:** Print; Online.

5549 ■ *"Boeing Partnership to Preserve Thousands of Acres of Threatened Wetlands in South Carolina"* in *Ecology, Environment & Conservation Business (August 2, 2014, pp. 3)*

Pub: NewsRX LLC.
Contact: Kalani Rosell, Contact

Description: U.S. Army Corps of Engineers approved Boeing's comprehensive wetlands mitigation plan to preserve about 4,000 acres of land, including more than 2,000 acres of wetlands near the Francis Marion National Forest in South Carolina Lowcountry. Boeing worked in partnership with federal, state and local agencies and conservation organizations to identify the tracts for preservation in order to achieve conservation goals of regional and national significance. **Availability:** Online.

5550 ■ *"Boston Cab Association Gets 2012 Green Business Award"* in *Professional Close-Up (April 28, 2012)*

Description: Boston Cab Association was awarded the 2012 Green Business Award for its conversion to all hybrid vehicles in its fleet. The company was the first to commit to the purchase of hybrids in 2006 as part of the City of Boston's Clean Air Cab program. **Availability:** Online.

5551 ■ *"Caber Engineering Helps to Reduce Canada's Carbon Footprint"* in *Ecology, Environment & Conservation Business (July 16, 2011, pp. 7)*

Description: Calgary-based Caber Engineering Inc. will assist in the engineering design of the Alberta Carbon Trunk Line (ACTL). The ACTL is Alberta's first sizable commercial carbon capture and storage project focusing on the reduction of environmental impacts while being economically beneficial. **Availability:** Online.

5552 ■ *"Calpine Gets Ready to Light It Up"* in *Barron's (Vol. 92, July 23, 2012, No. 30, pp. 15)*

Pub: Dow Jones & Company Inc.
Contact: Almar Latour, Chief Executive Officer

Ed: Jack Willoughby. **Description:** The stocks of electric power producer Calpine could gain value as natural gas-fired power plants increase their market share. The company's stock prices could rise by 50 percent from $17.50 but the company needs to complete its turnaround to fully realize these gains. **Availability:** Online.

5553 ■ *"Canada in 2020 Energy: Mr. Clean"* in *Canadian Business (Vol. 81, October 27, 2008, No. 18, pp. 74)*

Pub: Rogers Media Inc.
Contact: Neil Spivak, Chief Executive Officer

Ed: Rachel Pulfer. **Description:** Profile of Nicholas Parker, co-founder of Cleantech Group LLC, a pioneer in clean technology investing. Cleantech, now a global industry, accounts for 10 percent of all venture capital investments made by U.S. companies in 2007. **Availability:** Print; Online.

5554 ■ *"Canada's Largest Bakery Officially Opened Today"* in *Ecology, Environment & Conservation Business (October 15, 2011, pp. 7)*

Description: Maple Leaf Foods opened Canada's largest commercial bakery in Hamilton, Ontario. The firm's 385,000 square foot Trillium bakery benefits from efficient design flow and best-in-class technologies. **Availability:** Print; Online.

5555 ■ *"Canadian Hydronics Businesses Promote 'Beautiful Heat'"* in *Indoor Comfort Marketing (Vol. 70, September 2011, No. 9, pp. 20)*

Pub: Spray Technology & Marketing
Contact: Ava Caridad, Director, Editorial
E-mail: acaridad@spraytm.com

Released: September 01, 2011. **Description:** Canadian hydronics companies are promoting their systems as beautiful heat. Hydronics is the use of water as the heat-transfer medium in heating and cooling system. **Availability:** Print; Online.

5556 ■ *"Canadian Wind Farm Sued Due to Negative Health Effects"* in *PC Magazine Online (September 22, 2011)*

Pub: PC Magazine
Contact: Dan Costa, Editor-in-Chief
E-mail: dan_costa@pcmag.com

Ed: Andrew Webster. **Description:** Suncor Energy is being sued by a family in Ontario, Canada. The family claims that Suncor's wind turbines have created health problems for them, ranging from vertigo and sleep disturbance to depression and suicidal thoughts. The family's home is over 1,000 meters from the eight wind turbines, and according to Ontario officials, wind turbines must be a minimum of 550 meters from existing homes. **Availability:** Online.

5557 ■ *"CanWEA Unveils WindVision for BC: 5,250 MW of Wind Energy by 2025"* in *CNW Group (October 4, 2011)*

Pub: CNW Group Ltd.

Description: Wind industry leaders are asking British Columbia, Canada policy makers to created conditions to further develop and integrate wind energy in accordance with greenhouse gas emission targets and projected economic growth. Statistical data included. **Availability:** PDF; Online.

5558 ■ *"Case IH Announces Strategy to Meet 2014 Clean Air Standards"* in *Farm Industry News (September 15, 2011)*

Pub: Informa Business Media, Inc.
Contact: Charlie McCurdy, President

Ed: Jodie Wehrspann. **Description:** Case IH will meet EPA's stringent engine emissions limits imposed in 2014, called Tier 4. The limits call for a 90 percent reduction in particulate matter and nitrogen oxides (NOx) over the Tier 3 requirements from a few years ago. **Availability:** Print; Online.

5559 ■ *"Cash for Appliances Targets HVAC Products, Water Heaters"* in *Contractor (Vol. 56, October 2009, No. 10, pp. 1)*

Ed: Candace Roulo. **Description:** States and territories would need to submit a full application that specifies their implementation plans if they are interested in joining the Cash for Appliances program funded by the American Recovery and Reinvestment Act. The Department of Energy urges states to focus on heating and cooling equipment, appliances and water heaters since these offer the greatest energy savings potential. **Availability:** Print; Online.

5560 ■ *"Catch the Wind Announces Filing of Injunction Against Air Data Systems LLC and Philip Rogers"* in *CNW Group (September 30, 2011)*

Pub: CNW Group Ltd.

Description: Catch the Wind, providers of laser-based wind sensor products and technology, filed an injunction against Optical Air Data Systems (OADS) LLC and its former President and CEO Philip L. Rogers. The complaint seeks to have OADS and Rogers return tangible and intangible property owned by Catch the Wind, which the firm believes to be critical to the operations of their business. **Availability:** Online.

5561 ■ *"Catch the Wind to Hold Investor Update Conference Call on October 18, 2011"* in *CNW Group (October 4, 2011)*

Pub: CNW Group Ltd.

Description: Catch the Wind Ltd., providers of laser-based wind sensor products and technology, held a conference call for analysts and institutional investors. The high-growth technology firm is headquartered in Manassas, Virginia. **Availability:** Print; Online.

5562 ■ *"CE2 Carbon Capital and Dogwood Carbon Solutions Partner with Missouri Landowners to Generate High Quality Carbon Offsets from 300,000 Acres of Forest"* in *Nanotechnolgy Business Journal (January 25, 2010)*

Pub: Investment Weekly News

Description: Dogwood Carbon Solutions, a developer of agriculture and forestry based conservation projects, has partnered with CE2 Carbon Capital, one of the largest investors and owners of U.S. carbon commodities and carbon emissions reduction projects, to develop high-quality carbon offsets from over 30,000 acres of privately-owned non-industrial forest in the Ozark mountain region of Arkansas and Missouri. **Availability:** Print; Online.

5563 ■ *"CEO Forecast: With Cloudy Economy, Executives Turn to Government Contracting"* in *Hispanic Business (January-February 2009, pp. 34, 36)*

Ed: Jessica Haro, Richard Kaplan. **Description:** As economic uncertainty fogs the future, executives turn to government contracts in order to boost business. Revenue sources, health care challenges, environmental consulting and remediation services, as well as technological strides are discussed. **Availability:** Print; Online.

5564 ■ *"The CEO Poll: Fuel for Thought II Canadian Business Leaders on Energy Policy"* in *Canadian Business (Vol. 81, September 15, 2008, No. 14-15, pp. 12)*

Pub: Rogers Media Inc.
Contact: Neil Spivak, Chief Executive Officer

Ed: Joe Castaldo. **Description:** Most Canadian business leaders worry about the unreliability of the oil supply but feel that Canada is in a better position to benefit from the energy supply crisis than other countries. Many respondents also highlighted the need to invest in renewable energy sources. **Availability:** Online.

5565 ■ *"Charged Up for Sales"* in *Charlotte Business Journal (Vol. 25, October 15, 2010, No. 30, pp. 1)*

Description: Li-Ion Motors Corporation is set to expand its production lines of electric cars in Sacramento, California. The plan is seen to create up to 600 jobs. The company's total investment is seen to reach $500 million. **Availability:** Print; Online.

5566 ■ *"China's Transition to Green Energy Systems: The Economics of Home Solar Water Heaters and Their Popularization in Dezhou City"* in *Energy Policy (Vol. 39, October 2011, No. 10, pp. 5909-5919)*

Ed: Wei Li, Guojun Song, Melanie Beresford, Ben Ma. **Released:** 2011. **Description:** The economics of home solar water heaters and their growing popularity in Dezhous City, China is discussed. **Availability:** PDF; Online.

5567 ■ *"Clean-Tech Focus Sparks Growth"* in *Philadelphia Business Journal (Vol. 28, January 15, 2010, No. 48, pp. 1)*
Pub: Philadelphia Business Journal
Contact: Sierra Quinn, Director
E-mail: squinn@bizjournals.com

Ed: Peter Key. **Description:** Keystone Redevelopment Group and economic development organization Ben Franklin Technology Partners of Southeastern Pennsylvania have partnered in supporting the growth of new alternative energy and clean technology companies. Keystone has also been developing the Bridge Business Center. **Availability:** Online.

5568 ■ *"Co-Op Launches Revolving Loan Program for Farmers"* in *Bellingham Business Journal (Vol. February 2010, pp. 3)*
Pub: Sound Publishing Inc.
Contact: Josh O'Connor, President

Ed: Lance Henderson. **Description:** Community Food Co-op's Farm Fund received a $12,000 matching grant from the Sustainable Whatcom Fund of the Whatcom Community Foundation. The Farm Fund will create a new revolving loan program for local farmers committed to using sustainable practices.

5569 ■ *"Combo Dorm-Field House Built to Attain LEED Gold"* in *Contractor (Vol. 56, September 2009, No. 9, pp. 1)*

Ed: Candace Roulo, Robert P. Mader. **Description:** North Central College in Illinois has built a new dormitory that is expected to attain Leadership in Energy and Environmental Design Gold certification from the United States Green Building Council. The structure features a geo-exchange heat pump system and radiant floor heat. A description of the facility is also provided. **Availability:** Print; Online.

5570 ■ *"Coming Soon: Electric Tractors"* in *Farm Industry News (November 21, 2011)*
Pub: Informa Business Media, Inc.
Contact: Charlie McCurdy, President

Ed: Jodie Wehrspann. **Description:** The agricultural industry is taking another look at electric farm vehicles. John Deere Product Engineering Center said that farmers can expect to see more diesel-electric systems in farm tractors, sprayers, and implements. **Availability:** Online.

5571 ■ *"CommScope and Comsearch to Showcase Innovative Wind Power Solutions at WINDPOWER 2012 in Atlanta"* in *Benzinga.com (May 31, 2012)*
Pub: Benzinga.com
Contact: Jason Raznick, Founder

Ed: Aaron Wise. **Description:** CommScope Inc. and its subsidiary CommScope will highlight their complete wind power solution products during the WINDPOWER 2012 Conference and Exhibition in Atlanta, Georgia this year. CommScope's wind power products include fiber optic cabling solutions, while Comsearch offers wind energy services that address the siting challenges resulting from complex telecommunications issues. **Availability:** Print; PDF; Online.

5572 ■ *Consultants & Consulting Organizations Directory (CCOD)*
Pub: Gale, part of Cengage Group
Contact: Paul Gazzolo, General Manager Senior Vice President
URL(s): www.gale.com/ebooks/9780028668062/consultants--consulting-organizations-directory

Released: Latest 46th Edition. **Description:** Covers over 26,000 firms, individuals, and organizations active in consulting. **Entries include:** Individual or organization name, address, phone, fax, e-mail, URL, specialties, founding date, branch offices, names and titles of key personnel, number of employees, financial data, publications, seminars and workshops. **Arrangement:** By broad subject categories. **Indexes:** Subject, geographical, organization name. **Availability:** E-book; Download. **Type:** Directory.

5573 ■ *"Consumers Like Green, But Not Mandates"* in *Business Journal-Milwaukee (Vol. 28, December 10, 2010, No. 10, pp. A1)*
Pub: The Business Journal
Contact: Heather Ladage, President
E-mail: hladage@bizjournals.com

Ed: Sean Ryan. **Description:** Milwaukee, Wisconsin consumers are willing to spend more on green energy, a survey has revealed. Respondents also said they will pay more for efficient cars and appliances. Support for public incentives for homeowners and businesses that reduce energy use has also increased. **Availability:** Print; Online.

5574 ■ *"Consumers Want to Learn More About Green Business Efforts Despite Deep Doubt"* in *Benzinga.com (May 1, 2012)*
Pub: Benzinga.com
Contact: Jason Raznick, Founder

Ed: Aaron Wise. **Released:** May 01, 2012. **Description:** According to the third annual Gibbs & Soell Sense & Sustainability Study, 21 percent of Americans think the majority of businesses are working toward sustainable development, while 71 percent of consumer desire more knowledge about things corporations are doing to become sustainable and green. A majority of respondents believe the media is more likely to report green business when they can report bad news. **Availability:** Online.

5575 ■ *"Convert New Customers to Long Term Accounts"* in *Indoor Comfort Marketing (Vol. 70, February 2011, No. 2, pp. 22)*
Description: Marketing to new customers and suggestions for retaining them is covered. **Availability:** Online.

5576 ■ *"Corporate Responsibility"* in *Professional Services Close-Up (July 2, 2010)*
Description: List of firms awarded the inaugural Best Corporate Citizens in Government Contracting by the Corporate Responsibility Magazine is presented. The list is based on the methodology of the Magazine's Best Corporate Citizen's List, with 324 data points of publicly-available information in seven categories which include: environment, climate change, human rights, philanthropy, employee relations, financial performance, and governance. **Availability:** Online.

5577 ■ *"Battle-Tested Vestas Shrugs Off Ill Winds"* in *Business Journal Portland (Vol. 30, January 31, 2014, No. 48, pp. 4)*
Pub: American City Business Journals, Inc.
Contact: Mike Olivieri, Executive Vice President
Released: Weekly. **Price:** $4, Introductory 4-week offer(Digital & Print). **Description:** The revenues of Vestas-American Wind Technology are expected to increase by 12 percent in 2014, despite the decline in US turbine sales. The company holds the second-highest market share in the US. However, Vestas is struggling with tax incentives and increased competition. **Availability:** Print; Online.

5578 ■ *"Crude Awakening"* in *Canadian Business (Vol. 81, October 27, 2008, No. 18, pp. 14)*
Description: Jim Grays believes that a global liquid fuels crisis is coming and hopes the expected transition from oil dependence will be smooth. Charles Maxwell, on the other hand, predicts that a new world economy will arrive in three waves. Views of both experts are examined. **Availability:** Print; Online.

5579 ■ *"Customized Before Custom Was Cool"* in *Green Industry Pro (July 2011)*
Ed: Gregg Wartgow. **Description:** Profile of Turf Care Enterprises and owner Kevin Vogeler, who discusses his desire to use more natural programs using little or no chemicals in 1986. At that time, that sector represented 20 percent of his business, today it shares 80 percent. **Availability:** Online.

5580 ■ *"David Robinson Column"* in *Buffalo News (October 2, 2011)*
Pub: The Buffalo News, Inc.
Contact: Tom Wiley, President
E-mail: twiley@buffnews.com

Ed: David Robinson. **Description:** New York Power Authority ceased development of an offshore wind farm project. Wind farming in the waters of Lake Erie or Lake Ontario would be too costly. Details of the project are discussed. **Availability:** Online.

5581 ■ *"A Day Late and a Dollar Short"* in *Indoor Comfort Marketing (Vol. 70, March 2011, No. 3, pp. 30)*
Description: A discussion involving futures options and fuel oil prices is presented. **Availability:** Online.

5582 ■ *"DEM Says River Needs Cleanup"* in *Providence Business News (Vol. 28, January 6, 2014, No. 40, pp. 1)*
Pub: American City Business Journals, Inc.
Contact: Mike Olivieri, Executive Vice President

Released: January 04, 2014. **Description:** Rhode Island's Department of Environmental Management (DEM) called a meeting to gather information for its Ten Mile River water-quality-restoration plan. DEM announced the failure of the Ten Mile River and its impoundments to meet state water quality standards. The government grant received by Attleboro for the cleanup efforts is examined. **Availability:** Print; Online.

5583 ■ *"Despite Economic Upheaval Generation Y is Still Feeling Green: RSA Canada Survey"* in *CNW Group (October 28, 2010)*
Pub: CNW Group Ltd.

Description: Canadian Generation Y individuals believe it is important for their company to be environmentally-friendly and one-third of those surveyed would quit their job if they found their employer was environmentally irresponsible, despite the economy. **Availability:** Online.

5584 ■ *"Detroit Hosts Conferences on Green Building, IT, Finance"* in *Crain's Detroit Business (Vol. 25, June 1, 2009, No. 22, pp. 9)*
Pub: Crain Communications Inc.
Contact: Barry Asin, President

Ed: Tom Henderson. **Description:** Detroit will host three conferences in June 2009, one features green technology, one information technology and the third will gather black bankers and financial experts from across the nation. **Availability:** Online.

5585 ■ *"DeWind Delivering Turbines to Texas Wind Farm"* in *Professional Services Close-Up (September 25, 2011)*

Description: DeWind Company has begun shipment of turbines to the 20 MW Frisco Wind Farm located in Hansford County, Texas. DeWind is a subsidiary of Daewoo Shipbuilding and Marine Engineering Company. Details of the project are discussed. **Availability:** Online.

5586 ■ *"Dexter Gauntlett Gauges the Wind"* in *Business Journal Portland (Vol. 30, January 31, 2014, No. 48, pp. 6)*
Pub: American City Business Journals, Inc.
Contact: Mike Olivieri, Executive Vice President

Released: Weekly. **Price:** $4, Introductory 4-week offer(Digital & Print). **Description:** Navigant Research senior research analyst, Dexter Gauntlett says Vestas-American Wind Systems could boost its revenues. He added that the company has being hiring employees at its manufacturing plants. Gauntlett also said that wind energy will greatly boost state renewable portfolios. **Availability:** Print; Online.

5587 ■ *"DMW Gets MBE Certification"* in *Wireless News (July 29, 2012)*

Description: Towson, Maryland's Daft McCune Walker (DMW) received the Minority Business Enterprise (MBE) Certification from the State of Maryland for Engineering, Surveying, Environmental and CAD services. The firm is a multidisciplinary consulting organization and is woman-owned. **Availability:** Print; Online.

5588 ■ "Dog Marketplace: Pet Waste Products Pick Up Sales" in Pet Product News (Vol. 66, September 2012, No. 9, pp. 58)
Ed: Sandi Cain. Description: Pet supplies manufacturers are developing dog waste pickup bags and other convenient cleanup tools characterized by environment-friendliness and fashion. The demand for these cleanup tools has been motivated by dog owners' desire to minimize their and their dogs' environmental footprints. Availability: Online.

5589 ■ "Dow Champions Innovative Energy Solutions for Auto Industry at NAIAS" in Business of Global Warming (January 25, 2010, pp. 7)
Description: This year's North American International Auto Show in Detroit will host the "Electric Avenue" exhibit sponsored by the Dow Chemical Company. The display will showcase the latest in innovative energy solutions from Dow as well as electric vehicles and the technology supporting them. This marks the first time a non-automotive manufacturer is part of the main floor of the show. Availability: Print; PDF; Online.

5590 ■ "East Coast Solar" in Contractor (Vol. 57, February 2010, No. 2, pp. 17)
Ed: Dave Yates. Description: U.S. Department of Energy's Solar Decathlon lets 20 college student-led teams from around the world compete to design and build a solar-powered home. A mechanical contractor discusses his work as an advisor during the competition. Availability: Print; Online.

5591 ■ Eco Barons: The New Heroes of Environmental Activism
Pub: Ecco Books
Contact: Daniel Halpern, Founder
Ed: Edward Humes. Price: $18.99, hardcover. Description: Profiles of business leaders who have dedicated their lives to saving the planet from ecological devastation. Availability: E-book; Print; Download.

5592 ■ "Eco Smart Home Will Showcase Green Technology" in Contractor (Vol. 56, September 2009, No. 9, pp. 3)
Ed: Steve Spaulding. Description: Eco Smart World Wide is building the Eco Smart Demonstration House to promote the latest in sustainable, renewable and high-efficiency practices and products. The company will use insulated concrete forms in the construction of the building. Features and dimensions of the structure are also presented. Availability: Print; Online.

5593 ■ "Editorial: Find Private Money for FutureGen Plant" in Crain's Chicago Business (Vol. 34, September 12, 2011, No. 37, pp. 18)
Pub: Crain Communications Inc.
Contact: Barry Asin, President
Description: FutureGen is a clean-coal power plant being developed in Southern Illinois. The need for further funding is discussed. Availability: Print.

5594 ■ "Elon Musk's Solar Firm Is Nearly Doubling Its Massachusetts Workforce" in Boston Business Journal (Vol. 34, May 30, 2014, No. 17, pp. 3)
Pub: American City Business Journals, Inc.
Contact: Mike Olivieri, Executive Vice President
Released: Weekly. Description: SolarCity is planning to add 100 jobs to its Massachusetts operations. The solar panel firm opened a second operations center in the state. State business incentives have enabled the company to expand presence in the area. Availability: Print; Online.

5595 ■ "Emissions: Cloudy Skies" in Canadian Business (Vol. 81, October 27, 2008, No. 18, pp. 101)
Pub: Rogers Media Inc.
Contact: Neil Spivak, Chief Executive Officer
Ed: Andrew Wahl. Description: Canada's federal government is expected to implement its regulations on greenhouse-gas emissions by January 1, 2010, but companies are worried because the plan took so long and some details are yet to be revealed. Corporate Canada wants a firm, long-range plan similar to the European Union Emissions Trading Scheme in dealing with greenhouse-gas emissions. Availability: Online.

5596 ■ "Energy Consulting Company to Expand" in Austin Business JournalInc. (Vol. 28, November 7, 2008, No. 34, pp. A1)
Pub: Austin Business Journal
Contact: Rachel McGrath, Director
E-mail: rmcgrath@bizjournals.com
Ed: Kate Harrington. Description: CLEAResult Consulting Inc. is planning to increase its workforce and move its headquarters to a larger office. The company has posted 1,000 percent increase in revenues. The company's adoption of best practices and setting of benchmark goals are seen as the reason for its growth. Availability: Print; Online.

5597 ■ "Energy Efficiency Ordinance Softened" in Austin Business JournalInc. (Vol. 28, October 3, 2008, No. 29)
Pub: Austin Business Journal
Contact: Rachel McGrath, Director
E-mail: rmcgrath@bizjournals.com
Ed: Jean Kwon. Description: City of Austin has eliminated mandatory energy efficiency upgrades to single-family housing as a condition for selling or renting homes or buildings. The new law proposes that an energy performance audit be conducted on single-family homes before being sold and the results of the audit disclosed to perspectives buyers. Availability: Print; Online.

5598 ■ "Enriching the Ecosystem: A Four-Point Plan for Linking Innovation, Enterprises, and Jobs" in Harvard Business Review (Vol. 90, March 2012, No. 3, pp. 140)
Pub: Harvard Business Review Press
Contact: Moderna V. Pfizer, Contact
Ed: Rosabeth Moss Kanter. Price: $8.95, hardcopy black and white. Description: The four goals for enriching the ecosystem include: linking venture creation and knowledge creation to speed up the idea-to-enterprise transition; revitalizing small-, medium-, and large-sized firms via partnerships; improving matches between education and employment opportunities; and bringing together leaders across different sectors to create regional strategies. Availability: Print; PDF; Online.

5599 ■ "Environment Consulting Service Market Incredible Possibilities, Growth Analysis and Forecast to 2024" in Tech Mag (October 28, 2019)
URL(s): technologymagazine.org/environment-consulting-service-market-incredible-possibilities-growth-analysis-forecast-2024/
Ed: Partha Ray. Released: October 28, 2019. Description: An overview of the Environment Consulting Service Market study, which includes profitability prospects, growth dynamics, market size, market share forecast, and revenue estimation. Availability: Online.

5600 ■ Environmental Guide to the Internet
Contact: Carol Briggs Erickson, Author
URL(s): rowman.com/ISBN/9780865876439
Ed: Carol Briggs-Erickson, Toni Murphy. Released: Latest edition 4th. Price: $106, Individuals Paperback. Description: Covers 1,200 resources covering the environment on the Internet, including organizations, products, and resources, including discussion groups, electronic journals, newsgroups, and discussion groups. Entries include: Name, online address, description, e-mail address. Arrangement: Categories. Availability: Print.

5601 ■ "EPA Finalizes WaterSense for Homes" in Contractor (Vol. 57, January 2010, No. 1, pp. 70)
Ed: Robert P. Mader. Description: U.S. Environmental Protection Agency released its "final" version of the WaterSense for Homes standard. The standard's provisions that affect plumbing contractors include the specification that everything has to be leak tested and final service pressure cannot exceed 60 psi. Availability: Print; Online.

5602 ■ "EPA Grants E15 Waiver for 2001-2006 Vehicles" in Farm Industry News (January 21, 2011)
Pub: Informa Business Media, Inc.
Contact: Charlie McCurdy, President
Ed: Lynn Grooms. Description: U.S. Environmental Protection Agency waived a limitation on selling gasoline that contains more than 10 percent ethanol for model year 2001-2006 cars and light trucks, allowing fuel to contain up to 15 percent ethanol (E15) for these vehicles. Availability: Online.

5603 ■ "ESolar Partners With Penglai on Landmark Solar Thermal Agreement for China" in Business of Global Warming (January 25, 2010, pp. 8)
Description: Penglai Electric, a privately-owned Chinese electrical power equipment manufacturer, and eSolar, a global provider of cost-effective and reliable solar power plants, announced a master licensing agreement in which eSolar will build at least 2 gigawatts of solar thermal power plants in China over the next 10 years. Availability: Print; Online.

5604 ■ "Family Takes Wind Turbine Companies to Court Over Gag Clauses on Health Effects of Turbines" in CNW Group (September 12, 2011)
Pub: CNW Group Ltd.
Description: Shawn and Trisha Drennan are concerned about the negative experiences other have had with wind turbines close to their homes, including adverse health effects. The couple's home will be approximately 650 meters from the Kingsbridge II wind farm project in Ontario, Canada. Availability: Online.

5605 ■ "Federal Buildings to Achieve Zero-Net Energy by 2030" in Contractor (Vol. 56, December 2009, No. 12, pp. 5)
Ed: Candace Roulo. Description: United States president Barack Obama has issued sustainable goals for federal buildings. Federal agencies are also required to increase energy efficiency, conserve water and support sustainable communities. Obama has also announced a $3.4 billion investment in a smart energy creed. Availability: Print; Online.

5606 ■ "First Sustainability Standard for Household Portable and Floor Care Appliances Developed to Identify Environmentally Responsible Products" in Ecology, Environment & Conservation Business (September 13, 2014, pp. 39)
Pub: NewsRX LLC.
Contact: Kalani Rosell, Contact
Description: the Association of Home Appliance Manufacturers (AHAM), CSA Group, and the UL Environment released the AHAM 7002-2014/CSA SPE-7002-14/UL 7002, Sustainability Standard for Household Portable and Floor Care Appliances. This is the first voluntary sustainability standards for these appliances and is the third in a unit of product sustainability standards under development by the group. These standards are intended for use by manufacturers, governments, retailers, and others to identify products conforming to these standards in six key areas: materials, manufacturing and operations, energy consumption during use, end-of-life, consumables, and innovation. Availability: Online.

5607 ■ "First Suzlon S97 Turbines Arrive in North America for Installation" in PR Newswire (September 28, 2011)
Pub: PR Newswire Association LLC.
Description: Suzlon Energy Ltd., the world's fifth largest manufacturer of wind turbines, will install its first S97 turbine at the Amherst Wind Farm Project. These turbines will be installed on 90-meter hub height towers and at full capacity, will generate enough electricity to power over 10,000 Canadian homes. Availability: Online.

5608 ■ *The Flaw of Averages: Why We Underestimate Risk in the Face of Uncertainty*
Pub: John Wiley & Sons, Inc.
Contact: Christina Van Tassell, Executive Vice President Chief Financial Officer
Ed: Sam L. Savage. **Released:** March 26, 2012. **Price:** $19.95, paperback; $27.95, hardcover; $12.99, E-Book. **Description:** Personal and business plans are based on uncertainties on a daily basis. The common avoidable mistake individuals make in assessing risk in the face of uncertainty is defined. The explains why plans based on average assumptions are wrong, on average, in areas as diverse as finance, healthcare, accounting, the war on terror, and climate change. **Availability:** E-book; Print.

5609 ■ *"For Giving Us a Way To Say Yes To Solar: Lynn Jurich and Edward Fenster" in Inc. (Volume 32, December 2010, No. 10, pp. 110)*
Pub: Mansueto Ventures L.L.C.
Contact: Stephanie Mehta, Chief Executive Officer
Ed: Leigh Buchanan. **Released:** December 01, 2010. **Description:** Profile of entrepreneurs Lynn Jurich and Edward Fenster, cofounders of SunRun. The firm installs solar panels at little or no cost and homeowners sign 20-year contracts to buy power at a fixed price. **Availability:** Online.

5610 ■ *"For One Homebuilder, It's Pretty Easy Being Green, Even in Houston" in Houston Business Journal (Vol. 44, April 11, 2014, No. 49, pp. 7)*
Pub: American City Business Journals, Inc.
Contact: Mike Olivieri, Executive Vice President
Released: Weekly. **Price:** $4, introductory 4-week offer(Digital only). **Description:** Frankel Building Group vice president, Scott Frankel, says new housing projects in Houston, Texas have been getting bigger. He also said that industry members are facing the problem of lack of residential lots in the region. Frankel added that the company builds its homes to LEED-certified standards. **Availability:** Print; Online.

5611 ■ *"Former Tech Execs Want to Tap Building Trend in Austin" in Austin Business Journal (Vol. 31, May 13, 2011, No. 10, pp. A1)*
Pub: Austin Business Journal
Contact: Rachel McGrath, Director
E-mail: rmcgrath@bizjournals.com
Ed: Cody Lyon. **Description:** Falcon Containers moved to a 51-acre site in Far East Austin, Texas and started construction of a 2,500-square-foot headquarters made from eight 40-foot shipping containers. Falcon's CEO Stephen Shang plans to use his headquarters building as a showroom to attract upscale, urban hipsters. Insights on the construction's environmental and social impact are shared. **Availability:** Print; Online.

5612 ■ *"Fossil Fuel, Renewable Fuel Shares Expected to Flip Flop" in Farm Industry News (April 29, 2011)*
Pub: Informa Business Media, Inc.
Contact: Charlie McCurdy, President
Ed: Lynn Grooms. **Description:** Total energy use of fossil fuels is predicted to fall 5 percent by the year 2035, with renewable fuel picking it up. **Availability:** Online.

5613 ■ *"From the Moon to Malibu" in Canadian Business (Vol. 87, July 2014, No. 7, pp. 106)*
Description: The new BMW i8 plug-in hybrid sports car accelerates from zero to 100 kilometers per hour in 4.4 seconds but consumes fuel at an average of just 4.8 liters per 100 kilometers. The drivetrain features a 131-horsepower electric motor and a 231-horsepower internal combustion engine. **Availability:** Print; Online.

5614 ■ *"FSU's OGZEB Is Test Bed for Sustainable Technology" in Contractor (Vol. 56, October 2009, No. 10, pp. 1)*
Ed: Candace Roulo. **Description:** Florida State University has one of 14 off-grid zero emissions buildings (OGZEB) in the U.S.; it was built to research sustainable and alternative energy systems. The building produces electricity from 30 photovoltaic panels and it also has three AET water heating solar panels on the roof. **Availability:** Print; Online.

5615 ■ *"Fuel King: The Most Fuel-Efficient Tractor of the Decade is the John Deere 8295R" in Farm Industry News (November 10, 2011)*
Pub: Informa Business Media, Inc.
Contact: Charlie McCurdy, President
Description: Farm Industry News compiled a list of the most fuel-efficient tractors with help from the Nebraska Tractor Test Lab, with the John Deere 8295R PTO winner of the most fuel-efficient tractor of the decade. **Availability:** Print; Online.

5616 ■ *"GE Announces New Projects, Technology Milestone and New Service Program at AWEA Windpower 2012" in News Bites US (June 6, 2012)*
Description: General Electric announced plans at the AWEA Windpower 2012 for its two new wind turbine projects to be located in Michigan and Iowa. Details of these new wind turbine projects are included. **Availability:** Online.

5617 ■ *"GE Milestone: 1,000th Wind Turbine Installed in Canada" in CNW Group (October 4, 2011)*
Pub: CNW Group Ltd.
Description: GE installed its 1,000th wind turbine in Canada at Cartier Wind Energy's Gros Morne project in the Gaspesie Region of Quebec, Canada. As Canada continues to expand its use of wind energy, GE plans to have over 1,100 wind turbines installed in the nation by the end of 2011. **Availability:** Online.

5618 ■ *"General Electric Touts Going Green for Business Fleet Services" in America's Intelligence Wire (June 1, 2012)*
Description: General Capital Fleet Services if featuring alternative-fuel vehicles in Eden Prairie for its corporate customers. GE Capital is the world's largest fleet management service and is offering its customers the first of its kind service that allows corporate lease customers to test drive alternative fuel cars from 20 different manufacturers. **Availability:** Print; Online.

5619 ■ *"Germans Win Solar Decathlon Again" in Contractor (Vol. 56, November 2009, No. 11, pp. 1)*
Ed: Robert P. Mader. **Description:** Students from Technische Universtat Darmstadt won the U.S. Department of Energy's Solar Decathlon by designing and building the most attractive and efficient solar-powered home. The winner's design produced a surplus of power even during three days of rain and photovoltaic panels covered nearly every exterior surface. **Availability:** Print; Online.

5620 ■ *"Getting the Bioheat Word Out" in Indoor Comfort Marketing (Vol. 70, September 2011, No. 9, pp. 32)*
Description: Ways to market advanced liquid fuels to the public are outlined. **Availability:** Print; Online.

5621 ■ *"The Global Environment Movement is Bjorn Again" in Canadian Business (Vol. 83, September 14, 2010, No. 15, pp. 11)*
Pub: Rogers Media Inc.
Contact: Neil Spivak, Chief Executive Officer
Ed: Steve Maich. **Description:** Danish academic Bjorn Lomborg is in favor of decisive action to combat climate change in his new book and was given front page treatment by a London newspaper. Environmentalist groups see this as a victory since Lomborg had not previously considered climate change an immediate issue. **Availability:** Online.

5622 ■ *"Global Environmental Consulting Market Set to Surge" in Environmental Analyst (May 14, 2021)*
Released: May 14, 2021. **Description:** The environmental consulting market took a dip during the COVID-19 pandemic, but is set to soar in the coming years as society turns more and more towards caring for the planet. **Availability:** Online.

5623 ■ *"GM's Volt Woes Cast Shadow on E-Cars" in Wall Street Journal Eastern Edition (November 28, 2011, pp. B1)*
Pub: Dow Jones & Company Inc.
Contact: Almar Latour, Chief Executive Officer
Ed: Sharon Terlep. **Description:** The future of electric cars is darkened with the government investigation by the National Highway Traffic Safety Administration into General Motor Company's Chevy Volt after two instances of the car's battery packs catching fire during crash tests conducted by the Agency. **Availability:** Online.

5624 ■ *"Go Green Or Go Home" in Black Enterprise (Vol. 41, August 2010, No. 1, pp. 53)*
Pub: Earl G. Graves Ltd.
Contact: Earl Graves, Jr., President
Ed: Robinson M. Tennille. **Description:** The green economy has become an essential part of every business, however, small business owners need to learn how to participate, including minority owned entrepreneurs. **Availability:** Online.

5625 ■ *Good Green Guide for Small Businesses: How to Change the Way Your Business Works for the Better*
Pub: A. and C. Black
Contact: Jenny Ridout, Director
Released: First edition. **Description:** Guide for small businesses to take an environmental audit of their company and shows how to minimize the impact of office essentials such as utilities, insulation, recycling and waste, electrical equipment, water systems, lighting options, food and drink, and office cleaning arrangements and products. **Availability:** Print.

5626 ■ *"Governor Candidates Differ on Oregon's Green Streak" in Business Journal Portland (Vol. 27, October 22, 2010, No. 34, pp. 1)*
Pub: Portland Business Journal
Contact: Andy Giegerich, Managing Editor
E-mail: agiegerich@bizjournals.com
Ed: Andy Giegerich. **Description:** The views of Oregon gubernatorial candidates Chris Dudley and John Kitzhaber on the state's economy and on environmental policies are presented. Both Dudley, who is a Republican, and his Democratic challenger believe that biomass could help drive the state's economy. Both candidates also pledged changes in Oregon's business energy tax credit (BETC) program.

5627 ■ *"Grainger Show Highlights Building Green, Economic Recovery" in Contractor (Vol. 57, February 2010, No. 2, pp. 3)*
Ed: Candace Roulo. **Description:** Chief U.S. economist told attendees of the Grainger's 2010 Total MRO Solutions National Customer Show that the economic recovery would be subdued. Mechanical contractors who attended the event also learned about building sustainable, green products, and technologies, and economic and business challenges. **Availability:** Print; Online.

5628 ■ *"Grant Could Help Schools Harness Wind" in Dallas Business Journal (Vol. 37, April 11, 2014, No. 31, pp. 8)*
Pub: American City Business Journals, Inc.
Contact: Mike Olivieri, Executive Vice President
Released: Weekly. **Price:** $4, introductory 4-week offer(Digital only); $4, introductory 4-week offer(Digital & Print). **Description:** Five universities led by Texas A&M have received a $2.2 million grant from the Texas Emerging Technologies Fund for use in wind technology research. The research will focus on turbines that feature bigger blades to capture more wind. Technology developed by the universities will eventually be handed to the state. **Availability:** Print; Online.

5629 ■ *"Green Business Owners Share Secrets of Success In This Business Guide" in PRNewsChannel.com (March 1, 2012)*
Pub: Comtex News Network Inc.
Contact: Kan Devnani, President

Description: Business guide to help companies become sustainable and work to be a green business. **Availability:** Online.

5630 ■ *"Green Business Plan Competition" in Chemical & Engineering News (Vol. 90, July 9, 2012, No. 28, pp. 34)*
Pub: American Chemical Society Philadelphia Section
Contact: Dr. David Cichowicz, Director
Ed: Stephen K. Ritter. **Description:** Startup anticorrosion coatings firm AnCatt Inc. won the inaugural chemistry business plan competition at the Green Chemistry & Engineering Conference held in July 2012 in Washington, DC. AnCatt was honored for its conducting-polymer-based anticorrosion paint system aimed at replacing chromate, lead, and cadmium paint pigments. **Availability:** Online.

5631 ■ *"Green and Clean" in Retail Merchandiser (Vol. 51, July-August 2011, No. 4, pp. 56)*
Description: Green Valley Grocery partnered with Paragon Solutions consulting firm to make their stores environmentally green. **Availability:** Print; Online.

5632 ■ *"Green Collar: Green Buildings Support Job Creation, Workforce Transformation and Economic Recovery" in Environmental Design and Construction (Vol. 15, July 2012, No. 7, pp. 31)*
Pub: BNP Media
Contact: Harper Henderson, Owner Co-Chief Executive Officer
Ed: Maggie Comstock. **Description:** Despite construction being at an all-time low, green building construction has maintained its hold on nonresidential buildings. It has even shown growth in some sectors and accounts for over one-third of all nonresidential design and construction jobs and is expected to show further growth through 2014. Statistical details included.

5633 ■ *The Green Guide for Business: The Ultimate Environment for Businesses of All Sizes*
Pub: Profile Books Limited
Contact: Stephen Brough, Co-Founder
Ed: Chris Goodball, Roger East, Hannah Bullock. **Released:** March 09, 2010. **Description:** Everyone wants to go green these days, but for small businesses that's easier said than done. How do you measure a company's carbon footprint? Are dryers or hand towels more eco-friendly? Recycled paper or FSC-certified? All these questions and more are explored. **Availability:** E-book.

5634 ■ *"Green It Like You Mean It" in Special Events Magazine (Vol. 28, February 1, 2009, No. 2)*
Description: Eco-friendly party planners offer advice for planning and hosting green parties or events. Tips include information for using recycled paper products, organic food and drinks. The Eco Nouveau Fashion Show held by Serene Star Productions reused old garments to create new fashions as well as art pieces from discarded doors and window frames for the show; eco-friendly treats and gift bags were highlighted at the event.

5635 ■ *"Green Light" in The Business Journal-Portland (Vol. 25, July 11, 2008, No. 18, pp. 1)*
Description: Ecos Consulting, a sustainability consulting company based in Portland, Oregon, is seeing a boost in revenue as more businesses turn to sustainable practices. The company's revenue rose by 50 percent in 2007 and employees increased from 57 to 150. Other details about Ecos' growth are discussed. **Availability:** Print; Online.

5636 ■ *"Green Manufacturer Scouts Sites in Greater Cincinnati" in Business Courier (Vol. 27, July 23, 2010, No. 12, pp. 1)*
Pub: Business Courier

Ed: Dan Monk. **Description:** CresaPartners is searching for a manufacturing facility in Cincinnati, Ohio. The company is set to tour about ten sites in the area. **Availability:** Print; Online.

5637 ■ *"Green Rules To Drive Innovation: Charging for Carbon Can Inspire Conservation, Fuel Competition, and Enhance Competitiveness" in Harvard Business Review (Vol. 90, March 2012, No. 3, pp. 120)*
Pub: Harvard Business Review Press
Contact: Moderna V. Pfizer, Contact
Ed: Daniel C. Esty, Steve Charnovitz. **Price:** $8.95. **Description:** Along with carbon emissions charges, other green policy recommendations include expanding domestic renewable power and the use of natural gas, increasing federal funding of clean-energy research, utilizing incentive-based approaches to encourage the adoption of renewable energy, and implementing the World Trade Organization's Doha negotiations on sustainable development. **Availability:** Online; PDF.

5638 ■ *"Greenhouse Announces Reverse Merger With Custom Q, Inc." in Investment Weekly (January 30, 2010, pp. 338)*
Pub: Investment Weekly News
Description: In accordance with an Agreement and Plan of Share Exchange, GreenHouse Holdings, Inc., an innovative green solutions provider, has gone public via a reverse merger with Custom Q, Inc. **Availability:** Print; Online.

5639 ■ *Greening Your Small Business: How to Improve Your Bottom Line, Grow Your Brand, Satisfy Your Customers and Save the Planet*
Price: $19.95. **Description:** A definitive resource for anyone who wants their small business to be cutting-edge, competitive, profitable, and eco-conscious. Stories from small business owners address every aspect of going green, from basics such as recycling waste, energy efficiency, and reducing information technology footprint, to more in-depth concerns such as green marketing and communications, green business travel, and green employee benefits.

5640 ■ *"GreenTech Gears Up for Production" in Memphis Business Journal (Vol. 33, April 6, 2012, No. 52, pp. 1)*
Pub: Baltimore Business Journal
Contact: Rhonda Pringle, President
E-mail: rpringle@bizjournals.com
Description: GreenTech Automotive has broken ground for construction of a new production facility in Tunica, Tennessee. The company will focus its manufacturing operations in the new facility. **Availability:** Print; Online.

5641 ■ *Guerrilla Marketing Goes Green: Winning Strategies to Improve Your Profits and Your Planet*
Pub: John Wiley & Sons, Inc.
Contact: Christina Van Tassell, Executive Vice President Chief Financial Officer
Ed: Jay Conrad Levinson, Shel Horowitz, Jay Conrad Levinson. **Released:** 2010. **Description:** The latest tips on green marketing and sustainable business strategies are shared. **Availability:** E-book; Print; Electronic publishing; Online.

5642 ■ *"Habitat, Home Depot Expand Building Program" in Contractor (Vol. 56, September 2009, No. 9, pp. 16)*
Description: Habitat for Humanity International and The Home Depot Foundation are planning to expand their Partners in Sustainable Building program. The program will provide funds to help Habitat affiliates build 5,000 homes. Comments from executives are also included. **Availability:** Print; Online.

5643 ■ *"Harpoon Brewery Wins Boston Green Business Award for Sustainability and EnerNOC Energy Management Programs" in Investment Weekly News (May 12, 2012, No. 543)*
Description: Harpoon Brewery was awarded a 2012 Boston Green Business Award by Mayor Thomas Menino of Boston, Massachusetts. The brewery was cited for having an exceptional sustainability program that includes waste reduction, responsible chemical usage, and operational efficiency measures combined with energy management initiatives with EnerNOC. EnerNOC is a leading provider of energy management applications for commercial, industrial, and institutional energy users, including Harpoon. **Availability:** Online.

5644 ■ *"Hey, You Can't Do That" in Green Industry Pro (Vol. 23, September 2011)*
Ed: Rod Dickens. **Description:** Manufacturers of landscape equipment are making better use of energy resources, such as the use of fuel-injection systems instead of carburetors, lightweight materials, better lubricants, advanced battery technology, and innovative engine designs. **Availability:** Online.

5645 ■ *Housecleaning Business: Organize Your Business - Get Clients and Referrals - Set Rates and Services*
Ed: Laura Jorstad, Melinda Morse. **Price:** Paperback,softback. **Description:** This book shares insight into starting a housecleaning business. It shows how to develop a service manual, screen clients, serve customers, select cleaning products, competition, how to up a home office, using the Internet to grow the business and offering green cleaning options to clients. **Availability:** E-book; Print.

5646 ■ *"How Bad Is It?" in Hawaii Business (Vol. 54, July 2008, No. 1, pp. 35)*
Pub: PacificBasin Communications
Contact: Chuck Tindle, Director
E-mail: chuckt@pacificbasin.net
Ed: Jolyn Okimoto Rosa. **Description:** Donald G. Horner, chief executive officer of First Hawaiian Bank, says that the current Hawaiian economic situation is a cyclical slowdown. Maurice Kaya, an energy consultant, says the slowdown is due to overdependence on imported fuels. Other local leaders, such as Constance H. Lau, also discuss their view on the current economic situation in Hawaii.

5647 ■ *"How Green Is The Valley?" in Barron's (Vol. 88, July 4, 2008, No. 28, pp. 13)*
Description: San Jose, California has made a good start towards becoming a leader in alternative energy technology through the establishment of United Laboratories' own lab in the city. The certification process for photovoltaic cells will be dramatically shortened with this endeavor. **Availability:** Print.

5648 ■ *"How I Did It: Timberland's CEO On Standing Up to 65,000 Angry Activists" in Harvard Business Review (Vol. 88, September 2010, No. 9, pp. 39)*
Pub: Harvard Business Publishing
Contact: Diane Belcher, Managing Director
Ed: Jeff Swartz. **Price:** $8.95, PDF. **Description:** Timberland Company avoided a potential boycott by taking a two-way approach. It addressed a supplier issue that posed a threat to the environment, and launched an email campaign to keep Greenpeace activists informed of the development of a new supplier agreement. **Availability:** Online; PDF.

5649 ■ *"How to Reuse Or Recycle Your Old Tech: eWaste Is on the Rise but You Can Help Combat It By Using Old PCs and Electronics in Different Ways" in PC Magazine (Vol. 31, February 2012, No. 2, pp. 108)*
Description: US recycling businesses employ 30,000 workers to recycle 3.5 million tons of electronic waste, that does not include the number of devices that go to landfills. Simple and cheap ways to recycle or put old electronics to work are examined. **Availability:** Online.

5650 ■ *"How to... Harness Green Power" in The Caterer (July 20, 2012, No. 325)*
Pub: LNRS Data Services Limited
Contact: Mark Vickers Kelsey, Director

Description: Roger and Emma Stevens discuss their success as at winning the Considerate Hoteliers Association's award for Best Green Marketing Initiative. The couple discusses their restaurant and its partnership with tow nearby guesthouses. **Availability:** Online.

5651 ▪ *"IAPMO GTC Debates Supplement"* in *Contractor* (Vol. 56, September 2009, No. 9, pp. 3)
Ed: Robert P. Mader. **Description:** Green Technical Committee of the International Association of Plumbing and Mechanical Officials is developing a Green Plumbing and Mechanical Supplement. The supplement provides for installation of systems by licensed contractors and installers. Comments from officials are also presented. **Availability:** Print; Online.

5652 ▪ *"IAPMO GTC Votes to Limit Showers to 2.0-GPM"* in *Contractor* (Vol. 56, September 2009, No. 9, pp. 1)
Description: Green Technical Committee of the International Association of Plumbing and Mechanical Officials has voted to limit showers to 2.0 GPM. It is also developing a Green Plumbing and Mechanical Supplement. Comments from executives are also supplied. **Availability:** Print; Online.

5653 ▪ *"Independence Station Utilizes Sustainable Technologies"* in *Contractor* (Vol. 56, September 2009, No. 9, pp. 3)
Ed: Candace Roulo. **Description:** Independence Station building in Oregon is seen to receive the most LEED points ever awarded by the United States Green Building Council. The building will use an ice-based cooling storage system, biofuel cogeneration system and phovoltaic system. Other building features and dimensions are also supplied. **Availability:** Print; Online.

5654 ▪ *"IndieCompanyDk Offers Eco-Friendly Furniture That Stands Out"* in *Ecology, Environment & Conservation Business* (September 6, 2014, pp. 39)
Pub: NewsRX LLC.
Contact: Kalani Rosell, Contact
Description: A new manufacturer of eco-friendly furniture and interiors, IndieCompanyDk, is offering a new concept in sustainable furniture design, using exclusive and affordable smooth designs, which maintain the natural and raw look of quality reclaimed materials. **Availability:** Online.

5655 ▪ *"Industry Escalates Lobbying Efforts For Loan Program"* in *Crain's Detroit Business* (Vol. 24, September 22, 2008, No. 38, pp. 22)
Pub: Crain Communications Inc.
Contact: Barry Asin, President
Ed: Jay Greene, Ryan Beene, Harry Stoffer. **Description:** Auto suppliers such as Lear Corp., which is best known for vehicle seating, also supplies high-voltage wiring for Ford hybrids and is developing other hybrid components. These suppliers are joining automakers in lobbying for the loan program which would promote the accelerated development of fuel-efficient vehicles. **Availability:** Print; PDF; Online.

5656 ▪ *"Info Junkie: Karen Eng"* in *Crain's Chicago Business* (Vol. 34, October 24, 2011, No. 42, pp. 35)
Pub: Crain Communications Inc.
Contact: Barry Asin, President
Ed: Christina Le Beau. **Description:** Greg Colando, president of Flor Inc., an eco-friendly carpet company located I Chicago discusses his marketing program to increase sales. **Availability:** Online.

5657 ▪ *"Invest in Energy-Efficient Equipment for Your Pet Store"* in *Pet Product News* (Vol. 66, September 2012, No. 9, pp. 72)
Ed: Leila Meyer. **Description:** Aquatic retailers can achieve business growth by offering lighting products, pumps, heaters, filters, and other aquarium supplies that would help customers realize energy efficiency. Aside from offering an education in energy efficiency as a customer service opportunity, retailers are encouraged to determine what supplies are crucial in helping customers achieve energy usage goals. **Availability:** Online.

5658 ▪ *"Keene: Nominations are Being Sought by the Keene Cities for Climate Protection Committee for the Monadnock Green Business of the Year Award"* in *New Hampshire Business Review* (Vol. 34, February 24, 2012, No. 4, pp. 7)
Released: February 24, 2012. **Description:** Nominations are being sought by the Keene Cities for Climate Protection Committee for the Monadnock Green Business of the Year Award. The award recognizes socially and environmentally responsible companies in the region that have developed innovative practices or programs while contributing to the economic growth of the area.

5659 ▪ *"Kohler Building Earns LEED Silver Certification"* in *Contractor* (Vol. 56, September 2009, No. 9, pp. 12)
Description: United States Green Building Council has awarded Kohler Co. with the Silver Leadership in Energy and Environmental Design Status. The award has highlighted the company's work to transform its building into a more environmentally efficient structure. A description of the facility is also provided. **Availability:** Print; Online.

5660 ▪ *"Kroger Releases Annual Sustainability Report"* in *Ecology, Environment & Conservation Business* (July 26, 2014, pp. 46)
Pub: NewsRX LLC.
Contact: Kalani Rosell, Contact
Description: Kroger Company published its eighth annual sustainability report. The company is committed to reducing water consumption in its grocery stores by 5 percent in 2014. The report also provides a progress report on moving retail locations toward 'zero waste' and sourcing 100 percent certified palm oil. Statistical data included. **Availability:** Online.

5661 ▪ *"Large Homes can be Energy Efficient Too"* in *Contractor* (Vol. 56, October 2009, No. 10, pp. 5)
Ed: Candace Roulo. **Description:** Eco Estate at Briggs Chaney subdivision in Silver Spring, Maryland has model houses that use sustainable technologies and products and the homes that will be built on the subdivision will feature some of the technologies featured on the model home. The energy efficient HVAC system of the model homes are discussed. **Availability:** Print; Online.

5662 ▪ *"The Long View: Roberta Bondar's Unique Vision of Science, The Need for Education, and More"* in *Canadian Business* (Vol. 81, October 27, 2008, No. 18)
Pub: Rogers Media Inc.
Contact: Neil Spivak, Chief Executive Officer
Ed: Alex Mlynek. **Description:** Roberta Bondar believes that energy and renewable energy is a critical environmental issue faced by Canada today. Bondar is the first Canadian woman and neurologist in space. **Availability:** Online.

5663 ▪ *"Magpower May Build Solar Panels in Pflugerville"* in *Austin Business Journal* (Vol. 31, May 13, 2011, No. 10, pp. A1)
Pub: Austin Business Journal
Contact: Rachel McGrath, Director
E-mail: rmcgrath@bizjournals.com
Ed: Christopher Calnan. **Description:** RRE Austin Solar LLC CEO Doven Mehta has revealed plans to partner with Portugal-based Magpower SA, only if Austin energy buys electricity from planned solar energy farm in Pflugerville. Austin Energy has received 100 bids from 35 companies to supply 200 megawatts of solar- and wind-generated electricity. **Availability:** Print; Online.

5664 ▪ *"MFG Wind Launched at AWEA WindPower 2012 Conference and Exhibition"* in *Marketing Weekly News* (June 23, 2012, pp. 169)
Description: American Wind Energy Association's Conference & Exhibition was held in Atlanta, Georgia. The Molded Fiber Glass Companies (MFG) introduced MFG Wind, a new brand that stands for comprehensive wind-focused set of capabilities that it is bringing to the marketplace.

5665 ▪ *"Mixing Business and Pleasure On the Green"* in *Black Enterprise* (Vol. 41, October 2010, No. 3, pp. 65)
Description: Glow Golf, sponsored by Glow Sports, will offer instruction to 150 female corporate executives and entrepreneurs to learn the fundamentals of the game of golf. **Availability:** Print; Online.

5666 ▪ *The Necessary Revolution: Working Together to Create a Sustainable World*
Pub: Broadway Business
Ed: Peter M. Senge, Bryan Smith, Nina Kruschwitz, Joe Laur, Sara Schley. **Released:** April 06, 2010. **Price:** $20, paperback. **Description:** The book outlines various examples for companies to implement sustainable change and go green in the process. **Availability:** E-book; Print; Audio; Online.

5667 ▪ *"The New Alchemists"* in *Canadian Business* (Vol. 81, October 27, 2008, No. 18, pp. 22)
Description: Ethanol industry expects second-generation ethanol or cellulosic biofuels to provide ecologically friendly technologies than the ethanol made from food crops. Government and industries are investing on producing cellulosic biofuels. **Availability:** Print; Online.

5668 ▪ *"A New Alliance For Global Change"* in *Harvard Business Review* (Vol. 88, September 2010, No. 9, pp. 56)
Pub: Harvard Business Publishing
Contact: Diane Belcher, Managing Director
Ed: Bill Drayton, Valeria Budinich. **Price:** $8.95, PDF. **Description:** Collaboration between social organizations and for-profit firms through the development of hybrid value chains to target complex global issues is promoted. While social organizations offer links to communities and consumers, firms provide financing and scale expertise. **Availability:** Online; PDF.

5669 ▪ *"New Book Takes Alternate View on Ontario's Wind Industry"* in *CNW Group* (September 19, 2011)
Pub: CNW Group Ltd.
Description: Dirty Business: The Reality Behind Ontario's Rush to Wind Power, was written by editor and health care writer Jane Wilson of Ottawa, Ontario, Canada along with contributing editor Parker Gallant. The book contains articles and papers on the wind business, including information on illnesses caused from the environmental noise. **Availability:** Print; Online.

5670 ▪ *"A New Day is Dawning"* in *Indoor Comfort Marketing* (Vol. 70, August 2011, No. 8, pp. 18)
Description: New trends in the HVAC/R industry regarding biofuels and bioheat are explored. **Availability:** Online.

5671 ▪ *"New No. 1 at Element 8: Angel Group Brings on New Executive Director"* in *Puget Sound Business Journal* (Vol. 35, September 19, 2014, No. 22, pp. 6)
Pub: American City Business Journals, Inc.
Contact: Mike Olivieri, Executive Vice President
Description: Element 8 executive director, Kristi Growdon, says the company continues to find investment opportunities in the Pacific Northwest's clean technology sector. She also said the agricultural sector is a potentially lucrative investment destination. Growdon added that the company bases decisions on clean technology. **Availability:** Online.

5672 ▪ *"Next Stage of Green Building will be Water Efficiency"* in *Contractor* (Vol. 56, July 2009, No. 7, pp. 41)
Description: One market report says that water efficiency and conservation will become critical factors in green design, construction, and product selection in the next five years from 2009. The report outlines

how critical it will be for the construction industry to address responsible water practices in the future. **Availability:** Print; Online.

5673 ■ *"NStar Feels the Heat" in Cape Cod Times (September 30, 2011)*
Pub: Cape Cod Media Group
Contact: Anne Brennan, Executive Editor
E-mail: abrennan@capecodonline.com
Ed: Patrick Cassidy. **Description:** Massachusetts energy officials wish to delay a merger between NStar and Northeast Utilities until it is clear how the partnership would meet the state's green energy goals. Governor Deval Patrick supports the proposed Nantucket Sound wind farm. **Availability:** Online.

5674 ■ *"Nuclear Renaissance" in Canadian Business (Vol. 83, August 17, 2010, No. 13-14, pp. 46)*
Description: Nuclear energy has come back into the public's favor in Canada because it has virtually no emissions and is always available anytime of the day. Canada's nuclear industry has also achieved an incomparable record of safe, economic and reliable power generation in three provinces for 48 years. **Availability:** Online.

5675 ■ *"Out of Juice?" in Canadian Business (Vol. 81, October 27, 2008, No. 18, pp. 32)*
Description: Alternative energy experts suggest Canada should be more aggressive and should make major policy changes on energy alternatives despite an Ernst & Young research that rated the country high on renewable energy. **Availability:** Print; Online.

5676 ■ *"Overheating Taking Place? Pay Attention to Details.." in Indoor Comfort Marketing (Vol. 70, March 2011, No. 3)*
Description: Boiler facts are outlined to help the small HVAC company when servicing customers. **Availability:** PDF; Online.

5677 ■ *"An Overview of Energy Consumption of the Globalized World Economy" in Energy Policy (Vol. 39, October 2011, No. 10, pp. 5920-2928)*
Ed: Z. M. Chen, G. Q. Chen. **Released:** October 01, 2011. **Description:** Energy consumption and its impact on the global world economy is examined. **Availability:** Print; Online.

5678 ■ *"Paul Hawken and Other Top Lumnaries to Participate in Green Business BASE CAMP in Los Angeles" in Benzinga.com (April 19, 2012)*
Pub: Benzinga.com
Contact: Jason Raznick, Founder
Ed: Aaron Wise. **Description:** Paul Hawken, environmentalist, entrepreneur and author, is one of many people participating in the Green Business BASE CAMP, a four-day workshop for green business and cleantech entrepreneurs. The event will be held in Los Angeles, California from May 31 through June 3, 2012. Insider guidance will be offered to early-stage entrepreneurs seeking to compete within this sector. **Availability:** Online.

5679 ■ *"Pennsylvania DEP To Conduct Natural Gas Vehicle Seminar" in Travel & Leisure Close-Up (October 8, 2012)*
Description: Pennsylvania Department of Environmental Protection is holding a Natural Gas Vehicle seminar at the Bayfront Convention Center in Erie, PA, as well as other locations throughout the state. The seminars will help municipal and commercial fleet owners make better informed decisions when converting fleets from compressed natural gas and liquefied natural gas. **Availability:** Print; Online.

5680 ■ *"Planned CO2 Regulations Could Hit Region Hard" in Pittsburgh Business Times (Vol. 33, June 6, 2014, No. 47, pp. 9)*
Pub: American City Business Journals, Inc.
Contact: Mike Olivieri, Executive Vice President
Released: Weekly. **Price:** $4, introductory 4-week offer(Digital only). **Description:** The U.S. Environmental Protection Agency's (EPA's) proposed rules to cut carbon dioxide (CO2) emissions by 30 percent over 16 years could have an adverse impact on southwestern Pennsylvania. The draft regulations, announced June 2, 2014, will affect the Pennsylvania region's power-generation sector as well as its coal industry, thereby impacting the regional economy. **Availability:** Print; Online.

5681 ■ *"Pre-Certified LEED Hotel Prototype Reduces Energy Use, Conserves Water" in Contractor (Vol. 57, January 2010, No. 1, pp. 3)*
Pub: Informa USA, Inc.
Contact: Stephen A. Carter, Chief Executive Officer
Ed: Candace Roulo. **Released:** January 01, 2010. **Description:** Marriott International Inc.'s LEED pre-certified prototype hotel will reduce a hotel's energy and water consumption by 25 percent and save owners approximately $100,000. Their Courtyard Settler's Ridge in Pittsburgh will be the first hotel built based on the prototype.

5682 ■ *"PrintCity Shares Guide for Carbon Footprinting" in American Printer (Vol. 128, June 1, 2011, No. 6)*
Description: PrintCity Alliance published its new report, 'Carbon Footprint & Energy Reduction for Graphic Industry Value Chain.' The report aims to help improve the environmental performance of printers, converters, publishers, brand owners and their suppliers. **Availability:** Online.

5683 ■ *"Professional Grooming Marketplace: Cash In On Green Products and Services" in Pet Product News (Vol. 66, September 2012, No. 9, pp. 84)*
Ed: Lizett Bond. **Description:** Pet grooming salons can build customer reputation by providing sustainable and environment-friendly products and services. Energy efficiency and electricity conservation can also be focused upon as pet grooming salons aspire for green marketing goals. **Availability:** Online.

5684 ■ *"Programs Provide Education and Training" in Contractor (Vol. 56, September 2009, No. 9, pp. 56)*
Ed: William Feldman, Patti Feldman. **Description:** Opportunity Interactive's Showroom v2 software provides uses computer graphics to provide education and training on HVAC equipment and systems. It can draw heat pump balance points for a specific home. Meanwhile, Simutech's HVAC Training Simulators provide trainees with 'hands-on' HVACR training. **Availability:** Print; Online.

5685 ■ *"PSC Approves $130M TECO Solar Project" in Tampa Bay Business Journal (Vol. 30, December 18, 2009, No. 52, pp. 1)*
Pub: Tampa Bay Business Journal
Contact: Ian Anderson, President
E-mail: ianderson@bizjournals.com
Ed: Michael Hinman. **Description:** Florida's Public Service Commission has endorsed Tampa Electric Company's plan to add 25 megawatts of solar energy to its portfolio. TECO's plan needed the approval by PSC to defray additional costs for the project through ratepayers. **Availability:** Print; Online.

5686 ■ *"PSC Decision Could Help Bolster a Solar Market Supernova" in Tampa Bay Business Journal (Vol. 29, November 6, 2009, No. 46, pp. 1)*
Pub: Tampa Bay Business Journal
Contact: Ian Anderson, President
E-mail: ianderson@bizjournals.com
Ed: Michael Hinman. **Description:** Florida's Public Service Commission (PSC) decision on a power purchase agreement that could add 25 megawatts of solar energy on Tampa Electric Company's offerings is presented. The decision could support the growing market for suppliers and marketers of renewable energy such as Jabil Circuit Inc., which manufactures photovoltaic modules. Details of the agreement are discussed. **Availability:** Print; Online.

5687 ■ *"PSEG Queen Creek Solar Farm in Arizona Begins Commercial Operation" in Benzinga.com (October 4, 2012)*
Description: PSEG Solar Source will launch the commercial operation of the 25.2 megawatt DC (19 megawatt AC) Queen Creek Solar Farm in Queen Creek, Arizona. The Salt River Project (SRP) has a 20-year agreement to acquire acquire all of the solar energy generated by the project. More details are included.

5688 ■ *"PSI Repair Services to Showcase at Windpower Conference and Exhibition" in Entertainment Close-Up (May 19, 2012)*
Description: Subsidiary of Phillips Service Industries, PSI Repair Services, will highlight its off-warranty repair support for wind energy operations at the Windpower 2012 Conference and Exhibition. **Availability:** Online.

5689 ■ *"Recession Creating Surge in Business for Auto Recyclers" in Business Journal-Serving Phoenix & the Valley of the Sun (Vol. 31, November 12, 2010, No. 10, pp. 1)*
Pub: Phoenix Business Journal
Contact: Alex McAlister, Director
E-mail: amcalister@bizjournals.com
Ed: Patrick O'Grady. **Description:** Automotive parts recyclers in Arizona are benefiting from the challenging national economic conditions as well as from the green movement. Recyclers revealed that customers prefer recycled parts more because they are cheaper and are more environmentally friendly. Other information about the automotive parts recycling industry is presented. **Availability:** Print; Online.

5690 ■ *"Recycling 202: How to Take Your Recycling Practices to the Next Level" in Black Enterprise (Vol. 41, September 2010, No. 2, pp. 38)*
Pub: Earl G. Graves Ltd.
Contact: Earl Graves, Jr., President
Ed: Tamara E. Holmes. **Description:** Consumer Electronics Association and other organizations, manufacturers and retailers list ways to recycle all household items. **Availability:** Online.

5691 ■ *"Reducing the Book's Carbon Footprint" in American Printer (Vol. 128, July 1, 2011, No. 7)*
Description: Green Press Initiative's Book Industry Environmental Council is working to achieve a 20 percent reduction in the book industry's carbon footprint by 2020. The Council is made up of publishers, printers, paper suppliers, and non-governmental organizations. **Availability:** Online.

5692 ■ *"Region Wins as GE Puts Plants Close to R&D" in Business Review Albany (Vol. 41, July 4, 2014, No. 15, pp. 8)*
Pub: American City Business Journals, Inc.
Contact: Mike Olivieri, Executive Vice President
Description: General Electric Company (GE) invested over $400 million into the expansion of its health care, battery and renewable energy businesses in the Albany, New York region. The company's local growth secured about 7,000 private-sector jobs in the area and strengthened the relationship between GE research and manufacturing. **Availability:** Print; Online.

5693 ■ *"Reinventing Marketing to Manage the Environmental Imperative" in Journal of Marketing (Vol. 75, July 2011, No. 4, pp. 132)*
Pub: American Marketing Association
Contact: Bennie F. Johnson, Chief Executive Officer
Ed: Philip Kotler. **Description:** Marketers must now examine their theory and practices due to the growing recognition of finite resources and high environmental costs. Companies also need to balance more carefully their growth goals with the need to purse sustainability. Insights on the rise of demarketing and social marketing are also given. **Availability:** PDF.

5694 ■ "Renewable Energy Adoption in an Ageing Population: Heterogeneity in Preferences for Micro-Generation Technology Adoption" in Energy Policy (Vol. 39, October 2011, No. 10, pp. 6021-6029)
Ed: Ken Willis, Riccardo Scarpa, Rose Gilroy, Neveen Hamza. Released: October 01, 2011. Description: Attitudes and impacts of renewable energy adoption on an aging population is examined. Availability: Print; Online.

5695 ■ "Renewable Energy Market Opportunities: Wind Testing" in PR Newswire (September 22, 2011)
Pub: PR Newswire Association LLC.
Description: Global wind energy test systems markets are discussed. Research conducted covers both non-destructive test equipment and condition monitoring equipment product segments.

5696 ■ "Renewable Plants are Still On Valero Energy's Radar" in San Antonio Business Journal (Vol. 28, March 28, 2014, No. 7, pp. 10)
Pub: American City Business Journals, Inc.
Contact: Mike Olivieri, Executive Vice President
Released: Weekly. Price: $4, Introductory 4-week offer(Digital & Print). Description: Analysts believe that Valero Energy Corporation's recent purchase of an ethanol plant will not be its last. The company is considered to be the third-largest ethanol refiner in the U.S. The possibility of reopening Valero's other plants is also examined. Availability: Print; Online.

5697 ■ "Research and Markets Offers Report on US Business Traveler's Green, New Technology Views" in Airline Industry Information (July 30, 2012)
Description: The US Business Traveler Expectations of Green and Technology Initiatives in Hotels in 2012 contains comprehensive analysis on US business travelers views on green and technology initiative and socially responsible measures geared towards the business traveler. Availability: Print; Online.

5698 ■ "ReVenture Plan Appears Close to Landing Key N.C. Legislative Deal" in Charlotte Business Journal (Vol. 25, July 9, 2010, No. 16, pp. 1)
Pub: Charlotte Business Journal
Contact: Robert Morris, Editor
E-mail: rmorris@bizjournals.com
Ed: John Downey. Description: North Carolina lawmakers acted on special legislation that would boost development of Forsite Development 667-acre ReVenture Energy Park. The legislation could also improve chances that Duke Energy Carolinas will contract to purchase the power from the planned 50-megawatt biomass power plant located at the park. How utilities would benefit from the legislation is also discussed. Availability: Print; Online.

5699 ■ "R.I. Lags in Solar Incentives" in Providence Business News (Vol. 29, May 26, 2014, No. 8, pp. 1)
Pub: American City Business Journals, Inc.
Contact: Mike Olivieri, Executive Vice President
Released: May 24, 2014. Description: The state of Rhode Island has offered less in government renewable energy incentives than its neighboring states and has yet to experience the growth of residential solar energy projects. The Rhode Island Renewable Energy Fund allocated $800,000 to the small scale solar program in 2014. Availability: Print; Online.

5700 ■ "Richard Faulk Covers Climate in Copenhagen" in Houston Business Journal (Vol. 40, December 25, 2009, No. 33, pp. 1)
Pub: Houston Business Journal
Contact: Bob Charlet, President
E-mail: bcharlet@bizjournals.com
Ed: Ford Gunter. Description: Houston environmental attorney Richard Faulk talks to the United Nations Climate Change Conference in Copenhagen, Denmark. Faulk believes the conference failed due to political differences between countries like US and China. Faulk believed the discussion of developed and developing countries on verification and limits on carbon emissions is something good that came from the conference. Availability: Print; Online.

5701 ■ "Rosewood Site Faces Big Cleanup Before Stevenson Can Expand" in Baltimore Business Journal (Vol. 27, February 6, 2010, No. 40, pp. 1)
Pub: Baltimore Business Journal
Contact: Rhonda Pringle, President
E-mail: rpringle@bizjournals.com
Ed: Daniel J. Sernovitz. Description: Environmental assessment report states that Maryland's Rosewood Center for the Developmentally Disabled has significant amounts of toxic chemicals, which could impact Stevenson University's decision to purchase the property. Senator Robert A. Zirkin believes that the state should pay for the cleanup, which is expected to cost millions. Availability: Print; Online.

5702 ■ "Rough Headwinds" in Boston Business Journal (Vol. 30, November 12, 2010, No. 42, pp. 1)
Pub: Boston Business Journal
Contact: Carolyn M. Jones, President
E-mail: cmjones@bizjournals.com
Ed: Kyle Alspach. Description: Views of residents, as well as key information on First Wind's plan to install wind power turbines in Brimfield, Massachusetts are presented. Residents believe that First Wind's project will devalue properties, compromise quality of life, and ruin the rural quality of Brimfield. First Wind expects to produce 2,000 megawatts of power from wind by 2020. Availability: Online.

5703 ■ "Sales of What's Under Feet Add Up Fast" in Pet Product News (Vol. 66, September 2012, No. 9, pp. S8)
Description: Pet supplies retailers and manufacturers have been emphasizing the type of substances in creating new approaches to developing environment-friendly natural litters and beddings for small mammals and cats. Some of these approaches are highlighted, along with marketing strategies retailers have implemented. Availability: Print; Online.

5704 ■ "Saving the Planet: A Tale of Two Strategies: Thomas Malthus Advised Restraint; Robert Solow Promotes Innovation. Let's Pursue Both To Solve the Environmental Crisis" in Harvard Business Review (Vol. 90, April 2012, No. 4, pp. 48)
Pub: Harvard Business Review Press
Contact: Moderna V. Pfizer, Contact
Ed: Roger Martin, Alison Kemper. Price: $8.95, hardcover. Description: Theories of economists Thomas Malthus and Robert Solow are merged to address specific environmental problems. Malthusian restraint includes fuel economy, refillable bottles, and recycling. Solovian innovation includes water supply chlorination, solar cooking, and geothermal energy. Availability: PDF; Online.

5705 ■ "The Second Most Fuel-Efficient Tractor of the Decade: John Deere 8320R" in Farm Industry News (November 10, 2011)
Pub: Informa Business Media, Inc.
Contact: Charlie McCurdy, President
Description: John Deere's 8320R Tractor was ranked second in the Farm Industry News listing of the top 40 most fuel-efficient tractors of the decade, following the winner, John Deere's 8295R PTO tractor. Availability: Online.

5706 ■ "Six Arkansas Construction Projects Get LEED Certification" in Arkansas Business (Vol. 29, July 23, 2012, No. 30, pp. 19)
Pub: Arkansas Business Publishing Group
Contact: Mitch Bettis, President
Ed: Lance Turner. Description: State of Arkansas has bestowed its Leadership in Energy and Environmental Design certification on 55 projects throughout the state. Six projects are identified and described. A list of all projects is included. Availability: Online.

5707 ■ "Sky Harvest Windpower Corp. - Operational Update" in Investment Weekly News (March 10, 2012, pp. 744)
Pub: PR Newswire Association LLC.
Description: Sky Harvest Windpower Corporation is rebranding its focus on gas and power activities both nationally and internationally. The firm's Canadian projects are outlined as well as its commitment to purse the Green Options Partners Program in 2012. Availability: Online.

5708 ■ "Small Wind Power Market to Double by 2015 at $634 Million" in Western Farm Press (September 30, 2011)
Description: Small wind power provides cost-effective electricity on a highly localized level, in both remote settings as well as in conjunction with power from the utility grid. Government incentives are spurring new growth in the industry. Availability: Online.

5709 ■ "Solar Choices" in Contractor (Vol. 56, October 2009, No. 10, pp. 32)
Ed: Tom Scheel. Description: Price, performance, and ease of installation of a flat plate versus an evacuated tube collector for a plumbing and heating job are compared. The better choice with regards to weight, aesthetics, efficiency in warm or cool climates, year round load, and space heating is discussed. Availability: Print; Online.

5710 ■ "State Investment Goes Sour" in Business Journal Portland (Vol. 26, December 4, 2009, No. 39, pp. 1)
Pub: Portland Business Journal
Contact: Andy Giegerich, Managing Editor
E-mail: agiegerich@bizjournals.com
Ed: Erik Siemers. Description: Oregon might recoup only $500,000 of a $20 million loan to Vancouver-based Cascade Grain Products LLC. Cascade Grain's ethanol plant in Clatskanie, OR will be put into auction under the supervision of a bankruptcy court. Availability: Print; Online.

5711 ■ "Store Front: Invest in Energy-Efficient Equipment for Your Pet Store" in Pet Product News (Vol. 66, September 2012, No. 9, pp. 43)
Ed: Leila Meyer. Description: Developments in energy-efficient lighting, heating, and air conditioning have allowed pet supplies stores to conduct upgrades that result in savings. Pet supplies stores have also been impressing customers by obtaining Energy Start or LEED certification. Availability: Print; Online.

5712 ■ "The Superpower Dilemma" in Canadian Business (Vol. 83, August 17, 2010, No. 13-14, pp. 42)
Description: Canada has been an energy super-power partly because it controls the energy source and the production means, particularly of fossil fuels. However, Canada's status as superpower could diminish if it replaces petroleum exports with renewable technology for using sources of energy available globally. Availability: Online.

5713 ■ "Sustainability Is Top Priority for GreenTown Chicago" in Contractor (Vol. 56, November 2009, No. 11, pp. 1)
Ed: Candace Roulo. Description: GreenTown Chicago 2009 conference tackled energy-efficient practices and technologies, green design and building, and sustainable policies. Water conservation was also a topic at the conference and one mayor who made a presentation said that reducing the water loss in the system is a priority in the city's endeavor. Availability: Print; Online.

5714 ■ "Suzlon S88-Powered Wind Farm in Minnesota Secures Long-Term Financing" in PR Newswire (September 21, 2011)
Pub: PR Newswire Association LLC.
Description: Suzlon Energy Limited is the world's fifth largest manufacturer of wind turbines. Owners of the Grant County Wind Farm in Minnesota have secured a long-term financing deal for the ten Suzlon S88 2.1 MW wind turbines that generate enough electricity to power 7,000 homes.

5715 ■ "Taxis Are Set to Go Hybrid" in Philadelphia Business Journal (Vol. 30, September 16, 2011, No. 31, pp. 1)
Pub: Philadelphia Business Journal
Contact: Sierra Quinn, Director
E-mail: squinn@bizjournals.com
Ed: Natalie Kostelni. **Description:** Taxis are going hybrid in several major states such as New York, California and Maryland where it is mandated, but it is yet to happen in Philadelphia, Pennsylvania with the exception of one taxi company. Freedom Taxi is awaiting Philadelphia Parking Authority's sign off. **Availability:** Online.

5716 ■ "Thirsty? Now There's a Water Cooler to Suit Every Taste" in Inc. (Vol. 33, October 2011, No. 8, pp. 43)
Description: Brita's Hydration Station is a wall-mounted unit with a touch-free sensor for dispensing water. This water cooler cuts down on landfill waste and offers special features. **Availability:** Print; Online.

5717 ■ "Three Megatrends to Help Your Business Compete in 2014" in South Florida Business Journal (Vol. 34, January 3, 2014, No. 24, pp. 10)
Pub: American City Business Journals, Inc.
Contact: Mike Olivieri, Executive Vice President
Released: Weekly. **Price:** $8, Introductory 4-week offer(Digital & Print). **Description:** Businesses can improve their competitive edge in 2014 by adapting several mega small business trends in marketing and communications. Brands can use brand bridging to get customers attention, use wearable technology to increase their value, and adapt environmental sustainability and corporate social responsibility to keep their customers. **Availability:** Print; Online.

5718 ■ "Timken Features Solutions at AWEA WINDPOWER 2012" in PR Newswire (June 3, 2012)
Pub: PR Newswire Association LLC.
Description: The Timken Company plans to highlight its products and aftermarket solutions for the wind industry at the AWEA WINDPOWER 2012 Conference and Exhibition. Timken products help to maximize the performance of wind energy equipment. **Availability:** Online.

5719 ■ "Toolmakers' New Tack: Firms' Goal -- Advance Wind-Turbine Technology" in Crain's Detroit Business (Vol. 25, June 8, 2009,)
Pub: Crain Communications Inc.
Contact: Barry Asin, President
Ed: Ryan Beene, Amy Lane. **Description:** MAG Industrial Automation Systems LLC and Dowding Machining Inc. have partnered to advance wind-turbine technology. The goal is to cut costs of wind energy to the same level as carbon-based fuel. **Availability:** Print; Online.

5720 ■ "Ultra Low Sulfur Diesel: The Promise and the Reality" in Indoor Comfort Marketing (Vol. 70, July 2011, No. 7, pp. 22)
Description: Impacts of ultra low sulfur diesel are examined.

5721 ■ "Unilever to Sustainably Source All Paper and Board Packaging" in Ice Cream Reporter (Vol. 23, July 20, 2010, No. 8, pp. 1)
Description: Unilever, a leader in the frozen dessert market, has announced a new sustainable paper and board packaging sourcing policy that will reduce environmental impact by working with suppliers to source 75 percent of paper and board packaging from sustainably managed forests or from recycled material. Unilever is parent company to Breyers, Haagen-Dazs, Klondike, Popsicle and other ice cream brands.

5722 ■ "Valener Announces that Gaz Metro has Achieved a Key Step in Acquiring CVPS" in CNW Group (September 30, 2011)
Pub: CNW Group Ltd.
Description: Valener Inc., which owns about 29 percent of Gaz Metro Ltd. Partnership, announced that Gaz Metro welcomes the sale of Central Vermont Public Service Corporation (CVPS). Valener owns an indirect interest of 24.5 percent in the wind power projects jointly developed by Beaupre Eole General Partnership and Boralex Inc. on private lands in Quebec. Details of the deal are included. **Availability:** Print; Online.

5723 ■ "Volunteers Needed" in Canadian Business (Vol. 81, October 27, 2008, No. 18, pp. 60)
Description: Emissions-targeting regulations focus on the biggest polluters, missing out on other companies that leave carbon footprints in things such as shipping and travel. Some companies in Canada have initiated programs to offset their carbon emissions. Critics claim that offsetting does not reduce emissions and the programs merely justify pollution.

5724 ■ "Water Conservation Helps GC's Building Attain LEED Gold Status" in Contractor (Vol. 56, September 2009, No. 9, pp. 5)
Description: Green contractor Marshall Erdman has built a new office building using green design. The facility is seen to become a prime Leadership in Energy and Environmental Design (LEED) building model. Details of the building's design and features are also provided. **Availability:** Print; Online.

5725 ■ "Water-Recycling Trend Could Ease Demand for Injection Wells" in San Antonio Business Journal (Vol. 28, June 13, 2014, No. 18, pp. 6)
Pub: American City Business Journals, Inc.
Contact: Mike Olivieri, Executive Vice President
Released: Weekly. **Price:** $4, Introductory 4-week offer(Digital & Print). **Description:** Industry experts are encouraging oil and gas companies to consider investing in water recycling technology to ease the demand for wastewater disposal wells in South Texas. According to Pinnergy chief executive officer, Randy Taylor, the demand for disposal wells will not go away even with more water reuse in the area. **Availability:** Print; Online.

5726 ■ "Water Woes Force Big Brewers to Tighten the Tap" in Idaho Business Review (June 11, 2014)
Pub: BridgeTower Media
Contact: Adam Reinebach, President
Description: As drought or wildfires threated watersheds, large brewers across the nation are seeking to reduce their water-to-beer ratio in order to conserve the nation's water supply. Craft beer makers have expanded to its highest level since the 1870s. Statistical data included.

5727 ■ "What Is a Geothermal Heat Pump" in Indoor Comfort Marketing (Vol. 70, August 2011, No. 8, pp. 14)
Description: Examination of geothermal heat pumps is provided, citing new trends in the industry. **Availability:** Print; Online.

5728 ■ "Will Home Buyers Pay for Green Features?" in Contractor (Vol. 56, October 2009, No. 10, pp. 70)
Ed: Robert P. Mader. **Description:** National Association of Home Builders commissioned a survey which shows that homeowners are interested in green as long as they do not have to pay much for it. The association did not allow a board member to read the survey which raises questions about how the questions were phrased and how the sample was selected. **Availability:** Print; Online.

5729 ■ "Wind Farm Is Planned for Yolo Farmland" in Sacramento Business Journal (Vol. 29, September 21, 2012, No. 30, pp. 1)
Pub: Baltimore Business Journal
Contact: Rhonda Pringle, President
E-mail: rpringle@bizjournals.com
Ed: Melanie Turner. **Description:** Austin, Texas-based Pioneer Green Energy LLC has been planning to build as many as 400 wind turbines in Yolo County, California that could potentially generate up to 600 megawatts. The company has already raised $20 and it is expected to formally propose the project in early 2013. The economic impact on the farmers and landowners in the region is explored. **Availability:** Online.

5730 ■ "Wind Gets Knocked Out of Energy Farm Plan" in Buffalo News (September 28, 2011)
Description: New York Power Authority formally killed the proposal for a wind energy farm off the shores of Lake Erie and Lake Ontario. The Authority cited high subsidy costs would be required to make the wind farm economically feasible. Details of the proposal are outlined. **Availability:** Online.

5731 ■ "WindPower Solutions Announces Its Best In Class 'Next Gen' 85kw Wind Turbine" in Marketwired (June 6, 2012)
Pub: Comtex News Network Inc.
Contact: Kan Devnani, President
Description: WinPower Innovations Inc.'s subsidiary, WindPower Solutions, unveiled its next generation 85kw wind turbines that are available for sale. They are perfect for remote locations where there is a lot of wind and can be used locally or the site owner, if near the power grid, could sell the energy to the market. **Availability:** Online.

5732 ■ "Women Up: Kathleen Ligocki of Harvest Power Inc." in Boston Business Journal (Vol.. 34, April 11, 2014, No. 10)
Pub: American City Business Journals, Inc.
Contact: Mike Olivieri, Executive Vice President
Released: Weekly. **Price:** $4, introductory 4-week offer(Digital & Print). **Description:** Kathleen Ligocki is the CEO of Harvest Power Inc. of Massachusetts. The company diverts organic waste destined for landfills and produces green energy and soil enrichment products. The company was founded in 2008 and reported sales of over $130 million in 2013. **Availability:** Print; Online.

5733 ■ "Wood Increasingly Used in School Construction" in Arkansas Business (Vol. 29, July 23, 2012, No. 30, pp. 11)
Pub: Arkansas Business Publishing Group
Contact: Mitch Bettis, President
Ed: Jan Cottingham. **Description:** Arkansas state guidelines have increased the use of wood in school building construction. Wood is believed to provide strength and durability along with cost effectiveness and environmental benefits. **Availability:** Online.

5734 ■ "Yates Turns Log Home Green - Part Three" in Contractor (Vol. 57, January 2010, No. 1, pp. 5)
Released: January 12, 2010. **Description:** Dave Yates of F.W. Behler Inc. discusses remodeling a log home's HVAC system with geo-to-radiant heat and thermal-solar systems. The solar heater's installation is discussed.

5735 ■ "You're a What? Wind Turbine Service Technician" in Occupational Outlook Quarterly (Vol. 54, Fall 2010, No. 3, pp. 34)
Pub: U.S. Department of Labor Bureau of Labor Statistics
Contact: Amrit Kohli, Director
E-mail: kohli.amrit@bls.gov
Ed: Drew Liming. **Description:** Profile of Brandon Johnson, former member of the Air Force, found a career as a wind turbine service technician. **Availability:** Online; PDF.

5736 ■ "Yudelson Challenges San Antonio Groups" in Contractor (Vol. 56, October 2009, No. 10, pp. 6)
Description: Green building consultant and author Jerry Yudelson made a presentation for the Central Texas Green Building Council and Leadership San Antonio where he discussed the European approach to sustainability and how it can be used for designing

green buildings. Yudelson also discussed how to use sustainable practices for planning 25 years into the future. **Availability:** Print; Online.

STATISTICAL SOURCES

5737 ■ *Environmental Consulting Industry in the US - Market Research Report*
URL(s): www.ibisworld.com/united-states/market-research-reports/environmental-consulting-industry/
Price: $925. **Description:** Downloadable report analyzing the current and future trends in the environmental consulting industry. **Availability:** Download.

TRADE PERIODICALS

5738 ■ *Cal/EPA*
Pub: Inside Washington Publishers
Contact: Robert Woolard, Contact
URL(s): insideepa.com/topics/issue-inside-calepa
Description: Reports on environmental legislation, regulation, and litigation. **Availability:** Print.

5739 ■ *Clearwater Navigator*
Pub: Hudson River Sloop Clearwater
Contact: Greg Williams, Contact
URL(s): www.clearwater.org/about/publications-financials
Ed: Linda Richards. **Released:** Annual **Description:** Contains information on environmental issues, globally, nationally, and locally. Recurring features include letters to the editor, interviews, news of research, a calendar of events, and reports of meetings. **Availability:** PDF; Online.

5740 ■ *Composting News*
Pub: McEntee Media Corp.
URL(s): compostingnews.com
Facebook: www.facebook.com/CompostingNews
X (Twitter): x.com/CompostingNews
Released: Monthly **Price:** $83, Individuals for one year; $140, Individuals for two years. **Description:** Covers news and trends in the composting industry. Also reports on compost product prices. Recurring features include letters to the editor, interviews, news of research, a calendar of events, reports of meetings, and notices of publications available. **Availability:** Print; Download; Online.

5741 ■ *E-The Environmental Magazine*
Pub: Earth Action Network
Contact: Mha Atma Singh Khalsa, Contact
URL(s): emagazine.com
Facebook: www.facebook.com/askearthtalk
X (Twitter): x.com/EEnviroMag
Instagram: www.instagram.com/e_the_environmental_magazine
Ed: Roddy Scheer, Brita Belli. **Released:** Bimonthly **Description:** Clearinghouse of news, information and commentary on environmental issues. **Availability:** Online.

5742 ■ *Earth Island Journal: An International Environmental News Magazine*
Pub: Earth Island Institute
Contact: Josh Floum, President
URL(s): www.earthisland.org/journal
Facebook: www.facebook.com/EarthIslandJournal
Ed: Jason Mark. **Released:** Quarterly; Summer, Spring, Winter, autumn. **Price:** $25, for international addresses; $20, for award-winning. **Description:** Magazine publishing environmental alerts and success stories from around the world. **Availability:** Print; Online.

5743 ■ *Environmental Compliance Alert*
Pub: American Future Systems Inc.
Contact: Edward G. Rendell, Governor
URL(s): www.pbp.com/divisions/publishing/newsletters/regulations-compliance/environmental-compliance-alert
Released: Semimonthly **Description:** Explains the latest air, water and waste regulatory changes affect business in plain English. Recurring features include interviews, news of research, a calendar of events, news of educational opportunities, and a column titled Sharpen Your Judgment. **Availability:** Online.

5744 ■ *Environmental News Network (ENN)*
Pub: Environmental News Network
URL(s): www.enn.com
Facebook: www.facebook.com/TheEnnNews
Linkedin: www.linkedin.com/company/enn
X (Twitter): twitter.com/EnnNews
Ed: Allison Winter, Roger Greenway, Mohammad Munshed. **Released:** Daily **Description:** Online magazine covering environmental and science topics. **Availability:** Print; Online.

5745 ■ *Water Policy Report*
Pub: Inside Washington Publishers
Contact: Robert Woolard, Contact
URL(s): iwpnews.com/index.html#products
Released: Biweekly **Price:** $730, U.S. for per year; $730, Canada for per year; $780, Elsewhere for per year. **Description:** Reports on federal water quality programs and policies. Covers topics such as drinking water, toxics, enforcement, monitoring, and state/EPA relations. **Availability:** Online.

5746 ■ *Worm Digest: Worms Deepening Our Connection to Food and Soil*
Contact: Yu-Ting Lin, Editor
URL(s): www.wormdigest.org
Ed: Yu-Ting Lin. **Released:** Quarterly **Description:** Magazine reporting on worms and worm composting for organic waste utilization and soil enrichment. **Availability:** E-book; Print; Download; Online.

TRADE SHOWS AND CONVENTIONS

5747 ■ **GLOBE: Conference and Exhibition on Business and the Environment**
URL(s): 2016.globeseries.com
X (Twitter): twitter.com/GLOBE_Series
Frequency: Biennial. **Description:** Solutions for problems associated with climate change, energy security, and rising fuel prices. **Audience:** Business professionals. **Principal Exhibits:** Solutions for problems associated with climate change, energy security, and rising fuel prices.

CONSULTANTS

5748 ■ **Ardea Consulting**
PO Box 203
Minford, OH 45653
Ph: (530)669-1645
Co. E-mail: birdtox1@ardeacon.com
URL: http://ardeacon.com
Contact: Joseph P. Sullivan, Consultant Owner Principal
Description: Science-based consulting firm provides ecological risk assessments, avian and wildlife toxicology and ecotoxicology consulting services. **Founded:** 1997. **Publications:** "Estimating the response of ring-necked pheasants to the Conservation Reserve Program," 2008; "Identifying and handling contaminant-related wildlife mortality/morbidity," The Wildlife Society, 2005; "Productivity of American robins exposed to polychlorinated biphenyls," 2003; "Assessing impacts of environmental contaminants on wildlife". **Training:** Pheasant breeding bird survey response to the conservation reserve program, 2006; Society of Environmental Toxicology and Chemistry; Niov, 2006; Introduction and Demonstration of the Terrestrial Wildlife Exposure Model (TWEM), Nov, 2004; Society of Environmental Toxicology and Chemistry, Nov, 2004.

5749 ■ **EnviroBusiness Inc. (EBI)**
21 B St.
Burlington, MA 01803
Ph: (781)273-2500
Co. E-mail: info@ebiconsulting.com
URL: http://www.ebiconsulting.com
Contact: Nolan Previte, President
E-mail: nprevite@ebiconsulting.com
Facebook: www.facebook.com/EBIConsulting
Linkedin: www.linkedin.com/company/ebi-consulting
X (Twitter): x.com/ebiconsulting
YouTube: www.youtube.com/user/EBIConsulting
Description: Provider of environmental health and safety, architecture and engineering, due diligence, energy use reduction, management and engineering services for organizations. **Scope:** Provider of environmental health and safety, architecture and engineering, due diligence, energy use reduction, management and engineering services for organizations. **Founded:** 1989. **Training:** Marina Industry Regulatory Compliance Assistance, Mar, 2007; The Business of Boating in MA, Jan, 2007.

5750 ■ **Environmental Business Consultants (EBC)**
33 Wanita Rd.
Mississauga, ON, Canada L5G 1B3
Co. E-mail: info@ebccanada.com
URL: http://www.ebccanada.com/index.shtml
Contact: John Nicholson, President
E-mail: john.nicholson@ebccanada.com
Description: Firm provides consultation services in environmental and business management.

5751 ■ **Groupe DGE International Inc.**
1870, rue Cecile-Chabot
Sherbrooke, QC, Canada J1J 1P2
Ph: (819)820-8881
Co. E-mail: info@dgeinternational.ca
URL: http://dgeinternational.ca/en
Contact: Sophie Gauvin, President
E-mail: sgauvin@dgeinternational.ca
Description: Firm specializes in performing environmental management projects like the implementation of ISO 14000 environmental management system, the completion of studies and verifications as well as financial assistance requests for viability studies and implementation of international projects. **Scope:** Firm specializes in performing environmental management projects like the implementation of ISO 14000 environmental management system, the completion of studies and verifications as well as financial assistance requests for viability studies and implementation of international projects. **Founded:** 1999.

5752 ■ **J.L. Meaher and Associates Inc.**
107 St. Francis St., Ste. 1970
Mobile, AL 36602
Contact: Joseph L. Meaher, Contact
Description: Firm provides general forestry consulting, including advice on timber and timberland taxation, estate taxation, planning, timberland sales and purchases. **Scope:** Firm provides general forestry consulting, including advice on timber and timberland taxation, estate taxation, planning, timberland sales and purchases. **Founded:** 1974.

5753 ■ **Social Venture Partners (SVP)**
3815 S Othello St., Ste. 100 No. 374
Seattle, WA 98118
Ph: (206)471-0410
Co. E-mail: info@svpi.org
URL: http://www.socialventurepartners.org
Contact: Sudha Nandagopal, Chief Executive Officer
Facebook: www.facebook.com/SVPIntl
YouTube: www.youtube.com/user/SocialVenturePartner
Description: A philanthropic network principally engaged in providing tools, resources and consultancy services, including organizational management, program development and fundraising initiatives for not-for-profit organizations and social enterprises. **Founded:** 1997. **Publications:** "Voices That Matter: Paul Shoemaker, on Becoming a Social Entrepreneur," Oct, 2009; "Immerse Your Donors In You," The Nonprofit Times, Sep, 2009; "New Ideas Shouldn't Necessarily Spawn New Nonprofit Groups," Jan, 2009; "Inside Entrepreneurship: Nonprofit boards will welcome your talents," Dec, 2008; "Charity begins in the office," Nov, 2008.

FRANCHISES AND BUSINESS OPPORTUNITIES

5754 ■ Lord and Partners Ltd.
9-741 Muskoka Rd., Ste. 3 N
Huntsville, ON, Canada P1H 2L3
Description: Manufacturer and distributor of solvents, cleaners and specialty products for industries, automotive, aviation, government and others. **Training:** Provides 29 days training on the proven proprietary business, marketing systems, a demo "showroom on wheels," with ongoing support for a protected territory.

COMPUTERIZED DATABASES

5755 ■ *BioQUEST Library*
Beloit College BioQUEST Curriculum Consortium
700 College St.
Beloit, WI 53511
URL: http://www.bioquest.org
URL(s): qubeshub.org/community/groups/bioquest/about/history
Availability: Download; Online. **Type:** Full-text; Image.

5756 ■ *Earthquake Intensity Database, 1638-1985*
U.S. Department of Commerce National Oceanic and Atmospheric Administration National Centers for Environmental Information
E/NE42 325 Broadway
Boulder, CO 80305-3328
Fax: (303)497-6513
Co. E-mail: ncei.info@noaa.gov
URL: http://ngdc.noaa.gov
Contact: Dr. Eric Kihn, Director
E-mail: eric.a.kihn@noaa.gov
URL(s): www.ncei.noaa.gov/products/natural-hazards/tsunamis-earthquakes-volcanoes/earthquakes/intensity-database-1638-1985ngdc.noaa.gov/hazard/intintro.shtml
Availability: Download; Online. **Type:** Properties; Time Series.

5757 ■ *Environment Systems and Decisions*
Springer US
233 Spring St.
New York, NY 10013
Free: 866-839-0194
Fax: (212)460-1700
Co. E-mail: customerservice@springernature.com
URL: http://www.springer.com
Contact: Derk Haank, Chief Executive Officer
URL(s): link.springer.com/journal/10669
Released: Quarterly; March, June, September, December. **Description:** Journal covering environmental systems and decisions, with a focus on the perspectives and needs of infrastructure owners/operators, engineers, environmental professionals, and risk managers. **Availability:** Print; PDF; Download; Online. **Type:** Full-text.

5758 ■ *Environmental Law Reporter*
Environmental Law Institute
1730 M St. NW Ste. 700
Washington, DC 20036
Ph: (202)939-3800
Fax: (202)939-3868
Co. E-mail: law@eli.org
URL: http://www.eli.org
Contact: Jay Austin, Editor-in-Chief
E-mail: austin@eli.org
URL(s): www.elr.info
X (Twitter): twitter.com/EnvLawReporter
Released: Volume 54 Issue 4 — April 2024. **Price:** $800, for one year; $695, for print only. **Availability:** Print; Online. **Type:** Full-text.

5759 ■ *Environmental Sciences & Pollution Management*
ProQuest LLC
789 E Eisenhower Pky.
Ann Arbor, MI 48108
Ph: (734)761-4700
Free: 800-521-0600
URL: http://www.proquest.com
Contact: Matti Shem Tov, Chief Executive Officer
URL(s): about.proquest.com/en/products-services/natural_science
Availability: Online. **Type:** Bibliographic.

5760 ■ *Natural Hazards Image Database*
U.S. Department of Commerce National Oceanic and Atmospheric Administration National Centers for Environmental Information
E/NE42 325 Broadway
Boulder, CO 80305-3328
Fax: (303)497-6513
Co. E-mail: ncei.info@noaa.gov
URL: http://ngdc.noaa.gov
Contact: Dr. Eric Kihn, Director
E-mail: eric.a.kihn@noaa.gov
URL(s): www.ngdc.noaa.gov/hazardimages/#
Availability: Online. **Type:** Image.

5761 ■ *Significant Earthquake Database*
U.S. Department of Commerce National Oceanic and Atmospheric Administration National Centers for Environmental Information
E/NE42 325 Broadway
Boulder, CO 80305-3328
Fax: (303)497-6513
Co. E-mail: ncei.info@noaa.gov
URL: http://ngdc.noaa.gov
Contact: Dr. Eric Kihn, Director
E-mail: eric.a.kihn@noaa.gov
URL(s): www.ncei.noaa.gov/access/metadata/landing-page/bin/iso?id=gov.noaa.ngdc.mgg.hazards:G012153
Availability: Download; Online. **Type:** Full-text.

LIBRARIES

5762 ■ Appalachia-Science in the Public Interest (ASPI) - Resource Library
50 Lair St.
Mount Vernon, KY 40456
Ph: (606)256-0077
Co. E-mail: aspi@a-spi.org
URL: http://www.appalachia-spi.org
Contact: Al Fritsch, Contact
Facebook: www.facebook.com/Appalachia-Science-in-the-Public-Interest-158714454228646
X (Twitter): x.com/ASPIKentucky
Description: Publishes on environmental alternatives and sustainable development. Offers video cassettes, calendars, note cards and technical papers. Also offers a quarterly publication. Reaches market through direct mail. Does not accept unsolicited manuscripts. **Scope:** Public interest and educational materials. **Founded:** 1977. **Holdings:** Books; technical papers; newsletter. **Geographic Preference:** Local.

5763 ■ Beveridge and Diamond P.C. - AgTech Regulatory Resource Center
1900 N St. NW, Ste. 100
Washington, DC 20036
Ph: (202)789-6000
Co. E-mail: bdlaw@bdlaw.com
URL: http://www.bdlaw.com
Contact: Teresa Saulsby, Director
E-mail: tsaulsby@bdlaw.com
Facebook: www.facebook.com/BeveridgeDiamondPC
Linkedin: www.linkedin.com/company/beveridge-&-diamond-p-c
X (Twitter): x.com/bdlawfirm
Description: Provider of law and litigation support. **Scope:** Agriculture; biotechnology. **Founded:** 1974. **Holdings:** Figures not available.

5764 ■ Bryan Cave L.L.P., Law Library
1155 F St. NW, Ste. 700
Washington, DC 20004-1357
URL: http://www.bclplaw.com/en-US/people/pedro-j-martinez-fraga.html
Scope: Government and politics; law - commercial, corporate, environmental, intellectual property, taxation. **Services:** Interlibrary loan; copying; faxing; library open to the public with restrictions. **Founded:** 1978. **Holdings:** 11,000 volumes.

5765 ■ Cadwalader, Wickersham & Taft Library
700 6th St., NW
Washington, DC 20001
Ph: (202)862-2200
Co. E-mail: cwtinfo@cwt.com
URL: http://www.cadwalader.com
Scope: Law - antitrust, corporate, securities, taxation, business fraud. **Services:** Interlibrary loan; library open to the public by appointment (with restrictions). **Founded:** 1792. **Holdings:** 15,000 volumes; microforms; CD-ROM.

5766 ■ DLA Piper LLP US Library
500 8th St. NW
Washington, DC 20004
Ph: (202)799-4000
Fax: (202)799-5000
URL: http://www.dlapiper.com/en-cn/locations/washington-dc
Contact: William Minor, Partner
E-mail: william.minor@dlapiper.com

5767 ■ ERM - West Inc. Library
CA
Scope: Water management. **Services:** Interlibrary loan; library not open to the public. **Founded:** 1987. **Holdings:** Brewers documents.

5768 ■ Farmington River Watershed Association (FRWA) - Library
749 Hopmeadow St.
Simsbury, CT 06070
Ph: (860)658-4442
Fax: (860)651-7519
URL: http://frwa.org
Contact: Michael Feldman, President
Description: Corporations and individuals in Massachusetts and Connecticut. Protects and enhances the Farmington River. Acts as educational resource for information on water conservation and recreation issues. **Scope:** Research; water quality; education. **Founded:** 2006. **Holdings:** Figures not available. **Publications:** *Farmington River News* (Quarterly). **Geographic Preference:** Local.

5769 ■ General Engineering Laboratories Inc. Library (GEL)
2040 Savage Rd.
Charleston, SC 29407
Ph: (843)556-8171
Fax: (843)766-1178
Co. E-mail: info@gel.com
URL: http://www.gel.com
Contact: Joseoh M. Hodgson, Jr., President
Scope: Environmental analysis; environmental consulting; environmental regulations. **Founded:** 1981. **Holdings:** Figures not available.

5770 ■ Georgia Wildlife Federation Conservation Library (GWF)
11600 Hazelbrand Rd.
Covington, GA 30014
URL: http://gwf.org/acc
Contact: DeAnna Harris, Manager
E-mail: dharris@gwf.org
Founded: 1936.

5771 ■ Heartland Institute (HI) - Michael Parry Mazur Memorial Library
3939 N Wilke Rd.
Arlington Heights, IL 60004
Ph: (312)377-4000
Fax: (312)275-7942
Co. E-mail: database@heartland.org
URL: http://heartland.org
Contact: Wanda L. Davis, Director, Administration
E-mail: wdavis@heartland.org
Facebook: www.facebook.com/HeartlandInstitute
X (Twitter): x.com/heartlandinst
YouTube: www.youtube.com/user/HeartlandTube

Description: Privatization, deregulation, tax reform, education reform, healthcare policy, environmental policy, and telecommunications. Seeks alternatives to government-provided services at the national, state, and local levels. **Scope:** Privatization, deregulation, tax reform, education reform, healthcare policy, environmental policy, and telecommunications. Seeks alternatives to government-provided services at the national, state, and local levels. **Services:** Library open to the public by appointment; copying. **Founded:** 1984. **Holdings:** 20,000 books; journals. **Publications:** Privatization, deregulation, tax reform, education reform, healthcare policy, environmental policy, and telecommunications. Seeks alternatives to government-provided services at the national, state, and local levels. **Awards:** Heartland Liberty Prize (Irregular). **Geographic Preference:** National.

5772 ■ Illinois Sustainable Technology Center (ISTC) - Library
One Hazelwood Dr., MC-676
Champaign, IL 61820
Ph: (217)333-8940
Co. E-mail: info@istc.illinois.edu
URL: http://www.istc.illinois.edu
Contact: Kevin O'Brien, Director
E-mail: kcobrien@illinois.edu
Facebook: www.facebook.com/ISTCatUIUC
Linkedin: www.linkedin.com/company/illinois-sustainable-technology-center
X (Twitter): twitter.com/ISTCatUIUC
YouTube: www.youtube.com/user/4ISTC

Description: Integral unit of Office of Research and Scientific Analysis, Illinois Department of Natural Resources, affiliated with University of Illinois at Urbana-Champaign. Offers on-site disposal review, referral and consulting service, and waste reduction information and assistance. **Scope:** Integrates research, industrial and technical assistance, database management, laboratory services, and information resources in a program to manage and help solve Illinois' pollution and waste problems. Topics include characterization and assessment; environmental process and effects; prevention and source reduction; treatment, disposal, and remediation; risk assessment; river sediment reuse; and policy analysis. Collects, analyzes, synthesizes, and disseminates information on waste management. **Founded:** 1984. **Holdings:** Figures not available. **Publications:** *ISTC Factsheets*; *ISTC Research reports*; *ISTC Technical Reports*. **Educational Activities:** ISTC Conferences and seminars, Characterization and assessment, environmental process and effects.; Great Lake Regional Pollution Prevention Roundtable (Annual), Ensures information sharing, issue discussion and program development among member organizations to be primary goals.

5773 ■ Karpeles Manuscript Library - Duluth Museum
902 E 1st St.
Duluth, MN 55805
Co. E-mail: duluthkarpeles@gmail.com
URL: http://www.karpeles.com/visit/duluth-minnesota
Contact: Matthew Sjelin, Director

Scope: Literature; science; religion; political history; exploration; music and art. **Services:** Library open to the public. **Holdings:** Manuscripts; documents.

5774 ■ Keller and Heckman L.L.P. (KH) - Library
1001 G St. NW Ste. 500 W
Washington, DC 20001
Ph: (202)434-4100
Fax: (202)434-4646
Co. E-mail: info@khlaw.com
URL: http://www.khlaw.com
Contact: Janeanne R. Gorman, Executive Director
E-mail: gorman@khlaw.com
Linkedin: www.linkedin.com/company/keller-and-heckman-llp
X (Twitter): x.com/kellerandheck

Description: Firm provides legal, litigation and business transactions related services for domestic and international clients. **Scope:** Firm has a broad practice in the areas of regulatory law, litigation, and business transactions. Practice areas in advertising and promotion, antitrust, biotechnology, business counseling and transactional, chemical control, employment and labor, environmental, food and drug, government relations, health and safety compliance audit, insurance coverage, intellectual property, international regulatory affairs, litigation, pesticides, privacy and internet, product safety, REACH, telecommunications, trade and professional associations, transportation, and workplace safety and health. **Founded:** 1962. **Holdings:** Figures not available. **Publications:** "Electronic TSCA CDX Reporting Required Beginning April 7 2012," Apr, 2012; "Whistleblower Alert: OSHA's New Enforcement Memorandum Targets Disciplinary Policies, Incentive Programs," Mar, 2012; "Pole Attachment Make-Ready and Access Issues," Nov, 2009; "Telecom Business Alert," Nov, 2009. **Training:** UTC Joint Use Workshop, Nov, 2009; Issues with Wireless Providers Attaching to Distribution Systems. Oct, 2009; What is a Fair Pole Attachment Rate?, May, 2007.

5775 ■ Maritime College of Forest Technology Library (MCFT)
1350 Regent St.
Fredericton, NB, Canada E3C 2G6
Ph: (506)458-0199
Free: 866-619-9900
Co. E-mail: info@mcft.ca
URL: http://www.mcft.ca
Contact: Steven Hansen, Chairman
Facebook: www.facebook.com/MCFTfredericton
X (Twitter): x.com/mcftfredericton
Instagram: www.instagram.com/mcftfredericton
YouTube: www.youtube.com/channel/UCo8f2gjfTWaa7jkEO-TPc3Q

Description: Maritime College of forest technology library. **Scope:** Forestry; natural resources; environment; conservation. **Services:** Library not open to the public. **Founded:** 1946. **Holdings:** Figures not available.

5776 ■ PA Consulting Group (PA) - Reference Collection
The Chrysler Bldg., 45th Fl., 405 Lexington Ave.
New York, NY 10174
Ph: (212)973-5900
URL: http://www.paconsulting.com
Contact: John Alexander, Chairman
Linkedin: www.linkedin.com/company/pa-consulting
X (Twitter): x.com/PA_Consulting

Description: Publisher of books on marketing strategies, a broad spectrum of survey reports and other business sectors. **Scope:** Computers, telecommunications, and related aspects of information technology. **Founded:** 1972. **Holdings:** Figures not available.

5777 ■ San Francisco Public Library - Wallace Stegner Environmental Center
100 Larkin St., 5th Fl.
San Francisco, CA 94102
Ph: (415)557-4500
Co. E-mail: environmentalcenter@sfpl.org
URL: http://sfpl.org/locations/main-library/environmental-center

Scope: Environmental issues and the experiences of American Indians. **Services:** Center open to the public with restrictions; Interlibrary Loan; Photographs. **Founded:** 1996. **Holdings:** Books.

5778 ■ Saskatchewan Research Council (SRC) - Information Services
Bay 2D, 820 51st St., E
Saskatoon, SK, Canada S7K 0X8
Ph: (306)933-5400
Free: 877-772-7227
Co. E-mail: info@src.sk.ca
URL: http://www.src.sk.ca
Contact: Mike Crabtree, Secretary
X (Twitter): x.com/srcnews
YouTube: www.youtube.com/user/saskresearchcouncil

Description: Independent, nonprofit research organization located in Innovation Place research park in Saskatoon, affiliated with the University of Saskatchewan and University of Regina. **Scope:** SRC is Saskatchewan's leading provider of applied R&D and technology commercialization. We take the leading-edge knowledge developed in Saskatchewan and sell it to the world and, at the same time, bring the best knowledge the world has to offer and apply it to the unique Saskatchewan situations. **Services:** Interlibrary loan. **Founded:** 1947. **Holdings:** 8,600 monographs; 3,300 SRC-authored publications. **Publications:** *News Releases*; *SRC Annual report* (Annual).

5779 ■ Sedgwick County Zoo Library (SCZ)
5555 W Zoo Blvd.
Wichita, KS 67212
Ph: (316)660-9453
Fax: (316)942-3781
Co. E-mail: ask@scz.org
URL: http://scz.org
Contact: Jeff Ettling, President
E-mail: jeff.ettling@scz.org
Facebook: www.facebook.com/SedgwickCountyZoo
X (Twitter): x.com/SedgwickCoZoo
Instagram: www.instagram.com/sedgwickcountyzoo
YouTube: www.youtube.com/user/SedgwickCoZoo

Description: Aims to inspire discovery, appreciation, and respect for animals and nature. **Scope:** Zoology, wildlife conservation. **Services:** Interlibrary loan; copying; library open to the public. **Founded:** 1971. **Holdings:** 1000 books; 100 reports.

5780 ■ Stearns, Conrad and Schmidt Engineers Inc. - Library
3900 Kilroy Airport Way, Ste. 100
Long Beach, CA 90806-6816
Free: 800-767-4727
Fax: (562)427-0805
Co. E-mail: service@scsengineers.com
URL: http://www.scsengineers.com
Contact: James Walsh, President
E-mail: jwalsh@scsengineers.com
Facebook: www.facebook.com/scsengineersenvironmental
Linkedin: www.linkedin.com/company/scs-engineers
X (Twitter): x.com/SCSengineers
YouTube: www.youtube.com/channel/UCxtHOod4bo4pbjA_UBwQVnQ

Description: Firm offers environmental consulting construction services. **Scope:** Firm provides engineering and scientific services directed toward environmental protection and conservation of resources. Offers services in the areas of solid waste, environmental, field services, energy, secure, greenhouse gases and sustainability. **Founded:** 1970. **Holdings:** Figures not available. **Training:** The Twentieth Annual Arizona Solid Waste Management Seminar, 2010.

5781 ■ Tetra Tech NUS, Inc. Technical Information Center
117 Hearthstone Dr.
Aiken, SC 29803
Ph: (803)649-7963
URL: http://www.tetratech.com/cs/Satellite?c=Page&childpagename=TT%2FPage%2FLocationsSearch&cid=1388485287559&packedargs=isVanity%3Dfalse%26locale%3Den_US&pagename=TTWrapper&locsAction=doSearch&formFieldsToBePacked=locsAction%2ClocsCountryCode%2ClocsStateOrProvinceCo

Scope: Environment; nuclear energy. **Services:** Library not open to the public. **Founded:** 1966. **Holdings:** Reports. **Subscriptions:** 2 newspapers.

5782 ■ United Nations Association of Southern Arizona (UNASA) - Library
6242 E Speedway Blvd.
Tucson, AZ 85712
Ph: (520)881-7060
Co. E-mail: info@unasatucson.org
URL: http://www.unasatucson.org
Contact: John Dalton, Co-President
Facebook: www.facebook.com/UNASACenter
Instagram: www.instagram.com/unasacenter

Description: Individuals and organizations in Cochise, Greenlee, Pima, Pinal, and Santa Cruz counties, AZ committed to public education on the workings of the United Nations. Disseminates information on the role of the United Nations in world affairs and the United States role as a member of the United Nations. Promotes cooperative programs with community and civic organizations; makes available scholarships. Operates a U.N. Center whose profits are donated to UNICEF and local education programs about the UN. Operates occasional tours to countries in which there are United Nations projects and/or interests. **Scope:** Public education. **Founded:** 1975. **Holdings:** Figures not available. **Geographic Preference:** Local.

5783 ■ U.S. Environmental Protection Agency Headquarters and Chemical Libraries
Rm. 3340, William Jefferson Clinton W Bldg., 1301 Constitution Ave. NW
Washington, DC 20004
Ph: (202)566-0556
Co. E-mail: hqchemlibraries@epa.gov
URL: http://www.epa.gov/epalibraries/headquarters-and-chemical-libraries
Scope: Decision making and environmental awareness. **Services:** Interlibrary loan; library open to the public. **Holdings:** Figures not available. **Subscriptions:** 60 journals and other serials.

5784 ■ U.S. Environmental Protection Agency Headquarters Library
1200 Pennsylvania Ave., NW
Washington, DC 20460
URL: http://www.epa.gov/epalibraries/catalog
Scope: Water and environmental protection. **Services:** Interlibrary loan; SDI; library open to the public with restrictions. **Founded:** 1971. **Holdings:** Figures not available.

5785 ■ Williams College Center for Environmental Studies - Matt Cole Memorial Library
55 Mission Pk. Dr.
Williamstown, MA 01267
Co. E-mail: ces@williams.edu
URL: http://ces.williams.edu/publications/matt-cole-reading-room/matt-cole-library
Scope: Environmental issues; history. **Founded:** 1972. **Holdings:** Books; documents.

RESEARCH CENTERS

5786 ■ Center for Environmental Research (CER)
Hornsby Bend 2210 S FM 973
Austin, TX 78725
Ph: (512)972-1960
URL: http://austintexas.gov/department/center-environmental-research

Description: Joint urban ecology research and education facility between the Austin Water Utility, University of Texas and Texas AandM University. Offers educational tours and workshops. **Scope:** Urban ecology and sustainability, soil ecology and biosolids recycling, sustainable agriculture, riparian ecology and restoration, avian ecology and citizen science, urban biodiversity conservation, and environmental health education. **Founded:** 1987. **Publications:** *Discovering the Colorado: a vision for the Austin-Bastrop river corridor* (Monthly).

5787 ■ Harvard University - John F. Kennedy School of Government - Belfer Center for Science and International Affairs - Environment and Natural Resources Program (ENRP)
79 John F. Kennedy St.
Cambridge, MA 02138
URL: http://www.belfercenter.org/program/environment-and-natural-resources
Contact: Henry Lee, Director
Description: Integral unit of Belfer Center for Science and International Affairs, John F. Kennedy School of Government, Harvard University. **Scope:** Research focus includes environmental and energy issues; international security; and, public policy. Publishes discussion papers, research reports, newsletters, and policy reports. **Founded:** 1980. **Awards:** The Roy Family Award for Environmental Partnership (Biennial).

5788 ■ Holistic Management International (HMI)
2425 San Pedro NE Ste. A
Albuquerque, NM 87110
Ph: (505)842-5252
Fax: (505)843-7900
Co. E-mail: hmi@holisticmanagement.org
URL: http://holisticmanagement.org
Contact: Wayne Knight, Executive Director
Facebook: www.facebook.com/holisticmanagement
X (Twitter): x.com/hminternational
Instagram: www.instagram.com/hmi.holisticmanagement
YouTube: www.youtube.com/user/HolisticManagement
Description: Fosters citizen participation in sound resource management; works extensively on combating the desertification process. **Scope:** Evaluates effective policy analysis for planning and development to increase biodiversity and productivity of the land and communities. **Founded:** 1984. **Publications:** *In Practice* (Bimonthly); *Holistic Management In Practice* (Bimonthly). **Educational Activities:** HMI Holistic Management International Conferences. **Geographic Preference:** Multinational.

5789 ■ SUNY College of Environmental Science and Forestry - Randolph G. Pack Environmental Institute
1 Forestry Dr.
Syracuse, NY 13210
Ph: (315)470-6500
URL: http://www.esf.edu/envstudies/pack-institute.php
Contact: Benette Whitmore, Assistant Professor
E-mail: bwhitmor@esf.edu
Description: Integral unit of Faculty of Environmental Studies of SUNY College of Environmental Science and Forestry, a specialized college of State University of New York. Assistance offered to local groups on environmental equity projects (annual). **Scope:** Cultural environmental values, environmental communication, land information systems, water resources, sustainable development, and urban environmental systems. **Founded:** 1995. **Publications:** *Randolph G. Pack Environmental Institute Monographs*; *Randolph G. Pack Environmental Institute Papers*. **Educational Activities:** Day and half day trips.

5790 ■ Texas Center for Policy Studies (TCPS)
1206 San Antonio St.
Austin, TX 78701
Ph: (512)474-0811
Co. E-mail: tcps@texascenter.org
URL: http://www.texascenter.org
Contact: Richard Lowerre, President
Description: Independent, nonprofit organization. **Scope:** Environmental policy studies, including water quality, water supply, pollution, forestry development, habitat destruction, waste disposal, and rural economic development. **Founded:** 1982. **Publications:** *TCPS Newsletter* (Biennial); *Project Review*.

5791 ■ University of New Brunswick - New Brunswick Cooperative Fish and Wildlife Research Unit (NBCFWRU)
Department Of Biology
University of New Brunswick
Fredericton, NB, Canada E3B 6E1
Ph: (506)453-4929
Fax: (506)453-3538
Co. E-mail: forbes@unb.ca
URL: http://nbcfwru.ext.unb.ca
Contact: Dr. Graham J. Forbes, Director
E-mail: forbes@unb.ca
Description: Integral unit of University of New Brunswick. **Scope:** Management and conservation of wildlife and fisheries resources and their habitats within New Brunswick and Atlantic Canada. **Founded:** 1989.

Environmental Store

ASSOCIATIONS AND OTHER ORGANIZATIONS

5792 ■ **Center for Environmental Information (CEI) - Library**
700 W Metro Pk.
  Rochester, NY 14623
Ph: (585)233-6086
URL: http://geneseeriverwatch.org
Description: Disseminates information on environmental issues. Conducts annual climate issues conference. **Scope:** The environment; climate change. **Founded:** 1974. **Holdings:** Figures not available. **Publications:** *CEI Sphere* (Quarterly); *Directory of Environmental Organizations in the Rochester Area* (Annual). **Geographic Preference:** National.

5793 ■ **EarthSave International**
20555 Devonshire St., Ste. 105
  Chatsworth, CA 91311
Ph: (415)234-0829
Fax: (818)337-1957
Co. E-mail: info@earthsave.org
URL: http://www.earthsave.org
Contact: Jeff Nelson, Contact
Facebook: www.facebook.com/EarthSave-115440
  488483743
X (Twitter): x.com/earthsave
Description: Promotes food choices that are healthy for the planet. Seeks to educate, inspire and empower people to take positive action for all life on Earth. **Founded:** 1988. **Publications:** *EarthSave* (Quarterly). **Geographic Preference:** National.

5794 ■ **Environmental Business Council of New England (EBCNE)**
117 Kendrick St., Ste. 300
  Needham, MA 02494
Ph: (617)505-1818
Co. E-mail: ebc@ebcne.org
URL: http://ebcne.org
Contact: Ann Gisinger, President
E-mail: agisinger@ebcne.org
Linkedin: www.linkedin.com/company/environmental
  -business-council-of-new-england-inc-
X (Twitter): x.com/ebcne
YouTube: www.youtube.com/channel/UCLKLI
  6DmcaFbOwjJ2aB956g
Description: Fosters the development of an effective and competitive envirotech industry for the purpose of enhancing and maintaining a clean and productive environment. **Founded:** 1990. **Awards:** The Paul G. Keough Environmental-Energy Award for Government Service (Annual). **Geographic Preference:** National.

5795 ■ **Natural Products Marketing Council (NPMC)**
c/o NS Department of Agriculture
  Edward F. Lorraine Bldg., 74 Research Dr.
  Bible Hill, NS, Canada B6L 2R2
URL: http://novascotia.ca/agri/about-us/agencies
  -boards-and-commissions/natural-products-marke
  ting
Contact: Danielle Dorn Kouwenberg, Director (Acting)
E-mail: danielle.dornkouwenberg@novascotia.ca
Description: Producers and processors of natural food products and wool. Promotes growth and development of the natural products industries. Supervises natural product marketing boards. **Founded:** 1946. **Geographic Preference:** National.

5796 ■ **Organic Trade Association (OTA)**
444 N Capitol St. NW, Ste. 445A
  Washington, DC 20001
Ph: (202)403-8520
Co. E-mail: info@ota.com
URL: http://www.ota.com
Contact: Laura Batcha, Chief Executive Officer
Facebook: www.facebook.com/OrganicTrade
Linkedin: www.linkedin.com/company/organic-trade
  -association
X (Twitter): x.com/organictrade
Instagram: www.instagram.com/organictrade
Description: Producers, processors, distributors, retailers, individuals and others involved in the organic products industry. Promotes the industry; heightens production and marketing standards. Provides certification guidelines. **Founded:** 1985. **Publications:** *The Organic Report* (Semiannual); *The American Organic Standards* (Weekly); *Guide to the U.S. Organic Foods Production Act of 1990*; *How to Harvest the Profits of Organic Produce*; *The Organic Pages: Organic Trade Association's North American Resource Directory*. **Educational Activities:** All Things Organic Conference (Annual). **Awards:** OTA Organic Leadership Award (Annual). **Geographic Preference:** National.

REFERENCE WORKS

5797 ■ *"2010: Important Year Ahead for Waterfront"* in *Bellingham Business Journal* (Vol. March 2010, pp. 2)
Description: A tentative timeline has been established for the environmental impact statement (EIS) slated for completion in May 2010. The plan for the Waterfront District includes detailed economic and architectural analysis of the feasibility of reusing remaining structures and retaining some industrial icons. **Availability:** Print; Online.

5798 ■ *"2011 FinOvation Awards"* in *Farm Industry News* (January 19, 2011)
Pub: Informa Business Media, Inc.
Contact: Charlie McCurdy, President
Ed: Karen McMahon, Jodie Wehrspann. **Description:** The 2011 FinOvation Award winners are announced, covering new products that growers need for corn and soybean crops. Winners range from small turbines and a fuel-efficient pickup to a Class 10 combine and drought-tolerant hybrids. **Availability:** Online.

5799 ■ *"2011 a Record Year for New Wind Energy Installations in Canada"* in *CNW Group* (September 26, 2011)
Pub: CNW Group Ltd.
Description: Canada reports a record for new wind energy projects in 2011 with about 1,338 MW of newly installed wind energy capacity expected to come on line, compared to 690 MW installed in 2010. Statistical data included. **Availability:** Print; Online.

5800 ■ *"Acciona Windpower to Supply 3-Megawatt Turbines to Prince Edward Island Energy"* in *Professional Close-Up* (September 11, 2012)
Description: Acciona Windpower and Prince Edward Island Energy Corporation (PEIEC) have partnered to supply turbines for the Hermanville & Clear Springs Wind Project that will provide 10 Acciona Windpower AW3000/116 wind turbine generators with capacity of 3 megawatts and a rotor diameter of 116 meters. Acciona will operate and maintain the turbines for the first 15 years.

5801 ■ *"ACE Commits $300,000 to Support Environmental Conservation Initiatives and Green Business Entrepreneurs"* in *Insurance Business Weekly* (March 2, 2012, pp. 13)
Pub: NewsRX LLC.
Contact: Kalani Rosell, Contact
Description: ACE Charitable Foundation has commited to a two-year, $300,000 funding of The Conservation Fund for new initiatives that protect key watersheds, expand wildlife migration corridors and investment in local green economies in the United States. **Availability:** Online.

5802 ■ *"Acing the Test"* in *Contractor* (Vol. 57, January 2010, No. 1, pp. 32)
Pub: Informa USA, Inc.
Contact: Stephen A. Carter, Chief Executive Officer
Ed: Robert P. Mader. **Released:** January 01, 2010. **Description:** A ward winning mechanical system retrofitting of a middle school in Ohio is discussed. The school now operates at 37,800 Btu/sq. ft and reduced a significant amount of pollutants from being emitted into the environment.

5803 ■ *"Actiontec and Verizon Team Up for a Smarter Home"* in *Ecology,Environment & Conservation Business* (November 5, 2011, pp. 3)
Pub: Comtex News Network Inc.
Contact: Kan Devnani, President
Description: Verizon is implementing Actiontec Electronics' SG200 Service Gateway as a basic component of its Home Monitoring and Control service. This new smart home service allows customers to remotely check their homes, control locks and appliances, view home-energy use and more using a smartphone, PC, or FiOS TV. **Availability:** Online.

5804 ■ *"Adventures at Hydronicahh"* in *Contractor* (Vol. 56, September 2009, No. 9, pp. 52)
Ed: Mark Eatherton. **Released:** Part 6. **Description:** Installations of the heating system of a lakeview room

are described. The room's radiant windows are powered by electricity from a solar PV array and a propane-powered hydrogen fuel cell. The system will be programmed to use the most energy available. **Availability:** Print; Online.

5805 ■ *"Agana To Bottle Rain for Whole Foods" in Austin Business Journal (Vol. 32, March 30, 2012, No. 4, pp. 1)*
Pub: American City Business Journals, Inc.
Contact: Mike Olivieri, Executive Vice President
Ed: Vicky Garza. **Description:** Agana Rainwater has signed a deal to bottle rainwater for Whole Foods Market Inc. Rainwater bottling is seen as a conservation tools as it does not deplete the lake or aquifier. **Availability:** Online.

5806 ■ *"Agricultural Community Implements Green Technologies, Building Team" in Contractor (Vol. 56, September 2009, No. 9, pp. 5)*
Ed: Candace Roulo. **Description:** John DeWald and Associates has initiated a residential development project which uses green technologies in Illinois. The community features a community center, organic farm and recreational trails. Comments from executives are also provided. **Availability:** Print; Online.

5807 ■ *"Albuquerque Entrepreneurs Selected As Top Participants in USHCC Foundation Green Builds Business Program" in Marketing Weekly News (April 21, 2012)*
Description: Five winners of the 2012 Green Builds Business program was announced by the United States Hispanic Chamber of Commerce Foundation (USHCCF). These winners will receive a combined 24 hours of one-on-one green coaching with Bill Roth, the Green Business Coach for Entrepreneur.com and Founder of Earth 2017. Details are included. **Availability:** Print; Online.

5808 ■ *"Allowing Ethanol Tax Incentive to Expire Would Risk Jobs, RFA's Dinneen Says" in Farm Industry News (November 3, 2010)*
Pub: Informa Business Media, Inc.
Contact: Charlie McCurdy, President
Ed: Lynn Grooms. **Price:** $4, Print and Online; Special Offers only for 4 weeks. **Description:** Jobs would be at risk if the ethanol tax incentive expires. **Availability:** Print; Online.

5809 ■ *"Alstom Launches the ECO 122 - 2.7MW Wind Turbine for Low Wind Sites" in CNW Group (September 28, 2011)*
Pub: CNW Group Ltd.
Description: Alstom is launching its new ECO 122, a 2.7MW onshore wind turbine that combines high power and high capacity factor (1) to boost energy yield in low wind regions around the world. The ECO 122 will produce about 25 percent increased wind farm yield that current turbines and fewer turbines would be installed in areas. **Availability:** Print; Online.

5810 ■ *"Altera Ranks Among Top 25 Greenest Companies in U.S." in Ecology, Environment & Conservation Business (August 9, 2014, pp. 2)*
Pub: NewsRX LLC.
Contact: Kalani Rosell, Contact
Description: Altera Corporation was ranked 24 on the Newsweek Magazine 2014 Green Rankings of over 500 companies in the United States. These rankings are one of the world's most recognized assessments of corporate sustainability and environmental impact. Eight specific indicators were used, including conservation and sustainability efforts in the areas of energy, carbon, water, and waste productivity. **Availability:** Online.

5811 ■ *"Alternative Energy Calls for Alternative Marketing" in Indoor Comfort Marketing (Vol. 70, June 2011, No. 6, pp. 8)*
Pub: Spray Technology & Marketing
Contact: Ava Caridad, Director, Editorial
E-mail: acaridad@spraytm.com
Ed: Richard Rutigliano. **Released:** June 01, 2011. **Description:** Advice for marketing solar energy products and services is given. **Availability:** Print; Online.

5812 ■ *"Alternative Energy Is a Major Topic at Agritechnica 2011" in Farm Industry News (November 16, 2011)*
Pub: Informa Business Media, Inc.
Contact: Charlie McCurdy, President
Ed: Mark Moore. **Description:** Sustainable agricultural systems were a hot topic at this year's Agritechnia 2011, held in Germany. Germany is a leader in the development of on-farm biogas systems. **Availability:** Online.

5813 ■ *"Alternative Fuels Take Center Stage at Houston Auto Show" in Houston Business Journal (Vol. 44, January 31, 2014, No. 39, pp. 8)*
Pub: American City Business Journals, Inc.
Contact: Mike Olivieri, Executive Vice President
Released: January 31, 2014. **Price:** $4, Introductory 4-Week Offer(Digital & Print). **Description:** An energy summit was held at the Houston Auto Show in Texas on January 22, 2014, where energy executives discussed new technology and initiatives. They considered the market for electric and natural gas-fueled vehicles as well as other options including hydrogen, fuel cells, and biofuels. **Availability:** Print; Online.

5814 ■ *"American Chemistry Council Launches Flagship Blog" in Ecology, Environment & Conservation Business (October 29, 2011, pp. 5)*
Pub: PR Newswire Association LLC.
Description: American Chemistry Council (ACC) launched its blog, American Chemistry Matters, where interactive space allows bloggers to respond to news coverage and to discuss policy issues and their impact on innovation, competitiveness, job creation and safety. **Availability:** Online.

5815 ■ *"Answers About Commercial Wind Farms Could Come from Downstate" in Erie Times-News (September 27, 2011)*
Pub: Erie Times News
Contact: Christopher Millette, Managing Editor
E-mail: cmillette@timesnews.com
Ed: Valerie Myers. **Description:** Texas-based Pioneer Green Energy is measuring wind and leasing land in North East Township, Pennsylvania. The firm plans to build a 7,000-acre wind farm along wine-country ridges. About 70 turbines would harness wind in order to generate electricity that would be sold into the eastern power grid. **Availability:** Online.

5816 ■ *"Areva Diversifies Further Into Wind" in Wall Street Journal Eastern Edition (November 29, 2011, pp. B7)*
Pub: Dow Jones & Company Inc.
Contact: Almar Latour, Chief Executive Officer
Ed: Max Colchester, Noemie Bisserbe. **Description:** French engineering company Areva SA is diversifying and moving away from nuclear energy projects. One sign of that is its recent discussion to construct 120 wind turbines to be located at two German wind farms. Such a deal, if signed, would be worth about US$1.59 billion. **Availability:** Online.

5817 ■ *"Art Institute of Chicago Goes Green" in Contractor (Vol. 56, July 2009, No. 7, pp. 1)*
Ed: Candace Roulo. **Description:** Art Institute of Chicago's Modern Wing museum addition will receive a certification that makes them one of the most environmentally sound museum expansions in the U.S. A modified variable-air-volume system is being used to meet temperature and humidity requirements in the building and it also has a double curtain wall to capture summer heat. **Availability:** Print; Online.

5818 ■ *"Austin to Buy $1.1B of Wind Power from Two" in Austin Business Journal (Vol. 31, August 19, 2011, No. 24, pp. A1)*
Pub: Austin Business Journal
Contact: Rachel McGrath, Director
E-mail: rmcgrath@bizjournals.com
Ed: Vicky Garza. **Description:** Austin City Council is set to approve contracts to purchase wind energy from Duke Energy Corporation and MAP Royalty Inc. The city will get 200MW from Duke and 91MW from MAP and the total contract is estimated to be worth $1.1 million. **Availability:** Print; Online.

5819 ■ *"Award Win Highlights Slingsby's Green Credentials" in Ecology, Environment & Conservation Business (August 20, 2011, pp. 3)*
Description: Slingsby, an industrial and commercial equipment supplier, was joint winner with Hallmark Cards of the Baildon Business in the Community's Yorkshire and Humber Long Term Environmental Improvement Award. The firm cites its commitment to reducing environmental impact. **Availability:** Print; PDF; Online.

5820 ■ *"BARS+TONE Achieves Green Business Certification by the City and County of San Francisco" in Benzinga.com (April 26, 2012)*
Pub: Benzinga.com
Contact: Jason Raznick, Founder
Ed: Aaron Wise. **Description:** City and County of San Francisco, California presented a Green Business certification to BARS+TONE, a creative video agency. The certification is part of an ongoing effort to reduce environmental impact. **Availability:** Online.

5821 ■ *"Ben & Jerry's Introduces 'Green' Freezer" in Ice Cream Reporter (Vol. 21, October 20, 2008, No. 11, pp. 1)*
Description: Ben & Jerry's describes its latest concept as a cleaner, greener freezer. The hydrocarbon-based freezer provides great environmental benefits by minimizing the freezer's impact on global warming. **Availability:** Print; Online.

5822 ■ *"BETC Backers Plot Future" in Business Journal Portland (Vol. 27, December 10, 2010, No. 41, pp. 1)*
Pub: Portland Business Journal
Contact: Andy Giegerich, Managing Editor
E-mail: agiegerich@bizjournals.com
Ed: Erik Siemers. **Description:** A coalition of clean energy groups and industrial manufacturers have spearheaded a campaign aimed at persuading Oregon legislators that the state's Business Energy Tax Credit (BETC) is vital in job creation. Oregon's BETC grants tax credits for 50 percent of an eligible renewable or clean energy project's cost. However, some legislators propose BETC's abolition. **Availability:** Print; Online.

5823 ■ *"Beware of E15 Gasoline" in Rental Product News (Vol. 33, October 2011)*
Ed: Curt Bennink. **Description:** Environmental Protection Agency (EPA) set a new regulation that grants partial waivers to allow gasoline containing up to 15 percent ethanol (E15) to be introduced into commerce for use in model year 2001 and newer light-duty motor vehicles, subject to certain conditions. **Availability:** Online.

5824 ■ *"Beyond Meat (R) Completes Largest Financing Round to Date" in Ecology, Environment & Conservation Business (August 16, 2014, pp. 4)*
Pub: NewsRX LLC.
Contact: Kalani Rosell, Contact
Description: Beyond Meat (R) is the first company to recreate meat from plants and is dedicated to improving human health, positively impacting climate change, conserving natural resources and respecting animal welfare. The firm has completed its Series D financing round, which will also help the company promote consumer awareness and increase capacity at its manufacturing facility to meet demand. **Availability:** Online.

5825 ■ *"Biodiesel Poised to Regain Growth" in Farm Industry News (January 21, 2011)*
Pub: Informa Business Media, Inc.
Contact: Charlie McCurdy, President

Ed: Lynn Grooms. **Description:** According to Gary Haer, vice president of sales and marketing for Renewable Energy Group, the biodiesel industry is positioned to regain growth in 2011 with the reinstatement of the biodiesel blendersa tax credit of $1 per gallon. **Availability:** Print; Online.

5826 ■ *"Bioheat - Alternative for Fueling Equipment"* in *Indoor Comfort Marketing (Vol. 70, May 2011, No. 5, pp. 14)*
Description: Profile of Worley and Obetz, supplier of biofuels used as an alternative for fueling industry equipment. **Availability:** Print; Online.

5827 ■ *"Bitumen Oilsands: Slick Science"* in *Canadian Business (Vol. 81, September 15, 2008, No. 14-15, pp. 55)*
Pub: Rogers Media Inc.
Contact: Neil Spivak, Chief Executive Officer
Ed: Andrew Nikiforuk. **Description:** N-Solv Corp's John Nenniger has discovered a better alternative to steam-assisted gravity drainage methods for extracting bitumen. Nenniger's technique also relies on gravity but replaces steam with propane, which leaves behind impurities like asphaltenes and heavy metals that are too dirty to burn. **Availability:** Print; Mailing list; Online.

5828 ■ *"Blackwater Is LEED Golden for Port of Portland Building"* in *Contractor (Vol. 56, October 2009, No. 10, pp. 3)*
Ed: Robert P. Mader. **Description:** Worrel Water Technologies' Tidal Wetlands Living Machine recycles blackwater from the toilets and sends it right back to flush the toilets. The Technology is being installed in the new headquarters of the Port of Portland which aims to get awarded a gold certificate from the Leadership in Energy and Environmental Design. **Availability:** Print; Online.

5829 ■ *"Boston Cab Association Gets 2012 Green Business Award"* in *Professional Close-Up (April 28, 2012)*
Description: Boston Cab Association was awarded the 2012 Green Business Award for its conversion to all hybrid vehicles in its fleet. The company was the first to commit to the purchase of hybrids in 2006 as part of the City of Boston's Clean Air Cab program. **Availability:** Online.

5830 ■ *"Caber Engineering Helps to Reduce Canada's Carbon Footprint"* in *Ecology,Environment & Conservation Business (July 16, 2011, pp. 7)*
Description: Calgary-based Caber Engineering Inc. will assist in the engineering design of the Alberta Carbon Trunk Line (ACTL). The ACTL is Alberta's first sizable commercial carbon capture and storage project focusing on the reduction of environmental impacts while being economically beneficial. **Availability:** Online.

5831 ■ *"Calpine Gets Ready to Light It Up"* in *Barron's (Vol. 92, July 23, 2012, No. 30, pp. 15)*
Pub: Dow Jones & Company Inc.
Contact: Almar Latour, Chief Executive Officer
Ed: Jack Willoughby. **Description:** The stocks of electric power producer Calpine could gain value as natural gas-fired power plants increase their market share. The company's stock prices could rise by 50 percent from $17.50 but the company needs to complete its turnaround to fully realize these gains. **Availability:** Online.

5832 ■ *"Canada in 2020 Energy: Mr. Clean"* in *Canadian Business (Vol. 81, October 27, 2008, No. 18, pp. 74)*
Pub: Rogers Media Inc.
Contact: Neil Spivak, Chief Executive Officer
Ed: Rachel Pulfer. **Description:** Profile of Nicholas Parker, co-founder of Cleantech Group LLC, a pioneer in clean technology investing. Cleantech, now a global industry, accounts for 10 percent of all venture capital investments made by U.S. companies in 2007. **Availability:** Print; Online.

5833 ■ *"Canada's Largest Bakery Officially Opened Today"* in *Ecology,Environment & Conservation Business (October 15, 2011, pp. 7)*
Description: Maple Leaf Foods opened Canada's largest commercial bakery in Hamilton, Ontario. The firm's 385,000 square foot Trillium bakery benefits from efficient design flow and best-in-class technologies. **Availability:** Print; Online.

5834 ■ *"Canadian Hydronics Businesses Promote 'Beautiful Heat'"* in *Indoor Comfort Marketing (Vol. 70, September 2011, No. 9, pp. 20)*
Pub: Spray Technology & Marketing
Contact: Ava Caridad, Director, Editorial
E-mail: acaridad@spraytm.com
Released: September 01, 2011. **Description:** Canadian hydronics companies are promoting their systems as beautiful heat. Hydronics is the use of water as the heat-transfer medium in heating and cooling system. **Availability:** Print; Online.

5835 ■ *"Canadian Wind Farm Sued Due to Negative Health Effects"* in *PC Magazine Online (September 22, 2011)*
Pub: PC Magazine
Contact: Dan Costa, Editor-in-Chief
E-mail: dan_costa@pcmag.com
Ed: Andrew Webster. **Description:** Suncor Energy is being sued by a family in Ontario, Canada. The family claims that Suncor's wind turbines have created health problems for them, ranging from vertigo and sleep disturbance to depression and suicidal thoughts. The family's home is over 1,000 meters from the eight wind turbines, and according to Ontario officials, wind turbines must be a minimum of 550 meters from existing homes. **Availability:** Online.

5836 ■ *"CanWEA Unveils WindVision for BC: 5,250 MW of Wind Energy by 2025"* in *CNW Group (October 4, 2011)*
Pub: CNW Group Ltd.
Description: Wind industry leaders are asking British Columbia, Canada policy makers to created conditions to further develop and integrate wind energy in accordance with greenhouse gas emission targets and projected economic growth. Statistical data included. **Availability:** PDF; Online.

5837 ■ *"Case IH Announces Strategy to Meet 2014 Clean Air Standards"* in *Farm Industry News (September 15, 2011)*
Pub: Informa Business Media, Inc.
Contact: Charlie McCurdy, President
Ed: Jodie Wehrspann. **Description:** Case IH will meet EPA's stringent engine emissions limits imposed in 2014, called Tier 4. The limits call for a 90 percent reduction in particulate matter and nitrogen oxides (NOx) over the Tier 3 requirements from a few years ago. **Availability:** Print; Online.

5838 ■ *"Cash for Appliances Targets HVAC Products, Water Heaters"* in *Contractor (Vol. 56, October 2009, No. 10, pp. 1)*
Ed: Candace Roulo. **Description:** States and territories would need to submit a full application that specifies their implementation plans if they are interested in joining the Cash for Appliances program funded by the American Recovery and Reinvestment Act. The Department of Energy urges states to focus on heating and cooling equipment, appliances and water heaters since these offer the greatest energy savings potential. **Availability:** Print; Online.

5839 ■ *"Catch the Wind Announces Filing of Injunction Against Air Data Systems LLC and Philip Rogers"* in *CNW Group (September 30, 2011)*
Pub: CNW Group Ltd.
Description: Catch the Wind, providers of laser-based wind sensor products and technology, filed an injunction against Optical Air Data Systems (OADS) LLC and its former President and CEO Philip L. Rogers. The complaint seeks to have OADS and Rogers return tangible and intangible property owned by Catch the Wind, which the firm believes to be critical to the operations of their business. **Availability:** Online.

5840 ■ *"Catch the Wind to Hold Investor Update Conference Call on October 18, 2011"* in *CNW Group (October 4, 2011)*
Pub: CNW Group Ltd.
Description: Catch the Wind Ltd., providers of laser-based wind sensor products and technology, held a conference call for analysts and institutional investors. The high-growth technology firm is headquartered in Manassas, Virginia. **Availability:** Print; Online.

5841 ■ *"CE2 Carbon Capital and Dogwood Carbon Solutions Partner with Missouri Landowners to Generate High Quality Carbon Offsets from 300,000 Acres of Forest"* in *Nanotechnolgy Business Journal (January 25, 2010)*
Pub: Investment Weekly News
Description: Dogwood Carbon Solutions, a developer of agriculture and forestry based conservation projects, has partnered with CE2 Carbon Capital, one of the largest investors and owners of U.S. carbon commodities and carbon emissions reduction projects, to develop high-quality carbon offsets from over 30,000 acres of privately-owned non-industrial forest in the Ozark mountain region of Arkansas and Missouri. **Availability:** Print; Online.

5842 ■ *"CEO Forecast: With Cloudy Economy, Executives Turn to Government Contracting"* in *Hispanic Business (January-February 2009, pp. 34, 36)*
Ed: Jessica Haro, Richard Kaplan. **Description:** As economic uncertainty fogs the future, executives turn to government contracts in order to boost business. Revenue sources, health care challenges, environmental consulting and remediation services, as well as technological strides are discussed. **Availability:** Print; Online.

5843 ■ *"The CEO Poll: Fuel for Thought II Canadian Business Leaders on Energy Policy"* in *Canadian Business (Vol. 81, September 15, 2008, No. 14-15, pp. 12)*
Pub: Rogers Media Inc.
Contact: Neil Spivak, Chief Executive Officer
Ed: Joe Castaldo. **Description:** Most Canadian business leaders worry about the unreliability of the oil supply but feel that Canada is in a better position to benefit from the energy supply crisis than other countries. Many respondents also highlighted the need to invest in renewable energy sources. **Availability:** Online.

5844 ■ *"Charged Up for Sales"* in *Charlotte Business Journal (Vol. 25, October 15, 2010, No. 30, pp. 1)*
Description: Li-Ion Motors Corporation is set to expand its production lines of electric cars in Sacramento, California. The plan is seen to create up to 600 jobs. The company's total investment is seen to reach $500 million. **Availability:** Print; Online.

5845 ■ *"China's Transition to Green Energy Systems: The Economics of Home Solar Water Heaters and Their Popularization in Dezhou City"* in *Energy Policy (Vol. 39, October 2011, No. 10, pp. 5909-5919)*
Ed: Wei Li, Guojun Song, Melanie Beresford, Ben Ma. **Released:** 2011. **Description:** The economics of home solar water heaters and their growing popularity in Dezhous City, China is discussed. **Availability:** PDF; Online.

5846 ■ *"Clean-Tech Focus Sparks Growth"* in *Philadelphia Business Journal (Vol. 28, January 15, 2010, No. 48, pp. 1)*
Pub: Philadelphia Business Journal
Contact: Sierra Quinn, Director
E-mail: squinn@bizjournals.com

Ed: Peter Key. **Description:** Keystone Redevelopment Group and economic development organization Ben Franklin Technology Partners of Southeastern Pennsylvania have partnered in supporting the growth of new alternative energy and clean technology companies. Keystone has also been developing the Bridge Business Center. **Availability:** Online.

5847 ■ *"Co-Op Launches Revolving Loan Program for Farmers" in Bellingham Business Journal (Vol. February 2010, pp. 3)*
Pub: Sound Publishing Inc.
Contact: Josh O'Connor, President

Ed: Lance Henderson. **Description:** Community Food Co-op's Farm Fund received a $12,000 matching grant from the Sustainable Whatcom Fund of the Whatcom Community Foundation. The Farm Fund will create a new revolving loan program for local farmers committed to using sustainable practices.

5848 ■ *"Coming Soon: Electric Tractors" in Farm Industry News (November 21, 2011)*
Pub: Informa Business Media, Inc.
Contact: Charlie McCurdy, President

Ed: Jodie Wehrspann. **Description:** The agricultural industry is taking another look at electric farm vehicles. John Deere Product Engineering Center said that farmers can expect to see more diesel-electric systems in farm tractors, sprayers, and implements. **Availability:** Online.

5849 ■ *"CommScope and Comsearch to Showcase Innovative Wind Power Solutions at WINDPOWER 2012 in Atlanta" in Benzinga.com (May 31, 2012)*
Pub: Benzinga.com
Contact: Jason Raznick, Founder

Ed: Aaron Wise. **Description:** CommScope Inc. and its subsidiary CommScope will highlight their complete wind power solution products during the WINDPOWER 2012 Conference and Exhibition in Atlanta, Georgia this year. CommScope's wind power products include fiber optic cabling solutions, while Comsearch offers wind energy services that address the siting challenges resulting from complex telecommunications issues. **Availability:** Print; PDF; Online.

5850 ■ *"Consumers Like Green, But Not Mandates" in Business Journal-Milwaukee (Vol. 28, December 10, 2010, No. 10, pp. A1)*
Pub: The Business Journal
Contact: Heather Ladage, President
E-mail: hladage@bizjournals.com

Ed: Sean Ryan. **Description:** Milwaukee, Wisconsin consumers are willing to spend more on green energy, a survey has revealed. Respondents also said they will pay more for efficient cars and appliances. Support for public incentives for homeowners and businesses that reduce energy use has also increased. **Availability:** Print; Online.

5851 ■ *"Consumers Want to Learn More About Green Business Efforts Despite Deep Doubt" in Benzinga.com (May 1, 2012)*
Pub: Benzinga.com
Contact: Jason Raznick, Founder

Ed: Aaron Wise. **Released:** May 01, 2012. **Description:** According to the third annual Gibbs & Soell Sense & Sustainability Study, 21 percent of Americans think the majority of businesses are working toward sustainable development, while 71 percent of consumer desire more knowledge about things corporations are doing to become sustainable and green. A majority of respondents believe the media is more likely to report green business when they can report bad news. **Availability:** Online.

5852 ■ *"Convert New Customers to Long Term Accounts" in Indoor Comfort Marketing (Vol. 70, February 2011, No. 2, pp. 22)*
Description: Marketing to new customers and suggestions for retaining them is covered. **Availability:** Online.

5853 ■ *"Corporate Responsibility" in Professional Services Close-Up (July 2, 2010)*
Description: List of firms awarded the inaugural Best Corporate Citizens in Government Contracting by the Corporate Responsibility Magazine is presented. The list is based on the methodology of the Magazine's Best Corporate Citizen's List, with 324 data points of publicly-available information in seven categories which include: environment, climate change, human rights, philanthropy, employee relations, financial performance, and governance. **Availability:** Online.

5854 ■ *"Cost Remains Top Factor In Considering Green Technology" in Canadian Sailings (June 30, 2008)*
Description: Improving its environmental performance remains a priority in the shipping industry; however, testing new technologies can prove difficult due to the harsh conditions that ships endure as well as installation which usually requires a dry dock. **Availability:** Online.

5855 ■ *"Crude Awakening" in Canadian Business (Vol. 81, October 27, 2008, No. 18, pp. 14)*
Description: Jim Grays believes that a global liquid fuels crisis is coming and hopes the expected transition from oil dependence will be smooth. Charles Maxwell, on the other hand, predicts that a new world economy will arrive in three waves. Views of both experts are examined. **Availability:** Print; Online.

5856 ■ *"Customized Before Custom Was Cool" in Green Industry Pro (July 2011)*
Ed: Gregg Wartgow. **Description:** Profile of Turf Care Enterprises and owner Kevin Vogeler, who discusses his desire to use more natural programs using little or no chemicals in 1986. At that time, that sector represented 20 percent of his business, today it shares 80 percent. **Availability:** Online.

5857 ■ *"David Robinson Column" in Buffalo News (October 2, 2011)*
Pub: The Buffalo News, Inc.
Contact: Tom Wiley, President
E-mail: twiley@buffnews.com

Ed: David Robinson. **Description:** New York Power Authority ceased development of an offshore wind farm project. Wind farming in the waters of Lake Erie or Lake Ontario would be too costly. Details of the project are discussed. **Availability:** Online.

5858 ■ *"A Day Late and a Dollar Short" in Indoor Comfort Marketing (Vol. 70, March 2011, No. 3, pp. 30)*
Description: A discussion involving futures options and fuel oil prices is presented. **Availability:** Online.

5859 ■ *"DEM Says River Needs Cleanup" in Providence Business News (Vol. 28, January 6, 2014, No. 40, pp. 1)*
Pub: American City Business Journals, Inc.
Contact: Mike Olivieri, Executive Vice President

Released: January 04, 2014. **Description:** Rhode Island's Department of Environmental Management (DEM) called a meeting to gather information for its Ten Mile River water-quality-restoration plan. DEM announced the failure of the Ten Mile River and its impoundments to meet state water quality standards. The government grant received by Attleboro for the cleanup efforts is examined. **Availability:** Print; Online.

5860 ■ *"Despite Economic Upheaval Generation Y is Still Feeling Green: RSA Canada Survey" in CNW Group (October 28, 2010)*
Pub: CNW Group Ltd.

Description: Canadian Generation Y individuals believe it is important for their company to be environmentally-friendly and one-third of those surveyed would quit their job if they found their employer was environmentally irresponsible, despite the economy. **Availability:** Online.

5861 ■ *"Detroit Hosts Conferences on Green Building, IT, Finance" in Crain's Detroit Business (Vol. 25, June 1, 2009, No. 22, pp. 9)*
Pub: Crain Communications Inc.
Contact: Barry Asin, President

Ed: Tom Henderson. **Description:** Detroit will host three conferences in June 2009, one features green technology, one information technology and the third will gather black bankers and financial experts from across the nation. **Availability:** Online.

5862 ■ *"DeWind Delivering Turbines to Texas Wind Farm" in Professional Services Close-Up (September 25, 2011)*
Description: DeWind Company has begun shipment of turbines to the 20 MW Frisco Wind Farm located in Hansford County, Texas. DeWind is a subsidiary of Daewoo Shipbuilding and Marine Engineering Company. Details of the project are discussed. **Availability:** Online.

5863 ■ *"Dog Marketplace: Pet Waste Products Pick Up Sales" in Pet Product News (Vol. 66, September 2012, No. 9, pp. 58)*
Ed: Sandi Cain. **Description:** Pet supplies manufacturers are developing dog waste pickup bags and other convenient cleanup tools characterized by environment-friendliness and fashion. The demand for these cleanup tools has been motivated by dog owners' desire to minimize their and their dogs' environmental footprints. **Availability:** Online.

5864 ■ *"Dow Champions Innovative Energy Solutions for Auto Industry at NAIAS" in Business of Global Warming (January 25, 2010, pp. 7)*
Description: This year's North American International Auto Show in Detroit will host the "Electric Avenue" exhibit sponsored by the Dow Chemical Company. The display will showcase the latest in innovative energy solutions from Dow as well as electric vehicles and the technology supporting them. This marks the first time a non-automotive manufacturer is part of the main floor of the show. **Availability:** Print; PDF; Online.

5865 ■ *"East Coast Solar" in Contractor (Vol. 57, February 2010, No. 2, pp. 17)*
Ed: Dave Yates. **Description:** U.S. Department of Energy's Solar Decathlon lets 20 college student-led teams from around the world compete to design and build a solar-powered home. A mechanical contractor discusses his work as an advisor during the competition. **Availability:** Print; Online.

5866 ■ *Eco Barons: The New Heroes of Environmental Activism*
Pub: Ecco Books
Contact: Daniel Halpern, Founder

Ed: Edward Humes. **Price:** $18.99, hardcover. **Description:** Profiles of business leaders who have dedicated their lives to saving the planet from ecological devastation. **Availability:** E-book; Print; Download.

5867 ■ *"Eco Smart Home Will Showcase Green Technology" in Contractor (Vol. 56, September 2009, No. 9, pp. 3)*
Ed: Steve Spaulding. **Description:** Eco Smart World Wide is building the Eco Smart Demonstration House to promote the latest in sustainable, renewable and high-efficiency practices and products. The company will use insulated concrete forms in the construction of the building. Features and dimensions of the structure are also presented. **Availability:** Print; Online.

5868 ■ *"Editorial: Find Private Money for FutureGen Plant" in Crain's Chicago Business (Vol. 34, September 12, 2011, No. 37, pp. 18)*
Pub: Crain Communications Inc.
Contact: Barry Asin, President

Description: FutureGen is a clean-coal power plant being developed in Southern Illinois. The need for further funding is discussed. **Availability:** Print.

5869 ■ "Elon Musk's Solar Firm Is Nearly Doubling Its Massachusetts Workforce" in Boston Business Journal (Vol. 34, May 30, 2014, No. 17, pp. 3)
Pub: American City Business Journals, Inc.
Contact: Mike Olivieri, Executive Vice President
Released: Weekly. Description: SolarCity is planning to add 100 jobs to its Massachusetts operations. The solar panel firm opened a second operations center in the state. State business incentives have enabled the company to expand presence in the area. Availability: Print; Online.

5870 ■ "Emissions: Cloudy Skies" in Canadian Business (Vol. 81, October 27, 2008, No. 18, pp. 101)
Pub: Rogers Media Inc.
Contact: Neil Spivak, Chief Executive Officer
Ed: Andrew Wahl. Description: Canada's federal government is expected to implement its regulations on greenhouse-gas emissions by January 1, 2010, but companies are worried because the plan took so long and some details are yet to be revealed. Corporate Canada wants a firm, long-range plan similar to the European Union Emissions Trading Scheme in dealing with greenhouse-gas emissions. Availability: Online.

5871 ■ "Energy Consulting Company to Expand" in Austin Business JournalInc. (Vol. 28, November 7, 2008, No. 34, pp. A1)
Pub: Austin Business Journal
Contact: Rachel McGrath, Director
E-mail: rmcgrath@bizjournals.com
Ed: Kate Harrington. Description: CLEAResult Consulting Inc. is planning to increase its workforce and move its headquarters to a larger office. The company has posted 1,000 percent increase in revenues. The company's adoption of best practices and setting of benchmark goals are seen as the reason for its growth. Availability: Print; Online.

5872 ■ "Energy Efficiency Ordinance Softened" in Austin Business JournalInc. (Vol. 28, October 3, 2008, No. 29)
Pub: Austin Business Journal
Contact: Rachel McGrath, Director
E-mail: rmcgrath@bizjournals.com
Ed: Jean Kwon. Description: City of Austin has eliminated mandatory energy efficiency upgrades to single-family housing as a condition for selling or renting homes or buildings. The new law proposes that an energy performance audit be conducted on single-family homes before being sold and the results of the audit disclosed to perspectives buyers. Availability: Print; Online.

5873 ■ "Enriching the Ecosystem: A Four-Point Plan for Linking Innovation, Enterprises, and Jobs" in Harvard Business Review (Vol. 90, March 2012, No. 3, pp. 140)
Pub: Harvard Business Review Press
Contact: Moderna V. Pfizer, Contact
Ed: Rosabeth Moss Kanter. Price: $8.95, hardcopy black and white. Description: The four goals for enriching the ecosystem include: linking venture creation and knowledge creation to speed up the idea-to-enterprise transition; revitalizing small-, medium-, and large-sized firms via partnerships; improving matches between education and employment opportunities; and bringing together leaders across different sectors to create regional strategies. Availability: Print; PDF; Online.

5874 ■ *Environmental Guide to the Internet*
Contact: Carol Briggs Erickson, Author
URL(s): rowman.com/ISBN/9780865876439
Ed: Carol Briggs-Erickson, Toni Murphy. Released: Latest edition 4th. Price: $106, Individuals Paperback. Description: Covers 1,200 resources covering the environment on the Internet, including organizations, products, and resources, including discussion groups, electronic journals, newsgroups, and discussion groups. Entries include: Name, online address, description, e-mail address. Arrangement: Categories. Availability: Print.

5875 ■ "EPA Finalizes WaterSense for Homes" in Contractor (Vol. 57, January 2010, No. 1, pp. 70)
Ed: Robert P. Mader. Description: U.S. Environmental Protection Agency released its "final" version of the WaterSense for Homes standard. The standard's provisions that affect plumbing contractors include the specification that everything has to be leak tested and final service pressure cannot exceed 60 psi. Availability: Print; Online.

5876 ■ "EPA Grants E15 Waiver for 2001-2006 Vehicles" in Farm Industry News (January 21, 2011)
Pub: Informa Business Media, Inc.
Contact: Charlie McCurdy, President
Ed: Lynn Grooms. Description: U.S. Environmental Protection Agency waived a limitation on selling gasoline that contains more than 10 percent ethanol for model year 2001-2006 cars and light trucks, allowing fuel to contain up to 15 percent ethanol (E15) for these vehicles. Availability: Online.

5877 ■ "ESolar Partners With Penglai on Landmark Solar Thermal Agreement for China" in Business of Global Warming (January 25, 2010, pp. 8)
Description: Penglai Electric, a privately-owned Chinese electrical power equipment manufacturer, and eSolar, a global provider of cost-effective and reliable solar power plants, announced a master licensing agreement in which eSolar will build at least 2 gigawatts of solar thermal power plants in China over the next 10 years. Availability: Print; Online.

5878 ■ "Family Takes Wind Turbine Companies to Court Over Gag Clauses on Health Effects of Turbines" in CNW Group (September 12, 2011)
Pub: CNW Group Ltd.
Description: Shawn and Trisha Drennan are concerned about the negative experiences other have had with wind turbines close to their homes, including adverse health effects. The couple's home will be approximately 650 meters from the Kingsbridge II wind farm project in Ontario, Canada. Availability: Online.

5879 ■ "First Sustainability Standard for Household Portable and Floor Care Appliances Developed to Identify Environmentally Responsible Products" in Ecology, Environment & Conservation Business (September 13, 2014, pp. 39)
Pub: NewsRX LLC.
Contact: Kalani Rosell, Contact
Description: the Association of Home Appliance Manufacturers (AHAM), CSA Group, and the UL Environment released the AHAM 7002-2014/CSA SPE-7002-14/UL 7002, Sustainability Standard for Household Portable and Floor Care Appliances. This is the first voluntary sustainability standards for these appliances and is the third in a unit of product sustainability standards under development by the group. These standards are intended for use by manufacturers, governments, retailers, and others to identify products conforming to these standards in six key areas: materials, manufacturing and operations, energy consumption during use, end-of-life, consumables, and innovation. Availability: Online.

5880 ■ "First Suzlon S97 Turbines Arrive in North America for Installation" in PR Newswire (September 28, 2011)
Pub: PR Newswire Association LLC.
Description: Suzlon Energy Ltd., the world's fifth largest manufacturer of wind turbines, will install its first S97 turbine at the Amherst Wind Farm Project. These turbines will be installed on 90-meter hub height towers and at full capacity, will generate enough electricity to power over 10,000 Canadian homes. Availability: Online.

5881 ■ *The Flaw of Averages: Why We Underestimate Risk in the Face of Uncertainty*
Pub: John Wiley & Sons, Inc.
Contact: Christina Van Tassell, Executive Vice President Chief Financial Officer
Ed: Sam L. Savage. Released: March 26, 2012. Price: $19.95, paperback; $27.95, hardcover; $12.99, E-Book. Description: Personal and business plans are based on uncertainties on a daily basis. The common avoidable mistake individuals make in assessing risk in the face of uncertainty is defined. The explains why plans based on average assumptions are wrong, on average, in areas as diverse as finance, healthcare, accounting, the war on terror, and climate change. Availability: E-book; Print.

5882 ■ "Florida Harvest Power Converting Organic Biz Waste to Electricity" in Orlando Business Journal (Vol. 30, March 21, 2014, No. 39, pp. 3)
Pub: American City Business Journals, Inc.
Contact: Mike Olivieri, Executive Vice President
Released: Weekly. Price: $8, introductory 4-week offer(Digital & Print). Description: Florida Harvest Power is converting organic waste from local businesses into natural fertilizer and electricity in a new $30 million facility called the Central Florida Energy Garden. Regional vice president, Chris Peters, predicts that the facility will have 6,000 tons of fertilizer to sell annually. Availability: Print; Online.

5883 ■ "For Giving Us a Way To Say Yes To Solar: Lynn Jurich and Edward Fenster" in Inc. (Volume 32, December 2010, No. 10, pp. 110)
Pub: Mansueto Ventures L.L.C.
Contact: Stephanie Mehta, Chief Executive Officer
Ed: Leigh Buchanan. Released: December 01, 2010. Description: Profile of entrepreneurs Lynn Jurich and Edward Fenster, cofounders of SunRun. The firm installs solar panels at little or no cost and homeowners sign 20-year contracts to buy power at a fixed price. Availability: Online.

5884 ■ "For One Homebuilder, It's Pretty Easy Being Green, Even in Houston" in Houston Business Journal (Vol. 44, April 11, 2014, No. 49, pp. 7)
Pub: American City Business Journals, Inc.
Contact: Mike Olivieri, Executive Vice President
Released: Weekly. Price: $4, introductory 4-week offer(Digital only). Description: Frankel Building Group vice president, Scott Frankel, says new housing projects in Houston, Texas have been getting bigger. He also said that industry members are facing the problem of lack of residential lots in the region. Frankel added that the company builds its homes to LEED-certified standards. Availability: Print; Online.

5885 ■ "Former Tech Execs Want to Tap Building Trend in Austin" in Austin Business Journal (Vol. 31, May 13, 2011, No. 10, pp. A1)
Pub: Austin Business Journal
Contact: Rachel McGrath, Director
E-mail: rmcgrath@bizjournals.com
Ed: Cody Lyon. Description: Falcon Containers moved to a 51-acre site in Far East Austin, Texas and started construction of a 2,500-square-foot headquarters made from eight 40-foot shipping containers. Falcon's CEO Stephen Shang plans to use his headquarters building as a showroom to attract upscale, urban hipsters. Insights on the construction's environmental and social impact are shared. Availability: Print; Online.

5886 ■ "Fossil Fuel, Renewable Fuel Shares Expected to Flip Flop" in Farm Industry News (April 29, 2011)
Pub: Informa Business Media, Inc.
Contact: Charlie McCurdy, President
Ed: Lynn Grooms. Description: Total energy use of fossil fuels is predicted to fall 5 percent by the year 2035, with renewable fuel picking it up. Availability: Online.

5887 ■ "From Scarcity to Plenty" in Inc. (Vol. 36, March 2014, No. 2, pp. 76)
Pub: Mansueto Ventures L.L.C.
Contact: Stephanie Mehta, Chief Executive Officer

Description: Profile of Mom's Organic Market which started in Scott Nash's mom's garage. Nash describes the healthy food choices offered at the store as well as its Environmental Restoration program which addressed issues including carbon offsets, recycling, and composting. **Availability:** Print; Online.

5888 ■ *"FSU's OGZEB Is Test Bed for Sustainable Technology"* in Contractor (Vol. 56, October 2009, No. 10, pp. 1)

Ed: Candace Roulo. **Description:** Florida State University has one of 14 off-grid zero emissions buildings (OGZEB) in the U.S.; it was built to research sustainable and alternative energy systems. The building produces electricity from 30 photovoltaic panels and it also has three AET water heating solar panels on the roof. **Availability:** Print; Online.

5889 ■ *"Fuel King: The Most Fuel-Efficient Tractor of the Decade is the John Deere 8295R"* in Farm Industry News (November 10, 2011)

Pub: Informa Business Media, Inc.
Contact: Charlie McCurdy, President
Description: Farm Industry News compiled a list of the most fuel-efficient tractors with help from the Nebraska Tractor Test Lab, with the John Deere 8295R PTO winner of the most fuel-efficient tractor of the decade. **Availability:** Print; Online.

5890 ■ *"GE Announces New Projects, Technology Milestone and New Service Program at AWEA Windpower 2012"* in News Bites US (June 6, 2012)

Description: General Electric announced plans at the AWEA Windpower 2012 for its two new wind turbine projects to be located in Michigan and Iowa. Details of these new wind turbine projects are included. **Availability:** Online.

5891 ■ *"GE Milestone: 1,000th Wind Turbine Installed in Canada"* in CNW Group (October 4, 2011)

Pub: CNW Group Ltd.
Description: GE installed its 1,000th wind turbine in Canada at Cartier Wind Energy's Gros Morne project in the Gaspesie Region of Quebec, Canada. As Canada continues to expand its use of wind energy, GE plans to have over 1,100 wind turbines installed in the nation by the end of 2011. **Availability:** Online.

5892 ■ *"General Electric Touts Going Green for Business Fleet Services"* in America's Intelligence Wire (June 1, 2012)

Description: General Capital Fleet Services if featuring alternative-fuel vehicles in Eden Prairie for its corporate customers. GE Capital is the world's largest fleet management service and is offering its customers the first of its kind service that allows corporate lease customers to test drive alternative fuel cars from 20 different manufacturers. **Availability:** Print; Online.

5893 ■ *"Germans Win Solar Decathlon Again"* in Contractor (Vol. 56, November 2009, No. 11, pp. 1)

Ed: Robert P. Mader. **Description:** Students from Technische Universtat Darmstadt won the U.S. Department of Energy's Solar Decathlon by designing and building the most attractive and efficient solar-powered home. The winner's design produced a surplus of power even during three days of rain and photovoltaic panels covered nearly every exterior surface. **Availability:** Print; Online.

5894 ■ *"Getting the Bioheat Word Out"* in Indoor Comfort Marketing (Vol. 70, September 2011, No. 9, pp. 32)

Description: Ways to market advanced liquid fuels to the public are outlined. **Availability:** Print; Online.

5895 ■ *"The Global Environment Movement is Bjorn Again"* in Canadian Business (Vol. 83, September 14, 2010, No. 15, pp. 11)
Pub: Rogers Media Inc.
Contact: Neil Spivak, Chief Executive Officer

Ed: Steve Maich. **Description:** Danish academic Bjorn Lomborg is in favor of decisive action to combat climate change in his new book and was given front page treatment by a London newspaper. Environmentalist groups see this as a victory since Lomborg had not previously considered climate change an immediate issue. **Availability:** Online.

5896 ■ *"GM's Volt Woes Cast Shadow on E-Cars"* in Wall Street Journal Eastern Edition (November 28, 2011, pp. B1)
Pub: Dow Jones & Company Inc.
Contact: Almar Latour, Chief Executive Officer

Ed: Sharon Terlep. **Description:** The future of electric cars is darkened with the government investigation by the National Highway Traffic Safety Administration into General Motor Company's Chevy Volt after two instances of the car's battery packs catching fire during crash tests conducted by the Agency. **Availability:** Online.

5897 ■ *"Go Green Or Go Home"* in Black Enterprise (Vol. 41, August 2010, No. 1, pp. 53)
Pub: Earl G. Graves Ltd.
Contact: Earl Graves, Jr., President

Ed: Robinson M. Tennille. **Description:** The green economy has become an essential part of every business, however, small business owners need to learn how to participate, including minority owned entrepreneurs. **Availability:** Online.

5898 ■ *Good Green Guide for Small Businesses: How to Change the Way Your Business Works for the Better*
Pub: A. and C. Black
Contact: Jenny Ridout, Director

Released: First edition. **Description:** Guide for small businesses to take an environmental audit of their company and shows how to minimize the impact of office essentials such as utilities, insulation, recycling and waste, electrical equipment, water systems, lighting options, food and drink, and office cleaning arrangements and products. **Availability:** Print.

5899 ■ *"Got to be Smarter than the Average Bear"* in Contractor (Vol. 56, September 2009, No. 9, pp. 82)

Ed: Robert P. Mader. **Description:** International Association of Plumbing and Mechanical Officials Green Technical Committee has debated the need for contractors to have certifications in installing green plumbing. Some have argued that qualifications would discourage homeowners from improving their properties. Comments from executives are also included. **Availability:** Print; Online.

5900 ■ *"Governor Candidates Differ on Oregon's Green Streak"* in Business Journal Portland (Vol. 27, October 22, 2010, No. 34, pp. 1)
Pub: Portland Business Journal
Contact: Andy Giegerich, Managing Editor
E-mail: agiegerich@bizjournals.com

Ed: Andy Giegerich. **Description:** The views of Oregon gubernatorial candidates Chris Dudley and John Kitzhaber on the state's economy and on environmental policies are presented. Both Dudley, who is a Republican, and his Democratic challenger believe that biomass could help drive the state's economy. Both candidates also pledged changes in Oregon's business energy tax credit (BETC) program.

5901 ■ *"Grainger Show Highlights Building Green, Economic Recovery"* in Contractor (Vol. 57, February 2010, No. 2, pp. 3)

Ed: Candace Roulo. **Description:** Chief U.S. economist told attendees of the Grainger's 2010 Total MRO Solutions National Customer Show that the economic recovery would be subdued. Mechanical contractors who attended the event also learned about building sustainable, green products, and technologies, and economic and business challenges. **Availability:** Print; Online.

5902 ■ *"Green Business Owners Share Secrets of Success In This Business Guide"* in PRNewsChannel.com (March 1, 2012)
Pub: Comtex News Network Inc.
Contact: Kan Devnani, President
Description: Business guide to help companies become sustainable and work to be a green business. **Availability:** Online.

5903 ■ *"Green Business Plan Competition"* in Chemical & Engineering News (Vol. 90, July 9, 2012, No. 28, pp. 34)
Pub: American Chemical Society Philadelphia Section
Contact: Dr. David Cichowicz, Director

Ed: Stephen K. Ritter. **Description:** Startup anticorrosion coatings firm AnCatt Inc. won the inaugural chemistry business plan competition at the Green Chemistry & Engineering Conference held in July 2012 in Washington, DC. AnCatt was honored for its conducting-polymer-based anticorrosion paint system aimed at replacing chormate, lead, and cadmium paint pigments. **Availability:** Online.

5904 ■ *"Green and Clean"* in Retail Merchandiser (Vol. 51, July-August 2011, No. 4, pp. 56)
Description: Green Valley Grocery partnered with Paragon Solutions consulting firm to make their stores environmentally green. **Availability:** Print; Online.

5905 ■ *"Green Collar: Green Buildings Support Job Creation, Workforce Transformation and Economic Recovery"* in Environmental Design and Construction (Vol. 15, July 2012, No. 7, pp. 31)
Pub: BNP Media
Contact: Harper Henderson, Owner Co-Chief Executive Officer

Ed: Maggie Comstock. **Description:** Despite construction being at an all-time low, green building construction has maintained its hold on nonresidential buildings. It has even shown growth in some sectors and accounts for over one-third of all nonresidential design and construction jobs and is expected to show further growth through 2014. Statistical details included.

5906 ■ *The Green Guide for Business: The Ultimate Environment for Businesses of All Sizes*
Pub: Profile Books Limited
Contact: Stephen Brough, Co-Founder

Ed: Chris Goodball, Roger East, Hannah Bullock.
Released: March 09, 2010. **Description:** Everyone wants to go green these days, but for small businesses that's easier said than done. How do you measure a company's carbon footprint? Are dryers or hand towels more eco-friendly? Recycled paper or FSC-certified? All these questions and more are explored. **Availability:** E-book.

5907 ■ *"Green It Like You Mean It"* in Special Events Magazine (Vol. 28, February 1, 2009, No. 2)
Description: Eco-friendly party planners offer advice for planning and hosting green parties or events. Tips include information for using recycled paper products, organic food and drinks. The Eco Nouveau Fashion Show held by Serene Star Productions reused old garments to create new fashions as well as art pieces from discarded doors and window frames for the show; eco-friendly treats and gift bags were highlighted at the event.

5908 ■ *"Green Light"* in The Business Journal-Portland (Vol. 25, July 11, 2008, No. 18, pp. 1)
Description: Ecos Consulting, a sustainability consulting company based in Portland, Oregon, is seeing a boost in revenue as more businesses turn to sustainable practices. The company's revenue rose by 50 percent in 2007 and employees increased from 57 to 150. Other details about Ecos' growth are discussed. **Availability:** Print; Online.

Small Business Profiles

5909 ■ "Green Manufacturer Scouts Sites in Greater Cincinnati" in Business Courier (Vol. 27, July 23, 2010, No. 12, pp. 1)
Pub: Business Courier
Ed: Dan Monk. **Description:** CresaPartners is searching for a manufacturing facility in Cincinnati, Ohio. The company is set to tour about ten sites in the area. **Availability:** Print; Online.

5910 ■ "Green Rules To Drive Innovation: Charging for Carbon Can Inspire Conservation, Fuel Competition, and Enhance Competitiveness" in Harvard Business Review (Vol. 90, March 2012, No. 3, pp. 120)
Pub: Harvard Business Review Press
Contact: Moderna V. Pfizer, Contact
Ed: Daniel C. Esty, Steve Charnovitz. **Price:** $8.95. **Description:** Along with carbon emissions charges, other green policy recommendations include expanding domestic renewable power and the use of natural gas, increasing federal funding of clean-energy research, utilizing incentive-based approaches to encourage the adoption of renewable energy, and implementing the World Trade Organization's Doha negotiations on sustainable development. **Availability:** Online; PDF.

5911 ■ "Greenhouse Announces Reverse Merger With Custom Q, Inc." in Investment Weekly (January 30, 2010, pp. 338)
Pub: Investment Weekly News
Description: In accordance with an Agreement and Plan of Share Exchange, GreenHouse Holdings, Inc., an innovative green solutions provider, has gone public via a reverse merger with Custom Q, Inc. **Availability:** Print; Online.

5912 ■ Greening Your Small Business: How to Improve Your Bottom Line, Grow Your Brand, Satisfy Your Customers and Save the Planet
Price: $19.95. **Description:** A definitive resource for anyone who wants their small business to be cutting-edge, competitive, profitable, and eco-conscious. Stories from small business owners address every aspect of going green, from basics such as recycling waste, energy efficiency, and reducing information technology footprint, to more in-depth concerns such as green marketing and communications, green business travel, and green employee benefits.

5913 ■ "GreenTech Gears Up for Production" in Memphis Business Journal (Vol. 33, April 6, 2012, No. 52, pp. 1)
Pub: Baltimore Business Journal
Contact: Rhonda Pringle, President
E-mail: rpringle@bizjournals.com
Description: GreenTech Automotive has broken ground for construction of a new production facility in Tunica, Tennessee. The company will focus its manufacturing operations in the new facility. **Availability:** Print; Online.

5914 ■ Guerrilla Marketing Goes Green: Winning Strategies to Improve Your Profits and Your Planet
Pub: John Wiley & Sons, Inc.
Contact: Christina Van Tassell, Executive Vice President Chief Financial Officer
Ed: Jay Conrad Levinson, Shel Horowitz, Jay Conrad Levinson. **Released:** 2010. **Description:** The latest tips on green marketing and sustainable business strategies are shared. **Availability:** E-book; Print; Electronic publishing; Online.

5915 ■ "Harpoon Brewery Wins Boston Green Business Award for Sustainability and EnerNOC Energy Management Programs" in Investment Weekly News (May 12, 2012, No. 543)
Description: Harpoon Brewery was awarded a 2012 Boston Green Business Award by Mayor Thomas Menino of Boston, Massachusetts. The brewery was cited for having an exceptional sustainability program that includes waste reduction, responsible chemical usage, and operational efficiency measures combined with energy management initiatives with EnerNOC. EnerNOC is a leading provider of energy management applications for commercial, industrial, and institutional energy users, including Harpoon. **Availability:** Online.

5916 ■ "Hey, You Can't Do That" in Green Industry Pro (Vol. 23, September 2011)
Ed: Rod Dickens. **Description:** Manufacturers of landscape equipment are making better use of energy resources, such as the use of fuel-injection systems instead of carburetors, lightweight materials, better lubricants, advanced battery technology, and innovative engine designs. **Availability:** Online.

5917 ■ Housecleaning Business: Organize Your Business - Get Clients and Referrals - Set Rates and Services
Ed: Laura Jorstad, Melinda Morse. **Price:** Paperback, softback. **Description:** This book shares insight into starting a housecleaning business. It shows how to develop a service manual, screen clients, serve customers, select cleaning products, competition, how to up a home office, using the Internet to grow the business and offering green cleaning options to clients. **Availability:** E-book; Print.

5918 ■ "How Green Is The Valley?" in Barron's (Vol. 88, July 4, 2008, No. 28, pp. 13)
Description: San Jose, California has made a good start towards becoming a leader in alternative energy technology through the establishment of United Laboratories' own lab in the city. The certification process for photovoltaic cells will be dramatically shortened with this endeavor. **Availability:** Print.

5919 ■ "How I Did It: Timberland's CEO On Standing Up to 65,000 Angry Activists" in Harvard Business Review (Vol. 88, September 2010, No. 9, pp. 39)
Pub: Harvard Business Publishing
Contact: Diane Belcher, Managing Director
Ed: Jeff Swartz. **Price:** $8.95, PDF. **Description:** Timberland Company avoided a potential boycott by taking a two-way approach. It addressed a supplier issue that posed a threat to the environment, and launched an email campaign to keep Greenpeace activists informed of the development of a new supplier agreement. **Availability:** Online; PDF.

5920 ■ "How to... Harness Green Power" in The Caterer (July 20, 2012, No. 325)
Pub: LNRS Data Services Limited
Contact: Mark Vickers Kelsey, Director
Description: Roger and Emma Stevens discuss their success as at winning the Considerate Hoteliers Association's award for Best Green Marketing Initiative. The couple discusses their restaurant and its partnership with tow nearby guesthouses. **Availability:** Online.

5921 ■ "IndieCompanyDk Offers Eco-Friendly Furniture That Stands Out" in Ecology, Environment & Conservation Business (September 6, 2014, pp. 39)
Pub: NewsRX LLC.
Contact: Kalani Rosell, Contact
Description: A new manufacturer of eco-friendly furniture and interiors, IndieCompanyDk, is offering a new concept in sustainable furniture design, using exclusive and affordable smooth designs, which maintain the natural and raw look of quality reclaimed materials. **Availability:** Online.

5922 ■ "Industry Escalates Lobbying Efforts For Loan Program" in Crain's Detroit Business (Vol. 24, September 22, 2008, No. 38, pp. 22)
Pub: Crain Communications Inc.
Contact: Barry Asin, President
Ed: Jay Greene, Ryan Beene, Harry Stoffer. **Description:** Auto suppliers such as Lear Corp., which is best known for vehicle seating, also supplies high-voltage wiring for Ford hybrids and is developing other hybrid components. These suppliers are joining automakers in lobbying for the loan program which would promote the accelerated development of fuel-efficient vehicles. **Availability:** Print; PDF; Online.

5923 ■ "Info Junkie: Karen Eng" in Crain's Chicago Business (Vol. 34, October 24, 2011, No. 42, pp. 35)
Pub: Crain Communications Inc.
Contact: Barry Asin, President
Ed: Christina Le Beau. **Description:** Greg Colando, president of Flor Inc., an eco-friendly carpet company located I Chicago discusses his marketing program to increase sales. **Availability:** Online.

5924 ■ "Invest in Energy-Efficient Equipment for Your Pet Store" in Pet Product News (Vol. 66, September 2012, No. 9, pp. 72)
Ed: Leila Meyer. **Description:** Aquatic retailers can achieve business growth by offering lighting products, pumps, heaters, filters, and other aquarium supplies that would help customers realize energy efficiency. Aside from offering an education in energy efficiency as a customer service opportunity, retailers are encouraged to determine what supplies are crucial in helping customers achieve energy usage goals. **Availability:** Online.

5925 ■ "Keene: Nominations are Being Sought by the Keene Cities for Climate Protection Committee for the Monadnock Green Business of the Year Award" in New Hampshire Business Review (Vol. 34, February 24, 2012, No. 4, pp. 7)
Released: February 24, 2012. **Description:** Nominations are being sought by the Keene Cities for Climate Protection Committee for the Monadnock Green Business of the Year Award. The award recognizes socially and environmentally responsible companies in the region that have developed innovative practices or programs while contributing to the economic growth of the area.

5926 ■ "Kroger Releases Annual Sustainability Report" in Ecology, Environment & Conservation Business (July 26, 2014, pp. 46)
Pub: NewsRX LLC.
Contact: Kalani Rosell, Contact
Description: Kroger Company published its eighth annual sustainability report. The company is committed to reducing water consumption in its grocery stores by 5 percent in 2014. The report also provides a progress report on moving retail locations toward 'zero waste' and sourcing 100 percent certified palm oil. Statistical data included. **Availability:** Online.

5927 ■ "Large Homes can be Energy Efficient Too" in Contractor (Vol. 56, October 2009, No. 10, pp. 5)
Ed: Candace Roulo. **Description:** Eco Estate at Briggs Chaney subdivision in Silver Spring, Maryland has model houses that use sustainable technologies and products and the homes that will be built on the subdivision will feature some of the technologies featured on the model home. The energy efficient HVAC system of the model homes are discussed. **Availability:** Print; Online.

5928 ■ "The Long View: Roberta Bondar's Unique Vision of Science, The Need for Education, and More" in Canadian Business (Vol. 81, October 27, 2008, No. 18)
Pub: Rogers Media Inc.
Contact: Neil Spivak, Chief Executive Officer
Ed: Alex Mlynek. **Description:** Roberta Bondar believes that energy and renewable energy is a critical environmental issue faced by Canada today. Bondar is the first Canadian woman and neurologist in space. **Availability:** Online.

5929 ■ "Longtime Advocacy for Green Skin Care Is Paying Off" in Providence Business News (Vol. 29, June 2, 2014, No. 9, pp. 24)
Pub: American City Business Journals, Inc.
Contact: Mike Olivieri, Executive Vice President

Released: February 01, 2014. **Description:** Brenda Brock, entrepreneur and founder of Farmaesthetics, achieved success with her line of green, sustainable skin care products. She is now expanding her business to start new outlets. **Availability:** Print; Online.

5930 ■ *"Magpower May Build Solar Panels in Pflugerville" in Austin Business Journal (Vol. 31, May 13, 2011, No. 10, pp. A1)*
Pub: Austin Business Journal
Contact: Rachel McGrath, Director
E-mail: rmcgrath@bizjournals.com

Ed: Christopher Calnan. **Description:** RRE Austin Solar LLC CEO Doven Mehta has revealed plans to partner with Portugal-based Magpower SA, only if Austin energy buys electricity from planned solar energy farm in Pflugerville. Austin Energy has received 100 bids from 35 companies to supply 200 megawatts of solar- and wind-generated electricity. **Availability:** Print; Online.

5931 ■ *"MFG Wind Launched at AWEA WindPower 2012 Conference and Exhibition" in Marketing Weekly News (June 23, 2012, pp. 169)*

Description: American Wind Energy Association's Conference & Exhibition was held in Atlanta, Georgia. The Molded Fiber Glass Companies (MFG) introduced MFG Wind, a new brand that stands for comprehensive wind-focused set of capabilities that it is bringing to the marketplace.

5932 ■ *"Mixing Business and Pleasure On the Green" in Black Enterprise (Vol. 41, October 2010, No. 3, pp. 65)*

Description: Glow Golf, sponsored by Glow Sports, will offer instruction to 150 female corporate executives and entrepreneurs to learn the fundamentals of the game of golf. **Availability:** Print; Online.

5933 ■ *The Necessary Revolution: Working Together to Create a Sustainable World*
Pub: Broadway Business

Ed: Peter M. Senge, Bryan Smith, Nina Kruschwitz, Joe Laur, Sara Schley. **Released:** April 06, 2010. **Price:** $20, paperback. **Description:** The book outlines various examples for companies to implement sustainable change and go green in the process. **Availability:** E-book; Print; Audio; Online.

5934 ■ *"The New Alchemists" in Canadian Business (Vol. 81, October 27, 2008, No. 18, pp. 22)*

Description: Ethanol industry expects second-generation ethanol or cellulosic biofuels to provide ecologically friendly technologies than the ethanol made from food crops. Government and industries are investing on producing cellulosic biofuels. **Availability:** Print; Online.

5935 ■ *"A New Alliance For Global Change" in Harvard Business Review (Vol. 88, September 2010, No. 9, pp. 56)*
Pub: Harvard Business Publishing
Contact: Diane Belcher, Managing Director

Ed: Bill Drayton, Valeria Budinich. **Price:** $8.95, PDF. **Description:** Collaboration between social organizations and for-profit firms through the development of hybrid value chains to target complex global issues is promoted. While social organizations offer links to communities and consumers, firms provide financing and scale expertise. **Availability:** Online; PDF.

5936 ■ *"New Book Takes Alternate View on Ontario's Wind Industry" in CNW Group (September 19, 2011)*
Pub: CNW Group Ltd.

Description: Dirty Business: The Reality Behind Ontario's Rush to Wind Power, was written by editor and health care writer Jane Wilson of Ottawa, Ontario, Canada along with contributing editor Parker Gallant. The book contains articles and papers on the wind business, including information on illnesses caused from the environmental noise. **Availability:** Print; Online.

5937 ■ *"A New Day is Dawning" in Indoor Comfort Marketing (Vol. 70, August 2011, No. 8, pp. 18)*
Description: New trends in the HVAC/R industry regarding biofuels and bioheat are explored. **Availability:** Online.

5938 ■ *"New No. 1 at Element 8: Angel Group Brings on New Executive Director" in Puget Sound Business Journal (Vol. 35, September 19, 2014, No. 22, pp. 6)*
Pub: American City Business Journals, Inc.
Contact: Mike Olivieri, Executive Vice President

Description: Element 8 executive director, Kristi Growdon, says the company continues to find investment opportunities in the Pacific Northwest's clean technology sector. She also said the agricultural sector is a potentially lucrative investment destination. Growdon added that the company bases decisions on clean technology. **Availability:** Online.

5939 ■ *"The Next Great Canadian Idea: Peripiteia Generator" in Canadian Business (Vol. 81, July 21, 2008, No. 11, pp. 45)*
Pub: Rogers Media Inc.
Contact: Neil Spivak, Chief Executive Officer

Ed: Sharda Prashad. **Description:** Thane Heins has invented a generator that produces energy in an isolated system which contradicts the law of conservation of energy. Perepiteia generator is referred to as a 'perpetual motion machine.' Other inventions slated for the Canadian invention competition include Rob Matthies' batteries and Frank Naumann's Smart Trap. **Availability:** Online.

5940 ■ *"NStar Feels the Heat" in Cape Cod Times (September 30, 2011)*
Pub: Cape Cod Media Group
Contact: Anne Brennan, Executive Editor
E-mail: abrennan@capecodonline.com

Ed: Patrick Cassidy. **Description:** Massachusetts energy officials wish to delay a merger between NStar and Northeast Utilities until it is clear how the partnership would meet the state's green energy goals. Governor Deval Patrick supports the proposed Nantucket Sound wind farm. **Availability:** Online.

5941 ■ *"Nuclear Renaissance" in Canadian Business (Vol. 83, August 17, 2010, No. 13-14, pp. 46)*

Description: Nuclear energy has come back into the public's favor in Canada because it has virtually no emissions and is always available anytime of the day. Canada's nuclear industry has also achieved an incomparable record of safe, economic and reliable power generation in three provinces for 48 years. **Availability:** Online.

5942 ■ *"Out of Juice?" in Canadian Business (Vol. 81, October 27, 2008, No. 18, pp. 32)*
Description: Alternative energy experts suggest Canada should be more aggressive and should make major policy changes on energy alternatives despite an Ernst & Young research that rated the country high on renewable energy. **Availability:** Print; Online.

5943 ■ *"Overheating Taking Place? Pay Attention to Details.." in Indoor Comfort Marketing (Vol. 70, March 2011, No. 3)*
Description: Boiler facts are outlined to help the small HVAC company when servicing customers. **Availability:** PDF; Online.

5944 ■ *"An Overview of Energy Consumption of the Globalized World Economy" in Energy Policy (Vol. 39, October 2011, No. 10, pp. 5920-2928)*
Ed: Z. M. Chen, G. Q. Chen. **Released:** October 01, 2011. **Description:** Energy consumption and its impact on the global world economy is examined. **Availability:** Print; Online.

5945 ■ *"Paul Hawken and Other Top Lumnaries to Participate in Green Business BASE CAMP in Los Angeles" in Benzinga.com (April 19, 2012)*
Pub: Benzinga.com
Contact: Jason Raznick, Founder

Ed: Aaron Wise. **Description:** Paul Hawken, environmentalist, entrepreneur and author, is one of many people participating in the Green Business BASE CAMP, a four-day workshop for green business and cleantech entrepreneurs. The event will be held in Los Angeles, California from May 31 through June 3, 2012. Insider guidance will be offered to early-stage entrepreneurs seeking to compete within this sector. **Availability:** Online.

5946 ■ *"Pennsylvania DEP To Conduct Natural Gas Vehicle Seminar" in Travel & Leisure Close-Up (October 8, 2012)*
Description: Pennsylvania Department of Environmental Protection is holding a Natural Gas Vehicle seminar at the Bayfront Convention Center in Erie, PA, as well as other locations throughout the state. The seminars will help municipal and commercial fleet owners make better informed decisions when converting fleets from compressed natural gas and liquefied natural gas. **Availability:** Print; Online.

5947 ■ *"Planned CO2 Regulations Could Hit Region Hard" in Pittsburgh Business Times (Vol. 33, June 6, 2014, No. 47, pp. 9)*
Pub: American City Business Journals, Inc.
Contact: Mike Olivieri, Executive Vice President

Released: Weekly. **Price:** $4, introductory 4-week offer(Digital only). **Description:** The U.S. Environmental Protection Agency's (EPA's) proposed rules to cut carbon dioxide (CO2) emissions by 30 percent over 16 years could have an adverse impact on southwestern Pennsylvania. The draft regulations, announced June 2, 2014, will affect the Pennsylvania region's power-generation sector as well as its coal industry, thereby impacting the regional economy. **Availability:** Print; Online.

5948 ■ *"PrintCity Shares Guide for Carbon Footprinting" in American Printer (Vol. 128, June 1, 2011, No. 6)*
Description: PrintCity Alliance published its new report, 'Carbon Footprint & Energy Reduction for Graphic Industry Value Chain.' The report aims to help improve the environmental performance of printers, converters, publishers, brand owners and their suppliers. **Availability:** Online.

5949 ■ *"Professional Grooming Marketplace: Cash In On Green Products and Services" in Pet Product News (Vol. 66, September 2012, No. 9, pp. 84)*
Ed: Lizett Bond. **Description:** Pet grooming salons can build customer reputation by providing sustainable and environment-friendly products and services. Energy efficiency and electricity conservation can also be focused upon as pet grooming salons aspire for green marketing goals. **Availability:** Online.

5950 ■ *"Provinces Tackle E-Waste Problem" in Canadian Electronics (Vol. 23, June-July 2008, No. 4, pp. 1)*
Pub: Action Communication Inc.

Ed: Ken Manchen. **Description:** Canadian provinces are implementing measures concerning the safe and environmentally friendly disposal of electronic waste. Alberta, British Columbia, Nova Scotia, and Saskatchewan impose an e-waste recycling fee on electronic equipment purchases. **Availability:** Print; Online.

5951 ■ *"PSC Approves $130M TECO Solar Project" in Tampa Bay Business Journal (Vol. 30, December 18, 2009, No. 52, pp. 1)*
Pub: Tampa Bay Business Journal
Contact: Ian Anderson, President
E-mail: ianderson@bizjournals.com

Ed: Michael Hinman. **Description:** Florida's Public Service Commission has endorsed Tampa Electric Company's plan to add 25 megawatts of solar energy to its portfolio. TECO's plan needed the approval by PSC to defray additional costs for the project through ratepayers. **Availability:** Print; Online.

5952 ■ *"PSC Decision Could Help Bolster a Solar Market Supernova" in Tampa Bay Business Journal (Vol. 29, November 6, 2009, No. 46, pp. 1)*
Pub: Tampa Bay Business Journal
Contact: Ian Anderson, President

E-mail: ianderson@bizjournals.com
Ed: Michael Hinman. **Description:** Florida's Public Service Commission (PSC) decision on a power purchase agreement that could add 25 megawatts of solar energy on Tampa Electric Company's offerings is presented. The decision could support the growing market for suppliers and marketers of renewable energy such as Jabil Circuit Inc., which manufactures photovoltaic modules. Details of the agreement are discussed. **Availability:** Print; Online.

5953 ■ *"PSEG Queen Creek Solar Farm in Arizona Begins Commercial Operation"* in *Benzinga.com (October 4, 2012)*
Description: PSEG Solar Source will launch the commercial operation of the 25.2 megawatt DC (19 megawatt AC) Queen Creek Solar Farm in Queen Creek, Arizona. The Salt River Project (SRP) has a 20-year agreement to acquire acquire all of the solar energy generated by the project. More details are included.

5954 ■ *"PSI Repair Services to Showcase at Windpower Conference and Exhibition"* in *Entertainment Close-Up (May 19, 2012)*
Description: Subsidiary of Phillips Service Industries, PSI Repair Services, will highlight its off-warranty repair support for wind energy operations at the Windpower 2012 Conference and Exhibition. **Availability:** Online.

5955 ■ *"Recession Creating Surge in Business for Auto Recyclers"* in *Business Journal-Serving Phoenix & the Valley of the Sun (Vol. 31, November 12, 2010, No. 10, pp. 1)*
Pub: Phoenix Business Journal
Contact: Alex McAlister, Director
E-mail: amcalister@bizjournals.com
Ed: Patrick O'Grady. **Description:** Automotive parts recyclers in Arizona are benefiting from the challenging national economic conditions as well as from the green movement. Recyclers revealed that customers prefer recycled parts more because they are cheaper and are more environmentally friendly. Other information about the automotive parts recycling industry is presented. **Availability:** Print; Online.

5956 ■ *"Recycling 202: How to Take Your Recycling Practices to the Next Level"* in *Black Enterprise (Vol. 41, September 2010, No. 2, pp. 38)*
Pub: Earl G. Graves Ltd.
Contact: Earl Graves, Jr., President
Ed: Tamara E. Holmes. **Description:** Consumer Electronics Association and other organizations, manufacturers and retailers list ways to recycle all household items. **Availability:** Online.

5957 ■ *"Reducing the Book's Carbon Footprint"* in *American Printer (Vol. 128, July 1, 2011, No. 7)*
Description: Green Press Initiative's Book Industry Environmental Council is working to achieve a 20 percent reduction in the book industry's carbon footprint by 2020. The Council is made up of publishers, printers, paper suppliers, and non-governmental organizations. **Availability:** Online.

5958 ■ *"Region Wins as GE Puts Plants Close to R&D"* in *Business Review Albany (Vol. 41, July 4, 2014, No. 15, pp. 8)*
Pub: American City Business Journals, Inc.
Contact: Mike Olivieri, Executive Vice President
Description: General Electric Company (GE) invested over $400 million into the expansion of its health care, battery and renewable energy businesses in the Albany, New York region. The company's local growth secured about 7,000 private-sector jobs in the area and strengthened the relationship between GE research and manufacturing. **Availability:** Print; Online.

5959 ■ *"Reinventing Marketing to Manage the Environmental Imperative"* in *Journal of Marketing (Vol. 75, July 2011, No. 4, pp. 132)*
Pub: American Marketing Association
Contact: Bennie F. Johnson, Chief Executive Officer

Ed: Philip Kotler. **Description:** Marketers must now examine their theory and practices due to the growing recognition of finite resources and high environmental costs. Companies also need to balance more carefully their growth goals with the need to purse sustainability. Insights on the rise of demarketing and social marketing are also given. **Availability:** PDF.

5960 ■ *"Renewable Energy Adoption in an Ageing Population: Heterogeneity in Preferences for Micro-Generation Technology Adoption"* in *Energy Policy (Vol. 39, October 2011, No. 10, pp. 6021-6029)*
Ed: Ken Willis, Riccardo Scarpa, Rose Gilroy, Neveen Hamza. **Released:** October 01, 2011. **Description:** Attitudes and impacts of renewable energy adoption on an aging population is examined. **Availability:** Print; Online.

5961 ■ *"Renewable Energy Market Opportunities: Wind Testing"* in *PR Newswire (September 22, 2011)*
Pub: PR Newswire Association LLC.
Description: Global wind energy test systems markets are discussed. Research conducted covers both non-destructive test equipment and condition monitoring equipment product segments.

5962 ■ *"Renewable Plants are Still On Valero Energy's Radar"* in *San Antonio Business Journal (Vol. 28, March 28, 2014, No. 7, pp. 10)*
Pub: American City Business Journals, Inc.
Contact: Mike Olivieri, Executive Vice President
Released: Weekly. **Price:** $4, Introductory 4-week offer(Digital & Print). **Description:** Analysts believe that Valero Energy Corporation's recent purchase of an ethanol plant will not be its last. The company is considered to be the third-largest ethanol refiner in the U.S. The possibility of reopening Valero's other plants is also examined. **Availability:** Print; Online.

5963 ■ *"Research and Markets Offers Report on US Business Traveler's Green, New Technology Views"* in *Airline Industry Information (July 30, 2012)*
Description: The US Business Traveler Expectations of Green and Technology Initiatives in Hotels in 2012 contains comprehensive analysis on US business travelers views on green and technology initiative and socially responsible measures geared towards the business traveler. **Availability:** Print; Online.

5964 ■ *"ReVenture Plan Appears Close to Landing Key N.C. Legislative Deal"* in *Charlotte Business Journal (Vol. 25, July 9, 2010, No. 16, pp. 1)*
Pub: Charlotte Business Journal
Contact: Robert Morris, Editor
E-mail: rmorris@bizjournals.com
Ed: John Downey. **Description:** North Carolina lawmakers acted on special legislation that would boost development of Forsite Development 667-acre ReVenture Energy Park. The legislation could also improve chances that Duke Energy Carolinas will contract to purchase the power from the planned 50-megawatt biomass power plant located at the park. How utilities would benefit from the legislation is also discussed. **Availability:** Print; Online.

5965 ■ *"Richard Faulk Covers Climate in Copenhagen"* in *Houston Business Journal (Vol. 40, December 25, 2009, No. 33, pp. 1)*
Pub: Houston Business Journal
Contact: Bob Charlet, President
E-mail: bcharlet@bizjournals.com
Ed: Ford Gunter. **Description:** Houston environmental attorney Richard Faulk talks to the United Nations Climate Change Conference in Copenhagen, Denmark. Faulk believes the conference failed due to political differences between countries like US and China. Faulk believed the discussion of developed and developing countries on verification and limits on carbon emissions is something good that came from the conference. **Availability:** Print; Online.

5966 ■ *"The Rise of 'Zero-Waste' Grocery Stores"* in *Smithsonian.com (February 15, 2019)*
URL(s): www.smithsonianmag.com/innovation/rise-zero-waste-grocery-stores-180971495/
Ed: Emily Matchar. **Released:** February 15, 2019. **Description:** Plastic waste that ends up in landfills and oceans is starting to take a major toll on the environment. Some grocers are mindful of this and have introduced zero waste stores, where food is sold in bulk with consumers bringing their own containers, instead of wrapping everything in plastic. **Availability:** Online.

5967 ■ *"Rosewood Site Faces Big Cleanup Before Stevenson Can Expand"* in *Baltimore Business Journal (Vol. 27, February 6, 2010, No. 40, pp. 1)*
Pub: Baltimore Business Journal
Contact: Rhonda Pringle, President
E-mail: rpringle@bizjournals.com
Ed: Daniel J. Sernovitz. **Description:** Environmental assessment report states that Maryland's Rosewood Center for the Developmentally Disabled has significant amounts of toxic chemicals, which could impact Stevenson University's decision to purchase the property. Senator Robert A. Zirkin believes that the state should pay for the cleanup, which is expected to cost millions. **Availability:** Print; Online.

5968 ■ *"Rough Headwinds"* in *Boston Business Journal (Vol. 30, November 12, 2010, No. 42, pp. 1)*
Pub: Boston Business Journal
Contact: Carolyn M. Jones, President
E-mail: cmjones@bizjournals.com
Ed: Kyle Alspach. **Description:** Views of residents, as well as key information on First Wind's plan to install wind power turbines in Brimfield, Massachusetts are presented. Residents believe that First Wind's project will devalue properties, compromise quality of life, and ruin the rural quality of Brimfield. First Wind expects to produce 2,000 megawatts of power from wind by 2020. **Availability:** Online.

5969 ■ *"Sales of What's Under Feet Add Up Fast"* in *Pet Product News (Vol. 66, September 2012, No. 9, pp. S8)*
Description: Pet supplies retailers and manufacturers have been emphasizing the type of substances in creating new approaches to developing environment-friendly natural litters and beddings for small mammals and cats. Some of these approaches are highlighted, along with marketing strategies retailers have implemented. **Availability:** Print; Online.

5970 ■ *"Saving the Planet: A Tale of Two Strategies: Thomas Malthus Advised Restraint; Robert Solow Promotes Innovation. Let's Pursue Both To Solve the Environmental Crisis"* in *Harvard Business Review (Vol. 90, April 2012, No. 4, pp. 48)*
Pub: Harvard Business Review Press
Contact: Moderna V. Pfizer, Contact
Ed: Roger Martin, Alison Kemper. **Price:** $8.95, hardcover. **Description:** Theories of economists Thomas Malthus and Robert Solow are merged to address specific environmental problems. Malthusian restraint includes fuel economy, refillable bottles, and recycling. Solovian innovation includes water supply chlorination, solar cooking, and geothermal energy. **Availability:** PDF; Online.

5971 ■ *"The Second Most Fuel-Efficient Tractor of the Decade: John Deere 8320R"* in *Farm Industry News (November 10, 2011)*
Pub: Informa Business Media, Inc.
Contact: Charlie McCurdy, President
Description: John Deere's 8320R Tractor was ranked second in the Farm Industry News listing of the top 40 most fuel-efficient tractors of the decade, following the winner, John Deere's 8295R PTO tractor. **Availability:** Online.

5972 ■ "Should I or Shouldn't I?" in Indoor Comfort Marketing (Vol. 70, February 2011, No. 2, pp. 30)
Description: Investment tips are shared for investing in futures options. **Availability:** Print; Online.

5973 ■ "Six Arkansas Construction Projects Get LEED Certification" in Arkansas Business (Vol. 29, July 23, 2012, No. 30, pp. 19)
Pub: Arkansas Business Publishing Group
Contact: Mitch Bettis, President
Ed: Lance Turner. **Description:** State of Arkansas has bestowed its Leadership in Energy and Environmental Design certification on 55 projects throughout the state. Six projects are identified and described. A list of all projects is included. **Availability:** Online.

5974 ■ "Sky Harvest Windpower Corp. - Operational Update" in Investment Weekly News (March 10, 2012, pp. 744)
Pub: PR Newswire Association LLC.
Description: Sky Harvest Windpower Corporation is rebranding its focus on gas and power activities both nationally and internationally. The firm's Canadian projects are outlined as well as its commitment to purse the Green Options Partners Program in 2012. **Availability:** Online.

5975 ■ "Small Wind Power Market to Double by 2015 at $634 Million" in Western Farm Press (September 30, 2011)
Description: Small wind power provides cost-effective electricity on a highly localized level, in both remote settings as well as in conjunction with power from the utility grid. Government incentives are spurring new growth in the industry. **Availability:** Online.

5976 ■ "Solar Hot Water Sales Are Hot, Hot, Hot" in Contractor (Vol. 56, December 2009, No. 12, pp. 22)
Ed: Dave Yates. **Description:** Plumbing contractors in the United States can benefit from the increased sales of solar thermal water systems. Licensed plumbers have the base knowledge on the risks associated from heating and storing water. Safety issues associated with solar water heaters are also included. **Availability:** Online.

5977 ■ "State Investment Goes Sour" in Business Journal Portland (Vol. 26, December 4, 2009, No. 39, pp. 1)
Pub: Portland Business Journal
Contact: Andy Giegerich, Managing Editor
E-mail: agiegerich@bizjournals.com
Ed: Erik Siemers. **Description:** Oregon might recoup only $500,000 of a $20 million loan to Vancouver-based Cascade Grain Products LLC. Cascade Grain's ethanol plant in Clatskanie, OR will be put into auction under the supervision of a bankruptcy court. **Availability:** Print; Online.

5978 ■ "Store Front: Invest in Energy-Efficient Equipment for Your Pet Store" in Pet Product News (Vol. 66, September 2012, No. 9, pp. 43)
Ed: Leila Meyer. **Description:** Developments in energy-efficient lighting, heating, and air conditioning have allowed pet supplies stores to conduct upgrades that result in savings. Pet supplies stores have also been impressing customers by obtaining Energy Start or LEED certification. **Availability:** Print; Online.

5979 ■ "The Superpower Dilemma" in Canadian Business (Vol. 83, August 17, 2010, No. 13-14, pp. 42)
Description: Canada has been an energy superpower partly because it controls the energy source and the production means, particularly of fossil fuels. However, Canada's status as superpower could diminish if it replaces petroleum exports with renewable technology for using sources of energy available globally. **Availability:** Online.

5980 ■ "Sustainability Is Top Priority for GreenTown Chicago" in Contractor (Vol. 56, November 2009, No. 11, pp. 1)
Ed: Candace Roulo. **Description:** GreenTown Chicago 2009 conference tackled energy-efficient practices and technologies, green design and building, and sustainable policies. Water conservation was also a topic at the conference and one mayor who made a presentation said that reducing the water loss in the system is a priority in the city's endeavor. **Availability:** Print; Online.

5981 ■ "Suzlon S88-Powered Wind Farm in Minnesota Secures Long-Term Financing" in PR Newswire (September 21, 2011)
Pub: PR Newswire Association LLC.
Description: Suzlon Energy Limited is the world's fifth largest manufacturer of wind turbines. Owners of the Grant County Wind Farm in Minnesota have secured a long-term financing deal for the ten Suzlon S88 2.1 MW wind turbines that generate enough electricity to power 7,000 homes.

5982 ■ "Taxis Are Set to Go Hybrid" in Philadelphia Business Journal (Vol. 30, September 16, 2011, No. 31, pp. 1)
Pub: Philadelphia Business Journal
Contact: Sierra Quinn, Director
E-mail: squinn@bizjournals.com
Ed: Natalie Kostelni. **Description:** Taxis are going hybrid in several major states such as New York, California and Maryland where it is mandated, but it is yet to happen in Philadelphia, Pennsylvania with the exception of one taxi company. Freedom Taxi is awaiting Philadelphia Parking Authority's sign off. **Availability:** Online.

5983 ■ "Thirsty? Now There's a Water Cooler to Suit Every Taste" in Inc. (Vol. 33, October 2011, No. 8, pp. 43)
Description: Brita's Hydration Station is a wall-mounted unit with a touch-free sensor for dispensing water. This water cooler cuts down on landfill waste and offers special features. **Availability:** Print; Online.

5984 ■ "Timken Features Solutions at AWEA WINDPOWER 2012" in PR Newswire (June 3, 2012)
Pub: PR Newswire Association LLC.
Description: The Timken Company plans to highlight its products and aftermarket solutions for the wind industry at the AWEA WINDPOWER 2012 Conference and Exhibition. Timken products help to maximize the performance of wind energy equipment. **Availability:** Online.

5985 ■ "Toolmakers' New Tack: Firms' Goal -- Advance Wind-Turbine Technology" in Crain's Detroit Business (Vol. 25, June 8, 2009,)
Pub: Crain Communications Inc.
Contact: Barry Asin, President
Ed: Ryan Beene, Amy Lane. **Description:** MAG Industrial Automation Systems LLC and Dowding Machining Inc. have partnered to advance wind-turbine technology. The goal is to cut costs of wind energy to the same level as carbon-based fuel. **Availability:** Print; Online.

5986 ■ "Ultra Low Sulfur Diesel: The Promise and the Reality" in Indoor Comfort Marketing (Vol. 70, July 2011, No. 7, pp. 22)
Description: Impacts of ultra low sulfur diesel are examined.

5987 ■ "Unilever to Sustainably Source All Paper and Board Packaging" in Ice Cream Reporter (Vol. 23, July 20, 2010, No. 8, pp. 1)
Description: Unilever, a leader in the frozen dessert market, has developed a new sustainable paper and board packaging sourcing policy that will reduce environmental impact by working with suppliers to source 75 percent of paper and board packaging from sustainably managed forests or from recycled material. Unilever is parent company to Breyers, Haagen-Dazs, Klondike, Popsicle and other ice cream brands.

5988 ■ "Valener Announces that Gaz Metro has Achieved a Key Step in Acquiring CVPS" in CNW Group (September 30, 2011)
Pub: CNW Group Ltd.
Description: Valener Inc., which owns about 29 percent of Gaz Metro Ltd. Partnership, announced that Gaz Metro welcomes the sale of Central Vermont Public Service Corporation (CVPS). Valener owns an indirect interest of 24.5 percent in the wind power projects jointly developed by Beaupre Eole General Partnership and Boralex Inc. on private lands in Quebec. Details of the deal are included. **Availability:** Print; Online.

5989 ■ "Volunteers Needed" in Canadian Business (Vol. 81, October 27, 2008, No. 18, pp. 60)
Description: Emissions-targeting regulations focus on the biggest polluters, missing out on other companies that leave carbon footprints in things such as shipping and travel. Some companies in Canada have initiated programs to offset their carbon emissions. Critics claim that offsetting does not reduce emissions and the programs merely justify pollution.

5990 ■ "Water Conservation Helps GC's Building Attain LEED Gold Status" in Contractor (Vol. 56, September 2009, No. 9, pp. 5)
Description: Green contractor Marshall Erdman has built a new office building using green design. The facility is seen to become a prime Leadership in Energy and Environmental Design (LEED) building model. Details of the building's design and features are also provided. **Availability:** Print; Online.

5991 ■ "Wave of Resale, Consignment Shops Pop Up In Springs" in Gazette (March 19, 2012)
Ed: Bill Radford. **Description:** The depressed economy has spurred the growth of consignment shops across the nation. Colorado Springs, Colorado area urges people to shop at these resale locations because they promote green initiatives by recycling goods. WeeCycle, Knit Wits, Once Upon a Child and Re-Generation, Moutain Equipment Recyclers, and Gearonimo, are among the established consignment stores in the area. **Availability:** Print.

5992 ■ "What Is a Geothermal Heat Pump" in Indoor Comfort Marketing (Vol. 70, August 2011, No. 8, pp. 14)
Description: Examination of geothermal heat pumps is provided, citing new trends in the industry. **Availability:** Print; Online.

5993 ■ "Wind Farm Is Planned for Yolo Farmland" in Sacramento Business Journal (Vol. 29, September 21, 2012, No. 30, pp. 1)
Pub: Baltimore Business Journal
Contact: Rhonda Pringle, President
E-mail: rpringle@bizjournals.com
Ed: Melanie Turner. **Description:** Austin, Texas-based Pioneer Green Energy LLC has been planning to build as many as 400 wind turbines in Yolo County, California that could potentially generate up to 600 megawatts. The company has already raised $20 and it is expected to formally propose the project in early 2013. The economic impact on the farmers and landowners in the region is explored. **Availability:** Online.

5994 ■ "Wind Gets Knocked Out of Energy Farm Plan" in Buffalo News (September 28, 2011)
Description: New York Power Authority formally killed the proposal for a wind energy farm off the shores of Lake Erie and Lake Ontario. The Authority cited high subsidy costs would be required to make the wind farm economically feasible. Details of the proposal are outlined. **Availability:** Online.

5995 ■ "WindPower Solutions Announces Its Best In Class 'Next Gen' 85kw Wind Turbine" in Marketwired (June 6, 2012)
Pub: Comtex News Network Inc.
Contact: Kan Devnani, President

Description: WinPower Innovations Inc.'s subsidiary, WindPower Solutions, unveiled its next generation 85kw wind turbines that are available for sale. They are perfect for remote locations where there is a lot of wind and can be used locally or the site owner, if near the power grid, could sell the energy to the market. **Availability:** Online.

5996 ■ *"Women Up: Kathleen Ligocki of Harvest Power Inc." in Boston Business Journal (Vol.. 34, April 11, 2014, No. 10)*
Pub: American City Business Journals, Inc.
Contact: Mike Olivieri, Executive Vice President
Released: Weekly. **Price:** $4, introductory 4-week offer(Digital & Print). **Description:** Kathleen Ligocki is the CEO of Harvest Power Inc. of Massachusetts. The company diverts organic waste destined for landfills and produces green energy and soil enrichment products. The company was founded in 2008 and reported sales of over $130 million in 2013. **Availability:** Print; Online.

5997 ■ *"Wood Increasingly Used in School Construction" in Arkansas Business (Vol. 29, July 23, 2012, No. 30, pp. 11)*
Pub: Arkansas Business Publishing Group
Contact: Mitch Bettis, President
Ed: Jan Cottingham. **Description:** Arkansas state guidelines have increased the use of wood in school building construction. Wood is believed to provide strength and durability along with cost effectiveness and environmental benefits. **Availability:** Online.

5998 ■ *"Yates Turns Log Home Green - Part Three" in Contractor (Vol. 57, January 2010, No. 1, pp. 5)*
Released: January 12, 2010. **Description:** Dave Yates of F.W. Behler Inc. discusses remodeling a log home's HVAC system with geo-to-radiant heat and thermal-solar systems. The solar heater's installation is discussed.

5999 ■ *"You're a What? Wind Turbine Service Technician" in Occupational Outlook Quarterly (Vol. 54, Fall 2010, No. 3, pp. 34)*
Pub: U.S. Department of Labor Bureau of Labor Statistics
Contact: Amrit Kohli, Director
E-mail: kohli.amrit@bls.gov
Ed: Drew Liming. **Description:** Profile of Brandon Johnson, former member of the Air Force, found a career as a wind turbine service technician. **Availability:** Online; PDF.

6000 ■ *"Yudelson Challenges San Antonio Groups" in Contractor (Vol. 56, October 2009, No. 10, pp. 6)*
Description: Green building consultant and author Jerry Yudelson made a presentation for the Central Texas Green Building Council and Leadership San Antonio where he discussed the European approach to sustainability and how it can be used for designing green buildings. Yudelson also discussed how to use sustainable practices for planning 25 years into the future. **Availability:** Print; Online.

6001 ■ *Zero Waste Grocery Guide*
URL(s): www.litterless.com/wheretoshop
Description: An online database of where to grocery shop for bulk food that doesn't come in packaging. These stores encourage shoppers to bring their own containers to maintain a zero waste lifestyle. **Availability:** Online.

TRADE PERIODICALS

6002 ■ *Fifth Estate*
Pub: Fifth Estate
Facebook: www.facebook.com/FifthEstateMag
Released: Latest issues Fall 2023. **Price:** $4, Single issue for print Current issue Domestic U.S; $8, Other countries for print Current issue; $5, Single issue for print current issue; $6, Canada for print Current issue; $10, for Five random back issues; $20, for print. **Description:** Magazine covering anarchism and radical environmentalism. **Availability:** Print.

TRADE SHOWS AND CONVENTIONS

6003 ■ **GLOBE: Conference and Exhibition on Business and the Environment**
URL(s): 2016.globeseries.com
X (Twitter): twitter.com/GLOBE_Series
Frequency: Biennial. **Description:** Solutions for problems associated with climate change, energy security, and rising fuel prices. **Audience:** Business professionals. **Principal Exhibits:** Solutions for problems associated with climate change, energy security, and rising fuel prices.

FRANCHISES AND BUSINESS OPPORTUNITIES

6004 ■ **EnviroSpect Inc.**
422 Pine St.
 Williamsport, PA 17701
Contact: Jospeh M. Lyons, President
Description: Residential and commercial environmental inspections. **Founded:** 2004. **Training:** Available at headquarters: 52 hours minimum.

LIBRARIES

6005 ■ **AECOM - Library**
AECOM
 13355 Noel Rd., Ste. 400
 Dallas, TX 75240
Ph: (972)788-1000
Co. E-mail: info@aecom.com
URL: http://www.aecom.com
Contact: Lara Poloni, President
Facebook: www.facebook.com/
 AecomTechnologyCorporation
Linkedin: www.linkedin.com/company/aecom
X (Twitter): twitter.com/AECOM
Instagram: www.instagram.com/aecom
YouTube: www.youtube.com/user/
 AECOMTechnologyCorp
Description: Fully integrated provider of planning, consultation, architectural, and engineering design and construction services. **Scope:** Environment; air quality; hazardous waste. **Services:** Interlibrary loan; library not open to the public. **Founded:** 1990. **Holdings:** 5,000 books; technical and government reports; government agency rules and regulations. **Publications:** "Global Perspectives"; "Asia Beyond Growth"; "Climate Design"; "Water Reuse: Issues, Technologies, Applications"; "Wastewater Engineering: Treatment and Reuse"; "The Bigger Picture". **Educational Activities:** Air & Waste Management Association Annual Conference & Exhibition (ACE) (Annual); Core-Net Global Symposium (Irregular); American Planning Association Conference (APA) (Annual); IFMA's World Workplace Conference & Expo (Annual); ACENZ Annual Conference (Annual); ASFPM Annual National Conference (Annual); Airports Council International - Asia-Pacific Regional Assembly, Conference & Exhibition (Annual).

6006 ■ **Aullwood Audubon Center and Farm**
1000 Aullwood Rd.
 Dayton, OH 45414
Ph: (937)890-7360
Co. E-mail: askus@aullwood.org
URL: http://aullwood.audubon.org
Contact: Alexis R. Faust, Executive Director
Facebook: www.facebook.com/AullwoodAudubon
X (Twitter): x.com/AullwoodAudubon
YouTube: www.youtube.com/user/AullwoodAudubon
Description: Miscellaneous Publishing. **Founded:** 1957. **Publications:** *EE Bulletin* (Periodic). **Geographic Preference:** Local.

6007 ■ **Center for Environmental Information (CEI) - Library**
700 W Metro Pk.
 Rochester, NY 14623
Ph: (585)233-6086
URL: http://geneseeriverwatch.org
Description: Disseminates information on environmental issues. Conducts annual climate issues conference. **Scope:** The environment; climate change. **Founded:** 1974. **Holdings:** Figures not available. **Publications:** *CEI Sphere* (Quarterly); *Directory of Environmental Organizations in the Rochester Area* (Annual). **Geographic Preference:** National.

6008 ■ **General Engineering Laboratories Inc. Library (GEL)**
2040 Savage Rd.
 Charleston, SC 29407
Ph: (843)556-8171
Fax: (843)766-1178
Co. E-mail: info@gel.com
URL: http://www.gel.com
Contact: Joseoh M. Hodgson, Jr., President
Scope: Environmental analysis; environmental consulting; environmental regulations. **Founded:** 1981. **Holdings:** Figures not available.

6009 ■ **Gradient Corp. - Information Resource Center**
1 Beacon St., 17th Fl.
 Boston, MA 02108
Ph: (617)395-5000
URL: http://gradientcorp.com
Contact: Manu Sharma, President
E-mail: msharma@gradientcorp.com
Description: Environmental consulting firm specializing in risk assessment and risk-based agency negotiations. **Scope:** Environmental protection; pollution; environmental chemistry; toxicology; risk assessment. **Services:** Interlibrary loan; Center not open to the public. **Founded:** 1985. **Holdings:** 145,000 documents. **Training:** Endocrine Disruptor Screening Program, Marriot Metro Center, Washington, DC, May, 2010; These Kids are Driving me Crazy: The Science of Sensitive Sub-populations, New Orleans, LA, Mar, 2010; Novel Methods at the Intersection of Epidemiology and Policy-Making, Sep, 2009; Air Toxics; Risk Assessment. **Special Services:** GIS; Auto-CAD; ArcInfo; SITE-DB; Gradient CAAA Emission Inventory Database; Risk Ranger™; Risk Assessment Software.

6010 ■ **National Environmental Health Association (NEHA) - Library**
720 S Colorado Blvd., Ste. 105A
 Denver, CO 80246
Ph: (303)756-9090
Free: 844-331-2547
Fax: (303)691-9490
URL: http://www.neha.org
Contact: Roy Kroeger, President
E-mail: president@neha.org
Facebook: www.facebook.com/NEHA.org
Linkedin: www.linkedin.com/company/national
 -environmental-health-association
X (Twitter): x.com/nehaorg
Description: Represents all professionals in environmental health and protection, including Registered Sanitarians, Registered Environmental Health Specialists, Registered Environmental Health Technicians, Certified Environmental Health Technicians, Registered Hazardous Substances Professionals and Registered Hazardous Substances Specialists. Advances the environmental health and protection profession for the purpose of providing a healthful environment for all. Provides educational materials, publications, credentials and meetings to members and non-member professionals who strive to improve the environment. **Scope:** Health; environment. **Founded:** 1937. **Holdings:** Figures not available. **Publications:** *FOOD Environment News Digest*; *Directory of Environmental/Health Protection Providers* (Biennial); *Journal of Environmental Health: Dedicated to the Advancement of the Environmental Health Professional (JEH)* (10/year); *Sustaining and Educa* (10/year). **Educational Activities:** NEHA Annual Educational Conference (AEC) & Exhibition (Annual); Educational Conference and Exhibition (Annual). **Awards:** Samuel J. Crumbine Consumer Protection Award (Annual); NEHA/AAS Scholarship (Annual);

NEHA/AAS Scholarship Program (Annual); NEHA Certificates of Merit (Annual); Walter S. Mangold Award (Annual). **Geographic Preference:** National.

6011 ■ Tetra Tech NUS, Inc. Technical Information Center
117 Hearthstone Dr.
Aiken, SC 29803
Ph: (803)649-7963
URL: http://www.tetratech.com/cs/Satellite?c=Page
&childpagename=TT%2FPage%2FLoca
tionsSearch&cid=1388485287559&packedargs
=isVanity%3Dfalse%26locale%3Den_US
&pagename=TTWrapper&locsAction=doSearch
&formFieldsToBePacked=locsAction%2ClocsCoun
tryCode%2ClocsStateOrProvinceCo

Scope: Environment; nuclear energy. **Services:** Library not open to the public. **Founded:** 1966. **Holdings:** Reports. **Subscriptions:** 2 newspapers.

6012 ■ U.S. Environmental Protection Agency Headquarters and Chemical Libraries
Rm. 3340, William Jefferson Clinton W Bldg., 1301
   Constitution Ave. NW
   Washington, DC 20004
Ph: (202)566-0556
Co. E-mail: hqchemlibraries@epa.gov
URL: http://www.epa.gov/epalibraries/headquarters
   -and-chemical-libraries

Scope: Decision making and environmental awareness. **Services:** Interlibrary loan; library open to the public. **Holdings:** Figures not available. **Subscriptions:** 60 journals and other serials.

6013 ■ U.S. Environmental Protection Agency Headquarters Library
1200 Pennsylvania Ave., NW
   Washington, DC 20460
URL: http://www.epa.gov/epalibraries/catalog

Scope: Water and environmental protection. **Services:** Interlibrary loan; SDI; library open to the public with restrictions. **Founded:** 1971. **Holdings:** Figures not available.

6014 ■ Williams College Center for Environmental Studies - Matt Cole Memorial Library
55 Mission Pk. Dr.
   Williamstown, MA 01267
Co. E-mail: ces@williams.edu
URL: http://ces.williams.edu/publications/matt-cole
   -reading-room/matt-cole-library

Scope: Environmental issues; history. **Founded:** 1972. **Holdings:** Books; documents.

RESEARCH CENTERS

6015 ■ Clark University - George Perkins Marsh Institute - Center for Technology, Environment, and Development (CENTED)
950 Main St.
   Worcester, MA 01610-1477
URL: http://www.clarku.edu/offices
Contact: Pamela Dunkle, Manager, Operations
E-mail: pdunkle@clarku.edu

Description: Publishes on hazard assessment, energy studies, climate studies and international development. Aims to help determine and clarify issues surrounding major societal and global problems in the increasingly technological world of the late twentieth century. **Scope:** Risk analysis, global environmental change, environment and development, and technological hazards. **Founded:** 1978. **Publications:** *CENTED Research reports*; *CENTED Working papers*. **Educational Activities:** CENTED Distinguished Lecture Series, Research on human/environment interactions.

6016 ■ Green Seal (GS) - Library
601 13th St NW 12th Fl.
   Washington, DC 20005
Ph: (202)872-6400
Co. E-mail: standards@greenseal.org
URL: http://greenseal.org/splash
Contact: Doug Gatlin, Chief Executive Officer
E-mail: dgatlin@greenseal.org
Facebook: www.facebook.com/greenseal
Linkedin: www.linkedin.com/company/green-seal
X (Twitter): x.com/GreenSeal
YouTube: www.youtube.com/user/GreenSealVideos

Description: Environmental certification and consumer education organization. Establishes criteria and standards for consumer products, conducts product testing, and awards a seal of approval to products meeting standards. Offers membership program; Environmental Partners in which organizations receive assistance with green procurement. **Scope:** Analyzes effects of various consumer products on the environment, including toxic chemical pollution, energy consumption, depletion and pollution of water resources, waste of natural resources, destruction of the Earth's atmosphere, global warming, and harm to fish, wildlife, and natural areas. Tests products such as toilet and facial tissue, re-refined motor oil, light bulbs for home use, water conservation devices, fine paper, coffee filters, house paints, household cleaners, paper towels, and napkins. **Founded:** 1989. **Holdings:** Reports; manual; paper. **Publications:** *Hotel Green Buying Guide*; *Campus Green Buying Guide*; *Choose Green Report* (Monthly; Quarterly); *Green Seal Newsletter* (Quarterly); *Office Green Buying Guide*. **Awards:** Green Seal Internships. **Geographic Preference:** National.

6017 ■ Tellus Institute
37 Walker St.
   Cambridge, MA 02138
Ph: (617)266-5400
Co. E-mail: contact@tellus.org
URL: http://tellus.org
Contact: Dr. Paul Raskin, President
Facebook: www.facebook.com/TellusInstitute
X (Twitter): x.com/TellusInstitute

Description: Not-for-profit research and policy organization focusing on environmental and social issues, including energy, water, sustainable communities, corporate responsibility, and climate change. Provides technical advice and expert testimony to public agencies, consumer groups and private sector sponsors. **Scope:** Policy and planning issues in such areas as energy, water, waste, and land use. Analyzes evolving problems and evaluates options for technological and institutional change, develops and disseminates decision-support tools to strengthen capacity to develop effective resource and environmental strategies. **Founded:** 1976. **Publications:** "Worker Equity in Food and Agriculture," Tellus Institute and Sustainalytics, Oct, 2012; "The Century Ahead: Searching for Sustainability"; "Owning Our Future"; "Great Transition: The Promise and Lure of the Times Ahead"; "Frontiers of a Great Transition"; "Contours of the Future"; "Corporate Design". **Training:** Great Transition.

6018 ■ University of Colorado at Boulder - Environmental Program
2055 Regent Dr., Ste. 201
   UCB 214
   Boulder, CO 80309-0040
Ph: (303)492-7943
URL: http://www.colorado.edu/environmentalprogram
Contact: Bob Sievers, Director
E-mail: bob.sievers@colorado.edu

Description: Integral unit of University of Colorado at Boulder. **Scope:** Global change and environmental quality research, including global climate change, local and regional environmental quality, and sustainable development.

Estate Planning

REFERENCE WORKS

6019 ■ *4 Key Elements of a Small Business Owner's Estate Plan*
Ed: Beverly Davidek. **Description:** Passing your company onto your family is an important part of an estate plan that many small business owners don't often plan for. This article provides details on the importance of creating a comprehensive estate plan. **Availability:** Online.

6020 ■ *"7 Estate Planning Tips from Entrepreneurs" in The McKenzie Law Firm website (December 3, 2015)*
Ed: Daniel McKenzie. **Released:** December 03, 2015. **Description:** Provides seven estate planning tips from entrepreneurs that you may want to discuss with your estate planning lawyer to ensure that your small business wealth is protected. **Availability:** Online.

6021 ■ *"8 Reasons You May Need to Update Your Will" in NextAvenue.com (August 22, 2019)*
URL(s): www.nextavenue.org/update-your-will/
Ed: Patrick O'Brien. **Released:** August 22, 2019. **Description:** If you already have your will and estate planning complete, it may be time to open up the file and review what you have in it. Life changes and you may have sold a home, removed possessions, or downsized. These and several other life style changes could mean that you should update that will. **Availability:** Online.

6022 ■ *"Bank On It: New Year, New Estate Plan" in Hawaii Business (Vol. 53, February 2008, No. 8, pp. 54)*
Pub: PacificBasin Communications
Contact: Chuck Tindle, Director
E-mail: chuckt@pacificbasin.net
Ed: Antony M. Orme. **Description:** Discusses the start of the new year which can be a time to revise wills and estate plans as failure to do so may create problems of unequal inheritance and increase in estate tax exemption, which could disinherit beneficiaries. Other circumstances that can prompt changes in wills and estate plans are presented. **Availability:** Print; Online.

6023 ■ *"Eliminating All of Your Estate Tax Burden" in Contractor (Vol. 57, January 2010, No. 1, pp. 48)*
Ed: Irving L. Blackman. **Description:** Suggestions on how family owned businesses can minimize their estate tax burdens are discussed. One of these includes not using life insurance in a business succession plan to move stocks to the children and to never use Section 6166 as part of the overall estate tax plan. **Availability:** Print; Online.

6024 ■ *Estate Planning for Dummies*
Pub: John Wiley & Sons, Inc.
Contact: Christina Van Tassell, Executive Vice President Chief Financial Officer
URL(s): www.wiley.com/en-us/Estate+Planning+For +Dummies%2C+2nd+Edition-p-9781394158546
Ed: Jordan S. Simon, Joseph Mashinski. **Released:** 2nd edition. **Price:** $29.99, paperback. **Description:** Everything you need to know to start estate planning and securing your assets. New tax laws are discussed. **Availability:** Print.

6025 ■ *"Estate Planning for an Owner-Dependent Business" in Entrepreneur*
Ed: W. Rod Stern. **Description:** Because business owners likely have a significant portion of their wealth tied up in their business, it is important to have an estate plan. This article provides information for business owners who are owner dependent, multigenerational, or marketable and details information on how to create an appropriate estate plan. **Availability:** Online.

6026 ■ *Estate Planning for the Savvy Client: What You Need to Know Before You Meet with Your Lawyer*
Ed: Mary L. Barrow, Esq. **Released:** March 17, 2017. **Price:** $14.99, Paperback; $9.99, E-Book. **Description:** Attorney Mary L. Barrow guides the readers on what they should know before they start estate planning. Helps eliminate confusion by establishing clear goals and guides the reader in choosing the right attorney. **Availability:** E-book; Print.

6027 ■ *"Estate Planning for Small Business Owners in 8 Steps" in Fundera (October 28, 2020)*
Ed: Priyanka Prakash. **Released:** October 28, 2020. **Description:** Many small business owners are too busy taking care of the here and now to think about the future. Business estate planning helps ensure that your business matters are handled according to your wishes when you die or if you become disabled. This article details the importance of estate planning and provides 8 steps for small businesses to follow. **Availability:** Online.

6028 ■ *"Estate Planning Suggestions for Small Business Owners" in Stouffer Legal website (February 18, 2020)*
Released: February 18, 2020. **Description:** Personal estate planning coupled with a well-thought-out business succession plan is a necessity to prevent chaos in the event of the business owner's death or incapacity. This article provides suggestions from experienced estate planning attorneys to protect your small business. **Availability:** Online.

6029 ■ *"Estate Planning Tips for Food and Beverage Entrepreneurs" in Nutter Uncommon Law (March 9, 2020)*
Released: March 09, 2020. **Description:** Discuss what an estate plan is and why food and beverage entrepreneurs should set up an estate plan. Also provides information on core estate planning documents, tax information, and family protections for your small business. **Availability:** Online.

6030 ■ *"Estate Planning With Partnerships: Important New Considerations" in Stites & Harbison PLLC website (February 15, 2016)*
Released: February 15, 2016. **Description:** Discusses IRS audit rules and how they impact estate planning for business partnerships. This article discusses important legalities for partnerships, family limited partnerships, limited partnerships, limited liability partnerships and LLCs taxed as partnerships as they form their estate plan. **Availability:** Online.

6031 ■ *"Estate Tax Problems may Soon Disappear" in Contractor (Vol. 56, September 2009, No. 9, pp. 60)*
Ed: Irving L. Blackman. **Description:** Advice on how to effectively plan estate tax in the United States. Pending changes to US estate tax laws are seen to resolve inheritance problems. Captive insurance firms can lower property and casualty insurance costs to transfer businesses to children. **Availability:** Print; Online.

6032 ■ *Every Californian's Guide to Estate Planning*
Ed: Liza W. Hanks. **Released:** January 30, 2018. **Price:** $13.59, Paperback; $10.99, E-book. **Description:** A guide to help residents of California understand the basics of estate planning, inheritance, and taxes. **Availability:** E-book; Print.

6033 ■ *"Evolving from Practice to Enterprise" in Financial Advisor (November 1, 2019)*
URL(s): www.fa-mag.com/news/evolving-from-prac tice-to-enterprise-52345.html
Ed: Dawn Doebler, Michael Nathanson. **Released:** November 01, 2019. **Description:** A look at the financial advisory industry as smaller firms grow from a practice to a larger business and even to an enterprise. Gives definitions of each term and the qualifications each entity must possess. **Availability:** Online.

6034 ■ *"Expect Action on Health Care and the Economy" in Contractor (Vol. 57, January 2010, No. 1, pp. 30)*
Ed: Kevin Schwalb. **Description:** The Plumbing-Heating-Cooling Contractors National Association is working to solidify its standing in the public policy arena as the legislative agenda will focus on health care reform, estate tax and immigration reform, all of which will impact the industries. **Availability:** Print; Online.

6035 ■ *Family Trusts: A Guide for Beneficiaries, Trustees, Trust Protectors, and Trust Creators*
Ed: Hartley Goldstone, James E. Hughes, Jr., Keith Whitaker. **Released:** October 05, 2015. **Price:** $29.59, Hardcover; $21.59, E-Book. **Description:** A guide for anyone who is interested in creating a trust or who may be a beneficiary of a trust. Takes you through the entire process and discusses the positive and negative realities of dealing with trusts. **Availability:** E-book; Print.

6036 ■ Financial Planning & Analysis and Performance Management
Ed: Jack Alexander. **Released:** June 13, 2018. **Price:** $46.24, Hardcover; $36.79, E-book. **Description:** Comprehensive reference guide about financial planning for financial analysts working for organizations. Discussion topics include budget and forecasting, analysis, performance management, financial communication, metrics, benchmarking, and many others. **Availability:** E-book; Print.

6037 ■ Get a Financial Life: Personal Finance in Your Twenties and Thirties
Ed: Beth Kobliner. **Released:** March 21, 2017. **Price:** $10.27, Paperback; $12.99, E-book. **Description:** A guide for younger adults as they navigate the financial world and financial planning. **Availability:** E-book; Print.

6038 ■ Get Your Ducks in a Row: The Baby Boomers Guide to Estate Planning
Ed: Harry S. Margolis. **Released:** June 03, 2019. **Price:** $10.99, Paperback; $8.99, E-Book. **Description:** A guide to creating an estate plan for those who are older and have put off the task. Practical advice and easy to follow instructions are included. **Availability:** E-book; Print.

6039 ■ "Growing Expectations" in Financial Advisor (November 1, 2019)
URL(s): www.fa-mag.com/news/growing--expectations-52348.html
Ed: Christopher Robbins. **Released:** November 01, 2019. **Description:** During the National Association of Personal Financial Advisors' 2019 Fall Conference, the need to keep upgrading the clients' experiences with technology was one of the key takeaways of the event. With the majority of the current workforce part of the generations that grew up on modern tech, it is easy to see why they would want to have options beyond just phone calls and face-to-face meetings. **Availability:** Online.

6040 ■ "Guide to Estate Planning for Small Businesses" in Phillips & Blow Law website
Released: October 16, 2018. **Description:** Small business estate planning can help your heirs or successors navigate successfully in the event of your death. This article describes problems that may arise if you don't have an estate plan. **Availability:** Online.

6041 ■ "How to Find a Good Estate Planner" in NextAvenue.com (September 10, 2019)
URL(s): www.nextavenue.org/find-estate-planner/
Ed: Elizabeth Alterman. **Released:** September 10, 2019. **Description:** Helpful tips and resources for finding an estate planner. **Availability:** Online.

6042 ■ "Marketing the Modern Estate-Planning Practice" in WealthManagement.com (May 9, 2017)
Ed: Craig R. Hersch. **Released:** May 09, 2017. **Description:** Provides detailed information on how to market your estate planning business. Discusses traditional marketing, ineffective marketing, identification of target market, client value creation, and detailed marketing options. **Availability:** Online.

6043 ■ Plan Your Estate
Price: $26.49, Paperback; $25.17, E-Book. **Description:** Newly updated to reflect the Tax Cuts and Jobs Acts of 2017, the 14th edition is a complete guide to learning about estate planning. **Availability:** E-book; Print.

6044 ■ "Retailers, Your Will, and More" in Agency Sales Magazine (Vol. 39, July 2009, No. 7, pp. 46)
Description: IRS audit guide for small retail businesses is presented. Tips on how to make a will with multiple beneficiaries are discussed together with medical expenses that cannot be deducted.

6045 ■ The Simple Path to Wealth: Your Road Map to Financial Independence and a Rich, Free Life
Ed: JL Collins. **Price:** $15.11, Paperback; $9.99, E-book. **Description:** A guide about thinking about money and wealth, with practical, and humor-filled, discussions about a variety of topics involving investing. **Availability:** E-book; Print.

6046 ■ "Solutions to Family Business Problems" in Contractor (Vol. 56, October 2009, No. 10, pp. 51)
Ed: Irving L. Blackman. **Description:** Several common business problems that family owned firms face are presented together with their solutions. These problems include giving the children stock bonus options while another discusses the tax burden when a father wants to transfer the business to his son. **Availability:** Print; Online.

6047 ■ The Tools & Techniques of Estate Planning
Ed: Stephan Leimberg, L. Paul Hood, Edwin P. Morrow. **Released:** January 09, 2019. **Price:** $188, Paperback. **Description:** New updates reflecting changes to tax codes are included in the nineteenth edition of this book for estate planners. Includes easy-to-understand examples and techniques to help your clients make the best decisions for themselves their estates. **Availability:** Print.

6048 ■ "Using an LLC for Estate Planning" in Investopedia (July 29, 2020)
Ed: Michelle Ullman. **Released:** July 29, 2020. **Description:** Somewhere between a corporation and a partnership lies the limited liability company (LLC). This hybrid legal entity is beneficial for small business owners and is a powerful tool for estate planning. This article shares information on how to create an estate plan that will protect your assets and reduce taxes owed by you or your family members. **Availability:** Online.

6049 ■ "Wealth Advisory Firms Are Merging, but What's in It for Clients?" in The New York Times (September 13, 2019)
URL(s): www.nytimes.com/2019/09/13/your-money/wealth-advisers-mergers-clients.html
Ed: Paul Sullivan. **Released:** September 13, 2019. **Description:** Wealth management firms are being sold due to their high values to private equity firms looking to expand their inventory of profitable companies. But is this good for clients? Favorite and familiar advisers may be lost and getting used to a new replacement can lead to difficulties, plus other aspects of the move may not be seamless such using new platforms. But, clients dealing with smaller firms may actually benefit because this is an opportunity for more growth, which translates to bigger wealth. **Availability:** Online.

6050 ■ Your Complete Guide to a Successful & Secure Retirement
Ed: Larry Swedroe, Kevin Grogan. **Released:** January 07, 2019. **Price:** $11.88, Paperback; $8.19, E-book. **Description:** A helpful guide for those financially preparing for retirement. Discusses social security, medicare, investing, portfolio management, and more. **Availability:** E-book; Print.

TRADE PERIODICALS

6051 ■ Estate Planning Review--The Journal
URL(s): www.cchgroup.com/store/products/estate-planning-review-journal-19632000/journal-internet-19632000-journal-internet-19632000
Released: Monthly **Price:** $525, Individuals print; $475, Individuals internet. **Description:** Newsletter covering estate and financial planning issues for individuals. Includes coverage of retirement planning, insurance planning and investments. **Availability:** CD-ROM; Print; Online.

TRADE SHOWS AND CONVENTIONS

6052 ■ Annual Heckerling Institute on Estate Planning
URL(s): www.law.miami.edu/heckerling
Frequency: Annual. **Description:** Estate planning conference for attorneys, trust officers, accountants, insurance advisors, and wealth management professionals. **Principal Exhibits:** Estate planning conference for attorneys, trust officers, accountants, insurance advisors, and wealth management professionals.

FRANCHISES AND BUSINESS OPPORTUNITIES

6053 ■ American Prosperity Group (APG)
901 Rte. 23 S 2nd Fl.
  Pompton Plains, NJ 07444-1038
Ph: (973)831-4424
Free: 877-885-1APG
Co. E-mail: info@1apg.com
URL: http://1apg.com
Contact: Mark E. Charnet, Chief Executive Officer
E-mail: markcharnet@1apg.com
Facebook: www.facebook.com/AmericanProsperityGroup
YouTube: www.youtube.com/user/AmericanProsperity
Description: Provider of retirement and estate planning products and services. **Founded:** 2003. **Financial Assistance:** Yes **Training:** Offers 4 weeks at headquarters, 1 week onsite and ongoing support.

LIBRARIES

6054 ■ Adler Pollock & Sheehan, P.C. (AP&S) - Library
1 Citizens Plz., 8th Fl.
  Providence, RI 02903-1345
Ph: (401)274-7200
Fax: (401)751-0604
URL: http://www.apslaw.com
Contact: Robert P. Brooks, Managing Partner
E-mail: rbrooks@apslaw.com
Facebook: www.facebook.com/AdlerPollockSheehanPc
Linkedin: www.linkedin.com/company/adler-pollock-&-sheehan-p-c-
X (Twitter): x.com/AdlerPollock
Description: Service providers of legal assistance. **Scope:** Law - business, corporate, commercial, labor, tax, securities, environmental; estate planning; litigation; public utilities; telecommunications; energy; insurance. **Services:** Interlibrary loan (limited); library not open to the public. **Founded:** 1960. **Holdings:** 5,000 books; 500 bound periodical volumes. **Subscriptions:** 40 journals and other serials. **Awards:** The Honorable Walter R. Stone Diversity Fellowship (Annual).

6055 ■ Connecticut Judicial Branch - Putnam Law Library
Putnam Courthouse, 155 Church St.
  Putnam, CT 06260
Ph: (860)928-3716
Fax: (860)963-7531
URL: http://jud.ct.gov/lawlib
Scope: Law. **Services:** Copying; library open to the public; Interlibrary loan available, printing; microfiche; fax. **Holdings:** Books; journal; records.

6056 ■ Fasken Martineau DuMoulin L.L.P., Toronto Library
Bay Adelaide Ctr., 333 Bay St., Ste. 2400
  Toronto, ON, Canada M5H 2T6
Ph: (416)366-8381
Free: 800-268-8424
Fax: (416)364-7813
Co. E-mail: toronto@fasken.com
URL: http://www.fasken.com
Contact: Martin K. Denyes, Managing Partner Partner
E-mail: mdenyes@fasken.com
Facebook: www.facebook.com/FaskenLaw
X (Twitter): x.com/FaskenLaw
Instagram: www.instagram.com/faskenlaw
YouTube: www.youtube.com/channel/UCRZHjLjO0AiY4qE7Y7gWlbQ
Description: A full-service law firm with offices in Canada, the U.K., South Africa and China. **Scope:** Law - corporate, administrative, real estate, estate;

taxation; litigation. **Services:** Interlibrary loan. **Founded:** 2000. **Holdings:** 14,000 books; 50 bound periodical volumes; federal and provincial legislation.

6057 ■ Goodmans Library
Bay Adelaide Ctr., 333 Bay St., Ste. 3400
  Toronto, ON, Canada M5H 2S7
Ph: (416)979-2211
Fax: (416)979-1234
Co. E-mail: info@goodmans.ca
URL: http://www.goodmans.ca
Contact: Dale H. Lastman, Chairman
E-mail: dlastman@goodmans.ca
X (Twitter): x.com/GoodmansLLP
Description: Premier transaction law firms. **Scope:** Law - commercial, corporate, securities, bankruptcy, entertainment, planning, administrative; litigation; real estate; estates and trusts; taxation; e-commerce. **Services:** Interlibrary loan. **Founded:** 1962. **Holdings:** Figures not available.

6058 ■ Hancock & Estabrook Law Library
1800 AXA Twr. 1
  100 Madison St.
  Syracuse, NY 13202
Ph: (315)565-4500
URL: http://www.hancocklaw.com/our-firm
Contact: Cora A. Alsante, Partner
E-mail: calsante@hancocklaw.com
Facebook: www.facebook.com/HancockEstabrook
Linkedin: www.linkedin.com/company/hancock-estabrook-llp
X (Twitter): x.com/HancockLawLLP
Instagram: www.instagram.com/hancockestabrook
Description: It consists of books, journals, references, videos, and posters related to Law. **Scope:** New York state and federal law; labor relations; taxes; securities; estates and trusts; negligence; products liability; malpractice; municipalities; real property; the environment; healthcare. **Services:** Library not open to the public. **Founded:** 1889. **Holdings:** 20,000 books. **Subscriptions:** 200 journals and other serials.

6059 ■ Hinckley, Allen and Snyder L.L.P. - Library Services
100 Westminster St.
  Providence, RI 02903
Ph: (401)274-2000
Fax: (401)277-9600
URL: http://www.hinckleyallen.com
Contact: Adam M. Ramos, Partner
E-mail: aramos@hinckleyallen.com
Description: Law firm provides legal services and pragmatic business advice to regional, national and international clients including construction, corporate, litigation, real estate, trusts, and estates. **Scope:** Law: business litigation; construction litigation; tax; commercial/business; labor; health; trusts; estates; financial planning; real estate; intellectual property. **Services:** Interlibrary loan (limited); library not open to the public. **Founded:** 1906. **Holdings:** 8,000 books. **Educational Activities:** Bond Attorney's Workshop (Annual).

6060 ■ Irell & Manella Library
1800 Ave. of the Stars, Ste. 900
  Los Angeles, CA 90067
Ph: (310)277-1010
Fax: (310)203-7199
Co. E-mail: info@irell.com
URL: http://www.irell.com
Contact: Benjamin W. Hattenbach, Contact
E-mail: bhattenbach@irell.com
Linkedin: www.linkedin.com/company/19140
X (Twitter): x.com/IrellandManella
Scope: Law - intellectual property transactional, intellectual property litigation, federal and state litigation, tax, corporate, corporate securities, entertainment, antitrust, trusts and estates, probate, real estate, insurance, computer law, art law, aviation. **Services:** Library not open to the public. **Founded:** 1941. **Holdings:** 70,000 volumes; microfiche; audio- and videotapes; CD-ROMs.

6061 ■ Loeb & Loeb L.L.P., Law Library
10100 Santa Monica Blvd., Ste. 2200
  Los Angeles, CA 90067
Ph: (310)282-2000
Fax: (310)282-2200
URL: http://www.loeb.com/en
Contact: Paul W. A. Steverin, Vice Chairman of the Board
E-mail: pseverin@loeb.com
Facebook: www.facebook.com/LoebLoebLLP
Linkedin: www.linkedin.com/company/loeb-&-loeb-llp
X (Twitter): x.com/loeb_loebllp
Scope: Law taxation; litigation; insolvency and workout; entertainment; labor; real estate; corporate; estates and trusts; intellectual property. **Services:** Library not open to the public. **Founded:** 1909. **Holdings:** 34,000 volumes.

6062 ■ Lum, Drasco and Positan L.L.C., Law Library
103 Eisenhower Pky., Ste. 401
  Roseland, NJ 07068
Ph: (973)403-9000
Fax: (973)403-9021
URL: http://www.lumlaw.com
Contact: Steven J. Eisenstein, Member
E-mail: seisenstein@lumlaw.com
Scope: Law - taxation; labor and employment; corporate; banking; trust and estates; litigation. **Services:** Interlibrary loan; library not open to the public. **Founded:** 1870. **Holdings:** 20,000 volumes.

6063 ■ Nixon Peabody L.L.P., Law Library
1300 Clinton Sq.
  Rochester, NY 14604-1792
Ph: (585)263-1000
Fax: (585)263-1600
Co. E-mail: rluciano@nixonpeabody.com
URL: http://www.nixonpeabody.com/locations/rochester
Contact: Jared C. Lusk, Partner
E-mail: jlusk@nixonpeabody.com
Scope: Law - corporate, tax, estates, real estate, labor, environmental, litigation. **Services:** Interlibrary loan; library not open to the public. **Holdings:** Figures not available.

6064 ■ Venable L.L.P.
750 E Pratt St., Ste. 900
  Baltimore, MD 21202
Ph: (410)244-7400
Fax: (410)244-7742
URL: http://www.venable.com
Contact: Christopher J. Conoscenti, Partner
E-mail: cjconoscenti@venable.com
Linkedin: www.linkedin.com/company/venablellp
X (Twitter): x.com/Venablellp
YouTube: www.youtube.com/user/VenableLLP
Description: Law firm providing legal solutions. **Founded:** 1900.

Estate Sales Business

ASSOCIATIONS AND OTHER ORGANIZATIONS

6065 ■ **National Auctioneers Association (NAA)**
8880 Ballentine St.
Overland Park, KS 66214
Ph: (913)541-8084
Fax: (913)894-5281
Co. E-mail: support@auctioneers.org
URL: http://www.auctioneers.org
Contact: Beth Rose, President
E-mail: beth@bethroseauction.com
Facebook: www.facebook.com/naaauctioneers
X (Twitter): x.com/naaauctioneers
YouTube: www.youtube.com/user/NAAAuctioneers

Description: Provides continuing education classes for auctioneers, promotes use of the auction method of marketing in both the private and public sectors. Encourages the highest ethical standards for the profession. **Founded:** 1949. **Publications:** *Auction E-News* (Bimonthly); *Find an NAA Auction Professional*; *Auctioneer* (Bimonthly); *Auctioneer--Directory Issue* (Annual). **Educational Activities:** NAA Conference and Show (Annual). **Awards:** NAA Marketing Competition Award (Annual); International Auctioneer Championship (IAC) (Annual); National Auctioneers Association Hall of Fame (Annual). **Geographic Preference:** Multinational.

REFERENCE WORKS

6066 ■ *"10 Strategies for Estate Sale Leads" in EstateSales.org Blog*
Description: Provides fresh strategies gathered from estate sale professionals around the country to help gain estate sale leads. **Availability:** Online.

6067 ■ *"Building an Estate Sale Business by Franchising a Name and Brand" in The New York Times (May 4, 2016)*
URL(s): www.nytimes.com/2016/05/05/business/smallbusiness/building-an-estate-sale-business-with-franchises.html
Ed: Janet Morrissey. **Released:** May 04, 2016. **Description:** When it's time to hold an estate sale, it's often hard to choose an estate sale company because they are not required to be licensed and there are no regulations. Grasons Company Estate Sale Services is hoping to change this by building a stellar reputation within the industry and franchising the name. **Availability:** Online.

6068 ■ *"Dealing With Problem Estate Sale Customers" in EstateSales.org Blog*
Ed: Pascale Saliba. **Description:** Discusses the fact that estate sale businesses deal with a wide variety of customers and provides tips on managing difficult customers. **Availability:** Online.

6069 ■ *"Estate Sale Company Guide to Building an Online Presence" in EstateSales.org Blog*
Ed: Brandon Shinholser. **Description:** Discusses the importance of estate sale businesses establishing an online presence and explains how to do it. **Availability:** Online.

6070 ■ *"Estate Sale Contracts Guide" in EstateSales.org Blog*
Description: A guide to help you understand the different types of estate sale contracts, what to cover in your contract, best practices, regional differences, and sample contracts. **Availability:** Online.

6071 ■ *"A Guide to Managing Estate Sale Company Reviews" in EstateSales.org Blog*
Ed: Pascale Saliba. **Description:** As online reviews increase in popularity, your estate sale company's reviews have a ripple effect that can determines your company's reputation and continuity in the industry. This article discusses how to manage and navigate both positive and negative online reviews. **Availability:** Online.

6072 ■ *"In-Person vs Online Estate Sales" in EstateSales.org Blog*
Ed: Pascale Saliba. **Description:** While onsite traditional estate sales remain the preferred method of liquidating an estate, it's no secret that online sales have increased year after year. This article details how to incorporate online sales into your business to increase revenue, broaden your reach, and get the highest value for your clients' items. **Availability:** Online.

6073 ■ *"Managing Estate Sales Becomes Big Business" in The New York Times (March 11, 2015)*
URL(s): www.nytimes.com/2015/03/12/business/managing-estate-sales-becomes-big-business.html
Ed: Alan Feuer. **Released:** March 11, 2015. **Description:** Examines the growing industry of Estate Sale companies. While most are local small businesses, some are growing larger and expanding by franchising. **Availability:** Online.

6074 ■ *"Start an Estate Sale Company in 7 Steps" in EstateSales.org Blog*
Description: Estate liquidation is a great job for people who love learning about history and the provenance of things and for those with good people skills. This article discusses how to navigate the estate sale industry and how to start and market your business. **Availability:** Online.

6075 ■ *"Tech Tools of the Trade" in EstateSales.org Blog*
Description: Whether your estate sale business is a two-person mom and pop operation, or a large team with several employees, one thing is certain: buyers want speed and convenience when they're shopping. This article discusses technology tools you can use to enhance your business. **Availability:** Online.

6076 ■ *"What Is a Picker Sale? Estate Sales vs. Picker Sales" in EstateSales.org Blog*
Ed: Pascale Saliba. **Description:** Estate sales occur to liquidate the personal assets inside a home and Picker sales are a form of an estate sales in which none of the items are inventoried or tagged with a price. This article discusses when and why to hold a picker sale, how it may be run differently than an estate sale, and how to successfully market a picker sale. **Availability:** Online.

6077 ■ *"Your Guide to An Estate Sale Business Plan and Requirements" in EstateSales.org Blog*
Ed: Pascale Saliba. **Description:** Provides information you should know about putting together an estate sale business plan and what estate sale business requirements must be maintained. **Availability:** Online.

Event/Wedding Planning

START-UP INFORMATION

6078 ■ *Event Planning and Management: Principles, Planning and Practice*
Ed: Ruth Dowson, David Bassett. **Released:** November 03, 2018. **Description:** Discusses the theory of starting an event planning business. Includes sections on the planning stages, managing stakeholders, promotion, risk assessment, safety, and post-event evaluation. **Availability:** E-book.

6079 ■ *Wedding Services Industry in the US -Market Research Report*
URL(s): www.ibisworld.com/united-states/market-research-reports/wedding-services-industry/
Price: $925. **Description:** Downloadable report analyzing current and future trends in the wedding services industry. **Availability:** Download.

ASSOCIATIONS AND OTHER ORGANIZATIONS

6080 ■ **American Association of Certified Wedding Planners (AACWP)**
2150 W NW Hwy., Ste. 114-1039
Grapevine, TX 76051
Free: 844-202-2297
Co. E-mail: training@aacwp.org
URL: http://aacwp.org
Contact: Marsha Ballard French, President
E-mail: president@aacwp.org
Facebook: www.facebook.com/AACWP
Instagram: www.instagram.com/aacwp
Pinterest: www.pinterest.com/theaacwp

Description: Seeks to uphold best practices and standards of excellence in wedding planning. Offers networking and mentoring opportunities to certified wedding planners. **Founded:** 2007. **Geographic Preference:** National.

6081 ■ **International Live Events Association (ILEA)**
1660 International Dr., Ste. 600
McLean, VA 22102
Ph: (571)685-8010
Fax: (703)506-3266
Co. E-mail: info@ileahub.com
URL: http://www.ileahub.com
Contact: Melissa Jurcan, President
Facebook: www.facebook.com/ILEA.International.Live.Events.Association
Linkedin: www.linkedin.com/company/international-live-events-association-ilea-
Instagram: www.instagram.com/ileahq

Description: Seeks to educate, advance, and promote special events. **Founded:** 1987. **Publications:** *Event World* (Monthly); *ISES Membership Directory* (Annual). **Educational Activities:** Professional Development Conference (Annual). **Awards:** ILEA Esprit Awards (Annual); ILEA Spirit of Excellence Awards (Annual). **Geographic Preference:** National.

6082 ■ **Meeting Professionals International (MPI)**
2711 Lyndon B Johnson Fwy., Ste. 600
Dallas, TX 75234-7349
Ph: (972)702-3000
Free: 866-318-2743
Co. E-mail: feedback@mpi.org
URL: http://www.mpi.org
Contact: Paul van Deventer, President
Facebook: www.facebook.com/MPI
Linkedin: www.linkedin.com/company/mpi
X (Twitter): x.com/MPI

Description: Advances the meeting and event industry and the careers of the people in it. **Founded:** 1972. **Publications:** *Meeting Planners International--Oregon Chapter--Annual Membership Directory*; *The Meeting Professional* (8/year); *Meeting Professionals International Membership Directory*; *The Meeting Manager: The Official Publication of Meeting Professionals International* (Monthly). **Educational Activities:** MPI World Education Congress (WEC) (Annual); Professional Education Conference. **Awards:** Meeting Professional Awards-Planner/Supplier of the Year (Annual); MPI RISE Award - Member of the Year (Annual); MPI Chairman's/Chairwoman's Award (Annual). **Geographic Preference:** National.

6083 ■ **National Association for Catering and Events (NACE)**
10440 Little Patuxent Pky., Ste. 300
Columbia, MD 21044
Ph: (410)290-5410
Fax: (410)630-5768
Co. E-mail: info@nace.net
URL: http://www.nace.net
Contact: James Filtz, President
Facebook: www.facebook.com/NACENatl
Linkedin: www.linkedin.com/company/national-association-for-catering-and-events
X (Twitter): x.com/nacenational
Instagram: www.instagram.com/nacenational
YouTube: www.youtube.com/c/NationalAssociationforCateringandEventsNACE

Description: Addresses banquet facilities, off-premise, country club, military and resort catering. Provides continuing education, certification, networking and career support. **Founded:** 1958. **Publications:** *How To Get 5 Star Reviews*; *Legal Moves for a Successful 2022*; *Brand Authenticity Webinar*; *No Dozing on the Closing: 4 Tips to Win the Sale*; *5 Ways to Streamline Your Digital Marketing Webinar*; *Communication is Key: How to Communicate and Show Gratitude Effectively Amongst Colleagues*; *Don't Overlook the Obvious: Safety & Site Selection*; *Cultivating Comfort: The Key to Impeccable Client Experience*; *Prep, Reset & Revive for the New Year Webinar Series*; *Secrets of Highly Effective Networking to Build Brand Equity*; *Sorry, Not Sorry — How to Stop Over Apologizing and Feeling Guilty in Your Business*; *Uncovering Innovation in Events in 2022*; *Culture Eats Strategy for Breakfast*; *The Conversion Factor: How to Turn Inquiries into Bookings*; *Marketing Health Check: How to Know What Works and What Doesn't in Your Marketing Mix*; *The Impact of Operation on Your Business Longevity*; *The Wedding Roller Coaster and the Client Experience*; *Five Steps to Strategically Position Yourself in the Wedding Marketplace*; *A Look at Weddings in the New World: How Couples are Planning Weddings in the COVID Era*; *The Power of Language in Your Business*; *Beyond the Gram - Why Networking is Still the Most Powerful Marketing Tool*; *Springing into Sustainability: The What, Where, How, Why and Who of Food and Beverage Sustainability Part 1*; *Springing into Sustainability: The What, Where, How, Why and Who of Food and Beverage Sustainability Part 3*; *Stopping Business Takeover*; *Enslavement to Empowerment: How African Americans Molded Today's Catering Industry and It's Continued Evolution*; *NACE News Network* (Monthly); *Professional Caterer* (Quarterly). **Educational Activities:** National Association of Catering and Events Education Conference. **Awards:** NACE Chapter of the Year Award (Annual); George Zell Spirit of NACE Award (Annual). **Geographic Preference:** Multinational.

6084 ■ **Wedding International Professionals Association (WIPA)**
1205 Johnson Ferry Rd., Ste. 136-319
Marietta, GA 30068
Free: 844-444-9300
Co. E-mail: info@wipa.org
URL: http://www.wipa.org
Contact: Mara Mazdzer, President
Facebook: www.facebook.com/Wipausa
X (Twitter): x.com/WIPA_org
Instagram: www.instagram.com/wipa_org
Pinterest: www.pinterest.com/wipausa

Description: Promotes the wedding industry by enhancing professional growth and opportunities among its members. Educates the public on the value of employing qualified wedding specialists. Upholds the highest ethics and professional standards of performance for all members. **Founded:** 2008. **Geographic Preference:** Multinational.

REFERENCE WORKS

6085 ■ *Becoming and Event Planner*
Ed: Armand Limnander. **Released:** January 19, 2021. **Description:** An event planner details what it's really like to be an event planner and what it takes to set up a business in this industry. **Availability:** E-book.

6086 ■ *"Corporate Event Management Best Practices: 2020 Guide" in The Bizzabo Blog (January 9, 2020)*
Released: January 09, 2020. **Description:** Details best practices that lead to a strong corporate event management strategy. **Availability:** Online.

6087 ■ *Event Management: For Tourism, Cultural, Business and Sporting Events*
Ed: Lynn Van der Wagen, Lauren White. **Released:** February 16, 2018. **Description:** A learning resource for event management students. Includes case studies. **Availability:** Print.

6088 ■ *"Event Planning Guide 2020" in Cvent Blog (August 27, 2019)*
Ed: Madison Layman. **Released:** August 27, 2019. **Description:** A guide that walks through a basic event planning template, what it means to be an event planner, and how event management software can simplify the event planning process. **Availability:** Online.

6089 ■ *"The Event Planning Recipe for Success" in Entrepreneur*
Ed: Cheryl Kimball. **Description:** Explains how to get started in the event planning industry. Discusses part-time vs. full-time planning as well as a variety of party types, fundraisers, and product launches. **Availability:** Online.

6090 ■ *The Event Planning Toolkit: Your Guide to Organizing Extraordinary Meetings and Events*
Ed: Linda Joyce Jones. **Released:** November 12, 2020. **Description:** Information and organizational techniques to help run a successful event or meeting. **Availability:** E-book.

6091 ■ *"Event Postponement and Cancellation Guide" Cvent (May 15, 2020)*
Ed: Anna Linthicum. **Released:** May 15, 2020. **Description:** Provides details on making decisions about cancelling or postponing planned events, especially during uncertain times. Discusses best practices, cancellation insurance, and using event cancellations and postponements as opportunities. **Availability:** Online.

6092 ■ *"How to Become a Professional Wedding Planner" in The Spruce (October 3, 2019)*
Ed: Nina Callaway. **Released:** October 03, 2019. **Description:** Includes steps to launch a successful career in wedding planning. **Availability:** Online.

6093 ■ *"How to Start an Event Planning Business from Home" in EventMB (April 30, 2020)*
Ed: Becki Cross. **Released:** April 30, 2020. **Description:** Provides information that acts as a startup kit for anyone wanting to start their own event management company from home. **Availability:** Online.

6094 ■ *"How to Start a Wedding Planning Business" in Startup Jungle*
Ed: Kari Andrews. **Description:** Details how to start a wedding planning business including startup costs, marketing, required skills, license, and tax information. **Availability:** Online.

6095 ■ *"The Price Is Right: Turning a Profit in the Event Planning Business" in Entrepreneur*
Ed: Cheryl Kimball. **Description:** Details how to get started in the event planning industry as well as explains how to determine what to charge clients to turn a profit. **Availability:** Online.

6096 ■ *Simplified Events Management: A Text Book to Event Planning, Fundraising and Safety Managment*
Released: July 10, 2021. **Description:** Details the key aspects of event management, operations, objectives, staffing, logistics, safety, and careers within the industry. **Availability:** E-book.

6097 ■ *Start Your Own Event Planning Business*
Ed: Cheryl Kimball. **Released:** 4th Edition. **Price:** $19.95. **Description:** Provides advice and tools needed to start, run, and grow a successful event planning business. **Availability:** Paperback; Print.

6098 ■ *"Sustainable Is Attainable" in Cvent Blog (October 16, 2019)*
URL(s): www.cvent.com/en/blog/events/sustainable-attainable
Ed: Madison Layman. **Released:** October 16, 2019. **Description:** Podcast episode discussing environmentally conscious event planning. Learn how to make events more "green", from sourcing eco-friendly hotels and venues to waste reduction. **Availability:** Online.

STATISTICAL SOURCES

6099 ■ *U.S. The Future of Live Events Market Report 2021*
URL(s): store.mintel.com/report/us-the-future-of-live-events-market-report
Price: $4,366.35. **Description:** Downloadable report containing data on the live events market in the US and the impact COVID-19 has had on it. Report includes an executive summary, interactive databook, PowerPoint presentation, infographic overview, report PDF, and previous years data. **Availability:** PDF.

VIDEO/AUDIO MEDIA

6100 ■ *Buildng an Event Strategy that Connects with Your Community*
URL(s): ducttapemarketing.com/building-an-event-strategy-that-connects-with-your-community
Ed: John Jantsch. **Released:** July 20, 2023. **Description:** Podcast outlines the components of a successful event strategy: community engagement, consideration of available resources, and a clear event vision. Also discusses fostering relationships between the community and your business with Isaac Watson.

Executive Recruiting Agency

ASSOCIATIONS AND OTHER ORGANIZATIONS

6101 ■ **Association of Professional Recruiters of Canada (APRC)**
Ste. 2210 1081 Ambleside Dr.
Ottawa, ON, Canada K2B 8C8
Ph: (613)721-5957
Free: 888-441-0000
Fax: (866)340-3586
URL: http://www.workplace.ca/resources/aprc_assoc.html
Contact: Nathaly Pinchuk, Executive Director
E-mail: nat@workplace.ca

Description: Employment recruiters. Seeks to advance the practice of employment recruiting; promotes ongoing professional development of members. Serves as a forum for the exchange of information among members; sponsors educational programs. **Founded:** 1994. **Geographic Preference:** National.

REFERENCE WORKS

6102 ■ *"Altus Jobs Founders' Unique Operating System Generates Success"* in *Orlando Business Journal (Vol. 30, April 11, 2014, No. 42, pp. 3)*
Pub: American City Business Journals, Inc.
Contact: Mike Olivieri, Executive Vice President

Released: Weekly. **Price:** $8, introductory 4-week offer(Digital & Print). **Description:** Maitland, Florida-based Altus Jobs founders, Saum Sharifi and Augusto Guevara, have credited their unique operating sytem with their quick success in recruiting talent, specializing in high level engineering positions. The system allows employees to work from 9:30 a.m. to 3:30 p.m. in their casual office and motivates them to show entrepreneurship by offering commission on top of base salary. **Availability:** Print; Online.

6103 ■ *"America's Best Executive Recruiting Firms"* in *Forbes (March 27. 2019)*
URL(s): www.forbes.com/best-executive-recruiting-firms/#2768f79829be

Released: March 27, 2019. **Description:** A list of the best executive recruiting firms for 2019. The ones who made the list specialized in filling positions with salaries of at least $100,000. **Availability:** Online.

6104 ■ *"DHR Hires Carr for Sports Group"* in *Crain's Detroit Business (Vol. 25, June 8, 2009, No. 23, pp. 5)*
Pub: Crain Communications Inc.
Contact: Barry Asin, President

Ed: Sherri Begin Welch. **Description:** Lloyd Carr, former head football coach for University of Michigan, has taken a position with DHR International in order to expand its searches for collegiate and professional sports organizations, recruit athletic directors, head coaches and other executives. **Availability:** Print; Online.

6105 ■ *"Hello, and Goodbye"* in *Entrepreneur (June 2014)*

Released: December 19, 2015. **Description:** Companies must implement strategies to ensure the creation of an ethical workplace. They must be able to deal with clients that experience problems and try to bully their counterparts as a result. Executive search firms must be responsible for compensating new executive hires by helping them find new jobs. Businesses must communicate to their employees about their importance as a way of making them feel appreciated and, thus, contribute to ethical behavior. **Availability:** Online.

6106 ■ *"It's Not the How or the What but the Who: Succeed by Surrounding Yourself with the Best"*
Pub: Harvard Business Review Press
Contact: Moderna V. Pfizer, Contact

Released: June 03, 2014. **Price:** $32, Hardcover/Hardcopy. **Description:** Surrounding yourself with the best matters in every aspect of life and can mean the difference between success and failure. The author draws upon years of experience in global executive search and talent development, as well as the latest management and psychology research, to help improve the choices management makes about employees and mentors, business partners and friends, top corporate leaders and elected officials. **Availability:** E-book; Print.

6107 ■ *"Overseas Overtures"* in *Business Journal-Portland (Vol. 24, October 26, 2007, No. 35, pp. 1)*
Pub: Portland Business Journal
Contact: Andy Giegerich, Managing Editor
E-mail: agiegerich@bizjournals.com

Ed: Robin J. Mood. **Description:** Oregon has a workforce shortage, specifically for the health care industry. Recruiting agencies, such as the International Recruiting Network Inc., answers the high demand for workforce by recruiting foreign employees. The difficulties recruiting companies experience with regards to foreign labor laws are investigated. **Availability:** Print; Online.

6108 ■ *"Recruiting Diversifies"* in *Advertising Age (Vol. 83, October 8, 2012, No. 36, pp. 25)*

Description: Heidrick & Struggles launches a data and analytics practice that filles the void as marketing becomes more data-riven. H&S specializes in recruiting and filling CEO and other senior-level positions for human resource departments of large firms. **Availability:** Print; Online.

6109 ■ *"The Rise of the Supertemp: The Best Executive and Professional Jobs May No Longer Be Full-Time Gigs"* in *Harvard Business Review (Vol. 90, May 2012, No. 5, pp. 50)*
Pub: Harvard Business Review Press
Contact: Moderna V. Pfizer, Contact

Ed: Jody Grenstone Miller, Matt Miller. **Price:** $8.95, hardcopy and PDF. **Description:** Supertemps are independent contractors who perform mission-critical work on a project basis. Supertemps enjoy a high degree of flexibility and freedom, and offer companies new opportunities for innovation and growth. **Availability:** Print; Online; PDF.

6110 ■ *"Sign of the Times: Temp-To-Perm Attorneys"* in *HRMagazine (Vol. 54, January 2009, No. 1, pp. 24)*

Description: A growing number of law firms are hiring professional staff on a temp-to-perm basis according to the president of Professional Placement Services in Florida. Firms can save money while testing potential employees on a temporary basis. **Availability:** Print; Online.

6111 ■ *"Sleeping with Your Smartphone: How to Break the 24/7 Habit and Change the Way You Work"*
Pub: Harvard Business Review Press
Contact: Moderna V. Pfizer, Contact

Released: May 29, 2012. **Price:** $30, Hardcover/Hardcopy. **Description:** Harvard Business School professor, Leslie Perlow, reveals ways to become more productive after disconnecting from your smartphone. A six-person team was used in an experiment at The Boston Consulting Group, an elite management consulting firm, where teams changed the way they worked and became more efficient and effective by disconnecting. The team was better able to perform and recruit new talent. A step-by-step guide is offered to change your team. **Availability:** E-book; Print.

6112 ■ *"Staffing Firms are Picking Up the Pieces, Seeing Signs of Life"* in *Milwaukee Business Journal (Vol. 27, February 5, 2010, No. 19)*
Pub: The Business Journal
Contact: Heather Ladage, President
E-mail: hladage@bizjournals.com

Ed: Rich Rovito. **Description:** Milwaukee, Wisconsin-based staffing firms are seeing signs of economic rebound as many businesses turned to temporary employees to fill the demands for goods and services. Economic observers believe the growth in temporary staffing is one of the early indicators of economic recovery. **Availability:** Print; Online.

6113 ■ *"Wanted: African American Professional for Hire"* in *Black Enterprise (Vol. 37, November 2006, No. 4, pp. 93)*
Pub: Earl G. Graves Ltd.
Contact: Earl Graves, Jr., President

Ed: Joe Watson. **Description:** Excerpt from the book, Without Excuses: Unleash the Power of Diversity to Build Your Business, speaks to the lack of diversity in the corporate arena and why executives, recruiters, and HR professionals claim they are unable to find qualified individuals of different races when hiring. **Availability:** Online.

6114 ■ "Why Recruiters Need to Expand Their Reach" in Onrec.com (October 21, 2019)
URL(s): www.onrec.com/news/opinion/why-recruiters-need-to-expand-their-reach
Ed: Stuart Gentle. **Released:** October 21, 2019.
Description: Recruitment agencies are being encouraged to use new technologies and platforms to find employees who can fill open positions. With the advent of sites such as LinkedIn, companies can find potential candidates, but more often than not, these candidates have outdated profiles or profiles that have little substance. Challenges such as this are discusses along with possible solutions for recruiters.
Availability: Online.

FRANCHISES AND BUSINESS OPPORTUNITIES

6115 ■ Express Services, Inc.
Express Services, Inc.
9701 Boardwalk Blvd.
Oklahoma City, OK 73162
Ph: (405)840-5000
URL: http://www.expresspros.com
Facebook: www.facebook.com/ExpressEmploymentInternational
Linkedin: www.linkedin.com/company/expressemploymentinternational
X (Twitter): x.com/expresspros
Instagram: www.instagram.com/expressemploymentinternational
YouTube: www.youtube.com/user/expressep
Description: Firm provides staffing and recruitment services. **Founded:** 1983. **Financial Assistance:** Yes **Training:** 2 week initial training at headquarters, 1 week in certified training office and ongoing field training and support. Followed by additional time in new office with assigned field representative. **Educational Activities:** IFA Annual Convention (Annual).

6116 ■ F-O-R-T-U-N-E Personnel Consultants (FPC) [FPC National]
Lake Success, NY
Ph: (212)302-1141
Co. E-mail: info@fpcnational.com
URL: http://fpcnational.com
Contact: Jeff Herzog, President
Facebook: www.facebook.com/FPCNational
X (Twitter): x.com/fpcnational
YouTube: www.youtube.com/c/Fpcnational
Description: Operates a franchise network of recruiting firms specializing in executive and management placements. **Founded:** 1959. **Franchised:** 1973.
Financial Assistance: Yes **Training:** Offers 2 weeks training at headquarters, 5 days at franchisee's location with ongoing training, mentoring and coaching.

6117 ■ FPC/F-O-R-T-U-N-E Personnel Consultants (FPC)
Lake Success, NY
Ph: (212)302-1141
Co. E-mail: info@fpcnational.com
URL: http://fpcnational.com
Contact: Jeff Herzog, President
Facebook: www.facebook.com/FPCNational
Linkedin: www.linkedin.com/company/100753
X (Twitter): x.com/fpcnational
YouTube: www.youtube.com/user/fpcnational
Description: Firm provides executive search and recruiting services. **Founded:** 1959. **Training:** Yes.

6118 ■ Management Recruiters International Inc. (MRI)
1735 Market St., Ste. 200
Philadelphia, PA 19103
Contact: Michael S. Castleman, President
Description: Firm provides a complete range of recruitment and human resource services. **Scope:** Offers counsel to management in recruitment of management executives, sales managers and sales and marketing personnel, other administrative personnel, interim executive placement and interim sales managers, sales and marketing personnel and outplacement services. **Publications:** "10 Questions the Boss Should Ask Every Employee"; "10 Tips for Conducting Productive Employee Reviews"; "Behavioral Interviewing"; "Building Motivation Levels"; "Can You Attract Top Talent Without Top Dollars"; "Conducting Effective Meetings"; "Do You Refuse to Hear No"; "Get Your Underperforming Employee to Quit Try Counseling Out"; "How to Get the Most Value from Your Recruiter"; "How to Spot Red Flags on a Resume"; "Intergenerational Miscommunication in the Workplace"; "Managers as Motivators: Understand the Guiding Principles"; "New Employee Retention"; "Terminate 10% of Your Employees Each Year"; "Thinking Well Outside the Box"; "Working the Second Shift in Corporate America. How Managers Can Help Employees Improve Work-Family Balance"; "Will Passive Job Seekers Apply to Your Job"; "Why Conduct Quarterly Employee Reviews"; "Top 4 Strategic Interview Styles"; "Top 10 Recruiting Myths - Busted"; "Top 10 Interview No No's"; "Tips for Successfully On boarding New Employees". **Special Services:** MRINetwork Way™.

6119 ■ PrideStaff
7535 N Palm Ave., Ste. 101
Fresno, CA 93711
Free: 800-774-3316
Fax: (559)432-4371
Co. E-mail: info@pridestaff.com
URL: http://www.pridestaff.com
Contact: Rob Hale, Chief Information Officer
Facebook: www.facebook.com/PrideStaff
Linkedin: www.linkedin.com/company/pridestaff
X (Twitter): x.com/PrideStaff
Instagram: www.instagram.com/pridestaff
YouTube: www.youtube.com/channel/UCjjuj-VBhlwYBDK6gSPU9cQ
Description: Recruiting Agency. **No. of Franchise Units:** 36. **No. of Company-Owned Units:** 3. **Founded:** 1978. **Franchised:** 1995. **Equity Capital Needed:** $162,000-$237,000. **Franchise Fee:** $32,000. **Training:** Yes.

6120 ■ Sanford Rose Associates International Inc. (SRA)
Akron, OH
URL: http://sanfordrose.com
Description: Firm offers executive search solutions, globally, through its franchise network, the company specializes in retained search for experienced executives, management, and individual contributors, it assists clients in filling their mission-critical positions, for candidates, IT firm offers resume and interview preparation, and on-boarding resources. **Founded:** 1959.

Fashion Accessories/Design Business

START-UP INFORMATION

6121 ▪ *Start Your Own Fashion Accessories Business*
Pub: Entrepreneur Media Inc.
Contact: Dan Bova, Director
E-mail: dbova@entrepreneur.com
Ed: Eileen Figure Sandlin. **Released:** Second edition.
Description: Entrepreneurs wishing to start a fashion accessories business will find important information for setting up a home workshop and office, exploring the market, managing finances, publicizing and advertising the business and more.

ASSOCIATIONS AND OTHER ORGANIZATIONS

6122 ▪ **CFDA Foundation [Council of Fashion Designers of America (CFDA)]**
1350 Avenue of the Americas, 2nd Fl.
New York, NY 10019
Ph: (212)302-1821
Co. E-mail: info@cfda.com
URL: http://cfda.com/philanthropy/foundation
Facebook: www.facebook.com/cfda
X (Twitter): x.com/CFDA
Instagram: www.instagram.com/cfda
Description: Seeks "to further the position of fashion design as a recognized branch of American art and culture, to advance its artistic and professional standards, to establish and maintain a code of ethics and practices of mutual benefit in professional, public, and trade relations, and to promote and improve public understanding and appreciation of the fashion arts through leadership in quality and taste".
Founded: 1962. **Awards:** CFDA Fashion Awards (Annual). **Geographic Preference:** National.

REFERENCE WORKS

6123 ▪ *"Baby Fashion Accessories Market to Witness Steady Expansion During 2019 to 2025"* in *The Chicago Sentinel* (October 30, 2019)
URL(s): www.ccsentinel.com/business/baby-fashion-accessories-market-to-witness-steady-expansion-during-2019-to-2025-carters-gap-gerber-chil drenswear-ralph-lauren-the-childrens-place-baby-vision-barneys-new-york-etc/
Ed: Ava Saunders. **Released:** October 30, 2019.
Description: Baby fashion accessories are trending upwards and has had continuous growth, which is projected to continue. Big name manufacturers such as Carter's, Gap, Ralph Lauren, and The Children's Place are forecasted to keep growing their sales in this industry. **Availability:** Online.

6124 ▪ *"Better Than New Runs on Tried-and-True Model"* in *Bellingham Business Journal* (Vol. February 2010, pp. 16)
Pub: Sound Publishing Inc.
Contact: Josh O'Connor, President
Ed: Ashley Mitchell. **Description:** Profile of family owned Better Than New clothing store that sells overstock items from department stores and clothing manufacturers. The stores location makes it easy to miss and its only advertising is a large sign posted outside. This is the sixth store owned by the couple, Keijeo and Sirba Halmekanqas.

6125 ▪ *"The Bottom Line"* in *Retail Merchandiser* (Vol. 51, July-August 2011, No. 4, pp. 60)
Description: Hanky Panky believes that comfort and style don't have to be mutually exclusive when designing their line of intimate apparel for women. The lingerie retailer was launched in 1977. **Availability:** Print; PDF; Online.

6126 ▪ *"A Change Would Do You Good"* in *Canadian Business* (Vol. 80, November 19, 2007, No. 23, pp. 15)
Description: Western Glove Works will be manufacturing clothing offshore, including Sheryl Crow's jeans collection, in countries such as China and the Philippines. The company decided to operate offshore after 86 years of existence due to the high price of manufacturing jeans in Canada. Western Glove's focus on producing celebrity-endorsed goods is discussed. **Availability:** Print; Online.

6127 ▪ *"Consignment Shop Offers Children's Clothes, Products"* in *Frederick News-Post* (August 19, 2010)
Pub: Federick News-Post
Contact: Connie Hastings, Director
E-mail: chastings@newspost.com
Ed: Ed Waters, Jr. **Description:** Sweet Pea Consignments for Children offers used items for newborns to pre-teens. The shop carries name brand clothing as well as toys, books and baby products. **Availability:** Print; Online.

6128 ▪ *"Crowdsourcing their Way into One Big Mess"* in *Brandweek* (Vol. 51, October 25, 2010, No. 38, pp. 26)
Description: The Gap, was counting on crowdsourcing to provide feedback for its new logo, but it did not prove positive for the retailer. However, a massive outcry of negative opinion, via crowdsourcing, may not always equal valid, constructive criticism. **Availability:** Online.

6129 ▪ *"Design '07 (Fashion): Haute Flyers"* in *Canadian Business* (Vol. 80, November 19, 2007, No. 23, pp. 68)
Pub: Rogers Media Inc.
Contact: Neil Spivak, Chief Executive Officer
Ed: Rachel Pulfer. **Description:** Duckie Brown has been nominated by the Council of Fashion Designers of America as best menswear designer in the U.S. for 2007, along with leaders Calvin Klein and Ralph Lauren. The New York-based company was formed the day after September 11, 2001, but the timing did not hamper its growth. The works and plans of owners Steven Cox and Daniel Silver are described. **Availability:** Online.

6130 ▪ *"Escada Bought by US Private Equity Firm Regent"* in *Fashion Network* (October 30, 2019)
URL(s): us.fashionnetwork.com/news/Escada-bough t-by-us-private-equity-firm-regent,1153089.html
Released: October 30, 2019. **Description:** The Munich-based ready-to-wear label, Escada, was recently bought by US private equity firm Regent, which owns several other fashion-related companies. **Availability:** Online.

6131 ▪ *"Fall Fever"* in *Canadian Business* (Vol. 81, October 13, 2008, No. 17, pp. S12)
Description: Buyer's guide of men's suits and jackets for fall are presented, including a suit by Boss Hugo Boss recommended for fun in the city after finishing work. Designers Ermenegildo, Michael Kors, and Arnold Brant are also highlighted. **Availability:** Print; Online.

6132 ▪ *"Going Western with a Touch of Style"* in *Women In Business* (Vol. 63, Summer 2011, No. 2, pp. 8)
Pub: American Business Women's Association
Contact: Rene Street, Executive Director
Ed: Maureen Sullivan. **Released:** June 22, 2011.
Description: Tips on ways women should dress up in Western style are presented. The wearing of Western-style denims is recommended. Use of accessories such as belt buckles, boots and hats is also encouraged. **Availability:** Print; Online.

6133 ▪ *"H&M Offers a Dress for Less"* in *Canadian Business* (Vol. 83, September 14, 2010, No. 15, pp. 20)
Pub: Rogers Media Inc.
Contact: Neil Spivak, Chief Executive Officer
Ed: Laura Cameron. **Description:** Swedish clothing company H&M has implemented loss leader strategy by pricing some dresses at extremely low prices. The economy has forced retailers to keep prices down despite the increasing cost of manufacturing, partly due to Chinese labor becoming more expensive. How the trend will affect apparel companies is discussed. **Availability:** Print; Online.

6134 ▪ *"It's So You! Consignment Shop Owner Thrilled to See Vision Come to Fruition"* in *News-Herald* (August 27, 2010)
Pub: The News Herald
Contact: Tricia Ambrose, Executive Editor
E-mail: tambrose@news-herald.com
Ed: Brandon C. Baker. **Description:** Profile of Laurel Howes and her It's So You! Boutique. The consignment shop is located in Willoughby's Pine Ride Plaza in Ohio. The shop targets all women, but particularly those who are not that comfortable with shopping consignment. **Availability:** Online.

Fashion Accessories/Design Business

6135 ■ *"Izod, Loft Outlets Coming To Tanger"* in *New Hampshire Business Review (Vol. 33, March 25, 2011, No. 6, pp. 30)*
Description: Izod and Lots stores will open at the Tanger Outlet Center in Tilton, New Hampshire. Both stores will feature fashions and accessories. **Availability:** Online.

6136 ■ *"Life's Work: Manolo Blahnik"* in *Harvard Business Review (Vol. 88, December 2010, No. 12, pp. 144)*
Pub: Harvard Business Publishing
Contact: Diane Belcher, Managing Director
Ed: Alison Beard. **Price:** $8.95, PDF. **Description:** Shoe designer Manolo Blahnik recounts his beginnings in the shoe industry and the influence art has had on his work, as well as balancing art and commerce. He also discusses the importance of quality materials and craftsmanship and the benefits of managing an independent, family-owned business. **Availability:** Online; PDF.

6137 ■ *"Making It Work"* in *Retail Merchandiser (Vol. 51, July-August 2011, No. 4, pp. 43)*
Description: Profile of Anthony DiPaolo and his purchase of the Work 'N Gear retail store in 2002. The brick and mortar shop sells work wear and healthcare apparel and DiPaolo believes customer respect is essential to his success. **Availability:** Online.

6138 ■ *"Retail Happenings: Valentino Reopens Its O.C. Store with Big Focus on Menswear"* in *Los Angeles Times (October 30, 2019)*
URL(s): www.latimes.com/lifestyle/story/2019-10-30/retail-happenings-valentino-reopens-oc-store-big-focus-menswear-south-coast-plaza
Ed: Kavita Daswani. **Released:** October 30, 2019. **Description:** The new Valentino boutique that opened in South Coast Plaza will showcase the brand's newly launched VSling handbag. The reopening also features menswear such as tees, trench coats, and suits. **Availability:** Online.

6139 ■ *"Rule of the Masses: Reinventing Fashion Via Crowdsourcing"* in *WWD (Vol. 200, July 26, 2010, No. 17, pp. 1)*
Pub: Conde Nast Publications
Contact: Agnes Chu, President
Ed: Cate T. Corcoran. **Description:** Large apparel brands and retailers are crowdsourcing as a way to increase customer loyalty and to build their businesses. **Availability:** PDF; Download; Online.

6140 ■ *"These Clothes Use Outlandish Designs to Trick Facial Recognition Software into Thinking You're Not a Human"* in *Business Insider (October 12, 2019)*
URL(s): www.businessinsider.com/clothes-accessories-that-outsmart-facial-recognition-tech-2019-10
Ed: Aaron Holmes. **Released:** October 12, 2019. **Description:** With the rise of facial recognition technology, some designers are pushing back by designing clothes and accessories that make faces undetectable. Examples of what confuses this AI technology are given, such as masks and printed material. **Availability:** Online.

6141 ■ *"Well-Heeled Startup Plots Course for a Run at Garmin"* in *Business Journal Portland (Vol. 27, November 12, 2010, No. 37, pp. 1)*
Pub: Portland Business Journal
Contact: Andy Giegerich, Managing Editor
E-mail: agiegerich@bizjournals.com
Description: Oh! Shoes LLC expects to receive about $1.5 million in funding from angel investors, while marketing a new line of high heel shoes that are comfortable, healthy, and attractive. The new line of shoes will use the technology of athletic footwear while having the look of an Italian designer. Oh! Shoes hopes to generate $35 million in sales by 2014. **Availability:** Print; Online.

6142 ■ *"Zalondo Commits to Carbon Neutrality"* in *FashionUnited (October 30, 2019)*
URL(s): fashionunited.com/news/business/
Ed: Huw Hughes. **Released:** October 30, 2019. **Description:** The online fashion house Zalondo is planning on helping to meet the goals of the Paris climate agreement by committing to a net-zero carbon footprint. This will entail operations, deliveries, and returns. **Availability:** Online.

VIDEO/AUDIO MEDIA

6143 ■ *How I Built This: Advice Line with Joe Kudla of Vuori*
URL(s): wondery.com/shows/how-i-built-this/episode/10386-advice-line-with-joe-kudla-of-vuori
Ed: Guy Raz. **Released:** July 25, 2024. **Description:** Podcast works through business challenges with three early-stage founders in the clothing and accessories industry.

6144 ■ *How I Built This: Herschel Supply Co.: Jamie and Lyndon Cormack*
URL(s): wondery.com/shows/how-i-built-this/episode/10386-herschel-supply-co-jamie-and-lyndon-cormack
Ed: Guy Raz. **Released:** October 09, 2023. **Description:** Podcast explains how two brothers with no background in manufacturing learned to make bags by ripping old ones apart and found a factory through Google.

6145 ■ *Main Street Business Insights: Ebenezer Akakpo, Akakpo Design Group & Maine Culture*
URL(s): mainstreet.org/resources/knowledge-hub/podcast/ebenezer-akakpo-akakpo-design-group-maine-culture
Ed: Maggie Patterson. **Released:** July 31, 2024. **Description:** Podcast discusses the influence of cultural significance with a jewelry designer.

6146 ■ *Side Hustle to Small Business: Amity Gleason's Journery from Attorney to Jewelry Maker*
URL(s): sidehustletosmallbusiness.podbean.com/e/amity-gleason-s-journey-from-attorney-to-jewelry-maker
Ed: Sanjay Parekh. **Released:** October 30, 2024. **Description:** Podcast features a jewelry designer.

TRADE SHOWS AND CONVENTIONS

6147 ■ **Trendz Show**
Florida Fashion Focus, Inc.
URL(s): www.trendzshow.com/show-dates
Frequency: Irregular. **Description:** Ladies ready-to-wear clothing, handbags, jewelry, and accessories. Order-writing for future delivery. **Audience:** Industry professionals. **Principal Exhibits:** Ladies ready-to-wear clothing, handbags, jewelry, and accessories. Order-writing for future delivery. Dates and Locations: Palm Beach County Convention Center, Palm Beach, FL.

FRANCHISES AND BUSINESS OPPORTUNITIES

6148 ■ **Apricot Lane (ALB)**
3333 Vaca Valley Pkwy, Ste. 700
Vacaville, CA 95688
Ph: (707)451-6890
Fax: (707)451-0410
Co. E-mail: vacaville@apricotlaneusa.com
URL: http://apricotlaneboutique.com
Facebook: www.facebook.com/apricotlanevacaville
Instagram: www.instagram.com/apricotlanenuttree
Description: Retailer of casualwear, dressy fashions and accessories. **Founded:** 1991. **Franchised:** 1992. **Equity Capital Needed:** $290,000 ; $75,000 in cash or liquid assets. **Franchise Fee:** $29,500. **Financial Assistance:** No **Training:** Site selection and lease negotiation assistance; turnkey store design and construction; sales point system; home training program and onsite training; initial inventory orders; grand opening marketing kit; and onsite merchandising.

6149 ■ **Clothes Mentor (CM)**
14200 Wayzata Blvd.
Minnetonka, MN 55305
Ph: (952)303-6673
Co. E-mail: cmminnetonka@gmail.com
URL: http://minnetonkamn.clothesmentor.com
Facebook: www.facebook.com/ClothesMentorMinnetonka
Description: Retailer of women's apparel. **Founded:** 2001. **Financial Assistance:** Yes **Training:** Includes 2 weeks training at headquarters and ongoing support.

INTERNET DATABASES

6150 ■ *Fashion Industry: A Resource Guide*
URL(s): guides.loc.gov/fashion-industry
Description: An online resource providing links to topics for those in the fashion and apparel industry. Includes historical resources; retail, wholesale, manufacturing and trade; fashion magazines and trade literature; plus other internet sources. **Availability:** Online.

LIBRARIES

6151 ■ **Conde Nast Publications Library and Information Services**
1 World Trade Ctr.
New York, NY 10007
Co. E-mail: communications@condenast.com
URL: http://www.condenast.com
Contact: Roger Lynch, Chief Executive Officer
Linkedin: www.linkedin.com/company/conde-nast
X (Twitter): x.com/condenast
Instagram: www.instagram.com/condenast
Description: Produces in-depth research for the world's most celebrated media brands. **Scope:** Fashion; houses; gardens; home furnishings; interior design; health; personalities; photographs. **Services:** Library not open to public. **Founded:** 1935. **Holdings:** 7,000 volumes.

6152 ■ **George Brown College Archives**
500 Macpherson Ave., Rm. F-103
Toronto, ON, Canada M5R 1M1
Ph: (416)415-5000
Fax: (416)415-4772
URL: http://www.georgebrown.ca/about/archives
Contact: Clay Thibodeau, Archivist
E-mail: cthibodeau@georgebrown.ca
Facebook: www.facebook.com/georgebrowncollege
Linkedin: www.linkedin.com/school/george-brown-college
X (Twitter): x.com/GBCollege
Instagram: www.instagram.com/gbcollege
YouTube: www.youtube.com/user/georgebrowncollege
Scope: Education materials. **Services:** Copying; archives open to the public with restrictions and by appointment only. **Founded:** 1975. **Holdings:** 3,700 linear meters publications.

6153 ■ **State University of New York - Fashion Institute of Technology - Gladys Marcus Library**
227 W 27th St.
New York, NY 10001-5992
Ph: (212)217-7999
URL: http://www.fitnyc.edu/library/index.php
Description: Library supports the academic and research needs of the institute. **Scope:** Fashion, fashion history, textiles, fashion trend forecasting. **Services:** Interlibrary loan; library open by appointment. **Founded:** 1944. **Holdings:** 300,000 print, non-print, and electronic materials, including sketch collections, clipping files, and fashion show DVDs.

Film and Video Production Operation

START-UP INFORMATION

6154 ■ *"Katharine Grayson: Three Questions with John Brownlee, CEO of Vidscrip.com"* in *Business Journal (Vol. 32, June 27, 2014, No. 5, pp. 6)*
Pub: American City Business Journals, Inc.
Contact: Mike Olivieri, Executive Vice President
Description: John Brownlee, CEO of vidscrip.com, discusses the Minneapolis, Minnesota startup's deal with Partners HealthCare and what it means for the business. Partners HealthCare is using the vidscrip technology to create educational videos for patients.
Availability: Print; Online.

6155 ■ *"Legal Matters: 'Crowdfunding' a Boon for Entrepreneurs, If They Clear Regulatory Hurdles"* in *Finance and Commerce (July 17, 2012)*
Pub: BridgeTower Media
Contact: Adam Reinebach, President
Ed: Dan Heilman. **Description:** Part of the Jumpstart Our Business Startups Act (JOBS) is crowdfunding, which allows the funding of a company by selling small parts of equity to a group of investors. Kickstarter, a Website for raising funds for business entitites, is primarily used for film and book projects. Most businesses cannot adopt Kickstarter's model because of the legality of receiving investor funds without offering security.

ASSOCIATIONS AND OTHER ORGANIZATIONS

6156 ■ **Association Canadienne D'Etudes Cinematographiques (ACEC) [Film Studies Association of Canada (FSAC)]**
Victoria, BC, Canada
URL: http://www.filmstudies.ca
Contact: Andrew Burke, President
Facebook: www.facebook.com/FSAC.ACEC
Description: Promotes the study and appreciation of the history and art of film and related media. Conducts research and educational programs. **Founded:** 1977. **Publications:** *The Canadian Journal of Film Studies (CJFS)* (Semiannual); *Continuity* (Quarterly). **Awards:** Gerald Pratley Award (Annual). **Geographic Preference:** National.

6157 ■ **Association for Information Media and Equipment (AIME)**
PO Box 378
Coal Township, PA 17866
URL: http://aime.org
Contact: Geoff Craven, Executive Director
E-mail: geoff.c@craventech.com
Description: Promotes the use of motion media in the instructional and informational fields; works to educate schools and libraries regarding copyright laws as applied to film and video; offers networking opportunities among members and the sharing of information; lobbies for increased funds for school media materials; compiles statistics; sponsors market research. **Founded:** 1986. **Publications:** *AIME News* (Quarterly). **Geographic Preference:** National.

6158 ■ **Association of Moving Image Archivists (AMIA)**
1313 N Vine St.
Hollywood, CA 90028
Ph: (323)463-1500
Fax: (323)463-1506
Co. E-mail: amia@amianet.org
URL: http://amianet.org
Contact: Rachael Stoeltje, President
E-mail: amiapresident@amianet.org
Facebook: www.facebook.com/amiarchivists
X (Twitter): x.com/amianet
Instagram: www.instagram.com/amiarchivists
Description: Works to advance the field of moving image archiving by fostering cooperation among individuals and institutions concerned with the collection, description, preservation, exhibition, and use of moving image materials (film and video). **Founded:** 1991. **Publications:** *Association of Moving Image Archivists--Membership Directory* (Annual); *The Moving Image* (Semiannual). **Awards:** Rick Chace Foundation Scholarships; Kodak Fellowships in Film Preservation; Mary Pickford Scholarships; Sony Pictures Scholarship (Annual); Universal Studios Preservation Scholarships (Annual); AMIA Silver Light Award (Annual). **Geographic Preference:** Multinational.

6159 ■ **Audiovisual and Integrated Experience Association (AVIXA)**
11242 Waples Mill Rd., Ste. 200
Fairfax, VA 22030
Ph: (703)273-7200
Free: 800-659-7469
Co. E-mail: membership@avixa.org
URL: http://www.avixa.org
Contact: David Labuskes, Chief Executive Officer
Facebook: www.facebook.com/TheAVIXA
Linkedin: www.linkedin.com/company/theavixa
X (Twitter): x.com/AVIXA
Instagram: www.instagram.com/avixagram
YouTube: www.youtube.com/channel/UCLlhusbwAJ2zm2YIMfle_ew
Description: Producer of InfoComm tradeshows worldwide. A hub for professional collaboration, information, and community, and the leading resource for AV standards, certification, training, market intelligence and thought leadership. Members include manufacturers, systems integrators, dealers and distributors, consultants, programmers, rental and staging companies, technology managers, IT professionals, content producers, and multimedia professionals from more than 80 countries. **Founded:** 1939. **Publications:** *InfoCommunity News* (Quarterly); *ICIA Membership Directory* (Annual); *Directory of Multimedia Equipment, Software, and Services* (Annual); *International Communications Industries Association-- Membership Directory* (Annual); *Equipment Directory of Video, Computer and Audio-Visual Products* (Annual). **Educational Activities:** Integrated Systems Europe (ISE) (Annual); INFOCOMM (Annual). **Awards:** Mackey Barron Distinguished Achievement Award (Irregular). **Geographic Preference:** Multinational.

6160 ■ **Canadian Media Producers Association (CMPA)**
251 Laurier Ave. W, 11th Fl.
Ottawa, ON, Canada K1P 5J6
Ph: (613)233-1444
Free: 800-656-7440
Co. E-mail: ottawa@cmpa.ca
URL: http://cmpa.ca
Contact: Reynolds Mastin, President
Facebook: www.facebook.com/thecmpa
Linkedin: www.linkedin.com/company/canadian-media-producers-association-cmpa-
X (Twitter): x.com/the_cmpa
YouTube: www.youtube.com/user/cmpaonline
Description: Seeks to negotiate and manage labor agreements, and actively lobby the federal and provincial governments on various policy areas including taxation, trade, copyright, broadcasting and film. **Founded:** 2010. **Publications:** *Action Newsletter* (Quarterly); *Guide* (Annual). **Geographic Preference:** National.

6161 ■ **Center for Asian American Media (CAAM)**
145 9th St., Ste. 350
San Francisco, CA 94103
Ph: (415)863-0814
Fax: (415)863-7428
Co. E-mail: events@caamedia.org
URL: http://caamedia.org
Contact: Stephen Gong, Executive Director
E-mail: sgong@caamedia..org
Facebook: www.facebook.com/CAAMedia
X (Twitter): x.com/caam
Instagram: www.instagram.com/caamedia
YouTube: www.youtube.com/user/CAAMCHANNEL
Description: A nonprofit organization dedicated to presenting stories that convey the richness and diversity of Asian American experiences to the broadest audience possible. **Founded:** 1980. **Publications:** *CAAM Connect*; *Distribution Catalog*; *CAAMFest Program Guide* (Annual); *Year in Review* (Annual). **Educational Activities:** Film Festival (Annual). **Awards:** James T. Yee Fellowship Program; CAAM Open Door Completion Fund (Semiannual). **Geographic Preference:** National.

6162 ■ **Content Delivery and Security Association (CDSA)**
1775 W State St., No. 394
Boise, ID 83702
Ph: (208)629-1735
Co. E-mail: info@cdsaonline.org
URL: http://www.cdsaonline.org
Contact: Richard Atkinson, President
Facebook: www.facebook.com/CDSAonline
Linkedin: www.linkedin.com/company/cdsaonline
X (Twitter): x.com/CDSAonline

Description: Serves as the advocate for the growth and development of all recording media and as a forum for the exchange of information regarding global trends and innovations. Provides members an opportunity to join forces and be a strong industry voice allowing them to grow and expand their business. Encompasses all facets of the recording media. **Founded:** 1970. **Publications:** *Mediaware* (9/year); *IRMA International Source Directory* (Annual); *International Recording Media Associaton--Source Directory--the Buyer's Guide for the Recording Media Industry* (Annual). **Geographic Preference:** Multinational.

6163 ■ Documentaristes du Canada [Documentary Organization of Canada (DOC)]
401 Richmond St., W., Ste. 392
  Toronto, ON, Canada M5V 3A8
Ph: (647)846-7638
Co. E-mail: info@docorg.ca
URL: http://docorg.ca
Contact: Sarah Spring, Executive Director
E-mail: sarah@docorg.ca
Facebook: www.facebook.com/DOCorg
X (Twitter): x.com/DOCorg
Description: Association of independent filmmakers that promotes excellence in filmmaking, advances the economic interests of independent filmmakers, and provides professional development opportunities. Represents members' interests before government, industry organizations, and the public. Sponsors promotional programs. **Founded:** 1983. **Publications:** *POV* (Semiannual); *Point of View (POV)* (Semiannual). **Geographic Preference:** National.

6164 ■ Independent Media Arts Alliance (IMAA) [Alliance Des Arts Mediatiques Independants (AAMI)]
4580, Ave. de Lorimier
  Montreal, QC, Canada H2H 2B5
Ph: (514)522-8240
Co. E-mail: info@imaa.ca
URL: http://www.imaa.ca
Contact: Barbora Raceviciute, Director
E-mail: dir@imaa.ca
Facebook: www.facebook.com/AAMI.IMAA
X (Twitter): x.com/IMAA_AAMI
Instagram: www.instagram.com/imaa_aami
Description: Represents independent media organizations in Canada, including producers of film, video, and audio along with distributors and exhibitors. **Founded:** 1980. **Publications:** *Annual Review* (Annual). **Educational Activities:** IMAA National Indigenous Media Arts Conference. **Geographic Preference:** National.

6165 ■ International Association of Audio Visual Communicators (IAA-VC)
The Cindys
  PO Box 270779
  Flower Mound, TX 75022-5326
URL: http://www.cindys.com
Facebook: www.facebook.com/The-International-CINDY-Awards-705446786243008
X (Twitter): twitter.com/CindyAwards
Description: Organizes international media competition open to an array of media formats, including video, audio, online interactive media, mobile apps, and more. **Founded:** 1959. **Publications:** *International Association of Audio Visual Communicators--Membership Roster* (Annual). **Educational Activities:** International Association of Audio Visual Communicators Composium (Periodic); International Association of Audio Visual Communicators Competition. **Awards:** CINDY Sales and Marketing Awards (Annual). **Geographic Preference:** Multinational.

6166 ■ International Documentary Association (IDA) [International Documentary Foundation]
3600 Wilshire Blvd., Ste. 1810
  Los Angeles, CA 90010
Ph: (213)232-1660
Fax: (213)232-1669
Co. E-mail: info@documentary.org
URL: http://www.documentary.org
Contact: Rick Sigmund, Executive Director

Facebook: www.facebook.com/documentary.org
X (Twitter): x.com/IDAorg
Instagram: www.instagram.com/idaorg
YouTube: www.youtube.com/channel/UCsUYLxN5JtXGaIM459eYIkA
Description: Individuals and organizations involved in non-fiction film and video. Encourages the progress of the documentary arts and sciences and supports the efforts of nonfiction film and video makers throughout the world. Provides a forum for documentaries and allied members of the film and video industries to meet and discuss areas of mutual interest related to all aspects of nonfiction film and video arts, sciences, production, financing, and distribution. Holds screenings of all Oscar-nominated documentaries. **Founded:** 1982. **Publications:** *Documentary* (Quarterly). **Awards:** IDA Documentary Awards (Annual); IDA Career Achievement Award (Annual); Preservation and Scholarship Award (Annual); IDA AVID Excellence in Editing Award; Jacqueline Donnet Emerging Filmmaker Award (Annual); IDA ABCNews VideoSource Award (Annual); Pare Lorentz Award (Annual). **Geographic Preference:** Multinational.

6167 ■ La Guilde Canadienne des Realisateurs (GCR) [Directors Guild of Canada]
65 Heward Ave., Building A, Suite A201
  Toronto, ON, Canada M4M 2T5
Ph: (416)925-8200
Free: 888-972-0098
Fax: (416)925-8400
Co. E-mail: mail@dgc.ca
URL: http://www.dgc.ca/en/national
Contact: Warren P. Sonoda, President
X (Twitter): x.com/DGCTalent
Description: Promotes and seeks to advance the quality and vitality of Canadian feature film and television production. **Founded:** 1962. **Publications:** *Montage* (Semiannual); *Montage* (Semiannual). **Geographic Preference:** National.

6168 ■ Motion Picture Association-Canada (MPA) [MPA-Canada]
20 Eglinton Ave. W, Ste. 1004
  Toronto, ON, Canada M4R 1K8
Co. E-mail: mpa-canada@motionpictures.org
URL: http://www.mpa-canada.org
Contact: Wendy Noss, President
X (Twitter): x.com/MPACanada
Description: Film studios and distributors; marketers and distributors of television programming. Promotes increased distribution of American films in Canada. Conducts marketing and promotional activities. **Founded:** 1920. **Geographic Preference:** National.

6169 ■ POV
401 Richmond St., W., Ste. 392
  Toronto, ON, Canada M5V 3A8
Ph: (647)846-7638
Co. E-mail: info@docorg.ca
URL: http://docorg.ca
Contact: Sarah Spring, Executive Director
E-mail: sarah@docorg.ca
URL(s): povmagazine.com
Facebook: www.facebook.com/POVmag
X (Twitter): x.com/POVmagazine
Instagram: www.instagram.com/pov_magazine
YouTube: www.youtube.com/user/PointOfViewMagazine
Ed: Marc Glassman. **Released:** Semiannual; fall, winter. **Price:** C$12, Individuals for Canada; C$20, Individuals for international; C$45, Institutions for international; C$8, for pdf e-subscription; C$25, Institutions, Canada for online; C$1, Students, Canada for online; C$30, Institutions for online; C$15, Individuals for online. **Availability:** Print; Online.

6170 ■ Stuntwomen's Association of Motion Pictures (SA)
3760 Cahuenga Blvd., Ste. No 104
  Los Angeles, CA 90038
Ph: (818)762-0907
URL: http://stuntwomen.com
Contact: Katie Rowe, Contact
Facebook: www.facebook.com/SWAMPStuntwomen
X (Twitter): x.com/swampstuntwomen

Instagram: www.instagram.com/stuntwomensassociation
Description: Represents stunt actresses and stunt coordinators who belong to the Screen Actors Guild and/or to the American Federation of Television and Radio Artists and who have worked as professional stunt woman for a minimum of five years. **Founded:** 1967. **Geographic Preference:** National.

6171 ■ University Film and Video Association (UFVA)
Co. E-mail: home@ufva.org
URL: http://ufva.org
Contact: Wenhwa Tsao, President
E-mail: wtsao@colum.edu
Facebook: www.facebook.com/ufvaconnection
X (Twitter): x.com/UFVAtweets
Description: Professors and video/filmmakers concerned with the production and study of film and video in colleges and universities. Conducts research programs; operates placement service. **Founded:** 1947. **Publications:** *Journal of Film and Video (JFV)* (Quarterly). **Awards:** Carole Fielding Student Grant (Annual). **Geographic Preference:** National.

6172 ■ Wedding and Event Videographers Association International (WEVA)
5020 Clark Rd., No. 345
  Sarasota, FL 34233
Co. E-mail: info@weva.com
URL: http://www.weva.com/index.shtml
Contact: Roy Chapman, President
Description: Represents professional wedding and event videographers worldwide, providing resources in technical training, marketing, and networking. **Publications:** *Wedding & Event Videography Resource Guide* (Quarterly). **Awards:** WEVA Creative Excellence Award (Annual). **Geographic Preference:** Multinational.

REFERENCE WORKS

6173 ■ "Action: Huge Film Incentive Boost Eyed in Virginia" in Washington Business Journal (Vol. 32, January 3, 2014, No. 38, pp. 5)
Pub: American City Business Journals, Inc.
Contact: Mike Olivieri, Executive Vice President
Description: Senator John Watkins of Midlothian, Virginia is introducing a bill that would increase the film incentive program of the state from the existing 15 percent level to 20-25 percent and boost the credit fund from $5 million to $25 million every two years. The 15.7 percent increase in film industry employment in 2013 was credited by Governor Bob McDonnell to the government incentive program. **Availability:** Online.

6174 ■ "American Farmland Trust, The Culinary Institute of America, Fabulous Beekman Boys Hold Special Event to Raise Awareness in Culinary Students" in Ecology, Environment & Conservation Business (April 19, 2014, pp. 3)
Pub: NewsRX LLC.
Contact: Kalani Rosell, Contact
Description: American Farmland Trust and The Culinary Institute of American were joined by the Fabulous Beekman Boys, Brent Ridge and Josh Kilmer-Purcell of Beekman 1802, to host a screening of The First Season, a documentary film about dairy farming in New York. The event was held to raise awareness in culinary arts students about the issues faced by farmers today. **Availability:** Online.

6175 ■ "BARS+TONE Achieves Green Business Certification by the City and County of San Francisco" in Benzinga.com (April 26, 2012)
Pub: Benzinga.com
Contact: Jason Raznick, Founder
Ed: Aaron Wise. **Description:** City and County of San Francisco, California presented a Green Business certification to BARS+TONE, a creative video agency. The certification is part of an ongoing effort to reduce environmental impact. **Availability:** Online.

Small Business Profiles • Film and Video Production Operation ■ 6195

6176 ■ *Canadian Society of Cinematographers--Directory*
Pub: Canadian Society of Cinematographers
Contact: George Willis, CSC, SASC, President
URL(s): csc.ca/members
Description: Covers over 400 directors of photography, videographers, operators, assistants, and focus pullers in Canada. Entries include: Name, address, phone, fax, biographical data, description of activities. Arrangement: Alphabetical. Indexes: Geographical. Availability: Print.

6177 ■ *"Colorado's Hollywood Wager" in Denver Business Journal (Vol. 65, April 25, 2014, No. 50, pp. A4)*
Pub: American City Business Journals, Inc.
Contact: Mike Olivieri, Executive Vice President
Released: Weekly. Price: $4, introductory 4-week offer(Digital & Print). Description: The successes and controversies surrounding the film incentives program of Colorado are explored. Some critics question the incentive have been directed to people who paid for the lobbying of House Bill 1286, while others ask if incentives are a proper use of public funds. Availability: Print; Online.

6178 ■ *"Creativity, Inc.: Overcoming the Unseen Forces That Stand in the Way of True Inspiration"*
Pub: Penguin Random House
Contact: Nihar Malaviya, Chief Executive Officer
Released: April 08, 2014. Price: $28, hardcover, plus shipping charges; $2.99, e-book; $35, CD, plus shipping charges; $17.50, audiobook download; $16.89, Hardcover; $15.79, Paperback; $28.33, Audible Audiobook. Description: Ed Catmull, co-founder of Pixar Animation Studios, reaches out to managers who want to lead their employees to greater heights. Pixar has dominated the world of animated films for twenty years. Catmull addresses philosophies that protect the creative process and defy convention to inspire employees and create a successful small business. Availability: CD-ROM; E-book; Print; Audio.

6179 ■ *"Deal Made for Pontiac Home of Film Studio" in Crain's Detroit Business (Vol. 25, June 1, 2009, No. 22, pp. 3)*
Pub: Crain Communications Inc.
Contact: Barry Asin, President
Ed: Daniel Duggan. Description: Details of the $75 million movie production and training facility in Pontiac, Michigan are revealed. Availability: Print; Online.

6180 ■ *Directors Guild of America--Member Directory*
Pub: Directors Guild of America Inc.
Contact: Lesli Linka Glatter, President
URL(s): www.dga.org/The-Guild/Members.aspx
Ed: Darrell L. Hope. Description: Covers over 15,000 motion picture and television directors and their assistants providing films and tapes for entertainment, commercial, industrial, and other non-entertainment fields; international coverage. Entries include: DGA member name; contact or representative address, phone; specialty; brief description of experience and credits. Arrangement: Alphabetical. Indexes: Geographical, women and minority members, agents. Availability: Print.

6181 ■ *"Discovery Networks" in Brandweek (Vol. 49, April 21, 2008, No. 16, pp. SR9)*
Description: Provides contact information for sales and marketing personnel for the Discovery networks as well as a listing of the station's top programming and an analysis of the current season and the target audience for those programs running in the current season. The networks flagship station returned to the top 10 in 2007, averaging 1.28 million viewers.

6182 ■ *"Energy Exec Bankrolls Big-Budget UT Film" in Austin Business Journal (Vol. 34, June 6, 2014, No. 16, pp. A8)*
Pub: American City Business Journals, Inc.
Contact: Mike Olivieri, Executive Vice President
Released: Weekly. Price: $4, introductory 4-week offer(Digital only). Description: Bud Brigham, CEO of the energy firm Brigham Resources is bankrolling the film, "My All American" that focuses on University of Texas football coach Darrell K. Royal. The film is about his bond with star player Freddie Steinmark during the 1969 national championship season. Through this film, Brigham hopes to establish himself in Hollywood and dreams of being as big as Disney. Availability: Print; Online.

6183 ■ *"Ex-MP? Ex-con? Exactly!" in Canadian Business (Vol. 83, October 12, 2010, No. 17, pp. 16)*
Description: British author Jeffrey Archer's novels could be made into movies. Archer sold 250 million books in 63 countries, which include political thrillers, spy novels, and crime capers. Availability: Print; Online.

6184 ■ *"Explainer: The Rules for Shooting on Film Sets" in The Conversation (January 25, 2017)*
URL(s): theconversation.com/explainer-the-rules-for-shooting-on-film-sets-71797
Ed: David Court, Peter Millynn. Released: January 25, 2017. Description: Movies often feature characters using firearms to shoot each other, but who is responsible for ensuring safety on the set? Many safety protocols must be followed, especially in the use of blanks, which has caused injury and even death on some sets. Availability: Online.

6185 ■ *"Free Fall" in Canadian Business (Vol. 79, September 11, 2006, No. 18, pp. 28)*
Description: Second quarter results of Imax Corp are reviewed. The company's performance and its future prospects are also presented. Availability: Print; Online.

6186 ■ *"Georgia Looking to Expand Film Industry Tax Credits" in Atlanta Business Chronicle (June 27, 2014, pp. 3A)*
Pub: American City Business Journals, Inc.
Contact: Mike Olivieri, Executive Vice President
Released: Weekly. Price: $4, introductory 4-week offer(Digital only). Description: The lawmakers of the State of Georgia are looking to expand film tax incentives at a time when many states are eliminating or scaling back their film industry tax credits. A recently created legislative study committee will begin meeting to consider proposals to expand Georgia's film tax credit program to encourage an already rapidly growing industry. Availability: Print; Online.

6187 ■ *"Kokanee Films World's Longest Beer Commercial: Ready for a 90-Minute Feature Starring the Cast of Kokanee?" in Canadian Business (Vol. 85, July 16, 2012, No. 11-12, pp. 11)*
Ed: Jeff Beer. Description: Labatt Brewing Company and advertising agency Grip Ltd. produced a feature-length commercial for the Kokanee beer entitled, "The Movie Out Here", which centers on the reunion of friends in a ski town. As part of the marketing campaign, consumers can submit suggestions for props and set locations, audition for parts and vote online for the soundtrack. Availability: Online.

6188 ■ *"Lessons from SeaWorld's 'Blackfish' Nightmare" in Orlando Business Journal (Vol. 30, January 3, 2014, No. 28, pp. 7)*
Pub: American City Business Journals, Inc.
Contact: Mike Olivieri, Executive Vice President
Released: January 03, 2014. Price: $8, introductory 4-week offer(Digital only). Description: University of Florida's crisis communications specialist and public relations (PR) professor, W. Timothy Coombs, shares his views about the PR backlash from SeaWorld's refusal to participate in the filming of the documentary 'Blackfish'. Coombs believes SeaWorld must create a public statement that defends its character and actions. Availability: Print; Online.

6189 ■ *"The Life Changers" in Canadian Business (Vol. 81, October 27, 2008, No. 18, pp. 86)*
Description: The first season of 'The Life Changers' was produced in September 2007 to feature stories about research and development (R&D) efforts by universities in Atlantic Canada. The program addresses the need to inform the public about university R&D and its outcomes. Availability: Print; Online.

6190 ■ *"Lights, Camera, Action: Tools for Creating Video Blogs" in Inc. (Volume 32, December 2010, No. 09, pp. 57)*
Pub: Mansueto Ventures L.L.C.
Contact: Stephanie Mehta, Chief Executive Officer
Ed: John Brandon. Description: A video blog is a good way to spread company news, talk about products, and stand out among traditional company blogs. New editing software can create two- to four-minute blogs using a webcam and either Windows Live Essentials, Apple iLife 2011, Powerdirector 9 Ultra, or Adobe Visual Communicator 3. Availability: Online.

6191 ■ *"Local Film Industry Stands To Lose Jobs, Millions of Dollars Unless Florida Expands" in Orlando Business Journal (Vol. 30, March 14, 2014, No. 38, pp. 4)*
Pub: American City Business Journals, Inc.
Contact: Mike Olivieri, Executive Vice President
Released: Weekly. Price: $8, introductory 4-week offer(Digital & Print). Description: Central Florida's motion picture and TV production industries are in need of more government incentives. Many TV programs have been cancelled due to lack of this funding. Meanwhile, members of the sectors are set to lobby legislature to pass a $1.2 billion incentive package. Availability: Print; Online.

6192 ■ *"Long Days, Heady Loads: What the Best Boy Does on a Film Set" in The Conversation (October 27, 2019)*
URL(s): theconversation.com/long-days-heavy-loads-what-the-best-boy-does-on-a-film-set-123358
Ed: Lewis Fitz-Gerald. Released: October 27, 2019. Description: Describes the job of a best boy, or the gaffer's assistant, while filming and how the job evolved over time. The lighting in a production is one of the most important aspects of the film and often the best boy needs to be an effective manager and be able to work between apartments to be effective. Availability: Online.

6193 ■ *"Manitoba Tax Credits Create Film and TV Boom" in Canadian Business (Vol. 85, June 11, 2012, No. 10, pp. 11)*
Ed: Lyndsie Bourgon. Description: The province of Manitoba offers a 30 percent film and television tax credit on production costs to filmmakers and a 65 percent tax credit for local qualified labor, posting a record $145 million in 2008 and $90 million in 2011. Other Canadian provinces say the boost in film production is only temporary. Availability: Print; Online.

6194 ■ *"Md.'s Film Industry Professionals have to Leave the State to Find Work: Exiting Stage Left" in Baltimore Business Journal (Vol. 28, June 18, 2010, No. 6, pp. 1)*
Pub: Baltimore Business Journal
Contact: Rhonda Pringle, President
E-mail: rpringle@bizjournals.com
Ed: Scott Dance. Released: Weekly. Description: Film professionals including crew members and actors have been leaving Maryland to find work in other states such as Michigan, Louisiana, and Georgia where bigger budgets and film production incentives are given. Other consequences of this trend in local TV and film production are discussed. Availability: Print.

6195 ■ *"Megachurch Movie Mogul" in Dallas Business Journal (Vol. 37, June 6, 2014, No. 39, pp. 4)*
Pub: American City Business Journals, Inc.
Contact: Mike Olivieri, Executive Vice President
Description: Ordained minister and entrepreneur T.D. Jakes hopes to use the faith-based filmmaking business in Dallas-Fort Worth, Texas as a ministry tool while making huge profits. Jakes says Christian filmmaking represents about 60 percent of his revenue at TDJ Enterprises. Availability: Database; Online.

6196 ■ My Life From Scratch: A Sweet Journey of Starting Over, One Cake at a Time
Pub: Broadway Business

Ed: Gesine Bullock-Prado. **Released:** June 08, 2010. **Price:** $15, paperback; $10.99, e-book. **Description:** Lively account of Old World recipes, Bullock-Prado, a former Hollywood film developer and sister to actress Sandra Bullock, recounts the joys and heartbreak of running her own patisserie in Montpelier, Vermont. Having fled Los Angeles with her husband, Ray for the simpler pleasures of a small town near the Green Mountains, she opened her own bake shop, Gesine Confectionary in 2004, mostly on the fame of the macaroons she refashioned from her German mother's favorite almond treat, mandelhoernchen (and the casual mention of her sister in an interview). Her memoir follows one day in a busy baker's life, from waking at 3 a.m. to prepare the batter and bake her croissants, scones, and sticky buns, before opening her shop at 7 a.m., through the hectic lunch, and 3 p.m. tea time. **Availability:** E-book; Print.

6197 ■ "New Recession-Proof Internet Marketing Package Allows Businesses to Ramp Up Web Traffic and Profits" in PR Newswire (January 25, 2010)
Pub: PR Newswire Association LLC.

Description: Profile of Reel Web Design, a leading marketing firm in New York City that caters to small to medium sized businesses with smaller budgets that need substantial return on investment; Reel Web Design offers video production and submission, web design and maintenance and press release writing among additional services. **Availability:** Online.

6198 ■ "Online Marketing and Promotion of Canadian Films via Social Media Tools: Telefilm Launches New Initiative to Foster Innovative Distribution Strategies" in CNW Group (January 27, 2010)
Pub: Comtex News Network Inc.
Contact: Kan Devnani, President

Description: Telefilm Canada announced the launch of a pilot initiative aimed at encouraging the integration of online marketing and the use of social media tools into means of distribution ahead of a films' theatrical release. During this pilot phase Web-Cine 360 will target French-language feature films. **Availability:** Online.

6199 ■ "People; E-Commerce, Online Games, Mobile Apps" in Advertising Age (Vol. 80, October 19, 2009, No. 35, pp. 14)
Pub: Crain Communications, Inc.
Contact: Jessica Botos, Manager, Marketing
E-mail: jessica.botos@crainsnewyork.com

Ed: Nat Ives. **Description:** Profile of People Magazine and the ways in which the publisher is moving its magazine forward by exploring new concepts in a time of declining newsstand sales and advertising pages; among the strategies are e-commerce such as the brand People Style Watch in which consumers are able highlight clothing and jewelry and then connect to retailers' sites and a channel on Taxi TV, the network of video-touch screens in New Your City taxis. **Availability:** Online.

6200 ■ "Port in the Storm" in Canadian Business (Vol. 81, October 13, 2008, No. 17, pp. 101)

Description: Interport Inc.'s state-of-the-art studio complex in Toronto is discussed. The strong Canadian dollar, along with disputes within the movie industry, are creating challenges for the studio to secure Hollywood projects. Interport plans to compete for Hollywood projects based on quality. **Availability:** Print; Online.

6201 ■ "Q&A: Chuck Hughes, Celebrity Chef" in Canadian Business (Vol. 85, July 16, 2012, No. 11-12, pp. 65)

Ed: Nancy Won. **Description:** Celebrity chef Chuck Hughes feels blessed for the opportunity to work on a new cookbook based on the 'Chuck's Day Off' series and to start filming for a new U.S. show called 'Chuck Eats the Street'. For Hughes, cooking at the restaurant is the most rewarding and fulfilling job of all the things he does. **Availability:** Print; Online.

6202 ■ "The Rage Offstage at Marvel" in Barron's (Vol. 88, June 30, 2008, No. 26, pp. 19)
Pub: Dow Jones & Company Inc.
Contact: Almar Latour, Chief Executive Officer

Ed: Bill Alpert. **Description:** Lawsuits against Marvel Entertainment and Stan Lee are pushing the claims from Peter F. Paul that Stan Lee Media was undone by the actions of the accused. Paul's associates argue that Stan Lee Media owns rights to Marvel characters and that they want half the profits that Marvel is making. **Availability:** Online.

6203 ■ "Ready, Aim, (Cool) Fire" in Saint Louis Business Journal (Vol. 32, September 2, 2011, No. 1, pp. 1)
Pub: Saint Louis Business Journal
Contact: Robert Bobroff, President
E-mail: rbobroff@bizjournals.com

Ed: E.B. Solomont. **Description:** Coolfire Originals' CEO Jeff Keane is co-producing 'Welcome Sweetie Pie's' with Los Angeles, California-based Pilgrims Films and Television Films for the Oprah Winfrey Network. The reality show focuses on restaurant owner Robbie Montgomery of Sweetie Pie's in St. Louis, Missouri. **Availability:** Print; Online.

6204 ■ "Recovery on Tap for 2010?" in Orlando Business Journal (Vol. 26, January 1, 2010, No. 31, pp. 1)
Pub: Orlando Business Journal
Contact: Julie Swyers, Director
E-mail: jswyers@bizjournals.com

Ed: Melanie Stawicki Azam, Richard Bilbao, Christopher Boyd, Anjali Fluker. **Description:** Economic forecasts for Central Florida's leading business sectors in 2010 are presented. These sectors include housing, film and TV, sports business, law, restaurants, aviation, tourism and hospitality, banking and finance, commercial real estate, retail, health care, insurance, higher education, and manufacturing. According to some local executives, Central Florida's economy will slowly recover in 2010. **Availability:** Online.

6205 ■ "Regal Venture Puts Imax Back in the Spotlight" in Globe & Mail (March 13, 2007, pp. B5)

Ed: Shirley Won. **Description:** Imax Corp. has signed new contract with cinema hall operating giant Regal Entertainment Corp. for constructing two more giant screen theaters. Share prices of Imax Corp. have increased sharply after this announcement. **Availability:** Online.

6206 ■ "Revenge of the Scorned Protege" in Canadian Business (Vol. 85, September 17, 2012, No. 14, pp. 48)

Ed: Joanna Pachner. **Released:** September 17, 2012. **Description:** The prospect of a merger between Canadian distributor Alliance Films and international television and independent films distributor Entertainment One Group is expected to control the Canadian market and could rationalize competition in Great Britain. Entertainment One's offerings to broadcasters and other partners will be added with Alliance's 11,000 movie titles.

6207 ■ "ROIonline Announces Streaming Video Products" in Marketing Weekly News (December 5, 2009, pp. 155)
Pub: Investment Weekly News

Description: ROIonline LLC, an Internet marketing firm serving business-to-business and the industrial marketplace, has added streaming video options to the Internet solutions it offers its clients; due to the huge increase of broadband connections, videos are now commonplace on the Internet and can often convey a company's message in a must more efficient, concise and effective way that will engage a website's visitor thus delivering a high return on a company's investment. **Availability:** Print; Mailing list; Online.

6208 ■ The SHOOT Directory for Commercial Production and Postproduction
Contact: Roberta Griefer, Director, Editorial
E-mail: rgriefer@shootonline.com
URL(s): www.shootonline.comvariety411.com/biz/shoot-commercial-production-directory

Ed: Robert Goldrich. **Released:** Annual; latest edition June 2004. **Price:** $99, plus shipping and handling charges. **Description:** Covers companies that provide television commercial production and post-production services, including film video and audio production, duplication, editing, animation, film-to-tape transfer, and standards conversion in the U.S. and Canada. **Entries include:** Company name, address, phone, fax, names and titles of key personnel. **Arrangement:** Classified by type of company. **Indexes:** Geographical. **Availability:** Print; Online.

6209 ■ "Summit, Lions Gate are in Talks to Merge Studios" in Wall Street Journal Eastern Edition (November 29, 2011, pp. B2)
Pub: Dow Jones & Company Inc.
Contact: Almar Latour, Chief Executive Officer

Ed: Erica Orden, Michelle Kung. **Description:** Movie studio Summit Entertainment LLC is in talks with television producer Lions Gate Entertainment Corporation about a possible merger. Previous talks have taken place, but no deal was ever reached. Such a deal would create a large, independent studio able to compete in the market with the big Hollywood giants. **Availability:** Online.

6210 ■ "This Just In. State House Introduces Film-Industry Stimulus Bills" in Crain's Detroit Business (Vol. 24, March 3, 2008, No. 9)
Pub: Crain Communications Inc.
Contact: Barry Asin, President

Description: House Bills 5841-5856 would give Michigan the most competitive incentives in the U.S. to encourage projects by film industry. Provisions of the bill are outlined. **Availability:** Online.

STATISTICAL SOURCES

6211 ■ RMA Annual Statement Studies
Pub: Risk Management Association
Contact: Nancy Foster, President

Released: Annual. **Description:** Contains composite balance sheets and income statements for more than 360 industries, including the accounting, auditing, and bookkeeping industries. Also contains five years of comparative historical data for discerning trends. Includes 16 commonly used ratios, computed for most of the size groupings for nearly every industry.

TRADE PERIODICALS

6212 ■ ICG Magazine
Pub: International Cinematographers Guild
Contact: John Lindley, President
URL(s): www.icgmagazine.com/web
Facebook: www.facebook.com/theicgmag
X (Twitter): x.com/theicgmag
Instagram: www.instagram.com/theicgmag

Ed: David Geffner. **Released:** Monthly **Price:** $24, for 1 year online 10 digital issues; $88, Single issue. **Description:** Trade magazine covering cinematography lighting techniques in film and video. **Availability:** Print; PDF; Download; Online.

6213 ■ Journal of Film and Video (JFV)
Pub: University Film and Video Association
Contact: Wenhwa Tsao, President
E-mail: wtsao@colum.edu
URL(s): www.press.uillinois.edu/journals/?id=jfvufva.site-ym.com/page/journal

Ed: Stephen Tropiano, Michael Clarke. **Released:** Quarterly; spring, summer, fall, and winter. **Price:** $95, Individuals for print & online; $75, Individuals for print; $75, Individuals for online; $75, Institutions for print; $20, Single issue for back issue. **Description:** Film and video journal. **Availability:** Print; PDF; Download; Online.

Small Business Profiles — Film and Video Production Operation ■ 6223

VIDEO/AUDIO MEDIA

6214 ■ *How I Built My Small Business: Ross Jacobson - Behind the Scenes: Navigating Hollywood as an Indie Producer with 3311 Productions*
URL(s): www.annemcginty.com/transcripts/rossjacobson
Ed: Anne McGinty. **Released:** March 26, 2024.
Description: Podcast features the founder of a production company.

6215 ■ *How I Built This: ARRAY: Filmmaker Ava DuVernay*
URL(s): wondery.com/shows/how-i-built-this/episode/10386-array-filmmaker-ava-duvernay-2021
Ed: Guy Raz. **Description:** Podcast discusses how Ava DuVernay evolved from a publicity agent to the owner of a production and distribution company and helping change how movies get made and who gets to make them. .

CONSULTANTS

6216 ■ Continental Film Business Solutions (CFPC)
1466 Riverside Dr., Ste. E
Chattanooga, TN 37406
Ph: (423)622-1193
Fax: (423)629-0853
Co. E-mail: info@continentalfilm.com
URL: http://www.continentalfilm.com
Description: Firm offers expertise in system designing and integrating audiovisual systems and specializes in video production, video conferencing, system design and integration, digital signage, technical consultation, AV services and display calibration.
Scope: Firm offers expertise in system designing and integrating audiovisual systems and specializes in video production, video conferencing, system design and integration, digital signage, technical consultation, AV services and display calibration.
Founded: 1951.

6217 ■ Full Voice
9912B Holmes Rd., Ste. 237
Kansas City, MO 64131-4206
Description: Vocal performance training firm offering consulting services and personal training sessions in the implementation of effective vocal communication techniques for the development of business relationships and career enhancement. **Scope:** Vocal performance training firm offering consulting services and personal training sessions in the implementation of effective vocal communication techniques for the development of business relationships and career enhancement. **Publications:** "You Can Sound Like You Know What You're Saying". **Training:** You Can Sound Like You Know What You're Saying; The Psychology of Vocal Performance; Security. . .the Ability to Accept Change; Knowing. . .the Key to Relaxed Public Communication; The Effective Voice for Customer Service Enhancement; You Can Speak With Conviction; How To Make Yours a Championship Team; Functional English For Foreign Trade.
Special Services: FULL VOICE™.

FRANCHISES AND BUSINESS OPPORTUNITIES

6218 ■ Home Video Studio (HVS)
Apex, NC 27502
Free: 800-660-8273
Co. E-mail: info@homevideostudio.com
URL: http://apex.homevideostudio.com/169
Contact: Robert Hanley, President
Description: Firm offers video production services.
Founded: 1991. **Financial Assistance:** Yes **Training:** Yes.

COMPUTERIZED DATABASES

6219 ■ *Baseline Intelligence*
URL(s): www.baselineintel.com
Type: Full-text; Numeric.

LIBRARIES

6220 ■ California Film Commission (CFC) - Location Resource Center Library
7080 Hollywood Blvd., Ste. 900
Los Angeles, CA 90028
URL: http://film.ca.gov/locations/location-professionals
Scope: Motion picture film locations. **Services:** Library open to the public. **Founded:** 1985. **Holdings:** 500 books; 300,000 photographs.

6221 ■ University of North Carolina School of the Arts - Semans Library
1533 S Main St.
Winston Salem, NC 27127-2738
Ph: (336)770-3399
URL: http://www.uncsa.edu/faculty-staff-hub/around-campus/facilities-maintenance/design-and-construction-projects/semans-renovation.aspx
Description: Library collects, organizes, describes and preserves access to records of permanent administrative, legal, fiscal and historical value.
Scope: Art and design. **Services:** Interlibrary loan; library open to the public; copying; printing; scanning.
Founded: 1965. **Holdings:** Books; periodicals; music and media.

6222 ■ Watkins College of Art, Design, & Film Library
1900 Belmont Blvd.
Nashville, TN 37212
Co. E-mail: librarian@watkins.edu
URL: http://www.watkins.edu
Description: Watkins Library is a comprehensive nerve center of resources for Watkins students, staff, and faculty. **Scope:** Film; fine arts; visual arts; graphic design; photography. **Services:** Interlibrary loan; library open to the public for reference use only. **Holdings:** Books; films.

AWARDS AND HONORS

6223 ■ Stuntmen's Association of Motion Pictures (SAMP)
5200 Lankershim Blvd., Ste. 190
North Hollywood, CA 91601
Ph: (818)766-4334
Fax: (818)766-5943
Co. E-mail: stuntmen@sbcglobal.net
URL: http://www.stuntmen.com
Contact: Alex Daniels, Chief Executive Officer
Facebook: www.facebook.com/sampstuntmen
X (Twitter): x.com/SampStuntmen
Instagram: www.instagram.com/sampstuntmen
YouTube: www.youtube.com/channel/UCFnWcKJFXLEG6RxLdfaAGCw
Description: Men who do stunt work in motion pictures and television and who belong to the Screen Actors Guild and/or the American Federation of Television and Radio Artists Associations activities are primarily fraternal and charitable. Also seeks to improve working conditions for stuntmen and encourages members to uphold high professional standards.
Founded: 1961. **Geographic Preference:** National.

Financial Planning Service

START-UP INFORMATION

6224 ■ *"3 Question for Stephen Purpura, CEO of the Big-Data Startup Context Relevant"* in *Puget Sound Business Journal* (Vol. 35, May 23, 2014, No. 5, pp. 10)
Pub: American City Business Journals, Inc.
Contact: Mike Olivieri, Executive Vice President
Description: Stephne Purpura, CEO of Seattle, Washington-based big data startup, Context Relevant, shares his vision for the company in the financial industry data market. He explains why they decided to seek strategic investment in the company. **Availability:** Online.

6225 ■ *"On Their Own: Bronx High School Students Open a Bank Branch"* in *Black Enterprise* (Vol. 38, February 2008, No. 7, pp. 42)
Pub: Earl G. Graves Ltd.
Contact: Earl Graves, Jr., President
Ed: Jessica Jones. **Description:** Students at Fordham Leadership Academy for Business and Technology in New York City opened a student-run bank branch at their high school. The business paid high school seniors $11 per hour to work as tellers. Students were also taught interviewing basics. **Availability:** Online.

ASSOCIATIONS AND OTHER ORGANIZATIONS

6226 ■ **Accounting and Finance Benchmarking Consortium (AFBC)**
4606 FM 1960 Rd. W, Ste. 250
Houston, TX 77069-9949
Ph: (281)440-5044
URL: http://www.afbc.org
Description: Promotes the use of benchmarking, wherein businesses compare their processes with those of their competitors, as a means of improving corporate efficiency and profitability among accounting and finance managers; facilitates exchange of information among members; conducts target operations, procurement, development, and maintenance studies; and identifies model business practices. **Founded:** 1998. **Geographic Preference:** National.

6227 ■ **ADVOCIS**
10 Lower Spadina Ave.
Toronto, ON, Canada M5V 2Z2
Ph: (416)444-5251
Free: 877-773-6765
Co. E-mail: communications@advocis.ca
URL: http://www.advocis.ca
Contact: Greg Pollock, President
Facebook: www.facebook.com/pg/advocis/about
Linkedin: www.linkedin.com/company/advocis
X (Twitter): x.com/Advocis
YouTube: www.youtube.com/user/AdvocisTFAAC
Description: Voluntary professional membership association of financial advisors and planners in Canada. **Founded:** 1906. **Publications:** *Advisor Voice* (Monthly); *FORUM* (Quarterly); *Advocis* (Monthly). **Geographic Preference:** National.

6228 ■ **Canadian Association of Insolvency and Restructuring Professionals (CAIRP)**
277 Wellington St. W
Toronto, ON, Canada M5V 3H2
Ph: (647)695-3090
Co. E-mail: info@cairp.ca
URL: http://cairp.ca
Contact: Anne Wettlaufer, President
E-mail: anne.wettlaufer@cairp.ca
Facebook: www.facebook.com/CAIRP.ca
Linkedin: www.linkedin.com/company/canadian-association-of-insolvency-and-restructuring-professionals
X (Twitter): x.com/CAIRP_ACPIR
Description: Promotes excellence in the field of insolvency and business recovery services. Lobbies for reform of bankruptcy laws; sponsors continuing professional development courses; delivers qualification program for bankruptcy transfers in conjunction with the federal government. **Founded:** 1979. **Publications:** *Rebuilding Success* (Semiannual). **Awards:** Lloyd Houlden Fellowship (Annual). **Geographic Preference:** National.

6229 ■ **Canadian Institute of Financial Planning (CIFP)**
390 Brant St., Ste. 501
Burlington, ON, Canada L7R 4J4
Free: 866-635-5526
Co. E-mail: cifpgeneral@cifps.ca
URL: http://www.cifp.ca/Desktop/English/General/Home.asp
Contact: Keith Costello, President
Description: Works to promote excellence in the field of financial planning. Facilitates communication and cooperation among members, which includes financial planning professionals. Sponsors continuing professional education courses. **Geographic Preference:** National.

6230 ■ **Canadian Investor Relations Institute (CIRI) [Institut Canadien de Relations avec les Investisseurs]**
PO Box 76053
Oakville, ON, Canada L6M 3H5
Ph: (416)364-8200
Co. E-mail: enquiries@ciri.org
URL: http://www.ciri.org
Contact: Yvette Lokker, President
E-mail: ylokker@ciri.org
Facebook: www.facebook.com/CIRI.org
Linkedin: www.linkedin.com/company/canadianinvestorrelationsinstitute
X (Twitter): x.com/CIRINational
YouTube: www.youtube.com/user/CIRINational
Description: Executives responsible for communication between public corporations, investors and the financial community; dedicated to advancing the stature and credibility of the investor relations profession and the competency of members. **Publications:** *Newsline* (Bimonthly). **Geographic Preference:** National.

6231 ■ **Financial Managers Society (FMS)**
7918 Jones Branch Dr., 4th Fl.
McLean, VA 22102
Ph: (312)578-1300
Fax: (312)578-1308
Co. E-mail: info@fmsinc.org
URL: http://www.fmsinc.org
Contact: Alana Vartanian, President
E-mail: avartanian@fmsinc.org
Facebook: www.facebook.com/FinancialManagersSociety
Linkedin: www.linkedin.com/company/financial-managers-society
X (Twitter): x.com/FMS_Inc
Instagram: www.instagram.com/fms_inc
Description: Works for the needs of finance and accounting professionals from banks, thrifts and credit unions. Offers career-enhancing education, specialized publications, national leadership opportunities and worldwide connections with other industry professionals. **Founded:** 1948. **Publications:** *Record Retention Manual*; *Membership & Peer Consulting Directory*; *Financial Managers Society--Membership and Peer Consulting Directory* (Annual). **Educational Activities:** FMS Forum (Annual); The Finance & Accounting Forum for Financial Institutions (Annual). **Geographic Preference:** National.

6232 ■ **Financial Planning Association (FPA)**
1290 Broadway, Ste. 1625
Denver, CO 80203
Ph: (303)759-4900
Free: 800-322-4237
Co. E-mail: info@onefpa.org
URL: http://www.financialplanningassociation.org
Contact: Claudia Cypher Kane, President
Facebook: www.facebook.com/FinancialPlanningAssociation
Linkedin: www.linkedin.com/company/financial-planning-association
X (Twitter): x.com/fpassociation
YouTube: www.youtube.com/fpatelevision
Description: Works to support the financial planning process in order to help people achieve their goals and dreams. Believes that everyone needs objective advice to make smart financial decisions. **Founded:** 2000. **Publications:** *FPA This Week* (Weekly); *FPA Journal of Financial Planning* (Monthly). **Geographic Preference:** National.

6233 ■ **Financial Women's Association of New York (FWA)**
The FWA of New York Inc.
576 Fifth Ave., Ste. 903
New York, NY 10036-4762
Ph: (212)533-2141
Co. E-mail: fwaoffice@fwa.org
URL: http://www.fwa.org
Contact: Hermina Batson, President

E-mail: fwapresident@fwa.org
Facebook: www.facebook.com/fwany1956
Linkedin: www.linkedin.com/company/1636499
X (Twitter): x.com/FWANY
Instagram: www.instagram.com/fwanyc
Pinterest: www.pinterest.co.uk/pin/2441796110
16168791

Description: Persons of professional status in the field of finance in the New York metropolitan area. Works to promote and maintain high professional standards in the financial and business communities; provide an opportunity for members to enhance one another's professional contacts; achieve recognition of the contribution of women to the financial and business communities; encourage other women to seek professional positions within the financial and business communities. Activities include educational trips to foreign countries; college internship program including foreign student exchange; high school mentorship program; Washington and international briefings; placement service for members. Maintains speakers' bureau. **Founded:** 1956. **Publications:** *Financial Women's Association of New York--Directory* (Annual); *FWA Connections* (11/year); *Financial Women's Association of New York--Directory* (Annual). **Awards:** FWA Women of the Year Award (Annual). **Geographic Preference:** National.

6234 ■ Fondation Scolaire de l'Institut Canadien du Credit [Canadian Credit Institute Educational Foundation (CCIEF)]
c/o Credit Institute of Canada
219 Dufferin St., Ste. 216C
Toronto, ON, Canada M6K 3J1
Free: 888-447-3324
Co. E-mail: geninfo@creditedu.org
URL: http://www.creditedu.org/secure/EDUCATION/donationform.cfm
Contact: Nawshad Khadaroo, General Manager
E-mail: nkhadaroo@creditedu.org

Description: Financial institutions and providers of financial planning services. Promotes adherence to high standards of ethics and practice by members. Provides financial support to credit initiatives. **Founded:** 1967. **Geographic Preference:** National.

6235 ■ FORUM
10 Lower Spadina Ave.
Toronto, ON, Canada M5V 2Z2
Ph: (416)444-5251
Free: 877-773-6765
Co. E-mail: communications@advocis.ca
URL: http://www.advocis.ca
Contact: Greg Pollock, President
URL(s): www.advocis.ca/forum-magazine

Released: Quarterly **Description:** Contains columns and features on practice management, investing, insurance, financial planning, succession planning, and estate and tax planning. **Availability:** Print; PDF; Download; Online.

6236 ■ LIMRA International
LIMRA International
300 Day Hill Rd.
Windsor, CT 06095
Ph: (860)285-7789
Co. E-mail: customer.service@limra.com
URL: http://www.limra.com
Contact: David Levenson, President
Facebook: www.facebook.com/LIMRANews
Linkedin: www.linkedin.com/company/limra
X (Twitter): x.com/LIMRA
YouTube: www.youtube.com/user/limraloma

Description: Provides executive and field management development schools and seminars. Offers human resource development consulting services, including needs analysis and program design, evaluation, and implementation. **Scope:** Company research services apply scientific techniques to the areas of performance appraisal, manpower utilization, employee and consumer opinion sampling and market analysis. **Founded:** 1916. **Publications:** "28 Ways to Improve Your Sales Performance"; "Advanced Selection Interview Guide"; "LIMRA's Market Facts"; "Looking Ahead"; "Cross Selling". **Training:** Compensation and Motivation Plans that Deliver Results, Bangkok, Aug, 2009; Sales Compensation Seminar, Simsbury, May, 2009; Growth by Design; Strategic Marketing Review. **Educational Activities:** LIMRA International Conference (Annual). **Geographic Preference:** Multinational. **Special Services:** Career Profile.

6237 ■ National Association of Personal Financial Advisors (NAPFA)
8700 W Bryn Mawr Ave., Ste. 700N
Chicago, IL 60631
Ph: (847)483-5400
Free: 888-333-6659
Co. E-mail: info@napfa.org
URL: http://www.napfa.org
Contact: Geoffrey Brown, Chief Executive Officer
Facebook: www.facebook.com/NAPFAFeeOnly
X (Twitter): x.com/NAPFA
YouTube: www.youtube.com/channel/UCz5dfb
61JHACZuH3lNSwmwA

Description: Full-time, fee-only financial planners. Serves as a network for fee-only planners to discuss issues relating to practice management, client services, and investments selection. Works to encourage and advance the practice of fee-only financial planning by developing the skills of members and increasing the awareness of fee-only financial planning of consumers. **Founded:** 1983. **Publications:** *NAPFA Advisor* (Monthly); *NAPFA Membership Directory*; *NAPFA NewsLink*. **Awards:** NAPFA Special Membership Award (Irregular); NAPFA Special Achievement Award (Periodic). **Geographic Preference:** National.

6238 ■ Rebuilding Success
277 Wellington St. W
Toronto, ON, Canada M5V 3H2
Ph: (647)695-3090
Co. E-mail: info@cairp.ca
URL: http://cairp.ca
Contact: Anne Wettlaufer, President
E-mail: anne.wettlaufer@cairp.ca
URL(s): cairp.ca/rebuilding-success-magazine.html

Released: Semiannual **Availability:** PDF; Download; Online.

EDUCATIONAL PROGRAMS

6239 ■ WBENC Industry Spotlight
URL(s): www.wbenc.org/programs/industry-spotlight-series

Frequency: Irregular. **Description:** A series of webinars and resources for women business owners in order to learn about new trends, innovations, and sources of support in the automotive, food & beverage, utilities, healthcare, energy, financial services, and manufacturing sectors. **Principal Exhibits:** A series of webinars and resources for women business owners in order to learn about new trends, innovations, and sources of support in the automotive, food & beverage, utilities, healthcare, energy, financial services, and manufacturing sectors.

REFERENCE WORKS

6240 ■ "3Par: Storing Up Value" in Barron's (Vol. 90, August 30, 2010, No. 35, pp. 30)
Pub: Barron's Editorial & Corporate Headquarters

Ed: Mark Veverka. **Description:** Dell and Hewlett Packard are both bidding for data storage company 3Par. The acquisition would help Dell and Hewlett Packard provide customers with a one-stop shop as customers move to a private cloud in the Internet. **Availability:** Online.

6241 ■ "5 Things You Should Know If Your Bank Fails" in Black Enterprise (Vol. 41, December 2010, No. 5, pp. 29)
Pub: Earl G. Graves Ltd.
Contact: Earl Graves, Jr., President

Ed: John Simons. **Description:** The Federal Deposit Insurance Corporation announced that the number of banks in trouble has reached the highest level since March 1993. Advice from the FDIC is cited. Statistical data included. **Availability:** Online.

6242 ■ "113D Filings: Investors Report to the SEC" in Barron's (Vol. 88, March 24, 2008, No. 12, pp. M13)
Pub: Dow Jones & Company Inc.
Contact: Almar Latour, Chief Executive Officer

Released: April 02, 2016. **Description:** HealthCor Management called as problematic the plan of Magellan Health Services to use its high cash balances for acquisitions. Carlson Capital discussed with Energy Partners possible changes in the latter's board. Investor Carl Icahn suggested that Enzon Pharmaceuticals consider selling itself or divest some of its assets. **Availability:** Print; Online.

6243 ■ "A 16-Year Housing Slump? It Could Happen" in Barron's (Vol. 88, March 17, 2008, No. 11, pp. 27)
Pub: Dow Jones & Company Inc.
Contact: Almar Latour, Chief Executive Officer

Ed: Gene Epstein. **Description:** Housing remains a good protection against inflation but over very long periods. Inflation-adjusted stock prices did even better but have greater volatility. Commodities, on the other hand, underperformed both housing and stocks as inflation hedges. House prices tend to rise faster than the consumer price index is because land is inherently limited. **Availability:** Online.

6244 ■ "401(k) Keys to Stable Value" in Barron's (Vol. 88, March 10, 2008, No. 10, pp. 40)
Pub: Dow Jones & Company Inc.
Contact: Almar Latour, Chief Executive Officer

Ed: Tom Sullivan. **Description:** Stable-value funds offer investors stability in a period of volatility in financial markets, attracting $888 million in funds. The Securities and Exchange Commission approved the launch of actively managed exchange-traded funds. **Availability:** Online.

6245 ■ "ACE Agrees to Pay Out $266 Million to Investors" in Globe & Mail (February 17, 2006, pp. B1)

Ed: Brent Jang. **Description:** Canada-based commercial aviation firm ACE Aviation Holdings has agreed to pay 266 million dollars to its investors after filing a bankruptcy one year ago. Complete details of this pay off are discussed. **Availability:** Online.

6246 ■ "Advisory Firm Launches Own Foundation" in Financial Advisor (November 1, 2019)
URL(s): www.fa-mag.com/news/advisory-firm-launches-own-foundation-52360.html?issue=323

Ed: Jeff Schlegel. **Released:** November 01, 2019. **Description:** With the 50th anniversary of wealth management firm Bailard Inc. looming, the firm decided to start its own foundation, the Bailard Foundation. The goal is to create a fund where attorneys have discretion to give grants to clients who are about to lose their home. **Availability:** Online.

6247 ■ "Ag Firms Harvest Revenue Growth" in The Business Journal-Serving Metropolitan Kansas City (Vol. 26, July 18, 2008, No. 45, pp. 1)

Description: Five of the biggest agricultural companies in the Kansas City area, except one, reported multibillion-dollar revenue increases in 2007. The companies, which include Lansing Trade Group, posted a combined $9.5 billion revenue growth. The factors that affected the revenue increase in the area's agricultural companies, such as prices and high demand, are also examined. **Availability:** Print; Online.

6248 ■ "Air Canada Boss Gains $3.5-Million in Options" in Globe & Mail (January 19, 2007, pp. B5)

Ed: Brent Jang. **Description:** Air Canada chairman Robert Milton's sale of 200,000 shares in stock options is discussed. **Availability:** Online.

6249 ■ "Algoma Resolves Hedge Fund Fight" in Globe & Mail (March 8, 2006, pp. B1)

Ed: Greg Keenan. **Description:** Algoma Steel Inc. has ended a dispute with Paulson and Co., a New

York hedge fund, by offering to pay $200 million special dividend, appointing new directors, and continue to go for a sale. **Availability:** Print; Online.

6250 ■ *"All Eyes On Iris" in Canadian Business (Vol. 81, July 22, 2008, No. 12-13, pp. 20)*
Description: Provincial governments in Canada are believed to be awaiting Alberta Finance Minister Iris Evans' financial and investment policies as well as Evans' development of a new saving strategy. Alberta is the only Canadian province that is in position to invest in sovereign wealth funds after it eliminated its debt in 2005. **Availability:** Print; Online.

6251 ■ *"All-Star Advice 2010" in Black Enterprise (Vol. 41, October 2010, No. 3, pp. 97)*
Pub: Earl G. Graves Ltd.
Contact: Earl Graves, Jr., President
Ed: Renita Burns, Sheiresa Ngo, Marcia Wade Talbert. **Description:** Financial experts share tips on real estate, investing, taxes, insurance and debt management. **Availability:** Online.

6252 ■ *"All-Star Execs: Top CEO: Gordon Nixon" in Canadian Business (Vol. 80, November 24, 2008, No. 22, pp. 9)*
Pub: Rogers Media Inc.
Contact: Neil Spivak, Chief Executive Officer
Ed: Jeff Sanford. **Description:** Royal Bank of Canada (RBC) CEO, Gordon Nixon, believes the Canadian financial services segment is heavily regulated. Nixon also feels that it has become difficult for local banks to enter the market since foreign banks can easily come in and compete with them. His views on RBC's success are provided. **Availability:** Print; Online.

6253 ■ *"America's Top 40 Wealth Management Firms" in Barron's (Vol. 92, September 17, 2012, No. 38, pp. 28)*
Pub: Dow Jones & Company Inc.
Contact: Almar Latour, Chief Executive Officer
Description: The 40 largest wealth managers in the US are ranked according to client assets held in accounts worth $5 million or more as of June 30, 2012. Bank of America Global Wealth and Investment Management remained the largest, with $792 billion in assets under management. **Availability:** Online.

6254 ■ *"The Annual Entitlement Lecture Medicare Elephantiasis" in Barron's (March 31, 2008)*
Pub: Dow Jones & Company Inc.
Contact: Almar Latour, Chief Executive Officer
Ed: Thomas G. Donlan. **Description:** Expenditures on Medicare hospital insurance and the revenues available to pay for it have led to a gap of capital valued at $38.6 trillion. Slashing the benefits or raising taxes will not solve the gap which exists unless the government saves the money and invests it in private markets. **Availability:** Online.

6255 ■ *"Apartment Tower in River North Fetches More Than $90 Million" in Crain's Chicago Business (Vol. 34, October 24, 2011, No. 42, pp. 17)*
Pub: Crain Communications Inc.
Contact: Barry Asin, President
Ed: Alby Gallun. **Description:** Apartment tower in River North was sold for over $90 million to a Texas pension fund adviser. Details are included. **Availability:** Online.

6256 ■ *"Are You Ready for Dow 20,000?" in Barron's (Vol. 88, March 24, 2008, No. 12, pp. 26)*
Pub: Dow Jones & Company Inc.
Contact: Almar Latour, Chief Executive Officer
Ed: Jonathan R. Laing. **Description:** Stock strategist James Finucane forecasts that the Dow Jones Industrial Average will rise from its 12,361 level to as high as 20,000 from 2008 to 2009. He believes that stock liquidation and a buildup of cash provide the perfect conditions for a huge rally. **Availability:** Online.

6257 ■ *"As Capital Gains Tax Hike Looms, Baltimore's Merger Activity Percolates" in Baltimore Business Journal (Vol. 28, August 27, 2010, No. 16, pp. 1)*
Pub: Baltimore Business Journal
Contact: Rhonda Pringle, President
E-mail: rpringle@bizjournals.com
Ed: Scott Dance. **Description:** Concerns for higher capital gains taxes in 2011 have been provoking buyers and sellers to engage in mergers and acquisitions activity, which is expected to gain momentum before the end of 2010. Companies that had saved cash during the recession have been taking advantage of the buyer's market. Other trends in local and national mergers and acquisitions activity are presented. **Availability:** Print.

6258 ■ *"Asia Breathes a Sigh of Relief" in Business Week (September 22, 2008, No. 4100, pp. 32)*
Description: Foreign bankers, such as those in Asia, that had been investing heavily in the United States began to worry as the housing crisis deepened and the impact on Freddie Mac and Fannie Mae became increasingly clear. Due to the government bailout, however, central banks will most likely continue to buy American debt. **Availability:** Print; Online.

6259 ■ *"Au Revoir Or Goodbye?" in Barron's (Vol. 88, July 14, 2008, No. 28, pp. 5)*
Pub: Dow Jones & Company Inc.
Contact: Almar Latour, Chief Executive Officer
Ed: Alan Abelson. **Description:** Former Senator Phil Gramm's opinion that the U.S. is a "nation of whiners" as they moan about recession is another example of the disconnection between Washington and Wall Street on one hand and the real world on the other. It would be a catastrophe for most of the world if Fannie Mae and Freddie Mac were to go under and take their trillions of mortgage debt with them. **Availability:** Online.

6260 ■ *"Avalon Advisors Opens Alamo City Office" in San Antonio Business Journal (Vol. 28, April 18, 2014, No. 10, pp. 7)*
Pub: American City Business Journals, Inc.
Contact: Mike Olivieri, Executive Vice President
Released: Weekly. **Price:** $4, Introductory 4-week offer(Digital only). **Description:** Avalon Advisors LLC opened an office in San Antonio, Texas. The wealth management firm has been serving prominent clients in the city over the past few years. Rob McCaline, director of the company's new office, reveals that the business enjoyed tremendous growth in the city through referrals by existing clients. **Availability:** Print; Online.

6261 ■ *"BABs in Bond Land" in Barron's (Vol. 89, July 6, 2009, No. 27, pp. 14)*
Pub: Dow Jones & Company Inc.
Contact: Almar Latour, Chief Executive Officer
Ed: Jim McTague. **Description:** American Recovery and Reinvestment Act has created taxable Build America Bonds (BAB) to finance new construction projects. The issuance of the two varieties of taxable BABs is expected to benefit the municipal bond market. **Availability:** Online.

6262 ■ *"Back in the Race. New Fund Manager Has Whipped Sentinel International Equity Back into Shape" in Barron's (Vol. 88, March 17, 2008, No. 11, pp. 43)*
Pub: Dow Jones & Company Inc.
Contact: Almar Latour, Chief Executive Officer
Ed: Leslie P. Norton. **Description:** Katherine Schapiro was able to get Sentinel International Equity's Morningstar classification to blended fund from a value fund rating after joining Sentinel from her former jobs at Strong Overseas Fund. Schapiro aims to benefit from the global rebalancing as the U.S.'s share of the world economy shrinks. **Availability:** Online.

6263 ■ *"Back-Tested ETFs Draw Assets, Flub Returns" in Barron's (Vol. 92, July 23, 2012, No. 30, pp. 26)*
Pub: Dow Jones & Company Inc.
Contact: Almar Latour, Chief Executive Officer
Ed: Janet Paskin. **Description:** New exchange-traded funds are attracting investors by using 'back-tested' data offered by the indexes they track. Investors are substituting real performance for these hypothetical returns, which measure past performance of indexes had they been in existence. **Availability:** Online.

6264 ■ *"Bad Loans Start Piling Up" in Crain's New York Business (Vol. 24, January 6, 2008, No. 1, pp. 2)*
Pub: Crain Communications, Inc.
Contact: Jessica Botos, Manager, Marketing
E-mail: jessica.botos@crainsnewyork.com
Ed: Tom Fredrickson. **Description:** Problems in the subprime mortgage industry have extended to other lending activities as evidenced by bank charge-offs on bad commercial and industrial loans which have more than doubled in the third quarter.

6265 ■ *"Bad Paper" in Canadian Business (Vol. 80, November 19, 2007, No. 23, pp. 34)*
Description: The Canadian government froze the market for non-bank asset-backed commercial paper (ABCP) August 2007, which means holders will be unable to withdraw investments. The crisis and value of ABCP are discussed. **Availability:** Print; Online.

6266 ■ *"Bank Buys May Heat Up In Birmingham" in Birmingham Business Journal (Vol. 31, May 9, 2014, No. 19, pp. 8)*
Pub: American City Business Journals, Inc.
Contact: Mike Olivieri, Executive Vice President
Released: Weekly. **Price:** $4, introductory 4-week offer(Digital & Print). **Description:** The banking industry in Birmingham, Alabama is poised for more mergers and acquisitions in the next two years as bank failures drop and potential sellers look for protection from increasing regulations. Experts suggest Birmingham is an attractive market for potential buyers because of its rich history as a top financial center and its stable economic environment. **Availability:** Print; Online.

6267 ■ *"Bank On It: New Year, New Estate Plan" in Hawaii Business (Vol. 53, February 2008, No. 8, pp. 54)*
Pub: PacificBasin Communications
Contact: Chuck Tindle, Director
E-mail: chuckt@pacificbasin.net
Ed: Antony M. Orme. **Description:** Discusses the start of the new year which can be a time to revise wills and estate plans as failure to do so may create problems of unequal inheritance and increase in estate tax exemption, which could disinherit beneficiaries. Other circumstances that can prompt changes in wills and estate plans are presented. **Availability:** Print; Online.

6268 ■ *"The Bankrate Double Play, Bankrate Is Having Its Best Quarter Yet" in Barron's (Vol. 88, March 24, 2008, No. 12, pp. 27)*
Pub: Dow Jones & Company Inc.
Contact: Almar Latour, Chief Executive Officer
Ed: Neil A. Martin. **Description:** Shares of Bankrate may rise as much as 25 percent from their level of $45.08 a share due to a strong cash flow and balance sheet. The company's Internet business remains strong despite weakness in the online advertising industry and is a potential takeover target. **Availability:** Online.

6269 ■ *"Barbarians Set Bar Low With Lowly Canadian Telco" in Globe & Mail (March 31, 2007, pp. B1)*
Ed: Derek DeCloet. **Description:** The efforts of the private equity fund Kohlberg, Kravis, Roberts and Co. to acquire the Canadian telecommunications firm BCE are described. **Availability:** Online.

6270 ■ "Bargain Hunting In Vietnam" in Barron's (Vol. 88, July 14, 2008, No. 28, pp. M6)
Pub: Dow Jones & Company Inc.
Contact: Almar Latour, Chief Executive Officer
Ed: Elliot Wilson. **Description:** Vietnam's economy grew by just 6.5 percent for the first half of 2008 and its balance of payments ballooned to $14.4 billion. The falling stock prices in the country is a boon for bargain hunters and investing in the numerous domestic funds is one way of investing in the country. Some shares that investors are taking an interest in are also discussed. **Availability:** Online.

6271 ■ "Battered U.S. Auto Makers in Grip of Deeper Sales Slump" in Globe & Mail (April 4, 2007, pp. B1)
Ed: Greg Keenan. **Description:** The fall in Canadian sales and market share of Ford Motor Co., General Motors Corp. and Chrysler Group is discussed. **Availability:** Print; Online.

6272 ■ "Baupost Group Pours Money into Charlotte Real Estate Projects" in Charlotte Business Journal (Vol. 25, December 3, 2010, No. 37, pp. 1)
Pub: Charlotte Business Journal
Contact: Robert Morris, Editor
E-mail: rmorris@bizjournals.com
Ed: Will Boye. **Description:** Boston-based hedge fund Baupost Group has been financing real estate project in Charlotte, North Carolina including more than 80 acres just north of uptown. Aside from purchasing the $23.8 million note for the Rosewood Condominiums from Regions Financial Corporation, the Baupost Group is also negotiating with Regions to buy the $93.9 million debt of the EipCentre real estate project. **Availability:** Print; Online.

6273 ■ "BDC Launches New Online Business Advice Centre" in Marketwired (July 13, 2010)
Pub: Comtex News Network Inc.
Contact: Kan Devnani, President
Description: The Business Development Bank of Canada (BDC) offers entrepreneurs the chance to use their new online BDC Advice Centre in order to seek advice regarding the challenges of entrepreneurship. Free online business tools and information to help both startups and established firms are also provided. **Availability:** Print; Online.

6274 ■ "The Bear Stearns-JPMorgan Deal - Rhymes with Steal - Of A Lifetime" in Barron's (Vol. 88, March 24, 2008, No. 12, pp. 24)
Pub: Dow Jones & Company Inc.
Contact: Almar Latour, Chief Executive Officer
Ed: Andrew Bary. **Description:** JPMorgan Chase's impending acquisition of Bear Stearns for $2.50 a share is a huge steal for the former. JPMorgan is set to acquire a company with a potential annual earnings of $1 billion while the Federal Reserve funds Bear's illiquid assets by providing $30 billion in non-recourse loans. **Availability:** Online.

6275 ■ "The Bear's Back" in Barron's (Vol. 88, July 7, 2008, No. 27, pp. 17)
Pub: Dow Jones & Company Inc.
Contact: Almar Latour, Chief Executive Officer
Ed: Randall W. Forsyth, Vito Racanelli. **Description:** US stock markets have formally entered the bear market after the Dow Jones Industrial Average dropped 20 percent from its high as of June 2008. Investors remain uncertain as to how long the bear market will persist, especially with the US economy on the edge of recession. **Availability:** Online.

6276 ■ "The Beauty of Banking's Big Ugly" in Barron's (Vol. 89, July 27, 2009, No. 30, pp. 31)
Pub: Dow Jones & Company Inc.
Contact: Almar Latour, Chief Executive Officer
Ed: Andrew Bary. **Description:** Appeal of the shares of Citigroup comes from its sharp discount to its tangible book value and the company's positive attributes include a strong capital position, high loan-loss reserves, and their appealing global-consumer. The shares have the potential to generate nice profits and decent stock gains as the economy turns. **Availability:** Online.

6277 ■ "Behind the Numbers: When It Comes to Earnings, Look for Quality, Not Just Quantity" in Black Enterprise (Vol. 38, July 2008, pp. 35)
Pub: Earl G. Graves Ltd.
Contact: Earl Graves, Jr., President
Description: It is important for investors to examine the quality of a company's earnings rather than fixate on the quantity of those earnings. Advice is given regarding issues investors can look at when trying to determine the potential growth of a firm.

6278 ■ "Bertha's Birth Stirs Juice" in Barron's (Vol. 88, July 14, 2008, No. 28, pp. M11)
Pub: Dow Jones & Company Inc.
Contact: Almar Latour, Chief Executive Officer
Ed: Tom Sellen. **Description:** Price of frozen concentrated orange juice, which has risen to four-month highs of $1.3620 in July 2008 is due, in part, to the hurricane season that has come earlier than normal in the far eastern Atlantic thereby possibly harming the 2008-2009 Florida orange crop. Future tropical-storm development will affect the prices of this commodity. **Availability:** Online.

6279 ■ "Best Cash Flow Generators" in Canadian Business (Vol. 82, Summer 2009, No. 8, pp. 40)
Description: Agrium Inc. and FirstService Corporation are in the list of firms that are found to have the potential to be the best cash flow generators in Canada. The list also includes WestJet Airlines Ltd., which accounts for 385 flights each day. More than 80 percent of analysts rate the airline stocks a Buy. **Availability:** Print; Online.

6280 ■ "The Best Five-Month Run Since 1938" in Barron's (Vol. 89, August 3, 2009, No. 31, pp. M3)
Pub: Dow Jones & Company Inc.
Contact: Almar Latour, Chief Executive Officer
Ed: Kopin Tan, Andrew Bary. **Description:** US stock markets ended July 2009 registering the highest five-month rise since 1938. The shares of Cablevision could rise as the company simplifies its structure and spins off its Madison Square Garden unit. The shares of Potash Corp. could fall as the company faces lower earnings due to falling potash purchases. **Availability:** Online.

6281 ■ "Best Turnaround Stocks" in Canadian Business (Vol. 81, Summer 2008, No. 9, pp. 65)
Description: Share prices of Sierra Wireless Inc. and EXFO Electro Optical Engineering Inc. have fallen over the past year but have good chance at a rebound considering that the companies have free cash flow and no long-term debt. One-year stock performance analysis of the two companies is presented. **Availability:** Print; Online.

6282 ■ "Best Value Stocks" in Canadian Business (Vol. 81, Summer 2008, No. 9, pp. 63)
Description: Table showing the one-year performance of bargain or best-value stocks is presented. These stocks are undervalued compared to their North American peers, but it is projected that their five-year average return on equity is greater. **Availability:** Online.

6283 ■ "A Better Way to Tax U.S. Businesses" in (Vol. 90, July-August 2012, No. 7-8, pp. 134)
Pub: Harvard Business Review Press
Contact: Moderna V. Pfizer, Contact
Ed: Mihir A. Desai. **Price:** $8.95, PDF and hardcover black and white. **Description:** Correcting the US corporate tax code will require ending the disconnect between earnings stated to investors and taxable income, implementing rate reductions, eliminating the taxing of overseas income, and securing an agreement by business leaders to acknowledge taxes as a responsibility. **Availability:** Print; PDF; Online.

6284 ■ "Betting Big, Winning Big: Interview With Bruce Berkowitz, CEO of Fairholme Capital Management" in Barron's (Vol. 88, March 17, 2008, No. 11, pp. 49)
Pub: Dow Jones & Company Inc.
Contact: Almar Latour, Chief Executive Officer
Ed: Lawrence C. Strauss. **Description:** Bruce Berkowitz explains that the reason that his portfolio is concentrated is because getting more positions makes the portfolio more average compared to putting the money into your 10th or 20th-best idea. Berkowitz' picks include Berkshire Hathaway, Well-Care Health Plus, Sears Holdings, and Mohawk Industries. **Availability:** Online.

6285 ■ "Betting on a Happy Ending" in Barron's (Vol. 88, July 7, 2008, No. 27, pp. 14)
Pub: Dow Jones & Company Inc.
Contact: Almar Latour, Chief Executive Officer
Ed: Dimitra DeFotis. **Description:** Shares of Time Warner, priced at $14.69 each, appear under-priced as financial analysts discount the value of the company. The company should be worth more than $20 a share as the company is spinning off Time Warner Cable. **Availability:** Online.

6286 ■ "Betting On Volatile Materials" in Barron's (Vol. 88, July 14, 2008, No. 28, pp. M11)
Pub: Dow Jones & Company Inc.
Contact: Almar Latour, Chief Executive Officer
Ed: John Marshall. **Description:** Economic slowdowns in the U.S., Europe and China could cause sharp short-term declines in the materials sector. The S&P Materials sector is vulnerable to shifts in the flow of funds. Statistical data included. **Availability:** Online.

6287 ■ "Between the Lines: Intangible Assets" in Canadian Business (Vol. 79, July 17, 2006, No. 14-15, pp. 17)
Pub: Rogers Media Inc.
Contact: Neil Spivak, Chief Executive Officer
Ed: Al Rosen. **Description:** Need for investors to check the actual worth of a company and not to get carried away by the inflated claims made by the company is emphasized.

6288 ■ "Beware this Chinese Export" in Barron's (Vol. 90, August 30, 2010, No. 35, pp. 21)
Pub: Barron's Editorial & Corporate Headquarters
Ed: Bill Alpert, Leslie P. Norton. **Description:** A look at 158 China reverse-merger stocks in the U.S. reveal that the median underperformed the index of U.S. listed Chinese companies by 75 percent in their first three years. These reverse merger stocks also lagged the Russell 2000 index of small cap stocks by 66 percent. **Availability:** Online.

6289 ■ "Beware of Rotting Money" in Barron's (Vol. 89, July 13, 2009, No. 28, pp. 31)
Pub: Dow Jones & Company Inc.
Contact: Almar Latour, Chief Executive Officer
Ed: Thomas G. Donlan. **Description:** Inflation can take hold of a country and do it great harm; it is caused by people, most particularly central bankers in charge of the world's reserve currency. Arrogant economists pushed the belief that the government can engineer the economy and it is argued that there is trouble ahead when the government tries to control the economy. **Availability:** Online.

6290 ■ "Beyond Microsoft and Yahoo!: Some M&A Prospects" in Barron's (Vol. 88, March 17, 2008, No. 11, pp. 39)
Pub: Dow Jones & Company Inc.
Contact: Almar Latour, Chief Executive Officer
Ed: Eric J. Savitz. **Description:** Weak quarterly earnings report for Yahoo! could pressure the company's board to cut a deal with Microsoft. Electronic Arts is expected to win its hostile $26-a-share bid for Take-

Two Interactive Software. Potential targets and buyers for mergers and acquisitions are mentioned. **Availability:** Online.

6291 ■ *"Big Gains Brewing at Anheuser-Busch InBev"* in *Barron's (Vol. 90, August 30, 2010, No. 35, pp. 34)*
Pub: Barron's Editorial & Corporate Headquarters
Ed: Christopher C. Williams. **Description:** Anheuser-Busch InBev is realizing cost synergies and it posted better than expected returns two years after the merger that formed the company. One analyst believes its American depositary receipt could be worth as much as 72 in a year. **Availability:** Online.

6292 ■ *"The Big Idea: The Judgment Deficit"* in *Harvard Business Review (Vol. 88, September 2010, No. 9, pp. 44)*
Pub: Harvard Business Publishing
Contact: Diane Belcher, Managing Director
Ed: Amar Bhide. **Price:** $8.95. **Description:** The importance of individual, decentralized initiative and judgment in the capitalist system is outlined. While financial models have their use, they cannot always account appropriately for the inherent uncertainty in economic decision making. **Availability:** Online; PDF.

6293 ■ *"Big Oil: Picks and Pans"* in *Canadian Business (Vol. 79, August 14, 2006, No. 16-17, pp. 67)*
Description: A survey on investments in Canadian energy companies and the inflation caused by oil price hike, are discussed. **Availability:** Print; Online.

6294 ■ *"Big Trouble at Sony Ericsson"* in *Barron's (Vol. 88, March 24, 2008, No. 12, pp. M9)*
Pub: Dow Jones & Company Inc.
Contact: Almar Latour, Chief Executive Officer
Ed: Angelo Franchini. **Description:** Sony Ericsson is facing trouble as it warned that its sales and net income before taxes will fall by nearly half for the first quarter of 2008. The joint venture of Sony and Ericsson has a global mobile phone market share of nine percent as of 2007, fourth largest in the world. **Availability:** Online.

6295 ■ *"Blackstone Set to Sell Stake"* in *Globe & Mail (March 17, 2007, pp. B6)*
Description: The plan of Blackstone Group to sell 10 percent of its stake to raise $4 billion and its proposal to go for initial public offering is discussed.

6296 ■ *"Blackstone's Outlook Still Tough"* in *Barron's (Vol. 88, March 17, 2008, No. 11, pp. 19)*
Pub: Dow Jones & Company Inc.
Contact: Almar Latour, Chief Executive Officer
Ed: Andrew Bary. **Description:** Earnings for the Blackstone Group may not recover soon since the company's specialty in big leveraged buyouts is floundering and may not recover until 2009. The company earns lucrative incentive fees on its funds but those fees went negative in the fourth quarter of 2007 and there could be more fee reversals in the future. **Availability:** Online.

6297 ■ *"Bloody Monday for Bear?"* in *Barron's (Vol. 88, March 17, 2008, No. 11, pp. M14)*
Pub: Dow Jones & Company Inc.
Contact: Almar Latour, Chief Executive Officer
Ed: Steven M. Sears. **Description:** Shares of Bear Stearns could slip further at the start of the trading week unless the company is bought out or bolstered by some other development over the weekend. Prices of the company's shares in the options market suggests about a 30 percent chance that the stock falls below $20 before March expirations expire. **Availability:** Online.

6298 ■ *"Blue-Collar Broker Ranks in Nation's Elite"* in *Boston Business Journal (Vol. 31, July 15, 2011, No. 25, pp. 1)*
Pub: Boston Business Journal
Contact: Carolyn M. Jones, President
E-mail: cmjones@bizjournals.com

Ed: Tim McLaughlin. **Description:** Richard F. Connolly Jr. was ranked 91st in Barron's latest annual ranking of top financial advisers and his team at Morgan Stanley Smith Barney oversee an estimated $3.7 billion in assets. However, anyone who knew him knows that he's just a blue-collar broker from Woburn who loves golf. **Availability:** Print.

6299 ■ *"BMW Revs Up for a Rebound"* in *Barron's (Vol. 89, July 13, 2009, No. 28, pp. M7)*
Pub: Dow Jones & Company Inc.
Contact: Almar Latour, Chief Executive Officer
Ed: Jonathan Buck. **Description:** Investors may like BMW's stocks because the company has maintained its balance sheet strength and has an impressive production line of new models that should boost sales in the next few years. The company's sales are also gaining traction, although their vehicle delivery was down 1.7 percent year on year on June 2009, this was still the best monthly sales figure for 2009. **Availability:** Online.

6300 ■ *"Boar Market: Penny-Wise Consumers Favoring Pork"* in *Crain's Chicago Business (Vol. 31, April 14, 2008, No. 15, pp. 4)*
Pub: Crain Communications Inc.
Contact: Barry Asin, President
Ed: Bruce Blythe. **Description:** Interview with Alan Cole who is the president of Cedar Hill Associates Inc. and who discusses ways in which his company is taking advantage of the record highs of oil and natural gas as well as his overall outlook on the market. **Availability:** Online.

6301 ■ *"BofA May Part With U.S. Trust"* in *Boston Business Journal (Vol. 31, May 20, 2011, No. 17, pp. 1)*
Pub: Boston Business Journal
Contact: Carolyn M. Jones, President
E-mail: cmjones@bizjournals.com
Ed: Tim McLaughlin. **Description:** Bank of America Corporation is willing to sell its U.S. Trust private banking division to improve its capital ratio. The unit remains to be the corporation's core asset and posted $696 million revenue in the first quarter 2010 in contract with Merrill Lynch Global Wealth Management's $3.5 billion. Analysts say that U.S. Trust would fetch more than $3 billion. **Availability:** Print; Online.

6302 ■ *"BofA Will Reach the Top with Countrywide Deal"* in *Business North Carolina (Vol. 28, March 2008, No. 3, pp. 36)*
Description: Bank of America, headquartered in Charlotte, North Carolina, will add Countrywide to its let of credits. Countrywide is the largest U.S. mortgage lender. Statistical data included.

6303 ■ *"The Bogleheads' Guide to Investing"*
Pub: John Wiley & Sons, Inc.
Contact: Christina Van Tassell, Executive Vice President Chief Financial Officer
Released: Second edition. **Price:** $26.95, hardcover; $17.99, E-Book. **Description:** Advice that provides the first step to successful financial investments includes new information of backdoor Roth IRAs and ETFs as mainstream buy and hold investments, estate taxes and gifting, along with information on the changes in laws regarding Traditional and Roth IRAs and 401k and 403b retirement plans. The author teaches how to craft proven individual investment strategies. **Availability:** E-book; Print.

6304 ■ *"Bonds v. Stocks: Who's Right About Recession?"* in *Barron's (Vol. 90, August 23, 2010, No. 34, pp. M3)*
Pub: Barron's Editorial & Corporate Headquarters
Ed: Kopin Tan. **Description:** The future of treasury securities and stocks should the U.S. enter or avoid a recession are discussed. The back to school business climate and BHP Billiton's bid for Potash Corporation of Saskatchewan are also discussed. **Availability:** Online.

6305 ■ *"The Book On Indigo"* in *Canadian Business (Vol. 81, July 22, 2008, No. 12-13, pp. 29)*
Description: Indigo Books & Music Inc. reported record sales of $922 million resulting in a record net profit of $52.8 million for the 2008 fiscal year ended March 29, 2008. Earnings per share were $2.13, greater than Standard & Poor's expected $1.70 per share. Additional information concerning Indigo Books is presented.

6306 ■ *"Boomers' Spending Hurts Retirement"* in *Employee Benefit News (Vol. 25, November 1, 2011, No. 14, pp. 18)*
Pub: SourceMedia LLC
Contact: Gemma Postlethwaite, Chief Executive Officer
Ed: Ann Marsh. **Description:** Financial planners and employers need to educate clients and employees about retirement planning. Boomers are spending money that should be saved for their retirement.

6307 ■ *"Bottom-Fishing and Speed-Dating in India-How Investors Feel About the Indian Market"* in *Barron's (Vol. 88, March 24, 2008, No. 12, pp. M12)*
Pub: Dow Jones & Company Inc.
Contact: Almar Latour, Chief Executive Officer
Ed: Elliot Wilson. **Description:** Indian stocks have fallen hard in 2008, with Mumbai's Sensex 30 down 30 percent from its January 2008 peak of 21,000 to 14,995 in March. The India Private Equity Fair 2008 attracted 140 of the world's largest private equity firms and about 24 of India's fastest-growing corporations. Statistical data included. **Availability:** Online.

6308 ■ *"Bountiful Barrels: Where to Find $140 Trillion"* in *Barron's (Vol. 88, July 14, 2008, No. 28, pp. 40)*
Pub: Dow Jones & Company Inc.
Contact: Almar Latour, Chief Executive Officer
Ed: Andrew Bary. **Description:** Surge in oil prices has caused a large transfer of wealth to oil-producing countries thereby reshaping the global economy. Oil reserves of oil exporting countries are now valued at $140 trillion. Economist Stephen Jen believes that this wealth will be transformed into paper assets as these countries invest in global stocks and bonds. **Availability:** Online.

6309 ■ *"Bracing for a Bear of a Week"* in *Barron's (Vol. 88, March 17, 2008, No. 11, pp. 24)*
Pub: Dow Jones & Company Inc.
Contact: Almar Latour, Chief Executive Officer
Ed: Jacqueline Doherty. **Description:** JPMorgan Chase and the Federal Reserve Bank of New York's opening of a line of credit to Bear Stearns cut the stock price of Bear Stearns by 47 percent to 30 followed by speculation of an imminent sale. JP Morgan may be the only potential buyer for the firm and some investors say Bears could be sold at $20 to $30. Bears prime assets include its enormous asset base worth $395 billion. **Availability:** Online.

6310 ■ *"Briefly: Physician Groups Unite"* in *Crain's Detroit Business (Vol. 25, June 15, 2009, No. 24, pp. 18)*
Pub: Crain Communications Inc.
Contact: Barry Asin, President
Ed: Tom Henderson, Jay Greene. **Description:** Details of the merger between Planning Alternatives Ltd. and Oakland Wealth Management are highlighted. The two investment advisory firms will have a combined staff of 12 and will maintain two offices. **Availability:** Online.

6311 ■ *"A Bull Market in Finger-Pointing"* in *Barron's (Vol. 88, March 10, 2008, No. 10, pp. 9)*
Pub: Dow Jones & Company Inc.
Contact: Almar Latour, Chief Executive Officer
Ed: Michael Santoli. **Description:** Discusses who is to blame for the financial crisis brought about by the credit crunch in the United States; the country's

financial markets will eventually digest this crisis but will bottom out first before the situation improves. **Availability:** Online.

6312 ■ *"Bullish Alert: A Brave Market Call" in Barron's (Vol. 92, July 23, 2012, No. 30, pp. 12)*
Pub: Dow Jones & Company Inc.
Contact: Almar Latour, Chief Executive Officer
Ed: Jacqueline Doherty. **Description:** Seth Masters, chief investment officer of Bernstein Global Wealth Management, predicts that the Dow Jones will reach the 20,000 level within five years. He also predicts that the Standard & Poor's 500 index will rise to 2,000 points. **Availability:** Online.

6313 ■ *"Business Adventures by John Brooks - A 30-Minute Instaread Summay: Twelve Classic Tales from the World of Wall Street"*
Pub: CreateSpace
Released: May 26, 2015. **Price:** $1.74, paperback. **Description:** The concept of the stock market is chronicled. Joseph de la Vega is the stock trader who invented the stock market in Amsterdam in 1611. Insight into the crash in 1962 provides information about the way the market works. **Availability:** Print.

6314 ■ *Business Black Belt: Develop the Strength, Flexibility and Agility to Run Your Company*
Price: $15.99. **Description:** Manual offering insights that will enable anyone to become successful in small business. Seventy short chapters included topics such as attitude, management, marketing, selling, employees, money, MBAs, lawyers, consultants, and investors. **Availability:** Print.

6315 ■ *"The Business End of Staying in Business" in Contractor (Vol. 56, September 2009, No. 9, pp. 51)*
Ed: Al Schwartz. **Description:** Advice on how to manage a new plumbing business in the United States is offered. The transition from being a workman to an employer is seen as one that accompanies a steep learning curve. The importance of managing cash flow is also highlighted. **Availability:** Print; Online.

6316 ■ *"Calpine Gets Ready to Light It Up" in Barron's (Vol. 92, July 23, 2012, No. 30, pp. 15)*
Pub: Dow Jones & Company Inc.
Contact: Almar Latour, Chief Executive Officer
Ed: Jack Willoughby. **Description:** The stocks of electric power producer Calpine could gain value as natural gas-fired power plants increase their market share. The company's stock prices could rise by 50 percent from $17.50 but the company needs to complete its turnaround to fully realize these gains. **Availability:** Online.

6317 ■ *"Cameco to Supply Reactors With Recycled Nukem Warheads" in Canadian Business (Vol. 85, August 13, 2012, No. 13, pp. 10)*
Ed: Richard Warnica. **Description:** Cameco Corporation has acquired Nukem Energy gmbH from private equity firm Advent International for $136 million as part of the Canadian mining company's plan to double annual uranium production to 40 million pounds by 2018. Such agreement gives Cameco access to some of the last of the uranium supply in the Megatons to Megawatt deal between Russia and the U.S. which expires in 2013. **Availability:** Print; Online.

6318 ■ *"Canadian Banks Too Timid in China, Beijing Tells Flaherty" in Globe & Mail (January 22, 2007, pp. B1)*
Ed: Steven Chase. **Description:** The article discusses Canadian banks' investments on China according to the views of federal Finance Minister Jim Flaherty. **Availability:** Online.

6319 ■ *"The Canadians Are Coming!" in Canadian Business (Vol. 80, October 22, 2007, No. 21, pp. 15)*
Description: Toronto-Dominion Bank declared its acquisition of the New Jersey-based Commerce Bancorp for C$8.5 billion. Royal Bank of Canada has scooped up Trinidad-based Financial Group for C$2.2 billion. Details of the foreign acquisitions, as well as the impact of high Canadian dollars on the mergers are discussed. **Availability:** Online.

6320 ■ *"Candidates Won't Bash Fed; Rate Cuts Bash Savers" in Barron's (Vol. 88, March 24, 2008, No. 12, pp. 31)*
Pub: Dow Jones & Company Inc.
Contact: Almar Latour, Chief Executive Officer
Ed: Jim McTague. **Description:** Candidates in the 2008 US presidential election, like the current administration, do not and will not bash the Federal Reserve. The Federal Reserve's aggressive interest rate cuts hurt the incomes of people depending on their savings accounts. **Availability:** Online.

6321 ■ *"Capital One Expanding Campus in Plano" in Dallas Business Journal (Vol. 35, April 20, 2012, No. 2, pp. 1)*
Pub: Baltimore Business Journal
Contact: Rhonda Pringle, President
E-mail: rpringle@bizjournals.com
Ed: Candace Carlisle. **Description:** The financial services division of Capital One Financial Corporation in Plano, Texas will hire an additional 300 employees and start construction of two office buildings and 2,600-space parking garage in summer 2012. Cost of the 400,000-square-foot office space is estimated at $76 million and $19.5 million for the garage. **Availability:** Print; Online.

6322 ■ *"Capturing Generation Y: Ready, Set, Transform" in Credit Union Times (Vol. 21, July 14, 2010, No. 27, pp. 20)*
Ed: Senthil Kumar. **Description:** The financial services sector recognizes that Generation Y will have a definite impact on the way business is conducted in the future. The mindset of Generation Y is social and companies need to use networking tools such as Facebook in order to reach this demographic. **Availability:** Online.

6323 ■ *"The Case of the Deflated IPO" in Boston Business Journal (Vol. 29, June 24, 2011, No. 7, pp. 1)*
Pub: Boston Business Journal
Contact: Carolyn M. Jones, President
E-mail: cmjones@bizjournals.com
Ed: Scott Dance. **Description:** IPO market is on the rebound from the recession but for some companies in Maryland, the time is not yet ripe to go public. One of the companies that chooses to wait for better timing is SafeNet Inc. and it is eyeing some possible acquisitions while doing so. **Availability:** Print; Online.

6324 ■ *"Cemex Paves a Global Road to Solid Growth" in Barron's (Vol. 88, March 10, 2008, No. 10, pp. 24)*
Pub: Dow Jones & Company Inc.
Contact: Almar Latour, Chief Executive Officer
Ed: Sandra Ward. **Description:** Shares of Cemex are expected to perform well with the company's expected strong performance despite fears of a US recession. The company has a diverse geographical reach and benefits from a strong worldwide demand for cement. **Availability:** Online.

6325 ■ *"Chuck's Big Chance" in Barron's (Vol. 89, July 13, 2009, No. 28, pp. L3)*
Pub: Dow Jones & Company Inc.
Contact: Almar Latour, Chief Executive Officer
Ed: Leslie P. Norton. **Description:** Charles Schwab is cutting prices and rolling out new products to lure customers and the company is well positioned to benefit from Wall Street's misery. Their shares are trading at just 17 times earnings, which should be at least at a multiple of 20. **Availability:** Online.

6326 ■ *"CIBC Spends $1.1 Billion on Caribbean Expansion" in Globe & Mail (March 14, 2006, pp. B1)*
Ed: Sinclair Stewart. **Description:** Canadian Imperial Bank of Commerce (CIBC), the fifth-largest bank of Canada, is planning to spend $1.1billion to buy major share of Barbados-based First Caribbean International Bank. The details of the acquisition plan are presented. **Availability:** Print; Online.

6327 ■ *"Citadel Hires Three Lehman Execs" in Chicago Tribune (October 2, 2008)*
Description: Citadel Investment Group LLC, Chicago hedge-fund operator, has hired three former senior executives of bankrupt investment banker Lehman Brothers Holding Inc. Citadel believes that the company's hiring spree will help them to further expand the firm's capabilities in the global fixed income business. **Availability:** Online.

6328 ■ *"Citi Ruling Could Chill SEC, Street Legal Pacts" in Wall Street Journal Eastern Edition (November 29, 2011, pp. C1)*
Pub: Dow Jones & Company Inc.
Contact: Almar Latour, Chief Executive Officer
Ed: Jean Eaglesham, Chad Bray. **Description:** A $285 million settlement was reached between the Securities and Exchange Commission and Citigroup Inc. over allegations the bank misled investors over a mortgage-bond deal. Now, Judge Jed S. Rakoff has ruled against the settlement, a decision that will affect the future of such attempts to prosecute Wall Street fraud. Rakoff said that the settlement was "neither fair, nor reasonable, nor adequate, nor in the public interest." **Availability:** Online.

6329 ■ *"The Clash of the Cultures: Investment vs. Speculation"*
Pub: John Wiley & Sons, Inc.
Contact: Christina Van Tassell, Executive Vice President Chief Financial Officer
Released: August 05, 2012. **Price:** $29.95, hardcover; $19.99, e-book. **Description:** Founder of Vanguard Group urges a return to the common sense principles of long-term investing. John C. Bogle draws on his sixty-years of experience in the mutual fund industry to discuss his views on the changing culture in mutual fund investing, how speculation has invaded our national retirement system, the failure of institutional money managers to effectively participate in corporate governance, and the need for a federal standard of fiduciary duty. Bogle also discusses the history of the index mutual fund and how he created it. **Availability:** E-book; Print.

6330 ■ *"Clash of the Titans" in Canadian Business (Vol. 80, March 12, 2007, No. 6, pp. 27)*
Description: The frequent allegations of Google Inc. and Microsoft Corp. against each other over copyright and other legal issues, with a view to taking away other's market share, is discussed. **Availability:** Print; Online.

6331 ■ *"Climbing the Wall of Worry, Two Steps at a Time" in Barron's (Vol. 89, July 13, 2009, No. 28, pp. L16)*
Pub: Dow Jones & Company Inc.
Contact: Almar Latour, Chief Executive Officer
Ed: Brian Blackstone. **Description:** Statistical table that shows the performance of different mutual funds for the second quarter of 2009 is presented. The data shows that on average, the 8,272 diversified equity funds gained 17 percent for this quarter. **Availability:** Online.

6332 ■ *A Colossal Failure of Common Sense: The Inside Story of the Collapse of Lehman Brothers*
Pub: Currency
Contact: Penny Simon, Contact
E-mail: psimon@randomhouse.com
Ed: Lawrence G. McDonald, Patrick Robinson. **Released:** October 12, 2010. **Price:** $17, Paperback; $5.99; $20. **Description:** Former employee of Lehman Brothers details the failure of leadership that led to the demise of the company. **Availability:** E-book; Print; Audio.

6333 ■ "Column: Want People to Save? Force Them" in Harvard Business Review (Vol. 88, September 2010, No. 9, pp. 36)
Pub: Harvard Business Publishing
Contact: Diane Belcher, Managing Director
Ed: Dan Ariely. **Price:** $6, PDF. **Description:** Contrasts in U.S. attitudes towards savings and government regulation with those of Chile, where all employees are required to save 11 percent of their salary in a retirement account, are highlighted. **Availability:** Online; PDF.

6334 ■ "Coming: Cheaper Oil and a Stronger Buck" in Barron's (Vol. 88, March 24, 2008, No. 12, pp. 53)
Pub: Dow Jones & Company Inc.
Contact: Almar Latour, Chief Executive Officer
Ed: Lawrence C. Strauss. **Description:** Carl C. Weinberg, the chief economist of High Frequency Economics, forecasts that Chinese economic growth will slow down and that oil prices will drop to $80 a barrel in 2008. He also believes that the US dollar will start rising the moment the Federal Reserve stops cutting interest rates. **Availability:** Online.

6335 ■ "Coming Soon: Bailouts of Fannie and Freddie" in Barron's (Vol. 88, July 14, 2008, No. 28, pp. 14)
Pub: Dow Jones & Company Inc.
Contact: Almar Latour, Chief Executive Officer
Ed: Jonathan R. Laing. **Description:** Assurances from the government that Fannie Mae and Freddie Mac are adequately capitalized and able to carry on their duties as guarantors or owners of over $5 trillion of U.S. home mortgages are designed to keep both entities afloat until they attempt to raise $10 billion in new equity. The government would assume any losses in a bailout and owners of the banks' papers would profit as yields drop. **Availability:** Online.

6336 ■ "Coming: The End of Fiat Money" in Barron's (Vol. 92, July 23, 2012, No. 30, pp. 32)
Pub: Dow Jones & Company Inc.
Contact: Almar Latour, Chief Executive Officer
Ed: Leslie P. Norton. **Description:** Stephanie Pomboy, founder of MicroMavens, discusses her views on the global financial system. She believes that the global fiat currency system may collapse within five years and be replaced by a gold-backed currency system. **Availability:** Online.

6337 ■ "Commodity Speculation: Over the Top?" in Barron's (Vol. 89, July 13, 2009, No. 28, pp. 22)
Pub: Dow Jones & Company Inc.
Contact: Almar Latour, Chief Executive Officer
Ed: Gene Epstein. **Description:** Commodity Futures Trading Commission is planning to impose position limits on speculators of oil and other commodities as energy costs rebound from their lows. These regulations make much sense and these position limits would greatly diminish the cash commitment of the commodity index traders if these were imposed on speculators and swaps dealers properly. **Availability:** Online.

6338 ■ "Compelling Opportunities for Investors in Emerging Markets" in Barron's (Vol. 88, March 10, 2008, No. 10, pp. 39)
Pub: Dow Jones & Company Inc.
Contact: Almar Latour, Chief Executive Officer
Ed: Neil A. Martin. **Description:** Michael L. Reynal, portfolio manager of Principal International Emerging Markets Fund, is bullish on the growth prospects of stocks in emerging markets. He is investing big on energy, steel, and transportation companies. **Availability:** Online.

6339 ■ "Connect the Thoughts" in Canadian Business (Vol. 81, October 27, 2008, No. 18, pp. 8)
Description: Thomas Homer-Dixon believes the financial crisis that hit Wall Street is a systemic crisis and may result in the reconfiguration of financial markets in ways that people may never understand. He also thinks the U.S. may borrow against its assets, making it a weaker nation. **Availability:** Online.

6340 ■ "Consumer Contagion? A Bleak Earnings View" in Barron's (Vol. 88, March 10, 2008, No. 10, pp. 15)
Pub: Dow Jones & Company Inc.
Contact: Almar Latour, Chief Executive Officer
Ed: Robin Goldwyn Blumenthal. **Description:** Analysts expect consumer discretionary profits in the S&P 500 to drop 8.4 percent in the first quarter of 2008. A less confident consumer is expected to pull profits down, putting forecasts of earnings growth in the S&P 500 at risk. Statistical data included. **Availability:** Online.

6341 ■ "Consumers Turned Off? Not at Best Buy" in Barron's (Vol. 88, March 24, 2008, No. 12, pp. 29)
Pub: Dow Jones & Company Inc.
Contact: Almar Latour, Chief Executive Officer
Ed: Sandra Ward. **Description:** Shares of Best Buy, trading at $42.41 each, are expected to rise to an average of $52 a share due to the company's solid fundamentals. The company's shares have fallen 20 percent from their 52-week high and are attractive given the company's bright prospects in the video game sector and high-definition video. **Availability:** Online.

6342 ■ "Conversation Starters for the Holiday" in Barron's (Vol. 89, July 6, 2009, No. 27, pp. 7)
Pub: Dow Jones & Company Inc.
Contact: Almar Latour, Chief Executive Officer
Ed: Michael Santoli. **Description:** Investors are concerned that the US will experience high inflation due to low interest rates and improved money supply. US consumer spending has increased to 70 percent of gross domestic product, brought by health-care spending increases, while savings rates have risen to 6.9 percent. **Availability:** Online.

6343 ■ "A Conversation With: Ron Gantner, Jones Lang LaSalle" in Crain's Detroit Business (Vol. 24, October 6, 2008, No. 40, pp. 9)
Pub: Crain Communications Inc.
Contact: Barry Asin, President
Description: Interview with Ron Gantner who is a corporate real estate adviser with the real estate company Jones Lang LaSalle as well as the company's executive vice president and part of the tenant advisory team; Gantner speaks about the impact that the Wall Street crisis is having on the commercial real estate market in Detroit. **Availability:** Print; Online.

6344 ■ "Cool on Chicago Office Properties" in Crain's Chicago Business (Vol. 31, March 31, 2008, No. 13, pp. 16)
Pub: Crain Communications Inc.
Contact: Barry Asin, President
Ed: Eddie Baeb. **Description:** Investors predict values on Chicago office buildings to drop 1.3 percent over the next year. **Availability:** Online.

6345 ■ "Copy Karachi?" in Barron's (Vol. 88, June 30, 2008, No. 26, pp. 5)
Pub: Dow Jones & Company Inc.
Contact: Almar Latour, Chief Executive Officer
Ed: Randall W. Forsyth. **Description:** Karachi bourse had a historic 8.6 percent one-day gain because the bourse banned short-selling for a month and announced a 30 billion rupee fund to stabilize the market. The shares of General Motors are trading within the same values that it had in 1974. The reasons for this decline are discussed. **Availability:** Online.

6346 ■ "Cornerstone Seeks Investors for Hedge Fund" in Baltimore Business Journal (Vol. 32, June 20, 2014, No. 7, pp. 10)
Pub: American City Business Journals, Inc.
Contact: Mike Olivieri, Executive Vice President
Description: Cornerstone Advisory LLP is looking for investors to create a hedge fund that ties returns to various indices, real estate or commodity prices. Cornerstone hopes to raise between $30 million to $50 million and are planning a fall launch for the fund. They have hired New York law firm Thompson Hine LLP to draft the subscription agreement and NebraskaEs Gimini Fund Services LLC to run as third party administrator. **Availability:** Print; Online.

6347 ■ "Corus Eases Off Ailing Condo Market" in Crain's Chicago Business (April 28, 2008)
Pub: Crain Communications Inc.
Contact: Barry Asin, President
Ed: H. Lee Murphy. **Description:** Corus Bankshares Inc., a specialist in lending for the condominium high-rise construction market, is diversifying its portfolio by making loans to office developers and expects to be investing in hotels through the rest of the year. Corus' $7.57 billion loan portfolio is also discussed in detail as well as the company's earnings and share price. Statistical data included. **Availability:** Online.

6348 ■ "Cost Cuts Lead Dealers to Record Profits" in Globe & Mail (March 24, 2006, pp. B3)
Ed: Omar El Akkad. **Description:** The reasons behind posting of $4.3 billion profit by Canadian securities sector, for 2005, are presented. **Availability:** Online.

6349 ■ "CPI, Coal Lead Local Stock Decline" in Saint Louis Business Journal (Vol. 32, October 14, 2011, No. 7, pp. 1)
Pub: Saint Louis Business Journal
Contact: Robert Bobroff, President
E-mail: rbobroff@bizjournals.com
Ed: Greg Edwards. **Description:** Coal companies and CPI Corporation were among those whose stocks have declined in St. Louis, Missouri. The stocks of local firms have plunged by 28 percent during the first nine months of 2011. **Availability:** Print; Online.

6350 ■ "Crain's Picks Top '08 Stocks" in Crain's New York Business (Vol. 24, January 6, 2008, No. 1, pp. 3)
Pub: Crain Communications, Inc.
Contact: Jessica Botos, Manager, Marketing
E-mail: jessica.botos@crainsnewyork.com
Ed: Aaron Elstein. **Description:** Listing of five stocks that Crain's believes can deliver solid gains for shareholders. **Availability:** Online.

6351 ■ "Crash Landing? Serious Signal Flashing" in Barron's (Vol. 88, July 7, 2008, No. 27, pp. 11)
Pub: Dow Jones & Company Inc.
Contact: Almar Latour, Chief Executive Officer
Description: Discusses the Hindenburg Omen, named after the airship disaster of May 1937, which is considered a predictor of market crashes and has appeared twice in June 2008. There is a 25 percent probability that the US stock market will suffer a crash in the July-October 2008 period. **Availability:** Online.

6352 ■ Crash Proof 2.0: How to Profit From the Economic Collapse
Pub: John Wiley & Sons, Inc.
Contact: Christina Van Tassell, Executive Vice President Chief Financial Officer
Ed: Peter D. Schiff, John Downes. **Released:** Second edition. **Price:** $16.95, paperback; $27.95, hardcover; $18.99, e-book; $18.99, E-book. **Description:** Factors that will affect financial stability in the coming years are explained. A three step plan to battle the current economic downturn is also included. **Availability:** E-book; Print.

6353 ■ "The Credit Crisis Continues to Take Victims" in Barron's (Vol. 88, March 10, 2008, No. 10, pp. M12)
Pub: Dow Jones & Company Inc.
Contact: Almar Latour, Chief Executive Officer

Ed: Randall W. Forsyth. **Description:** Short-term Treasury yields dropped to new cyclical lows in early March 2008, with the yield for the two-year Treasury note falling to 1.532 percent. Spreads of the mortgage-backed securities of Fannie Mae and Freddie Mac rose on suspicion of collapses in financing. **Availability:** Online.

6354 ■ *"Cummins Is a Engine of Growth" in Barron's (Vol. 88, July 14, 2008, No. 28, pp. 43)*
Pub: Dow Jones & Company Inc.
Contact: Almar Latour, Chief Executive Officer
Ed: Shirley A. Lazo. **Description:** Engine maker Cummins increased its quarterly common dividend by 40 percent to 17.5 cents per share from 12.5 cents. CVS Caremark's dividend saw a hike of 18.4 percent from 9.5 cents to 11.25 cents per share while its competitor Walgreen is continuing its 75th straight year of dividend distribution and its 33rd straight year of dividend hikes. **Availability:** Online.

6355 ■ *Currency Internationalization: Global Experiences and Implications for the Renminbi*
Pub: Palgrave Macmillan
Released: First edition. **Description:** A collection of academic studies relating to the potential internationalization of China's remninbi. It also discusses the increasing use of China's remninbi currency in international trade and finance.

6356 ■ *"Deal Braces Cramer for Growth Run" in The Business Journal-Serving Metropolitan Kansas City (Vol. 26, July 4, 2008, No. 43, pp. 1)*
Description: Gardner, Kansas-based Cramer Products Inc. bought 100 percent of the stocks of Louisville, Kentucky-based Active Ankle Inc. from 26 private investors increasing its revenue by 20 percent. The latter is the second largest vendor of Cramer. Other details of the merger are presented. **Availability:** Print; Online.

6357 ■ *"Detroit Hosts Conferences on Green Building, IT, Finance" in Crain's Detroit Business (Vol. 25, June 1, 2009, No. 22, pp. 9)*
Pub: Crain Communications Inc.
Contact: Barry Asin, President
Ed: Tom Henderson. **Description:** Detroit will host three conferences in June 2009, one features green technology, one information technology and the third will gather black bankers and financial experts from across the nation. **Availability:** Online.

6358 ■ *Dictionary of Finance, Investment and Banking*
Pub: Palgrave Macmillan
Ed: Erik Banks. **Released:** First edition. **Description:** Comprehensive dictionary covering terms used in finance, investment and banking sectors.

6359 ■ *Dictionary of Real Estate Terms*
Pub: Barron's Educational Series Inc.
Contact: Manuel H. Barron, Contact
Ed: Jack P. Friedman, Jack C. Harris, J. Bruce Lindeman. **Released:** 9th edition. **Price:** $16.99, paperback, plus shipping charges $5.99. **Description:** More than 2,500 real estate terms relating to mortgages and financing, brokerage law, architecture, rentals and leases, property insurance, and more. **Availability:** E-book; Print.

6360 ■ *"Digging Deep for Gold: David Iben, Manager, Nuveen Tradewinds Value Opportunities Fund" in Barron's (Vol. 88, March 24, 2008, No. 12, pp. 49)*
Pub: Dow Jones & Company Inc.
Contact: Almar Latour, Chief Executive Officer
Ed: Suzanne McGee. **Description:** David Iben, manager of the Nuveen Tradewinds Value Opportunities Fund, looks for value in companies and industries where the consensus of analysts is negative. He started investing in gold stocks well before gold prices started to rise. **Availability:** Online.

6361 ■ *The Directory of Venture Capital & Private Equity Firms*
Pub: Grey House Publishing
Contact: Richard Gottlieb, President
Released: February 01, 2016. **Price:** $250, Softcover. **Description:** Updated and expanded edition that includes new entries offering access to more than 3,500 domestic and international venture capital and private equity firms; detailed contact information and extensive data on investments and funds is included. **Availability:** Print; Online.

6362 ■ *"Disappearing Act" in Globe & Mail (April 21, 2007, pp. B1)*
Description: The effects of the buyout of BCE Inc. on the trends of stock prices at the Toronto Stock Exchange are described. **Availability:** Online.

6363 ■ *"Discount Beers Take Fizz Out Of Molson" in Globe & Mail (February 10, 2006, pp. B3)*
Description: The reasons behind the decline in profits by 60 percent for Molson Coors Brewing Co., during fourth quarter 2005, are presented. **Availability:** Online.

6364 ■ *"Do-It-Yourself Portfolio Management" in Barron's (Vol. 89, July 13, 2009, No. 28, pp. 25)*
Pub: Dow Jones & Company Inc.
Contact: Almar Latour, Chief Executive Officer
Ed: Mike Hogan. **Description:** Services of several portfolio management web sites are presented. These web sites include MarketRiders E.Adviser, TD Ameritrade and E. **Availability:** Online.

6365 ■ *"Does Diversity Pay Dividends?" in Canadian Business (Vol. 87, October 2014, No. 10, pp. 89)*
Description: The growing interest in gender diversity-based investing can be driven in part by a rising number of women investors with progressive ideals. Alex Johnston of Catalyst Canada advocacy group predict the use of a diversity-based approach by institutional investors. **Availability:** Online.

6366 ■ *"The Dogs of TSX" in Canadian Business (Vol. 81, Summer 2008, No. 9, pp. 77)*
Description: Table showing the one-year stock performance of the ten highest dividend-yielding stocks on the S&P/TSX 60 Composite Index is presented. This technique is similar to the 'Dogs of the Dow' approach. The idea in this investment strategy is to buy equal amounts of stocks from these companies and selling them a year later, and then repeat the process. **Availability:** Online.

6367 ■ *"Don't Bet Against The House" in Barron's (Vol. 88, July 14, 2008, No. 28, pp. 20)*
Pub: Dow Jones & Company Inc.
Contact: Almar Latour, Chief Executive Officer
Ed: Sandra Ward. **Description:** Shares of Nasdaq OMX have lost more than 50 percent of their value from November 2007 to July 2008 but the value of these shares could climb 50 percent on the strength of world security exchanges. Only 15 percent of the company's revenues come from the U.S. and the shares are trading at 12.5 times the amount expected for 2008. **Availability:** Online.

6368 ■ *"Don't Fear the Phone" in Senior Market Advisor (Vol. 13, October 2012, No. 10, pp. 50)*
Description: Investment brokers and financial planning advisors must set aside time to make phone calls to clients as well as prospective clients. The article puts this process into perspective for setting appointments. **Availability:** Online.

6369 ■ *"Don't Hang Up On FairPoint" in Barron's (Vol. 88, July 7, 2008, No. 27, pp. M5)*
Description: Shares of FairPoint Communications, priced at $6.63 each, are undervalued and should be worth over $12 each. The company increased its size by more than five times by acquiring Verizon's local telephone operations in Vermont, New Hampshire, and Maine, but must switch customers in those areas into their system by the end of September 2007. **Availability:** Online.

6370 ■ *"Downtown Bank Got High Marks for Irwin Purchase, Is Looking For More" in Business Courier (Vol. 27, September 3, 2010, No. 18, pp. 1)*
Pub: Business Courier
Ed: Steve Watkins. **Price:** $4, Introductory 4-Week Offer(Digital & Print). **Description:** First Financial Bancorp is looking to acquire more troubled banks following its purchase of Irwin Union Bank. The bank has reported a $383 million bargain purchase gain during the third quarter of 2009. **Availability:** Print; Online.

6371 ■ *"Drilling Deep and Flying High" in Barron's (Vol. 88, June 30, 2008, No. 26, pp. 34)*
Pub: Dow Jones & Company Inc.
Contact: Almar Latour, Chief Executive Officer
Ed: Kenneth Rapoza. **Description:** Shares of Petrobras could rise another 25 percent if the three deepwater wells that the company has found proves as lucrative as some expect. Petrobras will become an oil giant if the reserves are proven. **Availability:** Online.

6372 ■ *"Drug, Seed Firms Offer Antidote For Inflation" in Crain's Chicago Business (Vol. 31, April 21, 2008, No. 16, pp. 4)*
Pub: Crain Communications Inc.
Contact: Barry Asin, President
Ed: Daniel Rome Levine. **Description:** Interview with Jerrold Senser, the CEO of Institutional Capital LLC in Chicago, in which he discusses the ways that the company is adjusting to the economic slowdown and rising inflation, his favorite firms for investment and his prediction of an economic turnaround; he also recommends five companies he feels are worth investing in. **Availability:** Online.

6373 ■ *"Drug Trial Halt at YM Sets Stage for Selloff" in Globe & Mail (January 31, 2007, pp. B3)*
Description: The decision of YM Biosciences Inc. to stop its trial of cancer drug tesmilifene and stocks following government concern over the safety of the drug is discussed. **Availability:** Online.

6374 ■ *"Dynamic Duo: Payouts Rise at General Dynamics, Steel Dynamics" in Barron's (Vol. 88, March 10, 2008, No. 10, pp. 45)*
Pub: Dow Jones & Company Inc.
Contact: Almar Latour, Chief Executive Officer
Ed: Shirley A. Lazo. **Description:** General Dynamics, the world's sixth-largest military contractor, raised its dividend payout by 20.7 percent from 29 cents to 35 cents a share. Steel Dynamics, producer of structural steel and steel bar products, declared a 2-for-1 stock split and raised its quarterly dividend by 33 percent to a split-adjusted 10 cents a share. **Availability:** Online.

6375 ■ *"Economic Recovery Prognosis: Four More Years" in Barron's (Vol. 89, July 13, 2009, No. 28, pp. 11)*
Pub: Dow Jones & Company Inc.
Contact: Almar Latour, Chief Executive Officer
Ed: Karen Hube. **Description:** Loomis Sayles Bond Fund manager Dan Fuss believes that the economy is bottoming and that recovery will be long and drawn out. Fuss guesses that the next peak in 10-year Treasury yields will be about 6.25% in around 4 and a half or five years ahead of 2009. **Availability:** Online.

6376 ■ *"An Educated Play on China" in Barron's (Vol. 88, June 30, 2008, No. 26, pp. M6)*
Pub: Dow Jones & Company Inc.
Contact: Almar Latour, Chief Executive Officer

Ed: Mohammed Hadi. **Description:** New Oriental Education & Technology Group sells English-language courses to an increasingly competitive Chinese workforce that values education. The shares in this company have been weighed down by worries on the impact of the Beijing Olympics on enrollment and the Sichuan earthquake. These shares could be a great way to get exposure to the long-term growth in China. **Availability:** Online.

6377 ■ *"The Education of Jack Bogle" in Philadelphia Business Journal (Vol. 33, April 4, 2014, No. 8, pp. 4)*
Pub: American City Business Journals, Inc.
Contact: Mike Olivieri, Executive Vice President
Description: Vanguard Group founder and now retired CEO, John C. Bogle, shares his views about life and starting the company. Bogle says Wellington Fund founder, Walter L. Morgan, made all the difference by having confidence in him and basically turned the company over to him when he was 37 years old. Bogle believes Philadelphia's mutual fund industry owes its significant growth to Vanguard. **Availability:** Online.

6378 ■ *"Egg Fight: The Yolk's on the Shorts" in Barron's (Vol. 88, July 7, 2008, No. 27, pp. 20)*
Pub: Dow Jones & Company Inc.
Contact: Almar Latour, Chief Executive Officer
Ed: Christopher C. Williams. **Description:** Shares of Cal-Maine Foods, the largest egg producer and distributor in the US, are due for a huge rise because of the increase in egg prices. Short sellers, however, continue betting that the stock, priced at $31.84 each, will eventually go down. **Availability:** Online.

6379 ■ *"The Emerging Capital Market for Nonprofits" in Harvard Business Review (Vol. 88, October 2010, No. 10, pp. 110)*
Pub: Harvard Business Publishing
Contact: Diane Belcher, Managing Director
Ed: Robert S. Kaplan, Allen S. Grossman. **Price:** $8.95, PDF. **Description:** Demonstration of how nonprofits can use intermediaries to grow their organizational structures, giving them improved scale and impact is offered. Some intermediaries play a mutual-fund role and conduct due diligence, while others act as venture capital funds and implement strategy. **Availability:** Online; PDF.

6380 ■ *"The Emperor Strikes Back" in Canadian Business (Vol. 80, March 26, 2007, No. 7, pp. 48)*
Description: The financial performance of Fairfax Financial Holdings Ltd. in 2006 is presented. The efforts of chief executive Prem Watsa to lead the company towards growth track are also presented. **Availability:** Online.

6381 ■ *"EnCana Axes Spending on Gas Wells" in Globe & Mail (February 16, 2006, pp. B1)*
Ed: Dave Ebner. **Description:** The reasons behind EnCana Corp.'s cost spending measures by $300 million on natural gas wells are presented. The company projects 2 percent cut in gas and oil sales for 2006. **Availability:** Print; Online.

6382 ■ *"End of the Beginning" in Canadian Business (Vol. 81, November 10, 2008, No. 19, pp. 17)*
Ed: David Wolf. **Released:** September 30, 2016. **Description:** The freeze in the money markets and historic decline in equity markets around the world finally forced governments into aggressive coordinated action. The asset price inflation brought on by cheap credit will now work in reverse and the tightening of credit will be difficult economically. Canada is exposed to the fallout everywhere, given that the U.S, the U.K. and Japan buy 30 percent of Canada's output. **Availability:** Print; Online.

6383 ■ *"End of an Era" in Barron's (Vol. 88, July 7, 2008, No. 27, pp. 3)*
Ed: Alan Abelson. **Released:** January 01, 2016. **Description:** June 2008 was a very bad month for US stocks, with investors losing as much as 41.9 percent in the first half of 2008 signaling an end to the financial environment that prevailed around the world since the 1980's. The US job market lost 62,000 jobs in June 2008. **Availability:** Print; Online.

6384 ■ *"Energy Firms Face Stricter Definitions" in Globe & Mail (March 26, 2007, pp. B3)*
Ed: David Ebner. **Description:** The Alberta Securities Commission has imposed strict securities regulations on oil and gas industries. Energy industries will have to submit revenue details to stake holders. **Availability:** Online.

6385 ■ *"Energy MPLs: Pipeline to Profits" in Barron's (Vol. 89, July 27, 2009, No. 30, pp. 9)*
Pub: Dow Jones & Company Inc.
Contact: Almar Latour, Chief Executive Officer
Ed: Dimitra DeFotis. **Description:** Energy master limited partnership stocks are range-bound in the next few months from July 2009 but there are there are some opportunities that remain. These include Energy Transfer Equity, Enterprise GP holdings, NuStar GP Holdings, and Plains All American Pipeline. **Availability:** Online.

6386 ■ *"Equal Weighting's Heavy Allure" in Barron's (Vol. 92, July 23, 2012, No. 30, pp. 27)*
Pub: Dow Jones & Company Inc.
Contact: Almar Latour, Chief Executive Officer
Ed: Brendan Conway. **Description:** Equal weight index exchange-traded funds are attracting investors due to their strong returns. This strategy gives investors a greater exposure to mid-capitalization companies and could provide strong returns over longer stretches. **Availability:** Online.

6387 ■ *"Essential Releases Record First Quarter Results" in Marketwired (May 14, 2007)*
Pub: Comtex News Network Inc.
Contact: Kan Devnani, President
Description: The first quarter of 2007 saw record financial performance despite numerous challenges for Essential Energy Services Trust. Statistical data included. **Availability:** Print; Online.

6388 ■ *"ETF Score Card" in Barron's (Vol. 89, July 13, 2009, No. 28, pp. 51)*
Pub: Dow Jones & Company Inc.
Contact: Almar Latour, Chief Executive Officer
Description: Statistical table is presented which shows the net assets of various exchange-traded funds are presented. The table also shows the total return of these funds up to a three-year time period. **Availability:** Online.

6389 ■ *"Europe's Meltdown" in Canadian Business (Vol. 83, June 15, 2010, No. 10, pp. 76)*
Description: As European countries such as Greece, Spain, and Portugal struggle with debt problems, it is worth noting that its equities trade at a 30 percent discount to the U.S. and that a 10 percent drop in the Euro translates to a 10 percent rise in profitability for exporters. Investors may also want to focus on business-to-business operations rather than consumer-focused ones. **Availability:** Online.

6390 ■ *"Everyone Out of the Pool" in Barron's (Vol. 89, July 20, 2009, No. 29, pp. 18)*
Pub: Dow Jones & Company Inc.
Contact: Almar Latour, Chief Executive Officer
Ed: Sandra Ward. **Description:** Shares of Pool Corp. could drop as continued weakness in the housing market weakens the market for swimming pool equipment. The company's shares are trading at $18.29, about 20 times projected 2009 earnings of $0.91 a share. **Availability:** Online.

6391 ■ *"Evolving from Practice to Enterprise" in Financial Advisor (November 1, 2019)*
URL(s): www.fa-mag.com/news/evolving-from-practice-to-enterprise-52345.html
Ed: Dawn Doebler, Michael Nathanson. **Released:** November 01, 2019. **Description:** A look at the financial advisory industry as smaller firms grow from a practice to a larger business and even to an enterprise. Gives definitions of each term and the qualifications each entity must possess. **Availability:** Online.

6392 ■ *"Falling Markets' Nastiest Habit" in Barron's (Vol. 88, July 7, 2008, No. 27, pp. 7)*
Pub: Dow Jones & Company Inc.
Contact: Almar Latour, Chief Executive Officer
Ed: Michael Santoli. **Description:** US market conditions reflect a bear market, with the S&P 500 index falling 20 percent below its recent high as of June 2008. The bear market is expected to persist in the immediate future, although bear market rallies are likely to occur. **Availability:** Online.

6393 ■ *"Falling Share Prices Will Convince Big Oil Producers to Pay Up to Drill" in Globe & Mail (April 21, 2007, pp. B1)*
Ed: Boyd Erman. **Description:** The effect of the increase in operational costs and the decline in share prices, on the exploration of petroleum deposits in Canada, is described. **Availability:** Online.

6394 ■ *"February Hot for Mutual Fund Sales" in Globe & Mail (March 3, 2006, pp. B10)*
Ed: Keith Damsell. **Description:** The details on Canadian mutual fund sector, which posted $4.7 billion for February 2005, are presented. **Availability:** Print; Online.

6395 ■ *"The Fed Still Has Ammunition" in Barron's (Vol. 90, August 30, 2010, No. 35, pp. M9)*
Pub: Barron's Editorial & Corporate Headquarters
Ed: Randall W. Forsyth. **Description:** Federal Reserve chairman Ben Bernanke said the agency still has tools to combat deflation and a second downturn but these strategies are not needed at this time. The prospects of the Federal Open Market Committee's purchasing of treasuries are also discussed. **Availability:** Online.

6396 ■ *"Fed Tackles Bear of a Crisis" in Barron's (Vol. 88, March 17, 2008, No. 11, pp. M10)*
Pub: Dow Jones & Company Inc.
Contact: Almar Latour, Chief Executive Officer
Ed: Randall W. Forsyth. **Description:** Emergency funding package for Bear Stearns from the Federal Reserve Bank of New York through JPMorgan Chase is one of the steps taken by the central bank shore up bank liquidity. Prior to the emergency funding, the central bank announced the Term Securities Lending Facility to allow dealers to borrow easily saleable Treasuries in exchange for less-liquid issues. **Availability:** Online.

6397 ■ *"Federal Bailout, Three Years Later" in Business Owner (Vol. 35, September-October 2011, No. 5, pp. 6)*
Description: State of the economy and small business sector three years after the government stimulus and bailout programs were instituted. **Availability:** Print; Online.

6398 ■ *"Fees Come Down; Markets Come Down More" in Barron's (Vol. 89, July 13, 2009, No. 28, pp. L8)*
Pub: Dow Jones & Company Inc.
Contact: Almar Latour, Chief Executive Officer
Ed: J.R. Brandstrader. **Description:** Investors spent less on mutual fund fees in 2009 than they did in the last 25 years. These fees include administration, accounting, and legal expense. Despite the popularity of money market funds which has contributed to this decline, the short-term yields of these funds fell in the last year. **Availability:** Online.

6399 ■ *"A Few Points of Contention" in Barron's (Vol. 88, July 14, 2008, No. 28, pp. 3)*
Pub: Dow Jones & Company Inc.
Contact: Almar Latour, Chief Executive Officer

Ed: Michael Santoli. **Description:** Headline inflation tends to revert to the lower core inflation, which excludes food and energy in its calculation over long periods. Prominent private equity figures believe that regulators should allow more than the de facto 10 percent to 25 percent limit of commercial banks to hasten the refunding of the financial sector. **Availability:** Online.

6400 ■ *Financial Planning & Analysis and Performance Management*

Ed: Jack Alexander. **Released:** June 13, 2018. **Price:** $46.24, Hardcover; $36.79, E-book. **Description:** Comprehensive reference guide about financial planning for financial analysts working for organizations. Discussion topics include budget and forecasting, analysis, performance management, financial communication, metrics, benchmarking, and many others. **Availability:** E-book; Print.

6401 ■ *"Financial Stability: Fraud, Confidence, and the Wealth of Nations"*

Pub: John Wiley & Sons, Inc.
Contact: Christina Van Tassell, Executive Vice President Chief Financial Officer

Released: September 2014. **Price:** $48.99, e-book; $75, hardcover. **Description:** Instruction is provided to help modern investors and finance professionals to learn from past successes and failures and to gauge future market threats. Insight into today's financial markets and the political economy will help craft a strategy that leads to financial stability. Topics covered include: capital; forecasting; political reaction; and past, present, and future applications within all areas of business. A companion Website offers additional data and research, providing a comprehensive resource for those wishing a better understanding of risk factors in investing. **Availability:** E-book; Print; Online; PDF.

6402 ■ *Financing Your Small Business*

Released: First edition. **Description:** Tips for raising venture capital, dealing with bank officials, and initiating public offerings of stock shares for small business.

6403 ■ *"Fine Wine, Poor Returns" in Barron's (Vol. 92, September 17, 2012, No. 38, pp. 11)*

Description: Investing in wines in not considered a good idea due to irrationally high wine prices. Wine collectors buying wines at very high prices are not expected to make money and are charged with a 28 percent 'collectibles' tax. **Availability:** Online.

6404 ■ *"FirstMerit's Top Executive Turns Around Credit Quality" in Crain's Cleveland Business (Vol. 28, October 15, 2007, No. 41, pp. 3)*

Pub: Crain Communications Inc.
Contact: K. C. Crain, President

Ed: Shawn A. Turner. **Description:** Discusses the ways in which chairman and CEO Paul Greig has been able to improve FirstMerit Corp.'s credit quality and profit margin. Strategies included selling more than $70 million in bad loans, hiring a new chief credit officer and redirecting its focus on cross-selling its wealth and investment services to its commercial customers. Statistical data included. **Availability:** Online.

6405 ■ *"FIS-Metavante Deal Paying Off for Many" in Business Journal-Milwaukee (Vol. 28, December 17, 2010, No. 11, pp. A1)*

Pub: The Business Journal
Contact: Heather Ladage, President
E-mail: hladage@bizjournals.com

Ed: Rich Kirchen. **Description:** Jacksonville, Florida-based Fidelity National Information Services Inc., also known as FIS, has remained committed to Milwaukee, Wisconsin more than a year after purchasing Metavante Technologies Inc. FIS has transferred several operations into Metropolitan Milwaukee and has continued its contribution to charitable organizations in the area. **Availability:** Print; Online.

6406 ■ *"Fiscal Cliff Notes" in Barron's (Vol. 92, September 15, 2012, No. 38, pp. 27)*

Pub: Dow Jones & Company Inc.
Contact: Almar Latour, Chief Executive Officer

Ed: Mike Hogan. **Description:** Websites and blogs dedicated to providing information on the economic effects of the 'fiscal cliff' are described. These sites discuss possible effects on the US economy, budget, and personal finances. **Availability:** Online.

6407 ■ *"Five Tips for Killer Landing Pages" in Retirement Advisor (Vol. 13, October 2012, No. 10, pp. 27)*

Ed: Amy McIlwain. **Description:** The importance of Web page design is highlighted. Five tips for creating a Webpage that encourages trust and informs users about the financial products and services you offer are are given. **Availability:** Print; Online.

6408 ■ *"A Flawed Yardstick for Banks" in Barron's (Vol. 88, July 14, 2008, No. 28, pp. M6)*

Pub: Dow Jones & Company Inc.
Contact: Almar Latour, Chief Executive Officer

Ed: Arindam Nag. **Description:** Return on equity is no longer the best measure for investors to judge banks by in a post-subprime-crises world. Investors should consider the proportion of a bank's total assets that are considered risky and look out for any write-downs of goodwill when judging a bank's financial health. **Availability:** Online.

6409 ■ *"Florida's Housing Gloom May Add To Woes of National City" in Crain's Cleveland Business (Vol. 28, October 29, 2007, No. 43, pp. 1)*

Pub: Crain Communications Inc.
Contact: K. C. Crain, President

Ed: Shawn A. Turner. **Description:** Already suffering by bad loans in the troubled mortgage market, National City Corp. is attempting to diversify its geographic presence beyond the slow-growth industrial Midwest by acquiring two Florida firms. Analysts worry that the acquisitions may end up making National City vulnerable to a takeover if the housing slump continues and credit quality becomes more of an issue for the bank. **Availability:** Online.

6410 ■ *Fooling Some of the People All of the Time*

Pub: John Wiley & Sons, Inc.
Contact: Christina Van Tassell, Executive Vice President Chief Financial Officer

Ed: David Einhorn. **Released:** January 2011. **Price:** $14.50, Paperback; $10.99, e-book. **Description:** A chronicle of the ongoing saga between author, David Einhorn's hedge fund, Greenlight Capital, and Allied Capital, a leader in the private finance industry. **Availability:** E-book; Print.

6411 ■ *"For Buffett Fans, the Price Is Right" in Barron's (Vol. 89, July 13, 2009, No. 28, pp. 17)*

Pub: Dow Jones & Company Inc.
Contact: Almar Latour, Chief Executive Officer

Ed: Andrew Bary. **Description:** Shares of Warren Buffett's Berkshire Hathaway have fallen to $85,000 and these are cheap since they are trading at just 1.2 times estimated book value and are well below its peak of $149,000. One fan of the stock expects it to top $110,000 in the next year from June 2009. **Availability:** Online.

6412 ■ *"For Gilead, Growth Beyond AIDS" in Barron's (Vol. 88, June 30, 2008, No. 26, pp. 18)*

Pub: Dow Jones & Company Inc.
Contact: Almar Latour, Chief Executive Officer

Ed: Jay Palmer. **Description:** First-quarter 2008 revenue for Gilead Sciences grew by 22 percent and an earnings gain of 19 percent thanks to their HIV-treatment drugs that comprised over two-thirds of the company's sales in 2007. An analyst has a 12-month target from June, 2008 of 65 per share. The factors behind the company's prospects are also discussed. **Availability:** Online.

6413 ■ *"Ford Canada's Edsel of a Year: Revenue Plummets 24 Percent in '05" in Globe & Mail (February 2, 2006, pp. B1)*

Description: Ford Motor Company of Canada Ltd. posted 24% decline in revenues for 2005. The drop in earnings is attributed to plant shutdown in Oaksville, Canada. **Availability:** Online.

6414 ■ *"Ford: Down, Not Out, and Still a Buy" in Barron's (Vol. 92, July 23, 2012, No. 30, pp. 14)*

Pub: Dow Jones & Company Inc.
Contact: Almar Latour, Chief Executive Officer

Ed: Vito J. Racanelli. **Description:** Stocks of Ford Motor Company could gain value as the company continues to improve its finances despite fears of slower global economic growth. The company's stock prices could double from $9.35 per share within three years. **Availability:** Online.

6415 ■ *"The Four Cheapest Plays in Emerging Markets" in Barron's (Vol. 89, July 27, 2009, No. 30, pp. 34)*

Pub: Dow Jones & Company Inc.
Contact: Almar Latour, Chief Executive Officer

Ed: Lawrence C. Strauss. **Description:** Portfolio manager Arjun Divecha of the GMO Emerging Markets III Fund says that the main thing in investing in emerging markets is getting the country right since getting it wrong makes it harder to add value. Divecha says that the four countries that they are positive on are Turkey, Russia, South Korea, and Thailand. **Availability:** Online.

6416 ■ *"Full-Court Press for Apple" in Barron's (Vol. 88, March 24, 2008, No. 12, pp. 47)*

Pub: Dow Jones & Company Inc.
Contact: Almar Latour, Chief Executive Officer

Ed: Mark Veverka. **Description:** Apple Inc. is facing more intellectual property lawsuits in 2008, with 30 patent lawsuits filed compared to 15 in 2007 and nine in 2006. The lawsuits, which involve products such as the iPod and the iPhone, present some concern for Apple's shareholders. **Availability:** Online.

6417 ■ *"Funds "Friend' Facebook" in Barron's (Vol. 89, July 27, 2009, No. 30, pp. 30)*

Pub: Dow Jones & Company Inc.
Contact: Almar Latour, Chief Executive Officer

Ed: Leslie P. Norton. **Description:** Mutual-fund companies are the latest entrants to the "social media" space and several companies have already set up Facebook and Twitter pages. The use of this technology pose special challenges for compliance and regulators especially since the Financial Industry Regulatory Authority reminds companies that advertising, sales and literature are governed by regulations. **Availability:** Online.

6418 ■ *"The Future of Private Equity" in Canadian Business (Vol. 80, March 26, 2007, No. 7, pp. 19)*

Description: The impact growing Canadian economy and competition in global business on the performance of private equity funds is analyzed. **Availability:** Online; PDF.

6419 ■ *"Future of the Street" in Barron's (Vol. 88, June 30, 2008, No. 26, pp. 27)*

Pub: Dow Jones & Company Inc.
Contact: Almar Latour, Chief Executive Officer

Ed: Michael Santoli. **Description:** Prospects of the securities industry in terms of jobs and profit sources are discussed. Suggestions on what the industry needs with regards to its use of capital are also discussed. **Availability:** Online.

6420 ■ *"Futures Shock for the CME" in Crain's Chicago Business (Vol. 31, November 10, 2008, No. 45, pp. 8)*

Pub: Crain Communications Inc.
Contact: Barry Asin, President

Ed: Ann Saphir. **Description:** Chicago-based CME Group Inc., the largest futures exchange operator in the U.S., is facing a potentially radically altered regulatory landscape as Congress weighs sweeping reform of financial oversight. The possible merger of the CFTC and the Securities and Exchange Commission are among CME's concerns. Other details of possible regulatory measures are provided. **Availability:** Online.

6421 ■ *"Generation Y - An Opportunity for a Fresh Financial Start"* in *(September 11, 2010, pp. 241)*
Pub: VerticalNews
Description: Eleanor Blayney, the consumer advocate for the Certified Financial Planner Board of Standards, offers a financial strategy for Generation Y individuals starting their financial planning. The first segment of the non-profit's Lifelong Financial Strategies initiative is called 'Starting Out', and focuses on ways Generation Y people can avoid pitfalls of earlier generations by making smart financial decisions. **Availability:** Print; Online.

6422 ■ *Get a Financial Life: Personal Finance in Your Twenties and Thirties*
Ed: Beth Kobliner. **Released:** March 21, 2017. **Price:** $10.27, Paperback; $12.99, E-book. **Description:** A guide for younger adults as they navigate the financial world and financial planning. **Availability:** E-book; Print.

6423 ■ *"Get Off The Rollercoaster"* in *Michigan Vue (Vol. 13, July-August 2008, No. 4, pp. 19)*
Description: Benefits of creating and implementing a solid financial plan during these rocky economic times are examined. Things to keep in mind before meeting with a financial planner include risk assessment, investment goals, the length of time required to meet those goals and the amount of money one has available to invest. **Availability:** Print; Online.

6424 ■ *"Getting In on the Ground Floor With World-Class Companies"* in *Barron's (Vol. 89, July 27, 2009, No. 30, pp. 32)*
Ed: Jacqueline Doherty. **Description:** Shares of AvalonBay Communities have fallen 61 percent in the past two and a half years to July 2009 but at $56, the stock is trading near the asset value. The shares could rise as the economy improves and if the recovery takes longer, investors will be rewarded with a yield of 3.5 percent. **Availability:** Online.

6425 ■ *"Getting More Out of Retirement"* in *Agency Sales Magazine (Vol. 39, November 2009, No. 10, pp. 48)*
Description: Overview of the Tax Increase Prevention and Reconciliation Act, which lets employees convert to a Roth IRA in 2010. The benefits of conversion depend on age and wealth and it is best to consult a tax advisor to determine the best strategy for retirement planners. **Availability:** Print; Online.

6426 ■ *"A Gift From Interactive Brokers"* in *Barron's (Vol. 92, July 23, 2012, No. 30, pp. M11)*
Pub: Dow Jones & Company Inc.
Contact: Almar Latour, Chief Executive Officer
Ed: Steven M. Sears. **Description:** Investors are advised to sell put options of Interactive Brokers stock in anticipation of lower share prices. This trade is also a hedge against a possible takeover but allows investors to buy into a company that pays regular dividends and is managed well. **Availability:** Online.

6427 ■ *"Global Steel Makers Circle Stelco"* in *Globe & Mail (April 19, 2007, pp. B3)*
Ed: Greg Keenan. **Description:** The details of the take over bids offered to Stelco Inc. are presented. Due to these bids the shares of Stelco Inc rose up to 70 percent. **Availability:** Online.

6428 ■ *"A Good Book Is Worth a Thousand Blogs"* in *Barron's (Vol. 88, July 14, 2008, No. 28, pp. 42)*
Pub: Dow Jones & Company Inc.
Contact: Almar Latour, Chief Executive Officer

Ed: Gene Epstein. **Description:** Nine summer book suggestions on economics are presented. The list includes 'The Revolution' by Ron Paul, 'The Forgotten Man' by Amity Shales, 'The Commitments of Traders Bible' by Stephen Briese, and 'Economic Facts and Fallacies' by Thomas Sowell. **Availability:** Online.

6429 ■ *"Good Going, Partners"* in *Barron's (Vol. 89, July 27, 2009, No. 30, pp. M8)*
Pub: Dow Jones & Company Inc.
Contact: Almar Latour, Chief Executive Officer
Ed: Shirley A. Lazo. **Description:** Four master limited partnerships boosted their dividends. Sunoco Logistics raised theirs by 11.2 percent, El Paso Pipeline by 12 percent, Holly Energy upped their dividends by a penny, and Western Gas hiked their dividend to 31 cents per unit. **Availability:** Online.

6430 ■ *"A Good Step, But There's a Long Way to Go"* in *Business Week (September 22, 2008, No. 4100, pp. 10)*
Ed: James C. Cooper. **Description:** Despite the historic action by the U.S. government to nationalize the mortgage giants Freddie Mac and Fannie Mae, rising unemployment rates may prove to be an even bigger roadblock to bringing back the economy from its downward spiral. The takeover is meant to restore confidence in the credit markets and help with the mortgage crisis but the rising rate in unemployment may make many households unable to take advantage of any benefits which arise from the bailout. Statistical data included. **Availability:** Online.

6431 ■ *"Google's Next Stop: Below 350?"* in *Barron's (Vol. 88, March 10, 2008, No. 10, pp. 17)*
Pub: Dow Jones & Company Inc.
Contact: Almar Latour, Chief Executive Officer
Ed: Jacqueline Doherty. **Description:** Share prices of Google Inc. are expected to drop from their level of $433 each to below $350 per share. The company is expected to miss its earnings forecast for the first quarter of 2008, and its continued aggressive spending on non-core areas will eventually bring down earnings. **Availability:** Online.

6432 ■ *"Graduates to the TSX in 2008"* in *Canadian Business (Vol. 81, Summer 2008, No. 9, pp. 79)*
Description: Table showing the market capitalization and stock performance of the companies that jumped to the TSX Venture Exchange is presented. The 17 companies that made the leap to the list will have an easier time raising capital, although leeway must be made in investing since they are still new businesses.

6433 ■ *"The Great Fall: Here Comes The Humpty Dumpty Economy"* in *Barron's (Vol. 88, March 10, 2008, No. 10, pp. 5)*
Pub: Dow Jones & Company Inc.
Contact: Almar Latour, Chief Executive Officer
Ed: Alan Abelson. **Description:** Discusses the US economy is considered to be in a recession, with the effects of the credit crisis expected to intensify as a result. Inflation is estimated at 4.3 percent in January 2008, while 63,000 jobs were lost in February 2008. **Availability:** Online.

6434 ■ *"The Great Moderation"* in *Canadian Business (Vol. 80, February 12, 2007, No. 4, pp. 25)*
Description: Caution over the changes to stock inventory levels and their adverse impact on the Canadian economy is discussed. **Availability:** Online.

6435 ■ *"The Green Trap"* in *Canadian Business (Vol. 80, April 9, 2007, No. 8, pp. 19)*
Description: Expert advice to companies on investing in environmental-friendly measures is presented. **Availability:** Online.

6436 ■ *"A Greenish Light for Financial-Sector Funds"* in *Barron's (Vol. 88, March 24, 2008, No. 12, pp. 52)*
Pub: Dow Jones & Company Inc.
Contact: Almar Latour, Chief Executive Officer

Ed: Tom Sullivan. **Description:** Financial sector funds have lost value in 2008 through 17 March, and investors are advised to reduce investments in the financial sector. Exchange-traded funds present a good way to own financial stocks. **Availability:** Online.

6437 ■ *"A Gripping Read: Bargains & Noble"* in *Barron's (Vol. 88, March 17, 2008, No. 11, pp. 20)*
Pub: Dow Jones & Company Inc.
Contact: Almar Latour, Chief Executive Officer
Ed: Jonathan R. Laing. **Description:** Barnes & Noble's earnings forecast for the fiscal year ending in January, 2008 to be $1.70 to $1.90 per share which is way lower than the $2.12 analyst consensus. The company also said that sales at stores one-year old or older dropped 0.5 percent in the fourth quarter. However, the shares are now cheap at 4.9 times enterprise value with some analysts putting a price target of 41 per share. **Availability:** Online.

6438 ■ *"Growing Expectations"* in *Financial Advisor (November 1, 2019)*
URL(s): www.fa-mag.com/news/growing--expectations-52348.html
Ed: Christopher Robbins. **Released:** November 01, 2019. **Description:** During the National Association of Personal Financial Advisors' 2019 Fall Conference, the need to keep upgrading the clients' experiences with technology was one of the key takeaways of the event. With the majority of the current workforce part of the generations that grew up on modern tech, it is easy to see why they would want to have options beyond just phone calls and face-to-face meetings. **Availability:** Online.

6439 ■ *"Growth Back on CIBC's Agenda"* in *Globe & Mail (March 3, 2006, pp. B1)*
Ed: Sinclair Stewart. **Description:** The details on business growth of Canadian Imperial Bank of Commerce, which posted $547 million profit for first quarter 2006, are presented. **Availability:** Online.

6440 ■ *"Handleman Liquidation Leaves Questions For Shareholders"* in *Crain's Detroit Business (Vol. 24, October 6, 2008, No. 40, pp. 4)*
Pub: Crain Communications Inc.
Contact: Barry Asin, President
Ed: Nancy Kaffer. **Description:** Discusses Handleman Co., a Troy-based music distribution company, and their plan of liquidation and dissolution as well as how shareholders will be affected by the company's plan. Handleman filed its plan to liquidate and dissolve assets with the Securities and Exchange Commission in mid-August, following several quarters of dismal earnings. **Availability:** Online.

6441 ■ *"Has Microsoft Found a Way to Get at Yahoo?"* in *Advertising Age (Vol. 79, July 7, 2008, No. 26, pp. 4)*
Pub: Crain Communications, Inc.
Contact: Jessica Botos, Manager, Marketing
E-mail: jessica.botos@crainsnewyork.com
Ed: Abbey Klaassen. **Description:** Microsoft's attempt to acquire Yahoo's search business is discussed as is Yahoo's plans for the future at a time when the company's shares have fallen dangerously low. **Availability:** Print; Online.

6442 ■ *"Headwinds From the New Sod Slow Aer Lingus"* in *Barron's (Vol. 88, March 10, 2008, No. 10, pp. M6)*
Pub: Dow Jones & Company Inc.
Contact: Almar Latour, Chief Executive Officer
Ed: Sean Walters, Arindam Nag. **Description:** Aer Lingus faces a drop in its share prices with a falling US market, higher jet fuel prices, and lower long-haul passenger load factors. British media companies Johnston Press and Yell Group are suffering from weaker ad revenue and heavier debt payments due to the credit crunch. **Availability:** Online.

6443 ■ *"The Heat Is On"* in *Crain's Chicago Business* (Vol. 31, April 28, 2008, No. 17, pp. 4)
Pub: Crain Communications Inc.
Contact: Barry Asin, President
Ed: Steve Daniels. **Description:** Discusses Nicor Inc., a natural-gas utility serving 2 million customers in Chicago's suburbs, and its potential acquirers; shares of the company have dropped 17 percent this year making Nicor the second-worst among 31 utilities in an index tracked by Standrd & Poor's. Statistical data included.

6444 ■ *"Hedge Funds for the Average Joe"* in *Canadian Business* (Vol. 85, August 13, 2012, No. 13, pp. 51)
Ed: Bryan Borzykowski. **Description:** The benefits of the Horizons Morningstar Hedge Fund Index ETF over traditional hedge funds are examined. Retail investors should avoid buying hedge fund exchange-traded funds (ETFs) because they are not actually buying into a hedge fund, the fund is just trying to emulate strategies that popular hedge funds use with derivatives. **Availability:** Print; Online.

6445 ■ *"Her Aim Is True"* in *Senior Market Advisor* (Vol. 13, October 2012, No. 10, pp. 40)
Description: Profile of Rebecca True, president of True Capital Advisors, discusses her approach to broad marketing plans for her company. True emphasizes on building relationships with women business owners and executives. **Availability:** Print; Online.

6446 ■ *"H.I.G. Capital Announces Acquisition of Next Generation Vending"* in *Benzinga.com* (October 29, 2011)
Pub: Benzinga.com
Contact: Jason Raznick, Founder
Description: H.I.G. Capital LLC, a leader in global private investments, acquired Next Generation Vending and Food Service Inc. Next Generation is a provider of vending services for corporate and institutional clients in Northeastern United States. **Availability:** Print; PDF; Online.

6447 ■ *"High-Yield Turns Into Road Kill"* in *Barron's* (Vol. 88, July 7, 2008, No. 27, pp. M7)
Pub: Dow Jones & Company Inc.
Contact: Almar Latour, Chief Executive Officer
Ed: Emily Barrett. **Description:** High-yield bonds have returned to the brink of collapse after profits have recovered from the shock brought about by the collapse of Bear Stearns. The high-yield bond market could decline again due to weakness in the automotive sector, particularly in Ford and General Motors. **Availability:** Online.

6448 ■ *"Higher Freight Rates Keep CPR Rolling in Profit"* in *Globe & Mail* (February 1, 2006, pp. B3)
Description: Canadian Pacific Railway Ltd. posted $135.4 million in revenues for fourth quarter 2005. The company's earnings projections for 2006 and workforce reduction plans are presented. **Availability:** Print; Online.

6449 ■ *"Higher Payouts Should Be In the Cards"* in *Barron's* (Vol. 92, July 23, 2012, No. 30, pp. 14)
Pub: Dow Jones & Company Inc.
Contact: Almar Latour, Chief Executive Officer
Ed: Michael Santoli. **Description:** Credit card companies Visa and MasterCard should be more generous to shareholders and pay higher dividends. Both have low dividend yields, with Visa paying $0.88/share a year and MasterCard paying $1.20/share annually. **Availability:** Online.

6450 ■ *"Hitting Bottom? Several Banks and Brokerages Are Ready to Pop Up for Air"* in *Barron's* (Vol. 88, March 24, 2008, No. 12, pp. 21)
Pub: Dow Jones & Company Inc.
Contact: Almar Latour, Chief Executive Officer
Ed: Jacqueline Doherty. **Description:** Brokerage houses and banks may stabilize in 2008 as a result of regulatory responses brought about by the near-collapse of Bear Stearns. Some of their shares may rise by as much as 20 percent from 2008 to 2009. **Availability:** Online.

6451 ■ *"Homebuilders Continue to be Our Nemesis"* in *Contractor* (Vol. 56, July 2009, No. 7, pp. 50)
Ed: Robert P. Mader. **Description:** Homebuilders rank high on the greed scale along with Wall Street brokers. There is this one instance when a builder gave copies of another contractor's quotes that have just been blackened out and another instance when one builder let other bidders visit a site while the current mechanical contractor is working. **Availability:** Print; Online.

6452 ■ *"Hong Kong's Boom in IPOs"* in *Barron's* (Vol. 89, July 13, 2009, No. 28, pp. M7)
Pub: Dow Jones & Company Inc.
Contact: Almar Latour, Chief Executive Officer
Ed: Nick Lord. **Description:** Hong Kong's IPO (initial public offering) market is booming with 13 Chinese IPOs already on the market for the year as July 2009. One of them is Bawang International which raised $214 million after generating $9 billion in order which makes it 42 times oversubscribed. **Availability:** Online.

6453 ■ *"How to Avoid the Most Common and Costliest Mistakes in Retirement Portfolio Investing"* in *Barron's* (Vol. 88, March 10, 2008, No. 10, pp. 30)
Pub: Dow Jones & Company Inc.
Contact: Almar Latour, Chief Executive Officer
Ed: Karen Hube. **Description:** Investors, particularly those having retirement investments, are advised to diversify their investments, refrain from market timing, and minimize payments to maximize investment gains. An investor committing these mistakes could lose as much as $375,000 dollars over ten years. **Availability:** Online.

6454 ■ *"How to Beat the Pros"* in *Canadian Business* (Vol. 81, Summer 2008, No. 9, pp. 59)
Description: Table showing the results of the Investor 500 beat the S&P/TSX composite index is presented. The average total return, best performing stocks and total return of the 2007 stock screen are provided. **Availability:** Online.

6455 ■ *"How CoolBrands' Thrills Turned to Chills"* in *Globe & Mail* (January 25, 2007, pp. B1)
Ed: Keith McArthur. **Description:** The key reasons behind the sudden share price fall of ice cream giant CoolBrands International Inc. are discussed. **Availability:** Print; Online.

6456 ■ *"How to Deal"* in *Canadian Business* (Vol. 81, November 10, 2008, No. 19, pp. 36)
Description: The Great Depression, Japan's Lost Decade, and the Swedish Banking Crisis is compared to the 2008 financial crisis in the U.S. The chances for recession in the U.S. are discussed along with investment strategies to survive.

6457 ■ *"How Foreigners Could Disrupt U.S. Markets"* in *Barron's* (Vol. 90, September 13, 2010, No. 37, pp. 30)
Pub: Barron's Editorial & Corporate Headquarters
Ed: Jim McTague. **Description:** An informal meeting by the House Homeland Security Panel concluded that U.S. stock exchanges and related trading routes can be the subject of attacks from rogue overseas traders. A drop in funding for the U.S. Department of Defense is discussed. **Availability:** Online.

6458 ■ *"How High Can Soybeans Fly?"* in *Barron's* (Vol. 88, March 10, 2008, No. 10, pp. M14)
Pub: Dow Jones & Company Inc.
Contact: Almar Latour, Chief Executive Officer
Ed: Kenneth Rapoza. **Description:** Prices of soybeans have risen to $14.0875 a bushel, up 8.3 percent for the week. Increased demand, such as in China and in other developing economies, and the investment-driven commodities boom are boosting prices. **Availability:** Online.

6459 ■ *"How Millionaire Mentor Cedric Nash Went from a $36,000 Salary to $90M in Annual Business Revenue"* in *Black Enterprise* (February 7, 2023)
URL(s): www.blackenterprise.com/how-millionaire-mentor-cedric-nash-man-went-from-a-36000-salary-to-90-million-in-annual-business-revenue/
Ed: Anne-Lyse Wealth. **Released:** February 07, 2023. **Description:** Founder of The Black Wealth Summit, Cedric Nash, discusses his rise in the financial advice world. **Availability:** Online.

6460 ■ *"How Not to Raise Bank Capital"* in *Barron's* (Vol. 88, June 30, 2008, No. 26, pp. M6)
Pub: Dow Jones & Company Inc.
Contact: Almar Latour, Chief Executive Officer
Ed: Sean Walters. **Description:** French bank Natixis wants to raise 1 billion euros from cash provided by their two major owners. Natixis will reimburse Banque Populaire and Caisses d'Epargne with hybrid securities so this move will not benefit Natixis' core Tier 1 ratio. This has also given the impression that the company is afraid of a full rights issue which could shake investors' faith in the bank. **Availability:** Online.

6461 ■ *"How Our Picks Beat The Bear"* in *Barron's* (Vol. 88, July 14, 2008, No. 28, pp. 18)
Pub: Dow Jones & Company Inc.
Contact: Almar Latour, Chief Executive Officer
Ed: Andrew Bary. **Description:** Performance of the stocks that Barron's covered in the first half of 2008 is discussed; some of the worst picks and most rewarding pans have been in the financial sector while the best plays were in the energy, materials, and the transportation sectors. **Availability:** Online.

6462 ■ *"How to Retire: Do's and Don'ts"* in *Canadian Business* (Vol. 79, July 17, 2006, No. 14-15, pp. 29)
Pub: Rogers Media Inc.
Contact: Neil Spivak, Chief Executive Officer
Ed: Andy Holloway, Erin Pooley, Thomas Watson. **Description:** Strategic tips for planning systematic investments, in order to make life more enjoyable after retirement, are elucidated. **Availability:** Print; Online.

6463 ■ *"How to Save More and Worry Less at Tax Time"* in *Canadian Business* (Vol. 85, August 13, 2012, No. 13, pp. 33)
Description: The top-down approach and the bottom-up approach are two cash-management strategies that are proven to make a person richer. The top-down approach to saving is best suitable to an analytical, detail-oriented person while the bottom-up approach can be effective to people who are having difficulties in keeping track of their spending. **Availability:** Online.

6464 ■ *"How Sweet It Will Be"* in *Barron's* (Vol. 89, July 13, 2009, No. 28, pp. M13)
Pub: Dow Jones & Company Inc.
Contact: Almar Latour, Chief Executive Officer
Ed: Debbie Carlson. **Description:** Raw sugar experienced a rally in the first half of 2009 and the long term outlook for sugar prices is still good. However, there is a likely near-term correction due to the onset of Brazilian harvest that could be 20.7 percent higher for 2009 as compared to the previous year and October contracts could fall to 15.61 cents per pound. **Availability:** Online.

6465 ■ *"How To Win the Fed's New Game"* in *Barron's* (Vol. 92, September 17, 2012, No. 38, pp. M10)
Description: Options trading strategies designed to take advantage of the US Federal Reserve's third quantitative easing program are discussed. Options traders are advised to invest in short-term options to maximize gains. **Availability:** Print; Online.

6466 ■ "I'll Have What She's Having" in Canadian Business (Vol. 85, September 17, 2012, No. 14, pp. 17)
Ed: Andrew Hallam. Description: Studies show that women have the higher tendency to follow responsible investing rules than men, earning more money in the process. Women were also found to perform better in bull markets as well as in the male-dominated hedge fund sector. Availability: Online.

6467 ■ "Imports Frothing Up Beer Market" in Globe & Mail (February 16, 2006, pp. B4)
Ed: Andy Hoffman. Description: The reasons behind the rise in market share of beer imports, in Canada, are presented. Availability: Online.

6468 ■ "In China, Railways to Riches" in Barron's (Vol. 88, July 7, 2008, No. 27, pp. M9)
Pub: Dow Jones & Company Inc.
Contact: Almar Latour, Chief Executive Officer
Ed: Assif Shameen. Description: Shares of Chinese railway companies look to benefit from multimillion-dollar investments aimed at upgrading the Chinese railway network. Investment in the sector is expected to reach $210 billion for the 2006-2010 period. Availability: Online.

6469 ■ "In the Hot Finance Jobs, Women Are Still Shut Out" in Harvard Business Review (Vol. 90, July-August 2012, No. 7-8, pp. 30)
Pub: Harvard Business Review Press
Contact: Moderna V. Pfizer, Contact
Ed: Nori Gerardo Lietz. Price: $6, PDF and hardcover black and white. Description: Although women constitute a significant proportion of business school graduates, the percentage of senior investment professionals who are female remain in a single-digit figure. Active effort will be needed to change corporate culture and industry awareness to raise this figure. Availability: Print; PDF; Online.

6470 ■ "In India, A Gold-Price Threat?" in Barron's (Vol. 88, June 30, 2008, No. 26, pp. M12)
Pub: Dow Jones & Company Inc.
Contact: Almar Latour, Chief Executive Officer
Ed: Melanie Burton. Description: Gold purchases in India are falling as record prices take its toll on demand. Gold imports to India fell by 52 percent in May 2008 from the previous year and local prices are higher by one-third from the previous year to 12,540 rupees for 10 grams. Availability: Online.

6471 ■ "In the Options Market, Financial-Sector Trading Is Moody and Paranoid" in Barron's (Vol. 88, March 10, 2008, No. 10, pp. M14)
Pub: Dow Jones & Company Inc.
Contact: Almar Latour, Chief Executive Officer
Ed: Steven M. Sears. Description: Discusses the options market which remains liquid but is cautious of possible failures, especially for financial companies. Investors are in absolute fear when trading with options involving the financial sector. Availability: Online.

6472 ■ "In Praise of How Not to Invest" in Barron's (Vol. 89, July 13, 2009, No. 28, pp. 11)
Pub: Dow Jones & Company Inc.
Contact: Almar Latour, Chief Executive Officer
Ed: Vito J. Racanelli. Description: One research study found that the shares of companies that have growing market shares and expanding asset bases underperform. This is contrary to the widely held premise that stock prices for these companies rise. It is argued that this result is caused by these companies' tendency to sacrifice profitability to grab market share and this is reflected in their stock prices. Availability: Online.

6473 ■ "In Surging Oil Industry, Good Fortune Comes In Stages" in Barron's (Vol. 88, July 7, 2008, No. 27, pp. 12)
Pub: Dow Jones & Company Inc.
Contact: Almar Latour, Chief Executive Officer
Ed: Sandra Ward. Description: Shares of US land oil and gas driller Helmerich and Payne, priced at $69 each, are estimated to be at peak levels. The shares are trading at 17 times 2008 earnings and could be in for some profit taking. Availability: Online.

6474 ■ "In the Wake of Pet-Food Crisis, Iams Sales Plummet Nearly 17 Percent" in Advertising Age (Vol. 78, May 14, 2007, No. 18, pp. 3)
Pub: Crain Communications, Inc.
Contact: Jessica Botos, Manager, Marketing
E-mail: jessica.botos@crainsnewyork.com
Ed: Jack Neff. Description: Although the massive U.S. pet-food recall impacted more than 100 brands, Procter & Gamble Co.'s Iams lost more sales and market share than any other industry player. According to Information Resources Inc. data, the brand's sales dropped 16.5 percent in the eight-week period ended April 22. Many analysts feel that the company could have handled the crisis in a better manner. Availability: Online.

6475 ■ "Incapital Set to Add Jobs, Expand Space" in South Florida Business Journal (Vol. 33, August 3, 2012, No. 1, pp. 1)
Pub: Baltimore Business Journal
Contact: Rhonda Pringle, President
E-mail: rpringle@bizjournals.com
Description: Chicago, Illinois-based Incapital has announced plans to hire 25 to 30 more financial professionals over the next 12 months. Incapital is also planning to expand its Boca Raton, Florida with construction totalling 5,000 additional square feet to accommodate future growth. Availability: Print; Online.

6476 ■ "The Incentive Bubble: Outsourcing Pay Decisions To Financial Markets Has Skewed Compensation and, With It, American Capitalism" in Harvard Business Review (Vol. 90, March 2012, No. 3, pp. 124)
Pub: Harvard Business Review Press
Contact: Moderna V. Pfizer, Contact
Ed: Mihir A. Desai. Price: $8.95. Description: Basing incentive contracts and executive compensation on financial markets actually rewards luck rather than performance, and can promote dangerous risk taking. This has led to America's two main crises of capitalism: growing income inequality and governance failures. Boards of directors must focus on performance rather than stocks, and endowments and foundations must focus on incentives for long-term growth. Availability: Online; PDF.

6477 ■ "Inland Snaps Up Rival REITs" in Crain's Chicago Business (Vol. 31, November 17, 2008, No. 46, pp. 3)
Pub: Crain Communications Inc.
Contact: Barry Asin, President
Ed: Alby Gallun. Description: Discusses Inland American Real Estate Trust Inc., a real estate investment trust that is napping up depressed shares of publicly traded competitors, a possible first step toward taking over these companies; however, with hotel and retail properties accounting for approximately 70 percent of its portfolio, the company could soon face its own difficulties. Availability: Online.

6478 ■ "Inmet Selling Nunavut Mining Properties" in Globe & Mail (February 15, 2006, pp. B6)
Ed: Allan Robinson. Description: The details on Wolfden Resources Inc.'s acquisition of mining assets of Inmet Mining Corp. are presented. Availability: Online.

6479 ■ "International ETFs: Your Passport to the World" in Barron's (Vol. 89, July 13, 2009, No. 28, pp. L10)
Pub: Dow Jones & Company Inc.
Contact: Almar Latour, Chief Executive Officer
Ed: John Hintze. Description: International exchange traded funds give investors more choices in terms of investment plays and there are 174 U.S. ETF listings worth $141 billion as of July 2009. Suggestions on how to invest in these funds based on one's conviction on how the global economy will unfold are presented. Availability: Online.

6480 ■ "Invest Like Harvard" in Barron's (Vol. 92, September 15, 2012, No. 38, pp. 32)
Pub: Dow Jones & Company Inc.
Contact: Almar Latour, Chief Executive Officer
Ed: Andrew Bary. Description: Asset management firms are offering endowment-style investment services that allow investors to invest in funds in the same way as foundations and endowments. High-Vista Strategies with $3.6 billion in assets under management, has produced a total return of 43.5 percent after fees from October 2005 to June 2012 using this strategy. Availability: Online.

6481 ■ "Investment Banks" in Black Enterprise (Vol. 44, June 2014, No. 10, pp. 88)
Pub: Earl G. Graves Ltd.
Contact: Earl Graves, Jr., President
Description: A ranking of the top 100 investment banks in the U.S. are presented.

6482 ■ "Investment Funds: Friends with Money" in Canadian Business (Vol. 81, May 22, 2008, No. 9, pp. 22)
Pub: Rogers Media Inc.
Contact: Neil Spivak, Chief Executive Officer
Ed: Jeff Stanford. Description: Two of the most well connected managers in Canadian capital markets Rob Farquharson and Brian Gibson will launch Panoply Capital Asset Management in June. The investment management company aims to raise a billion dollars from institutions and high-net worth individuals. Availability: Print; Online.

6483 ■ "Is Fannie Mae the Next Government Bailout?" in Barron's (Vol. 88, March 10, 2008, No. 10, pp. 21)
Pub: Dow Jones & Company Inc.
Contact: Almar Latour, Chief Executive Officer
Ed: Jonathan R. Laing. Description: Fannie Mae may need a government bailout as it faces huge hits brought about by the effects of the housing crisis. The shares of the government-sponsored enterprise have dropped 65 percent since the housing crisis began. Availability: Online.

6484 ■ "Is the VIX in Denial?" in Barron's (Vol. 88, July 7, 2008, No. 27, pp. M12)
Pub: Dow Jones & Company Inc.
Contact: Almar Latour, Chief Executive Officer
Ed: Lawrence McMillan. Description: Volatility Index (VIX) of the Chicago Board Options Exchange did not rise significantly despite the drop in the US stock markets, rising to near 25. This market decline, however, will eventually result in investor panic and the rise of the VIX. Availability: Online.

6485 ■ "It Could Be Worse" in Barron's (Vol. 89, July 27, 2009, No. 30, pp. 5)
Pub: Dow Jones & Company Inc.
Contact: Almar Latour, Chief Executive Officer
Ed: Alan Abelson. Description: Media sources are being fooled by corporate America who is peddling an economic recovery rather than reality as shown by the report of a rise in existing home sales which boosted the stock market even if it was a seasonal phenomenon. The phrase "things could be worse" sums up the reigning investment philosophy in the U.S. and this has been stirring up the market. Availability: Online.

6486 ■ "Ivernia Mine Closing Could Boost Lead" in Globe & Mail (April 4, 2007, pp. B5)
Ed: Andy Hoffman. Description: The closing of Ivernia Inc.'s mine in view of government investigation into alleged lead contamination at the port of Esperance is discussed. The likely increase in the price of lead is also discussed. Availability: Print; Online.

6487 ■ "Jacksonville Doing Well In Growing Economy" in Orlando Business Journal (Vol. 30, June 27, 2014, No. 53, pp. 8)
Pub: American City Business Journals, Inc.
Contact: Mike Olivieri, Executive Vice President

Released: June 27, 2014. **Description:** Jerry Mallot is the president of JaxUSA Partnership, the economic development arm of the Jax Chambers. According to Mallot, Northeast Florida's strongest selling points for business site or relocation there include advanced manufacturing, financial services, aviation and aerospace technology, life sciences, logistics and information technology.

6488 ■ *"Jamieson Eyes $175 Million Trust IPO"* in *Globe & Mail* (March 7, 2006, pp. B1)
Ed: Sinclair Stewart, Leonard Zehr. **Description:** The reasons behind $175 million initial public offering plans of Jamieson Laboratories Ltd. are presented. **Availability:** Print; Online.

6489 ■ *"J.C. Penney Head Shops for Shares"* in *Barron's* (Vol. 88, July 7, 2008, No. 27, pp. 29)
Pub: Dow Jones & Company Inc.
Contact: Almar Latour, Chief Executive Officer
Ed: Teresa Rivas. **Description:** Myron Ullman III, chairman and chief executive officer of J.C. Penney, purchased $1 million worth of shares of the company. He now owns 393,140 shares of the company and an additional 1,282 on his 401(k) plan. **Availability:** Online.

6490 ■ *"Jim Cramer's Get Rich Carefully"*
Pub: Penguin Publishing Group
Released: December 31, 2013 . **Price:** $17, paperback; $11.99, e-book; $20, audiobook download; $14.99. **Description:** Wall Street veteran and host of CNBC's Mad Money, Jim Cramer, provides a guide to high-yield, low-risk investing in a recovering economic market. **Availability:** audiobook; E-book; Print.

6491 ■ *"Judge Gives RIM One Last Chance"* in *Globe & Mail* (February 24, 2006, pp. B5)
Ed: Barrie McKenna, Paul Waldie. **Description:** United States District Court Judge James Spencer offers more time for Research In Motion Ltd. (RIM) to settle the patent infringement dispute with NTP Inc. RIM's shares increase by 6.2 percent following the decision. **Availability:** Online.

6492 ■ *"Juiced on Energy"* in *Barron's* (Vol. 88, July 14, 2008, No. 28, pp. 33)
Pub: Dow Jones & Company Inc.
Contact: Almar Latour, Chief Executive Officer
Ed: Leslie P. Norton. **Description:** Brad Evans and his team at Heartland Value Plus were able to outperform their peers by significantly undercommitting to financials and overexposing themselves with energy stocks. Brad Evans believes that there is a lot of value left in energy stocks such as natural gas. **Availability:** Online.

6493 ■ *"Just Hang Up"* in *Barron's* (Vol. 88, March 10, 2008, No. 10, pp. 45)
Description: Sprint's shares are expected to continue falling while the company attempts to attract subscribers by cutting prices, cutting earnings in the process. The company faces tougher competition from better-financed AT&T and Verizon Communications.

6494 ■ *"Keeping the Faith in Fuel-Tech"* in *Barron's* (Vol. 88, March 24, 2008, No. 12, pp. 20)
Pub: Dow Jones & Company Inc.
Contact: Almar Latour, Chief Executive Officer
Ed: Christopher C. Williams. **Description:** Shares of air pollution control company Fuel-Tech remain on track to reach $40 each from their $19 level due to a continued influx of contracts. The stock has suffered from lower-than-expected quarterly earnings and tougher competition but stand to benefit from increased orders. **Availability:** Online.

6495 ■ *"The Latin Beat Goes On"* in *Barron's* (Vol. 88, July 7, 2008, No. 27, pp. L5)
Pub: Dow Jones & Company Inc.
Contact: Almar Latour, Chief Executive Officer
Ed: Tom Sullivan. **Description:** Latin American stocks have outperformed other regional markets due to rising commodities prices and favorable economic climate. Countries such as Brazil, Mexico, Chile, and Peru provide investment opportunities, while Argentina and Venezuela are tougher places to invest. **Availability:** Online.

6496 ■ *"Leaders and Lagards"* in *Barron's* (Vol. 89, July 13, 2009, No. 28, pp. 14)
Description: Statistical table that shows the returns of different mutual funds in different categories that include U.S. stock funds, sector funds, world equity funds, and mixed equity funds is presented. The data presented is for the second quarter of 2009. **Availability:** Print; Online.

6497 ■ *"Legg Mason Compensation Committee Chair Defends CEO Fetting's Pay"* in *Baltimore Business Journal* (Vol. 29, July 22, 2011, No. 11, pp. 1)
Pub: Boston Business Journal
Contact: Carolyn M. Jones, President
E-mail: cmjones@bizjournals.com
Ed: Gary Haber. **Description:** Legg Mason Inc. CEO Mark R. Fetting has been awarded $5.9 million pay package and he expects to receive questions regarding it in the coming shareholders meeting. However, Baltimore, Maryland-based RKTL Associates chairman emeritus Harold R. Adams believes Fetting has done a tremendous job in bringing Legg's through a tough market. **Availability:** Print; Online.

6498 ■ *"Lending Door Slams"* in *Puget Sound Business Journal* (Vol. 29, October 24, 2008, No. 27, pp. 1)
Description: KeyBank's closure of its Puget Sound unit that services single-family homebuilders is part of a nationwide shutdown that includes similar closures in other cities. Bank of America is adopting more conservative terms for homebuilding loans while Union Bank of California is still offering credit for market rate housing. **Availability:** Print; Online.

6499 ■ *"Less Malaise in Malaysia"* in *Barron's* (Vol. 88, March 17, 2008, No. 11, pp. M12)
Pub: Dow Jones & Company Inc.
Contact: Almar Latour, Chief Executive Officer
Ed: Assif Shameen. **Description:** Shares of Malaysia's Bursa have been in freefall while the Malaysia government prolongs its pitch to sell a 10 percent stake of the exchange to NYSE Euronext. Asian bourses had produced very good returns for five years and charge some of the highest fees for exchanges. A key growth driver for Asian bourses could be the derivatives markets and exchange-traded funds. **Availability:** Online.

6500 ■ *"LIBOR's Hidden Lesson: Instant Messages Are Deadly"* in *Canadian Business* (Vol. 85, August 12, 2012, No. 14, pp. 75)
Ed: Vanessa Farquharson. **Description:** The appropriate use of instant messaging in the workplace is discussed. Employees involved in a business that deals with other people's finances or intellectual property are advised to keep all of their work and private email accounts separate. **Availability:** Print; Online.

6501 ■ *"Listen Up: There's a Revolution in the Cubicle"* in *Barron's* (Vol. 89, July 27, 2009, No. 30, pp. 18)
Pub: Dow Jones & Company Inc.
Contact: Almar Latour, Chief Executive Officer
Ed: Jay Palmer. **Description:** Plantronics will be among the first beneficiaries when the unified communications revolution arrives in the office. Plantronics' shares could rise to around 30 in 2009 from the 20s as of July 2009. Unified communications could create a huge new multimillion-dollar market for Plantronics. **Availability:** Online.

6502 ■ *"The Little Biotech that Could"* in *Barron's* (Vol. 89, July 27, 2009, No. 30, pp. 19)
Pub: Dow Jones & Company Inc.
Contact: Almar Latour, Chief Executive Officer
Ed: Christopher C. Williams. **Description:** OSI Pharmaceuticals' shares is a compelling investment bet among small biotech firms due to its Tarceva anticancer drug which has a 23 percent market share as well as their strong balance sheet. OSI is planning to expand the use of Tarceva which could re-ignite sales and one analyst expects the shares to trade in the 40s one year from July 2009. **Availability:** Online.

6503 ■ *"Long-Term Bull, Short-Term Bear"* in *Barron's* (Vol. 92, September 17, 2012, No. 38, pp. 24)
Description: Jason DeSena Trennert, managing partner at Strategas Research Partners, discusses his views on the financial markets and the US economy. He is bullish on the stocks of Merck, McDonalds, IBM and Oracle. **Availability:** Online.

6504 ■ *"Loonies Buy U.S. Cable"* in *Canadian Business* (Vol. 85, September 17, 2012, No. 14, pp. 8)
Ed: Jeff Beer. **Description:** The move by two Canadian companies to invest in the U.S. cable industry get mixed reactions from analyst and observers. Cogeco Cable purchased Atlantic Broadband for $1.36 billion while the Canada Pension Plan Investment Board announced its partnership with European private equity firm BC Partners to acquire Suddenlink Communications for $6.6 billion. **Availability:** Online.

6505 ■ *"Lotus Starts Slowly, Dodges Subprime Woes"* in *Crain's Detroit Business* (Vol. 24, April 14, 2008, No. 15, pp. 3)
Pub: Crain Communications Inc.
Contact: Barry Asin, President
Ed: Tom Henderson. **Description:** Discusses Lotus Bancorp Inc. and their business plan, which although is not right on target due to the subprime mortgage meltdown, is in a much better position than its competitors due to the quality of their loans. **Availability:** Online.

6506 ■ *"Lower Prices No Shoo-In as Telcos Near Deregulation"* in *Globe & Mail* (March 28, 2007, pp. B1)
Ed: Catherine McLean. **Description:** The fall in market share and low quality of service among other issues that may disallow telecommunication industries in Canada from setting their phone rates is discussed. **Availability:** Online.

6507 ■ *"Lundin Deal Leaves Nickel Market Thin"* in *Globe & Mail* (April 5, 2007, pp. B4)
Ed: Andy Hoffman. **Description:** The likely acquisition of Rio Narcea Gold Mines Ltd. by Lundin Mining Corp. and the decreasing number of nickel mining companies on the list of Toronto Stock Exchange are discussed. **Availability:** Online.

6508 ■ *"Magna Banks on Big Cash Hoard"* in *Globe & Mail* (March 1, 2006, pp. B3)
Ed: Greg Keenan. **Description:** The details on Magna International Inc., which posted decline in profits at $639 million for 2005, are presented. **Availability:** Online.

6509 ■ *"Making It Click: Annual Ranking Of the Best Online Brokers"* in *Barron's* (Vol. 88, March 17, 2008, No. 11, pp. 31)
Pub: Dow Jones & Company Inc.
Contact: Almar Latour, Chief Executive Officer
Ed: Theresa W. Carey. **Description:** Listing of 23 online brokers that are evaluated based on their trade experience, usability, range of offerings, research amenities, customer service and access, and costs. TradeStation Securities takes the top spot followed by thinkorswim by just a fraction. **Availability:** Online.

6510 ■ *"M&T On the March?"* in *Baltimore Business Journal* (Vol. 28, November 12, 2010, No. 27, pp. 1)
Pub: Baltimore Business Journal
Contact: Rhonda Pringle, President
E-mail: rpringle@bizjournals.com
Ed: Gary Haber. **Description:** Information on the growth of M&T Bank, as well as its expansion plans are presented. M&T recently acquired Wilmington Trust and took over $500 million in deposits from the failed K Bank. Analysts believe that M&T would continue its expansion through Washington DC and

Richmond, Virginia, especially after a bank executive acknowledged that the markets in those areas are attractive. **Availability:** Print; Online.

6511 ■ *"Many Roads Lead to Value Says David J. Williams, Manager of Excelsior Value & Restructuring Fund"* in Barron's (Vol. 88, March 10, 2008, No. 10, pp. 46)
Pub: Dow Jones & Company Inc.
Contact: Almar Latour, Chief Executive Officer

Ed: Lawrence C. Strauss. **Description:** David J. Williams, lead manager of Excelsior Value & Restructuring Fund, invests in struggling companies and those companies whose turnarounds show promise. Morgan Stanley, Lehman Brothers, and Petroleo Brasileiro are some of the companies he holds shares in, while he has unloaded shares of Citigroup, Freddie Mac, and Sallie Mae. **Availability:** Online.

6512 ■ *"Market Watch"* in Barron's (Vol. 88, March 24, 2008, No. 12, pp. M18)

Ed: Ashraf Laidi, Marc Pado, David Kotok. **Released:** 2018. **Description:** Latest measures implemented by the Federal Reserve to address the credit crisis did not benefit the US dollar, with the Japanese yen and the euro recouping earlier losses against the dollar. Goldman Sachs reported earnings of $3.23 per share, claiming a stronger liquidity position. The US markets bottomed early on 22 January 2007, according to evidence. **Availability:** Print; Online.

6513 ■ *"Market Watch: A Sampling of Advisory Opinion"* in Barron's (Vol. 88, March 17, 2008, No. 11, pp. M10)
Pub: Dow Jones & Company Inc.
Contact: Almar Latour, Chief Executive Officer

Ed: Paul Schatz, William Gibson, Michael Darda, Peter Greene, Ian Wyatt, Stephanie Pomboy. **Released:** January 25, 2014. **Description:** S&P 500 bank stocks were down 46 percent from their 2007 peak while the peak to through fall in 1989-1990 was just over 50 percent. This suggests that the bottom on the bank stocks could be near. The Federal Reserve Board announced they will lend up to $200 billion to primary lenders in exchange other securities. **Availability:** Print; Online.

6514 ■ *"Market Watch: A Sampling of Advisory Opinion US Stock Price Trends, Economic Effects of Global Trade, Chinese Economic Trends"* in Barron's (Vol. 92, July 23, 2012, No. 30, pp. M14)

Ed: Richard M. Salsman, Jack Ablin, Francois Sicart. **Description:** US stocks are considered inexpensive due to their low price-earnings ratios compared to levels before the global financial crisis. The US economy is becoming more dependent on the rest of the worldas a result of global trade. The Chinese economy continues to have strong economic growth despite a slowdown. **Availability:** Online.

6515 ■ *"Markets Defy the Doomsayers"* in Barron's (Vol. 88, March 24, 2008, No. 12, pp. M5)
Pub: Dow Jones & Company Inc.
Contact: Almar Latour, Chief Executive Officer

Ed: Leslie P. Norton. **Description:** US stock markets registered strong gains, with the Dow Jones Industrial Average rising 3.43 percent on the week to close at 12,361.32, in a rally that may be seen as short-covering. Shares of Hansen Natural are poised for further drops with a slowdown in the energy drink market. **Availability:** Online.

6516 ■ *"Markets: The Great Deleveraging"* in Canadian Business (Vol. 81, October 13, 2008, No. 17, pp. 45)
Pub: Rogers Media Inc.
Contact: Neil Spivak, Chief Executive Officer

Ed: Jeff Sanford. **Description:** 'Hell Week' of financial crisis on Wall Street is believed to have started with the downgrade of AIG Inc.'s credit rating. AIG is a major player in the credit derivatives market, and its bankruptcy would have affected firms on Wall Street. **Availability:** Online.

6517 ■ *"Mary Kramer: Good Things Happen When We Buy Local"* in Crain's Detroit Business (Vol. 24, October 6, 2008, No. 40, pp. 7)
Pub: Crain Communications Inc.
Contact: Barry Asin, President

Description: Michigan is facing incredibly difficult economic times. One way in which each one of us can help the state and the businesses located here is by purchasing our goods and services from local vendors. The state Agriculture Department projected that if Michigan households earmarked $10 per week in their grocery purchases to made-in-Michigan products, this would generate $30 million a week in economic impact. **Availability:** Online.

6518 ■ *The Match King: Ivar Kreuger, the Financial Genius Behind a Century of Wall Street Scandals*
Pub: PublicAffairs
Contact: Jaime Leifer, Director

Ed: Frank Partnoy. **Released:** March 09, 2010. **Price:** $16.99, paperback; $10.99, e-book. **Description:** Ivar Kreuger, the so-called Match King, used a pyramid scheme to become the financier to European leaders. **Availability:** E-book; Print.

6519 ■ *"McDonald's Loses Its Sizzle"* in Barron's (Vol. 88, March 17, 2008, No. 11, pp. 47)

Description: McDonald's has promised to return $15 billion to $17 billion to shareholders in 2007-2009 but headwinds are rising for the company. December, 2007 same-store sales were flat and the company's traffic growth in the U.S. is slowing. Its shares are likely to trade in tandem with the market until recession fears recede. **Availability:** Online.

6520 ■ *"Md.'s Boring Bonds Gain Pizzazz as Investors Flock to Debt Issues"* in Baltimore Business Journal (Vol. 28, June 11, 2010, No. 5, pp. 1)
Pub: Baltimore Business Journal
Contact: Rhonda Pringle, President
E-mail: rpringle@bizjournals.com

Ed: Gary Haber. **Description:** Companies and nonprofit organizations have increased the pace of bond offerings in order to take advantage of the bonds' appeal among willing investors. Companies mostly issued corporate bonds to replace existing debt at lower interest rates and save them money from interest payments.

6521 ■ *"Meet the Money Whisperer to the Super-Rich N.B.A. Elite"* in The New York Times (June 6, 2019)
URL(s): www.nytimes.com/2019/06/06/business/nba-wealth-manager-klay-thompson-joe-mclean.html

Ed: Devin Gordon. **Released:** June 06, 2019. **Description:** Profile of Joe McLean, a premier wealth manager for the NBA elite. Discusses his unusual strategies for managing wealth and how he earns the trust of his clients. **Availability:** Online.

6522 ■ *"Merrill Lynch in Talks to Buy BlackRock Stake"* in Globe & Mail (February 13, 2006, pp. B4)

Description: Financial services firm Merrill Lynch and Co. Inc. is planning to acquire money managing company BlackRock Inc. for 8 million dollars. Sources report that this deal would create 1-trillion dollar huge fund management venture. **Availability:** Online.

6523 ■ *"Microsoft's Big Gamble"* in Canadian Business (Vol. 81, March 3, 2008, No. 3, pp. 13)

Description: Microsoft Corp. is taking a big risk in buying Yahoo, as it is expected to pay more than $31 a share to finalize the acquisition. The deal would be seven and a half times bigger than any other that Microsoft has entered before, an execution of such deal is also anticipated to become a challenge for Microsoft. Recommendations on how Microsoft should handle the integration of the two businesses are given. **Availability:** Print; Online.

6524 ■ *"Millennial Money: How Young Investors Can Build a Fortune"*
Pub: Palgrave Macmillan

Released: October 14, 2014. **Price:** $26, hardcover. **Description:** Because the millennial generation won't be able to depend on pensions or social security for their retirement security, it is stressed that they save and invest their money wisely. As a generation, though, they are skeptical of advice from their elders, but are committed to passing wealth to future generations. A strategy for wise investments to help overcome shortcomings is included. **Availability:** E-book; Print.

6525 ■ *"Mine Woes Could Rouse Zinc"* in Barron's (Vol. 88, July 7, 2008, No. 27, pp. M12)
Pub: Dow Jones & Company Inc.
Contact: Almar Latour, Chief Executive Officer

Ed: Andrea Hotter. **Description:** Prices of zinc could increase due to supply problems in producing countries such as Australia and China. London Metal Exchange prices for the metal have dropped about 36 percent in 2008. **Availability:** Online.

6526 ■ *"Mining Goldman for Insight"* in Barron's (Vol. 89, July 20, 2009, No. 29, pp. M8)
Pub: Dow Jones & Company Inc.
Contact: Almar Latour, Chief Executive Officer

Ed: Steven M. Sears. **Description:** Methods of investing in options for companies with earnings estimates from Goldman Sachs are discussed. These methods take advantage of increased volatility generated by earnings revisions. **Availability:** Online.

6527 ■ *"A Mixed-Bag Quarter"* in Barron's (Vol. 88, July 7, 2008, No. 27, pp. 19)

Description: Seven component companies of the Dow Jones Industrial Average increased their dividend payouts in the second quarter of 2008 despite the weak performance of the index. Five companies in the Dow Jones Transportation index and three in the Dow Jones Utilities also increased their dividends. **Availability:** Online.

6528 ■ *"Money Basics: How to Handle a Bank Error"* in Black Enterprise (Vol. 41, December 2010, No. 5)
Pub: Earl G. Graves Ltd.
Contact: Earl Graves, Jr., President

Ed: Sheiresa Ngo. **Description:** Contact your bank or financial institution immediately after discovering an error in your account. **Availability:** Online.

6529 ■ *"More Gains in the Pipeline"* in Barron's (Vol. 89, August 3, 2009, No. 31, pp. M5)

Description: Shares of El Paso Corp. could recover as the company concludes a deal with a private-equity group to fund pipeline construction. The company's shares are trading at $10.06 and could move up to $12 as bad news has already been priced into the stock. **Availability:** Online.

6530 ■ *"Mover and Sheika"* in Conde Nast Portfolio (Vol. 2, June 2008, No. 6, pp. 104)

Ed: John Arlidge. **Description:** Profile of Princess Sheika Lubna who is the first female foreign trade minister in the Middle East, the United Arab Emirates biggest business envoy, paving the way for billions in new investment, and also a manufacturer of her own perfume line. **Availability:** Online.

6531 ■ *"A Neat SocialTrade"* in Barron's (Vol. 92, July 23, 2012, No. 30, pp. 23)
Pub: Dow Jones & Company Inc.
Contact: Almar Latour, Chief Executive Officer

Ed: Theresa W. Carey. **Description:** SocialTrade is a Website that allows users to exchange ideas and data with each other through video. Online broker DittoTrade launched a mobile applications that allows investors to connect to other traders and follow their trades. **Availability:** Online.

6532 ■ "Needed: A Strategy; Banking In China" in The Economist (Vol. 390, January 3, 2009, No. 8612, pp. 54)
Description: International banks are competing for a role in China but are finding obstacles in their paths such as a reduction in the credit their operations may receive from Chinese banks and the role they can play in the public capital markets which remain limited. **Availability:** Print; Online.

6533 ■ "The New Janus CEO of Battle-Hardened Money Manager Plots Comeback" in Denver Business Journal (Vol. 64, August 31, 2012, No. 15, pp. 1)
Pub: Baltimore Business Journal
Contact: Rhonda Pringle, President
E-mail: rpringle@bizjournals.com
Description: Richard Well, chief executive officer of Janus Capital Group Inc., discusses the strategic plans of the mutual fund company. He touches on the firm's alliance with Dai-chi Life Insurance Company Ltd., the future of equity markets, and the company's intelligent diversification strategy. **Availability:** Print; Online.

6534 ■ "A New Kid on the Block" in Barron's (Vol. 88, March 17, 2008, No. 11, pp. 58)
Pub: Dow Jones & Company Inc.
Contact: Almar Latour, Chief Executive Officer
Ed: Thomas G. Donlan. **Description:** Discusses the Federal Reserve which has offered to lend $100 billion in cash to banks and $200 billion in Treasuries to Wall Street investment banks that have problems with liquidity. The reluctance of the banks to lend money to meet a margin call on securities that could still depreciate is the reason why the agency is going into the direct loan business. **Availability:** Online.

6535 ■ "The New Nimble" in Barron's (Vol. 90, August 30, 2010, No. 35, pp. S12)
Pub: Barron's Editorial & Corporate Headquarters
Ed: Suzanne McGee. **Description:** Financial advisors are making investments based on short-lived market trends due to the uncertainty in the long-term market. This strategy can be demanding and advisors should only try it if they are confident about their skill in spotting short-term trends. **Availability:** Online.

6536 ■ "A New Way to Tell When to Fold 'Em" in Barron's (Vol. 88, July 7, 2008, No. 27, pp. 27)
Pub: Dow Jones & Company Inc.
Contact: Almar Latour, Chief Executive Officer
Ed: Theresa W. Carey. **Description:** Overview of the Online trading company SmartStops, a firm that aims to tell investors when to sell the shares of a particular company. The company's Web site categorizes stocks as moving up, down, or sideways, and calculates exit points for individual stocks based on an overall market trend. **Availability:** Online.

6537 ■ "Nightmare on Wall Street" in Canadian Business (Vol. 81, October 13, 2008, No. 17, pp. 9)
Description: Information on events that happened on Wall Street on the week that started September 15, 2008, as well on its effect on financial markets around the world, are presented. Lehman Brothers filed for bankruptcy on September 15, 2008 after negotiations with Barclays Group and Bank of America failed. Details on AIG and Morgan Stanley are also presented. **Availability:** Online.

6538 ■ "No Assets for Retirement? Eh, Who Cares?" in Financial Advisor (November, 2019)
URL(s): www.fa-mag.com/news/no-assets-for-retirement--eh--who-cares-52368.html?issue=323
Ed: Karen Demasters. **Released:** November 2019.
Description: About half of Americans have savings for retirement and those who do not, do not seem to care. With many people trying to pay bills and support themselves through the day, it's no wonder that many do not have savings set aside for the distant future.

6539 ■ "Nortel Plays Big to Settle Lawsuits" in Globe & Mail (February 9, 2006, pp. B1)
Description: The details on Nortel Networks Corp.'s settlement of cases with shareholders are presented. **Availability:** Online.

6540 ■ "Now in Play, Score Keeps Head Up and Stick on Ice" in Globe & Mail (January 20, 2007, pp. B5)
Ed: Grant Robertson. **Description:** The hike in the shares of Score Media Inc. due to its new services is presented. **Availability:** Online.

6541 ■ "Now That's Rich" in Canadian Business (Vol. 80, February 12, 2007, No. 4, pp. 92)
Description: The effort of chief executive officer of Stelco Inc. Rodney Mott in resolving the issue of financial loss of the company by taking up backdating options for share price is discussed. **Availability:** Print; Online.

6542 ■ "The Numbers Speak For Themselves" in Barron's (Vol. 88, July 14, 2008, No. 28, pp. 16)
Pub: Dow Jones & Company Inc.
Contact: Almar Latour, Chief Executive Officer
Ed: Bill Alpert. **Description:** Discusses quant fund managers versus traditional long-short equity funds after quants outperformed traditional funds in the year 2000. Causes for the underperformance are outlined and statistical data is included. **Availability:** Online.

6543 ■ "Nvidia Shares Clobbered After Gloomy Warning" in Barron's (Vol. 88, July 7, 2008, No. 27, pp. 25)
Pub: Dow Jones & Company Inc.
Contact: Almar Latour, Chief Executive Officer
Ed: Eric J. Savitz. **Description:** Shares of graphics chip manufacturer Nvidia suffered a 30 percent drop in its share price after the company warned that revenue and gross margin forecasts for the quarter ending July 27, 2008 will be below expectations. Stan Glasgow, chief operating officer of Sony Electronics, believes the US economic slowdown will not affect demand for the company's products. Statistical data included. **Availability:** Online.

6544 ■ "Nvidia's Picture Brighter Than Stock Price Indicates" in Barron's (Vol. 88, March 24, 2008, No. 12, pp. 46)
Pub: Dow Jones & Company Inc.
Contact: Almar Latour, Chief Executive Officer
Ed: Eric J. Savitz. **Description:** Shares of graphics chip maker Nvidia, priced at $18.52 each, do not indicate the company's strong position in the graphics chip market. The company's shares have dropped due to fears of slower demand for PCs, but the company is not as exposed to broader economic forces. **Availability:** Online.

6545 ■ "Nymex Dissidents Rattle Sabers" in Crain's Chicago Business (Vol. 31, April 21, 2008, No. 16, pp. 2)
Pub: Crain Communications Inc.
Contact: Barry Asin, President
Ed: Ann Saphir. **Description:** Two groups of New York Mercantile Exchange members say they have more than enough votes to stop CME Group Inc.'s $10 billion deal to acquire the oil and metals exchange and they are threatening a proxy fight if the Chicago exchange doesn't raise its offer. **Availability:** Online.

6546 ■ "Obama Orders Contractors To Raise Minimum Wage" in Atlanta Business Chronicle (June 20, 2014, pp. 9A)
Pub: American City Business Journals, Inc.
Contact: Mike Olivieri, Executive Vice President
Description: Discussion of the new rules set out by President Obama, which includes the minimum wage of employees and discrimination against employees doing business with the Federal government is presented. The minimum wage law will increase to $10 per hour from $7.25 per hour; and discrimination against employees on the basis of sexual orientation or gender identity will not be tolerated. **Availability:** Print; Online.

6547 ■ "October 2009: Recovery Plods Along" in Hispanic Business (October 2009, pp. 10-11)
Description: Economist reports on a possible economic recovery which will not be allowed to rely on a strong domestic demand in order to sustain it. Consumers, looking to counterbalance years of leverage financing based on unrealistic, ever-increasing home and portfolio valuations, are saving rather than spending money.

6548 ■ "Ohio Commerce Draws Closer to Profitability" in Crain's Cleveland Business (Vol. 28, October 29, 2007, No. 43, pp. 14)
Pub: Crain Communications Inc.
Contact: K. C. Crain, President
Ed: Shawn A. Turner. **Description:** Overview of the business plan of Ohio Commerce Bank, a de novo, or startup bank that is close to turning the corner to profitability. The bank opened in November 2006 and focuses on dealing with small businesses totaling $5 million or less in annual revenues. **Availability:** Online.

6549 ■ "Oil's Going Down, Down, Down" in Canadian Business (Vol. 79, October 9, 2006, No. 20, pp. 148)
Description: Strategies for investors to benefit from the fall in global crude oil prices are discussed. **Availability:** Print; Online.

6550 ■ "The Old Railway is on a Roll" in Globe & Mail (January 26, 2006, pp. B1)
Description: The reasons behind 5 percent rise in shares for Canadian National Railway Co. are presented. **Availability:** Online.

6551 ■ "One-Time Area Trust Executive Finds Trouble in N.H." in The Business Journal-Serving Metropolitan Kansas City (September 12, 2008)
Description: About 200 investors, some from Missouri's Kansas City area, claim that they had conducted business with Noble Trust Co. The trust company was placed under New Hampshire Banking Department's conservatorship after $15 million was discovered to be missing from its account. It is alleged that the money was lost in a Colorado Ponzi scheme. **Availability:** Print; Online.

6552 ■ "Opportunity Now Lies at Short End of the Market" in Barron's (Vol. 88, June 30, 2008, No. 26, pp. M9)
Pub: Dow Jones & Company Inc.
Contact: Almar Latour, Chief Executive Officer
Ed: Michael S. Derby. **Description:** Renewed credit concerns and the lesser chance of a Federal Reserve interest rate hike boosted the bond market. Some portfolio managers are more bullish on short-dated securities as they expect the market to adjust to a more appropriate outlook. **Availability:** Online.

6553 ■ "Oracle: No Profit of Doom" in Barron's (Vol. 88, March 31, 2008, No. 13, pp. 40)
Pub: Dow Jones & Company Inc.
Contact: Almar Latour, Chief Executive Officer
Ed: Mark Veverka. **Description:** Oracle's revenues grew by 21 percent but fell short of expectation and their profits came in at the low-end of expectations. The company's shares dropped 8 percent but investors are advised to pay more attention to the company's earnings expansion rather than revenue growth in a slow economy. Nokia's Rick Simonson points out that their markets in Asia and particularly India is growing so they are not as affected by the U.S. economic conditions. **Availability:** Online.

6554 ■ "Over A Barrel" in Canadian Business (Vol. 81, July 21, 2008, No. 11, pp. 13)
Description: Analysts predict that the skyrocketing price of fuel will cause a crackdown in the market as purported in the peak oil theory. It is forecasted that

the price of oil will reach $200 per barrel. Details of the effect of the increasing oil prices on the market are presented.

6555 ■ *"Packaging Firm Wraps Up Remake: Overseas Plants Help Firm Fatten Margins"* in *Crain's New York Business (January 6, 2008)*
Pub: Crain Communications, Inc.
Contact: Jessica Botos, Manager, Marketing
E-mail: jessica.botos@crainsnewyork.com
Description: Sealed Air Corp., a packaging manufacturer, has seen its share price fall nearly 20 percent over the past two years, making it one of the worst performers in the packaging sector. **Availability:** Online.

6556 ■ *Paper Fortunes: Modern Wall Street: Where It's Been and Where It's Going*
Ed: Roy C. Smith. **Released:** 2010. **Description:** Comprehensive history of Wall Street and lessons learned with insight into ways Wall Street will reinvent itself in this new economy. **Availability:** E-book.

6557 ■ *"Paterson Plots Comeback With Internet IPO"* in *Globe & Mail (February 20, 2006, pp. B1)*
Ed: Grant Robertson. **Description:** The initial public offering plans of chief executive officer Scott Paterson of JumpTV.com are presented. **Availability:** Online.

6558 ■ *"Perry Ellis and G-III Apparel--Out of Fashion, but Still in Style"* in *Barron's (Vol. 88, March 17, 2008, No. 11, pp. 48)*
Pub: Dow Jones & Company Inc.
Contact: Almar Latour, Chief Executive Officer
Ed: Robin Goldwyn Blumenthal. **Description:** Shares of Perry Ellis International and G-III Apparel Group have taken some beating in the market despite good growth earnings prospects. Perry Ellis sees earnings growth of 8 to 11 percent for fiscal 2009, while G-III Apparel expects earnings growth of 25 percent. **Availability:** Online.

6559 ■ *"Peter Bynoe Trades Up"* in *Black Enterprise (Vol. 38, July 2008, No. 12, pp. 30)*
Pub: Earl G. Graves Ltd.
Contact: Earl Graves, Jr., President
Description: Chicago-based Loop Capital Markets L.L.C. has named Peter Bynoe managing director of corporate finance. Bynoe was previously a senior partner at the law firm DLA Piper U.S. L.L.P., where he worked on stadium deals.

6560 ■ *"Place Restrictions on Your Stock Shares"* in *Business Owner (Vol. 35, July-August 2011, No. 4, pp. 14)*
Description: It is critical for any small business owner to be certain that the buyer or recipient of any part of the company represents that the stock is being acquired or given for investment purposes only. **Availability:** Online.

6561 ■ *"PNC Begins Search for New Baltimore-Area Headquarters"* in *Baltimore Business Journal (Vol. 28, June 4, 2010, No. 4, pp. 1)*
Pub: Baltimore Business Journal
Contact: Rhonda Pringle, President
E-mail: rpringle@bizjournals.com
Ed: Daniel J. Sernovitz. **Description:** PNC Financial Services Group Inc. is searching for a new headquarters building in Greater Baltimore, Maryland. The company is seeking about 150,000 square feet for its regional operations. However, PNC could also end up moving out of Baltimore for space in the surrounding suburbs. **Availability:** Print; Online.

6562 ■ *"The Power of Alumni Networks"* in *Harvard Business Review (Vol. 88, October 2010, No. 10, pp. 34)*
Pub: Harvard Business Publishing
Contact: Diane Belcher, Managing Director
Ed: Lauren H. Cohen, Christopher J. Malloy. **Price:** $6, PDF. **Description:** Research indicates that members of alumni associations tend to invest in similar ways; implications for the mutual funds sector are discussed. **Availability:** Online; PDF.

6563 ■ *"Private Equity Firms"* in *Black Enterprise (Vol. 44, June 2014, No. 10, pp. 89)*
Pub: Earl G. Graves Ltd.
Contact: Earl Graves, Jr., President
Description: A ranking of private equity firms in the U.S. is presented. **Availability:** Online.

6564 ■ *"Private Equity Firms Focus on Failing Banks"* in *Baltimore Business Journal (Vol. 28, July 16, 2010, No. 10, pp. 1)*
Pub: Baltimore Business Journal
Contact: Rhonda Pringle, President
E-mail: rpringle@bizjournals.com
Ed: Gary Haber. **Description:** Four deals in which assets of failed banks were acquired by private equity firms have been approved by the Federal Deposit Insurance Corporation in the past couple of years. Bay Bank FSK, for example, purchased Bay National Bank's assets in July 2010. Forecasts on more private equity acquisitions in the community banking industry are given. **Availability:** Print; Online.

6565 ■ *"Private TV Industry's Profit Climbs 4 Per Cent"* in *Globe & Mail (March 29, 2006, pp. B6)*
Ed: Simon Tuck. **Description:** The private television industry in Canada is experiencing 4 percent increase in its profits, i.e. $242.2 millions. The revenues of CTV contributed more to this increase in profits. **Availability:** Online.

6566 ■ *"Profits Without Prosperity: Stock Buybacks Manipulate the Market and Leave Most Americans Worse Off"* in *Harvard Business Review (Vol. 92, September 2014, No. 9, pp. 46)*
Pub: Harvard Business Publishing
Contact: Diane Belcher, Managing Director
Price: $8.95. **Description:** While stock prices rise due to stock buybacks, the long-term effects of buybacks are job instability, sluggish growth, and income inequality. Firms should not be permitted to repurchase their shares, and restrictions should be placed on stock-based pay. Profits should be invested in innovation. **Availability:** Online; PDF.

6567 ■ *"The Promise of the Promised Land"* in *San Francisco Business Times (Vol. 28, January 3, 2014, No. 24, pp. 4)*
Pub: American City Business Journals, Inc.
Contact: Mike Olivieri, Executive Vice President
Released: September 15, 2016. **Price:** $4, print. **Description:** San Francisco Bay Area in California has become the site selection for investment, technology and talent. The financing finding its way to the Bay Area has led to robust job creation, drawing people and increasing the population by 2.6 percent to 805,000. The impact of the Bay Area's technology boon in rents and home prices are also presented. **Availability:** Print; Online.

6568 ■ *"Putting SogoTrade Through Its Paces"* in *Barron's (Vol. 89, July 27, 2009, No. 30, pp. 27)*
Pub: Dow Jones & Company Inc.
Contact: Almar Latour, Chief Executive Officer
Ed: Theresa W. Carey. **Description:** SogoTrade options platform streams options quotes in real time and lets users place a trade in several ways. The site also features notable security tactics and is a reasonable choice for bargain-seekers. OptionsXpress' Xtend platform lets users place trades and get real time quotes. **Availability:** Online.

6569 ■ *"Putting the World at Your Fingertips"* in *Barron's (Vol. 88, July 7, 2008, No. 27, pp. L13)*
Pub: Dow Jones & Company Inc.
Contact: Almar Latour, Chief Executive Officer
Ed: Neil A. Martin. **Description:** Currency-traded exchange funds allow investors to diversify their assets and take advantage of investment opportunities such as speculation and hedging. Investors can use these funds to build positions in favor of or against the US dollar. **Availability:** Online.

6570 ■ *"Q&A: RBC's Gordon Nixon"* in *Canadian Business (Vol. 80, May 31, 2011, No. 22, pp. 9)*
Pub: Rogers Media Inc.
Contact: Neil Spivak, Chief Executive Officer
Ed: Rachel Pulfer. **Description:** Royal Bank of Canada (RBC) chief executive officer Gordon Nixon believes that the Canadian financial services segment is heavily regulated. Nixon also feels that it has become difficult for local banks to enter the market since foreign banks can easily come in and compete with Canadian banks. His views on RBC's success are provided. **Availability:** Online.

6571 ■ *"Q&A: The CAPP's Greg Stringham"* in *Canadian Business (Vol. 81, February 12, 2008, No. 3, pp. 8)*
Pub: Rogers Media Inc.
Contact: Neil Spivak, Chief Executive Officer
Ed: Michelle Magnan. **Description:** Canadian Association of Petroleum Producers' Greg Stringham thinks that the new royalty plan will result in companies pulling out their investments for Alberta's conventional oil and gas sector. Stringham adds that Alberta is losing its competitive advantage and companies must study their cost profiles to retrieve that advantage. The effects of the royalty system on Alberta's economy are examined further. **Availability:** Print; Online.

6572 ■ *"Quality at Bargain Prices"* in *Black Enterprise (Vol. 41, December 2010, No. 5, pp. 30)*
Description: Monica L. Walker, CEO of Holland Capital Management, suggests investors to watch prevailing trends in the financial market and to focus on using bottom-up analysis to identify companies meeting their investment criteria. **Availability:** Online.

6573 ■ *The Quants*
Released: January 25, 2011. **Price:** $22.50, audiobook. **Description:** The story of four rich and powerful men, along with Jim Simons, the founder of the most successful hedge fund in history and how they felt and what they thought in the days and weeks during the crash of Wall Street. **Availability:** E-book; Print; Audio.

6574 ■ *"A Questionable Chemical Romance"* in *Barron's (Vol. 88, July 14, 2008, No. 28, pp. 28)*
Pub: Dow Jones & Company Inc.
Contact: Almar Latour, Chief Executive Officer
Ed: Andrew Bary. **Description:** Dow Chemical paid $78-a-share for the surprise takeover of Rohm & Haas. The acquisition is reducing Dow Chemical's financial flexibility at a time when chemical companies are being affected by high costs and a weak U.S. economy. **Availability:** Online.

6575 ■ *"Quick Earnings Revival Unlikely"* in *Barron's (Vol. 88, June 30, 2008, No. 26, pp. 31)*
Description: Analysts are pushing back their prediction of a U.S. economy turnaround to 2009. A recession in the first half of 2008 may not have happened but unemployment is rising and house prices continue to fall.

6576 ■ *"Raptor Opens Austin Office"* in *Austin Business Journal (Vol. 31, July 8, 2011, No. 18, pp. 1)*
Pub: Austin Business Journal
Contact: Rachel McGrath, Director
E-mail: rmcgrath@bizjournals.com
Ed: Christopher Calnan. **Description:** Boston hedge fund operator Raptor Group launched Raptor Accelerator, a consulting business providing sales and advisory services to early-stage companies in Central Texas. Aside from getting involved with the startups in which the Raptor Group invests, Raptor Accelerator will target firms operating in the sports, media, entertainment, and content technology sectors. **Availability:** Print; Online.

6577 ■ "Raytheon Stock Up, Will Pay New Quarterly Dividend" in Barron's (Vol. 88, March 31, 2008, No. 13)
Pub: Dow Jones & Company Inc.
Contact: Almar Latour, Chief Executive Officer

Ed: Shirley A. Lazo. **Description:** Raytheon hiked their quarterly dividend to 28 cents per share from 25.5 cents. Aircastle slashed their quarterly common dividend by 64 percent for them to retain additional capital that can be used to increase their liquidity position. **Availability:** Online.

6578 ■ "The RBC Dynasty Continues" in Globe & Mail (January 30, 2006, pp. B1)
Description: The details on business growth of Royal Bank of Canada, under chief executive officer Gordon Nixon, are presented. **Availability:** Print; Online.

6579 ■ "Ready for a Rally?" in The Economist (Vol. 390, January 3, 2009, No. 8612, pp. 54)
Description: Analysts predict that the recession could end by 2010. The current economic crisis is presented in detail. **Availability:** Print; Online.

6580 ■ "Reflecting State Economy, Banks Less Profitable in 1Q" in Providence Business News (Vol. 29, July 14, 2014, No. 15, pp. 8)
Pub: American City Business Journals, Inc.
Contact: Mike Olivieri, Executive Vice President
URL(s): pbn.com/reflecting-state-economy-banks-less-profitable-in-1q98467
Description: Rhode Island banks posted an aggregate return on assets (ROA) of 0.60 percent for the first quarter (1Q) of 2014, slightly lower than the 0.66 percent in the same quarter 2013, reflecting the downturn in the state's economy and its high unemployment rate. However, two Rhode Island banks, Union Federal Savings Bank and The Washington Trust Company, reported higher ROA for 1Q than the national average at 3.98 percent and 1.19 percent respectively.

6581 ■ "Regulator Issues Warning On Reverse Mortgage Loans" in Retirement Advisor (Vol. 13, October 2012, No. 10, pp. 28)
Description: Reverse mortgages were first introduced in 1961 and are becoming popular now with aging baby boomers. The new Consumer Financial Protection Bureau warns the public to look closing before entering a reverse mortgage contract. The National Ethics Association encourages financial advisors to use the same caution and offers advise for advisors to help educate their clients about reverse mortgages. **Availability:** Print; Online.

6582 ■ "The REIT Stuff" in Canadian Business (Vol. 80, March 26, 2007, No. 7, pp. 72)
Description: The stock performance of various real estate investment trusts in Canada is analyzed. **Availability:** Online.

6583 ■ "REITs Decry Foreign Limits on Investment" in Globe & Mail (March 29, 2007, pp. B4)
Ed: Elizabeth Church. **Description:** The planned legislation by Canadian government for regulation foreign investments by real estate investment trusts is discussed. **Availability:** Online.

6584 ■ "Reports of Banks' Revival were Greatly Exaggerated" in Barron's (Vol. 88, July 7, 2008, No. 27, pp. L14)
Pub: Dow Jones & Company Inc.
Contact: Almar Latour, Chief Executive Officer

Ed: Jack Willoughby. **Description:** Performance of mutual funds improved for the second quarter of 2008 compared to the previous quarter, registering an average gain of 0.13 percent; funds focusing on natural resources rose the highest, their value rising by an average of 24.50 percent. **Availability:** Online.

6585 ■ "Research Reports" in Barron's (Vol. 88, March 24, 2008, No. 12, pp. M10)
Pub: Dow Jones & Company Inc.
Contact: Almar Latour, Chief Executive Officer

Ed: Anita Peltonen. **Description:** Investors are recommending purchasing shares of Ampco Pittsburgh due to an expected surge in earnings. Deteriorating credit quality presents problems for the shares of BankAtlantic Bancorp, whose price targets have been lowered from $7 to $5 each. Shares of Helicos Biosciences are expected to move sideways from their $6 level. Statistical data included.

6586 ■ "Research Reports" in Barron's (Vol. 90, August 23, 2010, No. 34, pp. M13)
Pub: Barron's Editorial & Corporate Headquarters
Description: Shares of Sirius XM Radio, Target and Deere and Company received an eBuyE rating, while shares of Research in Motion got an eNeutralE rating. **Availability:** Online.

6587 ■ "Research Reports: How Analysts Size Up Companies" in Barron's (Vol. 88, June 30, 2008, No. 26, pp. M11)
Availability: Online.

6588 ■ "Return to Wealth; Bank Strategy" in The Economist (Vol. 390, January 3, 2009, No. 8612, pp. 56)
Description: UBS' strategy to survive these trying economic times is presented. Statistical data included. UBS has a stronger balance-sheet than most of its investment-banking peers and has reduced its portfolio. **Availability:** Print; Online.

6589 ■ "The Right Time for REITs" in Barron's (Vol. 88, July 14, 2008, No. 28, pp. 32)
Pub: Dow Jones & Company Inc.
Contact: Almar Latour, Chief Executive Officer

Ed: Mike Hogan. **Description:** Discusses the downturn in U.S. real estate investment trusts so these are worth considering for investment. Several Websites that are useful for learning about real estate investment trusts for investment purposes are presented. **Availability:** Online.

6590 ■ "Risk and Reward" in Canadian Business (Vol. 81, October 13, 2008, No. 17, pp. 21)
Description: Macro-economist and currency analyst Mark Venezia believes that stable financial institutions, free-market reforms, and the role of central banks in keeping inflation and exchange rates stable could make emerging-market bonds strong performers for better future returns. Venezia's other views on emerging-market bonds are discussed. **Availability:** Print; Online.

6591 ■ "Rogue Caller Infiltrates Cincinnati Firms' Analyst Calls: 'Mr. CEO, Please Do Elaborate On Your Firm's Metrics'" in Business Courier (Vol. 24, February 28, 2008, No. 47, pp. 1)
Pub: American City Business Journals, Inc.
Contact: Mike Olivieri, Executive Vice President

Ed: Jon Newberry. **Description:** Discusses a rogue caller who goes by the name of Joe Herrick, Steven Nissan and Joe Harris has joined in over a dozen conference calls, asking chief executive officers on their plans and commenting on the companies' operations. The mystery caller attempts to pass himself off as a financial analyst. Transcripts of some conference calls, in which the rogue caller is involved, are provided. **Availability:** Online.

6592 ■ "Ryder's Shock Absorbers Are In Place" in Barron's (Vol. 88, March 24, 2008, No. 12, pp. 19)
Pub: Dow Jones & Company Inc.
Contact: Almar Latour, Chief Executive Officer

Ed: Christopher C. Williams. **Description:** Shares of Ryder System Inc. are expected to continue rising on the back of rising earnings, forecast at $5.20 a share for 2009. The shares of the truck freight company hit a 52-week high of $62.27 each and may reach $70 a share. **Availability:** Online.

6593 ■ Safety Net
Released: February 22, 2011. **Price:** $23, hardcover; $9.99, e-book. **Description:** Ways to build a financial investment strategy that protects you, while ensuring growth in a strong financial future are presented. **Availability:** E-book; Print.

6594 ■ "Score One for Barron's" in Barron's (Vol. 89, July 13, 2009, No. 28, pp. 14)
Pub: Dow Jones & Company Inc.
Contact: Almar Latour, Chief Executive Officer

Ed: Andrew Bary. **Description:** 57 companies that were bullishly covered on 'Barron's' for the first half of 2009 were up an average of 20.4 percent compared to the 10.2 percent gain in the relevant market indexes. The bearish stock picks by 'Barron's' were down 3.4 percent compared to a 6.4 percent for the benchmarks. **Availability:** Online.

6595 ■ "Scotiabank Targets More Baby Boomers" in Globe & Mail (March 4, 2006, pp. B5)
Ed: Elizabeth Church. **Description:** Bank of Nova Scotia posted $844 million profit for first quarter 2006. The plans of the bank to achieve baby boomer client base are presented. **Availability:** Online.

6596 ■ "Screening for the Best Stock Screens" in Barron's (Vol. 90, September 13, 2010, No. 37, pp. 36)
Pub: Barron's Editorial & Corporate Headquarters

Ed: Mike Hogan. **Description:** Pros and cons of the new and revised stock screening tools from Zack, Finviz.com, and GuruFocus are discussed. FinVix.com is more capable for screening through stocks and the service is free. **Availability:** Online.

6597 ■ "Sears' Lampert Solid in Game of Valuation Chicken" in Globe & Mail (February 25, 2006, pp. B2)
Ed: Eric Reguly. **Description:** The feasibility of share value of Sears Canada Inc., following Sears Holdings Corp.'s acquisition, is discussed. **Availability:** Online.

6598 ■ "SEC Report On Rating Agencies Falls Short" in Barron's (Vol. 88, July 14, 2008, No. 28, pp. 35)
Pub: Dow Jones & Company Inc.
Contact: Almar Latour, Chief Executive Officer

Ed: Jack Willoughby. **Description:** The Securities and Exchange Commissions report on credit-rating firms should have drawn attention to the slipshod practices in the offerings of collateralized debt obligations. The report fell short of prescribing correctives for the flawed system of these agencies' relationship with their clients. **Availability:** Online.

6599 ■ "Sense of Discovery" in Business Journal Portland (Vol. 27, November 19, 2010, No. 38, pp. 1)
Pub: Portland Business Journal
Contact: Andy Giegerich, Managing Editor
E-mail: agiegerich@bizjournals.com

Description: Tigard, Oregon-based Exterro Inc. CEO Bobby Balachandran announced plans to go public without the help of an institutional investor. Balachandran believes Exterro could grow to a $100 million legal compliance software company in the span of three years. Insights on Exterro's growth as market leader in the $1 billion legal governance software market are also given. **Availability:** Print; Online.

6600 ■ "Sentiment Split on Financials: Is the Worse Over or Still to Come?" in Barron's (Vol. 88, March 24, 2008, No. 12, pp. M14)
Pub: Dow Jones & Company Inc.
Contact: Almar Latour, Chief Executive Officer

Ed: Steven M. Sears. **Description:** Experts in the financial sector are split as to whether or not the worst of the financial crisis brought on by the credit crunch is over. Some options traders are trading on are defensive puts, expecting the worst, while investors buying calls are considered as bullish. **Availability:** Online.

6601 ■ *"Seven Things Great Employers Do (That Others Don't); Unusual, Innovative, and Proven Tactics To Create Productive and Profitable Working Environments"* in *Gallup Business Journal (April 15, 2014)*
Pub: Gallup, Inc.
Contact: Jon Clifton, Chief Executive Officer
Price: $8.95. **Description:** Seven unusual, innovative, and proven tactics that create productive and profitable working environments are examined through researching 32 companies. These firms represented many industries, including healthcare, financial services, hospitality, manufacturing, and retail throughout the world. **Availability:** Print; PDF; Online.

6602 ■ *"Should the Fed Regulate Wall Street?"* in *Barron's (Vol. 88, March 24, 2008, No. 12, pp. M15)*
Pub: Dow Jones & Company Inc.
Contact: Almar Latour, Chief Executive Officer
Ed: Randall W. Forsyth. **Description:** Greater regulation of the financial sector by the Federal Reserve is essential for it to survive the crisis it is experiencing. The resulting regulation could be in complete contrast with the deregulation the sector previously experienced. **Availability:** Online.

6603 ■ *"Should You Choose a Lump-Sum Pension Payout? Here's How Entrepreneur Ramona Harper Decided"* in *Black Enterprise (Vol. 44, June 2014, No. 10, pp. 27)*
Pub: Earl G. Graves Ltd.
Contact: Earl Graves, Jr., President
Description: Entrepreneur, Ramona Harper, chose a lump sum payout of her pension in order to start a new business. She used $110,000 to start her accessories boutique and put the remaining money into a small business 401(k), which helped her avoid a large tax. Tips to help individuals decide the best way to collect their pension are provided. **Availability:** Online.

6604 ■ *"Silver Standard Reports First Quarter 2007 Results"* in *Marketwired (May 14, 2007)*
Pub: Comtex News Network Inc.
Contact: Kan Devnani, President
Description: Silver Standard Resources Inc. reports a first quarter loss of $1.6 million compared with the first quarter of 2006 in which the loss was $1.1 million. Statistical data included. **Availability:** PDF; Online.

6605 ■ *The Simple Path to Wealth: Your Road Map to Financial Independence and a Rich, Free Life*
Ed: JL Collins. **Price:** $15.11, Paperback; $9.99, E-book. **Description:** A guide about thinking about money and wealth, with practical, and humor-filled, discussions about a variety of topics involving investing. **Availability:** E-book; Print.

6606 ■ *"Six Great Stock Funds for the Long Haul"* in *Barron's (Vol. 89, July 13, 2009, No. 28, pp. L5)*
Pub: Dow Jones & Company Inc.
Contact: Almar Latour, Chief Executive Officer
Ed: Lawrence C. Strauss, Tom Sullivan. **Description:** Six mutual funds that have solid long-term performance, transparency, savvy stock picking, and discipline are presented. The managers of these funds are also evaluated. These funds include the T. Rowe Price Emerging Market Stock Fund, Fairholme, and Dodge & Cox Stock. **Availability:** Online.

6607 ■ *"A Slice of Danish; Fixing Finance"* in *The Economist (Vol. 390, January 3, 2009, No. 8612, pp. 55)*
Description: Denmark's mortgage-holders and the county's lending system is presented. **Availability:** Print; Online.

6608 ■ *"Small Business Economic Trends: Moderate Improvement but No Clear Direction"* in *Small Business Economic Trends (March 2008, pp. 3)*
Pub: National Federation of Independent Business
Contact: Brad Close, President

Ed: William C. Dunkelberg, Holly Wade. **Description:** Commentary on the economic trends for small businesses in the U.S. is presented. Analysis of the labor market and low interest rates is given. The effect of the Federal Reserve's policy announcement on small business owner optimism is also discussed. **Availability:** Print; Online.

6609 ■ *"The Smell of Fear: Is a Bottom Near?"* in *Barron's (Vol. 88, March 17, 2008, No. 11, pp. M3)*
Pub: Dow Jones & Company Inc.
Contact: Almar Latour, Chief Executive Officer
Ed: Kopin Tan. **Description:** Liquidity problems at Bear Stearns frightened investors in markets around the world due to the fear of the prospects of a big bank's failure. Shares of health maintenance organizations got battered led by WellPoint, and Humana but longer-term investors who could weather short-term volatility may find value here. The value of J. Crew shares is also discussed. **Availability:** Online.

6610 ■ *"A Socko Payout Menu: Rural Phone Carrier Plots to Supercharge Its Shares"* in *Barron's (Vol. 88, June 30, 2008, No. 26, pp. M5)*
Description: CenturyTel boosted its quarterly common payout to 70 cents from 6.75 cents per share die to its strong cash flows and solid balance sheet. Eastman Kodak's plan for a buyback will be partially funded by its $581 million tax refund. CME Group will buyback stocks through 2009 worth $1.1 billion. **Availability:** Online.

6611 ■ *"Some Relief Possible Following Painful Week"* in *Barron's (Vol. 88, July 14, 2008, No. 28, pp. M3)*
Pub: Dow Jones & Company Inc.
Contact: Almar Latour, Chief Executive Officer
Ed: Kopin Tan. **Description:** Dow Chemical is offering a 74 percent premium to acquire Rohm & Haas' coatings and electronics materials operations. Frontline amassed a 5.6 percent stake in rival Overseas Shipholding Group and a merger between the two would create a giant global fleet with pricing power. Highlights of the U.S. stock market during the week that ended in July 11, 2008 are discussed. Statistical data included. **Availability:** Online.

6612 ■ *"Spectre of Iran War Spooks Oil Markets"* in *Globe & Mail (March 28, 2007, pp. B1)*
Ed: Shawn McCarthy. **Description:** The increase in the price of crude oil by $5 a barrel to reach $68 in the United States following speculation over war against Iran, is discussed. **Availability:** Online.

6613 ■ *"Spreading Your Wings"* in *Canadian Business (Vol. 81, March 17, 2008, No. 4, pp. 31)*
Ed: Megan Harman. **Released:** February 09, 2017. **Description:** Financing from angel investors is one avenue that should be explored by startups. Angel investors are typically affluent individuals who invest their own money. Angel investors usually want at least 10 times their initial investment within eight years but they benefit the businesses through their help in decision-making and the industry expertise they provide. **Availability:** Download; Online.

6614 ■ *"Stand-Up Guy: From Bear Stearns to Bear Market"* in *Barron's (Vol. 88, July 7, 2008, No. 27, pp. L11)*
Pub: Dow Jones & Company Inc.
Contact: Almar Latour, Chief Executive Officer
Ed: Suzanne McGee. **Description:** James O'Shaughnessy, a mutual fund manager with O'Shaughnessy Asset Management, is bullish on both financial and energy stocks. He was formerly involved with Bear Stearns until he left the firm in March 2008. **Availability:** Online.

6615 ■ *"Startup Lucena Taking On Wall Street"* in *Atlanta Business Chronicle (May 23, 2014, pp. 1A)*
Pub: American City Business Journals, Inc.
Contact: Mike Olivieri, Executive Vice President

Description: Lucena Research is a predictive analytics startup firm developing software for the financial investment sector. The company's software helps investment professionals identify trading strategies and investing trends to reduce risk and increase returns. **Availability:** Print; Online.

6616 ■ *"State of Play"* in *Canadian Business (Vol. 79, June 19, 2006, No. 13, pp. 25)*
Description: Top 100 information technology companies in Canada are ranked by their market capitalization as of June 1. The statistics that show the revenues of these companies are also presented. **Availability:** Print; Online.

6617 ■ *"State of the States"* in *Barron's (Vol. 92, August 27, 2012, No. 38, pp. 23)*
Pub: Dow Jones & Company Inc.
Contact: Almar Latour, Chief Executive Officer
Ed: Andrew Bary. **Description:** The strength of finances of US states are ranked based on their debt ad unfunded pensions compared with their gross domestic products. South Dakota is considered to have the healthiest finances, while those of Connecticut are the weakest. **Availability:** Online.

6618 ■ *"Stock Car Racing"* in *Canadian Business (Vol. 81, September 15, 2008, No. 14-15, pp. 29)*
Description: Some analysts predict a Chapter 11-style tune-up making GM and Ford a speculative turnaround stock. However, the price of oil could make or break the shares of the Big Three U.S. automobile manufacturers and if oil goes up too high then a speculative stock to watch is an electric car company called Zenn Motor Co. **Availability:** Online.

6619 ■ *"Stressed Out: 7 St. Louis Banks Rated 'At Risks'"* in *Saint Louis Business Journal (Vol. 32, September 16, 2011, No. 3, pp. 1)*
Pub: Saint Louis Business Journal
Contact: Robert Bobroff, President
E-mail: rbobroff@bizjournals.com
Ed: Greg Edwards. **Description:** St. Louis, Missouri has seven banks that are well above the 100 percent level that is considered 'at risk' based on a risk measurement called the Texas ratio. The banks are the Sun Security bank, 1st Advantage Bank, Superior Bank, Truman Bank, Reliance Bank, St. Louis Bank and Meramec Valley Bank. **Availability:** Online.

6620 ■ *"A Study in Diversity: What Women Want: There Are Fundamental Differences Between How Men and Women View Retirement Planning"* in *Senior Market Advisor (Vol. 13, October 2012, No. 10, pp. 36)*
Description: An overview of women's attitudes towards finances and retirement planning is provided. Contrasting views are even held by male and female financial advisors. **Availability:** Print; Online.

6621 ■ *"Stymiest's RBC Compensation Triggers Shareholder Outrage"* in *Gl obe & Mail (January 28, 2006, pp. B3)*
Description: The concerns of shareholders over the issue of Royal Bank of Canada's $6.6 million pay package for chief executive officer Barbara Stymiest, in 2004, are presented. **Availability:** Print; Online.

6622 ■ *"Subprime Mess Hits Huntington"* in *Business First-Columbus (November 26, 2007, pp. A1)*
Pub: Business First
Contact: Nick Fortine, President
E-mail: nfortine@bizjournals.com
Ed: Adrian Burns. **Description:** Huntington Bancshares Inc. picked up a $1.5 billion exposure to the country's subprime mortgage mess. It caused the bank to set aside $450 million to cover increases in loan losses. When Huntington acquired Sky Financial, it absorbed a 17-year relationship Sky had with Franklin Credit Corporation, which is a subprime lender and servicer. **Availability:** Print; Online.

6623 ■ "SunBank Plans Expansion Via Wal-Mart" in Business Journal-Serving Phoenix and the Valley of the Sun (Vol. 10, November 8, 2007)
Pub: Phoenix Business Journal
Contact: Alex McAlister, Director
E-mail: amcalister@bizjournals.com
Ed: Chris Casacchia. **Description:** SunBank plans to install 12 to 14 branches in Wal-Mart stores in Arizona and hire 100 bankers by the end of 2008. Wal-Mart also offers financial products at other stores through partnerships with other banks. **Availability:** Print; Online.

6624 ■ "Surprise Package" in Business Courier (Vol. 27, June 25, 2010, No. 8, pp. 1)
Pub: Business Courier
Ed: Dan Monk, Jon Newberry, Steve Watkins. **Description:** More than 60 percent of the chief executive officers (CEOs) in Greater Cincinnati's 35 public companies took a salary cut in 2009, but stock grants resulted in large paper gains for the CEOs. The salary cuts show efforts of boards of directors to observe austerity. Statistics on increased values of stock awards for CEOs, median pay for CEOs, and median shareholder return are also presented. **Availability:** Online.

6625 ■ "Surviving the Storm" in Canadian Business (Vol. 81, July 22, 2008, No. 12-13, pp. 50)
Description: Investment adviser Harry Dent and finance professor Paul Marsh discuss their views and forecasts on the United States' economic condition. Dent believes advisors should concentrate on wealth preservation rather than on returns. Other views regarding U.S. economic conditions are also presented. **Availability:** Print; Online.

6626 ■ "A Swifter, Better Marketplace" in Barron's (Vol. 89, July 13, 2009, No. 28, pp. M13)
Pub: Dow Jones & Company Inc.
Contact: Almar Latour, Chief Executive Officer
Ed: Eric W. Noll. **Description:** Listed-derivatives market is moving towards greater trading through computerized systems with an emphasis on speed and innovation. The market for listed options is also being changed by new techniques from other markets such as algorithmic trading, dark pools, and new-order priority systems. **Availability:** Online.

6627 ■ "Take It to the Bank" in Barron's (Vol. 89, July 13, 2009, No. 28, pp. 20)
Pub: Dow Jones & Company Inc.
Contact: Almar Latour, Chief Executive Officer
Ed: Jim McTague. **Description:** Banks are one of the safest place to put one's principal due to the temporary increase in the Federal Deposit Insurance Corp.'s insurance of bank accounts up to $250,000 and also because of the Cdars (Certificates of Deposit Registry Service) program which spreads the deposit to several banks thereby making the account covered as if the money was deposited at multiple banks. **Availability:** Online.

6628 ■ "Taking the Over-the-Counter Route to U.S." in Barron's (Vol. 88, July 7, 2008, No. 27, pp. 24)
Pub: Dow Jones & Company Inc.
Contact: Almar Latour, Chief Executive Officer
Ed: Eric Uhlfelder. **Description:** Many multinational companies have left the New York Stock Exchange and allowed their shares to trade over-the-counter. The companies have taken advantage of a 2007 SEC rule allowing publicly listed foreign companies to change trading venues if less than 5 percent of global trading volume in the past 12 months occurred in the US. **Availability:** Online.

6629 ■ "Tao of Downfall: the Failures of High-profile Entrepreneurs in the Chinese Economic Reform" in International Journal of Entrepreneurship and Small Business (Vol. 11, August 31, 2010, No. 2, pp. 121)
Ed: Wenxian Zhang, Ilan Alon. **Description:** Through historical reviews and case studies, this research seeks to understand why some initially successful entrepreneurs failed in the economic boom of past decades. Among various factors contributing to their downfall are a unique political and business environment, fragile financial systems, traditional cultural influences and personal characteristics. **Availability:** Online.

6630 ■ "TEDx Talk Puts the Pieces Together" in Philadelphia Business Journal (Vol. 33, April 4, 2014, No. 8, pp. 6)
Pub: American City Business Journals, Inc.
Contact: Mike Olivieri, Executive Vice President
Description: Gabriel Investments managing partner, Richard Vague, shares his views about entrepreneurs wanting to start a company. Vague says they should be relentless because it takes a long time to start and run a business and it is a challenge to recruit customers and grow rapidly. He also states his experience as an entrepreneur enables him to give advice and put things into perspective for the people he mentors. **Availability:** Online.

6631 ■ The Ten Laws of Enduring Success
Released: March 01, 2011. **Price:** $15, paperback; $4.99, e-book. **Description:** A new meaning for success is described by financial expert, Maria Bartiromo, with advice on how to adapt with the changing times. **Availability:** E-book; Print.

6632 ■ "That's About It for Quantitative Easing" in Barron's (Vol. 89, July 20, 2009, No. 29, pp. M11)
Pub: Dow Jones & Company Inc.
Contact: Almar Latour, Chief Executive Officer
Ed: Brian Blackstone. **Description:** US Federal Reserve appears to have decided to halt quantitative easing, causing bond prices to drop and yields to rise. The yield for the 1-year Treasury bond rose more than 0.3 percentage point to about 3.65 percent. **Availability:** Online.

6633 ■ "They've Fallen, But Can Senior-Housing Stocks Get Up" in Barron's (Vol. 88, March 10, 2008, No. 10, pp. 43)
Pub: Dow Jones & Company Inc.
Contact: Almar Latour, Chief Executive Officer
Ed: Kopin Tan. **Description:** Shares of senior housing companies present buying opportunities to investors because of their low prices. Companies such as Brookdale Senior Living are not as dependent on housing prices but have suffered declines in share prices. **Availability:** Online.

6634 ■ "Time to Leave the Party? Re-Evaluating Commodities" in Barron's (Vol. 88, March 24, 2008, No. 12, pp. M16)
Pub: Dow Jones & Company Inc.
Contact: Almar Latour, Chief Executive Officer
Ed: Andrea Hotter. **Description:** Prices of commodities such as gold, copper, crude oil, sugar, cocoa, and wheat have fallen from their all-time highs set in the middle of March 2008. Analysts, however, caution that this decline in prices may be temporary, and that a banking crisis may trigger new price rises in commodities. **Availability:** Online.

6635 ■ "Time for a Little Pruning?" in Barron's (Vol. 89, July 6, 2009, No. 27, pp. 13)
Pub: Dow Jones & Company Inc.
Contact: Almar Latour, Chief Executive Officer
Ed: Dimitra DeFotis. **Description:** Investors are advised to avoid the shares of Whole Foods, American Tower, T. Rowe Price, Iron Mountain, Intuitive Surgical, Salesforce.com, and Juniper Networks due to their high price to earnings ratios. The shares of Amazon.com, Broadcom, and Expeditors International of Washington remain attractive to investors despite their high price to earnings ratios due to their strong growth. **Availability:** Online.

6636 ■ "Too Much Information?" in Black Enterprise (Vol. 37, December 2006, No. 5, pp. 59)
Pub: Earl G. Graves Ltd.
Contact: Earl Graves, Jr., President
Ed: James C. Johnson. **Description:** African American business owners often face the dilemma of whether or not to divulge their minority status when soliciting new customers and financial institutions. The quality of the products or services is always the key factor and race should never define one's business; however, it is appropriate to market oneself as a minority- or women-owned business, especially if the company is in an industry where those clients are offered top-tier contracts. **Availability:** Online.

6637 ■ "Too Much Precaution About Biotech Corn" in Barron's (Vol. 88, March 17, 2008, No. 11, pp. 54)
Pub: Dow Jones & Company Inc.
Contact: Almar Latour, Chief Executive Officer
Ed: Mark I. Schwartz. **Description:** In the U.S., 90 percent of cultivated soybeans are biotech varietals as well as 60 percent of the corn. Farmers have significantly reduced their reliance on pesticides in the growing of biotech corn. Biotech cotton cultivation has brought hundreds of millions of dollars in net financial gains to farmers. The European Union has precluded the cultivation or sale of biotech crops within its border. **Availability:** Online.

6638 ■ "Tool-o-Rama" in Barron's (Vol. 90, September 6, 2010, No. 36)
Pub: Barron's Editorial & Corporate Headquarters
Ed: Theresa W. Carey. **Description:** New trading tool features from several online brokers are discussed. The new features from Fidelity, ChoiceTrade, JunoTrade and TradeKing are examined. Investors can now screen exchanged traded funds in the same way as stocks with Fidelity, while ChoiceTrade can run in any browser without the need to install additional plug-ins. **Availability:** Online.

6639 ■ "Top 10 Retirement Mistakes and How to Avoid Them" in Canadian Business (Vol. 83, July 20, 2010, No. 11-12, pp. 39)
Pub: Rogers Media Inc.
Contact: Neil Spivak, Chief Executive Officer
Ed: Jacqueline Nelson, Angelina Chapin. **Description:** Some of the top retirement mistakes are relying on selling one's house to find a retirement. Other mistakes are paying too much for investments and planning to work in retirement since no one can be sure that they will be healthy enough to accomplish this. Suggestions to avoid these pitfalls are discussed. **Availability:** Print; Online.

6640 ■ "Top 50 In Total Revenue" in Canadian Business (Vol. 81, Summer 2008, No. 9, pp. 119)
Description: Table showing the top 50 Canadian companies in terms of total revenue is presented. Manulife Financial Corp. topped the list with revenue of 34.5 billion. The financial services firm is the 6th largest provider of life insurance in the world and the second largest in North America. **Availability:** Print; Online.

6641 ■ "Top 100 Indy Advisors" in Barron's (Vol. 92, August 25, 2012, No. 38, pp. S2)
Pub: Dow Jones & Company Inc.
Contact: Almar Latour, Chief Executive Officer
Ed: Suzanne McGee. **Description:** Profiles of five independent financial advisors included the Barron's Top 100 independent financial advisor rankings for 2012 are included. Their investment strategies are also discussed. **Availability:** Online.

6642 ■ "Top Law Firms Join Forces" in Business Journal Portland (Vol. 27, December 3, 2010, No. 40, pp. 1)
Pub: Portland Business Journal
Contact: Andy Giegerich, Managing Editor
E-mail: agiegerich@bizjournals.com
Description: Law Firms Powell PC and Roberts Kaplan LLP will forge a collaboration, whereby 17 Roberts Kaplan attorneys will join the Portland, Oregon-based office of Lane Powell. The partnership is expected to strengthen the law firms' grip on Portland's banking clients. **Availability:** Print; Online.

6643 ■ *"Top Pension Fund Sends a Warning"* in Barron's (Vol. 92, July 23, 2012, No. 30, pp. M9)
Pub: Dow Jones & Company Inc.
Contact: Almar Latour, Chief Executive Officer
Ed: Michael Aneiro. **Description:** The California Public Employees' Retirement System reported a 1 percent return on investments for the fiscal year ended June 30, 2012. It lost 7.2 percent on stock investments, 11 percent on forest-land holdings and 2 percent on absolute-return assets, negating a 12.7 percent gain on its fixed-income investments. **Availability:** Online.

6644 ■ *"A Trader Gets a Better Deal From the IRS Than an Investor"* in Barron's (Vol. 88, March 31, 2008, No. 13, pp. 56)
Pub: Dow Jones & Company Inc.
Contact: Almar Latour, Chief Executive Officer
Ed: Dan McGuire. **Description:** There is a $3,000 a year annual limit to deducting investor's losses and normal investment expenses are purportedly deductible as miscellaneous expenses on Schedule A only to the extent that they exceed two percent of adjusted gross income. Professional gamblers who can use Schedule C are unable deduct a net gaming loss against income from any other sources. **Availability:** Online.

6645 ■ *"Traditional vs. Roth IRA"* in Black Enterprise (Vol. 37, October 2006, No. 3, pp. 58)
Pub: Earl G. Graves Ltd.
Contact: Earl Graves, Jr., President
Ed: K. Parker, Carolyn M. Brown. **Description:** Government taxes the traditional IRAs different than it taxes Roth IRAs. **Availability:** Online.

6646 ■ *"A Trend Is His Friend"* in Barron's (Vol. 89, July 27, 2009, No. 30, pp. 28)
Pub: Dow Jones & Company Inc.
Contact: Almar Latour, Chief Executive Officer
Ed: Eric Uhlfelder. **Description:** Global Diversified Program fund under Quality Capital Management is managed through a trading system called the Advanced Resource Allocator which rebalances short-term tactical moves to gather quick profits. CEO Aref Karim's allocations are based on risk and he says their sentiments toward the market conditions are agnostic. **Availability:** Online.

6647 ■ *"Trust Buyouts Not My Fault, Flaherty Says"* in Globe & Mail (April 3, 2007, pp. B1)
Ed: Tara Perkins, Doug Saunders, Steven Chase. **Description:** The causes of the acquisition of Canadian firms by foreign investors are discussed by the Canadian Finance Minister Jim Flaherty. **Availability:** Online.

6648 ■ *"Understanding Clients Her Key To Shaping Message"* in Providence Business News (Vol. 29, July 7, 2014, No. 14, pp. 10)
Pub: American City Business Journals, Inc.
Contact: Mike Olivieri, Executive Vice President
Released: July 05, 2014. **Description:** Kerry Chaffer, a partner at HCC Marketing, attributes her firm's success to their ability to understand clients, their business and the market. Chaffer discusses HCC's expertise in marketing community banks and commends engagement by local banks and their communities. **Availability:** Print; Online.

6649 ■ *"An Unfair Knock on Nokia"* in Barron's (Vol. 88, March 10, 2008, No. 10, pp. 36)
Pub: Dow Jones & Company Inc.
Contact: Almar Latour, Chief Executive Officer
Ed: Mark Veverka. **Description:** Discusses the decision by the brokerage house Exane to recommend a Sell on Nokia shares, presumably due to higher inventories, which is unfounded. The news that the company's inventories are rising is not an indicator of falling demand for its products. The company is also benefiting from solid management and rising market share. **Availability:** Online.

6650 ■ *"Unpleasant Surprise - When a Stock Distribution is Taxed as Dividend Income"* in Barron's (Vol. 88, March 24, 2008, No. 12, pp. 60)
Pub: Dow Jones & Company Inc.
Contact: Almar Latour, Chief Executive Officer
Ed: Shirley A. Lazo. **Description:** Discusses the $175 million that footwear company Genesco received in a settlement with Finish Line and UBS is considered as a stock distribution and is taxable as dividend income. Railroad company CSX raised its quarterly common payout from 15 cents to 18 cents. **Availability:** Online.

6651 ■ *"The Upside of Fear and Loathing"* in Barron's (Vol. 88, March 24, 2008, No. 12, pp. 11)
Pub: Dow Jones & Company Inc.
Contact: Almar Latour, Chief Executive Officer
Ed: Michael Santoli. **Description:** Fear and risk aversion prevalent among investors may actually serve to cushion the decline and spark a rally in US stock prices. Surveys of investors indicate rising levels of anxiety and bearishness, indicating a possible positive turnaround. **Availability:** Online.

6652 ■ *"Valener Announces that Gaz Metro has Achieved a Key Step in Acquiring CVPS"* in CNW Group (September 30, 2011)
Pub: CNW Group Ltd.
Description: Valener Inc., which owns about 29 percent of Gaz Metro Ltd. Partnership, announced that Gaz Metro welcomes the sale of Central Vermont Public Service Corporation (CVPS). Valener owns an indirect interest of 24.5 percent in the wind power projects jointly developed by Beaupre Eole General Partnership and Boralex Inc. on private lands in Quebec. Details of the deal are included. **Availability:** Print; Online.

6653 ■ *"Valenti: Roots of Financial Crisis Go Back to 1998"* in Crain's Detroit Business (Vol. 24, October 6, 2008, No. 40, pp. 25)
Pub: Crain Communications Inc.
Contact: Barry Asin, President
Ed: Tom Henderson, Nathan Skid. **Description:** Interview with Sam Valenti III who is the chairman and CEO of Valenti Capital L.L.C., a wealth-management firm; Valenti discusses in detail the history that led up to the current economic crisis as well as his prediction for the future of the country. **Availability:** Print; Online.

6654 ■ *"Virtue and Vice"* in Entrepreneur (September 2014)
Pub: Entrepreneur Media Inc.
Contact: Dan Bova, Director
E-mail: dbova@entrepreneur.com
Description: Socially responsible investments (SRI) are rising in the U.S., but many claim that vice funds offer better returns. Vice fund proponents argue that any profitable company deserves a place in a good investment portfolio. SRI proponents emphasize investments that benefit the society. Analysts note that investors who restrict their investment landscape by selecting only vice funds or only SRI funds may lead to lower returns. Other specialized funds attract activist investors supporting advocacies like gender equality or a positive work environment. **Availability:** PDF; Online.

6655 ■ *"Virtus.com Wins 'Best of Industry' WebAward for Excellence in Financial Services"* in Investment Weekly News (October 24, 2009, pp. 227)
Pub: Investment Weekly News
Description: Web Marketing Association honored Virtus.com, the Website of Virtus Investment Partners, Inc., for Outstanding Achievement in Web Development and Acsys Interactive was awarded the Financial Services Standard of Excellence Award for developing the site. The site was part of a rebranding effort and is a one-stop portal for both financial advisors and their investors. **Availability:** Online.

6656 ■ *"Voice: Rebuilding Trust"* in Business Strategy Review (Vol. 21, Summer 2010, No. 2, pp. 79-80)
Ed: David De Cremer. **Released:** June 24, 2010. **Description:** The financial world's attempts to rebuild trust are charted. Three steps to jump-start that process are outlined. **Availability:** Print; PDF; Online.

6657 ■ *"Wall Street Is No Friend to Radical Innovation"* in Harvard Business Review (Vol. 88, July-August 2010, No. 7-8, pp. 28)
Pub: Harvard Business Publishing
Contact: Diane Belcher, Managing Director
Ed: Julia Kirby. **Price:** $6, PDF. **Description:** Research indicates that investors are skittish about backing a business that proposes significant changes to its product or service status quo. **Availability:** Online; PDF.

6658 ■ *"Wealth Advisory Firms Are Merging, but What's in It for Clients?"* in The New York Times (September 13, 2019)
URL(s): www.nytimes.com/2019/09/13/your-money/wealth-advisers-mergers-clients.html
Ed: Paul Sullivan. **Released:** September 13, 2019. **Description:** Wealth management firms are being sold due to their high values to private equity firms looking to expand their inventory of profitable companies. But is this good for clients? Favorite and familiar advisers may be lost and getting used to a new replacement can lead to difficulties, plus other aspects of the move may not be seamless such using new platforms. But, clients dealing with smaller firms may actually benefit because this is an opportunity for more growth, which translates to bigger wealth. **Availability:** Online.

6659 ■ *"Weather Jitters Boost Coffee"* in Barron's (Vol. 92, July 23, 2012, No. 30, pp. M12)
Pub: Dow Jones & Company Inc.
Contact: Almar Latour, Chief Executive Officer
Ed: Alexandra Wexler. **Description:** Coffee futures prices rose by 20 percent as rains in Brazil sparked concerns about the crop's size and quality. Arabica futures for September 2012 delivery rose to $1.8695/pound and could exceed $2/pound by the end of the summer. **Availability:** Online.

6660 ■ *"A Week of the Worst Kind of Selling"* in Barron's (Vol. 88, June 30, 2008, No. 26, pp. M3)
Pub: Dow Jones & Company Inc.
Contact: Almar Latour, Chief Executive Officer
Ed: Kopin Tan. **Description:** In the week that ended in June 27, 2008 the selloff in the U.S. stock market was brought on by mounting bank losses and the spread of economic slowdown on top of high oil prices. The 31 percent decrease in the share price of Ingersoll-Rand since October 2007 may have factored in most of its risks. The company has completed its acquisition of Trane to morph into a refrigeration-equipment company. **Availability:** Online.

6661 ■ *"Well-Timed Entrance"* in Barron's (Vol. 92, July 23, 2012, No. 30, pp. 24)
Pub: Dow Jones & Company Inc.
Contact: Almar Latour, Chief Executive Officer
Ed: Michael Aneiro. **Description:** Dan Ivascyn, portfolio manager of Pimco Income Fund, discusses the fund's investment bonds. The fund is heavily invested in mortgage-backed securities and is positioned for a low-interest-rate environment well into 2014 or 2015. **Availability:** Online.

6662 ■ *"Wenzel Downhole Tools Ltd. Announces First Quarter Results for 2007"* in Marketwired (May 14, 2007)
Pub: Comtex News Network Inc.
Contact: Kan Devnani, President
Description: Wenzel Downhole Tools Ltd., a manufacturer, renter, and seller of drilling tools used in gas and oil exploration, announced its financial results for the first quarter ended March 31, 2007 which includes achieved revenues of $14.5 million. Statistical data included. **Availability:** Print; Online.

6663 ■ "Western & Southern to Trim Rich Retirement Plan" in Business Courier (Vol. 27, October 15, 2010, No. 24, pp. 1)
Pub: Business Courier
Ed: Dan Monk. Description: Insurance firm Western & Southern Financial Group announced that it will reduce the pension benefits of its 4,000 associates by more than 30 percent starting January 1, 2011. The move is expected to reduce annual retirement payments by several thousand dollars per associate. Western is a Fortune 500 company and has $34 billion in total assets. Availability: Print; Online.

6664 ■ "Weyerhaeuser's REIT Decision Shouldn't Scare Investors Away" in Barron's (Vol. 88, June 30, 2008, No. 26, pp. 18)
Pub: Dow Jones & Company Inc.
Contact: Almar Latour, Chief Executive Officer
Ed: Christopher Williams. Description: Weyerhaeuser Co.'s management said that a conversion to a real estate investment trust was not likely in 2009 since the move is not tax-efficient as of the moment and would overload its non-timber assets with debt. The company's shares have fallen by 19.5 percent. However, the company remains an asset-rich outfit and its activist shareholder is pushing for change. Availability: Online.

6665 ■ "What Comes After That Job Is Cut?" in Business Review Albany (Vol. 41, August 15, 2014, No. 21, pp. 4)
Released: Weekly. Price: $4, Print. Description: Former KeyBank regional president, Jeff Stone, has joined the list of well-known banking executives who have reinvented themselves as the financial industry transforms around the Albany, NY area. Stone, as well as other leading bank leaders, have transitioned to smaller banks or other industries. Insights into the Banking Industry's Act II are provided. Availability: Print; Online.

6666 ■ "What Has Sergey Wrought?" in Barron's (Vol. 89, July 13, 2009, No. 28, pp. 8)
Pub: Dow Jones & Company Inc.
Contact: Almar Latour, Chief Executive Officer
Ed: Alan Abelson. Description: Sergey Aleynikov is a computer expert that once worked for Goldman Sachs but he was arrested after he left the company and charged with theft for bringing with him the code for the company's proprietary software for high-frequency trading. The stock market has been down for four straight weeks as of July 13, 2009 which reflects the reality of how the economy is still struggling. Availability: Online.

6667 ■ "What Online Brokers Are Doing To Keep Their Customers' Accounts Safe" in Barron's (Vol. 88, March 10, 2008, No. 10, pp. 37)
Pub: Dow Jones & Company Inc.
Contact: Almar Latour, Chief Executive Officer
Ed: Theresa W. Carey. Description: Online brokerage firms employ different methods to protect the accounts of their customers from theft. These methods include secure Internet connections, momentary passwords, and proprietary algorithms. Availability: Online.

6668 ■ "Whatever Happened to TGIF? How Much Of the Recession Is Priced into Stocks?" in Barron's (Vol. 88, March 10, 2008, No. 10, pp. M3)
Pub: Dow Jones & Company Inc.
Contact: Almar Latour, Chief Executive Officer
Ed: Kopin Tan. Description: US stock markets fell in early March 2008 to their lowest level in 18 months, venturing close to entering a bear market phase. The S&P 500 has dropped an average of 0.78 percent on Fridays for 2008. Availability: Online.

6669 ■ "What's In a Relationship? The Case of Commercial Lending" in Business Horizons (Vol. 51, March-April 2008, No. 2, pp. 93)
Pub: Elsevier Advanced Technology Publications
Ed: Gregory F. Udell. Description: Academic literature on relationship lending and banking to small and medium enterprises is analyzed. This practice is best suited to some SME types but creates special challenges for bank managers. Relationship lending may also be better delivered by community banks. Availability: PDF; Online.

6670 ■ "What's More Important: Stag or Flation?" in Barron's (Vol. 88, July 14, 2008, No. 28, pp. M8)
Pub: Dow Jones & Company Inc.
Contact: Almar Latour, Chief Executive Officer
Ed: Randall W. Forsyth. Description: Economists are divided on which part of stagflation, an economic situation in which inflation and economic stagnation occur simultaneously and remain unchecked for a period of time, is more important. Some economists say that the Federal government is focusing on controlling inflation while others see the central bank as extending its liquidity facilities to the financial sector. Availability: Online.

6671 ■ "When to Roll Over" in Black Enterprise (Vol. 37, November 2006, No. 4, pp. 50)
Pub: Earl G. Graves Ltd.
Contact: Earl Graves, Jr., President
Ed: Carolyn M. Brown. Description: Being proactive and rolling over your funds if you own stock of your former employee will give you more control over your money, especially if the company merges or is sold. Availability: Online.

6672 ■ "Where the Money Is" in Conde Nast Portfolio (Vol. 2, June 2008, No. 6, pp. 113)
Description: Revenue generated from treatments for common brain disorders that are currently on the market are listed. Availability: Online.

6673 ■ "Where to Stash Your Cash" in Barron's (Vol. 88, March 17, 2008, No. 11, pp. 41)
Pub: Dow Jones & Company Inc.
Contact: Almar Latour, Chief Executive Officer
Ed: Mike Hogan. Description: Investors are putting their money in money-market mutual funds seeking fractionally better yields and a safe haven from the uncertainties that was brought about by subprime lending. These funds, however, are hovering near 3.20 percent which is less than the 4 percent inflation rate. Availability: Online.

6674 ■ "Whistling Past the Graveyard? Higher Quality Stocks Beckon to Investors?" in Barron's (Vol. 88, March 17, 2008, No. 11, pp. 15)
Pub: Dow Jones & Company Inc.
Contact: Almar Latour, Chief Executive Officer
Ed: Michael Santoli. Description: Discusses the Federal Reserve's move to provide $200 billion to the system which can be seen as an effort to avoid the liquidity problems that Bear Stearns suffered. The Federal Reserve's move seems to frighten investors rather than reassure them. Availability: Online.

6675 ■ "Why Asset Allocation Is Important: Don't Only Focus On Your Client's Finances, Start With Their Goals" in Retirement Advisor (Vol. 13, October 2012, No. 10, pp. 20)
Ed: Lloyd Lofton. Description: Asset allocation can help investors, particularly seniors, to manage risk when planning investments. Diversity means spreading assets into three major classes of stocks, bonds and fixed products. These investments should be reviewed annually. Availability: Print; Online.

6676 ■ "Why Intel Should Dump Its Flash-Memory Business" in Barron's (Vol. 88, March 10, 2008, No. 10, pp. 35)
Pub: Dow Jones & Company Inc.
Contact: Almar Latour, Chief Executive Officer
Ed: Eric J. Savitz. Description: Intel Corp. must sell its NAND flash-memory business as soon as it possibly can to the highest bidder to focus on its PC processor business and take advantage of other business opportunities. Apple should consider a buyback of 10 percent of the company's shares to lift its stock. Availability: Online.

6677 ■ "Why the Rout in Financials Isn't Over" in Barron's (Vol. 88, June 30, 2008, No. 26, pp. 23)
Pub: Dow Jones & Company Inc.
Contact: Almar Latour, Chief Executive Officer
Ed: Robin Goldwyn Blumenthal. Description: Top market technician Louise Yamada warns that the retreat in the shares of financial services is not yet over based on her analysis of stock charts. Yamada's analysis of the charts of Citigroup, Fifth Third Bancorp and Merrill Lynch are discussed together with the graphs for these shares. Statistical data included. Availability: Online.

6678 ■ "Why This Investing Expert Is Bullish On the Energy Sector: William Heard Expects the Changing Landscape to Lead to Greater Opportunities" in Black Enterprise (Vol. 45, July-August 2014, No. 1, pp. 25)
Pub: Earl G. Graves Ltd.
Contact: Earl Graves, Jr., President
Description: Profile of William Heard and his firm Heard Capital, LLC, the Chicago-based investment company that invests in telecommunications, media, technology, financials, industrials, and energy. Heard shares his investment philosophy and current investments.

6679 ■ "Why WestJet's Culture Guru Chooses to Fly Under the Radar" in Globe & Mail (January 22, 2007, pp. B1)
Ed: Brent Jang. Description: The views of co-founder Donald Bell of WestJet Airlines Ltd. on company's shares and services are presented. Availability: Online.

6680 ■ "Wielding a Big Ax" in Barron's (Vol. 89, July 13, 2009, No. 28, pp. 26)
Pub: Dow Jones & Company Inc.
Contact: Almar Latour, Chief Executive Officer
Ed: Shirley A. Lazo. Description: Weyerhaeuser cut their quarterly common payout by 80 percent from 25 cents to a nickel a share which they say will help them preserve their long-term value and improve their performance. Paccar also cut their quarterly dividend by half to nine cents a share. Walgreen however, boosted their quarterly dividend by 22.2 percent to 13.75 cents a share. Availability: Online.

6681 ■ "With Mine Approval, Crystallex's Value as Target Seen on Rise" in Globe & Mail (March 28, 2006, pp. B3)
Ed: Wendy Stueck. Description: Crystallex International Corp. obtains Venezuelan Ministry of Basic Industry and Mining's authorization on Las Cristinas mining project. The impact of the approval, which posted rise in shares by 21 percent for the company, is discussed.

6682 ■ "A World of Opportunity: Foreign Markets Offer Diversity to Keen Investors" in Canadian Business (Vol. 81, Summer 2008, No. 9)
Description: International Monetary Fund projected in its 'World Economy Outlook' that there is a 25 percent chance that a global recession will occur in 2008 and 2009. Global growth rate is forecasted at 3.7 percent in 2008. Inflation in Asia emerging markets and forecasts on stock price indexes are presented. Availability: Online.

6683 ■ "World's Best CEOs" in Barron's (Vol. 88, March 24, 2008, No. 12, pp. 33)
Pub: Dow Jones & Company Inc.
Contact: Almar Latour, Chief Executive Officer
Ed: Andrew Bary. Description: Listing of the 30 best chief executive officers worldwide which was compiled through interviews with investors and analysts, analysis of financial and stock market performance, and leadership and industry stature.

6684 ■ *"The Worst Lies Ahead for Wall Street: More Losses Certain; More Expensive Capital to Be Needed"* in Crain's New York Business (Vol. 24, January 20, 2008, No. 3, pp. 1)
Pub: Crain Communications, Inc.
Contact: Jessica Botos, Manager, Marketing
E-mail: jessica.botos@crainsnewyork.com
Ed: Aaron Elstein. **Description:** Due to the weakening economy, many financial institutions will face further massive losses forcing them to borrow more at higher interest rates and dragging down their earnings for years to come. The effects on commercial real estate and credit card loans are also discussed as well as the trend to investing in Asia and the Middle East. **Availability:** Online.

6685 ■ *"Xstrata's Takeover Bid Comes Up Short in Shareholders' Eyes"* in Globe & Mail (March 27, 2007, pp. B16)
Ed: Andy Hoffman. **Description:** The share holders of LionOre Mining International have expressed dissatisfaction over $4.6 billion take over by Xstrata PLC. Share holders are demanding more prices for share value. **Availability:** Online.

6686 ■ *"You Won't Go Broke Filling Up On The Stock"* in Barron's (Vol. 88, July 14, 2008, No. 28, pp. 38)
Pub: Dow Jones & Company Inc.
Contact: Almar Latour, Chief Executive Officer
Ed: Assif Shameen. **Description:** Due to high economic growth, pro-business policies and a consumption boom, the Middle East is a good place to look for equities. The best ways in which to gain exposure to this market include investing in the real estate industry and telecommunications markets as well as large banks that serve corporations and consumers. **Availability:** Online.

6687 ■ *"Young Money"*
Pub: Grand Central Publishing
Contact: Michael Pietsch, Chairman
Released: February 18, 2014. **Price:** $27, hardcover. **Description:** How the financial crisis of 2008 changed a generation and remade Wall Street is discussed. The author spent three years following eight entry-level workers at Goldman Sachs, Bank of America Merrill Lynch and other leading investment firms. These young bankers are exposed to the exhausting workloads, huge bonuses, and recreational drugs that have always characterized Wall Street life, but as they get their education and training, they face questions about ethics, prestige and the value of their work. **Availability:** E-book; Print; Audio.

6688 ■ *"Young People Speak Out On Credit Union Board Involvement"* in Credit Union Times (Vol. 21, July 14, 2010, No. 27, pp. 20)
Ed: Myriam DiGiovanni. **Description:** Results of a Credit Union Times survey of Generation Y individuals about serving on Credit Union boards across the country are examined. **Availability:** Online.

6689 ■ *Your Complete Guide to a Successful & Secure Retirement*
Ed: Larry Swedroe, Kevin Grogan. **Released:** January 07, 2019. **Price:** $11.88, Paperback; $8.19, E-book. **Description:** A helpful guide for those financially preparing for retirement. Discusses social security, medicare, investing, portfolio management, and more. **Availability:** E-book; Print.

6690 ■ *"Your Exposure to Bear Stearns"* in Barron's (Vol. 88, March 17, 2008, No. 11, pp. 45)
Pub: Dow Jones & Company Inc.
Contact: Almar Latour, Chief Executive Officer
Ed: Tom Sullivan, Jack Willoughby. **Description:** Bear Stearns makes up 5.5 percent of Pioneer Independence's portfolio, 1.4 percent of Vanguard Windsor II's portfolio, 1.2 percent of Legg Mason Value Trust, about 1 percent of Van Kampen Equity & Income, and 0.79 percent of Putnam Fund for Growth & Income. Ginnie Mae securities are now trading at 1.78 percentage points over treasuries due to the mortgage crises. **Availability:** Online.

6691 ■ *Your Guide to Arranging Bank & Debt Financing for Your Own Business in Canada*
Pub: Productive Publications
Contact: Iain Williamson, Author Publisher
Ed: Iain Williamson. **Released:** 2022-2023 Edition. **Price:** C$99.95, softcover, Postage/handling $19.95 on first title, Add postage/handling of $3.50 per title thereafter. **Description:** Bank financing for small businesses in Canada is discussed. **Availability:** Print.

6692 ■ *"Zara Eludes the Pain in Spain: Clothing Giant Inditex Sees Its First-Quarter Profits Rise By 30 Percent"* in Canadian Business (Vol. 85, September 17, 2012, No. 14, pp. 67)
Ed: Bryan Borzykowski. **Released:** September 17, 2012. **Description:** Clothing retailer Inditex reported a 30 percent increase in profit in the first quarter of 2012 and 15 percent increase in sales year over year. The company's unique business model was attributed to its growth, which also appeals to income investors.

6693 ■ *"Zell Takes a Gamble on Tribune"* in Globe & Mail (April 3, 2007, pp. B1)
Ed: Sinclair Stewart. **Description:** The purchase of the majority share in Tribune Co. by Samuel Zell is described. Samuel Zell's plans to keep the company's assets intact are discussed. **Availability:** Online.

TRADE PERIODICALS

6694 ■ *Fidelity Investor*
Contact: James H. Lowell, III, Editor
URL(s): fidelityinvestor.com
Ed: James H. Lowell, III. **Released:** Monthly **Price:** $99.95, Individuals; $189, Two years. **Description:** Contains investment advice covering Fidelity mutual funds. Recurring features include interviews, model portfolios, performance reviews, and best buys. **Availability:** Print; Online.

6695 ■ *FPA Journal of Financial Planning*
Pub: Financial Planning Association
Contact: Claudia Cypher Kane, President
URL(s): www.financialplanningassociation.org/learning/publications/journal
Released: Monthly **Description:** Provides coverage of industry events and developments as well as happenings within the association. Carries articles on regulatory, ethical, and public relations aspects of the industry. Recurring features include letters to the editor, news of members, a calendar of events, feature articles, and original contributions. **Availability:** Online.

6696 ■ *Global Custodian*
Contact: Jonathan Watkins, Editor
E-mail: jonathan.watkins@strategic-i.com
URL(s): www.globalcustodian.com/magazine/magazine_index.aspx
X (Twitter): twitter.com/globalcustodian
Ed: Jonathan Watkins. **Released:** 5/year **Price:** $565, Individuals For print only(1 year).; $830, Individuals For print only(2 year).; $715, Individuals For online only(1 year).; $1,185, Individuals For online only(2 year).; $890, Individuals For both print and online(1 year).; $1,310, Individuals For both print and online(2 year). **Description:** Business journal for global investment and operations professionals. **Availability:** Print; PDF; Online.

6697 ■ *International Tax and Public Finance*
Pub: Springer US
Contact: Derk Haank, Chief Executive Officer
URL(s): link.springer.com/journal/10797
Released: 6/year; February, April, June, August, October and December. **Description:** Journal covering tax and public finance worldwide. **Availability:** Print; PDF; Download; Online.

6698 ■ *Journal of IT Financial Management*
Pub: I.T. Financial Management Association
URL(s): www.itfma.com/default.aspx
Released: 3/year; Spring, Fall, Winter. **Description:** Journal covering financial management of information technology organizations. **Availability:** Print.

6699 ■ *Plan Sponsor: Insight on Plan Design & Investment Strategy*
Contact: Judy Faust Hartnett, Managing Editor
E-mail: jhartnett@assetinternational.com
URL(s): www.plansponsor.com/strategic-insight-acquires-brightscope
Linkedin: www.linkedin.com/groups/4902930/profile
X (Twitter): twitter.com/PLANSPONSOR
Released: Monthly **Description:** Trade magazine for pension fund and endowment executives. **Availability:** Print; Online.

TRADE SHOWS AND CONVENTIONS

6700 ■ *ABA Bank Marketing Conference*
American Bankers Association (ABA)
1120 Connecticut Ave. NW
Washington, DC 20036
Free: 800-226-5377
Co. E-mail: support@aba.com
URL: http://www.aba.com
Contact: Rob Nichols, President
URL(s): www.aba.com/training-events/conferences/bank-marketing-conference
Frequency: Irregular. **Description:** Marketing metrics, branch development, compliance, marketing trends, retail banking, customer profitability, branding, online marketing, employee retention, marketing research, and payments. **Audience:** Industry professionals. **Principal Exhibits:** Marketing metrics, branch development, compliance, marketing trends, retail banking, customer profitability, branding, online marketing, employee retention, marketing research, and payments. **Telecommunication Services:** reghousing@aba.com.

6701 ■ *ABA/BMA National Conference for Community Bankers*
Visa Inc.
900 Metro Center B
Foster City, CA 94404
Ph: (650)432-3200
Fax: (650)432-7436
URL: http://www.visa.com
Contact: Rajat Taneja, President
URL(s): www.aba.com/training-events/conferences/conference-for-community-bankers
Frequency: Annual. **Description:** Products and services related to investment management, customer service improvements, advertising, asset/liability management, bank management, electronic data interchange, employee recruitment/training, insurance, strategic planning models, including preparation for the 21st century, new revenue sourhttp://camsfdr.cams.cengage.info:8080/fdr/images/close.jpgces, cost control techniques, mainframe computers, market research, MCIF technology, minicomputers in community banking applications, software: platform, optical disk, and loan pricing, sweep accounts, and relationship banking for community bankers. **Audience:** Industry professionals. **Principal Exhibits:** Products and services related to investment management, customer service improvements, advertising, asset/liability management, bank management, electronic data interchange, employee recruitment/training, insurance, strategic planning models, including preparation for the 21st century, new revenue sourhttp://camsfdr.cams.cengage.info:8080/fdr/images/close.jpgces, cost control techniques, mainframe computers, market research, MCIF technology, minicomputers in community banking applications, software: platform, optical disk, and loan pricing, sweep accounts, and relationship banking for community bankers. Dates and Locations: 2025 Feb 16-18 JW Marriott Phoenix Desert Ridge, Phoenix, AZ. **Telecommunication Services:** reghousing@aba.com.

6702 ■ ACE Academy
Frequency: Annual. **Description:** Annual conference with a focus on investment, wealth management, and retirement and behavioral finance. **Principal Exhibits:** Annual conference with a focus on investment, wealth management, and retirement and behavioral finance.

6703 ■ FMS Forum
Financial Managers Society (FMS)
7918 Jones Branch Dr., 4th Fl.
McLean, VA 22102
Ph: (312)578-1300
Fax: (312)578-1308
Co. E-mail: info@fmsinc.org
URL: http://www.fmsinc.org
Contact: Alana Vartanian, President
E-mail: avartanian@fmsinc.org
URL(s): www.fmsinc.org/forum25-home.html
Frequency: Annual. **Description:** Offer exemplary teaching and training programs. **Audience:** Industry professionals. **Principal Exhibits:** Offer exemplary teaching and training programs. Dates and Locations: 2025 Jun 22-24 Omni Orlando Resort Champions-Gate, Orlando, FL. **Telecommunication Services:** info@fmsinc.org.

6704 ■ Futures and Options Expo
CME Group Inc.
20 S Wacker Dr.
Chicago, IL 60606
Ph: (312)930-1000
Free: 866-716-7274
Co. E-mail: info@cmegroup.com
URL: http://www.cmegroup.com
Contact: Terrence A. Duffy, Chief Executive Officer
URL(s): www.fia.org/fia/events/futures-options-expo
Frequency: Annual. **Description:** Includes keynote speakers, exhibits, and networking opportunities. **Audience:** Leaders and industry stakeholders. **Principal Exhibits:** Includes keynote speakers, exhibits, and networking opportunities. **Telecommunication Services:** tvitalechan@fia.org.

6705 ■ National Agricultural Bankers Conference
CHS Hedging, LLC
5500 Cenex Dr.
Inver Grove Heights, MN 55077
Free: 800-328-6530
Co. E-mail: support@chshedging.com
URL: http://chshedging.com
Contact: Nelson Neale, President
URL(s): www.aba.com/training-events/conferences/agricultural-bankers-conference
Frequency: Annual. **Description:** On topics related to latest developments in the agricultural lending business, as well as strategies for better market share, profitability, and customer service. Includes keynote speakers, workshops, and sessions. **Audience:** Industry professionals. **Principal Exhibits:** On topics related to latest developments in the agricultural lending business, as well as strategies for better market share, profitability, and customer service. Includes keynote speakers, workshops, and sessions. **Telecommunication Services:** mrogers@aba.com.

6706 ■ Wealth Management and Trust Conference
Alpha Core
URL(s): www.aba.com/training-events/conferences/wealth-management-trust-conference
Frequency: Annual. **Description:** Events for the wealth management and trust banking community. **Audience:** Industry professionals. **Principal Exhibits:** Events for the wealth management and trust banking community. Dates and Locations: 2025 Feb 24-26 Manchester Grand Hyatt, San Diego, CA. **Telecommunication Services:** kchancy@aba.com.

6707 ■ The Wealth and Retirement Management Advisor Forum
URL(s): investmentsandwealth.org/raf2022
Description: An educational conference for retirement advisors. **Principal Exhibits:** An educational conference for retirement advisors.

CONSULTANTS

6708 ■ Alan Biller and Associates
535 Middlefield Rd., Ste. 230
Menlo Park, CA 94025
Ph: (650)328-7283
Co. E-mail: info@alanbiller.com
URL: http://www.alanbiller.com
Contact: Asad Ali, President
Linkedin: www.linkedin.com/company/alan-biller-and-associates
Description: Firm provides consulting services to monitor over time of managers, rebalance portfolios, and much more. **Founded:** 1982. **Publications:** "Fourteen Things to Expect From Your Investment Consultant"; "First Principles of Performance Evaluation"; "Organization and Structure of a Fund"; "Hedge Fund Hoopla: As Taft-Hartley Funds Get Interested, What Should Trustees Ask?"; "Does Private Equity Have a Role in Your Portfolio?"; "Soft-Dollars Harm to Pension Funds, Markets"; "Baubles, Bangles and Bright Shiny Things"; "Equity Style Benchmarks for Fund Analysis"; "A Plan Sponsor's Guide to Commissions".

6709 ■ Arnold S. Goldin & Associates Inc.
PO Box 276158
Boca Raton, FL 33427
Ph: (561)994-5810
Fax: (561)431-3102
URL: http://www.arnoldgoldin.com
Description: An accounting and management consulting firm. Serves clients worldwide. Provides management services. Handles monthly write-ups and tax returns. **Scope:** An accounting and management consulting firm. Serves clients worldwide. Provides management services. Handles monthly write-ups and tax returns.

6710 ■ Olson Research Associates, Inc. (ORA)
2500 Wallington Way., No. 101
Marriottsville, MD 21104
Ph: (410)290-6999
Free: 888-657-6680
Co. E-mail: info@olsonresearch.com
URL: http://www.olsonresearch.com
Contact: Brad Olson, President
Description: Firm provides of financing consultants service. **Scope:** A firm of consultants, educators and publishers providing consulting services, simulation models, financial risk management reporting, educational programs and books for financial institutions. **Founded:** 1970. **Publications:** "Risk Management Digest"; "Strategic Financial Management," Ivy Press Inc; "The Double Whammy," Oct, 2000. **Training:** Policy Development Workshops; Seminars for Bank Directors; Financial Risk Management and Interest Rate Risk; Getting the Maximum Benefit From A/L Benchmarks; Revising Your ALCO Policies.

6711 ■ Rose & Crangle Ltd.
102 E Lincoln Ave.
Lincoln, KS 67455
Contact: S. Jeanne Crangle, Contact
Description: Provider of evaluation, planning and policy analyzes for universities, associations, foundations, governmental agencies and private companies engaged in scientific, technological or educational activities. Special expertise in the development of new institutions. Special skills in providing planning and related group facilitation workshops. **Scope:** Provider of evaluation, planning and policy analyzes for universities, associations, foundations, governmental agencies and private companies engaged in scientific, technological or educational activities. Special expertise in the development of new institutions. Special skills in providing planning and related group facilitation workshops. **Publications:** "Preface to Bulgarian Integration Into Europe and NATO: Issues of Science Policy And research Evaluation Practice," Ios Press, 2006; "Allocating Limited National Resources for Fundamental Research," 2005.

6712 ■ SS&C Technologies Inc.
SS&C Technologies Holdings, Inc.
100 S Wacker Dr. 19th Flr.
Chicago, IL 60606
Ph: (860)298-4500
Free: 800-234-0556
Co. E-mail: solution@sscinc.com
URL: http://www.ssctech.com
Contact: William C. Stone, Chief Executive Officer
Facebook: www.facebook.com/ssctechnologies
X (Twitter): x.com/SSCTechnologies
Instagram: www.instagram.com/ssctechnologies
YouTube: www.youtube.com/c/SsctechInc
Description: Firm provides the global financial services industry with a broad range of highly specialized software, software enabled-services and software as a service solutions for operational excellence. **Founded:** 1986. **Special Services:** Sun Solaris/MS NT Server Platforms. Software partners with Lotus Notes; Microsoft; Sybase; Ardent (Universe); and others.

FRANCHISES AND BUSINESS OPPORTUNITIES

6713 ■ 4Pillars Consulting Group Inc.
c/o Navaiz Chaudhry
13737-96th Ave., Ste. 201 Twr. 1
Surrey, BC, Canada V3V 0C6
Ph: (604)587-5577
Co. E-mail: navaizc@4pillars.ca
URL: http://www.4pillars.ca
Contact: Navaiz Chaudhry, Contact
E-mail: navaizc@4pillars.ca
Description: Consulting firm provides debt consolidation and restructuring, credit rebuilding, budgeting, financial literacy. **Financial Assistance:** Yes **Training:** Provides 2 weeks training and ongoing support.

6714 ■ The Comprehensive Financial Planning System, Inc. (CFPS)
3706 SW Topeka Blvd., Ste. 400
Topeka, KS 66609
Ph: (785)266-8333
Free: 800-550-2377
Fax: (785)266-7819
URL: http://t-mfinancial.com/cfps
Contact: Richard L. Miller, President
E-mail: rmiller@t-mfinancial.com
Description: Firm engaged in providing financial planning services to clients in the areas of insurance and investments. **No. of Franchise Units:** 5. **No. of Company-Owned Units:** 1. **Founded:** 1962. **Franchised:** 2004. **Equity Capital Needed:** $11,400. **Financial Assistance:** Yes **Training:** Yes.

6715 ■ The Interface Financial Group (IFG)
7910 Woodmont Ave., Ste. 1050
Bethesda, MD 20814
Free: 877-210-9748
Co. E-mail: info@interfacefinancial.com
URL: http://www.interfacefinancial.com
Contact: George Shapiro, Chief Executive Officer
Facebook: www.facebook.com/The-Interface-Financial-Group-111961404552
Linkedin: www.linkedin.com/company/the-interface-financial-group
YouTube: www.youtube.com/user/InvoiceFactoringForB
Description: Provider of invoice financial services for business growth. **Founded:** 1972. **Training:** Yes. **Educational Activities:** IFA Factoring Conference (Annual).

PUBLICATIONS

6716 ■ *Small Business Retirement Savings Advisor*
200 Constitution Ave. NW
Washington, DC 20210
Free: 866-487-2365
URL: http://www.dol.gov
Contact: Martin J. Walsh, Secretary
URL(s): webapps.dol.gov/elaws/ebsaplan.htm

Description: Aims to answer a variety of commonly asked questions about retirement savings options for small business employers and help you determine which program is most appropriate for your business. **Availability:** Print.

COMPUTERIZED DATABASES

6717 ■ ABI/INFORM
ProQuest LLC
789 E Eisenhower Pky.
Ann Arbor, MI 48108
Ph: (734)761-4700
Free: 800-521-0600
URL: http://www.proquest.com
Contact: Matti Shem Tov, Chief Executive Officer
URL(s): about.proquest.com/en/products-services/abi_inform_complete
Availability: Online. **Type:** Full-text; Bibliographic; Image.

6718 ■ Barron's
Dow Jones & Company Inc.
1211 Avenue of the Americas
New York, NY 10036
Free: 800-568-7625
Co. E-mail: support@dowjones.com
URL: http://dowjones.com
Contact: Almar Latour, Chief Executive Officer
URL(s): www.barrons.com
Facebook: www.facebook.com/barrons
Linkedin: www.linkedin.com/company/barrons
X (Twitter): x.com/barronsonline
Instagram: www.instagram.com/Barrons
Released: Daily **Price:** $8.50, Single issue; $1, for online Week/1 Year (digital Bundle print + online); $4, for 4 weeks/1 Year (digital Bundle-print + online); $2, for online 4 weeks/1 year. **Availability:** Print; Online. **Type:** Full-text; Numeric; Statistical.

6719 ■ Business Wire
Business Wire, Inc.
101 California St., 20th Fl.
San Francisco, CA 94111
Co. E-mail: info@businesswire.com
URL: http://www.businesswire.com
Contact: Geff Scott, Chief Executive Officer
Description: Contains more than 1.4 million records that make up the complete text of press releases from public and private companies and other organizations, such as hospitals and universities. **Availability:** Online. **Type:** Full-text.

6720 ■ Municipal Market Data-Line®
Thomson Reuters
22 Thomson Pl.
Boston, MA 02210
Ph: (617)856-2000
Free: 800-692-8833
Fax: (800)543-1983
URL: http://www.thomsonreuters.com
Contact: Peter DeBruyne, Director
URL(s): tm3.com
Type: Full-text; Numeric.

6721 ■ OTC Markets Newsletter
OTC Markets Group Inc.
300 Vesey St., 12th Fl.
New York, NY 10282
Ph: (212)896-4400
Free: 800-547-8682
Co. E-mail: info@otcmarkets.com
URL: http://www.otcmarkets.com
Contact: Cromwell R. Coulson, President
URL(s): www.otcmarkets.com/about/otc-markets-newsletter
Released: Monthly **Availability:** Print. **Type:** Full-text; Numeric.

6722 ■ U.S. Weekly Statistics
Haver Analytics
60 E 42nd St.
New York, NY 10165
Ph: (212)986-9300
Co. E-mail: sales@haver.com
URL: http://www.haver.com

Contact: Paul L. Kasriel, Contact
URL(s): haverproducts.com/products/market-data/#top
Released: Weekly **Availability:** Online. **Type:** Statistical; Numeric.

6723 ■ Value Line DataFile
Value Line, Inc.
551 5th Ave., 3rd Fl.
New York, NY 10176
Ph: (212)907-1500
Co. E-mail: vlcr@valueline.com
URL: http://www.valueline.com
Contact: Howard A. Brecher, Chief Executive Officer
URL(s): www.valuelinepro.com/value-line-data
Released: Weekly **Availability:** Online. **Type:** Numeric.

6724 ■ Value Line's Fundamental DataFile
Value Line, Inc.
551 5th Ave., 3rd Fl.
New York, NY 10176
Ph: (212)907-1500
Co. E-mail: vlcr@valueline.com
URL: http://www.valueline.com
Contact: Howard A. Brecher, Chief Executive Officer
URL(s): www.valuelinepro.com/fundamental-datafile
Availability: Online. **Type:** Time Series; Numeric.

INTERNET DATABASES

6725 ■ Fintech: Financial Technology Research Guide
URL(s): guides.loc.gov/fintech
Description: An online resource to find topics related to financial technology. **Availability:** Online.

LIBRARIES

6726 ■ Bank of Nova Scotia Archives [Scotiabank Archives]
44 King St. W
Toronto, ON, Canada M5H 1H1
Co. E-mail: archives@scotiabank.com
URL: http://www.scotiabank.com/ca/en/about/our-company/archives.html
Description: Banking industry in Canada. **Scope:** Cultural heritage community. **Founded:** 1967. **Holdings:** Reports.

6727 ■ Fiscal Agents - Financial Information Service - Research Department Library
25 Lakeshore Rd. W
Oakville, ON, Canada L6K 1C6
Ph: (905)844-7700
Free: 866-434-7225
Fax: (905)844-8552
URL: http://www.fiscalagents.com
Contact: David J. Newman, Contact
Scope: Industry, trust services, investment products, insurance. **Services:** Copying; library open to the public at librarian's discretion. **Founded:** 1977. **Holdings:** 12 reports.

6728 ■ Independent Community Bankers of America (ICBA)
Independent Community Bankers of America (ICBA)
1615 L St. NW, Ste. 900
Washington, DC 20036
Ph: (202)659-8111
Free: 800-422-8439
Fax: (202)659-3604
Co. E-mail: info@icba.org
URL: http://www.icba.org
Contact: Rebeca Romero Rainey, President
E-mail: rebeca.romerorainey@icba.org
Facebook: www.facebook.com/icbaorg
Linkedin: www.linkedin.com/company/icba
X (Twitter): x.com/ICBA
YouTube: www.youtube.com/user/CommunityBankChannel/featured
Description: Provides legislative and regulatory information and representation for community financial institutions and opposes "concentration of banking and commercial powers". Provides credit and debit cards, travelers checks, insurance, bank investment, mutual funds, credit and debit card programs, mortgages, check purchase protection, and group purchasing programs. **Founded:** 1930. **Publications:** *Independent Banker* (Monthly); *Community Bank Director Quarterly* (Quarterly); *Compliance Bulletin* (Periodic); *ICBA Community Reinvestment Act Deskbook*; *Washington Weekly Report*. **Educational Activities:** ICBA Live National Convention (Annual). **Awards:** ICBA National Community Bank Service Awards (Annual). **Geographic Preference:** National.

6729 ■ Ontario Teachers' Pension Plan Board (OTPP) - Knowledge Centre
Ontario Teachers' Pension Plan Board (OTPP)
5650 Yonge St.
Toronto, ON, Canada M2M 4H5
Ph: (416)228-5900
Free: 800-668-0105
Fax: (416)730-5349
Co. E-mail: communications@otpp.com
URL: http://www.otpp.com
Contact: Jo Taylor, President
Facebook: www.facebook.com/myOTPP
Linkedin: www.linkedin.com/company/ontario-teachers%E2%80%8B%27-pension-plan
X (Twitter): x.com/OTPPinfo
YouTube: www.youtube.com/user/otppinfo
Description: Engages in administering defined-benefit pensions for teachers. **Scope:** Pension management; investment; economics; finance. **Services:** Library not open to the public. **Founded:** 1989. **Holdings:** Books.

6730 ■ Principal Financial Group Inc. - Library
Principal Financial Group Inc.
711 High St.
Des Moines, IA 50392
Ph: (515)247-5111
Free: 800-986-3343
Fax: (866)894-2093
URL: http://www.principal.com
Contact: Daniel J. Houston, President
Facebook: www.facebook.com/PrincipalFinancial
Linkedin: www.linkedin.com/company/principal-financial-group
X (Twitter): twitter.com/Principal
YouTube: www.youtube.com/user/PrincipalFinancial
Description: Global investment management company offers retirement, asset management, and insurance products to small and medium-sized businesses, individuals, and institutional clients. **Founded:** 1879.

6731 ■ Russell Reynolds Associates Inc., Library
155 N Wacker Dr., Ste. 4100
Chicago, IL 60606-1732
Ph: (312)993-9696
URL: http://www.russellreynolds.com/en
Contact: Constantine Alexandrakis, Contact
Facebook: www.facebook.com/RussellReynoldsAssociates
Linkedin: www.linkedin.com/company/russell-reynolds-associates
X (Twitter): x.com/RRAonLeadership
Scope: Business, financial services, banking. **Services:** Interlibrary loan; copying; reference; library open to the public by appointment. **Holdings:** 1000 books; company annual reports; subject files.

6732 ■ Willamette Management Associates Library
8600 W Bryn Mawr Ave., Ste. 950 N
Chicago, IL 60631
Ph: (773)399-4300
Fax: (773)399-4310
URL: http://www.willamette.com
Contact: Robert F. Reilly, Managing Director
E-mail: rfreilly@willamette.com
Linkedin: www.linkedin.com/company/willamette-management-associates

Description: Business valuation, forensic analysis, and transaction financial advisory services. **Scope:** Business valuation; tax; estate; finance. **Services:** Interlibrary loan; copying; library not open to the public. **Founded:** 1969.

RESEARCH CENTERS

6733 ■ Boston University - Center for Finance, Law and Policy
121 Bay State Rd.
 Boston, MA 02215
Co. E-mail: login@bu.edu
URL: http://www.bu.edu/pardeeschool/tag/center-for-finance-law-and-policy

Description: Integral unit of School of Law, Boston University. **Scope:** Banking and financial institutions, particularly law and regulation of the financial services industry, pension and trust fund administration, law and regulation of depository institutions, securities activities of banks, deposit insurance funds, international banking, asset management, and financing. **Founded:** 1978. **Publications:** *Review of Financial Law* (Semiannual).

6734 ■ CFA Institute Research Foundation [Research Foundation of the Institute of Chartered Financial Analysts]
915 E High St.
 Charlottesville, VA 22902
Co. E-mail: rf@cfainstitute.org
URL: http://www.cfainstitute.org/en/research/foundation
Contact: Gary P. Brinson, President
Linkedin: www.linkedin.com/showcase/research-foundation
X (Twitter): twitter.com/CFAResearchFndn

Description: Publishes research on financial analysis and investment management. Accepts unsolicited manuscripts. **Scope:** Financial analysis and portfolio management. **Founded:** 1965. **Publications:** *Research Foundation of CFA Institute Monographs*. **Geographic Preference:** Regional.

6735 ■ Filene Research Institute (FRI)
5910 Mineral Point Rd.
 Madison, WI 53705
Ph: (608)661-3740
Co. E-mail: info@filene.org
URL: http://www.filene.org
Contact: Mark Meyer, President
Facebook: www.facebook.com/fileneresearch
Linkedin: www.linkedin.com/company/filene-research-institute
X (Twitter): x.com/fileneresearch

Description: Independent, nonprofit organization. Offers research colloquia workshops. **Scope:** Research on the economic, social and technological environment affecting the financial services sector, particularly credit unions; consumer finance issues; public policy and educational issues of credit unions, cooperatives and financial service providers. **Founded:** 1989. **Publications:** *Investigative reports*; *Filene Research Institute Research reports*.

6736 ■ McGill University - Desautels Faculty of Management - Desmarais Global Finance Research Centre
Bronfman Bldg.,
 1001 Sherbrooke St. W
 Montreal, QC, Canada H3A 1G5
URL: http://www.mcgill.ca/desautels/research/centres/dgfc
Contact: David Schumacher, Director
E-mail: david.schumacher@mcgill.ca

Description: Integral unit of Desautels Faculty of Management, McGill University. **Scope:** Modern finance, focusing on international financial markets, asset pricing and risk management, and corporate finance and governance. **Founded:** 1998. **Educational Activities:** DGFC Seminars, conferences.

6737 ■ Princeton University - Bendheim Center for Finance (BCF)
Julis Romo Rabinowitz Bldg., 20 Washington Rd.
 Princeton, NJ 08544
Ph: (609)258-0770
Fax: (609)258-0771
Co. E-mail: bcf@princeton.edu
URL: http://bcf.princeton.edu
Contact: Markus K. Brunnermeier, Director
E-mail: markus@princeton.edu
Linkedin: www.linkedin.com/school/princeton-bendheim-center-for-finance
X (Twitter): x.com/PrincetonBCF

Description: Integral unit of Princeton University. **Scope:** Research focuses on securities markets, credit markets, corporate finance, capital budgeting, and portfolio analysis. **Founded:** 1997. **Educational Activities:** BCF Conferences; BCF Seminars, Part of the finance seminar, with guest speakers who present on various topics relating to finance.

6738 ■ University of Chicago - Booth School of Business - Center for Research in Security Prices (CRSP)
105 W Adams St., Ste. 1700
 Chicago, IL 60603
Ph: (312)263-6400
Fax: (312)263-6430
Co. E-mail: support@crsp.org
URL: http://crsp.org
Contact: David Barclay, Chief Executive Officer
Linkedin: www.linkedin.com/company/center-for-research-in-security-prices-crsp

Description: Integral unit of Booth School of Business at University of Chicago. **Scope:** Historical financial data. **Founded:** 1960.

6739 ■ University of Pennsylvania - The Wharton School Finance Department - Rodney L. White Center for Financial Research
3254 Steinberg Hall-Dietrich Hall
 3620 Locust Walk
 Philadelphia, PA 19104-6367
Ph: (215)898-7616
Fax: (215)573-8084
Co. E-mail: rodneywhitecenter@wharton.upenn.edu
URL: http://rodneywhitecenter.wharton.upenn.edu
Contact: Itamar Drechsler, Director
E-mail: idrechsler@wharton.upenn.edu
X (Twitter): x.com/rodneycenter

Description: Integral unit of Wharton School at University of Pennsylvania. **Scope:** Finance, including financial management, money and capital markets, urban and real estate finance, and international finance and financial institutions, designed to accelerate the flow of applied and theoretical research to business and academic communities. **Founded:** 1969. **Educational Activities:** Rodney L. White Center for Financial Research Micro Seminars (Weekly).

Fish and Seafood Store

ASSOCIATIONS AND OTHER ORGANIZATIONS

6740 ■ **International Institute of Fisheries Economics and Trade (IIFET)**
Dept. of Agricultural and Resource Economics
Oregon State University
Corvallis, OR 97331-3601
URL: http://oregonstate.edu/dept/iifet
Contact: Kat Goetting, Executive Director
Facebook: www.facebook.com/International-Institute-of-Fisheries-Economics-Trade-IIFET-92047244451
X (Twitter): x.com/IIFETorg
Description: To advance the productive use of economic theory and analysis to answer critical questions surrounding the sustainable use of marine resources and to ensure future livelihoods of those who produce food from the sea. **Publications:** *IIFET Newsletter*; *International Institute of Fisheries Economics and Trade--Membership Directory*. **Educational Activities:** International Institute of Fisheries Economics and Trade Conference (Biennial). **Awards:** IIFET Best Student Paper Prize (Biennial); IIFET Distinguished Service Award (Biennial); IIFET Best Student Paper Award (Biennial); IIFET Distinguished Service Award (Biennial). **Geographic Preference:** Multinational.

6741 ■ **Maine Lobstermen's Association (MLA)**
2 Storer St., Ste. 203
Kennebunk, ME 04043
Ph: (207)967-4555
Fax: (866)407-3770
URL: http://www.mainelobstermen.org
Contact: Kristan Porter, President
Facebook: www.facebook.com/mainelobstermen
X (Twitter): x.com/mainelobstermen
Instagram: www.instagram.com/mainelobstermen
Description: Licensed lobstermen and supporting business. Gives Maine's lobstermen a voice and influence at the highest levels of government. **Founded:** 1954. **Geographic Preference:** National.

6742 ■ **Northwest Fisheries Association (NWFA)**
6523 California Ave. SW, No. 314
Seattle, WA 98136
Ph: (206)789-6197
Co. E-mail: info@northwestfisheries.org
URL: http://www.northwestfisheries.org
Contact: Katia Ionitsa, President
Facebook: www.facebook.com/northwestfisheries
Description: Primary and secondary seafood processors, seafood brokers, distributors, and direct support industries. Provides a positive business climate for members and enhances the flow of information throughout the Pacific fishing and seafood industry. **Founded:** 1951. **Geographic Preference:** National.

6743 ■ **Southeastern Association of Fish and Wildlife Agencies (SEAFWA)**
c/o Robert H. Boyles, President
Rembert C. Dennis Bldg.
Columbia, SC 29202
Ph: (803)734-4007
Co. E-mail: boylesr@dnr.sc.gov
URL: http://seafwa.org
Contact: Robert H. H. Boyles, President
E-mail: boylesr@dnr.sc.gov
Description: Directors of state game and fish commissions in 16 southern states, and the Commonwealth of Puerto Rico, and the Virgin Islands. Aims to: protect the right of jurisdiction of southeastern states over their wildlife resources on public and private lands; study state and federal wildlife legislation and regulations as they affect the area; consult with and make recommendations to federal wildlife and public land agencies on federal management programs and programs involving federal aid to southeastern states; serve as a clearinghouse for exchange of ideas on wildlife management and research techniques. Sponsors: Cooperative Fish Disease Study at Auburn University in Alabama; Cooperative Wildlife Disease Study at the University of Georgia in Athens. **Founded:** 1938. **Publications:** *Southeastern Association of Fish and Wildlife Agencies Proceedings*. **Educational Activities:** Southeastern Association of Fish and Wildlife Agencies Conference (Annual). **Geographic Preference:** National.

REFERENCE WORKS

6744 ■ *"21 Percent of Fish is Mislabeled in Restaurant and Stores"* in *U.S. News & World Report* (March 8, 2019)
URL(s): www.usnews.com/news/health-news/articles/2019-03-08/report-21-percent-of-fish-is-mislabeled-in-restaurants-and-stores
Ed: Alexa Lardieri. **Released:** March 08, 2019. **Description:** The conservation group Oceana's study on seafood concluded that about one-fifth of fish in restaurants is mislabeled. Sea bass and snapper were the most commonly mislabeled and were actually giant perch or nile tilapia and lavender jobfish. **Availability:** Online.

6745 ■ *"Baltimore's Steamed Crab Prices Reach New Highs: Paying the Price"* in *Baltimore Business Journal* (Vol. 28, July 9, 2010, No. 9, pp. 1)
Pub: Baltimore Business Journal
Contact: Rhonda Pringle, President
E-mail: rpringle@bizjournals.com
Ed: Emily Mullin. **Description:** Crab prices have never been higher in Baltimore, Maryland and businesses have been led to count on strengthening demand for seafood. For instance, the average price for a dozen large crabs has increased by 5 percent to $58.90. How restaurants have responded to the increase in prices is discussed, along with factors that might have caused the harvest of smaller crabs. **Availability:** Print.

6746 ■ *"Buyers Shouldn't Bank on Cheaper Fresh Atlantic Cod"* in *IntraFish* (November 2, 2019)
URL(s): www.intrafish.com/prices/buyers-shouldnt-bank-on-cheaper-fresh-atlantic-cod/2-1-686626
Ed: Nina Unlay. **Released:** November 02, 2019. **Description:** Discusses the rise in prices for consumer-favorite Atlantic cod and how it hasn't exactly been a deterrent for those dining out and ordering this fish. **Availability:** Online.

6747 ■ *"Convictions Under the Fisheries Act"* in *Marketwired* (May 16, 2007)
Pub: Comtex News Network Inc.
Contact: Kan Devnani, President
Description: Fisheries and Oceans Canada is mandated to protect and conserve marine resources and thus released a list of fishers fined for various offences under the Fisheries Act in March and April. **Availability:** Print; Online.

6748 ■ *"Counting Crabs: Supply Dips, Putting Crimp on Memorial Day Feast"* in *Boston Business Journal* (Vol. 29, June 3, 2011, No. 4, pp. 1)
Pub: Boston Business Journal
Contact: Carolyn M. Jones, President
E-mail: cmjones@bizjournals.com
Ed: Scott Dance. **Price:** $4, Introductory 4-Week Offer(Digital Only). **Description:** Restaurateurs in Baltimore City experienced low supply of crabs this Memorial Day 2011 owing to the early season and the fact that many small crabbers took time off during the weekend. Sales were cut in half compared with previous Memorial Day weekends and prices rose to as much as $185 to $200 per box of crabs. Normal supply is expected, though, as summer pushes on. **Availability:** Print; Online.

6749 ■ *"Life After Cod"* in *Globe & Mail* (March 18, 2006, pp. B1)
Pub: The Globe & Mail Inc.
Ed: Gordon Pitts. **Description:** Canadian fishing industry is under threat because of Chinese processing competition, high energy costs, rise of powerful retailers and the rise of Canadian dollar value. Fishing industry of Canada is analyzed. **Availability:** Print; PDF; Online.

6750 ■ *"Lobster Mania Hits China: They Just Had to Get Used to the Claws"* in *Canadian Business* (Vol. 85, July 16, 2012, No. 11-12, pp. 10)
Ed: Joe Castaldo. **Description:** Canadian lobster exports to China have tripled to almost $30 million annually since 2010 as a result of marketing efforts by Maritimes governments including pitching lobster to cooking shows and organizing training sessions for Chinese chefs. Canadian exporters must decide whether their lobster is a premium product or a commodity product to solidify its image in China. **Availability:** Print; Online.

6751 ■ *Seafood Festivals*
URL(s): www.fresh-seafood.net/directory/seafood-festivals/
Description: An online list of seafood festivals held throughout the United States. Includes a website for each entry and a brief description of the festival. **Availability:** Online.

6752 ■ "Seafood Sustainability — Consumer Preference Study" in Fresh Seafood (November 12, 2018)
URL(s): www.fresh-seafood.net/2018/11/seafood-sustainability-consumer-preference-study/
Released: November 12, 2018. **Description:** A recent study in a paper, "Measuring willingness to pay for environmental attributes in seafood," determined that consumers are willing to pay a premium for sustainable seafood. Americans consume about 15 pounds of seafood each per year, and labels with information about sustainability do affect their purchase decisions. **Availability:** Online.

6753 ■ "Time to Rethink Fishery Management?" in Providence Business News (Vol. 29, April 7, 2014, No. 1, pp. 1)
Pub: American City Business Journals, Inc.
Contact: Mike Olivieri, Executive Vice President
Released: April 05, 2014. **Description:** Mid-Atlantic Fishery Management Council has been examining how climate change impacts the way they think about fish stocks. The re-examination has prompted a new way of looking at fishery management that goes beyond the fishing effort. The changes that are happening in the waters off Rhode Island are also discussed. **Availability:** Print; Online.

LIBRARIES

6754 ■ Oregon State University (OSU) - Seafoods Research Laboratory Library
2001 Marine Dr.
Astoria, OR 97103
Ph: (503)325-4531
Fax: (503)325-2753
URL: http://osuseafoodlab.oregonstate.edu
Contact: Christina DeWitt, Director (Acting)

YouTube: www.youtube.com/user/SeafoodU
Description: Sea food research and education center. **Scope:** Marine food science and technology; fish processing; seafood safety; seafood processors; food educators. **Founded:** 1940. **Holdings:** 380 volumes.

RESEARCH CENTERS

6755 ■ Iowa State University - North Central Regional Aquaculture Center (NCRAC)
c/o Joseph Morris
111 Science Hall II
Ames, IA 50011-3221
Ph: (515)294-4622
Fax: (515)294-2995
Co. E-mail: jemorris@iastate.edu
URL: http://www.ncrac.org
Contact: Dr. Joseph E. Morris, Director
E-mail: jemorris@iastate.edu
Description: Aquaculture research, development, and demonstration center affiliated with the College of Agriculture and Natural Resources at Michigan State University; administered by its own board of directors with assistance from an industry advisory council and a technical committee. Offers information exchange between industry and researchers. **Scope:** Aquaculture products, focusing on increasing production of fish; improving breeding and culture technology for walleye, yellow perch, hybrid striped bass; and sunfish; developing techniques to preserve and transport gametes for year-round production; improving fish strains; enhancing development of domestic commercial aquaculture industry; and reducing foreign product dependency for the benefit of producers, consumers, and the economy. **Founded:** 1988. **Educational Activities:** NCRAC Extension educational programs.

6756 ■ Southern Regional Aquaculture Center (SRAC)
127 Experiment Station Rd.
Stoneville, MS 38776
Ph: (662)686-3269
Fax: (662)686-3320
URL: http://www.srac.msstate.edu
Contact: Dr. Jimmy Avery, Director
E-mail: javery@drec.msstate.edu
Description: Aquaculture research, development, and demonstration center affiliated with the Delta Research and Extension Center at Mississippi State University. **Scope:** Aquaculture and seafood products, focusing on increasing production of fish and shellfish, enhancing development of domestic commercial aquaculture industry, and reducing foreign product dependency for the benefit of producers, consumers, and the economy. **Founded:** 1987.

6757 ■ University of Maryland College of Agriculture and Natural Resources - Northeastern Regional Aquaculture Center (NRAC)
2113 Animal Sciences Bldg. 142
Ellicott City, MD 21042
Ph: (301)405-6511
Fax: (301)314-9412
URL: http://agnr.umd.edu/research/research-and-education-centers-locations/northeastern-regional-aquaculture-center
Contact: Dr. Reginal M. Harrell, Director
E-mail: rharrell@umd.edu
Description: One of five regional centers funded by the Department of Agriculture, representing 12 states and the District of Columbia, and located at University of Maryland. Offers information exchange between industry and researchers. **Scope:** Aquaculture in the Northeastern United States. **Founded:** 1985. **Publications:** *Northeastern Aquaculture*. **Educational Activities:** NRAC Extension educational programs.

Fish Farm

START-UP INFORMATION

6758 ■ *"No. 373: Back To the Roots"* **In** *Inc. (Vol. 36, September 2014, No. 7, pp. 82)*
Pub: Mansueto Ventures L.L.C.
Contact: Stephanie Mehta, Chief Executive Officer
Released: September 2014. **Description:** AquaFarm uses a technique called aquaponics which combines fish and plant cultivation by using fish waste to fertilize vegetation. The startup company prides itself on being part fish tank, part herb garden and sells a $60 kit for growing mushrooms. **Availability:** Print; Online.

6759 ■ *"Urban Organics Launches Aquaponic Farm in Old Hamm's Brewery"* in *Business Journal (Vol. 31, April 11, 2014, No. 46, pp. 4)*
Pub: American City Business Journals, Inc.
Contact: Mike Olivieri, Executive Vice President
Price: $4, Introductory 4-Week Offer(Digital & Print).
Description: Urban Organics launched its new aquaponics farm at the old site of Hamm's Brewery in St. Paul, Minnesota. The facility has four 3,000 gallon fish tanks that hold 1,000 fish which Urban Organics uses to grow fresh and healthy tilapia and vegetable produce. **Availability:** Print; Online.

ASSOCIATIONS AND OTHER ORGANIZATIONS

6760 ■ **American Fisheries Society (AFS)**
425 Barlow Pl., Ste. 110
Bethesda, MD 20814-2144
Ph: (301)897-8616
Fax: (301)897-8096
Co. E-mail: main@fisheries.org
URL: http://fisheries.org
Contact: Douglas Austen, Executive Director
E-mail: dausten@fisheries.org
Facebook: www.facebook.com/AmericanFisheriesSociety
Linkedin: www.linkedin.com/company/american-fisheries-society
X (Twitter): x.com/AmFisheriesSoc
Description: Fisheries and aquatic science professionals. Promotes the development of all branches of fishery science and practice, and the conservation, development, and wise utilization of fisheries, both recreational and commercial. Strengthens professional standards by certifying fisheries scientists, stressing professional ethics, and providing forums for the exchange of information. Represents members through written and verbal testimony before legislative and administrative bodies concerning aquatic environmental issues. **Founded:** 1870. **Publications:** *AFS Membership Directory and Handbook*; *Marine and Coastal Fisheries: Dynamics, Management, and Ecosystem Science* (6/year); *Fisheries* (Monthly); *North American Journal of Fisheries Management* (6/year); *North American Journal of Aquaculture* (Quarterly); *Transactions of the American Fisheries Society* (6/year); *Directory of North American Fisheries & Aquatic Scientists*; *Journal of Aquatic Animal Health (JAAH)* (Quarterly). **Educational Activities:** American Fisheries Society Annual Meeting (Annual). **Awards:** AFS Excellence in Fisheries Education Award (Annual); AFS Award of Excellence (Annual); AFS Distinguished Service Award (Annual); AFS Meritorious Service Award (Annual); J Frances Allen Scholarship Award (Annual); John E. Skinner Memorial Fund Award (Annual); Carl R. Sullivan Fishery Conservation Award (Annual); AFS Student Writing Contest (Annual); Carl R. Sullivan International Endowment Award; AFS President's Fishery Conservation Award (Annual); AFS Honorary Membership (Annual); William E. Ricker Resource Conservation Award (Annual). **Geographic Preference:** Multinational.

6761 ■ **American Institute of Fishery Research Biologists (AIFRB)**
PO Box 827
East Falmouth, MA 02536
URL: http://www.aifrb.org
Contact: Cate O'Keefe, President
E-mail: cokeefe@umassd.edu
X (Twitter): x.com/AIFRB_fisheries
Description: Professional scientific and educational organization formed to: advance the theory and practice of fishery science in pursuit of greater scientific understanding of living marine and freshwater natural resources, their habitat, their biological and physical environment, and their fisheries. **Founded:** 1954. **Publications:** *BRIEFS* (6/year). **Educational Activities:** AIFRB Board of Control (Annual). **Awards:** AIFRB Outstanding Achievement Award (Annual); AIFRB Clark Hubbs Research Assistance Award (Annual); W.F. Thompson Best Student Paper Award (Annual); AIFRB Distinguished Service Award (Annual); Outstanding Achievement Award - Individual (Annual); AIFRB Outstanding Achievement Award - Group (Annual); W. F. Thompson Award (Annual). **Geographic Preference:** National.

6762 ■ **Atlantic Salmon Federation (ASF)**
15 Rankine Mill Rd.
Chamcook, NB, Canada E5B 3B1
Ph: (506)529-4581
Free: 800-565-5666
Co. E-mail: savesalmon@asf.ca
URL: http://www.asf.ca
Contact: Bill Taylor, President
Facebook: www.facebook.com/ASFSalmon
X (Twitter): x.com/ASFSalmon
Description: Promotes the preservation and better management of Atlantic salmon stocks. **Founded:** 1948. **Publications:** *Atlantic Salmon Journal* (Quarterly); *Atlantic Salmon Journal: Conservation-Minded Salmon Angler* (Quarterly); *Atlantic Salmon Journal (ASJ)* (Quarterly). **Awards:** Olin Fellowships (Annual); Happy Fraser Award (Annual); Lee Wulff Conservation Award (Annual); T.B. (Happy) Fraser Award (Annual); Atlantic Salmon Federation Olin Fellowships (Annual). **Geographic Preference:** Regional; Multinational.

6763 ■ **Florida Tropical Fish Farms Association (FTFFA)**
PO Box 1519
Winter Haven, FL 33882
Ph: (863)293-5710
Fax: (863)299-5154
Co. E-mail: help@ftffa.com
URL: http://www.ftffa.com
Contact: Pierre LePochat, President
Facebook: www.facebook.com/Florida-Tropical-Fish-Farms-Association-945930095452059
Description: Growers of tropical fish and aquatic plants; associate members are manufacturers and suppliers of allied products in Florida and elsewhere in the U.S. Seeks to elevate trade standards and promote the industry. Sponsors quarterly meeting to hear speakers on the care of tropical fish, applicable laws, and other aspects of the trade. Resources include an organization-owned co-op. **Founded:** 1964. **Publications:** *Florida Tropical Fish Farms Association--Membership Directory*. **Awards:** FTFFA Hall of Fame (Irregular). **Geographic Preference:** National.

6764 ■ **International Association of Astacology (IAA)**
Swingle Hall Rm. 203
Arburn University
Auburn, AL 36849-5419
Ph: (334)844-9249
Co. E-mail: crayfish.org@gmail.com
URL: http://www.astacology.org/default.asp?uid=Guest
Contact: Dr. Javier Dieguez-Uribeondo, President
Facebook: www.facebook.com/CrayfishIAA
X (Twitter): x.com/CrayfishIAA
Description: Individuals from industry, academia, and state and federal government wildlife agencies. Promotes the scientific study and cultivation of freshwater crayfish. Sponsors working groups in areas such as biology, ecology, and zoogeography. Offers quarterly newsletter and journal. **Founded:** 1972. **Publications:** *Directory of Astacologists* (Biennial). **Geographic Preference:** Multinational.

6765 ■ **International Institute of Fisheries Economics and Trade (IIFET)**
Dept. of Agricultural and Resource Economics
Oregon State University
Corvallis, OR 97331-3601
URL: http://oregonstate.edu/dept/iifet
Contact: Kat Goetting, Executive Director
Facebook: www.facebook.com/International-Institute-of-Fisheries-Economics-Trade-IIFET-92047244451
X (Twitter): x.com/IIFETorg
Description: To advance the productive use of economic theory and analysis to answer critical questions surrounding the sustainable use of marine resources and to ensure future livelihoods of those who produce food from the sea. **Publications:** *IIFET Newsletter*; *International Institute of Fisheries Economics and Trade--Membership Directory*. **Educational Activities:** International Institute of Fisheries Economics and Trade Conference (Biennial).

Awards: IIFET Best Student Paper Prize (Biennial); IIFET Distinguished Service Award (Biennial); IIFET Best Student Paper Award (Biennial); IIFET Distinguished Service Award (Biennial). **Geographic Preference:** Multinational.

6766 ■ Journal of Northwest Atlantic Fishery Science (JNAFS)
1601 Lower Water St., Ste. 401
Halifax, NS, Canada B3J 3P6
Ph: (902)468-5590
Co. E-mail: info@nafo.int
URL: http://www.nafo.int
URL(s): journal.nafo.int
Ed: Tom Blasdale, Neil Campbell. **Availability:** Print; PDF; Download; Online.

6767 ■ NAFO Meeting Proceedings of the Commission
1601 Lower Water St., Ste. 401
Halifax, NS, Canada B3J 3P6
Ph: (902)468-5590
Co. E-mail: info@nafo.int
URL: http://www.nafo.int
URL(s): www.nafo.int/Library/Commission/Meeting-Proceedings-of-the-Commission
Released: Annual **Description:** Provides the contracting parties with a detailed consolidated text of all discussions initiated during the year. **Availability:** Print; Online; PDF.

6768 ■ National Shellfisheries Association (NSA)
815 Genevieve Dr.
Lafayette, LA 70503
URL: http://www.shellfish.org
Description: International organization dedicated to sustainable management of the shellfish industry, bringing together biologists, hydrographers, public health workers, shellfish producers, and fishery administrators. **Founded:** 1908. **Educational Activities:** National Shellfisheries Association Annual Meeting (Annual). **Awards:** David H. Wallace Award (Periodic). **Geographic Preference:** National.

6769 ■ North Pacific Anadromous Fish Commission (NPAFC) - Library
889 W Pender St., Ste. 502
Vancouver, BC, Canada V6C 3B2
Ph: (604)775-5550
Fax: (604)775-5577
URL: http://npafc.org
Contact: Vladimir Radchenko, Executive Director
E-mail: vlrad@npafc.org
Description: Represents administrators and scientists devoted to the conservation of salmon in the North Pacific Ocean. Seeks to prohibits commercial salmon fishing in the high seas of the Pacific, between the United States, Canada, Japan, Republic of Korea and Russian Federation. Coordinates fisheries enforcement and scientific researches on the high seas of the North Pacific. **Scope:** Fish; conservation. **Founded:** 1993. **Holdings:** Figures not available. **Publications:** *NPAFC Annual Report* (Annual); *NPAFC Bulletin*; *NPAFC Technical Report*; *Statistical Yearbook* (Annual). **Geographic Preference:** Multinational.

6770 ■ Northwest Atlantic Fisheries Organization (NAFO) - Library [Organisation des Peches de l'Atlantique Nord-Ouest]
1601 Lower Water St., Ste. 401
Halifax, NS, Canada B3J 3P6
Ph: (902)468-5590
Co. E-mail: info@nafo.int
URL: http://www.nafo.int
Facebook: www.facebook.com/NAFO.Info
Linkedin: www.linkedin.com/company/nafo1979
X (Twitter): x.com/NAFO1979
Description: Contracting parties working to investigate, protect, and conserve the fishery resources of the Northwest Atlantic Ocean. Provides resource management. Compiles statistics; maintains research programs. **Scope:** Fisheries science. **Founded:** 1979. **Holdings:** Publications; documents; annual reports. **Publications:** *Scientific Council Reports* (Annual); *NAFO List of Fishing Vessels* (Irregular); *Journal of Northwest Atlantic Fishery Science (JNAFS)*; *NAFO Meeting Proceedings of the Commission* (Annual). **Geographic Preference:** Multinational.

6771 ■ NPAFC Annual Report
889 W Pender St., Ste. 502
Vancouver, BC, Canada V6C 3B2
Ph: (604)775-5550
Fax: (604)775-5577
URL: http://npafc.org
Contact: Vladimir Radchenko, Executive Director
E-mail: vlrad@npafc.org
URL(s): www.npafc.org/annual-report
Released: Annual **Description:** Contains results of the Commission's major activities, including Annual Meetings, symposia, workshops, and other NPAFC events. **Availability:** Print; Online; Download; PDF.

6772 ■ NPAFC Technical Report
889 W Pender St., Ste. 502
Vancouver, BC, Canada V6C 3B2
Ph: (604)775-5550
Fax: (604)775-5577
URL: http://npafc.org
Contact: Vladimir Radchenko, Executive Director
E-mail: vlrad@npafc.org
URL(s): www.npafc.org/technical-report
Description: Contains abstracts of scientific presentations given at NPAFC workshops. **Availability:** Print; Download; PDF.

6773 ■ Pacific Coast Shellfish Growers Association (PCSGA)
1522-B Fourth Ave. E
Olympia, WA 98506
Ph: (360)754-2744
Fax: (360)754-2743
Co. E-mail: pcsga@pcsga.org
URL: http://pcsga.org
Contact: Connie Smith, Assistant Director
Facebook: www.facebook.com/Pacific-Coast-Shellfish-Growers-Association-191956388828
Description: Oyster, clam, mussel, scallop, geoduck growers, openers, packers and shippers in Alaska, California, Oregon, Washington, Hawaii and Mexico. **Founded:** 1930. **Geographic Preference:** Regional.

6774 ■ Pacific Salmon Commission (PSC) - Library
600-1155 Robson St.
Vancouver, BC, Canada V6E 1B5
Ph: (604)684-8081
Fax: (604)666-8707
Co. E-mail: info@psc.org
URL: http://www.psc.org
Contact: Teri Tarita, Manager
Description: Formed by treaty between Canada and the United States for the conservation, management and optimum production of Pacific Salmon. **Scope:** Fisheries management. **Founded:** 1985. **Holdings:** Reports; papers; maps; photographs; documents. **Publications:** *Fraser River Panel Annual Report* (Annual); *Pacific Salmon Commission Annual Report (PSC)* (Annual). **Geographic Preference:** Multinational.

6775 ■ Pacific Salmon Commission Annual Report (PSC)
600-1155 Robson St.
Vancouver, BC, Canada V6E 1B5
Ph: (604)684-8081
Fax: (604)666-8707
Co. E-mail: info@psc.org
URL: http://www.psc.org
Contact: Teri Tarita, Manager
URL(s): www.psc.org/publications/annual-reports/commission
Released: Annual **Availability:** PDF; Download.

6776 ■ Southeastern Fisheries Association (SFA)
1700 N Monroe St., No. 11-154
Tallahassee, FL 32303
Ph: (850)224-0612
Fax: (850)270-6464
Co. E-mail: info@sfaonline.org
URL: http://www.sfaonline.org
Contact: Tony Lombardi, President
Description: Producers, distributors and suppliers of seafood in the South Atlantic and Gulf of Mexico areas. Disseminates information on legislation, both proposed and implemented, that affects fishermen in that area. Promotes and represents commercial fishermen's interests in legislative, industrial and environmental matters. Provides HAACP training onsite. **Founded:** 1952. **Publications:** *International Conference on Shrimp Bycatch*. **Awards:** Aylesworth Scholarship (Annual). **Geographic Preference:** National.

6777 ■ U.S. Trout Farmers Association (USTFA)
3558 N Jefferson St., Ste. 5
Lewisburg, WV 24901-9504
Ph: (304)802-4901
Co. E-mail: ustroutfarmersassociation@gmail.com
URL: http://ustfa.org
Contact: Mark Ely, President
Facebook: www.facebook.com/USTroutFarmers
X (Twitter): x.com/ustroutfarmers
Description: Promotes the trout farming industry and recreational trout fishing. Establishes Trout Farmers Quality Assurance Program; monitors legislation related to the aquaculture industry. **Founded:** 1954. **Publications:** *Trout Talk* (Quarterly). **Educational Activities:** USTFA Fall Conference (Annual). **Geographic Preference:** National.

REFERENCE WORKS

6778 ■ "Back To the Roots Puts a Hold On Bad Phone Music" in San Francisco Business Times (Vol. 28, February 21, 2014, No. 31, pp. 3)
Pub: American City Business Journals, Inc.
Contact: Mike Olivieri, Executive Vice President
Released: Weekly. **Description:** Oakland, California-based Back to the Roots has changed its telephone-hold music into a silly employee-produced tune. Former employee, Dennis Byrd, recorded the music that has a catchy beat, while the lyrics induce giggles from customers. The lyrics of the song are also presented. Back to the Roots sells aqua farm garden kits and mushroom kits. **Availability:** Print; Online.

6779 ■ "Baltimore's Steamed Crab Prices Reach New Highs: Paying the Price" in Baltimore Business Journal (Vol. 28, July 9, 2010, No. 9, pp. 1)
Pub: Baltimore Business Journal
Contact: Rhonda Pringle, President
E-mail: rpringle@bizjournals.com
Ed: Emily Mullin. **Description:** Crab prices have never been higher in Baltimore, Maryland and businesses have been led to count on strengthening demand for seafood. For instance, the average price for a dozen large crabs has increased by 5 percent to $58.90. How restaurants have responded to the increase in prices is discussed, along with factors that might have caused the harvest of smaller crabs. **Availability:** Print.

6780 ■ "Counting Crabs: Supply Dips, Putting Crimp on Memorial Day Feast" in Boston Business Journal (Vol. 29, June 3, 2011, No. 4, pp. 1)
Pub: Boston Business Journal
Contact: Carolyn M. Jones, President
E-mail: cmjones@bizjournals.com
Ed: Scott Dance. **Price:** $4, Introductory 4-Week Offer(Digital Only). **Description:** Restaurateurs in Baltimore City experienced low supply of crabs this Memorial Day 2011 owing to the early season and the fact that many small crabbers took time off during the weekend. Sales were cut in half compared with previous Memorial Day weekends and prices rose to as much as $185 to $200 per box of crabs. Normal supply is expected, though, as summer pushes on. **Availability:** Print; Online.

**6781 ■ "Does Farming Drive Fish Disease?"
in The Scientist (April 19, 2017)**
URL(s): www.the-scientist.com/news-opinion/does
-farming-drive-fish-disease-31641
Ed: Claire Asher. **Released:** April 19, 2017. **Description:** Recent research points to diseases evolving in farmed fish that are more harmful than ever before. Bacteria, viruses, and parasites are harming these fish that are raised in high-density conditions and therefore are able to spread rapidly. This could cost the industry billions and even spread to the wild. **Availability:** Online.

6782 ■ Fisheries of the United States
Pub: National Marine Fisheries Service - Fisheries Statistics & Economics Division, F/ST1
Ed: Barbara K. O'Bannon. **Released:** Annual **Description:** Covers fisheries throughout the country as compiled in government statistical reports. Includes annual fishery statistics, such as worldwide consumption, supply, employment. **Availability:** Print; PDF.

6783 ■ "The Future of Fish Farming May Be Indoors" in Scientific American (September 17, 2018)
URL(s): www.scientificamerican.com/article/the-future
-of-fish-farming-may-be-indoors/
Ed: Laura Poppick. **Released:** September 17, 2019. **Description:** Discusses the technological advancements that have been made in water filtration and circulation, which is making fish farms more efficient and effective. **Availability:** Online.

6784 ■ "Life After Cod" in Globe & Mail (March 18, 2006, pp. B1)
Pub: The Globe & Mail Inc.
Ed: Gordon Pitts. **Description:** Canadian fishing industry is under threat because of Chinese processing competition, high energy costs, rise of powerful retailers and the rise of Canadian dollar value. Fishing industry of Canada is analyzed. **Availability:** Print; PDF; Online.

6785 ■ "Lobster Mania Hits China: They Just Had to Get Used to the Claws" in Canadian Business (Vol. 85, July 16, 2012, No. 11-12, pp. 10)
Ed: Joe Castaldo. **Description:** Canadian lobster exports to China have tripled to almost $30 million annually since 2010 as a result of marketing efforts by Maritimes governments including pitching lobster to cooking shows and organizing training sessions for Chinese chefs. Canadian exporters must decide whether their lobster is a premium product or a commodity product to solidify its image in China. **Availability:** Print; Online.

6786 ■ "Study Finds Epigenetic Differences Between Hatchery-Raised and Wild-Born Salmon" in The Scientist (March 1, 2018)
URL(s): www.the-scientist.com/notebook/study-finds
-epigenetic-differences-between-hatchery-raised-an
d-wild-born-salmon-30057
Ed: Shawna Williams. **Released:** March 01, 2018. **Description:** Researchers have discovered that hatchery-reared salmon do not survive as well as their wild-born relatives when they are released into the wild, and often produce fewer offspring if they make it that long. The results of studies are discussed which explain scientifically what is happening and why. **Availability:** Online.

6787 ■ "Time to Rethink Fishery Management?" in Providence Business News (Vol. 29, April 7, 2014, No. 1, pp. 1)
Pub: American City Business Journals, Inc.
Contact: Mike Olivieri, Executive Vice President
Released: April 05, 2014. **Description:** Mid-Atlantic Fishery Management Council has been examining how climate change impacts the way they think about fish stocks. The re-examination has prompted a new way of looking at fishery management that goes beyond the fishing effort. The changes that are happening in the waters off Rhode Island are also discussed. **Availability:** Print; Online.

TRADE PERIODICALS

6788 ■ Aquaculture Magazine
URL(s): www.aquaculturemag.com
Facebook: www.facebook.com/AquacultureMag
?ref=hl
X (Twitter): twitter.com/AquacultureMag
Released: Bimonthly **Price:** $45, for 2 years US; $100, for 2 years canada & mexico; $160, for 2 years outside america. **Description:** Magazine serving aqua culturists engaged in the production, processing, and marketing of finfish, shellfish, crustaceans, and aquatic plants. **Availability:** Print.

6789 ■ National Fisherman
Pub: National Fisherman
Contact: Bob Callahan, Director
E-mail: bcallahan@divcom.com
URL(s): www.nationalfisherman.com/about
Facebook: www.facebook.com/nationalfisherman
Linkedin: www.linkedin.com/company/na
tionalfisherman
X (Twitter): x.com/natfishmag
Instagram: www.instagram.com/nationalfisherman
Released: Quarterly **Price:** $22.95, U.S. for 2 year; $12.95, U.S. for one year. **Description:** Magazine covering commercial fishing and boat building. **Availability:** Print; Online.

6790 ■ North American Journal of Aquaculture
Pub: Wiley-Blackwell
URL(s): fisheries.org/about/governance/constitution
-and-rules/journalsafspubs.onlinelibrary.wiley.com/
journal/15488454
Ed: Christopher C. Kohler, Reginal M. Harrell. **Released:** Quarterly **Price:** $536, Institutions for online only; $602, Institutions for print and online; $558, Institutions for online US, Canada, India; $627, Institutions for print and online US, Canada, India; $2,214, Institutions for online only combined; $2,486, Institutions for print and online combined; $627, Institutions for print & online; $558, Institutions for online only. **Description:** Journal covering current research and practical experience in all areas of intensive and extensive fish culture, including broodstock selection and spawning; nutrition and feeding; health and water quality; facilities and production technology; and the management of ponds, pens, and raceways. Published by Wiley on behalf of the American Fisheries Society. **Availability:** Print; Download; PDF; Online.

TRADE SHOWS AND CONVENTIONS

6791 ■ American Fisheries Society Annual Meeting
American Fisheries Society (AFS)
425 Barlow Pl., Ste. 110
Bethesda, MD 20814-2144
Ph: (301)897-8616
Fax: (301)897-8096
Co. E-mail: main@fisheries.org
URL: http://fisheries.org
Contact: Douglas Austen, Executive Director
E-mail: dausten@fisheries.org
URL(s): afsannualmeeting.fisheries.org
Frequency: Annual. **Description:** Equipment, supplies, and services related to fishery and marine biology. **Audience:** Fisheries biologists, administrators, and professionals. **Principal Exhibits:** Equipment, supplies, and services related to fishery and marine biology. Dates and Locations: 2025 Aug 10-14 San Antonio, TX; 2026 Aug 30-Sep 03 Columbus, OH.

CONSULTANTS

6792 ■ Aquatic Control Inc.
418 W State Rd., Ste. 258
Seymour, IN 47274
Ph: (812)497-2410
Co. E-mail: sales@aquaticcontrol.com
URL: http://www.aquaticcontrol.com
Contact: Leah Essex, Chief Executive Officer
Facebook: www.facebook.com/AquaticControl
X (Twitter): x.com/Aquatic_Control
Description: Provider of consulting services in aquatic and terrestrial ecology such as aquatic vegetation and fisheries management, lake mapping, laboratory services, and much more. **Scope:** Provider of consulting services in aquatic and terrestrial ecology such as aquatic vegetation and fisheries management, lake mapping, laboratory services, and much more. **Founded:** 1966.

6793 ■ CEF Consultants Ltd.
3045 Robie St., Unit 5, Ste. 122
Halifax, NS, Canada B3K 4P6
URL: http://cefconsultants.ns.ca
Contact: Norval Collins, President
E-mail: ncollins@cefconsultants.ns.ca
Description: Firm provides environmental planning services including environmental effects monitoring, marine seismic survey reviews, impact, risk assessment, environmental, fisheries planning and environmental communications. **Scope:** Firm provides environmental planning services including environmental effects monitoring, marine seismic survey reviews, impact, risk assessment, environmental, fisheries planning and environmental communications. **Founded:** 1983. **Training:** Care of Live Shellfish During Shipping; Use of Fish Offal in Aquaculture Feed; Hold Live Fish and Shellfish; Exporting Goods and Services to the Caribbean.

6794 ■ Southern Fish Culturists Inc.
7608 US Hwy. 441 S
Leesburg, FL 34748
Contact: W. Chet Ross, President
Description: Provider of counseling services in problems of aquatic ecology such as effects of pollution on aquatic organisms, fish kill evaluations, environmental assessments, fish and bait culture, fisheries management and aquatic weed control. **Scope:** Provider of counseling services in problems of aquatic ecology such as effects of pollution on aquatic organisms, fish kill evaluations, environmental assessments, fish and bait culture, fisheries management and aquatic weed control. **Founded:** 1953.

LIBRARIES

6795 ■ Auburn University - College of Agriculture - School of Fisheries, Aquaculture and Aquatic Sciences - International Center for Aquaculture and Aquatic Environments (ICAAE) - Library
Auburn, AL 36849
URL: http://aurora.auburn.edu/handle/11200/1127
Description: Integral unit of College of Agriculture, Auburn University. Provides information on relevant technical subjects. **Scope:** Provides technical assistance to developing countries on use of inland fisheries and aquaculture to enhance the production of food and income. Conducts in-country surveys, prepares project proposals for international funding agencies, helps establish pond culture research and development stations, and assists in the implementations of research, training, and extension programs in the following areas: aquacultural economics, aquacultural extension, inventory of fish species, fish taxonomy, fish nutrition and feeding, fish diseases, fish culture, hatchery management, chemical and biological aquatic weed control, limnological surveys, water pollution control and abatement, pond engineering and facility design, and fish technology, processing and preservation. **Founded:** 1991. **Holdings:** 2,500 books; annual reports of the Fisheries Resources Unit, 1936 to present; 10,000 slides and pictures; 250 dissertations; 550 theses. **Publications:** ICAAE Abstracts; ICAAE Newsletter (Quarterly).

6796 ■ Columbia River Inter-Tribal Fish Commission (CRITFC) - Library
700 NE Multnomah St., Ste. 1200
Portland, OR 97232
Ph: (503)238-0667
Fax: (503)235-4228

Co. E-mail: fdsk@critfc.org
URL: http://www.critfc.org
Contact: Aja DeCoteau Yakama, Executive Director
E-mail: deca@critfc.org
Scope: Fisheries science; habitat and watersheds; fisheries management; Columbia River Basin fisheries and ecosystem. **Founded:** 1992. **Holdings:** 60,000 volumes; 20 journals and other serials. **Publications:** *The Dipnetter*. **Geographic Preference:** State.

6797 ■ Desmond-Fish Library
472 Rte. 403
 Garrison, NY 10524
Ph: (845)424-3020
Co. E-mail: staff@desmondfishlibrary.org
URL: http://desmondfishlibrary.org
Contact: Dede Farabaugh, Director
Facebook: www.facebook.com/desmondfishlibrary
X (Twitter): x.com/desmondfish
Instagram: www.instagram.com/desmondfishpubliclibrary
YouTube: www.youtube.com/channel/UC-MnaGezxB8StEcwnGv_NcQ/videos
Description: Contains reference materials, journals, books, online materials, and video and audio materials, and historical documents or records. **Scope:** Local history; adults; children and families. **Services:** Interlibrary loan; Wi-Fi; copying; library open to the public. **Founded:** 1980. **Holdings:** Book.

6798 ■ Fisheries Museum of the Atlantic Library
68 Bluenose Dr.
 Lunenburg, NS, Canada B0J 2C0
Ph: (902)634-4794
Free: 866-579-4909
Fax: (902)634-8990
Co. E-mail: fma@gov.ns.ca
URL: http://fisheriesmuseum.novascotia.ca/educational-resources
Contact: Angela Saunders, Manager
E-mail: angela.saunders@novascotia.ca
Scope: History. **Services:** Library open to the public. **Founded:** 1967. **Holdings:** 1,000 vessel photographs.

6799 ■ U.S. Department of Commerce - National Oceanic and Atmospheric Administration - Library and Information Services Division Central Library
1315 East-West Hwy. SSMC3, 2nd Fl.
 Silver Spring, MD 20910
Ph: (301)713-2600
Co. E-mail: library.reference@noaa.gov
URL: http://library.noaa.gov
Contact: Laura Newcomb, Director
E-mail: laura.newcomb@noaa.gov
X (Twitter): x.com/NOAALibrary
YouTube: www.youtube.com/channel/UCxK2oekvetMp6zPSTWN63_g
Scope: Ocean; coast; atmospheric science; fostering innovation; collaboration and discovery. **Services:** Interlibrary loan; Copying; library open to the public for reference use only. **Founded:** 1846. **Holdings:** 9,000 journals;120,000 eBooks.

RESEARCH CENTERS

6800 ■ Auburn University Alabama Agricultural Experiment Station - School of Fisheries, Aquaculture and Aquatic Sciences (FAAS)
203 Swingle Hall
 Auburn, AL 36849
Ph: (334)844-4786
Co. E-mail: fish@auburn.edu
URL: http://agriculture.auburn.edu/research/faas
Facebook: www.facebook.com/auschoolfish
X (Twitter): twitter.com/AuburnFisheries
Description: Integral unit of Alabama Agricultural Experiment Station at Auburn University. **Scope:** Aquaculture in fresh, brackish, and marine water; fisheries management in large and small impoundments, and rivers; aquatic plants management; nutrition and feeds; parasites and disease; limnology;

water quality and management for aquaculture; international development for fisheries and aquaculture; aquatic ecology and environmental assessment; environmental education. **Founded:** 1970. **Publications:** *Newsletter Quarterly* (Quarterly).

6801 ■ Maine Aquaculture Innovation Center (MAIC)
193 Clarks Cove Rd.
 Walpole, ME 04573
Ph: (207)832-1075
URL: http://www.maineaquaculture.org
Contact: Christopher V. Davis, Executive Director
E-mail: cdavis@midcoast.com
Description: Independent, nonprofit research organization. **Scope:** Aquaculture, including identification of suitable aquaculture sites, toxic phytoplankton monitoring lease sites, shellfish poisoning by toxic phytoplankton, shellfish genetics, public aquaculture of soft-shell clams, finfish health management, new and novel species, product quality control, aquaculture equipment, recycling fish processing wastes, and finfish feed technology, new species research, and environmental monitoring. **Founded:** 1988. **Geographic Preference:** National.

6802 ■ Memorial University of Newfoundland - Canadian Centre for Fisheries Innovation (CCFI)
155 Ridge Rd.
 Saint John's, NL, Canada A1B 5E7
URL: http://www.ccfi.ca
Contact: Keith Hutchings, Managing Director
E-mail: keith.hutchings@mi.mun.ca
URL(s): www.mun.ca/govern/administration/separately-incorporated-entities
X (Twitter): x.com/CCFI_MUN
Instagram: www.instagram.com/ccfi_mun
Description: Independent, nonprofit research and development organization affiliated with Memorial University of Newfoundland. Offers research and development, technology transfer, workshops, and information dissemination to the Canadian fishery and aquaculture industry. **Scope:** Deals with marine and freshwater fisheries, including aquaculture, harvesting and processing, and fisheries equipment development. Projects include design and development of harvesting technologies and vessels; fish product development; aquaculture issues; development of new fisheries; and fish genetics. **Publications:** *CCFI Annual report* (Annual); *Project Reports*.

6803 ■ Memorial University of Newfoundland - Fisheries and Marine Institute School of Fisheries - Centre for Aquaculture and Seafood Development (CASD)
PO Box 4920
 Saint John's, NL, Canada A1C 5R3
Ph: (709)778-0532
Fax: (709)778-0670
Co. E-mail: casd@mi.mun.ca
URL: http://www.mi.mun.ca/departments/centreforaquacultureandseafooddevelopment
Contact: Heather Burke, Director
E-mail: heather.burke@mi.mun.ca
Description: Integral unit of Fisheries and Marine Institute, Memorial University of Newfoundland. Offers analytical services such as nutritional, microbial, and quality assessments; provides assistance to companies in selecting equipment, processing, and quality control and productivity concerns; educational services and technical workshops. **Scope:** Development of new seafood products, added value products, equipment and process material development, and market base enhancement, techniques in food science and technology, food engineering, food safety, and marketing and management. Aquaculture research in areas of fish nutrition, shellfish culture, site evaluations, land based systems, and technical advisory services.

6804 ■ Oceanic Institute (OI)
41 202 Kalaniana " ole Hwy.
 Waimanalo, HI 96795-1820
Ph: (808)259-7951
Fax: (808)259-5971
Co. E-mail: admissions@hpu.edu

URL: http://www.hpu.edu/oi
Contact: Dr. Shaun Moss, Executive Director
E-mail: smoss@hpu.edu
Description: A research and development organization dedicated to marine aquaculture, biotechnology, and coastal resource management. Works to develop and transfer economically responsible technologies to increase aquatic food production while promoting the sustainable use of ocean resources. **Founded:** 1960. **Publications:** *OI Annual report* (Annual); *OI Research papers* (Periodic). **Educational Activities:** OI Training courses, Marine aquaculture focusing on technological development for commercial feasibility domestically and abroad, of finfish, ornamentals, and marine shrimp of all species.; OI Workshops, Offer exemplary teaching and training programs.

6805 ■ Stony Brook University - School of Marine and Atmospheric Sciences - Living Marine Resources Institute (LIMRI)
SoMAS, Stony Brook University
 Stony Brook, NY 11794-5000
URL: http://you.stonybrook.edu/somas/institutes/living-marine-resources-institute
Contact: Paul Shepson, Dean
E-mail: paul.shepson@stonybrook.edu
URL(s): somas.stonybrook.edu/about/facilities
Description: Research unit of the School of Marine and Atmospheric Sciences at Stony Brook University at Stony Brook. Offers public lectures. **Scope:** Conducts studies on the economic structure of living marine resource industries, the effects of development on fisheries habitat, and marine fisheries policy and management. **Founded:** 1985. **Educational Activities:** LIMRI Conferences and symposia, On issues related to fisheries and their effects on the environment.

6806 ■ University of British Columbia - Fisheries Centre (FC)
AERL, 2202 Main Mall
 Vancouver, BC, Canada V6T 1Z4
Ph: (604)822-2731
URL: http://oceans.ubc.ca/research/publications/research-reports
Contact: Dr. Tony Pitcher, Director
E-mail: t.pitcher@oceans.ubc.ca
Facebook: www.facebook.com/ubcoceans
Linkedin: www.linkedin.com/school/ubcoceans
X (Twitter): twitter.com/UBCoceans
YouTube: www.youtube.com/c/UBCInstitutefortheOceansandFisheries
Description: Integral unit of University of British Columbia, administered through the Faculty of Graduate Studies. **Scope:** Assessment and management of artisanal and commercial fisheries, impact of fisheries on aquatic ecosystems, recreational fisheries, coastal and watershed management, co-management of shared fishery resources and conflict resolution, and the conservation of endangered species and exploited aquatic animal resources. **Founded:** 1993. **Publications:** *Fisheries Centre Research reports* (Bimonthly). **Educational Activities:** Fisheries Centre Seminars, Focusing on freshwater systems, oceans and fisheries.; Fisheries Centre Workshops.

6807 ■ University of Idaho - Aquaculture Research Institute (ARI)
875 Perimeter Dr.
 Moscow, ID 83844
URL: http://www.uidaho.edu/research/entities/aquaculture
Contact: Brian C. Small, Director
E-mail: bcsmall@uidaho.edu
Description: Integral unit of University of Idaho Aquaculture Program. Provides opportunities for graduate student research across college lines. Aquaculture industry assistance available. **Scope:** Commercial and conservation aquaculture, including fish culture and production efficiency; fish nutrition and growth physiology; fish genetics and breeding; fish health and pathology; fish waste management and water quality assurance; aquaculture marketing and economics; aquaculture facility design; and fish behavior and life histories. Focus is on salmonids

and endangered species of the Pacific Northwest. **Founded:** 1988. **Publications:** *Idaho Aquaculture News* (Quarterly). **Educational Activities:** ARI K-12 outreach activities.

6808 ■ University of Maryland at College Park - College of Agriculture and Natural Resources - Department of Animal and Avian Sciences (CAF) - Crane Aquaculture Facility
Bldg. 142
8127 Regents Dr.
College Park, MD 20742-2311
URL: http://ansc.umd.edu/research/research-centers
Description: Cooperative private and public research facility owned by Baltimore Gas and Electric, licensed to the University of Maryland Agricultural Experiment Station. Provides juvenile to mature striped bass for outside research, demonstrations, and donations; technology transfer for aquaculture industry. **Scope:** Domestic and genetic selection of striped bass or rockfish for accelerated growth and earlier maturation. Other activities include striped bass reproduction, nutrition, disease prevention, stress physiology and cryobiology. **Founded:** 1983.

6809 ■ University of Memphis - College of Arts and Sciences - Department of Biological Sciences - Ecological Research Center (ERC)
Park Ave. Campus
The University of Memphis
Memphis, TN 38152
Ph: (901)678-2594
Co. E-mail: uuid@memphis.edu
URL: http://www.memphis.edu/erc
Contact: Dr. Bill Simco, Director
E-mail: bsimco@memphis.edu
Description: Integral unit of Department of Biological Sciences, College of Arts and Sciences, University of Memphis. **Scope:** Wildlife and fisheries studies and environmental assessments, including investigations of endangered species, wildlife management, and studies of migratory birds and wetlands. Also conducts aquaculture studies on channel catfish reproduction, factors limiting production, and stress responses to aquaculture practices. Research and graduate training in Urban Ecology. **Founded:** 1973.

6810 ■ University of New Hampshire - New Hampshire Sea Grant College Program
8 College Rd.
Durham, NH 03824
Ph: (603)862-6700
Free: 800-735-2964
Fax: (603)659-1304
Co. E-mail: nh.seagrant@unh.edu
URL: http://seagrant.unh.edu
Contact: Erik Chapman, Director
E-mail: erik.chapman@unh.edu
Facebook: www.facebook.com/nhseagrant
X (Twitter): twitter.com/NHSeaGrant
Instagram: www.instagram.com/nhseagrant
YouTube: www.youtube.com/NHSeaGrant
Description: Integral unit of the University of New Hampshire, part of the National Sea Grant College Program administered by the National Oceanic and Atmospheric Administration. **Scope:** Marine and estuarine sciences, including lobster resources and the lobster industry; social and scientific issues relating to fisheries management; fisheries development, marketing, harvesting, and processing; aquaculture; construction in the coastal zone; marine pollution; cumulative impacts of the coastal environment; coastal law and policy; marine biotechnology; and marine recreation and tourism, including environmental impact and use conflict, sport fishing, and economic development. **Founded:** 1966. **Educational Activities:** Great Bay Living Lab Program; Sea Grant Extension Program; Sea Trek Program; UNH Marine Docent Program.

6811 ■ Western Regional Aquaculture Center (WRAC)
1122 NE Boat St.
Seattle, WA 98105
URL: http://wracuw.org
Contact: Dr. Graham Young, Executive Director
E-mail: grahamy@uw.edu
Description: One of five regional centers funded by the Department of Agriculture, representing 12 states and located at the University of Washington. Offers information exchange between industry and researchers. **Scope:** Aquaculture and seafood products, focusing on increasing production of fish and shellfish, developing and testing vaccines for the IHN virus which affects commercial trout and salmon stocks, enhancing development of domestic commercial aquaculture industry, and reducing foreign product dependency for the benefit of producers, consumers, and the economy. **Founded:** 1985. **Publications:** *Waterlines* (Annual).

Fitness Service/Health Club/Personal Trainer

REFERENCE WORKS

6812 ■ *"5 Best Fitness Apps for Kids" in MentalUP(June 24, 2022)*
URL(s): www.mentalup.co/blog/fitness-apps-for-kids
Released: June 24, 2022. **Description:** Discusses the benefits of five difference fitness apps that are aimed at children and their physical fitness. **Availability:** Online.

6813 ■ *Building a Wellness Business That Lasts: How to Make a Great Living Doing What You Love*
URL(s): www.wiley.com/en-us/Building+a+Wellness+Business+That+Lasts%3A+How+to+Make+a+Great+Living+Doing+What+You+Love-p-9781119679066
Ed: Rick Stollmeyer. **Released:** October 2020. **Price:** $17, e-book; $28, hardcover. **Description:** There are a lot of business opportunities to bring wellness into the community, through gyms, spas, salons, etc. This book will help guide you on starting your own wellness small business. **Availability:** E-book; Print.

VIDEO/AUDIO MEDIA

6814 ■ *How I Built This: Orangetheory Fitness: Ellen Latham*
URL(s): wondery.com/shows/how-i-built-this/episode/10386-orangetheory-fitness-ellen-latham
Ed: Guy Raz. **Released:** April 10, 2023. **Description:** Podcast explains how a fired spa director developed a workout program that led to Orangetheory Fitness.

6815 ■ *Professional on the Go: What are the Best Tools for Health & Wellness Professinals?*
URL(s): www.spreaker.com/user/11226745/tools-for-health-and-wellness-professionals
Ed: Chinwe Onyeagoro. **Released:** July 01, 2019. **Description:** Podcast discusses solutions for fitness trainers, yoga and pilates instructors, and other service providers in the health/wellness community.

6816 ■ *Professional on the Go: The Business of Yoga from Expert Teacher Trainer*
URL(s): www.spreaker.com/user/11226745/episode-25-fifty-shades-of-yoga
Ed: Chinwe Onyeagoro. **Released:** December 22, 2019. **Description:** Podcast offers advice for those interested in starting/growing a yoga business.

6817 ■ *Side Hustle to Small Business: How Michele Riechman Is Empowering Women Over 40*
URL(s): www.hiscox.com/side-hustle-to-small-business/michele-riechman-personal-trainer-and-health-coach-podcast-season-4
Ed: Sanjay Parekh. **Released:** May 22, 2024. **Description:** Podcast features a personal trainer specializing in women over 40.

6818 ■ *Side Hustle to Small Business: How to Turn Past Experiences into Entrepreneurial Success*
URL(s): www.hiscox.com/side-hustle-to-small-business/matt-gluckman-think-fitness-life-podcast-season-4
Ed: Sanjay Parekh. **Released:** August 14, 2024. **Description:** Podcast explains how an entrepreneur uses communication skills from previous job experiences to run a remote personal training company.

PUBLICATIONS

6819 ■ *Club Business International (CBI)*
70 Fargo St.
Boston, MA 02210
Ph: (617)951-0055
Free: 800-228-4772
Co. E-mail: info@ihrsa.org
URL: http://www.ihrsa.org
Contact: Chris Craytor, Chairman of the Board
URL(s): www.healthandfitness.org/publications/type/cbi

Released: Monthly **Price:** $34.95, U.S. for per year; $129.95, for per year; $199.59, for 2 year international; $48, Members for per year. **Description:** Features the quality and profitability of commercial health, racquet, and sports clubs. **Availability:** Print; Online.

Floor Covering/Restoration Business

START-UP INFORMATION

6820 ■ *"No. 359: FlexGround: Recreational Surfaces"* in *Inc. (Vol. 36, September 2014, No. 7, pp. 130)*
Pub: Mansueto Ventures L.L.C.
Contact: Stephanie Mehta, Chief Executive Officer
Released: September 2014. **Description:** FlexGround was co-founded by Bill Stafford and his father, Bill Stafford Sr. The company makes flooring used on playgrounds that provides both grip and safety padding. FlexGround flowing is poured into place like concrete, but feels like a mix of a rubber mat and a trampoline and maintains its thickness no matter how high the traffic. **Availability:** Print; Online.

ASSOCIATIONS AND OTHER ORGANIZATIONS

6821 ■ **Association Canadienne De Terrazzo, Tuile et Marbre (ACTTM) [Terrazzo Tile and Marble Association of Canada (TTMAC)]**
163 Buttermill Ave., Unit 8
Concord, ON, Canada L4K 3X8
Ph: (905)660-9640
Free: 800-201-8599
Fax: (905)660-0513
Co. E-mail: association@ttmac.com
URL: http://www.ttmac.com/en
Contact: Tod Valickis, President
Facebook: www.facebook.com/TerrazzoTileMarbleAssociationofCanada
Linkedin: www.linkedin.com/company/terrazzo-tile-&-marble-association-of-canada
X (Twitter): x.com/TTMACCanada
YouTube: www.youtube.com/user/TTMACCanada
Description: Aims to develop a method of standardizing terrazzo, tile and marble installation techniques. Works as a technical resource and liaison for architects, designers and engineers. **Founded:** 1944. **Geographic Preference:** National.

6822 ■ **Carpet and Rug Institute (CRI)**
100 S Hamilton St.
Dalton, GA 30720
Ph: (706)278-3176
Fax: (706)278-8835
Co. E-mail: info@carpet-rug.org
URL: http://www.carpet-rug.org
Contact: Vance Bell, Chairman
Facebook: www.facebook.com/CarpetandRugInstitute
X (Twitter): x.com/CarpetRugInstit
Instagram: www.instagram.com/beauty.of.carpet
Pinterest: www.pinterest.com/carpetrug
Description: Represents the carpet and rug industry; sources of extensive carpet information for consumers, writers, interior designers, specifiers, facility managers, architects, builders and building owners and managers. **Founded:** 1791. **Publications:** *Directory of Carpet Style Names*; *Carpet and Rug Manufacturing Plants and Corporate Locations in the U.S. and Canada* (Annual); *Carpet and Rug Institute--Membership Directory* (Annual); *Carpet and Rug Manufacturing Plants and Corporate Locations United States and Canada*. **Geographic Preference:** National.

6823 ■ **Floor Covering Installation Contractors Association (FCICA)**
800 Roosevelt Rd., Bldg. C, Ste. 312
Glen Ellyn, IL 60137
Ph: (630)672-3702
Co. E-mail: info@fcica.com
URL: http://www.fcica.com
Facebook: www.facebook.com/FCICA2
Linkedin: www.linkedin.com/company/f-c-i-c-a-
X (Twitter): x.com/FCICA2
Instagram: www.instagram.com/flooringcontractors
YouTube: www.youtube.com/channel/UCjdNOdKOcz2KaWy31NUKGaw
Description: Represents installation contractors, carpet manufacturers, and suppliers to the installation trade. Aims to establish acceptable levels of performance for the carpet installation industry and promote standards of business ethics. Acts as liaison with retailers, manufacturers, and suppliers; represents the industry before government agencies. **Founded:** 1982. **Publications:** *The Flooring Contractor* (Quarterly); *FCICA Update* (Biweekly). **Educational Activities:** Mid-Year Meeting (Annual); Floor Covering Installation Contractors Association Annual Convention (Annual). **Geographic Preference:** National.

6824 ■ **Maple Flooring Manufacturers Association, Inc. (MFMA)**
1425 Tri State Pkwy., Ste. 110
Gurnee, IL 60031
Ph: (847)450-0050
Free: 888-480-9138
Co. E-mail: mfma@maplefloor.org
URL: http://www.maplefloor.org/Home.aspx
Contact: Steve Bernard, Executive Vice President
Facebook: www.facebook.com/MFMA1897
X (Twitter): x.com/MFMAsportsfloor
Instagram: www.instagram.com/mfma_sports_flooring_authority
YouTube: www.youtube.com/channel/UC_h5MnfEdlt22stf1GVlOEg
Description: Manufacturers and installers of Northern Maple hardwood flooring. Establishes uniform grades and standards for hard maple. **Founded:** 1897. **Educational Activities:** MFMA Conference (Biennial). **Geographic Preference:** Multinational.

6825 ■ **North American Association of Floor Covering Distributors (NAFCD)**
330 N Wabash Ave., Ste. 2000
Chicago, IL 60611-7621
Ph: (312)321-6836
Free: 800-383-3091
Fax: (312)673-6962
Co. E-mail: info@nafcd.org
URL: http://www.nafcd.org
Contact: A. J. Warne, President
Facebook: www.facebook.com/NAFCD
YouTube: www.youtube.com/user/nafcdfloorcovering
Description: The association provides critical benchmarking data from distributor members, economic data based on industry-specific indicators, and research on industry topics and trends related to flooring distribution. The economic trend reports are produced four times a year by senior economists at the Institute for Trend Research (ITR). **Founded:** 1971. **Publications:** *National Association of Floor Covering Distributors--Membership*; *North American Association of Floor Covering Distributors--Membership Directory*; *Strategy*. **Educational Activities:** University of Innovative Distribution (Annual). **Geographic Preference:** National.

6826 ■ **Resilient Floor Covering Institute (RFCI)**
115 Broad St., Ste. 201
Lagrange, GA 30240
URL: http://rfci.com
Contact: Bill Blackstock, Chief Executive Officer
Facebook: www.facebook.com/ResilientFloorCoveringInstitute
Linkedin: www.linkedin.com/company/resilient-floor-covering-institute
X (Twitter): x.com/rfci_official
Instagram: www.instagram.com/rfcinstitute
Description: Supports the manufacturers of vinyl composition tile, solid vinyl tile, or sheet vinyl and rubber tile and people who use its products. Provides technical information and data regarding the resilient flooring industry. **Founded:** 1976. **Geographic Preference:** National.

6827 ■ **World Floor Covering Association (WFCA)**
855 Abutment Rd., Ste. 1
Dalton, GA 30721-4474
Ph: (706)217-1183
Free: 855-330-1183
Fax: (706)217-1165
Co. E-mail: wfca@wfca.org
URL: http://wfca.org
Contact: Scott Humphrey, Chief Executive Officer
E-mail: shumphrey@wfca.org
Facebook: www.facebook.com/wfcaorg
Linkedin: www.linkedin.com/company/world-floor-covering-association
X (Twitter): x.com/WFCAorg
Instagram: www.instagram.com/worldfloorcoveringassociation
Description: Retail floorcovering store owners and managers; floorcovering distributors and manufacturers. Provides liaison, through a Washington, DC lobbyist, between the membership and government organizations that affect the business. Conducts seminars promoting professional development and increased profits; compiles business activity statistics; sponsors research. **Founded:** 1995. **Publications:** *World Floor Covering Association--Annual Management Report*. **Educational Activities:** The Interna-

tional Surface Event (TISE) (Annual). **Awards:** WFCA Hall of Fame (Annual). **Geographic Preference:** National.

REFERENCE WORKS

6828 ■ *"First Sustainability Standard for Household Portable and Floor Care Appliances Developed to Identify Environmentally Responsible Products"* in *Ecology, Environment & Conservation Business (September 13, 2014, pp. 39)*
Pub: NewsRX LLC.
Contact: Kalani Rosell, Contact
Description: the Association of Home Appliance Manufacturers (AHAM), CSA Group, and the UL Environment released the AHAM 7002-2014/CSA SPE-7002-14/UL 7002, Sustainability Standard for Household Portable and Floor Care Appliances. This is the first voluntary sustainability standards for these appliances and is the third in a unit of product sustainability standards under development by the group. These standards are intended for use by manufacturers, governments, retailers, and others to identify products conforming to these standards in six key areas: materials, manufacturing and operations, energy consumption during use, end-of-life, consumables, and innovation. **Availability:** Online.

6829 ■ *Floor Covering Product Resource Guide*
Pub: FCW
Contact: Mark Flinn, General Manager
E-mail: mflinn@hearst.com
URL(s): www.floorcoveringweekly.com/main/mediakit
Ed: Santiago Montero. **Released:** Annual **Description:** Publication includes lists of manufacturers and importers of carpet, rugs, carpet cushion, fiber, resilient wood, and ceramic floor coverings; separate listing of distributors by state, retail groups and associations. **Entries include:** For manufacturers--Company name, address, phone, regional sales offices, names and titles of key personnel, local distributors, products. For distributors--Company name, address, phone, manufacturers represented. **Arrangement:** Alphabetical. **Indexes:** Geographical by distributor. **Availability:** Print; PDF; Online.

6830 ■ *"Info Junkie: Karen Eng"* in *Crain's Chicago Business (Vol. 34, October 24, 2011, No. 42, pp. 35)*
Pub: Crain Communications Inc.
Contact: Barry Asin, President
Ed: Christina Le Beau. **Description:** Greg Colando, president of Flor Inc., an eco-friendly carpet company located I Chicago discusses his marketing program to increase sales. **Availability:** Online.

6831 ■ *North American Association of Floor Covering Distributors--Membership Directory*
Pub: North American Association of Floor Covering Distributors
Contact: A. J. Warne, President
URL(s): www.nafcd.org/page/Manufacturer
Description: Covers association happenings and approximately 300 member distributors and suppliers of floor coverings. **Entries include:** Company name, location (code indicates if a branch location), products, contacts. **Availability:** Print.

6832 ■ *"Take the Right Approach to Concrete Polishing Rentals"* in *Rental Product News (Vol. 33, June 2011)*
Description: A recent trend in flooring is concrete polishing for a practical, beautiful and sustainable way to decorate homes and businesses. Things to keep in mind when assessing the value of adding concrete polishing equipment to an existing rental store are evaluated. **Availability:** Online.

STATISTICAL SOURCES

6833 ■ *RMA Annual Statement Studies*
Pub: Risk Management Association
Contact: Nancy Foster, President
Released: Annual. **Description:** Contains composite balance sheets and income statements for more than 360 industries, including the accounting, auditing, and bookkeeping industries. Also contains five years of comparative historical data for discerning trends. Includes 16 commonly used ratios, computed for most of the size groupings for nearly every industry.

6834 ■ *Standard & Poor's Industry Surveys*
Pub: Standard And Poor's Financial Services LLC.
Contact: Douglas L. Peterson, President
Description: Two-volume book that examines the prospects for specific industries, including trucking. Also provides analyses of trends and problems, statistical tables and charts, and comparative company analyses.

TRADE PERIODICALS

6835 ■ *Floor Covering Weekly*
Pub: FCW
Contact: Mark Flinn, General Manager
E-mail: mflinn@hearst.com
Released: Weekly **Description:** Business newspaper of the floor covering industry. **Availability:** Print; Online.

6836 ■ *Floor Trends*
Pub: BNP Media
Contact: Harper Henderson, Owner Co-Chief Executive Officer
URL(s): www.floortrendsmag.com
Facebook: www.facebook.com/FloorTrendsMag
Linkedin: www.linkedin.com/company/floor-trends-mag
X (Twitter): x.com/floortrendsmag
Instagram: www.instagram.com/floortrendsmag
YouTube: www.youtube.com/floortrendsmag
Ed: Morgan Laidlaw. **Released:** Monthly **Description:** Trade magazine covering color & design trends for both commercial & residential professionals in the floor covering industry. **Availability:** Print.

6837 ■ *Rug News and Design*
Pub: Rug News Magazine
URL(s): rugnewsandesign.com
Facebook: www.facebook.com/rugnewsanddesign
X (Twitter): twitter.com/Rugnewsdesign
Instagram: www.instagram.com/rugnewsanddesign
Pinterest: www.pinterest.com/rugnewsdesign
Ed: Dasha Morgan. **Released:** Monthly **Price:** $39, for one year domestic; $100, for one year; $162, for international by air. **Description:** Trade magazine covering the area rug industry. **Availability:** Print; Online.

VIDEO/AUDIO MEDIA

6838 ■ *The How of Business: Bryan Park - Starting a Flooring Business*
URL(s): www.thehowofbusiness.com/487-bryan-park-starting-flooring-business
Ed: Henry Lopez. **Released:** August 28, 2023. **Description:** Podcast discusses the advantages and challenges of starting a flooring business.

FRANCHISES AND BUSINESS OPPORTUNITIES

6839 ■ **Floor Coverings International Ltd.**
FirstService Brands
5390 Triangle Pky., Ste. 125
Norcross, GA 30092
Free: 866-366-0420
Fax: (601)549-7973
URL: http://www.fsvbrands.com
Contact: Thomas W. Wood, Chief Executive Officer
URL(s): www.fsvbrands.com/our_companies/floor_coverings_international.html
Description: Firm provides flooring design and installation services. **Founded:** 1988. **Financial Assistance:** Yes **Training:** Yes.

6840 ■ **The Mad Matter**
The Mad Matter Franchise Corp.
PO Box 128
Cumming, GA 30028
Ph: (800)685-1144
Fax: (770)887-9240
Facebook: www.facebook.com/www.MadMatter.biz
Linkedin: www.linkedin.com/company/themadmatter
YouTube: www.youtube.com/channel/UC5xUVumoFb0d5RbTljqwQTQ
Description: Sale and installation of specialty flooring. **No. of Company-Owned Units:** 2. **Founded:** 1992. **Franchised:** 2003. **Equity Capital Needed:** Estimated $69,000-$121,000, includes franchise fee. **Franchise Fee:** $30,000-$50,000. **Training:** Yes.

6841 ■ **Marblelife, Inc.**
2800 W Airport Blvd., Ste100
Sanford, FL 32771
Contact: Alan G. Mayr, President
Description: Engaged in marble restoration and marble floor polishing, granite restoration, terrazzo restoration, limestone restoration, travertine restoration and grout cleaning. **Founded:** 1988.

6842 ■ **Mr. Sandless**
2970 Concord Rd.
Aston, PA 19014
Free: 877-966-3360
Fax: (610)364-2081
Co. E-mail: info@mrsandless.com
URL: http://www.mrsandless.com
Contact: Dan Praz, Owner Operator
Facebook: www.facebook.com/MrSandlessFloorRefinishing
X (Twitter): x.com/MrSandless
Instagram: www.instagram.com/mrsandless
Pinterest: www.pinterest.com/sandless
Description: Provider of wood refinishing services. **Founded:** 2004. **Franchised:** 2005. **Financial Assistance:** Yes **Training:** Provides 1 week at headquarters and ongoing support.

6843 ■ **N-Hance Wood Refinishing**
Logan, UT 84321
Free: 855-642-6230
URL: http://www.nhance.com
Contact: Mike Hilliard, Owner
X (Twitter): x.com/NHanceCorporate
Instagram: www.instagram.com/nhancewoodrefinishing
YouTube: www.youtube.com/channel/UCA34MtJ6T44pVBWG51J9giQ
Pinterest: www.pinterest.com/nhancerenews
Description: Provider of wood refinishing services. **Founded:** 2008. **Franchised:** 2003. **Financial Assistance:** Yes **Training:** Offers 1 week on training at headquarters and ongoing support.

6844 ■ **ProSource Wholesale**
13501 Shoreline Dr.
Earth City, MO 63045
Ph: (314)282-4798
Co. E-mail: info@prosourcecalifornia.com
URL: http://www.prosourcewholesale.com
Contact: Dana Hughes, Manager
Facebook: www.facebook.com/prosourcewholesale
Linkedin: www.linkedin.com/company/prosource-wholesale-floorcoverings
Instagram: www.instagram.com/prosource_wholesale
YouTube: www.youtube.com/user/ProSource2200
Pinterest: www.pinterest.com/pswholesale
Description: Firm provides home remodeling services including flooring, kitchen. **Founded:** 1991. **Franchised:** 1991. **Financial Assistance:** Yes **Training:** Initial training provided at headquarters in St. Louis and ongoing support.

Florist

START-UP INFORMATION

6845 ■ *"How to Open and Operate a Financially Successful Florist and Floral Business Online and Off"*
Pub: Atlantic Publishing Co.
Contact: Dr. Heather L. Johnson, Contact
Released: Revised second edition. **Description:** A concise and easy to follow guide for opening a retail florist or floral business online or a traditional brick and mortar store. Knowledge shared includes: cost control systems, retail math and competitive pricing, legal concerns, tax reporting requirements and reporting, profit and loss statements, management skills, sales advertising, and marketing techniques, customer service, direct sales, internal marketing ideas, and more. **Availability:** CD-ROM; Print; Online.

ASSOCIATIONS AND OTHER ORGANIZATIONS

6846 ■ **American Institute of Floral Designers (AIFD)**
2331 Rock Spring Rd.
Forest Hill, MD 21050
Ph: (443)966-3850
Co. E-mail: info@aifd.org
URL: http://aifd.org
Contact: Todd Sweeden, President
Facebook: www.facebook.com/AIFD.CFD
X (Twitter): x.com/AIFDHqtrs
YouTube: www.youtube.com/user/AIFDHqtrs
Description: Active floral designers, associates, retired floral designers and other individuals. Works to promote the profession and art of floral design. Maintains student chapter. **Founded:** 1965. **Awards:** AIFD Award of Design Influence (Annual); Award of Merit - Industry (Annual); Award of Merit - Non-Industry (Annual); Award of Design Influence (Annual); Award of Merit - Industry (Annual); Award of Distinguished Service to AIFD (Annual); AIFD Special Award of Recognition (Annual). **Geographic Preference:** National.

6847 ■ **Canadian Rose Society (CRS) - Library [CRS Library]**
45 O'Connor St., Ste. 1150
Ottawa, ON, Canada K1P 1A4
Co. E-mail: info@canarie.ca
URL: http://www.canarie.ca
Contact: Kathryn Anthonisen, President
E-mail: kathryn.anthonisen@canarie.ca
Facebook: www.facebook.com/canadianrosesociety
YouTube: www.youtube.com/channel/UCco2el5Y2r7 5885hJ3kTMmA
Description: Promotes the hobby of rose breeding and growing in Canada. Conducts educational programs; sponsors competitions; maintains speakers' bureau. **Scope:** Roses; flowers. **Founded:** 1914. **Holdings:** Figures not available. **Publications:** *Canadian Rosarian* (Annual); *The CRS CommPoster* (5/year). **Geographic Preference:** National.

6848 ■ **Flowers Canada (FC)**
45 Speedvale Ave., E Unit 7
Guelph, ON, Canada N1H 1J2
Ph: (519)836-5495
Free: 800-730-1020
Co. E-mail: flowers@fco.on.ca
URL: http://www.flowerscanadagrowers.com/home
Contact: Andrew Morse, Executive Director
Description: Retail florists, distributors, and greenhouse operators. Promotes growth and development in the domestic floriculture industry. Provides technical and promotional services; sponsors continuing professional development and educational programs for members. Represents members' interests before government agencies; serves as a liaison between members and related trade organizations. **Founded:** 1897. **Publications:** *News Vine* (Bimonthly). **Geographic Preference:** National.

6849 ■ **Heritage Rose Foundation (HRF)**
PO Box 831414
Richardson, TX 75083
URL: http://www.heritagerosefoundation.org
Contact: Stephen Scanniello, President
E-mail: stephenscanniello@gmail.com
Facebook: www.facebook.com/Heritage-Rose-Foundation-48238538257
Description: Collects, preserves, studies, and promotes old-fashioned roses. **Founded:** 1986. **Publications:** *Heritage Rose Foundation News*; *Rosa Mundi*. **Geographic Preference:** National.

6850 ■ **Society of American Florists (SAF)**
1001 N Fairfax St., Ste. 201
Alexandria, VA 22314
Ph: (703)836-8700
Fax: (703)836-8705
Co. E-mail: info@safnow.org
URL: http://safnow.org
Contact: Kate Penn, President
Facebook: www.facebook.com/SocietyofAmericanFlorists
X (Twitter): x.com/safdelivers
Instagram: www.instagram.com/societyofamericanflorists
YouTube: www.youtube.com/user/SAFVision
Description: Growers, wholesalers, retailers, and allied tradesmen in the floral industry. Lobbies Congress on behalf of the industry; sponsors educational programs; promotes the floral industry; prepares materials for consumers and for high school and college students; provides business resources. Sponsors Floricultural Hall of Fame, American Academy of Floriculture, and Professional Floral Commentators International. Compiles statistics; sponsors competitions. **Founded:** 1884. **Publications:** *Floral Management* (Bimonthly); *Floral Management--Buyers Guide Issue* (Irregular); *Dateline: Washington* (Biweekly); *SAF Floral Management* (Bimonthly); *Who's Who in Floriculture* (Biennial). **Educational Activities:** Annual SAF Congressional Action Days (Annual). **Awards:** Floriculture Hall of Fame (Irregular); Sylvia Cup Design Competition (Annual). **Geographic Preference:** National.

6851 ■ **Wholesale Florist and Florist Supplier Association (WF&FSA)**
529 14th St., NW, Ste. 1280
Washington, DC 20045
Ph: (410)940-6580
Free: 888-289-3372
Co. E-mail: info@wffsa.org
URL: http://www.wffsa.org/aws/WFFSA/pt/sp/home_page
Contact: Karen Oie, President
Facebook: www.facebook.com/WFFSAHQ
Linkedin: www.linkedin.com/company/wffsa
X (Twitter): x.com/wffsa
Instagram: www.instagram.com/wffsa
YouTube: www.youtube.com/channel/UCT9Tnw_jkgWDqwTvhZRzT7g
Description: Proprietorships, partnerships or corporations conducting wholesale businesses in fresh flowers or plants, or engaged in the manufacture and/or wholesaling of florist supplies; others actively engaged in the floral industry are associate members. Preserves and strengthens the wholesale florists' position in the floral industry. Provides a unified voice to promote the wholesalers' contributions to the industry. **Founded:** 1926. **Publications:** *Wholesale Florist & Florist Supplier Association--Membership Directory* (Daily). **Educational Activities:** University of Innovative Distribution (Annual). **Awards:** Leland T. Kintzele Distinguished Service Award (LTK) (Annual). **Geographic Preference:** National.

REFERENCE WORKS

6852 ■ *"7 Ways Event Planners Can Navigate the Current Flower Shortage"* in BizBash (September 23, 2021)
Ed: Claire Hoffman. **Released:** September 23, 2021. **Description:** Due to struggling farms and supply chain issues, many flowers are not readily available as they once were. Tips for navigating these effects and logistics are discussed.

6853 ■ *"Delaware Valley Floral Group Opens Long Island Distribution Center"* in The Produce News (October 9, 2019)
URL(s): http://www.theproducenews.com/more-floral-articles/floral/27700-delaware-valley-floral-group-opens-long-island-distribution-center
Released: October 09, 2019. **Description:** Announces Delaware Valley Floral Group's acquisition of several assets of C.P. Flowers Direct, Inc. along with the opening of their new distribution cener on Long Island. **Availability:** Online.

6854 ■ *"Floral-Design Kiosk Business Blossoming"* in Colorado Springs Business Journal (September 24, 2010)
Pub: Dolan Media Newswires
Ed: Monica Mendoza. **Description:** Profile of Shellie Greto and her mother Jackie Martin who started a wholesale flower business in their garage. The do-it-

yourself floral arrangement firm started a kiosk business in supermarkets called Complete Design. **Availability:** Online.

6855 ■ *"Flower Confidential" in Business Horizons (Vol. 51, January-February 2008, No. 1, pp. 73)*
Description: Review of the book, "Flower Confidential: The Good, the Bad, and the Beautiful Business of Flowers", which offers insight for anyone starting or running a successful flower shop. **Availability:** Online.

6856 ■ *"Flower Power" in Garden Center (November 4, 2019)*
URL(s): www.gardencentermag.com/article/feature-igc-trends-flower-power-floral-shops/
Ed: Brooke Bilyj. **Released:** November 04, 2019. **Description:** Independent Garden Centers are looking for ways to expand their business, and one way they are doing that is by bringing back floral departments. Some are snatching up florists that are closing and creating relationships with funeral homes, wedding venues, and other community events. **Availability:** Online.

6857 ■ *"Guide to Starting a Flower Delivery Business" in Home Business (Home Business (September 6, 2022)*
URL(s): homebusinessmag.com/business-start-up/how-to-guides/guide-starting-flower-delivery-business/
Released: September 06, 2022. **Description:** Itemizes the steps needed to take before starting a flower delivery service. **Availability:** Online.

6858 ■ *"Holiday Bloom: Event Designer Collin Abraham Heightens Glamour With Florals" in Black Enterprise (Vol. 41, November 2010, No. 4)*
Description: Profile of Collin Abraham, who works out of his Harlem boutique to arrange unique floral pieces to complement the social gatherings and main events he plans for his clients. **Availability:** Print; Online.

6859 ■ *"MyReviewsNow.net Announces New Affiliate Partner Gift Baskets Overseas" in M2 EquityBites (EQB) (June 22, 2012)*
Description: MyReviewsNow.net has partnered with Gift Baskets Overseas in order to offer gift baskets to be shipped overseas. Gift Baskets Oversease works with local florists and shippers worldwide. No financial details were disclosed. **Availability:** Online.

6860 ■ *"No. 252: H. Bloom: Floral Subscriptions" in Inc. (Vol. 36, September 2014, No. 7, pp. 132)*
Pub: Mansueto Ventures L.L.C.
Contact: Stephanie Mehta, Chief Executive Officer
Released: September 2014. **Description:** Spoilage is the largest problem facing flower shops. H. Bloom provides custom floral designs to high-end hotels, spas, restaurants, retailers, and apartment and office buildings through their subscription service. The firm found that regular orders provides better inventory control and less waste. Weekly, biweekly, or monthly deliveries are available. **Availability:** Print; Online.

6861 ■ *"Trammell Crow Facility in Houston is a Late Bloomer" in Houston Business Journal (Vol. 40, August 28, 2009, No. 16, pp. 1A)*
Pub: Houston Business Journal
Contact: Bob Charlet, President
E-mail: bcharlet@bizjournals.com
Ed: Jennifer Dawson. **Released:** Weekly. **Description:** Trammell Crow Company leased half of the 61,000 square foot IAH International Air Cargo Centre II to Tradewinds Cargo Handling. The facility, located at George Bush Intercontinental Airport, is intended to be a destination of fresh flowers and food from Latin America. **Availability:** Print; Online.

6862 ■ *"The Ultimate Guide to Active Selling" in The Produce News (October 9, 2019)*
URL(s): www.theproducenews.com/more-floral-articles/floral/27701-the-ultimate-guide-to-active-selling

Ed: Melissa Jones. **Released:** October 09, 2019. **Description:** Examines various selling techniques that can be used in floral shops to generate higher sales. **Availability:** Online.

6863 ■ *"VISA: Canadians Spend $97 Million on Mom This Mother's Day" in Canadian Corporate News (May 16, 2007)*
Description: Visa Canada finds that Canadians are spending more on Mother's Day in recent years. Since 2002, sales of jewelry, flowers, and cards have climbed steadily in the week before Mother's Day weekend. **Availability:** Print; Online.

6864 ■ *Wholesale Florist & Florist Supplier Association--Membership Directory*
Pub: Wholesale Florist and Florist Supplier Association
Contact: Karen Oie, President
URL(s): www.wffsa.org/aws/WFFSA/pt/sp/directory
Released: Daily **No. of Listings:** 1,275. **Entries include:** Company name, address, phone, names of executives, list of products or services. **Arrangement:** Geographical. **Indexes:** Alphabetical. **Availability:** Online.

STATISTICAL SOURCES

6865 ■ *Florists Industry in the US - Market Research Report*
URL(s): www.ibisworld.com/united-states/market-research-reports/florists-industry/
Price: $925. **Description:** Downloadable report analyzing the current and future trends in the florist industry. **Availability:** Online.

6866 ■ *RMA Annual Statement Studies*
Pub: Risk Management Association
Contact: Nancy Foster, President
Released: Annual. **Description:** Contains composite balance sheets and income statements for more than 360 industries, including the accounting, auditing, and bookkeeping industries. Also contains five years of comparative historical data for discerning trends. Includes 16 commonly used ratios, computed for most of the size groupings for nearly every industry.

TRADE PERIODICALS

6867 ■ *Florists' Review Magazine*
Contact: Travis Rigby, Publisher
E-mail: travis@floristsreview.com
URL(s): www.floristsreview.com
Facebook: www.facebook.com/FloristsReview/
X (Twitter): twitter.com/FloristsReview
Released: Monthly **Price:** $42, U.S. price for 12 issues; $72, U.S. price for 24 issues; $82, U.S. price for 36 issues; $55, Canada price for 12 issues; $85, Canada price for 24 issues; $60, price for 12 issues to International; $90, price for 24 issues to International. **Description:** Retail florist and wholesalers trade magazine. **Availability:** Print.

6868 ■ *Green Profit Magazine*
Pub: Ball Publishing
Contact: Jennifer Polanz, Managing Editor
E-mail: jpolanz@ballpublishing.com
URL(s): www.greenprofit.com
Facebook: www.facebook.com/springtrials
Ed: Dr. Matthew Chappell, Jennifer Polanz, Chris Beytes. **Released:** Monthly **Description:** Trade magazine for flower and plant retailers. **Availability:** Print; PDF; Online.

6869 ■ *Greenhouse Management*
Pub: GIE Media Inc.
Contact: Chris Foster, President
URL(s): www.greenhousemag.com
Facebook: www.facebook.com/GreenhouseManagementmag
Linkedin: www.linkedin.com/company/greenhouse-management-magazine
X (Twitter): x.com/Greenhousemag
Instagram: www.instagram.com/greenhousemanagement

Ed: Karen Varga. **Released:** Monthly **Description:** Commercial greenhouse growers magazine. **Availability:** Print; PDF; Online.

TRADE SHOWS AND CONVENTIONS

6870 ■ **Great Lakes Floral & Event Expo**
American Floral Endowment (AFE)
1001 N Fairfax St., Ste. 201
Alexandria, VA 22314
Ph: (703)838-5211
Co. E-mail: afe@endowment.org
URL: http://endowment.org
Contact: Debi Chedester, Executive Director
E-mail: dchedester@afeendowment.org
URL(s): glfee.com
Description: Floral equipment, supplies, and services. Event includes educational presentations, reception, recognition banquet and entertainment. **Audience:** Industry professionals. **Principal Exhibits:** Floral equipment, supplies, and services. Event includes educational presentations, reception, recognition banquet and entertainment. Dates and Locations: 2025 Feb 28-Mar 02 Devos Place, Grand Rapids, MI. **Telecommunication Services:** info@greatlakesfloralassociation.org.

6871 ■ **Northeast Floral Expo**
Connecticut Florists Association (CFA)
PO Box 110210
Cheshire, CT 06410
Ph: (203)268-9000
Co. E-mail: office@connecticutflorist.com
URL: http://www.connecticutflorist.com
Contact: Nicole Palazzo, President
URL(s): www.northeastfloralexpo.com
Frequency: Annual. **Description:** Florist supplies, cut flowers, potted plants, wire services, and dried and artificial flowers and plants. **Audience:** Florists and related trade professionals. **Principal Exhibits:** Florist supplies, cut flowers, potted plants, wire services, and dried and artificial flowers and plants.

6872 ■ **Northeast Texas Nursery Growers Association Trade Show**
URL(s): www.ntnga.org
Frequency: Annual. **Description:** Nursery and landscaper tradeshow featuring product vendors, educational opportunities, and networking. **Principal Exhibits:** Nursery and landscaper tradeshow featuring product vendors, educational opportunities, and networking.

6873 ■ **Nursery/Landscape Expo**
Texas Nursery & Landscape Association (TNLA)
7730 S IH-35
Austin, TX 78745-6698
Ph: (512)280-5182
Co. E-mail: info@tnlaonline.org
URL: http://www.tnlaonline.org
Contact: Amy Graham, President
E-mail: agraham@tnlaonline.org
URL(s): www.nurserylandscapeexpo.org
Frequency: Annual. **Description:** Plant materials including foliage, bedding plants, trees, and palms, allied products including machinery, equipment, and supplies for horticulture and landscape industry. **Audience:** Industry professionals. **Principal Exhibits:** Plant materials including foliage, bedding plants, trees, and palms, allied products including machinery, equipment, and supplies for horticulture and landscape industry. **Telecommunication Services:** expo@nurserylandsca.wpengine.com.

6874 ■ **Tropical Plant Industry Exhibition**
Florida Nursery, Growers and Landscape Association (FNGLA)
1533 Pk. Center Dr.
Orlando, FL 32835
Free: 800-375-3642
Co. E-mail: info@fngla.org
URL: http://www.fngla.org
Contact: Billy Deal, Director
E-mail: bdeal@fngla.org
URL(s): www.fngla.org/tpie

Frequency: Annual. **Description:** Large foliage plants, horticultural, interiorscape, florist, and interior foliage industry products. **Audience:** Tropical plant industry professionals and general public. **Principal Exhibits:** Large foliage plants, horticultural, interiorscape, florist, and interior foliage industry products.

FRANCHISES AND BUSINESS OPPORTUNITIES

6875 ■ Flowerama
320 W 1st St.
Cedar Falls, IA 50613
Ph: (319)277-5800
Free: 877-528-8187
Fax: (319)268-7357
Co. E-mail: floweramacedarfalls@gmail.com
URL: http://www.1800flowerscedarfalls.flowerama.com
Facebook: www.facebook.com/FloweramaCF
Linkedin: www.linkedin.com/company/flowerama-of-america-inc
X (Twitter): x.com/FloweramaCF
Instagram: www.instagram.com/floweramacedarfalls
Pinterest: www.pinterest.com/floweramacedarfalls
Description: Franchise program operates under the concepts of mass-merchandising and cash-and-carry floral sales. **Founded:** 1967. **Financial Assistance:** Yes **Training:** 4-6 week training program (held at the corporate offices in Waterloo, Iowa). Store layouts and design, assistance during construction, store set-up and product merchandising are provided.

6876 ■ Grower Direct Fresh Cut Flowers Inc.
6303 Wagner Rd.
Edmonton, AB, Canada T6E 4N4
Ph: (780)436-7774
Free: 877-277-4787
Fax: (780)436-3336
Co. E-mail: info@growerdirect.com
URL: http://growerdirect.com
X (Twitter): x.com/growerdirectflw
Description: Retailer of flowers such as cut flowers, gift and gourmet baskets, wedding flowers and funeral flowers. **Founded:** 1991. **Training:** Provides 10 days training.

6877 ■ Suspended In Time Inc.
122 S Mountain Way Dr.
Orem, UT 84058
Ph: (801)227-0075
Free: 866-756-0059
Co. E-mail: info@suspendedintime.com
URL: http://www.suspendedintime.com
Contact: Rachelle Adams, Contact
E-mail: rachelle@suspendedintime.com
Facebook: www.facebook.com/suspendedintime
X (Twitter): x.com/suspndedintime
Pinterest: www.pinterest.com/suspendedintime
Description: Provider of flower preservation for bridal bouquet, wedding bouquet flowers, preserved funeral floral and more. **Founded:** 1997. **Training:** Training provided at the corporate location 3, 10 hour days, which includes lunch - large discount on room accommodations and ongoing support as long as needed.

LIBRARIES

6878 ■ American Horticultural Society (AHS) - Library
7931 East Blvd. Dr.
Alexandria, VA 22308
Ph: (703)768-5700
Fax: (703)768-8700
URL: http://ahsgardening.org
Contact: Marcia Zech, Chairman of the Board
Facebook: www.facebook.com/americanhorticulturalsociety
Linkedin: www.linkedin.com/company/the-american-horticultural-society
X (Twitter): x.com/ahs_gardening
Instagram: www.instagram.com/ahs_gardening
YouTube: www.youtube.com/channel/UCXUu4FafeTTqC8S-VnnhPrg
Pinterest: www.pinterest.com/amhortsociety
Description: Represents amateur and professional gardeners. Aims to educate and inspire people of all ages to become successful and environmentally responsible gardeners by advancing the art and science of horticulture. **Scope:** Horticulture. **Founded:** 1922. **Holdings:** Figures not available. **Publications:** *North American Horticulture: A Reference Guide* (Irregular); *The American Gardener: The Magazine of the American Horticultural Society* (Bimonthly). **Awards:** Liberty Hyde Bailey Award (Irregular); Paul Ecke Jr. Commercial Award (Annual); G. B. Gunlogson Award (Annual); B.Y. Morrison Communication Award (Annual); AHS Horticultural Therapy Award (Irregular); AHS Landscape Design Award (Irregular); AHS Meritorious Service Award (Annual); Frances Jones Poetker Award (Irregular); AHS Professional Award (Irregular); H. Marc Cathey Award (Biennial); Catherine H. Sweeney Award (Periodic); AHS Teaching Award (Irregular); Community Greening Award (Annual); Horticultural Innovation Award (Biennial); Jane L. Taylor Award (Annual); American Horticultural Society Professional Award (Annual). **Geographic Preference:** National.

6879 ■ Garfield Park Conservatory Alliance - Garfield Park Conservatory - Library
300 N Central Pk. Ave.
Chicago, IL 60624
Ph: (773)638-1766
Co. E-mail: membership@garfieldpark.org
URL: http://garfieldconservatory.org
Contact: Jennifer Van Valkenburg, President
E-mail: jvanvalkenburg@garfieldpark.org
Facebook: www.facebook.com/GarfieldParkConservatory
Linkedin: www.linkedin.com/company/garfield-park-conservatory-alliance/about
X (Twitter): x.com/gpconservatory
Instagram: www.instagram.com/gpconservatory
YouTube: www.youtube.com/channel/UCn70zMRoK9xueMgdIP9PuIA
Scope: Horticulture. **Services:** Library not open to the public. **Founded:** 1908. **Holdings:** Books.

6880 ■ University of Georgia - State Botanical Garden of Georgia
2450 S Milledge Ave.
Athens, GA 30605
Ph: (706)542-1244
Co. E-mail: garden@uga.edu
URL: http://botgarden.uga.edu
Contact: Jennifer Cruse-Sanders, Director
E-mail: crusesanders@uga.edu
Facebook: www.facebook.com/botgarden
X (Twitter): twitter.com/botgardenGA
Instagram: www.instagram.com/botanicalgarden_ga
Description: Integral unit of University of Georgia, guided by its own advisory board. **Scope:** 313-acre site maintaining plant collections for research by scientists and students, including documented collections of native and cultivated plants, a plant evaluation site for woody ornamental plants in the Southeast, theme gardens and display collections of bulbs, annuals, perennials and woody plants, both native and exotic. **Services:** Library open to the public for reference use only. **Founded:** 1968. **Holdings:** 2,000 books; 85 videotapes; CD-ROMs; archives; manuscripts. **Subscriptions:** 14 journals and other serials. **Publications:** *Garden News Quarterly*.

Food Delivery Service

START-UP INFORMATION

6881 ■ **The Guide to a Successful Clean Eating Food Delivery Service**
Ed: Valeria Ray. **Released:** July 23, 2019. **Description:** Answers questions about starting your own full- or part-time clean food delivery service. **Availability:** Print.

6882 ■ **How to Start a Clean Eating Food Delivery Business**
Ed: Gordon Rock. **Released:** April 03, 2020. **Description:** As more and more people become interested in clean eating, starting a clean eating food delivery service may be an ideal work from home business. Included in this guide are recipes along with tips on starting a food delivery business. **Availability:** E-book.

6883 ■ **"How to Start a Delivery Service" in How to Start an LLC**
URL(s): howtostartanllc.com/business-ideas/delivery
Description: Presents information on how to start your own delivery service. Provides a ten-step process to follow.

6884 ■ **"How to Start a Food Delivery Business in 2022" in Circuit Blog (July 28, 2022)**
URL(s): getcircuit.com/teams/blog/how-to-start-a-food-delivery-business
Ed: Heather Reinblatt. **Released:** July 28, 2022. **Description:** Consumers love the convenience of food delivery. This article provides information on how to start your own food deliver service. **Availability:** Online.

6885 ■ **"How to Start a Food Delivery Service (with Templates)" in Paperform Blog (Aug. 11, 2022)**
URL(s): paperform.co/blog/how-to-start-a-food-delivery-service/
Ed: Eliza Frakes. **Released:** August 11, 2022. **Description:** Provides guidance to help you get your online food delivery service off the ground. Includes five steps to get you going. **Availability:** Online.

6886 ■ **"How to Start a Restaurant Delivery Service Business" in Chron (Feb. 4, 2019)**
URL(s): smallbusiness.chron.com/start-restaurant-delivery-service-business-4457.html
Ed: Devra Gartenstein. **Released:** February 04, 2019. **Description:** A well-run restaurant delivery service is a way to piggyback on existing businesses to provide a good customer experience and also to earn some money in the process. This article describes how to start a restaurant deliver service business by serving your local market. **Availability:** Online.

6887 ■ **"What Do I Need to Start a Lunchtime Delivery Food Service?" in Chron (April 11, 2019)**
URL(s): smallbusiness.chron.com/need-start-lunchtime-delivery-food-service-10245.html
Ed: Jordan Meyers. **Released:** April 11, 2019. **Description:** A lunchtime delivery food service can make a good business for someone who wants to work part-time yet offers the potential to earn a good deal of money. This article provides information on what you need to get started. **Availability:** Online.

ASSOCIATIONS AND OTHER ORGANIZATIONS

6888 ■ **Foodservice and Packaging Institute (FPI)**
PO Box 726
Falls Church, VA 22046
Ph: (703)592-9889
Fax: (703)592-9864
URL: http://fpi.org
Contact: Natha Dempsey, President
E-mail: ndempsey@fpi.org
Facebook: www.facebook.com/FoodservicePackagingInstitute
Linkedin: www.linkedin.com/company/foodservice-packaging-institute
X (Twitter): x.com/fpihq
Instagram: www.instagram.com/fpihq
YouTube: www.youtube.com/channel/UC9VBt9J75Ed_-AnB0RscPbA
Description: Manufacturers of raw material and machinery; suppliers and distributors of: single-use cups, plates and related items for service of food and/or beverages; nestable containers for food packaging and containers for oven usage, placemats and doilies, egg cartons and trays for prepackaging meat and produce. Promotes sanitation and the environmentally-responsible use of food and beverage packaging. **Founded:** 1933. **Publications:** *Executive Briefs* (Semimonthly); *Single Service News* (Semiannual). **Awards:** QSR-FPI Foodservice Packaging Awards (Semiannual). **Geographic Preference:** National.

6889 ■ **International Foodservice Manufacturers Association (IFMA)**
Two Prudential Plz.
180 N, Ste.tson Ave., Ste. 850
Chicago, IL 60601
Ph: (312)540-4400
Co. E-mail: ifma@ifmaworld.com
URL: http://www.ifmaworld.com
Contact: Phil Kafarakis, President
E-mail: phil@ifmaworld.com
Facebook: www.facebook.com/ifmaworldcom
Linkedin: www.linkedin.com/company/international-foodservice-manufacturers-association
X (Twitter): x.com/IFMAWORLD
Instagram: www.instagram.com/ifmaworld
Description: Aims to shape the future of food service by creating an environment for positive change and actionable solutions benefiting manufacturers and their food service channel partners. **Founded:** 1952. **Publications:** *Encyclopedia of the Foodservice Industry* (Irregular); *International Foodservice Manufacturers Association: Membership Directory*; *International Foodservice Manufacturers Association-- Membership Directory* (Annual); *IFMA World* (9/year). **Educational Activities:** Chain Operators Exchange (COEX) (Annual). **Awards:** IFMA Gold Plate Award (Annual); IFMA Silver Plate Award (Annual). **Geographic Preference:** Multinational.

6890 ■ **National Council of Chain Restaurants (NCCR)**
c/o National Retail Federation
1101 New York Ave. NW, Ste. 1200
Washington, DC 20005
Ph: (202)783-7971
Free: 800-673-4692
Co. E-mail: contact@nrf.com
URL: http://nrf.com/about-us/national-council-chain-restaurants
Contact: Matthew R. Shay, President
Description: Represents chain restaurant companies. Works to advance sound public policy that best serves the interests of restaurant businesses and the millions of people they employ. Major multiunit, multi-state foodservice, restaurant and lodging companies in the United States. **Founded:** 1965. **Educational Activities:** Membership, Tax Forum and Food Safety. **Geographic Preference:** National.

6891 ■ **National Restaurant Association Educational Foundation (NRAEF)**
2055 L St. NW
Washington, DC 20036
Free: 800-424-5156
Co. E-mail: comms@nraef.org
URL: http://chooserestaurants.org
Contact: Michelle Korsmo, Chief Executive Officer
Facebook: www.facebook.com/nraefoundation
Linkedin: www.linkedin.com/company/nraef
X (Twitter): x.com/nraef
Instagram: www.instagram.com/nraefoundation
YouTube: www.youtube.com/c/NRAEF
Description: Serves as an educational foundation supported by the National Restaurant Association and all segments of the foodservice industry including restaurateurs, foodservice companies, food and equipment manufacturers, distributors and trade associations. Advances the professional standards of the industry through education and research. Offers video training programs, management courses and careers information. Conducts research and maintains hall of fame. **Founded:** 1987. **Publications:** *Directory of Computer Hardware and Software for the Food Service Industry*; *Foodservice/Hospitality College Directory* (Irregular). **Educational Activities:** NSPA Conference. **Awards:** NRAEF Scholarships (Annual); Thad and Alice Eure Ambassador of Hospitality Award (Annual); Al Schuman/Ecolab Undergraduate Entrepreneurial Scholarship (Annual). **Geographic Preference:** National.

6892 ■ **Restaurants Canada - Library**
1155 Queen St. W
Toronto, ON, Canada M6J 1J4
Ph: (416)923-8416
Free: 800-387-5649

Fax: (416)923-1450
Co. E-mail: info@restaurantscanada.org
URL: http://www.restaurantscanada.org
Contact: Christian Buhagiar, Co-Chief Executive Officer Co-President
Facebook: www.facebook.com/RestaurantsCanada
Linkedin: www.linkedin.com/company/restaurants-canada
X (Twitter): x.com/RestaurantsCA
Instagram: www.instagram.com/RestaurantsCanada
YouTube: www.youtube.com/channel/UCxVckfCBIISII9LOuflNX8w

Description: Restaurant and food service corporations, hotels, caterers, and food service suppliers and educators, seeks to create a favorable business environment for members. **Scope:** Food service; quantity cooking; legislation; administration; management; statistics; training; customer attitude surveys. **Services:** Copying; open to the public on fee basis. **Founded:** 1944. **Publications:** *CRFA National Hospitality News*; *Canadian Foodservice Industry Operations Report* (Biennial); *Foodservice Facts* (Annual); *Legislation Guide* (Quarterly). **Educational Activities:** Restaurants Canada Show (Annual); ApEx. **Geographic Preference:** National.

REFERENCE WORKS

6893 ■ *"1 in 4 Food Delivery Drivers Admit to Eating Your Food" in NPR (July 30, 2019)*
URL(s): www.npr.org/2019/07/30/746600105/1-in-4-food-delivery-drivers-admit-to-eating-your-food
Released: June 30, 2019. **Description:** Results from a recent US Foods survey found that 54% of respondents, who are drivers for food delivery apps such as DoorDash, admit to being tempted by the smell of customers' food and half actually took a bite. To help solve this problem customers want tamper-evident stickers on their food containers. Other delivery services are stepping up and creating strategies to prevent this in the first place. **Availability:** Online.

6894 ■ *6 Unbelievably Eash Ways to Grow Your Food Delivery Business*
Ed: Swarnendu De. **Released:** November 27, 2017. **Description:** Provides details on how to build an on demand food delivery app. **Availability:** Online.

6895 ■ *"8 Unique Delivery Services" in Business News Daily (Oct. 20, 2022)*
URL(s): www.businessnewsdaily.com/8538-unique-delivery-businesses.html
Ed: Jennifer Post. **Released:** October 20, 2022. **Description:** Presents information on unique delivery services and how you might model your own delivery service should you choose to enter the delivery space. **Availability:** Online.

6896 ■ *10 Ideas to Start Your Own Food Delivery Business*
URL(s): spdload.com/blog/food-delivery-business-ideas/
Description: Delivery business ideas have become increasingly widespread and profitable. This article discusses reasons to look into some delivery service business ideas and presents ten ideas to watch for. **Availability:** Online.

6897 ■ *"85 Amazing Food Business Ideas You Could Start in 2023" in Small Business Trends(March 2, 2023)*
URL(s): smallbiztrends.com/2023/03/food-business-ideas.html
Ed: Annie Pilon. **Released:** March 02, 2023. **Description:** With the food service industry having changed and adapted to new norms after the pandemic, there are available many options for starting your own food-based small business. **Availability:** Online.

6898 ■ *"Amazon to End Its Restaurant Delivery Service" in The New York Times (June 11, 2019)*
URL(s): www.nytimes.com/2019/06/11/business/amazon-restaurant-delivery-service-ending.html
Ed: David Yaffe-Bellany. **Released:** June 11, 2019. **Description:** Amazon Restaurants will officially close on June 24 and according to Amazon the move will let them focus more on grocery delivery, since they now own Whole Foods. Amazon Restaurants never really took off in popularity as compared to the other food delivery apps and they can no longer keep up with the competition. **Availability:** Online.

6899 ■ *"Baltimore Vendors Brave Heat, Red Tape to Eke Out a Living: Working the Streets" in Baltimore Business Journal (Vol. 28, July 30, 2010, No. 12, pp. 1)*
Pub: Baltimore Business Journal
Contact: Rhonda Pringle, President
E-mail: rpringle@bizjournals.com
Ed: Amanda Pino. **Description:** Reports show that street vendors are popping up on new corners in Baltimore, Maryland, with city-inspected stainless steel food carts in tow. Applications for street vending licenses shot up at the end of 2009 and into this summer. It is believed that pinning down the exact number of vendors operating at any one point is difficult. **Availability:** Print.

6900 ■ *Best Practices for Safe Food Delivery, Take Out*
Description: Provides tips for safe carry out and delivery services for your business. **Availability:** Online.

6901 ■ *"Can You Cook Food from Home and Sell As a Delivery Business" in Marketing Food Online Blog (Jan. 24, 2022)*
URL(s): marketingfoodonline.com/blogs/news/can-you-cook-food-from-home-and-sell-as-a-delivery-business
Ed: Damian Roberti. **Released:** January 24, 2022. **Description:** Provides information on how to start your own food delivery service with food you've cooked at home. Discusses the legalities involved, which differ from state to state. **Availability:** Online.

6902 ■ *"Consumers Love Food Delivery. Restaurants and Grocers Hate It." in The Wall Street Journal (March 9. 2019)*
URL(s): www.wsj.com/articles/consumers-love-food-delivery-restaurants-and-grocers-hate-it-11552107610
Ed: Heather Haddon, Julie Jargon. **Released:** March 09, 2019. **Description:** Food delivery services are tricky for restaurants, with most being unprofitable due to the cost of delivery. Consumers have very high expectations because they are used to instant gratification with online services, but grocers and restaurants are struggling to keep up with the demand. **Availability:** Online.

6903 ■ *Food Delivery Tales: True Stories about Delivering Restaurant Food*
Ed: Scott Paulson. **Released:** September 15, 2019. **Description:** A Chicago Uber Eats delivery man tells his true stories about his experiences applying for the job and discusses the technology behind this industry. **Availability:** Print.

6904 ■ *Here Is a Brilliant Startup Idea of Online Office Food Ordering & Delivery Business*
Description: Food ordering and delivery has evolved with technology coming into the forefront and with the online office food ordering and delivery business playing a part. This article discusses how an online office food delivery business works and how to take advantage of this segment of the food tech industry. **Availability:** Online.

6905 ■ *"How to Make Third-Party Delivery Work For You in Any Market" in PMG Pizza Magazine (May 2019)*
Description: Discusses the use of third-party food delivery services and how to make the right service work for your business. **Availability:** Online.

6906 ■ *How to Optimize Your Small Business Delivery Services*
URL(s): optimoroute.com/small-business-delivery-services/
Released: August 26, 2022. **Description:** Discusses the importance of optimizing your small business delivery services and presents three options to choose from and offers information on how to decide which is right for your business. **Availability:** Online.

6907 ■ *How to Set Up a Delivery Service for Your Restaurant*
Released: March 23, 2020. **Description:** Food delivery and take-out services are two of the fastest growing segments of the restaurant industry. This article provides tips on how to add delivery services to your restaurant. **Availability:** Online.

6908 ■ *How to Start a Food Delivery Business*
Ed: Allison Tardelli. **Released:** July 25, 2020. **Description:** Provides advice on how to start a food delivery business from people who have done it. **Availability:** Online.

6909 ■ *How to Start a Food Delivery Business in Four Steps*
URL(s): www.nextinsurance.com/blog/how-to-start-a-food-delivery-business/
Ed: Matt Crawford. **Released:** August 31, 2022. **Description:** Food delivery services are playing a critical role in helping restaurants and food service professionals reach new customers in a constantly changing landscape. This article discusses the different types of food delivery businesses, the benefits of starting a food delivery business, specific steps for starting a food delivery business, and how to protect your business. **Availability:** Online.

6910 ■ *How to Start a Food Delivery Business From Home*
URL(s): www.entrepreneurshipinabox.com/17652/how-to-start-a-food-delivery-business-from-home/
Ed: Dragen Sutevski. **Description:** As more and more people are drawn to meal delivery subscriptions, food delivery businesses are booming. This article discusses how to start a home-based food delivery business. **Availability:** Online.

6911 ■ *"How To: Launching a Food Truck Catering Business" in FoodTruckOperator.com (October 5, 2020)*
Ed: Richard Traylor. **Released:** October 05, 2020. **Description:** Provides details on what is involved in a food truck-based catering operation and how to get started. **Availability:** Online.

6912 ■ *"Howl-o-ween" in Decatur Daily (October 25, 2011)*
Description: Animal Friends Humane Society provides free pet food and cat litter to Meals on Wheels clients. **Availability:** Online.

6913 ■ *"Kaiser Says Hospital Room Service Saves Money" in Pacific Business News (Vol. 26, August 22, 2014, No. 26, pp. 10)*
Pub: American City Business Journals, Inc.
Contact: Mike Olivieri, Executive Vice President
Released: Weekly. **Price:** $4, Introductory 4-week offer(Digital & Print). **Description:** Kaiser Permanente Hawaii's Moanalua Medical Center reveals that it has save nearly $1.5 million annually in food costs since it introduced in-house meal preparation and room service for patients two years ago. The hospital, which previous outsourced meal preparation to Aramark, finds that the new policy avoids waste by allowing patients to choose their own food as well as their mealtime. **Availability:** Print; Online.

6914 ■ *"Learn New Ideas from Experienced Menu Makers" in Nation's Restaurant News (Vol. 45, June 27, 2011, No. 13, pp. 82)*
Pub: Informa USA, Inc.
Contact: Stephen A. Carter, Chief Executive Officer
Ed: Nancy Kruse. **Released:** June 27, 2011. **Description:** National Restaurant Association Restaurant, Hotel-Motel Show featured the Food Truck Spot,

a firm committed to all aspects of mobile catering, foodtruck manufacturers, leasers of fully equipped truck and a food-truck franchising group.

6915 ■ "Meals on Wheels Filling 'Blizzard Bags" in Tulsa World (November 5, 2011)
Description: Cathy Perlingiere, director of volunteer services for Meals on Wheels of Metro Tulsa, Oklahoma reports that they do not deliver meals when the Tulsa Public Schools close because of weather so they try to prepare 'blizzard bags' with nonperishable food items to cover about three meals for when drivers cannot deliver. **Availability:** Print; Online.

6916 ■ "Oberweis Tests Home Ice Cream Delivery" in Ice Cream Reporter (Vol. 21, November 20, 2008, No. 12, pp. 1)
Description: Oberwies Dairy launched its Treat Delivery Program in the Saint Louis area. The program allows customers to order milkshakes, ice cream cones, sundaes and scoops of ice cream and they are delivered to their home or office. Oberweis is a fourth generation family run business. **Availability:** Print; Online.

6917 ■ "A Recipe for Food-Industry Growth?" in Providence Business News (Vol. 29, April 21, 2014, No. 3, pp. 1)
Pub: American City Business Journals, Inc.
Contact: Mike Olivieri, Executive Vice President
Released: April 19, 2014. **Description:** Industry experts believe that Rhode Island could become the 'Silicon Valley of Food'. The state is already known for its restaurants, chefs and ethnic cuisine, will host a Foods Innovation Summit in 2014. Ways that Rhode Island can take advantage of the economic benefits generated by the food industry are also examined. **Availability:** Print; Online.

6918 ■ Should I Use a Third-Party Delivery Service or Create My Own?
Description: The demand for food delivery from restaurant customers continues to climb. Restaurants face a tough decision when it comes to accommodating this guest preference. This article discusses the whether it's a better idea to sign up with a third-party delivery service or invest in developing a delivery channel for your restaurant. **Availability:** Online.

6919 ■ Small Business Ideas for Prepared Food Delivery
Ed: Shailynn Krow. **Description:** Prepared food delivery offers customers convenient, ready-to-eat meals for breakfast, lunch or dinner. This article details how to start a prepared food delivery service. **Availability:** Online.

6920 ■ "The Soon To Be $200B Online Food Delivery Is Rapidly Changing the Global Food Industry" in Forbes September 9, 2019)
URL(s): www.forbes.com/sites/sarwantsingh/2019/09/09/the-soon-to-be-200b-online-food-delivery-is-rapidly-changing-the-global-food-industry/#738268e0b1bc
Ed: Sarwant Singh. **Released:** September 09, 2019. **Description:** Discusses the growing demand for online food delivery services in the United States and worldwide. There are currently ten major players in this game just in the United States, and each is trying to take bigger and bigger pieces of the industry. **Availability:** Online.

6921 ■ "Substantial Deal Expected to Create Jobs, Help Industrial Market" in Tampa Bay Business Journal (Vol. 30, January 8, 2010, No. 3)
Pub: Tampa Bay Business Journal
Contact: Ian Anderson, President
E-mail: ianderson@bizjournals.com
Ed: Janet Leiser. **Description:** Food distribution firm Gordon Food Service (GFS) is on the brink of purchasing Albertson's million-square-foot warehouse along with 158 acres of space. The deal between GFS and Albertson's could expand GFS' presence in west Central Florida. A history of GFS' growth is included. **Availability:** Print; Online.

6922 ■ "Supersized: Delaware North Ready to Feed 80,000 NFL Fans" in Business First of Buffalo (Vol. 30, January 31, 2014, No. 20, pp. 3)
Pub: American City Business Journals, Inc.
Contact: Mike Olivieri, Executive Vice President
Released: January 31, 2014. **Description:** Delaware North is set to cater the food, retailing and beverage needs of 80,000 football fans at the Super Bowl games in New York. The company will bring 80 top venue managers and 30 high-level executive sous chefs to the event. Menu for the event is presented.

6923 ■ "Third-Party Food Delivery Service License Application Checklist" in NYC Consumer and Worker Protection
URL(s): www1.nyc.gov/site/dca/businesses/license-checklist-third-party-food-delivery-service.page
Description: A guide to third-party food delivery service licensing.

6924 ■ "Watch Out, Uber Eaters: Online Food Delivery Can Lead to Overspending and Isolation" in Tennessean (June 25, 2019)
URL(s): www.tennessean.com/story/money/2019/06/25/online-food-delivery-can-lead-addiction-overspending/1490064001/
Ed: Sandy Mazza, Brad Schmitt. **Released:** June 25, 2019. **Description:** Food delivery services and apps are quickly growing and people love the convenience they provide. However, it's often hard to stop ordering food online because it's so accessible and easy, which if not checked will lead to overspending. **Availability:** Online.

6925 ■ "West Sacramento Food Shipper Changes Hands" in Sacramento Business Journal (Vol. 31, May 30, 2014, No. 3)
Pub: American City Business Journals, Inc.
Contact: Mike Olivieri, Executive Vice President
Released: Weekly. **Price:** $4, Introductory 4-week offer(Digital & Print). **Description:** United Natural Foods Inc. (UNFI) is acquiring Tony's Fine Foods in a $195 million deal that brings together two companies native to Sacramento, California. Tony's is the leading distributor of perishable food products since 1934 and will operate as a wholly-owned subsidiary of UNFI as part of the deal. **Availability:** Print; Online.

6926 ■ What Type of License Does a Food Delivery Service Need?
URL(s): vakilsearch.com/advice/what-type-of-license-does-a-food-delivery-service-need/
Released: November 24, 2020. **Description:** Provides information on regulations and licensing needed to ensure that your new food delivery service is legally compliant. **Availability:** Online.

STATISTICAL SOURCES

6927 ■ Food Carryout and Delivery in the U.S.
URL(s): www.marketresearch.com/Packaged-Facts-v768/Food-Carryout-Delivery-Edition-31435487/
Price: $3,995. **Description:** Report focusing on carryout and delivery of prepared meals and food/beverages. Historical and projected foodservice revenues are provided, segmented by type of establishment. This report also provides historical and projected food carryout and delivery sales, segmented by carryout and delivery. **Availability:** Download.

6928 ■ Global Digital Food Delivery Market Size & Share to 2027
URL(s): www.marketresearch.com/Qualiket-Research-v4241/Global-Digital-Food-Delivery-Size-31451572/
Price: $3,950. **Description:** Report contains global digital food delivery market size, trends and growth, platform type, payment method, and regional forecasts to 2027. **Availability:** PDF.

6929 ■ Online Food Delivery Services Global Market Opportunities And Strategies To 2030
URL(s): www.marketresearch.com/Business-Research-Company-v4006/Online-Food-Delivery-Services-Global-31766663/

Price: $4,000. **Description:** Report covers market characteristics; size and growth; segmentation; regional and country breakdowns; competitive landscape; market shares; trends and strategies for the online food delivery market. It traces the market's historic and forecast market growth by geography. **Availability:** Download.

6930 ■ US Alcoholic Beverages Online Market Report 2021
URL(s): store.mintel.com/report/us-alcoholic-beverages-online-market-report
Price: $4,366.35. **Description:** When the Covid-19 pandemic hit, online alcoholic beverage sales went up, due to people not wanting to shop instore. This downloadable report covers the reasons online sources are used to purchase alcohol, barriers to doing so, and consumer behavior trends. Included are an executive summary, interactive databook, PowerPoint presentation, infographic overview, report PDF, and previous years data. **Availability:** PDF.

TRADE SHOWS AND CONVENTIONS

6931 ■ ApEx
Restaurants Canada
1155 Queen St. W
Toronto, ON, Canada M6J 1J4
Ph: (416)923-8416
Free: 800-387-5649
Fax: (416)923-1450
Co. E-mail: info@restaurantscanada.org
URL: http://www.restaurantscanada.org
Contact: Christian Buhagiar, Co-Chief Executive Officer Co-President
URL(s): www.apextradeshow.ca
Description: Products and services for the restaurant and hospitality industry, as well as institutions, convenience stores, delis and bakeries. **Audience:** Industry professionals. **Principal Exhibits:** Products and services for the restaurant and hospitality industry, as well as institutions, convenience stores, delis and bakeries. **Telecommunication Services:** chuckn@mediaedge.ca.

6932 ■ ProFood Tech
Arabian Exhibition Management WLL
PO Box 20200
Manama, Bahrain
Ph: 973 1755-0033
Co. E-mail: info@aemallworld.com
URL(s): www.idfa.org/profoodtech-2
Facebook: www.facebook.com/ProFoodTechShow
X (Twitter): twitter.com/profoodtech
Frequency: Biennial. **Description:** Food processing, packaging, ingredient, and distribution products and services. **Audience:** Processing and packaging professionals. **Principal Exhibits:** Food processing, packaging, ingredient, and distribution products and services.

FRANCHISES AND BUSINESS OPPORTUNITIES

6933 ■ Coffee Perks
2985 Mercury Rd.
Jacksonville, FL 32207
Ph: (904)737-7870
Fax: (904)737-7946
Co. E-mail: customercare@coffeeperks.com
URL: http://coffeeperks.com
Contact: Allicia Smith, Manager
Facebook: www.facebook.com/CoffeePerksCo
X (Twitter): x.com/Coffee_Perks
Description: Firm provides coffee, vending and water solutions for businesses. **Founded:** 1988. **Training:** Yes.

6934 ■ DoorDash Inc.
DoorDash Inc.
303 2nd St., South Tower, 8th Fl.
San Francisco, CA 94107
Ph: (650)487-3970
Free: 855-973-1040

Co. E-mail: support@doordash.com
URL: http://www.doordash.com
Contact: Tony Xu, Chief Executive Officer
Facebook: www.facebook.com/DoorDash
X (Twitter): twitter.com/doordash
Instagram: www.instagram.com/doordash
Description: Provider of on-demand food delivery services. **Founded:** 2013.

6935 ■ Farmer Boys Food, Inc.
3452 University Ave.
  Riverside, CA 92501
Ph: (951)275-9900
Free: 888-930-3276
URL: http://www.farmerboys.com
Contact: Mark Lobb, Contact
Facebook: www.facebook.com/FarmerBoysFood
X (Twitter): x.com/FarmerBoys
Instagram: www.instagram.com/farmerboysfood
YouTube: www.youtube.com/user/FarmerBoysFood
Description: Aim is to protect and serve farm fresh food. **Founded:** 1981. **Royalty Fee:** 5%. **Financial Assistance:** Yes **Training:** Yes.

6936 ■ Firkin Group of Pubs
20 Steelcase Rd. W, Unit 1C
  Markham, ON, Canada L3R 1B2
Ph: (905)305-9792
Co. E-mail: comments@firkinpubs.com
URL: http://www.firkinpubs.com
Facebook: www.facebook.com/firkinpubs
X (Twitter): x.com/FirkinPubs
Instagram: www.instagram.com/firkinpubs
Description: Chain of pubs. **Founded:** 1987. **Training:** Training provided at headquarters and ongoing support.

6937 ■ Grubhub Inc.
Just Eat Takeaway.com NV
  111 W Washington St., Ste. 2100
  Chicago, IL 60602
Co. E-mail: press@justeattakeaway.com
URL: http://www.justeattakeaway.com
Contact: Adam Dewitt, President
X (Twitter): x.com/grubhub
Instagram: www.instagram.com/grubhub
YouTube: www.youtube.com/user/grubhub
Description: Provider of online order and delivery portal services for a variety of restaurants. **Founded:** 2004.

6938 ■ Insomnia Cookies Franchising, LLC - 14th Street New York City
304 W 14th St.
  New York, NY 10014
Ph: (646)762-9313
Co. E-mail: customerservice@insomniacookies.com
URL: http://insomniacookies.com
Facebook: www.facebook.com/insomniacookies
X (Twitter): twitter.com/insomniacookies
Instagram: www.instagram.com/insomniacookies
Description: Chain of cookies shops. **No. of Company-Owned Units:** 14. **Founded:** 2003. **Franchised:** 2006. **Equity Capital Needed:** $65,600-$111,400. **Franchise Fee:** $25,000. **Royalty Fee:** 6%. **Training:** Offer 2-3 weeks training at headquarters, 2-3 weeks at franchisee's location, at other franchisee/corporate locations as needed and ongoing support.

6939 ■ The Lunch Lady Group Inc.
151 Spinnaker Way, Unit 4
  Concord, ON, Canada L4K 4C3
Ph: (905)660-5994
Co. E-mail: support@thelunchlady.ca
URL: http://thelunchlady.ca
Contact: Ruthie Burd, Founder
X (Twitter): x.com/LunchLadyGroup
Instagram: www.instagram.com/lunch_lady_group
Description: Provider of healthy lunches and nutritious meals for school children. **Founded:** 1993. **Training:** Offers 2 week training program and ongoing support.

6940 ■ Mancino's, Samuel Italian Eatery
401b N Clippert St.
  Lansing, MI 48912
Co. E-mail: info@samuelmancinos.com
URL: http://www.samuelmancinos.com
Description: Firm is a franchise of restaurants and provides food delivery services. **Franchised:** 1994. **Training:** Yes.

6941 ■ Padows's Hams & Deli, Inc.
11000 S Washington Hwy.
  Glen Allen, VA 23059
Ph: (804)965-6262
Fax: (804)965-9888
URL: http://www.padows.com
Contact: Sidney Padow, Contact
Description: Operator of restaurant offers hams, turkeys and much more. **Founded:** 1936. **Franchised:** 2000. **Training:** Yes.

6942 ■ Uber Eats
Uber Technologies, Inc.
  San Francisco, CA
Ph: (415)612-8582
Fax: (877)223-8023
Co. E-mail: business-support@uber.com
URL: http://www.uber.com
Facebook: www.facebook.com/UberEats
X (Twitter): x.com/ubereats
Instagram: www.instagram.com/ubereats
Description: Food delivery service. **Founded:** 2014.

6943 ■ VHooters of America LLC.
1815 The Exchange
  Atlanta, GA 30339
Ph: (770)951-2040
URL: http://www.hooters.com
Contact: Claudia Levitas, Officer
Facebook: www.facebook.com/hooters
X (Twitter): x.com/hooters
YouTube: www.youtube.com/hooters
Description: Business of restaurant and food delivery services. **No. of Franchise Units:** 416. **No. of Company-Owned Units:** 190. **Founded:** 1983. **Equity Capital Needed:** Net worth of $2,500,000; Liquidity of $1,500,000. **Franchise Fee:** $75,000. **Royalty Fee:** 5%. **Publications:** Hooters Magazine (Quarterly). **Training:** Yes.

LIBRARIES

6944 ■ The Coca-Cola Company
The Coca-Cola Company
  1 Coca-Cola Plz.
  Atlanta, GA 30313
Ph: (404)676-2121
Free: 800-438-2653
Co. E-mail: press@coca-cola.com
URL: http://www.coca-colacompany.com
Contact: John Murphy, President
Facebook: www.facebook.com/TheCocaColaCo
Linkedin: www.linkedin.com/company/the-coca-cola-company
X (Twitter): twitter.com/CocaCola
Instagram: www.instagram.com/cocacola
YouTube: www.youtube.com/user/CocaColaCo
Description: Producer and distributor of non-alcoholic beverages such as juices, ready-to-drink teas and coffees, sport, dairy and energy drinks. **Founded:** 1886. **Educational Activities:** GSF West; Sunshine Expo (Annual); Big Iron Farm Show and Exhibition (Annual).

6945 ■ Food Institute (FI)
330 Changebridge Rd., Ste. 101
  Pine Brook, NJ 07058
Ph: (201)791-5570
Free: 855-791-5570
Co. E-mail: questions@foodinstitute.com
URL: http://www.foodinstitute.com
Contact: Anika Wilson, Contact
E-mail: anika.wilson@foodinstitute.com
Facebook: www.facebook.com/foodinstitutenj
Linkedin: www.linkedin.com/company/the-food-institute
X (Twitter): x.com/FoodInstitute
Instagram: www.instagram.com/foodinstitute
YouTube: www.youtube.com/channel/UCYAPI0TXNtJa04aQre4h4pA
Description: Strives to provide food industry-related information to its members. **Scope:** The food industry. **Services:** Center open to the public on fee basis. **Founded:** 1928. **Holdings:** Figures not available. **Publications:** Today in Food; Get It Out, Get It Right, Get It Over! Avoiding Food Product Recalls; The Food Institute (Weekly); Almanac of the Canning, Freezing, Preserving Industries (Annual); Food Business Mergers and Acquisitions; OSHA Inspection Manual; Regulatory Directory (Periodic); Food Business Mergers & Acquisitions. **Geographic Preference:** Multinational.

6946 ■ Food Marketing Institute Information Service (FMI)
2345 Crystal Dr., Ste. 800
  Arlington, VA 22202
Ph: (202)452-8444
Fax: (202)429-4519
URL: http://www.fmi.org/membership/associate-membership
Scope: Food distribution. **Services:** Interlibrary loan; copying; service open to the public by appointment. **Founded:** 1952. **Holdings:** 7,000 volumes.

6947 ■ Technomic Inc. - Library
300 S Riverside Plz., Ste. 1600
  Chicago, IL 60606
Ph: (312)876-0004
Co. E-mail: info@technomic.com
URL: http://www.technomic.com
Contact: Alanna Young, President
Facebook: www.facebook.com/TechnomicInc
Linkedin: www.linkedin.com/company/technomic-inc
X (Twitter): x.com/technomic
Description: Firm provides food and foodservice industry data, intelligence and commentary, their proprietary research, trend analysis, forecasts, management consulting, and common-interest studies and reports provide channel-relevant strategic marketing insights and much more. **Scope:** Foodservice. **Founded:** 1966. **Holdings:** Figures not available. **Publications:** "MENU PRICING: Using consumer data to understand how price increases will impact your business"; "Top Growth Chains: Who They Are and Why They Succeed"; "Five Social Media Strategies for Restaurants"; "Defining the Social Media Opportunity for Foodservice Suppliers".

RESEARCH CENTERS

6948 ■ National Restaurant Association-Quality Assurance Executive Study Group
2055 L St. NW, Ste. 700
  Washington, DC 20036
Ph: (202)331-5900
Free: 800-424-5156
URL: http://www.restaurant.org/Events-Networking/Networking-Groups/Quality_Assurance/Overview
Contact: Tom Bene, President
Description: Group is a unit of the National Restaurant Association. **Scope:** Quality assurance and quality control in food service facilities. **Founded:** 1919. **Educational Activities:** Food Safety & Quality Assurance Executive Study Group; Quality Assurance Executive Study Group Study Group Meetings.

Food Truck

START-UP INFORMATION

6949 ■ *"Culinary School Puts a Food Truck on the Road"* in St. Louis Post-Dispatch (March 21, 2012)
Ed: Joe Bonwich. **Description:** Le Food Truck is a teach tool to help students learn about the fast-growing food truck market. Tony Hedger, instructor at L'Ecole Culinaire, a career college located in Laude, Missouri, coordinated the new program. The school also operates the Presentation Room, a restaurant used as part of the classroom. **Availability:** Print; Online.

6950 ■ *"Dining Notes: The Salty Fig is Jacksonville's Newest Food Truck"* in Florida Times-Union (July 13, 2012)
Ed: Gary T. Mills. **Description:** Jeff and John Stanford has selected locations throughout the city of Jacksonville, Florida to operate the food truck operation called, The Salty Fig. The brothers serve New American Southern style food along with a bar drink menu. The Salty Fig is named after the trees the boys enjoyed at their grandparent's home. **Availability:** Online.

6951 ■ *"Faces: Q&A With Katie Johnson, Co-Owner of Bloomy's Roast Beef Food Truck"* in Saint Paul Pioneer Press (June 13, 2012)
Ed: Kathie Jenkins. **Description:** Profile of Katie Johnson, 29 year old co-owner of Bloomy's Roast Beef food truck. Johnson discusses how her and her friend Ryan planned and started their food truck business and why they chose roast beef for their menu. **Availability:** Print; Online.

6952 ■ *Food Truck Business: Complete Guide for Beginners. How to Start, Manage & Grow YOUR OWN Food Truck Business*
Ed: Tony Smith. **Description:** As more and more people are enjoying the options available in food trucks, the opportunity to grow your own food truck business is growing. This guide discusses how to start, using social media, food safety, profits, plus more. **Availability:** Print.

6953 ■ *"The Food Truck Handbook: Start, Grow, and Succeed in the Mobile Food Business"*
Pub: John Wiley & Sons, Inc.
Contact: Christina Van Tassell, Executive Vice President Chief Financial Officer
Released: March 2012. **Price:** $19.95, paperback; $12.99, e-book. **Description:** Food truck businesses have grown so much in popularity, there are actually food truck competitions and was once a television show featuring them. A practical, step-by-step handbook is offered to help an entrepreneur start a mobile food delivery service. Information includes tips on choosing vending locations, opening and closing checklists; creation of a business plan with budget and finding vendor services, daily operation issues; common operating mistakes; and insight into delivery high quality food. **Availability:** E-book; Print.

6954 ■ *Mobile Vending: How to Run a Traveling Food or Merchandise Concession*
Ed: Jarvis Hooten. **Description:** Discusses strategies for starting and maintaining food trucks and festival food concession stands. **Availability:** Print.

6955 ■ *"So You Want To Be a Food Truck Vendor?"* in Philadelphia Business Journal (Vol. 33, August 15, 2014, No. 27, pp. 7)
Pub: American City Business Journals, Inc.
Contact: Mike Olivieri, Executive Vice President
Released: Weekly. **Price:** $4, introductory 4-week offer(Digital only). **Description:** Food truck vendors assert that the most challenging part of starting a food truck business is acquiring a license as well as the price and number of licenses and permits required. Other costs include additional fees to vend in prime locations, maintenance, and inventory. **Availability:** Print; Online.

6956 ■ *"Want to Start Your Own Food Truck? Read This First"* in Eater (November 21, 2019)
URL(s): www.eater.com/young-guns-rising-stars/2019/11/21/20970846/how-to-run-food-truck-business
Ed: Annie Burdick. **Released:** November 21, 2019. **Description:** More and more chefs are taking the plunge of opening up food trucks instead of a brick and mortar restaurant thinking it will be easier. Three food truck owners discuss their own experiences and successes in this industry. **Availability:** Online.

ASSOCIATIONS AND OTHER ORGANIZATIONS

6957 ■ **DER Kitchen**
2501 Main St.
Columbia, SC 29201
Ph: (803)779-3003
Co. E-mail: info@derkitchen.com
URL: http://www.derkitchen.com
Contact: Dave Roberts, Contact
Facebook: www.facebook.com/DERKitchen

Description: Kitchen incubator providing bakers, food truck operators and caterers a pay-by-the-hour base of operations without the need to build and equip a commercial kitchen.

6958 ■ **The Food Industry Association**
2345 Crystal Dr., Ste. 800
Arlington, VA 22202
Ph: (202)452-8444
URL: http://www.fmi.org
Linkedin: www.linkedin.com/company/fmithefoodindustryassociation
X (Twitter): x.com/FMI_ORG
Instagram: www.instagram.com/fmi_org
YouTube: www.youtube.com/user/FMIorg

Description: Works on behalf of the food industry to advance a safer, healthier, and more efficient consumer food supply chain. Provides members, from independent operators to the largest national and international players, a forum for actively coming together to engage in dialogue, collaboration and problem-solving as a community.

6959 ■ **Food Truck Association of Georgia (FTAG)**
PO Box 763
Holly Springs, GA 30142
Ph: (404)482-7502
Co. E-mail: info@foodtruckassociationofgeorgia.com
URL: http://foodtruckassociationofgeorgia.com/Home
Contact: Tony Harrison, President
Facebook: www.facebook.com/foodtruckassociationofgeorgia
Linkedin: www.linkedin.com/company/food-truck-association-of-georgia

Description: Represents food trucks, trailers, dessert trucks, and carts in Georgia. Advocates for the industry with local governments to help make areas more friendly towards these vendors. Educational materials and support is available for members. **Founded:** 2016.

6960 ■ **National Food Truck Association (NFTA)**
5792 W Jefferson Blvd.
Los Angeles, CA 90016
Ph: (202)644-8830
Co. E-mail: info@nationalfoodtrucks.org
URL: http://nationalfoodtrucks.org
Contact: Matt Geller, Chief Executive Officer
Facebook: www.facebook.com/nationalfoodtrucks
X (Twitter): x.com/natlfoodtrucks

Description: Provides access to resources and information for food truck owners. Offers location and management services.

6961 ■ **Roaming Hunger**
7561 W Sunset Blvd., Ste. 204
West Hollywood, CA 90046
Free: 800-568-9370
Co. E-mail: marketing@roaminghunger.com
Contact: Ross Resnick, Chief Executive Officer
Facebook: www.facebook.com/roaminghunger
Instagram: www.instagram.com/roaminghunger

Description: Organization provides national access to food trucks for promotions and catering events.

6962 ■ **Southern California Mobile Food Vendors Association**
Los Angeles, CA
Ph: (424)229-2874
Co. E-mail: socalmfva@gmail.com
URL: http://socalmfva.com
Facebook: www.facebook.com/SocalMFVA
X (Twitter): x.com/SoCalMFVA

Description: Provides information on owning and running a food truck in the Los Angeles area. Works with local governments and merchants to provide a positive impact in communities. Offers mentoring and a point of contact for members. **Founded:** 2010.

REFERENCE WORKS

6963 ■ *"6 Tips to Winterize Your Food Truck"* in FoodTruckOperator.com (October 3, 2019)
Ed: Richard Traylor. **Released:** October 03, 2019. **Description:** Winter is the most difficult season for many food trucks. This article discusses how changing your menu, working with local businesses and searching for events and catering opportunities, you can stay open and continue to make a profit. **Availability:** Online.

6964 ■ *"10 Things to Do Before Opening a Food Truck"* in Business News Daily (February 21, 2023)
URL(s): www.businessnewsdaily.com/8595-food-truck-tips.html
Ed: Brittney Morgan. **Released:** February 21, 2023. **Description:** Running a food truck can have its challenges. This article provides tips from food truck owners on what they did to thrive in the industry. **Availability:** Online.

6965 ■ *"85 Amazing Food Business Ideas You Could Start in 2023"* in Small Business Trends (March 2, 2023)
URL(s): smallbiztrends.com/2023/03/food-business-ideas.html
Ed: Annie Pilon. **Released:** March 02, 2023. **Description:** With the food service industry having changed and adapted to new norms after the pandemic, there are available many options for starting your own food-based small business. **Availability:** Online.

6966 ■ *"Aramark Rolls Out Ballpark Food Truck"* in Nation's Restaurant News (Vol. 45, August 8, 2011, No. 16, pp. 4)
Description: Aramark installed its first ballpark food truck serving Asian-inspired noodle bowls at the outfield concourse at Coors Field in Colorado. **Availability:** Print.

6967 ■ *"Buying a Food Truck: Advice, Insight on Customization, Design and Decor"* in FoodTruckOperator.com (March 9, 2020)
Ed: Richard Traylor. **Released:** March 09, 2020. **Description:** Provides tips about customization, design, and decor for your newly-purchased food truck. **Availability:** Online.

6968 ■ *"Conducting Effective Reference Checks For Your Food Truck"* in Mobile-Cuisine.com (2020)
Ed: Richard Myrick. **Description:** Provides steps on successfully hiring food truck staff members. **Availability:** Online.

6969 ■ *"Consumers Who Saw a Food Truck This Summer"* in Nation's Restaurant News (Vol. 45, September 26, 2011, No. 20, pp. 8)
Description: A guide to the number of customers encountering food trucks during summer 2011 is presented by region. **Availability:** Online.

6970 ■ *"Deep Dive: Does Your Food Truck Operation Need a Commissary Kitchen?"* in FoodTruckOperator.com (March 16, 2020)
Released: March 16, 2020. **Description:** Many food trucks are turning to a commissary kitchen for various reasons: need for space, ability to handle large event orders and to help reduce waste when it comes to time and resources. This article discusses what a commissary kitchen is all about and why it may be a good option for your food truck operation. **Availability:** Online.

6971 ■ *"Determining Your Food Truck Employee Needs"* in Mobile-Cuisine.com (September 8, 2020)
Ed: Richard Myrick. **Released:** September 08, 2020. **Description:** Detailed information on determining food truck employee wants and needs. **Availability:** Online.

6972 ■ *"Everything Food Truck Operators Need to Know About the Mobile POS"* in FoodTruckOperator.com (July 13, 2020)
Ed: Richard Traylor. **Released:** July 13, 2020. **Description:** Mobile payment has become a must-have technology for food truck operators. This article discusses how to adapt and change to utilize a mobile POS system. **Availability:** Online.

6973 ■ *"Faces: Q&A with Kevin Huyck, Chef/Owner of R.A. MacSammy's Food Truck Specializing in Mac and Cheese"* in Saint Paul Pioneer Press (March 28, 2012)
Ed: Kathie Jenkins. **Description:** Profile of 48 year old Kevin Huyck, chef and owner of his R.A. MacSammy food truck. Huyck specializes in serving a variety of macaroni and cheese dishes. He wanted to own his own restaurant but did not have the capital for such an investment at the time and hopes to expand with either another food truck or possibly a restaurant that features mac and cheese dishes. **Availability:** Online.

6974 ■ *"Farm to Fork: The Pros and Cons for Foodservice"* in FoodTruckOperator.com (August 5, 2019)
Ed: Richard Traylor. **Released:** August 05, 2019. **Description:** Sourcing food for your food truck from local farmers has many benefits. This article discusses both the advantages and disadvantages.

6975 ■ *"First Food Truck Festival Features Enticing Fare, Frustrating Waits"* in Saint Paul Pioneer Press (August 6, 2012)
Pub: McClatchy-Tribune Regional News
Ed: Megan Boldt. **Description:** The first Minnesota Food Truck Fest was held in downtown Minneapolis, Minnesota. Despite best intentions, attendees were left waiting in long lines and two vendors ran out of food in two hours. Fourteen food vendors and 25 craft beer trucks were representing this trend in food service. **Availability:** Print; Online.

6976 ■ *"Food Truck Group Backs Proposed Regulations"* in Buffalo News (January 18, 2012)
Ed: Aaron Besecker. **Description:** Food truck operators in the city of Buffalo, New York have accepted the newly created rules governing their operations in the city, despite the higher-than-expected $1,000 permit fee. An attorney for the Western New York Food Truck Association stated that the proposed rules would be acceptable to the membership. **Availability:** Print; Online.

6977 ■ *"Food-Truck Learnings Travel Indoors"* in Nation's Restaurant News (Vol. 45, June 27, 2011, No. 13, pp. 3)
Description: Challenges faced by owners of food truck businesses are discussed. Ways a food truck can be used to promote a restaurant's menu are covered. **Availability:** Print; Online.

6978 ■ *Food Truck Strategy: Simple Steps to Launch Your Own Food Truck*
Ed: Jeffrey S. Fulson, Sr. **Released:** December 29, 2017. **Price:** $9.99, Paperback. **Description:** Written by a food truck business owner. Organized and concise how-to manual covering essential areas of running a successful food truck. **Availability:** Print.

6979 ■ *"Food Truck Supplies 101: A Handy Checklist"* in FoodTruckOperator.com (August 16, 2017)
Ed: Richard Traylor. **Released:** August 16, 2017. **Description:** Provides a list of all of the important cooking, consumables, plating, cleaning, and safety supplies you should have on your food truck before you get started. **Availability:** Online.

6980 ■ *"Food Truck Weddings Gain Popularity, Buck Tradition"* in Tampa Tribune (June 24, 2012)
Ed: Jeff Houck. **Description:** A new trend crossing the nation is the use of a food truck for feeding guests as weddding receptions. Food trucks allow the bride and groom to provide a more casual atmosphere for their wedding party and is less expensive than a formal dinner. **Availability:** Print; Online.

6981 ■ *"Food Trucks Savor Rebirth in City"* in Providence Business News (Vol. 27, April 16, 2012, No. 2, pp. 1)
Description: Providence, Rhode Island has been experiencing the growth of the food truck business as the trucks and their devoted followers become regular fixtures in the city. Food trucks have a strong presence in the West Coast and have proliferated across the U.S. in recent years. Insights into Providence's food truck community are also given. **Availability:** Online.

6982 ■ *"Fuel Costs Curb Food Truck Trend"* in Tampa Tribune (March 26, 2012)
Ed: Jeff Houck. **Description:** Owner of Maggie on the Move food truck, Margaret Loflin, has had to raise the cost of drinks served in order to cover the increased cost of gasoline to run her business. She also added smaller, less costly items to her menu. Her husband has gone back to a part-time job in he hopes of keeping their food truck running. **Availability:** Print; Online.

6983 ■ *"A Guide to Starting a Food Truck Business"* in Home Business (June 30, 2022)
URL(s): homebusinessmag.com/business-start-up/how-to-guides/guide-starting-food-truck-business/
Released: June 30, 2022. **Description:** With the popularity of food trucks increasing, it could be the ideal time to start your own food truck business. Follow these steps to ensure you get the most out of the experience. **Availability:** Online.

6984 ■ *"How to Choose the Right Food Truck Oven"* in FoodTruckOperator.com (August 4, 2017)
Ed: Robert Simmelink. **Released:** August 04, 2017. **Description:** Space, utility costs and volume are key when operating a food truck. This article discusses how to choose the right oven for your food truck and how you can maximize your investment. **Availability:** Online.

6985 ■ *"How I... Operate a Food Truck on the Streets of Honolulu"* in Pacific Business News (Vol. 21, July 18, 2014, No. 21, pp. 19)
Pub: American City Business Journals, Inc.
Contact: Mike Olivieri, Executive Vice President
Released: Weekly. **Price:** $4, Introductory 4-week offer(Digital only). **Description:** Jennifer Hino, co-owner of The Girls Who Bake Next Door, believes that social media is important as it helps create and reach a wider customer base for her business, which she runs out of a food truck in Honolulu. She also posts photos on the site, which helps reinforce her brand. **Availability:** Print; Online.

6986 ■ *"How Mobile Devices Can Be Used in Food Truck Hiring"* in Mobile-Cuisine.com (September, 23, 2020)
Ed: Richard Myrick. **Released:** September 23, 2020. **Description:** Details how to utilize mobile devices in your recruiting and hiring processes. **Availability:** Online.

6987 ■ *"How to Optimize a Food truck Drive-Thru Service"* in FoodTruckOperator.com (June 15, 2020)
Ed: Richard Traylor. **Released:** June 15, 2020. **Description:** Discusses how to add a drive-thru window to your food truck as well as things to consider including safety protocols, adding online ordering, using touchless payment, and maintaining your drive-thru window. **Availability:** Online.

6988 ■ *How to Start a Food Truck Business in 2020*
Ed: Alex Johnson. **Released:** October 21, 2019. **Price:** $14.97, Paperback; $3.99, E-book. **Description:** An A-Z guide containing the most up-to-date information available on starting a food truck business. **Availability:** E-book; PDF.

Small Business Profiles   Food Truck ■ 7014

6989 ■ *"How To: Advertising Your Food Truck Without Spending a Dime"* in *FoodTruckOperator.com (March 26, 2020)*
Released: March 26, 2020. **Description:** Offers a variety of tips for food truck owners to use to promote and advertise their business without having to spend a lot of money. **Availability:** Online.

6990 ■ *"How To: Creating a Profitable Food Truck Patio Space"* in *FoodTruckOperator.com (September 14, 2020)*
Ed: Richard Traylor. **Released:** September 14, 2020. **Description:** Discusses how to create a patio area for your stationary food truck including tips on patio laws and regulations, design, inclement weather preparation, bug prevention, furniture and decor, and advertising. **Availability:** Online.

6991 ■ *"How To: Getting More Yelp Reviews"* in *FoodTruckOperator.com (October 5, 2020)*
Ed: Richard Traylor. **Released:** October 05, 2020. **Description:** Provides detail on how Yelp can help your food truck business and describes best practices to get more Yelp reviews. **Availability:** Online.

6992 ■ *"How To: Launching a Food Truck Catering Business"* in *FoodTruckOperator.com (October 5, 2020)*
Ed: Richard Traylor. **Released:** October 05, 2020. **Description:** Provides details on what is involved in a food truck-based catering operation and how to get started. **Availability:** Online.

6993 ■ *"How To: Preventing Cross-Contamination in the Food Truck Environment"* in *FoodTruckOperator.com (November 2, 2020)*
Ed: Richard Traylor. **Released:** November 02, 2020. **Description:** One of the biggest challenges food truck operators face is adhering to food safety guidelines and eliminating cross-contamination of harmful bacteria to other foods in your truck. This article discusses cross-contamination, how to prevent foodborne illness, proper food storage practices, food preparation practices, and general food safety. **Availability:** Online.

6994 ■ *"Install a Tasting System to Improve Food Truck Consistency"* in *Mobile-Cuisine.com*
Ed: Richard Myrick. **Description:** Provides information on how to implement a tasting system for your food truck to ensure consistency. **Availability:** Online.

6995 ■ *"Learn New Ideas from Experienced Menu Makers"* in *Nation's Restaurant News (Vol. 45, June 27, 2011, No. 13, pp. 82)*
Pub: Informa USA, Inc.
Contact: Stephen A. Carter, Chief Executive Officer
Ed: Nancy Kruse. **Released:** June 27, 2011. **Description:** National Restaurant Association Restaurant, Hotel-Motel Show featured the Food Truck Spot, a firm committed to all aspects of mobile catering, foodtruck manufacturers, leasers of fully equipped truck and a food-truck franchising group.

6996 ■ *"The Legal Side of Owning a Food Truck"* in *Entrepreneur (2020)*
Ed: Rich Mintzer. **Description:** Details the legal side of owning a food truck including licenses, permits, registrations, and laws. **Availability:** Online.

6997 ■ *"Longmont's Comida Food Truck Now a Brick-and-Mortar Restaurant, Too"* in *Las Cruces Sun-News (February 17, 2012)*
Pub: Tribune News Service
Contact: Jack Barry, Vice President, Operations
E-mail: jbarry@tribpub.com
Ed: Tony Kindelspire. **Description:** Rayme Rosello discusses her plans to open her new Mexican-style restaurant, Comida Cantina, which grew from her pink food truck. Rosello started her food truck in 2010 and has frequented neighborhood parties as well as office parks to build her business. Details of the new restaurant are provided. **Availability:** Print; Online.

6998 ■ *"A Look at 2020 Food Trends"* in *FoodTruckOperator.com (February 20, 2020)*.
Ed: Christine Potts. **Released:** February 20, 2020.

6999 ■ *"Meals on Wheels; Chicago Puts the Brakes on Upwardly Mobile Food Truck Operators"* in *Wall Street Journal (August 7, 2012, pp. A12)*
Pub: Dow Jones & Company Inc.
Contact: Almar Latour, Chief Executive Officer
Description: Details on the City of Chicago's move to regulate mobile food truck operators is presented. **Availability:** Online.

7000 ■ *"Mercyhurst Rolls Out Culinary Cab Food Truck"* in *Erie Times-News (June 19, 2012)*
Ed: Erica Erwin. **Description:** Mercyhurst University's food service company launched a Culinary Cab, or food truck, offering a variety of food choices to the campus community. Details of Parkhurst Dining Services plan for the mobile restaurant are outlined.

7001 ■ *"One of the First Food Trucks in Montreal"* in *America's Intelligence Wire (May 31, 2012)*
Description: Food Trucks in Montreal launched its grand opening June 1, 2012. La Mangeoire offers five types of sandwiches and will serve food at festivals and locations permitted by the city during the summer. **Availability:** Online.

7002 ■ *"PayDragon Brings Mobile Payment App to Food-Truck Vendors"* in *PaymentsSource (April 16, 2012)*
Pub: SourceMedia LLC
Contact: Gemma Postlethwaite, Chief Executive Officer
Ed: David Heun. **Description:** PayDragon is a new App for food truck vendors to collect payments. It is also used by other small merchants. Paperlinks, developed this unit to provide a fast technology that enables consumers to securely order and pay for food with credit and debit cards using email, which elimiantes these steps for the vendors. **Availability:** Print; Online.

7003 ■ *"Pot Watch: Magic Butter Delivers THC-infused Food Truck"* in *Puget Sound Business Journal (Vol. 35, May 30, 2014, No. 6, pp. 10)*
Pub: American City Business Journals, Inc.
Contact: Mike Olivieri, Executive Vice President
Description: Magical Butter is a startup in Seattle, Washington that sells a botanical extractor for infusing herbs into food ingredients like the active ingredient in marijuana known as THC into butter or oil. Career chef, Jeremy Cooper, has perfected the peanut butter and jelly sandwich with THC and sells them from the company's food truck business in Denver, Colorado. **Availability:** Online.

7004 ■ *"Pros and Cons of Joining a Group Purchasing Organization"* in *FoodTruckOperator.com (June 8, 2020)*
Ed: Richard Traylor. **Released:** June 08, 2020. **Description:** Saving on food costs is a prime focus for any food truck operator and one way may be joining a purchasing organization that provides a lower price point and sometimes unique produce and ingredients. But there are some downsides to the move as well. This article provides details on group purchasing organization pros and cons. **Availability:** Online.

7005 ■ *"Protecting Your Food Truck Recipes: Trade Secrets & Patents"* in *FoodTruckOperator.com (June 29, 2020)*
Ed: Richard Traylor. **Released:** June 29, 2020. **Description:** Many food trucks offer unique fare, often from family recipes and special ingredients, which are a valuable asset to the food truck operation. This article discusses how to protect your recipes as well as any food secrets. **Availability:** Online.

7006 ■ *"Radio Producer Launches Food Truck, New Show"* in *Dickinson Press (April 18, 2012)*
Description: Jason Spiess left his radio job to open The Rolling Stove mobile food truck in Dickinson, North Dakota. He will broadcast a new radio show from the food truck called, 'Talkin' Bakken' while serving breakfast and barbecue. He's using a 1973 Indian Winnebago that he bought from Craigslist.com and converted it into a barbecue smoker. **Availability:** Online.

7007 ■ *"Rice & Roll Onigiri Food Truck to Tour Los Angeles Area"* in *Entertainment Close-Up (July 30, 2012)*
Description: Rice & Roll Onigiri food truck service is entering the US market, offering Japanese stuffed rice balls in a variety of flavors and fillings. Asian cuisine is popular in restaurants and markets. The ten locations to visit Rice & Roll in California are listed.

7008 ■ *"Riverview Food Truck Event Draws Huge Crowds"* in *Tampa Tribune (January 25, 2012)*
Ed: Lois Kindle. **Description:** Brandon, Florida's first food truck rally offered sampling dishes to attendees. Over 6,000 people tasted food from 14 trucks serving gourmet and specialty foods. **Availability:** Print; Online.

7009 ■ *Running a Food Truck for Dummies*
Ed: Richard Myrick. **Released:** 2nd edition. **Price:** $17.99, Paperback. **Description:** Helps new food truck owners find their food niche, follow important rules of conducting business, outfitting your moving kitchen, meeting safety and sanitation requirements, and more. **Availability:** Print.

7010 ■ *"Sabra Food Truck Gives Canadians a New Reason to Take a Dip This Summer"* in *America's Intelligence Wire (August 1, 2012)*
Description: Sabra Canada Inc. is taking its food truck on tour of Canada's largest cities, offering people an opportunity to sample their hummus and dips. A schedule of the various stops is provided. **Availability:** Online.

7011 ■ *"Speed, Quality and Health: LA Smoothie Truck Combines Robotics with Self-Order Kiosks"* in *FoodTruckOperator.com (June 22, 2020)*
Ed: Elliot Maras. **Released:** June 22, 2020. **Description:** Profiles LA smoothie kitchen on wheels, Ono Blends, and their innovative method of offering their tasty treats prepared and served with state-of-the-art robotics. **Availability:** Online.

7012 ■ *"State Reverses Food Truck Order"* in *Cape Cod Times (May 15, 2012)*
Ed: Patrick Cassidy. **Description:** Massachusetts Department of Transportation is developing a plan that will allow food truck owners to operate under a new pilot program. Owners must obtain a license to operate through the Transportation Department's legal division. License requirements will be modeled on present license applications and some modifications may be necessary. Insurance issues must be addressed. **Availability:** Online.

7013 ■ *"Street Bistro Brings Food Truck Treats to Bangor"* in *Bangor Daily News (June 26, 2012)*
Ed: Emily Burnham. **Description:** Chef Kim Smith launched her food truck, Street Bistro in Bangor, Maine. Smith took a year off after closing her two restaurants called Unbridled Bistro and Bennett's Market. Smith and her husband purchased a Snap-On truck and redesigned it into a kitchen. Menu items range from French to Tex-Mex to Thai to American. **Availability:** Video; Online.

7014 ■ *"Tap Into Food Truck Trend to Rev Up Sales, Build Buzz"* in *Nation's Restaurant News (Vol. 45, February 7, 2011, No. 3, pp. 18)*
Ed: Brian Sacks. **Description:** Food truck trend is growing, particularly in New York City, Philadelphia, Washington DC, and Los Angeles, California. Man

entrepreneurs are using a mobile food component to market their food before opening a restaurant. **Availability:** Print; Online.

7015 ■ *"Thinking of Expanding Your Food Truck to a Physical Store? Learn the Costs Ahead of Time" in FoodTruckOperator.com (July 27, 2020)*
Ed: Richard Traylor. **Released:** July 27, 2020. **Description:** There are a number of food truck operators advancing their business into a physical brick-and-mortar store. This article provides details on startup costs associated with this endeavor. **Availability:** Online.

7016 ■ *"Understanding Food Truck Insurance Options, Costs" in FoodTruckOperator.com (November 23, 2020)*
Ed: Richard Taylor. **Released:** November 23, 2020. **Description:** If you're looking to start your own food truck, one of the most important business steps is investing in insurance. This article provides insight on how much food truck insurance might cost and which types of insurance you may need to keep your business protected. **Availability:** Online.

7017 ■ *"Use Perceived Value to Determine Your Food Truck Menu Prices" in Mobile-Cuisine.com (October 16, 2017)*
Ed: Richard Myrick. **Released:** October 16, 2017. **Description:** Provides details on using the perceived value of your food truck dishes and setting appropriate menu prices. **Availability:** Online.

7018 ■ *"Why Join a Food Truck Association" in mobile-cuisine.com*
URL(s): mobile-cuisine.com/business/join-a-food-truck-association
Description: Covers the benefits of joining a food truck association, including benefit programs and industry contacts. **Availability:** Online.

SOURCES OF SUPPLY

7019 ■ **Prestige Food Trucks**
Facebook: www.facebook.com/PrestigeFoodTrucks
X (Twitter): x.com/PrestigeFT
Instagram: www.instagram.com/prestigefoodtrucks
YouTube: www.youtube.com/user/PrestigeFoodTrucks
Description: Manufacturer of custom food trucks. **Founded:** 2012. **Publications:** *Prestige Food Trucks Blog*.

STATISTICAL SOURCES

7020 ■ *Food Trucks in the US - Industry Market Research Report*
URL(s): www.marketresearch.com/IBISWorld-v2487/Food-Trucks-Research-32383325/
Price: $1,020. **Description:** Report covering the scope, size, disposition and growth of the U.S. food truck industry, including the key sensitivities and success factors. Also included are five year industry forecasts, growth rates and an analysis of the industry key players and their market shares. **Availability:** Download.

7021 ■ *Global Food Trucks Services Market Growth (Status and Outlook) 2022-2028*
URL(s): www.marketresearch.com/LP-Information-Inc-v4134/Global-Food-Trucks-Services-Growth-32254476/
Price: $3,660. **Description:** Provides deep insight into the global food truck market, providing a comprehensive picture of the global market with quantitative and qualitative data. **Availability:** PDF.

7022 ■ *Street Vendors Industry in the US - Market Research Report*
URL(s): www.ibisworld.com/united-states/market-research-reports/street-vendors-industry/
Price: $925. **Description:** Downloadable report featuring key concepts and industry outlook for street vendors. **Availability:** Download.

Freight Forwarding Service

START-UP INFORMATION

7023 ■ *"No. 407: What I Learned in the Military, and What I Had to Unlearn"* in Inc. (Vol. 36, September 2014, No. 7, pp. 80)
Pub: Mansueto Ventures L.L.C.
Contact: Stephanie Mehta, Chief Executive Officer
Released: September 2014. **Description:** Profile of William Bailey, who served in the U.S. Army as information manager at the U.S. Military Academy at West Point. Bailey discusses his startup firm, Rapier Solutions, a government contractor providing IT, logistics, and social-work expertise. The firm has developed a new survivor outreach system for the U.S. Army. **Availability:** Print; Online.

ASSOCIATIONS AND OTHER ORGANIZATIONS

7024 ■ **National Customs Brokers and Forwarders Association of America, Inc. (NCBFAA)**
1200 18th St. NW, Ste. 901
Washington, DC 20036
Ph: (202)466-0222
Fax: (202)466-0226
Co. E-mail: development@ncbfaa.org
URL: http://www.ncbfaa.org
Contact: Jose D. Gonzalez, President
Facebook: www.facebook.com/NCBFAAFacebook
Linkedin: www.linkedin.com/company/national-customs-brokers-&-forwarders-association-of-america-inc
X (Twitter): x.com/NCBFAA
Instagram: www.instagram.com/ncbfaa
Description: Treasury-licensed customs brokers, FMC-licensed independent ocean freight forwarders, and CNS-registered air cargo agents; associate members in 25 foreign countries. Seeks to maintain high standards of business practice throughout the industry. Monitors legislative and regulatory issues affecting customs brokers and forwarders. **Founded:** 1897. **Publications:** *Membership Directory*; *National Customs Brokers & Forwarders Association of America Membership Directory* (Annual); *NCBFAA Membership Directory: The Who's Who of American Customs Brokers and International Freight Forwarders* (Annual); *National Customs Brokers & Forwarders Association of America--Membership Directory* (Annual). **Educational Activities:** Government Affairs Conference (GAC) (Annual). **Geographic Preference:** National.

7025 ■ **The National Industrial Transportation League (NITL)**
7918 Jones Branch Dr., Ste. 300
McLean, VA 22102
Ph: (703)524-5011
Co. E-mail: info@nitl.org
URL: http://www.nitl.org
Contact: Jennifer Hedrick, Executive Director
Facebook: www.facebook.com/National-Industrial-Transportation-League-143870279404142
Linkedin: www.linkedin.com/company/the-national-industrial-transportation-league
X (Twitter): x.com/NITL
Description: Seeks to promote adequate national and international transportation; encourages the exchange of ideas and information concerning traffic and transportation; and cooperates with regulatory agencies and other transportation companies in developing an understanding of legislation. **Founded:** 1907. **Publications:** *The Notice*, NITL (Weekly); *National Industrial Transportation League--Reference Manual* (Semiannual). **Educational Activities:** TransComp (Annual); National Industrial Transportation League Annual Meeting (Annual). **Geographic Preference:** National.

7026 ■ **Overseas Automotive Council (OAC)**
79 TW Alexander Dr. 4501 Research Commons, Ste. 200
Research Triangle Park, NC 27709
URL: http://www.mema.org/networking-groups/overseas-automotive-council
Contact: Ben Brucato, Contact
E-mail: bbrucato@mema.org
Description: Represents North American automotive aftermarket suppliers globally. Advocates for legislation beneficial to the industry and promotes the interests of members worldwide. **Founded:** 1923. **Publications:** *Overseas Automotive Council--Membership Roster* (Annual). **Geographic Preference:** National.

REFERENCE WORKS

7027 ■ *"13 Things You Need to Know about Freight Forwarding"* in UniversalCargo (December 19, 2017)
URL(s): www.universalcargo.com/13-things-you-need-to-know-about-freight-forwarding/
Ed: John Stuart. **Released:** December 19, 2017. **Description:** Defines freight forwarding and discusses thirteen things shippers should know about the business. **Availability:** Online.

7028 ■ *"66% of Consumers Expect Free Shipping on Every Purchase"* in Small Business Trends (August 10, 2021)
URL(s): smallbiztrends.com/2021/06/consumers-expecting-free-shipping.html
Ed: Gabrielle Pickard-Whitehead. **Released:** August 10, 2021. **Description:** A results from a Consumer Trends Report poll is discussed. Many consumers expect free shipping with their online purchases and their shopping habits are also discussed. **Availability:** Online.

7029 ■ *"Brent Leary on Partnering with Amazon for the Last Mile"* in Small Business Trends (September 20, 2022)
URL(s): smallbiztrends.com/2022/09/amazon-last-mile.html
Ed: Holly Chavez. **Released:** September 20, 2022. **Description:** Brent Leary, managing director at CRM Essentials, discusses the Atlanta Amazon delivery station and how small businesses can partner with Amazon. **Availability:** Online.

7030 ■ *"Central Freight Lines Relocates Irving Terminal"* in Dallas Business Journal (Vol. 35, March 2, 2012, No. 25, pp. 1)
Pub: Baltimore Business Journal
Contact: Rhonda Pringle, President
E-mail: rpringle@bizjournals.com
Description: Waco, Texas-based trucking firm Central Freight Lines Inc. is relocating its operational headquarters to Fort Worth from Irving. The relocation is the result of the changing vision for the old Texas stadium area, along with safety concerns related to highway and light rail construction. **Availability:** Print; Online.

7031 ■ *"The Chart that Organized the 20th Century"* in Harvard Business Review (Vol. 92, September 2014, No. 9, pp. 32)
Pub: Harvard Business Publishing
Contact: Diane Belcher, Managing Director
Price: $6. **Description:** An organizational chart from 1910 depicting the structure of the Southern Pacific and Union Pacific rail systems is presented. **Availability:** Online; PDF.

7032 ■ *"Coal Train Crush Feared"* in Puget Sound Business Journal (Vol. 33, July 6, 2012, No. 11, pp. 1)
Pub: Baltimore Business Journal
Contact: Rhonda Pringle, President
E-mail: rpringle@bizjournals.com
Ed: Steve Wilhelm. **Description:** Coal exports are seen to take up more rail capacity in Washington. The issue was raised in connection with the proposed Gateway Pacific Terminal at Cherry Point. The planned terminal has been opposed by environmental groups. **Availability:** Print; Online.

7033 ■ *"Con-Way Development Back in High Gear"* in Business Journal Portland (Vol. 27, November 5, 2010, No. 36, pp. 1)
Pub: Portland Business Journal
Contact: Andy Giegerich, Managing Editor
E-mail: agiegerich@bizjournals.com
Ed: Wendy Culverwell. **Description:** Trucking firm Con-Way Inc. intends to sell parcels of land from a property comprising 16 blocks and 20 prime acres west of the Pearl District in Portland, Oregon. In 2009, Con-Way abandoned plans to sell the property. As Con-Way reclaims control over design and usage of the property, it also expressed willingness to cooperate with a master developer on a related real estate project. **Availability:** Print; Online.

7034 ■ *"Conscious Capitalism: Liberating the Heroic Spirit of Business"*
Released: January 07, 2014. **Price:** $12.47, e-book; $16.79, paperback. **Description:** Conscious Capitalism companies include Whole Foods Market, South-

west Airlines, Costco, Google, Patagonia, The Container Store, UPS and others. These firms under the four specific tenants to success: higher purpose, stakeholder integration, conscious leadership, and conscious culture and management. These companies are able to create value for all stakeholders, including customers, employees, suppliers, investors, society, and the environment. A new preface by the authors is included. **Availability:** E-book; Print.

7035 ■ *Directory of Freight Forwarders and Custom House Brokers*
Pub: International Wealth Success Inc.
Contact: Tyler G. Hicks, Contact
URL(s): iwealthsuccess.com/product/iws-15-directory-of-freight-forwarders-and-customs-house-brokers
Price: $40, Single issue. **Description:** Contains lists of hundreds firms throughout the U.S. that helps export/import business. Covers several hundred freight forwarders and custom house brokers involved in international trade. **Entries include:** Company or firm name, address, phone. **Arrangement:** Geographical. **Availability:** E-book; PDF.

7036 ■ *"Fast 50: HNM Global Logistics" in Orlando Business Journal (Vol. 30, June 27, 2014, No. 53, pp. 8)*
Pub: American City Business Journals, Inc.
Contact: Mike Olivieri, Executive Vice President
Released: Weekly. **Description:** Tony L. McGee is the CEO of HNM Global Logistics, a full service freight forwarder that reduced its logistic spending by 22 percent in 2013. He believes that America will see a revival in manufacturing coupled with more free trade agreements. **Availability:** Print; Online.

7037 ■ *"Former Tech Execs Want to Tap Building Trend in Austin" in Austin Business Journal (Vol. 31, May 13, 2011, No. 10, pp. A1)*
Pub: Austin Business Journal
Contact: Rachel McGrath, Director
E-mail: rmcgrath@bizjournals.com
Ed: Cody Lyon. **Description:** Falcon Containers moved to a 51-acre site in Far East Austin, Texas and started construction of a 2,500-square-foot headquarters made from eight 40-foot shipping containers. Falcon's CEO Stephen Shang plans to use his headquarters building as a showroom to attract upscale, urban hipsters. Insights on the construction's environmental and social impact are shared. **Availability:** Print; Online.

7038 ■ *"How To Pirate-Proof a Freighter" in Canadian Business (Vol. 85, June 28, 2012, No. 11-12, pp. 20)*
Ed: Sarah Barmak. **Description:** Security experts offer advice on how to protect cargo ships and crew from pirate attacks. Some anti-piracy measures suggested include hiring a well-trained team of armed guards, securing lage coils of razor wire along the sides of the vessel and using the Long Range Acoustic Device to help distinguish pirates. **Availability:** Print; Online.

7039 ■ *"Kinek Offers Secure Prescription Drop-Off For Online Shoppers" in Pittsburgh Post-Gazette (June 14, 2012)*
Description: Canadian firm, Kinek, founded in 2009 in New Brunswick, provides drop-off point locations for online shoppers. Med-Fast Pharmacy in Western Pennsylvania joined the Kinek network to provide prescription pickup. The service can be used for most online purchases, including those made on Amazon or eBay. Some drop off sites charge a fee, others are free. **Availability:** Print; Online.

7040 ■ *"Maersk Targets Forwarders As Digital-First Revolution Spreads in Latin America" in The Load Star (April 11, 2019)*
URL(s): theloadstar.com/maersk-targets-forwarders-as-digital-first-revolution-spreads-in-latin-america/
Ed: Gavin van Marle. **Released:** April 11, 2019. **Description:** Maersk Line is looking to expand in Latin America and it's also been noted that digital-based shipping is starting to gain a foothold in the region. This new technology helps decrease costs for shippers, which every customer wants. **Availability:** Online.

7041 ■ *"No. 156: Divorced, But Still Running the Company Together" in Inc. (Vol. 36, September 2014, No. 7, pp. 78)*
Pub: Mansueto Ventures L.L.C.
Contact: Stephanie Mehta, Chief Executive Officer
Released: September 2014. **Description:** Co-founders, Lacy Starling and Tony Coutsoftides, of Legion Logistics discuss the challenges of running their family-owned business after their divorce. **Availability:** Print; Online.

7042 ■ *"Pegasus Logistics Expanding in Coppell" in Dallas Business Journal (Vol. 35, July 6, 2012, No. 43, pp. 1)*
Pub: Baltimore Business Journal
Contact: Rhonda Pringle, President
E-mail: rpringle@bizjournals.com
Ed: Candace Carlisle. **Description:** Coppell, Texas-based Pegasus Logistic Group has signed a lease with Teachers Insurance and Annuity Association - College Retirement Equities Fund for 255,000-square-foot office and industrial space at 301 Airport Drive. Pegasus plans to consolidate its corporate headquarters with its distribution to keep up with its growth. Details are included. **Availability:** Print; Online.

7043 ■ *"Port Canaveral Plans to Make Big Waves of Business in C. Fla." in Orlando Business Journal (Vol. 30, June 6, 2014, No. 50, pp. 4)*
Pub: American City Business Journals, Inc.
Contact: Mike Olivieri, Executive Vice President
Released: Weekly. **Price:** $8, Introductory 4-week offer(Digital & Print). **Description:** Port Canaveral CEO, John Walsh, has big plans for the expansion of the Port, which include a $500 million cargo and cruise expansion that could net billions of dollars in new economic impact and create more than 15,000 new jobs. Walsh plans to expand cargo capacity, dig deeper harbors for large cruise ships and build a rail transport cargo and, eventually, passengers in and out of the 380-acre Port Canaveral. The Port is the fifth-largest cargo port in Central Florida. **Availability:** Print; Online.

7044 ■ *"Ready for Our Ships to Come In" in Philadelphia Business Journal (Vol. 33, April 11, 2014, No. 9, pp. 4)*
Pub: American City Business Journals, Inc.
Contact: Mike Olivieri, Executive Vice President
Description: Philadelphia Regional Port Authority planned the construction of the Southport Marine Terminal in South Philadelphia at a cost of $300 million to capitalize on changes in the shipping industry. The Tioga Marine Terminal in Port Richmond is also being improved using a mix of public and private money. The growing competition among the East Coast ports is also discussed. **Availability:** Online.

7045 ■ *"RIAC: Green Air Link to Ireland No Flight of Fancy" in Providence Business News (Vol. 29, May 26, 2014, No. 8, pp. 1)*
Pub: American City Business Journals, Inc.
Contact: Mike Olivieri, Executive Vice President
URL(s): pbn.com/riac-green-air-link-to-ireland-no-fligh t-of-fancy97335
Ed: Kelly Anderson. **Description:** Rhode Island Airport Corporation president and CEO, Kelly Fredericks, joined the European trade mission led by the state government to pitch nonstop flights from T.F. Green Airport in Warwick, RI to Ireland. Fredericks is in discussions with Shannon Airport and Ireland West Airport Knock about cargo/freight forwarding and passenger services.

7046 ■ *"Same-Day Delivery's Second Act" in Inc. (Vol. 36, March 2014, No. 2, pp. 87)*
Pub: Mansueto Ventures L.L.C.
Contact: Stephanie Mehta, Chief Executive Officer
Description: New technology is helping electronic commerce to be reliable and profitable while offering same day delivery. Profiles of delivery services competing for retail contracts include Instacart, Zookal, Postmates, to name a few. Statistical data included. **Availability:** Online.

7047 ■ *"Senate Approval Adds Steam to Port of Savannah Project" in Atlanta Business Chronicle (May 30, 2014, pp. 18A)*
Pub: American City Business Journals, Inc.
Contact: Mike Olivieri, Executive Vice President
Description: U.S. Senate approved a budget for the long pending Savannah Harbor dredging project. The Senate approved $652 million for the dredging of the Savannah Harbor from 42 feet to 47 feet to enhance the port's ability to serve the new generation of supersized containerized cargo ships. **Availability:** Print; Online.

7048 ■ *"Sharp Restarts Toner Manufacturing: Production Moved from Japan to Serve China Market" in Memphis Business Journal (Vol. 34, May 11, 2012, No. 4, pp. 1)*
Pub: Baltimore Business Journal
Contact: Rhonda Pringle, President
E-mail: rpringle@bizjournals.com
Ed: Michael Sheffield. **Description:** Sharp Manufacturing Company of America has decided to reopen its ink toner production plant in Memphis, Tennessee because of cheaper material, labor and freight costs. The company's move was also attributed to local economic growth and the government support they received after a 2008 tornado hit the area surrounding the area. **Availability:** Print; Online.

7049 ■ *"StorageByMail Lets Customers Ship Away Their Clutter" in Inc. (Vol. 33, April 2011, No. 3, pp. 92)*
Pub: Inc. Magazine
Ed: Issie Lapowsky. **Description:** StorageByMail allows people to put items into storage by mailing them to the company. The firm charges a monthly fee, customers describe contents of each box, and ship to the Jersey City facility using a preprinted label. StorageByMail pays the $25 shipment charge. **Availability:** Online.

7050 ■ *"Trammell Crow Facility in Houston Is a Late Bloomer" in Houston Business Journal (Vol. 40, August 28, 2009, No. 16, pp. 1A)*
Pub: Houston Business Journal
Contact: Bob Charlet, President
E-mail: bcharlet@bizjournals.com
Ed: Jennifer Dawson. **Released:** Weekly. **Description:** Trammell Crow Company leased half of the 61,000 square foot IAH International Air Cargo Centre II to Tradewinds Cargo Handling. The facility, located at George Bush Intercontinental Airport, is intended to be a destination of fresh flowers and food from Latin America. **Availability:** Print; Online.

7051 ■ *"Union Pacific Railroad Receives Minority Business Exchange Award of Excellence" in News Bites US (July 7, 2012)*
Description: Union Pacific Railroad was given the Award of Excellence at the 2012 Iowa Minority Business Exchange held in Des Moines, Iowa. The award is part of the Wisconsin Iowa and Central Illinois Minority Supplier Development Council. Union Pacific has a history of purchasing from minority- and women-owned businesses. **Availability:** Print; Online.

7052 ■ *"Volvo: Logistics Agreement to Reduce Environmental Impact" in Ecology, Environment & Conservation Business (July 19, 2014, pp. 28)*
Pub: NewsRX LLC.
Contact: Kalani Rosell, Contact
Description: Scandinavian Logistics Partners AB (Scanlog) will sell surplus capacity in rail transport from Belgium to Sweden to the Volvo Group. The partnership benefits both costs and environmental impact. The Volvo group is committed to optimizing transport of their manufactured cars and trucks. **Availability:** Online.

7053 ■ "When One Business Model Isn't Enough: LAN Airlines Flourishes By Running Three Distinctly Different Operations at the Same Time" in Harvard Business Review (Vol. 90, January-February 2012, No.1-2, pp. 132)
Pub: Harvard Business Review Press
Contact: Moderna V. Pfizer, Contact
Ed: Ramon Casadesus-Masanell, Jorge Tarzijan. **Description:** Chilean carrier LAN Airlines successfully blends three distinct business models: a full-service international passenger airline, a no-frills domestic airline, and an air-cargo line. The cargo revenues complement the passenger business to ensure more fully loaded flights.

7054 ■ "Winners & Losers" in Canadian Business (Vol. 85, July 16, 2012, No. 11-12, pp. 22)
Description: Canadian Pacific Railway's 4,800 locomotive engineers and conductors walked out in protest of the proposed work rules and pension cuts. Shareholders rejected a $25-million bonus and retention payout to Astral Media chief executive officer Ian Greenburg. The Dragon spacecraft of Space Exploration Technologies delivered supplies and experiments to the International Space Station. **Availability:** Print.

STATISTICAL SOURCES

7055 ■ RMA Annual Statement Studies
Pub: Risk Management Association
Contact: Nancy Foster, President
Released: Annual. **Description:** Contains composite balance sheets and income statements for more than 360 industries, including the accounting, auditing, and bookkeeping industries. Also contains five years of comparative historical data for discerning trends. Includes 16 commonly used ratios, computed for most of the size groupings for nearly every industry.

TRADE PERIODICALS

7056 ■ Mailing Systems Technology (MAST)
Pub: RB Publishing Co.
URL(s): mailingsystemstechnology.com/flex-1-Home.html
Linkedin: www.linkedin.com/grp/home?gid=2076240
X (Twitter): twitter.com/MailSystemsTech
YouTube: www.youtube.com/channel/UCqW8H40P_daZu1VRWaUUoYA

Ed: Amanda Armendariz. **Released:** 6/year **Description:** Trade magazine covering mailing and office practices. **Availability:** Print; Online.

7057 ■ TransDigest
Pub: Transportation and Logistics Council, Inc.
Contact: Vikki Van Vliet, President
E-mail: vvanvliet@transaudit.com
URL(s): tlcouncil.org/transdigest
Ed: Stephen W. Beyer. **Released:** Monthly **Price:** $150, Nonmembers for per year. **Description:** Provides the shipping community with news relating to the transportation of goods, including agency actions and decisions, legislative developments, and court decisions. Recurring features include recent court decisions; questions & answers; tariff watch; notices of seminars and educational materials. **Availability:** Print; Online; PDF.

TRADE SHOWS AND CONVENTIONS

7058 ■ TransComp
The National Industrial Transportation League (NITL)
7918 Jones Branch Dr., Ste. 300
McLean, VA 22102
Ph: (703)524-5011
Co. E-mail: info@nitl.org
URL: http://www.nitl.org
Contact: Jennifer Hedrick, Executive Director
URL(s): www.nitl.org/trans.htm
Frequency: Annual. **Description:** For transportation service providers. **Audience:** Transportation professionals. **Principal Exhibits:** For transportation service providers. **Telecommunication Services:** gilanshah@nitl.org.

FRANCHISES AND BUSINESS OPPORTUNITIES

7059 ■ eShipping
10812 NW Hwy. 45
Parkville, MO 64152
Ph: (816)505-0198
Free: 866-890-3408
Fax: (816)880-0047
Co. E-mail: esupport@eshipping.biz
URL: http://www.eshipping.biz
Facebook: www.facebook.com/eShipping

Description: Provider of transportation management solutions and logistics services. **Founded:** 2001. **Training:** Provides 3-4 days training and ongoing support.

7060 ■ United Shipping Solutions
6900 S 900 E
Midvale, UT 84047
Description: Firm provides freight shipping services in the United States and internationally. **Founded:** 2002. **Franchised:** 2002. **Training:** Offers 7 days at headquarters, 7 days at franchisees location and ongoing training as needed (recurrent and/or advanced).

COMPUTERIZED DATABASES

7061 ■ MileMaker
Rand McNally and Co.
8770 W Bryn Mawr Ave.
Chicago, IL 60631
Free: 877-446-4863
URL: http://www.randmcnally.com
URL(s): www.milemaker.com
Linkedin: www.linkedin.com/company/milemaker
Availability: Online. **Type:** Directory; Numeric.

LIBRARIES

7062 ■ Airlines for America (A4A) - Library
1275 Pennsylvania Ave. NW, Ste. 1300
Washington, DC 20004
Ph: (202)626-4000
Co. E-mail: mediarelations@airlines.org
URL: http://www.airlines.org
Contact: Nicholas E. Calio, President
Facebook: www.facebook.com/AirlinesForAmerica
Linkedin: www.linkedin.com/company/airlines-for-america
X (Twitter): x.com/airlinesdotorg
Instagram: www.instagram.com/airlinesforamerica
YouTube: www.youtube.com/user/AirlinesForAmerica
Description: Airlines engaged in transporting persons, goods and mail by aircraft between fixed terminals on regular schedules. **Scope:** Airlines. **Founded:** 1936. **Holdings:** Figures not available. **Publications:** Air Transport (Annual); Economic (Annual). **Geographic Preference:** National.

Fund-Raising Consultant

START-UP INFORMATION

7063 ■ *"8 Ways to Make Your Crowdfunding Campaign Stand Out"* in *Entrepreneur (June 2014)*
Pub: Entrepreneur Media Inc.
Contact: Dan Bova, Director
E-mail: dbova@entrepreneur.com
Description: Business experts offer some tips to launch a successful crowdfunding campaign for startups. Entrepreneurs should create a solid plan and reach out to prospective backers before launching their campaigns. Richard Swart of the University of California, suggest hosting launch parties, organizing round table discussions, and establishing a presence at community events to garner support. A series of small campaigns builds brand loyalty over time and provides fans with additional opportunities to support the startup at different stages.

7064 ■ *"AccelerateMSP Picks CEO, Drops Plan for Seed Fund"* in *Business Journal (Vol. 31, March 28, 2014, No. 44, pp. 7)*
Pub: American City Business Journals, Inc.
Contact: Mike Olivieri, Executive Vice President
Released: April 28, 2014. **Description:** Nonprofit AccelerateMSPs chief executive officer, Pam York, reports that the organization is planning to work with early-stage startups. She stated the firm will also help these companies stimulate capital sources. York added that disagreements have led to the nonprofit's plan to establish seed funding. **Availability:** Print; Online.

7065 ■ *"After $4M Funding, ThisClicks CEO Talks What's Next"* in *Business Journal (Vol. 31, January 10, 2014, No. 33, pp. 7)*
Pub: American City Business Journals, Inc.
Contact: Mike Olivieri, Executive Vice President
Released: Weekly. **Price:** $4, Introductory 4-week offer(Digital & Print). **Description:** Chad Halvorson, CEO of technology startup ThisClicks, describes the fundraising process for the Roseville, Minnesota-based company. He discusses the factors driving the startup's growth and the firm's new products. **Availability:** Print; Online.

7066 ■ *"'Entrepreneurial Spirit' Leads Executives to Form New Tower Company"* in *South Florida Business Journal (Vol. 34, February 21, 2014, No. 31, pp. 6)*
Pub: American City Business Journals, Inc.
Contact: Mike Olivieri, Executive Vice President
Released: Weekly. **Price:** $8, Introductory 4-week offer(Digital & Print). **Description:** Phoenix Tower International is a new company in Boca Raton, Florida formed by the former executives of Global Tower Partners, a multibillion-dollar company that was sold in October 2013. Phoenix is self-funded and will focused on owning, leasing, and managing cellular phone service towers. **Availability:** Print; Online.

7067 ■ *"Made@Mayo: Mayo Professor Doubles As Founder of Text Tech Company"* in *Business Journal (Vol. 32, June 6, 2014, No. 2, pp. 10)*
Pub: American City Business Journals, Inc.
Contact: Mike Olivieri, Executive Vice President
Description: Rochester, Minnesota-based Mayo Clinic Ventures has managed the licensing of Mayo Clinic technologies and invests in startups. Mayo Clinic Ventures has a $100 million growth fund for investing in startups and two smaller funds worth about $500,000 combined. Insights on the stories of Mayo researchers leading startups are also provided. **Availability:** Online.

7068 ■ *"New Angel Group Aims To Keep Cash Local"* in *Puget Sound Business Journal (Vol. 35, September 26, 2014, No. 23, pp. 5)*
Pub: American City Business Journals, Inc.
Contact: Mike Olivieri, Executive Vice President
Description: Seattle Angel Fund head and angel investor, Susan Preston, shares her views about the need for another angel fund in Seattle, Washington. Preston says there are not many actual funds in the city, while there are so many young, aspiring and great companies in the area. She also believes Washington will lose companies when funding comes from out of state investors. **Availability:** Online.

7069 ■ *"Oliver Russell Acquiring Social Good Network"* in *Idaho Business Review (August 29, 2014)*
Pub: BridgeTower Media
Contact: Adam Reinebach, President
Description: Oliver Russell, owner of a Boise advertising firm, is acquiring the assets of startup Social Good Network, an online fundraising firm that was turned down for additional funding beyond its seed funding. Details of the deal and future plans are discussed.

7070 ■ *"Places for People Who Want to Make Things"* in *Philadelphia Business Journal (Vol. 28, May 4, 2012, No. 23, pp. 1)*
Pub: Baltimore Business Journal
Contact: Rhonda Pringle, President
E-mail: rpringle@bizjournals.com
Released: Weekly. **Description:** Entrepreneurs in Philadelphia, Pennsylvania have been opening businesses and nonprofits for people who have the urge to work in wood, sculpt or even make robots. Their sudden proliferation has provided people who like making things with their hands but can't afford the tools or don't have the space in which to do it where they live. **Availability:** Print; Online.

7071 ■ *"Take the Money and Run"* in *Entrepreneur (September 2014)*
Released: February 08, 2011. **Description:** Startup founders are encouraged to ask for more than they think they will need when raising capital. The tendency to think small when it comes to capital or staging rounds to preserve ownership is a mistake for founders. Securing a large amount of capital in the first round could help save the time and costs associated with raising the next round of funds. Venture capitalists welcome founders who ask for more money because they prefer to go bigger on a single bet and their focus is always on valuation. **Availability:** Online.

ASSOCIATIONS AND OTHER ORGANIZATIONS

7072 ■ **Association of Fund-Raising Distributors and Suppliers (AFRDS)**
5858 Lakehurst Dr.
Orlando, FL 32819
Ph: (407)821-8841
Fax: (407)854-9992
Co. E-mail: afrds@bmg1.com
URL: http://afrds.org
Contact: Jim Messina, President
Facebook: www.facebook.com/AFRDS
Description: Distributors, suppliers, and manufacturers of products sold to fundraising organizations. Seeks to enhance the image of the product fundraising industry. Works to establish a code of ethics; conducts public relations activities and seminars. **Founded:** 1992. **Geographic Preference:** National.

7073 ■ **Association of Fundraising Professionals (AFP)**
4300 Wilson Blvd. Ste. 300
Arlington, VA 22203-4167
Ph: (703)684-0410
Free: 800-666-3863
Fax: (703)684-1950
Co. E-mail: info@afpdc.org
URL: http://afpglobal.org
Contact: Kevin J. Foyle, Chairman
Facebook: www.facebook.com/AFPFan
Linkedin: www.linkedin.com/company/afpglobal
X (Twitter): x.com/afpihq
Description: Fundraising executives who work for non-profit and philanthropic organizations. Purposes are: to foster the development and growth of professional fundraising executives committed to the philanthropic process; to establish professional ethical standards and to require its members to adhere to those standards; to provide guidance and assistance to philanthropic institutions and agencies with fundraising programs; to offer continuing professional education and career enhancement services for philanthropic fundraising professionals. Maintains speakers' bureau. **Founded:** 1960. **Publications:** *Advancing Philanthropy: Journal of the National Society of Fund Raising Executives* (Quarterly); *NSFRE Directory* (Annual); *NSFRE-News*. **Educational Activities:** AFP ICONs (Annual). **Awards:** AFP Award for Outstanding Corporation (Annual); AFP Award for Outstanding Foundation (Annual); AFP Award for Outstanding Philanthropist (Annual); AFP Award for Outstanding Volunteer Fundraiser (Annual). **Geographic Preference:** Multinational.

7074 ■ Association of Fundraising Professionals - Edmonton and Area Chapter
PO Box 4355
 Spruce Grove, AB, Canada T7X 3B5
Ph: (780)224-4024
Co. E-mail: info@afpedmonton.ca
URL: http://www.afpedmonton.ca
Contact: Kelly Hoskins, President
E-mail: president@afpedmonton.ca
Facebook: www.facebook.com/AFPEdmonton
X (Twitter): x.com/AFPEdmonton
Instagram: www.instagram.com/afpedmonton

Description: Advances philanthropy through advocacy, research, education and certification programs within the Edmonton area and beyond. Organizes workshops and keynote presentations. Fosters high ethical standards and principles for its members. Represents the interests of the profession locally, provincially and nationally. **Founded:** 1996. **Geographic Preference:** Local.

7075 ■ Association of Fundraising Professionals Southeastern Wisconsin Chapter
PO Box 511400
 Milwaukee, WI 53203-0242
Ph: (414)399-0281
Co. E-mail: chapteradmin@afpsewi.org
URL: http://www.afpsewi.org
Contact: Dawn Groshek, President
Facebook: www.facebook.com/Association-of-Fundraising-Professionals-Southeastern-Wisconsin-Chapter-108137401537214
Linkedin: www.linkedin.com/company/association-of-fundraising-professionals-of-southeastern-wisconsin-afp-sewi-

Founded: 1973. **Geographic Preference:** Local.

7076 ■ Association of Professional Researchers for Advancement (APRA)
330 N Wabash Ave., Ste. 2000
 Chicago, IL 60611
Ph: (312)321-5196
Fax: (312)673-6966
Co. E-mail: info@aprahome.org
URL: http://www.aprahome.org
Contact: Melissa Bank Stepno, President
E-mail: melissa.stepno@blackbaud.com
Facebook: www.facebook.com/ApraInternational
Linkedin: www.linkedin.com/company/aprahq
X (Twitter): x.com/APRA_HQ
YouTube: www.youtube.com/channel/UCQXSWujD60TzqV1vk2IpZGQ/featured

Description: Facilitates education and dissemination of information about prospect research; encourages professional development and cooperative relationships among members. Prospect research is aimed at securing gifts, grants, and charitable donations for nonprofit organizations. **Founded:** 1998. **Publications:** *APRA Member Directory* (Annual); *Connections* (Quarterly). **Educational Activities:** APRA Annual Conference (Annual). **Awards:** Apra Margaret Fuhry Award (Periodic); APRA Visionary Award (Periodic); APRA Distinguished Service Award (Annual); The APRA Professional of the Year Award (Annual). **Geographic Preference:** National.

7077 ■ The Giving Institute (GI)
1660 International Dr., Ste. 600
 McLean, VA 22102
Ph: (312)981-6794
Co. E-mail: info@givinginstitute.org
URL: http://www.givinginstitute.org
Contact: Paul Koreen, Vice Chairman of the Board
Linkedin: www.linkedin.com/company/giving-institute

Description: Represents fund-raising counseling firms engaged in consulting on the management and planning of campaigns for hospitals, universities, religious groups, community funds, arts organizations, social service groups and other nonprofit institutions. Conducts research in philanthropy. **Founded:** 1935. **Publications:** *Giving Institute Membership Directory*. **Geographic Preference:** National.

7078 ■ National Association of Charitable Gift Planners (NACGP)
1075 Broad Ripple Ave. No.306
 Indianapolis, IN 46220-2034
Ph: (317)269-6274
Fax: (317)269-6268
Co. E-mail: info@charitablegiftplanners.org
URL: http://charitablegiftplanners.org
Contact: Michael Kenyon, President
Facebook: www.facebook.com/CGPnational
Linkedin: www.linkedin.com/company/national-association-of-charitable-gift-planners
X (Twitter): x.com/CGPnational

Description: Professional association of individuals from the fundraising, accounting, estate planning, insurance, and related fields. Members specialize in developing charitable gifts through bequests, trusts, annuities, life insurance, and real property. Provides education and networking opportunities. Conducts research. **Founded:** 1988. **Publications:** *The Journal of Gift Planning* (Quarterly); *Proceedings of the National Conference on Planned Giving* (Annual). **Educational Activities:** National Conference on Planned Giving (Annual). **Geographic Preference:** National.

REFERENCE WORKS

7079 ■ "ACE Commits $300,000 to Support Environmental Conservation Initiatives and Green Business Entrepreneurs" in Insurance Business Weekly (March 2, 2012, pp. 13)
Pub: NewsRX LLC.
Contact: Kalani Rosell, Contact

Description: ACE Charitable Foundation has commited to a two-year, $300,000 funding of The Conservation Fund for new initiatives that protect key watersheds, expand wildlife migration corridors and investment in local green economies in the United States. **Availability:** Online.

7080 ■ "American Indian College Fund to Support Environmental Science and Sustainability Programs, Fellowships, and Internships" in Ecology, Environment & Conservation Business (April 12, 2014, pp. 21)
Pub: NewsRX LLC.
Contact: Kalani Rosell, Contact

Description: Tribal colleges serve communities facing environmental issues, such as water quality, energy development, depletion of natural resources, and agricultural management. The American Indian College Fund has created a new Environmental Science and Sustainability Project of $1.35 million grant money to support tribal colleges and universities in select states that underwrite environmental science and sustainability programs of studies. Details of the project are included. **Availability:** Online.

7081 ■ "Artscape Looks for Last Big Donations" in Baltimore Business Journal (Vol. 32, July 11, 2014, No. 10, pp. 4)
Pub: American City Business Journals, Inc.
Contact: Mike Olivieri, Executive Vice President

Released: Weekly. **Price:** $4, introductory 4-week offer(Digital only). **Description:** Kathy Hornig, festivals director for Baltimore's Office of Promotion and the Arts, discusses last-minute efforts to raise the final $100,000 in donations for Artscape from mobile marketers and festival goers. The event, to be held July 18-23, 2014 in Baltimore, will focus on dance and movement. **Availability:** Print; Online.

7082 ■ "Azaya Therapeutics Taking Big Steps" in San Antonio Business Journal (Vol. 28, March 28, 2014, No. 7, pp. 8)
Pub: American City Business Journals, Inc.
Contact: Mike Olivieri, Executive Vice President

Released: Weekly. **Price:** $4, Introductory 4-week offer(Digital only). **Description:** Azaya Therapeutics believes that its $5 million funding round will be completed in 2014. The convertible-note bridge funding was initiated in October 2013. The company, which plans to pursue regulatory approval for its cancer medications, is also focusing on expanding the business. **Availability:** Print; Online.

7083 ■ "Back In the Black, Maryland Zoo Upgrades" in Baltimore Business Journal (Vol. 32, July 25, 2014, No. 12, pp. 4)
Pub: American City Business Journals, Inc.
Contact: Mike Olivieri, Executive Vice President

Released: Weekly. **Price:** $4, introductory 4-week offer(Digital only). **Description:** Maryland Zoo has stabilized its finances after several years of budgetary problems that nearly caused the zoo to lose its accreditation from the Association of Zoos and Aquariums. President Donald P. Hutchinson reveals the zoo has increased the number of private and corporate donors and is carrying out several upgrades, including new penguin and flamingo exhibits. **Availability:** Print; Online.

7084 ■ "Baltimore Businesses Put Cash Behind Bernstein" in Baltimore Business Journal (Vol. 28, August 20, 2010, No. 15, pp. 1)
Pub: Baltimore Business Journal
Contact: Rhonda Pringle, President
E-mail: rpringle@bizjournals.com

Ed: Scott Dance. **Description:** Baltimore, Maryland-based businesses have invested $40,000 to support lawyer Gregg L. Bernstein in the 2010 State Attorney election. The election campaign is being fueled by fear of a crime surge. Many businesses have been dealing with crimes such as muggings, shootings, and car break-ins. **Availability:** Print.

7085 ■ "Baltimore Grand Prix Week Schedule Filling Up With Galas, Nonprofit Fundraisers" in Baltimore Business Journal (Vol. 29, July 22, 2011, No. 11, pp. 1)
Pub: Boston Business Journal
Contact: Carolyn M. Jones, President
E-mail: cmjones@bizjournals.com

Ed: Alexander Jackson. **Description:** Baltimore, Maryland-based businesses and nonprofit groups have been planning their own events to coincide with the Baltimore Grand Prix during the Labor Day weekend. They also plan to partner with others in hopes of drumming up new business, raising money or to peddle their brands.

7086 ■ "Bonefish Grill Debuts New Cocktail to Benefit Conservation Foundation" in Ecology, Environment & Conservation Business (May 17, 2014, pp. 5)
Pub: NewsRX LLC.
Contact: Kalani Rosell, Contact

Description: Bonefish Grill has introduced the Ocean Trust Tropic Heat Martini to support the Ocean Trust, an ocean conservation foundation. The new drink contains house-made infused pineapple Absolut vodka, with fresh mango and a thin slice of jalapeno and served at their restaurants nationwide. **Availability:** Online.

7087 ■ "Bringing Charities More Bang for Their Buck" in Crain's Chicago Business (Vol. 34, May 23, 2011, No. 21, pp. 31)
Pub: Crain Communications Inc.
Contact: Barry Asin, President

Ed: Lisa Bertagnoli. **Description:** Marcy-Newberry Association connects charities with manufacturers in order to use excess items such as clothing, janitorial and office supplies. **Availability:** Online.

7088 ■ "Businesses Fret Over Crime Wave" in Philadelphia Business Journal (Vol. 31, February 10, 2012, No. 52, pp. 1)
Pub: Baltimore Business Journal
Contact: Rhonda Pringle, President
E-mail: rpringle@bizjournals.com

Description: Philadelphia, Pennsylvania-based businesses have expressed concern over the recent crime wave in the city. Businesses are raising $3 million to fund the Philadelphia Police Department's mounted patrol unit to ramp up security. **Availability:** Print; Online.

7089 ■ "Campaign Launches to Educate Hispanics on Tax Preparation" in Economics Week (February 3, 2012, pp. 35)
Pub: NewsRX LLC.
Contact: Kalani Rosell, Contact
Description: Hispanic Access Foundation has partnered with H&R Block to offer a program to help Hispanics file their taxes while avoiding fraud and misinformation. The campaign is called, 'Preparate Para Un Futuro Mejor' (Prepare Yourself for a Better Future) and will help fill the void for tax preparation education for Hispanics. Availability: Online.

7090 ■ "Canadian Pet Charities Won't Go Hungry" in Pet Product News (Vol. 66, September 2012, No. 9, pp. 15)
Description: Premium dog and cat food manufacturer Petcurean will donate more than 42,000 pounds of Go! and Now Fresh dry foods to 25 animal rescue organizations across Canada. The donation is deemed invaluable to Petcurean's network of dog and cat foster activities. Availability: Online.

7091 ■ "The Change Foundation Awards Northumberland Community Partnership $3 Million Project To Improve Seniors' Healthcare Transitions and Use Patient Input to Drive Redesign" in CNW Group (June 5, 2012)
Pub: Comtex News Network Inc.
Contact: Kan Devnani, President
Description: The Change Foundation has awarded the Northumberland Community Partnership with its $3 million project PATH-Partners Advancing Transitions in Healthcare for Ontario patients. The program brings together 12 health and social care organizations with patients and caregivers to identify healthcare transition issues in Central East Ontario, Canada. It will work with service providers to redesign care and to improve experiences. Availability: Online.

7092 ■ "Clash of the Titans" in San Francisco Business Times (Vol. 28, February 7, 2014, No. 29, pp. 4)
Pub: American City Business Journals, Inc.
Contact: Mike Olivieri, Executive Vice President
Released: September 01, 2017. Description: University of California, San Francisco (UCSF) Medical Center and Stanford Hospital and Clinics have been competing for dominance for San Francisco Bay Area's health care. Both medical centers are competing to affiliate with more doctors, gain more patients, and accomplish more fundraising. Ways the UCSF and Stanford plan to pursue their expansion and integration are also discussed. Availability: Print; Online.

7093 ■ "Consignment Shop Blends Business With a Giving Spirit" in Gazette (January 17, 2012)
Ed: Bill Radford. Description: Mountain Equipment Recyclers, located in Colorado Springs, Colorado, sells outdoor gear. Mike Mazzola, owner, has expanded his consignment shop to include a nonprofit entity to raise money for our veterans and their families. So far, he has exceeded his goal by giving five percent of sales of consigned gear and 50 percent of donated gear to three nonprofit organizations: AspenPoint, which helps veterans and their families; The Home Front Cares, supporting families of deployed soliders; and LifeQuest Transitions, which helps soldiers and veterans relearn life skills through cognitive exercises and adventure sports. The funds are split equally to the three agencies. Availability: Online.

7094 ■ "Cornerstone Seeks Investors for Hedge Fund" in Baltimore Business Journal (Vol. 32, June 20, 2014, No. 7, pp. 10)
Pub: American City Business Journals, Inc.
Contact: Mike Olivieri, Executive Vice President
Description: Cornerstone Advisory LLP is looking for investors to create a hedge fund that ties returns to various indices, real estate or commodity prices. Cornerstone hopes to raise between $30 million to $50 million and are planning a fall launch for the fund. They have hired New York law firm Thompson Hine LLP to draft the subscription agreement and NebraskaEs Gimini Fund Services LLC to run as third party administrator. Availability: Print; Online.

7095 ■ "Corporate Responsibility" in Professional Services Close-Up (July 2, 2010)
Description: List of firms awarded the inaugural Best Corporate Citizens in Government Contracting by the Corporate Responsibility Magazine is presented. The list is based on the methodology of the Magazine's Best Corporate Citizen's List, with 324 data points of publicly-available information in seven categories which include: environment, climate change, human rights, philanthropy, employee relations, financial performance, and governance. Availability: Online.

7096 ■ "Courier 250 Companies Hope to Rebound From 2009" in Business Courier (Vol. 27, July 16, 2010, No. 11, pp. 1)
Pub: Business Courier
Ed: Dan Monk, Jon Newberry. Description: Private companies that are featured in the Courier 250 publication have lost almost $4 billion in revenue, while combined sales dropped by 11 percent to 32 billion in 2009. Courier 250 is a guide to public companies, large nonprofits, private firms, and other related entities in Ohio's Cincinnati region. Availability: Online.

7097 ■ "Crowd Control" in Washington Business Journal (Vol. 33, August 15, 2014, No. 17, pp. 8)
Pub: American City Business Journals, Inc.
Contact: Mike Olivieri, Executive Vice President
Description: Washington DC's Department of Insurance, Securities and Banking issued a proposal that would create the legal framework by which companies can raise cash through crowdfunding. The DC proposal would allow District-based businesses to crowdfund from District-based backers. The advantages and drawbacks to the plan are examined. Availability: Online.

7098 ■ "Crowdfund Your Way to Millions: LeVar Burton's Kickstarter Campaign Raises $1 Million In Less Than 12 Hours" in Black Enterprise (Vol. 45, July-August 2014, No. 1, pp. 61)
Pub: Earl G. Graves Ltd.
Contact: Earl Graves, Jr., President
Description: Kickstarted is a viable option for funding a small business. Actor, LeVar Burton launched a Kickstarter campaign to help revive the learning show Reading Rainbow and raised $1 million in less than 12 hours. Information about six crowdfunding sites are listed, including: Kickstarter, Angellist, Rockethub, Crowdtilt, Indiegogo, and Rallyme.

7099 ■ "Crowdfunding Comes to Science's Aid as Budgets, Grants Face Squeeze" in Economic Times (July 10, 2012)
Pub: Bennett, Coleman & Company Ltd.
Ed: Rituparna Chattterjee. Description: Brian L. Fisher, entomologist studying ants in Madagascar raised $10,000 in 45 days from Petridish, a crowdfunding platform for scientists. Crowdfunding is where a group of investors fund projects. Availability: Online.

7100 ■ "CrowdFunding Made Simple Conference at University of Utah Ignites Ecosystem of Entrepreneurs and Investors" in Economics Week (June 29, 2012)
Description: The first national conference on crowdfunding was held at the University of Utah Guest House and Conference Center May 31 through June 1, 2012. The event, CrowdFunding Made Simple, gathered entrepreneurs, business owners, professional service providers, investors, government officials and students to provide understanding and potential of crowdfunding, including information on the Jumpstart Our Business Startups (JOBS) Act. Availability: Print; Online.

7101 ■ "Ditch the Pet Store! MindJolt SGN and The Humane Society of the United States Unleash Fluff Friends Rescue" in Benzinga.com (January 4, 2012)
Pub: Benzinga.com
Contact: Jason Raznick, Founder
Ed: Aaron Wise. Description: The Humane Society of the United States has partnered with MindJolt SGN, a multiplatform game developer and distributor, to release a mobile game called Fluff Friends Rescue. The game introduces players to the real-world challenges of rescuing pets by nursing animals back to health while running their own animal shelter.

7102 ■ "Early-Stage Biomed Firm Seeks Funds for First Device" in San Antonio Business Journal (Vol. 28, March 7, 2014, No. 4, pp. 6)
Pub: American City Business Journals, Inc.
Contact: Mike Olivieri, Executive Vice President
Released: Weekly. Price: $4, Introductory 4-week offer(Digital & Print). Description: Leto Solutions, an early stage medical device company, wants to raise $2 million in seed funding for the Aquilonix Prosthesis Cooling System. The thermoelectric temperature management is used to cool the prosthesis. A working prototype of the Aquilonix system has already been developed by the company. Availability: Print; Online.

7103 ■ "Economic Impact of the Arts: $125 Million" in Memphis Business Journal (Vol. 34, June 22, 2012, No. 10, pp. 1)
Pub: Baltimore Business Journal
Contact: Rhonda Pringle, President
E-mail: rpringle@bizjournals.com
Description: The culture industry in Memphis, Tennessee accounted for more than $125 million in combined spending from culturally-focused organizations and attendees in 2010 according to a study by the Americans for the Arts nonprofit group. Results indicate that the spending accounts form almost 4,000 jobs, over $100 million in household income and over $15 million in government revenue. Availability: Print; Online.

7104 ■ "The Emerging Capital Market for Nonprofits" in Harvard Business Review (Vol. 88, October 2010, No. 10, pp. 110)
Pub: Harvard Business Publishing
Contact: Diane Belcher, Managing Director
Ed: Robert S. Kaplan, Allen S. Grossman. Price: $8.95, PDF. Description: Demonstration of how nonprofits can use intermediaries to grow their organizational structures, giving them improved scale and impact is offered. Some intermediaries play a mutual-fund role and conduct due diligence, while others act as venture capital funds and implement strategy. Availability: Online; PDF.

7105 ■ "Endowments for Colleges Hit Hard In '09" in Milwaukee Business Journal (Vol. 27, February 12, 2010, No. 20, pp. A1)
Pub: The Business Journal
Contact: Heather Ladage, President
E-mail: hladage@bizjournals.com
Ed: Corrinne Hess. Description: Southeast Wisconsin college endowments declined by as much as 35 percent in 2009 due to the economic downturn. A list of 2009 endowments to colleges in southeast Wisconsin and their percent change from 2008 is presented. Availability: Print; Online.

7106 ■ "Equity 'Crowdfunding' Platform, RelayFund, Launched by Michigan Investor Group" in Economics Week (July 20, 2012)
Description: RelayFund was launched by a group of Michigan venture capitalists, entrepreneurs, and investment bankers to link small investors with startup firms under the new JOBS (Jumpstart Our Business Startups) Act. Crowdfunding is money raised for charities, projects or pre-selling products or services and allows online micro investments for startup companies.

7107 ■ "Extortion: How Politicians Extract Your Money, Buy Votes, and Line Their Own Pockets"
Pub: Mariner Books
Released: October 22, 2013. **Price:** $12.79, Paperback. **Description:** Politicians and lawmakers have developed a new set of legislative tactics designed to extort wealthy industries and donors into huge contributions. This money is then funneled into the pockets of their friends and family members. Schweizer reveals the secret 'fees' each political party charges politicians for top committee assignments; how fourteen members of Congress received hundreds of thousands of dollars using a self-loan loophole; how PAC money is used to bankroll their lavish lifestyles; and more. The first time these unethical issues have been reported to the public. **Availability:** E-book; Print.

7108 ■ "Falcons' Blank Kicking Off 'Westside Works' Job Training Program" in Atlanta Business Chronicle (May 30, 2014, pp. 6A)
Pub: American City Business Journals, Inc.
Contact: Mike Olivieri, Executive Vice President
Description: Arthur Blank, owner of the Atlanta Falcons, is kicking off 'Westside Works', an initiative to build a world-class football/soccer stadium in Atlanta and transform the adjacent communities. Westside Works, a partnership between The Arthur M. Blank Family Foundation, the Construction Education Foundation of Georgia, and Integrity CDC will provide construction jobs for at least 100 men and women from the Westside neighborhoods in the next 12 months. The program will also provide job training, skills assessment, adult education programs, interview preparedness, and job placement. **Availability:** Print; Online.

7109 ■ "Fight Ensues Over Irreplaceable Princess Diana Gowns" in Tampa Bay Business Journal (Vol. 30, January 15, 2010, No. 4, pp. 1)
Pub: Tampa Bay Business Journal
Contact: Ian Anderson, President
E-mail: ianderson@bizjournals.com
Ed: Janet Leiser. **Description:** People's Princess Charitable Foundation Inc. founder Maureen Rorech Dunkel has sought Chapter 11 bankruptcy protection before a state court decides on the fate of the five of 13 Princess Diana Gowns. Dunkel and the nonprofit were sued by Patricia Sullivan of HRH Venture LLC who claimed they defaulted on $1.5 million in loans. **Availability:** Print; Online.

7110 ■ "FIS-Metavante Deal Paying Off for Many" in Business Journal-Milwaukee (Vol. 28, December 17, 2010, No. 11, pp. A1)
Pub: The Business Journal
Contact: Heather Ladage, President
E-mail: hladage@bizjournals.com
Ed: Rich Kirchen. **Description:** Jacksonville, Florida-based Fidelity National Information Services Inc., also known as FIS, has remained committed to Milwaukee, Wisconsin more than a year after purchasing Metavante Technologies Inc. FIS has transferred several operations into Metropolitan Milwaukee and has continued its contribution to charitable organizations in the area. **Availability:** Print; Online.

7111 ■ "Funders Fuel Explosion of Biotech Activity" in Puget Sound Business Journal (Vol. 35, July 11, 2014, No. 12, pp. 3A)
Pub: American City Business Journals, Inc.
Contact: Mike Olivieri, Executive Vice President
Description: Washington's life sciences industry is experiencing problems due to a lack of support from state lawmakers, but the industry is receiving capital through initial public offerings, partnerships and venture equity. Joel Marcus of Alexandria Real Estate Equities claims that capital flows are at their highest levels since the dot-com bubble. **Availability:** Online.

7112 ■ "The Funding Is Out There!: Access the Cash You Need to Impact Your Business"
Pub: Morgan James Publishing L.L.C.
Contact: Amber Parrott, Director
Released: June 01, 2014. **Price:** $15.95, paperback; $9.99, e-book. **Description:** Thirty in-depth case studies are presented to show what actual business owners have done to acquire funding for their companies. Most small and medium sized businesses are unaware of the financing sources available to them. **Availability:** E-book; Print.

7113 ■ "GIV Mobile Announces New Partnership with American Forests, the Oldest National Nonprofit Conservation Organization in the Country" in Ecology, Environment & Conservation Business (January 25, 2014, pp. 34)
Pub: PR Newswire Association LLC.
Description: GIV Mobile has partnered with American Forests to restore and protect urban and rural forests in the nation. GIV is the first consumer conscious wireless network and operates on the 4G network of T-Mobile USA cellular service. **Availability:** Online.

7114 ■ "Giving In a New Age" in Denver Business Journal (Vol. 65, January 17, 2014, No. 36, pp. A4)
Pub: American City Business Journals, Inc.
Contact: Mike Olivieri, Executive Vice President
Description: Urban Peak's 921 Project was an online funding event that aims to get 921 people to participate in a group photo to raise awareness about youth homelessness in Denver, Colorado. The project, which was heavily promoted in social media, is symbolic of the sweeping changes in philanthropy in recent years. **Availability:** Online.

7115 ■ Giving Institute Membership Directory
Pub: The Giving Institute
Contact: Paul Koreen, Vice Chairman of the Board
URL(s): www.givinginstitute.org/news/673578/3-Strategic-Planning-Steps-for-Private-Family-Foundations.htm
Description: Covers member fund-raising consulting firms. Includes fair Practice Code; section on selection of counsel; brief historical introduction of AAFRC. **Entries include:** Company name, address, phone, fax, geographical area served, types of clients, description of services. **Arrangement:** Alphabetical. **Availability:** Print.

7116 ■ "Grant Program Boosting Biomedical Research" in Providence Business News (Vol. 28, February 24, 2014, No. 47, pp. 3)
Pub: American City Business Journals, Inc.
Contact: Mike Olivieri, Executive Vice President
Released: February 22, 2014. **Description:** The role played by the Institutional Development Award Network of Biomedical Research Excellence (INBRE) is boosting biomedical research in Rhode Island. According to researcher, Niall G. Howlett, procuring startup funding through INBRE led to receiving other grants and working with graduate students who have the potential to become part of the biomedical workforce. **Availability:** Print; Online.

7117 ■ "Hailey Is Getting an Indoor Ice Rink" in Idaho Business Review (August 27, 2014)
Pub: BridgeTower Media
Contact: Adam Reinebach, President
Description: Hailey Ice, a local nonprofit which built and operates outdoor rinks in the area, is donating $4 million towards the indoor ice skating rink. the money comes from various funds and foundations and collectively believe it to be a good investment in the community.

7118 ■ "Health Science Center's Capital Campaign Will Boost Local Research" in San Antonio Business Journal (Vol. 28, March 14, 2014, No. 5, pp. 8)
Pub: American City Business Journals, Inc.
Contact: Mike Olivieri, Executive Vice President
Description: The University of Texas Health Science Center at San Antonio's Campaign for the Future of fundraising project has been completed. The Health Science Center is expected to use the money to support research at the South Texas Medical Center. The capital campaign will allow the Health Science Center to become one of the most prominent universities in the U.S. **Availability:** Print; Online.

7119 ■ "Healthy Start for Medical Kiosks; Lions Kick in $20K" in Crain's Detroit Business" (Vol. 28, June 11, 2012, No. 24, pp. 18)
Pub: Crain Communications Inc.
Contact: Barry Asin, President
Ed: Jay Greene. **Description:** Detroit Lions Charities has given Henry Ford Health System's school-based and community health program money to purchase nine interactive health kiosks. These kiosks will be provided by Medical Imagineering LLC, a spinoff of Henry Ford's Innovation Institute and installed in elementary and middle schools in Detroit. **Availability:** Print; Online.

7120 ■ "How I Became a Serial Entrepreneur" in Baltimore Business Journal (Vol. 31, April 18, 2014, No. 51, pp. 26)
Pub: American City Business Journals, Inc.
Contact: Mike Olivieri, Executive Vice President
Description: Dr. Lisa Beth Ferstenberg, a physician by training, teaches a course at the Maryland Center for Entrepreneurship in Columbia to help CEOs attract prospective investors. Dr. Ferstenberg is also the chief medical officer at Sequella Inc. She reflects on the kind of personality required to become a successful entrepreneur and the mistakes entrepreneurs make in raising capital funding. **Availability:** Print; Online.

7121 ■ "How One Company Joins Corporate Public Relations and Community Engagement" in Denver Business Journal (Vol. 65, January 17, 2014, No. 36, pp. A6)
Pub: American City Business Journals, Inc.
Contact: Mike Olivieri, Executive Vice President
Description: Denver, Colorado-based Barefoot PR was formed by Cori Streetman and Sarah Hogan in 2010 to change corporate views on philanthropy. The partners made a commitment to make community investment the driving force of business. Insights on the next-generation of community relations consultants are also given. **Availability:** Online.

7122 ■ "How Young Professionals Can Position Themselves for Board Membership: 4 Quick Tips to Get You Started" in Black Enterprise (Vol. 45, July-August 2014, No. 1, pp. 46)
Pub: Earl G. Graves Ltd.
Contact: Earl Graves, Jr., President
Description: Four tips to help young professionals secure a position on a company's board focus on: starting with nonprofits, focus on key areas of interest, continue to growth through networking and training programs, and to gain global experience.

7123 ■ "Incubators Experiencing a Baby Boom" in Philadelphia Business Journal (Vol. 31, March 23, 2012, No. 6, pp. 1)
Pub: Baltimore Business Journal
Contact: Rhonda Pringle, President
E-mail: rpringle@bizjournals.com
Description: At least seven business incubators have opened in Philadelphia, Pennsylvania since November 2011. Five of the seven incubators are nonprofit organizations. **Availability:** Print; Online.

7124 ■ "Invest Like Harvard" in Barron's (Vol. 92, September 15, 2012, No. 38, pp. 32)
Pub: Dow Jones & Company Inc.
Contact: Almar Latour, Chief Executive Officer
Ed: Andrew Bary. **Description:** Asset management firms are offering endowment-style investment services that allow investors to invest in funds in the same way as foundations and endowments. High-Vista Strategies with $3.6 billion in assets under management, has produced a total return of 43.5 percent after fees from October 2005 to June 2012 using this strategy. **Availability:** Online.

7125 ■ "Katie's Cupcakes to Celebrate One-Year Anniversary" in Bellingham Business Journal (Vol. March 2010, pp. 3)
Pub: Sound Publishing Inc.
Contact: Josh O'Connor, President

Ed: Lance Henderson. **Description:** Katie Swanson, owner of Katie's Cupcakes, celebrated her firm's one-year anniversary with a fundraiser for the Whatcom Humane Society by offering free specialty cupcakes and other special events to the public. The specialty cupcakes will feature either a paw or bone and will be available throughout the month of March.

7126 ■ "Kineta Helps Grow Start Group of 5 Biotech Partners" in Puget Sound Business Journal (Vol. 35, June 13, 2014, No. 8, pp. 6)
Pub: American City Business Journals, Inc.
Contact: Mike Olivieri, Executive Vice President

Description: Kineta Inc is seeking new funding through its KPI Therapeutics. Kineta offers investors a return on their investments after three to five years. KPI Therapeutics is a new collaborative initiative between drug development firms and private investors. KPI's vision is to create a better way to develop early- and mid-stage therapies for patients and will act as an investment group and a strategic research hub. **Availability:** Print; Online.

7127 ■ "Largest North Texas Fundraising Events" in Dallas Business Journal (Vol. 37, March 7, 2014, No. 26, pp. 6)
Pub: American City Business Journals, Inc.
Contact: Mike Olivieri, Executive Vice President

Released: Weekly. **Price:** $25, Print. **Description:** Rankings of the largest North Texas fundraising events are presented. Rankings were based on the revenue from events held in 2013. **Availability:** Print; Online.

7128 ■ "A Lifetime of Giving: Food Bank CEO Fights Hunger One Mouth At a Time" in Black Enterprise (Vol. 41, November 2010, No. 4, pp. 86)
Pub: Earl G. Graves Ltd.
Contact: Earl Graves, Jr., President

Ed: Tamara E. Holmes. **Description:** Profile of Valerie Traore, CEO of Food Bank of South Jersey. Traore stresses the importance of volunteerism that she learned from her grandparents. Hunger relief became her passion when she served as a temp office worker for the Maryland Food Bank in Baltimore. She earned her Bachelor's of Science in management and has dedicated herself to a career in nonprofit service. **Availability:** Online.

7129 ■ "Many in Tech Look to Push More Community Involvement, But Not in Traditional Ways" in Boston Business Journal (Vol. 31, August 5, 2011, No. 28, pp. 1)
Pub: Boston Business Journal
Contact: Carolyn M. Jones, President
E-mail: cmjones@bizjournals.com

Ed: Mary Moore. **Released:** Weekly. **Price:** $4, Introductory 4-Week Offer(Digital Only). **Description:** Entrepreneurs and venture capitalists in Boston have launched Technology Underwriting Greater Good, the tech industry's answer to the criticism that they are not charitable. The foundation finances nonprofits that aid young people through entrepreneurship, education and life experience. Other tech firms in Boston doing charitable works are discussed. **Availability:** Print; Online.

7130 ■ "Maryland Nonprofits May Lose Minority Business Enterprise Status" in Baltimore Business Journal (Vol. 29, September 2, 2011, No. 17, pp. 1)
Pub: Boston Business Journal
Contact: Carolyn M. Jones, President
E-mail: cmjones@bizjournals.com

Ed: Scott Dance. **Description:** A business group has been pushing to bar nonprofits from Maryland's Minority Business program. Nonprofits have been found to take a large portion of state contracts intended for women- and minority-owned businesses. The group is also crafting proposed legislation to remove nonprofits from the program. **Availability:** Online.

7131 ■ "Mason Group Seeks $20M for 'Gray' Fund" in Business Courier Serving Cincinnati-Northern Kentucky (Vol. 29, June 15, 2012, No. 7, pp. 1)
Description: Nonprofit Link-age is seeking to raise $20 millin to fund a new revenue source for its members. The nonprofit is a senior care organization that buys food, medical supplies and medicine for senior members. **Availability:** Print; Online.

7132 ■ "Md.'s Boring Bonds Gain Pizzazz as Investors Flock to Debt Issues" in Baltimore Business Journal (Vol. 28, June 11, 2010, No. 5, pp. 1)
Pub: Baltimore Business Journal
Contact: Rhonda Pringle, President
E-mail: rpringle@bizjournals.com

Ed: Gary Haber. **Description:** Companies and nonprofit organizations have increased the pace of bond offerings in order to take advantage of the bonds' appeal among willing investors. Companies mostly issued corporate bonds to replace existing debt at lower interest rates and save them money from interest payments.

7133 ■ "Meals on Wheels Filling 'Blizzard Bags'" in Tulsa World (November 5, 2011)
Description: Cathy Perlingiere, director of volunteer services for Meals on Wheels of Metro Tulsa, Oklahoma reports that they do not deliver meals when the Tulsa Public Schools close because of weather so they try to prepare 'blizzard bags' with nonperishable food items to cover about three meals for when drivers cannot deliver. **Availability:** Print; Online.

7134 ■ "Medical-Device Firm Targets a Heart-Valve Market in Flux" in Philadelphia Business Journal (Vol. 33, May 9, 2014, No. 13, pp. 9)
Pub: American City Business Journals, Inc.
Contact: Mike Olivieri, Executive Vice President

Released: May 09, 2014. **Price:** $4, Introductory 4-week offer(Digital only). **Description:** Montgomery County-based medical products company, Thubrikar Aortic Valve Inc., is developing the Optimum TAV, a next-generation transcatheter aortic valve implantation (TAVI) device to treat heart patients with aortic stenosis. The company is raising funds to start clinical testing for the Optimum TAV in 2014, aiming to provide a more durable and efficient transcatheter aortic valve for lower-risk patients. **Availability:** Print; Online.

7135 ■ "Mercy Parent Nets Almost $1B in 2011" in Sacramento Business Journal (Vol. 28, September 30, 2011, No. 31, pp. 1)
Pub: Sacramento Business Journal
Contact: Stephanie Fretwell, Director
E-mail: sfretwell@blzjournals.com

Ed: Kathy Robertson. **Price:** $4, Print & Digital introductory 4-week offer; $4, Digital introductory 4-week offer. **Description:** Catholic Healthcare West has reported almost $1 billion in profits for 2010. The company has reported a profit margin of 8.7 percent. It also absorbed more than $1 billion in costs from charity care and government programs. **Availability:** Print; Online.

7136 ■ "Most Charitable Zip Codes" in Dallas Business Journal (Vol. 37, March 7, 2014, No. 26, pp. 8)
Pub: American City Business Journals, Inc.
Contact: Mike Olivieri, Executive Vice President

Released: Weekly. **Description:** Rankings of the most charitable zip codes in North Texas are presented. Rankings were based on cash contributions to charities in North Texas. **Availability:** Print; Online.

7137 ■ "A New Alliance For Global Change" in Harvard Business Review (Vol. 88, September 2010, No. 9, pp. 56)
Pub: Harvard Business Publishing
Contact: Diane Belcher, Managing Director

Ed: Bill Drayton, Valeria Budinich. **Price:** $8.95, PDF. **Description:** Collaboration between social organizations and for-profit firms through the development of hybrid value chains to target complex global issues is promoted. While social organizations offer links to communities and consumers, firms provide financing and scale expertise. **Availability:** Online; PDF.

7138 ■ "A New Approach to Funding Social Enterprises: Unbundling Societal Benefits and Financial Returns Can Dramatically Increase Investment" in Harvard Business Review (Vol. 90, January-February 2012, No.1-2, pp. 118)
Pub: Harvard Business Review Press
Contact: Moderna V. Pfizer, Contact

Ed: Bruce Kogut, Antony Bugg-Levine, Nalin Kulatilaka. **Price:** $8.95, PDF and hardcover black and white. **Description:** Identification of a range of financing arrangements that can maximize benefits delivered by social organizations. These include equity, quasi-equity debt, charitable giving, convertible debt, and securitized debt. The claims on assets and types of return for each are defined. **Availability:** Print; PDF; Online.

7139 ■ "The New Face of Aging: Chasing the Secret to Stopping the Clock" in San Francisco Business Times (Vol. 28, January 31, 2014, No. 28, pp. 4)
Pub: American City Business Journals, Inc.
Contact: Mike Olivieri, Executive Vice President

Released: Weekly. **Price:** $4, Introductory 4-week offer(Digital & Print). **Description:** San Francisco, California-based Calico has built a small team of star scientists to join research for finding the secret to stop human aging, with financial backing from Google. However, the Ellison Medical Foundation has stopped making new grants for aging research. The preventive approach of the aging research is also discussed. **Availability:** Print; Online.

7140 ■ "New Stem Cell Research Awareness Org Launched in Austin" in Austin Business Journal (Vol. 31, June 3, 2011, No. 13, pp. 1)
Pub: Austin Business Journal
Contact: Rachel McGrath, Director
E-mail: rmcgrath@bizjournals.com

Ed: Sandra Zaragoza. **Description:** MedRebels Foundation was launched in February 2011 with the goal of providing millions of dollars for research funding, education and advocacy for adult stem cell-focused medicine. The foundation, whose major contributor is SpineSmith LP, is a collaboration of other adult stem cell-related companies and nonprofit partners. It hopes to raise $200,000 by the end of 2011. **Availability:** Print; Online.

7141 ■ "One Laptop Per Child Weighs Going For-Profit" in Boston Business Journal (Vol. 31, May 20, 2011, No. 17, pp. 1)
Pub: Boston Business Journal
Contact: Carolyn M. Jones, President
E-mail: cmjones@bizjournals.com

Ed: Mary Moore. **Released:** Weekly. **Price:** $4, Print. **Description:** Nonprofit organization One Laptop Per Child is thinking of shifting into a for-profit structure in order to raise as much as $10 million in capital to achieve its goal of distributing more XO laptops to poor children worldwide. The organization has distributed 2 million computers since 2008 with Uruguay, Peru and Rwanda as its biggest markets. **Availability:** Print; Online.

7142 ■ "Outlook In Other Industries" in Crain's Detroit Business (Vol. 30, January 6, 2014, No. 1, pp. 3)
Pub: Crain Communications Inc.
Contact: Barry Asin, President

Released: January 6, 2014. **Description:** Outlook for industries in the Detroit area are listed, including small business growth, restaurants, defense contracts, nonprofits, transportation, auto suppliers, healthcare, bankruptcy, and government. **Availability:** Print; PDF; Online.

7143 ■ *"Pet Food Bank 'Shares the Love'"* in *Pet Product News* (Vol. 64, December 2010, No. 12, pp. 6)
Description: Winston-Salem, North Carolina-based nonprofit Share the Love Pet Food Bank has donated 60,000 pounds of pet food since its establishment in 2009. It has been linking pet food manufacturers and rescue groups to supply unsold pet food to needy animals. The nonprofit intends to reach out to more animal welfare groups by building more warehouses. **Availability:** Online.

7144 ■ *"Planet Dog Foundation Awards $25,000 In Grants"* in *Pet Product News* (Vol. 66, September 2012, No. 9, pp. 13)
Description: Portland, Maine-based Planet Dog Foundation has selected eight dog servic organizations to share $25,000 in grants. Aside from financing assitance dog, therapy dogs, and canine search and rescue programs across the U.S., the foundation supports programs that help children and adults. **Availability:** Online.

7145 ■ *"Points of Light Sells MissionFish to eBay"* in *Non-Profit Times* (Vol. 25, May 15, 2011, No. 7, pp. May 15, 2011)
Description: eBay purchased MissionFish, a subsidiary of Points of Light Institute for $4.5 million. MissionFish allows eBay sellers to give proceeds from sales to their favorite nonprofit organization and helps nonprofits raise funds by selling on eBay. **Availability:** Print; Online.

7146 ■ *"The Pre-Tail Revolution"* in *Canadian Business* (Vol. 87, October 2014, No. 10, pp. 10)
Description: A number of products that succeeded in security support from crowdfunding platforms, Kickstarter and Indiegogo, and those that failed are presented. Included are the do-it-yourself computer kit Kano, Bluetooth speakers Edge.sound, three-dimensional printer The Micro, Coolest Cooler the insect control device BugASalt, hexacopter Hexo+, and the Ubuntu Edge. **Availability:** Print; Online.

7147 ■ *"Preceptis Gets Gopher Angels' Biggest-Ever Investment"* in *Business Journal* (Vol. 31, January 31, 2014, No. 36, pp. 8)
Pub: American City Business Journals, Inc.
Contact: Mike Olivieri, Executive Vice President
Description: Preceptis Medical Inc. has secured $1.2 million in funding from Gopher Angels. The funding will help Preceptis to finance ongoing clinical studies and general operating expenses. The company develops surgical tools for pediatric ear-tube surgery. **Availability:** Print; Online.

7148 ■ *"Preserving a Nonprofit's Mission: YWCA to Absorb Key Programs as the Boston Center for Community and Justice Fades"* in *Boston Business Journal* (Vol. 31, June 17, 2011, No. 21, pp. 3)
Pub: Boston Business Journal
Contact: Carolyn M. Jones, President
E-mail: cmjones@bizjournals.com
Ed: Mary Moore. **Description:** Young Women's Christian Association Boston (YWCA) agreed to absorb the LeadBoston social issues and youth programs operated by the Boston Center for Community Justice. The BCCJ is scheduled to close after failing to stabilize its finances. **Availability:** Print; Online.

7149 ■ *"The Profits of Good Works"* in *Barron's* (Vol. 92, September 17, 2012, No. 38, pp. 14)
Description: The nonprofit organization B Lab is responsible for certifying companies as socially conscious and environmentally friendly. B Lab examines the impact of companies on workers, communities, and the environment as well as their internal governance. **Availability:** Online.

7150 ■ *Profits for Non-Profits: Running a Successful Non-Profit Gift Shop*
Ed: Nancy Kirk. **Released:** 4th edition. **Price:** $19.99, paperback. **Description:** Guide for managing a non-profit gift shop in a hospital, zoo, museum or any other non-profit entity. **Availability:** Print; Online.

7151 ■ *"PSCPets.com Gives Back to Support Military Working Dogs"* in *Pet Product News* (Vol. 66, September 2012, No. 9, pp. 17)
Description: Menomonie, Wisconsin-based online pet health and wellness products supplier PSCPets.com donated on $26.99 bottle of PSCPets Joint Support Military Working Dogs for every $5 donation for the company's Rescue Outreach Program. Each month, PSCPets.com uses the program to benefit animal welfare causes. How the effort to assist military working dogs started is discussed. **Availability:** Online.

7152 ■ *"Put the Good, the Bad and the Ugly on the Table"* in *South Florida Business Journal* (Vol. 35, September 19, 2014, No. 8, pp. 13)
Pub: American City Business Journals, Inc.
Contact: Mike Olivieri, Executive Vice President
Description: United Way of Broward County chief executive, Kathleen Cannon, says the creation of a macropractice for social work is the most rewarding part of her job. She also said teaching people how to give back is the most challenging part of her role.

7153 ■ *"Red Cross CEO Mark Beddingfield: This Work Is In His Blood"* in *Birmingham Business Journal* (Vol. 31, March 7, 2014, No. 10, pp. 11)
Pub: American City Business Journals, Inc.
Contact: Mike Olivieri, Executive Vice President
Description: American Red Cross Alabama Region CEO, Mark Beddingfield, says fundraising is the biggest challenge facing nonprofits in view of the weak economy. He believes nonprofits should always be ready to be able to serve clients. Beddingfield added that the organization continues to look for committed volunteers who are willing to serve people. **Availability:** Print; Online.

7154 ■ *"Research, Treatment to Expand"* in *Philadelphia Business Journal* (Vol. 28, June 22, 2012, No. 19, pp. 1)
Pub: Baltimore Business Journal
Contact: Rhonda Pringle, President
E-mail: rpringle@bizjournals.com
Description: Fox Chase Cancer Center and Temple University Health System have been planning several projects once their merger is completed. Their plans include the construction of a unit for cancer patients on the third floor of the Founder's Building at Jeanes Hospital and a granting mechanism to fund research collaborations. **Availability:** Print; Online.

7155 ■ *"Robai Aims to Commercialize Robot Arm for Manufacturers; Eyes Series A Funding"* in *Boston Business Journal* (Vol. 34, July 4, 2014, No. 22, pp. 5)
Pub: American City Business Journals, Inc.
Contact: Mike Olivieri, Executive Vice President
Released: June 25, 2014. **Description:** Robai aims to raise $5 million in funding to help commercialize a lightweight and easy to use robot arm, called Cyton. The robot arm operates much like a human arm with multiple ranges of motion. It weighs under five pounds, can be programmed in 15 minutes, has the ability to reach around obstacles, and is meant to do repetitive, mundane tasks for contract manufacturing companies. **Availability:** Print; Online.

7156 ■ *"Shelters Vie for $500,000 In Adoption Contest"* in *Pet Product News* (Vol. 66, September 2012, No. 9, pp. 19)
Description: Fifty shelters across the US will vie for more than $500,000 in grants through the American Society for the Prevention of Cruelty to Animals' Rachael Ray $100K Challenge. The shelters will aspire to adopt out at least 300 more cats and dogs from August through October 2012 than they did during the period one year ago. **Availability:** Online.

7157 ■ *"Shop Happy: Harvesting Happiness Announces Grassroots Crowdfunding Site for HH4Heroes"* in *Marketwired* (July 2, 2012)
Pub: Comtex News Network Inc.
Contact: Kan Devnani, President
Description: Shop Happy online store has created a fundraising aspect to their customers' shopping experience. Shoppers can assist in helping to heal post combat veterans suffering from PTSD, TBI, MST, andMSA who have served as combat warriors in Operations Iraqi and Enduring Freedom. Lisa Cypers Kamen, founder of Harvesting Happiness believes this program will help both veterans and customers to empower themselves and our veterans in a positive way (HH4Heroes.org).

7158 ■ *"Slater Progress Stalled"* in *Providence Business News* (Vol. 28, March 10, 2014, No. 49, pp. 1)
Pub: American City Business Journals, Inc.
Contact: Mike Olivieri, Executive Vice President
URL(s): pbn.com/slater-progress-stalled95603
Description: Slater Technology Fund has received only $1.9 million of the $9 million in expected federal funds. However, the venture capital firm decided to invest in some promising technology companies in Providence, Rhode Island. Slater senior managing director, Richard Horan, reveals that uncertainties with respect to grants have delayed private fundraising. **Availability:** Online.

7159 ■ *"SPOILED! Children's Consignment Boutique Now Collecting Donations To Support Baby2Baby & Help Children In Need"* in *Benzinga.com* (July 30, 2012)
Pub: Benzinga.com
Contact: Jason Raznick, Founder
Ed: Aaron Wise. **Description:** CeCe Hendriks opened her high-end children's consignment store in response to wanting to provide quality clothing for her son. Because children outgrow their clothing so fast, she decided a consignment shop is what all mom's needed. Hendriks offers a 50 percent consignment to donors and if the item isn't sold in 90 days, the consignee can choos to have the item returned or donate it to Baby2Baby. Hendriks also gives 10 percent of proceeds from sales to Baby2Baby, a nonprofit that works with homeles and domestic violence shelters. **Availability:** Online.

7160 ■ *"Steel Yard Eyes Funding Balance"* in *Providence Business News* (Vol. 29, May 26, 2014, No. 8, pp. 1)
Pub: American City Business Journals, Inc.
Contact: Mike Olivieri, Executive Vice President
Released: May 24, 2014. **Description:** Steel Yard is looking for new revenue to sustain its expansion as a nonprofit, metalwork training organization based in Providence, Rhode Island. The organization is applying for money from a proposed state funding pool of $590,000 for the first time to be used in 2014-2015 fiscal year. **Availability:** Print; Online.

7161 ■ *"Strategy Migration In a Changing Climate"* in *Harvard Business Review* (Vol. 92, May 2014, No. 5, pp. 42)
Pub: Harvard Business Publishing
Contact: Diane Belcher, Managing Director
Price: $6. **Description:** The CEO of World Wildlife Fund discusses the importance of ensuring reliable source supplies and mitigating reputational and financial risk in promoting corporate sustainability. Forging alliances to achieve goals is also key. **Availability:** Online; PDF.

7162 ■ *"Taking Off"* in *Puget Sound Business Journal* (Vol. 34, January 31, 2014, No. 42, pp. 4)
Pub: American City Business Journals, Inc.
Contact: Mike Olivieri, Executive Vice President
Description: Washington State is at the forefront of the U.S. space flight industry, as the federal government shrinks its role and entrepreneurs are filling the gap. The region is becoming a leader in the space sector because of its high-tech aerospace skills, software intellectuals, and investors willing to fund these enterprises. **Availability:** Online.

7163 ■ *"Ticketmaster Unveils Pink Tickets to Support Breast Cancer Awareness Month"* in *Travel & Leisure Close-Up* (October 8, 2012)
Description: National Football League is helping to raise awareness for the National Breast Cancer Awareness Month by issuing all tickets purchased

through Ticketmaster be pink. A portion of every NFL ticket sold on Ticketmaster and on NFL Ticket Exchange will go toward the American Cancer Society's fight against breast cancer. **Availability:** Print; Online.

7164 ■ *"Tim Tebow Foundation to Hold Pink 'Cleats for a Cure' Auction" in Travel & Leisure Close-Up (October 20, 2011)*
Pub: Close-Up Media Inc.
Contact: Caroline S. Moore, President
E-mail: cms@closeupmedia.com
Description: Tim Tebow Foundation partnered with XV Enterprises to hold the 'Cleats for a Cure' auction on eBay. Tebow is auctioning off a pair of pink cleans he wore during the Denver Broncos vs. Tennessee Titans game October 3, 2010. All funds will go toward finding a cure for breast cancer. **Availability:** Print; Online.

7165 ■ *"Top 21 Fundraising Consultants for Nonprofit Success" in Donorsearch (November 14, 2016)*
URL(s): www.donorsearch.net/top-fundraising-consultants/
Released: November 14, 2016. **Description:** Donorsearch reviews the top fundraising consultants, while listing each one's expertise, services, and contact info. **Availability:** Online.

7166 ■ *"Transfusion" in Puget Sound Business Journal (Vol. 33, August 31, 2012, No. 19, pp. 1)*
Released: July 12, 2019. **Description:** Seattle, Washington-based nonprofit biotechnology companies have been hiring people with fundraising and scientific skills. The development is part of efforts to find new funding resources. **Availability:** Online.

7167 ■ *"United Natural Foods Establishes Charitable Foundation to Support Healthy, Sustainable and Organic Food Systems" in United Natural Foods, Inc. (May 14, 2012)*
Pub: The Financial Times Ltd.
Contact: John Ridding, Chief Executive Officer
E-mail: john.ridding@ft.com
Description: United Natural Foods Inc. (UNFI) has established a foundation committed to supporting healthy, sustainable and organic food systems. UNFI distributes natural, organic and specialty foods and related products. **Availability:** PDF; Online.

7168 ■ *"Venture: Nonprofit Aims to Spur New Companies" in South Florida Business Journal (Vol. 34, April 18, 2014, No. 39, pp. 8)*
Pub: American City Business Journals, Inc.
Contact: Mike Olivieri, Executive Vice President
Released: Weekly. **Price:** $8, Introductory 4-week offer(Digital & Print). **Description:** The Scripps Research Institute has created the Scripps Advance group with an aim to turn early-stage research from its scientists in Jupiter, Florida and La Jolla, California into companies and to obtain venture capital funding to support clinical trials. Johnson and Johnson Innovation has become its first collaborator. The terms of the collaboration are also presented. **Availability:** Print; Online.

7169 ■ *"Veterans Train to Use Military Skills In Civilian Workforce" in South Florida Business Journal (Vol. 34, April 18, 2014, No. 39, pp. 10)*
Pub: American City Business Journals, Inc.
Contact: Mike Olivieri, Executive Vice President
Released: Weekly. **Price:** $8, Introductory 4-week offer(Digital & Print). **Description:** United Way of Broward County has launched the Mission United program that offers a one-stop shop of information and resources to meet the needs of military veterans. Mission United aims to reduce the jobless rate among veterans by creating two programs to help veterans and connect them with potential employers who are hiring. Details of the job training program is explored. **Availability:** Print; Online.

7170 ■ *"The Walmart Foundation and Leading Nonprofits Launch the MyFreeTaxes Program, Offering Eligible Taxpayers Free Tax Preparation in 2012" in Economics Week (February 10, 2012, pp. 274)*
Pub: PR Newswire Association LLC.
Description: United Way Worldwide, One Economy, and the National Disability Institute's Real Economic Impact Tour received funding in the amount of $4.35 million from Walmart Foundation to provide free tax filing services to eligible U.S. citizens. Earned Income Tax Credit (EITC), SNAP, and WIC eligibility education are also included in the program. The program will not only file income taxes for eligible individuals families, it will also educate them about rights and options. **Availability:** Online.

7171 ■ *"What Is Crowdfunding?" in Business News Daily (February 28, 2023)*
URL(s): www.businessnewsdaily.com/4134-what-is-crowdfunding.html
Ed: Simone Johnson. **Released:** February 28, 2023. **Description:** Defines and discusses crowdfunding in a small business context. **Availability:** Online.

7172 ■ *"What's That Business? Part of Savers Thrift Store Proceeds Go To Charity" in Duluth News-Tribune (February 27, 2012)*
Ed: Candace Renalls. **Description:** Savers Inc., a thrift store that sells housewares, furniture, clothing and collectibles allows customers to pick the charity it would like part of the store's proceeds to be given. The Duluth Savers Store has partnered with the Disabled American Veterans of Minnesota. Details of the stores, their customers and practices are highlighted. **Availability:** Online.

TRADE PERIODICALS

7173 ■ *The Chronicle of Philanthropy*
Pub: The Chronicle of Philanthropy
Contact: Stacy Palmer, Chief Executive Officer
URL(s): www.philanthropy.com/issue/current
Facebook: www.facebook.com/ChronicleOfPhilanthropy
Linkedin: www.linkedin.com/company/the-chronicle-of-philanthropy
X (Twitter): x.com/Philanthropy
Instagram: www.instagram.com/chronicleofphilanthropy
YouTube: www.youtube.com/channel/UCk0hYi2US2LASzODBika_6w
Pinterest: www.pinterest.com/cophilanthropy
Ed: Stacy Palmer. **Released:** Monthly **Price:** $8, for basic digital access month; $9, for all-access digital month; $10, for all-access print month. **Description:** Magazine covering fundraising, philanthropy, and non-profit organizations. Includes information on tax rulings, new grants, and statistics, reports on grant makers, and profiles of foundations. **Availability:** Print; Online.

7174 ■ *The Nonprofit Times*
Pub: NPT Publishing Group Inc.
URL(s): thenonprofittimes.com/about
Facebook: www.facebook.com/thenonprofittimes
X (Twitter): x.com/nonprofittimes
Released: Bimonthly **Price:** $59, for digital 1 year Canadian; $59, for digital only 1 year; $79, for digital 2 year; $79, for online only 2 year Canadian; $89, for print + online 1 year; $122, for print + online 2 year. **Description:** Trade journal serving nonprofit organizations. **Availability:** Print; Online.

VIDEO/AUDIO MEDIA

7175 ■ *Side Hustle to Small Business: Connecting Businesses with the Grants They Need*
URL(s): www.hiscox.com/side-hustle-to-small-business/danita-doleman-podcast-season-3
Ed: Sanjay Parekh. **Released:** July 25, 2023. **Description:** Podcast discusses grants for small businesses and how to identify the right ones for your business.

TRADE SHOWS AND CONVENTIONS

7176 ■ **AFP ICONs**
StratCom
URL(s): afpicon.com
Frequency: Annual. **Audience:** Fundraising professionals. **Telecommunication Services:** frp@maritz.com.

CONSULTANTS

7177 ■ **Ashland Group L.P.**
1560 W Bby Area Blvd. No. 350
Friendswood, TX 77546
Ph: (281)484-1700
Co. E-mail: info@ashlandgroup.com
URL: http://ashlandgroup.com
Contact: Dwayne Humphrey, Vice President, Business Development
Description: Government and political affairs agency that specializes in government relations, advocacy communications, media relations, campaign management and government contract lobbying. Offers creative and innovative tax issues. **Scope:** Government and political affairs agency that specializes in government relations, advocacy communications, media relations, campaign management and government contract lobbying. Offers creative and innovative tax issues. **Publications:** "State Tax Guide," Jan, 2009; "State Tax Guide," Jan, 2007.

7178 ■ **Essex & Drake Fund Raising Counsel**
PO Box 24231
San Jose, CA 95134
Ph: (408)601-0244
Co. E-mail: info@essexdrake.com
URL: http://www.essexdrake.com
Contact: Chelsey Souza, President
Facebook: www.facebook.com/essexdrake
Linkedin: www.linkedin.com/company/essex-&-drake-fund-raising-counsel
Description: Firm provides fundraising and marketing services to assist non-profits and public benefit organizations and specializes in board development including governance issues, organizes fundraising campaigns including feasibility studies, major gift campaigns, and strategy development, they also offer training in board excellence and in all areas of fundraising. **Scope:** Firm provides fundraising and marketing services to assist non-profits and public benefit organizations and specializes in board development including governance issues, organizes fundraising campaigns including feasibility studies, major gift campaigns, and strategy development, they also offer training in board excellence and in all areas of fundraising. **Founded:** 1977. **Publications:** "Fundraising for Nonprofits," Harper Collins. **Training:** Preparing for and Executing a Capital Campaign, San Francisco, Apr, 2013; Moves Management in Fundraising Campaigns, San Francisco, Mar, 2013; Major Gifts Solicitations, San Francisco, Mar, 2013; Managing a Successful Annual Campaign, San Francisco, Feb, 2013; Capital Campaigns that Really Work, 2012; Launching and Sustaining a Planned Giving Program in a Small Development Department, May, 2009; Web 2.0 for Nonprofits, San Francisco, Mar, 2009; Building and Sustaining a Board Driven Major Gifts Program, San Francisco; Marketing Your Organization for Fundraising Success; Strategies for a Successful Capital Campaign; Achieving Successful Online Fundraising; Identifying and Building Relationships with Major Donors; Best Practices in Managing a Capital, Endowment or Combination Campaign.

7179 ■ **Jeffrey Lant Associates, Inc. (JLA)**
50 Follen St., No. 507
Cambridge, MA 02138
Ph: (617)547-6372
Co. E-mail: drlant@drjeffreylant.com
URL: http://www.drjeffreylant.com
Description: Publishes technical assistance books for nonprofit organizations, consultants, independent professionals and small and home-based businesses.

Offers audio cassettes, workshops and consultation services. Also publish twice the monthly Worlgram newsletter. Reaches market through commission representatives, direct mail, telephone sales and the Internet. Accept unsolicited manuscripts. **Founded:** 1997. **Publications:** "E-mail El Dorado," JLA Publications, 1998; "Web Wealth: How to Turn the World Wide Web Into a Cash Hose for Your Business. Whatever You're Selling," 1997; "Multi-Level Money," JLA Publications, 1994; "No More Cold Calls," JLA Publications, 1997; "Cash Copy"; "How to make at least $100000 a year"; "E-Money". **Training:** Business and personal development, including Establishing and Operating Your Successful Consulting Business; Successfully Promoting Your Small Business and Professional Practice; Succeeding in Your Mail Order Business; Successfully Raising Money for Your Nonprofit Organization from Foundations, Corporations and Individuals; Money Making Marketing: Finding the People Who Need What You're Selling and Making Sure They Buy It; Getting Corporations, Foundations, and Individuals to Give You the Money Your Nonprofit Organization Needs.

7180 ■ Stevens, Reed, Curcio and Potholm Media
201 N Union St., Ste. 200
Alexandria, VA 22314
Ph: (703)683-8326
Co. E-mail: srcpmedia@srcpmedia.com
URL: http://srcpmedia.com
Contact: Ben Burger, Managing Partner
X (Twitter): x.com/srcpmedia

Description: Republican media consulting firm that specializes in media production, public opinion research, direct mail design, opposition research and political strategy. **Scope:** Republican media consulting firm that specializes in media production, public opinion research, direct mail design, opposition research and political strategy. **Founded:** 1993.

7181 ■ Strategic Business Alliance
1601 2nd Ave.
York, PA 17402

Description: Firm helps non-profit organizations develop projects and obtain grant funding and it prepares business plans and grant writing proposals for submission to state, federal and private funding sources and it also prepares requests for feasibility funding to compile studies on project feasibility. **Scope:** Firm helps non-profit organizations develop projects and obtain grant funding and it prepares business plans and grant writing proposals for submission to state, federal and private funding sources and it also prepares requests for feasibility funding to compile studies on project feasibility.

7182 ■ Triad Strategies L.L.C.
300 N 2nd St., Ste. 1200
Harrisburg, PA 17101
Ph: (717)238-2970
Co. E-mail: advocacy@triadstrategies.com
URL: http://www.triadstrategies.com
Contact: Roy Wells, President
E-mail: rwells@triadstrategies.com
Facebook: www.facebook.com/triadstrategies
Linkedin: www.linkedin.com/company/triad-strategies
X (Twitter): x.com/triadstrategies
Instagram: www.instagram.com/triadstrategies
YouTube: www.youtube.com/channel/UC_y9-DXXzey-oZPrH9K3fRA

Description: Government relations firm. Services include legislative and regulatory monitoring, legislative and executive branch lobbying, independent and quasi-public agency lobbying, issue research, issue management, grassroots organizing, public relations, strategic planning and network marketing. **Scope:** Government relations firm. Services include legislative and regulatory monitoring, legislative and executive branch lobbying, independent and quasi-public agency lobbying, issue research, issue management, grassroots organizing, public relations, strategic planning and network marketing. **Founded:** 2002.

FRANCHISES AND BUSINESS OPPORTUNITIES

7183 ■ Heavenly Gold Card
1724 N State
Big Rapids, MI 49307
URL: http://www.novamediainc.com/card
Contact: Tom Rundquist, Contact
E-mail: trund@netonecom.net

Description: Fund raising for non profit organizations. **Founded:** 1981. **Financial Assistance:** Yes **Training:** Yes.

LIBRARIES

7184 ■ Council for Advancement and Support of Education (CASE) - Library
1201 Eye St., NW, Ste. 300
Washington, DC 20005
Ph: (202)328-2273
Fax: (202)387-4973
Co. E-mail: insights@case.org
URL: http://www.case.org
Contact: Sue Cunningham, President
E-mail: president@case.org
Facebook: www.facebook.com/caseadvance
Linkedin: www.linkedin.com/company/case
X (Twitter): x.com/caseadvance
Instagram: www.instagram.com/caseadvance

Description: Members are colleges, universities, and independent elementary and secondary schools. Individual member representatives serve these institutions as alumni, fundraising, public relations, admissions, government relations, and publications officers. Serves as national clearinghouse for corporate matching gift information. Offers members professional training seminars and publications. Maintains reference library containing case studies, papers, and examples of reports and other campus publications. Conducts occasional research projects. Monitors federal legislation of interest to members. **Scope:** Advancement field; fundraising; alumni relations; communications and marketing. **Services:** Library open to the public; copying. **Founded:** 1974. **Holdings:** 15,000+ item. **Publications:** *Education Association Directory*; *CASE Directory of Member Institutions*; *Matching Gift Details: Guidebook to Corporate Matching Gift Programs* (Annual); *Council for Advancement and Support of Education--Membership Directory*; *Currents* (Bimonthly); *Profiles: Educational Institutions*. **Educational Activities:** Summit for Leaders in Advancement (Annual). **Awards:** CASE Chief Executive Leadership Award (Annual); CASE Circle of Excellence Awards (Annual); James L. Fisher Award for Distinguished Service to Education (Annual); John Grenzebach Award for Outstanding Research in Philanthropy for Educational Advancement (Annual). **Geographic Preference:** Multinational.

7185 ■ Council on Foundations Resource Center (COF)
1255 23rd St. NW, Ste. 200
Washington, DC 20037
Ph: (202)991-2225
Free: 800-673-9036
Co. E-mail: membership@cof.org
URL: http://cof.org
Contact: Kathleen P. Enright, President
E-mail: president@cof.org
Facebook: www.facebook.com/CouncilonFoundations
Linkedin: www.linkedin.com/company/council-on-foundations
X (Twitter): x.com/COF_
YouTube: www.youtube.com/user/CouncilOnFoundations

Scope: Legal information. **Services:** Library not open to the public. **Founded:** 1949. **Holdings:** Documents.

7186 ■ Foundation Center Cleveland Library
2121 Euclid Ave. Parker Hannifin Hall, 3rd Fl.
Cleveland, OH 44115-2214
URL: http://www.csuohio.edu/gsrc/foundation-center

Scope: Education materials. **Services:** Interlibrary loan; copying; instructional sessions in the use of specialized materials on grants; library open to the public. **Founded:** 1977. **Holdings:** Figures not available. **Subscriptions:** 25 journals and other serials.

7187 ■ Foundation Center, Washington, DC Library
32 Old Slip, 24th Fl.
New York, NY 10005-3500
URL: http://candid.org/improve-your-nonprofit/candid-in-your-community
Contact: Brian Trelstad, Treasurer

Scope: Private philanthropic giving; corporations; foundations. **Services:** Copying; library open to the public. **Founded:** 1964. **Holdings:** 2,500 volumes. **Subscriptions:** 50 journals and other serials.

7188 ■ Imagine Canada - John Hodgson Library
65 St. Clair Ave. E Ste. 700
Toronto, ON, Canada M4T 2Y3
Ph: (416)597-2293
Free: 800-263-1178
Co. E-mail: info@imaginecanada.ca
URL: http://www.imaginecanada.ca/en
Contact: Bruce MacDonald, President
E-mail: bmacdonald@imaginecanada.ca
Facebook: www.facebook.com/ImagineCanada
Linkedin: www.linkedin.com/company/imagine-canada
X (Twitter): x.com/ImagineCanada
Instagram: www.instagram.com/imaginecanada

Description: Provides contribution to social progress and vibrant communities. **Scope:** Issues of importance to the charitable and nonprofit sector as well as corporate citizenship. **Services:** Library not open to the public. **Founded:** 1981. **Holdings:** newspaper, pdf. **Subscriptions:** 7 journals and other serials. **Publications:** *Canadian Directory to Foundations & Corporations*; *Forefront/En Tete Magazine* (Semiannual); *Research Bulletin* (Semiannual). **Awards:** Imagine Canada Grants; Canadian Business and Community Partnership Awards (Annual). **Geographic Preference:** National.

7189 ■ Tucson Pima Public Library Grants and Nonprofit Information Collection
101 N Stone Ave.
Tucson, AZ 85701
Ph: (520)791-4010
Fax: (520)594-5621
URL: http://www.library.pima.gov
Contact: Amber Mathewson, Director

Scope: Grants; foundations; corporate philanthropy; fundraising; nonprofit management; charities; government grants. **Services:** Interlibrary loan; library open to the public. **Founded:** 1883. **Subscriptions:** newspapers; magazines 200 books; 50 reports.

RESEARCH CENTERS

7190 ■ Indiana University-Purdue University at Indianapolis - Lilly Family School of Philanthropy
301 University Blvd.
Indianapolis, IN 46202-5146
Ph: (317)274-4200
Fax: (317)278-8999
URL: http://philanthropy.iupui.edu
Contact: Amir Pasic, Dean
E-mail: ampasic@iupui.edu
Facebook: www.facebook.com/IULillyFamilySchoolofPhilanthropy
Linkedin: www.linkedin.com/school/indiana-university-lilly-family-school-of-philanthropy
X (Twitter): x.com/IUphilanthropy
Instagram: www.instagram.com/iu.philanthropy
YouTube: www.youtube.com/user/IUPhilanthropy

Description: Integral unit of Indiana University-Purdue University at Indianapolis. Offers research, surveys, project evaluation, etc. **Scope:** Theoretical, ethical, historical, practical, and applied aspects of philanthropy and non-profit management. **Founded:** 1987. **Publications:** *Indiana Gives*; *Million Dollar List* (Quarterly); *Philanthropic Giving Index* (Semiannual);

Philanthropy Matters. **Educational Activities:** Lilly Family School of Philanthropy Seminars; Lilly Family School of Philanthropy Symposium on fundraising (Annual).

7191 ■ New York University School of Law - National Center on Philanthropy and the Law (NCPL)
139 MacDougal St., 1st Fl.
New York, NY 10012-1076

Ph: (212)998-6168
Fax: (212)995-3149
Co. E-mail: ncpl.info@nyu.edu
URL: http://ncpl.law.nyu.edu
Contact: Jill S. Manny, Executive Director
E-mail: jill.manny@nyu.edu

Description: Research and educational unit of the School of Law at New York University. Offers courses on nonprofit law, tax aspects of charitable giving, and tax-exempt organizations. **Scope:** Researches on Philanthropy and the law. **Founded:** 1988. **Educational Activities:** NCPL Annual Conference (Annual). **Awards:** Rockefeller Brothers Fund Fellowship in Non-porifit Law (Annual); NCPL Fellowship in Non-profit Law (Annual); NCPL Open Society Presidential Fellowships (OSP) (Annual).

Funeral Service

ASSOCIATIONS AND OTHER ORGANIZATIONS

7192 ■ American Board of Funeral Service Education (ABFSE)
c/o Robert C. Smith III, Executive Director
992 Mantua Pk., Ste. 108
Woodbury Heights, NJ 08097
Ph: (816)233-3747
Fax: (856)579-7354
Co. E-mail: exdir@abfse.org
URL: http://www.abfse.org
Contact: Robert C. Smith, III, Executive Director
E-mail: exdir@abfse.org
Description: Representatives from National Funeral Directors Association, International Conference of Funeral Service Examining Boards of the United States, the National Funeral Directors and Mortuaries Association and college program representatives and public members. Seeks to: formulate and enforce rules and regulations setting up standards concerning the schools and colleges teaching mortuary science; accredit schools and colleges of mortuary science. Sponsors the National Scholarship for Funeral Service program to provide capable young men and women studying in the field with financial assistance. Compiles statistics. **Founded:** 1962. **Awards:** ABFSE National Scholarship Program (Annual); National Scholarship Program of the American Board of Funeral Service Education (Annual). **Geographic Preference:** National.

7193 ■ American Institute of Commemorative Art (AICA)
3 N Milpas St.
Santa Barbara, CA 93103
Ph: (805)886-8384
URL: http://www.monuments-aica.com
Contact: Jed Hendrickson, Contact
E-mail: jed@sbmonumental.com
Description: Retailers of memorials and cemetery monuments with strong interest in commemorative design. **Founded:** 1951. **Publications:** *Milestone*. **Awards:** Eugene H. Faehnle Award (Annual); Harold J. Schaller Award (Annual). **Geographic Preference:** National.

7194 ■ Casket and Funeral Supply Association of America (CFSA)
3502 Woodview Trace, Ste. 300
Indianapolis, IN 46268
Ph: (847)295-6630
Fax: (847)295-6647
Co. E-mail: info@cfsaa.org
URL: http://www.cfsaa.org
Contact: Justin Thacker, President
Facebook: www.facebook.com/funeralsuppliers
X (Twitter): x.com/CFSAmembers
Description: Manufacturers and distributors of burial caskets and other funeral supplies. **Founded:** 1913. **Publications:** *Casket & Funeral Supply Association of America Newsletter* (Biweekly). **Geographic Preference:** National.

7195 ■ Catholic Cemetery Conference (CCC)
1400 S Wolf Rd., Bldg. 3
Hillside, IL 60162-2197
Ph: (708)202-1242
Free: 888-850-8131
Fax: (708)202-1255
Co. E-mail: info@catholiccemeteryconference.org
URL: http://catholiccemeteryconference.org
Contact: Richard P. Peterson, President
E-mail: richp@mycatholiccemetery.org
Description: Archdiocesan and diocesan directors of Catholic cemeteries; provides cemetery advocacy and education. Associate members are administrators of Catholic cemeteries. **Founded:** 1949. **Publications:** *Catholic Cemetery* (Monthly); *Design and Construction Manual* (Periodic); *Field Operation Manual*; *Mausoleum Maintenance Manual*; *National Catholic Cemetery Conference--Membership and Resource Directory* (Annual). **Geographic Preference:** Multinational.

7196 ■ Cremation Association of North America (CANA) [Cremationist of North America]
499 Northgate Pky.
Wheeling, IL 60090-2646
Ph: (312)245-1077
Fax: (312)321-4098
Co. E-mail: info@cremationassociation.org
URL: http://www.cremationassociation.org
Contact: Barbara Kemmis, Executive Director
E-mail: barbara@cremationassociation.org
Facebook: www.facebook.com/CremationAssociation
Linkedin: www.linkedin.com/company/cremationassoc
X (Twitter): x.com/cremationassoc
Instagram: www.instagram.com/cremationassoc
Description: Seeks to increase public awareness and knowledge of cremation and memorialization. **Scope:** Cemeteries, crematories, funeral directors, and manufacturers. Seeks to increase public awareness and knowledge of cremation and memorialization. Conducts research; compiles statistics. Holds certification programs and trade show. **Founded:** 1913. **Publications:** *Newsletter Update* (Monthly); *Cremation Association of North America--Membership Directory*; *The Cremationist of North America* (Quarterly). **Educational Activities:** Cremation Association of North America Convention (Annual). **Geographic Preference:** Multinational.

7197 ■ Funeral Consumers Alliance (FCA)
33 Patchen Rd.
South Burlington, VT 05403
Ph: (802)865-8300
Co. E-mail: fca@funerals.org
URL: http://www.funerals.org
Contact: Joshua Slocum, Executive Director
E-mail: joshua@funerals.org
Description: Promotes a consumer's right to choose a dignified, meaningful, affordable funeral. Provides educational material to the public and affiliates. Monitors the funeral and cemetery industry for consumers nationwide. Responds to consumer complaints. Maintains speaker's bureau. **Founded:** 1963. **Publications:** *FCA Newsletter*; *Funeral Consumers Alliance*. **Geographic Preference:** National.

7198 ■ International Cemetery, Cremation and Funeral Association (ICCFA)
107 Carpenter Dr., Ste. 100
Sterling, VA 20164
Ph: (703)391-8400
Free: 800-645-7700
Fax: (703)391-8416
URL: http://iccfa.com
Contact: Gary Freytag, President
Facebook: www.facebook.com/ICCFACafe
Linkedin: www.linkedin.com/company/iccfa
X (Twitter): x.com/iccfa
Instagram: www.instagram.com/iccfa
Description: To provide exceptional education, networking and legislative guidance and support to progressive cemetery, funeral and cremation professionals worldwide. **Founded:** 1887. **Publications:** *ICFA Buyer's Guide and Membership Directory* (Annual); *Memento Mori* (10/year); *International Cemetery, Cremation & Funeral Association--Buyers Guide and Membership Directory* (Annual). **Educational Activities:** ICCFA Annual Convention & Exposition (Annual). **Awards:** ICCFA Keeping It Personal Awards (KIP) (Annual). **Geographic Preference:** National.

7199 ■ The Jewish Funeral Directors of America, Inc. (JFDA)
107 Carpenter Dr., Ste. 100
Sterling, VA 20164
Ph: (703)391-8400
Free: 800-645-7700
Fax: (703)391-8416
URL: http://iccfa.com/jfda
Contact: Albert Bloomfield, President
Description: Predominantly serves members of the Jewish faith. Assists people of the Jewish faith arrange meaningful and affordable funerals in the Jewish tradition. **Founded:** 1932. **Publications:** *How to Explain Death to Children*; *Jewish Funeral Director* (Annual). **Geographic Preference:** National.

7200 ■ Monument Builders of North America (MBNA)
3502 Woodview Trace, Ste. 300
Indianapolis, IN 46268
Free: 800-233-4472
Co. E-mail: info@monumentbuilders.org
URL: http://monumentbuilders.org
Contact: Matt Worthington, President
E-mail: matt@worthingtontx.com
Facebook: www.facebook.com/monumentbuildersofnorthamerica
Linkedin: www.linkedin.com/company/monument-builders-of-north-america
Instagram: www.instagram.com/monumentbuildersna
Description: Monument retailers, manufacturers, and wholesalers; bronze manufacturers and suppliers. Provides sales, advertising, and management materials to members. Develops modern and religious

memorial designs. Provides Affinity Programs such as discounts and low-cost credit card processing. Opposes "restrictive business practices and unfair competition". Compiles statistics; conducts specialized education and certification programs; maintains speaker's bureau. **Founded:** 1906. **Publications:** *Monument Builders of North America--Membership Roster* (Annual); *Monument Builders News* (Monthly). **Educational Activities:** MBNA Monument Industry Show (Annual). **Awards:** MBNA Aspire Awards (Annual). **Geographic Preference:** National.

7201 ■ National Concrete Burial Vault Association (NCBVA)
PO Box 8314
Greenville, SC 29604
Free: 888-886-2282
Co. E-mail: info@ncbva.org
URL: http://ncbva.org
Contact: Kyle York, President
Facebook: www.facebook.com/ncbva
Description: Represents manufacturers of concrete burial vaults. Provides a unified voice for the concrete burial vault industry regardless of product affiliation, brand recognition, or location. **Founded:** 1930. **Geographic Preference:** National.

7202 ■ National Funeral Directors Association (NFDA) - Howard C. Raether Library
13625 Bishop's Dr.
Brookfield, WI 53005
Ph: (262)789-1880
Free: 800-228-6332
Fax: (262)789-6977
Co. E-mail: nfda@nfda.org
URL: http://www.nfda.org
Contact: Christine Pepper, Chief Executive Officer
Facebook: www.facebook.com/NationalFuneralDirectorsAssociation
Linkedin: www.linkedin.com/company/national-funeral-directors-association
X (Twitter): x.com/nfda
Instagram: www.instagram.com/nfda_usa
YouTube: www.youtube.com/user/nfdaweb
Description: Federation of state funeral directors' associations with individual membership of funeral directors. Seeks to enhance the funeral service profession and promote quality services to the consumers. Conducts professional education seminars and home study courses. **Scope:** Death Care; Funeral service. **Services:** open to students; researchers by appointment only. **Founded:** 1882. **Holdings:** periodicals; artifacts; books; proceedings. **Publications:** *NFDA Bulletin* (Weekly); *The Director* (Monthly); *NFDA Directory of Members and Transportation Guide* (Annual); *The Director: Official Publication of the National Funeral Directors Association* (Monthly); *National Funeral Directors Association--Directory of Members*. **Educational Activities:** NFDA International Convention & Expo (Annual). **Awards:** NFDA Pursuit of Excellence Award (Annual). **Geographic Preference:** National.

7203 ■ National Funeral Directors and Morticians Association (NFDMA)
6290 Shannon Pky.
Union City, GA 30291
Ph: (770)969-0064
Free: 800-434-0958
Fax: (770)969-0505
URL: http://nfdma.com
Contact: George J. Durham, Jr., President
X (Twitter): x.com/nfdma
Description: State, district and local funeral directors and embalmers associations and their members. Promotes ethical practices; encourages just and uniform laws pertaining to funeral directing and embalming industry. **Founded:** 1924. **Educational Activities:** House of Representatives Meeting (Annual). **Awards:** NFDMA Scholarship Program (Annual). **Geographic Preference:** National.

7204 ■ Selected Independent Funeral Homes
One Overlook Point, Ste. 530
Lincolnshire, IL 60069
Free: 800-323-4219
Fax: (847)236-9968
Co. E-mail: info@selectedfuneralhomes.org
URL: http://www.selectedfuneralhomes.org
Contact: Robert Paterkiewicz, Chief Executive Officer
E-mail: robp@selectedfuneralhomes.org
Facebook: www.facebook.com/selectedFH
Linkedin: www.linkedin.com/company/selected-independent-funeral-homes
X (Twitter): x.com/selectedfh
Description: Establish a standard of service for the benefit of its consumers. Provides a continuing forum for the exchange, development and dissemination of knowledge and information beneficial to members and the public. **Founded:** 1917. **Geographic Preference:** Multinational.

REFERENCE WORKS

7205 ■ *"Balancing Freedom of Speech with the Right to Privacy: How to Legally Cope with the Funeral Protest Problem"* **in Pace Law Review (Fall 2007)**
Description: Information is offered to help authorities and funeral directors cope with protests occurring during a funeral. **Availability:** PDF; Online.

7206 ■ *"Bowman Funeral Directors Building New, Larger Facility in Garden City"* **in Idaho Business Review (March 13, 2014)**
Pub: BridgeTower Media
Contact: Adam Reinebach, President
Description: Bowman Funeral Directors has started construction of a 6,500 square foot building in Garden City, Idaho. Owner, Gary Bowman, is a licensed mortician and reports that the new funeral home will have a great room for services with audio and visual component services available, preparations and storage rooms, crematorium, offices, and a kitchen.

7207 ■ *"Cremation Popularity On the Rise"* **in Memphis Business Journal (Vol. 34, April 13, 2012, No. 53, pp. 1)**
Pub: Baltimore Business Journal
Contact: Rhonda Pringle, President
E-mail: rpringle@bizjournals.com
Description: Cremation has growing in popularity in the United States. The economic crisis is seen to drive the current trend. **Availability:** Print; Online.

7208 ■ *"The Funeral As We Know It Is Becoming a Relic — Just in Time for a Death Boom"* **in The Washington Post (April 15, 2019)**
URL(s): www.washingtonpost.com/lifestyle/style/the-funeral-as-we-know-it-is-becoming-a-relic--just-in-time-for-a-death-boom/2019/04/14/a49003c4-50c2-11e9-8d28-f5149e5a2fda_story.html
Ed: Karen Heller. **Released:** April 15, 2019. **Description:** A growing trend in the funeral industry is to replace traditional, embalmed-body visitations with memorial services centering around the life of the deceased. A party-like atmosphere with unique touches are becoming more common, along with cremations instead of embalming. Funeral homes are starting to adapt by hiring event planners and creating more friendly spaces within their old drab parlors. **Availability:** Online.

7209 ■ Funeral Consumers Alliance
Pub: Funeral Consumers Alliance
Contact: Joshua Slocum, Executive Director
E-mail: joshua@funerals.org
URL(s): funerals.org/affiliate-resources/affiliate-directory
Description: Covers over 120 nonprofit funeral consumer groups that educate the public about affordable funeral options. Monitors funeral industry practices for consumers. **Entries include:** Name, address, phone, email address. **Arrangement:** Geographical. **Availability:** Print; PDF.

7210 ■ *"Funeral Directors Get Creative As Boomers Near Great Beyond"* **in Advertising Age (Vol. 79, October 13, 2008, No. 38, pp. 30)**
Pub: Crain Communications, Inc.
Contact: Jessica Botos, Manager, Marketing
E-mail: jessica.botos@crainsnewyork.com
Ed: Lenore Skenazy. **Description:** Despite the downturn in the economy, the funeral business is thriving due to the number of baby boomers who realize the importance of making preparations for their death. Marketers are getting creative in their approach and many companies have taken into consideration the need for a more environmental friendly way to dispose of bodies and thus have created innovative businesses that reflect this need. **Availability:** Online.

7211 ■ *Funeral Home & Cemetery Directory--Buyer's Guide*
Pub: Nomis Publications Inc.
Contact: Chester E. Simon, Founder
URL(s): www.nomispublications.com/publications.aspx#TheBuyersGuide
Price: $40, for price 2024. **Description:** Covers over 2,000 suppliers to the funeral and cemetery industry. **Entries include:** Company name, address, phone, fax. **Arrangement:** Classified by product/service. **Indexes:** Product/service. **Availability:** Print; PDF; Online.

7212 ■ *"Funeral Picketing Laws and Free Speech"* **in Kansas Law Review (Vol. 55, April 2007, No. 3, pp. 575-627)**
Description: In-depth information covering laws governing protests and freedom of speech during funerals is presented. **Availability:** Download; PDF; Online.

7213 ■ *"A Grave Situation"* **in Chronicle of Higher Education (Vol. 54, November 30, 2007, No. 14)**
Description: W. Scott Walston has been selling funeral caskets with the University of Georgia's logo on them to graduates who pass away; however the University System of Georgia has a rule that forbids college logos on burial items. **Availability:** Print; Online.

7214 ■ *"Great News for the Dead: The Funeral Industry Is Being Disrupted"* **in The Economist (April 14, 2018)**
URL(s): www.economist.com/leaders/2018/04/14/great-news-for-the-dead-the-funeral-industry-is-being-disrupted
Released: April 14, 2018. **Description:** Old-fashioned funeral services typically cost around $9,000 with very few options for those left behind to deal with. However, with the advancement of online tools, those left grieving can search for options and compare competitors in the privacy of their own homes. **Availability:** Online.

7215 ■ *"With Funeral Home Rules Due for an Update, There's a Push for Online Prices"* **in The New York Times (March 29, 2019)**
URL(s): www.nytimes.com/2019/03/29/your-money/funeral-homes-pricing.html
Ed: Ann Carrns. **Released:** March 29, 2019. **Description:** Consumer advocates are pushing for change when it comes to funeral services by advocating for online pricing. Federal regulators are taking a look at an old rule that governs how funeral homes share information, and advocates want these prices online so that consumers can be better informed ahead of time. **Availability:** Online.

STATISTICAL SOURCES

7216 ■ *RMA Annual Statement Studies*
Pub: Risk Management Association
Contact: Nancy Foster, President
Released: Annual. **Description:** Contains composite balance sheets and income statements for more than 360 industries, including the accounting, auditing, and bookkeeping industries. Also contains five years

of comparative historical data for discerning trends. Includes 16 commonly used ratios, computed for most of the size groupings for nearly every industry.

TRADE PERIODICALS

7217 ■ Casket & Funeral Supply Association of America Newsletter
Pub: Casket and Funeral Supply Association of America
Contact: Justin Thacker, President
URL(s): www.cfsaa.org/advertising-opportunities

Released: Biweekly **Description:** Carries news items of interest to the funeral supply industry, including information on annual conventions, Federal Trade Commission regulations and other court rulings, and cost and pricing issues. **Availability:** Online.

7218 ■ The Director: Official Publication of the National Funeral Directors Association
Pub: National Funeral Directors Association
Contact: Christine Pepper, Chief Executive Officer
URL(s): nfda.org/resources/publications/the-director

Released: Monthly **Price:** $84, U.S. for 12 issues US; $96, Other countries for 12 issues International. **Description:** Magazine for the funeral service profession. Includes medical updates, business trends, federal regulations, and bereavement issues. **Availability:** Print; Online.

7219 ■ NFDA Bulletin
Pub: National Funeral Directors Association
Contact: Christine Pepper, Chief Executive Officer
URL(s): nfda.org/resources/publications/nfda-bulletin

Released: Weekly **Description:** Covers association activities and funeral business management topics. Reports on association news, government regulation, public relations issues, and local developments. **Availability:** Print; Online.

TRADE SHOWS AND CONVENTIONS

7220 ■ ICCFA Annual Convention & Exposition
International Cemetery, Cremation and Funeral Association (ICCFA)
107 Carpenter Dr., Ste. 100
Sterling, VA 20164
Ph: (703)391-8400
Free: 800-645-7700
Fax: (703)391-8416
URL: http://iccfa.com
Contact: Gary Freytag, President
URL(s): iccfa.com/annual

Frequency: Annual. **Description:** Exhibits related to lawn care machinery, backhoes, computer hardware/software, monuments, caskets/vaults/urns, memorials, software/management systems and direct sales materials. **Audience:** Cemetery, cremation and funeral service owners and managers from throughout North America and the world. **Principal Exhibits:** Exhibits related to lawn care machinery, backhoes, computer hardware/software, monuments, caskets/vaults/urns, memorials, software/management systems and direct sales materials. Dates and Locations: 2025 Apr 30-May 03 Mandalay Bay Resort & Casino, Las Vegas, NV. **Telecommunication Services:** lindsy@iccfa.com.

7221 ■ Ohio Funeral Directors Convention
Ohio Funeral Directors Association (OFDA)
2501 N Star Rd.
Columbus, OH 43221-0760
Ph: (614)486-5339
Free: 800-589-6332
Fax: (614)486-5358
Co. E-mail: melissa@ofdaonline.org
URL: http://ofdaonline.org/aws/OFDA/pt/sp/home_page
Contact: Lloyd E. Rankin, President
E-mail: lloydrankin16@gmail.com
URL(s): www.ofdaonline.org/aws/OFDA/pt/sp/convention_home_page

Frequency: Annual. **Description:** Exhibits relating to funerals and the funeral industry. **Audience:** Funeral directors. **Principal Exhibits:** Exhibits relating to funerals and the funeral industry. Dates and Locations: 2025 Apr 29-May 01; 2026 Apr 28-30. Hilton Easton Columbus, Columbus, OH. **Telecommunication Services:** info@ofdaonline.org.

7222 ■ Virginia Funeral Directors Association Conference
Virginia Funeral Directors Association (VFDA)
2706 N Main St.
South Boston, VA 24592
Ph: (804)264-0505
Co. E-mail: info@vfda.net
URL: http://www.vfda.net
Contact: Jay McIntyre, President
E-mail: jrmcintyre685@gmail.com
URL(s): vfda.net/tag/featured

Frequency: Annual. **Description:** Funeral. **Audience:** Members. **Principal Exhibits:** Funeral.

LIBRARIES

7223 ■ Funeral Consumers Alliance (FCA)
33 Patchen Rd.
South Burlington, VT 05403
Ph: (802)865-8300
Co. E-mail: fca@funerals.org
URL: http://www.funerals.org
Contact: Joshua Slocum, Executive Director
E-mail: joshua@funerals.org

Description: Promotes a consumer's right to choose a dignified, meaningful, affordable funeral. Provides educational material to the public and affiliates. Monitors the funeral and cemetery industry for consumers nationwide. Responds to consumer complaints. Maintains speaker's bureau. **Founded:** 1963. **Publications:** FCA Newsletter; Funeral Consumers Alliance. **Geographic Preference:** National.

7224 ■ National Funeral Directors Association (NFDA) - Howard C. Raether Library
13625 Bishop's Dr.
Brookfield, WI 53005
Ph: (262)789-1880
Free: 800-228-6332
Fax: (262)789-6977
Co. E-mail: nfda@nfda.org
URL: http://www.nfda.org
Contact: Christine Pepper, Chief Executive Officer
Facebook: www.facebook.com/NationalFuneralDirectorsAssociation
Linkedin: www.linkedin.com/company/national-funeral-directors-association
X (Twitter): x.com/nfda
Instagram: www.instagram.com/nfda_usa
YouTube: www.youtube.com/user/nfdaweb

Description: Federation of state funeral directors' associations with individual membership of funeral directors. Seeks to enhance the funeral service profession and promote quality services to the consumers. Conducts professional education seminars and home study courses. **Scope:** Death Care; Funeral service. **Services:** open to students; researchers by appointment only. **Founded:** 1882. **Holdings:** periodicals; artifacts; books; proceedings. **Publications:** NFDA Bulletin (Weekly); The Director (Monthly); NFDA Directory of Members and Transportation Guide (Annual); The Director: Official Publication of the National Funeral Directors Association (Monthly); National Funeral Directors Association-- Directory of Members. **Educational Activities:** NFDA International Convention & Expo (Annual). **Awards:** NFDA Pursuit of Excellence Award (Annual). **Geographic Preference:** National.

7225 ■ Northampton Community College - Paul and Harriett Mack Library
Bethlehem Campus College Ctr., 4th Flr.
Bethlehem, PA 18020
Ph: (610)861-5360
URL: http://www.northampton.edu/library.htm
Contact: Sandra Sander, Director, Library Services
E-mail: ssander@northampton.edu

Scope: Educational material. **Services:** Interlibrary loan; copying; center open to the public. **Founded:** 1967. **Holdings:** Figures not available.

Fur Farm

ASSOCIATIONS AND OTHER ORGANIZATIONS

7226 ■ **American Fur Council (AFC)**
PO Box 20272
New York, NY 10001
Co. E-mail: info@fur.org
URL: http://www.fur.org
Description: Fur retailers, manufacturers, and others involved in the fur industry. Aims to promote the fur industry and foster high standards, quality, and craftsmanship. Conducts public relations and advertising work. Committed to the wise use and humane care of animals; develops programs to ensure high standards for animal welfare in the fur industry; works with wildlife biologists to promote sound wildlife management. **Founded:** 1958. **Publications:** *American Fur Industry Fashion-Newsletter* (Annual); *Furs Naturally*. **Geographic Preference:** National.

7227 ■ **Conseil Canadien de la Fourrure (CCF) [Fur Council of Canada]**
1435 St. Alexandre, Ste. 1270
Montreal, QC, Canada H3A 2G4
Ph: (514)844-1945
Fax: (514)844-8593
Co. E-mail: info@furcouncil.com
URL: http://www.furcouncil.com/?lang=fr
Facebook: www.facebook.com/FurCouncilofCanada
X (Twitter): x.com/Councilfur
Instagram: www.instagram.com/furcouncilofcanada
YouTube: www.youtube.com/user/EcoFurs
Description: Fur trappers and processors and distributors of fur and fur apparel. Promotes increased demand for fur and fur clothing. Represents members' commercial interests; conducts promotional activities. **Educational Activities:** StyleLab Montreal. **Geographic Preference:** National.

REFERENCE WORKS

7228 ■ *"Fur Farms Still Unfashionably Cruel, Critics Say" in National Geographic (August 17, 2016)*
URL(s): www.nationalgeographic.com/news/2016/08/wildlife-china-fur-farming-welfare/
Ed: Rachael Bale. **Description:** Within the fashion industry, fur is making a comeback and to deal with the demand they are turning to Chinese mink farms for pelts, even though these farms are mostly unregulated. Animal advocates are trying to discourage the practice of animal fur farms, or at the very least make sure the animals are receiving proper welfare. **Availability:** Online.

7229 ■ *"Fur Helped Build the City. Now Its Sale May Be Banned." in The New York Times (May 16, 2019)*
URL(s): www.nytimes.com/2019/05/16/nyregion/newyorktoday/nyc-news-fur-ban.html
Ed: Corey Kilgannon. **Description:** The New York City Council has a proposed bill that would ban fur sales, introduced by Corey Johnson. Although the fur industry has declined in the city, it still exists and has the largest retail fur market in the country. **Availability:** Online.

7230 ■ *"Norway to Ban Fur Farms as Fox and Mink Go Out of Fashion" in Business of Fashion (January 15, 2018)*
URL(s): www.businessoffashion.com/articles/news-analysis/norway-to-ban-fur-farms-as-fox-and-mink-go-out-of-fashion
Released: January 15, 2018. **Description:** Norway is planning to phase out fur farms by 2025. Animal rights group Noah is celebrating this victory for animal rights, but on the other side of the debate are the 200 fur farms that employ 400 people, and the industry already adhered to strict rules for animal welfare. **Availability:** Online.

TRADE PERIODICALS

7231 ■ *Canadian Cooperative Wool Growers Magazine: Livestock Supply Catalogue*
Pub: Canadian Co-Operative Wool Growers Ltd.
Contact: David Mastine, President
URL(s): wool.ca/page/catalogue
Released: Annual **Description:** Company magazine covering wool marketing and livestock supplies. **Availability:** Print; PDF; Download.

Fur Store

ASSOCIATIONS AND OTHER ORGANIZATIONS

7232 ■ **American Fur Council (AFC)**
PO Box 20272
New York, NY 10001
Co. E-mail: info@fur.org
URL: http://www.fur.org
Description: Fur retailers, manufacturers, and others involved in the fur industry. Aims to promote the fur industry and foster high standards, quality, and craftsmanship. Conducts public relations and advertising work. Committed to the wise use and humane care of animals; develops programs to ensure high standards for animal welfare in the fur industry; works with wildlife biologists to promote sound wildlife management. **Founded:** 1958. **Publications:** *American Fur Industry Fashion-Newsletter* (Annual); *Furs Naturally*. **Geographic Preference:** National.

7233 ■ **Conseil Canadien de la Fourrure (CCF) [Fur Council of Canada]**
1435 St. Alexandre, Ste. 1270
Montreal, QC, Canada H3A 2G4
Ph: (514)844-1945
Fax: (514)844-8593
Co. E-mail: info@furcouncil.com
URL: http://www.furcouncil.com/?lang=fr
Facebook: www.facebook.com/FurCouncilofCanada
X (Twitter): x.com/Councilfur
Instagram: www.instagram.com/furcouncilofcanada
YouTube: www.youtube.com/user/EcoFurs
Description: Fur trappers and processors and distributors of fur and fur apparel. Promotes increased demand for fur and fur clothing. Represents members' commercial interests; conducts promotional activities. **Educational Activities:** StyleLab Montreal. **Geographic Preference:** National.

REFERENCE WORKS

7234 ■ *"The California Fur Ban and What It Means for You"* in The New York Times (October 14, 2019)
URL(s): www.nytimes.com/2019/10/14/style/fur-ban-california.html?action=click&module=RelatedCoverage&pgtype=Article&region=Footer
Ed: Vanessa Friedman. **Released:** October 14, 2019.
Description: California has become the first state to ban fur, meaning only the sale of new clothing and accessories are actually banned. The wearing of fur is still legal and any old fur still in circulation is acceptable as is any religious, traditional, or cultural fur. This is all due to a growing trend of people not purchasing fur due to animal welfare concerns and changing tastes in fashion with the younger generations. **Availability:** Online.

7235 ■ *"Fur Centre Stakes Former Byron Cade Spot in Clayton"* in St. Louis Business Journal (Vol. 33, August 10, 2012, No. 51, pp. 1)
Pub: Baltimore Business Journal
Contact: Rhonda Pringle, President
E-mail: rpringle@bizjournals.com
Description: The Fur & Leather Centre is relocating from 601 S. Lindbergh Blvd. to the Byron Cade Building at 7901 Clayton Road in Saint Louis, Missouri. The store purchased the building for an undisclosedprice, while its current lease is set to expire in March 2013. **Availability:** Print; Online.

7236 ■ *"Fur Helped Build the City. Now Its Sale May Be Banned."* in The New York Times (May 16, 2019)
URL(s): www.nytimes.com/2019/05/16/nyregion/newyorktoday/nyc-news-fur-ban.html
Ed: Corey Kilgannon. **Description:** The New York City Council has a proposed bill that would ban fur sales, introduced by Corey Johnson. Although the fur industry has declined in the city, it still exists and has the largest retail fur market in the country. **Availability:** Online.

7237 ■ *"Macy's, Home to $8,000 Mink Jackets, Will Stop Selling Fur Products by 2021"* in The New York Times (October 21, 2019)
URL(s): www.nytimes.com/2019/10/21/business/macys-fur-sales.html
Ed: Sapna Maheshwari. **Released:** October 21, 2019. **Description:** Macy's and Bloomingdale's department stores will stop selling fur by 2021, leading to the closure of 34 Fur Vaults at Macy's and 22 Maximilian salons at Bloomingdale's. The chain is taking on this change due to consumers who are buying less furs due to animal welfare concerns. **Availability:** Online.

Furniture Restoration Service

REFERENCE WORKS

7238 ■ *"5 Must-Have Tools for Refurbishing Wood Furniture"* in *The Spruce (February 2, 2019)*
URL(s): www.thespruce.com/top-supplies-to-refurbish-wood-furniture-2879094
Ed: Jami Delia. **Released:** February 11, 2019. **Description:** Breaks down the five most essential tools to keep around for restoring furniture. Also gives out practical tips for working with the tools. **Availability:** Online.

7239 ■ *Comprehensive Guide to Leather Repair and Restoration*
Ed: Kevin Gillan, Jason Murray. **Released:** May 2019. **Description:** A manual on how to restore furniture leather, automotive upholstery, and clothing. Beginning fundamentals are discussed and progresses to repair techniques and how to run your own leather restoration business.

7240 ■ *"Furniture Restoration and Design Firm Holds Grand Opening in Dunbar"* in *Charleston Gazette-Mail (July 18, 2019)*
URL(s): www.wvgazettemail.com/dailymailwv/daily_mail_news/furniture-restoration-and-design-firm-holds-grand-opening-in-dunbar/article_ad3e4568-871e-5c74-983f-6e3ace21bfbe.html
Ed: Clint Thomas. **Released:** July 18, 2019. **Description:** Appalachian Restoration and Design Company held it's grand opening on July 16. Owner Christina Deaton has been restoring furniture for well over a decade and decided it was time to open up a shop, which also included hand-painted vintage and antique furniture. **Availability:** Online.

7241 ■ *"How to Tell If Wood Furniture Is Worth Refinishing"* in *DIY Network*
URL(s): www.diynetwork.com/how-to/make-and-decorate/decorating/how-to-tell-if-wood-furniture-is-worth-refinishing
Ed: Karin Beuerlein. **Description:** A set of questions and answers to help restorers decide if fixing up that old piece of furniture is worthwhile. **Availability:** Online.

7242 ■ *"Keep Steel Wool Away from Your Antique Furniture; You'll Do More Harm Than Good"* in *Antique Trader (March 8, 2012)*
URL(s): www.antiquetrader.com/featured/keep-steel-wool-away-from-your-antique-furniture-you%E2%80%99ll-do-more-harm-than-good/
Ed: Fred Taylor. **Released:** March 08, 2012. **Description:** Discusses the many cons of using steel wool in the restoration process. Many people do not realize that the steel is coated with oil to prevent it from rusting, but this coating can come off and deposit rust onto your project. Alternative materials and processes are listed. **Availability:** Online.

7243 ■ *"Reduce, Reuse, Recycle, Reupholster, Is Motto of Willmar, Minn., Upholstery Hobbyist Turned Pro"* in *West Central Tribune (August 14, 2012)*
Ed: David Little. **Description:** American craftsmanship in furniture is foremost to Mr. Rousseau, owner of PrairieUpholstery of Willmar, Minnesota. He learned to reupholster furniture from an expert and opened his own shop in the historic downtown district. Rousseau will reupholster new and used furniture, car and truck seats, as well as boat seats and he can repair canvas. He also will rent upholstery cleaning and carpet shampoo machines, as well as refinishing wood furniture. **Availability:** Online.

7244 ■ *Rescue, Restore, Redecorate: Amy Howard's Guide to Refinishing Furniture and Accessories*
Ed: Amy Howard. **Released:** May 08, 2018. **Price:** $19.64, Paperback; $9.99, E-book. **Description:** Guides the user through restoring furniture and lists recipes, techniques, and tips to complete these refinishing projects. **Availability:** E-book; Print.

STATISTICAL SOURCES

7245 ■ *Furniture Repair & Reupholstery Industry in the US - Market Research Report*
URL(s): www.ibisworld.com/united-states/market-research-reports/furniture-repair-reupholstery-industry/
Price: $925. **Description:** Downloadable report analyzing current and future trends in the furniture repair and reupholstery industry. **Availability:** Download.

TRADE SHOWS AND CONVENTIONS

7246 ■ **AWFS Vegas**
Association of Woodworking and Furnishings Suppliers (AWFS)
2400 E Katella Ave., Ste. 340
Anaheim, CA 92806
Ph: (323)838-9440
Free: 800-946-2937
Fax: (323)838-9443
URL: http://www.awfs.org
Contact: Angela Hernandez, Executive Assistant
E-mail: angela@awfs.org
URL(s): www.awfsfair.org
Frequency: Annual. **Description:** Products manufactured by the woodworking and furnishings industries. **Audience:** Trade professionals and public. **Principal Exhibits:** Products manufactured by the woodworking and furnishings industries.

FRANCHISES AND BUSINESS OPPORTUNITIES

7247 ■ **CertiRestore Certified Furniture Restoration**
612 2nd Ave. NW, Ste. J
West Fargo, ND 58078
Ph: (701)364-0660
URL: http://www.certirestore.org
Description: Provider of furniture repair services and also retailer of furniture. **Royalty Fee:** 8%. **Financial Assistance:** Yes **Training:** Provides the tools, supplies, equipment, support and hands-on training. In their 11 day in-shop training class you will restore and repair several pieces of furniture, as well as marketing and business training.

7248 ■ **Furniture Medic of Canada**
8-60 E Bristol RD., Ste. 512.
Mississauga, ON, Canada L4Z 3K8
Ph: (905)670-0000
Free: 800-263-5928
Co. E-mail: info@furnituremedic.ca
URL: http://furnituremedic.ca
Description: Firm provides furniture repair and restoration services for commercial enterprises. **Founded:** 1992. **Financial Assistance:** Yes **Training:** Yes.

7249 ■ **Furniture Medic L.P.**
Roark Capital Group
150 Peabody Pl.
Memphis, TN 38103-3720
Ph: (404)591-5200
Fax: (404)591-5201
Co. E-mail: contact@roarkcapital.com
URL: http://www.roarkcapital.com
Description: Onsite furniture repair and restoration of furniture, antiques, cabinetry, paneled walls etc. **Founded:** 1992. **Training:** 5 week program, seminars, regional meetings, 24/7 technical assistance with key support in marketing, financial, customer acquisition and retention.

7250 ■ **Guardsman Furniture Professionals**
4999 36th St. S E
Grand Rapids, MI 49512
Free: 800-253-3957
URL: http://www.guardsman.com
Contact: Tim Mrotek, President
Linkedin: www.linkedin.com/company/guardsman-protection
Description: Provider of care and repair services to furniture industry. **Founded:** 1915. **Franchised:** 1994. **Financial Assistance:** Yes **Training:** All franchisee's receive complete technical and business training and provides quality onsite support.

7251 ■ **Leather Medic**
12901 Metro Pky.
Fort Myers, FL 33966
Ph: (239)482-2027
Fax: (239)277-5715
Co. E-mail: support@leathermedic.com
URL: http://leathermedic.com
Contact: Chade Life, Founder
Facebook: www.facebook.com/LeatherMedic/timeline
X (Twitter): x.com/Leather_Medic
YouTube: www.youtube.com/user/LeatherMedicHQ

Description: Firm engages in automotive leather and vinyl repair, leather furniture repair and refinishing. **No. of Franchise Units:** 22. **Founded:** 1988. **Franchise Fee:** $49,500. **Financial Assistance:** Yes **Training:** Offers 2 weeks of one-on-one training.

7252 ■ The Weathersby Guild, Inc.
403 Cimarron Pk.
  Peachtree City, GA 30269
Ph: (678)481-7518
Co. E-mail: info@weathersbyguild.com
URL: http://weathersbyguild.com
Contact: Steve Benz, Chief Executive Officer
Facebook: www.facebook.com/Weathersbyguild

Description: Provider of furniture repair and restoration services. **Founded:** 1972. **Training:** The guild concept reflects our focus on skill level. Our twenty-one day training course is intensive and includes on-the-job training with a specialty in service to the moving van industry. Provides ongoing training and support.

LIBRARIES

7253 ■ Bienenstock Furniture Library (BFL)
1009 N Main St.
  High Point, NC 27262
Ph: (336)883-4011
Co. E-mail: info@furniturelibrary.com
URL: http://www.furniturelibrary.com
Contact: Christi Spangle, President
Facebook: www.facebook.com/BienenstockFurnitureLibrary
X (Twitter): x.com/FurnLibrary
YouTube: www.youtube.com/channel/UCYD4raFGXFb9DcL6SRsF_lg

Scope: History and design of furniture; interiors, architecture; textiles; finishes and construction. **Services:** Photographing; library is open to the public. **Founded:** 1970. **Holdings:** 5,000 volumes; bound periodical volumes, including over 100 years of furniture catalogs; Furniture World; trade journals. **Subscriptions:** 10 journals and other serials.

7254 ■ Edward-Dean Museum & Gardens Art Reference Library
9401 Oak Glen Rd.
  Cherry Valley, CA 92223
URL: http://www.edward-deanmuseum.org/home-copy-copy

Scope: Science; botanicals; architecture; landscape; design; art; history; religion and fashion. **Services:** Library open to the public by special permission. **Founded:** 1964. **Holdings:** 2,700 Books.

7255 ■ Grand Rapids Public Library - Furniture Design Collection
111 Library St. NE
  Grand Rapids, MI 49503
URL: http://www.grpl.org/furniture-history

Scope: Furniture history and design. **Services:** Copying. **Founded:** 1913. **Holdings:** 4,000 items; books; eBooks; periodicals.

7256 ■ Kendall College of Art & Design Library (KCAD Library)
17 Fountain St., NW
  Grand Rapids, MI 49503
Ph: (616)259-1121
URL: http://ferris.libguides.com/kcad-library
X (Twitter): x.com/KCADofFSU
Instagram: www.instagram.com/kcadoffsu

Description: Kendall college of art and design library. **Scope:** Art education; art history; architecture; collaborative design; visual and critical studies. **Services:** Library open to the public. **Holdings:** 180 databases.

Gambling Organization/Service

ASSOCIATIONS AND OTHER ORGANIZATIONS

7257 ■ American Gaming Association (AGA)
799 9th St. NW, Ste. 700
Washington, DC 20001
Ph: (202)552-2675
Fax: (202)552-2676
Co. E-mail: press@americangaming.org
URL: http://www.americangaming.org
Contact: Bill Miller, President
Facebook: www.facebook.com/americangaming
Linkedin: www.linkedin.com/company/american-gaming-association
X (Twitter): x.com/AmericanGaming
Instagram: www.instagram.com/americangaming
YouTube: www.youtube.com/user/americangaming
Description: Represents the commercial casino entertainment industry by addressing federal legislative and regulatory issues affecting its members and their employees and customers; provides leadership in addressing newly emerging national issues and in developing industry wide programs on critical issues; serves as the industry's national information clearinghouse which provides the media, elected officials, other decision makers and the public with timely and accurate gaming industry data. **Founded:** 1995. **Publications:** *Inside the AGA* (Bimonthly); *Responsible Gaming Quarterly* (Quarterly). **Educational Activities:** Global Gaming Expo (G2E) (Annual). **Awards:** AGA Gaming Voice Award (Annual). **Geographic Preference:** National.

7258 ■ Casino Chip and Gaming Token Collectors Club (CC&GTCC)
c/o Jim Follis, Vice President
5466 Jacobs Field St.
Las Vegas, NV 89148
Co. E-mail: vicepresident@ccgtcc.com
URL: http://www.ccgtcc.com
Contact: Jim Follis, Vice President
E-mail: vicepresident@ccgtcc.com
Description: Member club of the American Numismatic Association. Collectors of casino gaming chips and tokens. Coordinates the exchange of information regarding gaming chips and tokens and the casinos where they are used. Conducts educational programs and competitions. **Founded:** 1988. **Publications:** *Casino Collectibles News* (Quarterly); *Club Directory*. **Awards:** CCGTCC Chip of the Year (Annual). **Geographic Preference:** National.

7259 ■ Casino Direct Marketing Association (CDMA)
3108 Colanthe Ave.
Las Vegas, NV 89102
Ph: (909)747-8181
Co. E-mail: casinodma@gmail.com
URL: http://casinodma.com
Contact: Linda Gordon, President
Linkedin: www.linkedin.com/company/casino-direct-marketing-association
X (Twitter): x.com/CasinoDMA

Description: A non-profit trade association that provides a national network forum for Casino Marketing Executives and their Industry Partners.

7260 ■ Fantasy Sports & Gaming Association (FSTA)
1818 Parmenter St., Ste. 300
Middleton, WI 53562
Ph: (608)310-7540
Co. E-mail: info@fsta.org
URL: http://thefsga.org
Contact: Christina McCoy, Executive Director
E-mail: cmccoy@thefsga.org
Facebook: www.facebook.com/TheFSGA
Linkedin: www.linkedin.com/company/fsga
X (Twitter): x.com/FSGAtweets
Description: Provides a forum for interaction between hundreds of existing and emerging companies in the fantasy sports industry. Serves the visionaries, innovators, investors, advisors, and sponsors that would like to network and learn more about the fantasy sports industry. **Founded:** 1999. **Geographic Preference:** National.

7261 ■ Gamblers Anonymous (GA) [Gamblers Anonymous Publishing Inc.; Gamblers Anonymous International Service Office]
1306 Monte Vista Ave., Ste. 5
Upland, CA 91786
Ph: (909)931-9056
Fax: (909)931-9059
Co. E-mail: isomain@gamblersanonymous.org
URL: http://www.gamblersanonymous.org/ga
Contact: G. Andre, Executive Secretary
Description: Men and women who have joined together in order to stop gambling and to help other compulsive gamblers do the same; is self-supporting, declines outside contributions, and neither opposes nor endorses outside causes. **Founded:** 1957. **Geographic Preference:** National.

7262 ■ Great Plains Indian Gaming Association
PO Box 1433
Bismarck, ND 58502
Ph: (701)255-9275
URL: http://gpiga.com
Contact: J. Kurt Luger, Executive Director
Description: A voluntary association comprised of 24 federally recognized Tribal Nations in the Great Plains region that works to protect and promote the Tribal gaming industry.

7263 ■ National Association of Administrators for Disordered Gambling Services
PO Box 572
Wheatland, CA 95692
Ph: (916)663-8714
URL: http://naadgs.org
Contact: Nancy Murray, President

Description: A national membership organization of state administrators of public funds for problem gambling services. **Founded:** 2000.

7264 ■ National Association of Casino Party Operators (NACPO)
712 H St. NE, Ste. 1079
Washington, DC 20002
Ph: (202)838-6843
Co. E-mail: admin@nacpo.org
URL: http://nacpo.org
Contact: Elaine Davidson, President
E-mail: info@elitecasinoevent.com
URL(s): nacpo.wildapricot.org
Facebook: www.facebook.com/nacpo
Linkedin: www.linkedin.com/company/national-association-of-casino-party-operators
YouTube: www.youtube.com/channel/UCWXsJx0GBzvLS-ZR-uxCdAA
Description: Casino party operators, party planners, party rental shop owners, theme party and special events operators, and others involved in casino party rental business. Strives to strengthen the casino and theme party industry and advance the industry into more geographical markets. Promotes members' interests. **Founded:** 1992. **Geographic Preference:** National.

7265 ■ National Council on Problem Gambling (NCPG)
730 11th St. NW, Ste. 601
Washington, DC 20001
Ph: (202)547-9204
Free: 800-522-4700
Fax: (202)547-9206
Co. E-mail: ncpg@ncpgambling.org
URL: http://www.ncpgambling.org
Contact: Phil Sherwood, President
Facebook: www.facebook.com/NCPGambling
Linkedin: www.linkedin.com/company/ncpg-usa
X (Twitter): x.com/NCPGambling
Instagram: www.instagram.com/ncpg_problemgambling
Description: Professionals in health, education, and law; recovering gamblers. Advocates for programs to assist problem gamblers and their families. Makes referrals for compulsive gamblers; seeks to stimulate the concern of the medical profession, educators, legislators, and the criminal justice system. Conducts training programs for professionals and information programs to encourage business management, educators, and the public to become aware of and to understand compulsive gambling. Compiles statistics; Administers national 24 hour toll-free helpline for individuals with gambling problems. **Founded:** 1972. **Geographic Preference:** National.

7266 ■ National Indian Gaming Association (NIGA)
224 2nd St. SE
Washington, DC 20003
Ph: (202)546-7711
URL: http://www.indiangaming.org
Contact: Jason Giles, Executive Director

Small Business Profiles · Gambling Organization/Service ■ 7283

E-mail: jramos@indiangaming.org
Facebook: www.facebook.com/IndianGaming1985
Linkedin: www.linkedin.com/company/indiangaming
  1985
X (Twitter): x.com/IndianGaming85
YouTube: www.youtube.com/channel/UC51-Hf
  _9Cw8bTlFmP5OQPQg
Description: Seeks to expand political self-determination of Indian nations. Cooperates with government agencies in the formulation and application of laws and regulations applicable to Indian gaming. Provides technical assistance and other support to tribal gaming establishments. **Founded:** 1985. **Educational Activities:** Election Meeting; National Indian Gaming Tradeshow & Convention (Annual). **Geographic Preference:** National.

7267 ■ National Indian Gaming Commission (NIGC)
90 K St. NE, Ste. 200
  Washington, DC 20002
Ph: (202)632-7003
Fax: (202)632-7066
Co. E-mail: contactus@nigc.gov
URL: http://www.nigc.gov
Contact: Sequoyah E. Simermeyer, Chairman
Facebook: www.facebook.com/NIGCgov
Linkedin: www.linkedin.com/company/national-indian
  -gaming-commission
X (Twitter): x.com/NIGCgov
YouTube: www.youtube.com/channel/
  UC9wbWwDJueEGSrswtzttL3Q
Description: An independent federal regulatory agency within the Department of the Interior and is committed to the prompt and efficient regulation of the Indian gaming industry. **Founded:** 1988.

7268 ■ National Tribal Gaming Commissioners & Regulators (NTGCR)
PO Box 454
  Oneida, WI 54155
Ph: (920)737-2814
Co. E-mail: dawnr@ntgcr.com
URL: http://www.ntgcr.com
Contact: Jamie Hummingbird, Chairman
Facebook: www.facebook.com/profile.php?id=1000
  64470860759
Description: An association that promotes cooperative relationships among the commissioners and regulators of Tribal gaming enterprises and other organizations. The organization also seeks to promote the exchange of thoughts, information and ideas which foster regulatory standards and enforcement that lead to consistent regulatory practices and methods of operations among its members.

7269 ■ North American Gaming Regulators Association (NAGRA)
1236 N Ave. W
  Missoula, MT 59801
Ph: (406)625-7051
Co. E-mail: info@nagra.org
URL: http://www.nagra.org
Contact: Jennifer LaMont, President
Facebook: www.facebook.com/NAGRA.org
Description: Works for the mutual exchange of regulatory techniques for training enforcement personnel; provides a medium for communication of common problems; offers resources to states enacting legislation; speaks on matters concerning nonprofit and related gambling. **Founded:** 1984. **Publications:** NAGRA News (Quarterly); Standards on Bingo; Standards on Pull-Tabs. **Geographic Preference:** Multinational.

7270 ■ VIXIO Regulatory Intelligence
1250 Connecticut Ave. NW, Ste. 700
  Washington, DC 20036
Ph: (202)261-3567
URL: http://vixio.com
Contact: Mike Woolfrey, Chief Executive Officer
Linkedin: www.linkedin.com/company/
  complianceonline-ltd
YouTube: www.youtube.com/channel/UCrM7RD
  1vGhmjD4sRi3Y1puw
Description: Provides businesses with the tools to easily understand, anticipate and comply with ever-changing regulation in the gambling regulation industry. **Founded:** 2006.

REFERENCE WORKS

7271 ■ "6 Ways Playing Poker Can Help You in Business (and 2 Ways It Can't)" in Entrepreneur (Oct. 23, 2015)
URL(s): www.entrepreneur.com/leadership/6-ways
  -playing-poker-can-help-you-in-business-an
  d-2-ways/250476
Ed: John Roa. **Released:** October 23, 2015. **Description:** Describes six ways in which playing poker can help you in business. **Availability:** Online.

7272 ■ "AG Warns Slots MBE Plan Risky" in Boston Business Journal (Vol. 29, May 27, 2011, No. 3, pp. 1)
Description: Attorney General Doug Gansler states that the law extending the minority business program on slots parlors contracting through 2018 could be open to lawsuits. He recommended that the state should conduct a study proving that minority- and women-owned businesses do not get a fair share in the gaming industry before it signs the bill to avoid lawsuits from majority-owned firms. **Availability:** Print; Online.

7273 ■ "Always Two Sides to a Chip: Sounding Off on the Issues" in South Florida Business Journal (Vol. 34, January 10, 2014, No. 25, pp. 14)
Pub: American City Business Journals, Inc.
Contact: Mike Olivieri, Executive Vice President
Released: January 10, 2014. **Price:** $4, Introductory 4-Week Offer(Digital & Print). **Description:** American Gaming Association CEO, Geoff Freeman and No Casinos president, John Sowinski, talk about gambling's track record in various cities in the U.S. Sowinski mentions that half of the casinos in Atlantic City, New Jersey have declared bankruptcy, while Freeman states that gambling is part of a multifaceted entertainment experience. **Availability:** Print; Online.

7274 ■ "As the Sports-Betting Industry Transforms, Entrepreneurs May Find It Hard to Get in on Gambling Profits -- but Related Businesses Will Thrive" in Entrepreneur (May 21, 2018)
URL(s): www.entrepreneur.com/starting-a-business/
  as-the-sports-betting-industry-transforms-en
  trepreneurs/313685
Ed: Kristi Dosh. **Released:** May 21, 2018. **Description:** Discusses how entrepreneurs may take advantage of opportunities to get in on gambling profits, but provides warnings about how to manage your risks. **Availability:** Online.

7275 ■ "Blatstein's North Broad St. Casino Plan in for Fight" in Philadelphia Business Journal (Vol. 28, April 20, 2012, No. 10, pp. 1)
Pub: Baltimore Business Journal
Contact: Rhonda Pringle, President
E-mail: rpringle@bizjournals.com
Price: $4, Introductory 4-Week Offer(Digital & Print). **Description:** There are concerns from the community about the proposed $500 million casino complex on North Broad Street in Philadelphia. A neighborhood association member does not see the casino as a positive development in the neighborhood while a local chef and business owner is calling on elected officials to oppose the casino. **Availability:** Print; Online.

7276 ■ "Caesars Deals a New Reality" in Memphis Business Journal (No. 35, April 4, 2014, No. 52, pp. 4)
Pub: American City Business Journals, Inc.
Contact: Mike Olivieri, Executive Vice President
Description: Caesars Entertainment Group has announced the closure of the Harrah's Tunica after attempts to sell it failed. Caesars lost $2.9 billion in 2013 after losing $1.5 billion in 2012 and is making moves to control the estimated $20 billion debt. The impact of the convention facility's closure to Tunica, Mississippi is also investigated. **Availability:** Print; Online.

7277 ■ Casino Gaming in the United States: A Research Guide
Pub: The Scarecrow Press Inc.
Contact: Jed Lyons, President
URL(s): rowman.com/Action/Search/_/Casino%
  20Gaming%20in%20the%20United%20States:%
  20A%20Research%20GuideCasino%20Gaming%
  20in%20the%20United%20States:%20A%20Re-
  search%20Guide
Description: Covers bibliography of nearly 900 books, articles, periodicals, Internet sites and government publications from 1985-94 on casino gambling. Also includes state gambling agencies, associations, Indian gaming locations, consultants, and public gaming companies. **Entries include:** For publications--Publication title, subject, author, web site address where applicable. For organizations--Name, address, phone. **Indexes:** Subject, author. **Availability:** Print.

7278 ■ "Casinos In Pitch Battle" in Philadelphia Business Journal (Vol. 28, July 20, 2012, No. 23, pp. 1)
Pub: Baltimore Business Journal
Contact: Rhonda Pringle, President
E-mail: rpringle@bizjournals.com
Description: The extent to which casinos in Philadelphia, Pennsylvania have invested in marketing and rebranding effortsin the Philadelphia-Atlantic City markets is explored. These efforts are part of the goal of the casinos to compete for customers considering that casinos contribute about $6 billion in taxes to Pennsylvania. Statistics pertaining to casinos and their advertising expenditures are presented. **Availability:** Print; Online.

7279 ■ "Designed to Deceive: How Gambling Distorts Reality and Hooks Your Brain" in The Conversation (August 13, 2018)
URL(s): theconversation.com/designed-to-deceive
  -how-gambling-distorts-reality-and-hooks-your-brain
  -91052
Ed: Mike Robinson. **Released:** August 13, 2018. **Description:** An addiction researcher examines the various aspects of gambling that make it so addictive and how the brain reacts to these types of situations. **Availability:** Online.

7280 ■ "A Dollar, a Dream, and a Cup of Joe" in Business Review Albany (Vol. 41, July 25, 2014, No. 18, pp. 6)
Description: Stewart Shops has boosted its revenues from selling lottery tickets. The company has reported $175.7 million in New York lottery sales in 2013. Steward also gets free publicity when there is a big winner. **Availability:** Print; Online.

7281 ■ "Entrepreneurs and Gamblers: Shared Traits" in Entrepreneur (Sept. 8, 2017)
URL(s): www.entrepreneur.com/en-za/starting-a-busi-
  ness/entrepreneurs-and-gamblers-shared-traits/
  330977
Ed: Jeff Broth. **Released:** September 08, 2017. **Description:** Describes the traits that successful business owners and gamblers may share and why it should come as no surprise that some of the most successful entrepreneurs are also big gamblers. **Availability:** Online.

7282 ■ "The Favorite In the Casino, Racino Race" in Business Review Albany (Vol. 41, July 25, 2014, No. 18, pp. 7)
Released: 2014. **Description:** The New York Government's plan to license four casinos could adversely impact the earnings of racinos. Racinos combine harness racing with video slot machines. The planned casinos are expected to attract racino customers creating competition. **Availability:** Print; Online.

7283 ■ "Fight Over Casino Funds Limits Kitty for MEDC" in Crain's Detroit Business (Vol. 24, January 21, 2008, No. 3, pp. 3)
Pub: Crain Communications Inc.
Contact: Barry Asin, President

Ed: Amy Lane. **Description:** Michigan Economic Development Corporation is facing uncertainty due to a Michigan American Indian tribe from the southwestern portion of the state withholding its 8 percent casino revenue share. **Availability:** Online.

7284 ■ *"Five Lessons in Entrepreneurship from the Worlds of Trading and Gambling" in Entrepreneur (Aug. 21, 2017)*
URL(s): www.entrepreneur.com/en-in/news-and-tren ds/five-lessons-in-entrepreneurship-from-the-worlds -of-trading/299047
Released: August 21, 2017. **Description:** Describes the parallels between trading and gambling on one hand and traditional entrepreneurship on the other. **Availability:** Online.

7285 ■ *"Former Prov. Mayor Sees Potential in Newport Grand" in Providence Business News (Vol. 29, July 21, 2014, No. 16, pp. 4)*
Pub: American City Business Journals, Inc.
Contact: Mike Olivieri, Executive Vice President
URL(s): pbn.com/former-prov-mayor-sees-potential -in-newport-grand98638
Description: Joseph R. Paolino, Jr., managing partner at Paolino Properties and former Providence Mayor, believes introducing table games to Newport Grand can help the gambling casino generate needed revenues. Paolino notes that if voters approve a ballot referendum to authorize table games in November, he and his partners will acquire and renovate Newport Grand as an entertainment center. **Telecommunication Services:** Daddona@pbn.com.

7286 ■ *"Gambling Firms See $7B to $8B Sports Betting Market by 2025" in The Chicago Tribune (November 5, 2019)*
URL(s): www.chicagotribune.com/sports/national -sports/sns-sports-gambling-betting-market-billions -dollars-20191105-pyvqzwbqxbesvccoovkftffqp4-s tory.html
Ed: Wayne Parry. **Released:** November 05, 2019. **Description:** Now that sports betting is legalized, the industry is quickly growing. The investment firm, Morgan Stanley, is predicting the market will generate $7 billion in revenue by 2025, with top-rated casinos making similar predictions. **Availability:** Online.

7287 ■ *"Gaming Infrastructure Paves Ready Path for Manufacturing" in Memphis Business Journal (No. 35, February 14, 2014, No. 45, pp. 4)*
Pub: American City Business Journals, Inc.
Contact: Mike Olivieri, Executive Vice President
Description: The city of Tunica, Mississippi is trying to expand its reputation as a gaming destination into manufacturing in an effort seek new opportunities for economic development and revenue. German crankshaft manufacturer, Feurer Powertrain, is building a $140 million manufacturing facility that will open in late 2014. **Availability:** Online.

7288 ■ *Gaming Means (Small) Business: How Casinos Boost Local Economies*
URL(s): www.americangaming.org/resources/new-stu dy-casino-industry-essential-to-small-business -growth/
Released: April 20, 2017. **Description:** Presents information on how the casino gaming industry is driving small business growth across the U.S. **Availability:** PDF.

7289 ■ *"Giant Garages Could Rise Up in Downtown Cincinnati" in Business Courier (Vol. 27, October 22, 2010, No. 25, pp. 1)*
Pub: Business Courier
Ed: Dan Monk. **Description:** More than 2,500 new parking spaces could rise up to the eastern edge of downtown Cincinnati, Ohio as public and private investors collect resources for new garage projects. These projects are expected to accommodate almost 1,500 monthly parkers who will lose access at Broadway Commons due to the construction of Harrah's casino. **Availability:** Print; Mailing list; Online.

7290 ■ *"Growth in Sleepy Perryville Hinges on Success of New Casino" in Baltimore Business Journal (Vol. 28, November 19, 2010, No. 28, pp. 1)*
Pub: Baltimore Business Journal
Contact: Rhonda Pringle, President
E-mail: rpringle@bizjournals.com
Ed: Rachel Bernstein. **Description:** Penn National Gaming Company's Hollywood Casino in Perryville, Maryland has been betting on the slot machines to lure slot players to the region to boost the town's growth. The success of Maryland's first casino is expected to lead to the development of land in the area. **Availability:** Print; Online.

7291 ■ *"Harrah's Tunica Shutting Down In June" in Memphis Business Journal (No. 35, March 28, 2014, No. 51, pp. 3)*
Pub: American City Business Journals, Inc.
Contact: Mike Olivieri, Executive Vice President
Released: Weekly. **Price:** $4, introductory 4-week offer(Digital only). **Description:** Caesars Entertainment Corporation is closing down Harrah's Tunica in June 2014 in an effort to ensure the long-term viability of its remaining operations in Memphis, Tennessee. The company will find positions for the displaced employees and some could be placed at Caesar's Horseshoe Casino & Hotel and Tunica Roadhouse. **Availability:** Print; Online.

7292 ■ *"Horse Racing Industry Cries Foul Over Budget Switch" in Philadelphia Business Journal (Vol. 31, March 23, 2012, No. 6, pp. 1)*
Pub: Baltimore Business Journal
Contact: Rhonda Pringle, President
E-mail: rpringle@bizjournals.com
Price: Introductory 4-Week Offer(Digital & Print); $4, Introductory 4-Week Offer(Digital Only). **Description:** Pennsylvania Governor Tom Corbett's proposal to slash $72 million from the Horse Racing Development Fund is seen to adversely impact the sector. The plan has been criticized by track operators, trainers, owners and horse breeders. **Availability:** Print; Online.

7293 ■ *"How to Get in on the Online Gambling Craze" in Entrepreneur (August 29, 2022)*
URL(s): www.entrepreneur.com/growing-a-business/ how-to-get-in-on-the-online-gambling-craze/431297
Ed: John Rampton. **Released:** August 29, 2022. **Description:** Includes information on how small business entrepreneurs can cash in on the online gambling craze. **Availability:** Online.

7294 ■ *"IGT Expands Partnership with Olympic Entertainment Group" in Travel & Leisure Close-Up (October 8, 2012)*
Description: International Game Technology is partnering with Olympic Jarve and Olympic Ulemiste properties by providing IGT Cloud solution. IGT is a provider of gaming systems technology which will increase the gambling experience for Olympic game players. **Availability:** Print; Online.

7295 ■ *"Internet Cafe Logging in to Chardon Plaza?" in News-Herald (July 16, 2011)*
Ed: Betsy Scott. **Description:** Pearl's High Rollers Inc. applied for an Internet sweepstakes cafe license that would reside in a vacant space in Chardon Plaza. City officials have created regulations for such businesses and Pearl's applied for a license and is awaiting approval. **Availability:** Online.

7296 ■ *"Las Vegas Casino Sues NHL's Evander Kane over $500K in Gambling Markers" in Las Vegas Review-Journal (November 11, 2019)*
URL(s): www.reviewjournal.com/crime/courts/las-ve gas-casino-sues-nhls-evander-kane-over-500k-in -gambling-markers-1886381/
Ed: Mick Akers. **Released:** November 05, 2019. **Description:** San Jose Sharks forward Evander Kane was sued by The Cosmopolitan for failing to pay back $500,000 worth of gambling markers. **Availability:** Online.

7297 ■ *"Lotteries Scratch Their Way to Billions" in Saint Louis Business Journal (Vol. 31, August 19, 2011, No. 52, pp. 1)*
Pub: Saint Louis Business Journal
Contact: Robert Bobroff, President
E-mail: rbobroff@bizjournals.com
Ed: Kelsey Volkmann. **Description:** Missouri Lottery reported $1 billion in sales in 2011. A six-fold increase in the lottery's advertising budget is seen to drive the revenue increase; a 4.5 percent rise in its scratch-off tickets and new sponsorships has also contributed to the development. **Availability:** Print; Online.

7298 ■ *"Maryland Casinos Face Atlantic City's $150M Might" in Baltimore Business Journal (Vol. 30, June 1, 2012, No. 4, pp. 1)*
Pub: American City Business Journals, Inc.
Contact: Mike Olivieri, Executive Vice President
Ed: Gary Haber. **Description:** Atlantic City has launched a campaign to attract visitors from the East Coast. The campaign is part of the city's $150 million marketing plan, which markets the city not for its casinos but as a shopping destination. Executive comments included. **Availability:** Online.

7299 ■ *"Maryland Ready to Defend Slots Minority Policy" in Boston Business Journal (Vol. 29, July 8, 2011, No. 9, pp. 3)*
Pub: Boston Business Journal
Contact: Carolyn M. Jones, President
E-mail: cmjones@bizjournals.com
Ed: Scott Dance. **Description:** The legality of Maryland's minority inclusion policy may be put under scrutiny once the lawsuit filed by rejected slots developer Baltimore City Entertainment Group on July 5, 2011 is heard in court. The lawsuit aims to stop the bidding process on a proposed casino in Baltimore because the minority policy amounts to reverse discrimination. **Availability:** Print; Online.

7300 ■ *"Massachusetts Gaming Commission Hiring Consultants for Sports Betting Launch" in PlayUSA (Oct. 14, 2022)*
URL(s): www.playusa.com/consultants-commission -investigations-massachusetts-sports-betting/
Ed: Nicholaus Garcia. **Released:** October 14, 2022. **Description:** Discusses the role Massachusetts sports betting consultants will play as sports betting launches in the state. **Availability:** Online.

7301 ■ *Massachusetts Gaming Regulators Contract Consultants to Expedite Sports Betting*
URL(s): www.casino.org/news/massachusetts-gam ing-regulators-contract-sports-betting-consultants/
Ed: Devin O'Connor. **Released:** October 14, 2022. **Description:** Discusses why the Massachusetts Gaming Commission has looked to hiring consultants and independent third parties to accelerate the process of legal sports betting operations. **Availability:** Online.

7302 ■ *"Much Work Still To Be Done on Meadows Deal" in Pittsburgh Business Times (Vol. 33, May 16, 2014, No. 44, pp. 3)*
Pub: American City Business Journals, Inc.
Contact: Mike Olivieri, Executive Vice President
Released: Weekly. **Price:** $4, introductory 4-week offer(Digital only). **Description:** Real estate investment trust, Gaming and Leisure Properties Inc., is acquiring the Meadows Racetrack & Casino in Washington, Pennsylvania from Cannery Casino & Resorts LLC in a $465 million deal. The process of finding an operator and getting the license transfers approved will be the next critical step following the deal. **Availability:** Print; Online.

7303 ■ *"New Jersey Passes Nevada in Sports Gambling — Should Las Vegas Be Worried?" in MarketWatch (November 5, 2019)*
URL(s): www.marketwatch.com/story/new-jersey -passed-nevada-in-sports-betting-last-month-shoul d-las-vegas-be-worried-2019-11-04?ns=prod/ accounts-mw

Ed: Weston Blasi. **Released:** November 05, 2019. **Description:** Individual states, thanks to the Supreme Court, can now decide if they will offer legalized sports betting. New Jersey is dominating this market, which is surpassing the gambling capital of Nevada. **Availability:** Online.

7304 ■ *"Online Gambling Businesses You Can Start from Home"* in *Home Business (Nov. 3, 2020)*
URL(s): homebusinessmag.com/businesses/special-types/online-gambling-businesses-start-home/
Released: November 03, 2020. **Availability:** Online.

7305 ■ *"Place Your Bets: Horse, Dog Racing Kiosks Bring the Track to Local Bars"* in *Dickinson Press (March 28, 2012)*
Pub: McClatchy Tribune Information Services
Contact: Patrick J. Talamantes, President
Description: MTPBets USA Inc., headquartered in Wilmington, Delaware, installed self-betting kiosks in businesses located in southwest North Dakota. The kiosks will feature live horse and dog races. **Availability:** Online.

7306 ■ *"Power Partnerships"* in *Business Courier (Vol. 27, October 22, 2010, No. 25, pp. 1)*
Description: The $400 million Harrah's casino and the $47 million redevelopment and expansion of Washington Park are project aimed at boosting the economy in downtown Cincinnati, Ohio. These projects will be done in cooperation with the National Association for the Advancement of Colored People. Insights into the role of minority-owned businesses in regional economic development are explored. **Availability:** Print; Online.

7307 ■ *"The Race Is On For High-Stakes Casino Gambling in Florida"* in *South Florida Business Journal (Vol. 34, January 10, 2014, No. 25, pp. 12)*
Pub: American City Business Journals, Inc.
Contact: Mike Olivieri, Executive Vice President
Released: Weekly. **Price:** $8, Introductory 4-week offer(Digital & Print). **Description:** The Florida Senate is considering the possibility of expanding the limits of gambling in the state by establishing destination casinos. However, Professor Bob Jarvis believes that placing limits on the gambling sector could hinder economic development. **Availability:** Print; Online.

7308 ■ *"The Real Risk of Entrepreneurial Strengths Becoming Addictive Weaknesses"* in *Entrepreneur (Oct. 18, 2016)*
URL(s): www.entrepreneur.com/living/the-real-risk-of-entrepreneurial-strengths-becoming/283574
Ed: Marvin Dumont. **Released:** October 18, 2016. **Description:** Provides information on why business entrepreneurs may be susceptible to gambling. **Availability:** Online.

7309 ■ *SBA Expands Loan Program to Include Small Gaming Companies*
URL(s): www.bhfs.com/insights/alerts-articles/2020/sba-expands-loan-program-to-include-small-gaming-companies
Ed: William Moschella. **Released:** April 24, 2020. **Description:** Discusses revised guidelines from the Small Business Administration that allow otherwise eligible small gaming businesses to be able to participate in the Paycheck Protection Program ("PPP"). **Availability:** Online.

7310 ■ *"Table Games Get a Leg Up"* in *Philadelphia Business Journal (Vol. 28, January 15, 2010, No. 48, pp. 1)*
Pub: Philadelphia Business Journal
Contact: Sierra Quinn, Director
E-mail: squinn@bizjournals.com
Ed: Athena D. Merritt, Peter Van Allen. **Description:** Casino operators expect the addition of live table games such as poker and blackjack at existing and planned casinos in Philadelphia will generate 1,000 new jobs. Most of the jobs will be dealers and floor supervisors. **Availability:** Online.

7311 ■ *"A Trader Gets a Better Deal From the IRS Than an Investor"* in *Barron's (Vol. 88, March 31, 2008, No. 13, pp. 56)*
Pub: Dow Jones & Company Inc.
Contact: Almar Latour, Chief Executive Officer
Ed: Dan McGuire. **Description:** There is a $3,000 a year annual limit to deducting investor's losses and normal investment expenses are purportedly deductible as miscellaneous expenses on Schedule A only to the extent that they exceed two percent of adjusted gross income. Professional gamblers who can use Schedule C are unable deduct a net gaming loss against income from any other sources. **Availability:** Online.

7312 ■ *"Tribes Roll Dice On Ventures as They Push Outside of Casinos"* in *Business Journal (Vol. 32, May 30, 2014, No. 1, pp. 8)*
Pub: American City Business Journals, Inc.
Contact: Mike Olivieri, Executive Vice President
Released: Weekly. **Price:** $4, introductory 4-week offer(Digital only). **Description:** The growing trend of American Indian tribes in Minnesota diversifying their investments in other sectors beyond gambling is examined. The Shakopee Mdewakanton Sioux Community invested in the 342-room JW Marriott hotel that is being built at the Mall of America. The Mille Lacs Band of Ojibwe also acquired Crowne Plaza St. Paul Riverfront Hotel and the Double Tree in early 2013. **Availability:** Print; Online.

7313 ■ *United States Online Gambling Market to Reach US 7.61 Billion by 2028*
URL(s): www.globenewswire.com/en/news-release/2022/09/01/2508751/0/en/United-States-Online-Gambling-Market-to-Reach-US-7-61-Billion-by-2028-BlueWeave-Consulting.html
Released: September 01, 2022. **Description:** Presents information from a study by BlueWeave Consulting that revealed statistics on the growing online gambling market. **Availability:** PDF; Online.

7314 ■ *"Wagering Opportunities"* in *Memphis Business Journal (No. 35, April 4, 2014, No. 52, pp. 8)*
Pub: American City Business Journals, Inc.
Contact: Mike Olivieri, Executive Vice President
Released: April 14, 2017. **Description:** Rankings of casino-hotels in the Memphis Metropolitan Area are presented. Rankings were based on the size of gaming space. **Availability:** Print; Online.

7315 ■ *"What Happens in Vegas Could Happen in Baltimore, Too"* in *Boston Business Journal (Vol. 29, June 17, 2011, No. 6, pp. 1)*
Pub: Boston Business Journal
Contact: Carolyn M. Jones, President
E-mail: cmjones@bizjournals.com
Ed: Daniel J. Sernovitz. **Description:** At least 36 companies expressed their interest in developing a casino in South Baltimore following the state commission's announcement for bids. Developers have until July 28, 2011 to submit their proposals. Baltimore's strong economy is the major factor for the interest, yet the fact that blackjack and poker are outlawed in Maryland could be a drawback. **Availability:** Print; Online.

STATISTICAL SOURCES

7316 ■ *Online Gambling Market in US 2022-2026*
URL(s): www.marketresearch.com/Infiniti-Research-Limited-v2680/Online-Gambling-30995627/
Price: $2,500. **Description:** Report offering an up-to-date analysis regarding the current U.S. gambling market scenario, latest trends and drivers, and the overall market environment. The market is driven by easing of government regulations and wider reach of online gambling. In addition, easing of government regulations is anticipated to boost the growth of the market as well. **Availability:** Download.

7317 ■ *Online Gambling Services in the US - Industry Market Research Report*
URL(s): www.marketresearch.com/IBISWorld-v2487/Online-Gambling-Services-Research-31871466/
Price: $1,020. **Description:** Report covering the scope, size, disposition and growth of the online gambling industry including the key sensitivities and success factors. Also included are five-year industry forecasts, growth rates and an analysis of the industry key players and their market shares. **Availability:** Download.

TRADE PERIODICALS

7318 ■ *Anthony Curtis' Las Vegas Advisor*
Pub: Huntington Press
Contact: Anthony Curtis, Publisher
E-mail: publisher@huntingtonpress.com
URL(s): www.lasvegasadvisor.com/newsletters
Facebook: www.facebook.com/lasvegasadvisor
X (Twitter): x.com/LVA_Tweet
YouTube: www.youtube.com/c/LasVegasAdvisorSHOW
Released: Monthly **Price:** $50, for per year. **Description:** Acts as a consumer's information source for Las Vegas visitors. Recurring features include letters to the editor, a calendar of events, book reviews, notices of publications available, and columns titled Couponomy, Top Ten Las Vegas Values, Dining, Entertainment News, Advance Planner, Letters & Tips, Gambling, Fast Track, Last Second Flash, Accommodations, Comp City, and Extra Stuff. **Availability:** Print; Download; Online.

7319 ■ *Current Blackjack News (CBJN)*
Pub: Pi Yee Press
URL(s): bj21.com/cbjn
Released: Monthly **Price:** $109, Individuals for per year; $42, for per quarter; $19, Single issue for pdf; $129, for per year; $17, Single issue. **Description:** Features reviews of rule changes for the game of blackjack and reports on casinos in Nevada, Mississippi, Louisiana, Illinois, Iowa, New Jersey, New York, Connecticut, Minnesota, and other areas with legalized casino gambling. Announces new casino openings, as well as highlighting profitable opportunities to win at casinos. **Availability:** Print; PDF; Online.

TRADE SHOWS AND CONVENTIONS

7320 ■ *NASPL Annual Conference*
North American Association of State and Provincial Lotteries (NASPL)
7757 Auburn Rd., Unit No. 7
Concord Township, OH 44077
Ph: (440)361-7962
Co. E-mail: info@nasplhq.org
URL: http://www.naspl.org
Contact: Gretchen Corbin, President
URL(s): www.naspl.org/events
Frequency: Annual. **Description:** Lottery equipment, supplies, and services. **Audience:** Industry professionals. **Principal Exhibits:** Lottery equipment, supplies, and services. Dates and Locations: 2025 Sep 09-12 Niagara Falls, ON; 2026 Sep 21-24 Orlando, FL.

CONSULTANTS

7321 ■ *The Casino Institute*
8152 Miramar Rd.
San Diego, CA 92126
Ph: (619)741-2200
Co. E-mail: info@thecasinoinstitute.com
URL: http://www.thecasinoinstitute.com
Contact: Allyson Ott, Chief Executive Officer
E-mail: allyson@thecasinoinstitute.com
Facebook: www.facebook.com/thecasinoinstitute
Instagram: www.instagram.com/thecasinoinstitute
Description: Specializes in casino consulting and table games dealer training services. **Founded:** 2004.

7322 ■ Gambling Consulting Expert
Calea Dorobantilor 17
Cluj Napoca, Romania
Ph: 40 773 939 033
Co. E-mail: hello@gamblingconsulting.expert
URL: http://gamblingconsulting.expert
Description: International gambling consultancy whose services include gambling licensing, offshore bank accounts, market research, and regulatory nees. **Founded:** 2004.

7323 ■ Global Promotional Sourcing Inc. (GPS)
12600 Chaparral Rd., Ste. 100
Henderson, NV 89044
Ph: (702)938-2250
Co. E-mail: info@gpsteam.com
URL: http://www.gpspromotions.com
Contact: Steve Raucher, President
Linkedin: www.linkedin.com/company/global-promotional-sourcing
Description: A marketing services company utilizing hard and soft goods to promote the brand and image of our clients, primarily in the gaming industry, and increase player loyalty. **Founded:** 2001.

7324 ■ The Innovation Group (TIG)
9200 E Mineral Ave., Ste. 100
Centennial, CO 80112
Ph: (303)798-7711
Co. E-mail: info@theinnovationgroup.com
URL: http://theinnovationgroup.com
Contact: Michael Soll, President
Facebook: www.facebook.com/innovgrp
Linkedin: www.linkedin.com/company/-tig-the-innovation-group
X (Twitter): x.com/InnovGrp
Description: A research and advisory firm in the gaming, entertainment, hospitality, tourism and leisure sectors. **Founded:** 1995.

7325 ■ L.E.K. Consulting LLC
75 State St., 19th Fl.
Boston, MA 02109
Contact: Kevin Parrales, Contact
Facebook: www.facebook.com/lekconsulting
Linkedin: www.linkedin.com/company/l-e-k--consulting
X (Twitter): x.com/LEK_Consulting
Instagram: www.instagram.com/lekconsulting
Description: Employs gaming consultants with expertise that spans lotteries, casinos, bingo, betting services, and online/mobile gaming. Offers services ranging from strategy development and business planning to strategy activation, mergers and acquisitions, and business performance improvement. Provides clients with a deep understanding of gaming markets and winning competitive strategies. **Scope:** Firm provides strategy consulting services. **Founded:** 1983. **Publications:** "Electric Perspectives: Rapid Response Planning"; "L.E.K. Publications in Chinese Media"; "Membership Has Its Share holder Rewards"; "Net Share holder Value"; "Creating Value Through Acquisitions," Journal of Business Strategy, Nov, 2007; "Translating Competitive Strength Into Bottom-Line Performance," Journal of Business Strategy, Sep, 2007; "The Mad Scramble for Market Share Can Trip Up Growth-Hungry Businesses," the Boston Globe, Aug, 2006; "Where Value Hides," 2006; "Expectations Investing," Harvard Business School Press, 2001; "Shareholder Value Insight"; "Executive Insights".

7326 ■ OC&C Strategy Consultants
3 Post Office Sq., Ste. 800, 8th Fl.
Boston, MA 02109
Ph: (212)301-0754
URL: http://www.occstrategy.com/en
Linkedin: www.linkedin.com/company/oc&c-strategy-consultants
Description: Advises businesses operating across a variety of models and channels, including fixed odds (e.g. casinos, lotteries), sportsbook (betting shops, online gambling) and gaming and e-sports.

7327 ■ Partis Solutions Ltd.
New York, NY
Ph: (415)694-0834
Co. E-mail: info@partissolutions.com
URL: http://partissolutions.com
Contact: Rob Dowling, Managing Partner
Description: Highly experienced in providing consulting and advisory services to the gaming and gambling sector worldwide.

7328 ■ SCCG Management
105 E Reno Ave., Ste. 8
Las Vegas, NV 89119
URL: http://sccgmanagement.com
Contact: Stephen Crystal, Chief Executive Officer
Description: Specializes in sports betting, iGaming, sports marketing, affiliate marketing, technology, intellectual property protection, product commercialization, esports, capital formation, M&A, joint ventures, casino management, and governmental and legal affairs for the casino and iGaming industry.

7329 ■ Spectrum Gaming Group
200 Lakeside Dr., Ste. 250
Horsham, PA 19044
Ph: (609)926-5100
Co. E-mail: solutions@spectrumgaming.com
URL: http://spectrumgaming.com
Contact: Fredric Gushin, Managing Director
Linkedin: www.linkedin.com/company/spectrum-gaming-group
X (Twitter): x.com/spectrumgaming
Description: A non-partisan consultancy that specializes in the economics, regulation and policy of legalized gambling worldwide. **Founded:** 1993.

7330 ■ Veriti Consulting LLC
8111 E Thomas Rd., Ste.120
Scottsdale, AZ 85251
Free: 877-520-1280
Co. E-mail: info@veriticonsulting.com
URL: http://truthbehindnumbers.com
Contact: Elizabeth B. Monty, Co-Founder Member
E-mail: lm@veriticonsulting.com
Description: Specializes in accounting and valuation services for the highly specialized casino and gaming industry. Our casino and gaming consultants have in-depth understanding of MICS/TICS, all state compact value drivers, gambling and casino valuation issues, and collaborating with gaming commissions and tribal government leaders.

PUBLICATIONS

7331 ■ *Casino Life*
Description: Daily source for up-to-date casino and gambling international industry news. Covers breaking gambling news, casino news stories, interviews and features. **Availability:** Electronic publishing.

7332 ■ *Casino Player Magazine*
URL(s): www.casinocenter.com/casino-player
Released: Monthly **Price:** $24, One year. Print and digital.; $37, Two years. Print and digital.; $53, Three years. Print and digital.; $9.95, One year. Digital only.
Description: Provides articles on casino life. **Availability:** Print; Online.

7333 ■ *Global Gaming Business Magazine*
URL(s): ggbmagazine.com
Released: Monthly **Description:** Monthly gaming trade publication focusing on the international casino industry. **Availability:** Online.

7334 ■ *Journal of Gambling Studies*
233 Spring St.
New York, NY 10013
Free: 866-839-0194
Fax: (212)460-1700
Co. E-mail: customerservice@springernature.com
URL: http://www.springer.com
Contact: Derk Haank, Chief Executive Officer
URL(s): link.springer.com/journal/10899
Released: Quarterly; March, June, September, December. **Description:** Journal covering research and discussion of the many and varied aspects of gambling behavior, both controlled and pathological. Disciplines covered include psychiatry, psychology, sociology, political science, criminology, and social work. **Availability:** Print; PDF; Download; Online.

7335 ■ *Strictly Slots*
URL(s): www.casinocenter.com/strictly-slots
Released: Monthly **Price:** $24, One year. Print and digital.; $37, Two years. Print and digital.; $53, Three years. Print and digital.; $9.95, One year. Digital only.
Description: Publishes articles concerning casino life and gambling. **Availability:** Print; Online.

7336 ■ *US Casino Magazine*
URL(s): uscasinomagazine.com
Description: A magazine that covers a variety of casino and gambling updates and stories. **Availability:** Online.

LIBRARIES

7337 ■ Atlantic City Free Public Library - Alfred M. Heston Collection
1 N Tennessee Ave.
Atlantic City, NJ 08401
URL: http://acfpl.org/ac-history-menu/atlantic-city-heritage-collections/15-heston-archives/50-alfred-m-heston.html
Description: Collection inlcudes Alfred Heston's contribution to the Atlantic city. **Scope:** Local History. **Services:** Copying; open to the public. **Founded:** 1901. **Holdings:** Collections. **Subscriptions:** journals; newspapers.

7338 ■ Loto-Quebec Centre de Documentation
500 Sherbrooke St. W
Montreal, QC, Canada H3A 3G6
URL: http://societe.lotoquebec.com/fr/medias-et-partenaires/centre-de-documentation
Scope: Lotteries, casinos, horse racing, video games, sports betting. **Services:** Interlibrary loan; copying; center open to the public. **Founded:** 1978. **Holdings:** 5,000 works created;1,200 artists. **Subscriptions:** 180 journals and other serials; 110 periodicals (includes journals).

7339 ■ University of Nevada, Las Vegas Special Collections Gaming Studies Collection
4505 S Maryland Pky.
Las Vegas, NV 89154-7010
URL: http://www.library.unlv.edu/speccol/collecting_strengths/gaming
Contact: William Eadington, Officer
Scope: Gambling; business of gaming; economic; social impacts; historical and cultural manifestations. **Services:** Copying; collection open to the public. **Founded:** 1966. **Holdings:** Figures not available.

7340 ■ Washoe County Law Library
Second Judicial District Ct.
75 Ct. St., Rm. 101
Reno, NV 89501
Ph: (775)328-3250
Co. E-mail: lawlibrary@washoecourts.us
URL: http://www.washoecourts.com/LawLibrary
Contact: Sarah Bates, Librarian, Law
Scope: Law. **Services:** Open to the public; copying; scanning; Wi-Fi; printing. **Founded:** 1915. **Holdings:** Figures not available.

RESEARCH CENTERS

7341 ■ McGill University - International Centre for Youth Gambling Problems and High-Risk Behaviors (YGI) [Centre International d'Étude sur le Je et les Comportements à Risque Chez les Jeunes]
3724, McTavish St.
Montreal, QC, Canada H3A 1Y2
Ph: (514)398-1391
Co. E-mail: ygi.educ@mcgill.ca
URL: http://www.youthgambling.com
Contact: Dr. Jeffrey Derevensky, Director

Facebook: www.facebook.com/International-Centre-for-Youth-Gambling-Problems-and-High-Risk-Behaviors-212440398797041
YouTube: www.youtube.com/user/YouthGamblingIntl
Description: Integral unit of McGill University. **Scope:** Youth gambling and risk-taking behaviors. **Founded:** 1992. **Publications:** *Journal of Gambling Studies*; *YGI Newsletter* (Quarterly).

7342 ■ Pennsylvania Family Institute (PFI)
23 N Front St.
 Harrisburg, PA 17101-1606
Ph: (717)545-0600
Fax: (717)545-8107
Co. E-mail: mail@pafamily.org
URL: http://pafamily.org
Facebook: www.facebook.com/PAFamily
X (Twitter): x.com/PFIpolicy
Instagram: www.instagram.com/pafamilycouncil
YouTube: www.youtube.com/channel/UCP2jA5MBIwEhPIswMYc9pxg
Description: Independent, nonprofit research and education association. Assists advocacy groups in planning seminars and conferences. **Scope:** Family issues as they relate to government policy, including divorce, day-care, parenting, drug abuse, abortion, welfare, gambling, youth culture, and education. **Founded:** 1989. **Publications:** *Pennsylvania Citizen Magazine Newsletter* (Quarterly); *Pennsylvania Families & Schools* (Quarterly); *PFI Research Reports*. **Educational Activities:** CME seminars in Pennsylvania on life issues; sex education and other topics; PFI Physicians Resource Council meetings.

Genealogy Service

ASSOCIATIONS AND OTHER ORGANIZATIONS

7343 ▪ Board for Certification of Genealogists (BCG)
PO Box 14291
 Washington, DC 20044
Co. E-mail: office@bcgcertification.org
URL: http://www.bcgcertification.org
Contact: Faye Jenkins Stallings, President
E-mail: president@bcgcertification.org
X (Twitter): x.com/BCGenealogists
Description: Administers standards of professional genealogical research. Grants certification in classifications of Certified Genealogists, Certified Genealogical Lecturers, and Certified Genealogical Instructors. **Founded:** 1964. **Publications:** Onboard (3/year). **Geographic Preference:** National.

7344 ▪ Czechoslovak Genealogical Society International (CGSI) - Research Collection
PO Box 16225
 Saint Paul, MN 55116-0225
Ph: (651)964-2322
Co. E-mail: info@cgsi.org
URL: http://cgsi.org
Contact: Kevin Hurbanis, President
Facebook: www.facebook.com/cgsi.org
YouTube: www.youtube.com/c/CGSIorg
Description: Promotes research and interest in Czechoslovakian culture and genealogy. Disseminates research materials. **Scope:** Czech and Slovak history; genealogy and culture. **Services:** Copying. **Holdings:** 1,200 volumes; Maps; gazetteers; books; directories. **Publications:** Czechoslovak Surname Index; Naše rodina (Quarterly). **Educational Activities:** CGSI Genealogical and Cultural Conference (Biennial). **Geographic Preference:** National.

7345 ▪ Gottscheer Heritage and Genealogy Association Inc. (GHGA)
PO Box 725
 Louisville, CO 80027-0725
Co. E-mail: rmrees58@socal.rr.com
URL: http://gottschee.org
Contact: Elfriede Stiene Stonitsch, President
E-mail: stonitsel@aol.com
Facebook: www.facebook.com/people/Gottscheer
 -Heritage-and-Genealogy-Association-GHGA/1000
 64549248077
Description: Preserves the history of the Gottschee region. Conducts historical and genealogical research on the Gottschee Region. **Founded:** 1992. **Publications:** The Gottscheer Tree (Quarterly); The Gottscheer Connection (Triennial). **Educational Activities:** Gottscheer Heritage and Genealogy Association Conference and Annual Meeting (Annual). **Geographic Preference:** National.

7346 ▪ Italian Genealogical Group (IGG)
PO Box 626
 Bethpage, NY 11714-0626
URL: http://www.italiangen.org
Contact: Michael Cassara, President
Facebook: www.facebook.com/I
 talianGenealogicalGroup
Description: Individuals of Italian descent. Promotes study of Italian family history and genealogy. Serves as a clearinghouse on Italian history, culture, and genealogy. **Founded:** 1993. **Publications:** Italian Genealogical Newsletter (Monthly). **Geographic Preference:** National.

7347 ▪ Lancaster Mennonite Historical Society (LMHS) - Library
2215 Millstream Rd.
 Lancaster, PA 17602-1499
Ph: (717)393-9745
Fax: (717)290-1585
Co. E-mail: customercare@mennonitelife.org
URL: http://www.lmhs.org
Facebook: www.facebook.com/MennoniteLife
X (Twitter): x.com/MennoniteLife
Instagram: www.instagram.com/mennonitelife
Description: Individuals interested in the historical background, religious thought and expression, culture, and genealogy of Mennonite- and Amish-related groups originating in Pennsylvania. Sponsors field trips and exhibits. Maintains speakers' bureau, library, archives and museum. Conducts historical and genealogical seminars, research publications, and children's programs. Compiles statistics. **Scope:** Mennonites and interrelated communities. **Services:** Open to the students; Nonmembers (5.00 per day). **Founded:** 1958. **Holdings:** Books; papers; artifacts. **Publications:** Pennsylvania Mennonite Heritage (Quarterly). **Educational Activities:** Lancaster Mennonite Historical Society Genealogy Conference (Annual). **Geographic Preference:** Multinational.

7348 ▪ National Public Records Research Association (NPRRA)
110 Horizon Dr., Ste. 210
 Raleigh, NC 27615
Ph: (919)459-2078
Fax: (919)459-2075
Co. E-mail: info@nprra.org
URL: http://nprra.org
Contact: Irene Motta, President
E-mail: imotta@ibcf.com
Facebook: www.facebook.com/nprra
X (Twitter): x.com/nprra
Description: Companies that provide research and information from public records. **Founded:** 1981. **Geographic Preference:** National.

7349 ▪ New Canaan Historical Society (NCHS) - Library
13 Oenoke Ridge Rd.
 New Canaan, CT 06840
Ph: (203)966-1776
Co. E-mail: info@nchistory.org
URL: http://www.nchistory.org
Contact: Lawrence Caldwell, President
Description: Individuals interested in the history of New Canaan, CT. Seeks to "bring together and arrange the historical events of the town of New Canaan and the genealogies of the families who have lived in town". Sponsors research and educational programs; serves as a clearinghouse on the history of New Canaan, CT; maintains six historical structures; operates museums within these structures. **Scope:** History of New Canaan; property; rural cemeteries; center school; town events; architecture and antiques. **Services:** Library open to the public. **Founded:** 1889. **Holdings:** 3,500 volumes; 30,000 papers; manuscripts; newspapers; photographs; records; documents; photographs. **Publications:** Tydings (Quarterly). **Educational Activities:** NCHS Ice Cream Social (Annual). **Geographic Preference:** National.

REFERENCE WORKS

7350 ▪ "10 Tools for Your Genealogy Research That You Never Thought You'd Need" in Ancestral Findings
URL(s): ancestralfindings.com/10-tools-for-your-ge
 nealogy-research-that-you-never-thought-you
 d-need/
Description: Researching genealogy can be challenging, and full of surprises. Listed here are ten tools the average researcher will find useful to help complete tasks. **Availability:** Online.

7351 ▪ "25 Best Genealogy Websites for Beginners" in Family Tree
URL(s): www.familytreemagazine.com/premium/
 25-best-genealogy-websites-for-beginners/
Ed: Sunny Jane Morton. **Description:** A list of the best internet resources available for those interested in conducting genealogy research. Gives the price and a description of the service, which services are free, and which are membership only. **Availability:** Online.

7352 ▪ Address Book for Germanic Genealogy
Pub: Genealogical Publishing Company Inc.
URL(s): genealogical.com/store/address-book-for
 -germanic-genealogy
Ed: Ernest Thode. **Released:** Published: 1997, Sixth Edition. **Price:** $31.50, Single issue. **Description:** Covers over 2,700 sources useful for genealogical researchers with interest in Germany, Austria, Switzerland, and other German-speaking areas; includes about 275 European genealogical societies, 282 European governmental archives, 194 American societies, 380 European religious archives, 175 American religious archives, 770 European municipal archives, 254 genealogists, and numerous libraries, publishers, museums, organizations, etc. **Entries include:** Name of source, address, brief description. **Arrangement:** By type of resource. **Availability:** Print; Online.

7353 ▪ Association of Professional Genealogists Directory
Pub: Association of Professional Genealogists
Contact: Annette Burke Burke Lyttle, President

URL(s): members.apgen.org/members/directory/search_APG.php?org_id=APG
Description: Covers member genealogists and related research services. **Entries include:** Genealogist's name or company name, address; telephone, fax, e-mail biography. **Arrangement:** Geographical. **Indexes:** Institutional members, geographical speciality, research speciality, related service, member residence by state. **Availability:** Online.

7354 ■ *"Blackstone to Acquire Ancestry.com for $4.7 Billion"* **in Reuters (August 5, 2020)**
Ed: Chibuike Oguh. **Released:** August 05, 2020. **Description:** Blackstone Group Inc. has agreed to acquire Ancestry.com Inc., which also includes its debt load, from fellow private equity firms Silver Lake, Spectrum Equity, and Permira. However, GIC will still retain a stake in the company. **Availability:** Online.

7355 ■ *Family Tree Home Business - Genealogy & Ancestry*
Ed: Kelly Land. **Released:** December 28, 2018. **Description:** Discusses the family tree business as a start up idea, beginning with your own family tree, how much a genealogy business can make, and tips on getting started. **Availability:** Online.

7356 ■ *The Family Tree Problem Solver: Tried-and-True Tactics for Tracing Elusive Ancestors*
Ed: Marsha Hoffman Rising. **Released:** Third edition. **Price:** $17.34, Paperback; $11.99, E-Book. **Description:** A guide to helping solve genealogy problems that researchers normally come across. Provides helpful tips and work-arounds to some common issues. **Availability:** E-book; Print.

7357 ■ *French and French-Canadian Family Research*
Pub: Ye Olde Genealogie Shoppe
URL(s): www.yogs.com/general/foreign.html#French_and_French-Canadian_Research
Description: Publication includes list of French and French Canadian genealogical societies and provincial archives in French and French Canadian provinces. **Entries include:** Institution name, and address. **Arrangement:** Alphabetical. **Indexes:** Organization name.

7358 ■ *Genealogical Periodical Annual Index: Key to the Genealogical Literature*
Pub: Heritage Books Inc.
Contact: Marlene Towle, Founder
URL(s): heritagebooks.com/products/101-g2556
Ed: Laird C. Towle. **Released:** Annual; latest Volume 41. **Description:** Publication includes contact information for about 330 periodicals published by genealogical societies and genealogists and used in indexing surnames, place names, and related topics for this book. **Entries include:** Name of publication, name of publisher, address, issues indexed, title abbreviation used in book. Publication mainly consists of an index containing 14,000 genealogical citations (surnames, place names, etc.). **Arrangement:** Alphabetical by title abbreviation. **Availability:** Print.

7359 ■ *The Genealogist's Address Book*
Pub: Genealogical Publishing Company Inc.
URL(s): genealogical.com/store/the-genealogists-addressbook-6th-edition
Ed: Elizabeth Petty Bentley. **Released:** Last Edition: 6th. **Price:** $46.95, Individuals for e-book; $83.50, Individuals for Paperback. **Description:** Covers 27,000 archives, historical societies, libraries, and genealogical societies; religious and ethnic organizations, research centers, surname registries, hereditary societies, and other groups useful to persons doing genealogical research. **Entries include:** Name, address, phone, name and title of contact. **Arrangement:** Geographical. **Availability:** E-book; Print.

7360 ■ *"A Genealogy Business Is About Family"* **in Extra Income Over 55**
Ed: Craig Wallin. **Description:** For those with a passion for research and history, working on your family history is likely something you've started. This article discusses turning your passion into a genealogy business. **Availability:** Online.

7361 ■ *"A Glimpse Into the Thriving Business of Family History"* **in Deseret News (April 9, 2014)**
Ed: Trent Toone. **Released:** April 09, 2014. **Description:** Family history is a lucrative business. This article discusses the family history business, success factors, challenges, and how to utilize technology in this industry. **Availability:** Online.

7362 ■ *"How to Become a Professional Genealogist"* **in How to Become a Professional Genealogist (October 10, 2018)**
Ed: Kimberly Powell. **Released:** October 10, 2018. **Description:** Provides a list of steps to see if you have the necessary skill, experience, and expertise to offer your genealogical services to others on a fee basis. Includes tips on becoming a certified or accredited genealogist. **Availability:** Online.

7363 ■ *How to Do Everything: Genealogy*
Ed: George Morgan. **Released:** Fourth edition. **Price:** $17.81, Paperback; $14.49, E-Book. **Description:** Newly revised edition covers the tools, techniques, and data needed to complete a genealogy project. **Availability:** E-book; Print.

7364 ■ *"How to Start a Genealogy Business"* **in The Balance Small Business (June 25, 2019)**
Ed: Leslie Truex. **Released:** June 25, 2019. **Description:** Details what genealogists do, pros and cons of starting a genealogy business, and eight steps to take to start a home-based genealogy business. **Availability:** Online.

7365 ■ *In Search of Your German Roots: A Complete Guide to Tracing Your Ancestors in the Germanic Areas of Europe*
Pub: Genealogical Publishing Company Inc.
URL(s): genealogical.com/store/in-search-of-your-german-roots
Ed: Angus Baxter. **Released:** Latest Edition 5th; 2015. **Price:** $33.50, for hardcover; $23.50, for paperback; $13.50, for e-book. **Description:** Publication includes lists of genealogical associations in Germany and German genealogical societies in the United States. **Entries include:** Association name and address, names and titles of key personnel, and description of services provided. Principal content of publication is researching techniques for genealogists. **Arrangement:** Alphabetical. **Availability:** E-book; Print.

7366 ■ *"Interactive Stores a Big Part of Borders' Turnaround Plan"* **in Crain's Detroit Business (Vol. 24, February 18, 2008, No. 7, pp. 4)**
Pub: Crain Communications Inc.
Contact: Barry Asin, President
Ed: Nathan Skid. **Description:** Borders Group Inc. is using digital technology and interactive media as a part of the firm's turnaround plan. The digital store will allow shoppers to create CDs, download audio books, publish their own works, print photos and search family genealogy. **Availability:** Online.

7367 ■ *International Vital Records Handbook*
Pub: Genealogical Publishing Company Inc.
URL(s): genealogical.com/store/international-vital-records-handbook-7th-edition
Ed: Thomas Jay Kemp. **Price:** $93, for paperback; $104, for hard Cover; $58.95, for e-book. **Description:** Covers vital records offices for 67 countries and territories in North America, the British Isles and other English-speaking countries, and Europe. **Entries include:** Office name, address, phone, application fees, method of payment, description of holdings, actual application forms to use in obtaining copies of records, and alternative record locations. **Arrangement:** Geographical. **Availability:** E-book; Print; PDF.

7368 ■ *"Making a Living from Genealogy"* **in ThoughtCo. (March 17, 2017)**
Ed: Kimberly Powell. **Released:** March 17, 2017. **Description:** A genealogy expert provides guidelines for starting your own genealogy business. **Availability:** Online.

7369 ■ *Organize Your Genealogy: Strategies and Solutions for Every Researcher*
Ed: Drew Smith. **Released:** July 01, 2016. **Price:** $17.96, Paperback; $5.99, E-book. **Description:** Shows how to use the latest tools and technology to organize your genealogy research. **Availability:** E-book; Print.

7370 ■ *Research Like a Pro: A Genealogist's Guide*
Ed: Diana Elder, Nicole Dyer. **Released:** May 19, 2018. **Price:** $18.99, Paperback; $4.99, E-book. **Description:** An expert genealogist shares her step-by-step methods for those who need help in their search to complete their family history. Also includes samples and templates. **Availability:** E-book; Print.

7371 ■ *"Starting Up As A Professional Genealogist"* **in Professional Family History Blog (November 22, 2018)**
Released: November 22, 2018. **Description:** Provides tips from a professional genealogist related to how to start your own genealogy business and how to get accredited. **Availability:** Online.

7372 ■ *"Starting Your Genealogy Business"* **in The Armchair Genealogist Blog**
Ed: Lynn Palermo. **Description:** Discusses the valuable guides for genealogists offered by Thomas MacEntee at GenBiz Solutions. These guides will position you to fast track your family history business. **Availability:** Online.

7373 ■ *"Turn Your Genealogy Hobby Into a Side Business"* **in Business.com (May 1, 2019)**
Released: May 01, 2019. **Description:** A guide to starting a home-based genealogy business that focuses on four main areas: validating your business idea, determining whether you'll need funding and how to get it, legal steps, and ideas for training. **Availability:** Online.

7374 ■ *"What Is the Average Income for Genealogists?"* **in Chron (June 16, 2020)**
Released: June 16, 2020. **Description:** Genealogists study family lineages in genetic and historical contexts. This article discusses education and training, certification requirements, average salary, and 10 steps on how to become a genealogy researcher. **Availability:** Online.

7375 ■ *Zotero for Genealogy: Harnessing the Power of Your Research*
Ed: Donna Cox Baker. **Price:** $21.99, Paperback; $9.99, E-book. **Description:** A guide on how to use the Zotero download for genealogy research. The product eliminates bulky files, binders, papers and allows the user to keep all notes and citations on any computing device. **Availability:** E-book; Print.

TRADE PERIODICALS

7376 ■ *Genealogical Journal of Jefferson County, New York*
Pub: NewYorkAncestry.com
Ed: Patricia R. James. **Released:** Quarterly **Price:** $20, Individuals plus postage. **Description:** Journal of genealogical information. **Availability:** Print.

7377 ■ *Hunterdon Historical Record*
Pub: Hunterdon County Historical Society
Contact: David Harding, Administrator
E-mail: hunterdonhistoryadm@gmail.com
URL(s): hunterdonhistory.org/newsletters
Released: 3/year; Winter, Spring, and Fall. **Description:** Publishes local history and genealogy articles, as well as Society news. Recurring features include a collection, book reviews, and Notes and Queries, Acquisitions, and Family Associations. **Availability:** Print; Download; PDF.

7378 ■ *Immigration Digest*
Pub: Genealogical Institute Inc.
Contact: Arlene H. Eakle, President
E-mail: arlene@arleneeakle.com
URL(s): arleneeakle.com/pages/bio.shtml

Description: Reports on new resources to link immigrant ancestors with their origins. Includes analytical reviews of source books and passenger lists. **Availability:** Print.

7379 ■ ISGS Newsletter
Pub: Illinois State Genealogical Society
Contact: Vicki Mattson, President
URL(s): ilgensoc.org/mo_newsletter.php
Released: Bimonthly **Description:** Keeps members abreast of what is going on in Illinois and surrounding areas in genealogy. Recurring features include a question and answer column. **Availability:** Print; PDF; Online.

7380 ■ Loyalist Gazette
Pub: United Empire Loyalists' Association of Canada
Contact: Patricia Groom, President
E-mail: president@uelac.org
URL(s): www.uelac.org/publications.php#gazette
Ed: Robert McBride. **Released:** Semiannual; spring, fall. **Description:** Scholarly journal covering history and genealogy related to the United Empire Loyalists and The Revolutionary War period. **Availability:** Print; PDF; Online.

7381 ■ The Maple Leaflet
Pub: French-Canadian Genealogical Society of Connecticut
Contact: Germaine Hoffman, Director
URL(s): www.fcgsc.org/publications
Released: Semiannual; March and September. **Description:** Contains articles on French-Canadian Genealogical Society of Connecticut's library events and new acquisitions. **Availability:** Online.

7382 ■ Missouri State Genealogical Association Journal
Pub: Missouri State Genealogical Association
Contact: Cheryl Lang, First Vice President
E-mail: firstvp@mosga.org
URL(s): www.mosga.org/cpage.php?pt=16
Released: Quarterly **Description:** Journal covering genealogy in Missouri. **Availability:** Print; PDF; Online.

7383 ■ New England Historical and Genealogical Register (NEHGS)
Pub: New England Historic Genealogical Society
Contact: D. Brenton Simons, President
URL(s): www.americanancestors.org/publications/register
Ed: Henry B. Hoff. **Released:** Quarterly; winter, spring, summer, and fall. **Price:** $20, for annual. **Description:** Scholarly journal focusing on genealogy and history. **Availability:** Print; Download; PDF; Online.

7384 ■ Northern Arizona Genealogical Society Bulletin
Pub: Northern Arizona Genealogical Society
Contact: Lee Campbell, President
URL(s): www.nagsprescott.org/newsletters.html
Released: Quarterly; January, April, July, October. **Description:** Focuses on the Society's activities and provides genealogical information. **Availability:** PDF.

7385 ■ OGS Quarterly
Pub: Oklahoma Genealogical Society
Contact: James Ike, President
E-mail: president@okgensoc.org
URL(s): www.okgensoc.org/store.php?sid=2
Released: Quarterly **Price:** $25, for DVD; $22, Members for DVD; $8, for softcover book; $7, Members for softcover book. **Description:** Features information pertaining to local genealogy and history. **Availability:** DVD; PDF.

7386 ■ THG: Connections
Pub: Indiana Historical Society Press
Contact: Jody Blankenship, President
E-mail: president@indianahistory.org
URL(s): indianahistory.org/explore/ihs-press/magazines
Ed: M. Teresa Baer. **Released:** Semiannual **Description:** Contains state and local historical and genealogical information. **Availability:** Online.

7387 ■ *Voyageur Magazine: Northeast Wisconsin's Historical Review*
Pub: Voyageur Magazine
Contact: Christine Dunbar, Manager
E-mail: chris@browncohistoricalsoc.org
Facebook: www.facebook.com/people/Voyageur-Northeast-Wisconsins-Historical-Review/100063644885502
X (Twitter): x.com/ReadVoyageur
Instagram: www.instagram.com/readvoyageurmagazine
Released: Semiannual; Summer / Fall 2024. **Price:** $20, for one issue. **Description:** Magazine on the history of a 26-county region of northeast Wisconsin. **Availability:** Print; PDF; Online.

FRANCHISES AND BUSINESS OPPORTUNITIES

7388 ■ Swyrich Corp.
633 Norris Crt, Units 1 & 2
Kingston, ON, Canada K7P 2R9
Ph: (613)384-9986
Co. E-mail: info@swyrich.com
URL: http://www.swyrich.com
Description: Firm provides heraldry software, custom design services, stock lapel pins and much more. **Founded:** 1991. **Training:** Yes.

COMPUTERIZED DATABASES

7389 ■ *Anthropological Literature*
Harvard University Peabody Museum of Archaeology and Ethnology
11 Divinity Ave.
Cambridge, MA 02138
Ph: (617)496-1027
Fax: (617)495-7535
Co. E-mail: pmreasrch@fas.harvard.edu
URL: http://peabody.harvard.edu
Contact: Kara Schneiderman, Director, Collections
E-mail: karaschneiderman@fas.harvard.edu
URL(s): peabody.harvard.edu/anthropological-literatureguides.library.harvard.edu/anthrolit
Released: Monthly **Availability:** Online. **Type:** Bibliographic.

7390 ■ *International Genealogical Index®*
Intellectual Reserve Inc.
50 E N Temple St.
Salt Lake City, UT 84150-0005
Fax: (801)240-1187
URL: http://www.churchofjesuschrist.org/comeuntochrist
Contact: Russell M. Nelson, President
URL(s): www.familysearch.org/search/collection/igi
Availability: Online. **Type:** Directory.

LIBRARIES

7391 ■ Adams County Genealogical Society (ACGS) - Library
PO Box 1254
Eastlake, CO 80614
Co. E-mail: info@adamscountygenealogy.org
URL: http://sites.google.com/view/adamscountygenealogicalsociety
Contact: Darby Wilcox, President
Description: Creates and fosters an interest in genealogy and to aid others in researching their family history. **Scope:** Genealogy; family histories; Adams County. **Services:** Copying; library open to the public on a limited schedule. **Founded:** 1979. **Holdings:** 1,200 books; 200 bound periodical volumes; 30 manuscripts; 50 archives; 100 reels of microfilm; 60 exchange newsletters. **Publications:** *Leafy Branches* (Quarterly). **Geographic Preference:** Local.

7392 ■ American-Canadian Genealogical Society (ACGS) - Library
1 Sundial Ave., Ste. 317N
Manchester, NH 03103
Ph: (603)622-1554
Co. E-mail: acgs@acgs.org
URL: http://acgs.org
Contact: Julie Smith, President
Facebook: www.facebook.com/ACGS.Society
Description: Genealogists interested in ancestries of French-Canadian origin. Serves as resource center for the collection and preservation of American-Canadian and Franco-American genealogical information. **Scope:** Church repertoires; histories of Quebec; the Maritimes; the New England states and Northern New York. **Services:** Open to public on Wednesdays and Saturdays; Scanning. **Founded:** 1973. **Holdings:** 10,000 reports; books; Journals; Records; Documents; directories; obituaries. **Educational Activities:** ACGS Annual Meeting and Fall Conference (Annual). **Geographic Preference:** Multinational.

7393 ■ American-French Genealogical Society (AFGS) - Library
78 Earle St.
Woonsocket, RI 02895-3108
Ph: (401)765-6141
Fax: (401)597-6290
Co. E-mail: info@afgs.org
URL: http://afgs.org
Contact: Normand Deragon, President
Facebook: www.facebook.com/American-French-Genealogical-Society-90894174795
Description: Seeks to study and preserve Franco-American heritage and French-Canadian culture in the U.S. by assisting members in researching their ancestors and the events that shaped their lives. Offers research services. Conducts educational programs. **Scope:** Family genealogy; history; and biography. **Founded:** 1978. **Holdings:** 20,000 vital statistics volumes; reference books; genealogical journals; publications; microfilm; CD records; church records; maps; charts. **Publications:** *Je Me Souviens* (Quarterly); *Beginning Franco-American Genealogy*; *La Cuisine de la Grandmere Volumes I and II*. **Awards:** AFGS French Canadian Hall of Fame (Annual); AFGS Special Achievement Awards (Annual). **Geographic Preference:** National.

7394 ■ American Jewish Historical Society (AJHS) - Library
15 W 16th St.
New York, NY 10011
Ph: (212)294-6160
Fax: (212)294-6161
Co. E-mail: info@ajhs.org
URL: http://www.ajhs.org
Contact: Felicia Herman, President
Facebook: www.facebook.com/AmericanJewishHistoricalSociety
X (Twitter): x.com/AJHSNYC
Instagram: www.instagram.com/ajhsnyc
YouTube: www.youtube.com/user/AJHSNYC
Description: Individuals and institutions interested in American Jewish history. Seeks to collect, display, preserve, and publish material on the history of the American Jewish community. **Scope:** American Jewish religious; Intellectual; Political and economic life; Jewish participation in the visual; Performing arts; The geographic origins of American Jewry; Jewish immigration to the Americas; Gender relations and family structure in American Jewish life. **Services:** Library open to the public for reference use only; Interlibray Loan. **Founded:** 1892. **Holdings:** 50,000 volumes; 3,000 volumes; 350 books and pamphlets; serials; journals; periodicals. **Publications:** *American Jewish History* (Quarterly). **Educational Activities:** AJHS Scholars' Conference (Biennial). **Awards:** Ruth B. Fein Prize; Pokross/Curhan Family Fund Prize; Lee Max Friedman Award Medal (Biennial); Saul Viener Book Prize (Biennial); The Henry L. Feingold Graduate Student Essay Prize; Emma Lazarus Statue of Liberty Award (Annual); Lee Max Friedman Memorial Award (Biennial); Saul Viener Prize (Biennial). **Geographic Preference:** National.

7395 ■ Annie Halenbake Ross Library - Special Collections
232 W Main St.
Lock Haven, PA 17745
Ph: (570)748-3321

Co. E-mail: ross1@rosslibrary.org
URL: http://rosslibrary.org/annie-halenbake-ross
Contact: Tammy Garrison, Director
Facebook: www.facebook.com/AHRLibrary
Scope: Genealogy. **Services:** Interlibrary loan; library open to the public. **Founded:** 1910. **Holdings:** 3000 DVD movies; books; 60 magazine.

7396 ■ Atchison Public Library (APL)
401 Kansas Ave.
Atchison, KS 66002
Ph: (913)367-1902
Fax: (913)367-2717
Co. E-mail: askus@atchisonlibrary.org
URL: http://www.atchisonlibrary.org
Contact: Nora McCrory, President
Scope: Local history; genealogy. **Services:** Library open to the public for reference use only. **Founded:** 1879. **Holdings:** 300 books; 10 bound periodical volumes; 34 reports; 30 microfiche; 400 reels of microfilm.

7397 ■ Barton County Historical Society (BCHS)
85 S Hwy. 281
Great Bend, KS 67530
Ph: (620)793-5125
URL: http://www.bartoncountymuseum.org
Contact: Richard Lartz, II, Director
Facebook: www.facebook.com/Barton-County-Historical-Society-Museum-and-Village-177104069604
Scope: Barton county and Kansas studies; genealogy. **Services:** Copying; library open to the public with restrictions. **Holdings:** Reports; manuscripts; archives; photographs.

7398 ■ Branches and Twigs Genealogical Society Collection
Kingman Carnegie Library
455 N Main St.
Kingman, KS 67068
Ph: (316)532-3061
Fax: (316)532-2528
Co. E-mail: nkostner@kingmanlibrary.org
URL: http://www.kingmanlibrary.org
Contact: Galene San Romani, President
Facebook: www.facebook.com/kingmankscarnegielibrary
Scope: Genealogy. **Services:** Interlibrary loan; copying; SDI; library open to the public. **Founded:** 1913. **Holdings:** 312 books; 8,000 microfiche; 210 reels of microfilm; manuscripts. **Subscriptions:** 3 journals and other serials; 2 newspapers.

7399 ■ Brigham Young University Family History Library (BYU)
2250 Harold B. Lee Library
Brigham Young University
Provo, UT 84602
Ph: (801)422-6200
Co. E-mail: family-history@byu.edu
URL: http://fh.lib.byu.edu
Contact: Joseph B. Everett, Librarian
E-mail: joe_everett@byu.edu
Facebook: www.facebook.com/byufhl
X (Twitter): x.com/BYUfam_hist_lib
YouTube: www.youtube.com/c/BYUFamilyHistoryLibrary
Scope: Genealogy and history. **Services:** Scanning; copying; center open to the public. **Founded:** 1964. **Holdings:** 35,000 journals, serials, and newspapers on microfilm; maps; online databases; primary and secondary source material in microform.

7400 ■ British Columbia Genealogical Society (BCGS) - BCGS Genealogical Library & Research Centre
Lansdowne Mall
Richmond, BC, Canada V6X 3T6
Ph: (604)502-9119
Co. E-mail: membership@bcgs.ca
URL: http://www.bcgs.ca
Contact: Eunice Robinson, President
X (Twitter): x.com/bcgs_ca
Description: Aims to preserve the family histories of British Columbians through access to genealogical records and effective research techniques. Maintains a library and resource center holding more than 15,000 genealogical publications and records. **Scope:** Genealogy. **Services:** Library open to the public on fee basis for non-members. **Founded:** 1971. **Holdings:** 18,000 books; magazines; maps; printed materials; periodicals. **Publications:** *British Columbia Genealogist* (Quarterly).

7401 ■ Chase County Historical Society & Museum Library
301/303 Broadway St.
Cottonwood Falls, KS 66845
URL: http://www.chasecountyhistoricalsocietymuseum.org/research
Scope: Chase county history. **Services:** Copying; library open to the public. **Founded:** 1934. **Holdings:** Figures not available.

7402 ■ Clarkesville-Habersham County Library
178 E Green St.
Clarkesville, GA 30523
Ph: (706)754-4413
Co. E-mail: folhabersham@gmail.com
URL: http://clarkesvillelibrary.org
Contact: Perry Rettig, Vice Chairperson
Description: Georgia library public information network for electronic services. **Scope:** Genealogy; history. **Services:** Copying; library open to the public; interlibrary loan (members only). **Founded:** 1940. **Holdings:** 40,000 items – DVDs, audio books, music's, print books.

7403 ■ Collin County Genealogical Society Library (CCGS)
PO Box 865052
Plano, TX 75086-5052
URL: http://www.collincountygenealogicalsociety.com/publications.html
Contact: W. O. Haggard, Jr., Contact
Scope: Genealogy; research. **Services:** Center not open to the public. **Founded:** 1970. **Holdings:** Books.

7404 ■ Connecticut Society of Genealogist Library (CSG Literary)
175 Maple St. E
Hartford, CT 06118-2634
Ph: (860)569-0002
URL: http://www.csginc.org
Contact: Pauline Merrick, President
E-mail: president@csginc.org
URL(s): csginc.org/visit
Scope: Genealogy. **Services:** Copying; library open to the public. **Founded:** 1968. **Holdings:** Books; manuscripts; microfiche; CD-ROM.

7405 ■ Connecticut State Library History and Genealogy Unit
231 Capitol Ave.
Hartford, CT 06106
URL: http://libguides.ctstatelibrary.org/hg/home
Scope: Genealogy; state history. **Services:** Library open to the public. **Holdings:** Books; bound periodical volumes; manuscripts; archives; microfiche; microfilms; patents; reports. **Subscriptions:** 75 journals and other serials; 75 newspapers.

7406 ■ Croatian Genealogical & Heraldic Society Library
c/o Adam S. Eterovich
2527 San Carlos Ave.
San Carlos, CA 94070
Ph: (650)592-1190
Co. E-mail: croatians@aol.com
URL: http://www.croatia.org/crown/croatians/www.croatians.com/CROATIAN%20GEN.htm
Contact: Adam S. Eterovich, Contact
Scope: Genealogy; heraldry; census. **Services:** Copying; library open to the public by appointment. **Holdings:** 2,000 books; 20 bound periodical volumes; 20 drawers of index cards; 30 manuscripts; internal database of Croatian pioneers.

7407 ■ Darke County Historical Society (DCHS)
205 N Broadway
Greenville, OH 45331
URL: http://www.garstmuseum.org
Contact: Steve Gruber, Contact
Description: Darke county historical society library and museum. **Scope:** Genealogy and native American historical information. **Services:** Library open to the public for reference use only. **Founded:** 1984. **Holdings:** 1,200 books; 20,000 microfiche; 5,000 surname folders.

7408 ■ Decatur Genealogical Society (DGS) - Library
1255 W S Side Dr.
Decatur, IL 62521
Contact: Linda L. Williams, Contact
Description: Encourages genealogical research in the area of Decatur and Macon County, Illinois. **Scope:** Genealogy; Macon County history; American history; black history; Church; Colonial & New England; immigration; land; military; native American. **Services:** Copying; library open to public. **Founded:** 1964. **Holdings:** Books; CDs; record; manuscripts; atlas; dictionary; heraldry; maps; newsletters.

7409 ■ Finney County Genealogical Society Library
PO Box 592
Garden City, KS 67846-0592
URL: http://sites.rootsweb.com/~ksfinney
Scope: Genealogy; local history. **Services:** Copying; library open to the public. **Founded:** 1967. **Holdings:** 1,025 books; 427 periodical volumes; 500 reports; 1,500 microfiche; 85 reels of microfilm. **Subscriptions:** 14 journals and other serials.

7410 ■ Firelands Historical Society Library
4 Case Ave.
Norwalk, OH 44857
Ph: (419)668-6038
Co. E-mail: curator@firelandsmuseum.com
URL: http://www.firelandsmuseum.com
Contact: Chris Hipp, President
Description: Museum and local history blog for tourists. **Scope:** Local history. **Founded:** 1857. **Holdings:** Figures not available.

7411 ■ Frederic Remington Area Historical Society Library
PO Box 133
Whitewater, KS 67154
URL: http://fredericremingtonareahistoricalsociety.org
Description: The library has collections of historical materials such as books, paper records, pictures, and photos. **Founded:** 1977.

7412 ■ French-Canadian Genealogical Society of Connecticut (FCGSC) - Library
53 Tolland Green
Tolland, CT 06084
Ph: (860)872-2597
Co. E-mail: info@fcgsc.org
URL: http://www.fcgsc.org
Contact: Germaine Hoffman, Director
Description: Aims to collect, preserve, and disseminate genealogical and historical information about the settlers of Quebec and Acadia, particularly those people of French-Canadian and Acadian heritage who settled in Connecticut, Massachusetts, New York, and throughout New England. **Scope:** French-Canadian genealogy and history. **Founded:** 1981. **Subscriptions:** 30 periodicals (includes journals) 3,000 books; 22 active serial titles; biographies; dictionaries; maps; miscellaneous reference materials; CD-ROMs. **Publications:** *The Maple Leaflet* (Semiannual).

7413 ■ German-Texan Heritage Society (GTHS) - Charles G. Trenckmann Family Library
507 E 10th St.
Austin, TX 78701
Ph: (512)467-4569
Co. E-mail: info@germantexans.org
URL: http://germantexans.org

Contact: Janis Gonser, President
E-mail: president@germantexans.org
Facebook: www.facebook.com/German-Texan-Heritage-Society-268699066333
X (Twitter): x.com/germantexans
Instagram: www.instagram.com/germantexans
Description: Promotes awareness and preservation of the German cultural heritage of Texas. Studies and disseminates information on folklore. Conducts research and educational programs. Produces cultural events and social gatherings. **Scope:** Genealogical studies. **Founded:** 1978. **Holdings:** Figures not available. **Publications:** *The Journal* (Quarterly). **Educational Activities:** German-Texan Heritage Society Annual Meeting (Annual). **Geographic Preference:** Multinational.

7414 ■ Godfrey Memorial Library (GML)
134 Newfield St., Rte. 3
Middletown, CT 06457
Ph: (860)346-4375
Co. E-mail: refdesk@godfrey.org
URL: http://www.godfrey.org/scholar/godfrey-home.html
Contact: Carol Ansel, Director
E-mail: carol.ansel@godfrey.org
Facebook: www.facebook.com/GodfreyMemorialLibrary
Instagram: www.instagram.com/godfreylibrary
Description: Publishes limited family research and provides photocopies from specified genealogies or histories. Accepts unsolicited manuscripts for use by the library's patrons, not for publishing. Reaches the market through direct mail and telephone sales. **Scope:** Genealogy; family history; local history. **Services:** Library open to the public. **Founded:** 1947. **Holdings:** 200,000 items - books, periodicals, biographies, history papers, directories, cemetery and funeral records, church records, military histories, newspapers, family bibles.

7415 ■ Greeley County Historical Society Library
510 Broadway
Tribune, KS 67879
URL: http://greeleycounty.org/library
Scope: Kansas history; genealogy; agriculture; poetry; diaries. **Services:** Copying; email; library open to the public. **Founded:** 1975. **Holdings:** 500 books, maps, newspapers, telephone directories, soldier's enrollments, Civil War and obituaries; reports; manuscripts; patents; archives; microfilm. **Subscriptions:** 4 journals and other serials.

7416 ■ Guysborough Historical Society
106 Church St.
Guysborough, NS, Canada B0H 1N0
Ph: (902)533-4008
Co. E-mail: guysborough.historical@ns.sympatico.ca
URL: http://www.guysboroughhistoricalsociety.ca
Contact: Chris Cook, President
Facebook: www.facebook.com/people/Guysborough-Historical-Society-Old-Court-House-Museum
X (Twitter): x.com/CourtHouse1843
Description: A non-profit, volunteer organization created to preserve the history of Guysborough County. **Founded:** 1973.

7417 ■ Harper County Genealogical Society Library (HCGS)
1002 Oak
Harper, KS 67058
Ph: (620)896-2959
URL: http://www.ksgenweb.org/harper/harpergenealogy/harperlibrary.htm
Contact: Paul Sanders, Contact
Description: HCGS genealogy library located in the harper public library. **Scope:** Harper county (Kansas) history; Kansas history; genealogy. **Services:** Library open to the public for reference use only. **Holdings:** Figures not available.

7418 ■ Houston Public Library (HPL) - Clayton Library Center for Genealogical Research
5300 Caroline St.
Houston, TX 77004
URL: http://houstonlibrary.org/clayton
Scope: Genealogy; history and social sciences. **Services:** Copying; center open to the public. **Founded:** 1968. **Holdings:** 100,000 books; 3,000 bound periodical volumes; 70,000 reels of microfilm; 60,000 microfiche; VF material.

7419 ■ Huguenot Society of America (HSA) - Library
20 W 44th St., Ste. 510
New York, NY 10036
Ph: (212)755-0592
Fax: (212)317-0676
Co. E-mail: hugsoc@verizon.net
URL: http://www.huguenotsocietyofamerica.org
Facebook: www.facebook.com/TheHuguenotSocietyofAmerica
Description: Seeks to promote history of the Huguenot settlers in America, to commemorate the principal events in the history of the Huguenots, and to promote the cause of religious freedom. **Scope:** History of Huguenots in France; history of Huguenots in other countries; church history; French history; American history; biography; genealogy; description and travel; theology; literature; miscellaneous. **Services:** Library open to the public by appointment. **Founded:** 1883. **Holdings:** Books; manuscripts; pamphlets; pictures.

7420 ■ Huguenot Society of South Carolina - Library
138 Logan St.
Charleston, SC 29401-1941
Ph: (843)723-3235
Fax: (843)853-8476
URL: http://www.huguenotsociety.org
Contact: Hagood S. Morrison, President
Description: Aims to preserve the memory of the Huguenots and promotes a better understanding of the values and culture of the Huguenots; maintains genealogical records of the immigrants to this country and their descendants. Maintains monuments at the locations of the six Huguenot churches and settlements in South Carolina. **Scope:** Local history. **Services:** Library open to the public by appointment. **Founded:** 1885. **Holdings:** Figures not available. **Awards:** Mary Mouzon Darby Undergraduate Scholarship (Annual); Huguenot Society of South Carolina Graduate Scholarship (Annual). **Geographic Preference:** National.

7421 ■ Huxford Genealogical Society, Inc. - Huxford-Spear Genealogical Library
20 S College St.
Homerville, GA 31634
Ph: (912)487-2310
Co. E-mail: huxford@windstream.net
URL: http://huxford.com
Scope: Genealogy. **Services:** Copying; research library open to nonmembers on a fee basis. **Founded:** 1972. **Holdings:** 4,000 volumes; 1,300 family surname files; 79 boxes of magazines; 600 boxes of microfilm; reports; manuscripts; archives; Georgia Death Index; Florida Death Index; CD-ROMs. **Subscriptions:** 2,000 journals and other serials.

7422 ■ Jackson County Public Library - Indiana & Jackson County History and Genealogy Collection
303 W 2nd St.
Seymour, IN 47274
URL: http://www.myjclibrary.org/local-history
Scope: History; genealogy. **Services:** Library open to the public. **Holdings:** Figures not available.

7423 ■ Kings County Museum Library
37 Cornwallis St.
Kentville, NS, Canada B4N 2E2
Ph: (902)678-6237
Co. E-mail: info@kingscountymuseum.ca
URL: http://www.kingscountymuseum.ca
Scope: Genealogy. **Founded:** 1980. **Holdings:** Figures not available.

7424 ■ Kittochtinny Historical Society Library
175 E King St.
Chambersburg, PA 17201
Ph: (717)264-1667
Co. E-mail: history@pa.net
URL: http://www.franklinhistorical.org
Contact: Ann Hull, Contact
E-mail: anubhull@comcast.net
Description: Organization of historical development. **Scope:** History; genealogy. **Services:** Library open to the public on a limited schedule; there will be a $5.00 a day charge for non-members to use the research facilities at the Old Jail. **Founded:** 1898. **Holdings:** Figures not available.

7425 ■ Lake Erie Islands Historical Society Library (LEIHS)
25 Town Hall Pl.
Put in Bay, OH 43456
Ph: (419)285-2804
Fax: (419)285-3804
Co. E-mail: director@leihs.org
URL: http://www.leihs.org
Contact: Maggie Beckford, President
Description: Lake Erie Islands Historical Society museum and resale shop. **Scope:** Local history. **Holdings:** Photographs; historical papers; artifacts.

7426 ■ Leavenworth County Historical Society and Museum Library
1128 5th Ave.
Leavenworth, KS 66048
URL: http://www.leavenworthhistory.org/museums.htm
Scope: History of Kansas; genealogy; Leavenworth county history. **Services:** Copying; library open to the public. **Founded:** 1954. **Holdings:** Figures not available.

7427 ■ Library of Congress Local History & Genealogy Reading Room
10 1st St., SE
Thomas Jefferson Bldg., LJ 100
Washington, DC 20540-4660
Ph: (202)707-3399
URL: http://www.loc.gov/research-centers/main/about-this-research-center
Contact: Carla Hayden, Librarian
Scope: Local history; genealogy. **Services:** Copying; section open to adults only. **Holdings:** 50,000 genealogies; 100,000 local histories; books; vertical files; manuscripts; microfilms; newspapers; photographs; maps; 6,000 guides.

7428 ■ Madison County Historical Society Library
260 E High St.
London, OH 43140
Ph: (740)852-2977
URL: http://www.madisonoh.ancestralsites.com/countylinks.php
Description: Deals with Madison county history and genealogy. **Scope:** Madison County history. **Services:** Library open to the public. **Founded:** 1980.

7429 ■ Manitoba Genealogical Society (MGS) - MGS Resource Center and Library
1045 Saint James St., Unit E
Winnipeg, MB, Canada R3H 1B1
Ph: (204)783-9139
Co. E-mail: contact@mbgenealogy.com
URL: http://mbgenealogy.com
Contact: Chris Irwin, President
E-mail: president@mbgenealogy.com
Facebook: www.facebook.com/mbgenealogy
X (Twitter): x.com/mbgenealogy
Description: Publishes on genealogy and family history. **Scope:** Genealogy; Manitoba local and family history. **Services:** Library open to the public on Tuesday to Thursday (free to members but $5 per day for visitors). **Founded:** 1976. **Holdings:** Books 900; 1400 Cemetery indexes; microfiche; maps; 60 journals. **Subscriptions:** newspapers. **Publications:** *Generations* (Quarterly).

Small Business Profiles — Genealogy Service ■ 7445

7430 ■ Marion Area Genealogical Society Library
c/o Warren G. Harding Presidential Library
380 Mt Vernon Ave.
Marion, OH 43302
URL: http://marionohmags.weebly.com
Contact: Susan Matthews, President
Scope: Marion county history; Ohio history; genealogy; Marion city history. **Services:** Copying; library open to the public. **Founded:** 1995. **Holdings:** 250 books; 100 bound periodical volumes; 50 reports.

7431 ■ McAllen Public Library (MPL)
4001 N 23rd St.
McAllen, TX 78504
Ph: (956)688-3300
Co. E-mail: referencelibrarian@mcallen.net
URL: http://www.mcallenlibrary.net
Contact: Kate P. Horan, Director
Facebook: www.facebook.com/mcallenlibrary
X (Twitter): x.com/mcallenlibrary
Instagram: www.instagram.com/mcallenlibrary
YouTube: www.youtube.com/user/mcallenlibrary
Scope: Local history. **Services:** Copying; library open to the public. **Founded:** 1975. **Holdings:** 6500 books; 640 bound periodical volumes.

7432 ■ Mennonite Historians of Eastern Pennsylvania (MHEP) - Mennonite Historical Library & Archives
565 Yoder Rd.
Harleysville, PA 19438-1020
Ph: (215)256-3020
Co. E-mail: info@mhep.org
URL: http://mhep.org
Contact: Christopher J. Detweiler, President
Description: Provider of preserving the heritage of Mennonite life and culture in Southeastern Pennsylvania. **Scope:** Mennonite life in the eastern Pennsylvania counties. **Services:** Copying; microfilm reader and printer; Library open to the public. **Founded:** 1967. **Holdings:** 86,000 records; 7,000 records; letter; newspapers; microfilm.

7433 ■ Milford Area Historical Society (GMAHS) - Leonard L. Harding, Jr. Library
906 Main St.
Milford, OH 45150
Ph: (513)248-0324
Co. E-mail: info@milfordhistory.net
URL: http://www.milfordhistory.net
Contact: Susan Vilardo, Contact
E-mail: info@milfordhistory.net
Facebook: www.facebook.com/promontevents
X (Twitter): x.com/Promont
Description: Aims to promote the history of Milford-Miami Township. **Scope:** History. **Founded:** 1797. **Holdings:** Books; photographs; plats; maps; ledger books; artifacts; personal memorabilia; local business memorabilia; yearbooks; scrapbooks; manuscripts; limited family archives.

7434 ■ The Montgomery County Genealogy Society Library
16501 Shady Grove Rd., No. 8262
Gaithersburg, MD 20898
URL: http://mocogensoc.org/cpage.php?pt=5
Contact: Jane C. Sween, Librarian
Scope: Genealogy. **Services:** Interlibrary loan; copying; library open to the public. **Founded:** 1970. **Holdings:** Archival materials; newspapers and censuses; microfiche; reels of microfilm; obits (1975-1995).

7435 ■ Napa Valley Genealogical Society Library
1701 Menlo Ave.
Napa, CA 94558
Ph: (707)252-2252
Co. E-mail: info@napagensoc.org
URL: http://napagensoc.org
Contact: Sandy Hoover, President
Facebook: www.facebook.com/Napa-Valley-Genealogical-Society-144039565764687
Scope: Genealogy. **Services:** Copying; library open to the public on fee basis. **Founded:** 1974. **Holdings:** Figures not available.

7436 ■ National Society of the Sons of Utah Pioneers (NSSUP)
3301 E 2920 S
Salt Lake City, UT 84109
Ph: (801)484-4441
Co. E-mail: supnatloffice@gmail.com
URL: http://www.sup1847.com
Contact: Larry Gibson, President
E-mail: larmgib@gmail.com
Description: Men ages 18 or older who are interested in preserving the history and names of the pioneers who settled in the West. Sponsors historical treks, promotes pageants, and conducts other historical activities. Participates in Pioneer Village, Farmington, UT, and in museums of life in the pioneer West. Conducts research. Maintains Pioneer Historical Gallery. **Founded:** 1933. **Awards:** SUP Tomorrow's Pioneers (Annual). **Geographic Preference:** National.

7437 ■ New York Genealogical and Biographical Society (NYG&B) - Library
36 W 44th St., 7th Fl., Ste. 711
New York, NY 10036-8105
Ph: (212)755-8532
Fax: (212)754-4218
Co. E-mail: education@nygbs.org
URL: http://www.newyorkfamilyhistory.org
Contact: Joshua D. Taylor, President
Facebook: www.facebook.com/nyfamilyhistory
X (Twitter): x.com/nyfamilyhistory
Description: Collects, preserves, and makes available to the public, information relating to genealogy, biography, and history, especially of the state of New York. **Scope:** Genealogy; census; immigration and naturalization. **Services:** Open to the public. **Founded:** 1869. **Holdings:** Records; maps; newspaper; periodicals; guides. **Publications:** The New York Genealogical and Biographical Record (NYG&B) (Quarterly). **Geographic Preference:** National.

7438 ■ Norfolk Historical Society (NHS)
420 Main St.
Port Dover, ON, Canada N0A 1N0
Free: 833-968-7647
Fax: (844)557-7733
Co. E-mail: info@norfolkhistoricalsociety.ca
URL: http://norfolkhistoricalsociety.ca
Contact: Michele Grant, President
Facebook: www.facebook.com/norfolkhistoricalsociety
Instagram: www.instagram.com/norfolkhistoricalsociety
Scope: History - local, Ontario, United States, Europe; census; vital statistics; cemeteries; churches. **Services:** Microfilm loan services; copying; library open to non-members for a fee. **Founded:** 1900. **Holdings:** 4,000 books; 3,000 bound periodical volumes; 1,000 microfiche; 2,000 reels of microfilm; archives.

7439 ■ Norwegian American Genealogical Center and Naeseth Library (NAGC & NL)
415 W Main St.
Madison, WI 53703-3116
Ph: (608)255-2224
Co. E-mail: genealogy@nagcnl.org
URL: http://www.nagcnl.org
Contact: Diane Maurer, Coordinator, Member Services
Facebook: www.facebook.com/NorAmGeneCtr
YouTube: www.youtube.com/channel/UCPMWqQlgD5-VzhDAjoeoWfg
Scope: Genealogical materials. **Services:** Copying. **Founded:** 1974. **Holdings:** Books.

7440 ■ Norwegian-American Historical Association Archives (NAHA)
1510 St. Olaf Ave.
Northfield, MN 55057
Ph: (507)786-3221
Co. E-mail: naha@stolaf.edu
URL: http://naha.stolaf.edu/archives
Contact: Scott Knudson, President
Description: Contains reference materials, journals, books, online materials, and video and audio materials on history. **Scope:** Norwegian-American history. **Services:** Interlibrary loan (through St. Olaf College Library; PALS); archives open to the public by appointment. **Founded:** 1925. **Holdings:** 8,000 books; 1,500 bound periodical volumes; newspapers; correspondence; diaries, scrapbooks; obituaries; photographs.

7441 ■ Ohio Genealogical Society - Coshocton County Chapter Library
PO Box 128
Coshocton, OH 43812-0128
URL: http://coshoctongenealogy.wordpress.com/program-schedule
Scope: Genealogy. **Founded:** 1904. **Holdings:** Figures not available.

7442 ■ Ohio Genealogical Society Perry County, Ohio Chapter Library
117 S Jackson St.
New Lexington, OH 43764
Ph: (740)342-4194
Fax: (740)342-4204
URL: http://www.pcdl.org
Contact: Melissa Marolt, Director
URL(s): www.perrycountyohio.net/county-resources/perry-county-foundations-and-societies/perry-county-chapter-ohio-genealogical-society
Facebook: www.facebook.com/perrycountydistrictlibrary
X (Twitter): x.com/PerryCoDistLib
Instagram: www.instagram.com/perrycountydistrictlibrary
Scope: Genealogy; history. **Services:** Copying; genealogical searches. **Founded:** 1983. **Holdings:** 2,000 books; 100 bound periodical volumes; 100 manuscripts; 100 microfiche; 43 microfilm; DVDs; audiobooks.

7443 ■ Perry Historians Library
763 Dix Hill Rd.
New Bloomfield, PA 17068
Ph: (717)582-4896
Co. E-mail: staff@theperryhistorians.org
URL: http://www.theperryhistorians.org
Contact: Donna Heller Zinn, Contact
E-mail: donna@theperryhistorians.org
Facebook: www.facebook.com/The-Perry-Historians-1601983876712194
Scope: Health resources. **Services:** Copying; library open to the public on a limited schedule; provides genealogical and historical research services. **Founded:** 1976. **Holdings:** 5,000 books; 500 reels of microfilm; 1,000 land drafts; 8,000 family and subject files; 800,000 cards; photographs.

7444 ■ Rock Island County Illinois Genealogical Society Library
822 11th Ave.
Moline, IL 61265-1221
Ph: (309)764-8590
Co. E-mail: librarian@ricigs.org
URL: http://ricigs.org
Contact: Ann Noyce, President
URL(s): www.richs.cc
Scope: Genealogy. **Services:** Library open to the public. **Founded:** 1972. **Holdings:** 2,000 books, publications, documents, CDs, and maps.

7445 ■ Ross County Genealogical Society (RCGS) - Library
PO Box 6352
Chillicothe, OH 45601
Ph: (740)773-2715
Co. E-mail: info@rcgsohio.org
URL: http://rcgsohio.org
Contact: Paul Hixon, President
Description: Works to collect, preserve, and make available genealogical and historical records. Promotes historical education. **Scope:** County Information. **Services:** Copying; library open to the public. **Founded:** 1973. **Holdings:** Books. **Publications:** Ross County Genealogical Society Newsletter. **Geographic Preference:** Local.

7446 ■ Russell County Historical Society & Genealogy Society Library (RCHS)
331 Kansas St.
Russell, KS 67665
Ph: (785)483-3637
Co. E-mail: rchs@russellks.net
URL: http://www.russellkshistory.com
Contact: Robert J. Dole, Contact
Scope: Genealogy; history county and general. **Services:** Copying; library open to the public. **Founded:** 1970. **Holdings:** Census records; books; maps.

7447 ■ St. Clair Shores Public Library - Local History Center
22500 11 Mile Rd.
Saint Clair Shores, MI 48081
Ph: (586)771-9020
URL: http://www.scslibrary.org/lhc.html
Contact: Eileen Sullivan, Contact
Scope: History of Michigan, Great Lakes and genealogy. **Services:** Library open to the public. **Founded:** 1939. **Holdings:** 4,000 volumes of books and periodicals; photographs.

7448 ■ St. Louis Genealogical Society (StLGS) - Research library
No. 4 Sunnen Dr., Ste. 140
Saint Louis, MO 63143
Ph: (314)647-8547
Co. E-mail: office@stlgs.org
URL: http://stlgs.org
Contact: Karen Goode, President
E-mail: president@stlgs.org
X (Twitter): x.com/stlgs
Description: Promotes family history research in the St. Louis, Missouri, area by providing education and research opportunities, offering community services, and collecting, preserving, and publishing genealogical and historical records. **Scope:** Genealogy; family histories. **Founded:** 1968. **Holdings:** 90,000 items; 20,000 books, journals, maps, CDs; microfilms. **Publications:** *Research Connections 2000--A Sourcebook of Genealogical Resources* (Annual).

7449 ■ Scarborough Historical Society - Scarborough Archives
6282 Kingston Rd.
Scarborough, ON, Canada M1C 1K9
Ph: (416)995-6930
Co. E-mail: archives@scarboroughhistorical.ca
URL: http://scarboroughhistorical.ca/archives-2/visit-the-archives
Contact: Carol Nelson, President
X (Twitter): x.com/ScarbArchives
Description: Promotes, preserves and stimulates an interest in the history of Scarborough, Ontario. **Scope:** History; genealogy. **Services:** Copying; microfilm/microfiche reading; archives open to the public by appointment. **Founded:** 1978. **Subscriptions:** newspapers published volumes; aerial photos; documents; maps; cemetery records; collection of local community histories; books.

7450 ■ Shenandoah County Library - Local History and Genealogy Collection
514 Stoney Creek Blvd.
Edinburg, VA 22824
Ph: (540)984-8200
Fax: (540)984-8207
URL: http://countylib.org
Contact: Sandy Whitesides, Director
E-mail: swhitesides@countylib.org
Description: Contains reference materials, journals, books, online materials, and video and audio materials on genealogy and historical studies. **Scope:** History; genealogical. **Services:** Copying; library open to the public. **Founded:** 1985. **Holdings:** Books; microforms; microfilm; records; photographs; letters; archival materials; Civil War materials.

7451 ■ Societe de Genealogie de Quebec Library
275 Dufferin, 2nd fl
Sherbrooke, QC, Canada J1H 4M5
Ph: (819)821-5414
Co. E-mail: info@sgce.qc.ca
URL: http://sgce.qc.ca/enregistrements-formations
Scope: Genealogy and local history. **Founded:** 1961. **Subscriptions:** 120 magazines Periodicals; monographs; newsletters; newspapers; dictionaries.

7452 ■ Sons of the American Revolution Genealogy Research Library (SAR Genealogical Research Library)
809 W Main St.
Louisville, KY 40202
Ph: (502)589-1776
Co. E-mail: library@sar.org
URL: http://www.sar.org
Contact: Cheri Daniels, Director
Facebook: www.facebook.com/sar.org
Scope: History and genealogy. **Services:** library open to the public on a fee basis. **Founded:** 1927. **Holdings:** Figures not available.

7453 ■ Southern Ohio Genealogical Society Research Library (SOGS)
North High Business Ctr.
1487 N High St., Ste. 450
Hillsboro, OH 45133
Co. E-mail: sogs414@gmail.com
URL: http://sogs.info/why-genealogy-research/sogs-research-library
Description: Southern Ohio Genealogical Society, has a genealogy research section located inside the Southern State Community College Library. **Scope:** Genealogy. **Services:** Library open to the public. **Founded:** 1976. **Holdings:** Books.

7454 ■ Thomas Raddall Research Centre Archives
Queens County Museum
109 Main St.
Liverpool, NS, Canada B0T 1K0
Ph: (902)354-4058
Fax: (902)354-2050
URL: http://www.raddallresearchcentre.com/Archives/archives.html
Contact: Linda Rafuse, Director
E-mail: rafusela@gov.ns.ca
Scope: Numerous history and genealogy. **Services:** Copying; library open to the public. **Founded:** 1929. **Subscriptions:** newspapers periodicals (includes journals) books; bound periodical volumes; archival files; microfiche; reels of microfilm; 3,000 photograph; records, grants and deeds; maps; diaries.

7455 ■ University of California, Berkeley - Magnes Collection of Jewish Art and Life - Western Jewish History Center (WJHC)
2121 Allston Way
Berkeley, CA 94720-6300
URL: http://magnes.berkeley.edu/research/magnes-history/people-and-institutions/institutions/western-jewish-history-center
Contact: Ruth Kelson Rafael, Archivist
Description: Integral unit of Magnes Collection of Jewish Art and Life, University of California Berkeley. **Scope:** History and the cultures of the Jews in the global diaspora and the American west. **Services:** Copying; Center open by appointment only. **Founded:** 1967. **Holdings:** 336 rolls of microfilm; 677 archival collections; 288 audio tapes (89 oral histories); books; vertical subject file; photographs.

7456 ■ W.A. Rankin Memorial Library
502 Indiana St.
Neodesha, KS 66757
Ph: (620)325-3275
Co. E-mail: neodeshalibrary@hotmail.com
URL: http://neodeshapubliclibrary.org
Facebook: www.facebook.com/WARankinMemLibraryNeodesha
Scope: Local history; family genealogy. **Services:** Interlibrary loan; copying; library open to the public. **Founded:** 1912. **Holdings:** Figures not available.

7457 ■ Warren County Genealogical Society (WCGS) - Library
406 Justice Dr.
Lebanon, OH 45036
Ph: (513)695-1144
Co. E-mail: wcgs@co.warren.oh.us
URL: http://www.wcgsoh.org
Contact: Bart C. Gibbons, President
Description: Genealogists and others with an interest in family history in Warren County, OH. Gathers and publishes local birth, marriage, court, death, and cemetery records. **Scope:** Genealogy. **Services:** Copying; research on Warren families for small fee; library open to the public. **Founded:** 1981. **Holdings:** Books; records. **Publications:** *Heir-Lines* (Quarterly). **Geographic Preference:** Local.

7458 ■ Washington County Historical & Genealogical Society Library (WCHGS)
216 Ballard St.
Washington, KS 66968
Ph: (785)325-2198
Fax: (785)325-2198
Co. E-mail: wchgs31@hotmail.com
URL: http://www.wchistoricalsociety.org
Contact: Jim Mooren, President
Scope: Local history and genealogy. **Founded:** 1983. **Holdings:** Figures not available.

7459 ■ West Hants Historical Society - Genealogies Collections
281 King St.
Windsor, NS, Canada B0N 2T0
Ph: (902)798-4706
Co. E-mail: info@westhantshistoricalsociety.ca
URL: http://westhantshistoricalsociety.ca/genealogy-services
Contact: Shirley Pineo, President
Facebook: www.facebook.com/westhantshistoricalsociety
X (Twitter): x.com/whhswindsor
Scope: Genealogy; community history. **Services:** Copying; library open to the public on a limited schedule and by appointment. **Holdings:** 400 books; 12 reels of microfilm; maps; scrapbooks; photographs.

7460 ■ Wichita Genealogical Society (WGS) - Library
PO Box 3705
Wichita, KS 67201-3705
Co. E-mail: info@wichitagensoc.org
URL: http://www.wichitagensoc.org
Contact: Rosie Wiley, Secretary
Description: Promotes genealogical and historical research in Wichita, Kansas. **Scope:** Genealogy; local history. **Services:** Library open to the public. **Founded:** 1987. **Holdings:** 23,000 books and magazines; 1,600 volumes; microfilm; records; newspapers.

RESEARCH CENTERS

7461 ■ College of Southern Maryland - Southern Maryland Studies Center (SMSC) - Archives
8730 Mitchell Rd.
La Plata, MD 20646
Ph: (301)934-7606
Co. E-mail: smsc@csmd.edu
URL: http://www.csmd.edu/student-services/library-services/southern-maryland-studies-center/index.html
Facebook: www.facebook.com/SouthernMarylandStudiesCenter
Description: Integral unit of College of Southern Maryland. **Scope:** Southern Maryland region, including culture and development of Calvert, Charles, St. Mary's and the southern areas of Anne Arundel and Prince George's counties. **Services:** Copying; center open to the public for reference use only. **Founded:** 1976. **Holdings:** 60,000 books; 2,000 reference volumes; 3,000 periodicals; 272 reels of microfilm; 5,000 audio/visual items; 209 manuscript collections.

7462 ■ Colorado Springs Pioneers Museum - Starsmore Center For Local History (SCLH) - Library
215 S Tejon St.
Colorado Springs, CO 80903
URL: http://www.cspm.org/collections/archives-collection

Contact: Hillary Mannion, Archivist
E-mail: hillary.mannion@coloradosprings.gov
Description: Integral unit of Colorado Springs Pioneers Museum, an independent, nonprofit organization. Offers consultation for paper and photograph preservation. **Scope:** Colorado history, local history, and genealogy. **Services:** Copying; Center open to the public by appointment. **Founded:** 1938. **Holdings:** Figures not available.

7463 ■ Historic Annapolis (HA) - fTexas Natural Resources Information System
18 Pinkney St.
  Annapolis, MD 21401
Ph: (410)267-7619
Co. E-mail: info@annapolis.org
URL: http://www.annapolis.org
Facebook: www.facebook.com/historicannapolis
Linkedin: www.linkedin.com/company/historic-annapolis-foundation
Instagram: www.instagram.com/historicannapolis
YouTube: www.youtube.com/channel/UCQ3y-8gNvNzo6L4mamCMBsw
Description: Represents individuals interested in preserving the history of Annapolis and Anne Arundel County, MD. Operates the William PACA House Museum and Garden built in 1765. **Scope:** State and local history, historic preservation, urban planning, and decorative arts. **Services:** Copying; Library open to the public by appointment. **Founded:** 1952. **Holdings:** Books; photos; slides; blueprints; maps; property histories; preservation files; archaeological reports; colonial research. **Publications:** *Historic Annapolis Foundation Journal* (Semiannual; Quarterly). **Awards:** Historic Annapolis Preservation Awards (Annual). **Geographic Preference:** Local.

7464 ■ Stearns History Museum (SHM) - Library
235 33rd Ave. S
  Saint Cloud, MN 56301
Ph: (320)253-8424
Co. E-mail: info@stearns-museum.org
URL: http://www.stearnshistorymuseum.org
Contact: Carie Essig, Executive Director
E-mail: cessig@stearns-museum.org
Facebook: www.facebook.com/StearnsHistoryMuseum
YouTube: www.youtube.com/c/StearnsHistoryMuseum
Description: Strives to nurture knowledge of and an appreciation for the history of Stearns County and Minnesota and cultivate in people the awareness and appreciation of local history. **Scope:** Genealogy, county history, architecture, agriculture, Luxembourg immigration, local sports, and granite industry. **Services:** Copying; center open to the public. **Founded:** 1936. **Holdings:** 2,150 books; 1,250 bound periodical volumes; 18 VF drawers of biographical and family files (16,000 names); 1,800 oral history tapes, 1975-2007, over 1,100 transcribed; 1,300 reels of microfilm of Stearns County newspapers; 17,500 photographs and 1500 slides; 22 reels of microfilm of Stearns County naturalization records, 1853-1954; 7 reels of microfilm of Stearns County Land Office tract index records, 1853-1910; St. Cloud city directories, 1888-2001; Stearns County birth records, 1870-1934; Stearns County death records, 1870-1928; Stearns County marriage index, 1855-1980; Stearns County marriage records, 1916-1979; Minneapolis Irish Standard, 1886-1920, reels of microfilm; Meyer's Ort German Empire Gazetteer, 1912; Austro-Hungarian Empire Gazetteer, 1845; Germans to America, 1840-1897; Trier Emigrants by Joseph Mergen, vols. 1-8; microfiche; manuscripts. **Subscriptions:** 18 journals and other serials. **Publications:** *Crossings* (Quarterly); *Crossings Magazine* (Bimonthly). **Educational Activities:** SHM Spring bus tour, Offers tours at a discount rate for groups of 12 or more booked at least three weeks in advance.; SHM Annual genealogical conference/workshop. **Geographic Preference:** Local.

7465 ■ University of Wisconsin - Green Bay - Archives and Area Research Center (ARC)
Cofrin Library, Rm. 705
  Green Bay, WI 54311
Ph: (920)465-2539
Co. E-mail: archives@uwgb.edu
URL: http://www.uwgb.edu/archives
Contact: Debra Anderson, Director
E-mail: andersod@uwgb.edu
Facebook: www.facebook.com/uwgbarchives
X (Twitter): x.com/uwgb_archives
Instagram: www.instagram.com/uwgbarchives
Description: Integral unit of University of Wisconsin—Green Bay. **Scope:** Local history and genealogy, Northeastern Wisconsin, Belgian Americans, and University records. **Founded:** 1972.

7466 ■ University of Wisconsin - Parkside - Archives and Area Research Center
900 Wood Rd.
  Kenosha, WI 53141-2000
Ph: (262)595-2411
Co. E-mail: archives@uwp.edu
URL: http://www.uwp.edu/learn/library/Archives
Facebook: www.facebook.com/uwparchives
Description: Integral unit of University of Wisconsin—Parkside. **Scope:** State and local history and genealogy. **Founded:** 1972.

Gift Basket Service

REFERENCE WORKS

7467 ■ *"Gift Baskets News and Trends" in Bespokebrow (June 15, 2018)*
URL(s): www.bespokebrowbands.com/gift-baskets-news-and-trends/
Ed: Doris Hardy. **Released:** June 15, 2018. **Description:** Discusses corporate gift basket giving and strategies for giving baskets that will make the best impact on your clients. **Availability:** Online.

7468 ■ *"Hollywood Baskets To Gift Nominees For the 2012 Teen Choice Awards July 22nd" in PR Newswire (July 16, 2012)*
Pub: PR Newswire Association LLC.
Description: Lisa Gal, founder of Hollywood Baskets, provided gift bags to the celebrities attending the 2012 Teen Choice Awards. **Availability:** Online.

7469 ■ *"MyReviewsNow.net Announces New Affiliate Partner Gift Baskets Overseas" in M2 EquityBites (EQB) (June 22, 2012)*
Description: MyReviewsNow.net has partnered with Gift Baskets Overseas in order to offer gift baskets to be shipped overseas. Gift Baskets Oversease works with local florists and shippers worldwide. No financial details were disclosed. **Availability:** Online.

TRADE PERIODICALS

7470 ■ *Gifts & Decorative Accessories*
Pub: Sandow
Contact: Peter Fain, Chief Operating Officer
URL(s): www.giftsanddec.com
Facebook: www.facebook.com/giftsanddecmag
Linkedin: www.linkedin.com/company/gifts-&-decorative-accessories-magazine
X (Twitter): x.com/Gifts_and_Dec
Instagram: www.instagram.com/gifts_and_dec
Released: Monthly **Price:** $55.97, for online 1 Year (11 issues); $68.97, for print and online 1 year (11 issues). **Description:** International magazine for retailers of gifts, greeting cards, decorative accessories, and stationery-related merchandise. **Availability:** Print; Online. **Type:** Full-text; Directory.

FRANCHISES AND BUSINESS OPPORTUNITIES

7471 ■ **Cookies in Bloom, Inc.**
7208 La Cosa Dr.
Dallas, TX 75248
Ph: (972)490-8644
URL: http://www.cookiesinbloom.com
Contact: Mary Pinac, President
Facebook: www.facebook.com/cookiesinbloom
Instagram: www.instagram.com/cookies.in.bloom
Description: Producer and retailer of cookies such as cookie bouquets, cookie cakes, gourmet cookie baskets and more. **Founded:** 1988. **Training:** 10 days at headquarters, 5 days at franchisee's location, on-the-job training at corporate approved shop and ongoing support.

7472 ■ **FruitFlowers/Incredibly Edible Delites**
1 Summit Ave.
Broomall, PA 19008
Ph: (610)353-8844
URL: http://www.ediblearrangements.com
Contact: Tariq Farid, Chief Executive Officer
Description: Floral fruit and vegetable bouquets. **Founded:** 1984. **Franchised:** 1993. **Financial Assistance:** Yes **Training:** Yes.

Gift/Card Shop

ASSOCIATIONS AND OTHER ORGANIZATIONS

7473 ■ **Souvenir Wholesale Distributors Association (SWDA)**
32770 Arapahoe Rd., No. 132-155
Lafayette, CO 80026
Free: 888-599-4474
Fax: (888)589-7610
Co. E-mail: swdabod1@gmail.com
URL: http://www.souvenircentral.org
Contact: Angie Rhonke, President
E-mail: angie@mtnstatesspecialties.com
Facebook: www.facebook.com/SWDA-73300987678
6736

Description: Represents distributors and manufacturers of post cards, souvenirs, and novelty items. **Founded:** 1973. **Educational Activities:** SWDA Annual Convention and Trade Show (Annual). **Awards:** SWDA Glassware Souvenir Award (Annual); SWDA Magnet Souvenir Award (Annual); SWDA Spoon Souvenir Award (Annual); SWDA Edibles Souvenir Award (Annual); SWDA Miscellaneous Souvenir Award (Annual); SWDA Allied Products Awards (Annual); SWDA Books Awards (Annual); SWDA Calendars Awards (Annual); SWDA Ceramics Souvenir Award (Annual); SWDA Key Chain Souvenir Award (Annual); SWDA Soft Goods Souvenir Award (Annual); SWDA Pens/Pencil Souvenir Award (Annual); SWDA Printer of the Year (Annual); SWDA Sunrise/Sunset Postcard Awards (Annual); SWDA Night Postcard Awards (Annual); SWDA Multiview Postcard Awards (Annual); SWDA Comic or Novelty Postcards Awards (Annual). **Geographic Preference:** National.

REFERENCE WORKS

7474 ■ *"21-Year-Old Opens Gift Shop in Midland Mall"* in *Midland Daily News* (November 2, 2019)
URL(s): www.ourmidland.com/news/article/21-year-old-opens-gift-shop-in-Midland-mall-14803248.php
Ed: Ashley Schafer. **Released:** November 02, 2019. **Description:** Outlife Collections in Midland Mall was recently opened by its 21-year-old owner Devin Dice. The store features unique American-Made products and CDB friendly products. **Availability:** Online.

7475 ■ *"Award Win Highlights Slingsby's Green Credentials"* in *Ecology,Environment & Conservation Business* (August 20, 2011, pp. 3)
Description: Slingsby, an industrial and commercial equipment supplier, was joint winner with Hallmark Cards of the Baildon Business in the Community's Yorkshire and Humber Long Term Environmental Improvement Award. The firm cites its commitment to reducing environmental impact. **Availability:** Print; PDF; Online.

7476 ■ *"Baltimore Entrepreneur Develops an Event-Themed Wish List App"* in *Baltimore Business Journal* (Vol. 32, July 25, 2014, No. 12, pp. 7)
Pub: American City Business Journals, Inc.
Contact: Mike Olivieri, Executive Vice President
Released: Weekly. **Price:** $4, introductory 4-week offer(Digital only). **Description:** Baltimore-based entrepreneur Patrick Nagle has developed an online event-themed gift registry named Glist, a mobile application (app) and Website that assists in gift buying. Glist allows users to photograph items they want, put them on the online birthday wish list, or 'glist', and share the registries via social media. **Availability:** Print; Online.

7477 ■ *Gifts and Decorative Accessories--Buyers Guide and Directory (New England)*
Pub: Gift and Decorative Accessories Center Association
URL(s): www.giftsanddec.com/company
Released: Continuous **Price:** Free. **Description:** Covers about 60 individuals who are giftware manufacturers' representatives in New England; also lists their manufacturers and suppliers. **Entries include:** For representatives--Name, address, phone, e-mail, manufacturers and products represented. **Arrangement:** Alphabetical. **Availability:** Print.

7478 ■ *"Halls Give Hospital Drive $11 Million Infusion"* in *The Business Journal-Serving Metropolitan Kansas City* (Vol. 26, July 18, 2008)
Description: Don Hall, chairman of Hallmark Cards Inc., and eight family members have announced that they will give $11 million to Children's Mercy Hospitals and Clinics for its $800 million expansion plan. Hall Family Foundation president Bill Hall that contributions such as that for Children's Mercy reflect the charitable interests of the foundation's board and founders. The possible impacts of the Hall's donation are analyzed.

7479 ■ *"Inside the New Amazon 4-Star Store, a Novelty Gift Shop"* in *The Wall Street Journal* (September 27, 2018)
URL(s): www.wsj.com/articles/inside-the-new-amazon-4-star-store-a-novelty-gift-shop-1538084782
Ed: Khadeeja Safdar, Laura Stevens. **Released:** September 27, 2018. **Description:** The Amazon 4-Star Store opened in New York City's SoHo neighborhood and carries a random variety of top-rated items. It also has a section for Amazon's own electric devices and products. **Availability:** Online.

7480 ■ *Profits for Non-Profits: Running a Successful Non-Profit Gift Shop*
Ed: Nancy Kirk. **Released:** 4th edition. **Price:** $19.99, paperback. **Description:** Guide for managing a non-profit gift shop in a hospital, zoo, museum or any other non-profit entity. **Availability:** Print; Online.

7481 ■ *"VISA: Canadians Spend $97 Million on Mom This Mother's Day"* in *Canadian Corporate News* (May 16, 2007)
Description: Visa Canada finds that Canadians are spending more on Mother's Day in recent years. Since 2002, sales of jewelry, flowers, and cards have climbed steadily in the week before Mother's Day weekend. **Availability:** Print; Online.

7482 ■ *"Worldwide Food Services (EREI) Tests Mini Dollar Store Program"* in *Marketwired* (August 6, 2009)
Pub: Comtex News Network Inc.
Contact: Kan Devnani, President
Description: Mini Dollar Stores and Eagle View LLC, wholly-owned subsidiaries of Worldwide Food Services, Inc., recently met with government officials and purchasing agents to lay out a test program which would distribute Mini Dollar Store items into VA hospital gift shops.

7483 ■ *"You Can Take It With You, and Museums Hope You Will"* and *The New York Times* (March 12, 2018)
URL(s): www.nytimes.com/2018/03/12/arts/museum-gift-shops-innovation.html
Ed: Claudia Dreifus. **Released:** March 12, 2018. **Description:** Examines several art museums around the world and their innovative gift shops. **Availability:** Online.

STATISTICAL SOURCES

7484 ■ *RMA Annual Statement Studies*
Pub: Risk Management Association
Contact: Nancy Foster, President
Released: Annual. **Description:** Contains composite balance sheets and income statements for more than 360 industries, including the accounting, auditing, and bookkeeping industries. Also contains five years of comparative historical data for discerning trends. Includes 16 commonly used ratios, computed for most of the size groupings for nearly every industry.

TRADE PERIODICALS

7485 ■ *Gifts & Decorative Accessories*
Pub: Sandow
Contact: Peter Fain, Chief Operating Officer
URL(s): www.giftsanddec.com
Facebook: www.facebook.com/giftsanddecmag
Linkedin: www.linkedin.com/company/gifts-&-decorative-accessories-magazine
X (Twitter): x.com/Gifts_and_Dec
Instagram: www.instagram.com/gifts_and_dec
Released: Monthly **Price:** $55.97, for online 1 Year (11 issues); $68.97, for print and online 1 year (11 issues). **Description:** International magazine for

retailers of gifts, greeting cards, decorative accessories, and stationery-related merchandise. **Availability:** Print; Online. **Type:** Full-text; Directory.

FRANCHISES AND BUSINESS OPPORTUNITIES

7486 ■ Party Land
113A W Ridge Pke.
 Plymouth Meeting, PA 19462
Description: Retailer of party products such as plates, cups, napkins, accessories, table covers, balloons. **Founded:** 1986. **Franchised:** 1988. **Training:** 1 week training.

LIBRARIES

7487 ■ Hallmark Cards, Inc.
Hallmark Cards, Inc.
 2501 McGee St.
 Kansas City, MO 64108
Ph: (816)274-5111
Free: 800-425-5627
URL: http://corporate.hallmark.com
Contact: Mike Perry, President
URL(s): www.hallmark.com
Facebook: www.facebook.com/Hallmark
X (Twitter): twitter.com/Hallmark
Instagram: www.instagram.com/hallmark
YouTube: www.youtube.com/user/hallmarkcards
Pinterest: www.pinterest.com/hallmark

Description: Manufacturer of greeting cards, stationery, and related products. **Founded:** 1910. **Educational Activities:** FMI Midwinter Executive Conference (Annual).

Glass Repair and Replacement Service

ASSOCIATIONS AND OTHER ORGANIZATIONS

7488 ■ **Independent Glass Association (IGA)**
14747 N Northsight Blvd., Ste. 111-387
  Scottsdale, AZ 85260
Co. E-mail: info@iga.org
URL: http://www.iga.org
Contact: Gary Hart, Executive Director
Facebook: www.facebook.com/iga.org
Description: Helps automotive and architectural glass retailers compete with the national chains. Unites the efforts, interests and ideas of its members. Offers marketing, billing, and purchasing programs and promotes a high standard for consumer safety, quality, service and fair trade principles. Encourages a competitive, free market environment and the independence of each member. **Founded:** 1995. **Publications:** *Beacon Bulletin* (Weekly). **Geographic Preference:** National.

7489 ■ **International Window Film Association (IWFA) - Library**
1103-A Brookdale St.
  Martinsville, VA 24112
Ph: (276)666-4932
Co. E-mail: admin@iwfa.com
URL: http://iwfa.com
Contact: Jack Mundy, President
E-mail: jack@ener-gard.com
Facebook: www.facebook.com/windowfilminfo
YouTube: www.youtube.com/user/WindowFilmIWFA
Description: Acts as a forum for communication and works to increase professionalism in the window film industry. Maintains educational programs and speakers' bureau. **Scope:** Window film. **Founded:** 1990. **Holdings:** Figures not available. **Publications:** *Flat Glass Training Manual* (Annual). **Geographic Preference:** Multinational.

7490 ■ **National Glass Association (NGA)**
1945 Old Gallows Rd., Ste. 750
  Vienna, VA 22182
Ph: (703)442-4890
Free: 866-342-5642
URL: http://www.glass.org
Contact: Nicole Harris, President
Linkedin: www.linkedin.com/company/national-glass-association
X (Twitter): x.com/natglassassoc
Description: Manufacturers, installers, retailers, distributors and fabricators of flat, architectural, automotive and specialty glass and metal products, mirrors, shower and patio doors, windows and tabletops. Provides informational, educational and technical services. **Founded:** 1948. **Publications:** *Window & Door* (6/year); *Glass Magazine--Directory of Suppliers Section* (Monthly); *Glass Magazine: The Voice of the Flat Glass and Metals Industry* (8/year); *AutoGlass: Glass on the Move*; *AutoGlass Installation Guide* (Annual); *Glass Magazine* (8/year). **Educational Activities:** National Auto Glass Conference (Semiannual); GlassBuild America: The Glass, Window and Door Expo (Annual); National Auto Glass Conference and Expo; The NGA Show: America's Glass Expo (Annual). **Geographic Preference:** National.

REFERENCE WORKS

7491 ■ *"Auto Glass Shortage Requires Creativity to Persevere"* in *Autobody News* (October 20, 2021)
Ed: Rebecca Barnabi. **Released:** October 20, 2021. **Description:** With the COVID-19 pandemic causing a glass shortage, auto glass shops are struggling to fill orders. However, manufacturers are trying to fulfill them as quickly as possible, but customers may still need to be patient and wait longer. **Availability:** Download.

7492 ■ *"Hanson's to Widen Marketing Window; Company Plans Mall Kiosks, to Attend Events"* in *Crain's Detroit Business* (Vol. 28, May 28, 2012, No. 22, pp. 3)
Pub: Crain Communications Inc.
Contact: Barry Asin, President
Ed: Sherri Welch. **Description:** Hanson's Window and Construction Company is expanding its presence through the use of kiosks installed at malls as well as attending local events in order to increase awareness of their firm. Las year Hanson spent nearly $9.2 million on marketing their vinyl replacement windows, siding and roofing for homes. **Availability:** Print; Online.

7493 ■ *"Healthcare Facilities Increasingly Embracing Dynamic Glass to Benefit Patients"* in *Ecology, Environment & Conservation Business* (May 24, 2014)
Pub: NewsRX LLC.
Contact: Kalani Rosell, Contact
Description: According to research, optimizing natural daylight and outdoor views in healthcare facilities helps to improve outcomes and shorter recovery times for patients. Therefore, a growing number of healthcare facilities are incorporating SageGlass(R) dynamic glass, a product of Saint-Gobain, into their new construction and remodeling/renovation designs. **Availability:** Online.

7494 ■ *"RavenBrick Ready to Manufacture Its High-Tech Windows"* in *Denver Business Journal* (Vol. 64, September 7, 2012, No. 16, pp. 1)
Pub: Baltimore Business Journal
Contact: Rhonda Pringle, President
E-mail: rpringle@bizjournals.com
Description: RavenBrick LLC is set to build a new manufacturing plant in Denver, Colorado. The company manufactures auto-darkening window films. RavenBrick has raised a total of $13.5 million in new investment capital. **Availability:** Print; Online.

7495 ■ *"Safelite Auto-Glass Replacement Practice Challenged by Glass-Repair Resin Maker"* in *The Columbus Dispatch* (February 13, 2018)
URL(s): www.dispatch.com/business/20180213/safelite-auto-glass-replacement-practice-challenged-by-glass-repair-resin-maker
Ed: Dan Gearino. **Released:** February 13, 2018. **Description:** Discusses the lawsuit against Safelite, the nation's largest retailer of auto glass products, as they defend claims that it is not spreading lies about the "six-inch" or "dollar-bill" rule for repairing windshields. **Availability:** Online.

7496 ■ *"When the Windshield Helps Drive the Car, a Repair Isn't So Simple"* in *The New York Times* (February 7, 2019)
URL(s): www.nytimes.com/2019/02/07/business/windshield-repairs.html
Released: February 07, 2019. **Description:** Today's newer vehicles come equipped with high-tech driver assistance features that are embedded into windshields, making any repairs difficult, time-consuming, and expensive. As drivers are depending more and more on these systems, making sure they are properly repaired is crucial for the safety of everyone driving in the car. **Availability:** Online.

STATISTICAL SOURCES

7497 ■ *Auto Windshield Repair Services Industry in the US - Market Research Report*
URL(s): www.ibisworld.com/united-states/market-research-reports/auto-windshield-repair-services-industry/
Price: $925. **Description:** Downloadable report analyzing the current and future trends in the auto windshield repair industry. **Availability:** Download.

TRADE PERIODICALS

7498 ■ *Glass Magazine: The Voice of the Flat Glass and Metals Industry*
Pub: National Glass Association
Contact: Nicole Harris, President
URL(s): www.glassmagazine.com
Facebook: www.facebook.com/glassmagazineNGA
X (Twitter): x.com/glassmag
Instagram: www.instagram.com/glassmagazinenga
YouTube: www.youtube.com/channel/UCNHAQHp2_mSR7XxU7DDwPEg
Ed: Katy Devlin. **Released:** 8/year; January/February, March, April, May/ June, July, August, September/ October and November/December. **Price:** $49.95, U.S.; $79.95, for outside. **Description:** Architectural glass magazine. **Availability:** Print; PDF; Online.

TRADE SHOWS AND CONVENTIONS

7499 ■ **NDGA Annual Convention with Glass Show and Sale**
National Depression Glass Association (NDGA)
  PO Box 156
  Wellington, KS 67152
Ph: (620)326-6400
Co. E-mail: convention@ndga.net
URL: http://www.ndga.net
Contact: Pam Meyer, President

E-mail: meyerantiques@juno.com
URL(s): www.ndga.net/pastconv/2024/conv2024.php
Frequency: Annual. **Description:** American-made glassworks, particularly those from the Depression era. **Audience:** Glass dealers and the public. **Principal Exhibits:** American-made glassworks, particularly those from the Depression era. **Telecommunication Services:** convention@ndga.net.

FRANCHISES AND BUSINESS OPPORTUNITIES

7500 ■ Apple Auto Glass
7111 Kennedy Rd., Unit 4
Mississauga, ON, Canada L5S 0A4
Free: 800-267-6105
Co. E-mail: info@appleautoglass.com
URL: http://www.appleautoglass.com
Contact: Gord Day, Owner
Description: Firm provides windshield repair and automotive glass replacement. **Founded:** 1983. **Training:** Training provided as required.

7501 ■ Atlantic Windshield Repair Inc.
449 Cambrian Ridge Trl.
Pelham, AL 35124
Contact: John L. Seale, President
Description: Firm provides windshield repair and services. **Training:** An initial 3 day training course covering windshield repair, insurance filing, customer service and advanced techniques and procedures. Ongoing video training and call in support available.

7502 ■ Belron Canada Inc. (BCI)
8288 Blvd. PIE-IX
Montreal, QC, Canada H1Z 3T6
Ph: (514)593-7000
Free: 800-363-7131
URL: http://www.belroncanada.com
Contact: Michel Savard, President
Linkedin: www.linkedin.com/company/belron-canada-inc
Description: Provider of automotive glass replacement, repair services and also glass distribution. **Founded:** 1965.

7503 ■ DURO vitres d'autos
8288, boul. Pie-IX
Montreal, QC, Canada H1Z 3T6
URL: http://www.durovitresdautos.com
Description: Provider of windshield repair and auto glass replacement and also retailer of antitheft devices, remote starters and other car accessories. **Founded:** 1954. **Training:** Yes.

7504 ■ Novus Glass
650 Pelham Blvd., Ste. 100
Saint Paul, MN 55114
Ph: (952)944-8000
Free: 800-776-6887
Co. E-mail: info@novusglass.com
URL: http://www.novusglass.com/en-us
Facebook: www.facebook.com/NovusGlassUSA
Linkedin: www.linkedin.com/company/novus-glass
X (Twitter): x.com/novusglobal
Instagram: www.instagram.com/novusmarketing
YouTube: www.youtube.com/c/NOVUSGlass
Description: Firm engages in auto glass repair and replacement services. **No. of Franchise Units:** 2,000. **Founded:** 1972. **Franchised:** 1985. **Equity Capital Needed:** $100,000 – Fixed Location Franchise ; $ 50,000 – Mobile Franchise ; 25% of total initial investment Fixed Location Franchise ; 25% of total initial investment Mobile Franchise. **Franchise Fee:** $14,995. **Royalty Fee:** 8% of gross revenue. **Financial Assistance:** Yes **Training:** Gives franchisee's the ongoing training and support needed to from their first day of training and throughout their career as a franchise owner. Offers complete technical and business training at the Minneapolis, MN headquarters. Offers one-on-one consultation with an 8-day program and teaches how to offer a full-service windshield repair franchise.

7505 ■ Synergistic International L.L.C.
Neighborly
133 N 1st St., Ste. 108
Hewitt, TX 76643
Free: 800-490-7501
Fax: (877)496-2356
URL: http://www.neighborlybrands.com
Description: Auto, commercial, and residential glass replacement. **Financial Assistance:** Yes **Training:** Yes.

RESEARCH CENTERS

7506 ■ Alfred University - Inamori School of Engineering - Center for Glass Research (CGR)
1 Saxon Dr.
Alfred, NY 14802
URL: http://www.alfred.edu/cact/center-for-glass-innovation.cfm
Contact: John Simmins, Director
Description: Integral unit of Inamori School of Engineering, Alfred University. Offers glass information and research. **Scope:** Manufacture, characterization, and properties of glass. **Founded:** 1985.

Golf Shop

ASSOCIATIONS AND OTHER ORGANIZATIONS

7507 ■ American Junior Golf Association (AJGA)
1980 Sports Club Dr.
Braselton, GA 30517
Ph: (770)868-4200
Free: 877-373-2542
Fax: (770)868-4211
Co. E-mail: ajga@ajga.org
URL: http://www.ajga.org
Contact: James E. Nugent, III, President
Facebook: www.facebook.com/AJGAGolf
X (Twitter): x.com/ajgaGolf
Instagram: www.instagram.com/ajgagolf
YouTube: www.youtube.com/AJGAvideos
Description: Works for the overall growth and development of young men and women through competitive junior golf. Provides exposure vehicle for college scholarships. **Founded:** 1978. **Publications:** Golfweek. **Awards:** Rolex Junior All-America Teams (Annual); AJGA Scholastic Junior All-America (Annual); Jerry Cole Sportsmanship Award (Annual); All-Time Rolex Junior Players of the Year (Annual). **Geographic Preference:** Multinational; Local.

7508 ■ Association of Golf Merchandisers (AGM)
2351 Sunset Blvd., Ste. 170 No. 331
Rocklin, CA 95765
Ph: (602)604-8250
Co. E-mail: info@agmgolf.org
URL: http://agmgolf.org
Contact: Desane Blaney, Executive Director
Facebook: www.facebook.com/AssociationGolfMerchandisers
Linkedin: www.linkedin.com/company/association-of-golf-merchandisers
Description: Dedicated to maximizing members' learning and earning capabilities. Conducts continuing educational programs; provides networking opportunities, scholarships and a forum for communication; compiles statistics. **Founded:** 1989. **Publications:** AGM Merchandise Manual. **Geographic Preference:** National.

7509 ■ Golf Range Association of America (GRAA)
CT
URL: http://www.golfrange.org
Contact: Brian Folino, President
E-mail: bfolino@golfrange.org
Description: Promotes growth and development of the golf industry. Gathers and disseminates information on economic and social trends affecting the golf industries; conducts educational programs. **Founded:** 1992. **Publications:** Golf Range Development and Operations; Golf Range Magazine (Monthly); Profile of Golf Practice Facility Operations 2003. **Geographic Preference:** National.

7510 ■ International Golf Federation (IGF)
Maison du Sport International
Av de Rhodanie 54
1007 Lausanne, Switzerland
Ph: 41 21 623-1212
Fax: 41 21 601-6477
Co. E-mail: info@igfmail.org
URL: http://www.igfgolf.org
Contact: Peter Dawson, President
Description: Strives to encourage the international development of golf, and to foster friendship and sportsmanship among the peoples of the world through the conduct of the biennial Amateur Team Championships for the Eisenhower Trophy and the Espirito Santo Trophy. **Founded:** 1958. **Awards:** Eisenhower Trophy (Biennial); Espirito Santo Trophy (Biennial). **Geographic Preference:** Multinational.

7511 ■ Ladies Professional Golf Association (LPGA)
100 International Golf Dr.
Daytona Beach, FL 32124-1092
Ph: (386)274-6200
Fax: (386)274-1099
Co. E-mail: tcpmembership@lpga.com
URL: http://www.lpga.com
Contact: Marvol Barnard, President
Facebook: www.facebook.com/LPGA
X (Twitter): x.com/lpga
Instagram: www.instagram.com/lpga_tour
YouTube: www.youtube.com/user/lpgavideo
Description: Represents and promotes women golfers, teachers and competitors. Compiles statistics on tournaments, money winnings, and scoring. **Founded:** 1950. **Publications:** Ladies Professional Golf Association--Schedule Directory (Annual); Player Guide (Annual). **Awards:** Patty Berg Award; LPGA Coach of the Year (Annual); Louise Suggs Rolex Rookie of the Year Award (Annual); LPGA T&CP Hall of Fame (Annual); Founders Award (Irregular); LPGA Professional of the Year (Annual); LPGA Rolex Player of the Year Award (Annual); LPGA Teacher of the Year (Annual); LPGA Vare Trophy (Annual); LPGA Commissioner's Award (Annual); Ellen Griffin Rolex Award (Annual). **Geographic Preference:** National; Regional.

7512 ■ National Golf Foundation (NGF)
501 N Hwy. A1A
Jupiter, FL 33477-4577
Ph: (561)744-6006
Free: 888-275-4643
Fax: (561)744-6107
Co. E-mail: general@ngf.org
URL: http://www.ngf.org
Contact: Joe Beditz, Executive Chairman of the Board
Facebook: www.facebook.com/NationalGolfFoundation
Linkedin: www.linkedin.com/company/national-golf-foundation
X (Twitter): x.com/ngf_golfbizinfo
Description: Golf-oriented businesses including: equipment and apparel companies; golf facilities; golf publications; golf course architects, developers and builders; companies offering specialized services to the golf industry; golf associations; teachers, coaches and instructors and other interested individuals. Serves as a market research and strategic planning organization for the golf industry. **Scope:** Golf consumers, golf courses, range operations and maintenance, industry sales, and golf facility development. **Founded:** 1936. **Publications:** The Graffis Report (Annual); Profile of Golf Practice Facility Operations 2003; Golf Course Directory (Annual); NGF Membership Directory (Quarterly); The NGF's Directory of Golf Retailers: Off-Course Golf Retail Stores in the U.S.; The NGF's Executive and Par-3 Golf Course Directory: A Viable Enterprise; The NGF's Golf Course Directory; The NGF's Golf Course Directory and Range Directory; The NGF's Golf Practice Range and Learning Center Directory; The NGF's Media Directory; Directory of Golf: The People and Businesses in Golf (Annual). **Educational Activities:** NGF Golf course management schools. **Geographic Preference:** National.

7513 ■ Professional Golfers' Association of America (PGA)
100 Ave. of the Champions
Palm Beach Gardens, FL 33418
Ph: (561)624-8400
Free: 877-410-7865
URL: http://www.pga.com
Contact: Jim Richerson, President
Facebook: www.facebook.com/PGAofAmerica
Instagram: www.instagram.com/Pga
YouTube: www.youtube.com/channel/UCnUYyAtDiyeaobSzKqVE_BA
Description: Trains, certifies, and advocates for professional golfers; certifies college programs in golf management at 14 universities. **Founded:** 1916. **Publications:** African American Golfer's Digest (Quarterly); PGA Merchandise Show. **Educational Activities:** PGA Merchandise Show (Annual). **Awards:** PGA Championship (Annual); PGA Professional Development Award (Annual); Bill Strausbaugh Award (Biennial); Teacher of the Year Award (Annual); Vardon Trophy (Annual); PGA of America Ryder Cup (Biennial); PGA Golf Professional of the Year (Annual); PGA Youth Player Development Award (Annual); PGA Merchandiser of the Year (Annual); PGA Player of the Year Award (Annual); PGA Teacher of the Year (Annual). **Geographic Preference:** National.

7514 ■ United States Golf Association (USGA) - Library
PO Box 708
Far Hills, NJ 07931
Ph: (908)234-2300
URL: http://www.usga.org
Contact: J. Stuart Francis, President
Facebook: www.facebook.com/USGA
Linkedin: www.linkedin.com/company/united-states-golf-association

X (Twitter): x.com/usga
Instagram: www.instagram.com/usga
YouTube: www.youtube.com/user/TheUSGA

Description: Serves as governing body for golf in the U.S. Turfgrass Visiting Service promotes scientific work in turf management. Provides data on rules, handicapping, amateur status, tournament procedure, turf maintenance, and golf balls and implements. **Scope:** Golf. **Founded:** 1894. **Holdings:** Figures not available. **Publications:** *Golf Journal: Official Publication of the United States Golf Association*; *Golf Journal* (9/year); *The Rules of Golf*, *Building a USGA Green*. **Awards:** Curtis Cup (Biennial); Walker Cup (Biennial); USGA Green Section Award (Annual); Bob Jones Award (Annual); Joe Dey Award (Annual); USGA U.S. Women's Open (Annual); USGA U.S. Senior Open (Annual); USGA U.S. Amateur Championship (Annual); USGA U.S. Women's Amateur (Annual); USGA/Chevron STEM Scholarship Program. **Geographic Preference:** National; Local.

REFERENCE WORKS

7515 ■ *"5 Ways to Create a Better Golf Shop"* in Golf Inc. (June 19, 2017)
URL(s): www.golfincmagazine.com/blog/5-ways-create-better-golf-shop
Ed: Jack Dillon. **Released:** June 19, 2017. **Description:** Discusses the five best tips for running a professional golf shop. **Availability:** Online.

7516 ■ *"Driving Passion"* in Small Business Opportunities (April 2008)
Pub: Harris Publishing, Inc.
Contact: Janet Chase, Contact
Ed: Chuck Green. **Description:** Profile of Joe Assell, founder of Golftec, a company offering golf instruction that uses the latest technology with professional teachers. **Availability:** Print; Online.

7517 ■ *"Golf Club Plan Raises Hackles"* in Philadelphia Business Journal (Vol. 31, April 6, 2012, No. 8, pp. 1)
Pub: Baltimore Business Journal
Contact: Rhonda Pringle, President
E-mail: rpringle@bizjournals.com
Description: VRJ Associates' proposal to redevelop its Westover Country Club golf course into an athletic and recreational facility has been opposed by neighboring residents. The proposed facility would include 12 tennis courts softball and baseball fields, among other things. **Availability:** Print; Online.

7518 ■ *"Golfsmith Goes On Offensive"* in Austin Business Journal (Vol. 32, April 27, 2012, No. 8, pp. A1)
Pub: American City Business Journals, Inc.
Contact: Mike Olivieri, Executive Vice President
Ed: Sandra Zaragoza. **Description:** Golfsmith International Holdings Inc. is targeting existing golfers with its marketing campaign as it attempts to increase its market share. The company aims to attract golfers by providing the right solutions to improving their games. **Availability:** Online.

7519 ■ *"Hit the Green: Golf Technology"* in Canadian Business (Vol. 79, August 14, 2006, No. 16-17, pp. 73)
Pub: Rogers Media Inc.
Contact: Neil Spivak, Chief Executive Officer
Ed: Andrew Wahl. **Description:** Reorganization of the bankrupt 4everSports golf company in the United States is discussed. **Availability:** Print; Online.

7520 ■ *"Hitting the Green"* in Canadian Business (Vol. 81, July 22, 2008, No. 12-13, pp. 34)
Description: RBC is sponsoring the Canadian Open golf tournament, which is the second-oldest event in the PGA Tour. RBC is expected to receive television exposure on CBS and the Golf Channel. Additional information relating to the sponsorship is presented. **Availability:** Print; Online.

7521 ■ *"How Has Cincinnati's City Golf Privatization Played?"* in Business Courier (Vol. 27, September 10, 2010, No. 19, pp. 1)
Pub: Business Courier
Ed: Dan Monk. **Description:** It was reported that private contractors are getting more revenue from fewer golfers on city-owned courses in Cincinnati, Ohio. In 1998, the city handed over seven municipal courses to private management. However, some believe that the city has escalated a price war among the region's golf courses. **Availability:** Print; Online.

7522 ■ *"Internal Auditor Wants Ethics Review of City's Billy Casper Golf Contract"* in Business Courier (Vol. 27, September 10, 2010, No. 19, pp. 1)
Pub: Business Courier
Ed: Dan Monk. **Description:** Mark Ashworth, an internal auditor for Cincinnati, Ohio is pushing for an ethics review of management contract for seven city-owned golf courses. Ashworth wants the Ohio Ethics Commission to investigate family ties between a superintendent for the Cincinnati Recreation Commission and Billy Casper Golf. **Availability:** Print; Online.

7523 ■ *"Major Golf Retail Show in the Rough for 2010"* in Orlando Business Journal (Vol. 26, January 15, 2010, No. 33, pp. 1)
Pub: Orlando Business Journal
Contact: Julie Swyers, Director
E-mail: jswyers@bizjournals.com
Ed: Anjali Fluker. **Description:** The 57th Annual PGA Merchandise Show in Orlando, Florida is projected to attract 39,000 attendees in 2010, compared with 41,000 in 2009. According to the Orange County Convention Center, economic benefits that could be obtained from the 2010 edition of the golf retail show might reach only $77 million, compared with $78 million generated last year. **Availability:** Print; Online.

7524 ■ *"Mixing Business and Pleasure On the Green"* in Black Enterprise (Vol. 41, October 2010, No. 3, pp. 65)
Description: Glow Golf, sponsored by Glow Sports, will offer instruction to 150 female corporate executives and entrepreneurs to learn the fundamentals of the game of golf. **Availability:** Print; Online.

7525 ■ *"On the Green: Sheila Johnson Adds $35 Million Golf Resort To Her Expanding Portfolio"* in Black Enterprise (January 2008)
Pub: Earl G. Graves Ltd.
Contact: Earl Graves, Jr., President
Ed: Donna M. Owens. **Description:** Profile of Sheila Johnson, CEO of Salamander Hospitality LLC, made history when she purchased the Innisbrook Resort and Golf Club, making her the first African American woman to own this type of property. The resort includes four championship golf courses, six swimming pools, four restaurants, eleven tennis courts, three conference halls, and a nature preserve. **Availability:** Online.

7526 ■ *"Sacramento Businesses Must Cut Water Use 20 Percent"* in Sacramento Business Journal (Vol. 30, January 17, 2014, No. 47, pp. 5)
Pub: American City Business Journals, Inc.
Contact: Mike Olivieri, Executive Vice President
Released: Weekly. **Price:** $4, introductory 4-week offer(Digital & Print). **Description:** The Sacramento, California City, California Council's decision to reduce water use by 20 percent could have a big impact on businesses. Hotels and restaurants are among the biggest commercial users of water, while golf courses generally use well water. The need for businesses to purchase more efficient fixtures is also discussed. **Availability:** Print; Online.

7527 ■ *"Seven Annoying People You'll Meet At Your Company Golf Day"* in Canadian Business (Vol. 85, August 29, 2012, No. 14, pp. 76)
Ed: Jeff Beer. **Description:** The characteristics of people one may meet on a company golf tournament are described. Tips on how to deal with negative attitudes are provided. **Availability:** Print; Online.

7528 ■ *"TopGolf Plans Three-Level Entertainment Center in S.A."* in San Antonio Business Journal (Vol. 27, January 10, 2014, No. 49, pp. 6)
Pub: American City Business Journals, Inc.
Contact: Mike Olivieri, Executive Vice President
Released: Weekly. **Price:** $4, Introductory 4-week offer(Digital & Print). **Description:** TopGolf plans to construct a golf entertainment complex in San Antonio, Texas. The proposed facility is expected to house about 2,900 square feet of private event space. The entertainment center could also attract around 400,000 visitors in the facility's first year of operation. **Availability:** Print; Online.

7529 ■ *"What Kind of Golfer Are You?"* in Baltimore Business Journal (Vol. 29, May 4, 2012, No. 53, pp. 1)
Ed: Gary Haber. **Description:** Businesspeople playing golf are classified into different profiles according to style. These profiles also describe the behavior of businessmen during and after playing golf. **Availability:** Print; Online.

7530 ■ *"Why Slacking Off Is Great For Business"* in Canadian Business (Vol. 85, August 13, 2012, No. 13, pp. 60)
Ed: Sarah Barmak. **Description:** Procrastination can be good for busy managers to develop creative thinking which may be good for business. Ways to enhance the brain's creative engine including taking a different route to the office, reading a best seller, or playing golf. **Availability:** Print; Online.

7531 ■ *"Winter Puts Golf Industry Off Course"* in Baltimore Business Journal (Vol. 31, April 4, 2014, No. 49, pp. 17)
Pub: American City Business Journals, Inc.
Contact: Mike Olivieri, Executive Vice President
Released: Weekly. **Price:** $4, introductory 4-week offer(Digital & Print). **Description:** Due to extreme cold and heavy snow in Maryland and the rest of the country, playing golf has become so impossible that the golf industry is struggling to stay on budget. Golf courses are closing down due to lack of revenue generation. Country clubs are working to be more creative with various winter events to supplement income. For example, one country club hosted a winter fest, indoor putting contests, a karaoke night, a comedy night, and a kids' activity day; while Waverly Woods Golf Club is offering members temperature pricing throughout the winter. **Availability:** Print; Online.

7532 ■ *"You'll Golf Better If You Think Tiger Has Used Your Clubs"* in Harvard Business Review (Vol. 90, July-August 2012, No. 7-8, pp. 32)
Pub: Harvard Business Review Press
Contact: Moderna V. Pfizer, Contact
Ed: Sally Linkenauger. **Description:** Golfers who were told that a professional had used the clubs they were given to use performed better than those who were told nothing about the clubs they were given. They perceived the hole to be 9 percent bigger in diamter than the control group, and were able to sink 32 percent more putts than did the control group.

TRADE PERIODICALS

7533 ■ *Golf*
Pub: EB Golf Media, LLC
Contact: David Maher, President
URL(s): golf.com
Facebook: www.facebook.com/golf
X (Twitter): twitter.com/golf_com
Instagram: www.instagram.com/golf_com
YouTube: www.youtube.com/channel/UCzdMqRWzdF0JUJRIVa-dgDw
Released: 8/year **Price:** $30, for 1 year; $50, for 2 year; $79.92, U.S. for annual cover; $87.92, Canada for annual cover. **Description:** Popular consumer magazine for golfers. **Availability:** Print; Online.

7534 ■ *Golf Digest*
Pub: Conde Nast Publications
Contact: Agnes Chu, President
URL(s): www.golfdigest.com
Facebook: www.facebook.com/GolfDigest
X (Twitter): twitter.com/GolfDigest
Instagram: www.instagram.com/golfdigest
YouTube: www.youtube.com/channel/UCkMO
 tD7MMYs1H55XH6CkWEw

Released: Monthly **Price:** $1.99, for online; $39.99, for print and online; $169.99, for all access. **Description:** International magazine for golfers. **Availability:** Print; Online.

TRADE SHOWS AND CONVENTIONS

7535 ■ GCSAA Education Conference
Golf Course Superintendents Association of America (GCSAA)
1421 Research Pk. Dr.
Lawrence, KS 66049
Ph: (785)841-2240
Free: 800-472-7878
Fax: (785)832-3643
Co. E-mail: inquiries@gcsaa.org
URL: http://www.gcsaa.org
Contact: Kevin P. Breen, President
URL(s): www.gcsaa.org/foundation/education

Frequency: Annual. **Description:** Equipment, supplies, and services for golf course and facility maintenance. **Audience:** Professionals, researchers, industry experts and superintendents. **Principal Exhibits:** Equipment, supplies, and services for golf course and facility maintenance.

7536 ■ Golf Course Superintendents Association of America Golf Industry Show
Golf Course Superintendents Association of America (GCSAA)
1421 Research Pk. Dr.
Lawrence, KS 66049
Ph: (785)841-2240
Free: 800-472-7878
Fax: (785)832-3643
Co. E-mail: inquiries@gcsaa.org
URL: http://www.gcsaa.org
Contact: Kevin P. Breen, President
URL(s): www.gcsaaconference.com

Frequency: Annual. **Description:** Exhibits relating to golf courses and facility management. **Audience:** Golf course superintendents, owners, general managers, builders, and architects. **Principal Exhibits:** Exhibits relating to golf courses and facility management. Dates and Locations: 2025 Feb 03-06 San Diego Convention Center, San Diego, CA; 2026 Jan 31-Feb 05 Orange County Convention Center, Orlando, FL. **Telecommunication Services:** cts@gcsaa.org.

7537 ■ PGA Merchandise Show
Professional Golfers' Association of America (PGA)
100 Ave. of the Champions
Palm Beach Gardens, FL 33418
Ph: (561)624-8400
Free: 877-410-7865
URL: http://www.pga.com
Contact: Jim Richerson, President
URL(s): www.pgashow.com
Facebook: www.facebook.com/PGAShow

Frequency: Annual. **Description:** Golf apparel, clubs, bags, balls, range equipment, club components, golf cars, golf shoes, and related equipment, supplies, and services. **Audience:** Golf professionals, retail buyers, club managers and superintendents. **Principal Exhibits:** Golf apparel, clubs, bags, balls, range equipment, club components, golf cars, golf shoes, and related equipment, supplies, and services. Dates and Locations: 2025 Jan 21-24 Orlando, FL. **Telecommunication Services:** inquiry@pga.reedexpo.com.

FRANCHISES AND BUSINESS OPPORTUNITIES

7538 ■ Golf USA Inc.
14040 Joel McDonald Dr.
Oklahoma City, OK 73134
Ph: (405)749-4653
Co. E-mail: mail@golfusa.com
URL: http://golfusa.com
Facebook: www.facebook.com/GolfUSA
X (Twitter): x.com/thegolfusa
Instagram: www.instagram.com/thegolfusa

Description: Operator of golf equipment, club repair, and services for golfers. **Founded:** 1986.

LIBRARIES

7539 ■ United States Golf Association (USGA) - Library
PO Box 708
Far Hills, NJ 07931
Ph: (908)234-2300
URL: http://www.usga.org
Contact: J. Stuart Francis, President
Facebook: www.facebook.com/USGA
Linkedin: www.linkedin.com/company/united-states
 -golf-association
X (Twitter): x.com/usga
Instagram: www.instagram.com/usga
YouTube: www.youtube.com/user/TheUSGA

Description: Serves as governing body for golf in the U.S. Turfgrass Visiting Service promotes scientific work in turf management. Provides data on rules, handicapping, amateur status, tournament procedure, turf maintenance, and golf balls and implements. **Scope:** Golf. **Founded:** 1894. **Holdings:** Figures not available. **Publications:** *Golf Journal: Official Publication of the United States Golf Association*; *Golf Journal* (9/year); *The Rules of Golf*; *Building a USGA Green*. **Awards:** Curtis Cup (Biennial); Walker Cup (Biennial); USGA Green Section Award (Annual); Bob Jones Award (Annual); Joe Dey Award (Annual); USGA U.S. Women's Open (Annual); USGA U.S. Senior Open (Annual); USGA U.S. Amateur Championship (Annual); USGA U.S. Women's Amateur (Annual); USGA/Chevron STEM Scholarship Program. **Geographic Preference:** National; Local.

Gourmet Coffee/Tea House

ASSOCIATIONS AND OTHER ORGANIZATIONS

7540 ■ **Café Association du Canada (CAC)**
[Coffee Association of Canada]
25 Adelaide St. E, Ste. 711
Toronto, ON, Canada M5C 3A1
Ph: (416)510-8032
Co. E-mail: info@coffeeassoc.com
URL: http://coffeeassoc.com
Contact: Robert Carter, President
Linkedin: www.linkedin.com/company/coffee-association-of-canada
X (Twitter): x.com/CoffeeAssociat1
Description: Seeks to make the coffee beverage experience a more integral and meaningful part of Canadian lives. Serves as a clearinghouse on the coffee industry. **Founded:** 1991. **Geographic Preference:** Multinational.

7541 ■ **National Coffee Association of U.S.A. Inc. (NCA)**
45 Broadway, Ste. 1140
New York, NY 10006
Ph: (212)766-4007
Fax: (212)766-5815
Co. E-mail: info@ncausa.org
URL: http://www.ncausa.org
Contact: William Murray, President
E-mail: wmmurray@ncausa.org
Facebook: www.facebook.com/nationalcoffeeassociation
X (Twitter): x.com/nationalcoffee
Description: Green coffee importers, jobbers, brokers, and agents; instant coffee and liquid extract processors; roasters and allied coffee industries; exporters; retailers. Promotes sound business relations and mutual understanding among members of the trade. Collects and publishes consumer, market and technical information on the coffee industry. **Founded:** 1911. **Publications:** *Coffee Reporter Weekly* (Weekly); *CoffeeTrax* (Quarterly); *National Coffee Data Trends (NCDT)* (Semiannual); *US Coffee Industry Review 2005*; *The Coffee Reporter* (Weekly). **Educational Activities:** National Coffee Association of U.S.A. Annual Convention (Annual). **Geographic Preference:** National.

7542 ■ **Specialty Coffee Association (SCA)**
117 W 4th St., Ste. 300
Santa Ana, CA 92701
Ph: (562)624-4100
Co. E-mail: membership@sca.coffee
URL: http://sca.coffee
Contact: Colleen Anunu, President
Facebook: www.facebook.com/SpecialtyCoffeeAssociation
Linkedin: www.linkedin.com/company/3481060
X (Twitter): x.com/SpecialtyCoffee
Instagram: www.instagram.com/specialtycoffeeassociation
YouTube: www.youtube.com/SpecialtyCoffeeAssociation/featured

Description: Coffee roasters, green coffee brokers, retailers, distributors, and others involved in the gourmet coffee industry. Provides business, professional, promotional, and educational assistance in the areas of cultivation, processing, preparation, and marketing of specialty coffee; increase consumer awareness, understanding, and consumption of specialty coffee. **Founded:** 2017. **Publications:** *Specialty Coffee Association of America--Member Directory*. **Educational Activities:** SCAA Planning Meeting; Re:co Symposium (Annual); SCAA Leadership Summit. **Awards:** SCAA Achievement Awards (Annual); SCAA Sustainability Award (Annual); SCAA Best New Product (Annual); Mose Drachman Sales and Service Award (Annual). **Geographic Preference:** National.

7543 ■ **Tea Association of the U.S.A. Inc. (TA)**
362 5th Ave., Ste. 1002
New York, NY 10001
Ph: (212)986-9415
Co. E-mail: info@teausa.com
URL: http://www.teausa.org
Contact: Peter F. Goggi, President
Description: Packers, importers, brokers, agents, and other firms dedicated to the interests and growth of the U.S. tea industry. **Founded:** 1899. **Geographic Preference:** National.

7544 ■ **Tea Council of the United States of America (TC)**
c/o Tea Association of the US A
362 5th Ave., Ste. 1002
New York, NY 10001
Ph: (212)986-9415
Co. E-mail: info@teausa.com
URL: http://www.teausa.com/14519/tea-council
Contact: Peter F. Goggi, Contact
E-mail: peter.goggi@teausa.org
Facebook: www.facebook.com/TeaCouncil
X (Twitter): x.com/TeaCouncil
Description: Represents companies and countries trading tea in the US. Works to increase tea consumption. **Founded:** 1950. **Publications:** *Tea World* (Annual); *TeaBits* (Quarterly). **Educational Activities:** TC World Tea Forum.

REFERENCE WORKS

7545 ■ *"Arvada Coffee Shop Wants To Be a Model for Employers"* in *Denver Business Journal* (Vol. 66, May 30, 2014, No. 2, pp. A5)
Pub: American City Business Journals, Inc.
Contact: Mike Olivieri, Executive Vice President
Released: Weekly. **Price:** $4, introductory 4-week offer(Digital only). **Description:** The Steamers Coffee Shop in Arvada, Colorado was initially created to provide work to people with developmental disabilities who are clients of Parker Personal Care Homes Inc. According to owner, Scott Parker, the coffee shop provided the most normal work setting possible to his client. **Availability:** Print; Online.

7546 ■ *"Caribou Coffee Kick-Starts Spring Planting with New Grounds for Your Ground Program in Time for Earth Day"* in *Ecology, Environment and Conservation Business* (May 3, 2014, pp. 5)
Pub: NewsRX LLC.
Contact: Kalani Rosell, Contact
Description: Caribou Coffee is providing customers and local gardening clubs in Minnesota free used espresso ground for their gardens. The Grounds for Your Grounds program allows customers to pick up five-pound recycled bags of used grounds from retail locations for use in their home garden or community garden. The firm is committed to supporting local gardens and gardening organizations with existing reusable resource-espresso grounds. **Availability:** Online.

7547 ■ *"Carrington Co. LLC Revolutionizes the Hot Tea Market with First-Ever, Organic Tea in Eco-Friendly Packaging"* in *Ecology, Environment & Conservation Business* (May 3, 2014, pp. 6)
Pub: NewsRX LLC.
Contact: Kalani Rosell, Contact
Description: Carrington Company makes organic non-genetically modified products including flax seeds, hemp, chia, and organic coconut oil and teas. The firm is launching its Carrington Organics Tea to its lineup of healthy products, packed in a 100 percent eco-friendly packaging that will fully and safely biodegrade when composted. It is the first tea available packaged in fully recyclable packaging. **Availability:** Online.

7548 ■ *"City Board Tweaks Internet Cafe Ordinance"* in *Ocala Star-Banner* (July 19, 2011)
Pub: Ocala Star-Banner
Contact: Austin L. Miller, Officer
E-mail: austin.miller@starbanner.com
Ed: Susan Latham Carr. **Description:** Ocala Planning and Zoning Commission revised the proposed draft of the Internet Cafe ordinance by eliminating the cap on the number of locations allowed, but keeping fees and number of devices the same. **Availability:** Online.

7549 ■ *"A Coffee Shop Owner's Guide to Handling Food & Dairy Allergies"* in *Perfect Daily Grind* (November 1, 2019)
URL(s): www.perfectdailygrind.com/2019/11/a-coffee-shop-owners-guide-to-handling-food-dairy-allergies/
Ed: Janice Kanniah. **Released:** November 01, 2019. **Description:** A practical guide to understanding common food allergies and how best to handle your coffee shop around this issue. **Availability:** Online.

7550 ■ *"Coinstar, Inc. and Seattle's Best Coffee Sign Exclusive Agreement to Roll Out Thousands of the New Rubi Kiosks in Grocery, Drug and Mass Channels"* in *Marketing Weekly News* (June 23 2012, pp. 77)
Pub: PR Newswire Association LLC.

Description: Seattles' Best Coffee, a firm of Starbucks Corporation, has partnered with Coinstar Inc. to install coffee kiosks in grocery, drug and mass merchant retailers featuring Seattle's Best coffee drinks. Rubi kiosk is the third automated kiosk owned by Coinstar. Details of the deal are included.

7551 ■ *"Colombia's Green Coffee Company Earns RA Certification for All It's Farms" in Daily Coffee News (November 26, 2021)*
Ed: Nick Brown. **Released:** November 26, 2021.
Description: Discusses Green Coffee Company attaining the Rainforest Alliance certification for all of its farms and how the company is looking to further enhance its sustainable practices.

7552 ■ *"Corner Bakery Readies Its Recipes for Growth" in Dallas Business Journal (Vol. 35, February 17, 2012, No. 23, pp. 1)*
Pub: Baltimore Business Journal
Contact: Rhonda Pringle, President
E-mail: rpringle@bizjournals.com
Description: Corner Bakery Cafe is planning to add 10 corporate locations and 15-20 franchise locations in 2012. The company was acquired by Roark Capital. **Availability:** Print; Online.

7553 ■ *"Drink Up!" in (Vol. 92, July 23, 2012, No. 30, pp. 19)*
Pub: Dow Jones & Company Inc.
Contact: Almar Latour, Chief Executive Officer
Ed: Robin Goldwyn Blumenthal. **Description:** Juice bars in the US are expanding as Americans increase the consumption of fresh vegetable and fruit juices. Coffeehouse chain Starbucks entered the market by introducing Evolution Fresh, a seller of coldpressed vegetable and fruit juices. The health benefits of fresh vegetable and fruit juice, however, remain uncertain. **Availability:** Online.

7554 ■ *"Dunnellon Welcomes Internet Cafe Jobs" in Ocala Star-Banner (August 18, 2011)*
Pub: Ocala Star-Banner
Contact: Austin L. Miller, Officer
E-mail: austin.miller@starbanner.com
Ed: Fred Hiers. **Description:** Despite the fact that a few Internet cafes offering patrons to win cash and are facing legal challenges, the city's planning commission would welcome the cafes in order to provide more jobs for its residents. **Availability:** Online.

7555 ■ *"A Guide to Different Heat Types in Roasting Equipment" in Perfect Daily Grind (October 4, 2019)*
URL(s): www.perfectdailygrind.com/2019/10/a-guide-to-different-heat-types-in-roasting-equipment/
Ed: Zach Latimore. **Released:** October 04, 2019.
Description: There is more to roasting coffee beans than just simply heating them up. There are a variety of techniques and equipment used, which are discussed here. **Availability:** Online.

7556 ■ *"The HBR Interview: "We Had to Own the Mistakes"" in Harvard Business Review (Vol. 88, July-August 2010, No. 7-8, pp. 108)*
Pub: Harvard Business Publishing
Contact: Diane Belcher, Managing Director
Ed: Adi Ignatius. **Description:** Interview with Howard Schultz, CEO of Starbucks, covers topics that include investment in retraining, the impact of competition, premium quality, authenticity, customer services, strategy development, work-and-life issues, and international presence. **Availability:** Online.

7557 ■ *"How Coffee Producers Can Adapt to Climate Change" in Perfect Daily Grind (November 7, 2019)*
URL(s): www.perfectdailygrind.com/2019/11/how-coffee-producers-can-adapt-to-climate-change/
Ed: Sarah Charles. **Released:** November 07, 2019.
Description: Examines how climate change can and will affect coffee producers since most growers are smaller farms and the crop needs a specific temperature and rainfall pattern. Pest and diseases are also detrimental to coffee crops and climate change has released these outbreaks as well. Included are suggestions to help offset damage from climate change. **Availability:** Online.

7558 ■ *"How to Make Your Coffee Shop More Accessible" in Perfect Daily Grind (August 12, 2019)*
URL(s): www.perfectdailygrind.com/2019/08/how-to-make-your-coffee-shop-more-accessible/
Ed: Tasmin Grant. **Released:** August 12, 2019.
Description: Addresses how coffee shops can make improvements in regards to accessibility for customers and employees with disabilities and impairments. **Availability:** Online.

7559 ■ *"Internet Cafe Logging in to Chardon Plaza?" in News-Herald (July 16, 2011)*
Ed: Betsy Scott. **Description:** Pearl's High Rollers Inc. applied for an Internet sweepstakes cafe license that would reside in a vacant space in Chardon Plaza. City officials have created regulations for such businesses and Pearl's applied for a license and is awaiting approval. **Availability:** Online.

7560 ■ *"Lux Coffees, Breads Push Chains to React" in Advertising Age (Vol. 77, June 26, 2006, No. 26, pp. S14)*
Pub: Crain Communications, Inc.
Contact: Jessica Botos, Manager, Marketing
E-mail: jessica.botos@crainsnewyork.com
Ed: Kate MacArthur. **Description:** Fast-food giants such as McDonald's, Burger King, Dunkin' Donuts and Subway have adjusted their menus in order to become more competitive with gourmet coffee shops and bakeries like Panera Bread and Starbucks which have taken a large share in the market. Statistical data included. **Availability:** Online.

7561 ■ *"Putting Customers' Wants First — Without Serving Bad Coffee" in Perfect Daily Grind (August 2, 2017)*
URL(s): www.perfectdailygrind.com/2017/08/putting-customers-wants-first-without-serving-bad-coffee/
Ed: Sam Koh. **Released:** August 02, 2017. **Description:** Baristas are often highly trained in the art of serving really good coffee, but what happens when a customer places an order that may not be that great, flavor-wise? Baristas need to provide great customer service as well, so they often have to delicately balance creating a great-tasting drink and not offending a paying customer. **Availability:** Online.

7562 ■ *"Real Estate Reinventions: Blue Tractor Barbeque and Brewery, Cafe Havana" in Crain's Detroit Business (Vol. 23, October 1, 2007, No. 40, pp. 15)*
Pub: Crain Communications Inc.
Contact: Barry Asin, President
Ed: Daniel Duggan. **Description:** Two restaurants are converted from a Buddhist Temple to become the most unique spaces in Ann Arbor, Michigan.

7563 ■ *"South Park Draws Brewers, Vintners" in Puget Sound Business Journal (Vol. 29, August 29, 2008, No. 19, pp. 1)*
Description: Craft breweries and wineries are moving into Seattle, Washington's South Park neighborhood due to the area's low rents, convenience, and ample equipment space. These industries bring a more upscale flavor to the heavily industrial area and the tastings and festivals draw people from throughout the Seattle region. **Availability:** Print; Online.

7564 ■ *"Starbucks' Wheel Strategy" in Puget Sound Business Journal (Vol. 29, October 3, 2008, No. 24, pp. 1)*
Description: Starbuck Corporation has placed drive-through windows in nearly 50 percent of its locations. Dorothy Kim, executive vice president of global strategy, revealed that the firm's transformation strategy includes the addition of even more drive-through windows since people want the car-friendly conveniences. **Availability:** Print; Online.

7565 ■ *"Subway Launches Expanded Cafes, Drive-Thru Window Locations" in South Florida Business Journal (Vol. 33, August 10, 2012, No. 2, pp. 1)*
Pub: Baltimore Business Journal
Contact: Rhonda Pringle, President
E-mail: rpringle@bizjournals.com
Description: Subway launched its larger cafe concept at Florida Atlantic University and plans to open more drive-thru restaurants in South Florida. This could change preferred leasing locations to Subway franchisees, which are also moving into nontraditional locations. Site selection issues are covered. **Availability:** Print; Online.

7566 ■ *VIDEO: Why Does Cold Brew Taste Different?*
URL(s): www.perfectdailygrind.com/2017/05/video-cold-brew-taste-different/
Released: May 08, 2017. **Description:** More than just cold coffee, cold brew has its own distinct flavor and properties. **Availability:** Online.

7567 ■ *"Zacks Industry Outlook Highlights: Starbucks, Nike, Big Lots, Deckers Outdoor and Family Dollar Stores" in PR Newswire (August 8, 2012)*
Pub: PR Newswire Association LLC.
Description: Zacks takes a look at the retail industry and covers the outlook for this highly competitive sector. Retailers discussed include: Starbucks Corporation, Nike Inc., Big Lots Inc., Deckers Outdoor Corporation, and Family Dollar Stores Inc. **Availability:** Online.

STATISTICAL SOURCES

7568 ■ *The Retail Market for Coffee Industry in the US - Market Research Report*
URL(s): www.ibisworld.com/united-states/market-research-reports/the-retail-market-for-coffee-industry/
Price: $925. **Description:** Downloadable report analyzing current and future trends in the retail coffee industry. **Availability:** Online.

7569 ■ *Standard & Poor's Industry Surveys*
Pub: Standard And Poor's Financial Services LLC.
Contact: Douglas L. Peterson, President
Description: Two-volume book that examines the prospects for specific industries, including trucking. Also provides analyses of trends and problems, statistical tables and charts, and comparative company analyses.

VIDEO/AUDIO MEDIA

7570 ■ *The How of Business: Coffee Shop Business Talk with Chris Deferio*
URL(s): www.thehowofbusiness.com/episode-333-chris-deferio
Ed: Henry Lopez. **Released:** October 05, 2020.
Description: Podcast discusses starting a coffee shop business.

FRANCHISES AND BUSINESS OPPORTUNITIES

7571 ■ **Barnie's Coffee and Tea Company Inc.**
1500 E Colonial Dr.
Orlando, FL 32803-4706
Ph: (407)896-8154
Co. E-mail: support@barniescoffee.com
URL: http://www.barniescoffee.com
Facebook: www.facebook.com/barniescoffeeandtea
Linkedin: www.linkedin.com/company/barnie%27s-coffeekitchen
X (Twitter): x.com/barniescoffee
Instagram: www.instagram.com/barniescoffeeandtea
Pinterest: www.pinterest.com/barniescoffee
Description: Gourmet coffee and tea. **Founded:** 1980. **Training:** Yes.

7572 ■ Gourmet Coffee/Tea House

7572 ■ The Bearclaw Coffee Co.
2460 Washtenaw Ave.
 Ann Arbor, MI 48104
Ph: (734)369-9660
Co. E-mail: logan@bearclawcoffee.com
URL: http://www.bearclawcoffee.com
Facebook: www.facebook.com/
 BearclawCoffeeCompany
Linkedin: www.linkedin.com/company/bearclaw
 -coffee-company
X (Twitter): x.com/bearclawcoffee
Instagram: www.instagram.com/
 bearclawcoffeecompany
Description: Company offers mobile coffee and event catering services. **Founded:** 2002. **Financial Assistance:** Yes **Training:** Provides 1 week at headquarters, at franchisee's location with ongoing support.

7573 ■ Cafe Ala Carte
19512 S Coquina Way
 Weston, FL 33332
Ph: (954)349-1030
Fax: (954)349-3100
URL: http://www.cafealacarte.com
Contact: Bonnie Fimiano, Contact
E-mail: dominick@cafealacarte.com
Facebook: www.facebook.com/cafealacarteofsou
 thflorida
X (Twitter): x.com/CafeAlaCarte
Instagram: www.instagram.com/cafealacartesou
 thflorida
Description: Provider of gourmet coffee catering service. **Founded:** 1994. **Financial Assistance:** Yes **Training:** Provides 1 week at headquarters, 1 week in Fort Lauderdale, FL with ongoing support.

7574 ■ Café Dépôt
162, blvd. Labelle
 Rosemere, QC, Canada J7A 2H1
Ph: (450)434-9693
Co. E-mail: info@cafedepot.ca
URL: http://cafedepot.com
Facebook: www.facebook.com/cafedepot.ca
Instagram: www.instagram.com/cafedepot
Description: Chain of coffee shop. **Founded:** 1994. **Training:** Yes.

7575 ■ The Coffee Beanery Ltd. (CB)
3429 Pierson Pl.
 Flushing, MI 48433
Ph: (810)733-1020
Free: 800-441-2255
Co. E-mail: marketplace@coffeebeanery.com
URL: http://www.coffeebeanery.com
Contact: Joanne Shaw, President
Facebook: www.facebook.com/CoffeeBeaneryHea
 dquarters
Linkedin: www.linkedin.com/company/coffee-beanery
X (Twitter): x.com/coffeebeaneryHQ
Instagram: www.instagram.com/coffeebeanery1976
YouTube: www.youtube.com/channel/UCpwD_5_ag
 1P5Ntb4mT1Zz2Q
Pinterest: www.pinterest.com/coffeebeanery
Description: Producer and retailer of whole bean coffees, tea and beverages such as flavored coffee, half caff coffee, green tea, herbal tea. Also provides gifts, brewers and accessories. **Founded:** 1976. **Training:** 4 weeks training at corporate headquarters plus 1 week orientation including customer service, merchandising, marketing & daily operations. Additional on-site training, site selection assistance, lease negotiation, layout & construction supervision and on.

7576 ■ Coffee News
PO Box 503
 Hampden, ME 04444
Ph: (207)217-3293
Co. E-mail: hello@mhcoffeenews.com
URL: http://www.coffeenewsbangor.com
Description: Weekly publication for distribution in coffee shops and restaurants. **Founded:** 1988. **Training:** Quarterly training sessions, open to all franchisees and personal mentor program.

7577 ■ Coffee Time Donuts Inc.
2195 Midland Ave.
 Scarborough, ON, Canada M1P 3E7
Ph: (647)351-8463
URL: http://coffeetime.com
Description: Chain of coffee shops. **Founded:** 1982. **Training:** Yes.

7578 ■ Country Style
2 E Beaver Creek Rd., Bldg. 1
 Richmond Hill, ON, Canada L4B 2N3
Description: Chain of coffee shop offers menu oatmeal, soup, sandwiches, salads and coffee. **Founded:** 1962. **Franchised:** 1963. **Equity Capital Needed:** total investment will vary depending on the size and condition of the premises. **Franchise Fee:** $35,000. **Royalty Fee:** 4.5% of gross. **Training:** Provides 4 weeks initial training.

7579 ■ Coyote Canyon
1359 Locke Dr.
 Bourbonnais, IL 60914
Ph: (815)936-0120
URL: http://www.stockadecompanies.com/OurRes
 taurants/CCHome
Facebook: www.facebook.com/Coyo
 teCanyonBourbonnais
Description: Chain of fast food restaurants. **Founded:** 1999. **Training:** Yes.

7580 ■ Dazbog Coffee Co.
1090 Yuma St.
 Denver, CO 80204
Ph: (303)892-9999
Free: 888-932-9264
Fax: (303)893-9999
Co. E-mail: feedback@dazbog.com
URL: http://www.dazbog.com
Contact: Leonid Yuffa, Contact
Facebook: www.facebook.com/dazbogcoffeeco
X (Twitter): x.com/dazbog
Instagram: www.instagram.com/dazbogcoffee
YouTube: www.youtube.com/channel/UCDaTuba32E
 t4jntB_fyZqxQ
Description: Coffee. **Founded:** 1996. **Franchise Fee:** $35,000. **Royalty Fee:** 6%.

7581 ■ Dunn Bros Coffee
111 3rd Ave. S, Ste. 130
 Minneapolis, MN 55401
Free: 888-417-0404
Co. E-mail: marketing@dunnbros.com
URL: http://dunnbrothers.com
Facebook: www.facebook.com/dunnbrotherscoffee
X (Twitter): x.com/dunnbroscoffees
Instagram: www.instagram.com/dunnbroscoffee
YouTube: www.youtube.com/channel/UCxw17GosC
 -F0HNqeVFbgqxQ
Description: Manufacturer and distributor of roasted coffee. **Founded:** 1987. **Equity Capital Needed:** $125,000 liquid assets and $500,000 net worth. **Franchise Fee:** $24,000. **Financial Assistance:** Yes **Training:** Offers 2 1/2 weeks at headquarters and ongoing support.

7582 ■ Ellianos Coffee Co.
2915 W US Hwy., 90
 Lake City, FL 32055
Ph: (386)752-0202
URL: http://www.ellianos.com
Contact: Mallory Pruitt, Executive Director
Facebook: www.facebook.com/lakecityellianos
Description: Chain of coffee shops. **Founded:** 2005. **Franchised:** 2003. **Equity Capital Needed:** net worth of $150,000 ; $50,000 in cash or liquid assets. **Training:** Coffee shop with outlets in many location.

7583 ■ Gloria Jean's Coffees USA
Retail Food Group Ltd. (RFG)
 17691 Mitchell N
 Irvine, CA 92614
Ph: 61 7 5591-3242
Co. E-mail: rfga@rfg.com.au
URL: http://www.rfg.com.au
Description: Retailer of the coffee store chain. **Founded:** 1979. **Financial Assistance:** No **Training:** Yes.

7584 ■ Good Earth Coffee House
4020 7th St. SE
 Calgary, AB, Canada T2G 2Y8
Ph: (403)294-9330
Free: 888-294-9330
Co. E-mail: franchise@goodearthcoffeehouse.com
URL: http://goodearthcoffeehouse.com
Contact: Gerry Docherty, President
Facebook: www.facebook.com/GoodEarthHQ
Linkedin: www.linkedin.com/company/good-earth
 -coffeehouse
X (Twitter): x.com/goodearthhq
Instagram: www.instagram.com/goodearthhq
Description: Production and retailer of coffee and bakery items. **Founded:** 1991. **Equity Capital Needed:** $425,000-$500,000. **Franchise Fee:** $35,000. **Royalty Fee:** 0.07. **Training:** Provides 6 weeks training.

7585 ■ A Grande Finale Franchise L.L.C.
965 Ash St.
 Broomfield, CO 80020
Contact: Nicole M. Hedlund, Contact
Description: Desserts, coffee and tea. **Founded:** 1999. **Royalty Fee:** 5-6%.

7586 ■ The Human Bean Drive Thru (THB)
623 Rossanley Dr.
 Medford, OR 97501
Ph: (541)608-0564
Free: 888-262-2215
Co. E-mail: info@thehumanbean.com
URL: http://thehumanbean.com
Contact: Scott Anderson, Chief Operating Officer
Facebook: www.facebook.com/thehumanbeancoffee
Linkedin: www.linkedin.com/company/
 thehumanbeancoffee
X (Twitter): x.com/HumanBeanInc
Instagram: www.instagram.com/thehumanbeancoffee
Pinterest: www.pinterest.com/humanbeancoffee
Description: Operator of coffee shop. **No. of Franchise Units:** 47. **Founded:** 1998. **Franchised:** 2002. **Equity Capital Needed:** $152,750-$617,000 . **Franchise Fee:** $20,000. **Royalty Fee:** No Royalty Fee. **Financial Assistance:** No **Training:** Offers 3 weeks training at headquarters and at franchisee's location at time of opening and ongoing support.

7587 ■ It's A Grind Coffee House
29641 The Old Rd.
 Castaic, CA 91384
Free: 877-320-5282
Co. E-mail: customerservice@itsagrind.com
URL: http://www.itsagrind.com
Contact: Peter George, Chairman
Facebook: www.facebook.com/itsagrind
X (Twitter): twitter.com/ITSAGRINDCoffee
YouTube: www.youtube.com/user/iagcoffeehouse
Description: Operator of coffee house. **Founded:** 1994. **Training:** A coffee shop.

7588 ■ Kelly's Coffee and Fudge Factory
444 N Rexford Dr.
 Beverly Hills, CA 90210
Ph: (310)550-9077
Fax: (310)550-9078
URL: http://kellyscoffeebh.com
Instagram: www.instagram.com/kellyscoffeebh
Description: Retailer of coffee products. **Training:** Yes.

7589 ■ Mountain Mudd Espresso
7265 Dixie Hwy / Route 4
 Fairfield, OH 45014
URL: http://www.mountainmuddfairfield.com
Description: Specialty coffee. **No. of Franchise Units:** 5. **No. of Company-Owned Units:** 12. **Founded:** 1994. **Franchised:** 2007. **Equity Capital Needed:** $22,500-$266,000 total investment. **Franchise Fee:** $5,000-$10,000. **Royalty Fee:** 4%. **Financial Assistance:** Yes **Training:** Provides 5 days training at headquarters and ongoing at franchisee's location.

7590 ■ PJ's Coffee of New Orleans
4480 LA 22, Ste. 2
 Mandeville, LA 70471

Ph: (985)792-7999
Co. E-mail: info@pjscoffee.com
URL: http://www.pjscoffee.com
Contact: David Mesa, Chief Development Officer
Facebook: www.facebook.com/pjscoffee
X (Twitter): x.com/pjscoffee
Instagram: www.instagram.com/pjscoffee
Pinterest: www.pinterest.com/pjscoffee
Description: Chain of retail coffee houses. **Founded:** 1978. **Training:** Raving Brands University classroom and onsite training provided. From register operation to food preparation, from hiring staff to accounting procedures, you'll improve your management skills, setup your back office and develop an airtight sales and marketing plan.

7591 ■ The Second Cup Ltd.
Aegis Brands Inc. (AB)
   5915 Airport Rd., Ste. 630.
   Mississauga, ON, Canada L4V 1T1
Ph: (437)747-4334
URL: http://aegisbrands.ca
Facebook: www.facebook.com/SecondCup
Instagram: www.instagram.com/secondcupcanada
Description: Chain of coffee shops. **Founded:** 1975. **Training:** Provides 6 weeks training.

7592 ■ Tapioca Express Inc.
1908 Central Ave.
   South El Monte, CA 91733
Free: 888-887-1616
Co. E-mail: marketing@tapiocaexpress.com
URL: http://www.tapiocaexpress.com
Contact: Cheng-Wei Lin, Chief Executive Officer
Facebook: www.facebook.com/TapiocaExpress
X (Twitter): x.com/tapioca_express
Instagram: www.instagram.com/
   tapiocaexpressofficial
YouTube: www.youtube.com/channel/
   UCGpniKlUiFTwZQjaiNtZOmA/featured
Description: Restaurant franchise known for their milk teas offers a variety of other specialty beverages and snack products inspired particularly by Taiwanese culture and cuisine. **Founded:** 1999. **Franchised:** 2000. **Training:** Offers 8 days at company store and ongoing support.

7593 ■ Tim Hortons Inc.
874 Sinclair Rd.
   Oakville, ON, Canada L6K 2Y1
Free: 888-601-1616
URL: http://www.timhortons.com
Facebook: www.facebook.com/TimHortons
X (Twitter): x.com/timhortons
Instagram: www.instagram.com/timhortonsus
YouTube: www.youtube.com/user/TimHortons
Description: Operator of fast food restaurant. **Founded:** 1964. **Franchised:** 1967. **Equity Capital Needed:** $1.5million in net worth and $500,000 liquid assets. **Franchise Fee:** $50,000. **Royalty Fee:** A weekly Royalty fee of 6% of gross sales.

Graphic Design

REFERENCE WORKS

7594 ■ *"The Logo Redesign That's Cheesier Than Most: JKR Introduces Velveeta's New Look" in PRINT (November 4, 2021)*
Ed: Chloe Gordon. **Released:** November 04, 2021.
Description: Starting in 2022, Velveeta is rolling out their new logo from Jones Knowles Ritchie. Discusses the impact the company hopes to have with the new branding.

STATISTICAL SOURCES

7595 ■ *Graphic Designers Industry in the US - Market Research Report*
URL(s): www.ibisworld.com/united-states/market-research-reports/graphic-designers-industry/
Price: $925. **Description:** Downloadable report analyzing current and future trends in the graphic design industry. **Availability:** Online.

VIDEO/AUDIO MEDIA

7596 ■ *How I Built My Small Business: Chelsea Bay Dennis - Creating a Sustainable Career as a Graphic Designer*
URL(s): www.annemcginty.com/transcripts/chelseabaydennis
Ed: Anne McGinty. **Released:** January 30, 2024.
Description: Podcast offers a conversation with a graphic designer, life coach, and storytelling event creator in Michigan.

7597 ■ *Side Hustle to Small Business: Passion to Profit: Transforming Hobbies into Side Hustles*
URL(s): www.hiscox.com/side-hustle-to-small-business/should-your-hobby-become-your-side-hustle-podcast-season-4
Ed: Sanjay Parekh. **Released:** April 17, 2024.
Description: Podcast discusses turning hobbies into thriving businesses.

7598 ■ *Small Business, Big Mindset: How to Create a Visual Brand*
URL(s): podcast.musclecreative.com/924061/episodes/12590853-how-to-create-a-visual-brand
Ed: Erin Geiger. **Released:** April 11, 2023. **Description:** Podcast discusses visual branding with a graphic desginer.

TRADE SHOWS AND CONVENTIONS

7599 ■ SGIA Expo
Specialty Graphic Imaging Association (SGIA)
10015 Main St.
Fairfax, VA 22031
Free: 888-385-3588
Co. E-mail: sgia@sgia.org
URL: http://www.sgia.org
Contact: Thomas Cooper, III, Chairman
URL(s): www.printingunited.com/general-information/future-printing-united-expo-dates
Facebook: www.facebook.com/SGIAORG
Frequency: Annual. **Description:** Includes over 2000 booths, more than 50 seminars, guest tours, golf tournament, social events, and printing awards competition. **Audience:** Industry professionals. **Principal Exhibits:** Includes over 2000 booths, more than 50 seminars, guest tours, golf tournament, social events, and printing awards competition. Dates and Locations: 2025 Oct 22-24 Orange County Convention Center, Orlando, FL; 2026 Oct 21-23 Las Vegas Convention Center, Las Vegas, NV.

Greenhouse/Garden Center/Nursery Business

START-UP INFORMATION

7600 ■ *How to Open & Operate a Financially Successful Landscaping, Nursery, or Lawn Service Business: With Companion CD-ROM*
Pub: Atlantic Publishing Co.
Contact: Dr. Heather L. Johnson, Contact
Ed: Lynn Wasnak. **Released:** 2010. **Description:** Guide provides understanding of the basic concepts of starting and running a service business, focusing on the operation of a small nursery, landscaping, or lawn service or combining the three operations. It also offers tips for running the business from the home. **Availability:** CD-ROM; Print; Online.

ASSOCIATIONS AND OTHER ORGANIZATIONS

7601 ■ **American Horticultural Society (AHS) - Library**
7931 East Blvd. Dr.
  Alexandria, VA 22308
Ph: (703)768-5700
Fax: (703)768-8700
URL: http://ahsgardening.org
Contact: Marcia Zech, Chairman of the Board
Facebook: www.facebook.com/americanhorticulturalsociety
Linkedin: www.linkedin.com/company/the-american-horticultural-society
X (Twitter): x.com/ahs_gardening
Instagram: www.instagram.com/ahs_gardening
YouTube: www.youtube.com/channel/UCXUu4FafeTTqC8S-VnnhPrg
Pinterest: www.pinterest.com/amhortsociety
Description: Represents amateur and professional gardeners. Aims to educate and inspire people of all ages to become successful and environmentally responsible gardeners by advancing the art and science of horticulture. **Scope:** Horticulture. **Founded:** 1922. **Holdings:** Figures not available. **Publications:** *North American Horticulture: A Reference Guide* (Irregular); *The American Gardener: The Magazine of the American Horticultural Society* (Bimonthly). **Awards:** Liberty Hyde Bailey Award (Irregular); Paul Ecke Jr. Commercial Award (Annual); G. B. Gunlogson Award (Annual); B.Y. Morrison Communication Award (Annual); AHS Horticultural Therapy Award (Irregular); AHS Landscape Design Award (Irregular); AHS Meritorious Service Award (Annual); Frances Jones Poetker Award (Irregular); AHS Professional Award (Irregular); H. Marc Cathey Award (Biennial); Catherine H. Sweeney Award (Periodic); AHS Teaching Award (Irregular); Community Greening Award (Annual); Horticultural Innovation Award (Biennial); Jane L. Taylor Award (Annual); American Horticultural Society Professional Award (Annual). **Geographic Preference:** National.

7602 ■ **American Hydrangea Society (AHS)**
Woodruff Auditorium in McElreath Hall, Atlanta History Center 130 W Paces Ferry Rd.
  Atlanta, GA 30350
Co. E-mail: membership@americanhydrangeasociety.org
URL: http://americanhydrangeasociety.org
Contact: Jennifer Petritz, President
Facebook: www.facebook.com/americanhydrangeasociety
Instagram: www.instagram.com/americanhydrangeasociety
YouTube: www.youtube.com/user/hydrangeavideos
Description: Represents growers and other individuals with an interest in the genus Hydrangea. Promotes the study of the cultivation of Hydrangea and related plant species. Conducts educational programs and serves as a clearinghouse on Hydrangea. Hosts members only garden tour each June. **Founded:** 1994. **Geographic Preference:** National.

7603 ■ **American Seed Trade Association (ASTA)**
1701 Duke St., Ste. 275
  Alexandria, VA 22314
Ph: (703)837-8140
Free: 888-890-7333
Fax: (703)837-9365
Co. E-mail: info@betterseed.org
URL: http://www.betterseed.org
Contact: Andrew W. LaVigne, President
Linkedin: www.linkedin.com/company/american-seed-trade-assn
X (Twitter): x.com/Better_Seed
Instagram: www.instagram.com/better_seed
YouTube: www.youtube.com/channel/UCeNdXgUMZy8a8_u0ZD_yrZQ
Description: Breeders, growers, assemblers, conditioners, wholesalers, and retailers of grain, grass, vegetable, flower, and other seed for planting purposes. **Founded:** 1883. **Publications:** *Corn and Sorghum Proceedings* (Annual); *Soybean Seed Proceedings* (Annual). **Geographic Preference:** National.

7604 ■ **AmericanHort**
525 9th St NW Ste. 800
  Washington, DC 20004
Ph: (202)789-2900
Co. E-mail: hello@americanhort.org
URL: http://www.americanhort.org
Contact: Ken Fisher, President
Facebook: www.facebook.com/AmericanHort
Linkedin: www.linkedin.com/company/americanhort
X (Twitter): x.com/American_Hort
Description: Vertical organization of wholesale growers; landscape firms; garden centers; mail order nurseries; suppliers. Promotes the industry and its products. Offers management and consulting services and public relations programs. Provides government representation and bank card plan for members. Maintains hall of fame. **Founded:** 1876. **Publications:** *American Nursery & Landscape Association--Member Directory: Who's Who in the Nursery Industry* (Annual); *Directory of Forest Tree Nurseries in the United States* (Irregular). **Educational Activities:** Farwest Show (Annual). **Geographic Preference:** National.

7605 ■ **Canadian Nursery Landscape Association (CNLA) [Association Candienne des Pepinieristes et des Paysagistes]**
7856 5th Line S
  Milton, ON, Canada L9T 2X8
Fax: (905)875-1840
Co. E-mail: info@cnla-acpp.ca
URL: http://cnla.ca
Contact: Anthony O'Neill, President
E-mail: aoneillnl@gmail.com
Facebook: www.facebook.com/canadanursery
X (Twitter): x.com/CNLA_ACPP
Description: Devises standards and develops and administers tests to ensure competence in nursery production, garden supply retailing, landscape contracting, and construction and maintenance. **Publications:** *CNLA Newsbrief* (Quarterly). **Awards:** CNLA Honorary Life Member (Periodic); CNLA President's Award (Periodic). **Geographic Preference:** National.

7606 ■ *CNLA Newsbrief*
7856 5th Line S
  Milton, ON, Canada L9T 2X8
Fax: (905)875-1840
Co. E-mail: info@cnla-acpp.ca
URL: http://cnla.ca
Contact: Anthony O'Neill, President
E-mail: aoneillnl@gmail.com
URL(s): cnla.ca/become-a-member
Released: Quarterly **Description:** Provides news and information of the association. **Availability:** Print.

7607 ■ **Flowers Canada (FC)**
45 Speedvale Ave., E Unit 7
  Guelph, ON, Canada N1H 1J2
Ph: (519)836-5495
Free: 800-730-1020
Co. E-mail: flowers@fco.on.ca
URL: http://www.flowerscanadagrowers.com/home
Contact: Andrew Morse, Executive Director
Description: Retail florists, distributors, and greenhouse operators. Promotes growth and development in the domestic floriculture industry. Provides technical and promotional services; sponsors continuing professional development and educational programs for members. Represents members' interests before government agencies; serves as a liaison between members and related trade organizations. **Founded:** 1897. **Publications:** *News Vine* (Bimonthly). **Geographic Preference:** National.

7608 ■ **Hobby Greenhouse Association (HGA)**
c/o Richard Schreiber, Membership Director
922 Norwood Dr.
  Norwalk, IA 50211-1329
Co. E-mail: hgamembershipdirector@hotmail.com
URL: http://www.hobbygreenhouse.org
Contact: Tom Karasek, President
E-mail: tomsherron@msn.com
Facebook: www.facebook.com/people/Hobby-Greenhouse-Association/100064755728438

Description: Greenhouse owners and those who grow plants indoors with lights; windowsill and porch gardeners. Promotes the hobby of greenhouse and indoor gardening. Provides information on plants and diseases, propagation of seeds, insect control, and greenhouse building and maintenance. **Founded:** 1976. **Publications:** *Hobby Greenhouse* (Quarterly); *HGA News* (Quarterly); *Directory of Manufacturers of Residential Greenhouses and Distributors of Imported Greenhouses* (Annual). **Geographic Preference:** Multinational.

7609 ■ National Gardening Association (NGA)

1100 Dorset St.
  South Burlington, VT 05403
URL: http://garden.org
Contact: Dave Whitinger, Executive Director
X (Twitter): x.com/NatlGardening
Instagram: www.instagram.com/nationalgar
  deningassoc
YouTube: www.youtube.com/user/nationalgardening
Pinterest: www.pinterest.com/ngagrows

Description: Serves as a clearinghouse for home, community and educational gardening information. **Founded:** 1971. **Publications:** *Environmental Survey* (Triennial); *Gardening with Kids* (Annual); *Growing Ideas* (Quarterly); *National Gardening Survey* (Annual); *What Gardeners Think* (Triennial); *Gardener's Dictionary: Breaking the garden language code*; *National Gardening: For the Food and Flower Gardening Enthusiast* (Bimonthly). **Awards:** NGA Subaru Healthy Sprouts Award (Annual); NGA Youth Garden Grant (Annual). **Geographic Preference:** National.

7610 ■ Nursery and Landscape Association Executives of North America (NLAE)

2130 Stella Ct.
  Columbus, OH 43215
Ph: (614)487-1117
Fax: (614)487-1216
Co. E-mail: nlae@americanhort.org
URL: http://www.nlae.org
Contact: Linda Reindl, President

Description: Professional society of executives of state, national, regional, and provincial nursery trade associations. **Founded:** 1947. **Geographic Preference:** National.

7611 ■ Ornamental Concrete Producers Association (OCPA)

KY
Ph: (270)230-2838
Co. E-mail: ocpa1990@gmail.com
Facebook: www.facebook.com/people/Ornamental
  -Concrete-Producers-Association/10005740
  5611807

Description: Producers of ornamental concrete products. Seeks to advance the ornamental concrete and related industries. Conducts educational programs; sponsors competitions; holds mold auctions. **Scope:** ornamental concrete. **Founded:** 1991. **Subscriptions:** video recordings. **Geographic Preference:** National.

REFERENCE WORKS

7612 ■ "All the Trimmings" in Green Industry Pro (Vol. 23, March 2011, No. 3, pp. 29)

Ed: Gregg Wartgow. **Description:** When choosing lawn mowing equipment, it is advised to purchase commercial-grade 21-inch walk mowers rather than less expensive consumer-grade mowers. John Deere is reentering the commercial 21-inch walk behind mower market after a five-year hiatus. **Availability:** Online.

7613 ■ "Customer Retention is Proportionate to Employee Retention" in Green Industry Pro (Vol. 23, September 2011)

Description: Presented in a question-answer format, information is provided to help retain customers as well as keeping workers happy. **Availability:** Online.

7614 ■ "Customized Before Custom Was Cool" in Green Industry Pro (July 2011)

Ed: Gregg Wartgow. **Description:** Profile of Turf Care Enterprises and owner Kevin Vogeler, who discusses his desire to use more natural programs using little or no chemicals in 1986. At that time, that sector represented 20 percent of his business, today it shares 80 percent. **Availability:** Online.

7615 ■ "Deep in the Heart of Drought" in Green Industry Pro (Vol. 23, October 2011)

Ed: Gregg Wartgow. **Description:** Challenges faced by landscape contractors during the recent drought in Texas are explored. Despite these challenges, opportunity for contractors providing irrigation services has risen. **Availability:** Online.

7616 ■ "Dozens 'Come Alive' in Downtown Chicago" in Green Industry Pro (July 2011)

Ed: Gregg Wartgow. **Description:** Highlights from the Come Alive Outside training event held in Chicago, Illinois July 14-15, 2011 are shared. Nearly 80 people representing 38 landscape companies attended the event that helps contractors review their services and find ways to sell them in new and various ways. **Availability:** Online.

7617 ■ "Evigence and Jarja Floral Partner to Create a Monitoring Device That Measures Flower Freshness" in Garden Center (October 21, 2019)

URL(s): www.gardencentermag.com/article/evigence
  -and-jarja-floral-partner-to-create-a-monitoring
  -device-that-mea

Ed: Julianne Mobilian. **Released:** October 21, 2019. **Description:** The new Floral Merchandising Aid (FMA) Sensor is being unveiled by Evigence Senors and tulip supplier Jarja Floral. The device indicates the remaining saleable life of a perishable product and should help florists better manage their merchandise. **Availability:** Online.

7618 ■ "Finding a Way to Continue Growing" in Green Industry Pro (Vol. 23, March 2011, No. 3, pp. 31)

Ed: Gregg Wartgow. **Description:** Profile of Brett Lemcke, VP of R.M. Landscape located in Rochester, New York. Lemcke tells how his Landscape Industry Certified credentials helped him to grow his business and beat out his competition. **Availability:** Online.

7619 ■ "Five Distinct Divisions, One Collective Focus" in Green Industry Pro (Vol. 23, October 2011)

Ed: Gregg Wartgow. **Description:** Profile of ACLS Inc., an amalgamation of All Commercial Landscape Service (commercial maintenance), All Custom Landscape Service (design/build), Fresno Tree Service, Certified Water Consulting (irrigation), and Tractor Service (disking and flailing services on everything from one-acre lots to hundreds of acres of open land). The firm discusses its rebranding effort in order to increase sales. **Availability:** Online.

7620 ■ "Flower Power" in Garden Center (November 4, 2019)

URL(s): www.gardencentermag.com/article/feature
  -igc-trends-flower-power-floral-shops/

Ed: Brooke Bilyj. **Released:** November 04, 2019. **Description:** Independent Garden Centers are looking for ways to expand their business, and one way they are doing that is by bringing back floral departments. Some are snatching up florists that are closing and creating relationships with funeral homes, wedding venues, and other community events. **Availability:** Online.

7621 ■ "Forward Motion" in Green Industry Pro (July 2011)

Ed: Gregg Wartgow. **Description:** Several landscape contractors have joined this publication's Working Smarter Training Challenge over the last year. This process is helping them develop ways to improve work processes, boost morale, drive out waste, reduce costs, improve customer service, and be more competitive. **Availability:** Print; Online.

7622 ■ "Gain the 'Come Alive Outside' Selling Edge" in Green Industry Pro (July 2011)

Ed: Jim Paluch. **Description:** Marketing the 'Come Alive Outside' slogan can help landscapers to increase their market share by identifying and applying these elements to each customer as well as their workers. **Availability:** Online.

7623 ■ "The Green Industry Jobs Gap" in Green Industry Pro (Vol. 23, October 2011)

Ed: Gregg Wartgow. **Description:** According to the U.S. Bureau of Labor Statistics, the landscaping industry employs over 829,000 workers. According to another private study, the industry would employ more if they were able to find more people interested in performing the required work. **Availability:** Online.

7624 ■ Greenhouse Growing

Ed: Elizatbeth Strong. **Released:** October 19, 2021. **Description:** Stories about people who invested in greenhouses and their experiences within this industry. **Availability:** E-book.

7625 ■ "Hey, You Can't Do That" in Green Industry Pro (Vol. 23, September 2011)

Ed: Rod Dickens. **Description:** Manufacturers of landscape equipment are making better use of energy resources, such as the use of fuel-injection systems instead of carburetors, lightweight materials, better lubricants, advanced battery technology, and innovative engine designs. **Availability:** Online.

7626 ■ "How to Develop an Active Sales Program" in Green Industry Pro (Vol. 23, September 2011)

Ed: Gregg Wartgow. **Description:** Craig den Hartog, owner of Emerald Magic Lawn Care located in Holtsville, New York, describes the various marketing tactics he has developed to increase sales in the current economic environment. Statistical data included. **Availability:** Online.

7627 ■ "How to Dominate in Residential Maintenance" in Green Industry Pro (Vol. 23, October 2011)

Ed: Gregg Wartgow. **Description:** Lawn care services were ranked among the most expendable consumer expenditures, according to the National Retail Federation data accumulated in early 2011. This makes it critical for any landscape firm to target sales efforts toward higher-income households and higher-value homes. **Availability:** Online.

7628 ■ "Labor of Love" in Green Industry Pro (Vol. 23, March 2011, No. 3, pp. 14)

Ed: Gregg Wartgow. **Description:** Profile of CLS Landscape Management in Chino, California and its owner who started the company when he was 21 years old. Kevin Davis built his landscape firm into a $20 million a year business without using any dedicated salesperson. **Availability:** Online.

7629 ■ "North Haven Gardens to Rebuild after Devastating Tornado" in GardenCenter (October 22, 2019)

URL(s): www.gardencentermag.com/article/north-ha
  ven-gardens-tornado/

Released: October 22, 2019. **Description:** After a tornado leveled North Haven Gardens in Dallas, the owners are promising to rebuild and are asking the public for input to make improvements before construction begins. **Availability:** Online.

7630 ■ "OSHA Begins Process of Creating Standard to Protect Workers From Hazardous Heat" in GardenCenter (October 26, 2021)

Ed: Chris Markham. **Released:** October 26, 2021. **Description:** With the warming temperatures spreading around the globe, workers are routinely exposed to extreme heat, which can prove to be fatal. OSHA is publishing an Advance Notice in order to deal with the situation and make it less hazardous for workers in fields. **Availability:** Online.

Small Business Profiles   Greenhouse/Garden Center/Nursery Business ■ 7650

7631 ■ "Paulino Gardens' Closure This Summer Was a Sign of the Times in Denver's Shifting Garden Center Industry" in The Denver Post (September 6, 2019)
URL(s): www.denverpost.com/2019/09/06/paulino-gardens-closure-denver-garden-center-industry/
Ed: Joe Rubino. **Released:** September 06, 2019. **Description:** Long-time staple in the Denver gardening industry, Paulino Gardens, closed it's doors after 62 years in business. **Availability:** Online.

7632 ■ "Problem Solving Requires Total Team Approach" in Green Industry Pro (Vol. 23, September 2011)
Ed: Bob Coulter. **Description:** Working Smarter Training Challenge teaches that leaders are able to carry out solutions directly into their organization, develop skills and drive business results in key areas by creating a culture of energized workers who are able to take ownership of their performance as well as the performance of the company as a whole. **Availability:** Online.

7633 ■ "Take Control of Your Company's Finances" in Green Industry Pro (Vol. 23, March 2011, No. 3, pp. 24)
Ed: Gregg Wartgow. **Description:** Understanding that when certain leading indicators that affect the outcome of certain lagging indicators are aligned, companies will be able to take control of their firm's finances. Ways to improve the processes that drive financial performance for landscape firms are outlined. **Availability:** Online.

7634 ■ "Take This Job and Love It" in Green Industry Pro (Vol. 23, October 2011)
Ed: Gregg Wartgow. **Description:** Details of the lawsuit filed by the Professional Landcare Network (PLANET) against the U.S. Department of Labor are explained. Challenges faced by landscape firms because of employment costs are outlined. Statistical data included. **Availability:** PDF; Online.

7635 ■ "Waterloo Gardens Files for Bankruptcy" in Philadelphia Business Journal (Vol. 28, July 20, 2012, No. 23, pp. 1)
Pub: Baltimore Business Journal
Contact: Rhonda Pringle, President
E-mail: rpringle@bizjournals.com
Description: Nursery and garden center Waterloo Gardens Inc. has voluntarily filed Chapter 11 bankruptcy protection in the Eastern District of Pennsylvania as it attempts to reorganize. Watrloos' Devon location will be closing, while its inventory will be relocated to its Exton location. Factors that might have contributed to the bankruptcy filing are also discussed. **Availability:** Print; Online.

7636 ■ "Way More Than Mowing" in Green Industry Pro (Vol. 23, September 2011)
Ed: Rod Dickens. **Description:** Shipp Shape Lawn Services located in Sylvester, Georgia now offers aeration, fertilizing and weed control, mulching, yard renovation, flowerbed maintenance, landscaping, as well as irrigation repairs and installation in order to diversify the business and stay competitive. **Availability:** Online.

STATISTICAL SOURCES

7637 ■ Landscaping Services Industry in the US - Market Research Report
URL(s): www.ibisworld.com/united-states/market-research-reports/landscaping-services-industry/
Price: $925. **Description:** Downloadable report analyzing current and future trends in the landscaping services industry. **Availability:** Download.

7638 ■ Nursery & Garden Stores Industry in the US - Market Research Report
URL(s): www.ibisworld.com/united-states/market-research-reports/nursery-garden-stores-industry/
Price: $925. **Description:** Downloadable report analyzing the current and future trends in the nursery and garden store industry. **Availability:** Download.

7639 ■ RMA Annual Statement Studies
Pub: Risk Management Association
Contact: Nancy Foster, President
Released: Annual. **Description:** Contains composite balance sheets and income statements for more than 360 industries, including the accounting, auditing, and bookkeeping industries. Also contains five years of comparative historical data for discerning trends. Includes 16 commonly used ratios, computed for most of the size groupings for nearly every industry.

TRADE PERIODICALS

7640 ■ Annals of the Missouri Botanical Garden
Pub: Missouri Botanical Garden Press
URL(s): www.mbgpress.org/Articles.asp?ID=253annals.mobot.org/index.php/annals
Ed: Allison Brock. **Released:** Annual **Price:** $125, Single issue for 1 issue. **Description:** Trade magazine covering original research in botany. **Availability:** Print; PDF; Online.

7641 ■ Chicago Home and Garden
Pub: Chicago Home & Garden
Ed: Jan Parr. **Description:** Magazine covering home and garden style in the Chicago, IL, area. **Availability:** Online.

7642 ■ FloraCulture International (FCI)
Pub: International Association of Horticultural Producers
Contact: Bernard Oosterom, President
URL(s): aiph.org/floraculture
Facebook: www.facebook.com/floracultureinternational
Linkedin: www.linkedin.com/company/floraculture-international
X (Twitter): x.com/FloraCulture_
YouTube: www.youtube.com/channel/UCmq5PUiwa1ybuH47Y38hxmQ
Released: 11/year; Jan-Feb, Mar-Apr, May-Jun, Jul-Aug, Sept-Oct, Nov - Dec. **Description:** Trade magazine for professional growers of cut flowers and flowering plants worldwide. **Availability:** Online.

7643 ■ Garden Center Products & Supplies: Professional Purchasing Guide for Garden Centers
Contact: Jim Gilbride, Publisher
E-mail: jgilbride@gie.net
URL(s): www.gardencentermag.com
Facebook: www.facebook.com/GardenCenterMagazine
X (Twitter): twitter.com/gardencentermag
Ed: Michelle Simakis. **Released:** Monthly **Description:** Catalog focusing on nursery and floral products and services. **Availability:** Handheld; Print; Online.

7644 ■ Green Profit Magazine
Pub: Ball Publishing
Contact: Jennifer Polanz, Managing Editor
E-mail: jpolanz@ballpublishing.com
URL(s): www.greenprofit.com
Facebook: www.facebook.com/springtrials
Ed: Dr. Matthew Chappell, Jennifer Polanz, Chris Beytes. **Released:** Monthly **Description:** Trade magazine for flower and plant retailers. **Availability:** Print; PDF; Online.

7645 ■ Greenhouse Management
Pub: GIE Media Inc.
Contact: Chris Foster, President
URL(s): www.greenhousemag.com
Facebook: www.facebook.com/GreenhouseManagementmag
Linkedin: www.linkedin.com/company/greenhouse-management-magazine
X (Twitter): x.com/Greenhousemag
Instagram: www.instagram.com/greenhousemanagement
Ed: Karen Varga. **Released:** Monthly **Description:** Commercial greenhouse growers magazine. **Availability:** Print; PDF; Online.

7646 ■ Landscape Trades: Canada's Premier Horticultural Trade Publication
Pub: Landscape Ontario Horticultural Trades Association
Contact: Joe Salemi, Director, Operations Deputy Director
E-mail: jsalemi@landscapeontario.com
URL(s): landscapetrades.com
Facebook: www.facebook.com/Landscape.Trades
X (Twitter): x.com/landscapetrades
Instagram: www.instagram.com/landscapetrades
Ed: Lee Ann Knudsen. **Released:** 6/year; February, March, may, August, October and December. **Price:** $84.74, Two years; $118.64, for 3 year; $46.90, for 1 year. **Description:** Landscape/nursery magazine. **Availability:** Print; Online.

7647 ■ Tree City U.S.A. Bulletin
Pub: Arbor Day Foundation
Contact: Dan Lambe, President
E-mail: dlambe@arborday.org
URL(s): www.arborday.org/trees/bulletins
Ed: James R. Fazio. **Released:** Bimonthly **Price:** $3, Single issue; $7.95, for 3-ring binder. **Description:** Features information on pruning, caring for storm-damaged trees, watering and fertilizing, and wise tree selection. **Availability:** Print; PDF; Download; Online.

7648 ■ Tri-Ology
Pub: Florida Department of Agriculture and Consumer Services Division of Plant Industry
Contact: Dr. Trevor Smith, Director
E-mail: plantindustry@fdacs.gov
URL(s): www.fdacs.gov/About-Us/Publications/Plant-Industry-Publications/TRI-OLOGY
Ed: P. J. Anderson, G. S. Hodges. **Released:** Quarterly **Description:** Government scientific publication covering plant pests and disease. **Availability:** Online; Download; PDF.

TRADE SHOWS AND CONVENTIONS

7649 ■ Farwest Show
AmericanHort
525 9th St NW Ste. 800
Washington, DC 20004
Ph: (202)789-2900
Co. E-mail: hello@americanhort.org
URL: http://www.americanhort.org
Contact: Ken Fisher, President
URL(s): www.farwestshow.com
X (Twitter): twitter.com/FarwestShow
Frequency: Annual. **Description:** Nursery stock, equipment, machinery, chemicals, and miscellaneous supplies and services for the wholesale and retail green industry. **Audience:** Industry professionals. **Principal Exhibits:** Nursery stock, equipment, machinery, chemicals, and miscellaneous supplies and services for the wholesale and retail green industry. **Telecommunication Services:** farwest@oan.org.

7650 ■ Nursery/Landscape Expo
Texas Nursery & Landscape Association (TNLA)
7730 S IH-35
Austin, TX 78745-6698
Ph: (512)280-5182
Co. E-mail: info@tnlaonline.org
URL: http://www.tnlaonline.org
Contact: Amy Graham, President
E-mail: agraham@tnlaonline.org
URL(s): www.nurserylandscapeexpo.org
Frequency: Annual. **Description:** Plant materials including foliage, bedding plants, trees, and palms, allied products including machinery, equipment, and supplies for horticulture and landscape industry. **Audience:** Industry professionals. **Principal Exhibits:** Plant materials including foliage, bedding plants, trees, and palms, allied products including machinery, equipment, and supplies for horticulture and landscape industry. **Telecommunication Services:** expo@nurserylandsca.wpengine.com.

7651 ■ St. Louis Builders Home & Garden Show
American Family Insurance Group
6000 American Pky.
Madison, WI 53783
Free: 800-692-6326
Co. E-mail: cfrsalessupport@amfam.com
URL: http://www.amfam.com
Contact: Bill Westrate, President
URL(s): www.stlhba.com/STLHBA/STLHBA/Events/Event_Display.aspx?EventKey=03_HG23
Frequency: Annual. **Description:** Exhibits relating to homes, pools, kitchen, baths, interior design, lawns, and gardens. **Audience:** General public and trade professionals. **Principal Exhibits:** Exhibits relating to homes, pools, kitchen, baths, interior design, lawns, and gardens. **Telecommunication Services:** ridgleyt@hbastl.com.

CONSULTANTS

7652 ■ Jobs In Horticulture Inc.
PO Box 521731
Longwood, FL 32752-1731
Free: 800-428-2474
Fax: (800)884-5198
Co. E-mail: info@hortjobs.com
URL: http://www.hortjobs.com
Contact: Armand Pichardo, Manager
X (Twitter): x.com/hortjobs
Description: Firm provides staffing and recruitment services. **Scope:** Firm provides staffing and recruitment services. **Founded:** 1993.

FRANCHISES AND BUSINESS OPPORTUNITIES

7653 ■ Grower Direct Fresh Cut Flowers Inc.
6303 Wagner Rd.
Edmonton, AB, Canada T6E 4N4
Ph: (780)436-7774
Free: 877-277-4787
Fax: (780)436-3336
Co. E-mail: info@growerdirect.com
URL: http://growerdirect.com
X (Twitter): x.com/growerdirectflw
Description: Retailer of flowers such as cut flowers, gift and gourmet baskets, wedding flowers and funeral flowers. **Founded:** 1991. **Training:** Provides 10 days training.

COMPUTER SYSTEMS/SOFTWARE

7654 ■ Advance Grower Solutions / Nursery/Greenhouse Accounting Software
URL(s): www.advgrower.com/solutions/wn/growpoint
Price: Prices vary depending on modules needed. **Description:** Available for IBM computers and compatibles. System provides accounting and report capabilities for nursery and landscaping businesses.

LIBRARIES

7655 ■ American Horticultural Society (AHS) - Library
7931 East Blvd. Dr.
Alexandria, VA 22308
Ph: (703)768-5700
Fax: (703)768-8700
URL: http://ahsgardening.org
Contact: Marcia Zech, Chairman of the Board
Facebook: www.facebook.com/americanhorticulturalsociety
Linkedin: www.linkedin.com/company/the-american-horticultural-society
X (Twitter): x.com/ahs_gardening
Instagram: www.instagram.com/ahs_gardening
YouTube: www.youtube.com/channel/UCXUu4FafeTTqC8S-VnnhPrg
Pinterest: www.pinterest.com/amhortsociety
Description: Represents amateur and professional gardeners. Aims to educate and inspire people of all ages to become successful and environmentally responsible gardeners by advancing the art and science of horticulture. **Scope:** Horticulture. **Founded:** 1922. **Holdings:** Figures not available. **Publications:** *North American Horticulture: A Reference Guide* (Irregular); *The American Gardener: The Magazine of the American Horticultural Society* (Bimonthly). **Awards:** Liberty Hyde Bailey Award (Irregular); Paul Ecke Jr. Commercial Award (Annual); G. B. Gunlogson Award (Annual); B.Y. Morrison Communication Award (Annual); AHS Horticultural Therapy Award (Irregular); AHS Landscape Design Award (Irregular); AHS Meritorious Service Award (Annual); Frances Jones Poetker Award (Irregular); AHS Professional Award (Irregular); H. Marc Cathey Award (Biennial); Catherine H. Sweeney Award (Periodic); AHS Teaching Award (Irregular); Community Greening Award (Annual); Horticultural Innovation Award (Biennial); Jane L. Taylor Award (Annual); American Horticultural Society Professional Award (Annual). **Geographic Preference:** National.

7656 ■ Atlanta Botanical Garden (ABG) - Sheffield Botanical Library
1345 Piedmont Ave., NE
Atlanta, GA 30309
Ph: (404)876-5859
Co. E-mail: info@atlantabg.org
URL: http://atlantabg.org
Contact: Mary Pat Matheson, President
E-mail: mpmatheson@atlantabg.org
Facebook: www.facebook.com/atlantabotanicalgarden
X (Twitter): x.com/AtlBotanical
Instagram: www.instagram.com/atlbotanical
YouTube: www.youtube.com/user/AtlBotanicalGarden
Pinterest: www.pinterest.com/atlantabg
Description: Services: Garden for preserving plant species and serving for research. **Scope:** Botany; horticulture. **Services:** Copying; library open to the public for reference use only. **Founded:** 1976.

7657 ■ Berkshire Botanical Garden (BBG)
5 W Stockbridge Rd.
Stockbridge, MA 01262
Ph: (413)298-3926
Co. E-mail: info@berkshirebotanical.org
URL: http://www.berkshirebotanical.org
Contact: Thaddeus Thompson, Executive Director
E-mail: tthompson@berkshirebotanical.org
Facebook: www.facebook.com/BerkshireBotanical
Instagram: www.instagram.com/berkshirebotanicalgarden
Description: Aims to fulfill the community's need for information, education and inspiration concerning the art and science of gardening and the preservation of the environment. **Founded:** 1934. **Geographic Preference:** Local.

7658 ■ Birmingham Botanical Gardens Library
2612 Ln. Pk. Rd.
Birmingham, AL 35223
Ph: (205)414-3950
URL: http://bbgardens.org/programs/library
Contact: Hope Long, Director, Library Services
E-mail: hlong@bbgardens.org
Facebook: www.facebook.com/BirminghamBotanicalGardens
Instagram: www.instagram.com/bbgardens
Scope: Gardening; horticulture. **Services:** Copying; printing (black and white, color); free wifi and internet access; library open to the public. **Holdings:** 14,000 books; DVDs; audiobooks; magazines; 65 magazines.

7659 ■ Brookgreen Gardens
1931 Brookgreen Dr.
Murrells Inlet, SC 29576
Ph: (843)235-6000
Fax: (843)235-6039
Co. E-mail: info@brookgreen.org
URL: http://www.brookgreen.org
Contact: Page Kiniry, President
Facebook: www.facebook.com/BrookgreenGardens
X (Twitter): x.com/BrookgreenSC
YouTube: www.youtube.com/BrookgreenGardensSC
Description: Publishes on art, horticulture, botany, gardening, natural history, and regional history. Offers a newsletter, workshop and program guides, calendars, posters, and postcards. Reaches the market through direct mail. **Founded:** 1931.

7660 ■ Brooklyn Botanic Garden (BBG) - Library
1000 Washington Ave.
Brooklyn, NY 11225
Ph: (718)623-7200
Co. E-mail: communications@bbg.org
URL: http://www.bbg.org
Contact: Adrian Benepe, President
Facebook: www.facebook.com/BrooklynBotanic
X (Twitter): x.com/brooklynbotanic
Instagram: www.instagram.com/brooklynbotanic
Description: Publishes on bonsai, designing with flowers, flowering shrubs, herbs, house plants, natural plant dyeing, propagation and pruning. **Scope:** Garden's plants. **Services:** Interlibrary loan. **Founded:** 1910. **Holdings:** 1,500 volume; books; serials; journals; image; photographs; records. **Publications:** *American Gardens: A Traveler's Guide*; *Garden News* (Quarterly).

7661 ■ California Botanic Garden (CALBG) - Library
1500 N College Ave.
Claremont, CA 91711
Ph: (909)625-8767
Co. E-mail: info@calbg.org
URL: http://www.calbg.org
Facebook: www.facebook.com/CaliforniaBotanicGarden
X (Twitter): twitter.com/CABotanicGarden
Instagram: www.instagram.com/californiabotanicgarden
Description: Independent, nonprofit, botanical garden and research organization. Community education programs and guided tours available. **Scope:** Systematics and evolutionary botany with emphasis on western North America and arid and semiarid regions of the world. Facilities are available for visiting scientists to study a collection of native California flora which can be grown in southern section of the state. **Services:** open to the public. **Founded:** 1927. **Holdings:** 56,000 books; 2,200 books; 1,000 print and e-journals; maps; newspaper; journal; article; reprints. **Publications:** *Aliso: A Journal of Systematic and Evolutionary Botany* (Semiannual); *Aliso* (Semiannual); *RSABG Newsletter* (Quarterly). **Educational Activities:** Out of the Wild and Into the Garden Horticultural Symposium; Southwestern Botanical Systematics Symposium.

7662 ■ Cheekwood Botanical Gardens Library
1200 Forrest Pk., Dr.
Nashville, TN 37205
Ph: (615)356-8000
Co. E-mail: info@cheekwood.org
URL: http://cheekwood.org
Contact: Jane O. MacLeod, President
Facebook: www.facebook.com/CheekwoodNashville
Linkedin: www.linkedin.com/company/cheekwood
X (Twitter): x.com/cheekwood
Instagram: www.instagram.com/cheekwood
Scope: Horticulture; landscape architecture; plant science; ecology; wildflowers; garden design; botanical art; orchids; herbs; natural history. **Services:** Interlibrary loan; copying; library open to the public with restrictions. **Founded:** 1929. **Holdings:** 4,750 books; 260 bound periodical volumes; 72 slide programs; 147 videocassettes; flower and seed catalogs. **Subscriptions:** 108 journals and other serials.

7663 ■ Cleveland Botanical Garden - Eleanor Squire Library
11030 E Blvd.
Cleveland, OH 44106
URL: http://holdenfg.org/attractions/cleveland-botanical-garden/elenor-squire-library

Scope: Ecology; urban; general gardening; sustainability; food plants; conservation. Services: open to the public; rare book. Founded: 1930. Holdings: Seed catalog; botanical prints; rare books.

7664 ■ Cornell University - Bailey Hortorium Library
177 Roberts Hall215 Garden Ave.
Ithaca, NY 14853
Co. E-mail: herbarium@cornell.edu
URL: http://cals.cornell.edu/school-integrative-plant-science/school-sections/plant-biology-section/bailey-hortorium
Contact: Dr. Kevin Nixon, Curator
E-mail: kcn2@cornell.edu
Scope: Taxonomic botany; horticulture; paleobotany. Services: Interlibrary loan; library open to the public. Founded: 1935. Holdings: 30,000 volumes; 200 journals.

7665 ■ Cylburn Arboretum Association Library
4915 Greenspring Ave.
Baltimore, MD 21209
Ph: (410)367-2217
Co. E-mail: info@cylburn.org
URL: http://cylburn.org
Contact: Rebecca Henry, President
Facebook: www.facebook.com/Cylburn
Instagram: www.instagram.com/cylburn
YouTube: www.youtube.com/channel/UCTSxHO8s63D0HIgoFVr42Pg
Scope: Horticulture; gardening; wild flowers; trees; shrubs. Services: Copying; library open to the public by appointment on a limited schedule. Holdings: 1,600 books; 2 VF drawers of clippings and pamphlets; seed catalogs.

7666 ■ Dawes Arboretum Library
7770 Jacksontown Rd.
Newark, OH 43056
Ph: (740)323-2355
Free: 800-443-2937
Co. E-mail: information@dawesarb.org
URL: http://dawesarb.org
Contact: Luke Messinger, Executive Director
Facebook: www.facebook.com/thedawesarboretum
X (Twitter): x.com/DawesArboretum
Instagram: www.instagram.com/dawesarboretum
YouTube: www.youtube.com/channel/UC5BwhH1X9q1unbwcult7Kiw
Description: The library consists of local history, journals, books, audio-visual materials, reference materials, computers, and Wi-Fi. Scope: Horticulture; botany; ecology; nature; forestry; gardening. Services: Copying; printing; Internet access; library open to the public for reference use only. Founded: 1929. Holdings: 1,400 books.

7667 ■ Denver Botanic Gardens - Helen Fowler Library
1007 York St.
Denver, CO 80206
Ph: (720)865-3500
Fax: (720)865-3713
Co. E-mail: info@botanicgardens.org
URL: http://www.botanicgardens.org
Contact: Brian Vogt, Chief Executive Officer
E-mail: vogtb@botanicgardens.org
Facebook: www.facebook.com/denverbotanicgardens
X (Twitter): x.com/denverbotanic
Instagram: www.instagram.com/denverbotanic
YouTube: www.youtube.com/user/DenverBotanicGardens
Description: Botanical garden with plants from the rocky mountain region. Scope: Gardening, botanical and horticultural topics. Founded: 1951.

7668 ■ Garfield Park Conservatory Alliance - Garfield Park Conservatory - Library
300 N Central Pk. Ave.
Chicago, IL 60624
Ph: (773)638-1766
Co. E-mail: membership@garfieldpark.org
URL: http://garfieldconservatory.org
Contact: Jennifer Van Valkenburg, President
E-mail: jvanvalkenburg@garfieldpark.org
Facebook: www.facebook.com/GarfieldParkConservatory
Linkedin: www.linkedin.com/company/garfield-park-conservatory-alliance/about
X (Twitter): x.com/gpconservatory
Instagram: www.instagram.com/gpconservatory
YouTube: www.youtube.com/channel/UCn70zMRoK9xueMgdlP9PulA
Scope: Horticulture. Services: Library not open to the public. Founded: 1908. Holdings: Books.

7669 ■ Harvard University - Botany Libraries
22 Divinity Ave.
Cambridge, MA 02138
Ph: (617)495-2366
Fax: (617)495-8654
Co. E-mail: botref@oeb.harvard.edu
URL: http://huh.harvard.edu/libraries
Contact: Amy S. Van Epps, Director (Acting)
E-mail: amy.vanepps@harvard.edu
X (Twitter): x.com/HarvardHerbaria
Scope: Systematic botany; floras; taxonomy; dendrology; early forestry. Services: Copying; library open to the public for reference use only. Founded: 1864. Holdings: Rare books; manuscripts; field notes; historical documents; monographs; journals; electronic media.

7670 ■ Holden Forests & Gardens - Warren H. Corning Library
9550 Sperry Rd.
Kirtland, OH 44094
Ph: (440)946-4400
Co. E-mail: editor@holdenfg.org
URL: http://holdenfg.org/holden-arboretum/plan-your-visit
Facebook: www.facebook.com/HoldenForestsandGardens
X (Twitter): x.com/hfandg
YouTube: www.youtube.com/channel/UC_an9IclNabrabD3PS9vEJw
Description: Miscellaneous Publishing. Scope: Conducts plant breeding of woody ornamental plants (rhododendron, magnolia, cornus, cercis, hamamelis). Studies reproductive biology and the use of biochemical markers. Services: Copying; library open to the public for reference use only. Founded: 1931. Holdings: 9,500 books and pamphlets; 10 VF drawers; 10,000 slides; 100 videocassettes; periodicals. Subscriptions: 125 journals and other serials. Publications: Holden Forests & Gardens (Quarterly; Quarterly); Leaves Class and Events Magazine (Quarterly). Awards: Holden Arboretum Internships (Annual).

7671 ■ Lenhardt Library of the Chicago Botanic Garden
1000 Lake Cook Rd.
Glencoe, IL 60022
Ph: (847)835-8201
Co. E-mail: library@chicagobotanic.org
URL: http://www.chicagobotanic.org/library
Contact: Leora Siegel, Senior Director
E-mail: lsiegel@chicagobotanic.org
Scope: Botany; horticulture; gardening; plant conservation; restoration ecology; horticultural therapy; Midwest flora; international flora; landscape design; garden design; phytopathology; soil science; pest and disease diagnosis. Services: Interlibrary loan; copying; library open to the public. Founded: 1951. Holdings: 125,000 volumes; 2,000 periodicals; 2,000 rare books; 600 DVDs and videos; 10,000 slides; 6,000 books; 1,000 catalogs; 250 linear feet archives.

7672 ■ Longwood Gardens - Library
1001 Longwood Rd.
Kennett Square, PA 19348
Ph: (610)388-1000
Co. E-mail: questions@longwoodgardens.org
URL: http://longwoodgardens.org
Contact: Paul B. Redman, President
E-mail: president@longwoodgardens.org
Facebook: www.facebook.com/LongwoodGardens
X (Twitter): x.com/longwoodgardens
Instagram: www.instagram.com/longwoodgardens
YouTube: www.youtube.com/user/LongwoodGardensInc
Scope: Botany; horticulture; allied arts and sciences. Services: Interlibrary loan; library and archives open to the public by appointment. Founded: 1961. Holdings: 31,000 volumes; monographs; periodicals; blueprints; photographs; maps; recordings; magazines. Subscriptions: 300 journals and other serials. Educational Activities: Conference on Landscape Architecture (Annual).

7673 ■ Los Angeles County Arboretum & Botanic Garden - Library
301 N Baldwin Ave.
Arcadia, CA 91007
Ph: (626)821-3213
Co. E-mail: education@arboretum.org
URL: http://www.arboretum.org
Contact: William Lincoln, President
Facebook: www.facebook.com/LAArboretum
X (Twitter): twitter.com/LAArboretum
Instagram: www.instagram.com/laarboretum
Description: Arboretum and botanical garden in Los Angeles. Scope: Botany; gardening; native plant life; environmental issues; agriculture. Services: Interlibrary loan; copying; circulating to Arboretum Foundation members; library open to the public. Founded: 1948. Holdings: 30,000 books; microfiche; maps; 25,000 books in open stacks (accessible through the online catalog); 5,000 E-book.; Books; magazines; government documents; pamphlets; audio-visual materials. Subscriptions: journals and other serials; magazines periodicals (includes journals).

7674 ■ Massachusetts Horticultural Society (MHS) - Library
The Garden at Elm Bank
900 Washington St.
Wellesley, MA 02482
Ph: (617)933-4900
Fax: (617)933-4901
Co. E-mail: membership@masshort.org
URL: http://www.masshort.org
Contact: James Hearsum, President
Facebook: www.facebook.com/MassHort
Linkedin: www.linkedin.com/company/massachusettshorticulturalsociety
Instagram: www.instagram.com/masshort
YouTube: www.youtube.com/channel/UCofIZ6pb4t4Xglack4IVQqw/featured
Description: Seeks to encourage the science and practice of horticulture throughout Massachusetts, and to develop the public's enjoyment, appreciation, and understanding of plants and the environment. Hosts classes and courses that explore plants, gardening, and the natural world. Maintains the Gardens at Elm Bank. Scope: Early agriculture; horticulture; landscape design. Services: open to the public by appointment. Founded: 1829. Holdings: 20,000 volumes; 5,000 rare books; manuscripts; prints; seed catalogs; slides; photographs; records. Geographic Preference: State.

7675 ■ Memphis Botanic Garden Foundation, Inc. - Goldsmith Civic Garden Center - Sybile Malloy Memorial Library
750 Cherry Rd.
Memphis, TN 38117
Ph: (901)636-4100
Co. E-mail: info@membg.org
URL: http://www.memphisbotanicgarden.com
Contact: Kim MacQueen, President
Scope: Horticulture, gardening, landscape design, flower arranging, environmental science, botany, agriculture. Services: Copying; library open to the public for reference use only. Founded: 1964. Holdings: 2,150 books; 10 bound periodical volumes; 200 horticultural magazines and pamphlets. Subscriptions: 15 journals and other serials.

7676 ■ Missouri Botanical Garden Library
4344 Shaw Blvd., Fourth fl., of The Bayer Ctr.
Saint Louis, MO 63110
Ph: (314)577-5155
Fax: (314)577-0840
Co. E-mail: library@mobot.

URL: http://www.missouribotanicalgarden.org/plant-science/plant-science/resources/raven-library
Contact: Andrew Colligan, Archivist
E-mail: andrew.colligan@mobot.org
Scope: Plant taxonomy and floristic; horticulture; botanical history and exploration. **Founded:** 1859. **Holdings:** 200,000 volumes of monographs and periodicals; 100,000 pamphlets; 35,000 slides; 7,000 vegetation and topographic maps; 220,000 archival items; 3,059 historic manuscripts; 40,000 microfiche of herbaria; 7,000 art works; 1,300 vertical files.

7677 ■ Morton Arboretum - Sterling Morton Library
4100 Illinois, Rte. 53
Lisle, IL 60532
Ph: (630)968-0074
Co. E-mail: trees@mortonarb.org
URL: http://mortonarb.org
Facebook: www.facebook.com/MortonArboretum
X (Twitter): twitter.com/MortonArboretum
YouTube: www.youtube.com/user/MortonArboretum
Pinterest: www.pinterest.com/mortonarboretum
Description: Non-profit educational and research museum. Offers a plant clinic as a free public service; answers inquiries about plant selection and care. **Scope:** Arboriculture and horticulture, including woodland plants, urban vegetation, natural area preservation, rare plant conservation, root and soil research studies, and urban tree breeding and selection. **Services:** Interlibrary loan; circulation; copying; library open to the public. **Founded:** 1922. **Holdings:** 5,000 volumes; Books; journals; artwork; correspondence; papers; maps; video and audio recordings; images; nursery catalogs. **Subscriptions:** 9000 journals. **Publications:** *Plant Health Care Reports* (Weekly); *Tree and Shrub Handbook*. **Educational Activities:** Education Programs, Includes classes for adults and children, dedicated to broader understanding of plants and nature.

7678 ■ National Gardening Association (NGA)
1100 Dorset St.
South Burlington, VT 05403
URL: http://garden.org
Contact: Dave Whitinger, Executive Director
X (Twitter): x.com/NatlGardening
Instagram: www.instagram.com/nationalgardeningassoc
YouTube: www.youtube.com/user/nationalgardening
Pinterest: www.pinterest.com/ngagrows
Description: Serves as a clearinghouse for home, community and educational gardening information. **Founded:** 1971. **Publications:** *Environmental Survey* (Triennial); *Gardening with Kids* (Annual); *Growing Ideas* (Quarterly); *National Gardening Survey* (Annual); *What Gardeners Think* (Triennial); *Gardener's Dictionary: Breaking the garden language code*; *National Gardening: For the Food and Flower Gardening Enthusiast* (Bimonthly). **Awards:** NGA Subaru Healthy Sprouts Award (Annual); NGA Youth Garden Grant (Annual). **Geographic Preference:** National.

7679 ■ New York Botanical Garden (NYBG) - LuEsther T. Mertz Library
2900 Southern Blvd.
Bronx, NY 10458
Ph: (718)817-8700
Co. E-mail: ticketingsupport@nybg.org
URL: http://www.nybg.org
Contact: J. Barclay Collins, II, Chairman
Facebook: www.facebook.com/NYBotanicalGarden
X (Twitter): x.com/NYBG
YouTube: www.youtube.com/c/newyorkbotanicalgardenbronx
Description: Independent, nonprofit research and educational organization. Offers guided tours of the garden grounds and the conservatory; home gardening online; plant information service. **Scope:** Plant systematics, floristics, economic botany, agroforestry, quantitative botanical inventory, biochemical and molecular systematics, genomics, systematic plant anatomy, and horticulture. Emphasizes monography, inventory, biodiversity studies, graduate training, and publication of floras of the New World. **Services:** Interlibrary loan; copying; scanning; library open to the public. **Founded:** 1891. **Holdings:** 575,000 volumes; 140,000 plans; 58,000 catalogs; 25,000 pieces; 42,000 e-journals; 16,000 serial titles; 9,600 books; 4,000 titles; documents; manuscripts; correspondence; working papers; field notebooks; photographs and maps. **Publications:** *Advances in Economic Botany*; *Botanical Review* (Quarterly); *Brittonia* (Quarterly); *Contributions from The New York Botanical Garden* (Occasionally); *Economic Botany*; *Flora Neotropica*; *New Flora of Vermont* (Irregular); *North American Flora* (Occasionally). **Educational Activities:** NYBG Seminars, Offer exemplary teaching programs. **Awards:** Rupert Barneby Award (Annual); Henry Allan Gleason Award (Annual).

7680 ■ Norfolk Botanical Garden Society - Frederic Heutte Memorial Library
6700 Azalea Garden Rd.
Norfolk, VA 23518-5337
Co. E-mail: library@nbgs.org
URL: http://norfolkbotanicalgarden.org/learn/horticulture/horticultural-library
Scope: Horticulture. **Services:** Library open to the public for reference use only. **Founded:** 1962. **Holdings:** 3,500 books.

7681 ■ Pennsylvania Horticultural Society (PHS) - McLean Library
100 N 20th St., 5th Fl.
Philadelphia, PA 19103
Ph: (215)988-8800
Co. E-mail: phs-info@pennhort.org
URL: http://phsonline.org
Contact: Matt Rader, President
Facebook: www.facebook.com/PHSgardening
Linkedin: www.linkedin.com/company/pennsylvania-horticultural-society
X (Twitter): x.com/PHSgardening
Instagram: www.instagram.com/phsgardening
YouTube: www.youtube.com/channel/UCK2tCVVaARp9MCLEm0t9TQw
Description: Seeks to use horticulture to advance the health and well-being of the greater Philadelphia region through four pillars: access to fresh food, healthy living environments, deep social connections, and economic opportunities. **Scope:** Gardening; historical; horticultural. **Services:** Library open to the public by appointment; interlibrary loan. **Founded:** 1827. **Holdings:** 15,000 books, DVDs; slides; videos. **Publications:** *PHS News* (6/year); *GROW* (Quarterly). **Educational Activities:** Philadelphia International Flower Show (Annual). **Geographic Preference:** State.

7682 ■ Planting Fields Arboretum - The Garden Library
1395 Planting Fields Rd.
Oyster Bay, NY 11771
URL: http://plantingfields.org/landscape
Scope: Horticulture; botany. **Services:** Library open to the public for browsing and reference use only (members of Planting Fields Foundation and Arboretum staff, as well as members of garden societies that meet on the grounds, have borrowing privileges). **Founded:** 1975. **Holdings:** 8,000 books.

7683 ■ Rodale Inc.
Rodale Inc.
PO Box 3064
Harlan, IA 51593-0128
Description: Publisher of health and wellness magazines. **Publications:** *Rodale's Organic Life* (Bimonthly); *Bike Tech* (Bimonthly); *Organic Gardening*; *Prevention: The Tools to Live Well*; *Runner's World: World's Leading Running Magazine* (Monthly); *Men's Health: Ton's of Useful Stuff*; *Prevention: The Magazine for Better Health* (Monthly); *Regeneration Gardeners' Network*; *Best Life*; *Children: The guide for parents* (Bimonthly); *Runner's World--Upcoming Races Section* (Monthly); *Destinations--Directory of Cross Country Ski Areas*; *Diane Magazine* (Quarterly); *Rodale's Fitness Swimmer* (Bimonthly); *Women's Health* (Bimonthly).

7684 ■ San Francisco Botanical Garden at Strybing Arboretum - Helen Crocker Russell Library of Horticulture
1199 9th Ave.
San Francisco, CA 94122
URL: http://cbhl.net/plant-libraries
Scope: Gardening; garden design; botanical art; ethno botany and pest management; horticultural history; plant lore; ethno botany and economic plants; medical botany; botanical art; illustration and crafts. gardening for biodiversity; ecological restoration. **Services:** Library open to the public; Internet access. **Founded:** 1972. **Holdings:** 27,000 volumes, including 300 rare volumes; 2,500 bound periodical volumes; 1 shelf of William Hammond Hall Archives; 3,000 slide transparencies of plants (accessible through online catalog); 26 VF drawers of brochures and pamphlets; 3,000 old and current nursery catalogs. **Subscriptions:** 250 periodicals (includes journals).

7685 ■ Santa Barbara Botanic Garden (SBBG) - Blaksley Library
1212 Mission Canyon Rd.
Santa Barbara, CA 93105
Ph: (805)682-4726
Co. E-mail: info@sbbotanicgarden.org
URL: http://sbbotanicgarden.org
Contact: Dr. Steve Windhager, Executive Director
E-mail: swindhager@sbbg.org
Facebook: www.facebook.com/sbbotanicgarden
Linkedin: www.linkedin.com/company/santa-barbara-botanic-garden
YouTube: www.youtube.com/channel/UCUkk2avxUVa9IciEomgSvWA
Description: Publishes on botany and horticulture. **Scope:** California native plants, including conservation biology, plant systematics and structural botany, particularly of the California Channel Islands. **Services:** Copying; open to the public by appointment. **Founded:** 1926. **Holdings:** 15,000 books; journals; 100,000 slides and photographs; manuscript; 1,500 nursery catalogs. **Publications:** *Garden Gazette* (Biweekly). **Educational Activities:** Special training, In botany and horticulture research and education.; Dara Emery Memorial Lecture (Annual); Santa Barbara Botanic Garden Master Gardener program; Annual Santa Barbara Botanic Garden Conservation Symposium (Annual), To provide a well-rounded discussion on the topic chosen. **Awards:** Dara Emery Memorial Lecture (Annual).

7686 ■ Texas Discovery Gardens Horticulture Library
3601 Martin Luther King Jr. Blvd.
Dallas, TX 75210
URL: http://txdg.org/history
Scope: Horticulture. **Founded:** 1941. **Holdings:** Figures not available.

7687 ■ University of Alberta - Botanic Garden - Library
c/o University of Alberta Central Receiving
116 St. & 85 Ave.
Edmonton, AB, Canada T6G 2R3
Ph: (780)492-3050
Co. E-mail: uabg.info@ualberta.ca
URL: http://www.ualberta.ca/botanic-garden/visit/hours-location.html
Contact: Carl Charest, Director
E-mail: charest@ualberta.ca
Facebook: www.facebook.com/UABotanicGarden
X (Twitter): twitter.com/UABotanicGarden
Instagram: www.instagram.com/uabotanicgarden
Pinterest: www.pinterest.ca/UABotanicGarden
Description: Integral unit of University of Alberta. **Scope:** Biodiversity and floristics bryophytes; taxonomy of microfungi. **Founded:** 1959. **Holdings:** Figures not available. **Publications:** *Kinnikinnick* (Quarterly).

7688 ■ University of California Botanical Garden at Berkeley - Myrtle R. Wolf Botanical & Horticultural Library
200 Centennial Dr.
Berkeley, CA 94720-5045

Ph: (510)643-2755
Fax: (510)642-5045
Co. E-mail: garden@berkeley.edu
URL: http://botanicalgarden.berkeley.edu
Contact: Dr. Lewis Feldman, Director
E-mail: lfeldman@berkeley.edu
Facebook: www.facebook.com/ucbgarden
Linkedin: www.linkedin.com/company/uc-botanical-garden
X (Twitter): x.com/ucbgarden
Instagram: www.instagram.com/ucbgarden
Description: The library has over 3,200 books and journals. **Scope:** Horticulture; floras; plant taxonomy; botanical gardens. **Services:** Library open to the public for reference use only. **Founded:** 1890. **Holdings:** 294 families; 2,485 genera; 10,880 taxa; 16,865 accessions.

7689 ■ University of Georgia - State Botanical Garden of Georgia
2450 S Milledge Ave.
Athens, GA 30605
Ph: (706)542-1244
Co. E-mail: garden@uga.edu
URL: http://botgarden.uga.edu
Contact: Jennifer Cruse-Sanders, Director
E-mail: crusesanders@uga.edu
Facebook: www.facebook.com/botgarden
X (Twitter): twitter.com/botgardenGA
Instagram: www.instagram.com/botanicalgarden_ga
Description: Integral unit of University of Georgia, guided by its own advisory board. **Scope:** 313-acre site maintaining plant collections for research by scientists and students, including documented collections of native and cultivated plants, a plant evaluation site for woody ornamental plants in the Southeast, theme gardens and display collections of the bulbs, annuals, perennials and woody plants, both native and exotic. **Services:** Library open to the public for reference use only. **Founded:** 1968. **Holdings:** 2,000 books; 85 videotapes; CD-ROMs; archives; manuscripts. **Subscriptions:** 14 journals and other serials. **Publications:** Garden News Quarterly.

7690 ■ University of Minnesota - Minnesota Landscape Arboretum - Andersen Horticultural Library
3675 Arboretum Dr.
Chaska, MN 55318
Co. E-mail: arbinfo@umn.edu
URL: http://arb.umn.edu
Contact: Jenny L. Verner, President
Facebook: www.facebook.com/MnArboretum
Description: The unit provides horticulture and gardening based courses. It offers adult classes, school programs and more. **Scope:** Landscape plant and fruit crop development, including breeding research to improve plant material and plant cold-hardiness to determine what plants are suited to the Minnesota environment. Studies include breeding, culture, and physiology of fruit and landscape and fruit plants. **Services:** Interlibrary loan (limited). **Founded:** 1958. **Holdings:** 20,000 books; magazines; newsletters; journals. **Publications:** Andersen Horticultural Library Source Lists of Plants and Seeds; Minnesota Landscape Arboretum Annual report (Annual); Plant Information Online; Member newsletter (Bimonthly); Progress reports. **Educational Activities:** Horticulture therapy; Special events, hiking, cross-country skiing, and tours, Engage members and visitors in the splendor of the gardens and beauty of nature during all four seasons. ; Minnesota Landscape Arboretum Photography Symposium; Minnesota Landscape Arboretum Workshops.

7691 ■ University of Pennsylvania - Morris Arboretum - Archives
100 E Northwestern Ave.
Philadelphia, PA 19118
Ph: (215)247-5777
Fax: (215)247-8128
Co. E-mail: info@morrisarboretum.org
URL: http://www.morrisarboretum.org
Contact: William Cullina, Executive Director
Facebook: www.facebook.com/morrisarboretum/
X (Twitter): twitter.com/morrisarboretum
Instagram: www.instagram.com/morrisarboretum/
YouTube: www.youtube.com/user/morrisarboretum
Description: Integral unit of University of Pennsylvania, but under its own advisory board of managers. Offers plant clinic. **Scope:** Taxonomy, pests and diseases of woody plants, history of landscape architecture, and flora of Pennsylvania, including exploration and introduction of plants from Asia, integrated pest management for ornamental plants, field studies of rare and endangered species. **Services:** Interlibrary loan; copying; reference services; library open to the public. **Founded:** 1933. **Holdings:** Documents; letters; maps; blueprints; drawings; ledgers; diaries; lantern slides; photos; negatives; books; newspapers; research material; reports. **Publications:** Morris Arboretum Impact Report (Annual); Morris Arboretum Newsletter- Seasons. **Educational Activities:** Morris Arboretum Development Courses, For arborists.; Morris Arboretum Workshops.

7692 ■ University of Washington Botanic Gardens - Elisabeth C. Miller Library
3501 NE 41st St.
Seattle, WA 98105
Ph: (206)543-0415
Fax: (206)897-1435
Co. E-mail: hortlib@uw.edu
URL: http://depts.washington.edu/hortlib
Contact: Brian Thompson, Manager
E-mail: bthomp@uw.edu
Facebook: www.facebook.com/ElisabethCMillerLibrary
Scope: Horticulture. **Services:** Copying; library open to the public. **Founded:** 1985. **Holdings:** 14,000 books; 30 linear feet of clipping files including pamphlets, copies of magazine articles on popular topics, and newspaper clippings; VHS tapes; DVDs; CDs; children's books. **Subscriptions:** 200 periodicals (includes journals).

7693 ■ Worcester County Horticultural Society Library
11 French Dr.
Boylston, MA 01505-0598
URL: http://nebg.org
Contact: Lisa McDonough, President
Scope: Agriculture; botany; conservation; gardening; fruit culture; general horticulture; landscape design. **Services:** Copying; library open to the public for reference use only. **Founded:** 1842. **Holdings:** newsletters; 8000 books; 1000 bound periodical volumes; 200 seed, tool, plant, and equipment catalogs; 14,500 slides.

RESEARCH CENTERS

7694 ■ Auburn University - Alabama Agricultural Experiment Station - Ornamental Horticulture Research Center (OHRC)
PO Box 8276.
Mobile, AL 36689
Co. E-mail: auohrc@gmail.com
URL: http://agriculture.auburn.edu/research/alabama-agricultural-experiment-station
Contact: Jeremy M. Pickens, Assistant Professor
E-mail: pickejm@auburn.edu
Facebook: www.facebook.com/AAES.OHRC
Description: Integral unit of Alabama Agricultural Experiment Station at Auburn University. **Scope:** Pest control, including insects, diseases, and weeds; culture of container-grown woody ornamentals and greenhouse crops, including propagation, fertilization, growing media, and environmental effects; and growth regulators. Applied research conducted in support of commercial nursery industry. **Founded:** 1928.

7695 ■ Horticultural Research Institute (HRI)
80 M St. SE
Washington, DC 20003
Ph: (202)789-2900
URL: http://www.hriresearch.org
Contact: Jennifer Gray, Contact
E-mail: jenniferg@americanhort.org
Facebook: www.facebook.com/hriresearch
Linkedin: www.linkedin.com/company/hriresearch
X (Twitter): x.com/HORTRESEARCH
Description: Nursery firms; nursery supply companies; state and regional nurserymen's associations. Conducts nursery industry research in areas of management, marketing, production, integrated pest management, water use, and a continuing study of the industry scope. Administered by the staff of the American Nursery and Landscape Association. **Scope:** Problems and opportunities in the nursery and landscape industry. **Founded:** 1962. **Publications:** Journal of Environmental Horticulture (Quarterly); New Horizons (Semiannual). **Awards:** Mugget Scholarship (Annual); Susie & Bruce Usrey Education Scholarship (Annual); Gunter Mecking Memorial Scholarship (Annual); Wright Family of Alabama Scholarship (Annual); Bryan A. Champion Memorial Scholarship (Annual); HRI Research Competitive Grants (Annual); Carville M. Akehurst Memorial Scholarship (Annual); Spring Meadow - Proven Winners Scholarship (Annual); Timothy S. and Palmer W. Bigelow, Jr. Scholarship (Annual); Usrey Family Scholarship (Annual). **Geographic Preference:** National.

7696 ■ Ohio State University - Agricultural Technical Institute (ATI) - Library
1328 Dover Rd.
Wooster, OH 44691
Ph: (330)287-1331
Free: 800-647-8283
Fax: (330)287-1333
Co. E-mail: ati@osu.edu
URL: http://ati.osu.edu
Contact: Dr. Kristina Boone, Director
E-mail: boone.3@osu.edu
Facebook: www.facebook.com/ohiostateatiadmissions
X (Twitter): x.com/OhioStateATI
YouTube: www.youtube.com/user/ohiostateati
Description: Integral unit of Ohio State University. Telephone reference service. **Scope:** Floriculture, landscape science, nursery, turf, crops, greenhouse production, agricultural engineering and mechanics, agronomic industries, soil and water management, dairy and livestock science, and construction. **Services:** Interlibrary loan; printing; copying. **Founded:** 1969. **Holdings:** DVDs; magazines; journals; books and textbooks. **Educational Activities:** ATI Continuous education and distance learning.

Greeting Card Publishing

ASSOCIATIONS AND OTHER ORGANIZATIONS

7697 ■ Greeting Card Association (GCA)
2851 S Parker Rd., Ste. 1210
Aurora, CO 80014
Ph: (202)216-9627
Fax: (303)200-7099
Co. E-mail: gca@greetingcard.org
URL: http://www.greetingcard.org
Contact: Amy McAnarney, President
Facebook: www.facebook.com/GreetingCardAssociationUSA
X (Twitter): x.com/USGCA
Instagram: www.instagram.com/usagca
YouTube: www.youtube.com/channel/UCSKQgg_quiTUUVxhLWgLbZA

Description: Publishers of greeting cards and suppliers of materials. **Founded:** 1941. **Publications:** CardTalk (6/year); Directory of Greeting Card Sales Representatives and Distributors (Biennial); Greeting Card Industry Directory (Biennial). **Educational Activities:** National Stationery Show (NSS). **Awards:** LOUIE Awards (Annual). **Geographic Preference:** National.

7698 ■ Souvenir Wholesale Distributors Association (SWDA)
32770 Arapahoe Rd., No. 132-155
Lafayette, CO 80026
Free: 888-599-4474
Fax: (888)589-7610
Co. E-mail: swdabod1@gmail.com
URL: http://www.souvenircentral.org
Contact: Angie Rhonke, President
E-mail: angie@mtnstatesspecialties.com
Facebook: www.facebook.com/SWDA-733009876786736

Description: Represents distributors and manufacturers of post cards, souvenirs, and novelty items. **Founded:** 1973. **Educational Activities:** SWDA Annual Convention and Trade Show (Annual). **Awards:** SWDA Glassware Souvenir Award (Annual); SWDA Magnet Souvenir Award (Annual); SWDA Spoon Souvenir Award (Annual); SWDA Edibles Souvenir Award (Annual); SWDA Miscellaneous Souvenir Award (Annual); SWDA Allied Products Awards (Annual); SWDA Books Awards (Annual); SWDA Calendars Awards (Annual); SWDA Ceramics Souvenir Award (Annual); SWDA Key Chain Souvenir Award (Annual); SWDA Soft Goods Souvenir Award (Annual); SWDA Pens/Pencil Souvenir Award (Annual); SWDA Printer of the Year (Annual); SWDA Sunrise/Sunset Postcard Awards (Annual); SWDA Night Postcard Awards (Annual); SWDA Multiview Postcard Awards (Annual); SWDA Comic or Novelty Postcards Awards (Annual). **Geographic Preference:** National.

REFERENCE WORKS

7699 ■ "Award Win Highlights Slingsby's Green Credentials" in Ecology, Environment & Conservation Business (August 20, 2011, pp. 3)

Description: Slingsby, an industrial and commercial equipment supplier, was joint winner with Hallmark Cards of the Baildon Business in the Community's Yorkshire and Humber Long Term Environmental Improvement Award. The firm cites its commitment to reducing environmental impact. **Availability:** Print; PDF; Online.

7700 ■ "E-Cards Are Back, Thanks to the Pandemic" in The New York Times (June 22, 2021)

Ed: Anna Schaverien. **Released:** June 22, 2021. **Description:** Due to the COVID-19 pandemic causing stores to close and reducing social gatherings, many people resurrected the old e-card to send along over the internet in order to stay connected. **Availability:** Online.

7701 ■ "Greeting Card Companies Need a Sympathy Card: CVS, Walmart Poised to Cut Back" in USA Today (March 26, 2019)
URL(s): www.usatoday.com/story/money/2019/03/26/walmart-cvs-may-cut-greeting-card-space-as-cards-decline/3243515002/

Ed: Nathan Bomey. **Released:** March 26, 2019. **Description:** Although the greeting card industry has seen some gains in a few sectors such as premium cards and budget cards, most people are not buying as many cards as they used to. With the decline in greeting cards, stores such as CVS and Walmart are cutting back on the amount of space dedicated to cards. **Availability:** Online.

7702 ■ "Halls Give Hospital Drive $11 Million Infusion" in The Business Journal-Serving Metropolitan Kansas City (Vol. 26, July 18, 2008)

Description: Don Hall, chairman of Hallmark Cards Inc., and eight family members have announced that they will give $11 million to Children's Mercy Hospitals and Clinics for its $800 million expansion plan. Hall Family Foundation president Bill Hall that contributions such as that for Children's Mercy reflect the charitable interests of the foundation's board and founders. The possible impacts of the Hall's donation are analyzed.

7703 ■ "Search and Discover New Opportunities" in DM News (Vol. 31, December 14, 2009, No. 29, pp. 13)
Pub: Haymarket Media Inc.
Contact: Kevin Costello, Chief Executive Officer

Ed: Chantal Tode. **Description:** Although other digital strategies are gaining traction in Internet marketing, search marketing continues to dominate this advertising forum. Companies like American Greetings, which markets e-card brands online, are utilizing social networking sites and affiliates to generate a higher demand for their products. **Availability:** Print; Online.

7704 ■ "You Won't Believe How Much the Greeting Card Industry Is Worth" in Southern Living (May 9, 2018)
URL(s): www.southernliving.com/culture/greeting-card-industry-worth

Released: May 09, 2018. **Description:** The greeting card industry is alive and doing well, to the tune of $7.5 billion. Consumers are still enjoying the old-fashioned pastime of sending and receiving cards, especially Christmas cards and it doesn't look to be slowing down anytime soon. **Availability:** Online.

STATISTICAL SOURCES

7705 ■ Online Greeting Card Sales Industry in the US - Market Research Report
URL(s): www.ibisworld.com/united-states/market-research-reports/online-greeting-card-sales-industry/

Price: $925. **Description:** Downloadable report analyzing the online greeting card industry. **Availability:** Online.

TRADE SHOWS AND CONVENTIONS

7706 ■ National Stationery Show (NSS)
Greeting Card Association (GCA)
2851 S Parker Rd., Ste. 1210
Aurora, CO 80014
Ph: (202)216-9627
Fax: (303)200-7099
Co. E-mail: gca@greetingcard.org
URL: http://www.greetingcard.org
Contact: Amy McAnarney, President
URL(s): nynow.com

Description: Greeting cards, social stationery, and related products such as calendars, desk accessories, small leather goods, photo frames, party goods, home office products, prints and posters, postcards, note paper, games, toys, balloons, wedding products, back-to-school supplies, and holiday supplies. **Audience:** Importers and distributors, buyers, licensors, special-event planners, mass retailers, and corporate marketers. **Principal Exhibits:** Greeting cards, social stationery, and related products such as calendars, desk accessories, small leather goods, photo frames, party goods, home office products, prints and posters, postcards, note paper, games, toys, balloons, wedding products, back-to-school supplies, and holiday supplies.

LIBRARIES

7707 ■ Hallmark Cards, Inc.
Hallmark Cards, Inc.
 2501 McGee St.
 Kansas City, MO 64108
Ph: (816)274-5111
Free: 800-425-5627
URL: http://corporate.hallmark.com
Contact: Mike Perry, President
URL(s): www.hallmark.com
Facebook: www.facebook.com/Hallmark
X (Twitter): twitter.com/Hallmark
Instagram: www.instagram.com/hallmark
YouTube: www.youtube.com/user/hallmarkcards
Pinterest: www.pinterest.com/hallmark
Description: Manufacturer of greeting cards, stationery, and related products. **Founded:** 1910. **Educational Activities:** FMI Midwinter Executive Conference (Annual).

Grocery Store

ASSOCIATIONS AND OTHER ORGANIZATIONS

7708 ■ Consumer Brands Association (CBA)
1001 19th St. N
Arlington, VA 22209
Ph: (571)378-6760
Fax: (571)378-6759
Co. E-mail: info@consumerbrandsassociation.org
URL: http://consumerbrandsassociation.org
Contact: Stacy Papadopoulos, Chief Executive Officer (Acting)
Facebook: www.facebook.com/ConsumerBrandsAssociation
Linkedin: www.linkedin.com/company/consumerbrandsassociation
X (Twitter): x.com/consumerbrands
YouTube: www.youtube.com/channel/UCtUehfpXw8vm2O4mgGRHCPQ

Description: Grocery manufacturers' associations of Australia, Austria, Belgium, Brazil, Canada, Denmark, France, Germany, Italy, Japan, Mexico, New Zealand, South Africa, Switzerland, the United Kingdom, the United States, and Venezuela. Promotes high standards in the manufacture and distribution of grocery products. Coordinates activities of grocery manufacturers worldwide. **Founded:** 1982. **Publications:** *ASMC's Directory of Members* (Annual); *Association of Sales & Marketing Companies--Directory of Members* (Annual); *Newsline* (Bimonthly); *Sales & Marketing Magazine*; *Sales Training*; *GMA Executive Update* (Monthly); *GMA State Legislative Report*; *GMA Washington Report* (Monthly). **Educational Activities:** Executive Conference. **Geographic Preference:** Multinational; National.

7709 ■ Fédération Canadienne des Épiciers Indépendants (FCEI)
105 Gordon Baker Rd., Ste. 401
North York, ON, Canada M2H 3P8
Ph: (416)492-2311
Fax: (800)661-2344
Co. E-mail: info@cfig.ca
URL: http://www.cfig.ca
Contact: Tom Shurrie, President
E-mail: tshurrie@cfig.ca
Facebook: www.facebook.com/CFIGFCEI
X (Twitter): x.com/cfigfcei

Description: Promotes growth and development of members' businesses. Represents the commercial and regulatory interests of independent grocers; conducts promotional activities. **Founded:** 1962. **Educational Activities:** Grocery Innovations Canada (GIC) (Annual); GSF West. **Awards:** Master Merchandiser Awards (Annual); Canadian Federation of Independent Grocers National Scholarship (Annual). **Geographic Preference:** National.

7710 ■ Food Industry Association Executives (FIAE)
c/o Bev Lynch, President
664 Sandipiper Bay Dr. SW
Sunset Beach, NC 28468
Ph: (215)499-6284
Co. E-mail: bev@mgmt57.com
URL: http://www.foodindustryassociationexecutives.com
Contact: Bev Lynch, President

Description: Professional executives of local, state, and national retail grocers associations. **Founded:** 1927. **Geographic Preference:** National.

7711 ■ Food Institute (FI)
330 Changebridge Rd., Ste. 101
Pine Brook, NJ 07058
Ph: (201)791-5570
Free: 855-791-5570
Co. E-mail: questions@foodinstitute.com
URL: http://www.foodinstitute.com
Contact: Anika Wilson, Contact
E-mail: anika.wilson@foodinstitute.com
Facebook: www.facebook.com/foodinstitutenj
Linkedin: www.linkedin.com/company/the-food-institute
X (Twitter): x.com/FoodInstitute
Instagram: www.instagram.com/foodinstitute
YouTube: www.youtube.com/channel/UCYAPI0TXNtJa04aQre4h4pA

Description: Strives to provide food industry-related information to its members. **Scope:** The food industry. **Services:** Center open to the public on fee basis. **Founded:** 1928. **Holdings:** Figures not available. **Publications:** *Today in Food*; *Get It Out, Get It Right, Get It Over! Avoiding Food Product Recalls*; *The Food Institute* (Weekly); *Almanac of the Canning, Freezing, Preserving Industries* (Annual); *Food Business Mergers and Acquisitions*; *OSHA Inspection Manual*; *Regulatory Directory* (Periodic); *Food Business Mergers & Acquisitions*. **Geographic Preference:** Multinational.

7712 ■ Food Marketing Institute (FMI)
2345 Crystal Dr., Ste. 800
Arlington, VA 22202
Ph: (202)452-8444
Fax: (202)429-4519
URL: http://www.fmi.org
Contact: Leslie G. Sarasin, President
Linkedin: www.linkedin.com/company/fmithefoodindustryassociation
X (Twitter): x.com/FMI_ORG
Instagram: www.instagram.com/fmi_org
YouTube: www.youtube.com/user/FMIorg

Description: Grocery retailers and wholesalers. Maintains liaison with government and consumers. Conducts 30 educational conferences and seminars per year. Conducts research programs; compiles statistics. **Scope:** Retail and wholesale grocery operations, food industry research, and consumer behavior and attitudes regarding grocery shopping. **Founded:** 1977. **Publications:** *FMI Newsletter*; *FMI News: Aisle by Aisle* (Monthly); *Advantage* (Monthly); *Information Systems Directory* (Biennial); *Facts About Supermarket Development* (Annual); *Food Marketing Industry Speaks* (Annual); *Food Retailing Industry Speaks* (Annual); *Operating Results of Independent Supermarkets*. **Educational Activities:** FMI Midwinter Executive Conference (Annual). **Awards:** William H. Albers Industry Relations Award (Annual); Esther Peterson Consumer Service Award (Periodic); Sidney R. Rabb Award for Statesmanship (Annual). **Geographic Preference:** National.

7713 ■ Michigan Distributors and Vendors Association (MDVA)
120 N Washington Sq., Ste. 110B
Lansing, MI 48933
Ph: (517)372-2323
Fax: (517)372-4404
URL: http://mdva.org
Contact: Polly T. Reber, President

Description: Represents two significant business segments in the grocery and convenience products industry in Michigan. Advocates for and supports the distributors and food service industries. **Founded:** 1947. **Geographic Preference:** State.

7714 ■ National Frozen and Refrigerated Foods Association (NFRA)
4755 Linglestown Rd., Ste. 300
Harrisburg, PA 17112
Ph: (717)657-8601
Fax: (717)657-9862
Co. E-mail: nfra@nfraweb.org
URL: http://nfraweb.org
Contact: Jeff Rumachik, President
E-mail: jeff@nfraweb.org
X (Twitter): x.com/nfraweb

Description: More than 400 member companies representing the frozen and refrigerated dairy foods industry. Promotes the sales and consumption of frozen and refrigerated foods through education, training, research and menu development and provides a forum for industry dialogue. Sponsors National Frozen Food Month, in March; June Dairy Month; June and July Ice Cream and Novelties Promotion; Frozen and Refrigerated Foods Festival, in October; and Bring Us To Your Table! Freezer Favorites. **Founded:** 1945. **Publications:** *The Frozen Food Executive* (Monthly); *New Products Newsletter* (Quarterly); *National Frozen and Refrigerated Foods Association--Membership Directory*. **Educational Activities:** NFRA Convention; NFRA Annual Executive Conference (Annual). **Awards:** NFRA Golden Penguin Awards (Annual). **Geographic Preference:** Multinational.

7715 ■ National Grocers Association (NGA)
601 Pennsylvania Ave. NW, Ste. 375N
Washington, DC 20004
Ph: (202)938-2570
Fax: (202)938-2574
Co. E-mail: communications@nationalgrocers.org
URL: http://www.nationalgrocers.org
Contact: Greg Ferrara, President
Facebook: www.facebook.com/NationalGrocersAssn
Linkedin: www.linkedin.com/company/national-grocers-association
X (Twitter): x.com/NationalGrocers
Instagram: www.instagram.com/nationalgrocers
YouTube: www.youtube.com/NationalGrocers

Description: Independent food retailers; wholesale food distributors servicing 29,000 food stores. Promotes industry interests and works to advance understanding, trade and cooperation among all sectors of the food industry. Represents member's interests before the government. Aids in the development of programs designed to improve the productivity and efficiency of the food distribution industry. **Founded:** 1980. **Publications:** *Congressional or Regulatory Update* (Periodic). **Educational Activities:** NGA Show (Annual); The NGA Show; America's Supermarket Showcase (Annual). **Awards:** Clarence G. Adamy Great American Award (Annual); NGA Spirit of America Award (Annual). **Geographic Preference:** National.

7716 ■ Natural Grocer Association
Description: Association that works to elevate, unify, and serve the independent grocer industry.

7717 ■ Women Grocers of America (WGA)
601 Pennsylvania Ave., NW N Bldg., Ste. 375
Washington, DC 20004
Ph: (202)938-2570
Fax: (202)938-2574
Co. E-mail: nga-foundation@nationalgrocers.org
URL: http://www.nationalgrocers.org/foundation/women-grocers-of-america
Contact: Chelsea Matzen, Vice President
Facebook: www.facebook.com/NGAFoundation
Linkedin: www.linkedin.com/company/national-grocers-association
X (Twitter): x.com/NGA_Foundation
Instagram: www.instagram.com/nationalgrocers
YouTube: www.youtube.com/user/NationalGrocers

Description: Information and advisory arm to the National Grocers Association. Encourages the education of students pursuing grocery industry-related careers in the independent segment of the industry through its scholarship program. Encourages all segments of the food industry to promote breast cancer awareness and prevention. Participates in and supports the programs offered by the National Grocers Association. **Founded:** 1982. **Awards:** Mary Macey Scholarship (Annual); WGA Woman of the Year (Annual). **Geographic Preference:** National.

INCUBATORS/RESEARCH AND TECHNOLOGY PARKS

7718 ■ Plug and Play - Food and Beverage
440 N Wolfe Rd.
Sunnyvale, CA 94085
URL: http://www.plugandplaytechcenter.com/industries/food-and-beverage

Description: An accelerator for startups in the food and beverage industry. Provides support with venture and angel partners, mentorship, a data center, office space, and networking opportunities. This program has a focus on the following: personalized nutrition, food freshness and safety, automation, functional foods, protein and ingredient alternatives, asset tracking, distribution, and waste reduction.

REFERENCE WORKS

7719 ■ "Agana To Bottle Rain for Whole Foods" in Austin Business Journal (Vol. 32, March 30, 2012, No. 4, pp. 1)
Pub: American City Business Journals, Inc.
Contact: Mike Olivieri, Executive Vice President

Ed: Vicky Garza. **Description:** Agana Rainwater has signed a deal to bottle rainwater for Whole Foods Market Inc. Rainwater bottling is seen as a conservation tools as it does not deplete the lake or aquifer. **Availability:** Online.

7720 ■ "Baking Up a Bigger Lance" in Charlotte Business Journal (Vol. 25, December 3, 2010, No. 37, pp. 1)
Pub: Charlotte Business Journal
Contact: Robert Morris, Editor
E-mail: rmorris@bizjournals.com

Ed: Ken Elkins. **Description:** Events that led to the merger between Charlotte, North Carolina-based snack food manufacturer Lance Inc. and Pennsylvania-based pretzel maker Snyder's of Hanover Inc. are discussed. The merger is expected to help Lance in posting a 70 percent increase in revenue, which reached $900 million in 2009. How the merger would affect Snyder's of Hanover is also described. **Availability:** Print; Online.

7721 ■ "Baltimore Shopping Centers Go On the Block as Sellers See Demand" in Baltimore Business Journal (Vol. 29, September 2, 2011, No. 17, pp. 1)
Pub: Boston Business Journal
Contact: Carolyn M. Jones, President
E-mail: cmjones@bizjournals.com

Ed: Daniel J. Sernovitz. **Description:** Maryland-based investors have been choosing to put their money in the supermarket business. Retail property sales have increased during the second quarter of 2011. **Availability:** Online.

7722 ■ "Bankruptcies" in Crain's Detroit Business (Vol. 24, March 24, 2008, No. 12, pp. 6)
Pub: Crain Communications Inc.
Contact: Barry Asin, President

Description: Current list of business that filed for Chapter 7 or 11 protection in U.S. Bankruptcy Court in Detroit include a construction company, a medical care company, a physical therapy firm and a communications firm. **Availability:** Online.

7723 ■ "Basics Market Expands Beyond Portland's City Limits" in Grocery Dive (November 4, 2019)
URL(s): www.grocerydive.com/news/basics-market-expands-beyond-portlands-city-limits/566532/
Ed: Lauren Stine. **Released:** November 04, 2019.
Description: After debuting last year, Basics Market has opened it's third location in Oregon and has plans for a fourth. The market features products from local producers while being organized for easy access to ingredients. **Availability:** Online.

7724 ■ "Battered Loblaw Makes Deep Job Cuts" in Globe & Mail (January 23, 2007)
Ed: Marina Strauss. **Description:** Loblaw Companies Ltd., supermarket giant, is eliminating up to 1,000 administrative jobs and shifting more buying responsibilities to its suppliers. The grocer will also introduce a national inventory strategy called "category management". **Availability:** Online.

7725 ■ "Bertha's Birth Stirs Juice" in Barron's (Vol. 88, July 14, 2008, No. 28, pp. M11)
Pub: Dow Jones & Company Inc.
Contact: Almar Latour, Chief Executive Officer

Ed: Tom Sellen. **Description:** Price of frozen concentrated orange juice, which has risen to four-month highs of $1.3620 in July 2008 is due, in part, to the hurricane season that has come earlier than normal in the far eastern Atlantic thereby possibly harming the 2008-2009 Florida orange crop. Future tropical-storm development will affect the prices of this commodity. **Availability:** Online.

7726 ■ "Better Made's Better Idea: Diversify Despite Rising Costs" in Crain's Detroit Business (Vol. 24, September 22, 2008, No. 38, pp. 18)
Pub: Crain Communications Inc.
Contact: Barry Asin, President

Ed: Nathan Skid. **Description:** Better Made Snack Foods Inc. is planning to expand its product lines and market reach as well as boost manufacturing capability during a time in which the company is being buffeted by rising commodity and fuel costs. The company feels that diversification is the key to maintain sales and growth. **Availability:** Online.

7727 ■ "Bonuses In Bad Times: In a Recession, How Should a Supermarket Chain Acknowledge Its Employees' Extra Effort?" in Harvard Business Review (Vol. 90, July 2012, No. 7-8, pp. 153).
Pub: Harvard Business Review Press
Contact: Moderna V. Pfizer, Contact

Ed: Daniela Beyersdorfer, Vincent Dessain, Zeynep Ton. **Price:** $6, hardcopy black and white; $7.46, hardcopy and PDF. **Description:** A fictional case study offering advice on how to acknowledge efforts made by workers during a recession. **Availability:** Print; Online.

7728 ■ "Coca-Cola FEMSA, Family Dollar, Other Dividend Payers On a Roll" in Benzinga.com (June 21, 2012)
Pub: Benzinga.com
Contact: Jason Raznick, Founder

Ed: Nelson Hem. **Description:** Dividend paying companies showing upward price trends are outlined. The firms highlighted include: Agnico-Eagle Mines, Coca-Cola FEMSA, Dean Foods, Expedia, Family Dollar Stores, Ferrellgas Partners, and InterContinental Hotels. **Availability:** Print; Online.

7729 ■ "Coinstar, Inc. and Seattle's Best Coffee Sign Exclusive Agreement to Roll Out Thousands of the New Rubi Kiosks in Grocery, Drug and Mass Channels" in Marketing Weekly News (June 23 2012, pp. 77)
Pub: PR Newswire Association LLC.

Description: Seattles' Best Coffee, a firm of Starbucks Corporation, has partnered with Coinstar Inc. to install coffee kiosks in grocery, drug and mass merchant retailers featuring Seattle's Best coffee drinks. Rubi kiosk is the third automated kiosk owned by Coinstar. Details of the deal are included.

7730 ■ "Competitors Eye Whole Foods" in Sacramento Business Journal (Vol. 31, August 8, 2014, No. 24, pp. 6)
Pub: American City Business Journals, Inc.
Contact: Mike Olivieri, Executive Vice President

Released: Weekly. **Price:** $4, Introductory 4-week offer(Digital & Print). **Description:** Whole Foods Market has confirmed its plans to open a store in midtown Sacramento, California. However, Sacramento Natural Foods Co-op and Gluten Free Specialty says the announcement would not affect their own expansion plans into the same neighborhood. The proposed mixed-use building that will house the Whole Foods healthy grocery store is also discussed. **Availability:** Print; Online.

7731 ■ "Does the Gig Economy Have a Future in Grocery Stores?" in Grocery Dive (November 7, 2019)
URL(s): www.grocerydive.com/news/does-the-gig-economy-have-a-future-in-grocery-stores/566797/
Ed: Jeff Wells. **Released:** November 07, 2019.
Description: The gig economy has entered the grocery business by filling jobs for workers who shop for customers and deliver the goods. This type of work is expanding in the market as e-commerce demand accelerates, and traditional grocers have taken notice and started to provide their own on-demand labor. **Availability:** Online.

7732 ■ "Drink Up!" in (Vol. 92, July 23, 2012, No. 30, pp. 19)
Pub: Dow Jones & Company Inc.
Contact: Almar Latour, Chief Executive Officer

Ed: Robin Goldwyn Blumenthal. **Description:** Juice bars in the US are expanding as Americans increase the consumption of fresh vegetable and fruit juices. Coffeehouse chain Starbucks entered the market by introducing Evolution Fresh, a seller of coldpressed vegetable and fruit juices. The health benefits of fresh vegetable and fruit juice, however, remain uncertain. **Availability:** Online.

7733 ■ "Eastern Market's New Bite?" in Washington Business Journal (Vol. 33, August 8, 2014, No. 16, pp. 6)
Pub: American City Business Journals, Inc.
Contact: Mike Olivieri, Executive Vice President

Price: $4, Introductory 4-Week Offer(Digital & Print). **Description:** Eastern Market continues to operate despite allegations of financial mismanagement on the part of Washington DC auditors. Many of the market's vendors have been operating their stands with expired leases for more than five years. However, the Department of General Services has vowed to draw a new standard contract for renting and renegotiate new leases. **Availability:** Print; Online.

7734 ■ *"Egg Fight: The Yolk's on the Shorts"* in Barron's (Vol. 88, July 7, 2008, No. 27, pp. 20)
Pub: Dow Jones & Company Inc.
Contact: Almar Latour, Chief Executive Officer

Ed: Christopher C. Williams. **Description:** Shares of Cal-Maine Foods, the largest egg producer and distributor in the US, are due for a huge rise because of the increase in egg prices. Short sellers, however, continue betting that the stock, priced at $31.84 each, will eventually go down. **Availability:** Online.

7735 ■ *"Floral-Design Kiosk Business Blossoming"* in Colorado Springs Business Journal (September 24, 2010)
Pub: Dolan Media Newswires

Ed: Monica Mendoza. **Description:** Profile of Shellie Greto and her mother Jackie Martin who started a wholesale flower business in their garage. The do-it-yourself floral arrangement firm started a kiosk business in supermarkets called Complete Design. **Availability:** Online.

7736 ■ *"The Freshest Ideas Are in Small Grocery Stores"* in The New York Times (July 31, 2018)
URL(s): www.nytimes.com/2018/07/31/dining/grocery-store.html

Released: July 31, 2018. **Description:** Smaller grocery stores are starting to make headway in the industry, as consumers' shopping habits change. More younger customers are interested in "food experiences" and shop more than once a week while looking for curated items and more innovations. Smaller stores are complying and are able to give their customers what they want, which is often a zero waste store and healthier options. **Availability:** Online.

7737 ■ *"From Scarcity to Plenty"* in Inc. (Vol. 36, March 2014, No. 2, pp. 76)
Pub: Mansueto Ventures L.L.C.
Contact: Stephanie Mehta, Chief Executive Officer

Description: Profile of Mom's Organic Market which started in Scott Nash's mom's garage. Nash describes the healthy food choices offered at the store as well as its Environmental Restoration program which addressed issues including carbon offsets, recycling, and composting. **Availability:** Print; Online.

7738 ■ *"'Frozen' Assets: Refrigeration Goes High Tech as Hussmann Invests $7 Million in Global Hub"* in St. Louis Business Journal (Vol. 33, September 21, 2012, No. 4, pp. 1)
Pub: Baltimore Business Journal
Contact: Rhonda Pringle, President
E-mail: rpringle@bizjournals.com

Description: Hussmann Corporation is spending $7 million to create a high-tech innovation and clients collaboration center that will be called Global Hub, a venue for grocery food retailers, industry trend setters and through leaders. The company is also focusing on tapping the potential of convenience marts and dollar-store retailers. **Availability:** Print.

7739 ■ *"GM's Decision to Boot Dealer Prompts Sale"* in Baltimore Business Journal (Vol. 27, November 6, 2009, No. 26, pp. 1)
Pub: Baltimore Business Journal
Contact: Rhonda Pringle, President
E-mail: rpringle@bizjournals.com

Ed: Daniel J. Sernovitz. **Description:** General Motors Corporation's (GM) decision to strip Baltimore's Anderson Automotive Group Inc. of its GM franchise has prompted the owner, Bruce Mortimer, to close the automotive dealership and sell the land to a developer. The new project could make way for new homes, a shopping center and supermarket. **Availability:** Print; Online.

7740 ■ *"Green and Clean"* in Retail Merchandiser (Vol. 51, July-August 2011, No. 4, pp. 56)
Description: Green Valley Grocery partnered with Paragon Solutions consulting firm to make their stores environmentally green. **Availability:** Print; Online.

7741 ■ *"Grocers Fight Food Stamp Plan"* in Philadelphia Business Journal (Vol. 30, January 20, 2012, No. 49, pp. 1)
Pub: Baltimore Business Journal
Contact: Rhonda Pringle, President
E-mail: rpringle@bizjournals.com

Description: Grocers in Philadelphia, Pennsylvania have opposed the state's plan to eliminate food stamps for individuals and families with more than $2,000 in savings and other assets. About one-third of Philadelphia's population is eligible for food stamps. **Availability:** Print; Online.

7742 ■ *"Growing Grocer"* in Washington Business Journal (Vol. 32, March 21, 2014, No. 49, pp. 6)
Pub: American City Business Journals, Inc.
Contact: Mike Olivieri, Executive Vice President

Description: Scott Allhouse, the regional president of Whole Foods Markets for the Mid-Atlantic region, discusses the grocer's expansion plans in the Washington DC area. The company wants to open a store at the Walter Reed redevelopment and plans to open two more stores in Washington DC. **Availability:** Online.

7743 ■ *"The Harris Teeter Grocery Chain Has Started a New Ice Cream Club for Shoppers"* in Ice Cream Reporter (Vol. 21, July 20, 2008)
Description: Store loyalty cards are being issued to Harris Teeter customers to purchase any variety of Ben & Jerry's, Haagen-Dazs, Dove, Starbucks, Ciao Bella, Clemmy's, Purely Decadent, So Delicious, Harris Teeter Naturals, HT Traders, Hunter Farms or Denali Ice Cream. One point is earned for every dollar spent, 30 total points earns a $5 electronic coupon towards the next purchase. **Availability:** Print; Online.

7744 ■ *"In the Wake of Pet-Food Crisis, Iams Sales Plummet Nearly 17 Percent"* in Advertising Age (Vol. 78, May 14, 2007, No. 18, pp. 3)
Pub: Crain Communications, Inc.
Contact: Jessica Botos, Manager, Marketing
E-mail: jessica.botos@crainsnewyork.com

Ed: Jack Neff. **Description:** Although the massive U.S. pet-food recall impacted more than 100 brands, Procter & Gamble Co.'s Iams lost more sales and market share than any other industry player. According to Information Resources Inc. data, the brand's sales dropped 16.5 percent in the eight-week period ended April 22. Many analysts feel that the company could have handled the crisis in a better manner. **Availability:** Online.

7745 ■ *"Kroger Family of Pharmacies to Offer Health Assessment Kiosks at Locations Nationwide"* in Entertainment Close-Up (August 22, 2012)
Pub: Close-Up Media Inc.
Contact: Caroline S. Moore, President
E-mail: cms@closeupmedia.com

Description: Kroger HealthCENTER kiosks will be placed in Kroger Company Family of Pharmacies in 1,950 locations across the country. The kiosks are provided by Styhealthy, a wellness solutions firm and will offer self-use health screening to customers. **Availability:** Online.

7746 ■ *"Kroger Launches Car-Buying Program"* in Supermarket News (November 7, 2019)
URL(s): www.supermarketnews.com/retail-financial/kroger-launches-car-buying-program
Ed: Russell Redman. **Released:** November 07, 2019. **Description:** Kroger is entering the car buying industry by partnering with TrueCar Inc. to form Kroger Auto, Powered by TrueCar. Kroger customers can now access vehicle pricing information to compare savings plus receive discounts on new and used vehicles. Consumers who participate will also receive a free Fuel VIP membership. **Availability:** Online.

7747 ■ *"Kroger Recasts Its Brand"* in Supermarket News (November 6, 2019)
URL(s): www.supermarketnews.com/retail-financial/kroger-recasts-its-brand
Ed: Russell Redman. **Released:** November 06, 2019. **Description:** The Kroger Co. has unveiled a new logo and a new brand identity that emphasizes "food first." Their new slogan is "Fresh for Everyone" while still maintaining an updated version of its classic Kroger logo. **Availability:** Online.

7748 ■ *"Kroger Releases Annual Sustainability Report"* in Ecology, Environment & Conservation Business (July 26, 2014, pp. 46)
Pub: NewsRX LLC.
Contact: Kalani Rosell, Contact

Description: Kroger Company published its eighth annual sustainability report. The company is committed to reducing water consumption in its grocery stores by 5 percent in 2014. The report also provides a progress report on moving retail locations toward 'zero waste' and sourcing 100 percent certified palm oil. Statistical data included. **Availability:** Online.

7749 ■ *"LCB Puts a Cork in Kiosk Wine Sales"* in Times Leader (December 22, 2010)
Ed: Andrew M. Seder. **Description:** The Pennsylvania Liquor Control Board closed down thirty Pronto Wine Kiosks located in supermarkets throughout the state. The Board cited mechanical and technological issues such as products not dispensing. **Availability:** Online.

7750 ■ *"Liquor-Sales Issue in Kansas Creates Strange Bedfellows"* in Wichita Business Journal (Vol. 27, February 10, 2012, No. 6, pp. 1)
Pub: Baltimore Business Journal
Contact: Rhonda Pringle, President
E-mail: rpringle@bizjournals.com

Description: How the business community in Kansas has reacted to House Bill 2532, a legislation that would alter the way liquor is sold in the state, is presented. Under the legislation, groceries and convenience stores would be allowed to get licenses to sell liquor, wine and full-strength beer. On the other hand, liquor stores would be permitted to sell other products on the premises. **Availability:** Print; Online.

7751 ■ *"Liquor Stores Feeling Financial Impact Six Months after Grocery Stores Allowed to Sell Wine on Sundays"* in wsmv.com (June 26, 2019)
URL(s): www.wsmv.com/news/liquor-stores-feeling-financial-impact-six-months-after-grocery-stores/article_89c13f36-987f-11e9-bb72-8f7b70b01ee4.html
Ed: Cameron Taylor. **Released:** June 26, 2019. **Description:** Six months after a new Tennessee law went info effect allowing grocery stores to sell liquor on Sundays, local liquor stores noticed they are losing profits. Since it's easier to pick up alcohol while doing grocery shopping, there is no longer an incentive to visit the liquor store and make a purchase. **Availability:** Online.

7752 ■ *"Marketer Bets Big on U.S.'s Growing Canine Obsession"* in Advertising Age (Vol. 79, April 14, 2008, No. 15, pp. 14)
Pub: Crain Communications, Inc.
Contact: Jessica Botos, Manager, Marketing
E-mail: jessica.botos@crainsnewyork.com

Ed: Emily Bryson York. **Description:** Overview of FreshPet, a New Jersey company that began marketing two brands of refrigerated dog food-Deli Fresh and FreshPet Select-which are made from fresh ingredients such as beef, rice and carrots. The company projects continued success due to the amount of money consumers spend on their pets as well as fears derived from the 2007 recalls that inspired consumers to look for smaller, independent manufacturers that are less likely to source ingredients from China. **Availability:** Online.

7753 ■ *"Mary Kramer: Good Things Happen When We Buy Local" in Crain's Detroit Business (Vol. 24, October 6, 2008, No. 40, pp. 7)*
Pub: Crain Communications Inc.
Contact: Barry Asin, President
Description: Michigan is facing incredibly difficult economic times. One way in which each one of us can help the state and the businesses located here is by purchasing our goods and services from local vendors. The state Agriculture Department projected that if Michigan households earmarked $10 per week in their grocery purchases to made-in-Michigan products, this would generate $30 million a week in economic impact. **Availability:** Online.

7754 ■ *"Men and Menu: A Switch in the Kitchen" in Barron's (Vol. 88, March 24, 2008, No. 12, pp. 17)*
Pub: Dow Jones & Company Inc.
Contact: Almar Latour, Chief Executive Officer
Ed: Robin Goldwyn Blumenthal. **Description:** Men are doing more kitchen duties, with 18 percent of meals at home being made by men in 2007 compared to 11 percent four years previously. Young wives, however, choose to forgo work and stay at home. **Availability:** Online.

7755 ■ *"Modern Meal Offers Recipe Inspiration, Curation and Home Delivery" in Orlando Business Journal (Vol. 30, April 4, 2014, No. 41, pp. 3)*
Pub: American City Business Journals, Inc.
Contact: Mike Olivieri, Executive Vice President
Released: Weekly. **Price:** $8, introductory 4-week offer(Digital & Print). **Description:** Modern Meal LLC's CEO, Mark Hudgins, works to get people to the dinner table for a good meal. The social network with a Pinterest look is in early-beta-launch and users are trying out the features by curating recipes from popular cooking Websites and looking at recipes of other users. Modern' Meal's plan to tap into the e-grocery market is also discussed. **Availability:** Print; Online.

7756 ■ *National Frozen and Refrigerated Foods Association--Membership Directory*
Pub: National Frozen and Refrigerated Foods Association
Contact: Jeff Rumachik, President
E-mail: jeff@nfraweb.org
URL(s): nfraweb.org/membership/member-categories/manufacturers
Description: Covers 800 member companies worldwide, including distributors, manufacturers, sales agents, logistics providers, suppliers, retailers, and food service operators. **Entries include:** Company name, address, phone, names of executives, products or services, trade and brand names. **Arrangement:** Geographical within membership category; supplier members and manufacturer members listed in product classifications. **Indexes:** Company name. **Availability:** Online.

7757 ■ *"Need Fiber in Your Diet? Pour Some Milk" in Globe & Mail (April 10, 2007, pp. B7)*
Ed: William Illsey Atkinson. **Description:** The growing market and demand for functional foods and neutraceuticals in Canada is discussed. The research being conducted by University of Manitoba's Richardson Centre for Functional Foods and Nutraceuticals to explore new health compounds in food is highlighted. **Availability:** Online.

7758 ■ *"Neighbors Rally for Dollar Store" in Chattanooga Times/Free Press (August 4, 2010)*
Pub: Chattanooga Publishing Company Inc.
Description: Neighbors are rallying to keep the Family Dollar Store in their city open. The proposed new store would expand the grocery portion of its retail discount shop. **Availability:** Print; Online.

7759 ■ *"Nicholas Markets Joins Wakefern, Rebrands as The Fresh Grocer" in Grocery Dive (November 1, 2019)*
URL(s): www.grocerydive.com/news/nicholas-markets-joins-wakefern-rebrands-as-the-fresh-grocer/566434/
Ed: Lauren Stine. **Released:** November 01, 2019. **Description:** Wakefern Food Corp. now owns New Jersey-based Nicholas Markets and the four stores will now be rebranded under The Fresh Grocer name. **Availability:** Online.

7760 ■ *"No Trader Joe's for Mid-South" in Memphis Business Journal (Vol. 34, July 13, 2012, No. 13, pp. 1)*
Pub: Baltimore Business Journal
Contact: Rhonda Pringle, President
E-mail: rpringle@bizjournals.com
Ed: Andy Ashby. **Description:** Trader Joe's Company Inc. has been planning 20 new locations in the next 12 months that would be added to its more than 350 stores. However, the specialty grocery store chain has not included Memphis, Tennessee in its two-year plan. **Availability:** Print; Online.

7761 ■ *"Patience May Pay Off" in Barron's (Vol. 89, July 13, 2009, No. 28, pp. 30)*
Description: New CEO Craig Herkert can turn around Supervalu and their shares could double to $30 in three years from June 2009 according to one investment officer. Herkert knows how to run a lean and tight operation since he has worked for Albertsons and Wal-Mart in the past. **Availability:** Online.

7762 ■ *"Phillips Edison Launches $1.8B Retail REIT" in Business Courier (Vol. 27, October 15, 2010, No. 24, pp. 1)*
Pub: Business Courier
Ed: Dan Monk. **Description:** Retail center operator Phillips Edison & Company is organizing a real estate investment trust (REIT) to raise $1.8 billion to finance the planned purchase of 150 grocery-centered shopping centers around the U.S. The offering would be Phillips largest. Phillips Edison employs 174 workers and operates 250 shopping centers nationwide. **Availability:** Print; Online.

7763 ■ *"Private Label Is More Influential Than Ever in Determining Store Choice, Report Says" in Grocery Dive (November 8, 2019)*
URL(s): www.grocerydive.com/news/private-label-is-more-influential-than-ever-in-determining-store-choice-re/566939/
Ed: Krishna Thakker. **Released:** November 08, 2019. **Description:** Grocers are seeing more sales from their own private label lines recently, mostly because they are no longer just copying national brands but using those labels to create innovative products. This has been noticed by consumers who welcome the brands and develop a loyalty to them. **Availability:** Online.

7764 ■ *Progressive Grocer's Marketing Guidebook: The Comprehensive Source for Grocery, Drug and Mass Merchant Insights*
URL(s): retailbuyers.net/custom-retail-database-solutions/marketing-guidebook
Released: Annual; latest edition 2015. **Price:** $1,085, Individuals ADVANTAGE (Includes more than 10,500 personal e-Mail addresses); $685, Individuals (Personal e-Mail addresses not included). **Description:** Covers over 2,800 U.S. and Canadian supermarket chains, large independents and wholesalers; also includes 350 specialty distributors include smaller food wholesalers, food brokers, non-food distributors, and candy/tobacco/media distributors and over 24,800 key executives and buyers. **Entries include:** For retailers and wholesalers--Company name, address, phone, email and websites, number of stores operated or served, areas of operation, major grocery supplier, three-year financial summary, buying policies, private label information, lists of executives, buyers, and merchandisers. For specialty distributors--Name, address, phone, list of key personnel including buyers' categories, list of items handled, URL. **Arrangement:** Alphabetical by hierarchy, geographical by eight regions and 50 market areas. **Indexes:** Grocery related organizations, chain and wholesalers, state index, store operating name/parent company reference. **Availability:** CD-ROM; Print.

7765 ■ *"Publix Could Be Downtown's Tipping Point" in Birmingham Business Journal (Vol. 31, May 23, 2014, No. 21, pp. 6)*
Pub: American City Business Journals, Inc.
Contact: Mike Olivieri, Executive Vice President
Released: Weekly. **Price:** $4, introductory 4-week offer(Digital & Print). **Description:** Publix Super Markets is planning to open a grocery store and pharmacy in downtown Birmingham, Alabama. Customer demand is expected to increase due to the development of hundreds of apartments in the area. The project is also expected to boost the local real estate industry. **Availability:** Print; Online.

7766 ■ *"Putting 'Great' Back Into A&P" in Crain's New York Business (Vol. 24, January 6, 2008, No. 1, pp. 3)*
Pub: Crain Communications, Inc.
Contact: Jessica Botos, Manager, Marketing
E-mail: jessica.botos@crainsnewyork.com
Description: After five straight years ending in 2005, A&P Grocery lost revenue; due to a sweeping plan to freshen up its supermarkets the company returned to growth mode and was able to acquire longtime competitor Pathmark Stores.

7767 ■ *"Ralcorp Investigated for Rejecting ConAgra Bid" in Saint Louis Business Journal (Vol. 32, September 16, 2011, No. 3, pp. 1)*
Pub: Saint Louis Business Journal
Contact: Robert Bobroff, President
E-mail: rbobroff@bizjournals.com
Ed: Evan Binns. **Description:** New York-based Levi & Korsinsky started investigating Ralcorp Holidngs Inc. after it rejected ConAgra Foods Inc.'s third and latest takeover bid of $5.17 billion. The investigation would determine whether Ralcorp's directors had acted on behalf of shareholders' best interest. **Availability:** Print; Online.

7768 ■ *"Real Deals for Vacant Big Boxes" in Memphis Business Journal (Vol. 33, January 6, 2012, No. 39, pp. 1)*
Pub: Baltimore Business Journal
Contact: Rhonda Pringle, President
E-mail: rpringle@bizjournals.com
Ed: Andy Ashby. **Description:** VH Foods Inc. is planning to relocate to a retail facility at Cross Creek Shopping Center in Memphis, Tennessee. The company will expand its grocery food offerings at the new location. **Availability:** Print; Online.

7769 ■ *"Report: Grocery Stores Upcoming from Amazon" in Supermarket News (October 1, 2019)*
URL(s): www.supermarketnews.com/retail-financial/report-grocery-stores-upcoming-amazon
Ed: Russell Redman. **Released:** October 01, 2019. **Description:** Plans are in the works for Amazon to move beyond its Whole Foods Market to open a new chain of grocery stores. At the time, this is mostly speculation but the retail giant has been signing leases in several markets throughout the US. **Availability:** Online.

7770 ■ *"Retail Loyalty in the Digital Age is Focus of Retail Insights Southeast (RISE) Event" in GlobeNewswire (August 21, 2012)*
Pub: Comtex News Network Inc.
Contact: Kan Devnani, President
Description: The first annual Retail Insights Southeast (RISE) retail/shopper marketing event was held in Charlotte, North Carolina September 18, 2012. Representatives from retailers such as Family Dollar and Food Lion as well as brands like Coca-Cola, Clorox, Kraft Foods and Unilever were in attendance. **Availability:** Print; Online.

7771 ■ *"Roundy's Pushing Chicago Expansion"* in *Milwaukee Business Journal (Vol. 27, February 12, 2010, No. 20, pp. A1)*
Pub: The Business Journal
Contact: Heather Ladage, President
E-mail: hladage@bizjournals.com

Ed: Rich Kirchen. **Description:** Roundy Supermarkets Inc. is expanding in Chicago, Illinois as the Milwaukee-based company is set to open one store in downtown Chicago and another in the Arlington suburb. The store openings have been pushed back to spring and early summer in 2010 due to the economic downturn. **Availability:** Print; Online.

7772 ■ *"Save-A-Lot Adds Amazon PayCode and Hub Locker to St. Louis Stores"* in *Grocery Dive (November 5, 2019)*
URL(s): www.grocerydive.com/news/save-a-lot-adds-amazon-paycode-and-hub-locker-to-st-louis-stores/566608/

Ed: Lauren Stine. **Released:** November 05, 2019. **Description:** Save-A-Lot is adding Amazon PayCode to several stores in St. Louis, which allows for picking up and paying for Amazon packages with cash. Amazon Hub Locker will also be available. **Availability:** Online.

7773 ■ *"Silver Springs Creamery Opens Retail Store"* in *Bellingham Business Journal (Vol. March 2010, pp. 3)*
Pub: Sound Publishing Inc.
Contact: Josh O'Connor, President

Ed: Isaac Bonnell. **Description:** Eric Sundstrom, owner of Silver Springs Creamery, announced the opening of its on-site retail store that will sell the farm's goat and cow cheese, yogurt, ice cream and flesh milk.

7774 ■ *"Sprouts Farmers Market Reexamines Marketing Strategy to Increase Sales"* in *Supermarket News (November 5, 2021)*
URL(s): www.supermarketnews.com/retail-financial/sprouts-farmers-market-reexamines-marketing-strategy-increase-sales

Ed: Victoria A.F. Camron. **Released:** November 05, 2021. **Description:** Due to not communicating its pricing strategy, Sprouts Farmers Market failed to meet third quarter expectations. In order to improve sales, CEO Jack Sinclair said the company is now going to focus on delivering a clear message to their customers.

7775 ■ *"Still Stretching"* in *Business Courier (Vol. 24, December 28, 2008, No. 37, pp. 1)*

Description: Minority-owned businesses have experienced growth in 2007 as Cincinnati and Hamilton County used a workforce development and economic inclusion policy. Kroger Co., for example, has been inducted to the Billion Dollar Roundtable in 2007 for attaining $1 billion in annual spending with suppliers that are minority- owned. The need for more progress within the minority-owned enterprises is discussed. **Availability:** Online.

7776 ■ *"A Stock Worth Trading Down To"* in *Barron's (Vol. 88, July 14, 2008, No. 28, pp. 36)*
Pub: Dow Jones & Company Inc.
Contact: Almar Latour, Chief Executive Officer

Ed: Alexander Eule. **Description:** Shares of Ralcorp Holdings are cheap at around $49.95 after slipping 20 percent prior to their acquisition of Post cereals from Kraft. Some analysts believe its shares could climb over 60 percent to $80 as value-seeking consumers buy more private label products. **Availability:** Print; Online.

7777 ■ *"Substantial Deal Expected to Create Jobs, Help Industrial Market"* in *Tampa Bay Business Journal (Vol. 30, January 8, 2010, No. 3)*
Pub: Tampa Bay Business Journal
Contact: Ian Anderson, President
E-mail: ianderson@bizjournals.com

Ed: Janet Leiser. **Description:** Food distribution firm Gordon Food Service (GFS) is on the brink of purchasing Albertson's million-square-foot warehouse along with 158 acres of space. The deal between GFS and Albertson's could expand GFS' presence in west Central Florida. A history of GFS' growth is included. **Availability:** Print; Online.

7778 ■ *"Supermercado El Rancho Chain Grows Along with Hispanic Population"* in *Dallas Business Journal (Vol. 35, July 13, 2012, No. 44, pp. 1)*
Pub: Baltimore Business Journal
Contact: Rhonda Pringle, President
E-mail: rpringle@bizjournals.com

Ed: Matt Joyce. **Description:** Garland, Texas-based Supermercado El Rancho has grown rapidly wit its take on the Hispanic grocery market and is planning to open 12 stores in six years. La Bodega Meat Inc., the chain's affiliate distribution company, is planning a $13.1 million renovation and double the size of its warehouse to accommodate the plans for more stores.

7779 ■ *Top Grocery Trends of 2021*
URL(s): www.supermarketnews.com/consumer-trends/top-grocery-trends-2021?PK=UMblock
Released: September 08, 2021. **Description:** Downloadable PDF report contains sales trends, insights on consumer behavior changes, challenges and supply chain issues for retailers, plus more. **Availability:** PDF.

7780 ■ *"Trader Joe's Secret Sauce? An Army of Influencers"* in *Grocery Dive (November 8, 2019)*
URL(s): www.grocerydive.com/news/trader-joes-secret-sauce-an-army-of-influencers/566912/

Ed: Jennifer Sweeney. **Released:** November 08, 2019. **Description:** Influencer marketing is giving Trader Joe's a boost on Instagram thanks to several social media accounts from fans of the company. Featuring products and recipes, these digital influencers have inadvertently created a whole marketing campaign for the grocer. **Availability:** Online.

7781 ■ *"Trader Joe's Warehouse May Bring More Business to Daytona"* in *Orlando Business Journal (Vol. 30, March 14, 2014, No. 38, pp. 8)*
Pub: American City Business Journals, Inc.
Contact: Mike Olivieri, Executive Vice President

Released: March 14, 2014. **Price:** $8, introductory 4-week offer(Digital only). **Description:** Trader Joe's plan to open a retail warehouse grocery store in Daytona, Florida would benefit the city's economy. The firm is set to receive an incentive package from the Volusia County government. The new facility is expected to generate hundreds of jobs. **Availability:** Print; Online.

7782 ■ *"Transparency Tops Tate & Lyle's List of Trends"* in *Food Business News (November 18,2021)*
URL(s): www.foodbusinessnews.net/articles/20075-transparency-tops-tate-and-lyles-list-of-trends

Ed: Jeff Gelski. **Released:** November 18, 2021. **Description:** Six trends in the food and beverage industry are driving the needs of consumers. The top one, transparency, is based on customers wanting to know what the products they are eating and drinking are made of. **Availability:** Online.

7783 ■ *"USDA Invests $270 Million to Assist Meat, Poultry Producers"* in *Meat+Poultry (November 24, 2021)*
Ed: Erica Shaffer. **Released:** November 24, 2021. **Description:** Due to the COVID-19 pandemic, some contract producers of livestock and poultry experienced some revenue declines and the Consolidated Appropriations Act is giving some relief in the form of direct checks.

7784 ■ *"Village at Waugh Chapel $275M Expansion Begins"* in *Baltimore Business Journal (Vol. 28, August 27, 2010, No. 16, pp. 1)*
Pub: Baltimore Business Journal
Contact: Rhonda Pringle, President
E-mail: rpringle@bizjournals.com

Ed: Daniel J. Sernovitz. **Description:** Developer Greenberg Gibbons Corporation has broken ground on a $275 million, 1.2 million-square-foot addition to its Village at the Waugh Chapel mixed-use complex. Aside from creating 2,600 permanent jobs, the addition, named Village South, is expected to lure Target and Wegmans Food Markets to Crofton, Maryland. Funding for this project is discussed. **Availability:** Print.

7785 ■ *"Wakefern's ShopRite Tests Online Meal Planning Service"* in *Supermarket News (November 4, 2019)*
URL(s): www.supermarketnews.com/online-retail/wakefern-s-shoprite-tests-online-meal-planning-service

Ed: Russell Redman. **Released:** November 04, 2019. **Description:** Wakefern Food Corp. is partnering with Locai Solutions and piloting an online meal planning and recipe experience called CookIt. The technology uses artificial intelligence which recommends recipes based off of customers' online shopping baskets. **Availability:** Online.

7786 ■ *"'Wal-Mart Effect' Feeds Grocer Price Wars"* in *Globe & Mail (March 15, 2007, pp. B14)*

Ed: Marina Strauss. **Description:** The decrease in profit reports by Canadian grocery giants amidst high expansion plans by Wal-Mart Stores Inc. are discussed. This industry is witnessing the most severe pricing competitions in recent times. **Availability:** Print; Online.

7787 ■ *"Wegmans Adding 1,600-Plus Jobs Here Over the Next Year"* in *Boston Business Journal (Vol. 34, February 14, 2014, No. 2, pp. 3)*
Pub: American City Business Journals, Inc.
Contact: Mike Olivieri, Executive Vice President

Description: Wegmans, a family-owned grocery chain, is planning to add the most jobs of any firm in Massachusetts in 2014. The company will create more than 1,600 full- and part-time positions by opening three stores. Bill Congdon, Wegmans' New England division manager, reveals that the company is also planning to open a store in the city of Boston. **Availability:** Print; Online.

7788 ■ *"Wegmans Uses Database for Recall"* in *Supermarket News (Vol. 56, September 22, 2008, No. 38)*
Pub: Informa USA, Inc.
Contact: Stephen A. Carter, Chief Executive Officer

Ed: Carol Angrisani. **Description:** Wegmans used data obtained through its loyalty card that, in turn, sent automated telephone calls to every customer who had purchased tainted pet food when Mars Petcare recalled dog food products.

7789 ■ *"Whole Foods: A Big Boost for Midtown"* in *Sacramento Business Journal (Vol. 31, August 1, 2014, No. 23, pp. 3)*
Pub: American City Business Journals, Inc.
Contact: Mike Olivieri, Executive Vice President

Description: Whole Foods Market is opening a 40,000-square-foot grocery store anchoring a six-story mixed-us project at 2001 L Street in midtown Sacramento, California. The store is expected to draw shoppers from East Sacramento, Curtis Park, West Sacramento, and Natomas and raise property values around the area. **Availability:** Print; Online.

7790 ■ *Wholesale Grocer & Foodservice Distributor Leads*
Pub: Chain Store Guide
Contact: Kaitlyn Toner, Account Manager
URL(s): www.chainstoreguide.com/c-88-wholesale-grocer-foodservice-distributor-leads-plus.aspx

Description: Covers about 4,700 companies in the United States and Canada with at least $500,000 in sales to foodservice companies. Included companies must distribute more than one product line and obtain no more than 95% of its total sales volume from self-manufactured merchandise. **Entries include:** Company name, address, phone and fax numbers, e-mail and web addresses; Internet order processing indicator and sales percentage; total sales; foodservice and wholesale sales; product lines; total units served; foodservice accounts served; trading areas; distribution center locations; markets served; buying/marketing group name and location; subsidiaries names and locations; divisional, regional and branch office locations; year founded; public company indicator; key personnel with titles; 21,700 foodservice distribution contacts; 9,642 Name, address, phone, fax. **Arrangement:** Geographical. **Indexes:** Product lines, alphabetical, exclusions. **Availability:** Download; Online.

7791 ▪ "Your Merchandising and Promotions Exchange: Web Coupon Users Shop More" in Pet Product News (Vol. 66, September 2012, No. 9, pp. 101)

Description: A survey on behalf of Coupons.com shows that consumers who use digital coupons make 22 percent more supermarket trips annually than conventional shoppers and spend 23 percent more per trip. The findings suggest that digital coupon sites should be taken into consideration by brands intending to reach heavy grocery spenders. **Availability:** Online.

7792 ▪ Zero Waste Grocery Guide
URL(s): www.litterless.com/wheretoshop
Description: An online database of where to grocery shop for bulk food that doesn't come in packaging. These stores encourage shoppers to bring their own containers to maintain a zero waste lifestyle. **Availability:** Online.

STATISTICAL SOURCES

7793 ▪ Impact of Private Label in the Online Food and Drink Market - US - February 2019
URL(s): store.mintel.com/report/impact-of-private-label-in-the-online-food-and-drink-market-us-february-2019?_ga=2.169804129.1182593580.1637273274-1258978629.1637273274
Price: $4,366.35. **Description:** Downloadable report examining food and beverage shopping habits. Includes an executive summary, interactive databook, PowerPoint presentation, infographic overview, report PDF, and previous years data. **Availability:** PDF.

7794 ▪ Meat Markets Industry in the US - Market Research Report
URL(s): www.ibisworld.com/united-states/market-research-reports/meat-markets-industry/
Price: $925. **Description:** Downloadable report analyzing the current and future trends in the meat market industry. **Availability:** Online.

7795 ▪ RMA Annual Statement Studies
Pub: Risk Management Association
Contact: Nancy Foster, President
Released: Annual. **Description:** Contains composite balance sheets and income statements for more than 360 industries, including the accounting, auditing, and bookkeeping industries. Also contains five years of comparative historical data for discerning trends. Includes 16 commonly used ratios, computed for most of the size groupings for nearly every industry.

7796 ▪ Standard & Poor's Industry Surveys
Pub: Standard And Poor's Financial Services LLC.
Contact: Douglas L. Peterson, President
Description: Two-volume book that examines the prospects for specific industries, including trucking. Also provides analyses of trends and problems, statistical tables and charts, and comparative company analyses.

7797 ▪ US Grocery Retailing Industry Report 2021
URL(s): store.mintel.com/report/us-grocery-retailing-market-report
Price: $4,366.35. **Description:** Downloadable report discussing the current trends in how consumers shop at grocery stores, especially during and after the Covid-19 Pandemic. The rise of online grocery shopping was one of the biggest changes and challenges for grocers. Report includes an executive summary, interactive databook, PowerPoint presentation, infographic overview, report PDF, and previous years data. **Availability:** PDF.

7798 ▪ US The Natural/Organic Food Shopper Market Report 2020
URL(s): store.mintel.com/report/us-the-natural-and-organic-food-shopper-market-report
Price: $4,366.35. **Description:** Downloadable report discussing data on the natural and organic food industry and the effects of COVID-19. Report includes an executive summary, interactive databook, PowerPoint presentation, infographic overview, report PDF, and previous years data. **Availability:** PDF.

TRADE PERIODICALS

7799 ▪ The Food & Beverage International
Contact: Ellen Walsh, Editor
E-mail: ewalsh@fbworld.com
URL(s): www.fandbi.com
Ed: Ellen Walsh. **Description:** Trade magazine covering the food and beverage industry. **Availability:** Print.

7800 ▪ The Food Institute
Pub: Food Institute
Contact: Anika Wilson, Contact
E-mail: anika.wilson@foodinstitute.com
URL(s): foodinstitute.com/about
Released: Weekly **Description:** Reports on developments in the food industry, including new products, the food service industry, mergers and acquisitions, current legislation and regulations, judicial decisions, and financial and marketing information. **Availability:** Print.

7801 ▪ Food Trade News
Pub: Best-Met Publishing Company Inc.
Contact: Jeffrey W. Metzger, President
E-mail: jmetzger@best-met.com
URL(s): www.foodtradenews.com
Facebook: www.facebook.com/foodtradenews
X (Twitter): x.com/foodtradenews
Ed: Jeffrey Metzger. **Released:** Monthly **Price:** $138, Two years for print; $69, for print 1 year. **Description:** Newspaper for the retail supermarket industry. **Availability:** Print.

7802 ▪ Iowa Grocer
Pub: Iowa Grocery Industry Association
Contact: Michelle Hurd, President
E-mail: mhurd@iowagrocers.com
URL(s): www.iowagrocers.com/iowa-grocer-magazine.html
Released: Quarterly **Description:** Magazine for grocery industry - retail and supply. **Availability:** Online.

7803 ▪ The Packer: The Business Newspaper of the Produce Industry
Contact: Fred Wilkinson, Managing Editor
E-mail: fwilkinson@thepacker.com
URL(s): www.thepacker.com
Facebook: www.facebook.com/packernews
X (Twitter): twitter.com/thepacker
Released: Weekly **Price:** $99, per year price. **Description:** Newspaper on produce marketing. **Availability:** Print; Online.

7804 ▪ Progressive Grocer: The Industry's Source for News Analysis and Marketing Tactics
Pub: EnsembleIQ
Contact: Jennifer Litterick, Chief Executive Officer
URL(s): www.progressivegrocer.com
Facebook: www.facebook.com/progressivegrocer
Linkedin: www.linkedin.com/groups/1775564/profile
X (Twitter): twitter.com/pgrocer
Instagram: www.instagram.com/progressive_grocer
YouTube: www.youtube.com/channel/UCYgh6JPIuY5J0b4SE8C3rwA
Released: Monthly **Price:** $14, Single issue; $16, Single issue for foreign; $125, for per year; $230, for two year; $150, Canada and Mexico for per year; $270, Canada and Mexico for two year; $170, for foreign per year; $325, for foreign two year; $87, for digital per year; $161, for digital two year. **Description:** Magazine for chain and independent supermarkets and wholesale grocers. **Availability:** Print; Online.

7805 ▪ Shelby Report of the Southeast
Pub: Shelby Publishing Company Inc.
Contact: Stephanie Reid, President
E-mail: s.reid@shelbypublishing.com
URL(s): www.theshelbyreport.com
Facebook: www.facebook.com/theshelbyreport
Linkedin: www.linkedin.com/company/shelby-publishing
YouTube: www.youtube.com/channel/UCflOfdAjfQvnfl30YhujSfg
Released: Monthly **Price:** $95.35, for 2 Years print; $132.43, for 3 year print; $45, for digital 1 year; $81, for online two year subscription; $112.50, for online three year subscription; $56.97, for print + online 1 year; $102.55, for print + online 2 year; $142.43, for print + online 3 years; $52.97, for print 1 years. **Description:** Retail and wholesale food trade newspaper. **Availability:** Print; Online.

7806 ▪ Shelby Report of the Southwest
Pub: Shelby Publishing Company Inc.
Contact: Stephanie Reid, President
E-mail: s.reid@shelbypublishing.com
URL(s): www.theshelbyreport.com/category/southwest
Ed: Terrie Ellerbee, Lorrie Griffith. **Released:** Monthly **Price:** $52.97, for 1 year print; $95.35, for 2 year print; $132.43, for 3 year print; $45, for 1 year digital; $81, for 2 yr. digital; $112.50, for 3 yr. digital; $56.97, for print and digital, 1 year; $102.55, for print and digital, 2 year; $142.43, for print and digital, 3 year. **Description:** Retail and wholesale food trade newspaper. **Availability:** Print; Online.

TRADE SHOWS AND CONVENTIONS

7807 ▪ America's Supermarket Showcase
National Grocers Association (NGA)
601 Pennsylvania Ave. NW, Ste. 375N
Washington, DC 20004
Ph: (202)938-2570
Fax: (202)938-2574
Co. E-mail: communications@nationalgrocers.org
URL: http://www.nationalgrocers.org
Contact: Greg Ferrara, President
URL(s): www.thengashow.com
Frequency: Annual. **Description:** Food and non-food consumer goods and services. Fixtures, equipment and technology for supermarket operations. **Audience:** Independent retailers and wholesalers, food retail industry executives, food/CPG manufacturers, and service providers. **Principal Exhibits:** Food and non-food consumer goods and services. Fixtures, equipment and technology for supermarket operations.

7808 ▪ CheeseCon
Wisconsin Cheese Makers' Association (WCMA)
5117 W Ter. Dr., Ste. 402
Madison, WI 53718
Ph: (608)286-1001
Co. E-mail: jkeller@wischeesemakers.org
URL: http://www.wischeesemakersassn.org
Contact: Steve Bechel, President
URL(s): www.cheesecon.org/index.cfm
Frequency: Biennial. **Description:** Tabletop mini expo of cheese making machinery and related equipment, supplies, and services. **Audience:** Cheese industry professionals, and public. **Principal Exhibits:** Tabletop mini expo of cheese making machinery and related equipment, supplies, and services. Dates and Locations: 2025 Apr 15-17; 2027 Apr 20-22; 2029 Apr 10-12; 2031 Apr 08-10. Alliant Energy Center, Madison, WI. **Telecommunication Services:** events@wischeesemakers.org.

7809 ■ Fancy Food Show
Specialty Food Association Inc.
  136 Madison Ave., 12th Fl.
  New York, NY 10016-6788
Ph: (212)482-6440
Fax: (212)482-6459
URL: http://www.specialtyfood.com
Contact: Phil Kafarakis, President
URL(s): www.specialtyfood.com/fancy-food-shows
X (Twitter): twitter.com/Specialty_Food

Frequency: Semiannual. **Description:** Specialty foods and confectionery equipment, supplies, and services. **Audience:** Industry professionals. **Principal Exhibits:** Specialty foods and confectionery equipment, supplies, and services. Dates and Locations: 2025 Jan 19-21 Las Vegas Convention Center, Las Vegas, NV; 2025 Jun 29-Jul 01 Javits Center, New York City, NY. **Telecommunication Services:** membership@specialtyfood.com.

7810 ■ Food Northwest Process & Packaging Expo
Food Northwest (NWFPA)
  8338 NE Alderwood Rd., Ste. 160
  Portland, OR 97220
Ph: (503)327-2200
URL: http://www.foodnorthwest.org
Contact: Pam Barrow, Vice President
E-mail: pbarrow@foodnw.org
URL(s): web.cvent.com/event/fc3d7c2a-f7e6-4126-8 3f1-4481b8457646/websitePage:b5ff82bf-4966-47 df-9b1b-681d20f18c44?previewToken=323b2a4e 424bbb153f91b4518ddc3b62

Frequency: Annual. **Description:** Food processing industry equipment, supplies, and services. **Audience:** Industry professionals. **Principal Exhibits:** Food processing industry equipment, supplies, and services. Dates and Locations: Oregon Convention Center, Portland, OR. **Telecommunication Services:** kurt@foodnw.org.

7811 ■ Great Lakes Ice Cream and Fast Food Trade Show
URL(s): www.glicffa.com/convention-trade-show

Frequency: Annual. **Description:** Ice cream, frozen desserts, and fast food products for those who have purchasing power for their companies and markets. **Audience:** Qualified buyers for the frozen dessert and fast food industry. **Principal Exhibits:** Ice cream, frozen desserts, and fast food products for those who have purchasing power for their companies and markets.

7812 ■ Groceryshop
URL(s): groceryshop.com

Frequency: Annual. **Description:** Educational topics and workshops concerning the grocery store industry, including digital growth strategies, online grocery shopping, and new technologies. **Principal Exhibits:** Educational topics and workshops concerning the grocery store industry, including digital growth strategies, online grocery shopping, and new technologies.

7813 ■ Michigan Grocers Association Annual Convention and Trade Show
Michigan Grocers Association (MGA)
  603 S Washington Ave.
  Lansing, MI 48933
Ph: (517)372-5656
Free: 800-366-3699
Fax: (517)372-1303
Co. E-mail: mra@retailers.com
URL: http://www.retailers.com/about-us/mra-divisions
URL(s): www.retailers.com/about-us/mra-divisions

Frequency: Annual. **Description:** Opportunity to network with and learn from each other and to discover new products coming into the market. **Audience:** Chain and independent grocers, convenience store operators and food, beverage, and equipment manufacturers, brokers, wholesalers, distributors, and service providers. **Principal Exhibits:** Opportunity to network with and learn from each other and to discover new products coming into the market.

7814 ■ National Fiery Foods and Barbeque Show
URL(s): www.fieryfoodsshow.com

Facebook: www.facebook.com/FieryFoodsShow
X (Twitter): twitter.com/fieryfoodsshow
Instagram: www.instagram.com/fieryfoodsshow

Frequency: Annual. **Description:** Tradeshow featuring hot and spicy foods and condiments. Live demonstrations and networking. **Principal Exhibits:** Tradeshow featuring hot and spicy foods and condiments. Live demonstrations and networking.

7815 ■ NFRA Convention
American Frozen Food Institute (AFFI)
  1210 S Glebe Rd.
  Arlington, VA 22204-9998
Ph: (703)821-0770
Fax: (703)342-0343
Co. E-mail: info@affi.com
URL: http://AmericanFrozenFoodInstitut
Contact: Alison Bodor, President
E-mail: abodor@affi.com
URL(s): nfraconvention.org/sponsorships

Description: Products and services for frozen and refrigerated food manufacturing and retailing. Includes meetings, networking, and entertainment. **Audience:** Frozen food buyers, brokers, manufacturers, suppliers, distributors, warehouse personnel, retailers, sales agents, and logistics providers. **Principal Exhibits:** Products and services for frozen and refrigerated food manufacturing and retailing. Includes meetings, networking, and entertainment. **Telecommunication Services:** nfra@nfraweb.org.

7816 ■ Oklahoma Super Trade Show
URL(s): oklahomasupertradeshow.com

Frequency: Annual. **Description:** An in-depth tradeshow featuring products from grocers and wholesalers. **Principal Exhibits:** An in-depth tradeshow featuring products from grocers and wholesalers.

7817 ■ Refrigerated Foods Association Expo
URL(s): www.refrigeratedfoods.org/rfa-conference

Frequency: Annual. **Description:** Networking and seminars about current trends in chilled foods, safety, and packaging. **Principal Exhibits:** Networking and seminars about current trends in chilled foods, safety, and packaging.

7818 ■ Sweets & Snacks Expo
National Confectioners Association (NCA)
  1101 30th St. NW, Ste. 200
  Washington, DC 20007
Ph: (202)534-1440
Co. E-mail: info@candyusa.com
URL: http://candyusa.com
Contact: John H. Downs, President
E-mail: john.downs@candyusa.com
URL(s): sweetsandsnacks.com
Facebook: www.facebook.com/SWEETSan dSNACKS

Frequency: Annual. **Description:** Showcases new products in the sweets and snacks industry. **Audience:** Buyers, merchandisers, operations managers, executives and store owners from supermarkets, convenience stores, warehouse clubs, mass and dollar merchants, drug stores, vending, wholesalers, theaters, specialty and department stores, confectionery and snack professionals. **Principal Exhibits:** Showcases new products in the sweets and snacks industry. Dates and Locations: 2025 May 13-15 Indiana Convention Center, Indianapolis, IN; 2026 May 19-21 Las Vegas Convention Center, Las Vegas, NV; 2027 May 18-20 Indiana Convention Center, Indianapolis, IN; 2028 May 16-18 Indiana Convention Center, Indianapolis, IN; 2029 May 15-17 Las Vegas Convention Center, Las Vegas, NV; 2030 May 14-16 Indiana Convention Center, Indianapolis, IN; 2031 May 13-15 Indiana Convention Center, Indianapolis, IN; 2032 May 18-20 Las Vegas Convention Center, Las Vegas, NV. **Telecommunication Services:** attendeehelp@sweetsandsnacks.com.

7819 ■ TGCSA Convention & Expo
Tennessee Grocers and Convenience Store Association (TGCSA)
  414 Union St., Ste. 1900
  Nashville, TN 37219
Ph: (615)889-0136
URL: http://www.tngrocer.org

Contact: Rob Ikard, President
E-mail: rikard@tngrocer.org
URL(s): www.tgcsaexpo.com

Frequency: Annual. **Description:** Food products and equipment, supplies, and services. **Audience:** Food wholesalers, retail grocers, and retail industry personnels. **Principal Exhibits:** Food products and equipment, supplies, and services. Dates and Locations: 2025 Jun 02-04 Muscle Shoals, AL.

7820 ■ United Fresh Convention
Fresh Produce and Floral Council (FPFC)
  PO Box 3627
  Lake Arrowhead, CA 92352
Ph: (714)739-0177
Fax: (714)739-0226
Co. E-mail: info@fpfc.org
URL: http://www.fpfc.org
Contact: Don Gann, President
E-mail: don@fpfc.org
URL(s): www.fpfc.org/fpfc-2021-calendar-of-events

Frequency: Annual. **Description:** It's the place where leaders are ready to forge new connections, make purchases and see cutting-edge products and services for the fresh produce industry. **Audience:** General public. **Principal Exhibits:** It's the place where leaders are ready to forge new connections, make purchases and see cutting-edge products and services for the fresh produce industry.

7821 ■ Viva Fresh Expo
URL(s): vivafreshexpo.com

Frequency: Annual. **Description:** Provides networking and education for the produce industry. **Principal Exhibits:** Provides networking and education for the produce industry.

7822 ■ Western Association of Food Chains Annual Convention
URL(s): www.wafc.com/convention

Description: Provides education and networking for the food industry. **Principal Exhibits:** Provides education and networking for the food industry.

FRANCHISES AND BUSINESS OPPORTUNITIES

7823 ■ The Honey Baked Ham Company L.L.C. (HBH)
3875 Mansell Rd.
Alpharetta, GA 30022
Free: 800-367-7720
URL: http://www.honeybaked.com/home
Contact: Harry J. Hoenselaar, Founder
Facebook: www.facebook.com/HoneyBake dHamOfficial
X (Twitter): x.com/honeybakedham
Instagram: www.instagram.com/honeybaked_ham
YouTube: www.youtube.com/channel/UCCG-6tQN0T dL20TECiHyGWQ
Pinterest: www.pinterest.com/honeybaked_ham

Description: Producer and retailer of ham and turkey products. **Founded:** 1957. **Training:** Comprehensive 14 day program at corporate training store.

LIBRARIES

7824 ■ Food Institute (FI)
330 Changebridge Rd., Ste. 101
Pine Brook, NJ 07058
Ph: (201)791-5570
Free: 855-791-5570
Co. E-mail: questions@foodinstitute.com
URL: http://www.foodinstitute.com
Contact: Anika Wilson, Contact
E-mail: anika.wilson@foodinstitute.com
Facebook: www.facebook.com/foodinstitutenj
Linkedin: www.linkedin.com/company/the-food-insti tute
X (Twitter): x.com/FoodInstitute
Instagram: www.instagram.com/foodinstitute

YouTube: www.youtube.com/channel/UCYAPI0TXN tJa04aQre4h4pA

Description: Strives to provide food industry-related information to its members. **Scope:** The food industry. **Services:** Center open to the public on fee basis. **Founded:** 1928. **Holdings:** Figures not available. **Publications:** *Today in Food*; *Get It Out, Get It Right, Get It Over! Avoiding Food Product Recalls*; *The Food Institute* (Weekly); *Almanac of the Canning, Freezing, Preserving Industries* (Annual); *Food Business Mergers and Acquisitions*; *OSHA Inspection Manual*; *Regulatory Directory* (Periodic); *Food Business Mergers & Acquisitions*. **Geographic Preference:** Multinational.

RESEARCH CENTERS

7825 ■ St. Joseph's University - Erivan K. Haub School of Business - Academy of Food Marketing
5600 City Ave.
 Philadelphia, PA 19131
Ph: (610)660-1600
Co. E-mail: bursarsoffice@sju.edu
URL: http://www.sju.edu/haub-school-business/afm
Contact: Joseph J. Bivona, Executive Director

Description: Integral unit of Erivan K. Haub School of Business, Saint Joseph's University, but operating under its own board of control. **Scope:** Food marketing from farm gate to table, including analysis and evaluation of concepts, precepts, and practices of the food industry in America and elsewhere. Conducts special studies on problems of food marketing in urban low-income areas, in-home electronic shopping, household buying behavior, national and international food consumption, and nutrient intake. Also seeks to improve efficiency in retail and wholesale operations, evaluates procedures for development of new products, examines aspects of consumer research, analyzes the effectiveness of coupons and in-store promotions, and investigates bulk foods and warehouse productivity. **Founded:** 1962. **Educational Activities:** Academy of Food Marketing Industry seminars.

Gunsmith/Gun Shop

START-UP INFORMATION

7826 ■ *"No. 381: Metallica and Other Forms of Hardware"* in *Inc.* (Vol. 36, September 2014, No. 7, pp. 107)
Pub: Mansueto Ventures L.L.C.
Contact: Stephanie Mehta, Chief Executive Officer
Released: August 20, 2014. **Description:** Profile of Mikhail Orlov, who stayed in American instead of fighting a war he did not believe in while living in Chechnya, Russia. Orlov discovered his entrepreneurial spirit when he began importing Russian army surplus gear. He operates his startup online store selling guns, ammo, and hunting accessories. **Availability:** Print; Online.

ASSOCIATIONS AND OTHER ORGANIZATIONS

7827 ■ **American Custom Gunmakers Guild (ACGG)**
7810 County Rd.
Napoleon, OH 43545
Ph: (719)645-0335
Co. E-mail: admin@acgg.org
URL: http://www.acgg.org
Contact: Steve Durren, President
E-mail: president@acgg.org
Facebook: www.facebook.com/American-Custom-Gunmakers-Guild-165054520257083
Description: Seeks to preserve and promote the art of fine custom gun making. **Founded:** 1983. **Publications:** *Gunmaker* (Quarterly); *Directory of Regular Members* (Biennial); *Realizing Your Dream: A Client's Guide to Building a Custom Gun*; *Directory of Custom Gunmaking Services* (Semiannual). **Educational Activities:** ACGG Annual Exhibition (Annual). **Geographic Preference:** National.

7828 ■ **Gun Owners of America (GOA)**
8001 Forbes Pl., Ste. 102
Springfield, VA 22151
Ph: (703)321-8585
URL: http://www.gunowners.org
Contact: Sam Paredes, Executive Director
Facebook: www.facebook.com/GunOwners
X (Twitter): x.com/GunOwners
Instagram: www.instagram.com/gunownersofamerica
YouTube: www.youtube.com/user/GunOwnersofAmerica
Description: Works to educate the public about the Second Amendment. **Founded:** 1976. **Publications:** *GOA Newsletter*. **Geographic Preference:** National.

7829 ■ **Second Amendment Foundation (SAF) - Library**
12500 NE 10th Pl.
Bellevue, WA 98005
Ph: (425)454-7012
Co. E-mail: info@saf.org
URL: http://www.saf.org
Contact: Massad Ayoob, President
X (Twitter): x.com/2afdn

Instagram: www.instagram.com/secondamendmentfoundation
Description: Individuals dedicated to promoting a better understanding of "your constitutional right to privately own and possess firearms." Compiles statistics. **Scope:** Firearms rights. **Founded:** 1974. **Subscriptions:** 2 journals and other serials 200 books; 30 reports. **Publications:** *Women and Guns*; *The Gottlieb-Tartaro Report* (Monthly); *Gun Week Newspaper* (Periodic); *Publications Catalog*; *Second Amendment Reporter* (Quarterly); *TheGunMag.com* (Monthly). **Educational Activities:** Gun Rights Policy Conference (Annual). **Geographic Preference:** National.

7830 ■ **Sporting Arms and Ammunition Manufacturers' Institute (SAAMI)**
11 Mile Hill Rd.
Newtown, CT 06470
Ph: (203)426-4358
URL: http://saami.org
Contact: Joe Bartozzi, President
Description: Creates technical, performance, and safety standards for the firearms, ammunition, and propellants industry, promotes safety and responsibility when handling and using firearms, and shares knowledge regarding new technology, challenges, and trends in the field. **Founded:** 1926. **Geographic Preference:** National.

REFERENCE WORKS

7831 ■ *"Bankruptcies"* in *Crain's Detroit Business* (Vol. 24, March 24, 2008, No. 12, pp. 6)
Pub: Crain Communications Inc.
Contact: Barry Asin, President
Description: Current list of business that filed for Chapter 7 or 11 protection in U.S. Bankruptcy Court in Detroit include a construction company, a medical care company, a physical therapy firm and a communications firm. **Availability:** Online.

7832 ■ *"Beware the Amateur Gunsmith"* in *Ammoland* (January 30, 2019)
URL(s): www.ammoland.com/2019/01/beware-the-amateur-gunsmith/#axzz64jWC8GlT
Ed: David LaPell. **Released:** January 30, 2019. **Description:** Discusses what to look for when evaluating the work of a gunsmith to help determine if the firearm is safe or not. Also gives tips on looking for gunsmiths who are good at their job and who display the proper qualifications. **Availability:** Online.

7833 ■ *"Dick's Sporting Goods Distances Itself further from Firearms"* in *USA Today* (October 6, 2019)
URL(s): www.usatoday.com/story/money/2019/10/06/dicks-sporting-goods-distances-itself-further-from-firearms/40243337/
Ed: Rich Duprey. **Released:** October 06, 2019. **Description:** After implementing new policies to restrict access to firearms in its stores and lobbying for more gun control laws Dick's Sporting Goods is poised to exit the hunting and firearms market. It already agreed to sell several of its Field & Stream stores. **Availability:** Online.

7834 ■ *"EOTech Product Improves Holographic Gun Sights"* in *Crain's Detroit Business* (Vol. 24, February 4, 2008, No. 5, pp. 9)
Pub: Crain Communications Inc.
Contact: Barry Asin, President
Ed: Chad Halcom. **Description:** L-3 Communications EOTech Inc. procured new business contracts to fulfill military and law enforcement's demand for improved holographic sites used on handheld weapons. **Availability:** Online.

7835 ■ *"Fire Destroys Surplus Store, Sets Off Live Rounds Near Jacksonville NAS"* in *Florida Times-Union* (December 5, 2010)
Pub: Florida Times-Union
Ed: John Leacock. **Description:** Fire which caused numerous explosions at a military surplus store near Jacksonville Naval Air Station is under investigation. Heat and flames ignited lighter fluid and set off live rounds of ammunition sold in the store. **Availability:** Print; Online.

7836 ■ *Lethal Logic: Exploding the Myths that Paralyze American Gun Policy*
Pub: Potomac Books Inc.
Ed: Dennis A, Henigan. **Released:** June 01, 2009. **Price:** $34.95, hardcover. **Description:** Marketing tactics being used by gun manufacturers regarding possible new gun control laws are examined. **Availability:** E-book; Print; PDF.

7837 ■ *The World Directory of Custom Bullet Makers*
Pub: Corbin Manufacturing & Supply Inc.
Contact: Dave Corbin, Contact
E-mail: dave@corbins.com
URL(s): www.corbins.com/wd-1-e.htm
Description: Covers 300 manufacturers of custom projectiles for small arms (to 20 mm). **Entries include:** Company name, address, phone, telex, names and titles of key personnel, subsidiary and branch names and locations, description of products and services provided, including specific calibers of bullets produced. **Arrangement:** Alphabetical. **Indexes:** Product/service, geographical. **Availability:** CD-ROM; E-book; Print; PDF.

TRADE PERIODICALS

7838 ■ *Firearms News*
Pub: KSE Outdoor Sportsman Group LLC.
URL(s): www.firearmsnews.com
Facebook: www.facebook.com/FirearmsNewsMag
X (Twitter): x.com/firearmsnewsmag
Instagram: www.instagram.com/firearmsnews
Pinterest: www.pinterest.com/firearmsnewsmag

Released: 24/Year. **Price:** $15, for print 15 issues. **Description:** Gun sales magazine for collectors, dealers and hunters. **Availability:** Print; Online.

7839 ■ *Rifle: The Sporting Firearms Journal*
Pub: Wolfe Publishing Company
Contact: Jeremiah Polacek, Manager
E-mail: jeremiah@wolfepub.com
URL(s): www.riflemagazine.com
Facebook: www.facebook.com/RifleMag
Ed: Dave Scovill. **Released:** Bimonthly; january-february, march-April, may-June, July-august, september-october, november-december. **Price:** $23.97, for digital only 1 year; $22.99, for print only 1 year; $10, Single issue; $39, U.S. for 2 years; $29, for foreign one year; $51, for foreign 2 years. **Description:** Covers all types of rifles-centerfires, rimfires, air rifles and muzzle loaders. **Availability:** Print; Online.

LIBRARIES

7840 ■ Brady Campaign to Prevent Gun Violence [Brady]
840 1st St. NE Ste. 400
 Washington, DC 20002
Ph: (202)370-8100
Co. E-mail: brady@bradyunited.org
URL: http://www.bradyunited.org
Contact: Kris Brown, President
Facebook: www.facebook.com/bradycampaign
Linkedin: www.linkedin.com/company/brady-united
X (Twitter): x.com/bradybuzz
YouTube: www.youtube.com/user/BradyCampaign
Description: Serves as the education, legal advocacy, and research affiliate of Handgun Control, Inc. Sponsors prevention programs for parents and youth on the risks associated with guns; legal representation for gun violence victims; and outreach to the entertainment community to encourage deglamorization of guns in the media. **Scope:** Aims to create a safer America by cutting gun deaths in half by 2025. **Founded:** 1974. **Publications:** *Legal Action Report* (Quarterly); *Progress Report* (3/year). **Geographic Preference:** National.

7841 ■ Francis Marion University - James A. Rogers Library Special Collections
4822 E Palmetto St.
 Florence, SC 29506
Ph: (843)661-1300
URL: http://www.fmarion.edu/library
Contact: Suzanne Singleton, Librarian, Reference
E-mail: msingleton@fmarion.edu
Facebook: www.facebook.com/francismarionu
X (Twitter): x.com/FrancisMarionU
Instagram: www.instagram.com/francismarionu
YouTube: www.youtube.com/user/FrancisMarionU
Scope: Rogers history; educational material. **Services:** Interlibrary loan; copying; library open to the public with restrictions on borrowing. **Founded:** 1970. **Holdings:** 10,000 books; 30 manuscripts. **Subscriptions:** 978 journals and other serials; 28 newspapers.

7842 ■ NRA-ILA Library
11250 Waples Mill Rd.
 Fairfax, VA 22030
Free: 800-392-8683
URL: http://www.nraila.org
Scope: Firearms and hunting; criminal justice; natural resources; legislative issues. **Founded:** 1976. **Holdings:** Figures not available.

7843 ■ Ontario Ministry of Community Safety and Correctional Services - Centre of Forensic Sciences (CFS) - Library
25 Morton Shulman Ave.
 Toronto, ON, Canada M3M 0B1
Ph: (647)329-1320
Co. E-mail: cfs.feedback@ontario.ca
URL: http://cfs.mcscs.jus.gov.on.ca
Linkedin: www.linkedin.com/company/centre-of-forensic-sciences
Scope: Forensic science; toxicology; biology; chemistry; engineering; firearms; photography; questioned documents. **Services:** Interlibrary loan; copying (limited); library open to criminal justice and medical professionals by appointment. **Founded:** 1967. **Holdings:** Figures not available.

7844 ■ U.S. Bureau of Alcohol, Tobacco and Firearms - National Laboratory Center Library (NLC)
Ammendale, MD
URL: http://www.atf.gov/laboratories
Contact: Marvin G. Richardson, Deputy Director
Scope: Alcohol; analytical techniques; forensic sciences; firearms; tobacco; explosives. **Services:** Library not open to the public. **Holdings:** 5,700 books; 4,000 bound periodical volumes; 200 total journal titles; government documents; archives.

Hair Replacement/Electrolysis Clinic

ASSOCIATIONS AND OTHER ORGANIZATIONS

7845 ■ **American Electrology Association (AEA) [American Electrolysis Association]**
c/o Pearl G. Warner, President
4711 Midlothian Tpke. 13
Crestwood, IL 60418
Ph: (708)293-1400
Fax: (708)293-1405
Co. E-mail: presaea@electrology.com
URL: http://www.electrology.com
Contact: Pearl G. Warner, President
E-mail: presaea@electrology.com
Description: Electrologists united for education, professional advancement, and protection of public welfare. Promotes uniform legislative standards throughout the states. Coordinates efforts of affiliated associations in dealing with problems of national scope. Sponsors the International Board of Electrologist Certification and Council on Accreditation of Electrology Schools/Programs. **Founded:** 1958. **Publications:** *American Electrology Association--Roster*; *Journal of Electrology* (Semiannual). **Educational Activities:** American Electrology Association Annual Convention (Annual). **Geographic Preference:** National.

7846 ■ **American Hair Loss Council (AHLC)**
222 Everbright Ave.
Franklin, TN 37064
Ph: (615)721-8085
Co. E-mail: info@ahlc.org
URL: http://ahlc.org
Contact: Joseph Ellis, President
Facebook: www.facebook.com/TheAHLC
Linkedin: www.linkedin.com/company/the-american-hair-loss-council
Instagram: www.instagram.com/americanhairlosscouncil
Description: Provides nonbiased information regarding treatments for hair loss in both men and women. Facilitates communication and information exchange between professionals in different areas of specialization. Conducts educational programs; compiles statistics. **Founded:** 1985. **Publications:** *AHLC News* (Quarterly). **Geographic Preference:** National.

7847 ■ **Society for Clinical and Medical Hair Removal (SCMHR)**
2424 American Ln.
Madison, WI 53704-3102
Ph: (608)443-2470
Fax: (608)333-0310
Co. E-mail: homeoffice@scmhr.org
URL: http://www.scmhr.org
Contact: Elin Ayala, President
E-mail: elina@scmhr.org
Facebook: www.facebook.com/SCMHR
X (Twitter): x.com/scmhr
Description: Professional society of electrologists (persons engaged in the removal of superfluous hair by galvanic blend or short wave methods for cosmetic and medical purposes). Conducts continuing education and leadership development seminars. **Founded:** 1985. **Publications:** *SCME Directory of Membership* (Annual); *National Commission for Electrologist Certification--Directory of Certified Clinical Electrologists* (Annual). **Awards:** Dr. Bordier Award (Annual). **Geographic Preference:** Multinational.

REFERENCE WORKS

7848 ■ *"Laser Hair Removal vs. Electrolysis: Which Is Better?" in Healthline (May 17, 2017)*
URL(s): www.healthline.com/health/beauty-skin-care/laser-hair-removal-vs-electrolysis
Ed: Kristeen Cherney. **Released:** May 17, 2017.
Description: Discusses the differences, benefits, and risks of laser hair removal and electrolysis. **Availability:** Online.

7849 ■ *"What Are the Costs Involved with a Hair Transplant?" in Medical News Today (November 26, 2017)*
URL(s): www.medicalnewstoday.com/articles/320 153.php#what-is-the-cost-of-a-hair-transplant
Ed: Jayne Leonard. **Released:** November 26, 2017.
Description: Defines the medical hair transplant procedure along with examining all of the costs associated and if insurance will cover it. **Availability:** Online.

FRANCHISES AND BUSINESS OPPORTUNITIES

7850 ■ **Women's Health Boutique (WHB)**
605 N 6th St.
Longview, TX 75601
Ph: (903)758-9904
Free: 800-525-2420
Fax: (903)236-9786
Co. E-mail: info@whblongview.com
URL: http://www.mywhb.com
Contact: Vicki Jones, President
Facebook: www.facebook.com/womenshealthboutique
X (Twitter): x.com/WHBgirls
Pinterest: www.pinterest.com/whbladies
Description: Products and services related to pre and postnatal care, post-mastectomy, compression therapy, hair loss, incontinence, and skin care. **No. of Franchise Units:** 13. **Founded:** 1991. **Franchised:** 1994. **Equity Capital Needed:** $49,000 minimum start-up cash. **Training:** Yes.

Hair Salon/Barber Shop

ASSOCIATIONS AND OTHER ORGANIZATIONS

7851 ▪ Allied Beauty Association (ABA)
Cityside Postal Outlet
 Mississauga, ON, Canada L4Z 3L3
Ph: (905)568-0158
Free: 800-268-6644
Co. E-mail: communication@abacanada.com
URL: http://abacanada.com/about-aba
Contact: Dave Basi, Contact
Facebook: www.facebook.com/ABACanada
X (Twitter): x.com/abacanada
Instagram: www.instagram.com/user/ABACanada
YouTube: www.youtube.com/user/TheABACanada

Description: Promotes growth and development of members' businesses. Represents members' interests, conducts public relations campaigns and serves as a clearinghouse on the Canadian beauty industries. **Founded:** 1934. **Publications:** *Riben Nehrah Quarterly* (Quarterly). **Educational Activities:** Calgary Beauty Show; Allied Beauty Association British Columbia Beauty Convention; Saskatchewan Beauty Convention. **Geographic Preference:** National.

7852 ▪ American Association of Cosmetology Schools (AACS)
20 F St., NW, Ste. 700
 Washington, DC 20001
Ph: (202)963-5730
Co. E-mail: info@beautyschools.org
URL: http://myaacs.org
Contact: Cecil Kidd, Executive Director
E-mail: cecil@myaacs.org
Facebook: www.facebook.com/AmericanAssocia
 tionOfCosmetologySchools
Linkedin: www.linkedin.com/company/american
 -association-of-cosmetology-schools
X (Twitter): x.com/AACSchools
Instagram: www.instagram.com/aacschools

Description: Owners and teachers in cosmetology schools. **Founded:** 1924. **Publications:** *CEA Update* (Quarterly); *Salon City Star*; *Skin Inc.* (Monthly). **Educational Activities:** AACS Annual Convention & Expo (Annual). **Awards:** N.F. Cimaglia Educator of the Year (Annual). **Geographic Preference:** National.

7853 ▪ Intercoiffure America/Canada (ICA)
c/o Robin Doty
 5149 Wheelis Dr.
 Memphis, TN 38117
Ph: (901)484-7708
Co. E-mail: info@intercoiffure.com
URL: http://www.intercoiffure.com
Contact: Robin Doty, Contact
Facebook: www.facebook.com/in
 tercoiffureamericacanada
X (Twitter): x.com/intercoiffureac
Instagram: www.instagram.com/intercoiffureac

Description: Owners of beauty salons in the United States and Canada who meet the ethical standards set down by Intercoiffure. Seeks to make the women of America the best in hair fashion. **Founded:** 1915. **Geographic Preference:** Multinational.

7854 ▪ National Accrediting Commission of Career Arts and Sciences (NACCAS)
3015 Colvin St.
 Alexandria, VA 22314
Ph: (703)600-7600
Fax: (703)379-2200
Co. E-mail: filecomplaint@naccas.org
URL: http://naccas.org
Contact: Darin M. Wallace, Executive Director
E-mail: dwallace@naccas.org

Description: Accrediting body for schools of cosmetology; presently there are 1030 accredited schools. Objectives are to: raise standards of cosmetology schools throughout the country; encourage use of modern educational methods and techniques; stimulate self-improvement by the schools. Sponsors standards and professional team training workshops. **Founded:** 1981. **Publications:** *NACCAS Review* (3/year); *Directory of Accredited Cosmetology Schools* (Annual). **Geographic Preference:** National.

7855 ▪ National Association of Barber Boards of America (NABBA)
c/o 3336 Cypresswood Dr. S
 Jacksonville, FL 32257
Free: 888-338-0101
URL: http://www.nationalbarberboards.com
Contact: Paul Robinson, President

Description: Improves standards and procedures for examining barbers and regulates the barber industry. Furthers continuing education and development of curricula for educating barbers. Devises procedures for ensuring that consumers are informed and protected. Maintains library. **Founded:** 1926. **Educational Activities:** NABBA Annual Conference (Annual). **Geographic Preference:** National.

7856 ▪ National Beauty Culturists' League, Inc. (NBCL)
25 Logan Cir., NW
 Washington, DC 20005-3725
Ph: (202)332-2695
Fax: (202)332-0940
URL: http://www.nbcl.info
Contact: Dr. Katie B. Catalon, President

Description: Encourages standardized, scientific, and approved methods of hair, scalp, and skin treatments. Offers scholarships and plans to establish a research center. **Founded:** 1919. **Educational Activities:** National Beauty Culturists' League Annual Trade Show (Annual). **Geographic Preference:** National.

7857 ▪ National-Interstate Council of State Boards of Cosmetology (NIC)
7622 Briarwood Cir.
 Little Rock, AR 72205
Ph: (501)227-8262
URL: http://nictesting.org
Contact: Anwar Saleem, President

Description: Persons commissioned by 50 state governments as administrators of cosmetology laws and examiners of applicants for licenses to practice cosmetology. **Founded:** 1956. **Educational Activities:** National - Interstate Council of State Boards of Cosmetology Seminar. **Geographic Preference:** National.

7858 ▪ Professional Beauty Association (PBA)
7755 E Gray Rd.
 Scottsdale, AZ 85260-3459
Ph: (480)281-0424
Free: 800-468-2274
Co. E-mail: info@probeauty.org
URL: http://www.probeauty.org
Contact: Nina Daily, Executive Director
Facebook: www.facebook.com/professionalbeau
 tyassociation
Linkedin: www.linkedin.com/company/professional
 -beauty-association
X (Twitter): x.com/probeautyassoc
Instagram: www.instagram.com/probeautyassoc
YouTube: www.youtube.com/user/professionalbeauty

Description: Manufacturer of beauty and barber products, cosmetics, equipment, and supplies used in or resold by beauty salons or barbershops. **Founded:** 1985. **Publications:** *American Salon Magazine* (Quarterly); *PBA Progress*. **Educational Activities:** Professional Beauty Africa (Annual); National Beauty Show - HAIRWORLD (Annual); Cosmoprof North America (CPNA) (Annual); International Salon & Spa Expo (Annual). **Awards:** Sally Beauty Scholarships for High School Graduates (Annual). **Geographic Preference:** National.

REFERENCE WORKS

7859 ▪ "The 6 Secrets That Will Help Your Hair Salon and Day Spa Succeed" in Entrepreneur (September 30, 2014)
Ed: Eileen Figure Sandlin. **Released:** September 30, 2014. **Description:** Reveals six aspects of your business that can help make your salon or day spa profitable. **Availability:** Online.

7860 ▪ "10 Things to Do Before Opening a Salon" in Business News Daily (June 16, 2020)
Ed: Sammi Caramela. **Released:** June 16, 2020. **Description:** Details ten things to think about before opening a salon including costs, financing, and marketing plans. **Availability:** Online.

7861 ▪ "Barbering Is an Art" in The New York Times (May 4, 2018)
URL(s): www.nytimes.com/2018/05/04/nyregion/
 barbering-is-an-art.html
Ed: Corey Kilgannon. **Released:** May 04, 2018. **Description:** Profile of Arthur Rubinoff and his barbershop that also holds a museum. Vintage and

7862 ■ Hair Salon/Barber Shop

antique barber equipment are on display and customers can also get a haircut in antique chairs. **Availability:** Online.

7862 ■ *Barbershop Elevates Marketing to Support Expansion*
Description: Details the story of a barbershop, its changes through generations, and its current methods of operation which have led to major expansion. **Availability:** Online.

7863 ■ *"Barbershops Are Back and Bucking Retail Trends" in Forbes (July 6, 2017)*
URL(s): www.forbes.com/sites/bisnow/2017/07/06/barbershops-are-back-and-bucking-retail-trends/#1ae251c03fe9
Ed: Kyle Hagerty. **Released:** July 06, 2017. **Description:** From the early 1990s to about 2012, there was a decrease in barbershops across the nation. Starting in 2013 that trend reversed and now barbershops and shave shops are booming. In fact, barbering is one of the fastest-growing professions in the country and landlords are looking to fill vacant retail shops, making this a perfect combo for consumers. **Availability:** Online.

7864 ■ *Beauty Salon Industry Analysis*
Ed: Nancy Wagner. **Description:** Gives an overview of the beauty salon industry and projects where the industry is headed in the next few years. **Availability:** Online.

7865 ■ *"Check It Out! The Professional Beauty Association Launches New Website" in Modern Salong (November 11, 2019)*
URL(s): www.modernsalon.com/618285/check-it-out-the-professional-beauty-association-launches-new-website
Released: November 11, 2019. **Description:** The Professional Beauty Association launched a new website. The newly enhanced site includes sections on member resources, events and programming, advocacy, and also has expanded resources for inspiration. **Availability:** Online.

7866 ■ *"Factors to Consider When Opening a New Location for Your Salon" in Millennium Systems International (November 11, 2019)*
URL(s): www.millenniumsi.com/blog/open-a-new-location/
Ed: Jason Everett. **Released:** November 01, 2019. **Description:** Discusses the pros and cons of opening a new location for an already existing salon. **Availability:** Online.

7867 ■ *"Here Are the Right Ways to Dispose of Your Spa's Hazardous Waste" in American Spa (March 25, 2019)*
Ed: Maricha Ellis. **Released:** March 25, 2019. **Description:** Discusses the importance of hazardous waste disposal in salons and spas. what types of products are considered hazardous waste, and how to maintain compliance. **Availability:** Online.

7868 ■ *How to Make Money Running a Barbershop*
Ed: Alicia Bodine. **Description:** Modern barber shops offer many services in addition to cutting hair, they shave, trim facial hair, style hair, dye hair, among other things. This article details things that are important to think about as you open a barber shop including location, permits, equipment, licensing, advertising, and networking. **Availability:** Online.

7869 ■ *"How Much Money Do Beauty Salon Owners Make?" in Chron (March 8, 2019)*
Ed: K.A. Francis. **Released:** March 08, 2019. **Description:** How much a beauty salon owner makes will depend on the number of employees the salon has, the services provided, the salon's geographic location and the condition of the economy. This articles explains each of these areas and looks at future growth in the industry. **Availability:** Online.

7870 ■ *Is Owning a Hair Salon Profitable?*
Ed: John Hallberg. **Description:** Explains the concepts of salon revenue and profit and how you can influence those things as a small business owner. **Availability:** Online.

7871 ■ *"Mother and Daughter Create Tool to Unbraid 8 Braids at One Time" in Black Enterprise(February 25, 2023)*
URL(s): www.blackenterprise.com/mother-and-daughter-create-tool-to-unbraid-8-braids-at-one-time/
Released: February 25, 2023. **Description:** A mother and daughter duo launched a company to develop and create The Original Unbraider, which is being used in salons and sold at hair shows. **Availability:** Online.

7872 ■ *"The Pros and Cons of Starting a Barbershop or Salon from Scratch" in American Barber (October 14, 2018)*
Released: October 14, 2018. **Description:** Provides a detailed list of pros and cons to familiarize yourself with if you are starting a barbershop or salon from scratch. **Availability:** Online.

7873 ■ *"Quintessential Gentleman: Going Old-School on Calvert" in Baltimore Business Journal (Vol. 31, February 7, 2014, No. 41, pp. 6)*
Pub: American City Business Journals, Inc.
Contact: Mike Olivieri, Executive Vice President
Description: Quintessential Gentleman owner, Craig Martin shares his vintage idea in the expansion of his men's barbershop, spa, and tailor business in the Jewelers Building at South Calvert Street in downtown Baltimore, Maryland. Martin says his idea is to bring back tradition combined with modern amenities. He also shares his plan to model the business on a department store. **Availability:** Print; Online.

7874 ■ *"A Shave, a Haircut — and a Blood Pressure Check" in U.S. News & World Report (April 15, 2019)*
URL(s): www.usnews.com/news/healthiest-communities/articles/2019-04-15/battling-high-blood-pressure-at-the-barber
Ed: Joseph P. Williams. **Released:** April 15, 2019. **Description:** More than 50 barbershops in the Los Angeles County area are participating in a program that allows customers to check their blood pressure and to receive follow up training and care from an on-site pharmacist. The goal is to successfully treat men, especially African American men, who may not know they are suffering from this condition. So far, the results have been positive and more programs like it are being introduced around the country. **Availability:** Online.

7875 ■ *"Shear Savvy" in Puget Sound Business Journal (Vol. 35, July 25, 2014, No. 14, pp. 14)*
Pub: American City Business Journals, Inc.
Contact: Mike Olivieri, Executive Vice President
Description: Gene Juarez has returned to Gene Juarez Salons and Spas as a board advisor. Juarez sold the company he founded for an undisclosed sum to the Seattle, Washington-based Evergreen Pacific in 2006. The salon offers hair cuts and hair treatment for men and women and bridal parties, as well as makeup applications. Massage therapy is also offered. **Availability:** PDF; Online.

7876 ■ *"Top 5 Barber Business Trends in 2021" in UpMetrics (November 2, 2021)*
Released: November 02, 2021. **Description:** Barbering is making a comeback and the industry as a whole is growing, but shop owners still need to protect their barber startup from the ups and downs of the economy. Discussed are current trends that attract new customers and keep them coming back. **Availability:** Online.

7877 ■ *"What Are the Real Costs of Running a Barber Shop?" in Appointfix (February 17, 2020)*
Released: February 17, 2020. **Description:** Looks at the challenges faced by salon and barbershop owners as they work to manage overall business costs and set appropriate pricing strategies for the services you provide. **Availability:** Online.

7878 ■ *"Why Hair Salons and Day Spas Fail" in Entrepreneur (September 9, 2014)*
Ed: Eileen Figure Sandlin. **Released:** September 09, 2014. **Description:** Reveals problems that can sink even the most well-thought-out business ideas including outside market conditions, financing problems, tax-related issues, poor planning, and mismanagement. **Availability:** Online.

STATISTICAL SOURCES

7879 ■ *Barber Shops Industry in the US - Market Research Report*
URL(s): www.ibisworld.com/united-states/market-research-reports/barber-shops-industry/
Price: $925. **Description:** Downloadable report analyzing the current and future trends in the barber shop industry. **Availability:** Download.

7880 ■ *Hair & Nail Salons Industry in the US - Market Research Report*
URL(s): www.ibisworld.com/united-states/market-research-reports/hair-nail-salons-industry/
Price: $925. **Description:** Downloadable report analyzing current and future trends in the hair and nail salon industries. **Availability:** Download.

7881 ■ *RMA Annual Statement Studies*
Pub: Risk Management Association
Contact: Nancy Foster, President
Released: Annual. **Description:** Contains composite balance sheets and income statements for more than 360 industries, including the accounting, auditing, and bookkeeping industries. Also contains five years of comparative historical data for discerning trends. Includes 16 commonly used ratios, computed for most of the size groupings for nearly every industry.

TRADE PERIODICALS

7882 ■ *The Beauty Industry Report (BIR)*
Pub: The Beauty Industry Report
Contact: Jayne Morehouse, Chief Executive Officer
E-mail: jayne@bironline.com
URL(s): www.bironline.com/about-bir
Released: Monthly **Price:** $29.95, for email only one year. **Description:** Dedicated to the professional beauty salon and store industry. Recurring features include columns titled Guest Column. **Availability:** Print; Online.

VIDEO/AUDIO MEDIA

7883 ■ *Professional on the Go: Top Trends in the Esthetics Industry*
URL(s): www.spreaker.com/user/11226756/top-rends/esthetics-industry
Ed: Chinwe Onyeagoro. **Released:** June 30, 2019. **Description:** Podcast discusses trends that are impacting estheticians, skincare professionals, and other service providers in the spa/salon industry.

CONSULTANTS

7884 ■ *Art of Business*
345 Morgantown Rd.
 Reading, PA 19611
URL: http://www.raylon.com
Contact: Joe Hafetz, Founder
Description: Business management and personnel relations for salon professionals and manufacturers of professional beauty and barber salon products and consultation services for salon owners include compensation systems, staff retention, client retention, communications, promotion and public relations and serves professional beauty salon industry. **Scope:** Business management and personnel relations for salon professionals and manufacturers of professional beauty and barber salon products and consultation services for salon owners include compensation systems, staff retention, client retention, communications, promotion and public relations and serves professional beauty salon industry. **Founded:** 1953. **Training:** How to Triple Your

Income; The New Psy-Cosmetologist; The Receptionist; Managing Conversion: How to Convert Your Sales Force from Sales Reps to Sales Consultants.

FRANCHISES AND BUSINESS OPPORTUNITIES

7885 ■ Cartoon Cuts
927 N University Dr.
  Coral Springs, FL 33071
URL: http://cartooncuts.com
X (Twitter): x.com/cartooncuts
Instagram: www.instagram.com/cartooncuts
Description: Hair salons for children. **Founded:** 1991. **Training:** Yes.

7886 ■ Chatters Salon
271 Burnt Park Dr.
  Red Deer County, AB, Canada T4S 0K7
Ph: (403)356-2734
Free: 877-820-9365
Co. E-mail: customerservice@chatters.ca
URL: http://chatters.ca
Facebook: www.facebook.com/ChattersHairSalon
X (Twitter): x.com/ChattersHair
Instagram: www.instagram.com/chattershairsalon
YouTube: www.youtube.com/channel/UCRF3o
  5RcvXz0x0plSdCkAsQ
Pinterest: www.pinterest.ca/ChattersSalons
Description: Provider of salon services such as hair cuts, lashes, brows, waxing, perms, colors and other services for men, women and children. **Founded:** 1991.

7887 ■ City Looks
3900 Grant Ave., Ste. 11
  Winnipeg, MB, Canada R3R 3C2
Ph: (204)896-3177
Co. E-mail: info@citylooks.ca
URL: http://www.citylooks.ca
Contact: N. Nicole, Specialist
X (Twitter): x.com/CityLooks
YouTube: www.youtube.com/user/CityLooksTraining
Description: Provider of salon and spa services including wig, scalp services and more. **Founded:** 1996. **Training:** Provides training and ongoing support.

7888 ■ Cookie Cutters Haircuts for Kids
55 S Raceway Rd., Ste.700
  Indianapolis, IN 46231
Ph: (317)271-3855
Co. E-mail: sheltonlr@haircutsarefun.com
URL: http://www.haircutsarefun.com
Facebook: www.facebook.com/CookieCuttersHaircutsForKidsAvon
Description: Firm provides interactive hair care for children. **Franchised:** 1995. **Equity Capital Needed:** $90,500 - $261,000. **Franchise Fee:** $35,000 ; second location for an additional $20,000 ; three or more locations for an additional $10,000 each. **Royalty Fee:** 5% of Gross Sales. **Training:** Yes.

7889 ■ Cost Cutters Family Hair Care
3003 Nicollet Ave. S
  Minneapolis, MN 55408
URL: http://www.costcutters.com/home
Facebook: www.facebook.com/CostCutters
X (Twitter): twitter.com/costcutters
Instagram: www.instagram.com/costcutters
YouTube: www.youtube.com/channel/UCoY37bh
  -cfchivHad0bCdYg
Description: Provides salon service such as haircuts, styling and color services. **No. of Operating Units:** 740. **Founded:** 1986. **Equity Capital Needed:** $150,000 liquid assets ; $500,000 net worth. **Financial Assistance:** Yes **Training:** 1 week onsite training with ongoing support.

7890 ■ Fantastic Sams International Corporation (FSIC) [Fantastic Sams Cut & Color; Fantastic Sams Hair Salons]
45 Enon St.
  Beverly, MA 01915
Ph: (978)921-1888
Co. E-mail: marketing@fantasticsams.com
URL: http://www.fantasticsams.com
Contact: Kathie Lee, President
Facebook: www.facebook.com/fantasticsamscutandcolor
X (Twitter): x.com/FSHairSalons
Pinterest: www.pinterest.com/fantasticsams
Description: Full service family hair salons. **Founded:** 1974. **Franchised:** 1976. **Training:** Yes.

7891 ■ First Choice Haircutters, Ltd. (FCH)
Regis Corporation
  6085 Creditview Rd., Unit 21
  Mississauga, ON, Canada L5V 2A8
Ph: (952)947-7777
Co. E-mail: InvestorRelations@regiscorp.com
URL: http://www.regiscorp.com
Facebook: www.facebook.com/FirstChoice
Instagram: www.instagram.com/firstchoicehair
Description: Operator of haircut saloons. **No. of Operating Units:** 400. **Founded:** 1980. **Franchised:** 1982. **Equity Capital Needed:** $150,000 liquid assets ; $500,000 net worth for single or multiple units. **Training:** Provides 1 week managerial and technical training, 1 week onsite training with support in all areas including real estate, grand opening, staffing, marketing and ongoing support.

7892 ■ Great Clips Inc.
4400 W 78th Str., Ste. 700
  Minneapolis, MN 55435
Free: 800-999-5959
Co. E-mail: customerservice@greatclips.com
URL: http://www.greatclips.com
Contact: Rob Goggins, President
Facebook: www.facebook.com/GreatClips
X (Twitter): x.com/greatclips
Instagram: www.instagram.com/greatclips
YouTube: www.youtube.com/user/greatclips
Pinterest: www.pinterest.com/greatclips
Description: High-volume, quality hair salons that specialize in cuts and perms for the entire family. Unique and attractive decor and quality advertising. Emphasis on strong, hands-on support to franchisee's. Definite opportunity for growth in a fast-growing industry. directors. **Founded:** 1982. **Training:** Training begins with New Franchisee Orientation & Training. This 5 day session covers all aspects of the Great Clips operating systems. All style and employee training is provided through our field staff and our area training centers.

7893 ■ Lemon Tree Family Hair Salon
55 Eagle Rock Ave.
  East Hanover, NJ 07936
URL: http://lemontree.com
Contact: Jonathan Shaw, President
Linkedin: www.linkedin.com/company/lemon-tree-salon
Description: Offers franchises for unisex hair care services. **No. of Franchise Units:** 45. **Founded:** 1972. **Franchised:** 1976. **Equity Capital Needed:** $55,100-$87,700. **Franchise Fee:** $9,000. **Training:** Includes 1 week of training at corporate headquarters and a company representative spends 1 week at salon grand opening.

7894 ■ Magicuts, Ltd.
Regis Corporation
  777 Bay St., Unit M216
  Toronto, ON, Canada M5G 2C8
Ph: (952)947-7777
Co. E-mail: InvestorRelations@regiscorp.com
URL: http://www.regiscorp.com
Facebook: www.facebook.com/MagicutsSalons
Description: Provider of salon services including haircut, shampoo, style dry, perms, specialty perms, color services and highlights. **Training:** Full training and support.

7895 ■ Regal Nails, Salon and Spa L.L.C.
5150 Florida Blvd.
  Baton Rouge, LA 70806
Free: 888-414-6245
Co. E-mail: comments@regalnails.com
URL: http://regalnails.com
Contact: David Nguyen, Manager
Facebook: www.facebook.com/RegalNailsLLC
Linkedin: www.linkedin.com/company/regal-nails
  -salon-&-spa-llc
X (Twitter): x.com/regalnailsllc
Instagram: www.instagram.com/regalnailsllc
YouTube: www.youtube.com/channel/
  UC9F9BTEZfUQ1b6gRat7qqNQ
Pinterest: www.pinterest.com/regalnailsllc
Description: Operator of salon. **Founded:** 1997.

7896 ■ Roosters MGC International LLC [Roosters Men's Grooming Center]
Regis Corporation
  37619 W Twelve Mile Rd.
  Farmington Hills, MI 48331
Ph: (952)947-7777
Co. E-mail: InvestorRelations@regiscorp.com
URL: http://www.regiscorp.com
Description: Operator of men beauty salons. **No. of Operating Units:** 76. **Founded:** 1999. **Franchised:** 1999. **Equity Capital Needed:** $150,000 - $500,000. **Financial Assistance:** No **Training:** Yes.

7897 ■ Sport Clips Haircuts
110 Sports Clips Way
  Georgetown, TX 78628
Ph: (512)869-1201
Free: 800-872-4247
Co. E-mail: goodtobeaguy@sportclips.com
URL: http://www.sportclips.com
Contact: Gordon Logan, Chief Executive Officer
Facebook: www.facebook.com/SportClipsHaircuts
X (Twitter): x.com/SportClips
Instagram: www.instagram.com/sportclipshaircuts
YouTube: www.youtube.com/user/SportClipsOfficial/videos
Description: Men's hair care centers with sports theme. **Founded:** 1993. **Financial Assistance:** No **Training:** Initial and ongoing technical and management training by Sport Clips area Coaches.

7898 ■ Supercuts
Facebook: www.facebook.com/Supercuts
X (Twitter): twitter.com/supercuts
Description: The franchise offers affordable hair care. **No. of Franchise Units:** 15. **No. of Company-Owned Units:** 37. **Founded:** 1975. **Franchised:** 1978. **Equity Capital Needed:** $100,000 liquid assets; $300,000 net worth. **Franchise Fee:** $22,500 first salon; $12,500 each additional. **Training:** Initial and ongoing support.

7899 ■ Supercuts Inc.
Regis Corporation
  3701 Wayzata Blvd., Ste. 600
  Minneapolis, MN 55416
Ph: (952)947-7777
Co. E-mail: InvestorRelations@regiscorp.com
URL: http://www.regiscorp.com
Contact: Matthew Doctor, Chief Executive Officer
Facebook: www.facebook.com/Supercuts
X (Twitter): x.com/supercuts
Instagram: www.instagram.com/supercuts
YouTube: www.youtube.com/user/SupercutsUS
Description: Franchisee offering haircutting services for men, women, and children. **Financial Assistance:** Yes **Training:** Provides 1 week managerial and technical training, 1 week on-site training. Support in all areas including real estate, grand opening, staffing, marketing and ongoing support.

LIBRARIES

7900 ■ Aesthetics International Association (AIA) - Library
1910 Pacific Ave., Ste. 8030
Dallas, TX 75201
Free: 800-961-3777
Co. E-mail: info@dermascope.com
URL: http://www.dermascope.com/aia
Contact: Amanda Strunk Miller, Editor-in-Chief
E-mail: amanda@dermascope.com
Facebook: www.facebook.com/dermascope
Pinterest: www.pinterest.com/dermascope
Description: Aestheticians (persons licensed to manage or own a skin care salon) and students of certified schools; associate members are manufacturers and distributors representing the cosmetic industry. Seeks to improve the education and upgrade the standards of aestheticians, cosmetologists, and related persons in the industry. Promotes public awareness of research results and information relating to the professions of aesthetics and cosmetology. Educates the public and the aesthetic and cosmetology professions through seminars and lectures. **Scope:** Skin care. **Founded:** 1972. **Holdings:** Figures not available. **Publications:** *DERMASCOPE Magazine* (Monthly); *Dermascope* (Monthly). **Geographic Preference:** National.

Handwriting Analysis Consultant

ASSOCIATIONS AND OTHER ORGANIZATIONS

7901 ■ American Association of Handwriting Analysts (AAHA)
c/o Jane O'Brien, Treasurer
4143 Lorna Ct. SE
Lacey, WA 98503
Co. E-mail: aahahandwriting@gmail.com
URL: http://www.aahahandwriting.org
Contact: Cindy G. Cheaves, President
E-mail: aahahandwriting@gmail.com
Description: Persons who have completed courses in handwriting analysis, passed examinations by a committee of the Association, and displayed proficiency in the science; individuals who have passed an exam on the guiding principles of graphology. Serves as a forum for the exchange of information on graphology and research in the field. Seeks public recognition of handwriting analysis as an important aid in the solution of problems involving personality and identification of signatures or writing. Promotes research in handwriting analysis. **Founded:** 1962. **Awards:** AAHA Honorary Membership (Annual). **Geographic Preference:** National.

7902 ■ American Handwriting Analysis Foundation (AHAF) - Library
6 Orchard Loop N
Tonasket, WA 98855
Ph: (509)592-1388
Co. E-mail: ahaf@ahafhandwriting.org
URL: http://ahafhandwriting.org
Contact: Lauren Mooney Bear, President
E-mail: mooneybear19@gmail.com
Facebook: www.facebook.com/people/American-Handwriting-Analysis-Foundation/100062411005390
Instagram: www.instagram.com/ahaf_news
Description: Individuals interested in handwriting analysis. Seeks to advance graphology (the art and science of determining qualities of the personality from the script) as a helping profession; provide certification program for members; establish a code of ethics; foster research in handwriting analysis and cooperation among all handwriting analysts and handwriting societies. **Scope:** Handwriting analysis. **Services:** Interlibrary loan; open to the public with appointment. **Founded:** 1967. **Holdings:** Books; monographs. **Publications:** *AHAF Journal* (Quarterly); *Guide to Self-Published Papers*; *International Bibliography of Graphological Journal Articles 1968-1988*; *Manual for Graphological Researchers*. **Awards:** Flandrin/Michon Life Achievement Award. **Geographic Preference:** Multinational.

7903 ■ Association of Forensic Document Examiners (AFDE) - Library
c/o Lynda D. Hartwick., 34 Bluff Ridge Dr., Ste. 1c
Lake Ozark, MO 65049
Ph: (573)964-5159
Co. E-mail: info@afde.org
URL: http://afde.org
Contact: Lynda D. Hartwick, President
E-mail: docsndispt@aol.com
Description: Represents forensic document examiners and students of document examination. Sponsors annual continuing education conferences and offers a certification program. **Scope:** Forensic science. **Founded:** 1986. **Holdings:** Figures not available. **Publications:** *Journal of Forensic Document Examination* (Annual). **Geographic Preference:** Multinational.

7904 ■ International Graphoanalysis Society (IGAS) - Library
842 5th Ave.
New Kensington, PA 15068
Ph: (724)472-9701
Fax: (267)501-1931
URL: http://www.igas.com
Description: Represents handwriting analysts and identification experts. Maintains hall of fame and speakers' bureau. Compiles statistics; conducts research programs, specialized education, and placement service. **Scope:** Handwriting analysis. **Founded:** 1929. **Holdings:** Figures not available. **Publications:** *Journal of Graphoanalysis*. **Geographic Preference:** National.

REFERENCE WORKS

7905 ■ *Handwriting Analysis Plain & Simple: The Only Book You'll Ever Need*
Released: February 01, 2019. **Price:** $11.26, Paperback; $10.49, E-book. **Description:** Explains graphology, or handwriting analysis, and how it can be used to complete a personality profile. A brief history of the art is included. **Availability:** E-book; Print.

7906 ■ *Handwriting Psychology: Personality Reflected in Handwriting*
Ed: Dr. Helmut Ploog. **Released:** January 14, 2013. **Price:** $14.54, Paperback; $21.40, Hardcover; $3.99, E-book. **Description:** Teaches how to analyze handwriting to help reveal insights about a person. **Availability:** E-book; Print.

7907 ■ *"The Latest: Handwriting Expert to Examine Franklin Will' in U.S. News & World Report (August 6, 2019)*
URL(s): www.usnews.com/news/best-states/michigan/articles/2019-08-06/the-latest-handwriting-expert-to-examine-franklin-will
Released: August 06, 2019. **Description:** After Aretha Franklin's death, several additional wills were discovered in her couch cushions, leading a Michigan judge to grant permission for a handwriting expert to examine them. **Availability:** Online.

CONSULTANTS

7908 ■ All Handwriting Services, LLC
728 Pk. Shadows Cir.
Bountiful, UT 84010
Contact: Linda L. Cropp, Contact
Description: Firm provides forgery authentication, graffiti identification, depositions and much more. **Scope:** Firm provides forgery authentication, graffiti identification, depositions and much more. **Training:** Basics of Handwriting Analysis; Know Yourself and Others Through Handwriting Analysis; The Troubled Teen; Introduction to Handwriting Analysis; Pre-employment Screening and Handwriting Analysis; How to Hire a Document Examiner: Credentials, Expertise, Certifications, Fees; When to Hire document Examiner; Detect Violence in the Workplace Through Handwriting Analysis; The Dishonest/Abusive Personality.

LIBRARIES

7909 ■ American Association of Handwriting Analysts (AAHA)
c/o Jane O'Brien, Treasurer
4143 Lorna Ct. SE
Lacey, WA 98503
Co. E-mail: aahahandwriting@gmail.com
URL: http://www.aahahandwriting.org
Contact: Cindy G. Cheaves, President
E-mail: aahahandwriting@gmail.com
Description: Persons who have completed courses in handwriting analysis, passed examinations by a committee of the Association, and displayed proficiency in the science; individuals who have passed an exam on the guiding principles of graphology. Serves as a forum for the exchange of information on graphology and research in the field. Seeks public recognition of handwriting analysis as an important aid in the solution of problems involving personality and identification of signatures or writing. Promotes research in handwriting analysis. **Founded:** 1962. **Awards:** AAHA Honorary Membership (Annual). **Geographic Preference:** National.

Hardware Store

ASSOCIATIONS AND OTHER ORGANIZATIONS

7910 ■ Builders Hardware Manufacturers Association (BHMA)
355 Lexington Ave., 15th Fl.
New York, NY 10017
Ph: (212)297-2122
Fax: (212)370-9047
Co. E-mail: bhma@kellencompany.com
URL: http://buildershardware.com
Contact: Mark Bloom, President
Linkedin: www.linkedin.com/company/builders-hardware-manufacturers-association
Description: Manufacturers of builders' hardware, both contract and stock. Provides statistical services; maintains standardization program; sponsors certification programs for locks, latches, door closers, and cabinet hardware. Maintains 12 product sections. **Founded:** 1925. **Geographic Preference:** National.

7911 ■ Canadian Institute of Plumbing and Heating (CIPH)
295 The W Mall, ste.504
Toronto, ON, Canada M9C 4Z4
Ph: (416)695-0447
Free: 800-639-2474
Co. E-mail: info@ciph.com
URL: http://www.ciph.com
Contact: Ralph Suppa, President
E-mail: r.suppa@ciph.com
Facebook: www.facebook.com/CIPHnews
Linkedin: www.linkedin.com/company/ciph
X (Twitter): x.com/ciphnews
Instagram: www.instagram.com/ciphnews
YouTube: www.youtube.com/channel/UCx8_LwmTSuOmOr0Iyp7sLGQ
Description: Seeks to improve plumbing and heating practice and technology in Canada. Promotes advancement of members' businesses. **Founded:** 1933. **Publications:** *Canadian Institute of Plumbing and Heating Pipeline.* **Educational Activities:** University of Innovative Distribution (Annual); CIPHEX West (Biennial); CMPX: Canadian Mechanical & Plumbing Exposition (CMPX) (Biennial); MCEE: Mecanex/Climatex/Expolectriq/Eclairage (MECANEX) (Biennial). **Geographic Preference:** National.

7912 ■ LBMAO Reporter
120 Traders Blvd E, Unit 112
Mississauga, ON, Canada L4Z 2H7
Ph: (905)625-1084
Free: 888-365-2626
Fax: (905)625-3006
URL: http://www.lbmao.on.ca
Contact: Rebecca Gravelle, Chairman
URL(s): www.lbmao.on.ca/publications/reporter-magazine
Released: Bimonthly **Description:** Contains timely and informative articles of particular interest to lumber and building materials and hardware retailers. **Availability:** Online.

7913 ■ The Lumber and Building Materials Association of Ontario, Inc (LBMAO)
120 Traders Blvd E, Unit 112
Mississauga, ON, Canada L4Z 2H7
Ph: (905)625-1084
Free: 888-365-2626
Fax: (905)625-3006
URL: http://www.lbmao.on.ca
Contact: Rebecca Gravelle, Chairman
Facebook: www.facebook.com/LBMAO
X (Twitter): x.com/LBMAO
Description: Seeks to advance the lumber and building supplies industries. Facilitates communication and cooperation among members; represents members' interests before labor and industrial organizations, government agencies, and the public. **Founded:** 1917. **Publications:** *LBMAO Reporter* (Bimonthly); *The LBMAO Reporter* (Bimonthly); *Directory of Ontario Lumber and Building Materials, Hardware and Home Improvement Retailers* (Annual). **Educational Activities:** Fall/Winter Buying Show (Annual). **Geographic Preference:** National.

7914 ■ National Lumber and Building Material Dealers Association (NLBMDA)
2001 K St. NW, 3rd Fl., N
Washington, DC 20006
Ph: (202)367-1169
Co. E-mail: info@dealer.org
URL: http://www.dealer.org
Contact: Jonathan M. Paine, President
E-mail: jonathon@dealer.org
Facebook: www.facebook.com/nlbmda
Linkedin: www.linkedin.com/company/national-lumber-&-building-material-dealers-association-nlbmda-
X (Twitter): x.com/NLBMDA
Description: Represents more than 8,000 lumber and building material companies with over 400,000 employees, 20 state and regional associations and the industry's leading manufacturers and service providers. **Founded:** 1917. **Publications:** *Building Material Dealer; Cost of Doing Business (CODB)* (Annual); *Forklift and You; NLBMDA Advocate* (Monthly); *Nuts & Bolts; ProSales* (Monthly); *Risk Management Best Practices; Your National Perspective* (Quarterly). **Educational Activities:** ProDealer Industry Summit (Annual); Annual Spring Meeting & Legislative Conference (Annual). **Awards:** NLBMDA Grassroots Dealer of the Year (Annual). **Geographic Preference:** National.

7915 ■ North American Retail Hardware Association (NRHA)
1025 E 54th St.
Indianapolis, IN 46220
Free: 800-772-4424
Co. E-mail: nrha@nrha.org
URL: http://yournhpa.org/media
Contact: Scott Wright, Executive Director
E-mail: swright@nrha.org
Facebook: www.facebook.com/NorthAmericanHardwareandPaintAssociation
Linkedin: www.linkedin.com/company/north-american-hardware-and-paint-association
X (Twitter): x.com/Your_NHPA
Instagram: www.instagram.com/your_nhpa
YouTube: www.youtube.com/user/nrhatv
Description: Represents independent family-owned hardware/home improvement retailers. Sponsors correspondence courses in hardware and building materials retailing; conducts annual cost-of-doing-business study. **Publications:** *Buyer's Book; North American Hardware Association Cost of Doing Business Study* (Annual); *Hardware Retailing: Serving Hardware, Home Center, Building Material Retailers* (Monthly). **Awards:** Young Retailer of the Year Award (Annual). **Geographic Preference:** National.

REFERENCE WORKS

7916 ■ "Ace Retailers Provide Meaningful Yard Makeovers" in Hardware Retailing (November 6, 2019)
URL(s): www.hardwareretailing.com/ace-retailers-provide-meaningful-yard-makeovers/
Ed: Kate Klein. **Released:** November 06, 2019. **Description:** Several locally-owned Ace Hardware Stores in Florida partnered up with nonprofit organizations to help families in need with yard makeovers. This community project was the result of a challenge from a TV station and the owners of the Ace Hardware Stores did their best to respond and provide great-looking finished projects. **Availability:** Online.

7917 ■ "CEOs Keep Bringing Home the Perks" in Baltimore Business Journal (Vol. 30, May 18, 2012, No. 2, pp. 1)
Pub: American City Business Journals, Inc.
Contact: Mike Olivieri, Executive Vice President
Ed: Gary Haber. **Description:** According to the annual proxy statement of Baltimore-based Stanley Black & Decker, executive chairman Nolan D. Archibald received a $12.3 million compensation package in 2011. According to the company, Archibald's perks are part of his employment agreement which was duly approved by the shareholders during the merger of Stanley Works and Black & Decker. **Availability:** Print; Online.

7918 ■ "Code Name: Inventors: Go from Golden Idea to Agent of Invention" in Black Enterprise (Vol. 41, November 2010, No. 4, pp. 78)
Pub: Earl G. Graves Ltd.
Contact: Earl Graves, Jr., President
Ed: Renita Burns. **Description:** Profile of Andre Woolery, inventor of a magnetic wristband that holds small nails, screws, drill bits, and small tools, allowing handymen to keep essential tools at hand while working. **Availability:** Online.

7919 ■ "Do It Best Celebrates New Products, Expands Paint Options at 2019 Fall Market" in Hardware Retailing (October 21, 2019)
URL(s): www.hardwareretailing.com/do-it-best-celebrates-new-products-expands-paint-options-at-2019-fall-market/

Ed: Melanie Moul. **Released:** October 21, 2019. **Description:** The Do It Best Fall Market featured many new vendors and The Launch Zone, which debuted last year, highlights new and innovative products. This year, a new relationship with Benjamin Moore and it's PPG Glidden paint line were also a big hit, since paint is one of the top-selling items in hardware stores. **Availability:** Online.

7920 ■ *"Home Depot Co-Founder Ken Langone Talks About Business" in Atlanta Business Chronicle (April 11, 2014)*
Pub: American City Business Journals, Inc.
Contact: Mike Olivieri, Executive Vice President
Description: Ken Langone spoke on April 7, 2014 at Fairfield University in Connecticut. He is one of the co-founders of Home Depot home improvement chain. He provided the funds to start the chain in 1978 after Arthur Blank and Bernie Marcus were let go from their jobs at Handy Dan. **Availability:** Print; Online.

7921 ■ *"Inside True Value's $150M Supply Chain Investment" in Hardware Retailing (November 11, 2019)*
URL(s): www.hardwareretailing.com/inside-true-values-150m-supply-chain-investment/
Ed: Todd Taber. **Released:** November 11, 2019. **Description:** True Value opened up its newest regional distribution center, which is set to help modernize its supply chain for independent retailers. **Availability:** Online.

7922 ■ *"Knife Sharpening Tools – Your List for Starting a Business" in Small Business Trends(March 2, 2023)*
URL(s): smallbiztrends.com/2023/03/knife-sharpening-tools.html
Ed: Rob Starr. **Released:** March 02, 2023. **Description:** Discusses operating a knife sharpening businesses as a side-hustle or as a small business. **Availability:** Online.

7923 ■ *"Most Popular Tools? The Survey Says" in Contractor (Vol. 57, February 2010, No. 2, pp. 1)*
Ed: Robert P. Mader. **Description:** According to a survey of individuals in the field, mechanical contractors are purchasing more of their tools at home centers and they are also increasingly working in the service, repair, and retrofit markets. The survey also found that the reciprocating saw is the most used corded power tool. Additional purchasing habits of mechanical contractors are listed. **Availability:** Print; Online.

7924 ■ *"'Top Guns' Take Aim at Industry Issues" in HBS Dealer (November 8, 2021)*
Ed: Ken Clark. **Released:** November 08, 2021. **Description:** Supply chain issues are hitting local hardware stores, so several of the 'Top Gun' award-winning heads of hardware retailers discuss what they believe is causing the problems and what to do about them.

7925 ■ *"True Value Ranks No. 1 in National Customer Service Poll" in Hardware Retailing (November 1, 2019)*
URL(s): www.hardwareretailing.com/true-value-ranks-no-1-in-national-customer-service-poll/
Ed: Todd Taber. **Released:** November 01, 2019. **Description:** Topping Newsweek's 2020 list of America's Best Customer Service Brands in the "Home Improvement Stores" category is True Value. Their commitment to customer care has led to a trustworthy brand that customers come back to over and over again. **Availability:** Online.

STATISTICAL SOURCES

7926 ■ *Hardware Stores Industry in the US - Market Research Report*
URL(s): www.ibisworld.com/united-states/market-research-reports/hardware-stores-industry/
Price: $925. **Description:** Downloadable report analyzing current and future trends in the hardware store industry. **Availability:** Online.

7927 ■ *RMA Annual Statement Studies*
Pub: Risk Management Association
Contact: Nancy Foster, President
Released: Annual. **Description:** Contains composite balance sheets and income statements for more than 360 industries, including the accounting, auditing, and bookkeeping industries. Also contains five years of comparative historical data for discerning trends. Includes 16 commonly used ratios, computed for most of the size groupings for nearly every industry.

7928 ■ *Standard & Poor's Industry Surveys*
Pub: Standard And Poor's Financial Services LLC.
Contact: Douglas L. Peterson, President
Description: Two-volume book that examines the prospects for specific industries, including trucking. Also provides analyses of trends and problems, statistical tables and charts, and comparative company analyses.

TRADE SHOWS AND CONVENTIONS

7929 ■ **Door and Hardware Institute Annual Convention and Exposition**
URL(s): www.dhiconextions.org
Frequency: Annual. **Description:** Doors, hardware, and specialty building products. **Audience:** Industry distributors, sales representatives, manufacturers, engineers and facility administrators. **Principal Exhibits:** Doors, hardware, and specialty building products.

7930 ■ **Northwestern Building Products Expo**
Northwestern Lumber Association (NLA)
701 Decatur Ave. N, Ste. 105
Golden Valley, MN 55427
Ph: (763)544-6822
Free: 888-544-6822
Fax: (763)595-4060
Co. E-mail: info@nlassn.org
URL: http://www.nlassn.org
Contact: Cody Nuernberg, President
E-mail: cnuernberg@nlassn.org
URL(s): www.nlassn.org/page/Expos
Frequency: Annual. **Description:** Any product or service that is ultimately sold or used by retail lumber and building material dealers. **Audience:** Industry professionals. **Principal Exhibits:** Any product or service that is ultimately sold or used by retail lumber and building material dealers.

FRANCHISES AND BUSINESS OPPORTUNITIES

7931 ■ **Matco Tools Corp.**
Fortive Corporation
4403 Allen Rd.
Stow, OH 44224
Ph: (425)446-5000
Co. E-mail: investors@fortive.com
URL: http://www.fortive.com
Contact: Timothy J. Gilmore, President
Facebook: www.facebook.com/matcotools
X (Twitter): x.com/matcotools
Instagram: www.instagram.com/matcotools
YouTube: www.youtube.com/matcotoolsvideos
Pinterest: www.pinterest.com/matcotools
Description: Matco Tools is a provider of precision mechanics hand tools, service equipment, and diagnostic computers that are distributed through franchised mobile tool distributors. From well-stocked Matco Tools trucks, Matco Distributors provide weekly service to customers at their place of employment. **Founded:** 1946. **Franchise Fee:** None. **Financial Assistance:** Yes **Training:** Yes.

7932 ■ **Snap-on Incorporated**
Snap-on Incorporated
2801 80th St.
Kenosha, WI 53141
Ph: (262)656-5200
Free: 877-762-7664
Co. E-mail: questions@snapon.com
URL: http://www.snapon.com
Contact: Nicholas T. Pinchuk, President
Facebook: www.facebook.com/snapontools
Linkedin: www.linkedin.com/company/snap-on-tools
X (Twitter): twitter.com/snapon_tools
Instagram: www.instagram.com/snapon_official/
YouTube: www.youtube.com/user/snaponscanner
Description: Manufacturer and marketer of tools, equipment, diagnostics, repair information, and systems solutions for professional users such as mechanics, the firm specializes in hand and power tools, and tool storage products. **Founded:** 1920.

7933 ■ **Woodcraft Franchise L.L.C.**
1177 Rosemar Rd.
Parkersburg, WV 26102-0245
Ph: (304)422-5412
Free: 855-WCD-REAM
Fax: (304)422-5417
Co. E-mail: woodcraftfranchise@woodcraft.com
URL: http://www.woodcraft.com
X (Twitter): x.com/woodcraft
YouTube: www.youtube.com/woodcraftmarketing
Pinterest: www.pinterest.com/woodcraftsupply
Description: Retailer of woodworking tools and equipment. **No. of Franchise Units:** 66.0. **No. of Company-Owned Units:** 6. **No. of Operating Units:** 72.0. **Founded:** 1928. **Franchised:** 1997. **Equity Capital Needed:** Required Worth $750,000 ; Liquid Assets $200,000. **Franchise Fee:** $50,000. **Royalty Fee:** 5% of gross revenues. **Financial Assistance:** No **Training:** Yes.

Hat Store

REFERENCE WORKS

7934 ■ *"Bethesda Firm Aims to Revitalize Hat Chain Lids" in Washington Business Journal (March 15, 2019)*
URL(s): www.bizjournals.com/washington/news/2019/03/15/bethesda-firm-aims-to-revitalize-hat-chain-lids.html
Ed: Katishi Maake. **Released:** March 15, 2019. **Description:** Ames Watson LLC acquired Lids Sports Group and is looking to have the chain sell more than just hats. This is due in part to consolidating Lids with Fanzz, a sports apparel retailer, which will offer customers a larger selection of items to choose from. **Availability:** Online.

7935 ■ *"Oldest Hat Retailer in the United States Contemplates Future in Changing Detroit" in Crain's Detroit (June 25, 2017)*
URL(s): www.crainsdetroit.com/article/20170625/news/632431/oldest-hat-retailer-united-states-contemplates-future-changing-detroit
Ed: Aaron Mondry. **Released:** June 25, 2017. **Description:** Profile of Henry the Hatter, the iconic hat store located in Downtown Detroit. With raising rents in the area, it's possible the store may have to move soon to another cheaper location. **Availability:** Online.

LIBRARIES

7936 ■ **Fashion Institute of Design and Merchandising (FIDM) - Library**
919 S Grand Ave.
  Los Angeles, CA 90015
Ph: (213)624-1200
Free: 800-624-1200
URL: http://fidm.edu
Contact: Tonian Hohberg, President
Facebook: www.facebook.com/FIDMCollege
Linkedin: www.linkedin.com/school/fidm
X (Twitter): x.com/FIDM
YouTube: www.youtube.com/fidm
Pinterest: www.pinterest.com/fidm
Scope: Textile design and research; fashion; business and marketing; interior design; retailing and costumes. **Services:** Copying; interlibrary loan. **Founded:** 1969. **Subscriptions:** 200 magazines Books; periodicals; publications; newspapers; DVDs; CDs.

7937 ■ **Fashion Institute of Design & Merchandising (FIDM) - Orange County Library**
17590 Gillette Ave.
  Irvine, CA 92614
URL: http://fidm.edu/en/majors/merchandise+marketing/experience/bios/molly+stolen
Scope: Textile design; textile design; marketing; interior design; retailing; costumes. **Services:** Copying; library open to the public by appointment. **Founded:** 1980. **Holdings:** 3,000 books; 130 bound periodical volumes; 40 pamphlet headings; 475 videotapes; 135 slide sets; 300 retail catalogs; 100 annual reports; 50 CD-ROMs. **Subscriptions:** 80 journals and other serials; 8 newspapers.

7938 ■ **State University of New York - Fashion Institute of Technology - Gladys Marcus Library**
227 W 27th St.
  New York, NY 10001-5992
Ph: (212)217-7999
URL: http://www.fitnyc.edu/library/index.php

Description: Library supports the academic and research needs of the institute. **Scope:** Fashion, fashion history, textiles, fashion trend forecasting. **Services:** Interlibrary loan; library open by appointment. **Founded:** 1944. **Holdings:** 300,000 print, non-print, and electronic materials, including sketch collections, clipping files, and fashion show DVDs.

Hazardous Waste Disposal Business

ASSOCIATIONS AND OTHER ORGANIZATIONS

7939 ■ Council on Safe Transportation of Hazardous Articles, Inc. (COSTHA)
101 Ridge St., Ste. I
Glens Falls, NY 12801
Ph: (518)761-0389
Fax: (518)792-7781
URL: http://www.costha.com
Contact: Anne Barry, Director, Communications Director, Marketing
E-mail: anne@costha.com
Linkedin: www.linkedin.com/company/the-council-on-safe-transportation-of-hazardous-articles-costha

Description: Participates in international harmonization efforts. Promotes regulatory compliance and safety in the hazardous materials transportation industry. Promotes the growth and development of its members as Hazardous Materials Professionals. **Founded:** 1972. **Publications:** *COSTHA Quarterly* (Bimonthly). **Geographic Preference:** National.

7940 ■ Dangerous Goods Advisory Council (DGAC) [Hazardous Materials Advisory Council]
7501 Greenway Center Dr., Ste. 760
Greenbelt, MD 20770
Ph: (202)289-4550
Co. E-mail: info@dgac.org
URL: http://dgac.org
Contact: Vaughn Arthur, President
Facebook: www.facebook.com/people/Dangerous-Goods-Advisory-Council/100064661052955
X (Twitter): x.com/dgac_hmac

Description: Works to promote safe transportation of these materials; provides assistance in answering regulatory questions, guidance to appropriate governmental resources, and advice in establishing corporate compliance and safety programs. Conducts seminars on domestic and international hazardous materials packaging and transporting. **Founded:** 1978. **Publications:** *Hazardous Materials Advisory Council--Directory* (Annual). **Awards:** George L. Wilson Memorial Award (Annual). **Geographic Preference:** National.

7941 ■ National Waste and Recycling Association (NWRA)
1550 Crystal Dr., Ste. 804
Arlington, VA 22202
Ph: (202)244-4700
Free: 800-424-2869
Fax: (202)966-4824
Co. E-mail: membership@wasterecycling.org
URL: http://wasterecycling.org
Contact: Darrell Smith, President
E-mail: dsmith@wasterecycling.org
Facebook: www.facebook.com/wasterecycling
Linkedin: www.linkedin.com/company/nwra
X (Twitter): x.com/wasterecycling
Instagram: www.instagram.com/_wasterecycling

YouTube: www.youtube.com/channel/UCsfdUSRuvAbQWQYfdDG0VCQ

Description: Manufacturers, designers, and distributors of waste collection, treatment, and storage equipment; waste handling consultants. Promotes effective processing of solid and hazardous wastes and more extensive use of recycling. Represents members' interests; conducts research and educational programs; maintains hall of fame; compiles statistics. **Founded:** 1962. **Publications:** *Waste Age--Waste Industry Yellow Pages* (Annual); *Legal Bulletin* (Quarterly); *Manual of Recommended Safety Practices*; *Waste Industry Marketplace* (Annual); *Waste Age--Refuse Truck Body Buyer's Guide Issue* (Annual); *National Solid Wastes Management Association: Member Companies*; *Waste Industry News* (Monthly; Quarterly); *Directory of Chemical Waste Transporters* (Biennial); *Listing of Rated Stationary Compactors* (3/year); *Products and Services Directory* (Annual); *WASTEC E-News* (8/year); *WASTEC's Equipment Technology News* (Quarterly); *IWED Guide to Waste Equipment Distributors*; *National Contract Sweepers' Institute--Directory*; *Waste Age--Resource Recovery Activities Update Issue*; *Waste Age--Waste Industry Buyer Guide* (Annual); *Chemical Waste Transportation Institute Directory*; *Recycling Times: The Newspaper For Recycling and Waste Professionals* (Biweekly); *Waste Industry Buyers Guide* (Annual); *Directory of Hazardous Waste Management Service Firms* (Irregular). **Educational Activities:** Waste Expo (Annual); Waste Equipment Technology Association Roundtable. **Awards:** NWRA Distinguished Service Award (Annual); NWRA Hall of Fame Award (Annual); NWRA Chapter Leadership Award (Annual). **Geographic Preference:** Multinational; National.

REFERENCE WORKS

7942 ■ *4 Ways Small Businesses Benefit from Responsible Waste Management*
Description: Provides four advantages that small businesses can gain from practicing responsible waste management. **Availability:** Online.

7943 ■ *"5 Reasons Why E-Waste Management Is a Must for Small Businesses - And What You Can Do About It"* in Credibly Blog
Description: E-waste is becoming one of the largest sources of waste in the world. This includes gadgets, devices, appliances, and equipment. This article discusses five big reasons why e-waste management should be a priority for your small business. **Availability:** Online.

7944 ■ *"6 Tips for Growing a Waste Management Business"* in Fundbox Blog (April 27, 2017)
Ed: Rieva Lesonsky. **Released:** April 27, 2017. **Description:** Discusses the variety of opportunities in the waste management industry as well as how to grow a waste management business. **Availability:** Online.

7945 ■ *"22 Top Recycling Tips for the Workplace That You Can Implement Today"* in Recycle Coach (October 9, 2020)
URL(s): recyclecoach.com/blog/22-top-recycling-tips-for-the-workplace-that-you-can-implement-today-rcaw/
Released: October 09, 2020. **Description:** As more companies turn to green policies, more ways to recycle are becoming available. Listed are 22 ways to incorporate recycling and how to get employees on board in participating.

7946 ■ *"Altera Ranks Among Top 25 Greenest Companies in U.S."* in Ecology, Environment & Conservation Business (August 9, 2014, pp. 2)
Pub: NewsRX LLC.
Contact: Kalani Rosell, Contact

Description: Altera Corporation was ranked 24 on the Newsweek Magazine 2014 Green Rankings of over 500 companies in the United States. These rankings are one of the world's most recognized assessments of corporate sustainability and environmental impact. Eight specific indicators were used, including conservation and sustainability efforts in the areas of energy, carbon, water, and waste productivity. **Availability:** Online.

7947 ■ *"Arkansas Receives EPA Grant to Tackle Hazardous Waste"* in Waste Today (November 6, 2019)
URL(s): www.wastetodaymagazine.com/article/arkansas-receives-epa-grant-tackle-hazardous-waste/
Ed: Theresa Cottom. **Released:** November 06, 2019. **Description:** The Arkansas Department of Environmental Quality was awarded over $380,000 to support programs that manage and reduce hazardous waste. This includes controlling the generation, transportation, treatment, storage, and disposal of waste, minimizing its production, and protecting public health. **Availability:** Online.

7948 ■ *"DEM Says River Needs Cleanup"* in Providence Business News (Vol. 28, January 6, 2014, No. 40, pp. 1)
Pub: American City Business Journals, Inc.
Contact: Mike Olivieri, Executive Vice President

Released: January 04, 2014. **Description:** Rhode Island's Department of Environmental Management (DEM) called a meeting to gather information for its Ten Mile River water-quality-restoration plan. DEM announced the failure of the Ten Mile River and its impoundments to meet state water quality standards. The government grant received by Attleboro for the cleanup efforts is examined. **Availability:** Print; Online.

7949 ■ *"EPA Announces Funding for Gulf of Mexico Waterway Cleanup"* in Waste Today (September 24, 2019)
URL(s): www.wastetodaymagazine.com/article/epa-funding-gulf-mexico-waterway-cleanup/

Ed: Theresa Cotton. **Released:** September 24, 2019. **Description:** The EPA's Gulf of Mexico Division is providing grant funding for innovative projects that will help reduce the amount of trash in the water. This allows recipients to incorporate prevention, removal, and outreach that will protect local beaches and the water. **Availability:** Online.

7950 ■ *"EPA Removes New York Scrap Dealer from Superfund List" in Waste Today (October 30, 2019)*
URL(s): www.wastetodaymagazine.com/article/ ellenville-scrap-iron-and-metal-cleanup/
Ed: Kelly Maile. **Released:** October 30, 2019. **Description:** Ellenville Scrap Iron and Metal was on the EPA's list of hazardous sites in need of cleanup, and after extensive work was completed on the property, the once contaminated land is now a safe and productive site. **Availability:** Online.

7951 ■ *"EPA Removes Strasburg Landfill from National Priorities List" in Waste Today (September 6, 2019)*
URL(s): www.wastetodaymagazine.com/article/epa -removes-strasburg-landfill-superfund-site-national -priorities-list/
Ed: Theresa Cottom. **Released:** September 06, 2019. **Description:** The Strasburg Landfill Superfund Site in Pennsylvania was removed from the EPA's National Priorities List after nearly 30 years of cleanup. Moving forward, the site will only need to be monitored as all cleanup goals have now been met. **Availability:** Online.

7952 ■ *"Hazardous Waste Management - Types, Regulations, & How Different Businesses Can Handle It" in OH&S (August 31, 2020)*
Ed: Amanda Wilson. **Released:** August 31, 2020. **Description:** Hazardous waste is an environmental responsibility for small businesses. This article discusses the strict guidelines set by governmental agencies to efficiently manage, transport and recycle or dispose of hazardous waste. **Availability:** Online.

7953 ■ *"Healing Power from Medical Waste" in Memphis Business Journal (Vol. 33, March 30, 2012, No. 51, pp. 1)*
Pub: Baltimore Business Journal
Contact: Rhonda Pringle, President
E-mail: rpringle@bizjournals.com
Description: Tennessee-based BioD LLC has been using amniotic fluid in placenta from cesarian section births, which was considered as biomedical waste, to make various compounds that are used to develop stem cell-based healing products. BioD has sales of $3 million in 2011 and it expects sales of $6 million in 2012. **Availability:** Print; Online.

7954 ■ *"Here Are the Right Ways to Dispose of Your Spa's Hazardous Waste" in American Spa (March 25, 2019)*
Ed: Maricha Ellis. **Released:** March 25, 2019. **Description:** Discusses the importance of hazardous waste disposal in salons and spas. what types of products are considered hazardous waste, and how to maintain compliance. **Availability:** Online.

7955 ■ *"How Small Businesses Can Manage Hazardous Waste: A Guide" in MultiBriefs: Exclusive (August 28, 2020)*
Ed: Amanda Wilson. **Released:** August 28, 2020. **Description:** Many small businesses are not even aware that they generate hazardous waste. This article includes the types of businesses that typically generate hazardous waste, why hazardous waste is important, how to identify wastes, how to get an EPA identification number, and how to avoid violations. **Availability:** Online.

7956 ■ *"How to Start a Hazardous Waste Disposal Business" in Gaebler Ventures*
Description: Starting a hazardous waste disposal business is an excellent entrepreneurial opportunity if you have the creativity and tenacity necessary to be a successful entrepreneur. This article offers tips and advice that instructs you on how to start your business.

7957 ■ *"Kinderhook Acquires Chemtron Corp." in Waste Today (August 23, 2019)*
URL(s): www.wastetodaymagazine.com/article/kin derhook-acquires-chemtron-corp/
Ed: Adam Redling. **Released:** August 23, 2019. **Description:** The hazardous and non-hazardous waste management provider, Chemtron, was acquired by Kinderhook Industries LLC. **Availability:** Online.

7958 ■ *"PaintCare Celebrates 10 Years with 10 Paint Recycling Programs" in Waste Today (October 29, 2019)*
URL(s): www.wastetodaymagazine.com/article/exten ded-producer-responsibly-paint-recycling/
Ed: Kelly Maile. **Released:** October 29, 2019. **Description:** The national nonprofit, PaintCare, is celebrating 10 years of providing consumer education and recycling for households, businesses, and institutions that purchase paint, stain, and varnish. Leftovers from these products are often collected in government-run hazardous waste programs, so there is a need for PaintCare to step in and provide this type of waste collection. **Availability:** Online.

7959 ■ *"Pep Boys to Pay $3.7M for Illegally Disposing of Hazardous Waste" in Waste Today (October 1, 2019)*
URL(s): www.wastetodaymagazine.com/article/pep -boys-hazardous-waste-lawsuit/
Ed: Adam Redling. **Released:** October 01, 2019. **Description:** After disposing toxic waste from automotive fluids into municipal landfills, Pep Boys must pay a $3.7 million settlement. This is based off of undercover inspections and charges were brought forth by the Alameda County District Attorney's Office Environmental Protection Unit. **Availability:** Online.

7960 ■ *"Quasar Energy Group Completes Project in Ohio Wastewater Treatment Plant" in Waste Today (November 8, 2019)*
URL(s): www.wastetodaymagazine.com/article/qua -sar-energy-group-project-ohio-wastewater-treatmen t-plant/
Ed: Theresa Cottom. **Released:** November 08, 2019. **Description:** Quasar Energy Group has completed its project in Alliance, OH to provide technology and equipment to that biosolids generated at the plant can be designated as Class A/EQ Quality. This material can then by used on area farms as natural fertilizer, taking the place of commercial fertilizers. **Availability:** Online.

7961 ■ *"Small Businesses and Disposal of Hazardous Waste" in HG.org Legal Resources*
Description: Small businesses are able to ensure that hazardous waste and other protocols are adhered to while working under the U.S. Environmental Protection Agency. This article details how to ensure that harmful chemicals and substances are transferred to disposal units properly. **Availability:** Online.

7962 ■ *"Uranium Energy Corp Provides an Update on Its Goliad Operations" in Canadian Corporate News (May 16, 2007)*
Description: Complaints against Uranium Energy Corp. and its Goliad Project in South Texas have been dismissed. The Railroad Commission of Texas (RRC), the regulatory authority which oversees mineral exploration in Texas, concluded that Uranium Energy Corp.'s drilling activities on the Goliad Project have not contaminated certain water wells or the related aquifer. **Availability:** Print; Online.

7963 ■ *"Waste Management Exec First 'Undercover Boss' in Series Kicking Off on Super Bowl Sunday" in Houston Business Journal (Vol. 40, January 22, 2010, No. 37, pp. A1)*
Pub: Houston Business Journal
Contact: Bob Charlet, President
E-mail: bcharlet@bizjournals.com
Ed: Christine Hall. **Description:** Houston, Texas-based Waste Management Inc.'s president and chief operation officer, Larry O'Donnell shares some of his experience as CBS Television Network reality show 'Undercover Boss' participant. O'Donnell believes the show was a great way to show the customers how tough their jobs are and reveals that the most difficult job was being a sorter at the recycling center. **Availability:** Print; Online.

7964 ■ *"Water-Recycling Trend Could Ease Demand for Injection Wells" in San Antonio Business Journal (Vol. 28, June 13, 2014, No. 18, pp. 6)*
Pub: American City Business Journals, Inc.
Contact: Mike Olivieri, Executive Vice President
Released: Weekly. **Price:** $4, Introductory 4-week offer(Digital & Print). **Description:** Industry experts are encouraging oil and gas companies to consider investing in water recycling technology to ease the demand for wastewater disposal wells in South Texas. According to Pinnergy chief executive officer, Randy Taylor, the demand for disposal wells will not go away even with more water reuse in the area. **Availability:** Print; Online.

7965 ■ *"What to Do with Business Waste" in ERC Blog*
Description: Discusses how business recycling can benefit your small business, how to develop a plan for business waste, and how to update your workplace procedures. **Availability:** Online.

7966 ■ *"Women Up: Kathleen Ligocki of Harvest Power Inc." in Boston Business Journal (Vol.. 34, April 11, 2014, No. 10)*
Pub: American City Business Journals, Inc.
Contact: Mike Olivieri, Executive Vice President
Released: Weekly. **Price:** $4, introductory 4-week offer(Digital & Print). **Description:** Kathleen Ligocki is the CEO of Harvest Power Inc. of Massachusetts. The company diverts organic waste destined for landfills and produces green energy and soil enrichment products. The company was founded in 2008 and reported sales of over $130 million in 2013. **Availability:** Print; Online.

STATISTICAL SOURCES

7967 ■ *Portable Toilet Rental & Septic Tank Cleaning Industry in the US - Market Research Report*
URL(s): www.ibisworld.com/united-states/market-re search-reports/portable-toilet-rental-septic-tank -cleaning-industry/
Price: $925. **Description:** Downloadable report analyzing current and future trends in the portable toilet rental and septic tank cleaning industry. **Availability:** Download.

7968 ■ *Remediation & Environmental Cleanup Services Industry in the US - Market Research Report*
URL(s): www.ibisworld.com/united-states/market-re search-reports/remediation-environmental-cleanup -services-industry/
Price: $925. **Description:** Downloadable report analyzing data about current and future trends in the remediation and environmental cleanup services industry. **Availability:** Download.

7969 ■ *Waste Collection Services Industry in the US - Market Research Report*
URL(s): www.ibisworld.com/united-states/market-re search-reports/waste-collection-services-industry/
Price: $925. **Description:** Downloadable report analyzing current and future trends in the waste collection industry. **Availability:** Download.

7970 ■ *Waste Treatment & Disposal Services Industry in the US - Market Research Report*
URL(s): www.ibisworld.com/united-states/market-re search-reports/waste-treatment-disposal-services-in dustry/
Price: $925. **Description:** Downloadable report analyzing current and future trends in the waste treatment industry. **Availability:** Download.

TRADE PERIODICALS

7971 ■ Environmental Engineering Science
Pub: Mary Ann Liebert Inc. Publishers
Contact: Mary Ann Liebert, Founder
URL(s): www.liebertpub.com/loi/ees
Released: Monthly; current volume: 41. **Description:** Journal on environmental and industrial waste technology. **Availability:** Print; Download; PDF; Online.

CONSULTANTS

7972 ■ Baxter & Woodman Inc.
8678 Ridgefield Rd.
Crystal Lake, IL 60012
Ph: (815)459-1260
Co. E-mail: marketing@baxterwoodman.com
URL: http://www.baxterwoodman.com
Contact: John V. Ambrose, President
Facebook: www.facebook.com/BaxterWoodman
Linkedin: www.linkedin.com/company/baxter-&-woodman
X (Twitter): x.com/BaxterWoodman
Description: Firm is engaged in architecture, engineering and construction services. **Founded:** 1946.

7973 ■ Dangerous Goods Council, Inc. (DGC)
PO Box 7325
York, PA 17404
Ph: (717)848-8840
Fax: (717)848-8841
Co. E-mail: hazmat@hazshipper.com
URL: http://www.hazshipper.com
Description: Academic institution that promotes safety in transporting and handling of hazardous materials both domestically and internationally. **Scope:** Academic institution that promotes safety in transporting and handling of hazardous materials both domestically and internationally. **Publications:** "PHMSA-02-11989 (HM-224C) and PHMSA-04-19886 (HM-224E): Hazardous Materials; Transportation of Lithium Batteries," 2008; "Hazardous Materials Regulations: Transportation of Compressed Oxygen, Other Oxidizing Gases and Chemical Oxygen Generators on Aircraft; correction," 2007; "Hazardous Materials: Security Requirements for Offerors and Transporters of Hazardous Materials," 2003. **Training:** Initial and recurrent training for dangerous goods; Awareness/familiarization training for dangerous goods; Safety training for dangerous goods, Hazmat Training. **Special Services:** Haz-Shipper™.

7974 ■ Haztrain Inc.
3460 Rockefeller Ct.
Waldorf, MD 20602
Ph: (301)932-0994
Free: 800-258-7501
Fax: (301)934-9584
URL: http://www.haztrain.com
Contact: Timothy J. Czysz, President
E-mail: timczysz@haztrain.com
Description: Consultants in hazardous waste management. Specialists in the development of site specific, employee hazardous waste training to most major industries dealing with hazardous waste, specifically the automobile and transportation industries. Industries served: Auto, manufacturing and government agencies. **Scope:** Consultants in hazardous waste management. Specialists in the development of site specific, employee hazardous waste training to most major industries dealing with hazardous waste, specifically the automobile and transportation industries. Industries served: Auto, manufacturing and government agencies. **Founded:** 1983.

7975 ■ Kimmel & Associates, Inc.
25 Page Ave.
Asheville, NC 28801
Ph: (828)251-9900
Fax: (828)251-9955
Co. E-mail: kimmel@kimmel.com
URL: http://kimmel.com
Contact: Charlie Kimmel, President
E-mail: charlie@kimmel.com
Facebook: www.facebook.com/Kimmel.Associates
Linkedin: www.linkedin.com/company/kimmel-&-associates
X (Twitter): x.com/KimmelAssociate
Instagram: www.instagram.com/kimmelassociates
Description: Firm offers executive search and personnel consulting, management practices consultation and merger and acquisition consultation. **Scope:** Firm offers executive search and personnel consulting, management practices consultation and merger and acquisition consultation. **Founded:** 1981. **Publications:** "GRAY POWER can give you an EDGE," ENR magazine; "A Guide to Hiring Forwarder Talent," CNS Focus Magazine, 2004.

7976 ■ MVTL Laboratories Inc.
1126 N Front St.Bldg. No 2
New Ulm, MN 56073
Free: 800-782-3557
Fax: (507)359-2890
Co. E-mail: crc@mvtl.com
URL: http://www.mvtl.com
Contact: Thomas R. Berg, Chief Executive Officer
Description: Firm provides environmental, agricultural, food science and energy technology testing services. **Scope:** Firm provides environmental, agricultural, food science and energy technology testing services. **Founded:** 1951. **Publications:** "What You Need to Know About Salmonella," 2007; "The What, Where, Why of Natamycin," Apr, 2007; "Why Gluten Testing is needed," Apr, 2007; "Sulfates in Your Well," 2007; "What Is Your Well Water Telling You". **Training:** Soil Seminar, 2008.

LIBRARIES

7977 ■ Air & Waste Management Association (A&WMA) - Library
436 Seventh Ave., Ste. 2100
Pittsburgh, PA 15219
Ph: (412)232-3444
Free: 800-270-3444
Fax: (412)232-3450
Co. E-mail: info@awma.org
URL: http://www.awma.org
Contact: Stephanie Glyptis, Executive Director
E-mail: sglyptis@awma.org
Facebook: www.facebook.com/AirandWasteManagementAssociation
Linkedin: www.linkedin.com/company/air-&-waste-management-association
X (Twitter): x.com/AirandWaste
Description: Serves as environmental, educational, and technical organization. Seeks to provide a neutral forum for the exchange of technical information on a wide variety of environmental topics. **Scope:** The environment. **Founded:** 1907. **Holdings:** Figures not available. **Publications:** Air and Waste Management Association Government Agencies Directory (Annual); Environmental Manager (Monthly); Air Pollution Engineering Manual; Journal of the Air & Waste Management Association (Monthly); EM Magazine (Monthly). **Educational Activities:** Air & Waste Management Association Annual Conference & Exhibition (ACE) (Annual). **Awards:** Milton Feldstein Memorial Scholarships; Richard Stessel Memorial Scholarship (Annual); Dave Benforado Scholarship (Annual); George T. Minasian Award; Frank A. Chambers Excellence in Air Pollution Control Award (Irregular); S. Smith Griswold Outstanding Air Pollution Official Award (Annual); Honorary A&WMA Membership (Annual); Richard Beatty Mellon Environmental Stewardship Award (Annual); Lyman A. Ripperton Environmental Educator Award (Annual); Richard I. Stessel Waste Management Award (Annual); Jacqueline Shields Memorial Scholarship (Annual); Local A&WMA Sections and Chapter Scholarships (Annual); J. Deane Sensenbaugh Environmental Technology Award (Annual); A&WMA Outstanding Young Professional Award (OYP) (Annual). **Geographic Preference:** National.

7978 ■ Brown and Caldwell
201 N Civic Dr., No. 300
Walnut Creek, CA 94596
Ph: (925)937-9010
Free: 800-727-2224
Fax: (925)937-9026
Co. E-mail: info@brwncald.com
URL: http://brownandcaldwell.com
Contact: Rich D'Amato, President
Facebook: www.facebook.com/BrownAndCaldwell
Linkedin: www.linkedin.com/company/brown-and-caldwell
X (Twitter): twitter.com/brwncald
Instagram: www.instagram.com/brownandcaldwell/
YouTube: www.youtube.com/user/BCWaterNews
Description: Firm that provides environmental engineering services. **Scope:** Full-service environmental engineering and consulting firm that provides innovative solutions that preserve the health of ecosystems and improve the lives of employees of a workplace, clients and community. Caters to municipal, federal and private agencies. Provides business consulting practices like financial planning services for utility managers, design build services, operational services and more. Environmental services include groundwater modeling, litigation support, mining services and risk assessment. Information technology services rendered by the firm include custom software solutions for industry and municipal agencies. Other services include solid waste management, startup assistance and lake and reservoir water quality management. **Founded:** 1947. **Publications:** Promotes sustainable water practices in developing countries. **Training:** Supports companies that are dedicated to promoting sustainable water practices in developing countries.

7979 ■ Brown University - Institute at Brown for Environment & Society (IBES)
85 Waterman St.
Providence, RI 02912
Ph: (401)863-3449
Fax: (401)863-3839
Co. E-mail: environment@brown.edu
URL: http://ibes.brown.edu
Contact: Michael Burger, Executive Director
Facebook: www.facebook.com/brownenvsoc
X (Twitter): x.com/brownenvt
YouTube: www.youtube.com/channel/UCwi73X-v_0N1v2qdHMvy4Aw
Description: Integral unit of Brown University. Offers science and policy-related courses. **Scope:** Environmental studies with a focus on natural systems, food and water, human health and well-being, equity and governance, climate science, land change science, conservation science, environmental health, and institutions and human behavior. **Services:** Library open to the public for reference use only. **Holdings:** 500 books; 200 reports.

7980 ■ California Department of Conservation - Division of Recycling - Resource Center
801 K St., MS 24-01
Sacramento, CA 95814
URL: http://www.conservation.ca.gov/dlrp/watershedportal/InformationResources/Pages/informationResources.aspx
Contact: David Shabazian, Director
Scope: Recycling; waste reduction; resource conservation. **Services:** Copying; library open to the public with restrictions. **Founded:** 1989. **Holdings:** 300 books; 400 reports; 277 videocassettes.

7981 ■ Center For Health, Environment and Justice (CHEJ)
7139 Shreve Rd.
Falls Church, VA 22046
Ph: (703)237-2249
Co. E-mail: info@chej.org
URL: http://chej.org
Contact: Lois Marie Gibbs, Founder
E-mail: lgibbs@chej.org
Facebook: www.facebook.com/CHEJfans
X (Twitter): x.com/chej
Instagram: www.instagram.com/chej_org
YouTube: www.youtube.com/channel/UCxVIsudFDVZGpjOuRAEAnPQ

Description: Promotes environmental justice and empowerment through community organization. **Founded:** 1981. **Publications:** *Journal of the Grassroots Movement*; *Everyone's Backyard* (Quarterly). **Geographic Preference:** National.

7982 ■ Illinois Sustainable Technology Center (ISTC) - Library
One Hazelwood Dr., MC-676
Champaign, IL 61820
Ph: (217)333-8940
Co. E-mail: info@istc.illinois.edu
URL: http://www.istc.illinois.edu
Contact: Kevin O'Brien, Director
E-mail: kcobrien@illinois.edu
Facebook: www.facebook.com/ISTCatUIUC
Linkedin: www.linkedin.com/company/illinois-sustainable-technology-center
X (Twitter): twitter.com/ISTCatUIUC
YouTube: www.youtube.com/user/4ISTC
Description: Integral unit of Office of Research and Scientific Analysis, Illinois Department of Natural Resources, affiliated with University of Illinois at Urbana-Champaign. Offers on-site disposal review, referral and consulting service, and waste reduction information and assistance. **Scope:** Integrates research, industrial and technical assistance, database management, laboratory services, and information resources in a program to manage and help solve Illinois' pollution and waste problems. Topics include characterization and assessment; environmental process and effects; prevention and source reduction; treatment, disposal, and remediation; risk assessment; river sediment reuse; and policy analysis. Collects, analyzes, synthesizes, and disseminates information on waste management. **Founded:** 1984. **Holdings:** Figures not available. **Publications:** *ISTC Factsheets*; *ISTC Research reports*; *ISTC Technical Reports*. **Educational Activities:** ISTC Conferences and seminars, Characterization and assessment, environmental process and effects.; Great Lake Regional Pollution Prevention Roundtable (Annual), Ensures information sharing, issue discussion and program development among member organizations to be primary goals.

7983 ■ Long Island Lighting Company Resource Center
131 S Hoffman Ln.
Islandia, NY 11749
Free: 800-490-0075
URL: http://www.psegliny.com
Scope: Energy, electricity, public utilities, business management. **Services:** Library not open to the public. **Founded:** 1986. **Holdings:** 1570 books; 100 periodical titles; videocassettes; audiocassettes.

7984 ■ Pennsylvania Environmental Council (PEC) - Library
1617 JFK Blvd., Ste. 543
Philadelphia, PA 19103
Ph: (215)545-4570
Co. E-mail: paenvironmentalcouncil@gmail.com
URL: http://pecpa.org
Contact: Tom Gilbert, President
Facebook: www.facebook.com/PennsylvaniaEnvironmentalCouncil
X (Twitter): twitter.com/pecpa
YouTube: www.youtube.com/channel/UCfKnE95ObJLP-A3zie0JtMw
Description: Independent, nonprofit advocacy organization. **Scope:** Growth management, land use, air quality and transportation; water resource allocation, groundwater, wetlands, open space preservation. **Services:** Copying; faxing; library open to the public by appointment. **Founded:** 1969. **Holdings:** 400 books; 100 reports; 40 videotapes; 10 slide shows. **Subscriptions:** 200 journals and other serials. **Publications:** *PEC Fact Sheets*; *Pennsylvania Environmentalist*; *Special Reports*. **Educational Activities:** PEC Seminars; Speakers; PEC Deep Decarbonization Conferences; PEC Annual Members Meeting; Slide Shows and videos.

7985 ■ U.S. Environmental Protection Agency Headquarters Library
1200 Pennsylvania Ave., NW
Washington, DC 20460
URL: http://www.epa.gov/epalibraries/catalog
Scope: Water and environmental protection. **Services:** Interlibrary loan; SDI; library open to the public with restrictions. **Founded:** 1971. **Holdings:** Figures not available.

RESEARCH CENTERS

7986 ■ The Nature Conservancy - Ohio Chapter
6375 Riverside Dr., Ste. 100
Dublin, OH 43017
Ph: (614)717-2770
Co. E-mail: ohio@tnc.org
URL: https://www.nature.org/en-us/about-us/where-we-work/united-states/ohio
Contact: Jennifer Morris, Chief Executive Officer
Facebook: www.facebook.com/ohionatureconservancy
X (Twitter): twitter.com/nature_ohio
Description: Strives to preserve biological diversity through land and water protection of natural areas in Ohio. **Scope:** Owns and manages 35 preserves throughout Ohio to protect habitat; preserves serve as living laboratories to apply conservation science and methods. Current projects include Southern Appalachian forests (edge of Appalachia Preserve System); Ohio River Watershed/Drainage basin (Darby Creek Watershed); Lake Erie Watershed/Drainage basin (Grand River Watershed, Oak Openings Region, Akron Kames). Also studies invasive species and compatible agriculture. **Founded:** 1958. **Publications:** *Nature Conservancy Magazine* (Quarterly); *Ohio Chapter Newsletter* (Monthly). **Educational Activities:** Ohio Chapter Prescribed burn and land management training; Ohio Chapter Annual Membership meeting; Ohio Chapter Volunteer Award Dinner.

7987 ■ University of Florida - Hinkley Center for Solid and Hazardous Waste Management (FCSHWM)
2320 Surge Area Dr., Bldg., 226
Gainesville, FL 32608
Co. E-mail: hinkleycenter@hinkleycenter.org
URL: http://www.hinkleycenter.org
Contact: Timothy Townsend, Executive Director
E-mail: ttown@ufl.edu
Description: Integral unit of University of Florida and State University System of Florida; information dissemination, publications listing. **Scope:** Construction and demolition debris, hazardous waste management, medical waste management, pollution prevention, socioeconomic issues, special wastes, waste reduction, wetlands management, sustainability. **Founded:** 1988. **Publications:** *Annual Research Booklet*; *FCSHWM Newsletter* (Quarterly).

7988 ■ University of Iowa - Center for Health Effects of Environmental Contamination (CHEEC)
251 North Capitol St. Chemistry Bldg. Rm. W195
Iowa City, IA 52242
Ph: (319)335-4550
Co. E-mail: cheec@uiowa.edu
URL: http://www.cheec.uiowa.edu
Contact: Peter Weyer, Officer
E-mail: peter-weyer@uiowa.edu
Facebook: www.facebook.com/pg/UICHEEC/posts
X (Twitter): x.com/UICHEEC
Description: Integral unit of University of Iowa. Develops and maintains environmental databases that can be accessed by state agencies. Offers engineering, health, and laboratory consultations and health assessments at hazardous waste disposal sites. Responds to public inquiries regarding health effects of exposure to environmental contaminants. **Scope:** Fate and transport of toxic substances in the environment, radon and indoor air contaminants, non-point source chemical contamination of water supplies, and epidemiologic studies that relate the occurrence of diseases to contaminant exposure. **Founded:** 1987. **Publications:** *CHEEC Annual Report* (Annual); *CHEEC Newsletter*; *CHEEC Technical Report*. **Awards:** CHEEC Seed Grant Program.

7989 ■ University of Northern Iowa - Iowa Waste Reduction Center (IWRC)
Business & Community Services Bldg., Ste. 113
University of Northern Iowa
Cedar Falls, IA 50614
Ph: (319)273-8905
Free: 800-422-3109
Fax: (319)273-6582
Co. E-mail: iwrc@uni.edu
URL: http://iwrc.uni.edu
Contact: Joe Bolick, Director
E-mail: mjbolick@uni.edu
Facebook: www.facebook.com/iowaenviroassist
Linkedin: www.linkedin.com/company/iowa-waste-reduction-center
X (Twitter): x.com/iowaenviro
YouTube: www.youtube.com/user/iowaenviroassist
Description: Independent, nonprofit research organization. Offers consulting for the Iowa Automobile Dealers Service and painting technicians; maintains mobile exhibits that travel to small companies and rural areas. **Scope:** Environmentally safe ways to reduce and manage waste from small business, including hazardous waste, air emissions, used oil, air-conditioning and coolant waste, wastewater, and solid waste. **Founded:** 1987. **Publications:** *The Closed Loop* (Annual); *Point Source Newsletter*.

Health Food Store

START-UP INFORMATION

7990 ■ *"Aubry & Kale Walch, Herbivorous Butcher"* in *Business Journal (Vol. 32, August 29, 2014, No. 14, pp. 6)*
Pub: American City Business Journals, Inc.
Contact: Mike Olivieri, Executive Vice President
Released: August 29, 2014. **Description:** Kale and Aubry Walch, founders of family-owned The Herbivorous Butcher, reveal that the process of formulating recipes for their shop took years. Aubry said that she and her brother used to make fake meats for themselves. Their plan to open a full-scale vegan butcher shop is also discussed. **Availability:** Print; Online.

7991 ■ *"No. 479: SeaSnax Seaweed Snacks"* in *Inc. (Vol. 36, September 2014, No. 7, pp. 44)*
Pub: Mansueto Ventures L.L.C.
Contact: Stephanie Mehta, Chief Executive Officer
Released: September 2014. **Description:** SeaSnax make a perfect snack for children's lunchboxes. These crispy sheets of seaweed made the 500 Inc. list of outstanding entrepreneurial startups and are now sold in Whole Food Stores. **Availability:** Print; Online.

7992 ■ *"Organic Chain Scouting Cincinatti Sites, Including Kenwood"* in *Business Courier (Vol. 27, December 3, 2010, No. 31, pp. 1)*
Pub: Business Courier
Ed: Tom Demeropolis. **Description:** Asheville, North Carolina-based Earth Fare has been planning to add a total of six stores in 2011, including the potential opening of more than one store in the Greater Cincinnati area market. Earth Fare has not named specific locations but Kenwood area was reportedly being considered for its first location. Insights on growing trends toward health food stores are also given. **Availability:** Print; Online.

7993 ■ *"Sustainable Advantage"* in *Inc. (Vol. 36, September 2014, No. 7, pp. 86)*
Pub: Mansueto Ventures L.L.C.
Contact: Stephanie Mehta, Chief Executive Officer
Price: $8.95, hardcopy black and white. **Description:** Four startup companies committed to providing sustainable, eco-friendly products and services while protecting the environment and bettering human health are profiled. Holganix(TM) offers organic lawn care products; Motiv Power Systems electrifies large vehicles; Clean Energy Collective Solar Power builds lareg community solar panel arrays; and Protein Bar offers healthy alternatives to fast food in its chain of restaurants. The company also works with nonprofits focused on wellness and education and has created 167 Learning Gardens nationwide. **Availability:** Print; PDF; Online.

7994 ■ *"Urban Organics Launches Aquaponic Farm in Old Hamm's Brewery"* in *Business Journal (Vol. 31, April 11, 2014, No. 46, pp. 4)*
Pub: American City Business Journals, Inc.
Contact: Mike Olivieri, Executive Vice President
Price: $4, Introductory 4-Week Offer(Digital & Print). **Description:** Urban Organics launched its new aquaponics farm at the old site of Hamm's Brewery in St. Paul, Minnesota. The facility has four 3,000 gallon fish tanks that hold 1,000 fish which Urban Organics uses to grow fresh and healthy tilapia and vegetable produce. **Availability:** Print; Online.

ASSOCIATIONS AND OTHER ORGANIZATIONS

7995 ■ **Canadian Health Food Association (CHFA) [Association Canadienne des Aliements de Sante]**
235 Yorkland Blvd., Ste. 201
Toronto, ON, Canada M2J 4Y8
Free: 800-661-4510
Co. E-mail: info@chfa.ca
URL: http://chfa.ca/en
Contact: Aaron Skelton, President
Facebook: www.facebook.com/CAhealthfood
X (Twitter): x.com/cdnhealthfood
Instagram: www.instagram.com/cahealthfood
YouTube: www.youtube.com/user/cdnhealthfood
Description: Seeks to advance the health food industries. Facilitates communication and cooperation among members; represents the commercial and regulatory interests of the health food industries; sponsors educational and promotional programs. **Publications:** *The Natural Voice* (5/year). **Educational Activities:** CHFA West (Annual); CHFA East Tradeshow (Annual). **Geographic Preference:** National.

7996 ■ **The Food Industry Association**
2345 Crystal Dr., Ste. 800
Arlington, VA 22202
Ph: (202)452-8444
URL: http://www.fmi.org
Linkedin: www.linkedin.com/company/fmithefoodindustryassociation
X (Twitter): x.com/FMI_ORG
Instagram: www.instagram.com/fmi_org
YouTube: www.youtube.com/user/FMIorg
Description: Works on behalf of the food industry to advance a safer, healthier, and more efficient consumer food supply chain. Provides members, from independent operators to the largest national and international players, a forum for actively coming together to engage in dialogue, collaboration and problem-solving as a community.

7997 ■ **Health Information Resource Center (HIRC)**
328 W Lincoln Ave., Ste. 10
Libertyville, IL 60048-2725
Ph: (847)816-8660
Free: 800-828-8225
Fax: (847)816-8662
Co. E-mail: info@healthawards.com
URL: http://healthawards.com/dha/aboutus.html
Description: Clearinghouse for consumer health information. Provides information and referral services to many organizations that use or produce consumer health information materials. Conducts market research. **Founded:** 1993. **Publications:** *Health and Medical Media: The Comprehensive Sourcebook of Media Contacts for Healthcare Professionals* (Biennial). **Awards:** HIRC National Health Information Awards (Annual); HIRC Digital Health Awards (Annual). **Geographic Preference:** National.

7998 ■ **Independent Natural Food Retailers Association (INFRA)**
2356 University Ave. W, Ste. 200
Saint Paul, MN 55114
Ph: (651)888-4700
Co. E-mail: info@infretailers.com
URL: http://www.naturalfoodretailers.com/home
Contact: Emily Kanter, Chairman of the Board
Facebook: www.facebook.com/infretailers
Instagram: www.instagram.com/infretailers
Description: Supports independent natural and organic food retailers of all sizes. **Founded:** 2005.

7999 ■ **National Association of Health Stores (NAHS)**
PO Box 14177
Tranent EH34 5WX, United Kingdom
Ph: 44 1875 341 408
Co. E-mail: nahsoffice@gmail.com
URL: http://www.nahs.co.uk
Contact: Gary Trickett, Member
URL(s): bira.co.uk/sectors/nationalassociationofhealthstores
Facebook: www.facebook.com/NationalAssociationofHealthStores
X (Twitter): x.com/ukhealthstores
YouTube: www.youtube.com/user/scottie8438
Description: Supports independent health product retailers in the United Kingdom. Seeks to promote to the public the benefits of shopping in locally owned, independent health stores, and to ensure a high standard of customer advice in member stores. **Founded:** 1931.

8000 ■ **Natural Products Association (NPA)**
440 1st St. NW Ste. 520
Washington, DC 20001
Ph: (202)223-0101
Fax: (202)223-0250
Co. E-mail: natural@npanational.org
URL: http://www.npanational.org
Contact: Daniel Fabricant, President
Facebook: www.facebook.com/NaturalProductsAssociation
X (Twitter): x.com/NPANational
Instagram: www.instagram.com/npanational
YouTube: www.youtube.com/channel/UC0w3VqZZIStYtinFxGYJ7qw
Description: Represents retailers, wholesalers, brokers, distributors and manufacturers of natural, nutritional, dietetic foods, supplements, services and natural body and home care products. **Founded:** 1936. **Educational Activities:** Natural Products Day

8001 ■ Health Food Store

(Annual); NNFA Market Place/National Nutritional Foods Association (Annual). **Awards:** NPA President's Award (Annual); NPA Clinician Award (Annual); Burton Kallman Scientific Award (Annual); Rachel Carson Environmental Award (Annual); The Natural Products Association Clinician Award (Annual); Statesman/Stateswoman Award (Annual); NPA Industry Champion Award (Annual); NPA Socially Responsible Retailer Award (Annual). **Geographic Preference:** National.

8001 ■ Organic & Natural Health Association
PO Box 42385
Washington, DC 20015
Co. E-mail: info@organicandnatural.org
URL: http://organicandnatural.org
Contact: Karen Howard, Chief Executive Officer
Facebook: www.facebook.com/organicandnaturalhealthassociation
Linkedin: www.linkedin.com/company/organic-and-natural-health-association
X (Twitter): x.com/orgnathealth
YouTube: www.youtube.com/user/OrgNatHealth
Description: Dedicated to creating and promoting transparent business practices that safeguard access to organic and natural food, products and services. **Founded:** 2014.

8002 ■ Specialty Food Association Inc.
136 Madison Ave., 12th Fl.
New York, NY 10016-6788
Ph: (212)482-6440
Fax: (212)482-6459
URL: http://www.specialtyfood.com
Contact: Phil Kafarakis, President
Facebook: www.facebook.com/SpecialtyFoodAssociation
Linkedin: www.linkedin.com/company/specialty-food-association
X (Twitter): x.com/Specialty_Food
Instagram: www.instagram.com/specialtyfoodassociation
YouTube: www.youtube.com/user/NASFT
Pinterest: www.pinterest.com/craftcarejoy
Description: Manufacturers, distributors, processors, importers, retailers, and brokers of specialty and gourmet foods. Fosters trade, commerce and interest in the specialty food industry. **Founded:** 1952. **Publications:** Specialty Food Magazine. **Educational Activities:** Fancy Food Show (Semiannual); Specialty Food Association Winter Fancy Food Show (Annual); Summer Fancy Food Show (Annual). **Awards:** Sofi Awards (Annual). **Geographic Preference:** National.

REFERENCE WORKS

8003 ■ *"Agana To Bottle Rain for Whole Foods"* in Austin Business Journal (Vol. 32, March 30, 2012, No. 4, pp. 1)
Pub: American City Business Journals, Inc.
Contact: Mike Olivieri, Executive Vice President
Ed: Vicky Garza. **Description:** Agana Rainwater has signed a deal to bottle rainwater for Whole Foods Market Inc. Rainwater bottling is seen as a conservation tools as it does not deplete the lake or aquifer. **Availability:** Online.

8004 ■ *"Almost Like Home"* in Pet Product News (Vol. 66, September 2012, No. 9, pp. S18)
Description: Treats Unleashed, a natural and functional pet foods and supplies store chain in Midwestern U.S., has been known for creating an aura that kept customers returning to each of its seven stores. It has also been reputed for a laidback atmosphere hat prioritizes customer education over sales. The chain's promotional and growth-related plans are also discussed. **Availability:** Online.

8005 ■ *"Ben & Jerry's Changing Some 'All Natural' Labels"* in Ice Cream Reporter (Vol. 23, October 20, 2010, No. 11, pp. 1)
Description: Following criticism from the Center for Science in the Public Interest, Ben & Jerry's will omit the term 'All Natural' from its labeling, however the firm reports it will continue to use the most natural ingredients they can find for its products. **Availability:** Print; Online.

8006 ■ *"A Better-For-You Grocery Pops Up in NYC"* in Supermarket News (September 20, 2019)
URL(s): www.supermarketnews.com/retail-financial/better-you-grocery-pops-nyc
Ed: Holly Petre. **Released:** September 20, 2019. **Description:** Emily Schildt, founder of Pop Up Grocer, is bringing the hybrid grocery store/bodega to NYC for a month. The store will feature fresh produce, snacks, beverages, supplements, wellness essentials, household items, and pet supplies. **Availability:** Online.

8007 ■ *"Beyond Meat (R) Completes Largest Financing Round to Date"* in Ecology, Environment & Conservation Business (August 16, 2014, pp. 4)
Pub: NewsRX LLC.
Contact: Kalani Rosell, Contact
Description: Beyond Meat (R) is the first company to recreate meat from plants and is dedicated to improving human health, positively impacting climate change, conserving natural resources and respecting animal welfare. The firm has completed its Series D financing round, which will also help the company promote consumer awareness and increase capacity at its manufacturing facility to meet demand. **Availability:** Online.

8008 ■ *"Canine Cuisine: AKC Tips for a Healthful Diet"* in Seattle Times (September 13, 2008, pp. D9)
Pub: Associated Press
Contact: Ken Dale, Chief Financial Officer Senior Vice President
Description: The American Kennel Club recommends feeding dogs food with balanced essential nutrients, including proteins, carbohydrates, fats, vitamins, minerals, and water; types of food, feeding practices and what not to feed a dog is discussed. **Availability:** Online.

8009 ■ *"Careers in Organic Food Production"* in Occupational Outlook Quarterly (Vol. 54, Fall 2010, No. 3, pp. 3)
Pub: U.S. Department of Labor Bureau of Labor Statistics
Contact: Amrit Kohli, Director
E-mail: kohli.amrit@bls.gov
Ed: Adam Bibler. **Description:** Organic methods of food production, including methods that combine science with traditional farming practices, are outlined. Facts regarding careers in organic food preparation are presented. **Availability:** Online; PDF.

8010 ■ *"Carrington Co. LLC Revolutionizes the Hot Tea Market with First-Ever, Organic Tea in Eco-Friendly Packaging"* in Ecology, Environment & Conservation Business (May 3, 2014, pp. 6)
Pub: NewsRX LLC.
Contact: Kalani Rosell, Contact
Description: Carrington Company makes organic non-genetically modified products including flax seeds, hemp, chia, and organic coconut oil and teas. The firm is launching its Carrington Organics Tea to its lineup of healthy products, packed in a 100 percent eco-friendly packaging that will fully and safely biodegrade when composted. It is the first tea available packaged in fully recyclable packaging. **Availability:** Online.

8011 ■ *"Competitors Eye Whole Foods"* in Sacramento Business Journal (Vol. 31, August 8, 2014, No. 24, pp. 6)
Pub: American City Business Journals, Inc.
Contact: Mike Olivieri, Executive Vice President
Released: Weekly. **Price:** $4, Introductory 4-week offer(Digital & Print). **Description:** Whole Foods Market has confirmed its plans to open a store in midtown Sacramento, California. However, Sacramento Natural Foods Co-op and Gluten Free Specialty says the announcement would not affect their own expansion plans into the same neighborhood. The proposed mixed-use building that will house the Whole Foods healthy grocery store is also discussed. **Availability:** Print; Online.

8012 ■ *"Conscious Capitalism: Liberating the Heroic Spirit of Business"*
Released: January 07, 2014. **Price:** $12.47, e-book; $16.79, paperback. **Description:** Conscious Capitalism companies include Whole Foods Market, Southwest Airlines, Costco, Google, Patagonia, The Container Store, UPS and others. These firms under the four specific tenants to success: higher purpose, stakeholder integration, conscious leadership, and conscious culture and management. These companies are able to create value for all stakeholders, including customers, employees, suppliers, investors, society, and the environment. A new preface by the authors is included. **Availability:** E-book; Print.

8013 ■ *"Consumer Tastes Are Redefining Convenience Retail"* in Food Business News (July 2, 2019)
URL(s): www.foodbusinessnews.net/articles/14055-consumer-tastes-are-redefining-convenience-retail
Ed: Monica Watrous. **Released:** July 02, 2019. **Description:** Moving away from traditional unhealthy snacks and other offerings, convenience stores are now starting to sell fresh and healthy food and premium coffee. This is actually taking away market share from other health food stores. **Availability:** Online.

8014 ■ *"Despite Higher Prices, Organic Food Gains"* in MMR (Vol. 29, February 20, 2012, No. 4, pp. 39)
Description: Despite higher prices, consumers are buying organic food products at a high rate. Total sales of organic products rose 15 to 20 percent due to shoppers increasing the number and variety of organic products they bought. Statistical data included. **Availability:** Print; Online.

8015 ■ *"Dream Town Launches Organic Food Delivery for Its Employees"* in Internet Wire (June 28, 2012)
Pub: Comtex News Network Inc.
Contact: Kan Devnani, President
Description: Local organics were spotlighted by Chicago real estate online firm, Dream Team, who held a special event for its employees and special guests at the Landmark Century Cinema. Robert Kenner's Food Inc. presented Irv and Shelly's Fresh Picks. Dream Team is committed to helping first time home buyers. **Availability:** Print; Online.

8016 ■ *"Drink Up!"* in (Vol. 92, July 23, 2012, No. 30, pp. 19)
Pub: Dow Jones & Company Inc.
Contact: Almar Latour, Chief Executive Officer
Ed: Robin Goldwyn Blumenthal. **Description:** Juice bars in the US are expanding as Americans increase the consumption of fresh vegetable and fruit juices. Coffeehouse chain Starbucks entered the market by introducing Evolution Fresh, a seller of coldpressed vegetable and fruit juices. The health benefits of fresh vegetable and fruit juice, however, remain uncertain. **Availability:** Online.

8017 ■ *"Effort Is Growing to Offer Healthier Choices in Vending Machines"* in Philadelphia Inquirer (July 29, 2011)
Ed: Don Sapatkin. **Description:** Since Boston's mayor announced a ban on the sale of all sugar sweetened beverages on city properties, it seems more cities, states, hospitals, businesses, and even park systems are following suit. Thus, vending machines are beginning to offer healthier snacks and drinks to consumers.

8018 ■ *"Environmental Working Group Names Whole Foods Market (R) Leading National Retailer for 'Green' Sunscreen"* in Ecology, Environment & Conservation Business (June 14, 2014, pp. 5)
Pub: NewsRX LLC.
Contact: Kalani Rosell, Contact

Description: Whole Foods Market has been named as the leading retailer selling the largest selection of 'green' rated sunscreen to shoppers. **Availability:** Online.

8019 ■ *"Facials for Fido? Retail: Kriser's Pet Store Grows With High-End Pet Products Market"* in *San Fernando Valley Business Journal* (Vol. 17, February 20, 2012, No. 4, pp. 1)
Description: Sherman Oaks all-natural pet food and supply retailer, Kriser's, is expanding with seven new stores. The company is known for its health options in pet food, tasty treats, and fancy toys by catering to a high-end clientele. They also offer upscale pet grooming services, including blueberry facials and de-shedding treatments. **Availability:** Online.

8020 ■ *"From Scarcity to Plenty"* in *Inc.* (Vol. 36, March 2014, No. 2, pp. 76)
Pub: Mansueto Ventures L.L.C.
Contact: Stephanie Mehta, Chief Executive Officer
Description: Profile of Mom's Organic Market which started in Scott Nash's mom's garage. Nash describes the healthy food choices offered at the store as well as its Environmental Restoration program which addressed issues including carbon offsets, recycling, and composting. **Availability:** Print; Online.

8021 ■ *"Global Organic Food"* in *Investment Weekly News* (January 21, 2012, pp. 272)
Description: Research and Markets has added 'Global Organic Food' to its reporting of industry profiles. The report will offer top-line qualitative and quantitative summary information including, market size, description of leading players with key financial metrics and analysis of competitive pressures within the market covering the global organic food market. Market size and segmentation data, textual and graphical analysis of market growth trends, leading companies and macroeconomic information will be provided. **Availability:** Online.

8022 ■ *"Good News If You Buy Organic Food — It's Getting Cheaper"* in *MarketWatch* (January 24, 2019)
URL(s): www.marketwatch.com/story/heres-why
-prices-of-organic-food-are-dropping-2019-0
1-24?ns=prod/accounts-mw
Released: January 24, 2019. **Description:** Even though organic produce is still more expensive, it's prices have been coming down. That also goes for items such as baby food in a jar and soy milk. Organic farmers are actually saving money by not using pesticides or synthetic fertilizers and demand is also higher than it used to be. **Availability:** Online.

8023 ■ *"Hain Celestial Acquires Greek Gods Yogurt"* in *Ice Cream Reporter* (Vol. 23, July 20, 2010, No. 8, pp. 1)
Description: Hain Celestial Group acquired The Greek Gods LLC. Hain Celestial is a natural and organic products company and Greek Gods makes all natural, Greek-style yogurt and ice cream. **Availability:** Print; Online.

8024 ■ *"Half Empty or Half Full"* in *Crain's Chicago Business* (Vol. 31, March 24, 2008, No. 12, pp. 4)
Pub: Crain Communications Inc.
Contact: Barry Asin, President
Ed: Meghan Streit. **Description:** Lifeway Foods Inc., the health food company which manufactures a yogurt-like drink called kefir, is being negatively affected by the soaring price of milk; however, the fact that probiotics are picking up in the market may mean that Lifeway stands a good chance of bouncing back and the company's lower share price could be an opportunity for long-term investors who have a tolerance for risk. **Availability:** Online.

8025 ■ *"Harvest Cafe Builds Strong Following for Healthy Foodservice"* in *Supermarket News* (September 5, 2019)
URL(s): www.supermarketnews.com/prepared-foods/
harvest-caf-builds-strong-following-healthy-foodser
vice

Ed: Mark Hamstra. **Released:** September 05, 2019.
Description: One of the top organic restaurants in Wisconsin, Harvest Cafe, is actually located inside a grocery store. Good Harvest Market relocated its store, which allowed it to expand its prepared foods and seating for in-store dining with the Harvest Cafe. **Availability:** Online.

8026 ■ *"Healthy Fast Food Acquires Rights to U-Swirl Yogurt"* in *Ice Cream Reporter* (Vol. 21, October 20, 2008, No. 11, pp. 5)
Description: Healthy Fast Food Inc. will acquire worldwide rights to U-Swirl Frozen Yogurt; the firm will use the new acquisition to create a yogurt superstore in a cafe setting concept for its operations. **Availability:** Print; Online.

8027 ■ *"In the Raw: Karyn Calabrese Brings Healthy Dining to a New Sophisticated Level"* in *Black Enterprise* (Vol. 41, September 2010)
Pub: Earl G. Graves Ltd.
Contact: Earl Graves, Jr., President
Ed: Sonia Alleyne. **Description:** Profile of Karyn Calabrese whose businesses are based in Chicago, Illinois. Calabrese has launched a complete line of products (vitamins and beauty items), services (spa, chiropractic, and acupuncture treatments), and restaurants to bring health dining and lifestyles to a better level. **Availability:** Online.

8028 ■ *"Medicine Men"* in *Canadian Business* (Vol. 80, February 12, 2007, No. 4, pp. 19)
Description: The effort of HPI Health Products' owners Dong Pedersen and Kent Pedersen to popularize their pain reliever product 'Lakota' is discussed. **Availability:** Online.

8029 ■ *"Meet the New Convenience Store"* in *Supermarket News* (August 3, 2018)
URL(s): www.supermarketnews.com/retail-financial/
meet-new-convenience-store

Ed: Gloria Dawson. **Released:** August 03, 2018.
Description: Convenience stores have grown from a place to grab some candy, pop, and other snacks to offering more and better options for healthier pre-packed food. Consumers are craving more high-end products, and these new stores are delivering and growing the trend. **Availability:** Online.

8030 ■ *"Men and Menu: A Switch in the Kitchen"* in *Barron's* (Vol. 88, March 24, 2008, No. 12, pp. 17)
Pub: Dow Jones & Company Inc.
Contact: Almar Latour, Chief Executive Officer
Ed: Robin Goldwyn Blumenthal. **Description:** Men are doing more kitchen duties, with 18 percent of meals at home being made by men in 2007 compared to 11 percent four years previously. Young wives, however, choose to forgo work and stay at home. **Availability:** Online.

8031 ■ *"The More Incredible Egg"* in *Entrepreneur* (June 2014)
Pub: Entrepreneur Media Inc.
Contact: Dan Bova, Director
E-mail: dbova@entrepreneur.com
Description: San Francisco, California-based startup Hampton Creek has developed a plant-based alternative to eggs. The startup touts it as a healthier, more humane and environment-friendly egg alternative. The company used several varieties of the yellow pea and discovered that its properties mimic egg emulsion. Hampton Creek's first food product was Beyond Eggs, a powder that allows food manufacturers to eliminate eggs from food products. It also developed Just Mayo, an egg-free mayonnaise substitute, and is developing Eat the Dough, an egg-free substitute for cookie dough. **Availability:** Print; Online.

8032 ■ *"Need Fiber in Your Diet? Pour Some Milk"* in *Globe & Mail* (April 10, 2007, pp. B7)
Ed: William Illsey Atkinson. **Description:** The growing market and demand for functional foods and neutraceuticals in Canada is discussed. The research being conducted by University of Manitoba's Richardson Centre for Functional Foods and Nutraceuticals to explore new health compounds in food is highlighted. **Availability:** Online.

8033 ■ *"New Recipes Added to IAMS Naturals Pet Food Line"* in *MMR* (Vol. 28, August 1, 2011, No. 11, pp. 17)
Description: Procter & Gamble Company's IAMS brand has created a new pet food line called IAMS Naturals for pet owners wishing to feed their pets natural, wholesome food. IAMS Sensitive Naturals has ocean fish and its first ingredient for dogs with sensitivities. IAMS Simple & Natural features chicken with no fillers. **Availability:** Print; Online.

8034 ■ *"New York's Duane Reade Adds In-Store Yogurt Kiosks"* in *ADWEEK* (Vol. 53, February 6, 2012, No. 5, pp. 16)
Description: Fifty year old chain, Pinkberry, is adding self-serve frozen kiosks to select stores in the New York area. Duane Reade, owner of Pinkberry, is refocusing the business to a health and daily-living destination. **Availability:** Online.

8035 ■ *"Optimum Nutrition, Maximum Profit"* in *Pet Product News* (Vol. 66, September 2012, No. 9, pp. S1)
Description: How pet food manufacturers have expanded brand lines to address pet owners' demand for fresh, balanced superfood diets that provide optimum pet nutrtion and foster rapid digestion among pets is explored. Retailers have been maximizing profits by guiding pet owners in selecting he appropriate superfood brands for their pets. **Availability:** Online.

8036 ■ *"Organic Dog Food Options"* in *Pet Product News* (Vol. 66, September 2012, No. 9, pp. 54)
Ed: Keith Loria. **Description:** How pet supplies manufacturers have responded to dog owners' demand for natural and organic dog food is discussed. This demand has been generated by increasing health-consciousness, leading to greater tendency to look more closely at food ingredients. Reasons why the switch to organic dog food should be done are presented, along with marketing tips for organic dog food products. **Availability:** Print; Online.

8037 ■ *"Organic Dog Treats"* in *Veterinary Economics* (Vol. 49, November 2008, No. 11, pp. 52)
Description: Wet Noses all-natural dog treats come in six flavors: dogranola, pumpkin, sweet potato curry, apples and carrots, cheddar, and peanut butter and molasses. The treats are made without animal by-products, added chemicals, preservatives, corn, soy or wheat. **Availability:** Online.

8038 ■ *"Organic Food Company's a Hit With the Sippy-Cup Crowd"* in *Investor's Business Daily* (March 27, 2012, pp. A5)
Description: Cofounder Annie Withy of Annie's Homegrown Inc. is profiled along with the firm's packaged foods that appeal to children. Statistical data included. **Availability:** Online.

8039 ■ *"Organic Food Industry Goes to College"* in *USA Today* (April 9, 2012)
Ed: Chuck Raasch. **Description:** With the organic food industry growing the US Department of Agriculture is has pumped $117 million into organic research in the last three years. According to a recent report by the Organic Farming Research Foundation (OFRF), the number of states committing land for organic research has nearly doubled from 2003 to 2011. Universities offering academic programs in organic farming rose from none to nine. The OFRF supports organic farmers and producers. **Availability:** Online.

8040 ■ *"People Want Organic Food Because of What Isn't On It, Local Producers Say"* in *Republican & Herald* (September 24, 2012)
Released: September 24, 2012. **Description:** Local producers believe that people want organically grown food because it is free of pesticides and toxins, thus making it healthier. **Availability:** Print; Online.

8041 ■ "Perry's Goes Organic" in Ice Cream Reporter (Vol. 22, December 20, 2008, No. 1, pp. 1)
Description: Family-owned Perry's Ice Cream is starting a new line of organic ice cream in both vanilla and chocolate flavors. All Perry's products are made with milk and cream from local dairy farmers. **Availability:** Print; Online.

8042 ■ "Q&A: PSU's Tom Gillpatrick on How Quirkiness Gives Portland Its Edge" in Business Journal Portland (Vol. 30, January 17, 2014, No. 46, pp. 6)
Pub: American City Business Journals, Inc.
Contact: Mike Olivieri, Executive Vice President
Released: Weekly. **Price:** $4, introductory 4-week offer(Digital only). **Description:** Portland State University Food Industry Leadership Center executive director, Tom Gillpatrick, says consumers now prefer healthier food brands. He also stated the Portland, Oregon's food sector has grown owing to that trend. Gillpatrick added that the state's reputation for being different has also helped the sector. **Availability:** Print; Online.

8043 ■ "R&R Launches Upscale Spoony's and Low Fat Dragon's Den" in Ice Cream Reporter (Vol. 23, August 20, 2010, No. 9, pp. 3)
Description: European ice cream manufacturer R&R has acquired French ice cream maker Rolland and will position itself as an upscale challenger to brands like Ben & Jerry's. **Availability:** Print; Online.

8044 ■ "Red Mango Set to Grow in Florida" in Ice Cream Reporter (Vol. 23, September 20, 2010, No. 10, pp. 2)
Description: Red Mango will add 12 new locations throughout Florida. The stores offer healthy, nutritious frozen yogurt, smoothies and parfaits. **Availability:** Print; Online.

8045 ■ "Secaucus-Based Freshpet is Barking Up the Right Tree" in Record (September 8, 2011)
Pub: North Jersey Media Group
Contact: Scott Muller, Director
E-mail: muller@northjersey.com
Ed: Rebecca Ollales. **Description:** Freshpet produces a variety of nutritious, refrigerated pet foods and treats for cats and dogs. The firm introduced five new recipes and treats to its grain-free line called Vital line. The Vital line mimics the ancestral diets of dogs and cats. **Availability:** Online.

8046 ■ "Sell a Movement Within a Smoothie" in Canadian Business (Vol. 87, July 2014, No. 7, pp. 58)
Description: Vega is a nutritional and fitness supplement maker based in Vancouver, British Columbia that has increased its sales sevenfold from 2008 to 2013, earning the 9th spot in the 2014 Profit 500 ranking of fastest growing companies in Canada. The firm's strategy is to promote its flagship product Vega One using an in-store bicycle-powered blender. **Availability:** Online.

8047 ■ "Sodexo Upgrades Healthy Vending Initiative" in Entertainment Close-Up (September 25, 2011)
Description: Sodexo launched its Your Health Your Way On-the-Go program for its vending machines across the nation. **Availability:** Online.

8048 ■ "Specialize in Cat Nutrition" in Pet Product News (Vol. 66, September 2012, No. 9, pp. 80)
Ed: Karen Shugart. **Description:** Cat food manufacturers have been developing a widely expanding variety of specialty diets that target numerous feline needs as cat owners' interest in their pets' nutrition becomes more intense. In view of this trend, insights into the growth of specialty diets in the cat food category are presented, along with descriptions of some of these diets. **Availability:** Online.

8049 ■ "Sprouts Farmers Market Reexamines Marketing Strategy to Increase Sales" in Supermarket News (November 5, 2021)
URL(s): www.supermarketnews.com/retail-financial/sprouts-farmers-market-reexamines-marketing-strategy-increase-sales
Ed: Victoria A.F. Camron. **Released:** November 05, 2021. **Description:** Due to not communicating its pricing strategy, Sprouts Farmers Market failed to meet third quarter expectations. In order to improve sales, CEO Jack Sinclair said the company is now going to focus on delivering a clear message to their customers.

8050 ■ "Tabs Says Organic Food Sales Hit Record in 2011. Sales Jump 15-20 Percent" in Entertainment Close-Up (February 21, 2012)
Description: Tabs Group reported it found an increase in American consumers reporting they purchased organic products along with a rise in overall sales in its Annual Organic Product Survey. Statistical data included.

8051 ■ "Tapping the 'Well' in Wellness" in Pet Product News (Vol. 64, November 2010, No. 11, pp. 1)
Ed: Wendy Bedwell-Wilson. **Description:** Healthy food and treats are among the leading wellness products being sought by customers from specialty retailers to keep their pets healthy. With this demand for pet wellness products, retailers suggest making sure that staff know key ingredients to emphasize to customers. Other insights into this trend and ways to engage customers are discussed. **Availability:** Online.

8052 ■ Top Grocery Trends of 2021
URL(s): www.supermarketnews.com/consumer-trends/top-grocery-trends-2021?PK=UMblock
Released: September 08, 2021. **Description:** Downloadable PDF report contains sales trends, insights on consumer behavior changes, challenges and supply chain issues for retailers, plus more. **Availability:** PDF.

8053 ■ "Transgenerational Trend: New Fans for Fresh Fare" in Barron's (Vol. 92, July 7, 2012, No. 28, pp. 15)
Pub: Dow Jones And Co.
Contact: Almar Latour, Chief Executive Officer
Ed: Robin Goldwyn Blumenthal. **Description:** The preference for natural and organic food is shared by baby boomers and millennials. Spending on natural and organic food is projected to rise along with rising food spending. **Availability:** Online.

8054 ■ "United Natural Foods Establishes Charitable Foundation to Support Healthy, Sustainable and Organic Food Systems" in United Natural Foods, Inc. (May 14, 2012)
Pub: The Financial Times Ltd.
Contact: John Ridding, Chief Executive Officer
E-mail: john.ridding@ft.com
Description: United Natural Foods Inc. (UNFI) has established a foundation committed to supporting healthy, sustainable and organic food systems. UNFI distributes natural, organic and specialty foods and related products. **Availability:** PDF; Online.

8055 ■ "United State Organic Food Market Retains Robust Growth amid the Pandemic: Projected to Grow at a CAGR of 8.7% during 2021-2027" in GlobeNewswire (Jan. 25, 2022)
URL(s): www.globenewswire.com/news-release/2022/01/25/2372820/0/en/United-State-Organic-Food-Market-Retains-Robust-Growth-Amid-the-Pandemic-Projected-to-Grow-at-a-CAGR-of-8-7-during-2021-2027-BlueWeave.html
Released: January 25, 2022. **Description:** Presents statistics on the growing U.S. organic food market based on a recent study by BlueWeave Consulting. **Availability:** Online.

8056 ■ "Wegmans, Fairway Lead Off Impossible Burger's East Coast Launch" in Supermarket News (September 25, 2019)
URL(s): www.supermarketnews.com/organic-natural/wegmans-fairway-lead-impossible-burger-s-east-coast-launch
Released: September 25, 2019. **Description:** The plant-based Impossible Burger is set to be sold in all 100 Wegman stores in seven states and two Fairway locations in Manhattan. This is due to a growing demand for plant-based options. **Availability:** Online.

8057 ■ "Whole Foods: A Big Boost for Midtown" in Sacramento Business Journal (Vol. 31, August 1, 2014, No. 23, pp. 3)
Pub: American City Business Journals, Inc.
Contact: Mike Olivieri, Executive Vice President
Description: Whole Foods Market is opening a 40,000-square-foot grocery store anchoring a six-story mixed-us project at 2001 L Street in midtown Sacramento, California. The store is expected to draw shoppers from East Sacramento, Curtis Park, West Sacramento, and Natomas and raise property values around the area. **Availability:** Print; Online.

8058 ■ "Whole Foods' Local Foragers Fill Store Shelves" in Supermarket News (October 22, 2019)
URL(s): www.supermarketnews.com/organic-natural/whole-foods-local-foragers-fill-store-shelves
Ed: Hannah Esper. **Released:** October 22, 2019. **Description:** Kelly Landrieu from Whole Foods Market, runs a program with the company that has team members find the best new local suppliers. This keeps each store supplied with local produce and other retail goods. **Availability:** Online.

8059 ■ "Yogun Fruz Adds First Location in Southern New York State" in Ice Cream Reporter (Vol. 23, September 20, 2010, No. 10, pp. 2)
Description: Yogen Fruz signed a master franchise agreement to expand into the southern counties of New York State. The firm offers a healthy and beneficial option to fast food and typical dessert choices. **Availability:** Print; Online.

STATISTICAL SOURCES

8060 ■ Impact of Private Label in the Online Food and Drink Market - US - February 2019
URL(s): store.mintel.com/report/impact-of-private-label-in-the-online-food-and-drink-market-us-february-2019?_ga=2.169804129.1182593580.1637273274-1258978629.1637273274
Price: $4,366.35. **Description:** Downloadable report examining food and beverage shopping habits. Includes an executive summary, interactive databook, PowerPoint presentation, infographic overview, report PDF, and previous years data. **Availability:** PDF.

8061 ■ RMA Annual Statement Studies
Pub: Risk Management Association
Contact: Nancy Foster, President
Released: Annual. **Description:** Contains composite balance sheets and income statements for more than 360 industries, including the accounting, auditing, and bookkeeping industries. Also contains five years of comparative historical data for discerning trends. Includes 16 commonly used ratios, computed for most of the size groupings for nearly every industry.

8062 ■ US Grocery Retailing Industry Report 2021
URL(s): store.mintel.com/report/us-grocery-retailing-market-report
Price: $4,366.35. **Description:** Downloadable report discussing the current trends in how consumers shop at grocery stores, especially during and after the Covid-19 Pandemic. The rise of online grocery shopping was one of the biggest changes and challenges for grocers. Report includes an executive summary, interactive databook, PowerPoint presentation, infographic overview, report PDF, and previous years data. **Availability:** PDF.

8063 ■ US The Natural/Organic Food Shopper Market Report 2020
URL(s): store.mintel.com/report/us-the-natural-and-organic-food-shopper-market-report

Price: $4,366.35. **Description:** Downloadable report discussing data on the natural and organic food industry and the effects of COVID-19. Report includes an executive summary, interactive databook, PowerPoint presentation, infographic overview, report PDF, and previous years data. **Availability:** PDF.

TRADE PERIODICALS

8064 ■ Nutrition Action Healthletter
Pub: Center for Science in the Public Interest
Contact: Dr. Peter Lurie, President
E-mail: plurie@cspinet.org
URL(s): www.cspinet.org/page/nutrition-action
Released: 10/year **Price:** $25, U.S. for print one year; $43, U.S. for print two years; $59, U.S. for print three years; $40, for print one year Canada and international; $73, for print two years Canada and international; $104, for print three years Canada and international; $25, U.S. for online one year Canada and international; $43, U.S. for online two years Canada and international; $59, U.S. for online three years Canada and international. **Description:** Covers food and nutrition, the food industry, and relevant government regulations and legislation. Focuses on the connections among diet, lifestyle, and disease. Includes nutritional comparisons of food products, reader questions and answers, and health-promoting recipes. **Availability:** Print; Online.

8065 ■ Whole Foods: Informing and Educating Natural Products Retailers on Dietary Supplements, Herbs, HBC, Homeopathy, Foods
Pub: WFC Inc.
Contact: Maggie Jaqua, Director
E-mail: maggiejaqua@wfcinc.com
URL(s): www.wholefoodsmagazine.com
Facebook: www.facebook.com/WholeFoodsM
Linkedin: www.linkedin.com/company/wholefoods-magazine
X (Twitter): x.com/WholeFoodsMag
Instagram: www.instagram.com/wholefoodsmag
YouTube: www.youtube.com/channel/UCo0Fx8qFBjLCtNygoo3T2QA
Ed: Kaylynn Chiarello-Ebner. **Released:** 10/year; combined Jan/Feb issue and June/July issue and May. **Price:** $80, for Canada and Mexico per year; $12, Single issue; $75, for except may source book; $20, for march retailer survey; $10, for reprints each; $195, for foreign subscriptions per year; $70, for per year non-qualified; $80, for 2 year non-qualified. **Description:** Natural product retailer magazine. **Availability:** Print; PDF; Online.

TRADE SHOWS AND CONVENTIONS

8066 ■ CHFA East Tradeshow
Canadian Health Food Association (CHFA)
235 Yorkland Blvd., Ste. 201
Toronto, ON, Canada M2J 4Y8
Free: 800-661-4510
Co. E-mail: info@chfa.ca
URL: http://chfa.ca/en
Contact: Aaron Skelton, President
URL(s): ww.chfanow.ca/toronto/
Frequency: Annual. **Description:** Health-related products, including vitamin, mineral, and herbal supplements; cosmetics; foods; exercise equipment; publications; body care products; and small appliances. **Audience:** Industry professionals. **Principal Exhibits:** Health-related products, including vitamin, mineral, and herbal supplements; cosmetics; foods; exercise equipment; publications; body care products; and small appliances. Dates and Locations: 2025 Sep 18-21 Enercare Centre, Toronto, ON; 2026 Sep 24-27 Enercare Centre, Toronto, ON. **Telecommunication Services:** info@chfa.ca.

CONSULTANTS

8067 ■ Ainsley Ideas Inc. [Health Food & Beverage Group]
Toronto, ON, Canada
Description: Works with new and established healthy food or beverage companies to build their brand, grow their sales, and make an impact on the food industry.

8068 ■ Emerge Natural Sales Solutions
San Francisco, CA
Ph: (415)407-3660
URL: http://www.emergenaturalsalessolutions.com
Contact: Jason Werner, Founder
Facebook: www.facebook.com/emergenaturalsalessolutions
Linkedin: www.linkedin.com/in/jason-werner-2b01a054
X (Twitter): x.com/EmergebyJason
Instagram: www.instagram.com/emergenaturalsalessolutions
Description: A consultant in natural products that provides outsourced sales management solutions for implementing your sales channel in the natural trade.

8069 ■ Good Food Consulting
CA
Ph: (510)316-2224
Co. E-mail: brian@goodfoodconsulting.com
URL: http://www.goodfoodconsulting.com
Contact: Brian Bigelow, Owner
Description: Provides management consulting for established and startup manufacturers and food and dining operations specializing in gluten free, organic, vegan, or natural and sustainable food products. We help with your overall business operations, financial management, and new store openings.

8070 ■ Marisa Moore Nutrition, LLC
2625 Piedmont Rd., Ste. 56-160
Atlanta, GA 30324
Co. E-mail: questions@marisamoore.com
URL: http://marisamoore.com
Contact: Marisa Moore, Contact
E-mail: marisa@marisamoore.com
Facebook: www.facebook.com/MarisaMooreNutrition
X (Twitter): x.com/marisamoore
Instagram: www.instagram.com/MarisaMoore
Pinterest: www.pinterest.com/marisamoore
Description: Food and nutrition expert working on the business side of health and wellness. Works with startups, chefs, food vendors, marketers, food scientists, brand managers, nutritionists, and researchers.

8071 ■ Natural Products Consulting LLC
8 Cobblestone Ln.
Andover, MA 01810
Ph: (978)886-1052
URL: http://www.naturalconsulting.com
Contact: Bob Burke, Consultant Founder
E-mail: bob@naturalconsulting.com
Description: Provides assistance in bringing natural, organic and specialty products to market across most classes of trade. **Scope:** Provides assistance in bringing natural, organic and specialty products to market across most classes of trade. **Founded:** 1998. **Publications:** "Natural Products Field Manual," 2009; "Staking Out Space on the Supermarket Shelf," 2003; "The Sales Manager's Handbook," 2003. **Training:** Becoming a More Effective Sales Manager in the Natural and Specialty Channel, San Mateo, CA, 2010; What's Hot in Natural and Organic New Product Trends, Mar, 2009; Selling Natural and Specialty products and Trade Spending Management.

8072 ■ OF+ Consulting
London, United Kingdom
URL: http://ofplus.com
Contact: Simon Wright, Founder
E-mail: simon@ofplus.com
Description: Helps food and drink companies develop and market their products.

8073 ■ Ripple Effect Sales Management
516 Upper Weadley Rd.
Wayne, PA 19087
Ph: (610)254-0101
Fax: (610)254-0101
URL: http://www.rippleeffectsalesmgmt.com
Contact: Jeff Krinsky, Owner Founder
E-mail: jeff@rippleeffectsalesmgmt.com
Facebook: www.facebook.com/RippleEffectSalesManagement
X (Twitter): x.com/RE_SalesMgmt
Description: Works with clients to grow sales and build brands of natural, organic, and specialty foods.

8074 ■ Taste Profit Marketing, LLC
54 Pleasant St., Unit 9
Concord, NH 03301
Ph: (617)833-2417
Co. E-mail: info@tasteprofit.com
URL: http://tasteprofit.com
Contact: Noah Munro, Founder
Facebook: www.facebook.com/TasteProfitMarketing
Linkedin: www.linkedin.com/company/taste-profit
X (Twitter): x.com/tasteprofit
Instagram: www.instagram.com/tasteprofit
Description: Helps food entrepreneurs grow profitable food businesses and become better marketing managers. Services include website development, eCommerce development, branding, email automation, SEO, food photography, graphic design, blogging, and marketing planning. **Founded:** 2015.

FRANCHISES AND BUSINESS OPPORTUNITIES

8075 ■ Berrybrook Farm Natural Food Pantry
1257 E Blvd.
Charlotte, NC 28203
Ph: (704)334-6528
Co. E-mail: berrybrookfarm@bellsouth.net
URL: http://www.berrybrookfarm.com
Facebook: www.facebook.com/berrybrookfarmnaturalfoods
X (Twitter): x.com/berrybrookfarm1
Description: Retailer of soups, vegetarian wraps, smoothies, sandwiches, salads. **Founded:** 1972. **Royalty Fee:** 5%. **Training:** Provides 16 days at headquarters, 14 days onsite with ongoing support.

8076 ■ Booster Juice Inc.
8915-51 Ave., Ste. 205
Edmonton, AB, Canada T6E 5J3
Ph: (780)440-6770
Co. E-mail: support@boosterjuice.com
URL: http://boosterjuice.com
Contact: Dale Wishewan, President
Facebook: www.facebook.com/boosterjuice
X (Twitter): twitter.com/boosterjuice
Instagram: www.instagram.com/boosterjuice
Description: To create long-standing customer relationships by consistently delivering an incredibly delicious, convenient and nutritious product, perfectly suited for an active lifestyle. **No. of Franchise Units:** 280. **Founded:** 1999. **Franchised:** 1999. **Equity Capital Needed:** Net Worth of $350,000; Liquid Assets of $100,000. **Franchise Fee:** $20,000. **Royalty Fee:** 6% of gross sales. **Training:** Training includes 2 weeks at head office and ongoing support.

8077 ■ Sangster's Health Centres
Canada
Free: 877-951-2224
URL: http://sangsters.com
Facebook: www.facebook.com/sangsters
X (Twitter): twitter.com/sangsters
Instagram: www.instagram.com/sangsterscanada
Description: Retail sale of vitamins, herbs, natural cosmetics, natural foods, body building and supplies, specializing in their own name-brand products and also national company brands. **No. of Franchise Units:** 36. **No. of Company-Owned Units:** 5. **Founded:** 1971. **Franchised:** 1978. **Equity Capital Needed:** $30,000 minimum. **Franchise Fee:** $25,000. **Training:** Yes.

8078 ■ Smoothie King
1412 N Hwy. 190
Covington, LA 70433
Ph: (985)809-9722
Free: 800-577-4200
URL: http://www.smoothieking.com
Facebook: www.facebook.com/SmoothieKing
X (Twitter): x.com/SmoothieKing

Instagram: www.instagram.com/smoothieking
YouTube: www.youtube.com/channel/UCvydHFk0PuOLmqekEo18a4A
Pinterest: www.pinterest.com/smoothiekingus

Description: Offers guests the industry's first, original nutritional fruit and function based fresh-blended smoothies. **Founded:** 1989. **Financial Assistance:** Yes **Training:** Provides 1 day pre-opening (orientation), 14 days management training at Corporate store, 8 days store opening (14 days before open & 4 days after opening) onsite. Assistance in real estate, design and construction. **Educational Activities:** Multi-Unit Foodservice Operators Conference (MUFSO) (Annual).

8079 ■ Uncle Louie G Inc.
115 Johnson St.
Staten Island, NY 10309
Ph: (718)966-3763
Fax: (718)966-3764
Co. E-mail: unclelouiegee@me.com
URL: http://unclelouiegee.com
Contact: Dino Russo, Contact
Facebook: www.facebook.com/UncleLouieG

Description: Retailer of ice creams. **Founded:** 1998. **Financial Assistance:** Yes **Training:** Yes.

LIBRARIES

8080 ■ Academy of Nutrition and Dietetics (AND) - Library
120 S Riverside Plz., Ste. 2190
Chicago, IL 60606-6995
Ph: (312)899-0040
Free: 800-877-1600
URL: http://www.eatright.org
Contact: Kevin L. Sauer, President
X (Twitter): x.com/eatright
YouTube: www.youtube.com/user/EatRightTV
Pinterest: www.pinterest.com/kidseatright

Description: Represents food and nutrition professionals. Promotes nutrition, health and well-being. **Scope:** Food and nutrition. **Services:** Library not open to the public. **Founded:** 1917. **Holdings:** Figures not available. **Publications:** *Weight Loss Matters: Your Weight and Your Health Pamphlet*; *Find a Nutrition Professional Consumer Search*; *Directory of Columbus Registered Dietitians*; *Directory of Registered Dietitians*; *Directory of Dietetics Programs* (Annual); *Directory of Consulting Dietitians in Private Practice*; *Journal of the Academy of Nutrition and Dietetics* (Monthly). **Educational Activities:** Food Nutrition Conference Expo (FNCE) (Annual).

8081 ■ Geisinger Medical Center (GMC) - Health Sciences Library
100 N Academy Ave.
Danville, PA 17822
Ph: (570)271-6211
URL: http://www.geisinger.org/patient-care/find-a-location/geisinger-medical-center

Description: Community radio station currently operating out of the French Quarter in New Orleans. **Scope:** Medical. **Services:** Library not open to public. **Founded:** 1996. **Holdings:** Figures not available.

8082 ■ Lemmen-Holton Cancer Pavilion Library
145 Michigan St. NE
Grand Rapids, MI 49503
Ph: (616)486-5700
URL: http://findadoctor.spectrumhealth.org/location/profile/7989

Description: Provide a full range of cancer services including, prevention, screening and diagnosis, personalized cancer treatment, integrative therapies, supportive care services, access to clinical trials and leading edge technology. **Scope:** Medicine; literature. **Holdings:** Books.

8083 ■ Price-Pottenger Nutrition Foundation (PPNF) - Library [Health and Healing Wisdom; PPNF]
7890 Broadway
Lemon Grove, CA 91945
Ph: (619)462-7600
Free: 800-366-3748
Co. E-mail: info@price-pottenger.org
URL: http://price-pottenger.org
Contact: Mark Bielsky, President
Facebook: www.facebook.com/pricepottenger
Linkedin: www.linkedin.com/company/price-pottenger-nutrition-foundation
Instagram: www.instagram.com/pricepottenger
YouTube: www.youtube.com/user/PricePottengerNF

Description: Seeks to increase awareness of natural health, organic gardening, nutrition and ecology. Disseminates information to the medical and dental professions, as well as to the public, through publications, seminars, classes, study groups, and scientific exhibits. Stresses the benefits of chemically-untreated "whole" foods. Named in honor of Weston A. Price, DDS and Francis M. Pottenger, Jr., MD, known for their work in nutrition research. Publishes nutritional books. Reaches market through direct mail and wholesalers. **Scope:** Health, organic gardening, nutrition, and the environment. **Founded:** 1952. **Holdings:** 5,000 health books. **Publications:** *Price-Pottenger Journal of Health and Healing* (Quarterly). **Geographic Preference:** Multinational.

8084 ■ U.S.D.A. National Agricultural Library (NAL) - Food and Nutrition Information Center (FNIC)
10301 Baltimore Ave.
Beltsville, MD 20705
Ph: (301)504-5414
URL: http://www.nal.usda.gov/programs/fnic
Contact: James Cain, Contact
E-mail: james.cain@usda.gov

Scope: Food; human nutrition education. **Services:** library not open to the public. **Founded:** 1977. **Holdings:** Figures not available.

8085 ■ Voice for Animals, Inc. (VOICE) - Library
PO Box 120095
San Antonio, TX 78212
Ph: (210)737-3138
Co. E-mail: voice@voiceforanimals.org
URL: http://www.voiceforanimals.org
Contact: Rachel Z. Wolf, Contact

Description: Individuals with an interest in animal rights. Seeks to raise public awareness of animal rights issues. Works to abolish "the systematic abuse of nonhuman animals." Conducts educational programs. **Scope:** Animal rights. **Founded:** 1987. **Holdings:** Figures not available. **Geographic Preference:** National.

www.ingramcontent.com/pod-product-compliance
Lightning Source LLC
Jackson TN
JSHW060747100425
82367JS00003B/54